SCOTT

2022
STANDARD POSTAGE
STAMP CATALOGUE

ONE HUNDRED AND SEVENTY-EIGHTH EDITION IN SIX VOLUMES

Volume 1A
U.S., U.N., A-Australia

EDITOR-IN-CHIEF	Jay Bigalke
EDITOR-AT-LARGE	Donna Houseman
CONTRIBUTING EDITOR	Charles Snee
EDITOR EMERITUS	James E. Kloetzel
SENIOR EDITOR /NEW ISSUES AND VALUING	Martin J. Frankevicz
ADMINISTRATIVE ASSISTANT/CATALOGUE LAYOUT	Eric Wiessinger
PRINTING AND IMAGE COORDINATOR	Stacey Mahan
SENIOR GRAPHIC DESIGNER	Cinda McAlexander
SALES DIRECTOR	David Pistello
SALES DIRECTOR	Eric Roth

Released April 2021

Includes New Stamp Listings through the February 2021 Linn's Stamp News Monthly Catalogue Update

Copyright© 2021 by

AMOS MEDIA

1660 Campbell Road, Suite A, Sidney, OH 45365

Publishers of *Linn's Stamp News, Linn's Stamp News Monthly, Coin World* and *Coin World Monthly*.

Table of contents

See the following volumes for other country listings:
Volume 1B through 6B for Countries of the World, Austria-Z
Volume 1B: Austria-B
Volume 2A: C Cur; Volume 2B: Cyp-F
Volume 3A: G; Volume 3B: H-I
Volume 4A: J-L; Volume 4B: M
Volume 5A: N-Phil; Volume 5B: Pit-Sam
Volume 6A: San-Tete; Volume 6B: Thai-Z

Scott Catalogue Mission Statement

The Scott Catalogue Team exists to serve the recreational, educational and commercial hobby needs of stamp collectors and dealers.

We strive to set the industry standard for philatelic information and products by developing and providing goods that help collectors identify, value, organize and present their collections.

Quality customer service is, and will continue to be, our highest priority. We aspire toward achieving total customer satisfaction.

What's new for 2022 Scott Standard Volume 1?

Another catalog season is upon us as we continue the journey of the 153-year history of the Scott catalogs. The 2022 volumes are the 178th edition of the Scott *Standard Postage Stamp Catalogue*. Volume 1A includes listings for the United States, United Nations, and countries of the world Aden through Australia. Listings for Austria through B countries of the world can be found in Vol. 1B.

This year's covers feature the United States 1922 5¢ Theodore Roosevelt stamp (Scott 557) on the Vol. 1A catalog and the Austria 1936 5-shilling Construction Workers stamp (379) on Vol. 1B.

Because Vol. 1B is a continuation of the first part of the Vol. 1 catalog, the introduction pages are not repeated in each volume this year.

Much of the review for this year's catalog took place throughout 2020 and into 2021. The world was interrupted by the COVID-19 pandemic, and the effects of that hit the stamp world in multiple ways. Some collectors returned to collecting, auction houses saw increases in realizations, traditional in-person stamp shows took a pause, and collectors shifted to purchasing more online. Some of these situations impacted valuing decisions this year and could lead to more changes as we continue our reviews.

For the United States, our editorial analysis corresponds closely to Scott advisors' general feelings that current Scott values accurately reflect market values for very fine stamps. There are always exceptions, and this year's Vol. 1A shows slight advances for the majority of the 1893 Columbian stamps (Scott 230-245) in unused original gum and mint never hinged conditions.

Quite a number of the 1914-17 Washington-Franklin issues make significant advances in value in unused, original gum condition and mint, never-hinged condition, especially in the No. 462-478 set. Scott 465, the 4¢ orange brown, jumps to $60 unused and $125 mint from $45 and $105, respectively, in the 2021 Scott Specialized Catalogue of United States Stamps and Covers. Similar gains are seen for almost all stamps from Nos. 468 through 476.

Scott 485, the 1917 5¢ carmine imperforate error of color, moves from $9,000 in unused, original gum condition last year to $10,000 in the 2022 Vol. 1A. When was the last time you saw this stamp in this condition offered for sale?

In the Air Post section, the 1930 Graf Zeppelins (Scott C13-C15) move ahead very slightly after a long period of dormancy.

The 2020 auction season saw the appearance of many rare and high-quality Confederate States postmasters' provisionals. Buyer response was decidedly mixed. Some of the rarest items sold for excellent prices, such as the 3¢ Tuscumbia, Ala., handstamped envelope (Scott 6AXU1), which leaps to $30,000 from just $17,500 last year. The used Beaumont, Texas, 10¢ black on pink stamp (Scott 12X2) jumps to $30,000 from its 2021 value of $20,000.

Moving in the opposite direction were items such as the Athens, Ga., 5¢ red type II stamp (Scott 5X2), which drops from $5,750 used last year to $3,000 in this Vol. 1A. A larger loss was felt by the Independence, Texas, 10¢ black on buff stamp with small "10" and manuscript "Pd," which is only known on cover. Its value plummeted to $20,000 from a lofty $32,500 last year. The unique Mt. Lebanon, La., stamp on cover (60X1) disappointingly did not sell at auction when offered in 2020. Other stamps and covers that move either up or down in value are sprinkled throughout the Postmasters' Provisional Issues section, with declines somewhat outnumbering the gains.

STANDARD POSTAGE STAMP CATALOGUE
2022 | VOL. 1A
United States, United Nations, A-Australia

STANDARD POSTAGE STAMP CATALOGUE
2022 | VOL. 1B
Austria-B

In-period uses of modern U.S. postal stationery were looked at, and a number of increases in values were made.

Several new U.S. errors were discovered since the 2021 catalog season and make their first appearance in this Vol. 1A. Included are Scott 527d, the 2¢ carmine Washington type V offset issue with all color missing (from a foldover), and Scott B5b, an imperforate error of the 1998 type of the Breast Cancer Awareness semipostal that can be differentiated from imperfs from uncut press sheets by having normal roulette die cuts on the reverse of the stamps, which are omitted on the imperforate uncut press sheets. Also new is an imperforate 22¢ Official coil (Scott O136b), currently recorded only used.

Other new errors include an example of one of the Presidential Ameripex souvenir sheets with a double impression of red error (Scott 2216q) and a die-cutting-omitted block of four of the Santa Claus Christmas stamps of 2018 (5335c).

This year Argentina received a close look with almost 1,300 value changes made, most of which were increases. An inverted overprint error of the Zeppelin First Flight airmail stamp of 1930 (Scott C20a) appears for the first time in this catalog.

We have begun a review of Australian States for this edition. For New South Wales approximately 1,100 value changes were made, and 575 changes were made for Queensland.

Austria and Austria Offices in Crete were looked at closely with approximately 2,500 and 10 value changes made, respectively. A number of recent stamp issues included as gifts with standing orders, which are noted but not listed, are valued for the first time.

Many other countries received reviews that are not noted in this letter. We encourage you to pay special attention to the Number Additions, Deletions and Changes listing in this volume. We also suggest reading the catalog introduction, which includes an abundance of useful information.

Lastly, the new Scott *Stamp Illustrated Identifier*, formerly included as the Illustrated Identifier in each Scott Standard catalog volume, is now a separate publication. The softcover 6-inch-by-9-inch booklet will make it easier to identify stamps while consulting listings in the Scott catalog without having to flip back and forth. To purchase, visit online at www.amosadvantage.com.

Best wishes in your stamp collecting pursuits!

Jay Bigalke, Scott catalog editor-in-chief

Acknowledgments

Our appreciation and gratitude go to the following individuals who have assisted us in preparing information included in this year's Scott catalogues. Some helpers prefer anonymity. These individuals have generously shared their stamp knowledge with others through the medium of the Scott catalogue.

Those who follow provided information that is in addition to the hundreds of dealer price lists and advertisements and scores of auction catalogues and realizations that were used in producing the catalogue values. It is from those noted here that we have been able to obtain information on items not normally seen in published lists and advertisements. Support from these people goes beyond data leading to catalogue values, for they also are key to editorial changes.

A special acknowledgment to Liane and Sergio Sismondo of The Classic Collector for their assistance and knowledge sharing that have aided in the preparation of this year's Standard and Classic Specialized Catalogues.

Clifford J. Alexander
  (Carriers and Locals Society)
Roland Austin
Michael & Cecilia Ball (A To Z Stamps)
Jim Bardo (Bardo Stamps)
John Birkinbine II
Brian M. Bleckwenn
  (The Philatelic Foundation)
Les Bootman
Roger S. Brody
Tom Brougham
  (Canal Zone Study Group)
Paul and Josh Buchsbayew
  (Cherrystone Auctions, Inc.)
Timothy Bryan Burgess
Tina and John Carlson (JET Stamps)
Jay Carrington
Carlson Chambliss
Bob Coale
Tony L. Crumbley
  (Carolina Coin and Stamp, Inc.)
Christopher Dahle
Charles Deaton
Bob and Rita Dumaine
  (Sam Houston Duck Co.)
Charles Epting (H.R. Harmer)
Mike Farrell
David Feldman International Auctioneers
Robert A. Fisher
Jeffrey M. Forster
Robert S. Freeman
Henry L. Gitner
  (Henry Gitner Philatelists, Inc.)
Stan Goldfarb

Marc E. Gonzales
Daniel E. Grau
Bruce Hecht (Bruce L. Hecht Co.)
Eric Jackson
Michael Jaffe (Michael Jaffe Stamps, Inc.)
William A. (Bill) Jones
Allan Katz (Ventura Stamp Co.)
Patricia A. Kaufmann
  (Civil War Philatelic Society)
Jon Kawaguchi
  (Ryukyu Philatelic Specialist Society)
Han Ki Kim
Ingert Kuzych
Ulf Lindahl (Ethiopian Philatelic Society)
Ignacio Llach (Filatelia Llach, S.L.)
William K. McDaniel
Pat McElroy
Brian Metz
Mark S. Miller (India Study Circle)
Gary Morris (Pacific Midwest Co.)
Peter Mosiondz Jr.
Bruce M. Moyer
  (Moyer Stamps & Collectables)
Scott Murphy
Dr. Tiong Tak Ngo
Nik & Lisa Oquist
Don Peterson
  (International Philippine Philatelic
  Society)
Stanley M. Piller
  (Stanley M. Piller & Associates)
Dr. Charles Posner
Peter W. W. Powell
Ed Reiser (Century Stamp Co.)

Ghassan D. Riachi
Robert G. Rufe
Theodosios D. Sampson Ph.D.
Dennis W. Schmidt
Joyce & Chuck Schmidt
Guy Shaw
  (Mexico-Elmhurst Philatelic Society
  International)
J. Randall Shoemaker
  (Philatelic Stamp Authentication and
  Grading, Inc.)
Sergio and Liane Sismondo
  (The Classic Collector)
Jay Smith
Telah Smith
Mark Stelmacovich
Scott R. Trepel
  (Siegel Auction Galleries, Inc.)
Dan Undersander
Steven Unkrich
Herbert R. Volin
Philip T. Wall
Val Zabijaka (Zabijaka Auctions)

Addresses, telephone numbers, web sites, email addresses of general and specialized philatelic societies

Collectors can contact the following groups for information about the philately of the areas within the scope of these societies, or inquire about membership in these groups. Aside from the general societies, we limit this list to groups that specialize in particular fields of philately, particular areas covered by the Scott *Standard Postage Stamp Catalogue*, and topical groups. Many more specialized philatelic society exist than those listed below. These addresses are updated yearly, and they are, to the best of our knowledge, correct and current. Groups should inform the editors of address changes whenever they occur. The editors also want to hear from other such specialized groups not listed.

Unless otherwise noted all website addresses begin with http://

General Societies

American Philatelic Society, 100 Match Factory Place, Bellefonte, PA 16823-1367; (814) 933-3803; https://stamps.org; apsinfo@stamps.org

International Society of Worldwide Stamp Collectors, Joanne Murphy, M.D., P.O. Box 19006, Sacramento, CA 95819; www.iswsc.org; executivedirector@iswsc.org

Royal Philatelic Society of Canada, P.O. Box 69080, St. Clair Post Office, Toronto, ON M4T 3A1 Canada; (888) 285-4143; www.rpsc.org; info@rpsc.org

Royal Philatelic Society London, 15 Abchurch Lane, London EX4N 7BW, United Kingdom; +44 (0) 20 7486 1044; www.rpsl.org.uk; secretary@rpsl.org.uk

Libraries, Museums, and Research Groups

American Philatelic Research Library, 100 Match Factory Place, Bellefonte, PA 16823; (814) 933-3803; www.stamplibrary.org; library@stamps.org.

V. G. Greene Philatelic Research Foundation, P.O. Box 69100, St. Clair Post Office, Toronto, ON M4T 3A1, Canada; (416) 921-2073; info@greenefoundation.ca

Aero/Astro Philately

American Air Mail Society, Stephen Reinhard, P.O. Box 110, Mineola, NY 11501; www.americanairmailsociety.org; sreinhard1@optonline.net

Postal History

Auxiliary Markings Club, Jerry Johnson, 6621 W. Victoria Ave., Kennewick, WA 99336; www.postal-markings.org; membership-2010@postal-markings.org

Postage Due Mail Study Group, Bob Medland, Camway Cottage, Nanny Hurn's Lane, Cameley, Bristol BS39 5AJ, United Kingdom; 01761 45959; www.postageduemail.org.uk; secretary.pdmsg@gmail.com

Postal History Society, Yamil Kouri, 405 Waltham St. #347, Lexington, MA 02421; www.postalhistorysociety.org; yhkouri@massmed.org

Post Mark Collectors Club, Bob Milligan, 7014 Woodland Oaks Drive, Magnolia, TX 77354; (281) 259-2735; www.postmarks.org; bob.milligan0@gmail.com

U.S. Cancellation Club, Roger Curran, 18 Tressler Blvd., Lewisburg, PA 17837; rdcnrc@ptd.net

Revenues and Cinderellas

American Revenue Association, Lyman Hensley, 473 E. Elm St., Sycamore, IL 60178-1934; www.revenuer.org; ilrno2@netzero.net

Christmas Seal and Charity Stamp Society, John Denune Jr., 234 E. Broadway, Granville, OH 43023; (740) 814-6031; www.seal-society.org

National Duck Stamp Collectors Society, Anthony J. Monico, P.O. Box 43, Harleysville, PA 19438-0043; www.ndscs.org; ndscs@ndscs.org

State Revenue Society, Kent Gray, P.O. Box 67842, Albuquerque, NM 87193; www.staterevenue.org; srssecretary@comcast.net

Thematic Philately

Americana Unit, Dennis Dengel, 17 Peckham Road, Poughkeepsie, NY 12603-2018; www.americanaunit.org; ddengel@americanaunit.org

American Topical Association, Jennifer Miller, P.O. Box 2143, Greer, SC 29652-2143; (618) 985-5100; americantopical.org; ata@americantopical.org

Astronomy Study Unit, Leonard Zehr, 1411 Chateau Ave., Windsor, ON N8P 1M2, Canada; (416) 833-9317; www.astronomystudyunit.net; lenzehr@gmail.com

Bicycle Stamps Club, Corey Hjalseth, 1102 Broadway, Suite 200, Tacoma, WA 98402; (253) 318-6222; www.bicyclestampsclub.org; coreyh@evergreenhomeloans.com

Biology Unit, Chris Dahle, 1401 Linmar Drive NE, Cedar Rapids, IA 52402-3724; www.biophilately.org; chris-dahle@biophilately.org

Bird Stamp Society, Mr. S. A. H. (Tony) Statham, Ashlyns Lodge, Chesham Road, Berkhamsted, Herts HP4 2ST United Kingdom; www.bird-stamps.org/bss; tony.statham@sky.com

Captain Cook Society, Jerry Yucht, 8427 Leale Ave., Stockton, CA 95212, www.captaincooksociety.com; us@captaincooksociety.com

The CartoPhilatelic Society, Marybeth Sulkowski, 2885 Sanford Ave., SW, #32361, Grandville, MI 49418-1342; www.mapsonstamps.org; secretary@mapsonstamps.org

Casey Jones Railroad Unit, Jeff Lough, 2612 Redbud Land, Apt. C, Lawrence, KS 66046; www.uqp.de/cjr; jeffydplaugh@gmail.com

Cats on Stamps Study Unit, Robert D. Jarvis, 2731 Teton Lane, Fairfield, CA 94533; www.catstamps.info; catmews1@yahoo.com

Chemistry and Physics on Stamps Study Unit, Dr. Roland Hirsch, 13830 Metcalf Ave., Apt. 15218, Overland Park, KS 66223-8017; (301) 792-6296; www.cpossu.org; rfhirsch@cpossu.org

Chess on Stamps Study Unit, Barry Keith, 511 First St. N., Apt. 106; Charlottesville, VA 22902; www.chessonstamps.org; keithfam@embarqmail.com

Cricket Philatelic Society, A. Melville-Brown, 11 Weppons, Ravens Road, Shoreham-by-Sea, West Sussex BN43 5AW, United Kingdom; www.cricketstamp.net; mel.cricket.100@googlemail.com

Earth's Physical Features Study Group, Fred Klein, 515 Magdalena Ave., Los Altos, CA 94024; http://epfsu.jeffhayward.com; epfsu@jeffhayward.com

Ebony Society of Philatelic Events and Reflections (ESPER); Don Neal, P.O. Box 5245, Somerset, NJ 08875-5245; www.esperstamps.org; esperdon@verizon.net

Europa Study Unit, Tonny E. Van Loij, 3002 S. Xanthia St.; Denver, CO 80231-4237; (303) 752-0189; www.europastudyunit.org; tvanloij@gmail.com

Fire Service in Philately, John Zaranek, 81 Hillpine Road, Cheektowaga, NY 14227-2259; (716) 668-3352; jczaranek@roadrunner.com

Gastronomy on Stamps Study Unit, David Wolfersburger, 5062 NW 35th Lane Road, Ocala, FL 34482; (314) 494-3795; www.gastronomystamps.org

Gay and Lesbian History on Stamps Club, Joe Petronie, P.O. Box 190842, Dallas, TX 75219-0842; www.glhsonline.org; glhsc@aol.com

Gems, Minerals and Jewelry Study Unit, Fred Haynes, 10 Country Club Drive, Rochester, NY 14618-3720; fredmhaynes55@gmail.com

Graphics Philately Association, Larry Rosenblum. 1030 E. El Camino Real, PMB 107, Sunnyvale, CA 94087-3759; www.graphics-stamps.org; larry@graphics-stamps.org

Journalists, Authors and Poets on Stamps, Christopher D. Cook, 7222 Hollywood Road, Berrien Springs, MI 49103; cdcook2@gmail.com

Lighthouse Stamp Society; www.lighthousestampsociety.org; dalene@lighthousestampsociety.org

Lions International Stamp Club, David McKirdy, s-Gravenwetering 248, 3062 SJ Rotterdam, Netherlands; 31(0) 10 212 0313; www.lisc.nl; davidmckirdy@aol.com

Masonic Study Unit, Gene Fricks, 25 Murray Way, Blackwood, NJ 08012-4400; genefricks@comcast.net

Medical Subjects Unit, Dr. Frederick C. Skvara, P.O. Box 6228, Bridgewater, NJ 08807; fcskvara@optonline.net

Napoleonic Age Philatelists, Ken Berry, 4117 NW 146th St., Oklahoma City, OK 73134-1746; (405) 748-8646; www.nap-stamps.org; krb4117@att.net

Old World Archaeological Study Unit, Caroline Scannell, 14 Dawn Drive, Smithtown, NY 11787-176; www.owasu.org; editor@owasu.org

Petroleum Philatelic Society International, Feitze Papa, 922 Meander Drive, Walnut Creek, CA 94598-4239; www.ppsi.org.uk; oildad@astound.net

Rotary on Stamps Fellowship, Gerald L. Fitzsimmons, 105 Calle Ricardo, Victoria, TX 77904; www.rotaryonstamps.org; glfitz@suddenlink.net

Scouts on Stamps Society International, Woodrow (Woody) Brooks, 498 Baldwin Road, Akron, OH 44312; (330) 612-1294; www.sossi.org; secretary@sossi.org

Ships on Stamps Unit, Erik Th. Matzinger, Voorste Havervelden 30, 4822 AL Breda, Netherlands; www.shipsonstamps.org; erikships@gmail.com

Space Topic Study Unit, David Blog, P.O. Box 174, Bergenfield, NJ 07621; www.space-unit.com; davidblognj@gmail.com

Stamps on Stamps Collectors Club, Michael Merritt, 73 Mountainside Road, Mendham, NJ 07945; www.stampsonstamps.org; michael@mischu.me

Windmill Study Unit, Walter J. Hallien, 607 N. Porter St., Watkins Glenn, NY 14891-1345; (607) 229-3541; www.windmillworld.com

Wine On Stamps Study Unit, David Wolfersburger, 5062 NW 35th Lane Road, Ocala, FL 34482; (314) 494-3795; www.wine-on-stamps.org;

United States

American Air Mail Society, Stephen Reinhard, P.O. Box 110, Mineola, NY 11501; www.americanairmailsociety.org; sreinhard1@optonline.net

American First Day Cover Society, P.O. Box 246, Colonial Beach VA 22443-0246; (520) 321-0880; www.afdcs.org; afdcs@afdcs.org

Auxiliary Markings Club, Jerry Johnson, 6621 W. Victoria Ave., Kennewick, WA 99336; www.postal-markings.org; membership-2010@postal-markings.org

American Plate Number Single Society, Rick Burdsall, APNSS Secretary, P.O. BOX 1023, Palatine, IL 60078-1023; www.apnss.org; apnss.sec@gmail.com

American Revenue Association, Lyman Hensley, 473 E. Elm St., Sycamore, IL 60178-1934; www.revenuer.org; ilrno2@netzero.net

American Society for Philatelic Pages and Panels, Ron Walenciak, P.O. Box 1042, Washington Township, NJ 07676; www.asppp.org; ron.walenciak@asppp.org

Canal Zone Study Group, Mike Drabik, P.O. Box 281, Bolton, MA 01740, www.canalzonestudygroup.com; czsgsecretary@gmail.com

Carriers and Locals Society, John Bowman, 14409 Pentridge Drive, Corpus Christi, TX 78410; (361) 933-0757; www.pennypost.org; jbowman@stx.rr.com

Christmas Seal & Charity Stamp Society, John Denune Jr., 234 E. Broadway, Granville, OH 43023; (740) 814-6031; www.seal-society.org; john@christmasseals.net

Civil War Philatelic Society , Patricia A. Kaufmann, 10194 N. Old State Road, Lincoln, DE 19960-3644; (302) 422-2656; www.civilwarphilatelicsociety.org; trishkauf@comcast.net

Error, Freaks, and Oddities Collectors Club, Scott Shaulis, P.O. Box 549, Murrysville, PA 15668-0549; (724) 733-4134; www.efocc.org; scott@shaulisstamps.com

National Duck Stamp Collectors Society, Anthony J. Monico, P.O. Box 43, Harleysville, PA 19438-0043; www.ndscs.org; ndscs@ndscs.org

Plate Number Coil Collectors Club (PNC3), Gene Trinks, 16415 W. Desert Wren Court, Surprise, AZ 85374; (623) 322-4619; www.pnc3.org; gctrinks@cox.net

Post Mark Collectors Club, Bob Milligan, 7014 Woodland Oaks Drive, Magnolia, TX 77354; (281) 259-2735; www.postmarks.org; bob.milligan0@gmail.com

Souvenir Card Collectors Society, William V. Kriebel, www.souvenircards.org; kriebewv@drexel.edu

United Postal Stationery Society, Dave Kandziolka, 404 Sundown Drive, Knoxville, TN 37934; www.upss.org; membership@upss.org

U.S. Cancellation Club; Roger Curran, 18 Tressler Blvd., Lewisburg, PA 17837; rdcnrc@ptd.net

U.S. Philatelic Classics Society; Rob Lund, 2913 Fulton St., Everett, WA 98201-3733; www.uspcs.org; membershipchairman@uspcs.org

US Possessions Philatelic Society, Daniel F. Ring, P.O. Box 113, Woodstock, IL 60098; http://uspps.tripod.com; danielfring@hotmail.com

United States Stamp Society, Rod Juell, P.O. Box 3508, Joliet, IL 60434-3508; www.usstamps.org; execsecretary@usstamps.org

Africa

Bechuanalands and Botswana Society, Otto Peetoom, Roos, East Yorkshire HU12 0LD, United Kingdom; 44(0)1964 670239; www.bechuanalandphilately.com; info@bechuanalandphilately.com

Egypt Study Circle, Mike Murphy, 11 Waterbank Road, Bellingham, London SE6 3DJ United Kingdom; (44) 0203 6737051; www.egyptstudycircle.org.uk; secretary@egyptstudycircle.org.uk

Ethiopian Philatelic Society, Ulf Lindahl, 21 Westview Place, Riverside, CT 06878; (203) 722-0769; https://ethiopianphilatelicsociety.weebly.com; ulindahl@optonline.net

Liberian Philatelic Society, P.O. Box 1570, Parker, CO 80134; www.liberiastamps.org; liberiastamps@comcast.net

Orange Free State Study Circle, J. R. Stroud, RDPSA, 24 Hooper Close, Burnham-on-sea, Somerset TA8 1JQ United Kingdom; 44 1278 782235; www.orangefreestatephilately.org.uk; richard@richardstroud.plus.com

Philatelic Society for Greater Southern Africa, David McNamee, 15 Woodland Drive, Alamo, CA 94507; www.psgsa.org; alan.hanks@sympatico.ca

Rhodesian Study Circle, William R. Wallace, P.O. Box 16381, San Francisco, CA 94116; (415) 564-6069; www.rhodesianstudycircle.org.uk; bwall8rscr@earthlink.net

Society for Moroccan and Tunisian Philately, S.P.L.M., 206, Bld Pereire, 75017 Paris, France; http://splm-philatelie.org; splm206@aol.com

South Sudan Philatelic Society, William Barclay, 1370 Spring Hill Road, South Londonderry, VT 05155; barclayphilatelics@gmail.com

Sudan Study Group, Andy Neal, Bank House, Coedway, Shrewsbury SY5 9AR United Kingdom; www.sudanstamps.org; andywneal@gmail.com

Transvaal Study Circle, c/o 9 Meadow Road, Gravesend, Kent DA11 7LR United Kingdom; www.transvaalstamps.org.uk; transvaalstudycircle@aol.co.uk

West Africa Study Circle, Martin Bratzel, 1233 Virginia Ave., Windsor, ON N8S 2Z1 Canada; www.wasc.org.uk; marty_bratzel@yahoo.ca

Asia

Aden & Somaliland Study Group, Malcom Lacey, 108 Dalestorth Road, Sutton-in-Ashfield, Nottinghamshire NG17 3AA, United Kingdom; www.stampdomain.com/aden; neil53williams@yahoo.co.uk

Burma (Myanmar) Philatelic Study Circle, Michael Whittaker, 1, Ecton Leys, Hillside, Rugby, Warwickshire CV22 5SL United Kingdom; https://burmamyanmarphilately.wordpress.com/burma-myanmar-philatelic-study-circle; manningham8@mypostoffice.co.uk

Ceylon Study Circle, Rodney W. P. Frost, 42 Lonsdale Road, Cannington, Bridgwater, Somerset TA5 2JS United Kingdom; 01278 652592; www.ceylonsc.org; rodney.frost@tiscali.co.uk

China Stamp Society, H. James Maxwell, 1050 W. Blue Ridge Blvd., Kansas City, MO 64145-1216; www.chinastampsociety.org; president@chinastampsociety.org

Hong Kong Philatelic Society, John Tang, G.P.O. Box 446, Hong Kong; www.hkpsociety.com; hkpsociety@outlook.com

Hong Kong Study Circle, Robert Newton, www.hongkongstudycircle.com/index.html; newtons100@gmail.com

India Study Circle, John Warren, P.O. Box 7326, Washington, DC 20044; (202) 488-7443; https://indiastudycircle.org; jw-kbw@earthlink.net

International Philippine Philatelic Society, James R. Larot, Jr., 4990 Bayleaf Court, Martinez, CA 94553; (925) 260-5425; www.theipps.info; jlarot@ccwater.com

International Society for Japanese Philately, P.O. Box 1283, Haddonfield NJ 08033; www.isjp.org; secretary@isjp.org

Iran Philatelic Study Circle, Nigel Gooch, Marchwood, 56, Wickham Ave., Bexhill-on-Sea, East Sussex TN39 3ER United Kingdom; www.iranphilately.org; nigelmgooch@gmail.com

Korea Stamp Society, Peter Corson, 1109 Gunnison Place, Raleigh, NC 27609; (919) 787-7611; koreastampsociety.org; pbcorson@aol.com

Nepal & Tibet Philatelic Study Circle, Colin Hepper, 12 Charnwood Close, Peterborough, Cambs PE2 9BZ United Kingdom; http://fuchs-online.com/ntpsc; ntpsc@fuchs-online.com

Pakistan Philatelic Study Circle, Jeff Siddiqui, P.O. Box 7002, Lynnwood, WA 98046; jeffsiddiqui@msn.com

Society of Indo-China Philatelists, Ron Bentley, 2600 N. 24th St., Arlington, VA 22207; (703) 524-1652; www.sicp-online.org; ron.bentley@verizon.net

Society of Israel Philatelists, Inc., Sarah Berezenko, 100 Match Factory Place, Bellefonte, PA 16823-1367; (814) 933-3803 ext. 212; www.israelstamps.com; israelstamps@gmail.com

Australasia and Oceania

Australian States Study Circle of the Royal Sydney Philatelic Club, Ben Palmer, G.P.O. 1751, Sydney, NSW 2001 Australia; http://club.philas.org.au/states

Fellowship of Samoa Specialists, Trevor Shimell, 18 Aspen Drive, Newton Abbot, Devon TQ12 4TN United Kingdom; www.samoaexpress.org; trevor.shimell@gmail.com

Malaya Study Group, Michael Waugh, 151 Roker Lane, Pudsey, Leeds LS28 9ND United Kingdom; http://malayastudygroup.com; mawpud43@gmail.com

New Zealand Society of Great Britain, Michael Wilkinson, 121 London Road, Sevenoaks, Kent TN13 1BH United Kingdom; 01732 456997; www.nzsgb.org.uk; mwilkin799@aol.com

Pacific Islands Study Circle, John Ray, 24 Woodvale Ave., London SE25 4AE United Kingdom; www.pisc.org.uk; secretary@pisc.org.uk

Papuan Philatelic Society, Steven Zirinsky, P.O. Box 49, Ansonia Station, New York, NY 10023; (718) 706-0616; www.papuanphilatelicsociety.com; szirinsky@cs.com

Pitcairn Islands Study Group, Dr. Everett L. Parker, 207 Corinth Road, Hudson, ME 04449-3057; (207) 573-1686; www.pisg.net; eparker@hughes.net

Ryukyu Philatelic Specialist Society, Laura Edmonds, P.O. Box 240177, Charlotte, NC 28224-0177; (336) 509-3739; www.ryukyustamps.org; secretary@ryukyustamps.org

Society of Australasian Specialists / Oceania, Steve Zirinsky, P.O. Box 230049, New York, NY 10023-0049; www.sasoceania.org; president@sosoceania.org

Sarawak Specialists' Society, Stephen Schumann, 2417 Cabrallo Drive, Hayward, CA 94545; (510) 785-4794; www.britborneostamps.org.uk; vpnam@s-s-s.org.uk

Western Australia Study Group, Brian Pope, P.O. Box 423, Claremont, WA 6910 Australia; (61) 419 843 943; www.wastudygroup.com; wastudygroup@hotmail.com

Europe

American Helvetia Philatelic Society, Richard T. Hall, P.O. Box 15053, Asheville, NC 28813-0053; www.swiss-stamps.org; secretary2@swiss-stamps.org

American Society for Netherlands Philately, Hans Kremer, 50 Rockport Court, Danville, CA 94526; (925) 820-5841; www.asnp1975.com; hkremer@usa.net

Andorran Philatelic Study Circle, David Hope, 17 Hawthorn Drive, Stalybridge, Cheshire SK15 1UE United Kingdom; www.andorranpsc.org.uk; andorranpsc@btinternet.com

Austria Philatelic Society, Ralph Schneider, P.O. Box 978, Iowa Park, TX 76376; (940) 213-5004; www.austriaphilatelicsociety.com; rschneiderstamps@gmail.com

Channel Islands Specialists Society, Richard Flemming, Burbage, 64 Falconers Green, Hinckley, Leicestershire, LE102SX, United Kingdom; www.ciss.uk; secretary@ciss.uk

Cyprus Study Circle, Rob Wheeler, 47 Drayton Ave., London W13 0LE United Kingdom; www.cyprusstudycircle.org; robwheeler47@aol.com

Danish West Indies Study Unit of Scandinavian Collectors Club, Arnold Sorensen, 7666 Edgedale Drive, Newburgh, IN 47630; (812) 480-6532; www.scc-online.org; valbydwi@hotmail.com

Eire Philatelic Association, John B. Sharkey, 1559 Grouse Lane, Mountainside, NJ 07092-1340; www.eirephilatelicassoc.org; jsharkeyepa@me.com

Faroe Islands Study Circle, Norman Hudson, 40 Queen's Road, Vicar's Cross, Chester CH3 5HB United Kingdom; www.faroeislandssc.org; jntropics@hotmail.com

France & Colonies Philatelic Society, Edward Grabowski, 111 Prospect St., 4C, Westfield, NJ 07090; (908) 233-9318; www.franceandcolsps.org; edjjg@alum.mit.edu

Germany Philatelic Society, P.O. Box 6547, Chesterfield, MO 63006-6547; www.germanyphilatelicusa.org; info@germanyphilatelicsocietyusa.org

Gibraltar Study Circle, Susan Dare, 22, Byways Park, Strode Road, Clevedon, North Somerset BS21 6UR United Kingdom; www.gibraltarstudycircle.wordpress.com; smldare@yahoo.co.uk

International Society for Portuguese Philately, Clyde Homen, 1491 Bonnie View Road, Hollister, CA 95023-5117; www.portugalstamps.com; ispp1962@sbcglobal.net

Italy and Colonies Study Circle, Richard Harlow, 7 Duncombe House, 8 Manor Road, Teddington, Middlesex TW118BE United Kingdom; 44 208 977 8737; www.icsc-uk.com; richardharlow@outlook.com

Liechtenstudy USA, Paul Tremaine, 410 SW Ninth St., Dundee, OR 97115-9731; (503) 538-4500; www.liechtenstudy.org; tremaine@liechtenstudy.org

Lithuania Philatelic Society, Audrius Brazdeikis, 9915 Murray Landing, Missouri City, TX 77459; (281) 450-6224; www.lithuanianphilately.com/lps; audrius@lithuanianphilately.com

Luxembourg Collectors Club, Gary B. Little, 7319 Beau Road, Sechelt, BC V0N 3A8 Canada; (604) 885-7241; http://lcc.luxcentral.com; gary@luxcentral.com

Plebiscite-Memel-Saar Study Group of the German Philatelic Society, Clayton Wallace, 100 Lark Court, Alamo, CA 94507; claytonwallace@comcast.net

Polonus Polish Philatelic Society, Daniel Lubelski, P.O. Box 2212, Benicia, CA 94510; (419) 410-9115; www.polonus.org; info@polonus.org

Rossica Society of Russian Philately, Alexander Kolchinsky, 1506 Country Lake Drive, Champaign, IL 61821-6428; www.rossica.org; alexander.kolchinsky@rossica.org

Scandinavian Collectors Club, Alan Warren, Scandinavian Collectors Club, P.O. Box 39, Exton PA 19341-0039; (612) 810-8640; www.scc-online.org; alanwar@att.net

Society for Czechoslovak Philately, Tom Cossaboom, P.O. Box 4124, Prescott, AZ 86302; (928) 771-9097; www.csphilately.org; klfck1@aol.com

Society for Hungarian Philately, Alan Bauer, P.O. Box 4028, Vineyard Haven, MA 02568; (617) 645-4045; www.hungarianphilately.org; alan@hungarianstamps.com

Spanish Study Circle, Edith Knight, www.spaincircle.wixsite.com/spainstudycircle; spaincircle@gmail.com

Ukrainian Philatelic & Numismatic Society, Martin B. Tatuch, 5117 8th Road N., Arlington, VA 22205-1201; www.upns.org; treasurer@upns.org

Vatican Philatelic Society, Dennis Brady, 4897 Ledyard Drive, Manlius NY 13104-1514; www.vaticanphilately.org; dbrady7534@gmail.com

Yugoslavia Study Group, Michael Chant, 1514 N. Third Ave., Wausau, WI 54401; 208-748-9919; www.yugosg.org; membership@yugosg.org

Interregional Societies

American Society of Polar Philatelists, Alan Warren, P.O. Box 39, Exton, PA 19341-0039; (610) 321-0740; www.polarphilatelists.org; alanwar@att.net

First Issues Collector's Club, Kurt Streepy, 3128 E. Mattatha Drive, Bloomington, IN 47401; www.firstissues.org; secretary@firstissues.org

Former French Colonies Specialist Society, Col.fra, BP 628, 75367 Paris, France; www.colfra.org; postmaster@colfra.org

France & Colonies Philatelic Society, Edward Grabowski, 111 Prospect St., 4C, Westfield, NJ 07090; (908) 233-9318, www.franceandcolsps.org; edjjg@alum.mit.edu

Joint Stamp Issues Society, Richard Zimmermann, 29A, Rue Des Eviats, 67220 Lalaye, France; www.philarz.net; richard.zimmermann@club-internet.fr

The King George VI Collectors Society, Brian Livingstone, 21 York Mansions, Prince of Wales Drive, London SW11 4DL United Kingdom; www.kg6.info; livingstone484@btinternet.com

International Society of Reply Coupon Collectors, Peter Robin, P.O. Box 353, Bala Cynwyd, PA 19004; peterrobin@verizon.net

Italy and Colonies Study Circle, Richard Harlow, 7 Duncombe House, 8 Manor Road, Teddington, Middlesex TW118BE United Kingdom; 44 208 977 8737; www.icsc-uk.com; richardharlow@outlook.com

St. Helena, Ascension & Tristan Da Cunha Philatelic Society, Dr. Everett L. Parker, 207 Corinth Road, Hudson, ME 04449-3057; (207) 573-1686; www.shatps.org; eparker@hughes.net

United Nations Philatelists, Blanton Clement, Jr., P.O. Box 146, Morrisville, PA 19067-0146; www.unpi.com; bclemjunior@gmail.com

Latin America

Asociación Filatélica de Panamá, Edward D. Vianna B. ASOFILPA, 0819-03400, El Dorado, Panama; http://asociacionfilatelicadepanama.blogspot.com; asofilpa@gmail.com

Asociacion Mexicana de Filatelia (AMEXFIL), Alejandro Grossmann, Jose Maria Rico, 129, Col. Del Valle, 3100 Mexico City, DF Mexico; www.amexfil.mx; amexfil@gmail.com

Associated Collectors of El Salvador, Pierre Cahen, Vipsal 1342, P.O. Box 02-5364, Miami FL 33102; www.elsalvadorphilately.org; sfes-aces@elsalvadorphilately.org

Association Filatelic de Costa Rica, Giana Wayman (McCarty), #SJO 4935, P.O. Box 025723, Miami, FL 33102-5723; 011-506-2-228-1947; scotland@racsa.co.cr

Brazil Philatelic Association, William V. Kriebel, www.brazilphilatelic.org, info@brazilphilatelic.org

Canal Zone Study Group, Mike Drabik, P.O. Box 281, Bolton, MA 01740; www.canalzonestudygroup.com; czsgsecretary@gmail.com

Colombia-Panama Philatelic Study Group, Allan Harris, 26997 Hemmingway Ct, Hayward CA 94542-2349; www.copaphil.org; copaphilusa@aol.com

Falkland Islands Philatelic Study Groups, Morva White, 42 Colton Road, Shrivenham, Swindon SN6 8AZ United Kingdom; 44(0) 1793 783245; www.fipsg.org.uk; morawhite@supanet.com

Federacion Filatelica de la Republica de Honduras, Mauricio Mejia, Apartado Postal 1465, Tegucigalpa, D.C. Honduras; 504 3399-7227; www.facebook.com/filateliadehonduras; ffrh@hotmail.com

International Cuban Philatelic Society (ICPS), Ernesto Cuesta, P.O. Box 34434, Bethesda, MD 20827; (301) 564-3099; www.cubafil.org; ecuesta@philat.com

International Society of Guatemala Collectors, Jaime Marckwordt, 449 St. Francis Blvd., Daly City, CA 94015-2136; (415) 997-0295; www.guatemalastamps.com; president@guatamalastamps.com

Mexico-Elmhurst Philatelic Society International, Eric Stovner, P.O. Box 10097, Santa Ana, CA 92711-0097; www.mepsi.org; treasurer@mepsi.org

Nicaragua Study Group, Erick Rodriguez, 11817 S. W. 11th St., Miami, FL 33184-2501; nsgsec@yahoo.com

North America (excluding United States)

British Caribbean Philatelic Study Group, Bob Stewart, 7 West Dune Lane, Long Beach Township, NJ 08008; (941) 379-4108; www.bcpsg.com; bcpsg@comcast.net

British North America Philatelic Society, Andy Ellwood, 10 Doris Ave., Gloucester, ON K1T 3W8 Canada; www.bnaps.org; secretary@bnaps.org

British West Indies Study Circle, Steve Jarvis, 5 Redbridge Drive, Andover, Hants SP10 2LF United Kingdom; 01264 358065; www.bwisc.org; info@bwisc.org

Bermuda Collectors Society, John Pare, 405 Perimeter St., Mount Horeb, WI 53572; (608) 852-7358; www.bermudacollectorssociety.com; pare16@mhtc.net

Haiti Philatelic Society, Ubaldo Del Toro, 5709 Marble Archway, Alexandria, VA 22315; www.haitiphilately.org; u007ubi@aol.com

Hawaiian Philatelic Society, Gannon Sugimura, P.O. Box 10115, Honolulu, HI 96816-0115, www.hpshawaii.com; hiphilsoc@gmail.com

Stamp Dealer Associations

American Stamp Dealers Association, Inc., P.O. Box 513, Centre Hall PA 16828; (800) 369-8207; www.americanstampdealer.com; asda@americanstampdealer.com

National Stamp Dealers Association, Sheldon Ruckens, President, 3643 Private Road 18, Pinckneyville, IL 62274-3426; (618) 357-5497; www.nsdainc.org; nsda@nsdainc.org

Youth Philately

Young Stamp Collectors of America, 100 Match Factory Place, Bellefonte, PA 16823; (814) 933-3803; https://stamps.org/learn/youth-in-philately; ysca@stamps.org

ORGANIZE YOUR COLLECTION WITH
STOCK SHEETS

VARIO STOCK SHEETS

Vario stock sheets offer unparalleled quality and versatility. They're a convenient and easy way to store and organize stamps. Vario stock sheets are carefully manufactured to be free of harmful plasticized PVC, and softeners. Vario stock will fit all standard 3-ring binders and are available in a variety of sizes.

NOTE: Black sheets have pockets on both sides. Clear sheets have pockets on one side only. "S" in item number denotes black page. "C" in item number denotes clear page.

SOLD IN PACKAGES OF 5. RETAIL – $5.85 AA* – $4.98

10⅛" / 258 mm / 195 mm / 7⅝"	128 mm / 5"	5" / 128 mm / 3¾" / 96 mm	84 mm / 3¼"
V1S V1C	V2S V2C	V2ST	V3S V3C

63 mm / 2½" / 97mm / 3¾"	63 mm / 2½"	48 mm / 1⅞"	39 mm / 1½"
V4VC	V4S V4C	V5S V5C	V6S

33 mm / 1¼"	29mm / 1⅛"	10⅛" / 258 mm / 216 mm / 7⅝"
V7S	V8S	VIB

PRINZ STOCK SHEETS

Prinz stock pages offer convenience and flexibility. Pages are produced on thick, archival-quality paper with acetate pockets glued from the bottom of each pocket. They're ideal for the topical collector who may require various page styles to store a complete collection. **Sold in packages of 10.**

- Black background makes beautiful stamp presentation.
- Pockets use pull away/snap back principle.
- Multi-hole punch fits most binder types.
- Available in 9 different page formats. 8½" x 11"

Available with pockets on one side or both sides. "D" in item number denotes two-sided page.

Item		Retail	AA*	Item		Retail	AA*
S1	1 Pocket 242 mm	$11.99	$8.75	S5D	5 Pockets 45 mm	$17.99	$12.99
S1D	1 Pocket 242 mm	$17.99	$12.99	S6	6 Pockets 37 mm	$11.99	$8.75
S2	2 Pockets 119 mm	$11.99	$8.75	S6D	6 Pockets 37 mm	$17.99	$12.99
S2D	2 Pockets 119 mm	$17.99	$12.99	S7	7 Pockets 31 mm	$11.99	$8.75
S3	3 Pockets 79 mm	$11.99	$8.75	S7D	7 Pockets 31 mm	$17.99	$12.99
S3D	3 Pockets 79 mm	$17.99	$12.99	S8	8 Pockets 27 mm	$11.99	$8.75
S4	4 Pockets 58 mm	$11.99	$8.75	S8D	8 Pockets 27 mm	$17.99	$12.99
S4D	4 Pockets 58 mm	$17.99	$12.99	S9	Multi-Pockets	$11.99	$8.75
S5	5 Pockets 45 mm	$11.99	$8.75	S9D	Multi-Pockets	$17.99	$12.99

HAGNER STOCK SHEETS

The original Hagner Stock sheets are made from archival quality pH board and feature pure polyester film pockets that are glued to each page with special chemically inert glue. For more than 40 years, collectors all over the world have come to rely on Hagner stock sheets for their long-term stamp protection. Single-sided stock sheets are available in black or white. **Sold in packages of 5.**

Item				Retail	AA*
HGB01	One Pocket 242 mm		Black (Single-sided)	$7.25	$6.50
HGB11	One Pocket 242 mm		Black (Double-sided)	$11.75	$8.99
HGB02	Two Pocket 119 mm		Black (Single-sided)	$7.25	$6.50
HGB22	Two Pocket 119 mm		Black (Double-sided)	$11.75	$8.99
HGB03	Three Pocket 79 mm		Black (Single-sided)	$7.25	$6.50
HGB33	Three Pocket 79 mm		Black (Double-sided)	$11.75	$8.99
HGB04	Four Pocket 58 mm		Black (Single-sided)	$7.25	$6.50
HGB44	Four Pocket 58 mm		Black (Double-sided)	$11.75	$8.99
HGB05	Five Pocket 45 mm		Black (Single-sided)	$7.25	$6.50
HGB55	Five Pocket 45 mm		Black (Double-sided)	$11.75	$8.99
HGB06	Six Pocket 37 mm		Black (Single-sided)	$7.25	$6.50
HGB66	Six Pocket 37 mm		Black (Double-sided)	$11.75	$8.99
HGB07	Seven Pocket 31 mm		Black (Single-sided)	$7.25	$6.50
HGB77	Seven Pocket 31 mm		Black (Double-sided)	$11.75	$8.99
HGB08	Eight Pocket 27 mm		Black (Single-sided)	$7.25	$6.50
HGB88	Eight Pocket 27 mm		Black (Double-sided)	$11.75	$8.99
HGB09	Multi Pocket		Black (Single-sided)	$7.25	$6.50
HGB99	Multi Pocket		Black (Double-sided)	$11.75	$8.99

(Pocket sizes on Multi-pocket stock sheet are 36 mm, 67mm and 139mm).

3-RING BINDER WITH SLIPCASE

We have the binders for you! Take a look at our handsome matching binder and slipcase set. These great binder, slipcase sets are available in blue or black. If you want a heavy duty binder, checkout our metal-hinged, thick panel, 3-ring binder. What are you waiting for?

Item		Retail	AA*
SSBSBL	Blue 3-Ring Binder and Slipcase	$24.99	$19.99
SSBSBK	Black 3-Ring Binder and Slipcase	$24.99	$19.99
SSBMBK	Black Metal Hinged 3-Ring Binder	$24.99	$19.99

Get yours today by visiting www.AmosAdvantage.com

Or call 1-800-572-6885• Outside U.S. & Canada Call: 1-937-498-0800
P.O. Box 4129, Sidney, OH 45365

Expertizing services

The following organizations will, for a fee, provide expert opinions about stamps submitted to them. Collectors should contact these organizations to find out about their fees and requirements before submitting philatelic material to them. The listing of these groups here is not intended as an endorsement by Amos Media Co.

General Expertizing Services

American Philatelic Expertizing Service (a service of the American Philatelic Society)
100 Match Factory Place
Bellefonte PA 16823-1367
(814) 237-3803
www.stamps.org/stamp-authentication
apex@stamps.org
Areas of Expertise: Worldwide

BPA Expertising, Ltd.
P.O. Box 1141
Guildford, Surrey, GU5 0WR
United Kingdom
www.bpaexpertising.com
sec@bpaexpertising.org
Areas of Expertise: British Commonwealth, Great Britain, Classics of Europe, South America and the Far East

Philatelic Foundation
22 E. 35th St., 4th Floor
New York NY 10016
(212) 221-6555
www.philatelicfoundation.org
philatelicfoundation@verizon.net
Areas of Expertise: U.S. & Worldwide

Philatelic Stamp Authentication and Grading, Inc.
P.O. Box 41-0880
Melbourne FL 32941-0880
(305) 345-9864
www.psaginc.com
info@psaginc.com
Areas of Expertise: U.S., Canal Zone, Hawaii, Philippines, Canada & Provinces

Professional Stamp Experts
P.O. Box 539309
Henderson NV 89053-9309
(702) 776-6522
www.gradingmatters.com
www.psestamp.com
info@gradingmatters.com
Areas of Expertise: Stamps and Covers of U.S., U.S. Possessions, British Commonwealth

Royal Philatelic Society London Expert Committee
15 Abchurch Lane
London, EX4N 7BW
United Kingdom
www.rpsl.limited/experts.aspx
experts@rpsl.limited
Areas of Expertise: Worldwide

Expertizing Services Covering Specific Fields or Countries

China Stamp Society Expertizing Service
1050 W. Blue Ridge Blvd.
Kansas City MO 64145
(816) 942-6300
hjmesq@aol.com
Areas of Expertise: China

Civil War Philatelic Society Authentication Service
C/O Stefan T. Jaronski
P.O. Box 232
Sidney, MT 59270-0232
www.civilwarphilatelicsociety.org/authentication/
authentication@civilwarphilatelicsociety.org
Areas of Expertise: Confederate stamps and postal history

Errors, Freaks and Oddities Collectors Club Expertizing Service
138 East Lakemont Drive
Kingsland GA 31548
(912) 729-1573
Areas of Expertise: U.S. errors, freaks and oddities

Hawaiian Philatelic Society Expertizing Service
P.O. Box 10115
Honolulu HI 96816-0115
www.stampshows.com/hps.html
hiphilsoc@gmail.com
Areas of Expertise: Hawaii

Hong Kong Stamp Society Expertizing Service
P.O. Box 206
Glenside PA 19038
Areas of Expertise: Hong Kong

International Association of Philatelic Experts United States Associate members:
Paul Buchsbayew
119 W. 57th St.
New York NY 10019
(212) 977-7734
Areas of Expertise: Russia, Soviet Union

William T. Crowe
P.O. Box 2090
Danbury CT 06813-2090
wtcrowe@aol.com
Areas of Expertise: United States

John Lievsay
(see American Philatelic Expertizing Service and Philatelic Foundation)
Areas of Expertise: France

Robert W. Lyman
P.O. Box 348
Irvington on Hudson NY 10533
(914) 591-6937
Areas of Expertise: British North America, New Zealand

Robert Odenweller
P.O. Box 401
Bernardsville NJ 07924-0401
(908) 766-5460
Areas of Expertise: New Zealand, Samoa to 1900

Sergio Sismondo
The Regency Tower, Suite 1109
770 James St.
Syracuse NY 13203
(315) 422-2331
Areas of Expertise: British East Africa, Camerouns, Cape of Good Hope, Canada, British North America

International Society for Japanese Philately Expertizing Committee
132 North Pine Terrace
Staten Island NY 10312-4052
(718) 227-5229
Areas of Expertise: Japan and related areas, except WWII Japanese Occupation issues

International Society for Portuguese Philately Expertizing Service
P.O. Box 43146
Philadelphia PA 19129-3146
(215) 843-2106
s.s.washburne@worldnet.att.net
Areas of Expertise: Portugal and Colonies

Mexico-Elmhurst Philatelic Society International Expert Committee
Expert Committee Administrator
Marc E. Gonzales
P.O. Box 29040
Denver CO 80229-0040
www.mepsi.org/expert_committeee.htm
expertizations@mepsi.org
Areas of Expertise: Mexico

Ukrainian Philatelic & Numismatic Society Expertizing Service
30552 Dell Lane
Warren MI 48092-1862
Areas of Expertise: Ukraine, Western Ukraine

V. G. Greene Philatelic Research Foundation
P.O. Box 69100
St. Clair Post Office
Toronto, ON M4T 3A1
Canada
(416) 921-2073
www.greenefoundation.ca
info@greenefoundation.ca
Areas of Expertise: British North America

Information on catalogue values, grade and condition

Catalogue value

The Scott Catalogue value is a retail value; that is, an amount you could expect to pay for a stamp in the grade of Very Fine with no faults. Any exceptions to the grade valued will be noted in the text. The general introduction on the following pages and the individual section introductions further explain the type of material that is valued. The value listed for any given stamp is a reference that reflects recent actual dealer selling prices for that item.

Dealer retail price lists, public auction results, published prices in advertising and individual solicitation of retail prices from dealers, collectors and specialty organizations have been used in establishing the values found in this catalogue. Amos Media Co. values stamps, but Amos Media is not a company engaged in the business of buying and selling stamps as a dealer.

Use this catalogue as a guide for buying and selling. The actual price you pay for a stamp may be higher or lower than the catalogue value because of many different factors, including the amount of personal service a dealer offers, or increased or decreased interest in the country or topic represented by a stamp or set. An item may occasionally be offered at a lower price as a "loss leader," or as part of a special sale. You also may obtain an item inexpensively at public auction because of little interest at that time or as part of a large lot.

Stamps that are of a lesser grade than Very Fine, or those with condition problems, generally trade at lower prices than those given in this catalogue. Stamps of exceptional quality in both grade and condition often command higher prices than those listed.

Values for pre-1900 unused issues are for stamps with approximately half or more of their original gum. Stamps with most or all of their original gum may be expected to sell for more, and stamps with less than half of their original gum may be expected to sell for somewhat less than the values listed. On rarer stamps, it may be expected that the original gum will be somewhat more disturbed than it will be on more common issues. Post-1900 unused issues are assumed to have full original gum. From breakpoints in most countries' listings, stamps are valued as never hinged, due to the wide availability of stamps in that condition. These notations are prominently placed in the listings and in the country information preceding the listings. Some countries also feature listings with dual values for hinged and never-hinged stamps.

Grade

A stamp's grade and condition are crucial to its value. The accompanying illustrations show examples of Very Fine stamps from different time periods, along with examples of stamps in Fine to Very Fine and Extremely Fine grades as points of reference. When a stamp seller offers a stamp in any grade from fine to superb without further qualifying statements, that stamp should not only have the centering grade as defined, but it also should be free of faults or other condition problems.

FINE stamps (illustrations not shown) have designs that are quite off center, with the perforations on one or two sides very close to the design but not quite touching it. There is white space between the perforations and the design that is minimal but evident to the unaided eye. Imperforate stamps may have small margins, and earlier issues may show the design just touching one edge of the stamp design. Very early perforated issues normally will have the perforations slightly cutting into the design. Used stamps may have heavier than usual cancellations.

FINE-VERY FINE stamps will be somewhat off center on one side, or slightly off center on two sides. Imperforate stamps will have two margins of at least normal size, and the design will not touch any edge. For perforated stamps, the perfs are well clear of the design, but are still noticeably off center. *However, early issues of a country may be printed in such a way that the design naturally is very close to the edges. In these cases, the perforations may cut into the design very slightly.* Used stamps will not have a cancellation that detracts from the design.

VERY FINE stamps will be just slightly off center on one or two sides, but the design will be well clear of the edge. The stamp will present a nice, balanced appearance. Imperforate stamps will be well centered within normal-sized margins. *However, early issues of* many countries may be printed in such a way that the perforations may touch the design on one or more sides. Where this is the case, a boxed note will be found defining the centering and margins of the stamps being valued. Used stamps will have light or otherwise neat cancellations. This is the grade used to establish Scott Catalogue values.

EXTREMELY FINE stamps are close to being perfectly centered. Imperforate stamps will have even margins that are slightly larger than normal. Even the earliest perforated issues will have perforations clear of the design on all sides.

Amos Media Co. recognizes that there is no formally enforced grading scheme for postage stamps, and that the final price you pay or obtain for a stamp will be determined by individual agreement at the time of transaction.

Condition

Grade addresses only centering and (for used stamps) cancellation. *Condition* refers to factors other than grade that affect a stamp's desirability.

Factors that can increase the value of a stamp include exceptionally wide margins, particularly fresh color, the presence of selvage, and plate or die varieties. Unusual cancels on used stamps (particularly those of the 19th century) can greatly enhance their value as well.

Factors other than faults that decrease the value of a stamp include loss of original gum, regumming, a hinge remnant or foreign object adhering to the gum, natural inclusions, straight edges, and markings or notations applied by collectors or dealers.

Faults include missing pieces, tears, pin or other holes, surface scuffs, thin spots, creases, toning, short or pulled perforations, clipped perforations, oxidation or other forms of color changelings, soiling, stains, and such man-made changes as reperforations or the chemical removal or lightening of a cancellation.

Grading illustrations

On the following two pages are illustrations of various stamps from countries appearing in this volume. These stamps are arranged by country, and they represent early or important issues that are often found in widely different grades in the marketplace. The editors believe the illustrations will prove useful in showing the margin size and centering that will be seen on the various issues.

In addition to the matters of margin size and centering, collectors are reminded that the very fine stamps valued in the Scott catalogues also will possess fresh color and intact perforations, and they will be free from defects.

Examples shown are computer-manipulated images made from single digitized master illustrations.

Stamp illustrations used in the catalogue

It is important to note that the stamp images used for identification purposes in this catalogue may not be indicative of the grade of stamp being valued. Refer to the written discussion of grades on this page and to the grading illustrations on the following two pages for grading information.

Fine-Very Fine →

SCOTT CATALOGUES VALUE STAMPS IN THIS GRADE

Very Fine →

Extremely Fine →

Fine-Very Fine →

SCOTT CATALOGUES VALUE STAMPS IN THIS GRADE

Very Fine →

Extremely Fine →

Gum Conditions

For purposes of helping to determine the gum condition and value of an unused stamp, Scott presents the following chart which details different gum conditions and indicates how the conditions correlate with the Scott values for unused stamps. Used together, the Illustrated Grading Chart on the previous pages and this Illustrated Gum Chart should allow catalogue users to better understand the grade and gum condition of stamps valued in the Scott catalogues.

Never Hinged (NH; ★★): A never-hinged stamp will have full original gum that will have no hinge mark or disturbance. The presence of an expertizer's mark does not disqualify a stamp from this designation.

Original Gum (OG; ★): Pre-1900 stamps should have approximately half or more of their original gum. On rarer stamps, it may be expected that the original gum will be somewhat more disturbed than it will be on more common issues. Post-1900 stamps should have full original gum. Original gum will show some disturbance caused by a previous hinge(s) which may be present or entirely removed. The actual value of a post-1900 stamp will be affected by the degree of hinging of the full original gum.

Disturbed Original Gum: Gum showing noticeable effects of humidity, climate or hinging over more than half of the gum. The significance of gum disturbance in valuing a stamp in any of the Original Gum categories depends on the degree of disturbance, the rarity and normal gum condition of the issue and other variables affecting quality.

Regummed (RG; (★)): A regummed stamp is a stamp without gum that has had some type of gum privately applied at a time after it was issued. This normally is done to deceive collectors and/or dealers into thinking that the stamp has original gum and therefore has a higher value. A regummed stamp is considered the same as a stamp with none of its original gum for purposes of grading.

Gum Categories:	MINT N.H.	ORIGINAL GUM (O.G.)				NO GUM
	Mint Never Hinged *Free from any disturbance*	**Lightly Hinged** *Faint impression of a removed hinge over a small area*	**Hinge Mark or Remnant** *Prominent hinged spot with part or all of the hinge remaining*	**Large part o.g.** *Approximately half or more of the gum intact*	**Small part o.g.** *Approximately less than half of the gum intact*	**No gum** *Only if issued with gum*
Commonly Used Symbol:	★★	★	★	★	★	(★)
Pre-1900 Issues (Pre-1881 for U.S.)	*Very fine pre-1900 stamps in these categories trade at a premium over Scott value*			Scott Value for "Unused"		Scott "No Gum" listings for selected unused classic stamps
From 1900 to breakpoints for listings of never-hinged stamps	Scott "Never Hinged" listings for selected unused stamps	Scott Value for "Unused" (Actual value will be affected by the degree of hinging of the full o.g.)				
From breakpoints noted for many countries	Scott Value for "Unused"					

Understanding the listings

On the opposite page is an enlarged "typical" listing from this catalogue. Below are detailed explanations of each of the highlighted parts of the listing.

1 Scott number — Scott catalogue numbers are used to identify specific items when buying, selling or trading stamps. Each listed postage stamp from every country has a unique Scott catalogue number. Therefore, Germany Scott 99, for example, can only refer to a single stamp. Although the Scott catalogue usually lists stamps in chronological order by date of issue, there are exceptions. When a country has issued a set of stamps over a period of time, those stamps within the set are kept together without regard to date of issue. This follows the normal collecting approach of keeping stamps in their natural sets.

When a country issues a set of stamps over a period of time, a group of consecutive catalogue numbers is reserved for the stamps in that set, as issued. If that group of numbers proves to be too few, capital-letter suffixes, such as "A" or "B," may be added to existing numbers to create enough catalogue numbers to cover all items in the set. A capital-letter suffix indicates a major Scott catalogue number listing. Scott generally uses a suffix letter only once. Therefore, a catalogue number listing with a capital-letter suffix will seldom be found with the same letter (lower case) used as a minor-letter listing. If there is a Scott 16A in a set, for example, there will seldom be a Scott 16a. However, a minor-letter "a" listing may be added to a major number containing an "A" suffix (Scott 16Aa, for example).

Suffix letters are cumulative. A minor "b" variety of Scott 16A would be Scott 16Ab, not Scott 16b.

There are times when a reserved block of Scott catalogue numbers is too large for a set, leaving some numbers unused. Such gaps in the numbering sequence also occur when the catalogue editors move an item's listing elsewhere or have removed it entirely from the catalogue. Scott does not attempt to account for every possible number, but rather attempts to assure that each stamp is assigned its own number.

Scott numbers designating regular postage normally are only numerals. Scott numbers for other types of stamps, such as air post, semi-postal, postal tax, postage due, occupation and others have a prefix consisting of one or more capital letters or a combination of numerals and capital letters.

2 Illustration number — Illustration or design-type numbers are used to identify each catalogue illustration. For most sets, the lowest face-value stamp is shown. It then serves as an example of the basic design approach for other stamps not illustrated. Where more than one stamp use the same illustration number, but have differences in design, the design paragraph or the description line clearly indicates the design on each stamp not illustrated. Where there are both vertical and horizontal designs in a set, a single illustration may be used, with the exceptions noted in the design paragraph or description line.

When an illustration is followed by a lower-case letter in parentheses, such as "A2(b)," the trailing letter indicates which overprint or surcharge illustration applies.

Illustrations normally are 70 percent of the original size of the stamp. Oversized stamps, blocks and souvenir sheets are reduced even more. Overprints and surcharges are shown at 100 percent of their original size if shown alone, but are 70 percent of original size if shown on stamps. In some cases, the illustration will be placed above the set, between listings or omitted completely. Overprint and surcharge illustrations are not placed in this catalogue for purposes of expertizing stamps.

3 Paper color — The color of a stamp's paper is noted in italic type when the paper used is not white.

4 Listing styles — There are two principal types of catalogue listings: major and minor.

Major listings are in a larger type style than minor listings. The catalogue number is a numeral that can be found with or without a capital-letter suffix, and with or without a prefix.

Minor listings are in a smaller type style and have a small-letter suffix or (if the listing immediately follows that of the major number) may show only the letter. These listings identify a variety of the major item. Examples include perforation and shade differences, multiples (some souvenir sheets, booklet panes and se-tenant combinations), and singles of multiples.

Examples of major number listings include 16, 28A, B97, C13A, 10N5, and 10N6A. Examples of minor numbers are 16a and C13Ab.

5 Basic information about a stamp or set — Introducing each stamp issue is a small section (usually a line listing) of basic information about a stamp or set. This section normally includes the date of issue, method of printing, perforation, watermark and, sometimes, some additional information of note. *Printing method, perforation and watermark apply to the following sets until a change is noted.* Stamps created by overprinting or surcharging previous issues are assumed to have the same perforation, watermark, printing method and other production characteristics as the original. Dates of issue are as precise as Scott is able to confirm and often reflect the dates on first-day covers, rather than the actual date of release.

6 Denomination — This normally refers to the face value of the stamp; that is, the cost of the unused stamp at the post office at the time of issue. When a denomination is shown in parentheses, it does not appear on the stamp. This includes the nondenominated stamps of the United States, Brazil and Great Britain, for example.

7 Color or other description — This area provides information to solidify identification of a stamp. In many recent cases, a description of the stamp design appears in this space, rather than a listing of colors.

8 Year of issue — In stamp sets that have been released in a period that spans more than a year, the number shown in parentheses is the year that stamp first appeared. Stamps without a date appeared during the first year of the issue. Dates are not always given for minor varieties.

9 Value unused and Value used — The Scott catalogue values are based on stamps that are in a grade of Very Fine unless stated otherwise. Unused values refer to items that have not seen postal, revenue or any other duty for which they were intended. Pre-1900 unused stamps that were issued with gum must have at least most of their original gum. Later issues are assumed to have full original gum. From breakpoints specified in most countries' listings, stamps are valued as never hinged. Stamps issued without gum are noted. Modern issues with PVA or other synthetic adhesives may appear ungummed. Unused self-adhesive stamps are valued as appearing undisturbed on their original backing paper. Values for used self-adhesive stamps are for examples either on piece or off piece. For a more detailed explanation of these values, please see the "Catalogue Value," "Condition" and "Understanding Valuing Notations" sections elsewhere in this introduction.

In some cases, where used stamps are more valuable than unused stamps, the value is for an example with a contemporaneous cancel, rather than a modern cancel or a smudge or other unclear marking. For those stamps that were released for postal and fiscal purposes, the used value represents a postally used stamp. Stamps with revenue cancels generally sell for less.

Stamps separated from a complete se-tenant multiple usually will be worth less than a pro-rated portion of the se-tenant multiple, and stamps lacking the attached labels that are noted in the listings will be worth less than the values shown.

10 Changes in basic set information — Bold type is used to show any changes in the basic data given for a set of stamps. These basic data categories include perforation gauge measurement, paper type, printing method and watermark.

11 Total value of a set — The total value of sets of three or more stamps issued after 1900 are shown. The set line also notes the range of Scott numbers and total number of stamps included in the grouping. The actual value of a set consisting predominantly of stamps having the minimum value of 25 cents may be less than the total value shown. Similarly, the actual value or catalogue value of se-tenant pairs or of blocks consisting of stamps having the minimum value of 25 cents may be less than the catalogue values of the component parts.

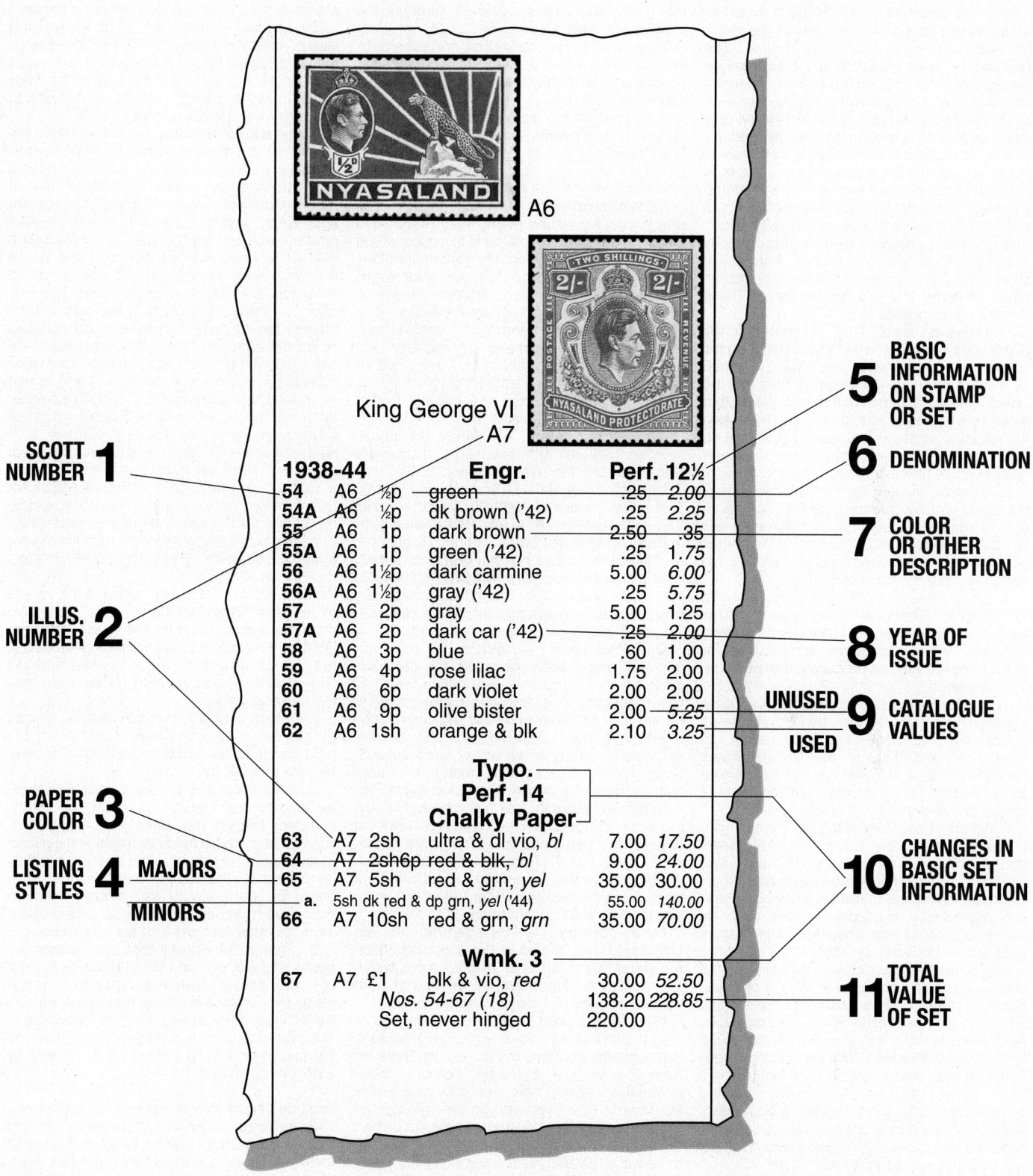

SCOTT NUMBER **1**

ILLUS. NUMBER **2**

PAPER COLOR **3**

LISTING STYLES **4** MAJORS MINORS

A6

King George VI
A7

5 BASIC INFORMATION ON STAMP OR SET

6 DENOMINATION

7 COLOR OR OTHER DESCRIPTION

8 YEAR OF ISSUE

9 CATALOGUE VALUES   UNUSED   USED

10 CHANGES IN BASIC SET INFORMATION

11 TOTAL VALUE OF SET

1938-44			Engr.	Perf. 12½	
54	A6	½p	green	.25	*2.00*
54A	A6	½p	dk brown ('42)	.25	*2.25*
55	A6	1p	dark brown	2.50	.35
55A	A6	1p	green ('42)	.25	1.75
56	A6	1½p	dark carmine	5.00	*6.00*
56A	A6	1½p	gray ('42)	.25	5.75
57	A6	2p	gray	5.00	1.25
57A	A6	2p	dark car ('42)	.25	*2.00*
58	A6	3p	blue	.60	1.00
59	A6	4p	rose lilac	1.75	2.00
60	A6	6p	dark violet	2.00	2.00
61	A6	9p	olive bister	2.00	*5.25*
62	A6	1sh	orange & blk	2.10	3.25

Typo.
Perf. 14
Chalky Paper

63	A7	2sh	ultra & dl vio, *bl*	7.00	*17.50*
64	A7	2sh6p	red & blk, *bl*	9.00	*24.00*
65	A7	5sh	red & grn, *yel*	35.00	30.00
a.			5sh dk red & dp grn, *yel* ('44)	55.00	*140.00*
66	A7	10sh	red & grn, *grn*	35.00	*70.00*

Wmk. 3

67	A7	£1	blk & vio, *red*	30.00	*52.50*
			Nos. 54-67 (18)	138.20	*228.85*
			Set, never hinged	220.00	

Catalogue listing policy

It is the intent of Amos Media Co. to list all postage stamps of the world in the Scott *Standard Postage Stamp Catalogue*. The only strict criteria for listing is that stamps be decreed legal for postage by the issuing country and that the issuing country actually have an operating postal system. Whether the primary intent of issuing a given stamp or set was for sale to postal patrons or to stamp collectors is not part of our listing criteria. Scott's role is to provide basic comprehensive postage stamp information. It is up to each stamp collector to choose which items to include in a collection.

It is Scott's objective to seek reasons why a stamp should be listed, rather than why it should not. Nevertheless, there are certain types of items that will not be listed. These include the following:

1. Unissued items that are not officially distributed or released by the issuing postal authority. If such items are officially issued at a later date by the country, they will be listed. Unissued items consist of those that have been printed and then held from sale for reasons such as change in government, errors found on stamps or something deemed objectionable about a stamp subject or design.

2. Stamps "issued" by non-existent postal entities or fantasy countries, such as Nagaland, Occusi-Ambeno, Staffa, Sedang, Torres Straits and others. Also, stamps "issued" in the names of legitimate, stamp-issuing countries that are not authorized by those countries.

3. Semi-official or unofficial items not required for postage. Examples include items issued by private agencies for their own express services. When such items are required for delivery, or are valid as prepayment of postage, they are listed.

4. Local stamps issued for local use only. Postage stamps issued by governments specifically for "domestic" use, such as Haiti Scott 219-228, or the United States nondenominated stamps, are not considered to be locals, since they are valid for postage throughout the country of origin.

5. Items not valid for postal use. For example, a few countries have issued souvenir sheets that are not valid for postage. This area also includes a number of worldwide charity labels (some denominated) that do not pay postage.

6. Egregiously exploitative issues such as stamps sold for far more than face value, stamps purposefully issued in artificially small quantities or only against advance orders, stamps awarded only to a selected audience such as a philatelic bureau's standing order customers, or stamps sold only in conjunction with other products. All of these kinds of items are usually controlled issues and/or are intended for speculation. These items normally will be included in a footnote.

7. Items distributed by the issuing government only to a limited group, club, philatelic exhibition or a single stamp dealer or other private company. These items normally will be included in a footnote.

8. Stamps not available to collectors. These generally are rare items, all of which are held by public institutions such as museums. The existence of such items often will be cited in footnotes.

The fact that a stamp has been used successfully as postage, even on international mail, is not in itself sufficient proof that it was legitimately issued. Numerous examples of so-called stamps from non-existent countries are known to have been used to post letters that have successfully passed through the international mail system.

There are certain items that are subject to interpretation. When a stamp falls outside our specifications, it may be listed along with a cautionary footnote.

A number of factors are considered in our approach to analyzing how a stamp is listed. The following list of factors is presented to share with you, the catalogue user, the complexity of the listing process.

Additional printings — "Additional printings" of a previously issued stamp may range from an item that is totally different to cases where it is impossible to differentiate from the original. At least a minor number (a small-letter suffix) is assigned if there is a distinct change in stamp shade, noticeably redrawn design, or a significantly different perforation measurement. A major number (numeral or numeral and capital-letter combination) is assigned if the editors feel the "additional printing" is sufficiently different from the original that it constitutes a different issue.

Commemoratives — Where practical, commemoratives with the same theme are placed in a set. For example, the U.S. Civil War Centennial set of 1961-65 and the Constitution Bicentennial series of 1989-90 appear as sets. Countries such as Japan and Korea issue such material on a regular basis, with an announced, or at least predictable, number of stamps known in advance. Occasionally, however, stamp sets that were released over a period of years have been separated. Appropriately placed footnotes will guide you to each set's continuation.

Definitive sets — Blocks of numbers generally have been reserved for definitive sets, based on previous experience with any given country. If a few more stamps were issued in a set than originally expected, they often have been inserted into the original set with a capital-letter suffix, such as U.S. Scott 1059A. If it appears that many more stamps than the originally allotted block will be released before the set is completed, a new block of numbers will be reserved, with the original one being closed off. In some cases, such as the U.S. Transportation and Great Americans series, several blocks of numbers exist. Appropriately placed footnotes will guide you to each set's continuation.

New country — Membership in the Universal Postal Union is not a consideration for listing status or order of placement within the catalogue. The index will tell you in what volume or page number the listings begin.

"No release date" items — The amount of information available for any given stamp issue varies greatly from country to country and even from time to time. Extremely comprehensive information about new stamps is available from some countries well before the stamps are released. By contrast some countries do not provide information about stamps or release dates. Most countries, however, fall between these extremes. A country may provide denominations or subjects of stamps from upcoming issues that are not issued as planned. Sometimes, philatelic agencies, those private firms hired to represent countries, add these later-issued items to sets well after the formal release date. This time period can range from weeks to years. If these items were officially released by the country, they will be added to the appropriate spot in the set. In many cases, the specific release date of a stamp or set of stamps may never be known.

Overprints — The color of an overprint is always noted if it is other than black. Where more than one color of ink has been used on overprints of a single set, the color used is noted. Early overprint and surcharge illustrations were altered to prevent their use by forgers.

Personalized Stamps — Since 1999, the special service of personalizing stamp vignettes, or labels attached to stamps, has been offered to customers by postal administrations of many countries. Sheets of these stamps are sold, singly or in quantity, only through special orders made by mail, in person, or through a sale on a computer website with the postal administrations or their agents for which an extra fee is charged, though some countries offer to collectors at face value personalized stamps having generic images in the vignettes or on the attached labels. It is impossible for any catalogue to know what images have been chosen by customers. Images can be 1) owned or created by the customer, 2) a generic image, or 3) an image pulled from a library of stock images on the stamp creation website. It is also impossible to know the quantity printed for any stamp having a particular image. So from a valuing standpoint, any image is equivalent to any other image for any personalized stamp having the same catalogue number. Illustrations of personalized stamps in the catalogue are not always those of stamps having generic images.

Personalized items are listed with some exceptions. These include:

1. Stamps or sheets that have attached labels that the customer cannot personalize, but which are nonetheless marketed as "personalized," and are sold for far more than the franking value.

2. Stamps or sheets that can be personalized by the customer, but where a portion of the print run must be ceded to the issuing country for sale to other customers.

3. Stamps or sheets that are created exclusively for a particular commercial client, or clients, including stamps that differ from any similar stamp that has been made available to the public.

4. Stamps or sheets that are deliberately conceived by the issuing authority that have been, or are likely to be, created with an excessive number of different face values, sizes, or other features that are changeable.

5. Stamps or sheets that are created by postal administrations using the same system of stamp personalization that has been put in place for use by the public that are printed in limited quantities and sold above face value.

6. Stamps or sheets that are created by licensees not directly affiliated or controlled by a postal administration.

Excluded items may or may not be footnoted.

Se-tenants — Connected stamps of differing features (se-tenants) will be listed in the format most commonly collected. This includes pairs, blocks or larger multiples. Se-tenant units are not always symmetrical. An example is Australia Scott 508, which is a block of seven stamps. If the stamps are primarily collected as a unit, the major number may be assigned to the multiple, with minors going to each component stamp. In cases where continuous-design or other unit se-tenants will receive significant postal use, each stamp is given a major Scott number listing. This includes issues from the United States, Canada, Germany and Great Britain, for example.

Special notices

Classification of stamps

The Scott Standard Postage Stamp Catalogue lists stamps by country of issue. The next level of organization is a listing by section on the basis of the function of the stamps. The principal sections cover regular postage, semi-postal, air post, special delivery, registration, postage due and other categories. Except for regular postage, catalogue numbers for all sections include a prefix letter (or number-letter combination) denoting the class to which a given stamp belongs. When some countries issue sets containing stamps from more than one category, the catalogue will at times list all of the stamps in one category (such as air post stamps listed as part of a postage set).

The following is a listing of the most commonly used catalogue prefixes.

Prefix.......Category
C..........Air Post
M.........Military
P..........Newspaper
N..........Occupation - Regular Issues
O..........Official
Q.........Parcel Post
J..........Postage Due
RA.......Postal Tax
B..........Semi-Postal
E..........Special Delivery
MR.......War Tax

Other prefixes used by more than one country include the following:
H..........Acknowledgment of Receipt
I...........Late Fee
CO.......Air Post Official
CQ.......Air Post Parcel Post
RAC.....Air Post Postal Tax
CF........Air Post Registration
CB.......Air Post Semi-Postal
CBO ....Air Post Semi-Postal Official
CE ......Air Post Special Delivery
EY........Authorized Delivery
S..........Franchise
G..........Insured Letter
GY.......Marine Insurance
MC.......Military Air Post
MQ ......Military Parcel Post
NC.......Occupation - Air Post
NO.......Occupation - Official
NJ........Occupation - Postage Due
NRA.....Occupation - Postal Tax
NB.......Occupation - Semi-Postal
NE ......Occupation - Special Delivery
QY.......Parcel Post Authorized Delivery
AR ....Postal-fiscal
RAJ......Postal Tax Due
RAB.....Postal Tax Semi-Postal
F..........Registration
EB........Semi-Postal Special Delivery
EO ....Special Delivery Official
QE ....Special Handling

New issue listings

Updates to this catalogue appear each month in the *Linn's Stamp News* monthly magazine. Included in this update are additions to the listings of countries found in the Scott *Standard Postage Stamp Catalogue* and the *Specialized Catalogue of United States Stamps and Covers,* as well as corrections and updates to current editions of this catalogue.

From time to time there will be changes in the final listings of stamps from the *Linn's Stamp News* magazine to the next edition of the catalogue. This occurs as more information about certain stamps or sets becomes available.

The catalogue update section of the *Linn's Stamp News* magazine is the most timely presentation of this material available. Annual subscriptions to *Linn's Stamp News* are available from Linn's Stamp News, Box 4129, Sidney, OH 45365-4129.

Number additions, deletions and changes

A listing of catalogue number additions, deletions and changes from the previous edition of the catalogue appears in each volume. See Catalogue Number Additions, Deletions & Changes in the table of contents for the location of this list.

Understanding valuing notations

The *minimum catalogue value* of an individual stamp or set is 25 cents. This represents a portion of the cost incurred by a dealer when he prepares an individual stamp for resale. As a point of philatelic-economic fact, the lower the value shown for an item in this catalogue, the greater the percentage of that value is attributed to dealer mark up and profit margin. In many cases, such as the 25-cent minimum value, that price does not cover the labor or other costs involved with stocking it as an individual stamp. The sum of minimum values in a set does not properly represent the value of a complete set primarily composed of a number of minimum-value stamps, nor does the sum represent the actual value of a packet made up of minimum-value stamps. Thus a packet of 1,000 different common stamps — each of which has a catalogue value of 25 cents — normally sells for considerably less than $250!

The *absence of a retail value* for a stamp does not necessarily suggest that a stamp is scarce or rare. A dash in the value column means that the stamp is known in a stated form or variety, but information is either lacking or insufficient for purposes of establishing a usable catalogue value.

Stamp values in *italics* generally refer to items that are difficult to value accurately. For expensive items, such as those priced at $1,000 or higher, a value in italics indicates that the affected item trades very seldom. For inexpensive items, a value in italics represents a warning. One example is a "blocked" issue where the issuing postal administration may have controlled one stamp in a set in an attempt to make the whole set more valuable. Another example is an item that sold at an extreme multiple of face value in the marketplace at the time of its issue.

One type of warning to collectors that appears in the catalogue is illustrated by a stamp that is valued considerably higher in used condition than it is as unused. In this case, collectors are cautioned to be certain the used version has a genuine and contemporaneous cancellation. The type of cancellation on a stamp can be an important factor in determining its sale price. Catalogue values do not apply to fiscal, telegraph or non-contemporaneous postal cancels, unless otherwise noted.

Some countries have released back issues of stamps in canceled-to-order form, sometimes covering as much as a 10-year period. The Scott Catalogue values for used stamps reflect canceled-to-order material when such stamps are found to predominate in the marketplace for the issue involved. Notes frequently appear in the stamp listings to specify which items are valued as canceled-to-order, or if there is a premium for postally used examples.

Many countries sell canceled-to-order stamps at a marked reduction of face value. Countries that sell or have sold canceled-to-order stamps at *full* face value include United Nations, Australia, Netherlands, France and Switzerland. It may be almost impossible to identify such stamps if the gum has been removed, because official government canceling devices are used. Postally used examples of these items on cover, however, are usually worth more than the canceled-to-order stamps with original gum.

Abbreviations

Scott uses a consistent set of abbreviations throughout this catalogue to conserve space, while still providing necessary information.

Color Abbreviations

amb	amber	crim	crimson	ol	olive
anil	aniline	cr	cream	olvn	olivine
ap	apple	dk	dark	org	orange
aqua	aquamarine	dl	dull	pck	peacock
az	azure	dp	deep	pnksh	pinkish
bis	bister	db	drab	Prus	Prussian
bl	blue	emer	emerald	pur	purple
bld	blood	gldn	golden	redsh	reddish
blk	black	grysh	grayish	res	reseda
bril	brilliant	grn	green	ros	rosine
brn	brown	grnsh	greenish	ryl	royal
brnsh	brownish	hel	heliotrope	sal	salmon
brnz	bronze	hn	henna	saph	sapphire
brt	bright	ind	indigo	scar	scarlet
brnt	burnt	int	intense	sep	sepia
car	carmine	lav	lavender	sien	sienna
cer	cerise	lem	lemon	sil	silver
chlky	chalky	lil	lilac	sl	slate
cham	chamois	lt	light	stl	steel
chnt	chestnut	mag	magenta	turq	turquoise
choc	chocolate	man	manila	ultra	ultramarine
chr	chrome	mar	maroon	Ven	Venetian
cit	citron	mv	mauve	ver	vermilion
cl	claret	multi	multicolored	vio	violet
cob	cobalt	mlky	milky	yel	yellow
cop	copper	myr	myrtle	yelsh	yellowish

When no color is given for an overprint or surcharge, black is the color used. Abbreviations for colors used for overprints and surcharges include: "(B)" or "(Blk)," black; "(Bl)," blue; "(R)," red; and "(G)," green.

Additional abbreviations in this catalogue are shown below:

Adm.	Administration
AFL	American Federation of Labor
Anniv.	Anniversary
APS	American Philatelic Society
Assoc.	Association
ASSR.	Autonomous Soviet Socialist Republic
b	Born
BEP	Bureau of Engraving and Printing
Bicent.	Bicentennial
Bklt.	Booklet
Brit.	British
btwn	Between
Bur.	Bureau
c. or ca.	Circa
Cat.	Catalogue
Cent.	Centennial, century, centenary
CIO	Congress of Industrial Organizations
Conf.	Conference
Cong.	Congress
Cpl.	Corporal
CTO	Canceled to order
d	Died
Dbl.	Double
EDU	Earliest documented use
Engr.	Engraved
Exhib.	Exhibition
Expo.	Exposition
Fed	Federation
GB	Great Britain
Gen.	General
GPO	General post office
Horiz.	Horizontal
Imperf.	Imperforate
Impt.	Imprint
Intl.	International

Invtd.	Inverted
L	Left
Lieut., lt.	Lieutenant
Litho.	Lithographed
LL	Lower left
LR	Lower right
mm	Millimeter
Ms.	Manuscript
Natl.	National
No.	Number
NY	New York
NYC	New York City
Ovpt.	Overprint
Ovptd.	Overprinted
P	Plate number
Perf.	Perforated, perforation
Phil.	Philatelic
Photo.	Photogravure
PO	Post office
Pr.	Pair
P.R.	Puerto Rico
Prec.	Precancel, precanceled
Pres.	President
PTT	Post, Telephone and Telegraph
R	Right
Rio	Rio de Janeiro
Sgt.	Sergeant
Soc.	Society
Souv.	Souvenir
SSR	Soviet Socialist Republic, see ASSR
St.	Saint, street
Surch.	Surcharge
Typo.	Typographed
UL	Upper left
Unwmkd.	Unwatermarked
UPU	Universal Postal Union
UR	Upper Right
US	United States
USPOD	United States Post Office Department
USSR	Union of Soviet Socialist Republics
Vert.	Vertical
VP	Vice president
Wmk.	Watermark
Wmkd.	Watermarked
WWI	World War I
WWII	World War II

Examination

Amos Media Co. will not comment upon the genuineness, grade or condition of stamps, because of the time and responsibility involved. Rather, there are several expertizing groups that undertake this work for both collectors and dealers. Neither will Amos Media Co. appraise or identify philatelic material. The company cannot take responsibility for unsolicited stamps or covers sent by individuals.

All letters, emails, etc. are read attentively, but they are not always answered because of time considerations.

How to order from your dealer

When ordering stamps from a dealer, it is not necessary to write the full description of a stamp as listed in this catalogue. All you need is the name of the country, the Scott catalogue number and whether the desired item is unused or used. For example, "Japan Scott 422 unused" is sufficient to identify the unused stamp of Japan listed as "422 A206 5y brown."

Basic stamp information

A stamp collector's knowledge of the combined elements that make a given stamp issue unique determines his or her ability to identify stamps. These elements include paper, watermark, method of separation, printing, design and gum. On the following pages each of these important areas is briefly described.

Paper

Paper is an organic material composed of a compacted weave of cellulose fibers and generally formed into sheets. Paper used to print stamps may be manufactured in sheets, or it may have been part of a large roll (called a web) before being cut to size. The fibers most often used to create paper on which stamps are printed include bark, wood, straw and certain grasses. In many cases, linen or cotton rags have been added for greater strength and durability. Grinding, bleaching, cooking and rinsing these raw fibers reduces them to a slushy pulp, referred to by paper makers as "stuff." Sizing and, sometimes, coloring matter is added to the pulp to make different types of finished paper.

After the stuff is prepared, it is poured onto sieve-like frames that allow the water to run off, while retaining the matted pulp. As fibers fall onto the screen and are held by gravity, they form a natural weave that will later hold the paper together. If the screen has metal bits that are formed into letters or images attached, it leaves slightly thinned areas on the paper. These are called watermarks.

When the stuff is almost dry, it is passed under pressure through smooth or engraved rollers — dandy rolls — or placed between cloth in a press to be flattened and dried.

Wove — **Laid** — **Granite**

Quadrille — **Oblong Quadrille** — **Laid Batonne**

Stamp paper falls broadly into two types: wove and laid. The nature of the surface of the frame onto which the pulp is first deposited causes the differences in appearance between the two. If the surface is smooth and even, the paper will be of fairly uniform texture throughout. This is known as wove paper. Early papermaking machines poured the pulp onto a continuously circulating web of felt, but modern machines feed the pulp onto a cloth-like screen made of closely interwoven fine wires. This paper, when held to a light, will show little dots or points very close together. The proper name for this is "wire wove," but the type is still considered wove. Any U.S. or British stamp printed after 1880 will serve as an example of wire wove paper.

Closely spaced parallel wires, with cross wires at wider intervals, make up the frames used for what is known as laid paper. A greater thickness of the pulp will settle between the wires. The paper, when held to a light, will show alternate light and dark lines. The spacing and the thickness of the lines may vary, but on any one sheet of paper they are all alike. See Russia Scott 31-38 for examples of laid paper.

Batonne, from the French word meaning "a staff," is a term used if the lines in the paper are spaced quite far apart, like the printed ruling on a writing tablet. Batonne paper may be either wove or laid. If laid, fine laid lines can be seen between the batons.

Quadrille is the term used when the lines in the paper form little squares. Oblong quadrille is the term used when rectangles, rather than

squares, are formed. Grid patterns vary from distinct to extremely faint. See Mexico-Guadalajara Scott 35-37 for examples of oblong quadrille paper.

Paper also is classified as thick or thin, hard or soft, and by color. Such colors may include yellowish, greenish, bluish and reddish.

Brief explanations of other types of paper used for printing stamps, as well as examples, follow.

Colored — Colored paper is created by the addition of dye in the paper-making process. Such colors may include shades of yellow, green, blue and red. Surface-colored papers, most commonly used for British colonial issues in 1913-14, are created when coloring is added only to the surface during the finishing process. Stamps printed on surface-colored paper have white or uncolored backs, while true colored papers are colored through. See Jamaica Scott 71-73.

Pelure — Pelure paper is a very thin, hard and often brittle paper that is sometimes bluish or grayish in appearance. See Serbia Scott 169-170.

Native — This is a term applied to handmade papers used to produce some of the early stamps of the Indian states. Stamps printed on native paper may be expected to display various natural inclusions that are normal and do not negatively affect value. Japanese paper, originally made of mulberry fibers and rice flour, is part of this group. See Japan Scott 1-18.

Manila — This type of paper is often used to make stamped envelopes and wrappers. It is a coarse-textured stock, usually smooth on one side and rough on the other. A variety of colors of manila paper exist, but the most common range is yellowish-brown.

Silk — Introduced by the British in 1847 as a safeguard against counterfeiting, silk paper contains bits of colored silk thread scattered throughout. The density of these fibers varies greatly and can include as few as one fiber per stamp or hundreds. U.S. revenue Scott R152 is a good example of an easy-to-identify silk paper stamp.

Silk-thread paper has uninterrupted threads of colored silk arranged so that one or more threads run through the stamp or postal stationery. See Great Britain Scott 5-6 and Switzerland Scott 14-19.

Granite — Filled with minute cloth or colored paper fibers of various colors and lengths, granite paper should not be confused with either type of silk paper. Austria Scott 172-175 and a number of Swiss stamps are examples of granite paper.

Chalky — A chalk-like substance coats the surface of chalky paper to discourage the cleaning and reuse of canceled stamps, as well as to provide a smoother, more acceptable printing surface. Because the designs of stamps printed on chalky paper are imprinted on what is often a water-soluble coating, any attempt to remove a cancellation will destroy the stamp. Do not soak these stamps in any fluid. To remove a stamp printed on chalky paper from an envelope, wet the paper from underneath the stamp until the gum dissolves enough to release the stamp from the paper. See St. Kitts-Nevis Scott 89-90 for examples of stamps printed on this type of chalky paper.

India — Another name for this paper, originally introduced from China about 1750, is "China Paper." It is a thin, opaque paper often used for plate and die proofs by many countries.

Double — In philately, the term double paper has two distinct meanings. The first is a two-ply paper, usually a combination of a thick and a thin sheet, joined during manufacture. This type was used experimentally as a means to discourage the reuse of stamps.

The design is printed on the thin paper. Any attempt to remove a cancellation would destroy the design. U.S. Scott 158 and other Banknote-era stamps exist on this form of double paper.

The second type of double paper occurs on a rotary press, when the end of one paper roll, or web, is affixed to the next roll to save time feeding the paper through the press. Stamp designs are printed over the joined paper and, if overlooked by inspectors, may get into post office stocks.

Goldbeater's Skin — This type of paper was used for the 1866 issue of Prussia, and was a tough, translucent paper. The design was printed in reverse on the back of the stamp, and the gum applied over the printing. It is impossible to remove stamps printed on this type of paper from the paper to which they are affixed without destroying the design.

Ribbed — Ribbed paper has an uneven, corrugated surface made by passing the paper through ridged rollers. This type exists on some copies of U.S. Scott 156-165.

Various other substances, or substrates, have been used for stamp manufacture, including wood, aluminum, copper, silver and gold foil, plastic, and silk and cotton fabrics.

Watermarks

Watermarks are an integral part of some papers. They are formed in the process of paper manufacture. Watermarks consist of small designs, formed of wire or cut from metal and soldered to the surface of the mold or, sometimes, on the dandy roll. The designs may be in the form of crowns, stars, anchors, letters or other characters or symbols. These pieces of metal — known in the paper-making industry as "bits" — impress a design into the paper. The design sometimes may be seen by holding the stamp to the light. Some are more easily seen with a watermark detector. This important tool is a small black tray into which a stamp is placed face down and dampened with a fast-evaporating watermark detection fluid that brings up the watermark image in the form of dark lines against a lighter background. These dark lines are the thinner areas of the paper known as the watermark. Some watermarks are extremely difficult to locate, due to either a faint impression, watermark location or the color of the stamp. There also are electric watermark detectors that come with plastic filter disks of various colors. The disks neutralize the color of the stamp, permitting the watermark to be seen more easily.

Multiple watermarks of Crown Agents and Burma

Watermarks of Uruguay, Vatican City and Jamaica

WARNING: Some inks used in the photogravure process dissolve in watermark fluids (Please see the section on Soluble Printing Inks). Also, see "chalky paper."

Watermarks may be found normal, reversed, inverted, reversed and inverted, sideways or diagonal, as seen from the back of the stamp. The relationship of watermark to stamp design depends on the position of the printing plates or how paper is fed through the press. On machine-made paper, watermarks normally are read from right to left. The design is repeated closely throughout the sheet in a "multiple-watermark design." In a "sheet watermark," the design appears only once on the sheet, but extends over many stamps. Individual stamps may carry only a small fraction or none of the watermark.

"Marginal watermarks" occur in the margins of sheets or panes of stamps. They occur on the outside border of paper (ostensibly outside the area where stamps are to be printed). A large row of letters may spell the name of the country or the manufacturer of the paper, or a border of lines may appear. Careless press feeding may cause parts of these letters and/or lines to show on stamps of the outer row of a pane.

Soluble printing inks

WARNING: Most stamp colors are permanent; that is, they are not seriously affected by short-term exposure to light or water. Many colors, especially of modern inks, fade from excessive exposure to light. There are stamps printed with inks that dissolve easily in water or in fluids used to detect watermarks. Use of these inks was intentional to prevent the removal of cancellations. Water affects all aniline inks, those on so-called safety paper and some photogravure printings - all such inks are known as fugitive colors. Removal from paper of such stamps requires care and alternatives to traditional soaking.

Separation

"Separation" is the general term used to describe methods used to separate stamps. The three standard forms currently in use are perforating, rouletting and die-cutting. These methods are done during the stamp production process, after printing. Sometimes these methods are done on-press or sometimes as a separate step. The earliest issues, such as the 1840 Penny Black of Great Britain (Scott 1), did not have any means provided for separation. It was expected the stamps would be cut apart with scissors or folded and torn. These are examples of imperforate stamps. Many stamps were first issued in imperforate formats and were later issued with perforations. Therefore, care must be observed in buying single imperforate stamps to be certain they were issued imperforate and are not perforated copies that have been altered by having the perforations trimmed away. Stamps issued imperforate usually are valued as singles. However, imperforate varieties of normally perforated stamps should be collected in pairs or larger pieces as indisputable evidence of their imperforate character.

PERFORATION

The chief style of separation of stamps, and the one that is in almost universal use today, is perforating. By this process, paper between the stamps is cut away in a line of holes, usually round, leaving little bridges of paper between the stamps to hold them together. Some types of perforation, such as hyphen-hole perfs, can be confused with roulettes, but a close visual inspection reveals that paper has been removed. The little perforation bridges, which project from the stamp when it is torn from the pane, are called the teeth of the perforation.

As the size of the perforation is sometimes the only way to differentiate between two otherwise identical stamps, it is necessary to be able to accurately measure and describe them. This is done with a perforation gauge, usually a ruler-like device that has dots or graduated lines to show how many perforations may be counted in the space of two centimeters. Two centimeters is the space universally adopted in which to measure perforations.

Perforation gauge

To measure a stamp, run it along the gauge until the dots on it fit exactly into the perforations of the stamp. If you are using a graduated-line perforation gauge, simply slide the stamp along the surface until the lines on the gauge perfectly project from the center of the bridges or holes. The number to the side of the line of dots or lines that fit the stamp's perforation is the measurement. For example, an "11" means that 11 perforations fit between two centimeters. The description of the stamp therefore is "perf. 11." If the gauge of the perforations on the top and bottom of a stamp differs from that on the sides, the result is what is known as compound perforations. In measuring compound perforations, the gauge at top and bottom is always given first, then the sides. Thus, a stamp that measures 11 at top and bottom and 10½ at the sides is "perf. 11 x 10½." See U.S. Scott 632-642 for examples of compound perforations.

Stamps also are known with perforations different on three or all four sides. Descriptions of such items are clockwise, beginning with the top of the stamp.

A perforation with small holes and teeth close together is a "fine perforation." One with large holes and teeth far apart is a "coarse perforation." Holes that are jagged, rather than clean-cut, are "rough perforations." *Blind perforations* are the slight impressions left by the perforating pins if they fail to puncture the paper. Multiples of stamps showing blind perforations may command a slight premium over normally perforated stamps.

The term *syncopated perfs* describes intentional irregularities in the perforations. The earliest form was used by the Netherlands from 1925-33, where holes were omitted to create distinctive patterns. Beginning in 1992, Great Britain has used an oval perforation to help prevent counterfeiting. Several other countries have started using the oval perfs or other syncopated perf patterns.

A new type of perforation, still primarily used for postal stationery, is known as microperfs. Microperfs are tiny perforations (in some cases hundreds of holes per two centimeters) that allows items to be intentionally separated very easily, while not accidentally breaking apart as easily as standard perforations. These are not currently measured or differentiated by size, as are standard perforations.

perce en arc

perce en lignes

perce en points

oblique roulette

perce en scie

perce serpentin

ROULETTING

In rouletting, the stamp paper is cut partly or wholly through, with no paper removed. In perforating, some paper is removed. Rouletting derives its name from the French roulette, a spur-like wheel. As the wheel is rolled over the paper, each point makes a small cut. The number of cuts made in a two-centimeter space determines the gauge of the roulette, just as the number of perforations in two centimeters determines the gauge of the perforation.

The shape and arrangement of the teeth on the wheels varies. Various roulette types generally carry French names:

Perce en lignes — rouletted in lines. The paper receives short, straight cuts in lines. This is the most common type of roulette. See Mexico Scott 500.

Perce en points — pin-rouletted or pin-perfed. This differs from a small perforation because no paper is removed, although round, equidistant holes are pricked through the paper. See Mexico Scott 242-256.

Perce en arc and perce en scie — pierced in an arc or saw-toothed designs, forming half circles or small triangles. See Hanover (German States) Scott 25-29.

Perce en serpentin — serpentine roulettes. The cuts form a serpentine or wavy line. See Brunswick (German States) Scott 13-18.

Once again, no paper is removed by these processes, leaving the stamps easily separated, but closely attached.

DIE-CUTTING

The third major form of stamp separation is die-cutting. This is a method where a die in the pattern of separation is created that later cuts the stamp paper in a stroke motion. Although some standard stamps bear die-cut perforations, this process is primarily used for self-adhesive postage stamps. Die-cutting can appear in straight lines, such as U.S. Scott 2522, shapes, such as U.S. Scott 1551, or imitating the appearance of perforations, such as New Zealand Scott 935A and 935B.

Printing processes

ENGRAVING (Intaglio, Line-engraving, Etching)

Master die — The initial operation in the process of line engraving is making the master die. The die is a small, flat block of softened steel upon which the stamp design is recess engraved in reverse.

Photographic reduction of the original art is made to the appropriate size. It then serves as a tracing guide for the initial outline of the design. The engraver lightly traces the design on the steel with his graver, then slowly works the design until it is completed. At various points during the engraving process, the engraver hand-inks the die and makes an impression to check his progress. These are known as progressive die proofs. After completion of the engraving, the die is hardened to withstand the stress and pressures of later transfer operations.

Transfer roll

Transfer roll — Next is production of the transfer roll that, as the name implies, is the medium used to transfer the subject from the master die to the printing plate. A blank roll of soft steel, mounted on a mandrel, is placed under the bearers of the transfer press to allow it to roll freely on its axis. The hardened die is placed on the bed of the press and the face of the transfer roll is applied to the die, under pressure. The bed or the roll is then rocked back and forth under increasing pressure, until the soft steel of the roll is forced into every engraved line of the die. The resulting impression on the roll is known as a "relief" or a "relief transfer." The engraved image is now positive in appearance and stands out from the steel. After the required number of reliefs are "rocked in," the soft steel transfer roll is hardened.

Different flaws may occur during the relief process. A defective relief may occur during the rocking in process because of a minute piece of foreign material lodging on the die, or some other cause. Imperfections in the steel of the transfer roll may result in a breaking away of parts of the design. This is known as a relief break, which will show up on finished stamps as small, unprinted areas. If a damaged relief remains in use, it will transfer a repeating defect to the plate. Deliberate alterations of reliefs sometimes occur. "Altered reliefs" designate these changed conditions.

Plate — The final step in pre-printing production is the making of the printing plate. A flat piece of soft steel replaces the die on the bed of the transfer press. One of the reliefs on the transfer roll is positioned over this soft steel. Position, or layout, dots determine the correct position on the plate. The dots have been lightly marked on the plate in advance. After the correct position of the relief is determined, the design is rocked in by following the same method used in making the transfer roll. The difference is that this time the image is being transferred from the transfer roll, rather than to it. Once the design is entered on the plate, it appears in reverse and is recessed. There are as many transfers entered on the plate as there are subjects printed on the sheet of stamps. It is during this process that double and shifted transfers occur, as well as re-entries. These are the result of improperly entered images that have not been properly burnished out prior to rocking in a new image.

Modern siderography processes, such as those used by the U.S. Bureau of Engraving and Printing, involve an automated form of rocking designs in on preformed cylindrical printing sleeves. The same process also allows for easier removal and re-entry of worn images right on the sleeve.

Transferring the design to the plate

Following the entering of the required transfers on the plate, the position dots, layout dots and lines, scratches and other markings generally are burnished out. Added at this time by the siderographer are any required guide lines, plate numbers or other marginal markings. The plate is then hand-inked and a proof impression is taken. This is known as a plate proof. If the impression is approved, the plate is machined for fitting onto the press, is hardened and sent to the plate vault ready for use.

On press, the plate is inked and the surface is automatically wiped clean, leaving ink only in the recessed lines. Paper is then forced under pressure into the engraved recessed lines, thereby receiving the ink. Thus, the ink lines on engraved stamps are slightly raised, and slight depressions (debossing) occur on the back of the stamp. Prior to the advent of modern high-speed presses and more advanced ink formulations, paper had to be dampened before receiving the ink. This sometimes led to uneven shrinkage by the time the stamps were perforated, resulting in improperly perforated stamps, or misperfs. Newer presses use drier paper, thus both *wet and dry printings* exist on some stamps.

Rotary Press — Until 1914, only flat plates were used to print engraved stamps. Rotary press printing was introduced in 1914, and slowly spread. Some countries still use flat-plate printing.

After approval of the plate proof, older rotary press plates require additional machining. They are curved to fit the press cylinder. "Gripper slots" are cut into the back of each plate to receive the "grippers," which hold the plate securely on the press. The plate is then hardened. Stamps printed from these bent rotary press plates are longer or wider than the same stamps printed from flat-plate presses. The stretching of the plate during the curving process is what causes this distortion.

Re-entry — To execute a re-entry on a flat plate, the transfer roll is re-applied to the plate, often at some time after its first use on the press. Worn-out designs can be resharpened by carefully burnishing out the original image and re-entering it from the transfer roll. If the original impression has not been sufficiently removed and the transfer roll is not precisely in line with the remaining impression, the resulting double transfer will make the re-entry obvious. If the registration is true, a re-entry may be difficult or impossible to distinguish. Sometimes a stamp printed from a successful re-entry is identified by having a much sharper and clearer impression than its neighbors. With the advent of rotary presses, post-press re-entries were not possible. After a plate was curved for the rotary press, it was impossible to make a re-entry. This is because the plate had already been bent once (with the design distorted).

However, with the introduction of the previously mentioned modern-style siderography machines, entries are made to the preformed cylindrical printing sleeve. Such sleeves are dechromed and softened. This allows individual images to be burnished out and re-entered on the curved sleeve. The sleeve is then rechromed, resulting in longer press life.

Double Transfer — This is a description of the condition of a transfer on a plate that shows evidence of a duplication of all, or a portion of the design. It usually is the result of the changing of the registration between the transfer roll and the plate during the rocking in of the original entry. Double transfers also occur when only a portion of the design has been rocked in and improper positioning is noted. If the worker elected not to burnish out the partial or completed design, a strong double transfer will occur for part or all of the design.

It sometimes is necessary to remove the original transfer from a plate and repeat the process a second time. If the finished re-worked image shows traces of the original impression, attributable to incomplete burnishing, the result is a partial double transfer.

With the modern automatic machines mentioned previously, double transfers are all but impossible to create. Those partially doubled images on stamps printed from such sleeves are more than likely re-entries, rather than true double transfers.

Re-engraved — Alterations to a stamp design are sometimes necessary after some stamps have been printed. In some cases, either the original die or the actual printing plate may have its "temper" drawn (softened), and the design will be re-cut. The resulting impressions from such a re-engraved die or plate may differ slightly from the original issue, and are known as "re-engraved." If the alteration was made to the master die, all future printings will be consistently different from the original. If alterations were made to the printing plate, each altered stamp on the plate will be slightly different from each other, allowing specialists to reconstruct a complete printing plate.

Dropped Transfers — If an impression from the transfer roll has not been properly placed, a dropped transfer may occur. The final stamp image will appear obviously out of line with its neighbors.

Short Transfer — Sometimes a transfer roll is not rocked its entire length when entering a transfer onto a plate. As a result, the finished transfer on the plate fails to show the complete design, and the finished stamp will have an incomplete design printed. This is known as a "short transfer." U.S. Scott No. 8 is a good example of a short transfer.

TYPOGRAPHY (Letterpress, Surface Printing, Flexography, Dry Offset, High Etch)

Although the word "Typography" is obsolete as a term describing a printing method, it was the accepted term throughout the first century of postage stamps. Therefore, appropriate Scott listings in this catalogue refer to typographed stamps. The current term for this form of printing, however, is "letterpress."

As it relates to the production of postage stamps, letterpress printing is the reverse of engraving. Rather than having recessed areas trap the ink and deposit it on paper, only the raised areas of the design are inked. This is comparable to the type of printing seen by inking and using an ordinary rubber stamp. Letterpress includes all printing where the design is above the surface area, whether it is wood, metal or, in some instances, hardened rubber or polymer plastic.

For most letterpress-printed stamps, the engraved master is made in much the same manner as for engraved stamps. In this instance, however, an additional step is needed. The design is transferred to another surface before being transferred to the transfer roll. In this way, the transfer roll has a recessed stamp design, rather than one done in relief. This makes the printing areas on the final plate raised, or relief areas.

For less-detailed stamps of the 19th century, the area on the die not used as a printing surface was cut away, leaving the surface area raised. The original die was then reproduced by stereotyping or electrotyping. The resulting electrotypes were assembled in the required number and format of the desired sheet of stamps. The plate used in printing the stamps was an electroplate of these assembled electrotypes.

Once the final letterpress plates are created, ink is applied to the raised surface and the pressure of the press transfers the ink impression to the paper. In contrast to engraving, the fine lines of letterpress are impressed on the surface of the stamp, leaving a debossed surface. When viewed from the back (as on a typewritten page), the corresponding line work on the stamp will be raised slightly (embossed) above the surface.

PHOTOGRAVURE (Gravure, Rotogravure, Heliogravure)

In this process, the basic principles of photography are applied to a chemically sensitized metal plate, rather than photographic paper. The design is transferred photographically to the plate through a halftone, or dot-matrix screen, breaking the reproduction into tiny dots. The plate is treated chemically and the dots form depressions, called cells, of varying depths and diameters, depending on the degrees of shade in the design. Then, like engraving, ink is applied to the plate and the surface is wiped clean. This leaves ink in the tiny cells that is lifted out and deposited on the paper when it is pressed against the plate.

Gravure is most often used for multicolored stamps, generally using the three primary colors (red, yellow and blue) and black. By varying the dot matrix pattern and density of these colors, virtually any color can be reproduced. A typical full-color gravure stamp will be created from four printing cylinders (one for each color). The original multicolored image will have been photographically separated into its component colors.

Modern gravure printing may use computer-generated dot-matrix screens, and modern plates may be of various types including metal-coated plastic. The catalogue designation of Photogravure (or "Photo") covers any of these older and more modern gravure methods of printing.

For examples of the first photogravure stamps printed (1914), see Bavaria Scott 94-114.

LITHOGRAPHY (Offset Lithography, Stone Lithography, Dilitho, Planography, Collotype)

The principle that oil and water do not mix is the basis for lithography. The stamp design is drawn by hand or transferred from engraving to the surface of a lithographic stone or metal plate in a greasy (oily) substance. This oily substance holds the ink, which will later be transferred to the paper. The stone (or plate) is wet with an acid fluid, causing it to repel the printing ink in all areas not covered by the greasy substance.

Transfer paper is used to transfer the design from the original stone or plate. A series of duplicate transfers are grouped and, in turn, transferred to the final printing plate.

Photolithography — The application of photographic processes to lithography. This process allows greater flexibility of design, related to use of halftone screens combined with line work. Unlike photogravure or engraving, this process can allow large, solid areas to be printed.

Offset — A refinement of the lithographic process. A rubber-covered blanket cylinder takes the impression from the inked lithographic plate. From the "blanket" the impression is offset or transferred to the paper. Greater flexibility and speed are the principal reasons offset printing has largely displaced lithography. The term "lithography" covers both processes, and results are almost identical.

EMBOSSED (Relief) Printing

Embossing, not considered one of the four main printing types, is a method in which the design first is sunk into the metal of the die. Printing is done against a yielding platen, such as leather or linoleum. The platen is forced into the depression of the die, thus forming the design on the paper in relief. This process is often used for metallic inks.

Embossing may be done without color (see Sardinia Scott 4-6); with color printed around the embossed area (see Great Britain Scott 5 and most U.S. envelopes); and with color in exact registration with the embossed subject (see Canada Scott 656-657).

HOLOGRAMS

For objects to appear as holograms on stamps, a model exactly the same size as it is to appear on the hologram must be created. Rather than using photographic film to capture the image, holography records an image on a photoresist material. In processing, chemicals eat away at certain exposed areas, leaving a pattern of constructive and destructive interference. When the photoresist is developed, the result is a pattern of uneven ridges that acts as a mold. This mold is then coated with metal, and the resulting form is used to press copies in much the same way phonograph records are produced.

A typical reflective hologram used for stamps consists of a reproduction of the uneven patterns on a plastic film that is applied to a reflective background, usually a silver or gold foil. Light is reflected off the background through the film, making the pattern present on the film visible. Because of the uneven pattern of the film, the viewer will perceive the objects in their proper three-dimensional relationships with appropriate brightness. The first hologram on a stamp was produced by Austria in 1988 (Scott 1441).

FOIL APPLICATION

A modern technique of applying color to stamps involves the application of metallic foil to the stamp paper. A pattern of foil is applied to the stamp paper by use of a stamping die. The foil usually is flat, but it may be textured. Canada Scott 1735 has three different foil applications in pearl, bronze and gold. The gold foil was textured using a chemical-etch copper embossing die. The printing of this stamp also involved two-color offset lithography plus embossing.

THERMOGRAPHY

In the 1990s stamps began to be enhanced with thermographic printing. In this process, a powdered polymer is applied over a sheet that has just been printed. The powder adheres to ink that lacks drying or hardening agents and does not adhere to areas where the ink has these agents. The excess powder is removed and the sheet is briefly heated to melt the powder. The melted powder solidifies after cooling, producing a raised, shiny effect on the stamps. See Scott New Caledonia C239-C240.

COMBINATION PRINTINGS

Sometimes two or even three printing methods are combined in producing stamps. In these cases, such as Austria Scott 933 or Canada 1735 (described in the preceding paragraph), the multiple-printing technique can be determined by studying the individual characteristics of each printing type. A few stamps, such as Singapore Scott 684-684A, combine as many as three of the four major printing types (lithography, engraving and typography). When this is done it often indicates the incorporation of security devices against counterfeiting.

INK COLORS

Inks or colored papers used in stamp printing often are of mineral origin, although there are numerous examples of organic-based pigments. As a general rule, organic-based pigments are far more subject to varieties and change than those of mineral-based origin.

The appearance of any given color on a stamp may be affected by many aspects, including printing variations, light, color of paper, aging and chemical alterations.

Numerous printing variations may be observed. Heavier pressure or inking will cause a more intense color, while slight interruptions in the ink feed or lighter impressions will cause a lighter appearance. Stamps printed in the same color by water-based and solvent-based inks can differ significantly in appearance. This affects several stamps in the U.S. Prominent Americans series. Hand-mixed ink formulas (primarily from the 19th century) produced under different conditions (humidity and temperature) account for notable color variations in early printings of the same stamp (see U.S. Scott 248-250, 279B, for example). Different sources of pigment can also result in significant differences in color.

Light exposure and aging are closely related in the way they affect stamp color. Both eventually break down the ink and fade colors, so that a carefully kept stamp may differ significantly in color from an identical copy that has been exposed to light. If stamps are exposed to light either intentionally or accidentally, their colors can be faded or completely changed in some cases.

Papers of different quality and consistency used for the same stamp printing may affect color appearance. Most pelure papers, for example, show a richer color when compared with wove or laid papers. See Russia Scott 181a, for an example of this effect.

The very nature of the printing processes can cause a variety of differences in shades or hues of the same stamp. Some of these shades are scarcer than others, and are of particular interest to the advanced collector.

Luminescence

All forms of tagged stamps fall under the general category of luminescence. Within this broad category is fluorescence, dealing with forms of tagging visible under longwave ultraviolet light, and phosphorescence, which deals with tagging visible only under shortwave light. Phosphorescence leaves an afterglow and fluorescence does not. These treated stamps show up in a range of different colors when exposed to UV light. The differing wavelengths of the light activates the tagging material, making it glow in various colors that usually serve different mail processing purposes.

Intentional tagging is a post-World War II phenomenon, brought about by the increased literacy rate and rapidly growing mail volume. It was one of several answers to the problem of the need for more automated mail processes. Early tagged stamps served the purpose of triggering machines to separate different types of mail. A natural outgrowth was to also use the signal to trigger machines that faced all envelopes the same way and canceled them.

Tagged stamps come in many different forms. Some tagged stamps have luminescent shapes or images imprinted on them as a form of security device. Others have blocks (United States), stripes, frames (South Africa and Canada), overall coatings (United States), bars (Great Britain and Canada) and many other types. Some types of tagging are even mixed in with the pigmented printing ink (Australia Scott 366, Netherlands Scott 478 and U.S. Scott 1359 and 2443).

The means of applying taggant to stamps differs as much as the intended purposes for the stamps. The most common form of tagging is a coating applied to the surface of the printed stamp. Since the taggant ink is frequently invisible except under UV light, it does not interfere with the appearance of the stamp. Another common application is the use of phosphored papers. In this case the paper itself either has a coating of taggant applied before the stamp is printed, has taggant applied during the papermaking process (incorporating it into the fibers), or has the taggant mixed into the coating of the paper. The latter method, among others, is currently in use in the United States.

Many countries now use tagging in various forms to either expedite mail handling or to serve as a printing security device against counterfeiting. Following the introduction of tagged stamps for public use in 1959 by Great Britain, other countries have steadily joined the parade. Among those are Germany (1961); Canada and Denmark (1962); United States, Australia, France and Switzerland (1963); Belgium and Japan (1966); Sweden and Norway (1967); Italy (1968); and Russia (1969). Since then, many other countries have begun using forms of tagging, including Brazil, China, Czechoslovakia, Hong Kong, Guatemala, Indonesia, Israel, Lithuania, Luxembourg, Netherlands, Penrhyn Islands, Portugal, St. Vincent, Singapore, South Africa, Spain and Sweden to name a few.

In some cases, including United States, Canada, Great Britain and Switzerland, stamps were released both with and without tagging. Many of these were released during each country's experimental period. Tagged and untagged versions are listed for the aforementioned countries and are noted in some other countries' listings. For at least a few stamps, the experimentally tagged version is worth far more than its untagged counterpart, such as the 1963 experimental tagged version of France Scott 1024.

In some cases, luminescent varieties of stamps were inadvertently created. Several Russian stamps, for example, sport highly fluorescent ink that was not intended as a form of tagging. Older stamps, such as early U.S. postage dues, can be positively identified by the use of UV light, since the organic ink used has become slightly fluorescent over time. Other stamps, such as Austria Scott 70a-82a (varnish bars) and Obock Scott 46-64 (printed quadrille lines), have become fluorescent over time.

Various fluorescent substances have been added to paper to make it appear brighter. These optical brighteners, as they are known, greatly affect the appearance of the stamp under UV light. The brightest of these is known as Hi-Brite paper. These paper varieties are beyond the scope of the Scott Catalogue.

Shortwave UV light also is used extensively in expertizing, since each form of paper has its own fluorescent characteristics that are impossible to perfectly match. It is therefore a simple matter to detect filled thins, added perforation teeth and other alterations that involve the addition of paper. UV light also is used to examine stamps that have had cancels chemically removed and for other purposes as well.

Gum

The Illustrated Gum Chart in the first part of this introduction shows and defines various types of gum condition. Because gum condition has an important impact on the value of unused stamps, we recommend studying this chart and the accompanying text carefully.

The gum on the back of a stamp may be shiny, dull, smooth, rough, dark, white, colored or tinted. Most stamp gumming adhesives use gum arabic or dextrine as a base. Certain polymers such as polyvinyl alcohol (PVA) have been used extensively since World War II.

The *Scott Standard Postage Stamp Catalogue* does not list items by types of gum. The *Scott Specialized Catalogue of United States Stamps and Covers* does differentiate among some types of gum for certain issues.

Reprints of stamps may have gum differing from the original issues. In addition, some countries have used different gum formulas for different seasons. These adhesives have different properties that may become more apparent over time.

Many stamps have been issued without gum, and the catalogue will note this fact. See, for example, United States Scott 40-47. Sometimes, gum may have been removed to preserve the stamp. Germany Scott B68, for example, has a highly acidic gum that eventually destroys the stamps. This item is valued in the catalogue with gum removed.

Reprints and reissues

These are impressions of stamps (usually obsolete) made from the original plates or stones. If they are valid for postage and reproduce obsolete issues (such as U.S. Scott 102-111), the stamps are reissues. If they are from current issues, they are designated as *second, third*, etc., *printing*. If designated for a particular purpose, they are called *special printings*.

When special printings are not valid for postage, but are made from original dies and plates by authorized persons, they are *official reprints*. *Private reprints* are made from the original plates and dies by private hands. An example of a private reprint is that of the 1871-1932 reprints made from the original die of the 1845 New Haven, Conn., postmaster's provisional. *Official reproductions* or imitations are made from new dies and plates by government authorization. Scott will list those reissues that are valid for postage if they differ significantly from the original printing.

The U.S. government made special printings of its first postage stamps in 1875. Produced were official imitations of the first two stamps (listed as Scott 3-4), reprints of the demonetized pre-1861 issues (Scott 40-47) and reissues of the 1861 stamps, the 1869 stamps and the then-current 1875 denominations. Even though the official imitations and the reprints were not valid for postage, Scott lists all of these U.S. special printings.

Most reprints or reissues differ slightly from the original stamp in some characteristic, such as gum, paper, perforation, color or watermark. Sometimes the details are followed so meticulously that only a student of that specific stamp is able to distinguish the reprint or reissue from the original.

Remainders and canceled to order

Some countries sell their stock of old stamps when a new issue replaces them. To avoid postal use, the remainders usually are canceled with a punch hole, a heavy line or bar, or a more-or-less regular-looking cancellation. The most famous merchant of remainders was Nicholas F. Seebeck. In the 1880s and 1890s, he arranged printing contracts between the Hamilton Bank Note Co., of which he was a director, and several Central and South American countries. The contracts provided that the plates and all remainders of the yearly issues became the property of Hamilton. Seebeck saw to it that ample stock remained. The "Seebecks," both remainders and reprints, were standard packet fillers for decades.

Some countries also issue stamps *canceled-to-order (CTO)*, either in sheets with original gum or stuck onto pieces of paper or envelopes and canceled. Such CTO items generally are worth less than postally used stamps. In cases where the CTO material is far more prevalent in the marketplace than postally used examples, the catalogue value relates to the CTO examples, with postally used examples noted as premium items. Most CTOs can be detected by the presence of gum. However, as the CTO practice goes back at least to 1885, the gum inevitably has been soaked off some stamps so they could pass as postally used. The normally applied postmarks usually differ slightly from standard postmarks, and specialists are able to tell the difference. When applied individually to envelopes by philatelically minded persons, CTO material is known as *favor canceled* and generally sells at large discounts.

Cinderellas and facsimiles

Cinderella is a catch-all term used by stamp collectors to describe phantoms, fantasies, bogus items, municipal issues, exhibition seals, local revenues, transportation stamps, labels, poster stamps and many other types of items. Some cinderella collectors include in their collections local postage issues, telegraph stamps, essays and proofs, forgeries and counterfeits.

A *fantasy* is an adhesive created for a nonexistent stamp-issuing authority. Fantasy items range from imaginary countries (Occusi-Ambeno, Kingdom of Sedang, Principality of Trinidad or Torres Straits), to non-existent locals (Winans City Post), or nonexistent transportation lines (McRobish & Co.'s Acapulco-San Francisco Line).

On the other hand, if the entity exists and could have issued stamps (but did not) or was known to have issued other stamps, the items are considered bogus stamps. These would include the Mormon postage stamps of Utah, S. Allan Taylor's Guatemala and Paraguay inventions, the propaganda issues for the South Moluccas and the adhesives of the Page & Keyes local post of Boston.

Phantoms is another term for both fantasy and bogus issues.

Facsimiles are copies or imitations made to represent original stamps, but which do not pretend to be originals. A catalogue illustration is such a facsimile. Illustrations from the Moens catalogue of the last century were occasionally colored and passed off as stamps. Since the beginning of stamp collecting, facsimiles have been made for collectors as space fillers or for reference. They often carry the word "facsimile," "falsch" (German), "sanko" or "mozo" (Japanese), or "faux" (French) overprinted on the face or stamped on the back. Unfortunately, over the years a number of these items have had fake cancels applied over the facsimile notation and have been passed off as genuine.

Forgeries and counterfeits

Forgeries and counterfeits have been with philately virtually from the beginning of stamp production. Over time, the terminology for the two has been used interchangeably. Although both forgeries and counterfeits are reproductions of stamps, the purposes behind their creation differ considerably.

Among specialists there is an increasing movement to more specifically define such items. Although there is no universally accepted terminology, we feel the following definitions most closely mirror the items and their purposes as they are currently defined.

Forgeries (also often referred to as Counterfeits) are reproductions of genuine stamps that have been created to defraud collectors. Such spurious items first appeared on the market around 1860, and most old-time collections contain one or more. Many are crude and easily spotted, but some can deceive experts.

An important supplier of these early philatelic forgeries was the Hamburg printer Gebruder Spiro. Many others with reputations in this craft included S. Allan Taylor, George Hussey, James Chute, George Forune, Benjamin & Sarpy, Julius Goldner, E. Oneglia and L.H. Mercier. Among the noted 20th-century forgers were Francois Fournier, Jean Sperati and the prolific Raoul DeThuin.

Forgeries may be complete replications, or they may be genuine stamps altered to resemble a scarcer (and more valuable) type. Most forgeries, particularly those of rare stamps, are worth only a small fraction of the value of a genuine example, but a few types, created by some of the most notable forgers, such as Sperati, can be worth as much or more than the genuine. Fraudulently produced copies are known of most classic rarities and many medium-priced stamps.

In addition to rare stamps, large numbers of common 19th- and early 20th-century stamps were forged to supply stamps to the early packet trade. Many can still be easily found. Few new philatelic forgeries have appeared in recent decades. Successful imitation of well-engraved work is virtually impossible. It has proven far easier to produce a fake by altering a genuine stamp than to duplicate a stamp completely.

Counterfeit (also often referred to as Postal Counterfeit or Postal Forgery) is the term generally applied to reproductions of stamps that have been created to defraud the government of revenue. Such items usually are created at the time a stamp is current and, in some cases, are hard to detect. Because most counterfeits are seized when the perpetrator is captured, postal counterfeits, particularly used on cover, are usually worth much more than a genuine example to specialists. The first postal counterfeit was of Spain's 4-cuarto carmine of 1854 (the real one is Scott 25). Apparently, the counterfeiters were not satisfied with their first version, which is now very scarce, and they soon created an engraved counterfeit, which is common. Postal counterfeits quickly followed in Austria, Naples, Sardinia and the Roman States. They have since been created in many other countries as well, including the United States.

An infamous counterfeit to defraud the government is the 1-shilling Great Britain "Stock Exchange" forgery of 1872, used on telegraph forms at the exchange that year. The stamp escaped detection until a stamp dealer noticed it in 1898.

Fakes

Fakes are genuine stamps altered in some way to make them more desirable. One student of this part of stamp collecting has estimated that by the 1950s more than 30,000 varieties of fakes were known. That number has grown greatly since then. The widespread existence of fakes makes it important for stamp collectors to study their philatelic holdings and use relevant literature. Likewise, collectors should buy from reputable dealers who guarantee their stamps and make full and prompt refunds should a purchased item be declared faked or altered by some mutually agreed-upon authority. Because fakes always have some genuine characteristics, it is not always possible to obtain unanimous agreement among experts regarding specific items. These students may change their opinions as philatelic knowledge increases. More than 80 percent of all fakes on the philatelic market today are regummed, reperforated (or perforated for the first time), or bear forged overprints, surcharges or cancellations.

Stamps can be chemically treated to alter or eliminate colors. For example, a pale rose stamp can be re-colored to resemble a blue shade of high market value. In other cases, treated stamps can be made to resemble missing color varieties. Designs may be changed by painting, or a stroke or a dot added or bleached out to turn an ordinary variety into a seemingly scarcer stamp. Part of a stamp can be bleached and reprinted in a different version, achieving an inverted center or frame. Margins can be added or repairs done so deceptively that the stamps move from the "repaired" into the "fake" category.

Fakers have not left the backs of the stamps untouched either. They may create false watermarks, add fake grills or press out genuine grills. A thin India paper proof may be glued onto a thicker backing to create the appearance an issued stamp, or a proof printed on cardboard may be shaved down and perforated to resemble a stamp. Silk threads are impressed into paper and stamps have been split so that a rare paper variety is added to an otherwise inexpensive stamp. The most common treatment to the back of a stamp, however, is regumming.

Some in the business of faking stamps have openly advertised foolproof application of "original gum" to stamps that lack it, although most publications now ban such ads from their pages. It is believed that very few early stamps have survived without being hinged. The large number of never-hinged examples of such earlier material offered for sale thus suggests the widespread extent of regumming activity. Regumming also may be used to hide repairs or thin spots. Dipping the stamp into watermark fluid, or examining it under longwave ultraviolet light often will reveal these flaws.

Fakers also tamper with separations. Ingenious ways to add margins are known. Perforated wide-margin stamps may be falsely represented as imperforate when trimmed. Reperforating is commonly done to create scarce coil or perforation varieties, and to eliminate the naturally occurring straight-edge stamps found in sheet margin positions of many earlier issues. Custom has made straight-edged stamps less desirable. Fakers have obliged by perforating straight-edged stamps so that many are now uncommon, if not rare.

Another fertile field for the faker is that of overprints, surcharges and cancellations. The forging of rare surcharges or overprints began in the 1880s or 1890s. These forgeries are sometimes difficult to detect, but experts have identified almost all. Occasionally, overprints or cancellations are removed to create non-overprinted stamps or seemingly unused items. This is most commonly done by removing a manuscript cancel to make a stamp resemble an unused example. "SPECIMEN" overprints may be removed by scraping and repainting to create non-overprinted varieties. Fakers use inexpensive revenues or pen-canceled stamps to generate unused stamps for further faking by adding other markings. The quartz lamp or UV lamp and a high-powered magnifying glass help to easily detect removed cancellations.

The bigger problem, however, is the addition of overprints, surcharges or cancellations — many with such precision that they are very difficult to ascertain. Plating of the stamps or the overprint can be an important method of detection.

Fake postmarks may range from many spurious fancy cancellations to a host of markings applied to transatlantic covers, to adding normally appearing postmarks to definitives of some countries with stamps that are valued far higher used than unused. With the increased popularity of cover collecting, and the widespread interest in postal history, a fertile new field for fakers has come about. Some have tried to create entire covers. Others specialize in adding stamps, tied by fake cancellations, to genuine stampless covers, or replacing less expensive or damaged stamps with more valuable ones. Detailed study of postal rates in effect at the time a cover in question was mailed, including the analysis of each handstamp used during the period, ink analysis and similar techniques, usually will unmask the fraud.

Restoration and repairs

Scott bases its catalogue values on stamps that are free of defects and otherwise meet the standards set forth earlier in this introduction. Most stamp collectors desire to have the finest copy of an item possible. Even within given grading categories there are variances. This leads to a controversial practice that is not defined in any universal manner: stamp *restoration*.

There are broad differences of opinion about what is permissible when it comes to restoration. Carefully applying a soft eraser to a stamp or cover to remove light soiling is one form of restoration, as is washing a stamp in mild soap and water to clean it. These are fairly accepted forms of restoration. More severe forms of restoration include pressing out creases or removing stains caused by tape. To what degree each of these is acceptable is dependent upon the individual situation. Further along the spectrum is the freshening of a stamp's color by removing oxide build-up or the effects of wax paper left next to stamps shipped to the tropics.

At some point in this spectrum the concept of *repair* replaces that of restoration. Repairs include filling thin spots, mending tears by reweaving or adding a missing perforation tooth. Regumming stamps may have been acceptable as a restoration or repair technique many decades ago, but today it is considered a form of fakery.

Restored stamps may or may not sell at a discount, and it is possible that the value of individual restored items may be enhanced over that of their pre-restoration state. Specific situations dictate the resultant value of such an item. Repaired stamps sell at substantial discounts from the value of sound stamps.

Terminology

Booklets — Many countries have issued stamps in small booklets for the convenience of users. This idea continues to become increasingly popular in many countries. Booklets have been issued in many sizes and forms, often with advertising on the covers, the panes of stamps or on the interleaving.

The panes used in booklets may be printed from special plates or made from regular sheets. All panes from booklets issued by the United States and many from those of other countries contain stamps that are straight edged on the sides, but perforated between. Others are distinguished by orientation of watermark or other identifying features. Any stamp-like unit in the pane, either printed or blank, that is not a postage stamp, is considered to be a *label* in the catalogue listings.

Scott lists and values booklet panes. Modern complete booklets also are listed and valued. Individual booklet panes are listed only when they are not fashioned from existing sheet stamps and, therefore, are identifiable from their sheet stamp counterparts.

Panes usually do not have a used value assigned to them because there is little market activity for used booklet panes, even though many exist used and there is some demand for them.

Cancellations — The marks or obliterations put on stamps by postal authorities to show that they have performed service and to prevent their reuse are known as cancellations. If the marking is made with a pen, it is considered a "pen cancel." When the location of the post office appears in the marking, it is a "town cancellation." A "postmark" is technically any postal marking, but in practice the term generally is applied to a town cancellation with a date. When calling attention to a cause or celebration, the marking is known as a "slogan cancellation." Many other types and styles of cancellations exist, such as duplex, numerals, targets, fancy and others. See also "precancels," below.

Coil Stamps — These are stamps that are issued in rolls for use in dispensers, affixing and vending machines. Those coils of the United States, Canada, Sweden and some other countries are perforated horizontally or vertically only, with the outer edges imperforate. Coil stamps of some countries, such as Great Britain and Germany, are perforated on all four sides and may in some cases be distinguished from their sheet stamp counterparts by watermarks, counting numbers on the reverse or other means.

Covers — Entire envelopes, with or without adhesive postage stamps, that have passed through the mail and bear postal or other markings of philatelic interest are known as covers. Before the introduction of envelopes in about 1840, people folded letters and wrote the address on the outside. Some people covered their letters with an extra sheet of paper on the outside for the address, producing the term "cover." Used airletter sheets, stamped envelopes and other items of postal stationery also are considered covers.

Errors — Stamps that have some major, consistent, unintentional deviation from the normal are considered errors. Errors include, but are not limited to, missing or wrong colors, wrong paper, wrong watermarks, inverted centers or frames on multicolor printing, inverted or missing surcharges or overprints, double impressions, missing perforations, unintentionally omitted tagging and others. Factually wrong or misspelled information, if it appears on all examples of a stamp, are not considered errors in the true sense of the word. They are errors of design. Inconsistent or randomly appearing items, such as misperfs or color shifts, are classified as freaks.

Color-Omitted Errors — This term refers to stamps where a missing color is caused by the complete failure of the printing plate to deliver ink to the stamp paper or any other paper. Generally, this is caused by the printing plate not being engaged on the press or the ink station running dry of ink during printing.

Color-Missing Errors — This term refers to stamps where a color or colors were printed somewhere but do not appear on the finished stamp. There are four different classes of color-missing errors, and the catalog indicates with a two-letter code appended to each such listing what caused the color to be missing. These codes are used only for the United States' color-missing error listings.

FO = A *foldover* of the stamp sheet during printing may block ink from appearing on the face of a stamp. Instead, the color will appear on the back of the foldover (where it might fall on the back of the selvage or perhaps a bit on the back of the stamp or on the back of another stamp. FO also will be used in the case of foldunders, where the paper may fold underneath the other stamp paper and the color will print on the platen.

EP = When the extraneous paper is removed, an unprinted area of stamp paper remains and may show a color or colors to be totally missing on the finished stamp.

CM = A misregistration of the printing plates during printing will result in a *color misregistration*, and such a misregistraion may result in a color not appearing on the finished stamp.

PS = A *perforation shift* after printing may remove a color from the finished stamp. Normally, this will occur on a row of stamps at the edge of the stamp pane.

Measurements – When measurements are given in the Scott catalogues for stamp size, grill size or any other reason, the first measurement given is always for the top and bottom dimension, while the second measurement will be for the sides (just as perforation gauges are measured). Thus, a stamp size of 15mm x 21mm will indicate a vertically oriented stamp 15mm wide at top and bottom, and 21mm tall at the sides. The same principle holds for measuring or counting items such as U.S. grills. A grill count of 22x18 points (B grill) indicates that there are 22 grill points across by 18 grill points down.

Overprints and Surcharges — Overprinting involves applying wording or design elements over an already existing stamp. Overprints can be used to alter the place of use (such as "Canal Zone" on U.S. stamps), to adapt them for a special purpose ("Porto" on Denmark's 1913-20 regular issues for use as postage due stamps, Scott J1-J7) or to commemorate a special occasion (United States Scott 647-648).

A *surcharge* is a form of overprint that changes or restates the face value of a stamp or piece of postal stationery.

Surcharges and overprints may be handstamped, typeset or, occasionally, lithographed or engraved. A few hand-written overprints and surcharges are known.

Personalized Stamps — In 1999, Australia issued stamps with se-tenant labels that could be personalized with pictures of the customer's choice. Other countries quickly followed suit, with some offering to print the selected picture on the stamp itself within a frame that was used exclusively for personalized issues. As the picture used on these stamps or labels vary, listings for such stamps are for any picture within the common frame (or any picture on a se-tenant label), be it a "generic" image or one produced especially for a customer, almost invariably at a premium price.

Precancels — Stamps that are canceled before they are placed in the mail are known as precancels. Precanceling usually is done to expedite the handling of large mailings and generally allow the affected mail pieces to skip certain phases of mail handling.

In the United States, precancellations generally identified the point of origin; that is, the city and state. This information appeared across the face of the stamp, usually centered between parallel lines. More recently, bureau precancels retained the parallel lines, but the city and state designations were dropped. Recent coils have a service inscription that is present on the original printing plate. These show the mail service paid for by the stamp. Since these stamps are not intended to receive further cancellations when used as intended, they are considered precancels. Such items often do not have parallel lines as part of the precancellation.

In France, the abbreviation *Affranchts* in a semicircle together with the word *Postes* is the general form of precancel in use. Belgian precancellations usually appear in a box in which the name of the city appears. Netherlands precancels have the name of the city enclosed between concentric circles, sometimes called a "lifesaver." Precancellations of other countries usually follow these patterns, but may be any arrangement of bars, boxes and city names.

Precancels are listed in the Scott catalogues only if the precancel changes the denomination (Belgium Scott 477-478); if the precanceled stamp is different from the non-precanceled version (such as untagged U.S. precancels); or if the stamp exists only precanceled (France Scott 1096-1099, U.S. Scott 2265).

Proofs and Essays — Proofs are impressions taken from an approved die, plate or stone in which the design and color are the same as the stamp issued to the public. Trial color proofs are impressions taken from approved dies, plates or stones in colors that vary from the final version. An essay is the impression of a design that differs in some way from the issued stamp. "Progressive die proofs" generally are considered to be essays.

Provisionals — These are stamps that are issued on short notice and intended for temporary use pending the arrival of regular issues. They usually are issued to meet such contingencies as changes in government or currency, shortage of necessary postage values or military occupation.

During the 1840s, postmasters in certain American cities issued stamps that were valid only at specific post offices. In 1861, postmasters of the Confederate States also issued stamps with limited validity. Both of these examples are known as "postmaster's provisionals."

Se-tenant — This term refers to an unsevered pair, strip or block of stamps that differ in design, denomination or overprint.

Unless the se-tenant item has a continuous design (see U.S. Scott 1451a, 1694a) the stamps do not have to be in the same order as shown in the catalogue (see U.S. Scott 2158a).

Specimens — The Universal Postal Union required member nations to send samples of all stamps they released into service to the International Bureau in Switzerland. Member nations of the UPU received these specimens as samples of what stamps were valid for postage. Many are overprinted, handstamped or initial-perforated "Specimen," "Canceled" or "Muestra." Some are marked with bars across the denominations (China-Taiwan), punched holes (Czechoslovakia) or back inscriptions (Mongolia).

Stamps distributed to government officials or for publicity purposes, and stamps submitted by private security printers for official approval, also may receive such defacements.

The previously described defacement markings prevent postal use, and all such items generally are known as "specimens."

Tete-Beche — This term describes a pair of stamps in which one is upside down in relation to the other. Some of these are the result of intentional sheet arrangements, such as Morocco Scott B10-B11. Others occurred when one or more electrotypes accidentally were placed upside down on the plate, such as Colombia Scott 57a. Separation of the tete-beche stamps, of course, destroys the tete beche variety.

Pronunciation Symbols

ə .... banana, collide, abut

'ə, ˌə .... humdrum, abut

ə .... immediately preceding \l\, \n\, \m\, \ŋ\, as in battle, mitten, eaten, and sometimes open \'ō-pᵊm\, lock and key \-ᵊŋ-\; immediately following \l\, \m\, \r\, as often in French table, prisme, titre

ər .... further, merger, bird

'ər-
'ə-r } .... as in two different pronunciations of hurry \'hər-ē, 'hə-rē\

a .... mat, map, mad, gag, snap, patch

ā .... day, fade, date, aorta, drape, cape

ä .... bother, cot, and, with most American speakers, father, cart

ȧ .... father as pronunced by speakers who do not rhyme it with bother; French patte

au̇ .... now, loud, out

b .... baby, rib

ch .... chin, nature \'nā-chər\

d .... did, adder

e .... bet, bed, peck

'ē, ˌē .... beat, nosebleed, evenly, easy

ē .... easy, mealy

f .... fifty, cuff

g .... go, big, gift

h .... hat, ahead

hw .... whale as pronounced by those who do not have the same pronunciation for both whale and wail

i .... tip, banish, active

ī .... site, side, buy, tripe

j .... job, gem, edge, join, judge

k .... kin, cook, ache

k̲ .... German ich, Buch; one pronunciation of loch

l .... lily, pool

m .... murmur, dim, nymph

n .... no, own

ⁿ .... indicates that a preceding vowel or diphthong is pronounced with the nasal passages open, as in French un bon vin blanc \œⁿ-bōⁿ-vaⁿ-bläⁿ\

ŋ .... sing \'siŋ\, singer \'siŋ-ər\, finger \'fiŋ-gər\, ink \'iŋk\

ō .... bone, know, beau

ȯ .... saw, all, gnaw, caught

œ .... French boeuf, German Hölle

œ̄ .... French feu, German Höhle

ȯi .... coin, destroy

p .... pepper, lip

r .... red, car, rarity

s .... source, less

sh .... as in shy, mission, machine, special (actually, this is a single sound, not two); with a hyphen between, two sounds as in grasshopper \'gras-ˌhä-pər\

t .... tie, attack, late, later, latter

th .... as in thin, ether (actually, this is a single sound, not two); with a hyphen between, two sounds as in knighthood \'nīt-ˌhu̇d\

th̲ .... then, either, this (actually, this is a single sound, not two)

ü .... rule, youth, union \'yün-yən\, few \'fyü\

u̇ .... pull, wood, book, curable \'kyu̇r-ə-bəl\, fury \'fyu̇r-ē\

ue .... German füllen, hübsch

ūe .... French rue, German fühlen

v .... vivid, give

w .... we, away

y .... yard, young, cue \'kyü\, mute \'myüt\, union \'yün-yən\

ʸ .... indicates that during the articulation of the sound represented by the preceding character the front of the tongue has substantially the position it has for the articulation of the first sound of yard, as in French digne \dēnʸ\

z .... zone, raise

zh .... as in vision, azure \'a-zhər\ (actually, this is a single sound, not two); with a hyphen between, two sounds as in hogshead \'hȯgz-ˌhed, 'hägz-\

\ .... slant line used in pairs to mark the beginning and end of a transcription: \'pen\

ˈ .... mark preceding a syllable with primary (strongest) stress: \'pen-mən-ˌship\

ˌ .... mark preceding a syllable with secondary (medium) stress: \'pen-mən-ˌship\

- .... mark of syllable division

( ) .... indicate that what is symbolized between is present in some utterances but not in others: factory \'fak-t(ə-)rē\

÷ .... indicates that many regard as unacceptable the pronunciation variant immediately following: cupola \'kyü-pə-lə, ÷-ˌlō\

SHOWGARD MOUNTS

Showgard mounts are manufactured with the highest archival qualities in mind. The foil used to produce the mounts is acid free and stronger than other mounts for maximum protection and durability. Selecting the right size mount for your stamp is easy. Simply use a millimeter ruler to measure the stamps' width then the height. Showgard incorporates these measurements into their product numbers to insure you get the right size. Mounts available with clear (c) or black (b) backgrounds, with a few exceptions. Please specify background preference when ordering.

Item	Description	Mounts	Retail	AA*
SGC50X31	50/31 U.S. Jumbo Singles - Horizontal	40	$3.95	$2.85
SGCV31X50	31/50 U.S. Jumbo Singles - Vertical	40	$3.95	$2.85
SGJ40X25	40/25 U.S. Commem. - Horizontal	40	$3.95	$2.85
SGJV25X40	25/40 U.S. Commem. - Vertical	40	$3.95	$2.85
SGE22X25	22/25 U.S. Regular Issues - Vertical	40	$3.95	$2.85
SGEH25X22	25/22 U.S. Regular Issues - Horizontal	40	$3.95	$2.85
SGT25X27	25/27 U.S. Famous Americans	40	$3.95	$2.85
SGU33X27	33/27 U.N., Germany	40	$3.95	$2.85
SGN40X27	40/27 United Nations	40	$3.95	$2.85
SGAH41X31	41/31 U.S. Semi Jumbo - Horizontal	40	$3.95	$2.85
SGAV31X41	31/41 U.S. Semi Jumbo - Vertical	40	$3.95	$2.85
SGDH52X36	52/36 U.S. Duck Stamps	30	$3.95	$2.85
SGS31X31	31/31 U.S. Celebrate the Century	30	$3.95	$2.85
SGUS2	Cut Style with Tray-8 Sizes	320	$32.95	$23.50
SGUS3	Strip Style w/Tray-No. 22 thru No. 52	75	$49.95	$35.75
SGUS1	U.S. Strip Sizes No. 22 thru No. 52	50	$24.50	$17.50
SG67X25	67/25 U.S. Coil Strips of 3	40	$8.35	$5.95
SG57X55	57/55 U.S. Regular Issue	25	$8.35	$5.95
SG106X55	106/55 U.S. 3¢, 4¢ Commemoratives	20	$8.35	$5.95
SG105X57	105/57 U.S. Giori Press Issues	20	$8.35	$5.95
SG127X70	127/70 U.S. Jumbo Issues	10	$8.35	$5.95
SG140X89	140/89 Postcards, Souvenir Sheets	10	$8.35	$5.95
SG165X94	165/94 First Day Covers	10	$8.35	$5.95
SG20	215/20 U.S. Mini Stamps, etc.	22	$9.75	$6.95
SG22	215/22 Narrow U.S. Airs	22	$9.75	$6.95
SG24	215/24 U.K. and Canada, early U.S.	22	$9.75	$6.95
SG25	215/25 U.S. Commem. & Regular Issues	22	$9.75	$6.95
SG27	215/27 U.S. Famous Americans, U.N.	22	$9.75	$6.95
SG28	215/28 Switzerland, Liechtenstein	22	$9.75	$6.95
SG30	215/30 U.S. Special Stamps, Jamestown	22	$9.75	$6.95
SG31	315/31 U.S. Squares & Semi Jumbo	22	$9.75	$6.95
SG33	215/33 U.K. Issues, Misc. Foreign	22	$9.75	$6.95
SG36	215/36 Duck Stamps, Misc. Foreign	15	$9.75	$6.95
SG39	215/39 U.S. Magsaysay, Misc. Foreign	15	$9.75	$6.95
SG41	215/41 U.S. Vertical Commem. Israel Tabs	15	$9.75	$6.95
SG44	215/44 Booklet Panes, Hatteras Quartet	15	$9.75	$6.95
SG48	215/48 Canada Reg. Issue & Comm Blocks	15	$9.75	$6.95
SG50	215/50 U.S. Plain Blocks of 4	15	$9.75	$6.95
SG52	215/52 France Paintings, Misc. Foreign	15	$9.75	$6.95
SG57	215/57 U.S. Commem. Plate Blocks	15	$9.75	$6.95
SG61	215/61 Souvenir Sheets, Tab Singles, etc.	15	$9.75	$6.95
SG63	240/63 U.S. Semi Jumbo Blocks	10	$11.95	$8.75
SG66	240/66 U.S. ATM Panes, SA Duck Panes	10	$11.95	$8.75
SG68	240/68 Canadian Plate Blocks, etc.	10	$11.95	$8.75
SG74	240/74 U.N. Inscription Blocks of 4	10	$11.95	$8.75
SG80	240/80 U.S. Commem. Blocks	10	$11.95	$8.75
SG82	240/82 U.N. Chagall SS, Canada Plate Blocks	10	$11.95	$8.75
SG84	240/84 Israel Plate Blocks, etc.	10	$11.95	$8.75
SG89	240/89 U.N. Inscription Blocks of 6	10	$11.95	$8.75
SG100	240/100 U.S. Squares Plate Blocks	7	$11.95	$8.75
SG120	240/120 Miniature Sheets	7	$11.95	$8.75
SG70	264/70 U.S. Jumbo Plate Blocks	10	$16.25	$11.50
SG91	264/91 U.K. Souvenir Sheets	10	$16.25	$11.50
SG105	264/105 U.K. Blocks, Covers, etc.	10	$16.25	$11.50
SG107	264/107 U.S. Plate No. Strip of 20	10	$16.25	$11.50
SG111	264/111 U.S. Floating Plate No. Strips of 20	5	$10.75	$7.75
SG127	264/127 Modern U.S. Definitive Sheets of 20	5	$11.95	$8.50
SG137	264/137 U.N. SS, U.K. Coronation	5	$12.95	$9.50
SG158	264/158 Miniature Sheets, Apollo Soyuz PB	5	$14.50	$10.50
SG175	264/175 U.S. Sheets-Pan American Reissues	5	$15.95	$11.75
SG188	264/188 U.S. Miniature Sheets-Hollywood, etc.	5	$16.95	$11.95
SG198	264/198 U.S. Miniature Sheets	5	$17.25	$12.50
SGMPK	Assortment No. 22 thru No. 41	12	$7.50	$5.50
SGMPK2	Assortment No. 76 thru No. 171	15	$32.75	$23.75
SGAB	U.S. SS to 1975-except White Plains	11	$8.75	$6.50
SGWSE	World Stamp Expo Souvenir Sheets	3	$2.75	$1.95
SGRP94	U.S. 1994 Souvenir Sheets (Black Only)	5	$10.25	$7.50
SGRPAC97	Pacific 97 Issues	7	$5.75	$4.25
SGDC2006	Washington 2006 Souvenir Sheets (Black Only)	4	$7.95	$5.75
SGTM	Trans-Mississippi Issues	11	$5.75	$4.25
SGSPC	Space Exploration Sheets	5	$7.25	$5.25
SGNY2016	New York 2016 WWS Releases		$12.50	$10.00
SG265X231	265/231 U.S. Full Sheets & Souvenir Cards	5	$21.25	$15.25
SG260X25	260/25 U.S. Coil Strips of up to 11 stamps	25	$12.75	$8.95
SG293X30	293/30 U.S. American Eagle Coil Strips of up to 11 stamps	5	$4.25	$3.25

Item	Description	Mounts	Retail	AA*
SG260X40	260/40 U.S. Postal People Full Strip	10	$10.50	$7.50
SG260X46	260/46 U.S. Vending Booklets	10	$10.50	$7.50
SG260X55	260/55 U.S. 13¢ Eagle Full Strip	10	$10.50	$7.50
SG260X59	260/59 U.S. Double Press Reg. Iss. Strips of 20	10	$10.50	$7.50
SG111X91	111/91 U.S. Columbian Souvenir Sheets	6	$5.50	$3.95
SG229X131	229/131 U.S. WWII Sheets, Looney Tunes	5	$10.75	$7.75
SG187X144	187/144 U.N. Flag Sheetlets	10	$18.50	$12.95
SG204X153	204/153 U.S. Commem. Sheets, Bicentennial	5	$11.25	$8.25
SG120X207	120/207 U.S. Ameripex Presidential Sheetlets	4	$7.75	$5.75
SG192X201	192/201 U.S. Classics Mini-Sheets	5	$13.50	$9.75
SG280X228	280/228 U.S. Greetings From America Sheets	5	$20.50	$14.75
SG191X229	191/229 U.S. Celebrate The Century Sheets	5	$15.25	$11.25
SG146X84	146/84 Distinguished Americans, Cycling Souvenir Sheet and other miniature panes	3	$3.75	$2.75
SG203X146	203/146 Hanukkah, Kwanzaa, Eid, Wedding Cake Series, Ronald Reagan, Dogs at Work, Jose Ferrer, Samuel de Champlain SS, etc.	3	$7.50	$5.50
SG178X181	178/181 Butterfly Series, Carmel Mission Express Mail, Celebrate Scouting, Cranes, etc.	3	$7.50	$5.50
SG148X196	148/196 $5.00 Waves of Color, Moon Landing 25th Anniversary, etc.	3	$7.50	$5.50
SG76	264/76 BEP SS, Booklets, Plate Blocks	5	$11.95	$8.75
SG96	264/96 Souvenir Sheets, Panes	5	$11.95	$8.75
SG109	264/109 Foreign Miniature Sheets	5	$11.95	$8.75
SG115	264/115 Foreign Miniature Sheets	5	$11.95	$8.75
SG117	264/117 Foreign Miniature Sheets	5	$11.95	$8.75
SG121	264/121 Foreign Miniature Sheets	5	$11.95	$8.75
SG131	264/131 Looney Toons, Misc. Sheetlets	5	$11.95	$8.75
SG135	264/135 Foreign Miniature Sheets	5	$11.95	$8.75
SG139	264/139 White House Pane, etc.	5	$11.95	$8.75
SG143	264/143 Victorian Love, Misc. Sheets	5	$11.95	$8.75
SG147	264/147 Cinco de Mayo, etc.	5	$14.95	$10.75
SG151	264/151 Antique Auto, Communication, etc.	5	$15.50	$11.08
SG163	264/163 Tropical Flowers, UN Human Rights	5	$14.95	$10.75
SG167	264/167 Misc. U.S. Sheetlets	5	$14.95	$10.75
SG171	264/171 Helping Children Learn, etc.	5	$14.95	$10.75
SG181	264/181 U.S. Sheets–Calder, All Aboard, etc.	5	$18.50	$13.25
SG201	264/201 Dinosaurs, etc.	5	$18.50	$13.25
SG215	264/215 U.S. Sheets–Arctic Animals, Ballet, etc.	5	$18.50	$13.25

7" LIGHTHOUSE STAMP MOUNT CUTTER

This affordable and versatile mount cutter features an attachable measuring scale up to 7" (180mm) with an adjustable stop for accurate and clean cuts every time.

Item	Retail	AA*
LH180MC	$24.95	$19.95

AMOS ADVANTAGE

Call **1-800-572-6885**

Outside U.S. & Canada: (937) 498-0800

Visit **www.AmosAdvantage.com**

Mail orders to: P.O. Box 4129, Sidney, OH 45365

COMMON DESIGN TYPES

Pictured in this section are issues where one illustration has been used for a number of countries in the Catalogue. Not included in this section are overprinted stamps or those issues which are illustrated in each country. Because the location of Never Hinged breakpoints varies from country to country, some of the values in the listings below will be for unused stamps that were previously hinged.

EUROPA
Europa, 1956

The design symbolizing the cooperation among the six countries comprising the Coal and Steel Community is illustrated in each country.

Belgium	496-497
France	805-806
Germany	748-749
Italy	715-716
Luxembourg	318-320
Netherlands	368-369

Nos. 496-497 (2)	9.00	.50
Nos. 805-806 (2)	5.25	1.00
Nos. 748-749 (2)	7.40	1.10
Nos. 715-716 (2)	9.25	1.25
Nos. 318-320 (3)	65.50	42.00
Nos. 368-369 (2)	25.75	1.50
Set total (13) Stamps	122.15	47.35

Europa, 1958

"E" and Dove — CD1

European Postal Union at the service of European integration.

1958, Sept. 13

Belgium	527-528
France	889-890
Germany	790-791
Italy	750-751
Luxembourg	341-343
Netherlands	375-376
Saar	317-318

Nos. 527-528 (2)	3.75	.60
Nos. 889-890 (2)	1.65	.55
Nos. 790-791 (2)	2.95	.60
Nos. 750-751 (2)	1.05	.60
Nos. 341-343 (3)	1.35	.90
Nos. 375-376 (2)	1.25	.75
Nos. 317-318 (2)	1.05	2.30
Set total (15) Stamps	13.05	6.30

Europa, 1959

6-Link Enless Chain — CD2

1959, Sept. 19

Belgium	536-537
France	929-930
Germany	805-806
Italy	791-792
Luxembourg	354-355
Netherlands	379-380

Nos. 536-537 (2)	1.55	.60
Nos. 929-930 (2)	1.40	.80
Nos. 805-806 (2)	1.35	.60
Nos. 791-792 (2)	.80	.50
Nos. 354-355 (2)	2.65	1.00
Nos. 379-380 (2)	2.10	1.85
Set total (12) Stamps	9.85	5.35

Europa, 1960

19-Spoke Wheel CD3

First anniverary of the establishment of C.E.P.T. (Conference Europeenne des Administrations des Postes et des Telecommunications.) The spokes symbolize the 19 founding members of the Conference.

1960, Sept.

Belgium	553-554
Denmark	379
Finland	376-377
France	970-971
Germany	818-820
Great Britain	377-378
Greece	688
Iceland	327-328
Ireland	175-176
Italy	809-810
Luxembourg	374-375
Netherlands	385-386
Norway	387
Portugal	866-867
Spain	941-942
Sweden	562-563
Switzerland	400-401
Turkey	1493-1494

Nos. 553-554 (2)	1.25	.55
No. 379 (1)	.55	.50
Nos. 376-377 (2)	1.70	1.80
Nos. 970-971 (2)	.50	.50
Nos. 818-820 (3)	1.90	1.35
Nos. 377-378 (2)	8.00	5.00
No. 688 (1)	4.25	1.75
Nos. 327-328 (2)	1.30	1.85
Nos. 175-176 (2)	47.50	27.50
Nos. 809-810 (2)	.50	.50
Nos. 374-375 (2)	1.00	.80
Nos. 385-386 (2)	2.00	2.00
No. 387 (1)	1.00	.80
Nos. 866-867 (2)	3.00	1.75
Nos. 941-942 (2)	1.50	.75
Nos. 562-563 (2)	1.05	.55
Nos. 400-401 (2)	1.75	.75
Nos. 1493-1494 (2)	2.10	1.35
Set total (34) Stamps	80.85	50.05

Europa, 1961

19 Doves Flying as One — CD4

The 19 doves represent the 19 members of the Conference of European Postal and Telecommunications Administrations C.E.P.T.

1961-62

Belgium	572-573
Cyprus	201-203
France	1005-1006
Germany	844-845
Great Britain	382-384
Greece	718-719
Iceland	340-341
Italy	845-846
Luxembourg	382-383
Netherlands	387-388
Spain	1010-1011
Switzerland	410-411
Turkey	1518-1520

Nos. 572-573 (2)	.75	.50
Nos. 201-203 (3)	2.10	1.20
Nos. 1005-1006 (2)	.50	.50
Nos. 844-845 (2)	.60	.75
Nos. 382-384 (3)	.75	.75
Nos. 718-719 (2)	.80	.50
Nos. 340-341 (2)	1.10	1.60
Nos. 845-846 (2)	.50	.50
Nos. 382-383 (2)	.55	.55
Nos. 387-388 (2)	.50	.50
Nos. 1010-1011 (2)	.60	.50
Nos. 410-411 (2)	1.90	.60
Nos. 1518-1520 (3)	1.55	.90
Set total (29) Stamps	12.20	9.35

Europa, 1962

Young Tree with 19 Leaves CD5

The 19 leaves represent the 19 original members of C.E.P.T.

1962-63

Belgium	582-583
Cyprus	219-221
France	1045-1046
Germany	852-853
Greece	739-740
Iceland	348-349
Ireland	184-185
Italy	860-861
Luxembourg	386-387
Netherlands	394-395
Norway	414-415
Switzerland	416-417
Turkey	1553-1555

Nos. 582-583 (2)	.65	.65
Nos. 219-221 (3)	76.25	6.75
Nos. 1045-1046 (2)	.60	.50
Nos. 852-853 (2)	.65	.75
Nos. 739-740 (2)	2.00	1.15
Nos. 348-349 (2)	.85	.85
Nos. 184-185 (2)	2.00	.50
Nos. 860-861 (2)	1.00	.55
Nos. 386-387 (2)	.75	.55
Nos. 394-395 (2)	1.35	.90
Nos. 414-415 (2)	1.75	1.70
Nos. 416-417 (2)	1.65	1.00
Nos. 1553-1555 (3)	2.05	1.10
Set total (28) Stamps	91.55	16.95

Europa, 1963

Stylized Links, Symbolizing Unity — CD6

1963, Sept.

Belgium	598-599
Cyprus	229-231
Finland	419
France	1074-1075
Germany	867-868
Greece	768-769
Iceland	357-358
Ireland	188-189
Italy	880-881
Luxembourg	403-404
Netherlands	416-417
Norway	441-442
Switzerland	429
Turkey	1602-1603

Nos. 598-599 (2)	1.60	.55
Nos. 229-231 (3)	64.00	9.40
No. 419 (1)	1.25	.55
Nos. 1074-1075 (2)	.60	.50
Nos. 867-868 (2)	.50	.55
Nos. 768-769 (2)	4.65	1.65
Nos. 357-358 (2)	1.20	1.20
Nos. 188-189 (2)	4.75	3.25
Nos. 880-881 (2)	.50	.50
Nos. 403-404 (2)	.75	.55
Nos. 416-417 (2)	1.30	1.00
Nos. 441-442 (2)	2.60	2.40
No. 429 (1)	.90	.60
Nos. 1602-1603 (2)	1.20	.50
Set total (27) Stamps	85.80	23.20

Europa, 1964

Symbolic Daisy — CD7

5th anniversary of the establishment of C.E.P.T. The 22 petals of the flower symbolize the 22 members of the Conference.

1964, Sept.

Austria	738
Belgium	614-615
Cyprus	244-246
France	1109-1110
Germany	897-898
Greece	801-802
Iceland	367-368
Ireland	196-197
Italy	894-895
Luxembourg	411-412
Monaco	590-591
Netherlands	428-429
Norway	458
Portugal	931-933
Spain	1262-1263
Switzerland	438-439
Turkey	1628-1629

No. 738 (1)	1.10	.25
Nos. 614-615 (2)	1.40	.60
Nos. 244-246 (3)	32.25	5.10
Nos. 1109-1110 (2)	.50	.50
Nos. 897-898 (2)	.50	.50
Nos. 801-802 (2)	4.15	1.55
Nos. 367-368 (2)	1.40	1.15
Nos. 196-197 (2)	17.00	4.25
Nos. 894-895 (2)	.50	.50
Nos. 411-412 (2)	.75	.55
Nos. 590-591 (2)	2.50	.70
Nos. 428-429 (2)	.75	.60
No. 458 (1)	3.50	3.50
Nos. 931-933 (3)	10.00	2.00
Nos. 1262-1263 (2)	1.15	.80
Nos. 438-439 (2)	1.65	.50
Nos. 1628-1629 (2)	2.00	.80
Set total (34) Stamps	81.10	23.85

Europa, 1965

Leaves and "Fruit" CD8

1965

Belgium	636-637
Cyprus	262-264
Finland	437
France	1131-1132
Germany	934-935
Greece	833-834
Iceland	375-376
Ireland	204-205
Italy	915-916
Luxembourg	432-433
Monaco	616-617
Netherlands	438-439
Norway	475-476
Portugal	958-960
Switzerland	469
Turkey	1665-1666

Nos. 636-637 (2)	.50	.50
Nos. 262-264 (3)	25.35	6.00
No. 437 (1)	1.25	.55
Nos. 1131-1132 (2)	.70	.55
Nos. 934-935 (2)	.50	.50
Nos. 833-834 (2)	2.25	1.15
Nos. 375-376 (2)	2.50	1.75
Nos. 204-205 (2)	16.00	3.35
Nos. 915-916 (2)	.50	.50
Nos. 432-433 (2)	.75	.55
Nos. 616-617 (2)	3.25	1.65
Nos. 438-439 (2)	.55	.50
Nos. 475-476 (2)	2.40	1.90
Nos. 958-960 (3)	10.00	2.75
No. 469 (1)	1.15	.50
Nos. 1665-1666 (2)	2.00	1.25
Set total (32) Stamps	69.65	23.95

Europa, 1966

Symbolic Sailboat — CD9

1966, Sept.

Andorra, French	172
Belgium	675-676
Cyprus	275-277
France	1163-1164
Germany	963-964

Greece..................................862-863
Iceland..................................384-385
Ireland..................................216-217
Italy.......................................942-943
Liechtenstein 415
Luxembourg................................440-441
Monaco..................................639-640
Netherlands................................441-442
Norway 496-497
Portugal................................980-982
Switzerland................................477-478
Turkey 1718-1719

No. 172 (1)	3.00	3.00
Nos. 675-676 (2)	.80	.55
Nos. 275-277 (3)	4.75	2.75
Nos. 1163-1164 (2)	.55	.50
Nos. 963-964 (2)	.50	.55
Nos. 862-863 (2)	2.10	1.05
Nos. 384-385 (2)	4.50	3.50
Nos. 216-217 (2)	6.75	2.00
Nos. 942-943 (2)	.50	.50
No. 415 (1)	.40	.35
Nos. 440-441 (2)	.70	.55
Nos. 639-640 (2)	2.00	.65
Nos. 441-442 (2)	.85	.50
Nos. 496-497 (2)	2.35	2.15
Nos. 980-982 (3)	9.75	2.25
Nos. 477-478 (2)	1.40	.60
Nos. 1718-1719 (2)	3.35	1.75
Set total (34) Stamps	44.25	23.15

Europa, 1967

Cogwheels
CD10

1967

Andorra, French 174-175
Belgium..................................688-689
Cyprus..................................297-299
France..................................1178-1179
Germany..................................969-970
Greece..................................891-892
Iceland..................................389-390
Ireland..................................232-233
Italy.......................................951-952
Liechtenstein 420
Luxembourg................................449-450
Monaco..................................669-670
Netherlands................................444-447
Norway 504-505
Portugal................................994-996
Spain..................................1465-1466
Switzerland................................482
Turkey B120-B121

Nos. 174-175 (2)	10.75	6.25
Nos. 688-689 (2)	1.05	.55
Nos. 297-299 (3)	4.25	2.50
Nos. 1178-1179 (2)	.55	.50
Nos. 969-970 (2)	.55	.55
Nos. 891-892 (2)	3.05	.85
Nos. 389-390 (2)	3.00	2.00
Nos. 232-233 (2)	5.90	2.30
Nos. 951-952 (2)	.60	.50
No. 420 (1)	.45	.40
Nos. 449-450 (2)	1.00	.70
Nos. 669-670 (2)	2.75	.70
Nos. 444-447 (4)	2.70	2.05
Nos. 504-505 (2)	2.00	1.80
Nos. 994-996 (3)	9.50	1.85
Nos. 1465-1466 (2)	.50	.50
No. 482 (1)	.60	.30
Nos. B120-B121 (2)	2.50	2.00
Set total (38) Stamps	51.70	26.30

Europa, 1968

Golden Key
with
C.E.P.T.
Emblem
CD11

1968

Andorra, French 182-183
Belgium..................................705-706
Cyprus..................................314-316
France..................................1209-1210
Germany..................................983-984
Greece..................................916-917
Iceland..................................395-396
Ireland..................................242-243
Italy.......................................979-980

Liechtenstein 442
Luxembourg................................466-467
Monaco..................................689-691
Netherlands................................452-453
Portugal................................1019-1021
San Marino................................687
Spain..................................1526
Switzerland................................488
Turkey 1775-1776

Nos. 182-183 (2)	16.50	10.00
Nos. 705-706 (2)	1.25	.50
Nos. 314-316 (3)	2.90	2.50
Nos. 1209-1210 (2)	.85	.55
Nos. 983-984 (2)	.50	.55
Nos. 916-917 (2)	3.10	1.45
Nos. 395-396 (2)	3.00	2.20
Nos. 242-243 (2)	3.30	2.25
Nos. 979-980 (2)	.50	.50
No. 442 (1)	.45	.40
Nos. 466-467 (2)	.80	.70
Nos. 689-691 (3)	5.40	.95
Nos. 452-453 (2)	1.05	.70
Nos. 1019-1021 (3)	9.75	2.10
No. 687 (1)	.55	.35
No. 1526 (1)	.25	.25
No. 488 (1)	.40	.25
Nos. 1775-1776 (2)	2.50	1.25
Set total (35) Stamps	53.05	27.45

Europa, 1969

"EUROPA"
and "CEPT"
CD12

Tenth anniversary of C.E.P.T.

1969

Andorra, French 188-189
Austria 837
Belgium..................................718-719
Cyprus..................................326-328
Denmark..................................458
Finland..................................483
France..................................1245-1246
Germany..................................996-997
Great Britain 585
Greece..................................947-948
Iceland..................................406-407
Ireland..................................270-271
Italy.......................................1000-1001
Liechtenstein 453
Luxembourg................................475-476
Monaco..................................722-724
Netherlands................................475-476
Norway 533-534
Portugal................................1038-1040
San Marino................................701-702
Spain..................................1567
Sweden..................................814-816
Switzerland................................500-501
Turkey 1799-1800
Vatican..................................470-472
Yugoslavia 1003-1004

Nos. 188-189 (2)	18.50	12.00
No. 837 (1)	.55	.25
Nos. 718-719 (2)	.75	.50
Nos. 326-328 (3)	3.00	2.25
No. 458 (1)	.75	.75
No. 483 (1)	3.50	.75
Nos. 1245-1246 (2)	.55	.50
Nos. 996-997 (2)	.70	.50
No. 585 (1)	.25	.25
Nos. 947-948 (2)	4.00	1.25
Nos. 406-407 (2)	4.20	2.40
Nos. 270-271 (2)	3.50	2.00
Nos. 1000-1001 (2)	.50	.50
No. 453 (1)	.45	.45
Nos. 475-476 (2)	.95	.50
Nos. 722-724 (3)	10.50	2.00
Nos. 475-476 (2)	1.35	1.00
Nos. 533-534 (2)	2.20	1.95
Nos. 1038-1040 (3)	17.75	2.40
Nos. 701-702 (2)	.90	.90
No. 1567 (1)	.25	.25
Nos. 814-816 (3)	4.00	2.85
Nos. 500-501 (2)	1.85	1.00
Nos. 1799-1800 (2)	2.50	1.65
Nos. 470-472 (3)	.75	.75
Nos. 1003-1004 (2)	4.00	4.00
Set total (51) Stamps	88.20	43.60

Europa, 1970

Interwoven
Threads
CD13

1970

Andorra, French 196-197
Belgium..................................741-742
Cyprus..................................340-342
France..................................1271-1272
Germany..................................1018-1019
Greece..................................985, 987
Iceland..................................420-421
Ireland..................................279-281
Italy.......................................1013-1014
Liechtenstein 470
Luxembourg................................489-490
Monaco..................................768-770
Netherlands................................483-484
Portugal................................1060-1062
San Marino................................729-730
Spain..................................1607
Switzerland................................515-516
Turkey 1848-1849
Yugoslavia 1024-1025

Nos. 196-197 (2)	20.00	8.50
Nos. 741-742 (2)	1.10	.55
Nos. 340-342 (3)	2.70	2.75
Nos. 1271-1272 (2)	.65	.50
Nos. 1018-1019 (2)	.60	.50
Nos. 985,987 (2)	6.35	1.60
Nos. 420-421 (2)	6.00	4.00
Nos. 279-281 (3)	7.50	2.50
Nos. 1013-1014 (2)	.50	.50
No. 470 (1)	.45	.45
Nos. 489-490 (2)	.80	.55
Nos. 768-770 (3)	6.35	2.10
Nos. 483-484 (2)	1.30	1.15
Nos. 1060-1062 (3)	9.75	2.35
Nos. 729-730 (2)	.90	.55
No. 1607 (1)	.25	.25
Nos. 515-516 (2)	1.85	.70
Nos. 1848-1849 (2)	2.50	1.50
Nos. 1024-1025 (2)	.80	.80
Set total (40) Stamps	70.35	31.80

Europa, 1971

"Fraternity,
Cooperation,
Common
Effort"
CD14

1971

Andorra, French 205-206
Belgium..................................803-804
Cyprus..................................365-367
Finland..................................504
France..................................1304
Germany..................................1064-1065
Greece..................................1029-1030
Iceland..................................429-430
Ireland..................................305-306
Italy.......................................1038-1039
Liechtenstein 485
Luxembourg................................500-501
Malta..................................425-427
Monaco..................................797-799
Netherlands................................488-489
Portugal................................1094-1096
San Marino................................749-750
Spain..................................1675-1676
Switzerland................................531-532
Turkey 1876-1877
Yugoslavia 1052-1053

Nos. 205-206 (2)	20.00	7.75
Nos. 803-804 (2)	1.30	.55
Nos. 365-367 (3)	2.60	3.25
No. 504 (1)	5.00	.75
No. 1304 (1)	.45	.40
Nos. 1064-1065 (2)	.60	.50
Nos. 1029-1030 (2)	4.00	1.80
Nos. 429-430 (2)	5.00	3.75
Nos. 305-306 (2)	4.50	1.50
Nos. 1038-1039 (2)	.65	.50
No. 485 (1)	.45	.45
Nos. 500-501 (2)	1.00	.65
Nos. 425-427 (3)	.80	.80
Nos. 797-799 (3)	15.00	2.80
Nos. 488-489 (2)	1.20	.95
Nos. 1094-1096 (3)	9.75	1.75
Nos. 749-750 (2)	.65	.55
Nos. 1675-1676 (2)	.75	.55
Nos. 531-532 (2)	1.85	.65
Nos. 1876-1877 (2)	2.50	1.25
Nos. 1052-1053 (2)	.50	.50
Set total (43) Stamps	78.55	31.65

Europa, 1972

Sparkles, Symbolic
of Communications
CD15

1972

Andorra, French 210-211
Andorra, Spanish 62
Belgium..................................825-826
Cyprus..................................380-382
Finland..................................512-513
France..................................1341
Germany..................................1089-1090
Greece..................................1049-1050
Iceland..................................439-440
Ireland..................................316-317
Italy.......................................1065-1066
Liechtenstein 504
Luxembourg................................512-513
Malta..................................450-453
Monaco..................................831-832
Netherlands................................494-495
Portugal................................1141-1143
San Marino................................771-772
Spain..................................1718
Switzerland................................544-545
Turkey 1907-1908
Yugoslavia 1100-1101

Nos. 210-211 (2)	21.00	7.00
No. 62 (1)	60.00	60.00
Nos. 825-826 (2)	.95	.55
Nos. 380-382 (3)	5.95	4.25
Nos. 512-513 (2)	7.00	1.40
No. 1341 (1)	.50	.35
Nos. 1089-1090 (2)	1.10	.55
Nos. 1049-1050 (2)	2.00	1.55
Nos. 439-440 (2)	2.90	2.65
Nos. 316-317 (2)	13.00	4.50
Nos. 1065-1066 (2)	.55	.50
No. 504 (1)	.45	.45
Nos. 512-513 (2)	.95	.65
Nos. 450-453 (4)	1.05	1.40
Nos. 831-832 (2)	5.00	1.40
Nos. 494-495 (2)	1.20	.90
Nos. 1141-1143 (3)	9.75	1.50
Nos. 771-772 (2)	.70	.50
No. 1718 (1)	.50	.40
Nos. 544-545 (2)	1.65	.60
Nos. 1907-1908 (2)	4.00	2.00
Nos. 1100-1101 (2)	1.20	1.20
Set total (44) Stamps	141.40	94.25

Europa, 1973

Post Horn
and Arrows
CD16

1973

Andorra, French 219-220
Andorra, Spanish 76
Belgium..................................839-840
Cyprus..................................396-398
Finland..................................526
France..................................1367
Germany..................................1114-1115
Greece..................................1090-1092
Iceland..................................447-448
Ireland..................................329-330
Italy.......................................1108-1109
Liechtenstein 528-529
Luxembourg................................523-524
Malta..................................469-471
Monaco..................................866-867
Netherlands................................504-505
Norway 604-605
Portugal................................1170-1172
San Marino................................802-803
Spain..................................1753
Switzerland................................580-581
Turkey 1935-1936
Yugoslavia 1138-1139

Nos. 219-220 (2)	20.00	11.00
No. 76 (1)	1.25	.85
Nos. 839-840 (2)	1.00	.65
Nos. 396-398 (3)	4.25	3.85
No. 526 (1)	1.25	.55
No. 1367 (1)	1.25	.75
Nos. 1114-1115 (2)	.85	.50
Nos. 1090-1092 (3)	2.10	1.40
Nos. 447-448 (2)	6.65	3.35

Nos. 329-330 (2)	5.25	2.00
Nos. 1108-1109 (2)	.50	.50
Nos. 528-529 (2)	.60	.60
Nos. 523-524 (2)	.90	.75
Nos. 469-471 (3)	.90	1.20
Nos. 866-867 (2)	15.00	2.40
Nos. 504-505 (2)	1.20	.95
Nos. 604-605 (2)	4.00	1.80
Nos. 1170-1172 (3)	13.00	2.15
Nos. 802-803 (2)	1.00	.60
No. 1753 (1)	.35	.25
Nos. 580-581 (2)	1.55	.60
Nos. 1935-1936 (2)	4.15	2.25
Nos. 1138-1139 (2)	1.15	1.10
Set total (46) Stamps	88.15	40.05

Europa, 2000

CD17

2000

Albania	2621-2622
Andorra, French	522
Andorra, Spanish	262
Armenia	610-611
Austria	1814
Azerbaijan	698-699
Belarus	350
Belgium	1818
Bosnia & Herzegovina (Moslem)	358
Bosnia & Herzegovina (Serb)	111-112
Croatia	428-429
Cyprus	959
Czech Republic	3120
Denmark	1189
Estonia	394
Faroe Islands	376
Finland	1129
Aland Islands	166
France	2771
Georgia	228-229
Germany	2086-2087
Gibraltar	837-840
Great Britain (Jersey)	935-936
Great Britain (Isle of Man)	883
Greece	1959
Greenland	363
Hungary	3699-3700
Iceland	910
Ireland	1230-1231
Italy	2349
Latvia	504
Liechtenstein	1178
Lithuania	668
Luxembourg	1035
Macedonia	187
Malta	1011-1012
Moldova	355
Monaco	2161-2162
Poland	3519
Portugal	2358
Portugal (Azores)	455
Portugal (Madeira)	208
Romania	4370
Russia	6589
San Marino	1480
Slovakia	355
Slovenia	424
Spain	3036
Sweden	2394
Switzerland	1074
Turkey	2762
Turkish Rep. of Northern Cyprus	500
Ukraine	379
Vatican City	1152

Nos. 2621-2622 (2)	11.00	11.00
No. 522 (1)	2.00	1.00
No. 262 (1)	1.75	.80
Nos. 610-611 (2)	4.75	4.75
No. 1814 (1)	1.25	1.25
Nos. 698-699 (2)	6.00	6.00
No. 350 (1)	1.75	1.75
No. 1818 (1)	1.40	.60
No. 358 (1)	4.75	4.75
Nos. 111-112 (2)	110.00	110.00
Nos. 428-429 (2)	6.25	6.25
No. 959 (1)	2.10	1.40
No. 3120 (1)	1.20	.40
No. 1189 (1)	3.50	2.25
No. 394 (1)	1.25	1.25
No. 376 (1)	2.40	2.40
No. 1129 (1)	2.00	.60
No. 166 (1)	2.00	1.10
No. 2771 (1)	1.25	.40
Nos. 228-229 (2)	9.00	9.00
Nos. 2086-2087 (2)	4.35	2.10
Nos. 837-840 (4)	5.50	5.30

Nos. 935-936 (2)	2.40	2.40
No. 883 (1)	1.75	1.75
No. 363 (1)	1.90	1.90
Nos. 3699-3700 (2)	6.50	2.50
No. 910 (1)	1.60	1.60
Nos. 1230-1231 (2)	4.35	4.35
No. 2349 (1)	1.50	.40
No. 504 (1)	5.00	2.40
No. 1178 (1)	2.25	1.75
No. 668 (1)	1.50	1.50
No. 1035 (1)	1.40	.85
No. 187 (1)	3.00	3.00
Nos. 1011-1012 (2)	4.35	4.35
No. 355 (1)	3.50	3.50
Nos. 2161-2162 (2)	2.80	1.40
No. 3519 (1)	1.25	.75
No. 2358 (1)	1.25	.65
No. 455 (1)	1.25	.50
No. 208 (1)	1.25	.50
No. 4370 (1)	2.50	1.25
No. 6589 (1)	4.00	.85
No. 1480 (1)	1.00	1.00
No. 355 (1)	1.60	.80
No. 424 (1)	3.25	3.25
No. 3036 (1)	1.00	.40
No. 2394 (1)	3.00	1.50
No. 1074 (1)	2.10	1.05
No. 2762 (1)	2.75	2.00
No. 500 (1)	2.50	2.50
No. 379 (1)	4.50	3.00
No. 1152 (1)	1.25	1.25
Set total (68) Stamps	263.70	229.25

The Gibraltar stamps are similar to the stamp illustrated, but none have the design shown above. All other sets listed above include at least one stamp with the design shown, but some include stamps with entirely different designs. Bulgaria Nos. 4131-4132, Guernsey Nos. 802-803 and Yugoslavia Nos. 2485-2486 are Europa stamps with completely different designs.

PORTUGAL & COLONIES
Vasco da Gama

Fleet Departing
CD20

Fleet Arriving at Calicut — CD21

Embarking at Rastello
CD22

Muse of History
CD23

San Gabriel, da Gama and Camoens
CD24

Archangel Gabriel, the Patron Saint
CD25

Flagship San Gabriel — CD26

Vasco da Gama — CD27

Fourth centenary of Vasco da Gama's discovery of the route to India.

1898

Azores	93-100
Macao	67-74
Madeira	37-44
Portugal	147-154
Port. Africa	1-8
Port. Congo	75-98
Port. India	189-196
St. Thomas & Prince Islands	170-193
Timor	45-52

Nos. 93-100 (8)	113.50	73.50
Nos. 67-74 (8)	138.75	91.75
Nos. 37-44 (8)	60.55	37.25
Nos. 147-154 (8)	155.00	50.25
Nos. 1-8 (8)	35.00	23.50
Nos. 75-98 (24)	52.15	41.65
Nos. 189-196 (8)	25.25	15.50
Nos. 170-193 (24)	56.30	43.00
Nos. 45-52 (8)	39.75	27.25
Set total (104) Stamps	676.25	403.65

Pombal
POSTAL TAX
POSTAL TAX DUES

Marquis de Pombal — CD28

Planning Reconstruction of Lisbon, 1755 — CD29

Pombal Monument, Lisbon — CD30

Sebastiao Jose de Carvalho e Mello, Marquis de Pombal (1699-1782), statesman, rebuilt Lisbon after earthquake of 1755. Tax was for the erection of Pombal monument. Obligatory on all mail on certain days throughout the year. Postal Tax Dues are inscribed "Multa."

1925

Angola	RA1-RA3, RAJ1-RAJ3
Azores	RA9-RA11, RAJ2-RAJ4
Cape Verde	RA1-RA3, RAJ1-RAJ3
Macao	RA1-RA3, RAJ1-RAJ3
Madeira	RA1-RA3, RAJ1-RAJ3
Mozambique	RA1-RA3, RAJ1-RAJ3
Nyassa	RA1-RA3, RAJ1-RAJ3
Portugal	RA11-RA13, RAJ2-RAJ4
Port. Guinea	RA1-RA3, RAJ1-RAJ3
Port. India	RA1-RA3, RAJ1-RAJ3
St. Thomas & Prince Islands	RA1-RA3, RAJ1-RAJ3
Timor	RA1-RA3, RAJ1-RAJ3

Nos. RA1-RA3,RAJ1-RAJ3 (6)	6.60	6.60
Nos. RA9-RA11,RAJ2-RAJ4 (6)	6.60	6.60
Nos. RA1-RA3,RAJ1-RAJ3 (6)	4.50	3.90
Nos. RA1-RA3,RAJ1-RAJ3 (6)	21.25	13.20
Nos. RA1-RA3,RAJ1-RAJ3 (6)	7.95	14.70
Nos. RA1-RA3,RAJ1-RAJ3 (6)	2.40	2.55
Nos. RA1-RA3,RAJ1-RAJ3 (6)	63.00	63.00
Nos. RA11-RA13,RAJ2-RAJ4 (6)	5.95	5.20
Nos. RA1-RA3,RAJ1-RAJ3 (6)	5.10	4.65
Nos. RA1-RA3,RAJ1-RAJ3 (6)	3.45	3.45
Nos. RA1-RA3,RAJ1-RAJ3 (6)	4.50	4.50
Nos. RA1-RA3,RAJ1-RAJ3 (6)	2.10	3.90
Set total (72) Stamps	133.40	132.25

Vasco da Gama
CD34

Mousinho de Albuquerque
CD35

Dam
CD36

Prince Henry the Navigator
CD37

Affonso de Albuquerque
CD38

Plane over Globe
CD39

1938-39

Angola	274-291, C1-C9
Cape Verde	234-251, C1-C9
Macao	289-305, C7-C15
Mozambique	270-287, C1-C9
Port. Guinea	233-250. C1-C9
Port. India	439-453, C1-C8
St. Thomas & Prince Islands	302-319, 323-340, C1-C18
Timor	223-239, C1-C9

Nos. 274-291,C1-C9 (27)	129.40	22.85
Nos. 234-251,C1-C9 (27)	87.00	27.15
Nos. 289-305,C7-C15 (26)	495.70	149.20
Nos. 270-287,C1-C9 (27)	63.45	11.20
Nos. 233-250,C1-C9 (27)	130.20	49.15
Nos. 439-453,C1-C8 (23)	82.75	30.95
Nos. 302-319,323-340,C1-C18 (54)	467.70	244.80
Nos. 223-239,C1-C9 (26)	193.55	94.50
Set total (237) Stamps	1,650.	629.80

Lady of Fatima

Our Lady of the Rosary, Fatima, Portugal — CD40

1948-49

Angola	315-318
Cape Verde	266
Macao	336
Mozambique	325-328
Port. Guinea	271
Port. India	480
St. Thomas & Prince Islands	351
Timor	254

Nos. 315-318 (4)	68.00	17.25
No. 266 (1)	8.50	4.50
No. 336 (1)	42.50	12.00
Nos. 325-328 (4)	73.25	16.85
No. 271 (1)	6.50	3.50
No. 480 (1)	4.50	3.00
No. 351 (1)	8.50	7.00
No. 254 (1)	6.00	6.00
Set total (14) Stamps	217.75	70.10

A souvenir sheet of 9 stamps was issued in 1951 to mark the extension of the 1950 Holy Year. The sheet contains: Angola No. 316, Cape Verde No. 266, Macao No. 336, Mozambique No. 325, Portuguese Guinea No. 271, Portuguese India Nos. 480, 485, St. Thomas & Prince Islands No. 351, Timor No. 254. The sheet also contains a portrait of Pope Pius XII and is inscribed "Encerramento do

Ano Santo, Fatima 1951." It was sold for 11 escudos.

Holy Year

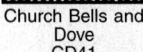

Church Bells and Dove
CD41

Angel Holding Candelabra
CD42

Holy Year, 1950.

1950-51

Angola	331-332
Cape Verde	268-269
Macao	339-340
Mozambique	330-331
Port. Guinea	273-274
Port. India	490-491, 496-503
St. Thomas & Prince Islands	353-354
Timor	258-259

Nos. 331-332 (2)	7.60	1.35
Nos. 268-269 (2)	5.50	3.50
Nos. 339-340 (2)	60.00	14.00
Nos. 330-331 (2)	3.00	1.10
Nos. 273-274 (2)	11.25	3.50
Nos. 490-491,496-503 (10)	10.40	4.95
Nos. 353-354 (2)	7.75	4.90
Nos. 258-259 (2)	8.00	4.00
Set total (24) Stamps	113.50	37.30

A souvenir sheet of 8 stamps was issued in 1951 to mark the extension of the Holy Year. The sheet contains: Angola No. 331, Cape Verde No. 269, Macao No. 340, Mozambique No. 331, Portuguese Guinea No. 275, Portuguese India No. 490, St. Thomas & Prince Islands No. 354, Timor No. 258, some with colors changed. The sheet contains doves and is inscribed 'Encerramento do Ano Santo, Fatima 1951.' It was sold for 17 escudos.

Holy Year Conclusion

Our Lady of Fatima — CD43

Conclusion of Holy Year. Sheets contain alternate vertical rows of stamps and labels bearing quotation from Pope Pius XII, different for each colony.

1951

Angola	357
Cape Verde	270
Macao	352
Mozambique	356
Port. Guinea	275
Port. India	506
St. Thomas & Prince Islands	355
Timor	270

No. 357 (1)	5.25	1.50
No. 270 (1)	1.50	1.25
No. 352 (1)	45.00	10.00
No. 356 (1)	2.25	1.00
No. 275 (1)	1.75	.90
No. 506 (1)	2.50	1.00
No. 355 (1)	3.00	2.00
No. 270 (1)	5.75	2.40
Set total (8) Stamps	67.00	20.05

Medical Congress

CD44

First National Congress of Tropical Medicine, Lisbon, 1952. Each stamp has a different design.

1952

Angola	358
Cape Verde	287
Macao	364

Mozambique	359
Port. Guinea	276
Port. India	516
St. Thomas & Prince Islands	356
Timor	271

No. 358 (1)	1.50	.50
No. 287 (1)	.75	.60
No. 364 (1)	10.00	6.00
No. 359 (1)	1.25	.55
No. 276 (1)	1.00	.45
No. 516 (1)	5.50	2.00
No. 356 (1)	.35	.30
No. 271 (1)	2.50	1.30
Set total (8) Stamps	22.85	11.70

Postage Due Stamps

CD45

1952

Angola	J37-J42
Cape Verde	J31-J36
Macao	J53-J58
Mozambique	J51-J56
Port. Guinea	J40-J45
Port. India	J47-J52
St. Thomas & Prince Islands	J52-J57
Timor	J31-J36

Nos. J37-J42 (6)	4.30	2.55
Nos. J31-J36 (6)	2.80	2.30
Nos. J53-J58 (6)	17.45	6.85
Nos. J51-J56 (6)	1.80	1.55
Nos. J40-J45 (6)	2.55	2.55
Nos. J47-J52 (6)	6.10	6.10
Nos. J52-J57 (6)	3.85	3.85
Nos. J31-J36 (6)	6.20	3.50
Set total (48) Stamps	45.05	29.25

Sao Paulo

Father Manuel da Nobrega and View of Sao Paulo — CD46

Founding of Sao Paulo, Brazil, 400th anniv.

1954

Angola	385
Cape Verde	297
Macao	382
Mozambique	395
Port. Guinea	291
Port. India	530
St. Thomas & Prince Islands	369
Timor	279

No. 385 (1)	.80	.50
No. 297 (1)	.70	.60
No. 382 (1)	15.00	6.00
No. 395 (1)	.40	.30
No. 291 (1)	.35	.25
No. 530 (1)	.80	.40
No. 369 (1)	.70	.50
No. 279 (1)	3.00	1.25
Set total (8) Stamps	21.75	9.80

Tropical Medicine Congress

CD47

Sixth International Congress for Tropical Medicine and Malaria, Lisbon, Sept. 1958. Each stamp shows a different plant.

1958

Angola	409
Cape Verde	303
Macao	392
Mozambique	404
Port. Guinea	295
Port. India	569
St. Thomas & Prince Islands	371

Timor	289

No. 409 (1)	3.50	1.10
No. 303 (1)	5.50	2.10
No. 392 (1)	10.00	5.00
No. 404 (1)	2.50	.85
No. 295 (1)	3.00	1.10
No. 569 (1)	1.75	.75
No. 371 (1)	2.75	2.00
No. 289 (1)	3.50	2.75
Set total (8) Stamps	32.50	15.65

Sports

CD48

Each stamp shows a different sport.

1962

Angola	433-438
Cape Verde	320-325
Macao	394-399
Mozambique	424-429
Port. Guinea	299-304
St. Thomas & Prince Islands	374-379
Timor	313-318

Nos. 433-438 (6)	5.50	3.20
Nos. 320-325 (6)	15.25	5.20
Nos. 394-399 (6)	68.65	14.60
Nos. 424-429 (6)	5.70	2.45
Nos. 299-304 (6)	6.00	3.00
Nos. 374-379 (6)	6.75	3.20
Nos. 313-318 (6)	9.15	5.05
Set total (42) Stamps	117.00	36.70

Anti-Malaria

Anopheles Funestus and Malaria Eradication Symbol — CD49

World Health Organization drive to eradicate malaria.

1962

Angola	439
Cape Verde	326
Macao	400
Mozambique	430
Port. Guinea	305
St. Thomas & Prince Islands	380
Timor	319

No. 439 (1)	1.75	.90
No. 326 (1)	1.40	.90
No. 400 (1)	7.00	2.25
No. 430 (1)	1.40	.40
No. 305 (1)	1.25	.45
No. 380 (1)	2.25	1.25
No. 319 (1)	1.50	1.00
Set total (7) Stamps	16.55	7.15

Airline Anniversary

Map of Africa, Super Constellation and Jet Liner — CD50

Tenth anniversary of Transportes Aereos Portugueses (TAP).

1963

Angola	490
Cape Verde	327
Mozambique	434
Port. Guinea	318
St. Thomas & Prince Islands	381

No. 490 (1)	1.00	.35
No. 327 (1)	1.10	.70
No. 434 (1)	.40	.25

No. 318 (1)	.65	.35
No. 381 (1)	.80	.50
Set total (5) Stamps	3.95	2.15

National Overseas Bank

Antonio Teixeira de Sousa — CD51

Centenary of the National Overseas Bank of Portugal.

1964, May 16

Angola	509
Cape Verde	328
Port. Guinea	319
St. Thomas & Prince Islands	382
Timor	320

No. 509 (1)	.90	.30
No. 328 (1)	1.10	.75
No. 319 (1)	.65	.40
No. 382 (1)	.70	.50
No. 320 (1)	1.50	.85
Set total (5) Stamps	4.85	2.80

ITU

ITU Emblem and the Archangel Gabriel — CD52

International Communications Union, Cent.

1965, May 17

Angola	511
Cape Verde	329
Macao	402
Mozambique	464
Port. Guinea	320
St. Thomas & Prince Islands	383
Timor	321

No. 511 (1)	1.25	.65
No. 329 (1)	2.10	1.40
No. 402 (1)	6.00	2.25
No. 464 (1)	.45	.25
No. 320 (1)	1.90	.75
No. 383 (1)	2.00	1.00
No. 321 (1)	1.50	.90
Set total (7) Stamps	15.20	7.20

National Revolution

CD53

40th anniv. of the National Revolution. Different buildings on each stamp.

1966, May 28

Angola	525
Cape Verde	338
Macao	403
Mozambique	465
Port. Guinea	329
St. Thomas & Prince Islands	392
Timor	322

No. 525 (1)	.50	.25
No. 338 (1)	.60	.45
No. 403 (1)	9.00	2.25
No. 465 (1)	.50	.30
No. 329 (1)	.55	.35
No. 392 (1)	.80	.50
No. 322 (1)	1.75	.95
Set total (7) Stamps	13.70	5.05

Navy Club

CD54

Centenary of Portugal's Navy Club. Each stamp has a different design.

1967, Jan. 31

Angola		527-528
Cape Verde		339-340
Macao		412-413
Mozambique		478-479
Port. Guinea		330-331
St. Thomas & Prince Islands		393-394
Timor		323-324

Nos. 527-528 (2)	1.75	.75
Nos. 339-340 (2)	2.00	1.40
Nos. 412-413 (2)	11.25	4.00
Nos. 478-479 (2)	1.40	.65
Nos. 330-331 (2)	1.20	.90
Nos. 393-394 (2)	3.30	1.30
Nos. 323-324 (2)	4.65	1.90
Set total (14) Stamps	25.55	10.90

Admiral Coutinho

CD55

Centenary of the birth of Admiral Carlos Viegas Gago Coutinho (1869-1959), explorer and aviation pioneer. Each stamp has a different design.

1969, Feb. 17

Angola		547
Cape Verde		355
Macao		417
Mozambique		484
Port. Guinea		335
St. Thomas & Prince Islands		397
Timor		335

No. 547 (1)	.85	.35
No. 355 (1)	.50	.25
No. 417 (1)	5.00	1.75
No. 484 (1)	.25	.25
No. 335 (1)	.35	.25
No. 397 (1)	.60	.35
No. 335 (1)	2.50	1.05
Set total (7) Stamps	10.05	4.25

Administration Reform

Luiz Augusto Rebello da Silva — CD56

Centenary of the administration reforms of the overseas territories.

1969, Sept. 25

Angola		549
Cape Verde		357
Macao		419
Mozambique		491
Port. Guinea		337
St. Thomas & Prince Islands		399
Timor		338

No. 549 (1)	.35	.25
No. 357 (1)	.50	.25
No. 419 (1)	6.00	1.00
No. 491 (1)	.25	.25
No. 337 (1)	.25	.25
No. 399 (1)	.45	.45
No. 338 (1)	1.25	.50
Set total (7) Stamps	9.05	2.95

Marshal Carmona

CD57

Birth centenary of Marshal Antonio Oscar Carmona de Fragoso (1869-1951), President of Portugal. Each stamp has a different design.

1970, Nov. 15

Angola		563
Cape Verde		359
Macao		422
Mozambique		493
Port. Guinea		340
St. Thomas & Prince Islands		403
Timor		341

No. 563 (1)	.45	.25
No. 359 (1)	.55	.35
No. 422 (1)	2.00	1.00
No. 493 (1)	.40	.25
No. 340 (1)	.35	.25
No. 403 (1)	.75	.40
No. 341 (1)	1.00	.35
Set total (7) Stamps	5.50	2.85

Olympic Games

CD59

20th Olympic Games, Munich, Aug. 26-Sept. 11. Each stamp shows a different sport.

1972, June 20

Angola		569
Cape Verde		361
Macao		426
Mozambique		504
Port. Guinea		342
St. Thomas & Prince Islands		408
Timor		343

No. 569 (1)	.65	.25
No. 361 (1)	.85	.30
No. 426 (1)	4.25	1.00
No. 504 (1)	.30	.25
No. 342 (1)	.45	.25
No. 408 (1)	.45	.25
No. 343 (1)	1.60	.80
Set total (7) Stamps	8.55	3.10

Lisbon-Rio de Janeiro Flight

CD60

50th anniversary of the Lisbon to Rio de Janeiro flight by Arturo de Sacadura and Coutinho, March 30-June 5, 1922. Each stamp shows a different stage of the flight.

1972, Sept. 20

Angola		570
Cape Verde		362
Macao		427
Mozambique		505
Port. Guinea		343
St. Thomas & Prince Islands		409
Timor		344

No. 570 (1)	.35	.25
No. 362 (1)	1.50	.30
No. 427 (1)	22.50	8.50
No. 505 (1)	.25	.25
No. 343 (1)	.25	.25
No. 409 (1)	.50	.25
No. 344 (1)	1.40	.60
Set total (7) Stamps	26.75	10.40

WMO Centenary

WMO Emblem — CD61

Centenary of international meterological cooperation.

1973, Dec. 15

Angola		571
Cape Verde		363
Macao		429
Mozambique		509
Port. Guinea		344
St. Thomas & Prince Islands		410
Timor		345

No. 571 (1)	.45	.25
No. 363 (1)	.65	.30
No. 429 (1)	6.00	1.75
No. 509 (1)	.30	.25
No. 344 (1)	.45	.35
No. 410 (1)	.60	.50
No. 345 (1)	4.25	2.50
Set total (7) Stamps	12.70	5.90

FRENCH COMMUNITY
**Upper Volta can be found under
Burkina Faso in Vol. 1
Madagascar can be found under
Malagasy in Vol. 3
Colonial Exposition**

People of French Empire CD70

Women's Heads CD71

France Showing Way to Civilization CD72

"Colonial Commerce" CD73

International Colonial Exposition, Paris.

1931

Cameroun		210-216
Chad		60-63
Dahomey		97-100
Fr. Guiana		152-155
Fr. Guinea		116-119
Fr. India		100-103
Fr. Polynesia		76-79
Fr. Sudan		102-105
Gabon		120-123
Guadeloupe		138-141
Indo-China		140-142
Ivory Coast		92-95
Madagascar		169-172
Martinique		129-132
Mauritania		65-68
Middle Congo		61-64
New Caledonia		176-179
Niger		73-76
Reunion		122-125
St. Pierre & Miquelon		132-135
Senegal		138-141
Somali Coast		135-138
Togo		254-257
Ubangi-Shari		82-85
Upper Volta		66-69
Wallis & Futuna Isls.		85-88

Nos. 213-216 (4)	23.00	18.25
Nos. 60-63 (4)	22.00	22.00
Nos. 97-100 (4)	26.00	26.00
Nos. 152-155 (4)	22.00	22.00
Nos. 116-119 (4)	19.75	19.75
Nos. 100-103 (4)	18.00	18.00
Nos. 76-79 (4)	30.00	30.00
Nos. 102-105 (4)	19.00	19.00
Nos. 120-123 (4)	17.50	17.50
Nos. 138-141 (4)	19.00	19.00
Nos. 140-142 (3)	12.00	11.50
Nos. 92-95 (4)	22.50	22.50
Nos. 169-172 (4)	9.25	6.50
Nos. 129-132 (4)	21.00	21.00
Nos. 65-68 (4)	22.00	22.00
Nos. 61-64 (4)	20.00	18.50
Nos. 176-179 (4)	24.00	24.00
Nos. 73-76 (4)	20.50	20.50
Nos. 122-125 (4)	22.00	22.00
Nos. 132-135 (4)	24.00	24.00
Nos. 138-141 (4)	20.00	20.00
Nos. 135-138 (4)	22.00	22.00
Nos. 254-257 (4)	22.00	22.00

Timor		345

Paris International Exposition Colonial Arts Exposition

"Colonial Resources"
CD74   CD77

Overseas Commerce CD75

Exposition Building and Women CD76

"France and the Empire" CD78

Cultural Treasures of the Colonies CD79

Souvenir sheets contain one imperf. stamp.

1937

Cameroun		217-222A
Dahomey		101-107
Fr. Equatorial Africa		27-32, 73
Fr. Guiana		162-168
Fr. Guinea		120-126
Fr. India		104-110
Fr. Polynesia		117-123
Fr. Sudan		106-112
Guadeloupe		148-154
Indo-China		193-199
Inini		41
Ivory Coast		152-158
Kwangchowan		132
Madagascar		191-197
Martinique		179-185
Mauritania		69-75
New Caledonia		208-214
Niger		77-83
Reunion		167-173
St. Pierre & Miquelon		165-171
Senegal		172-178
Somali Coast		139-145
Togo		258-264
Wallis & Futuna Isls.		89

Nos. 82-85 (4)	21.00	21.00
Nos. 66-69 (4)	19.00	19.00
Nos. 85-88 (4)	31.00	35.00
Set total (103) Stamps	548.50	543.00

Nos. 217-222A (7)	18.80	20.30
Nos. 101-107 (7)	23.60	27.60
Nos. 27-32, 73 (7)	28.10	32.10
Nos. 162-168 (7)	22.50	24.50
Nos. 120-126 (7)	24.00	28.00
Nos. 104-110 (7)	21.15	36.50
Nos. 117-123 (7)	58.50	75.00
Nos. 106-112 (7)	23.60	27.60
Nos. 148-154 (7)	19.55	21.05
Nos. 193-199 (7)	17.70	19.70
No. 41 (1)	21.00	27.50
Nos. 152-158 (7)	22.20	26.20
No. 132 (1)	9.25	11.00
Nos. 191-197 (7)	19.25	21.75
Nos. 179-185 (7)	19.95	21.70
Nos. 69-75 (7)	20.50	24.50
Nos. 208-214 (7)	39.00	50.50
Nos. 73-83 (11)	40.60	45.10
Nos. 167-173 (7)	21.70	23.20
Nos. 165-171 (7)	49.60	64.00
Nos. 172-78 (7)	21.00	23.80
Nos. 139-145 (7)	25.60	32.60
Nos. 258-264 (7)	20.40	20.40
No. 89 (1)	19.00	37.50
Set total (154) Stamps	606.55	742.10

Curie

Pierre and Marie Curie CD80

40th anniversary of the discovery of radium. The surtax was for the benefit of the Intl. Union for the Control of Cancer.

1938

Cameroun	B1
Cuba	B1-B2
Dahomey	B2
France	B76
Fr. Equatorial Africa	B1
Fr. Guiana	B3
Fr. Guinea	B2
Fr. India	B6
Fr. Polynesia	B5
Fr. Sudan	B1
Guadeloupe	B3
Indo-China	B14
Ivory Coast	B2
Madagascar	B2
Martinique	B2
Mauritania	B3
New Caledonia	B4
Niger	B1
Reunion	B4
St. Pierre & Miquelon	B3
Senegal	B3
Somali Coast	B2
Togo	B1

No. B1 (1)	10.00	10.00
Nos. B1-B2 (2)	12.00	3.35
No. B2 (1)	9.50	9.50
No. B76 (1)	21.00	24.00
No. B1 (1)	24.00	24.00
No. B3 (1)	13.50	13.50
No. B2 (1)	8.75	8.75
No. B6 (1)	10.00	10.00
No. B5 (1)	20.00	20.00
No. B1 (1)	12.50	12.50
No. B3 (1)	11.00	10.50
No. B14 (1)	12.00	12.00
No. B2 (1)	11.00	7.50
No. B2 (1)	11.00	11.00
No. B2 (1)	13.00	13.00
No. B3 (1)	7.75	7.75
No. B4 (1)	16.50	17.50
No. B1 (1)	16.50	16.50
No. B4 (1)	14.00	14.00
No. B3 (1)	21.00	22.50
No. B3 (1)	10.50	10.50
No. B2 (1)	7.75	7.75
No. B1 (1)	20.00	20.00
Set total (24) Stamps	313.25	294.60

Caillie

Rene Caillie and Map of Northwestern Africa — CD81

Death centenary of Rene Caillie (1799-1838), French explorer. All three denominations exist with colony name omitted.

1939

Dahomey	108-110
Fr. Guinea	161-163
Fr. Sudan	113-115
Ivory Coast	160-162
Mauritania	109-111
Niger	84-86
Senegal	188-190
Togo	265-267

Nos. 108-110 (3)	1.20	3.60
Nos. 161-163 (3)	1.20	3.20
Nos. 113-115 (3)	1.20	3.20
Nos. 160-162 (3)	1.05	2.55
Nos. 109-111 (3)	1.05	3.80
Nos. 84-86 (3)	2.35	2.35
Nos. 188-190 (3)	1.05	2.90
Nos. 265-267 (3)	1.05	3.30
Set total (24) Stamps	10.15	24.90

New York World's Fair

Natives and New York Skyline CD82

1939

Cameroun	223-224
Dahomey	111-112
Fr. Equatorial Africa	78-79
Fr. Guiana	169-170
Fr. Guinea	164-165
Fr. India	111-112
Fr. Polynesia	124-125
Fr. Sudan	116-117
Guadeloupe	155-156
Indo-China	203-204
Inini	42-43
Ivory Coast	163-164
Kwangchowan	133-134
Madagascar	209-210
Martinique	186-187
Mauritania	112-113
New Caledonia	215-216
Niger	87-88
Reunion	174-175
St. Pierre & Miquelon	205-206
Senegal	191-192
Somali Coast	179-180
Togo	268-269
Wallis & Futuna Isls.	90-91

Nos. 223-224 (2)	2.80	2.40
Nos. 111-112 (2)	1.60	3.20
Nos. 78-79 (2)	1.60	3.20
Nos. 169-170 (2)	2.60	2.60
Nos. 164-165 (2)	1.60	3.20
Nos. 111-112 (2)	3.00	8.00
Nos. 124-125 (2)	4.80	4.80
Nos. 116-117 (2)	1.60	3.20
Nos. 155-156 (2)	2.50	2.50
Nos. 203-204 (2)	2.05	2.05
Nos. 42-43 (2)	7.50	9.00
Nos. 163-164 (2)	1.50	3.00
Nos. 133-134 (2)	2.50	2.50
Nos. 209-210 (2)	1.50	2.50
Nos. 186-187 (2)	2.35	2.35
Nos. 112-113 (2)	1.40	2.80
Nos. 215-216 (2)	3.35	3.35
Nos. 87-88 (2)	1.60	2.80
Nos. 174-175 (2)	2.80	2.80
Nos. 205-206 (2)	4.80	6.00
Nos. 191-192 (2)	1.40	2.80
Nos. 179-180 (2)	1.40	2.80
Nos. 268-269 (2)	1.40	2.80
Nos. 90-91 (2)	5.00	6.00
Set total (48) Stamps	62.65	86.65

French Revolution

Storming of the Bastille CD83

French Revolution, 150th anniv. The surtax was for the defense of the colonies.

1939

Cameroun	B2-B6
Dahomey	B3-B7
Fr. Equatorial Africa	B4-B8, CB1
Fr. Guiana	B4-B8, CB1
Fr. Guinea	B3-B7
Fr. India	B7-B11
Fr. Polynesia	B6-B10, CB1
Fr. Sudan	B2-B6
Guadeloupe	B4-B8
Indo-China	B15-B19, CB1
Inini	B1-B5
Ivory Coast	B3-B7
Kwangchowan	B1-B5
Madagascar	B3-B7, CB1
Martinique	B3-B7
Mauritania	B4-B8
New Caledonia	B5-B9, CB1
Niger	B2-B6
Reunion	B5-B9, CB1
St. Pierre & Miquelon	B4-B8
Senegal	B4-B8, CB1
Somali Coast	B3-B7
Togo	B4-B8
Wallis & Futuna Isls.	B1-B5

Nos. B2-B6 (5)	60.00	60.00
Nos. B3-B7 (5)	47.50	47.50
Nos. B4-B8,CB1 (6)	120.00	120.00
Nos. B4-B8,CB1 (6)	79.50	79.50
Nos. B3-B7 (5)	47.50	47.50
Nos. B7-B11 (5)	28.75	32.50
Nos. B6-B10,CB1 (6)	122.50	122.50
Nos. B2-B6 (5)	50.00	50.00
Nos. B4-B8 (5)	50.00	50.00
Nos. B15-B19,CB1 (6)	85.00	85.00
Nos. B1-B5 (5)	80.00	100.00
Nos. B3-B7 (5)	43.75	43.75
Nos. B1-B5 (5)	46.25	46.25
Nos. B3-B7,CB1 (6)	65.50	65.50
Nos. B3-B7 (5)	52.50	52.50
Nos. B4-B8 (5)	42.50	42.50
Nos. B5-B9,CB1 (6)	101.50	101.50
Nos. B2-B6 (5)	60.00	60.00
Nos. B5-B9,CB1 (6)	87.50	87.50
Nos. B4-B8 (5)	67.50	72.50
Nos. B4-B8,CB1 (6)	56.50	56.50
Nos. B3-B7 (5)	45.00	45.00
Nos. B2-B6 (5)	42.50	42.50
Nos. B1-B5 (5)	80.00	110.00
Set total (128) Stamps	1,562.	1,621.

Plane over Coastal Area CD85

All five denominations exist with colony name omitted.

1940

Dahomey	C1-C5
Fr. Guinea	C1-C5
Fr. Sudan	C1-C5
Ivory Coast	C1-C5
Mauritania	C1-C5
Niger	C1-C5
Senegal	C12-C16
Togo	C1-C5

Nos. C1-C5 (5)	4.00	4.00
Nos. C1-C5 (5)	4.00	4.00
Nos. C1-C5 (5)	4.00	4.00
Nos. C1-C5 (5)	3.80	3.80
Nos. C1-C5 (5)	3.50	3.50
Nos. C1-C5 (5)	3.50	3.50
Nos. C12-C16 (5)	3.50	3.50
Nos. C1-C5 (5)	3.15	3.15
Set total (40) Stamps	29.45	29.45

Defense of the Empire

Colonial Infantryman — CD86

1941

Cameroun	B13B
Dahomey	B13
Fr. Equatorial Africa	B8B
Fr. Guiana	B10
Fr. Guinea	B13
Fr. India	B13
Fr. Polynesia	B12
Fr. Sudan	B12
Guadeloupe	B10
Indo-China	B19B
Inini	B7
Ivory Coast	B13
Kwangchowan	B7
Madagascar	B9
Martinique	B9
Mauritania	B14
New Caledonia	B11
Niger	B12
Reunion	B11
St. Pierre & Miquelon	B8B
Senegal	B14
Somali Coast	B9
Togo	B10B
Wallis & Futuna Isls.	B7

No. B13B (1)	1.60
No. B13 (1)	1.20
No. B8B (1)	3.50
No. B10 (1)	1.40
No. B13 (1)	1.40
No. B13 (1)	1.25
No. B12 (1)	3.50
No. B12 (1)	1.40
No. B10 (1)	1.00
No. B19B (1)	3.00
No. B7 (1)	1.75
No. B13 (1)	1.25
No. B7 (1)	.85

No. B9 (1)	1.50
No. B9 (1)	1.40
No. B14 (1)	.95
No. B12 (1)	1.40
No. B11 (1)	1.60
No. B8B (1)	4.50
No. B14 (1)	1.25
No. B9 (1)	1.60
No. B10B (1)	1.10
No. B7 (1)	1.75
Set total (23) Stamps	40.15

Each of the CD86 stamps listed above is part of a set of three stamps. The designs of the other two stamps in the set vary from country to country. Only the values of the Common Design stamps are listed here.

Colonial Education Fund

CD86a

1942

Cameroun	CB3
Dahomey	CB4
Fr. Equatorial Africa	CB5
Fr. Guiana	CB4
Fr. Guinea	CB4
Fr. India	CB3
Fr. Polynesia	CB4
Fr. Sudan	CB4
Guadeloupe	CB3
Indo-China	CB5
Inini	CB3
Ivory Coast	CB4
Kwangchowan	CB4
Malagasy	CB5
Martinique	CB3
Mauritania	CB4
New Caledonia	CB4
Niger	CB4
Reunion	CB4
St. Pierre & Miquelon	CB3
Senegal	CB5
Somali Coast	CB3
Togo	CB3
Wallis & Futuna	CB3

No. CB3 (1)	1.10	
No. CB4 (1)	.80	5.50
No. CB5 (1)	.80	
No. CB4 (1)	1.10	
No. CB3 (1)	.40	5.50
No. CB4 (1)	.90	
No. CB3 (1)	2.00	
No. CB4 (1)	.40	5.50
No. CB3 (1)	1.10	
No. CB5 (1)	2.00	
No. CB3 (1)	1.25	
No. CB4 (1)	1.00	5.50
No. CB4 (1)	1.00	
No. CB5 (1)	.65	
No. CB3 (1)	1.00	
No. CB4 (1)	.80	
No. CB4 (1)	2.25	
No. CB4 (1)	.35	
No. CB4 (1)	.90	
No. CB3 (1)	7.00	
No. CB5 (1)	.80	6.50
No. CB3 (1)	.70	
No. CB3 (1)	.35	
No. CB3 (1)	2.00	
Set total (24) Stamps	30.65	28.50

Cross of Lorraine & Four-motor Plane CD87

1941-5

Cameroun	C1-C7
Fr. Equatorial Africa	C17-C23
Fr. Guiana	C9-C10
Fr. India	C1-C6
Fr. Polynesia	C3-C9
Fr. West Africa	C1-C3
Guadeloupe	C1-C2
Madagascar	C37-C43

Martinique.................................C1-C2
New Caledonia........................C7-C13
Reunion C18-C24
St. Pierre & Miquelon.................C1-C7
Somali Coast.............................C1-C7

Nos. C1-C7 (7)	6.30	6.30
Nos. C17-C23 (7)	10.40	6.35
Nos. C9-C10 (2)	3.80	3.10
Nos. C1-C6 (6)	9.30	15.00
Nos. C3-C9 (7)	13.75	10.00
Nos. C1-C3 (3)	9.50	3.90
Nos. C1-C2 (2)	3.75	2.50
Nos. C37-C43 (7)	5.60	3.80
Nos. C1-C2 (2)	3.00	1.60
Nos. C7-C13 (7)	8.85	7.30
Nos. C18-C24 (7)	7.05	5.00
Nos. C1-C7 (7)	11.60	9.40
Nos. C1-C7 (7)	13.95	11.10
Set total (71) Stamps	106.85	85.35

Somali Coast stamps are inscribed "Djibouti".

Transport Plane CD88

Caravan and Plane CD89

1942

Dahomey C6-C13
Fr. Guinea C6-C13
Fr. Sudan................................C6-C13
Ivory Coast..............................C6-C13
Mauritania...............................C6-C13
Niger C6-C13
Senegal C17-C25
Togo.......................................C6-C13

Nos. C6-C13 (8)	7.15	
Nos. C6-C13 (8)	5.75	
Nos. C6-C13 (8)	8.00	
Nos. C6-C13 (8)	11.15	
Nos. C6-C13 (8)	9.75	
Nos. C6-C13 (8)	6.20	
Nos. C17-C25 (9)	9.45	
Nos. C6-C13 (8)	0.75	
Set total (65) Stamps	64.20	

Red Cross

Marianne CD90

The surtax was for the French Red Cross and national relief.

1944

Cameroun.....................................B28
Fr. Equatorial Africa B38
Fr. Guiana B12
Fr. India B14
Fr. Polynesia................................B13
Fr. West Africa B1
Guadeloupe.................................B12
Madagascar.................................B15
Martinique...................................B11
New Caledonia.............................B13
Reunion B15
St. Pierre & Miquelon....................B13
Somali Coast...............................B13
Wallis & Futuna Isls. B9

No. B28 (1)	2.00	1.60
No. B38 (1)	1.60	1.20
No. B12 (1)	1.75	1.25
No. B14 (1)	1.50	1.25
No. B13 (1)	2.00	1.60
No. B1 (1)	6.50	4.75
No. B12 (1)	1.40	1.00
No. B15 (1)	.90	.90
No. B11 (1)	1.20	1.20
No. B13 (1)	1.50	1.50
No. B15 (1)	1.60	1.10
No. B13 (1)	2.60	2.60
No. B13 (1)	1.75	2.00
No. B9 (1)	3.00	3.00
Set total (14) Stamps	29.30	24.95

Eboue

CD91

Felix Eboue, first French colonial administrator to proclaim resistance to Germany after French surrender in World War II.

1945

Cameroun.................................296-297
Fr. Equatorial Africa 156-157
Fr. Guiana 171-172
Fr. India 210-211
Fr. Polynesia............................150-151
Fr. West Africa 15-16
Guadeloupe.............................187-188
Madagascar.............................259-260
Martinique...............................196-197
New Caledonia.........................274-275
Reunion 238-239
St. Pierre & Miquelon................322-323
Somali Coast...........................238-239

Nos. 296-297 (2)	2.40	1.95
Nos. 156-157 (2)	2.55	2.00
Nos. 171-172 (2)	2.45	2.00
Nos. 210-211 (2)	2.20	1.95
Nos. 150-151 (2)	3.60	2.85
Nos. 15-16 (2)	2.40	2.40
Nos. 187-188 (2)	2.05	1.60
Nos. 259-260 (2)	2.00	1.45
Nos. 196-197 (2)	2.05	1.55
Nos. 274-275 (2)	3.40	3.00
Nos. 238-239 (2)	2.40	2.00
Nos. 322-323 (2)	4.40	3.45
Nos. 238-239 (2)	2.45	2.10
Set total (26) Stamps	34.35	28.30

Victory

Victory — CD92

European victory of the Allied Nations in World War II.

1946, May 8

Cameroun......................................C8
Fr. Equatorial Africa C24
Fr. Guiana C11
Fr. India C7
Fr. Polynesia................................C10
Fr. West Africa C4
Guadeloupe..................................C3
Indo-China..................................C19
Madagascar................................C44
Martinique....................................C3
New Caledonia.............................C14
Reunion C25
St. Pierre & Miquelon......................C8
Somali Coast................................C8
Wallis & Futuna Isls. C1

No. C8 (1)	1.60	1.20
No. C24 (1)	1.60	1.25
No. C11 (1)	1.75	1.25
No. C7 (1)	1.00	4.00
No. C10 (1)	2.75	2.00
No. C4 (1)	1.60	1.20
No. C3 (1)	1.25	1.00
No. C19 (1)	1.00	.55
No. C44 (1)	1.00	.35
No. C3 (1)	1.30	1.00
No. C14 (1)	1.50	1.25
No. C25 (1)	1.10	.90
No. C8 (1)	2.10	2.10
No. C8 (1)	1.75	1.40
No. C1 (1)	2.25	1.90
Set total (15) Stamps	23.55	21.35

Chad to Rhine

Leclerc's Departure from Chad — CD93

Battle at Cufra Oasis — CD94

Tanks in Action, Mareth — CD95

Normandy Invasion — CD96

Entering Paris — CD97

Liberation of Strasbourg — CD98

"Chad to the Rhine" march, 1942-44, by Gen. Jacques Leclerc's column, later French 2nd Armored Division.

1946, June 6

Cameroun.................................C9-C14
Fr. Equatorial Africa C25-C30
Fr. Guiana C12-C17
Fr. India C8-C13
Fr. Polynesia..........................C11-C16
Fr. West Africa C5-C10
Guadeloupe..............................C4-C9
Indo-China.............................C20-C25
Madagascar...........................C45-C50
Martinique................................C4-C9
New Caledonia.......................C15-C20
Reunion C26-C31
St. Pierre & Miquelon..............C9-C14
Somali Coast.........................C9-C14
Wallis & Futuna Isls. C2-C7

Nos. C9-C14 (6)	12.05	9.70
Nos. C25-C30 (6)	14.70	10.80
Nos. C12-C17 (6)	12.65	10.35
Nos. C8-C13 (6)	12.80	15.00
Nos. C11-C16 (6)	17.55	13.40
Nos. C5-C10 (6)	16.05	11.95
Nos. C4-C9 (6)	12.00	9.60
Nos. C20-C25 (6)	6.40	6.40
Nos. C45-C50 (6)	10.30	8.40
Nos. C4-C9 (6)	8.85	7.30
Nos. C15-C20 (6)	13.40	11.90
Nos. C26-C31 (6)	10.25	6.55
Nos. C9-C14 (6)	17.30	14.35

Nos. C9-C14 (6)	18.10	12.65
Nos. C2-C7 (6)	13.75	10.45
Set total (90) Stamps	196.15	158.80

UPU

French Colonials, Globe and Plane — CD99

Universal Postal Union, 75th anniv.

1949, July 4

Cameroun..C29
Fr. Equatorial Africa C34
Fr. India C17
Fr. Polynesia....................................C20
Fr. West Africa C15
Indo-China......................................C26
Madagascar.....................................C55
New Caledonia..................................C24
St. Pierre & Miquelon.........................C18
Somali Coast....................................C18
Togo...C18
Wallis & Futuna Isls. C10

No. C29 (1)	8.00	4.75
No. C34 (1)	16.00	12.00
No. C17 (1)	11.50	8.75
No. C20 (1)	20.00	15.00
No. C15 (1)	12.00	8.75
No. C26 (1)	4.75	4.00
No. C55 (1)	4.00	2.75
No. C24 (1)	7.50	5.00
No. C18 (1)	20.00	12.00
No. C18 (1)	14.00	10.50
No. C18 (1)	8.50	7.00
No. C10 (1)	11.00	8.25
Set total (12) Stamps	137.25	98.75

Tropical Medicine

Doctor Treating Infant CD100

The surtax was for charitable work.

1950

Cameroun......................................B29
Fr. Equatorial Africa B39
Fr. India B15
Fr. Polynesia..................................B14
Fr. West Africa B3
Madagascar...................................B17
New Caledonia................................B14
St. Pierre & Miquelon.......................B14
Somali Coast..................................B14
Togo...B11

No. B29 (1)	7.25	5.50
No. B39 (1)	7.25	5.50
No. B15 (1)	6.00	4.00
No. B14 (1)	10.50	8.00
No. B3 (1)	9.50	7.25
No. B17 (1)	5.50	5.50
No. B14 (1)	6.75	5.25
No. B14 (1)	16.00	15.00
No. B14 (1)	7.75	6.25
No. B11 (1)	5.00	3.50
Set total (10) Stamps	81.50	65.75

Military Medal

Medal, Early Marine and Colonial Soldier — CD101

Centenary of the creation of the French Military Medal.

1952

Cameroun.....................................322
Comoro Isls...................................39
Fr. Equatorial Africa 186

Fr. India 233
Fr. Polynesia...................................179
Fr. West Africa 57
Madagascar.....................................286
New Caledonia.................................295
St. Pierre & Miquelon....................345
Somali Coast 267
Togo..327
Wallis & Futuna Isls. 149

No. 322 (1)	7.25	3.25
No. 39 (1)	45.00	37.50
No. 186 (1)	8.00	5.50
No. 233 (1)	5.50	7.00
No. 179 (1)	13.50	10.00
No. 57 (1)	8.75	6.50
No. 286 (1)	3.75	2.50
No. 295 (1)	6.50	6.00
No. 345 (1)	16.00	15.00
No. 267 (1)	9.00	8.00
No. 327 (1)	5.50	4.75
No. 149 (1)	7.25	7.25
Set total (12) Stamps	136.00	113.25

Liberation

Allied Landing, Victory Sign and Cross of Lorraine — CD102

Liberation of France, 10th anniv.

1954, June 6

Cameroun.......................................C32
Comoro Isls. C4
Fr. Equatorial Africa C38
Fr. India C18
Fr. Polynesia...................................C22
Fr. West Africa C17
Madagascar.....................................C57
New Caledonia.................................C25
St. Pierre & Miquelon....................C19
Somali Coast C19
Togo..C19
Wallis & Futuna Isls. C11

No. C32 (1)	7.25	4.75
No. C4 (1)	32.50	19.00
No. C38 (1)	12.00	8.00
No. C18 (1)	11.00	8.00
No. C22 (1)	10.00	8.00
No. C17 (1)	12.00	5.50
No. C57 (1)	3.25	2.00
No. C25 (1)	7.50	5.00
No. C19 (1)	19.00	12.00
No. C19 (1)	10.50	8.50
No. C19 (1)	7.00	5.50
No. C11 (1)	11.00	8.25
Set total (12) Stamps	143.00	94.50

FIDES

Plowmen
CD103

Efforts of FIDES, the Economic and Social Development Fund for Overseas Possessions (Fonds d' Investissement pour le Developpement Economique et Social). Each stamp has a different design.

1956

Cameroun.................................326-329
Comoro Isls. 43
Fr. Equatorial Africa 189-192
Fr. Polynesia...................................181
Fr. West Africa 65-72
Madagascar.............................292-295
New Caledonia.................................303
St. Pierre & Miquelon....................350
Somali Coast...........................268-269
Togo..331

Nos. 326-329 (4)	6.90	3.20
No. 43 (1)	2.25	1.60
Nos. 189-192 (4)	3.20	1.65
No. 181 (1)	4.00	2.00
Nos. 65-72 (8)	16.00	6.35
Nos. 292-295 (4)	2.25	1.20
No. 303 (1)	1.90	1.10
No. 350 (1)	6.00	4.00

Nos. 268-269 (2)	5.35	3.15
No. 331 (1)	4.25	2.10
Set total (27) Stamps	52.10	26.35

Flower

CD104

Each stamp shows a different flower.

1958-9

Cameroun..333
Comoro Isls. 45
Fr. Equatorial Africa 200-201
Fr. Polynesia...................................192
Fr. So. & Antarctic Terr. 11
Fr. West Africa 79-83
Madagascar.............................301-302
New Caledonia.........................304-305
St. Pierre & Miquelon....................357
Somali Coast 270
Togo..348-349
Wallis & Futuna Isls. 152

No. 333 (1)	1.60	.80
No. 45 (1)	5.25	4.25
Nos. 200-201 (2)	3.60	1.60
No. 192 (1)	6.50	4.00
No. 11 (1)	8.75	7.50
Nos. 79-83 (5)	10.45	5.60
Nos. 301-302 (2)	1.60	.60
Nos. 304-305 (2)	8.00	3.00
No. 357 (1)	4.50	2.25
No. 270 (1)	4.25	1.40
Nos. 348-349 (2)	1.10	.50
No. 152 (1)	3.25	3.25
Set total (20) Stamps	58.85	34.75

Human Rights

Sun, Dove and U.N. Emblem CD105

10th anniversary of the signing of the Universal Declaration of Human Rights.

1958

Comoro Isls. 44
Fr. Equatorial Africa 202
Fr. Polynesia...................................191
Fr. West Africa 85
Madagascar.....................................300
New Caledonia.................................306
St. Pierre & Miquelon....................356
Somali Coast 274
Wallis & Futuna Isls. 153

No. 44 (1)	9.00	9.00
No. 202 (1)	2.40	1.25
No. 191 (1)	13.00	8.75
No. 85 (1)	2.40	2.00
No. 300 (1)	.80	.40
No. 306 (1)	2.00	1.50
No. 356 (1)	3.50	2.50
No. 274 (1)	3.50	2.10
No. 153 (1)	4.50	4.50
Set total (9) Stamps	41.10	32.00

C.C.T.A.

CD106

Commission for Technical Cooperation in Africa south of the Sahara, 10th anniv.

1960

Cameroun..339
Cent. Africa 3
Chad..66
Congo, P.R..90
Dahomey 138
Gabon..150
Ivory Coast 180
Madagascar.....................................317

Mali..9
Mauritania...117
Niger..104
Upper Volta..89

No. 339 (1)	1.60	.75
No. 3 (1)	1.60	.75
No. 66 (1)	1.75	.50
No. 90 (1)	1.00	1.00
No. 138 (1)	.50	.25
No. 150 (1)	1.25	1.10
No. 180 (1)	1.10	.50
No. 317 (1)	.60	.30
No. 9 (1)	1.20	.50
No. 117 (1)	.75	.40
No. 104 (1)	.85	.45
No. 89 (1)	.65	.40
Set total (12) Stamps	12.85	6.90

Air Afrique, 1961

Modern and Ancient Africa, Map and Planes — CD107

Founding of Air Afrique (African Airlines).

1961-62

Cameroun...C37
Cent. Africa C5
Chad..C7
Congo, P.R..C5
Dahomey C17
Gabon..C5
Ivory Coast C18
Mauritania...C17
Niger..C22
Senegal C31
Upper Volta..C4

No. C37 (1)	1.00	.50
No. C5 (1)	1.00	.65
No. C7 (1)	1.00	.25
No. C5 (1)	1.75	.90
No. C17 (1)	.80	.40
No. C5 (1)	11.00	6.00
No. C18 (1)	2.00	1.25
No. C17 (1)	2.40	1.25
No. C22 (1)	1.75	.90
No. C31 (1)	.80	.30
No. C4 (1)	3.50	1.75
Set total (11) Stamps	27.00	14.15

Anti-Malaria

CD108

World Health Organization drive to eradicate malaria.

1962, Apr. 7

Cameroun...B36
Cent. Africa B1
Chad..B1
Comoro Isls. B1
Congo, P.R..B3
Dahomey B15
Gabon..B4
Ivory Coast B15
Madagascar.......................................B19
Mali..B1
Mauritania...B16
Niger..B14
Senegal B16
Somali Coast B15
Upper Volta..B1

No. B36 (1)	1.00	.45
No. B1 (1)	1.40	1.40
No. B1 (1)	1.00	.50
No. B1 (1)	3.50	3.50
No. B3 (1)	1.40	1.00
No. B15 (1)	.75	.75
No. B4 (1)	1.00	1.00
No. B15 (1)	1.25	1.25
No. B19 (1)	.75	.50
No. B1 (1)	1.25	.60
No. B16 (1)	.50	.50
No. B14 (1)	.75	.75

No. B16 (1)	1.10	.65
No. B15 (1)	7.00	7.00
No. B1 (1)	.75	.70
Set total (15) Stamps	23.40	20.55

Abidjan Games

CD109

Abidjan Games, Ivory Coast, Dec. 24-31, 1961. Each stamp shows a different sport.

1962

Cent. Africa 19-20, C6
Chad......................................83-84, C8
Congo, P.R.........................103-104, C7
Gabon.................................163-164, C6
Niger..................................109-111
Upper Volta........................103-105

Nos. 19-20,C6 (3)	4.15	2.85
Nos. 83-84,C8 (3)	5.80	1.55
Nos. 103-104,C7 (3)	3.85	1.80
Nos. 163-164,C6 (3)	5.00	3.00
Nos. 109-111 (3)	2.60	1.25
Nos. 103-105 (3)	2.80	1.75
Set total (18) Stamps	24.20	12.20

African and Malagasy Union

Flag of Union CD110

First anniversary of the Union.

1962, Sept. 8

Cameroun..373
Cent. Africa 21
Chad..85
Congo, P.R..105
Dahomey 155
Gabon..165
Ivory Coast 198
Madagascar.....................................332
Mauritania...170
Niger..112
Senegal 211
Upper Volta..106

No. 373 (1)	2.00	.75
No. 21 (1)	1.25	.75
No. 85 (1)	1.25	.25
No. 105 (1)	1.50	.50
No. 155 (1)	1.25	.90
No. 165 (1)	1.60	1.25
No. 198 (1)	2.10	.75
No. 332 (1)	.80	.50
No. 170 (1)	.75	.50
No. 112 (1)	.80	.50
No. 211 (1)	.80	.50
No. 106 (1)	1.10	.75
Set total (12) Stamps	15.20	8.20

Telstar

Telstar and Globe Showing Andover and Pleumeur-Bodou — CD111

First television connection of the United States and Europe through the Telstar satellite, July 11-12, 1962.

1962-63

Andorra, French 154
Comoro Isls. C7
Fr. Polynesia...................................C29
Fr. So. & Antarctic Terr. C5
New Caledonia.................................C33
St. Pierre & Miquelon....................C26
Somali Coast C31
Wallis & Futuna Isls. C17

No. 154 (1)	2.00	1.60
No. C7 (1)	4.50	2.75
No. C29 (1)	11.50	8.00

No. C5 (1)	29.00	21.00
No. C33 (1)	25.00	18.50
No. C26 (1)	7.25	4.50
No. C31 (1)	1.00	1.00
No. C17 (1)	3.75	3.75
Set total (8) Stamps	84.00	61.10

Freedom From Hunger

World Map and Wheat Emblem CD112

U.N. Food and Agriculture Organization's "Freedom from Hunger" campaign.

1963, Mar. 21

Cameroun	B37-B38
Cent. Africa	B2
Chad	B2
Congo, P.R.	B4
Dahomey	B16
Gabon	B5
Ivory Coast	B16
Madagascar	B21
Mauritania	B17
Niger	B15
Senegal	B17
Upper Volta	B2

Nos. B37-B38 (2)	2.25	.75
No. B2 (1)	1.25	1.25
No. B2 (1)	1.10	.50
No. B4 (1)	1.40	1.00
No. B16 (1)	.80	.80
No. B5 (1)	1.00	1.00
No. B16 (1)	1.50	1.50
No. B21 (1)	.60	.45
No. B17 (1)	.60	.60
No. B15 (1)	.75	.75
No. B17 (1)	.80	.50
No. B2 (1)	.75	.70
Set total (13) Stamps	12.80	9.80

Red Cross Centenary

CD113

Centenary of the International Red Cross.

1963, Sept. 2

Comoro Isls.	55
Fr. Polynesia	205
New Caledonia	328
St. Pierre & Miquelon	367
Somali Coast	297
Wallis & Futuna Isls.	165

No. 55 (1)	7.50	6.00
No. 205 (1)	15.00	12.00
No. 328 (1)	8.00	6.75
No. 367 (1)	12.00	5.50
No. 297 (1)	6.25	6.25
No. 165 (1)	4.00	4.00
Set total (6) Stamps	52.75	40.50

African Postal Union, 1963

UAMPT Emblem, Radio Masts, Plane and Mail CD114

Establishment of the African and Malagasy Posts and Telecommunications Union.

1963, Sept. 8

Cameroun	C47
Cent. Africa	C10
Chad	C9
Congo, P.R.	C13

Dahomey	C19
Gabon	C13
Ivory Coast	C25
Madagascar	C75
Mauritania	C22
Niger	C27
Rwanda	36
Senegal	C32
Upper Volta	C9

No. C47 (1)	2.25	1.00
No. C10 (1)	1.90	.90
No. C9 (1)	1.80	.60
No. C13 (1)	1.40	.75
No. C19 (1)	.75	.25
No. C13 (1)	1.90	.80
No. C25 (1)	2.50	1.50
No. C75 (1)	1.25	.80
No. C22 (1)	1.50	.60
No. C27 (1)	1.25	.60
No. 36 (1)	1.00	.50
No. C32 (1)	1.75	.50
No. C9 (1)	1.50	.75
Set total (13) Stamps	20.75	9.80

Air Afrique, 1963

Symbols of Flight — CD115

First anniversary of Air Afrique and inauguration of DC-8 service.

1963, Nov. 19

Cameroun	C48
Chad	C10
Congo, P.R.	C14
Gabon	C18
Ivory Coast	C26
Mauritania	C26
Niger	C35
Senegal	C33

No. C48 (1)	1.25	.40
No. C10 (1)	1.80	.60
No. C14 (1)	1.60	.60
No. C18 (1)	1.25	.65
No. C26 (1)	1.00	.50
No. C26 (1)	.70	.25
No. C35 (1)	1.00	.55
No. C33 (1)	2.00	.65
Set total (8) Stamps	10.60	4.20

Europafrica

Europe and Africa Linked — CD116

Signing of an economic agreement between the European Economic Community and the African and Malagasy Union, Yaounde, Cameroun, July 20, 1963.

1963-64

Cameroun	402
Cent. Africa	C12
Chad	C11
Congo, P.R.	C16
Gabon	C19
Ivory Coast	217
Niger	C43
Upper Volta	C11

No. 402 (1)	2.25	.60
No. C12 (1)	2.50	1.75
No. C11 (1)	1.60	.50
No. C16 (1)	1.60	1.00
No. C19 (1)	1.25	.75
No. 217 (1)	1.10	.35
No. C43 (1)	.85	.50
No. C11 (1)	1.50	.80
Set total (8) Stamps	12.65	6.25

Human Rights

Scales of Justice and Globe CD117

15th anniversary of the Universal Declaration of Human Rights.

1963, Dec. 10

Comoro Isls.	56
Fr. Polynesia	206
New Caledonia	329
St. Pierre & Miquelon	368
Somali Coast	300
Wallis & Futuna Isls.	166

No. 56 (1)	7.50	6.00
No. 205 (1)	15.00	12.00
No. 329 (1)	7.00	6.00
No. 368 (1)	7.00	3.50
No. 300 (1)	8.50	8.50
No. 166 (1)	7.00	7.00
Set total (6) Stamps	52.00	43.00

PHILATEC

Stamp Album, Champs Elysees Palace and Horses of Marly CD118

Intl. Philatelic and Postal Techniques Exhibition, Paris, June 5-21, 1964.

1963-64

Comoro Isls.	60
France	1078
Fr. Polynesia	207
New Caledonia	341
St. Pierre & Miquelon	369
Somali Coast	301
Wallis & Futuna Isls.	167

No. 60 (1)	4.00	3.50
No. 1078 (1)	.25	.25
No. 200 (1)	16.00	10.00
No. 341 (1)	6.50	6.50
No. 369 (1)	11.00	8.00
No. 301 (1)	7.75	7.75
No. 167 (1)	3.00	3.00
Set total (7) Stamps	47.50	39.00

Cooperation

CD119

Cooperation between France and the French-speaking countries of Africa and Madagascar.

1964

Cameroun	409-410
Cent. Africa	39
Chad	103
Congo, P.R.	121
Dahomey	193
France	1111
Gabon	175
Ivory Coast	221
Madagascar	360
Mauritania	181
Niger	143
Senegal	236
Togo	495

Nos. 409-410 (2)	2.50	.50
No. 39 (1)	.90	.50
No. 103 (1)	1.00	.25
No. 193 (1)	.90	.35
No. 1111 (1)	.25	.25
No. 175 (1)	.90	.60
No. 221 (1)	1.10	.35

No. 360 (1)	.60	.25
No. 181 (1)	.60	.35
No. 143 (1)	.80	.40
No. 236 (1)	1.60	.85
No. 495 (1)	.70	.25
Set total (14) Stamps	12.65	5.25

ITU

Telegraph, Syncom Satellite and ITU Emblem CD120

Intl. Telecommunication Union, Cent.

1965, May 17

Comoro Isls.	C14
Fr. Polynesia	C33
Fr. So. & Antarctic Terr.	C8
New Caledonia	C40
New Hebrides	124-125
St. Pierre & Miquelon	C29
Somali Coast	C36
Wallis & Futuna Isls.	C20

No. C14 (1)	18.00	10.00
No. C33 (1)	80.00	52.50
No. C8 (1)	200.00	160.00
No. C40 (1)	10.00	8.00
Nos. 124-125 (2)	32.25	27.25
No. C29 (1)	24.00	11.50
No. C36 (1)	15.00	9.00
No. C20 (1)	16.00	16.00
Set total (9) Stamps	395.25	293.25

French Satellite A-1

Diamant Rocket and Launching Installation — CD121

Launching of France's first satellite, Nov. 26, 1965.

1965-66

Comoro Isls.	C16a
France	1138a
Reunion	359a
Fr. Polynesia	C41a
Fr. So. & Antarctic Terr.	C10a
New Caledonia	C45a
St. Pierre & Miquelon	C31a
Somali Coast	C40a
Wallis & Futuna Isls.	C23a

No. C16a (1)	9.00	9.00
No. 1138a (1)	.65	.65
No. 359a (1)	3.50	3.00
No. C41a (1)	14.00	14.00
No. C10a (1)	29.00	24.00
No. C45a (1)	7.00	7.00
No. C31a (1)	14.50	14.50
No. C40a (1)	7.00	7.00
No. C23a (1)	8.50	8.50
Set total (9) Stamps	93.15	87.65

French Satellite D-1

D-1 Satellite in Orbit — CD122

Launching of the D-1 satellite at Hammaguir, Algeria, Feb. 17, 1966.

1966

Comoro Isls.	C17
France	1148

Fr. Polynesia.................................C42
Fr. So. & Antarctic Terr. C11
New Caledonia..............................C46
St. Pierre & Miquelon....................C32
Somali Coast.................................C49
Wallis & Futuna Isls. C24

No. C17 (1) 4.00 4.00
No. 1148 (1) .25 .25
No. C42 (1) 7.00 4.75
No. C11 (1) 57.50 40.00
No. C46 (1) 2.25 2.00
No. C32 (1) 9.00 6.00
No. C49 (1) 4.25 2.75
No. C24 (1) 3.50 3.50
Set total (8) Stamps 87.75 63.25

Air Afrique, 1966

Planes and Air Afrique
Emblem — CD123

Introduction of DC-8F planes by Air Afrique.

1966

Cameroun.......................................C79
Cent. Africa C35
Chad...C26
Congo, P.R......................................C42
Dahomey..C42
Gabon...C47
Ivory Coast.....................................C32
Mauritania......................................C57
Niger...C63
Senegal...C47
Togo..C54
Upper Volta.....................................C31

No. C79 (1) .80 .25
No. C35 (1) 1.00 .50
No. C26 (1) .85 .25
No. C42 (1) 1.00 .25
No. C42 (1) .75 .25
No. C47 (1) .90 .35
No. C32 (1) 1.00 .60
No. C57 (1) .60 .30
No. C63 (1) .70 .35
No. C47 (1) .80 .30
No. C54 (1) .80 .25
No. C31 (1) .75 .50
Set total (12) Stamps 9.95 4.15

African Postal Union, 1967

Telecommunications Symbols and Map
of Africa — CD124

Fifth anniversary of the establishment of the African and Malagasy Union of Posts and Telecommunications, UAMPT.

1967

Cameroun.......................................C90
Cent. Africa C46
Chad...C37
Congo, P.R......................................C57
Dahomey..C61
Gabon...C58
Ivory Coast.....................................C34
Madagascar....................................C85
Mauritania......................................C65
Niger...C75
Rwanda...C1-C3
Senegal...C60
Togo..C81
Upper Volta.....................................C50

No. C90 (1) 2.40 .65
No. C46 (1) 2.25 .85
No. C37 (1) 2.00 .60
No. C57 (1) 1.60 .60
No. C61 (1) 1.75 .95
No. C58 (1) 2.00 .85
No. C34 (1) 3.50 1.50
No. C85 (1) 1.25 .60
No. C65 (1) 1.25 .60
No. C75 (1) 1.40 .60

Nos. C1-C3 (3) 2.30 1.25
No. C60 (1) 1.75 .50
No. C81 (1) 1.90 .30
No. C50 (1) 1.80 .70
Set total (16) Stamps 27.15 10.55

Monetary Union

Gold Token of the
Ashantis, 17-18th
Centuries — CD125

West African Monetary Union, 5th anniv.

1967, Nov. 4

Dahomey 244
Ivory Coast.....................................259
Mauritania......................................238
Niger...204
Senegal...294
Togo..623
Upper Volta.....................................181

No. 244 (1) .65 .65
No. 259 (1) .85 .40
No. 238 (1) .45 .25
No. 204 (1) .55 .25
No. 294 (1) .60 .25
No. 623 (1) .60 .25
No. 181 (1) .65 .35
Set total (7) Stamps 4.35 2.40

WHO Anniversary

 Sun, Flowers and WHO Emblem CD126

World Health Organization, 20th anniv.

1968, May 4

Afars & Issas..................................317
Comoro Isls.....................................73
Fr. Polynesia...................................241-242
Fr. So. & Antarctic Terr. 31
New Caledonia................................367
St. Pierre & Miquelon.....................377
Wallis & Futuna Isls. 169

No. 317 (1) 3.00 3.00
No. 73 (1) 2.40 1.75
Nos. 241-242 (2) 22.00 12.75
No. 31 (1) 62.50 47.50
No. 367 (1) 4.00 2.25
No. 377 (1) 12.00 9.00
No. 169 (1) 5.75 5.75
Set total (8) Stamps 111.65 82.00

Human Rights Year

 Human Rights Flame — CD127

1968, Aug. 10

Afars & Issas..........................322-323
Comoro Isls.....................................76
Fr. Polynesia...................................243-244
Fr. So. & Antarctic Terr. 32
New Caledonia................................369
St. Pierre & Miquelon.....................382
Wallis & Futuna Isls. 170

Nos. 322-323 (2) 6.75 4.00
No. 76 (1) 3.25 3.25
Nos. 243-244 (2) 24.00 14.00
No. 32 (1) 55.00 47.50
No. 369 (1) 2.75 1.50
No. 382 (1) 8.00 5.50
No. 170 (1) 3.25 3.25
Set total (9) Stamps 103.00 79.00

2nd PHILEXAFRIQUE

CD128

Opening of PHILEXAFRIQUE, Abidjan, Feb. 14. Each stamp shows a local scene and stamp.

1969, Feb. 14

Cameroun.......................................C118
Cent. Africa C65
Chad...C48
Congo, P.R......................................C77
Dahomey..C94
Gabon...C82
Ivory Coast............................C38-C40
Madagascar....................................C92
Mali...C65
Mauritania......................................C80
Niger...C104
Senegal...C68
Togo..C104
Upper Volta.....................................C62

No. C118 (1) 3.25 1.25
No. C65 (1) 1.75 1.75
No. C48 (1) 2.40 1.00
No. C77 (1) 2.00 1.75
No. C94 (1) 2.25 2.25
No. C82 (1) 2.00 2.00
Nos. C38-C40 (3) 14.50 14.50
No. C92 (1) 1.75 .85
No. C65 (1) 1.75 1.00
No. C80 (1) 1.90 .75
No. C104 (1) 3.00 1.90
No. C68 (1) 2.00 1.40
No. C104 (1) 2.25 .45
No. C62 (1) 4.00 3.25
Set total (16) Stamps 44.80 34.10

Concorde

Concorde in
Flight
CD129

First flight of the prototype Concorde supersonic plane at Toulouse, Mar. 1, 1969.

1969

Afars & Issas..................................C56
Comoro Isls.....................................C29
France...C42
Fr. Polynesia...................................C50
Fr. So. & Antarctic Terr. C18
New Caledonia................................C63
St. Pierre & Miquelon.....................C40
Wallis & Futuna Isls. C30

No. C56 (1) 26.00 16.00
No. C29 (1) 18.00 12.00
No. C42 (1) .75 .35
No. C50 (1) 55.00 35.00
No. C18 (1) 55.00 37.50
No. C63 (1) 27.50 20.00
No. C40 (1) 32.50 11.00
No. C30 (1) 15.00 10.00
Set total (8) Stamps 229.75 141.85

Development Bank

 Bank Emblem — CD130

African Development Bank, fifth anniv.

1969

Cameroun.......................................499
Chad...217
Congo, P.R..............................181-182

Ivory Coast.....................................281
Mali...127-128
Mauritania......................................267
Niger...220
Senegal 317-318
Upper Volta.....................................201

No. 499 (1) .80 .25
No. 217 (1) .90 .25
Nos. 181-182 (2) 1.00 .50
No. 281 (1) .70 .40
Nos. 127-128 (2) 1.00 .50
No. 267 (1) .60 .25
No. 220 (1) .70 .30
Nos. 317-318 (2) 1.55 .50
No. 201 (1) .65 .30
Set total (12) Stamps 7.90 3.25

ILO

ILO Headquarters, Geneva, and
Emblem — CD131

Intl. Labor Organization, 50th anniv.

1969-70

Afars & Issas..................................337
Comoro Isls.....................................83
Fr. Polynesia...................................251-252
Fr. So. & Antarctic Terr. 35
New Caledonia................................379
St. Pierre & Miquelon.....................396
Wallis & Futuna Isls. 172

No. 337 (1) 2.75 2.00
No. 83 (1) 1.25 .75
Nos. 251-252 (2) 24.00 12.50
No. 35 (1) 15.00 10.00
No. 379 (1) 2.25 1.10
No. 396 (1) 10.00 5.50
No. 172 (1) 2.75 2.75
Set total (8) Stamps 58.00 34.60

ASECNA

 Map of Africa, Plane and Airport CD132

10th anniversary of the Agency for the Security of Aerial Navigation in Africa and Madagascar (ASECNA, Agence pour la Securite de la Navigation Aerienne en Afrique et a Madagascar).

1969-70

Cameroun.......................................500
Cent. Africa 119
Chad...222
Congo, P.R......................................197
Dahomey..269
Gabon...260
Ivory Coast.....................................287
Mali...130
Niger...221
Senegal 321
Upper Volta.....................................204

No. 500 (1) 2.00 .60
No. 119 (1) 2.00 .80
No. 222 (1) 1.00 .25
No. 197 (1) 2.00 .40
No. 269 (1) .90 .55
No. 260 (1) 1.75 .75
No. 287 (1) .90 .40
No. 130 (1) .90 .40
No. 221 (1) 1.40 .70
No. 321 (1) 1.60 .50
No. 204 (1) 1.75 1.00
Set total (11) Stamps 16.20 6.35

U.P.U. Headquarters

 CD133

New Universal Postal Union headquarters, Bern, Switzerland.

1970

Afars & Issas		342
Algeria		443
Cameroun		503-504
Cent. Africa		125
Chad		225
Comoro Isls.		84
Congo, P.R.		216
Fr. Polynesia		261-262
Fr. So. & Antarctic Terr.		36
Gabon		258
Ivory Coast		295
Madagascar		444
Mali		134-135
Mauritania		283
New Caledonia		382
Niger		231-232
St. Pierre & Miquelon		397-398
Senegal		328-329
Tunisia		535
Wallis & Futuna Isls.		173

No. 342 (1)	2.50	1.40
No. 443 (1)	1.10	.40
Nos. 503-504 (2)	2.60	.55
No. 125 (1)	1.75	.70
No. 225 (1)	1.20	.25
No. 84 (1)	5.50	2.00
No. 216 (1)	1.00	.25
Nos. 261-262 (2)	20.00	10.00
No. 36 (1)	40.00	27.50
No. 258 (1)	.90	.55
No. 295 (1)	1.10	.50
No. 444 (1)	.55	.25
Nos. 134-135 (2)	1.05	.50
No. 283 (1)	.60	.30
No. 382 (1)	3.00	1.50
Nos. 231-232 (2)	1.50	.60
Nos. 397-398 (2)	34.00	16.25
Nos. 328-329 (2)	1.55	.55
No. 535 (1)	.60	.25
No. 173 (1)	3.25	3.25
Set total (26) Stamps	123.75	67.55

De Gaulle

CD134

First anniversary of the death of Charles de Gaulle (1890-1970), President of France.

1971-72

Afars & Issas		356-357
Comoro Isls.		104-105
France		1325a
Fr. Polynesia		270-271
Fr. So. & Antarctic Terr.		52-53
New Caledonia		393-394
Reunion		380a
St. Pierre & Miquelon		417-418
Wallis & Futuna Isls.		177-178

Nos. 356-357 (2)	12.50	7.50
Nos. 104-105 (2)	9.00	5.75
No. 1325a (1)	3.00	2.50
Nos. 270-271 (2)	51.50	29.50
Nos. 52-53 (2)	40.00	29.50
Nos. 393-394 (2)	23.00	11.75
No. 380a (1)	9.25	8.00
Nos. 417-418 (2)	56.50	31.00
Nos. 177-178 (2)	20.00	16.25
Set total (16) Stamps	224.75	141.75

African Postal Union, 1971

UAMPT Building, Brazzaville, Congo — CD135

10th anniversary of the establishment of the African and Malagasy Posts and Telecommunications Union, UAMPT. Each stamp has a different native design.

1971, Nov. 13

Cameroun		C177
Cent. Africa		C89
Chad		C94
Congo, P.R.		C136
Dahomey		C146
Gabon		C120
Ivory Coast		C47
Mauritania		C113
Niger		C164
Rwanda		C8
Senegal		C105
Togo		C166
Upper Volta		C97

No. C177 (1)	2.00	.50
No. C89 (1)	2.25	.85
No. C94 (1)	1.50	.50
No. C136 (1)	1.60	.75
No. C146 (1)	1.75	.80
No. C120 (1)	1.75	.70
No. C47 (1)	2.00	1.00
No. C113 (1)	1.10	.65
No. C164 (1)	1.25	.60
No. C8 (1)	2.75	2.50
No. C105 (1)	1.60	.50
No. C166 (1)	1.25	.40
No. C97 (1)	1.50	.70
Set total (13) Stamps	22.30	10.45

West African Monetary Union

African Couple, City, Village and Commemorative Coin — CD136

West African Monetary Union, 10th anniv.

1972, Nov. 2

Dahomey		300
Ivory Coast		331
Mauritania		299
Niger		258
Senegal		374
Togo		825
Upper Volta		280

No. 300 (1)	.65	.25
No. 331 (1)	1.00	.50
No. 299 (1)	.75	.25
No. 258 (1)	.65	.30
No. 374 (1)	.50	.30
No. 825 (1)	.60	.25
No. 280 (1)	.60	.25
Set total (7) Stamps	4.75	2.10

African Postal Union, 1973

Telecommunications Symbols and Map of Africa — CD137

11th anniversary of the African and Malagasy Posts and Telecommunications Union (UAMPT).

1973, Sept. 12

Cameroun		574
Cent. Africa		194
Chad		294
Congo, P.R.		289
Dahomey		311
Gabon		320
Ivory Coast		361
Madagascar		500
Mauritania		304
Niger		287
Rwanda		540
Senegal		393
Togo		849
Upper Volta		297

No. 574 (1)	1.75	.40
No. 194 (1)	1.25	.75
No. 294 (1)	1.75	.40
No. 289 (1)	1.60	.50
No. 311 (1)	1.25	.55
No. 320 (1)	1.40	.75
No. 361 (1)	2.50	1.00
No. 500 (1)	1.10	.35
No. 304 (1)	1.10	.40
No. 287 (1)	.90	.60
No. 540 (1)	4.00	2.00
No. 393 (1)	1.60	.50
No. 849 (1)	1.00	.35
No. 297 (1)	1.25	.70
Set total (14) Stamps	22.45	9.25

Philexafrique II — Essen

CD138

CD139

Designs: Indigenous fauna, local and German stamps. Types CD138-CD139 printed horizontally and vertically se-tenant in sheets of 10 (2x5). Label between horizontal pairs alternately commemorates Philexafrique II, Libreville, Gabon, June 1978, and 2nd International Stamp Fair, Essen, Germany, Nov. 1-5.

1978-1979

Benin		C286a
Central Africa		C201a
Chad		C239a
Congo Republic		C246a
Djibouti		C122a
Gabon		C216a
Ivory Coast		C65a
Mali		C357a
Mauritania		C186a
Niger		C292a
Rwanda		C13a
Senegal		C147a
Togo		C364a

No. C286a (1)	9.00	8.50
No. C201a (1)	7.50	7.50
No. C239a (1)	7.50	4.00
No. C246a (1)	7.00	7.00
No. C122a (1)	6.50	6.50
No. C216a (1)	6.50	4.00
No. C65a (1)	9.00	9.00
No. C357a (1)	5.00	3.00
No. C186a (1)	5.50	5.00
No. C292a (1)	6.00	6.00
No. C13a (1)	4.00	4.00
No. C147a (1)	10.00	4.00
No. C364a (1)	3.00	1.50
Set total (13) Stamps	86.50	70.00

BRITISH COMMONWEALTH OF NATIONS

The listings follow established trade practices when these issues are offered as units by dealers. The Peace issue, for example, includes only one stamp from the Indian state of Hyderabad. The U.P.U. issue includes the Egypt set. Pairs are included for those varieties issued with bilingual designs se-tenant.

Silver Jubilee

Windsor Castle and King George V CD301

Reign of King George V, 25th anniv.

1935

Antigua		77-80
Ascension		33-36
Bahamas		92-95
Barbados		186-189
Basutoland		11-14
Bechuanaland Protectorate		117-120
Bermuda		100-103
British Guiana		223-226
British Honduras		108-111
Cayman Islands		81-84
Ceylon		260-263
Cyprus		136-139
Dominica		90-93
Falkland Islands		77-80
Fiji		110-113
Gambia		125-128
Gibraltar		100-103
Gilbert & Ellice Islands		33-36
Gold Coast		108-111
Grenada		124-127
Hong Kong		147-150
Jamaica		109-112
Kenya, Uganda, Tanzania		42-45
Leeward Islands		96-99
Malta		184-187
Mauritius		204-207
Montserrat		85-88
Newfoundland		226-229
Nigeria		34-37
Northern Rhodesia		18-21
Nyasaland Protectorate		47-50
St. Helena		111-114
St. Kitts-Nevis		72-75
St. Lucia		91-94
St. Vincent		134-137
Seychelles		118-121
Sierra Leone		166-169
Solomon Islands		60-63
Somaliland Protectorate		77-80
Straits Settlements		213-216
Swaziland		20-23
Trinidad & Tobago		43-46
Turks & Caicos Islands		71-74
Virgin Islands		69-72

The following have different designs but are included in the omnibus set:

Great Britain		226-229
Offices in Morocco (Sp. Curr.)		67-70
Offices in Morocco (Br. Curr.)		226-229
Offices in Morocco (Fr. Curr.)		422-425
Offices in Morocco (Tangier)		508-510
Australia		152-154
Canada		211-216
Cook Islands		98-100
India		142-148
Nauru		31-34
New Guinea		46-47
New Zealand		199-201
Niue		67-69
Papua		114-117
Samoa		163-165
South Africa		68-71
Southern Rhodesia		33-36
South-West Africa		121-124

Nos. 77-80 (4)	20.25	23.25
Nos. 33-36 (4)	58.50	127.50
Nos. 92-95 (4)	25.00	46.00
Nos. 186-189 (4)	30.00	50.30
Nos. 11-14 (4)	11.60	21.25
Nos. 117-120 (4)	15.75	36.00
Nos. 100-103 (4)	16.80	58.50
Nos. 223-226 (4)	22.35	35.50
Nos. 108-111 (4)	15.25	16.35
Nos. 81-84 (4)	21.60	24.50
Nos. 260-263 (4)	10.40	21.60
Nos. 136-139 (4)	39.75	34.40
Nos. 90-93 (4)	18.85	19.85
Nos. 77-80 (4)	55.00	14.75
Nos. 110-113 (4)	20.25	34.00
Nos. 125-128 (4)	13.05	25.25
Nos. 100-103 (4)	28.75	42.75
Nos. 33-36 (4)	36.80	67.00
Nos. 108-111 (4)	25.75	78.10
Nos. 124-127 (4)	16.70	40.60
Nos. 147-150 (4)	59.00	18.75
Nos. 109-112 (4)	17.00	39.00
Nos. 42-45 (4)	8.75	11.00
Nos. 96-99 (4)	35.75	49.60
Nos. 184-187 (4)	22.00	33.70
Nos. 204-207 (4)	44.60	58.25
Nos. 85-88 (4)	10.25	30.25
Nos. 226-229 (4)	17.50	12.05
Nos. 34-37 (4)	17.50	70.00
Nos. 18-21 (4)	17.00	15.00
Nos. 47-50 (4)	39.75	80.25
Nos. 111-114 (4)	31.15	36.50
Nos. 72-75 (4)	10.80	18.65
Nos. 91-94 (4)	16.00	20.80
Nos. 134-137 (4)	9.45	21.25
Nos. 118-121 (4)	15.75	40.00
Nos. 166-169 (4)	23.60	50.35
Nos. 60-63 (4)	29.00	38.00
Nos. 77-80 (4)	17.00	48.25
Nos. 213-216 (4)	15.00	25.50
Nos. 20-23 (4)	6.80	18.25
Nos. 43-46 (4)	14.05	27.75
Nos. 71-74 (4)	9.90	14.50
Nos. 69-72 (4)	25.00	55.25
Nos. 226-229 (4)	5.15	4.40

Nos. 67-70 (4)	14.35	26.10
Nos. 226-229 (4)	8.20	28.90
Nos. 422-425 (4)	3.90	2.00
Nos. 508-510 (3)	18.80	23.85
Nos. 152-154 (3)	49.50	45.35
Nos. 211-216 (6)	23.85	13.35
Nos. 98-100 (3)	9.65	12.00
Nos. 142-148 (7)	28.85	14.00
Nos. 31-34 (4)	9.90	9.90
Nos. 46-47 (2)	4.35	1.70
Nos. 199-201 (3)	23.00	28.50
Nos. 67-69 (3)	11.80	26.50
Nos. 114-117 (4)	9.20	17.50
Nos. 163-165 (3)	4.40	6.50
Nos. 68-71 (4)	57.50	153.00
Nos. 33-36 (4)	27.75	45.25
Nos. 121-124 (4)	13.00	36.10
Set total (245) Stamps	1,338.	2,145.

Coronation

Queen Elizabeth and King George VI
CD302

1937

Aden	13-15
Antigua	81-83
Ascension	37-39
Bahamas	97-99
Barbados	190-192
Basutoland	15-17
Bechuanaland Protectorate	121-123
Bermuda	115-117
British Guiana	227-229
British Honduras	112-114
Cayman Islands	97-99
Ceylon	275-277
Cyprus	140-142
Dominica	94-96
Falkland Islands	81-83
Fiji	114-116
Gambia	129-131
Gibraltar	104-106
Gilbert & Ellice Islands	37-39
Gold Coast	112-114
Grenada	128-130
Hong Kong	151-153
Jamaica	113-115
Kenya, Uganda, Tanzania	60-62
Leeward Islands	100-102
Malta	188-190
Mauritius	208-210
Montserrat	89-91
Newfoundland	230-232
Nigeria	50-52
Northern Rhodesia	22-24
Nyasaland Protectorate	51-53
St. Helena	115-117
St. Kitts-Nevis	76-78
St. Lucia	107-109
St. Vincent	138-140
Seychelles	122-124
Sierra Leone	170-172
Solomon Islands	64-66
Somaliland Protectorate	81-83
Straits Settlements	235-237
Swaziland	24-26
Trinidad & Tobago	47-49
Turks & Caicos Islands	75-77
Virgin Islands	73-75

The following have different designs but are included in the omnibus set:

Great Britain	234
Offices in Morocco (Sp. Curr.)	82
Offices in Morocco (Fr. Curr.)	439
Offices in Morocco (Tangier)	514
Canada	237
Cook Islands	109-111
Nauru	35-38
Newfoundland	233-243
New Guinea	48-51
New Zealand	223-225
Niue	70-72
Papua	118-121
South Africa	74-78
Southern Rhodesia	38-41
South-West Africa	125-132

Nos. 13-15 (3)	2.70	5.65
Nos. 81-83 (3)	1.85	8.00
Nos. 37-39 (3)	2.75	2.75
Nos. 97-99 (3)	1.05	3.05
Nos. 190-192 (3)	1.10	1.95
Nos. 15-17 (3)	1.15	3.00
Nos. 121-123 (3)	.95	3.35
Nos. 115-117 (3)	1.25	5.00
Nos. 227-229 (3)	1.45	3.05
Nos. 112-114 (3)	1.20	2.40
Nos. 97-99 (3)	1.10	2.70
Nos. 275-277 (3)	8.25	10.35

Nos. 140-142 (3)	3.75	6.50
Nos. 94-96 (3)	.85	2.40
Nos. 81-83 (3)	2.90	2.30
Nos. 114-116 (3)	1.35	5.75
Nos. 129-131 (3)	.85	3.95
Nos. 104-106 (3)	2.25	6.45
Nos. 37-39 (3)	.85	2.15
Nos. 112-114 (3)	3.10	10.00
Nos. 128-130 (3)	1.00	.85
Nos. 151-153 (3)	23.00	12.50
Nos. 113-115 (3)	1.25	1.25
Nos. 60-62 (3)	1.00	2.35
Nos. 100-102 (3)	1.55	4.00
Nos. 188-190 (3)	1.25	1.60
Nos. 208-210 (3)	1.75	3.50
Nos. 89-91 (3)	1.00	3.35
Nos. 230-232 (3)	7.00	2.80
Nos. 50-52 (3)	3.25	8.50
Nos. 22-24 (3)	.95	2.25
Nos. 51-53 (3)	1.05	1.30
Nos. 115-117 (3)	1.45	2.05
Nos. 76-78 (3)	.95	2.15
Nos. 107-109 (3)	1.05	2.05
Nos. 138-140 (3)	.80	4.75
Nos. 122-124 (3)	1.20	1.90
Nos. 170-172 (3)	1.95	5.65
Nos. 64-66 (3)	.90	2.00
Nos. 81-83 (3)	1.10	3.50
Nos. 235-237 (3)	3.25	1.60
Nos. 24-26 (3)	.75	2.70
Nos. 47-49 (3)	1.00	1.00
Nos. 75-77 (3)	2.25	1.55
Nos. 73-75 (3)	2.20	6.90
No. 234 (1)	.25	.25
No. 82 (1)	.80	.80
No. 439 (1)	.35	.25
No. 514 (1)	.55	.55
No. 237 (1)	.85	.25
Nos. 109-111 (3)	.85	.80
Nos. 35-38 (4)	1.10	5.50
Nos. 233-243 (11)	41.90	30.40
Nos. 48-51 (4)	1.40	7.90
Nos. 223-225 (3)	1.75	2.25
Nos. 70-72 (3)	.80	2.05
Nos. 118-121 (4)	1.60	5.25
Nos. 74-78 (5)	7.60	9.35
Nos. 38-41 (4)	3.55	15.50
Nos. 125-132 (8)	5.00	8.40
Set total (189) Stamps	171.45	262.30

Peace

King George VI and Parliament Buildings, London
CD303

Return to peace at the close of World War II.

1945-46

Aden	28-29
Antigua	96-97
Ascension	50-51
Bahamas	130-131
Barbados	207-208
Bermuda	131-132
British Guiana	242-243
British Honduras	127-128
Cayman Islands	112-113
Ceylon	293-294
Cyprus	156-157
Dominica	112-113
Falkland Islands	97-98
Falkland Islands Dep.	1L9-1L10
Fiji	137-138
Gambia	144-145
Gibraltar	119-120
Gilbert & Ellice Islands	52-53
Gold Coast	128-129
Grenada	143-144
Jamaica	136-137
Kenya, Uganda, Tanzania	90-91
Leeward Islands	116-117
Malta	206-207
Mauritius	223-224
Montserrat	104-105
Nigeria	71-72
Northern Rhodesia	46-47
Nyasaland Protectorate	82-83
Pitcairn Islands	9-10
St. Helena	128-129
St. Kitts-Nevis	91-92
St. Lucia	127-128
St. Vincent	152-153
Seychelles	149-150
Sierra Leone	186-187
Solomon Islands	80-81
Somaliland Protectorate	108-109
Trinidad & Tobago	62-63
Turks & Caicos Islands	90-91
Virgin Islands	88-89

The following have different designs but are included in the omnibus set:

Great Britain	264-265
Offices in Morocco (Tangier)	523-524
Aden	
Kathiri State of Seiyun	12-13
Qu'aiti State of Shihr and Mukalla	12-13
Australia	200-202
Basutoland	29-31
Bechuanaland Protectorate	137-139
Burma	66-69
Cook Islands	127-130
Hong Kong	174-175
India	195-198
Hyderabad	51-53
New Zealand	247-257
Niue	90-93
Pakistan-Bahawalpur	O16
Samoa	191-194
South Africa	100-102
Southern Rhodesia	67-70
South-West Africa	153-155
Swaziland	38-40
Zanzibar	222-223

Nos. 28-29 (2)	.95	2.50
Nos. 96-97 (2)	.50	.80
Nos. 50-51 (2)	.80	2.00
Nos. 130-131 (2)	.50	1.40
Nos. 207-208 (2)	.50	1.10
Nos. 131-132 (2)	.55	.55
Nos. 242-243 (2)	1.05	1.40
Nos. 127-128 (2)	.50	.50
Nos. 112-113 (2)	.80	.80
Nos. 293-294 (2)	.60	2.10
Nos. 156-157 (2)	.90	.70
Nos. 112-113 (2)	.50	.50
Nos. 97-98 (2)	.90	1.35
Nos. 1L9-1L10 (2)	1.30	1.00
Nos. 137-138 (2)	.75	1.75
Nos. 144-145 (2)	.50	.95
Nos. 119-120 (2)	.75	1.00
Nos. 52-53 (2)	.50	1.10
Nos. 128-129 (2)	1.85	3.75
Nos. 143-144 (2)	.50	.95
Nos. 136-137 (2)	.80	12.50
Nos. 90-91 (2)	.65	.65
Nos. 116-117 (2)	.50	1.50
Nos. 206-207 (2)	.65	2.00
Nos. 223-224 (2)	.50	1.05
Nos. 104-105 (2)	.50	.50
Nos. 71-72 (2)	.70	2.75
Nos. 46-47 (2)	1.25	2.00
Nos. 82-83 (2)	.50	.50
Nos. 9-10 (2)	1.40	1.40
Nos. 128-129 (2)	.65	.70
Nos. 91-92 (2)	.50	.50
Nos. 127-128 (2)	.50	.60
Nos. 152-153 (2)	.50	.50
Nos. 149-150 (2)	.55	.50
Nos. 186-187 (2)	.50	.50
Nos. 80-81 (2)	.50	1.50
Nos. 108-109 (2)	.70	.50
Nos. 62-63 (2)	.50	.50
Nos. 90-91 (2)	.50	.50
Nos. 88-89 (2)	.50	.50
Nos. 264-265 (2)	.50	.50
Nos. 523-524 (2)	1.50	3.00
Nos. 12-13 (2)	.50	.90
Nos. 12-13 (2)	.50	1.25
Nos. 200-202 (3)	1.60	1.25
Nos. 29-31 (3)	2.10	2.60
Nos. 137-139 (3)	2.05	4.75
Nos. 66-69 (4)	1.50	1.25
Nos. 127-130 (4)	2.00	1.85
Nos. 174-175 (4)	6.75	3.15
Nos. 195-198 (4)	5.60	5.50
Nos. 51-53 (3)	1.50	1.70
Nos. 247-257 (11)	3.35	3.65
Nos. 90-93 (4)	1.70	2.20
No. O16 (1)	5.50	7.00
Nos. 191-194 (4)	2.05	1.00
Nos. 100-102 (3)	1.00	3.25
Nos. 67-70 (4)	1.40	1.75
Nos. 153-155 (3)	1.85	3.25
Nos. 38-40 (3)	2.40	5.50
Nos. 222-223 (2)	.65	1.00
Set total (151) Stamps	74.55	114.15

Silver Wedding

King George VI and Queen Elizabeth
CD304   CD305

1948-49

Aden	30-31
Kathiri State of Seiyun	14-15
Qu'aiti State of Shihr and Mukalla	14-15

Antigua	98-99
Ascension	52-53
Bahamas	148-149
Barbados	210-211
Basutoland	39-40
Bechuanaland Protectorate	147-148
Bermuda	133-134
British Guiana	244-245
British Honduras	129-130
Cayman Islands	116-117
Cyprus	158-159
Dominica	114-115
Falkland Islands	99-100
Falkland Islands Dep.	1L11-1L12
Fiji	139-140
Gambia	146-147
Gibraltar	121-122
Gilbert & Ellice Islands	54-55
Gold Coast	142-143
Grenada	145-146
Hong Kong	178-179
Jamaica	138-139
Kenya, Uganda, Tanzania	92-93
Leeward Islands	118-119
Malaya	
Johore	128-129
Kedah	55-56
Kelantan	44-45
Malacca	1-2
Negri Sembilan	36-37
Pahang	44-45
Penang	1-2
Perak	99-100
Perlis	1-2
Selangor	74-75
Trengganu	47-48
Malta	223-224
Mauritius	229-230
Montserrat	106-107
Nigeria	73-74
North Borneo	238-239
Northern Rhodesia	48-49
Nyasaland Protectorate	85-86
Pitcairn Islands	11-12
St. Helena	130-131
St. Kitts-Nevis	93-94
St. Lucia	129-130
St. Vincent	154-155
Sarawak	174-175
Seychelles	151-152
Sierra Leone	188-189
Singapore	21-22
Solomon Islands	82-83
Somaliland Protectorate	110-111
Swaziland	48-49
Trinidad & Tobago	64-65
Turks & Caicos Islands	92-93
Virgin Islands	90-91
Zanzibar	224-225

The following have different designs but are included in the omnibus set:

Great Britain	267-268
Offices in Morocco (Sp. Curr.)	93-94
Offices in Morocco (Tangier)	525-526
Bahrain	62-63
Kuwait	82-83
Oman	25-26
South Africa	106
South-West Africa	159

Nos. 30-31 (2)	40.40	56.50
Nos. 14-15 (2)	17.85	16.00
Nos. 14-15 (2)	18.55	12.50
Nos. 98-99 (2)	13.55	15.75
Nos. 52-53 (2)	55.55	50.45
Nos. 148-149 (2)	45.25	40.30
Nos. 210-211 (2)	18.55	13.55
Nos. 39-40 (2)	52.80	55.25
Nos. 147-148 (2)	42.85	47.75
Nos. 133-134 (2)	47.75	55.25
Nos. 244-245 (2)	24.25	28.45
Nos. 129-130 (2)	25.25	53.20
Nos. 116-117 (2)	25.25	33.50
Nos. 158-159 (2)	58.50	78.05
Nos. 114-115 (2)	25.25	32.75
Nos. 99-100 (2)	112.10	76.10
Nos. 1L11-1L12 (2)	4.25	6.00
Nos. 139-140 (2)	18.20	11.50
Nos. 146-147 (2)	21.25	21.25
Nos. 121-122 (2)	61.00	78.00
Nos. 54-55 (2)	14.25	26.25
Nos. 142-143 (2)	35.25	48.20
Nos. 145-146 (2)	21.75	21.75
Nos. 178-179 (2)	283.50	96.50
Nos. 138-139 (2)	27.85	60.25
Nos. 92-93 (2)	50.25	67.75
Nos. 118-119 (2)	7.00	8.25
Nos. 128-129 (2)	29.25	53.25
Nos. 55-56 (2)	35.25	50.25
Nos. 44-45 (2)	35.75	62.75
Nos. 1-2 (2)	35.40	49.75
Nos. 36-37 (2)	28.10	38.20
Nos. 44-45 (2)	28.00	38.05
Nos. 1-2 (2)	40.50	37.80

Nos. 99-100 (2)	27.80	37.75
Nos. 1-2 (2)	33.50	58.00
Nos. 74-75 (2)	30.25	25.30
Nos. 47-48 (2)	32.75	61.75
Nos. 223-224 (2)	40.55	45.25
Nos. 229-230 (2)	19.25	45.25
Nos. 106-107 (2)	8.75	17.25
Nos. 73-74 (2)	17.85	22.80
Nos. 238-239 (2)	35.30	45.75
Nos. 48-49 (2)	100.30	90.25
Nos. 85-86 (2)	18.25	30.25
Nos. 11-12 (2)	44.75	48.50
Nos. 130-131 (2)	32.80	42.80
Nos. 93-94 (2)	11.25	10.50
Nos. 129-130 (2)	22.25	40.25
Nos. 154-155 (2)	27.75	30.25
Nos. 174-175 (2)	50.40	52.90
Nos. 151-152 (2)	16.25	48.25
Nos. 188-189 (2)	25.25	29.75
Nos. 21-22 (2)	116.00	45.40
Nos. 82-83 (2)	13.40	13.40
Nos. 110-111 (2)	8.40	8.75
Nos. 48-49 (2)	40.30	47.75
Nos. 64-65 (2)	32.75	38.25
Nos. 92-93 (2)	14.25	20.25
Nos. 90-91 (2)	16.25	22.25
Nos. 224-225 (2)	29.60	38.00
Nos. 267-268 (2)	30.40	25.25
Nos. 93-94 (2)	20.10	25.35
Nos. 525-526 (2)	23.10	29.25
Nos. 62-63 (2)	38.50	57.75
Nos. 82-83 (2)	69.50	45.50
Nos. 25-26 (2)	41.00	42.50
No. 106 (1)	.80	1.00
No. 159 (1)	1.10	.35
Set total (136) Stamps	2,491.	2,685.

U.P.U.

Mercury and Symbols of Communications — CD306

Plane, Ship and Hemispheres — CD307

Mercury Scattering Letters over Globe CD308

U.P.U. Monument, Bern CD309

Universal Postal Union, 75th anniversary.

1949

Aden	32-35
Kathiri State of Seiyun	16-19
Qu'aiti State of Shihr and Mukalla	
	16-19
Antigua	100-103
Ascension	57-60
Bahamas	150-153
Barbados	212-215
Basutoland	41-44
Bechuanaland Protectorate	149-152
Bermuda	138-141
British Guiana	246-249
British Honduras	137-140
Brunei	79-82
Cayman Islands	118-121
Cyprus	160-163
Dominica	116-119
Falkland Islands	103-106
Falkland Islands Dep.	1L14-1L17
Fiji	141-144
Gambia	148-151
Gibraltar	123-126

Gilbert & Ellice Islands	56-59
Gold Coast	144-147
Grenada	147-150
Hong Kong	180-183
Jamaica	142-145
Kenya, Uganda, Tanzania	94-97
Leeward Islands	126-129
Malaya	
Johore	151-154
Kedah	57-60
Kelantan	46-49
Malacca	18-21
Negri Sembilan	59-62
Pahang	46-49
Penang	23-26
Perak	101-104
Perlis	3-6
Selangor	76-79
Trengganu	49-52
Malta	225-228
Mauritius	231-234
Montserrat	108-111
New Hebrides, British	62-65
New Hebrides, French	79-82
Nigeria	75-78
North Borneo	240-243
Northern Rhodesia	50-53
Nyasaland Protectorate	87-90
Pitcairn Islands	13-16
St. Helena	132-135
St. Kitts-Nevis	95-98
St. Lucia	131-134
St. Vincent	170-173
Sarawak	176-179
Seychelles	153-156
Sierra Leone	190-193
Singapore	23-26
Solomon Islands	84-87
Somaliland Protectorate	112-115
Southern Rhodesia	71-72
Swaziland	50-53
Tonga	87-90
Trinidad & Tobago	66-69
Turks & Caicos Islands	101-104
Virgin Islands	92-95
Zanzibar	226-229

The following have different designs but are included in the omnibus set:

Great Britain	276-279
Offices in Morocco (Tangier)	546-549
Australia	223
Bahrain	68-71
Burma	116-121
Ceylon	304-306
Egypt	281-283
India	223-226
Kuwait	89-92
Oman	31-34
Pakistan-Bahawalpur	26-29, O25-O28
South Africa	109-111
South-West Africa	160-162

Nos. 32-35 (4)	5.85	8.45
Nos. 16-19 (4)	2.75	16.00
Nos. 16-19 (4)	2.60	8.00
Nos. 100-103 (4)	3.60	7.70
Nos. 57-60 (4)	11.10	9.00
Nos. 150-153 (4)	5.35	9.30
Nos. 212-215 (4)	4.40	14.85
Nos. 41-44 (4)	4.75	10.00
Nos. 149-152 (4)	3.35	7.25
Nos. 138-141 (4)	4.75	6.15
Nos. 246-249 (4)	2.75	4.20
Nos. 137-140 (4)	3.30	6.35
Nos. 79-82 (4)	9.50	8.45
Nos. 118-121 (4)	3.60	7.25
Nos. 160-163 (4)	4.60	10.70
Nos. 116-119 (4)	2.30	5.65
Nos. 103-106 (4)	14.00	17.10
Nos. 1L14-1L17 (4)	14.60	14.50
Nos. 141-144 (4)	3.35	15.75
Nos. 148-151 (4)	2.75	7.10
Nos. 123-126 (4)	5.90	8.75
Nos. 56-59 (4)	4.30	13.00
Nos. 144-147 (4)	2.55	10.35
Nos. 147-150 (4)	2.15	3.55
Nos. 180-183 (4)	57.25	18.25
Nos. 142-145 (4)	2.25	2.45
Nos. 94-97 (4)	2.90	3.40
Nos. 126-129 (4)	3.05	9.60
Nos. 151-154 (4)	4.70	8.90
Nos. 57-60 (4)	4.80	12.00
Nos. 46-49 (4)	4.25	12.65
Nos. 18-21 (4)	4.25	17.30
Nos. 59-62 (4)	3.50	10.75
Nos. 46-49 (4)	3.00	7.25
Nos. 23-26 (4)	5.10	11.75
Nos. 101-104 (4)	3.65	10.75
Nos. 3-6 (4)	3.95	14.25
Nos. 76-79 (4)	4.90	12.30
Nos. 49-52 (4)	5.55	12.25
Nos. 225-228 (4)	4.50	4.85
Nos. 231-234 (4)	3.70	7.05
Nos. 108-111 (4)	3.30	4.35
Nos. 62-65 (4)	1.60	4.25
Nos. 79-82 (4)	15.40	22.00

Nos. 75-78 (4)	2.80	9.25
Nos. 240-243 (4)	7.15	6.50
Nos. 50-53 (4)	5.00	6.50
Nos. 87-90 (4)	4.05	4.05
Nos. 13-16 (4)	18.50	16.50
Nos. 132-135 (4)	4.85	7.10
Nos. 95-98 (4)	3.35	5.55
Nos. 131-134 (4)	2.55	3.85
Nos. 170-173 (4)	2.20	5.05
Nos. 176-179 (4)	8.15	10.85
Nos. 153-156 (4)	3.00	5.15
Nos. 190-193 (4)	2.90	9.15
Nos. 23-26 (4)	19.00	13.70
Nos. 84-87 (4)	4.05	4.90
Nos. 112-115 (4)	3.95	8.70
Nos. 71-72 (2)	1.95	2.25
Nos. 50-53 (4)	2.80	4.65
Nos. 87-90 (4)	3.00	5.25
Nos. 66-69 (4)	3.15	3.15
Nos. 101-104 (4)	3.05	8.90
Nos. 92-95 (4)	2.60	5.90
Nos. 226-229 (4)	5.45	13.50
Nos. 276-279 (4)	1.35	1.00
Nos. 546-549 (4)	3.20	10.15
No. 223 (1)	.40	.40
Nos. 68-71 (4)	4.75	16.50
Nos. 116-121 (6)	7.30	5.35
Nos. 304-306 (3)	3.35	4.25
Nos. 281-283 (3)	5.75	2.70
Nos. 223-226 (4)	27.25	10.50
Nos. 89-92 (4)	6.10	10.25
Nos. 31-34 (4)	8.00	15.75
Nos. 26-29, O25-O28 (8)	2.00	42.00
Nos. 109-111 (3)	2.00	2.70
Nos. 160-162 (3)	3.00	5.50
Set total (313) Stamps	453.70	723.20

University

Arms of University College CD310

Alice, Princess of Athlone CD311

1948 opening of University College of the West Indies at Jamaica.

1951

Antigua	104-105
Barbados	228-229
British Guiana	250-251
British Honduras	141-142
Dominica	120-121
Grenada	164-165
Jamaica	146-147
Leeward Islands	130-131
Montserrat	112-113
St. Kitts-Nevis	105-106
St. Lucia	149-150
St. Vincent	174-175
Trinidad & Tobago	70-71
Virgin Islands	96-97

Nos. 104-105 (2)	1.35	3.75
Nos. 228-229 (2)	1.75	2.65
Nos. 250-251 (2)	1.10	1.25
Nos. 141-142 (2)	1.40	2.20
Nos. 120-121 (2)	1.40	1.75
Nos. 164-165 (2)	1.20	1.60
Nos. 146-147 (2)	.90	.70
Nos. 130-131 (2)	1.35	4.00
Nos. 112-113 (2)	.85	2.00
Nos. 105-106 (2)	.90	2.25
Nos. 149-150 (2)	1.40	1.50
Nos. 174-175 (2)	1.00	2.15
Nos. 70-71 (2)	.75	.75
Nos. 96-97 (2)	1.50	3.75
Set total (28) Stamps	16.85	30.30

Coronation

Queen Elizabeth II — CD312

1953

Aden	47
Kathiri State of Seiyun	28

Qu'aiti State of Shihr and Mukalla	
	28
Antigua	106
Ascension	61
Bahamas	157
Barbados	234
Basutoland	45
Bechuanaland Protectorate	153
Bermuda	142
British Guiana	252
British Honduras	143
Cayman Islands	150
Cyprus	167
Dominica	141
Falkland Islands	121
Falkland Islands Dependencies	1L18
Fiji	145
Gambia	152
Gibraltar	131
Gilbert & Ellice Islands	60
Gold Coast	160
Grenada	170
Hong Kong	184
Jamaica	153
Kenya, Uganda, Tanzania	101
Leeward Islands	132
Malaya	
Johore	155
Kedah	82
Kelantan	71
Malacca	27
Negri Sembilan	63
Pahang	71
Penang	27
Perak	126
Perlis	28
Selangor	101
Trengganu	74
Malta	241
Mauritius	250
Montserrat	127
New Hebrides, British	77
Nigeria	79
North Borneo	260
Northern Rhodesia	60
Nyasaland Protectorate	96
Pitcairn Islands	19
St. Helena	139
St. Kitts-Nevis	119
St. Lucia	156
St. Vincent	185
Sarawak	196
Seychelles	172
Sierra Leone	194
Singapore	27
Solomon Islands	88
Somaliland Protectorate	127
Swaziland	54
Trinidad & Tobago	84
Tristan da Cunha	13
Turks & Caicos Islands	118
Virgin Islands	114

The following have different designs but are included in the omnibus set:

Great Britain	313-316
Offices in Morocco (Tangier)	579-582
Australia	259-261
Bahrain	92-95
Canada	330
Ceylon	317
Cook Islands	145-146
Kuwait	113-116
New Zealand	280-284
Niue	104-105
Oman	52-55
Samoa	214-215
South Africa	192
Southern Rhodesia	80
South-West Africa	244-248
Tokelau Islands	4

No. 47 (1)	1.25	1.25
No. 28 (1)	.75	1.50
No. 28 (1)	1.10	.60
No. 106 (1)	.40	.75
No. 61 (1)	1.25	2.75
No. 157 (1)	1.40	.75
No. 234 (1)	1.00	.25
No. 45 (1)	.50	.60
No. 153 (1)	.75	.35
No. 142 (1)	.85	.50
No. 252 (1)	.45	.25
No. 143 (1)	.60	.40
No. 150 (1)	.40	1.75
No. 167 (1)	1.60	.25
No. 141 (1)	.40	.40
No. 121 (1)	.90	1.50
No. 1L18 (1)	1.80	1.40
No. 145 (1)	1.00	.50
No. 152 (1)	.50	.50
No. 131 (1)	.50	.50
No. 60 (1)	.65	2.25
No. 160 (1)	1.00	.25

No. 170 (1)	.30	.25
No. 184 (1)	6.00	.35
No. 153 (1)	.70	.25
No. 101 (1)	.40	.25
No. 132 (1)	1.00	2.25
No. 155 (1)	1.40	.30
No. 82 (1)	2.25	.60
No. 71 (1)	1.60	1.60
No. 27 (1)	1.10	1.50
No. 63 (1)	1.40	.65
No. 71 (1)	2.25	.25
No. 27 (1)	1.75	.30
No. 126 (1)	1.60	.25
No. 28 (1)	1.75	4.00
No. 101 (1)	1.75	.25
No. 74 (1)	1.50	1.00
No. 241 (1)	.50	.25
No. 250 (1)	1.10	.25
No. 127 (1)	.60	.45
No. 77 (1)	.75	.60
No. 79 (1)	.45	.25
No. 260 (1)	1.75	1.00
No. 60 (1)	.70	.25
No. 96 (1)	.75	.75
No. 19 (1)	2.25	2.25
No. 139 (1)	1.25	1.25
No. 119 (1)	.35	.25
No. 156 (1)	.70	.35
No. 185 (1)	.50	.30
No. 196 (1)	2.00	1.75
No. 172 (1)	.80	.80
No. 194 (1)	.40	.40
No. 27 (1)	2.50	.40
No. 88 (1)	1.00	1.00
No. 127 (1)	.40	.25
No. 54 (1)	.30	.25
No. 84 (1)	.25	.25
No. 13 (1)	1.00	1.75
No. 118 (1)	.40	1.10
No. 114 (1)	.40	1.00
Nos. 313-316 (4)	16.35	5.95
Nos. 579-582 (4)	7.40	5.20
Nos. 259-261 (3)	3.60	2.75
Nos. 92-95 (4)	15.25	12.75
No. 330 (1)	.25	.25
No. 317 (1)	1.40	.25
Nos. 145-146 (2)	2.65	2.65
Nos. 113-116 (4)	16.00	8.50
Nos. 280-284 (5)	3.30	4.55
Nos. 104-105 (2)	1.60	1.60
Nos. 52-55 (4)	14.25	6.50
Nos. 214-215 (2)	2.50	.80
No. 192 (1)	.45	.30
No. 80 (1)	7.25	7.25
Nos. 244-248 (5)	3.00	2.35
No. 4 (1)	2.75	2.75
Set total (106) Stamps	164.90	115.45

Separate designs for each country for the visit of Queen Elizabeth II and the Duke of Edinburgh.

Royal Visit 1953

1953

Aden		62
Australia		267-269
Bermuda		163
Ceylon		318
Fiji		146
Gibraltar		146
Jamaica		154
Kenya, Uganda, Tanzania		102
Malta		242
New Zealand		286-287

No. 62 (1)	.65	4.00
Nos. 267-269 (3)	2.75	2.05
No. 163 (1)	.50	.25
No. 318 (1)	1.00	.25
No. 146 (1)	.65	.35
No. 146 (1)	.50	.30
No. 154 (1)	.50	.25
No. 102 (1)	.50	.25
No. 242 (1)	.35	.25
Nos. 286-287 (2)	.50	.50
Set total (13) Stamps	7.90	8.45

West Indies Federation

Map of the Caribbean
CD313

Federation of the West Indies, April 22, 1958.

1958

Antigua		122-124
Barbados		248-250
Dominica		161-163
Grenada		184-186
Jamaica		175-177
Montserrat		143-145
St. Kitts-Nevis		136-138
St. Lucia		170-172

St. Vincent		198-200
Trinidad & Tobago		86-88

Nos. 122-124 (3)	5.80	3.80
Nos. 248-250 (3)	1.60	2.90
Nos. 161-163 (3)	1.95	1.85
Nos. 184-186 (3)	1.50	1.20
Nos. 175-177 (3)	2.65	3.45
Nos. 143-145 (3)	2.35	1.35
Nos. 136-138 (3)	3.00	3.10
Nos. 170-172 (3)	2.05	2.80
Nos. 198-200 (3)	1.50	1.75
Nos. 86-88 (3)	.75	.90
Set total (30) Stamps	23.15	23.10

Freedom from Hunger

Protein Food
CD314

U.N. Food and Agricultural Organization's "Freedom from Hunger" campaign.

1963

Aden		65
Antigua		133
Ascension		89
Bahamas		180
Basutoland		83
Bechuanaland Protectorate		194
Bermuda		192
British Guiana		271
British Honduras		179
Brunei		100
Cayman Islands		168
Dominica		181
Falkland Islands		146
Fiji		198
Gambia		172
Gibraltar		161
Gilbert & Ellice Islands		76
Grenada		190
Hong Kong		218
Malta		291
Mauritius		270
Montserrat		150
New Hebrides, British		93
North Borneo		296
Pitcairn Islands		35
St. Helena		173
St. Lucia		179
St. Vincent		201
Sarawak		212
Seychelles		213
Solomon Islands		109
Swaziland		108
Tonga		127
Tristan da Cunha		68
Turks & Caicos Islands		138
Virgin Islands		140
Zanzibar		280

No. 65 (1)	1.50	1.75
No. 133 (1)	.35	.35
No. 89 (1)	1.00	.50
No. 180 (1)	.65	.65
No. 83 (1)	.50	.25
No. 194 (1)	.50	.50
No. 192 (1)	1.00	.50
No. 271 (1)	.45	.25
No. 179 (1)	.60	.25
No. 100 (1)	3.25	2.25
No. 168 (1)	.55	.30
No. 181 (1)	.30	.30
No. 146 (1)	10.50	2.50
No. 198 (1)	3.50	2.25
No. 172 (1)	.50	.25
No. 161 (1)	4.00	2.25
No. 76 (1)	1.40	.40
No. 190 (1)	.30	.25
No. 218 (1)	47.50	7.50
No. 291 (1)	2.00	2.00
No. 270 (1)	.45	.25
No. 150 (1)	.55	.35
No. 93 (1)	.60	.25
No. 296 (1)	1.90	.75
No. 35 (1)	10.00	4.50
No. 173 (1)	2.25	1.10
No. 179 (1)	.40	.40
No. 201 (1)	.90	.50
No. 212 (1)	1.60	1.75
No. 213 (1)	.85	.35
No. 109 (1)	3.00	.85
No. 108 (1)	.50	.50
No. 127 (1)	.60	.35
No. 68 (1)	.75	.35
No. 138 (1)	.50	.25
No. 140 (1)	.50	.50
No. 280 (1)	1.50	.80
Set total (37) Stamps	107.20	39.05

Red Cross Centenary

Red Cross and Elizabeth II
CD315

1963

Antigua		134-135
Ascension		90-91
Bahamas		183-184
Basutoland		84-85
Bechuanaland Protectorate		195-196
Bermuda		193-194
British Guiana		272-273
British Honduras		180-181
Cayman Islands		169-170
Dominica		182-183
Falkland Islands		147-148
Fiji		203-204
Gambia		173-174
Gibraltar		162-163
Gilbert & Ellice Islands		77-78
Grenada		191-192
Hong Kong		219-220
Jamaica		203-204
Malta		292-293
Mauritius		271-272
Montserrat		151-152
New Hebrides, British		94-95
Pitcairn Islands		36-37
St. Helena		174-175
St. Kitts-Nevis		143-144
St. Lucia		180-181
St. Vincent		202-203
Seychelles		214-215
Solomon Islands		110-111
South Arabia		1-2
Swaziland		109-110
Tonga		134-135
Tristan da Cunha		69-70
Turks & Caicos Islands		139-140
Virgin Islands		141-142

Nos. 134-135 (2)	1.00	2.00
Nos. 90-91 (2)	6.75	3.35
Nos. 183-184 (2)	2.30	2.80
Nos. 84-85 (2)	1.20	.90
Nos. 195-196 (2)	.95	.85
Nos. 193-194 (2)	3.00	2.80
Nos. 272-273 (2)	.85	.60
Nos. 180-181 (2)	1.00	2.50
Nos. 169-170 (2)	1.10	3.00
Nos. 182-183 (2)	.70	1.05
Nos. 147-148 (2)	18.00	5.50
Nos. 203-204 (2)	3.25	2.80
Nos. 173-174 (2)	.75	1.00
Nos. 162-163 (2)	6.25	5.40
Nos. 77-78 (2)	2.00	3.50
Nos. 191-192 (2)	.80	.50
Nos. 219-220 (2)	35.00	7.35
Nos. 203-204 (2)	.75	1.65
Nos. 292-293 (2)	2.50	4.75
Nos. 271-272 (2)	.85	.50
Nos. 151-152 (2)	1.00	.75
Nos. 94-95 (2)	1.00	.50
Nos. 36-37 (2)	6.50	5.50
Nos. 174-175 (2)	1.70	2.30
Nos. 143-144 (2)	.90	.90
Nos. 180-181 (2)	1.25	1.25
Nos. 202-203 (2)	.90	.90
Nos. 214-215 (2)	1.00	1.50
Nos. 110-111 (2)	1.25	1.15
Nos. 1-2 (2)	1.25	1.25
Nos. 109-110 (2)	1.10	1.10
Nos. 134-135 (2)	1.00	1.25
Nos. 69-70 (2)	1.15	.80
Nos. 139-140 (2)	.85	.75
Nos. 141-142 (2)	.80	1.25
Set total (70) Stamps	110.65	73.95

Shakespeare

Shakespeare Memorial Theatre, Stratford-on-Avon — CD316

400th anniversary of the birth of William Shakespeare.

1964

Antigua		151
Bahamas		201
Bechuanaland Protectorate		197
Cayman Islands		171

Dominica		184
Falkland Islands		149
Gambia		192
Gibraltar		164
Montserrat		153
St. Lucia		196
Turks & Caicos Islands		141
Virgin Islands		143

No. 151 (1)	.35	.25
No. 201 (1)	.60	.35
No. 197 (1)	.35	.35
No. 171 (1)	.35	.30
No. 184 (1)	.35	.35
No. 149 (1)	1.60	.50
No. 192 (1)	.35	.25
No. 164 (1)	.65	.55
No. 153 (1)	.35	.25
No. 196 (1)	.45	.25
No. 141 (1)	.40	.25
No. 143 (1)	.45	.45
Set total (12) Stamps	6.25	4.10

ITU

ITU Emblem
CD317

Intl. Telecommunication Union, cent.

1965

Antigua		153-154
Ascension		92-93
Bahamas		219-220
Barbados		265-266
Basutoland		101-102
Bechuanaland Protectorate		202-203
Bermuda		196-197
British Guiana		293-294
British Honduras		187-188
Brunei		116-117
Cayman Islands		172-173
Dominica		185-186
Falkland Islands		154-155
Fiji		211-212
Gibraltar		167-168
Gilbert & Ellice Islands		87-88
Grenada		205-206
Hong Kong		221-222
Mauritius		291-292
Montserrat		157-158
New Hebrides, British		108-109
Pitcairn Islands		52-53
St. Helena		180-181
St. Kitts-Nevis		163-164
St. Lucia		197-198
St. Vincent		224-225
Seychelles		218-219
Solomon Islands		126-127
Swaziland		115-116
Tristan da Cunha		85-86
Turks & Caicos Islands		142-143
Virgin Islands		159-160

Nos. 153-154 (2)	1.45	.85
Nos. 92-93 (2)	1.90	1.30
Nos. 219-220 (2)	1.35	1.50
Nos. 265-266 (2)	1.50	1.25
Nos. 101-102 (2)	.85	.65
Nos. 202-203 (2)	1.10	.75
Nos. 196-197 (2)	2.15	2.25
Nos. 293-294 (2)	.50	.50
Nos. 187-188 (2)	.75	.75
Nos. 116-117 (2)	1.75	1.75
Nos. 172-173 (2)	1.00	.85
Nos. 185-186 (2)	.55	.55
Nos. 154-155 (2)	6.75	3.15
Nos. 211-212 (2)	2.00	1.05
Nos. 167-168 (2)	9.00	5.95
Nos. 87-88 (2)	.85	.60
Nos. 205-206 (2)	.50	.50
Nos. 221-222 (2)	24.50	3.80
Nos. 291-292 (2)	1.10	.50
Nos. 157-158 (2)	1.05	1.15
Nos. 108-109 (2)	.65	.50
Nos. 52-53 (2)	6.25	4.30
Nos. 180-181 (2)	.80	.60
Nos. 163-164 (2)	.60	.60
Nos. 197-198 (2)	1.25	1.25
Nos. 224-225 (2)	.80	.90
Nos. 218-219 (2)	.75	.60
Nos. 126-127 (2)	.70	.55
Nos. 115-116 (2)	.70	.70
Nos. 85-86 (2)	1.00	.65
Nos. 142-143 (2)	.75	.50
Nos. 159-160 (2)	.85	.85
Set total (64) Stamps	75.70	42.15

Intl. Cooperation Year

ICY Emblem CD318

1965

Antigua	155-156
Ascension	94-95
Bahamas	222-223
Basutoland	103-104
Bechuanaland Protectorate	204-205
Bermuda	199-200
British Guiana	295-296
British Honduras	189-190
Brunei	118-119
Cayman Islands	174-175
Dominica	187-188
Falkland Islands	156-157
Fiji	213-214
Gibraltar	169-170
Gilbert & Ellice Islands	104-105
Grenada	207-208
Hong Kong	223-224
Mauritius	293-294
Montserrat	176-177
New Hebrides, British	110-111
New Hebrides, French	126-127
Pitcairn Islands	54-55
St. Helena	182-183
St. Kitts-Nevis	165-166
St. Lucia	199-200
Seychelles	220-221
Solomon Islands	143-144
South Arabia	17-18
Swaziland	117-118
Tristan da Cunha	87-88
Turks & Caicos Islands	144-145
Virgin Islands	161-162

Nos. 155-156 (2)	.55	.50
Nos. 94-95 (2)	1.30	1.40
Nos. 222-223 (2)	.65	1.90
Nos. 103-104 (2)	.75	.85
Nos. 204-205 (2)	.85	1.00
Nos. 199-200 (2)	2.05	1.25
Nos. 295-296 (2)	.55	.50
Nos. 189-190 (2)	.60	.55
Nos. 118-119 (2)	.85	.85
Nos. 174-175 (2)	1.00	.75
Nos. 187-188 (2)	.55	.55
Nos. 156-157 (2)	6.00	1.65
Nos. 213-214 (2)	1.95	1.25
Nos. 169-170 (2)	1.25	2.75
Nos. 104-105 (2)	.85	.60
Nos. 207-208 (2)	.50	.50
Nos. 223-224 (2)	22.00	3.10
Nos. 293-294 (2)	.65	.50
Nos. 176-177 (2)	.80	.65
Nos. 110-111 (2)	.50	.50
Nos. 126-127 (2)	12.00	12.00
Nos. 54-55 (2)	6.35	4.50
Nos. 182-183 (2)	.95	.50
Nos. 165-166 (2)	.80	.60
Nos. 199-200 (2)	.55	.55
Nos. 220-221 (2)	.80	.60
Nos. 143-144 (2)	.70	.60
Nos. 17-18 (2)	1.20	.50
Nos. 117-118 (2)	.75	.75
Nos. 87-88 (2)	1.05	.65
Nos. 144-145 (2)	.65	.50
Nos. 161-162 (2)	.65	.50
Set total (64) Stamps	70.65	43.85

Churchill Memorial

Winston Churchill and St. Paul's, London, During Air Attack — CD319

1966

Antigua	157-160
Ascension	96-99
Bahamas	224-227
Barbados	281-284
Basutoland	105-108
Bechuanaland Protectorate	206-209
Bermuda	201-204
British Antarctic Territory	16-19
British Honduras	191-194
Brunei	120-123
Cayman Islands	176-179
Dominica	189-192
Falkland Islands	158-161
Fiji	215-218

Gibraltar	171-174
Gilbert & Ellice Islands	106-109
Grenada	209-212
Hong Kong	225-228
Mauritius	295-298
Montserrat	178-181
New Hebrides, British	112-115
New Hebrides, French	128-131
Pitcairn Islands	56-59
St. Helena	184-187
St. Kitts-Nevis	167-170
St. Lucia	201-204
St. Vincent	241-244
Seychelles	222-225
Solomon Islands	145-148
South Arabia	19-22
Swaziland	119-122
Tristan da Cunha	89-92
Turks & Caicos Islands	146-149
Virgin Islands	163-166

Nos. 157-160 (4)	3.05	3.05
Nos. 96-99 (4)	10.00	6.40
Nos. 224-227 (4)	2.30	3.20
Nos. 281-284 (4)	3.00	4.95
Nos. 105-108 (4)	2.80	3.25
Nos. 206-209 (4)	2.50	2.50
Nos. 201-204 (4)	4.00	4.75
Nos. 16-19 (4)	41.20	18.00
Nos. 191-194 (4)	2.45	1.30
Nos. 120-123 (4)	7.65	6.55
Nos. 176-179 (4)	3.10	3.65
Nos. 189-192 (4)	1.15	1.15
Nos. 158-161 (4)	12.75	9.55
Nos. 215-218 (4)	4.40	3.00
Nos. 171-174 (4)	3.05	5.30
Nos. 106-109 (4)	1.50	1.30
Nos. 209-212 (4)	1.10	1.10
Nos. 225-228 (4)	52.50	11.40
Nos. 295-298 (4)	3.70	3.75
Nos. 178-181 (4)	1.60	1.55
Nos. 112-115 (4)	2.30	1.00
Nos. 128-131 (4)	8.35	8.35
Nos. 56-59 (4)	11.00	6.75
Nos. 184-187 (4)	1.85	1.95
Nos. 167-170 (4)	1.50	1.70
Nos. 201-204 (4)	1.50	1.50
Nos. 241-244 (4)	1.50	1.75
Nos. 222-225 (4)	3.20	4.35
Nos. 145-148 (4)	1.50	1.60
Nos. 19-22 (4)	2.95	2.20
Nos. 119-122 (4)	1.70	2.55
Nos. 89-92 (4)	5.95	2.70
Nos. 146-149 (4)	1.60	1.75
Nos. 163-166 (4)	1.90	1.90
Set total (136) Stamps	210.60	135.75

Royal Visit, 1966

Queen Elizabeth II and Prince Philip CD320

Caribbean visit, Feb. 4 - Mar. 6, 1966.

1966

Antigua	161-162
Bahamas	228-229
Barbados	285-286
British Guiana	299-300
Cayman Islands	180-181
Dominica	193-194
Grenada	213-214
Montserrat	182-183
St. Kitts-Nevis	171-172
St. Lucia	205-206
St. Vincent	245-246
Turks & Caicos Islands	150-151
Virgin Islands	167-168

Nos. 161-162 (2)	3.50	2.60
Nos. 228-229 (2)	3.05	3.05
Nos. 285-286 (2)	3.00	2.00
Nos. 299-300 (2)	2.35	.85
Nos. 180-181 (2)	3.45	1.80
Nos. 193-194 (2)	3.00	.60
Nos. 213-214 (2)	.80	.50
Nos. 182-183 (2)	2.00	1.00
Nos. 171-172 (2)	.90	.75
Nos. 205-206 (2)	1.50	1.35
Nos. 245-246 (2)	2.75	1.35
Nos. 150-151 (2)	1.20	.55
Nos. 167-168 (2)	1.75	1.75
Set total (26) Stamps	29.25	18.15

World Cup Soccer

Soccer Player and Jules Rimet Cup CD321

World Cup Soccer Championship, Wembley, England, July 11-30.

1966

Antigua	163-164
Ascension	100-101
Bahamas	245-246
Bermuda	205-206
Brunei	124-125
Cayman Islands	182-183
Dominica	195-196
Fiji	219-220
Gibraltar	175-176
Gilbert & Ellice Islands	125-126
Grenada	230-231
New Hebrides, British	116-117
New Hebrides, French	132-133
Pitcairn Islands	60-61
St. Helena	188-189
St. Kitts-Nevis	173-174
St. Lucia	207-208
Seychelles	226-227
Solomon Islands	167-168
South Arabia	23-24
Tristan da Cunha	93-94

Nos. 163-164 (2)	.80	.85
Nos. 100-101 (2)	2.50	2.00
Nos. 245-246 (2)	.65	.65
Nos. 205-206 (2)	1.75	1.75
Nos. 124-125 (2)	1.30	1.25
Nos. 182-183 (2)	.75	.65
Nos. 195-196 (2)	1.20	.75
Nos. 219-220 (2)	1.70	.60
Nos. 175-176 (2)	1.85	1.75
Nos. 125-126 (2)	.70	.60
Nos. 230-231 (2)	.65	.95
Nos. 116-117 (2)	1.00	1.00
Nos. 132-133 (2)	7.00	7.00
Nos. 60-61 (2)	5.50	5.00
Nos. 188-189 (2)	1.25	.60
Nos. 173-174 (2)	.85	.80
Nos. 207-208 (2)	1.15	.90
Nos. 226-227 (2)	.85	.75
Nos. 167-168 (2)	1.10	1.10
Nos. 23-24 (2)	1.90	.55
Nos. 93-94 (2)	1.25	.90
Set total (42) Stamps	35.70	30.30

WHO Headquarters

World Health Organization Headquarters, Geneva — CD322

1966

Antigua	165-166
Ascension	102-103
Bahamas	247-248
Brunei	126-127
Cayman Islands	184-185
Dominica	197-198
Fiji	224-225
Gibraltar	180-181
Gilbert & Ellice Islands	127-128
Grenada	232-233
Hong Kong	229-230
Montserrat	184-185
New Hebrides, British	118-119
New Hebrides, French	134-135
Pitcairn Islands	62-63
St. Helena	190-191
St. Kitts-Nevis	177-178
St. Lucia	209-210
St. Vincent	247-248
Seychelles	228-229
Solomon Islands	169-170
South Arabia	25-26
Tristan da Cunha	99-100

Nos. 165-166 (2)	1.15	.55
Nos. 102-103 (2)	6.60	3.35
Nos. 247-248 (2)	.80	.80
Nos. 126-127 (2)	1.35	1.35
Nos. 184-185 (2)	2.25	1.20
Nos. 197-198 (2)	.75	.75
Nos. 224-225 (2)	4.70	3.30
Nos. 180-181 (2)	6.50	4.50
Nos. 127-128 (2)	.80	.70
Nos. 232-233 (2)	.80	.50
Nos. 229-230 (2)	11.25	2.30
Nos. 184-185 (2)	1.00	1.00
Nos. 118-119 (2)	.75	.50
Nos. 134-135 (2)	8.50	8.50
Nos. 62-63 (2)	7.25	6.50
Nos. 190-191 (2)	3.50	1.50
Nos. 177-178 (2)	.60	.60
Nos. 209-210 (2)	.80	.80
Nos. 247-248 (2)	1.15	1.05
Nos. 228-229 (2)	1.25	.65
Nos. 169-170 (2)	.95	.80

Nos. 25-26 (2)	2.10	.70
Nos. 99-100 (2)	1.90	1.25
Set total (46) Stamps	66.70	43.15

UNESCO Anniversary

"Education" — CD323

"Science" (Wheat ears & flask enclosing globe). "Culture" (lyre & columns). 20th anniversary of the UNESCO.

1966-67

Antigua	183-185
Ascension	108-110
Bahamas	249-251
Barbados	287-289
Bermuda	207-209
Brunei	128-130
Cayman Islands	186-188
Dominica	199-201
Gibraltar	183-185
Gilbert & Ellice Islands	129-131
Grenada	234-236
Hong Kong	231-233
Mauritius	299-301
Montserrat	186-188
New Hebrides, British	120-122
New Hebrides, French	136-138
Pitcairn Islands	64-66
St. Helena	192-194
St. Kitts-Nevis	179-181
St. Lucia	211-213
St. Vincent	249-251
Seychelles	230-232
Solomon Islands	171-173
South Arabia	27-29
Swaziland	123-125
Tristan da Cunha	101-103
Turks & Caicos Islands	155-157
Virgin Islands	176-178

Nos. 183-185 (3)	1.90	2.50
Nos. 108-110 (3)	11.00	5.80
Nos. 249-251 (3)	2.35	2.35
Nos. 287-289 (3)	2.35	2.15
Nos. 207-209 (3)	3.80	3.90
Nos. 128-130 (3)	4.65	5.40
Nos. 186-188 (3)	2.50	1.50
Nos. 199-201 (3)	1.60	.75
Nos. 183-185 (3)	6.50	3.25
Nos. 129-131 (3)	2.50	2.45
Nos. 234-236 (3)	1.10	1.20
Nos. 231-233 (3)	69.50	17.50
Nos. 299-301 (3)	2.10	1.50
Nos. 186-188 (3)	2.40	2.40
Nos. 120-122 (3)	1.90	1.90
Nos. 136-138 (3)	7.75	7.75
Nos. 64-66 (3)	7.10	4.75
Nos. 192-194 (3)	5.25	3.65
Nos. 179-181 (3)	.90	.90
Nos. 211-213 (3)	1.15	1.15
Nos. 249-251 (3)	2.30	1.35
Nos. 230-232 (3)	2.40	2.40
Nos. 171-173 (3)	2.00	1.50
Nos. 27-29 (3)	5.50	5.50
Nos. 123-125 (3)	1.40	1.40
Nos. 101-103 (3)	2.00	1.40
Nos. 155-157 (3)	1.05	.90
Nos. 176-178 (3)	1.40	1.30
Set total (84) Stamps	156.35	88.50

Silver Wedding, 1972

Queen Elizabeth II and Prince Philip — CD324

Designs: borders differ for each country.

1972

Anguilla	161-162
Antigua	295-296
Ascension	164-165
Bahamas	344-345
Bermuda	296-297
British Antarctic Territory	43-44
British Honduras	306-307
British Indian Ocean Territory	48-49

Brunei	186-187
Cayman Islands	304-305
Dominica	352-353
Falkland Islands	223-224
Fiji	328-329
Gibraltar	292-293
Gilbert & Ellice Islands	206-207
Grenada	466-467
Hong Kong	271-272
Montserrat	286-287
New Hebrides, British	169-170
New Hebrides, French	188-189
Pitcairn Islands	127-128
St. Helena	271-272
St. Kitts-Nevis	257-258
St. Lucia	328-329
St. Vincent	344-345
Seychelles	309-310
Solomon Islands	248-249
South Georgia	35-36
Tristan da Cunha	178-179
Turks & Caicos Islands	257-258
Virgin Islands	241-242

Nos. 161-162 (2)	1.10	1.50
Nos. 295-296 (2)	.50	.50
Nos. 164-165 (2)	.70	.70
Nos. 344-345 (2)	.60	.60
Nos. 296-297 (2)	.50	.65
Nos. 43-44 (2)	6.50	5.65
Nos. 306-307 (2)	.80	.80
Nos. 48-49 (2)	2.00	1.00
Nos. 186-187 (2)	.70	.70
Nos. 304-305 (2)	.75	.75
Nos. 352-353 (2)	.65	.65
Nos. 223-224 (2)	1.00	1.15
Nos. 328-329 (2)	.70	.70
Nos. 292-293 (2)	.50	.50
Nos. 206-207 (2)	.50	.50
Nos. 466-467 (2)	.70	.70
Nos. 271-272 (2)	1.70	1.50
Nos. 286-287 (2)	.50	.50
Nos. 169-170 (2)	.50	.50
Nos. 188-189 (2)	1.25	1.25
Nos. 127-128 (2)	.90	.85
Nos. 271-272 (2)	.60	1.20
Nos. 257-258 (2)	.65	.50
Nos. 328-329 (2)	.75	.75
Nos. 344-345 (2)	.55	.55
Nos. 309-310 (2)	.90	.90
Nos. 248-249 (2)	.50	.50
Nos. 35-36 (2)	1.40	1.40
Nos. 178-179 (2)	.70	.70
Nos. 257-258 (2)	.50	.50
Nos. 241-242 (2)	.50	.50
Set total (62) Stamps	30.10	29.15

Princess Anne's Wedding

Princess Anne and Mark Phillips — CD325

Wedding of Princess Anne and Mark Phillips, Nov. 14, 1973.

1973

Anguilla	179-180
Ascension	177-178
Belize	325-326
Bermuda	302-303
British Antarctic Territory	60-61
Cayman Islands	320-321
Falkland Islands	225-226
Gibraltar	305-306
Gilbert & Ellice Islands	216-217
Hong Kong	289-290
Montserrat	300-301
Pitcairn Islands	135-136
St. Helena	277-278
St. Kitts-Nevis	274-275
St. Lucia	349-350
St. Vincent	358-359
St. Vincent Grenadines	1-2
Seychelles	311-312
Solomon Islands	259-260
South Georgia	37-38
Tristan da Cunha	189-190
Turks & Caicos Islands	286-287
Virgin Islands	260-261

Nos. 179-180 (2)	.55	.55
Nos. 177-178 (2)	.60	.60
Nos. 325-326 (2)	.50	.50
Nos. 302-303 (2)	.50	.50
Nos. 60-61 (2)	1.10	1.10
Nos. 320-321 (2)	.50	.50

Nos. 225-226 (2)	.70	.60
Nos. 305-306 (2)	.55	.55
Nos. 216-217 (2)	.50	.50
Nos. 289-290 (2)	2.65	2.00
Nos. 300-301 (2)	.55	.55
Nos. 135-136 (2)	.70	.60
Nos. 277-278 (2)	.50	.50
Nos. 274-275 (2)	.50	.50
Nos. 349-350 (2)	.50	.50
Nos. 358-359 (2)	.50	.50
Nos. 1-2 (2)	.50	.50
Nos. 311-312 (2)	.65	.65
Nos. 259-260 (2)	.70	.70
Nos. 37-38 (2)	.75	.75
Nos. 189-190 (2)	.50	.50
Nos. 286-287 (2)	.50	.50
Nos. 260-261 (2)	.50	.50
Set total (46) Stamps	15.50	14.65

Elizabeth II Coronation Anniv.

CD326   CD327

CD328

Designs: Royal and local beasts in heraldic form and simulated stonework. Portrait of Elizabeth II by Peter Grugeon. 25th anniversary of coronation of Queen Elizabeth II.

1978

Ascension	229
Barbados	474
Belize	397
British Antarctic Territory	71
Cayman Islands	404
Christmas Island	87
Falkland Islands	275
Fiji	384
Gambia	380
Gilbert Islands	312
Mauritius	464
New Hebrides, British	258
New Hebrides, French	278
St. Helena	317
St. Kitts-Nevis	354
Samoa	472
Solomon Islands	368
South Georgia	51
Swaziland	302
Tristan da Cunha	238
Virgin Islands	337

No. 229 (1)	2.00	2.00
No. 474 (1)	1.35	1.35
No. 397 (1)	1.40	1.75
No. 71 (1)	6.00	6.00
No. 404 (1)	2.00	2.00
No. 87 (1)	3.50	4.00
No. 275 (1)	4.00	5.50
No. 384 (1)	1.75	1.75
No. 380 (1)	1.50	1.50
No. 312 (1)	1.25	1.25
No. 464 (1)	2.10	2.10
No. 258 (1)	1.75	1.75
No. 278 (1)	3.50	3.50
No. 317 (1)	1.75	1.75
No. 354 (1)	1.00	1.00
No. 472 (1)	2.10	2.10
No. 368 (1)	2.50	2.50
No. 51 (1)	3.00	3.00
No. 302 (1)	1.60	1.60
No. 238 (1)	1.50	1.50
No. 337 (1)	1.80	1.80
Set total (21) Stamps	47.35	49.70

Queen Mother Elizabeth's 80th Birthday

CD330

Designs: Photographs of Queen Mother Elizabeth. Falkland Islands issued in sheets of 50; others in sheets of 9.

1980

Ascension	261
Bermuda	401
Cayman Islands	443
Falkland Islands	305
Gambia	412
Gibraltar	393
Hong Kong	364
Pitcairn Islands	193
St. Helena	341
Samoa	532
Solomon Islands	426
Tristan da Cunha	277

No. 261 (1)	.40	.40
No. 401 (1)	.45	.75
No. 443 (1)	.40	.40
No. 305 (1)	.40	.40
No. 412 (1)	.40	.50
No. 393 (1)	.35	.35
No. 364 (1)	1.10	1.25
No. 193 (1)	.60	.60
No. 341 (1)	.50	.50
No. 532 (1)	.55	.55
No. 426 (1)	.50	.50
No. 277 (1)	.45	.45
Set total (12) Stamps	6.10	6.65

Royal Wedding, 1981

Prince Charles and Lady Diana — CD331   CD331a

Wedding of Charles, Prince of Wales, and Lady Diana Spencer, St. Paul's Cathedral, London, July 29, 1981.

1981

Antigua	623-627
Ascension	294-296
Barbados	547-549
Barbuda	497-501
Bermuda	412-414
Brunei	268-270
Cayman Islands	471-473
Dominica	701-705
Falkland Islands	324-326
Falkland Islands Dep.	1L59-1L61
Fiji	442-444
Gambia	426-428
Ghana	759-764
Grenada	1051-1055
Grenada Grenadines	440-443
Hong Kong	373-375
Jamaica	500-503
Lesotho	335-337
Maldive Islands	906-909
Mauritius	520-522
Norfolk Island	280-282
Pitcairn Islands	206-208
St. Helena	353-355
St. Lucia	543-549
Samoa	558-560
Sierra Leone	509-518
Solomon Islands	450-452
Swaziland	382-384
Tristan da Cunha	294-296
Turks & Caicos Islands	486-489
Caicos Island	8-11
Uganda	314-317
Vanuatu	308-310
Virgin Islands	406-408

Nos. 623-627 (5)	6.55	2.55
Nos. 294-296 (3)	1.00	1.00

Nos. 547-549 (3)	.90	.90
Nos. 497-501 (5)	10.95	10.95
Nos. 412-414 (3)	2.00	2.00
Nos. 268-270 (3)	2.15	4.50
Nos. 471-473 (3)	1.20	1.30
Nos. 701-705 (5)	8.35	2.35
Nos. 324-326 (3)	1.65	1.70
Nos. 1L59-1L61 (3)	1.45	1.45
Nos. 442-444 (3)	1.35	1.35
Nos. 426-428 (3)	.80	.80
Nos. 759-764 (9)	6.20	6.20
Nos. 1051-1055 (5)	9.85	1.85
Nos. 440-443 (4)	2.35	2.35
Nos. 373-375 (3)	3.05	2.85
Nos. 500-503 (4)	1.45	1.35
Nos. 335-337 (3)	.90	.90
Nos. 906-909 (4)	1.55	1.55
Nos. 520-522 (3)	2.15	2.15
Nos. 280-282 (3)	1.75	1.75
Nos. 206-208 (3)	1.10	1.10
Nos. 353-355 (3)	.85	.85
Nos. 543-549 (5)	7.00	7.00
Nos. 558-560 (3)	.85	.85
Nos. 509-518 (10)	15.50	15.50
Nos. 450-452 (3)	1.25	1.25
Nos. 382-384 (3)	1.30	1.25
Nos. 294-296 (3)	.90	.90
Nos. 486-489 (4)	2.20	2.20
Nos. 8-11 (4)	5.00	5.00
Nos. 314-317 (4)	3.30	3.00
Nos. 308-310 (3)	1.15	1.15
Nos. 406-408 (3)	1.10	1.10
Set total (131) Stamps	109.10	92.95

Princess Diana

CD332

CD333

Designs: Photographs and portrait of Princess Diana, wedding or honeymoon photographs, royal residences, arms of issuing country. Portrait photograph by Clive Friend. Souvenir sheet margins show family tree, various people related to the princess. 21st birthday of Princess Diana of Wales, July 1.

1982

Antigua	663-666
Ascension	313-316
Bahamas	510-513
Barbados	585-588
Barbuda	544-547
British Antarctic Territory	92-95
Cayman Islands	486-489
Dominica	773-776
Falkland Islands	348-351
Falkland Islands Dep.	1L72-1L75
Fiji	470-473
Gambia	447-450
Grenada	1101A-1105
Grenada Grenadines	485-491
Lesotho	372-375
Maldive Islands	952-955
Mauritius	548-551
Pitcairn Islands	213-216
St. Helena	372-375
St. Lucia	591-594
Sierra Leone	531-534
Solomon Islands	471-474
Swaziland	406-409
Tristan da Cunha	310-313
Turks and Caicos Islands	531-534
Virgin Islands	430-433

Nos. 663-666 (4)	8.25	7.35
Nos. 313-316 (4)	3.50	3.50
Nos. 510-513 (4)	6.00	3.85
Nos. 585-588 (4)	3.40	3.25
Nos. 544-547 (4)	9.75	7.70
Nos. 92-95 (4)	4.25	3.45
Nos. 486-489 (4)	4.75	2.70
Nos. 773-776 (4)	7.05	7.05
Nos. 348-351 (4)	2.95	2.95
Nos. 1L72-1L75 (4)	2.50	2.60
Nos. 470-473 (4)	3.25	2.95
Nos. 447-450 (4)	2.85	2.85
Nos. 1101A-1105 (7)	16.05	15.55

Nos. 485-491 (7)	17.65	17.65
Nos. 372-375 (4)	4.00	4.00
Nos. 952-955 (4)	5.50	3.90
Nos. 548-551 (4)	5.00	5.00
Nos. 213-216 (4)	2.15	2.15
Nos. 372-375 (4)	2.00	2.00
Nos. 591-594 (4)	8.70	8.70
Nos. 531-534 (4)	7.20	7.20
Nos. 471-474 (4)	2.90	2.90
Nos. 406-409 (4)	3.85	2.25
Nos. 310-313 (4)	3.65	1.45
Nos. 486-489 (4)	2.20	2.20
Nos. 430-433 (4)	3.00	3.00
Set total (110) Stamps	142.35	128.15

250th anniv. of first edition of Lloyd's List (shipping news publication) & of Lloyd's marine insurance.

CD335

Designs: First page of early edition of the list; historical ships, modern transportation or harbor scenes.

1984

Ascension	351-354
Bahamas	555-558
Barbados	627-630
Cayes of Belize	10-13
Cayman Islands	522-526
Falkland Islands	404-407
Fiji	509-512
Gambia	519-522
Mauritius	587-590
Nauru	280-283
St. Helena	412-415
Samoa	624-627
Seychelles	538-541
Solomon Islands	521-524
Vanuatu	368-371
Virgin Islands	466-469

Nos. 351-354 (4)	2.90	2.55
Nos. 555-558 (4)	4.15	2.95
Nos. 627-630 (4)	6.10	5.15
Nos. 10-13 (4)	2.65	2.65
Nos. 522-526 (5)	9.30	8.45
Nos. 404-407 (4)	3.50	3.65
Nos. 509-512 (4)	5.30	4.90
Nos. 519-522 (4)	4.20	4.30
Nos. 587-590 (4)	9.40	9.40
Nos. 280-283 (4)	2.40	2.35
Nos. 412-415 (4)	2.40	2.40
Nos. 624-627 (4)	2.55	2.35
Nos. 538-541 (4)	5.00	5.00
Nos. 521-524 (4)	4.65	3.95
Nos. 368-371 (4)	2.40	2.40
Nos. 466-469 (4)	4.25	4.25
Set total (65) Stamps	71.15	66.70

Queen Mother 85th Birthday

CD336

Designs: Photographs tracing the life of the Queen Mother, Elizabeth. The high value in each set pictures the same photograph taken of the Queen Mother holding the infant Prince Henry.

1985

Ascension	372-376
Bahamas	580-584
Barbados	660-664
Bermuda	469-473
Falkland Islands	420-424
Falkland Islands Dep.	1L92-1L96
Fiji	531-535
Hong Kong	447-450
Jamaica	599-603
Mauritius	604-608
Norfolk Island	364-368
Pitcairn Islands	253-257
St. Helena	428-432
Samoa	649-653

Seychelles	567-571
Zil Elwannyen Sesel	101-105
Solomon Islands	543-547
Swaziland	476-480
Tristan da Cunha	372-376
Vanuatu	392-396

Nos. 372-376 (5)	4.65	4.65
Nos. 580-584 (5)	7.70	6.45
Nos. 660-664 (5)	8.00	6.70
Nos. 469-473 (5)	9.40	9.40
Nos. 420-424 (5)	7.35	6.65
Nos. 1L92-1L96 (5)	8.00	8.00
Nos. 531-535 (5)	6.15	6.15
Nos. 447-450 (4)	9.50	8.50
Nos. 599-603 (5)	6.15	7.00
Nos. 604-608 (5)	11.30	11.30
Nos. 364-368 (5)	5.00	5.00
Nos. 253-257 (5)	5.25	5.95
Nos. 428-432 (5)	5.25	5.25
Nos. 649-653 (5)	8.40	7.55
Nos. 567-571 (5)	8.70	8.70
Nos. 101-105 (5)	6.60	6.60
Nos. 543-547 (5)	3.95	3.95
Nos. 476-480 (5)	7.75	7.25
Nos. 372-376 (5)	5.40	5.40
Nos. 392-396 (5)	5.25	5.25
Set total (99) Stamps	139.75	135.70

Queen Elizabeth II, 60th Birthday

CD337

1986, April 21

Ascension	389-393
Bahamas	592-596
Barbados	675-679
Bermuda	499-503
Cayman Islands	555-559
Falkland Islands	441-445
Fiji	544-548
Hong Kong	465-469
Jamaica	620-624
Kiribati	470-474
Mauritius	629-633
Papua New Guinea	640-644
Pitcairn Islands	270-274
St. Helena	451-455
Samoa	670-674
Seychelles	592-596
Zil Elwannyen Sesel	114-118
Solomon Islands	562-566
South Georgia	101-105
Swaziland	490-494
Tristan da Cunha	388-392
Vanuatu	414-418
Zambia	343-347

Nos. 389-393 (5)	2.80	3.30
Nos. 592-596 (5)	2.75	3.70
Nos. 675-679 (5)	3.25	3.10
Nos. 499-503 (5)	4.65	5.15
Nos. 555-559 (5)	4.55	5.60
Nos. 441-445 (5)	3.95	4.95
Nos. 544-548 (5)	3.00	3.00
Nos. 465-469 (5)	8.75	6.75
Nos. 620-624 (5)	2.75	2.70
Nos. 470-474 (5)	2.10	2.10
Nos. 629-633 (5)	3.50	3.50
Nos. 640-644 (5)	4.10	4.10
Nos. 270-274 (5)	2.70	2.70
Nos. 451-455 (5)	2.50	3.05
Nos. 670-674 (5)	2.55	2.55
Nos. 592-596 (5)	2.70	2.70
Nos. 114-118 (5)	2.15	2.15
Nos. 562-566 (5)	2.90	2.90
Nos. 101-105 (5)	3.30	3.65
Nos. 490-494 (5)	2.15	2.15
Nos. 388-392 (5)	3.00	3.00
Nos. 414-418 (5)	3.10	3.10
Nos. 343-347 (5)	1.75	1.75
Set total (115) Stamps	74.95	77.65

Royal Wedding

Marriage of Prince Andrew and Sarah Ferguson
CD338

1986, July 23

Ascension	399-400
Bahamas	602-603
Barbados	687-688

Cayman Islands	560-561
Jamaica	629-630
Pitcairn Islands	275-276
St. Helena	460-461
St. Kitts	181-182
Seychelles	602-603
Zil Elwannyen Sesel	119-120
Solomon Islands	567-568
Tristan da Cunha	397-398
Zambia	348-349

Nos. 399-400 (2)	1.60	1.60
Nos. 602-603 (2)	2.75	2.75
Nos. 687-688 (2)	2.00	1.25
Nos. 560-561 (2)	1.70	2.35
Nos. 629-630 (2)	1.35	1.35
Nos. 275-276 (2)	2.40	2.40
Nos. 460-461 (2)	1.05	1.05
Nos. 181-182 (2)	1.50	2.25
Nos. 602-603 (2)	2.50	2.50
Nos. 119-120 (2)	2.30	2.30
Nos. 567-568 (2)	1.00	1.00
Nos. 397-398 (2)	1.40	1.40
Nos. 348-349 (2)	1.10	1.30
Set total (26) Stamps	22.65	23.50

Queen Elizabeth II, 60th Birthday

Queen Elizabeth II & Prince Philip, 1947 Wedding Portrait — CD339

Designs: Photographs tracing the life of Queen Elizabeth II.

1986

Anguilla	674-677
Antigua	925-928
Barbuda	783-786
Dominica	950-953
Gambia	611-614
Grenada	1371-1374
Grenada Grenadines	749-752
Lesotho	531-534
Maldive Islands	1172-1175
Sierra Leone	760-763
Uganda	495-498

Nos. 674-677 (4)	8.00	8.00
Nos. 925-928 (4)	5.50	6.20
Nos. 783-786 (4)	8.15	8.15
Nos. 950-953 (4)	7.25	7.25
Nos. 611-614 (4)	8.25	7.90
Nos. 1371-1374 (4)	6.80	6.80
Nos. 749-752 (4)	6.75	6.75
Nos. 531-534 (4)	5.25	5.25
Nos. 1172-1175 (4)	6.25	6.25
Nos. 760-763 (4)	5.25	5.25
Nos. 495-498 (4)	8.50	8.50
Set total (44) Stamps	90.95	91.30

Royal Wedding, 1986

CD340

Designs: Photographs of Prince Andrew and Sarah Ferguson during courtship, engagement and marriage.

1986

Antigua	939-942
Barbuda	809-812
Dominica	970-973
Gambia	635-638
Grenada	1385-1388
Grenada Grenadines	758-761
Lesotho	545-548
Maldive Islands	1181-1184
Sierra Leone	769-772
Uganda	510-513

Nos. 939-942 (4)	7.00	8.75
Nos. 809-812 (4)	14.55	14.55
Nos. 970-973 (4)	7.25	7.25
Nos. 635-638 (4)	7.80	7.80
Nos. 1385-1388 (4)	8.30	8.30
Nos. 758-761 (4)	9.00	9.00

Nos. 545-548 (4)	7.45	7.45
Nos. 1181-1184 (4)	8.45	8.45
Nos. 769-772 (4)	5.35	5.35
Nos. 510-513 (4)	9.25	10.00
Set total (40) Stamps	84.40	86.90

Lloyds of London, 300th Anniv.

CD341

Designs: 17th century aspects of Lloyds, representations of each country's individual connections with Lloyds and publicized disasters created by the organization.

1986

Ascension	454-457
Bahamas	655-658
Barbados	731-734
Bermuda	541-544
Falkland Islands	481-484
Liberia	1101-1104
Malawi	534-537
Nevis	571-574
St. Helena	501-504
St. Lucia	923-926
Seychelles	649-652
Zil Elwannyen Sesel	146-149
Solomon Islands	627-630
South Georgia	131-134
Trinidad & Tobago	484-487
Tristan da Cunha	439-442
Vanuatu	485-488

Nos. 454-457 (4)	5.00	5.00
Nos. 655-658 (4)	8.90	4.95
Nos. 731-734 (4)	12.50	8.35
Nos. 541-544 (4)	8.00	6.60
Nos. 481-484 (4)	5.45	3.85
Nos. 1101-1104 (4)	4.25	4.25
Nos. 534-537 (4)	11.00	7.85
Nos. 571-574 (4)	8.35	8.35
Nos. 501-504 (4)	8.70	7.15
Nos. 923-926 (4)	8.80	8.80
Nos. 649-652 (4)	12.85	12.85
Nos. 146-149 (4)	11.25	11.25
Nos. 627-630 (4)	7.00	4.45
Nos. 131-134 (4)	6.30	3.70
Nos. 484-487 (4)	10.25	6.35
Nos. 439-442 (4)	7.60	7.60
Nos. 485-488 (4)	5.90	5.90
Set total (68) Stamps	142.10	117.25

Moon Landing, 20th Anniv.

CD342

Designs: Equipment, crew photographs, spacecraft, official emblems and report profiles created for the Apollo Missions. Two stamps in each set are square in format rather than like the stamp shown; see individual country listings for more information.

1989

Ascension	468-472
Bahamas	674-678
Belize	916-920
Kiribati	517-521
Liberia	1125-1129
Nevis	586-590
St. Kitts	248-252
Samoa	760-764
Seychelles	676-680
Zil Elwannyen Sesel	154-158
Solomon Islands	643-647
Vanuatu	507-511

Nos. 468-472 (5)	9.40	8.60
Nos. 674-678 (5)	23.00	19.70
Nos. 916-920 (5)	22.85	18.10
Nos. 517-521 (5)	12.50	12.50
Nos. 1125-1129 (5)	8.50	8.50
Nos. 586-590 (5)	7.50	7.50

Nos. 248-252 (5)	8.00	8.25
Nos. 760-764 (5)	9.85	9.30
Nos. 676-680 (5)	16.05	16.05
Nos. 154-158 (5)	26.85	26.85
Nos. 643-647 (5)	9.00	6.75
Nos. 507-511 (5)	9.90	9.90
Set total (60) Stamps	163.40	152.00

Queen Mother, 90th Birthday

CD343   CD344

Designs: Portraits of Queen Elizabeth, the Queen Mother. See individual country listings for more information.

1990

Ascension	491-492
Bahamas	698-699
Barbados	782-783
British Antarctic Territory	170-171
British Indian Ocean Territory	106-107
Cayman Islands	622-623
Falkland Islands	524-525
Kenya	527-528
Kiribati	555-556
Liberia	1145-1146
Pitcairn Islands	336-337
St. Helena	532-533
St. Lucia	969-970
Seychelles	710-711
Zil Elwannyen Sesel	171-172
Solomon Islands	671-672
South Georgia	143-144
Swaziland	565-566
Tristan da Cunha	480-481

Nos. 491-492 (2)	4.75	4.75
Nos. 698-699 (2)	5.25	5.25
Nos. 782-783 (2)	4.00	3.70
Nos. 170-171 (2)	6.00	6.00
Nos. 106-107 (2)	18.00	18.50
Nos. 622-623 (2)	4.00	5.50
Nos. 524-525 (2)	4.75	4.75
Nos. 527-528 (2)	7.00	7.00
Nos. 555-556 (2)	4.75	4.75
Nos. 1145-1146 (2)	3.25	3.25
Nos. 336-337 (2)	4.25	4.25
Nos. 532-533 (2)	5.25	5.25
Nos. 969-970 (2)	4.60	4.60
Nos. 710-711 (2)	6.60	6.60
Nos. 171-172 (2)	8.25	8.25
Nos. 671-672 (2)	5.00	5.30
Nos. 143-144 (2)	5.50	6.50
Nos. 565-566 (2)	4.10	4.10
Nos. 480-481 (2)	5.50	5.60
Set total (38) Stamps	110.90	113.90

Queen Elizabeth II, 65th Birthday, and Prince Philip, 70th Birthday

CD345

CD346

Designs: Portraits of Queen Elizabeth II and Prince Philip differ for each country. Printed in sheets of 10 + 5 labels (3 different) between. Stamps alternate, producing 5 different triptychs.

1991

Ascension	506a
Bahamas	731a
Belize	970a
Bermuda	618a
Kiribati	572a
Mauritius	734a
Pitcairn Islands	349a
St. Helena	555a
St. Kitts	319a
Samoa	791a
Seychelles	724a
Zil Elwannyen Sesel	178a
Solomon Islands	689a
South Georgia	150a
Swaziland	587a
Vanuatu	541a

No. 506a (1)	3.50	3.75
No. 731a (1)	4.00	4.00
No. 970a (1)	3.75	3.75
No. 618a (1)	3.50	4.00
No. 572a (1)	4.00	4.00
No. 734a (1)	4.00	4.00
No. 349a (1)	3.25	3.25
No. 555a (1)	2.75	2.75
No. 319a (1)	3.00	3.00
No. 791a (1)	3.75	3.75
No. 724a (1)	5.00	5.00
No. 178a (1)	6.25	6.25
No. 689a (1)	3.75	3.75
No. 150a (1)	4.75	7.00
No. 587a (1)	4.00	4.00
No. 541a (1)	2.50	2.50
Set total (16) Stamps	61.75	64.75

Royal Family Birthday, Anniversary

CD347

Queen Elizabeth II, 65th birthday, Charles and Diana, 10th wedding anniversary: Various photographs of Queen Elizabeth II, Prince Philip, Prince Charles, Princess Diana and their sons William and Henry.

1991

Antigua	1446-1455
Barbuda	1229-1238
Dominica	1328-1337
Gambia	1080-1089
Grenada	2006-2015
Grenada Grenadines	1331-1340
Guyana	2440-2451
Lesotho	871-875
Maldive Islands	1533-1542
Nevis	666-675
St. Vincent	1485-1494
St. Vincent Grenadines	769-778
Sierra Leone	1387-1396
Turks & Caicos Islands	913-922
Uganda	918-927

Nos. 1446-1455 (10)	21.70	20.05
Nos. 1229-1238 (10)	125.00	119.50
Nos. 1328-1337 (10)	30.20	30.20
Nos. 1080-1089 (10)	24.65	24.40
Nos. 2006-2015 (10)	25.45	22.10
Nos. 1331-1340 (10)	23.85	23.35
Nos. 2440-2451 (12)	21.40	21.15
Nos. 871-875 (5)	13.55	13.55
Nos. 1533-1542 (10)	28.10	28.10
Nos. 666-675 (10)	23.65	23.65
Nos. 1485-1494 (10)	26.75	25.90
Nos. 769-778 (10)	25.40	25.40
Nos. 1387-1396 (10)	26.35	26.35
Nos. 913-922 (10)	27.50	25.30
Nos. 918-927 (10)	26.60	26.60
Set total (147) Stamps	470.15	455.60

Queen Elizabeth II's Accession to the Throne, 40th Anniv.

CD348

Various photographs of Queen Elizabeth II with local Scenes.

1992

Antigua	1513-1518
Barbuda	1306-1311
Dominica	1414-1419
Gambia	1172-1177
Grenada	2047-2052
Grenada Grenadines	1368-1373
Lesotho	881-885
Maldive Islands	1637-1642
Nevis	702-707
St. Vincent	1582-1587
St. Vincent Grenadines	829-834
Sierra Leone	1482-1487
Turks and Caicos Islands	978-987
Uganda	990-995
Virgin Islands	742-746

Nos. 1513-1518 (6)	15.00	15.10
Nos. 1306-1311 (6)	125.25	83.65
Nos. 1414-1419 (6)	12.50	12.50
Nos. 1172-1177 (6)	14.95	14.85
Nos. 2047-2052 (6)	15.95	15.95
Nos. 1368-1373 (6)	17.00	15.35
Nos. 881-885 (5)	11.90	11.90
Nos. 1637-1642 (6)	17.55	17.55
Nos. 702-707 (6)	13.55	13.55
Nos. 1582-1587 (6)	14.40	14.40
Nos. 829-834 (6)	19.65	19.65
Nos. 1482-1487 (6)	22.50	22.50
Nos. 913-922 (10)	27.50	25.30
Nos. 990-995 (6)	19.50	19.50
Nos. 742-746 (5)	15.50	15.50
Set total (92) Stamps	362.70	317.25

CD349

1992

Ascension	531-535
Bahamas	744-748
Bermuda	623-627
British Indian Ocean Territory	119-123
Cayman Islands	648-652
Falkland Islands	549-553
Gibraltar	605-609
Hong Kong	619-623
Kenya	563-567
Kiribati	582-586
Pitcairn Islands	362-366
St. Helena	570-574
St. Kitts	332-336
Samoa	805-809
Seychelles	734-738
Zil Elwannyen Sesel	183-187
Solomon Islands	708-712
South Georgia	157-161
Tristan da Cunha	508-512
Vanuatu	555-559
Zambia	561-565

Nos. 531-535 (5)	6.10	6.10
Nos. 744-748 (5)	6.90	4.70
Nos. 623-627 (5)	7.40	7.55
Nos. 119-123 (5)	22.75	19.25
Nos. 648-652 (5)	7.60	6.60
Nos. 549-553 (5)	5.95	5.90
Nos. 605-609 (5)	5.15	5.50
Nos. 619-623 (5)	5.10	5.25
Nos. 563-567 (5)	9.10	9.10
Nos. 582-586 (5)	3.85	3.85
Nos. 362-366 (5)	5.35	5.35
Nos. 570-574 (5)	5.70	5.70
Nos. 332-336 (5)	6.60	6.50
Nos. 805-809 (5)	7.85	5.90
Nos. 734-738 (5)	10.55	10.55
Nos. 183-187 (5)	9.40	9.40
Nos. 708-712 (5)	5.00	5.30
Nos. 157-161 (5)	5.60	5.90
Nos. 508-512 (5)	8.75	8.30
Nos. 555-559 (5)	3.65	3.65
Nos. 561-565 (5)	5.60	5.60
Set total (105) Stamps	153.95	144.95

Royal Air Force, 75th Anniversary

CD350

1993

Ascension	557-561
Bahamas	771-775
Barbados	842-846
Belize	1003-1008
Bermuda	648-651
British Indian Ocean Territory	136-140
Falkland Is.	573-577
Fiji	687-691
Montserrat	830-834

St. Kitts	351-355

Nos. 557-561 (5)	15.60	14.60
Nos. 771-775 (5)	24.65	21.45
Nos. 842-846 (5)	14.15	12.85
Nos. 1003-1008 (6)	16.55	16.50
Nos. 648-651 (4)	9.65	10.45
Nos. 136-140 (5)	16.10	16.10
Nos. 573-577 (5)	10.85	10.85
Nos. 687-691 (5)	17.75	17.40
Nos. 830-834 (5)	14.10	14.10
Nos. 351-355 (5)	22.80	23.55
Set total (50) Stamps	162.20	157.85

Royal Air Force, 80th Anniv.

Design CD350 Re-inscribed

1998

Ascension	697-701
Bahamas	907-911
British Indian Ocean Terr	198-202
Cayman Islands	754-758
Fiji	814-818
Gibraltar	755-759
Samoa	957-961
Turks & Caicos Islands	1258-1265
Tuvalu	763-767
Virgin Islands	879-883

Nos. 697-701 (5)	16.10	16.10
Nos. 907-911 (5)	13.60	12.65
Nos. 136-140 (5)	16.10	16.10
Nos. 754-758 (5)	15.25	15.25
Nos. 814-818 (5)	14.00	12.75
Nos. 755-759 (5)	9.70	9.70
Nos. 957-961 (5)	15.70	14.90
Nos. 1258-1265 (2)	27.50	27.50
Nos. 763-767 (5)	9.75	9.75
Nos. 879-883 (5)	15.00	15.00
Set total (47) Stamps	152.70	149.70

End of World War II, 50th Anniv.

CD351

CD352

1995

Ascension	613-617
Bahamas	824-828
Barbados	891-895
Belize	1047-1050
British Indian Ocean Territory	163-167
Cayman Islands	704-708
Falkland Islands	634-638
Fiji	720-724
Kiribati	662-668
Liberia	1175-1179
Mauritius	803-805
St. Helena	646-654
St. Kitts	389-393
St. Lucia	1018-1022
Samoa	890-894
Solomon Islands	799-803
South Georgia	198-200
Tristan da Cunha	562-566

Nos. 613-617 (5)	21.50	21.50

Nos. 824-828 (5)	22.00	18.70
Nos. 891-895 (5)	14.20	11.90
Nos. 1047-1050 (4)	6.05	5.90
Nos. 163-167 (5)	16.25	16.25
Nos. 704-708 (5)	17.65	13.95
Nos. 634-638 (5)	18.65	17.15
Nos. 720-724 (5)	17.50	14.50
Nos. 662-668 (7)	16.30	16.30
Nos. 1175-1179 (5)	15.25	11.15
Nos. 803-805 (3)	7.50	7.50
Nos. 646-654 (9)	26.10	26.10
Nos. 389-393 (5)	16.40	16.40
Nos. 1018-1022 (5)	12.25	10.15
Nos. 890-894 (5)	15.25	14.50
Nos. 799-803 (5)	14.75	14.75
Nos. 198-200 (3)	14.50	15.50
Nos. 562-566 (5)	20.10	20.10
Set total (91) Stamps	292.20	272.30

UN, 50th Anniv.

CD353

1995

Bahamas	839-842
Barbados	901-904
Belize	1055-1058
Jamaica	847-851
Liberia	1187-1190
Mauritius	813-816
Pitcairn Islands	436-439
St. Kitts	398-401
St. Lucia	1023-1026
Samoa	900-903
Tristan da Cunha	568-571
Virgin Islands	807-810

Nos. 839-842 (4)	7.15	6.40
Nos. 901-904 (4)	7.00	5.75
Nos. 1055-1058 (4)	4.70	4.70
Nos. 847-851 (5)	5.40	5.45
Nos. 1187-1190 (4)	9.65	9.65
Nos. 813-816 (4)	4.55	4.55
Nos. 436-439 (4)	8.15	8.15
Nos. 398-401 (4)	6.15	7.15
Nos. 1023-1026 (4)	7.50	7.25
Nos. 900-903 (4)	9.35	8.20
Nos. 568-571 (4)	13.50	13.50
Nos. 807-810 (4)	7.45	7.45
Set total (49) Stamps	90.55	88.20

Queen Elizabeth, 70th Birthday

CD354

1996

Ascension	632-635
British Antarctic Territory	240-243
British Indian Ocean Territory	176-180
Falkland Islands	653-657
Pitcairn Islands	446-449
St. Helena	672-676
Samoa	912-916
Tokelau	223-227
Tristan da Cunha	576-579
Virgin Islands	824-828

Nos. 632-635 (4)	5.30	5.30
Nos. 240-243 (4)	9.45	8.15
Nos. 176-180 (5)	11.50	11.50
Nos. 653-657 (5)	13.55	11.20
Nos. 446-449 (4)	8.60	8.60
Nos. 672-676 (5)	12.45	12.70
Nos. 912-916 (5)	10.50	10.50
Nos. 223-227 (5)	10.50	10.50
Nos. 576-579 (4)	8.35	8.35
Nos. 824-828 (5)	11.30	11.30
Set total (46) Stamps	101.50	98.10

Diana, Princess of Wales (1961-97)

CD355

1998

Ascension	696
Bahamas	901A-902
Barbados	950
Belize	1091
Bermuda	753
Botswana	659-663
British Antarctic Territory	258
British Indian Ocean Terr.	197
Cayman Islands	752A-753
Falkland Islands	694
Fiji	819-820
Gibraltar	754
Kiribati	719A-720
Namibia	909
Niue	706
Norfolk Island	644-645
Papua New Guinea	937
Pitcairn Islands	487
St. Helena	711
St. Kitts	437A-438
Samoa	955A-956
Seycelles	802
Solomon Islands	866-867
South Georgia	220
Tokelau	252B-253
Tonga	980
Niuafo'ou	201
Tristan da Cunha	618
Tuvalu	762
Vanuatu	718A-719
Virgin Islands	878

No. 696 (1)	5.25	5.25
Nos. 901A-902 (2)	5.30	5.30
No. 950 (1)	6.25	6.25
No. 1091 (1)	5.00	5.00
No. 753 (1)	5.00	5.00
Nos. 659-663 (5)	8.25	8.80
No. 258 (1)	5.50	5.50
No. 197 (1)	5.50	5.50
Nos. 752A-753 (3)	7.40	7.40
No. 694 (1)	5.00	5.00
Nos. 819-820 (2)	5.25	5.25
No. 754 (1)	4.75	4.75
Nos. 719A-720 (2)	4.85	4.85
No. 909 (1)	1.75	1.75
No. 706 (1)	5.50	5.50
Nos. 644-645 (2)	5.60	5.60
No. 937 (1)	6.25	6.25
No. 487 (1)	4.75	4.75
No. 711 (1)	4.25	4.25
Nos. 437A-438 (2)	5.15	5.15
Nos. 955A-956 (2)	7.00	7.00
No. 802 (1)	6.25	6.25
Nos. 866-867 (2)	5.40	5.40
No. 220 (1)	4.50	5.00
Nos. 252B-253 (2)	6.00	6.00
No. 980 (1)	5.75	5.75
No. 201 (1)	6.50	6.50
No. 618 (1)	5.00	5.00
No. 762 (1)	4.00	4.00
Nos. 718A-719 (2)	8.00	8.00
No. 878 (1)	4.50	4.50
Set total (46) Stamps	169.45	170.50

Wedding of Prince Edward and Sophie Rhys-Jones

CD356

1999

Ascension	729-730
Cayman Islands	775-776
Falkland Islands	729-730
Pitcairn Islands	505-506
St. Helena	733-734
Samoa	971-972
Tristan da Cunha	636-637

Virgin Islands	908-909

Nos. 729-730 (2)	4.50	4.50
Nos. 775-776 (2)	4.95	4.95
Nos. 729-730 (2)	14.00	14.00
Nos. 505-506 (2)	7.00	7.00
Nos. 733-734 (2)	5.00	5.00
Nos. 971-972 (2)	5.00	5.00
Nos. 636-637 (2)	7.50	7.50
Nos. 908-909 (2)	7.50	7.50
Set total (16) Stamps	55.45	55.45

1st Manned Moon Landing, 30th Anniv.

CD357

1999

Ascension	731-735
Bahamas	942-946
Barbados	967-971
Bermuda	778
Cayman Islands	777-781
Fiji	853-857
Jamaica	889-893
Kirbati	746-750
Nauru	465-469
St. Kitts	460-464
Samoa	973-977
Solomon Islands	875-879
Tuvalu	800-804
Virgin Islands	910-914

Nos. 731-735 (5)	12.80	12.80
Nos. 942-946 (5)	14.10	14.10
Nos. 967-971 (5)	9.45	8.25
No. 778 (1)	9.00	9.00
Nos. 777-781 (5)	9.25	9.25
Nos. 853-857 (5)	9.25	8.45
Nos. 889-893 (5)	8.30	7.18
Nos. 746-750 (5)	8.85	8.85
Nos. 465-469 (5)	9.25	8.00
Nos. 460-464 (5)	11.35	11.65
Nos. 973-977 (5)	12.60	12.45
Nos. 875-879 (5)	7.50	7.50
Nos. 800-804 (5)	7.45	7.45
Nos. 910-914 (5)	11.75	11.75
Set total (66) Stamps	110.00	126.90

Queen Mother's Century

CD358

1999

Ascension	736-740
Bahamas	951-955
Cayman Islands	782-786
Falkland Islands	734-738
Fiji	858-862
Norfolk Island	688-692
St. Helena	740-744
Samoa	978-982
Solomon Islands	880-884
South Georgia	231-235
Tristan da Cunha	638-642
Tuvalu	805-809

Nos. 736-740 (5)	15.50	15.50
Nos. 951-955 (5)	13.75	12.65
Nos. 782-786 (5)	8.35	8.35
Nos. 734-738 (5)	30.00	28.25
Nos. 858-862 (5)	12.80	13.25
Nos. 688-692 (5)	9.50	9.50
Nos. 740-744 (5)	16.15	16.15
Nos. 978-982 (5)	12.50	12.10
Nos. 880-884 (5)	7.50	7.00
Nos. 231-235 (5)	29.75	30.00
Nos. 638-642 (5)	18.00	18.00
Nos. 805-809 (5)	8.65	8.65
Set total (60) Stamps	182.45	179.40

Prince William, 18th Birthday

CD359

2000

Ascension	755-759
Cayman Islands	797-801
Falkland Islands	762-766
Fiji	889-893
South Georgia	257-261
Tristan da Cunha	664-668
Virgin Islands	925-929

Nos. 755-759 (5)	15.50	15.50
Nos. 797-801 (5)	11.15	10.90
Nos. 762-766 (5)	24.60	22.50
Nos. 889-893 (5)	12.90	12.90
Nos. 257-261 (5)	29.00	28.75
Nos. 664-668 (5)	21.50	21.50
Nos. 925-929 (5)	14.50	14.50
Set total (35) Stamps	129.15	126.55

Reign of Queen Elizabeth II, 50th Anniv.

CD360

2002

Ascension	790-794
Bahamas	1033-1037
Barbados	1019-1023
Belize	1152-1156
Bermuda	822-826
British Antarctic Territory	307-311
British Indian Ocean Territory	239-243
Cayman Islands	844-848
Falkland Islands	804-808
Gibraltar	896-900
Jamaica	952-956
Nauru	491-495
Norfolk Island	758-762
Papua New Guinea	1019-1023
Pitcairn Islands	552
St. Helena	788-792
St. Lucia	1146-1150
Solomon Islands	931-935
South Georgia	274-278
Swaziland	706-710
Tokelau	302-306
Tonga	1059
Niuafo'ou	239
Tristan da Cunha	706-710
Virgin Islands	967-971

Nos. 790-794 (5)	14.10	14.10
Nos. 1033-1037 (5)	15.25	15.25
Nos. 1019-1023 (5)	12.90	12.90
Nos. 1152-1156 (5)	12.65	12.25
Nos. 822-826 (5)	18.00	18.00
Nos. 307-311 (5)	23.00	23.00
Nos. 239-243 (5)	19.40	19.40
Nos. 844-848 (5)	13.25	13.25
Nos. 804-808 (5)	23.00	22.00
Nos. 896-900 (5)	6.65	6.65
Nos. 952-956 (5)	16.65	16.65
Nos. 491-495 (5)	17.75	17.75
Nos. 758-762 (5)	15.90	15.90
Nos. 1019-1023 (5)	14.50	14.50
No. 552 (1)	9.25	9.25
Nos. 788-792 (5)	19.75	19.75
Nos. 1146-1150 (5)	12.25	12.25
Nos. 931-935 (5)	12.40	12.40
Nos. 274-278 (5)	28.00	28.50
Nos. 706-710 (5)	12.50	12.50
Nos. 302-306 (5)	14.50	14.50
No. 1059 (1)	8.50	8.50
No. 239 (1)	8.75	8.75
Nos. 706-710 (5)	18.50	18.50
Nos. 967-971 (5)	16.50	16.50
Set total (113) Stamps	383.90	383.00

Queen Mother Elizabeth (1900-2002)

CD361

2002

Ascension		799-801
Bahamas		1044-1046
Bermuda		834-836
British Antarctic Territory		312-314
British Indian Ocean Territory		245-247
Cayman Islands		857-861
Falkland Islands		812-816
Nauru		499-501
Pitcairn Islands		561-565
St. Helena		808-812
St. Lucia		1155-1159
Seychelles		830
Solomon Islands		945-947
South Georgia		281-285
Tokelau		312-314
Tristan da Cunha		715-717
Virgin Islands		979-983

Nos. 799-801 (3)	8.85	8.85
Nos. 1044-1046 (3)	9.10	9.10
Nos. 834-836 (3)	12.25	12.25
Nos. 312-314 (3)	18.75	18.75
Nos. 245-247 (3)	17.35	17.35
Nos. 857-861 (5)	15.00	15.00
Nos. 812-816 (5)	28.50	28.50
Nos. 499-501 (3)	14.00	14.00
Nos. 561-565 (5)	15.25	15.25
Nos. 808-812 (5)	12.00	12.00
Nos. 1155-1159 (5)	12.00	12.00
No. 830 (1)	6.50	6.50
Nos. 945-947 (3)	9.25	9.25
Nos. 281-285 (5)	19.50	19.50
Nos. 312-314 (3)	11.85	11.85
Nos. 715-717 (3)	16.25	16.25
Nos. 979-983 (5)	23.50	23.50
Set total (63) Stamps	249.90	249.90

Head of Queen Elizabeth II

CD362

2003

Ascension		822
Bermuda		865
British Antarctic Territory		322
British Indian Ocean Territory		261
Cayman Islands		878
Falkland Islands		828
St. Helena		820
South Georgia		294
Tristan da Cunha		731
Virgin Islands		1003

No. 822 (1)	12.50	12.50
No. 865 (1)	50.00	50.00
No. 322 (1)	9.50	9.50
No. 261 (1)	11.00	11.00
No. 878 (1)	14.00	14.00
No. 828 (1)	9.00	9.00
No. 820 (1)	9.00	9.00
No. 294 (1)	8.50	8.50
No. 731 (1)	10.00	10.00
No. 1003 (1)	10.00	10.00
Set total (10) Stamps	143.50	143.50

Coronation of Queen Elizabeth II, 50th Anniv.

CD363

2003

Ascension		823-825

Bahamas		1073-1075
Bermuda		866-868
British Antarctic Territory		323-325
British Indian Ocean Territory		262-264
Cayman Islands		879-881
Jamaica		970-972
Kiribati		825-827
Pitcairn Islands		577-581
St. Helena		821-823
St. Lucia		1171-1173
Tokelau		320-322
Tristan da Cunha		732-734
Virgin Islands		1004-1006

Nos. 823-825 (3)	12.50	12.50
Nos. 1073-1075 (3)	13.00	13.00
Nos. 866-868 (2)	14.25	14.25
Nos. 323-325 (3)	23.00	23.00
Nos. 262-264 (3)	28.00	28.00
Nos. 879-881 (3)	19.25	19.25
Nos. 970-972 (3)	10.00	10.00
Nos. 825-827 (3)	13.50	13.50
Nos. 577-581 (5)	14.40	14.40
Nos. 821-823 (3)	7.25	7.25
Nos. 1171-1173 (3)	8.75	8.75
Nos. 320-322 (3)	17.25	17.25
Nos. 732-734 (3)	16.75	16.75
Nos. 1004-1006 (3)	25.00	25.00
Set total (43) Stamps	222.90	222.90

Prince William, 21st Birthday

CD364

2003

Ascension		826
British Indian Ocean Territory		265
Cayman Islands		882-884
Falkland Islands		829
South Georgia		295
Tokelau		323
Tristan da Cunha		735
Virgin Islands		1007-1009

No. 826 (1)	7.25	7.25
No. 265 (1)	8.00	8.00
Nos. 882-884 (3)	6.95	6.95
No. 829 (1)	13.50	13.50
No. 295 (1)	8.50	8.50
No. 323 (1)	7.25	7.25
No. 735 (1)	6.00	6.00
Nos. 1007-1009 (3)	10.00	10.00
Set total (12) Stamps	67.45	67.45

British Commonwealth of Nations

Dominions, Colonies, Territories, Offices and Independent Members

Comprising stamps of the British Commonwealth and associated nations.

A strict observance of technicalities would bar some or all of the stamps listed under Burma, Ireland, Kuwait, Nepal, New Republic, Orange Free State, Samoa, South Africa, South-West Africa, Stellaland, Sudan, Swaziland, the two Transvaal Republics and others but these are included for the convenience of collectors.

1. Great Britain

Great Britain: Including England, Scotland, Wales and Northern Ireland.

2. The Dominions, Present and Past

AUSTRALIA

The Commonwealth of Australia was proclaimed on Jan. 1, 1901. It consists of six former colonies as follows:

New South Wales	Victoria
Queensland	Tasmania
South Australia	Western Australia

The following islands and territories are, or have been, administered by Australia: Australian Antarctic Territory, Christmas Island, Cocos (Keeling) Islands, Nauru, New Guinea, Norfolk Island, Papua.

CANADA

The Dominion of Canada was created by the British North America Act in 1867. The following provinces were former separate colonies and issued postage stamps:

British Columbia and Vancouver Island	Newfoundland
New Brunswick	Nova Scotia
	Prince Edward Island

FIJI

The colony of Fiji became an independent nation with dominion status on Oct. 10, 1970.

GHANA

This state came into existence March 6, 1957, with dominion status. It consists of the former colony of the Gold Coast and the Trusteeship Territory of Togoland. Ghana became a republic July 1, 1960.

INDIA

The Republic of India was inaugurated on Jan. 26, 1950. It succeeded the Dominion of India which was proclaimed Aug. 15, 1947, when the former Empire of India was divided into Pakistan and the Union of India. The Republic is composed of about 40 predominantly Hindu states of three classes: governor's provinces, chief commissioner's provinces and princely states. India also has various territories, such as the Andaman and Nicobar Islands.

The old Empire of India was a federation of British India and the native states. The more important princely states were autonomous. Of the more than 700 Indian states, these 43 are familiar names to philatelists because of their postage stamps.

CONVENTION STATES

Chamba	Jhind
Faridkot	Nabha
Gwalior	Patiala

FEUDATORY STATES

Alwar	Jammu and Kashmir
Bahawalpur	Jasdan
Bamra	Jhalawar
Barwani	Jhind (1875-76)
Bhopal	Kashmir
Bhor	Kishangarh
Bijawar	Kotah
Bundi	Las Bela
Bussahir	Morvi
Charkhari	Nandgaon
Cochin	Nowanuggur
Dhar	Orchha
Dungarpur	Poonch
Duttia	Rajasthan
Faridkot (1879-85)	Rajpeepla
Hyderabad	Sirmur
Idar	Soruth
Indore	Tonk
Jaipur	Travancore
Jammu	Wadhwan

NEW ZEALAND

Became a dominion on Sept. 26, 1907. The following islands and territories are, or have been, administered by New Zealand:

Aitutaki	Ross Dependency
Cook Islands (Rarotonga)	Samoa (Western Samoa)
Niue	Tokelau Islands
Penrhyn	

PAKISTAN

The Republic of Pakistan was proclaimed March 23, 1956. It succeeded the Dominion which was proclaimed Aug. 15, 1947. It is made up of all or part of several Moslem provinces and various districts of the former Empire of India, including Bahawalpur and Las Bela. Pakistan withdrew from the Commonwealth in 1972.

SOUTH AFRICA

Under the terms of the South African Act (1909) the self-governing colonies of Cape of Good Hope, Natal, Orange River Colony and Transvaal united on May 31, 1910, to form the Union of South Africa. It became an independent republic May 3, 1961.

Under the terms of the Treaty of Versailles, South-West Africa, formerly German South-West Africa, was mandated to the Union of South Africa.

SRI LANKA (CEYLON)

The Dominion of Ceylon was proclaimed Feb. 4, 1948. The island had been a Crown Colony from 1802 until then. On May 22, 1972, Ceylon became the Republic of Sri Lanka.

3. Colonies, Past and Present; Controlled Territory and Independent Members of the Commonwealth

Abu Dhabi	Barbuda
Aden	Basutoland
Aitutaki	Batum
Alderney	Bechuanaland
Anguilla	Bechuanaland Prot.
Antigua	Belize
Ascension	Bermuda
Australia	Botswana
Bahamas	British Antarctic Territory
Bahrain	British Central Africa
Bangladesh	British Columbia and
Barbados	Vancouver Island

British East Africa
British Guiana
British Honduras
British Indian Ocean Territory
British New Guinea
British Solomon Islands
British Somaliland
Brunei
Burma
Bushire
Cameroons
Canada
Cape of Good Hope
Cayman Islands
Christmas Island
Cocos (Keeling) Islands
Cook Islands
Crete,
  British Administration
Cyprus
Dominica
East Africa & Uganda
  Protectorates
Egypt
Falkland Islands
Fiji
Gambia
German East Africa
Ghana
Gibraltar
Gilbert Islands
Gilbert & Ellice Islands
Gold Coast
Grenada
Griqualand West
Guernsey
Guyana
Heligoland
Hong Kong
Indian Native States
  (see India)
Ionian Islands
Jamaica
Jersey

Jordan
Kenya
Kenya, Uganda & Tanzania
Kiribati
Kuwait
Labuan
Lagos
Leeward Islands
Lesotho
Madagascar
Malawi
Malaya
  Federated Malay States
  Johore
  Kedah
  Kelantan
  Malacca
  Negri Sembilan
  Pahang
  Penang
  Perak
  Perlis
  Selangor
  Singapore
  Sungei Ujong
  Trengganu
Malaysia
Maldive Islands
Malta
Man, Isle of
Mauritius
Mesopotamia
Montserrat
Mozambique
Muscat
Namibia
Natal
Nauru
Nevis
New Britain
New Brunswick
Newfoundland
New Guinea
New Hebrides

New Republic
New South Wales
New Zealand
Niger Coast Protectorate
Nigeria
Niue
Norfolk Island
North Borneo
Northern Nigeria
Northern Rhodesia
North West Pacific Islands
Nova Scotia
Nyasaland Protectorate
Oman
Orange River Colony
Pakistan
Palestine
Papua New Guinea
Penrhyn Island
Pitcairn Islands
Prince Edward Island
Qatar
Queensland
Rhodesia
Rhodesia & Nyasaland
Ross Dependency
Rwanda
Sabah
St. Christopher
St. Helena
St. Kitts
St. Kitts-Nevis-Anguilla
St. Lucia
St. Vincent
Samoa
Sarawak
Seychelles
Sierra Leone
Singapore
Solomon Islands
Somaliland Protectorate
South Africa
South Arabia
South Australia

South Georgia
Southern Nigeria
Southern Rhodesia
South-West Africa
Sri Lanka
Stellaland
Straits Settlements
Sudan
Swaziland
Tanganyika
Tanzania
Tasmania
Tobago
Togo
Tokelau Islands
Tonga
Transvaal
Trinidad
Trinidad and Tobago
Tristan da Cunha
Trucial States
Turks and Caicos
Turks Islands
Tuvalu
Uganda
United Arab Emirates
Vanuatu
Victoria
Virgin Islands
Western Australia
Zambia
Zanzibar
Zimbabwe
Zululand

**POST OFFICES IN
FOREIGN COUNTRIES**
Africa
  East Africa Forces
  Middle East Forces
Bangkok
China
Morocco
Turkish Empire

Colonies, former colonies, offices, territories controlled by parent states

Belgium
Belgian Congo
Ruanda-Urundi

Denmark
Danish West Indies
Faroe Islands
Greenland
Iceland

Finland
Aland Islands

France

COLONIES PAST AND PRESENT, CONTROLLED TERRITORIES
Afars & Issas, Territory of
Alaouites
Alexandretta
Algeria
Alsace & Lorraine
Anjouan
Annam & Tonkin
Benin
Cambodia (Khmer)
Cameroun
Castellorizo
Chad
Cilicia
Cochin China
Comoro Islands
Dahomey
Diego Suarez
Djibouti (Somali Coast)
Fezzan
French Congo
French Equatorial Africa
French Guiana
French Guinea
French India
French Morocco
French Polynesia (Oceania)
French Southern & Antarctic Territories
French Sudan
French West Africa
Gabon
Germany
Ghadames
Grand Comoro
Guadeloupe
Indo-China
Inini
Ivory Coast
Laos
Latakia
Lebanon
Madagascar
Martinique
Mauritania
Mayotte
Memel
Middle Congo
Moheli
New Caledonia
New Hebrides
Niger Territory

Nossi-Be
Obock
Reunion
Rouad, Ile
Ste.-Marie de Madagascar
St. Pierre & Miquelon
Senegal
Senegambia & Niger
Somali Coast
Syria
Tahiti
Togo
Tunisia
Ubangi-Shari
Upper Senegal & Niger
Upper Volta
Viet Nam
Wallis & Futuna Islands

POST OFFICES IN FOREIGN COUNTRIES
China
Crete
Egypt
Turkish Empire
Zanzibar

Germany

EARLY STATES
Baden
Bavaria
Bergedorf
Bremen
Brunswick
Hamburg
Hanover
Lubeck
Mecklenburg-Schwerin
Mecklenburg-Strelitz
Oldenburg
Prussia
Saxony
Schleswig-Holstein
Wurttemberg

FORMER COLONIES
Cameroun (Kamerun)
Caroline Islands
German East Africa
German New Guinea
German South-West Africa
Kiauchau
Mariana Islands
Marshall Islands
Samoa
Togo

Italy

EARLY STATES
Modena
Parma
Romagna
Roman States
Sardinia
Tuscany
Two Sicilies
 Naples
 Neapolitan Provinces
 Sicily

FORMER COLONIES, CONTROLLED TERRITORIES, OCCUPATION AREAS
Aegean Islands
 Calimno (Calino)
 Caso
 Cos (Coo)
 Karki (Carchi)
 Leros (Lero)
 Lipso
 Nisiros (Nisiro)
 Patmos (Patmo)
 Piscopi
 Rodi (Rhodes)
 Scarpanto
 Simi
 Stampalia
Castellorizo
Corfu
Cyrenaica
Eritrea
Ethiopia (Abyssinia)
Fiume
Ionian Islands
 Cephalonia
 Ithaca
 Paxos
Italian East Africa
Libya
Oltre Giuba
Saseno
Somalia (Italian Somaliland)
Tripolitania

POST OFFICES IN FOREIGN COUNTRIES
"ESTERO"*
Austria
China
 Peking
 Tientsin
Crete
Tripoli
Turkish Empire
 Constantinople
 Durazzo
 Janina
Jerusalem
Salonika
Scutari
Smyrna
Valona
*Stamps overprinted "ESTERO" were used in various parts of the world.

Netherlands
Aruba
Caribbean Netherlands
Curacao
Netherlands Antilles (Curacao)
Netherlands Indies
Netherlands New Guinea
St. Martin
Surinam (Dutch Guiana)

Portugal

COLONIES PAST AND PRESENT, CONTROLLED TERRITORIES
Angola
Angra
Azores

Cape Verde
Funchal
Horta
Inhambane
Kionga
Lourenco Marques
Macao
Madeira
Mozambique
Mozambique Co.
Nyassa
Ponta Delgada
Portuguese Africa
Portuguese Congo
Portuguese Guinea
Portuguese India
Quelimane
St. Thomas & Prince Islands
Tete
Timor
Zambezia

Russia

ALLIED TERRITORIES AND REPUBLICS, OCCUPATION AREAS
Armenia
Aunus (Olonets)
Azerbaijan
Batum
Estonia
Far Eastern Republic
Georgia
Karelia
Latvia
Lithuania
North Ingermanland
Ostland
Russian Turkestan
Siberia
South Russia
Tannu Tuva
Transcaucasian Fed. Republics
Ukraine
Wenden (Livonia)
Western Ukraine

Spain

COLONIES PAST AND PRESENT, CONTROLLED TERRITORIES
Aguera, La
Cape Juby
Cuba
Elobey, Annobon & Corisco
Fernando Po
Ifni
Mariana Islands
Philippines
Puerto Rico
Rio de Oro
Rio Muni
Spanish Guinea
Spanish Morocco
Spanish Sahara
Spanish West Africa

POST OFFICES IN FOREIGN COUNTRIES
Morocco
Tangier
Tetuan

Dies of British colonial stamps

DIE A:

1. The lines in the groundwork vary in thickness and are not uniformly straight.

2. The seventh and eighth lines from the top, in the groundwork, converge where they meet the head.

3. There is a small dash in the upper part of the second jewel in the band of the crown.

4. The vertical color line in front of the throat stops at the sixth line of shading on the neck.

DIE B:

1. The lines in the groundwork are all thin and straight.

2. All the lines of the background are parallel.

3. There is no dash in the upper part of the second jewel in the band of the crown.

4. The vertical color line in front of the throat stops at the eighth line of shading on the neck.

DIE I:

1. The base of the crown is well below the level of the inner white line around the vignette.

2. The labels inscribed "POSTAGE" and "REVENUE" are cut square at the top.

3. There is a white "bud" on the outer side of the main stem of the curved ornaments in each lower corner.

4. The second (thick) line below the country name has the ends next to the crown cut diagonally.

DIE II:

1. The base of the crown is aligned with the underside of the white line around the vignette.

2. The labels curve inward at the top inner corners.

3. The "bud" has been removed from the outer curve of the ornaments in each corner.

4. The second line below the country name has the ends next to the crown cut vertically.

DIE Ia.	DIE Ib.
1 as die II.	1 and 3 as die II.
2 and 3 as die I.	2 as die I.

Wmk. 1
Crown and C C

Wmk. 2
Crown and C A

Wmk. 3
Multiple Crown
and C A

Wmk. 4
Multiple Crown
and Script C A

Wmk. 4a

Wmk. 46

Wmk. 314
St. Edward's Crown
and C A Multiple

Wmk. 373

Wmk. 384

Wmk. 406

British Colonial and Crown Agents watermarks

Watermarks 1 to 4, 314, 373, 384 and 406, common to many British territories, are illustrated here to avoid duplication.

The letters "CC" of Wmk. 1 identify the paper as having been made for the use of the Crown Colonies, while the letters "CA" of the others stand for "Crown Agents." Both Wmks. 1 and 2 were used on stamps printed by De La Rue & Co.

Wmk. 3 was adopted in 1904; Wmk. 4 in 1921; Wmk. 46 in 1879; Wmk. 314 in 1957; Wmk. 373 in 1974; Wmk. 384 in 1985; Wmk 406 in 2008.

In Wmk. 4a, a non-matching crown of the general St. Edwards type (bulging on both sides at top) was substituted for one of the Wmk. 4 crowns which fell off the dandy roll. The non-matching crown occurs in 1950-52 printings in a horizontal row of crowns on certain regular stamps of Johore and Seychelles, and on various postage due stamps of Barbados, Basutoland, British Guiana, Gold Coast, Grenada, Northern Rhodesia, St. Lucia, Swaziland and Trinidad and Tobago. A variation of Wmk. 4a, with the non-matching crown in a horizontal row of crown-CA-crown, occurs on regular stamps of Bahamas, St. Kitts-Nevis and Singapore.

Wmk. 314 was intentionally used sideways, starting in 1966. When a stamp was issued with Wmk. 314 both upright and sideways, the sideways varieties usually are listed also — with minor numbers. In many of the later issues, Wmk. 314 is slightly visible.

Wmk. 373 is usually only faintly visible.

UNITED STATES

yu-ˌnī-təd ˈstāts

GOVT. — Republic
AREA — 3,615,211 sq. mi.
POP. — 308,745,538 (2010)
CAPITAL — Washington, DC

In addition to the 50 States and the District of Columbia, the Republic includes Guam, the Commonwealth of Puerto Rico, the Virgin Islands, American Samoa, Wake, Midway, and a number of small islands in the Pacific Ocean, all of which use stamps of the United States.

100 Cents = 1 Dollar

Catalogue values for unused stamps in this country are for Never Hinged items, beginning with Scott 772 in the regular postage section, Scott C19 in the air post section, Scott E17 in the special delivery section, Scott FA1 in the certified mail section, Scott O127 in officials section, Scott J88 in the postage due section, Scott RW1 in the hunting permit stamps section.

Watermarks

Wmk. 190 — "USPS" in Single-lined Capitals

Wmk. 191 — Double-lined "USPS" in Capitals

Watermark 191 has 9 letters for each horizontal row of 10 stamps. Watermark 190 has 8 to 9 letters for each horizontal row. Each watermark has 9 letters for each vertical row of 10 stamps. This results in a number of stamps in each pane showing only a small portion of 1 or more watermark letters. This is especialy true of watermark 190.

Wmk. 190PI — PIPS, used in the Philippines
Wmk. 191PI — PIPS, used in the Philippines
Wmk. 191C — US-C, used for Cuba
Wmk. 191R — USIR

PROVISIONAL ISSUES BY POSTMASTERS

Values for Envelopes are for entires.

ALEXANDRIA, VA.

A1

A2

All known examples are cut to shape.
Type I — 40 asterisks in circle.
Type II — 39 asterisks in circle.

1846		Typeset		Imperf.
1X1	A1	5c black, *buff,* type I		325,000.
a.		5c black, *buff,* type II		625,000.
1X2	A2	5c black, *blue,* type I, on cover		1,180,000.

ANNAPOLIS, MD.

E1

1846

2XU1	E1	5c carmine red, *white*		500,000.

Handstamped impressions of the circular design with "2" in blue or red exist on envelopes and letter sheets. Values: blue $17,500, red $30,000.
A letter sheet exists with circular design and "5" handstamped in red. Values: blue $10,000, red $12,500.
A similar circular design in blue was used as a postmark.

BALTIMORE, MD.

Signature of Postmaster — A1

Printed from a plate of 12 (2x6) containing nine 5c stamps and three 10c.

1845		Engr.		Imperf.
3X1	A1	5c black		6,000.
3X2	A1	10c black, on cover		80,000.
3X3	A1	5c black, *bluish*	65,000.	6,000.
3X4	A1	10c black, *bluish*		50,000.

Nos. 3X1-3X4 were printed from a plate of 12 (2x6) containing nine 5c and three 10c.

Envelopes

E1

The color given is that of the "PAID 5" and oval. "James M. Buchanan" is handstamped in black, blue or red. The paper is manila, buff, white, salmon or grayish.

1845			Handstamped
		Various Papers	
3XU1	E1	5c blue	4,500.
3XU2	E1	5c red	10,000.
3XU3	E1	10c blue	20,000.
3XU4	E1	10c red	20,000.

On the formerly listed "5+5" envelopes, the second "5" in oval is believed not to be part of the basic prepaid marking.

BOSCAWEN, N. H.

A1

1846 (?)		Typeset		Imperf.
4X1	A1	5c dull blue, *yellowish,* on cover		300,000.

BRATTLEBORO, VT.

Initials of Postmaster (FNP) — A1

Plate of 10 (5x2).

1846				Imperf.
	Thick Softwove Paper Colored Through			
5X1	A1	5c black, *buff*		7,500.

LOCKPORT, N. Y.

A1

"Lockport, N.Y." oval and "PAID" separately handstamped in red, "5" in black ms.

1846				Imperf.
6X1	A1	5c red, *buff,* on cover		120,000.

MILLBURY, Mass.

George Washington — A1

Printed from a woodcut, singly, on a hand press.

1846				Imperf.
7X1	A1	5c black, *bluish*	—	50,000.

NEW HAVEN, CONN.

ENVELOPES

E1

Impressed from a brass handstamp at upper right of envelope.
Signed in blue, black or magenta ms., as indicated in parentheses.

1845

8XU1	E1	5c red (M)		100,000.
8XU2	E1	5c red, *light bluish* (Bk)		125,000.
8XU3	E1	5c dull blue, *buff* (Bl)		75,000.
8XU4	E1	5c dull blue (Bl)		60,000.

Values of Nos. 8XU1-8XU4 are a guide to value. They are based on auction realizations and other sales, and take condition into consideration. All New Haven envelopes are of

---

equal rarity (each is unique), with the exception of No. 8XU2, of which two exist. An entire of No. 8XU2 is the finest example known, and this is reflected in the value shown. The other envelopes are valued according to condition, and cut squares also are valued according to condition as much as rarity.

Reprints were made at various times between 1871 and 1932. They can be distinguished from the originals, primarily due to differences in paper. See the Scott Specialized Catalogue of United States Stamps and Covers for more detail and values.

NEW YORK, N. Y.

George Washington — A1

Plate of 40 (5x8). Nos. 9X1-9X3 and varieties unused are valued without gum. Examples with original gum are extremely scarce and will command higher prices.

9X1	A1	5c black, signed ACM, connected, *1846*	1,500.	450.
a.		Signed ACM, AC connected	1,750.	550.
b.		Signed A.C.M.	4,500.	675.
c.		Signed MMJr		10,000.
d.		Signed RHM	13,000.	3,500.
e.		Without signature	3,750.	900.

These stamps were usually initialed "ACM" in magenta ink, as a control, before being sold or passed through the mails.
A plate of 9 (3x3) was made from which proofs were printed in black on white and deep blue papers; also in blue, green, brown and red on white bond paper. Stamps from this plate were not issued, and it is possible that it is an essay, as the design differs slightly from the issued stamps from the sheet of 40. No examples from the plate of nine are known used.

1847		Engr.		Imperf.
		Blue Wove Paper		
9X2	A1	5c black, signed ACM connected	6,500.	3,750.
a.		Signed RHM		
b.		Signed ACM, AC connected		8,000.
d.		Without signature	25,000.	7,500.

All used true blue examples carry "ACM" without periods; of the three unused examples, two lack initials.
On the only example known of No. 9X2a the "R" is illegible and does not match those of the other "RHM" signatures.
No. 9X2b is unique.

1847		Engr.		Imperf.
		Gray Wove Paper		
9X3	A1	5c black, signed ACM connected	5,250.	2,250.
a.		Signed RHM		8,500.
b.		Without signature		13,000.

PROVIDENCE, R. I.

A1 & A2

10X1	A1	5c gray black	350.	2,250.
10X2	A2	10c gray black	1,150.	16,500.
a.		Se-tenant with 5c	2,000.	

Plate of 12 (3x4) contains 11-5c and 1-10c.
Reprints were made in 1898. Each stamp bears one of the following letters on the back: B. O. G. E. R. T. D. U. R. B. I. N. Value of 5c, $65; 10c, $160; sheet, $1,000.
Reprint singles or sheets without back print sell for more.

ST. LOUIS, MO.

A1

A2

Missouri Coat of Arms — A3

Nos. 11X1-11X8 unused are valued without gum.

Wove Paper Colored Through

1845, Nov.-1846   *Imperf.*

11X1	A1	5c black, greenish	50,000.	8,000.
11X2	A2	10c black, greenish	50,000.	8,000.
11X3	A3	20c black, greenish	160,000.	

Printed from Plate 1 (3 varieties each of the 5c and 10c) and Plate 2 (1 variety of the 5c, 3 of the 10c, 2 of the 20c).

1846

11X4	A1	5c black, (III), gray lilac	—	55,000.
11X5	A2	10c black, gray lilac	50,000.	12,500.
11X6	A3	20c black, gray lilac	100,000.	60,000.

One variety of 5c, 3 of 10c, 2 of 20c.
No. 11X6 unused is unique. It is in the grade of fine and valued thus.

1847   **Pelure Paper**

11X7	A1	5c black, bluish	—	11,000.
11X8	A2	10c black, bluish	17,500.	15,000.
a.		Impression of 5c on back		77,500.

Three varieties of 5c, 3 of 10c.
Values of Nos. 11X7-11X8 reflect the usual poor condition of these stamps, which were printed on fragile pelure paper. Attractive examples with minor defects sell for considerably more.
Used values are for pen-canceled stamps.
No. 11X8a is unique.

Please Note:

Stamps are valued in the grade of very fine unless otherwise indicated.
Values for early and valuable stamps are for examples with certificates of authenticity from acknowledged expert committees, or examples sold with the buyer having the right of certification. This applies to examples with original gum as well as examples without gum. Beware of stamps offered "as is," as the gum on some unused stamps offered with "original gum" may be fraudulent, and stamps offered as unused without gum may in some cases be altered or faintly canceled used stamps.

Manuscript Cancels on Used Stamps

Manuscript (pen) cancels reduce the value of used stamps by about 50%. See the Scott U.S. Specialized Catalogue for individual valuations.

GENERAL ISSUES
All Issues from 1847 through 1894 are unwatermarked.

Benjamin Franklin — A1

1847, July 1   **Engr.**   *Imperf.*
Thin Bluish Wove Paper

1	A1	5c red brown	6,000.	350.
		No gum	2,100.	
a.		5c dark brown	7,000.	450.
		No gum	2,400.	
b.		5c orange brown	10,000.	675.
		No gum	3,500.	
c.		5c red orange	25,000.	8,500.
		No gum	9,500.	
d.		5c brown orange	—	1,000.
		No gum	4,500.	

George Washington — A2

2	A2	10c black	35,000.	750.
		No gum	15,000.	

REPRODUCTIONS of 1847 ISSUE

A3

A4

Actually, official imitations made from new plates of 50 subjects made by the Bureau of Engraving and Printing by order of the Post Office Department. These were not valid for postal use.

5c. On the originals the left side of the white shirt frill touches the oval on a level with the top of the "F" of "Five." On the reproductions it touches the oval about on a level with the top of the figure "5." On the originals, the bottom of the right leg of the "N" in "CENTS" is blunt. On the reproductions, the "N" comes to a point at the bottom.

10c. On the reproductions, line of coat at left points to right tip of "X" and line of coat at right points to center of "S" of CENTS. On the originals, line of coat points to "T" of TEN and between "T" and "S" of CENTS. The bottom of the right leg of the "N" of "CENTS" shows the same difference as on the 5c originals and reproductions. On the reproductions, the gap between the bottom legs of the left "X" is noticeably wider than the gap on the right "X." On the originals, the gaps are of equal width. On the reproductions, the eyes have a sleepy look, the line of the mouth is straighter, and in the curl of hair near the left cheek is a strong black dot, while the originals have only a faint one.

(See Nos. 948a and 948b for 1947 reproductions — 5c blue and 10c brown orange in larger size.)

1875   *Imperf.*
Bluish paper, without gum

3	A3	5c red brown	900.
4	A4	10c black	1,150.

Numbers in parentheses are quantities sold.

Except as noted here and in footnotes for selected issues, values for 1851-57 issues are for examples that clearly show all of the illustrated type characteristics. Stamps that have weakly defined or missing type characteristics sell for less.
In Nos. 5-17, the 1¢, 3¢ and 12¢ have very small margins between the stamps. The 5¢ and 10¢ have moderate size margins. The values of these stamps take the margin size into consideration.
Values for Nos. 5A, 6b and 19b are for the less distinct positions. Best examples sell for more.
Values for No. 16 are for outer line recut at top. Other recuts sell for more.

Franklin — A5

Type I

Type Ib

ONE CENT
Type I. Has complete curved lines outside the labels with "U. S. Postage" and "One Cent." The scrolls below the lower label are turned under, forming little balls. The ornaments at top are substantially complete.
Type Ib. As type I, but balls below bottom label are not as clear. Plume-like scrolls at bottom are incomplete.

1851-57   *Imperf.*

5	A5	1c blue, type I (7R1E)	125,000.	55,000.
5A	A5	1c blue, type 1b	32,500.	6,750.
		No gum	12,000.	

A6

Type Ic

Type Ia. Same as type I at bottom, but top ornaments and outer line at top are partly cut away.
Type Ic. Same as type Ia, but bottom right plume and ball ornament incomplete. Bottom left plume is complete or nearly complete.

6	A6	1c blue, type 1a ('57)	45,000.	9,250.
		No gum	20,000.	
6b	A6	1c blue, type 1c	7,000.	3,500.
		No gum	3,000.	

A7

Type II — Same as Type I at top, but the little balls of the bottom scrolls and the bottoms of the lower plume ornaments are missing. The side ornaments are substantially complete.

7	A7	1c blue, type II	1,000.	135.
		No gum		375.

A8

It takes a team of philately's most qualified professionals
to create the finest auction catalog ever produced.

Put us to work for you.

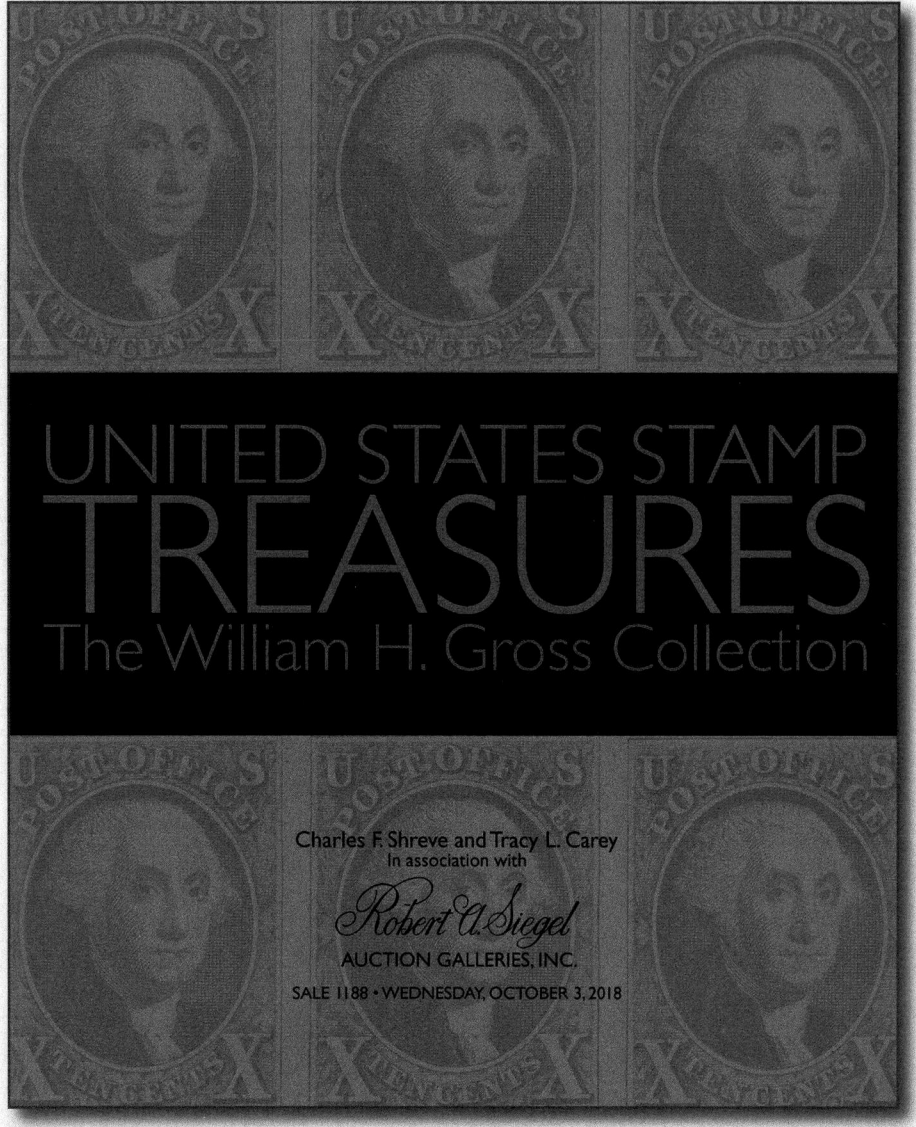

To discuss the sale of your U.S. stamps or postal history, call Scott Trepel at 212-753-6421.
If you have a worldwide collection, call Charles Shreve at 214-754-5991.

Robert A. Siegel

AUCTION GALLERIES, INC.

siegelauctions.com

Type IIIa

Type III. The top and bottom curved lines outside the labels are broken in the middle. The side ornaments are substantially complete.

Type IIIa. Similar to type III with the outer line broken at top or bottom but not both.

8   A8   1c blue, type
             III   25,000.   1,500.
        No gum   7,500.

Values for type III are for at least a 2mm break in each outer line. Examples of type III with wider breaks in outer lines command higher prices; those with smaller breaks sell for much less.

8A A8   1c blue, type
             IIIa   6,000.   800.
        No gum   2,250.

Stamps of type IIIa with bottom line broken command higher prices than those with top line broken. See note after No. 8 on width of break of outer lines.

A9

Type IV. Similar to type II, but with the curved lines outside the labels recut at top or bottom or both.

9   A9   1c blue, type
             IV ('52)   725.00   95.00
        No gum   240.00
  a.   Printed on both sides,
        reverse inverted   50,000.

        No. 9a is unique.

The No. 9b cover, a printed-matter circular mailed in 1853, is unique. The circular likely should have been sent at the 1c rate for printed matter in effect at the time. However, both the sending (New Haven, Conn.) and receiving (Hartford, Conn.) post offices treated it as fully prepaid with ½c postage applied. Value is based on 2013 auction realization.

Washington — A10

All of the 3c stamps of the 1851 and 1857 issues were recut at least to the extent of the outer frame lines, sometimes the inner lines at the sides (type II stamps), and often other lines in triangles, diamond blocks, label blocks and/or top/bottom frame lines. Some of the most prominent varieties are listed below each major listing (others are described in "The 3c Stamp of U.S. 1851-57 Issue," by Carroll Chase).

OUTER FRAME LINE

Type I

THREE CENTS

Type I — There is an outer frame line on all four sides. The outer frame lines at the sides are always recut.

10 A10 3c org brown,
             type I   4,000.   185.00
        No gum   1,500.

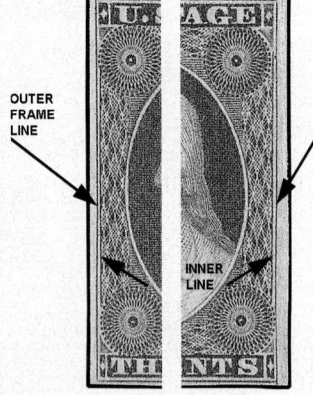

OUTER FRAME LINE

INNER LINE

Type II

Type II — As type I, but with the inner lines at the sides added by recutting on the plate.

10A A10 3c org brown,
             type II   3,500.   150.00
        No gum   1,350.
  b.   Printed on both sides   55,000.

Only one example of No. 10Ab is recorded.

11 A10 3c dull red,
             type I
             ('55)   250.00   17.50
        No gum   100.00
11A A10 3c dull red,
             type II
             ('53-'55)   250.00   15.00
        No gum   85.00
  e.   Double impression   30,000.

Thomas Jefferson — A11

FIVE CENTS

Type I — Projections on all four sides.

12 A11 5c red brown,
             type I
             ('56)   30,000.   750.00
        No gum   11,000.

Washington — A12

A13

TEN CENTS

Type I — The "shells" at the lower corners are practically complete. The outer line below the label is very nearly complete. The outer lines are broken above the middle of the top label and the "X" in each upper corner.

13 A12 10c green, type
             I ('55)   19,000.   750.
        No gum   8,500.

Type II — The design is complete at the top. The outer line at the bottom is broken in the middle. The shells are partly cut away, as shown.

14 A13 10c green, type
             II ('55)   5,000.   145.
        No gum   1,800.

A14

Type III — The outer lines are broken above the top label and the "X" numerals. The outer line at the bottom and the shells are partly cut away, as shown, similar to type II.

15 A14 10c green, type
             III ('55)   5,000.   145.
        No gum   1,800.

A15

Type IV. The outer lines have been recut at top or bottom or both.

Types I, II, III and IV have complete ornaments at the sides of the stamps and three pearls at each outer edge of the bottom panel.

16 A15 10c green, type
             IV ('55)   37,500.   1,600.
        No gum   20,000.

Washington — A16

17 A16 12c gray black   6,250.   250.
        No gum   2,100.
  c.   Printed on both sides   40,000.

Values for 1857-61 issues are for examples that clearly show all the illustrated type characteristics. Stamps that have weakly defined or missing type characteristics sell for less.

Nos. 18-39 have small or very small margins. The values take into account the margin size. See footnotes for more specific information on selected issues.

SAME DESIGNS AS 1851-57 ISSUES
1857-61   *Perf. 15½*

18 A5   1c blue, type I
             ('61)   2,100.   475.
        No gum   800.
             short ornaments at ei-
             ther top or bottom   —
19 A6   1c blue, type Ia   42,500.   9,000.
        No gum   20,000.
  b.   blue, type Ic   4,250.   3,500.
        No gum   1,750.
20 A7   1c blue, type II   850.   275.
        No gum   375.
21 A8   1c blue, type III   17,500.   1,500.
        No gum   6,000.
  a.   Horiz. pair, imperf. be-
        tween   20,000.
22 A8   1c blue, type
             IIIa   2,200.   475.
        No gum   825.

Beware of pairs of No. 22 with faint blind perforations between that sometimes are offered as pairs imperf. between.

23 A9   1c blue, type IV   10,000.   550.
        No gum   4,250.

Franklin — A20

Type V — Similar to type III of 1851-57 but with side ornaments partly cut away. About one-half of all positions have side scratches. Wide breaks in top and bottom framelines.

Type Va — Stamps from Plate 5 with almost complete ornaments at right side and no side scratches. Many, but not all, stamps from

Plate 5 are Type Va, the remainder being Type V.

24	A20	1c blue, type V	140.00	37.50
		No gum	60.00	
b.		Laid paper		7,500.
25	A10	3c rose, type I	2,750.	180.00
		No gum	950.	
b.		Vert. pair, imperf. horizontally		25,000.
25A	A10	3c rose, type II	9,000.	850.
		No gum	4,000.	

CONTINUOUS FRAME LINE — CONTINUOUS FRAME LINE

Washington Type III — A21

Type III — There are no outer frame lines at top and bottom. The side frame lines were recut so as to be continuous from the top to the bottom of the plate. **Stamps from the top or bottom rows show the ends of the side frame lines and may be mistaken for Type IV.**

26	A21	3c dull red, type III	65.00	10.00
		No gum	27.50	
b.		Horiz. pair, imperf. vertically	14,000.	
c.		Vert. pair, imperf. horizontally		16,000.
d.		Horizontal pair, imperf. between		
e.		Double impression	15,000.	

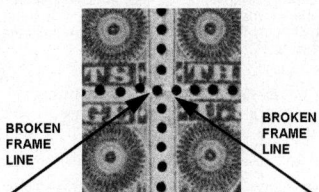

BROKEN FRAME LINE — BROKEN FRAME LINE

Washington Type IV — A21a

Type IV — As type III, but the side frame lines extend only to the top and bottom of the stamp design. All Type IV stamps are from plates 10 and 11 (each of which exists in three states), and these plates produced only Type IV. The side frame lines were recut individually for each stamp, thus being broken between the stamps vertically.

Beware of type III stamps with frame lines that stop at the top of the design (from top row of plate) or bottom of the design (from bottom row of plate). These are often mistakenly offered as No. 26A.

26A	A21a	3c dull red, type IV	600.00	150.00
		No gum	260.00	
f.		Horiz. strip of 3, imperf. vert., on cover		27,000.

No. 26Af is unique.

27	A11	5c brick red, type I ('58)	80,000.	1,450.
		No gum	20,000.	
		N.Y. Ocean Mail		+1,000.
28	A11	5c red brown, type I	60,000.	1,050.
		No gum	15,000.	
b.		Bright red brown	70,000.	2,250.
		No gum	20,000.	
28A	A11	5c Indian red, type I ('58)	160,000.	3,500.
		No gum	40,000.	

No. 28A unused is valued in the grade of fine. Only four examples are recorded with any amount of gum.

| 29 | A11 | 5c brown, type I ('59) | 5,500. | 325. |
| | | No gum | 1,750. | |

Jefferson — A22

FIVE CENTS.

Type II — The projections at top and bottom are partly cut away.

30	A22	5c orange brown, type II ('61)	1,200.	1,300.
		No gum	500.	
30A	A22	5c brown, type II ('60)	2,250.	300.
		No gum	850.	
b.		Printed on both sides		35,000.
31	A12	10c green, type I	35,000.	1,100.
		No gum	11,500.	
32	A13	10c green, type II	5,750.	190.
		No gum	2,000.	
33	A14	10c green, type III	5,750.	190.
		No gum	2,000.	
34	A15	10c green, type IV	50,000.	2,100.
		No gum	20,000.	

Example I   Example II

Washington (Two typical examples) — A23

TEN CENTS

Type V — The side ornaments are slightly cut away. Usually only one pearl remains at each end of the lower label, but some copies show two or three pearls at the right side. At the bottom the outer line is complete and the shells nearly so. The outer lines at top are complete except over the right "X."

| 35 | A23 | 10c green, type V ('59) | 210.00 | 55.00 |
| | | No gum | 95.00 | |

No. 36 outer frame lines recut on plate

TWELVE CENTS. Printed from two plates. Plate 1 (No. 36) — Outer frame lines were recut on the plate and are complete. Very narrow spacing of stamps on the plate.

36	A16	12c black (Plate 1)	1,700.	300.
		No gum	500.	
c.		Horizontal pair, imperf. between		12,500.

Typical No. 36B, outer frame lines not recut

Plate III (No. 36B) — Weak outer frame lines from the die were not recut and are noticeably uneven or broken, sometimes partly missing. Somewhat wider spacing of stamps on the plate.

| 36B | A16 | 12c black, plate III ('59) | 700. | 250. |
| | | No gum | 325. | |

Washington A17

Franklin A18

37	A17	24c gray lilac ('60)	1,450.	400.
a.		24c gray	1,450.	400.
		No gum	500.	
38	A18	30c orange ('60)	1,900.	450.
		No gum	700.	

Washington — A19

| 39 | A19 | 90c blue ('60) | 3,000. | 10,500. |
| | | No gum | 1,400. | |

See Die and Plate proofs in the Scott United States Specialized Catalogue for imperfs. of the 12c, 24c, 30c, 90c.

Genuine cancellations on the 90c are rare. Used examples must be accompanied by certificates of authenticity issued by recognized expertizing committees.

REPRINTS OF 1857-60 ISSUE
White paper, without gum.

1875				Perf. 12
40	A5	1c bright blue	600.	
41	A10	3c scarlet	2,850.	
42	A22	5c orange brown	1,200.	
43	A12	10c blue green	2,500.	13,000.
44	A16	12c greenish black	2,750.	
45	A17	24c blackish violet	3,000.	10,000.
46	A18	30c yellow orange	3,000.	
47	A19	90c deep blue	3,600.	

Nos. 41-46 are valued in the grade of fine.

Nos. 40-47 exist imperforate. Very infrequent sales preclude establishing a value at this time. One set of imperforate pairs is recorded and it sold for $110,000 in a 2009 auction.

Essays-Trial Color Proofs

The paper of former Nos. 55-62 (Nos. 63E11e, 65-E15h, 67-E9e, 69-E6e, 72-E7h, Essay section, Nos. 70eTC, 71bTC, Trial Color Proof section, Scott U.S. Specialized) is thin and semitransparent. That of the postage issues is thicker and more opaque, except Nos. 62B, 70c and 70d.

Franklin — A24

A24

Washington — A25

A25

Jefferson — A26

A26

Washington — A27

A27

A27a

Washington — A28

A28

Washington
A29

Franklin
A30

Washington — A31

A31

1c — There is a dash under the tip of the ornament at right of the numeral in upper left corner.

3c — Ornaments at corners end in a small ball.

5c — There is a leaflet in the foliated ornaments at each corner.

10c (A27) — A heavy curved line has been cut below the stars and an outer line added to the ornaments above them.

12c — There are corner ornaments consisting of ovals and scrolls.

90c — Parallel lines form an angle above the ribbon with "U. S. Postage"; between these lines there is a row of dashes and a point of color at the apex of the lower line.

1861   *Perf. 12*

62B	A27a	10c dark green	8,500.	1,700.
		No gum	3,600.	

1861-62   *Perf. 12*

63	A24	1c blue	275.00	45.00
		No gum	100.00	
a.		1c ultramarine	2,500.	1,900.
		No gum	1,000.	
b.		1c dark blue	800.00	875.00
		No gum	300.00	
c.		Laid paper, horiz. or vert.	8,500.	4,500.
d.		Vertical pair, imperf. horiz.	—	—
e.		Printed on both sides, reverse inverted	—	35,000.

The editors would like to see authenticated evidence of the existence of No. 63d.

64	A25	3c pink	14,000.	550.00
		No gum	5,000.	
a.		3c pigeon blood pink	50,000.	4,250.
		No gum	15,000.	
b.		3c rose pink, Aug. 17, 1861	600.00	140.00
		No gum	250.00	
65	A25	3c rose	125.00	3.00
		No gum	50.00	
b.		Laid paper, horiz. or vert.	—	1,100.
c.		Vertical pair, imperf. horiz.	12,500.	1,500.
		No gum	5,000.	
e.		Printed on both sides, reverse inverted	40,000.	8,000.
f.		Double impression	—	12,500.

The 3c lake can be found under No. 66 in the Trial Color Proofs section of the Scott U.S. Specialized Catalogue. The imperf 3c lake under No. 66P is in the same section. The imperf 3c rose can be found in the Die and Plate Proofs section of the Specialized.

67	A26	5c buff	27,500.	750.
		No gum	10,500.	
a.		5c brown yellow	30,000.	1,100.
		No gum	11,500.	
b.		5c olive yellow	—	4,750.

Values of Nos. 67, 67a, 67b reflect the normal small margins.

68	A27	10c green	950.	55.00
		No gum	375.	
a.		10c dark green	1,350.	85.00
		No gum	500.	
b.		Vertical pair, imperf. horiz.	—	30,000.
69	A28	12c black	1,700.	95.00
		No gum	675.	
70	A29	24c red lilac ('62)	3,000.	300.00
		No gum	1,150.	
a.		24c brown lilac	3,250.	325.00
		No gum	1,250.	
b.		24c steel blue ('61)	16,500.	825.00
		No gum	6,250.	
c.		24c violet, thin paper, Aug. 20, 1861	35,000.	2,250.
		reddish violet No gum	13,500.	
d.		24c pale gray violet, thin paper	25,000.	3,000.
		No gum	6,000.	

There are numerous shades of the 24c stamp in this and the following issue.

Color changelings, especially of No. 78, are frequently offered as No. 70b. Obtaining a certificate from an acknowledged expert committee is strongly advised.

Nos. 70c and 70d are on a thinner, harder and more transparent paper than Nos. 70, 70a, 70b or the latter Nos. 78, 78a, 78b and 78c.

71	A30	30c orange	2,600.	225.
		No gum	950.	
a.		Printed on both sides	—	—

Values for No. 71 are for examples with small margins, especially at sides. Large-margined examples sell for much more.

72	A31	90c blue	3,000.	600.
		No gum	1,200.	
a.		90c pale blue	3,000.	650.
		No gum	1,200.	
b.		90c dark blue	3,750.	950.
		No gum	1,500.	

Please Note:

Stamps are valued in the grade of very fine unless otherwise indicated.

Values for early and valuable stamps are for examples with certificates of authenticity from acknowledged expert committees, or examples sold with the buyer having the right of certification.

This applies to examples with original gum as well as examples without gum.

Beware of stamps offered "as is," as the gum on some unused stamps offered with "original gum" may be fraudulent, and stamps offered as unused without gum may in some cases be altered or faintly canceled used stamps.

DESIGNS AS 1861 ISSUE

Andrew
Jackson
A32

Abraham
Lincoln
A33

1861-66   *Perf. 12*

73	A32	2c black ('63)	350.00	55.00
		No gum	150.00	
f.		Printed on both sides, reverse not inverted	—	27,500.
g.		Laid paper	—	11,500.

No. 73f unused is unique. It has perfs cut off on two sides and is valued thus.

The 3c scarlet can be found under No. 74 in the Scott U.S. Specialized Catalogue Trial Color Proofs section.

75	A26	5c red brown ('62)	5,750.	425.
		No gum	2,100.	

Values for No. 75 reflect the normal small margins.

76	A26	5c brown ('63)	1,400.	125.
		No gum	550.	
a.		5c black brown	2,250.	400.
		No gum	850.	
b.		Laid paper	—	—

Values of Nos. 76, 76a reflect the normal small margins.

77	A33	15c black ('66)	5,000.	175.
		No gum	1,900.	
78	A29	24c lilac ('62)	2,750.	400.
		No gum	950.	
a.		24c grayish lilac	2,750.	425.
		No gum	950.	
b.		24c gray	2,750.	450.
		No gum	950.	
c.		24c blackish violet	95,000.	17,000.
		No gum	30,000.	

Only three examples are recorded of No. 78c unused with original gum. No. 78c unused with and without gum are valued in the grade of fine-very fine.

d.		Printed on both sides, reverse inverted	—	22,500.

SAME DESIGNS AS 1861-66 ISSUES

Grill

Embossed with grills of various sizes. Some authorities believe that more than one size of grill probably existed on one of the grill rolls.

A peculiarity of the United States issues from 1867 to 1870 is the grill or embossing. The object was to break the fiber of the paper so that the ink of the canceling stamp would soak in and make washing for a second using impossible. The exact date at which grilled stamps came into use is unsettled. Luff's "Postage Stamps of the United States" places the date as probably August 8, 1867.

Horizontal measurements are given first.

GRILL WITH POINTS UP

Grills A and C were made by a roller covered with ridges shaped like an inverted V. Pressing the ridges into the stamp paper forced the paper into the pyramidal pits between the ridges, causing irregular breaks in the paper. Grill B was made by a roller with raised bosses.

A. GRILL COVERING THE ENTIRE STAMP

1867-68   *Perf. 12*

79	A25	3c rose	8,500.	1,300.
		No gum	2,750.	
b.		Printed on both sides	—	—

Nos. 79, 79b, are valued for fine-very fine centering but with minor perforation faults.

An essay which is often mistaken for No. 79 (#79-E15) shows the points of the grill as small squares faintly impressed in the paper, but not cutting through it.

On No. 79 the grill breaks through the paper. Examples free from defects are rare.

80	A26	5c brown		400,000.
a.		5c dark brown		400,000.
81	A30	30c orange		225,000.

Four examples of Nos. 80 and 80a (two of each shade), and eight examples of No. 81 (one in the New York Public Library Miller collection and not available to collectors) are known. All are more or less faulty and/or off center. Values are for off-center examples with small perforation faults.

B. GRILL ABOUT 18x15mm (22x18 POINTS)

82	A25	3c rose	900,000.

The four known examples of No. 82 are valued in the grade of fine.

Earliest documented use: Feb. 1?, 1869 (dated cancel on off-cover stamp).

C. GRILL ABOUT 13x16mm (16 TO 17 BY 18 TO 21 POINTS)

The grilled area on each of four C grills in the sheet may total about 18x15mm when a normal C grill adjoins a fainter grill extending to the right or left edge of the stamp.

This is caused by a partial erasure on the grill roller when it was changed to produce C grills instead of the all-over A grill.

The imperf. can be found in the Scott U.S. Specialized Catalogue Die and Plate Proofs section.

83	A25	3c rose	5,500.	1,100.
		No gum	2,000.	

GRILL WITH POINTS DOWN

The grills were produced by rollers with the surface covered, or partly covered, by pyramidal bosses. On the D, E and F grills the tips of the pyramids are vertical ridges. On the Z grill the ridges are horizontal.

D. GRILL ABOUT 12x14mm (15 BY 18 TO 19 POINTS)

84	A32	2c black	16,000.	5,000.
		No gum	6,500.	

No. 84 is valued in the grade of fine.

85	A25	3c rose	8,000.	1,100.
		No gum	2,400.	

Z. GRILL ABOUT 11x14mm (14 TO 15 BY 17 OR 18 POINTS)

(1c, 10c, 15c 17 rows; 2c, 3c, 12c 18 rows)

85A	A24	1c blue		3,000,000.

Two examples of No. 85A are currently recorded. One is contained in the New York Public Library collection, which is on long-term loan to the Smithsonian National Postal Museum.

85B	A32	2c black	17,500.	1,100.
		No gum	6,750.	
85C	A25	3c rose	25,000.	3,250.
		No gum	9,000.	
85D	A27	10c green		750,000.

Six examples of No. 85D are known. One is contained in the New York Public Library collection. Value is for a well-centered example with small faults.

85E	A28	12c intense black	25,000.	2,300.
		No gum	8,500.	
85F	A33	15c black		2,000,000.

Two examples of No. 85F are documented, one in the grade of very good, the other extremely fine. Value is for the extremely fine example.

E. GRILL ABOUT 11x13mm (14 BY 16 TO 18 POINTS)

86	A24	1c blue	3,000.	450.
		No gum	1,100.	
a.		1c dull blue	3,000.	425.
		No gum	1,100.	
87	A32	2c black	1,700.	200.
		No gum	650.	
88	A25	3c rose	950.	30.00
		No gum	350.	
a.		3c lake red	1,250.	80.00
		No gum	475.	
89	A27	10c green	5,000.	325.
		No gum	2,000.	
90	A28	12c black	4,750.	375.
		No gum	1,900.	
91	A33	15c black	12,500.	575.
		No gum	4,500.	

F. GRILL ABOUT 9x13mm (12 BY 16 TO 18 POINTS)

92	A24	1c blue	2,800.	425.
		No gum	925.	
a.		1c pale blue	2,300.	375.
		No gum	700.	
93	A32	2c black	450.	55.00
		No gum	155.	
94	A25	3c red	350.	12.50
a.		3c rose	350.	12.50
		No gum	150.	
c.		Vertical pair, imperf. horiz.	15,000.	
d.		Printed on both sides	9,000.	42,500.

The imperf. 3c can be found in the Scott U.S. Specialized Catalogue Die and Plate Proofs section.

95	A26	5c brown	3,250.	850.
		No gum	1,250.	
a.		5c black brown	5,000.	2,300.
		No gum	2,000.	

Values of Nos. 95, 95a reflect the normal small margins.

96	A27	10c yel grn	2,500.	250.
97	A28	12c black	2,800.	250.
		No gum	1,000.	
98	A33	15c black	4,250.	275.
		No gum	1,600.	
99	A29	24c gray lilac	8,500.	1,500.
		No gum	3,250.	
100	A30	30c orange	9,000.	950.
		No gum	3,300.	

Values for No. 100 are for examples with small margins, especially at sides. Large-margined examples sell for much more.

101	A31	90c blue	14,500.	2,500.
		No gum	5,750.	

RE-ISSUE OF 1861-66 ISSUES
Without Grill, Hard White Paper
White Crackly Gum

1875   *Perf. 12*

102	A24	1c blue	750.	1,700.
		No gum	350.	
103	A32	2c black	3,500.	10,500.
		No gum	1,600.	
104	A25	3c brown red	3,750.	13,000.
		No gum	1,700.	
105	A26	5c brown	2,500.	6,000.
		No gum	1,150.	

106	A27	10c	green	2,900.	115,000.
	No gum			1,400.	
107	A28	12c	black	3,500.	12,000.
	No gum			1,600.	
108	A33	15c	black	4,500.	30,000.
	No gum			2,100.	
109	A29	24c	deep violet	6,000.	16,500.
	No gum			2,750.	
110	A30	30c	brownish org	5,750.	16,500.
	No gum			2,800.	
111	A31	90c	blue	7,000.	225,000.
	No gum			3,500.	

These stamps can be distinguished from the 1861-66 issues by the shades and the paper which is hard and very white instead of yellowish. The gum is white and crackly.

Franklin — A34

Post Horse and Rider — A35

G. Grill measuring 9½x9mm (12 by 11 to 11½ points)

1869   Hard Wove Paper   Perf. 12

112	A34	1c	buff	575.	130.
	No gum			210.	
b.	Without grill			32,500.	
113	A35	2c	brown	500.	80.
	No gum			190.	
b.	Without grill			14,000.	
d.	Printed on both sides				62,500.

Locomotive A36

Washington A37

114	A36	3c ultramarine	225.	16.00
	No gum		90.	
a.	Without grill		13,000.	18,000.
	Without grill, gray paper			3,750.
d.	Double impression		15,000.	
e.	Printed on both sides, reverse inverted			55,000.

Two examples recorded of No. 114a on normal paper: one with pen cancel but with original gum, 1994 Philatelic Foundation certificate; and one lifted from a cover, original gum adhering, examined, and placed back, 2011 Philatelic Foundation certificate. Also, four examples of No. 114a on gray paper: a single lifted from cover, examined, and hinged back in place, 1991 Philatelic Foundation certificate; and a strip of three on piece, mostly detached from piece, with full gum, 1978 and 2006 Philatelic Foundation certificates.

Nos. 114d and 114e each are unique. No. 114d has a pre-printing paper fold. The existence of a genuine example of No. 114d has been questioned by specialists. The editors would like to see evidence of its existence with an updated certificate.

115	A37	6c ultramarine	2,500.	225.
	No gum		1,000.	

Shield and Eagle — A38

S. S. Adriatic — A39

116	A38	10c yellow	1,850.	110.
	No gum		750.	
117	A39	12c green	1,850.	130.
	No gum		725.	

Landing of Columbus — A40

Type I. Picture unframed.
No. 118 has horizontal shading lines at the left and right sides of the vignette.

118	A40	15c brn & bl, type I	9,000.	825.
	No gum		3,250.	
a.	Without grill		11,500.	

A40a

No. 119 has diagonal shading lines at the left and right sides of the vignette.

119	A40a	15c brn & bl, type II	2,750.	190.
	No gum		975.	
b.	Center inverted		1,000,000.	22,500.
c.	Center double, one inverted		700,000.	80,000.

Declaration of Independence — A41

120	A41	24c green & violet	7,500.	600.
	No gum		2,700.	
a.	Without grill		14,000.	
b.	Center inverted		750,000.	37,500.

Shield, Eagle and Flags — A42

Lincoln — A43

121	A42	30c ultra & carmine	4,000.	375.
	No gum		1,450.	
a.	Without grill		10,000.	
b.	Flags inverted		750,000.	90,000.
	No gum		300,000.	

Seven examples of No. 121b unused are recorded. Only one has part of its original gum.

122	A43	90c carmine & black	11,000.	1,800.
	No gum		4,000.	
a.	Without grill		22,500.	

Values of varieties of Nos. 112-122 without grill are for examples with original gum.

Most examples of Nos. 119b, 120b are faulty. Values are for stamps with fine centering and only minimal faults. No. 120b unused is valued without gum, as all of the three examples available to collectors are without gum.

RE-ISSUE OF 1869 ISSUE
Without grill, hard white paper, with white crackly gum.

The gum is almost always somewhat yellowed with age, and unused stamps with original gum are valued with such gum.

A new plate of 150 subjects was made for the 1c. The plate for the frame of the 15c was made using the same die as that used to make the type I frame for No. 118. For No. 118, the lines on each side of the vignette area were entered onto the plate itself, one position at a time. Upon close examination, each stamp position will be found to exhibit minute differences in these horizontal fringe lines.

1875   Perf. 12

123	A34	1c buff	525.	425.
	No gum		220.	

124	A35	2c brown	600.	750.
	No gum		250.	
125	A36	3c blue	5,000.	27,500.
	No gum		2,500.	

Used value for No. 125 is for an attractive fine to very fine example with minimal faults.

126	A37	6c blue	1,900.	3,000.
	No gum		850.	
127	A38	10c yellow	1,600.	1,800.
	No gum		700.	
128	A39	12c green	2,000.	3,000.
	No gum		900.	

A40b

No. 129 (type III) is similar to No. 118 (type I) but without the shading lines at each side of the vignette.

129	A40b	15c brn & bl, Type III	1,300.	1,000.
	No gum		625.	
a.	Imperf. horizontally, single		14,000.	30,000.
	No gum		5,000.	

Two used examples of No. 129a are recorded. Both have faults and are valued thus.

130	A41	24c grn & violet	2,000.	1,600.
	No gum		900.	
131	A42	30c ultra & car	2,250.	2,750.
	No gum		1,000.	
132	A43	90c car & blk	3,750.	6,000.
	No gum		1,500.	

Soft Porous Paper
1880-82

133	A34	1c buff, issued with gum	350.	550.
	No gum		145.	
a.	1c brown orange, issued without gum ('81 and '82)		350.	650.

Beware of No. 133 unused without gum offered as No. 133a. Certification is recommended for No. 133a.

PRODUCED BY THE NATIONAL BANK NOTE COMPANY

Franklin — A44

A44

Jackson — A45

A45

Washington — A46

A46

Lincoln — A47

A47

Edwin M.
Stanton — A48

A48

Jefferson — A49

A49

Henry Clay — A50

A50

Daniel Webster — A51

A51

Gen. Winfield
Scott
A52

Alexander
Hamilton
A53

Commodore O.H.
Perry — A54

H. GRILL ABOUT 10x12mm (11 TO 13 BY 14 TO 16 POINTS)

The "H" grills can be separated into early state and late state, based on the shape of the tip of the grill. Early-state grills show a point or very small vertical line at the tip of the pyramid, while late-state grills show the pyramid tips truncated and flat.

Early-state "H" grills tend to be on vertical-mesh wove paper, while later printings and all late-state grills were printed on horizontal-mesh wove paper, resulting in stamp designs being approximately ¼mm shorter than the designs printed on vertical-mesh wove paper. The late-stage "H" grills virtually all seem to have been used only after Jan. 1873.

Poor printing quality often resulted in grills that show only a few grill points or a very few rows of points. This is especially true of the "H" grills. When there are not enough grill points to clearly identify whether the grill is an "H" or an "I," it must be assumed it is the lower-valued "H" grill variety. Authentication is advised for these stamps with high catalogue values.

White Wove Paper, Thin to Medium Thick.

1870-71   **Perf. 12**

134	A44	1c ultramarine	2,000.	200.00
		No gum	700.	
135	A45	2c red brown	1,000.	80.00
		No gum	360.	
136	A46	3c green	575.	32.50
		No gum	190.	
b.		Printed on both sides	—	

The imperf. 3c can be found in the Scott U.S. Specialized Catalogue Die and Plate Proofs section.

137	A47	6c carmine	5,000.	425.
		No gum	1,750.	
b.		Pair, one without grill	—	
138	A48	7c vermilion	4,250.	525.
		No gum	1,550.	
b.		Pair, one without grill	—	
139	A49	10c brown	7,500.	800.
		No gum	2,700.	
140	A50	12c dull violet	32,500.	3,750.
		No gum	17,500.	
141	A51	15c orange	7,500.	1,500.
		No gum	2,500.	
142	A52	24c purple	—	6,500.
143	A53	30c black	20,000.	3,750.
		No gum	7,500.	
144	A54	90c carmine	25,000.	2,250.
		No gum	10,000.	

I. GRILL ABOUT 8½x10mm (10 TO 11 BY 10 TO 13 POINTS)

The "I" grills can be separated into early state and late state, based on the shape of the tip of the grill. Early state grills show small tips of the pyramid, while late state grills show the pyramid tips truncated and flat.

Early state "I" grills tend to be on vertical-mesh wove paper, while later printings and all late-state grills were printed on horizontal-mesh wove paper, resulting in stamp designs being approximately ¼mm shorter than the designs printed on vertical-mesh wove paper. The late-stage "I" grills all seem to have been used only after Jan. 1873.

Values are for stamps with grills that are clearly identifiable. Poor printing quality often resulted in grills that show only a few points or a very few rows of points. When there are not enough grill points to clearly identify whether the grill is an "H" or an "I," it must be assumed it is the lower-valued "H" grill variety. Authentication is advised for these stamps with high catalogue values.

134A	A44	1c ultra	2,750.	375.00
		No gum	800.00	
135A	A45	2c red brown	2,000.	300.00
136A	A46	3c green	850.00	90.00
a.		Pair, one without grill	—	
137A	A47	6c carmine	8,500.	900.00
		On cover		1,250.
		Strip of 3	—	
138A	A48	7c vermilion ('71)	6,500.	750.00
		No gum	2,200.	
139A	A49	10c brown	17,500.	10,000.

There are two unused examples of No. 139A recorded. One is fine and the other is very fine plus. The catalogue value is for the latter.

140A	A50	12c dull violet	30,000.	

Two examples are recorded of No. 140A unused, and it is valued in the grade of fine.

141A	A51	15c orange	16,500.	8,500.

Three singles and a block of 4 are recorded of No. 141A unused. Value for unused single is for a fine example.

143A	A53	30c black	75,000.	

Only one recorded example of No. 143A, which is valued in the grade of fine-very fine.

144A	A54	90c carmine	—	15,000.

The unused No. 144A has a vertically split grill and is unique.

White Wove Paper Without Grill.

1870-71   **Perf. 12**

145	A44	1c ultra	650.	20.00
		No gum	240.	
146	A45	2c red brown	325.	17.50
		No gum	135.	
d.		Double impression	9,000.	
147	A46	3c green	200.	1.80
		No gum	80.	
a.		Printed on both sides, reverse inverted	17,500.	
b.		Double impression	30,000.	

Nos. 147a and 147b are valued in the grade of fine.

The imperf. 3c can be found in the Scott U.S. Specialized Catalogue Die and Plate Proofs section.

148	A47	6c carmine	900.	22.50
		No gum	290.	
c.		Double paper	—	100.00

No. 148b is unique.

149	A48	7c ver ('71)	900.	100.00
		No gum	290.	
150	A49	10c brown	2,000.	35.00
		No gum	800.	
151	A50	12c dull violet	2,850.	200.00
		No gum	1,050.	
152	A51	15c brt org	3,500.	210.00
		No gum	1,300.	
a.		Double impression	—	9,000.

No. 152a is unique. It has fine centering and faults and is valued thus.

153	A52	24c purple	1,700.	210.00
		No gum	650.	
a.		Double paper	—	—
154	A53	30c black	7,000.	275.00
		No gum	2,600.	
155	A54	90c carmine	5,000.	325.00
		No gum	1,800.	

PRINTED BY THE CONTINENTAL BANK NOTE COMPANY

Designs of the 1870-71 Issue with secret marks on the values from 1c to 15c, as described and illustrated:

The object of secret marks was to provide a simple and positive proof that these stamps were produced by the Continental Bank Note Company and not by their predecessors.

Almost all of the stamps of the Continental Bank Note Co. printing including the Department stamps and some of the Newspaper stamps may be found upon a paper that shows more or less the characteristics of a ribbed paper. The ribbing may be oriented either vertically or horizontally, with horizontal ribbing being far more common than vertical ribbing. Values are for the most common varieties.

Franklin — A44a

1c. In the pearl at the left of the numeral "1" there is a small crescent.

Jackson — A45a

2c. Under the scroll at the left of "U. S." there is a small diagonal line. This mark seldom shows clearly. The stamp, No. 157, can be distinguished by its color.

Washington — A46a

3c. The under part of the upper tail of the left ribbon is heavily shaded.

Lincoln — A47a

6c. The first four vertical lines of the shading in the lower part of the left ribbon have been strengthened.

Stanton — A48a

7c. Two small semi-circles are drawn around the ends of the lines that outline the ball in the lower right hand corner.

Jefferson — A49a

10c. There is a small semi-circle in the scroll at the right end of the upper label.

Clay — A50a

12c. The balls of the figure "2" are crescent shaped.

Webster — A51a

15c. In the lower part of the triangle in the upper left corner two lines have been made heavier forming a "V." This mark can be found on some of the Continental and American (1879) printings, but not all stamps show it.

Secret marks were added to the dies of the 24c, 30c and 90c but new plates were not made from them. The various printings of the 30c and 90c can be distinguished only by the shades and paper.

Experimental J. Grill about 7x9½mm exists on all values except 24c and 90c. Grill is composed of truncated pyramids and was so strongly impressed that some points often broke through the paper.

White Wove Paper, Thin to Thick Without Grill

1873, July (?)   **Perf. 12**

156	A44a	1c ultra	200.	5.75
		No gum	90.	
e.		With grill	2,000.	
f.		Imperf., pair	—	1,500.
157	A45a	2c brown	325.	25.00
		No gum	125.	
c.		With grill	1,850.	750.00
d.		Double impression	—	16,500.

No. 157d is unique.

158	A46a	3c green	110.	1.00
		No gum	40.	
e.		With grill	550.	

h. Horizontal pair, imperf. vert. — —
i. Horizontal pair, imperf. between — 1,300.
j. Double impression — 7,000.
k. Printed on both sides — 20,000.

Nos. 158j and 158k are valued in the grade of fine.

The imperf 3c, with and without grill, can be found in the Scott U.S. Specialized Catalogue Die and Plate Proofs section.

159	A47a	6c dull pink	375.	18.00
	No gum		120.	
b.	With grill		1,800.	
160	A48a	7c org ver	1,000.	85.00
	No gum		350.	
a.	With grill		3,500.	
161	A49a	10c brown	800.	25.00
	No gum		250.	
c.	With grill		3,750.	
d.	Horizontal pair, imperf. between		15,000.	
162	A50a	12c blkish vio	2,200.	135.00
	No gum		725.	
a.	With grill		5,500.	
163	A51a	15c yel org	1,900.	150.00
	No gum		650.	
a.	With grill		5,750.	
164	A52	24c purple	357,500.	

The Philatelic Foundation has certified as genuine a 24c on vertically ribbed paper, and that is the unique stamp listed as No. 164. Specialists believe that only Continental used ribbed paper. It is not known for sure whether or not Continental also printed the 24c value on regular paper; if it did, specialists currently are not able to distinguish these from No. 153. The catalogue value represents a 2004 auction sale price realized.

165	A53	30c gray black	3,750.	135.
	No gum		1,200.	
c.	With grill		22,500.	
166	A54	90c rose car	2,100.	300.00
	No gum		700.	

Special Printing of the 1873 Issue
Hard, White Wove Paper
Without Gum

1875   **Perf. 12**

167	A44a	1c ultramarine	14,000.	
168	A45a	2c dark brown	6,000.	
169	A46a	3c blue green	21,500.	—
170	A47a	6c dull rose	18,000.	
171	A47a	7c reddish ver	4,000.	
172	A49a	10c pale brown	17,000.	
173	A50a	12c dark violet	5,500.	
174	A51a	15c bright org	15,500.	
175	A52	24c dull purple	3,400.	22,500.
176	A53	30c greenish blk	12,000.	
177	A54	90c vio carmine	18,000.	

Although perforated, these stamps were usually cut apart with scissors. As a result, the perforations are often much mutilated and the design is frequently damaged.

These can be distinguished from the 1873 issue by the shades; also by the paper, which is very white instead of yellowish.

These and the subsequent issues listed under the heading of "Special Printings" are special printings of stamps then in current use which, together with the reprints and re-issues, were made for sale to collectors. They were available for postage except for the Officials, Newspaper and Periodical, and demonetized issues.

Only three examples of No. 175 used have been certified. They all have small faults and are valued thus.

Yellowish Wove Paper

1875   **Perf. 12**

178	A45a	2c vermilion	325.	15.00
	No gum		100.	
c.	With grill		1,200.	2,750.

The imperf 2c can be found in the Scott U.S. Specialized Catalogue Die and Plate Proofs section.

Zachary Taylor — A55

179	A55	5c blue	700.	27.50
	No gum		225.	
c.	With grill		9,500.	

SPECIAL PRINTING OF 1875 ISSUE
Hard, White Wove Paper
Without Gum

1875

180	A45a	2c carmine ver	70,000.	
181	A55	5c bright blue	450,000.	

Unlike Nos. 167-177, Nos. 180-181 were seldom cut apart with scissors.

IMPORTANT INFORMATION REGARDING VALUES FOR NEVER-HINGED STAMPS

Collectors should be aware that the values given for never-hinged stamps from No. 182 on are for stamps in the grade of very fine, just as the values for all stamps in the catalogue are for very fine stamps unless indicated otherwise. The never-hinged premium as a percentage of value will be larger for stamps in extremely fine or superb grades, and the premium will be smaller for fine-very fine, fine or poor examples. This is particularly true of the issues of the late-19th and early-20th centuries.

VALUES FOR NEVER-HINGED STAMPS PRIOR TO SCOTT 182

This catalogue does not value pre-1879 stamps in never-hinged condition. Premiums for never-hinged condition in the classic era invariably are even larger than those premiums listed for the 1879 and later issues. Generally speaking, the earlier the stamp is listed in the catalogue, the larger will be the never-hinged premium.

For values of the most popular U.S. stamps in various conditions, including never hinged from No. 182 on, and in the grades of very good, fine, fine to very fine, very fine, very fine to extremely fine, extremely fine, extremely fine to superb, and superb, see the *Scott Stamp Values U.S. Specialized by Grade*, updated and issued each year as part of the U.S. specialized catalogue.

PRINTED BY THE AMERICAN BANK NOTE COMPANY
SAME AS 1870-75 ISSUES
Soft Porous Paper
Varying from Thin to Thick

1879   **Perf. 12**

182	A44a	1c dark ultra	200.	6.00
	Never hinged		675.	
	No gum		80.	
183	A45a	2c vermilion	100.	5.00
	Never hinged		370.	
	No gum		40.	
a.	Double impression		—	5,500.

No. 183a is valued in the grade of fine.

184	A46a	3c green	90.	1.00
	Never hinged		325.	
	No gum		35.	
b.	Double impression		—	5,000.

No. 184b is valued in the grade of fine.

The imperf 3c can be found in the Scott U.S. Specialized Catalogue Die and Plate Proofs section.

185	A55	5c blue	500.	16.00
	Never hinged		1,600.	
	No gum		155.	
186	A47a	6c pink	900.	22.50
	Never hinged		3,100.	
	No gum		275.	
187	A49	10c brn, without secret mark	3,000.	40.00
	Never hinged		10,000.	
	No gum		1,000.	
a.	Double paper		10,000.	—
188	A49a	10c brn, with secret mark	1,800.	30.00
	Never hinged		6,000.	
	No gum		650.	
189	A51a	15c red orange	180.	27.50
	Never hinged		600.	
	No gum		70.	
190	A53	30c full black	850.	90.00
	Never hinged		2,800.	
	No gum		300.	

191	A54	90c carmine	2,100.	375.00
	Never hinged		7,250.	
	No gum		700.	

The Continental Bank Note Co. was consolidated with the American Bank Note Co. on February 4, 1879. The American Bank Note Company used many plates of the Continental Bank Note Company to print the ordinary postage, Departmental and Newspaper stamps. Therefore, stamps bearing the Continental Company's imprint were not always its product. The A. B. N. Co. also used the 30c and 90c plates of the N. B. N. Co. Some of No. 190 and all of No. 217 were from A. B. N. Co. plate 405.

Early printings of No. 188 were from Continental plates 302 and 303 which contained the normal secret mark of 1873. After those plates were re-entered by the A. B. N. Co. in 1880, pairs or multiple pieces contained combinations of normal, hairline or missing marks. The pairs or other multiples usually found contain at least one hairline mark which tended to disappear as the plate wore.

A. B. N. Co. plates 377 and 378 were made in 1881 from the National transfer roll of 1870. No. 187 from these plates has no secret mark. The imperf. 90c can be found in the Scott U.S. Specialized Catalogue Die and Plate Proofs section.

Special Printing of the 1879 Issue
Soft Porous Paper
Without Gum

1880   **Perf. 12**

192	A44a	1c dark ultra	57,500.
193	A45a	2c black brown	16,000.
194	A46a	3c blue green	120,000.
195	A47a	6c dull rose	67,500.
196	A48a	7c scarlet ver	6,750.
197	A49a	10c deep brown	37,500.
198	A50a	12c blkish pur	9,500.
199	A51a	15c orange	30,000.
200	A52	24c dark violet	9,000.
201	A53	30c grnish blk	22,500.
202	A54	90c dull carmine	30,000.
203	A45a	2c scarlet ver	100,000.
204	A55	5c deep blue	240,000.

Nos. 192 and 194 are valued in the grade of fine.

No. 197 was printed from Continental plate 302 (or 303) after plate was re-entered. Therefore, the stamp may show normal, hairline or missing secret mark.

The Post Office Department did not keep separate records of the 1875 and 1880 Special Printings of the 1873 and 1879 issues, but the total quantity sold of both is recorded. Census research indicates that numbers sold of the two sets were approximately equal.

Unlike the 1875 hard-paper Special Printings (Nos. 167-177), the 1880 soft-paper Special Printings were never cut apart with scissors.

While use of Nos. 192-204 for postage was legal, no used examples are recorded. Expertization by competent authorities would be required to establish use.

James A. Garfield — A56

1882

205	A56	5c yellow brown	240.	15.00
	Never hinged		775.	
	No gum		90.	

Special Printing
1882   **Perf. 12**
Soft porous paper, without gum

205C	A56	5c gray brown	50,000.	

DESIGNS OF 1873 RE-ENGRAVED

Franklin — A44b

1c — The vertical lines in the upper part of the stamp have been so deepened that the background often appears to be solid. Lines of shading have been added to the upper arabesques.

1881-82

206	A44b	1c gray blue	70.00	1.00
	Never hinged		225.00	
	No gum		25.00	
a.	Double impression		—	

No. 206a is a partial double impression, with "ONE 1 CENT," etc. at bottom doubled.
Earliest documented use: Oct. 11, 1881.

Washington — A46b

3c. The shading at the sides of the central oval appears only about one-half the previous width. A short horizontal dash has been cut about 1mm below the "TS" of "CENTS."

207	A46b	3c blue green	80.00	.80
	Never hinged		250.00	
	No gum		27.50	
c.	Double impression		5,000.	

Lincoln — A47b

6c. On the original stamps four vertical lines can be counted from the edge of the panel to the outside of the stamp. On the re-engraved stamps there are but three lines in the same place.

208	A47b	6c rose	825.	110.00
	Never hinged		2,600.	
	No gum		250.	
a.	6c deep brown red		600.	190.00
	Never hinged		1,900.	
	No gum		170.	

Jefferson — A49b

10c. On the original stamps there are five vertical lines between the left side of the oval and the edge of the shield. There are only four lines on the re-engraved stamps. In the lower part of the latter, also, the horizontal lines of the background have been strengthened.

209	A49b	10c brown	160.	6.00
	Never hinged		475.	
	No gum		65.	
b.	10c black brown		3,000.	375.00
	Never hinged		6,000.	
	No gum		950.	
c.	Double impression		—	

Specimen stamps (usually overprinted "Sample") without overprint exist in a brown shade that differs from No. 209. The unoverprinted brown specimen is cheaper than No. 209. Expertization is recommended.

Washington — A57   Jackson — A58

Nos. 210-211 were issued to meet the reduced first class rate of 2 cents for each half ounce, and the double rate, which Congress approved Mar. 3, 1883, effective Oct. 1, 1883.

1883, Oct. 1   **Perf. 12**

210	A57	2c red brown	45.	.75
	Never hinged		135.	
	No gum		17.	
211	A58	4c blue green	225.	25.00
	Never hinged		800.	
	No gum		80.	

Imperfs can be found in the Scott U.S. Specialized Catalogue Die and Plate Proofs section.

Special Printing
1883-85 Soft porous paper *Perf. 12*
211B A57 2c pale red brn,
         with gum
         ('85)   400.   —
         Never hinged   950.
         No gum   140.
    c.   Horizontal pair, imperf.
         between   2,250.
         Never hinged   3,250.
211D A58 4c deep blue grn   47,500.

No. 211D is without gum.

Franklin — A59

1887   *Perf. 12*
212 A59 1c ultramarine   90.00   2.50
         Never hinged   290.00
         No gum   35.00
213 A57 2c green   40.00   .60
         Never hinged   120.00
         No gum   15.00
    b.   Printed on both sides   —

Imperf 1c, 2c can be found in the Scott U.S. Specialized Catalogue Die and Plate Proofs section.

214 A46b 3c vermilion   60.00   50.00
         Never hinged   190.00
         No gum   25.00
         Nos. 212-214 (3)   190.00   53.10

1888   *Perf. 12*
215 A58 4c carmine   180.00   30.00
         Never hinged   525.
         No gum   60.
216 A56 5c indigo   210.00   20.00
         Never hinged   650.
         No gum   75.
217 A53 30c orange brn   300.00   90.00
         Never hinged   1,075.
         No gum   90.
218 A54 90c purple   800.00   225.00
         Never hinged   2,500.
         No gum   250.
         Nos. 215-218 (4)   1,490.   365.00

Imperfs can be found in the Scott U.S. Specialized Catalogue Die and Plate Proofs section.

Franklin
A60

Washington
A61

Jackson
A62

Lincoln
A63

Ulysses S.
Grant
A64

Garfield
A65

William T.
Sherman
A66

Daniel
Webster
A67

Henry Clay
A68

Jefferson
A69

Perry — A70

1890-93   *Perf. 12*
219 A60 1c dull blue   20.00   .75
         Never hinged   65.00
219D A61 2c lake   150.00   5.75
         Never hinged   475.00
220 A61 2c carmine   20.00   .70
         Never hinged   60.00
    a.   Cap on left "2"   150.00   12.50
         Never hinged   425.00
    c.   Cap on both "2's"   650.00   35.00
         Never hinged   1,800.
221 A62 3c purple   55.00   9.00
         Never hinged   175.00
222 A63 4c dark brown   80.00   4.75
         Never hinged   240.00
223 A64 5c chocolate   60.00   4.75
         Never hinged   185.00
224 A65 6c brown red   50.00   25.00
         Never hinged   160.00
225 A66 8c lilac ('93)   45.00   17.00
         Never hinged   135.00
226 A67 10c green   160.00   5.00
         Never hinged   475.00
227 A68 15c indigo   180.00   25.00
         Never hinged   550.00
228 A69 30c black   280.00   30.00
         Never hinged   850.00
229 A70 90c orange   450.00   140.00
         Never hinged   1,500.
         Nos. 219-229 (12)   1,550.   267.70

The No. 220 with "cap on right 2" variety is due to imperfect inking, not a plate defect.
Imperfs. can be found in the *Scott U.S. Specialized Catalogue* Die and Plate Proofs section.

COLUMBIAN EXPOSITION ISSUE

Columbus in
Sight of
Land — A71

Landing of
Columbus
A72

Flagship of
Columbus
A73

Fleet of
Columbus
A74

Columbus
Soliciting Aid
from Isabella
A75

Columbus
Welcomed at
Barcelona
A76

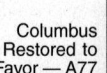

Columbus
Restored to
Favor — A77

Columbus
Presenting
Natives
A78

Columbus
Announcing
his Discovery
A79

Columbus at
La Rábida
A80

Recall of
Columbus
A81

Isabella
Pledging her
Jewels
A82

Columbus in
Chains
A83

Columbus
Describing
his Third
Voyage
A84

Isabella &
Columbus
A85

Columbus
A86

1893   *Perf. 12*
230 A71 1c deep blue   14.00   .40
         Never hinged   32.50
231 A72 2c brn vio   12.50   .30
         Never hinged   31.00
232 A73 3c green   35.00   15.00
         Never hinged   97.50
233 A74 4c ultra   55.00   8.00
         Never hinged   150.00
    a.   4c blue (error)   17,500.   16,500.
         Never hinged   32,500.

No. 233a exists in two shades. No. 233a used is valued with small faults, as almost all examples come thus.

234 A75 5c chocolate   55.00   8.50
         Never hinged   150.00
235 A76 6c purple   55.00   22.50
         Never hinged   150.00
    a.   6c red violet   55.00   22.50
         Never hinged   150.00
236 A77 8c magenta   50.00   10.00
         Never hinged   140.00

237 A78 10c blk brn   95.00   8.00
         Never hinged   265.00
238 A79 15c dark green   200.00   72.50
         Never hinged   600.00
239 A80 30c org brn   225.00   90.00
         Never hinged   675.00
240 A81 50c slate blue   450.00   175.00
         Never hinged   1,400.
         No gum   200.
241 A82 $1 salmon   1,000.   525.00
         Never hinged   3,400.
         No gum   500.
242 A83 $2 brown red   1,100.   525.00
         Never hinged   3,600.
         No gum   550.
243 A84 $3 yel grn   1,500.   775.00
         Never hinged   4,750.
         No gum   750.
    a. $3 olive green   1,400.   775.00
         Never hinged   4,350.
         No gum   700.
244 A85 $4 crim lake   2,100.   975.00
         Never hinged   7,250.
         No gum   1,100.
    a. $4 rose carmine   2,000.   975.00
         Never hinged   7,000.
         No gum   1,000.
245 A86 $5 black   2,400.   1,175.00
         Never hinged   9,750.
         No gum   1,250.

World's Columbia Expo., Chicago, May 1-Oct. 30, 1893.
Nos. 230-245 are known imperf., but were not regularly issues.
See Scott U.S. Specialized Catalogue Die and Plate Proofs section for the 2c.

Never-Hinged Stamps
See note before No. 182 regarding premiums for never-hinged stamps.

Bureau Issues
Starting in 1894, the Bureau of Engraving and Printing at Washington produced most U.S. postage stamps.

Until 1965 Bureau-printed stamps were engraved except Nos. 525-536 which were offset.

The combination of lithography and engraving (see #1253) was first used in 1964, and photogravure (see #1426) in 1971.

Franklin
A87

Washington
A88

Jackson
A89

Lincoln
A90

Grant
A91

Garfield
A92

Sherman
A93

Webster
A94

Clay
A95

Jefferson
A96

Perry
A97

James
Madison
A98

John Marshall — A99

1894   **Unwmk.**   *Perf. 12*
246 A87 1c ultramarine   30.00   7.00
    Never hinged   90.00
247 A87 1c blue   62.50   4.00
    Never hinged   180.00

Triangle A
(Type I)

TWO CENTS
Type I (Triangle A). The horizontal lines of the ground work run across the triangle and are of the same thickness within it as without.

Triangle B
(Type II)

Type II (Triangle B). The horizontal lines cross the triangle but are thinner within it than without. Other minor design differences exist, but the change to Triangle B is a sufficient determinant.

Triangle C
(Types III and IV)

Type III (Triangle C). The horizontal lines do not cross the double lines of the triangle. The lines within the triangle are thin, as in Type II. The rest of the design is the same as Type II, except that most of the designs had the dot in the "S" of "CENTS" removed. Stamps with this dot present are listed; some specialists refer to them as "Type IIIa" varieties.

Type IV

Type IV (Triangle C). See No. 279B and its varieties. Type IV is from a new die with many major and minor design variations including, (1) re-cutting and lengthening of hairline, (2) shaded toga button, (3) strengthening of lines

on sleeve, (4) additional dots on ear, (5) "T" of "TWO" straight at right, (6) background lines extend into white oval opposite "U" of "UNITED." Many other differences exist.

For further information concerning type IV, see also George Brett's article in the Sept. 1993 issue of the "The United States Specialist" and the 23-part article by Kenneth Diehl in the Dec. 1994 through Aug. 1997 issues of the "The United States Specialist."

248 A88 2c pink, type I   32.50   10.00
    Never hinged   97.50
  a. Vert. pair, imperf. horiz.   5,500.00
249 A88 2c car. lake,
    type I   150.00   7.00
    Never hinged   450.00
  a. Double impression   —
250 A88 2c car, type I   29.00   3.00
    Never hinged   85.00
  a. 2c rose, type I   36.00   8.50
    Never hinged   105.00
  b. 2c scarlet, type I   26.00   2.75
    Never hinged   80.00
  d. Horizontal pair, imperf.
    between   2,000.00
251 A88 2c car, type II   400.00   14.00
    Never hinged   1,200.00
  a. 2c scarlet, type II   375.00   13.00
    Never hinged   1,125.00
252 A88 2c car, type III   135.00   13.00
    Never hinged   400.00
    On cover   22.50
  a. 2c scarlet, type III   120.00   15.00
    Never hinged   360.00
  b. Horiz. pair, imperf.
    vert.   5,000.00
  c. Horiz. pair, imperf. be-
    tween   5,500.00

No. 252b is unique and exists only as a horizontal top plate-number strip of 3. A vertical right plate-number strip of 3 from the same plate exists containing three stamps imperforate at left and right.

253 A89 3c purple   120.00   12.00
    Never hinged   360.00
254 A90 4c dark brown   200.00   11.00
    Never hinged   600.00
255 A91 5c chocolate   120.00   9.00
    Never hinged   360.00
  c. Vert. pair, imperf.
    horiz.   3,500.00
256 A92 6c dull brown   160.00   27.50
    Never hinged   475.00
  a. Vert. pair, imperf.
    horiz.   3,000.00
257 A93 8c vio brn   160.00   20.00
    Never hinged   475.00
258 A94 10c dark green   275.00   20.00
    Never hinged   850.00
259 A95 15c dark blue   275.00   65.00
    Never hinged   850.00
260 A96 50c orange   475.   140.
    Never hinged   1,425.

Type I

Type II

ONE DOLLAR
Type I. The circles enclosing "$1" are broken where they meet the curved line below "One Dollar."
Type II. The circles are complete.

261 A97 $1 blk, type I   1,000.   350.
    Never hinged   3,150.
    No gum   400.
261A A97 $1 blk, type II   2,100.   800.
    Never hinged   6,500.
    No gum   850.
262 A98 $2 bright blue   2,750.   1,200.
    Never hinged   8,750.
    No gum   1,100.
263 A99 $5 dark green   4,000.   2,600.
    Never hinged   14,000.
    No gum   2,100.

For imperfs. and the 2c pink, vert. pair, imperf. hoirz., see Scott U.S. Specialized Catalogue Die and plate Proofs.

Same as 1894 Issue
Wmk. 191 Horizontally or Vertically
1895   *Perf. 12*
264 A87 1c blue   6.00   .60
    Never hinged   17.50
265 A88 2c car, type I   35.00   3.50
    Never hinged   105.00
266 A88 2c car, type II   40.00   15.00
    Never hinged   120.00
267 A88 2c car, type III   5.50   .60
    Never hinged   16.00
  a. 2c pink, type III   20.00   5.00
    Never hinged   60.00
  b. 2c vermilion, type III   50.00   15.00
  c. 2c rose carmine, type III

The three left vertical rows from plate 170 are type II, the balance being type III.

268 A89 3c purple   37.50   2.25
    Never hinged   115.00
269 A90 4c dark brown   42.50   3.50
    Never hinged   125.00
270 A91 5c chocolate   35.00   3.50
    Never hinged   105.00
271 A92 6c dull brown   110.00   8.50
    Never hinged   325.00
  a. Wmkd. USIR   15,000.   8,500.
272 A93 8c violet brown   70.00   2.75
    Never hinged   210.00
  a. Wmkd. USIR   6,000.   950.00
273 A94 10c dark green   95.00   2.25
    Never hinged   280.00
274 A95 15c dark blue   200.00   17.50
    Never hinged   600.00
275 A96 50c orange   240.   40.00
    Never hinged   725.
  a. 50c red orange   325.   47.50
    Never hinged   975.
276 A97 $1 black, type I   600.   95.
    Never hinged   1,800.
    No gum   250.
276A A97 $1 black, type II   1,250.   200.
    Never hinged   3,750.
    No gum   500.
277 A98 $2 bright blue   900.   400.
    Never hinged   2,900.
    No gum   375.
  a. $2 dark blue   900.   400.
    Never hinged   2,900.
    No gum   375.
278 A99 $5 dark green   2,000.   600.
    Never hinged   6,250.
    No gum   800.

For imperfs. and the 1c horiz. imperf. vert., see Scott U.S. Specialized Catalogue Die and Plate Proofs.
For "I.R." overprints see Nos. R155, R156-R158.
No. 271a unused is valued in the grade of fine.

Wmk. 191 Horizontally or Vertically
1897-1903   *Perf. 12*
279 A87 1c dp grn,
    horiz.
    wmk ('98)   9.00   .50
    Never hinged   25.00
  a. Vert. wmk (error)   50.00   7.50
    Never hinged   150.00
279B A88 2c red, type
    IV ('99)   9.00   .40
    Never hinged   25.00
  c. 2c rose carmine, type
    IV ('99)   275.00   230.00
    Never hinged   850.00
  d. 2c orange red, type
    IV, horiz. wmk. ('00)   11.50   2.00
    Never hinged   32.50
  e. 2c orange red, type
    IV, vert. wmk.   55.00   12.50
    Never hinged   170.00
  f. 2c carmine, type IV   10.00   2.00
    Never hinged   27.50
  g. 2c pink, type IV   55.00   7.50
    Never hinged   165.00
  h. 2c vermilion, type IV
    ('99)   12.50   3.00
    Never hinged   35.00
  i. 2c brown org, type IV
    ('99)   400.00   100.00
    Never hinged   950.00
  j. Booklet pane of 6,
    red, type IV, horiz.
    wmk. ('00)   500.00   3,000.
    Never hinged   1,000.
  k. Booklet pane of 6,
    red, type IV, vertical
    watermark ('02)   500.00   —
    Never hinged   1,000.
  l. As No. 279B, all color
    missing (FO)   500.00

No. 279Bl must be collected se-tenant with a partially printed stamp.

280 A90 4c rose brn
    ('98)   30.00   3.25
    Never hinged   80.00
  a. 4c lilac brown   30.00   3.25
    Never hinged   80.00
  b. 4c orange brown   30.00   3.00
    Never hinged   80.00
281 A91 5c dk blue
    ('98)   32.50   2.25
    Never hinged   100.00
282 A92 6c lake ('98)   45.00   6.50
    Never hinged   140.00
  a. 6c purple lake   80.00   20.00
    Never hinged   240.00

Type I. The tips of the foliate ornaments do not impinge on the white curved line below "ten cents."

282C A94 10c brn, type I
    ('98)   175.00   6.50
    Never hinged   525.00

Type II. The tips of the ornaments break the curved line below the "e" of "ten" and the "t" of "cents."

283 A94 10c org brn,
    type II,
    horiz.
    wmk.   150.00   6.00
    Never hinged   450.00
  a. Vert. wmk. ('00)   250.00   15.00
    Never hinged   775.00
284 A95 15c ol grn ('98)   150.00   13.00
    Never hinged   475.00
  Nos. 279-284 (8)   600.50   38.40

For "I.R." overprints, see Nos. R153-R155A.

VALUES FOR VERY FINE STAMPS
    Please note: Stamps are valued in the grade of Very Fine unless otherwise indicated.

TRANS-MISSISSIPPI EXPOSITION ISSUE

Marquette on the Mississippi
A100

Farming in the West — A101

Indian Hunting Buffalo
A102

Frémont on the Rocky Mountains
A103

Troops Guarding Wagon Train — A104

Hardships of Emigration
A105

Western Mining Prospector
A106

Western Cattle in Storm
A107

Mississippi River Bridge
A108

1898, June 17   Wmk. 191   *Perf. 12*
285 A100 1c dk yel grn   27.50   7.00
    Never hinged   75.00
286 A101 2c copper red   25.00   2.75
    Never hinged   72.50
287 A102 4c orange   110.00   25.00
    Never hinged   330.00

288	A103	5c dull blue	100.00	25.00
		Never hinged	300.00	
289	A104	8c violet brown	140.00	47.50
		Never hinged	430.00	
a.		Vert. pair, imperf. horiz.	27,500.	
290	A105	10c gray vio	140.00	35.00
		Never hinged	425.00	
291	A106	50c sage grn	600.00	175.00
		Never hinged	1,750.	
292	A107	$1 black	1,500.	700.
		Never hinged	3,750.	
		No gum	850.	
293	A108	$2 org brn	1,900.	1,050.
		Never hinged	5,750.	
		No gum	950.	
		Nos. 285-293 (9)	4,543.	2,067.

Trans-Mississippi Exposition, Omaha, Neb., June 1 to Nov. 1, 1898.
For "I.R" overprints see #R158A-R158B.

Never-Hinged Stamps

See note before No. 182 regarding premiums for never-hinged stamps.

PAN-AMERICAN EXPOSITION ISSUE

Fast Lake Navigation A109

"Empire State" Express A110   Electric Automobile A111

Bridge at Niagara Falls — A112   Canal Locks at Sault Ste. Marie — A113

Fast Ocean Navigation — A114

1901, May 1   Wmk. 191   Perf. 12

294	A109	1c grn & blk	16.00	3.00
		Never hinged	40.00	
a.		Center inverted	12,500.	25,000.
		Never hinged	22,500.	
295	A110	2c car & blk	15.00	1.00
		Never hinged	37.50	
a.		Center inverted	50,000.	55,000.
296	A111	4c dp red brn & blk	70.00	18.00
		Never hinged	170.00	
a.		Center inverted	85,000.	—
297	A112	5c ultra & black	75.00	17.00
		Never hinged	180.00	
298	A113	8c brn vio & blk	90.00	50.00
		Never hinged	230.00	
299	A114	10c yel brn & blk	115.00	30.00
		Never hinged	300.00	
		Nos. 294-299 (6)	381.00	119.00
		Nos. 294-299, never hinged	957.50	

No. 296a was a special printing. Almost all unused examples of Nos. 295a and 296a have partial or disturbed gum. Values are for examples with full original gum that is slightly disturbed.

Franklin A115   Washington A116

Jackson A117   Grant A118

Lincoln A119   Garfield A120

Martha Washington A121   Webster A122

Benjamin Harrison A123   Clay A124

Jefferson A125   David G. Farragut A126

Madison A127   Marshall A128

1902-03   Wmk. 191   Perf. 12

300	A115	1c blue grn ('03)	12.00	.25
		Never hinged	30.00	
b.		Booklet pane of 6	600.00	11,500.
		Never hinged	1,150.	
		Wmk. horiz.	2,000.	
301	A116	2c car ('03)	15.00	.50
		Never hinged	37.50	
c.		Booklet pane of 6	500.00	6,000.
		Never hinged	950.00	
302	A117	3c brt vio ('03)	55.00	3.75
		Never hinged	140.00	
303	A118	4c brn ('03)	55.00	2.25
		Never hinged	140.00	
304	A119	5c blue ('03)	60.00	2.00
		Never hinged	150.00	
305	A120	6c claret ('03)	60.00	5.50
		Never hinged	150.00	
306	A121	8c vio black	45.00	3.25
		Never hinged	110.00	
307	A122	10c pale red brn ('03)	60.00	3.00
		Never hinged	150.00	
308	A123	13c purple blk	40.00	10.00
		Never hinged	100.00	
309	A124	15c ol grn ('03)	185.00	12.50
		Never hinged	475.00	
310	A125	50c org ('03)	425.	35.00
		Never hinged	1,225.	
311	A126	$1 black ('03)	600.00	90.00
		Never hinged	1,800.	
		No gum	240.00	
312	A127	$2 dk bl ('03)	825.00	200.00
		Never hinged	2,500.	
		No gum	325.00	
313	A128	$5 dk grn ('03)	2,100.	700.00
		Never hinged	6,250.	
		No gum	800.00	
		Nos. 300-313 (14)	4,537.	1,068.

For listings of designs A127 and A128 with Perf. 10 see Nos. 479 and 480.

1906-08   Imperf.

314	A115	1c blue green	14.00	17.50
		Never hinged	30.00	
314A	A118	4c brn ('08)	100,000.	50,000.
		Never hinged	230,000.	
315	A119	5c blue ('08)	300.	1,250.
		Never hinged	575.	

No. 314A was issued imperforate but all examples were privately perforated with large

oblong perforations at the sides (Schermack type III).
Beware of examples of No. 303 with trimmed perforations and fake private perfs added.
Used examples of Nos. 314 and 315 must have contemporaneous cancels.

COIL STAMPS

Warning! Imperforate stamps are known fraudulently perforated to resemble coil stamps and part-perforate varieties. Fully perforated stamps and booklet stamps also are known with perforations fraudulently trimmed off to resemble coil stamps.

1908   Perf. 12 Horizontally

316	A115	1c blue green	160,000.	
317	A119	5c blue	6,000.	—
		Never hinged	12,000.	

Perf. 12 Vertically

318	A115	1c blue green	4,500.	
		Never hinged	9,500.	

Coil stamps for use in vending and affixing machines are perforated on two sides only, either horizontally or vertically.
They were first issued in 1908, using perf. 12. This was changed to 8½ in 1910, and to 10 in 1914.
Imperforate sheets of certain denominations were sold to the vending machine companies which applied a variety of private perforations and separations.
Several values of the 1902 and later issues are found on an apparently coarse ribbed paper caused by worn blankets on the printing press and are not true paper varieties.
No. 316 is valued in the grade of fine to very fine. There are no very fine examples recorded.
All examples of Nos. 316-318 must be accompanied by certificates of authenticity issued by recognized expertizing committees.
No. 318 mint never hinged is valued in the grade of fine.

Washington — A129

Type I

Type II

The two large arrows in the illustrations highlight the two major differences of the type II stamps: closing of the thin left border line next to the laurel leaf, and strengthening of the inner frame line at the lower left corner. The small arrows point out three minor differences that are not always easily discernible: strengthening of shading lines on the ribbon just above the "T" of "TWO," a shorter shading line to the left of the "P" in "POSTAGE," and shortening of a shading line in the left side ribbon.

Type I

1903, Nov. 12   Wmk. 191   Perf. 12

319	A129	2c car, type I	6.00	.25
		Never hinged	15.00	
a.		2c lake	—	
b.		2c carmine rose	15.00	.40
		Never hinged	45.00	
c.		2c scarlet	10.00	.30
		Never hinged	25.00	
d.		Vert. pair, imperf. horiz., No. 319	7,500.	
		Never hinged	17,500.	
e.		Vert. pair, imperf. between		
r.		Vert. pair, rouletted between	4,000.	

During the use of No. 319, the postmaster of San Francisco discovered in his stock panes that had the perforations missing between the top two rows of stamps. To facilitate their separation, the imperf rows were rouletted, and the stamps were sold over the counter. These vertical pairs with regular perfs all around and rouletted between are No. 319r. No 319e is from a different source. One example has been authenticated, and collectors are warned that other pairs exist with faint blind perfs or indentations from the perforating machine.

g.	Booklet pane of 6, carmine	125.00	450.00
	Never hinged	240.00	
n.	Booklet pane of 6, carmine rose	275.00	700.00
	Never hinged	500.00	
p.	Booklet pane of 6, scarlet	185.00	625.00
	Never hinged	350.00	

Type II

1908   Wmk. 191   Perf. 12

319F	A129	2c lake	10.00	.30
		Never hinged	25.00	
i.		2c carmine	65.00	50.00
		Never hinged	150.00	
j.		2c carmine rose	100.00	1.75
		Never hinged	225.00	
k.		2c scarlet	70.00	2.00
		Never hinged	160.00	
l.		Booklet pane of 6, scarlet	—	
q.		Booklet pane of 6, lake	300.00	800.00
		Never hinged	575.00	

Type I

1906, Oct. 2   Wmk. 191   Imperf.

320	A129	2c carmine	15.00	19.00
		Never hinged	32.50	
c.		2c carmine rose	75.00	42.50
		Never hinged	150.00	

Type II

1908   Wmk. 191   Imperf.

320A	A129	2c lake	45.00	50.00
		Never hinged	100.00	
d.		2c carmine	135.00	—
		Never hinged	200.00	

No. 320Ad was issued imperforate, but all examples were privately perforated with large oblong perforations at the sides (Schermack type III).

COIL STAMPS

1908   Perf. 12 Horizontally

321	A129	2c car, type I, pair	600,000.	300,000.

Four authenticated unused pairs of No. 321 are known and available to collectors. A fifth, unauthenticated pair is in the New York Public Library Miller collection, which is on long-term loan to the Smithsonian National Postal Museum. The value for an unused pair is for a fine-very fine example. Two fine pairs are recorded and one very fine pair.
There are no authenticated unused or off-cover used single stamps recorded. The used value is for a single on cover, of which two authenticated examples are known, both used from Indianapolis in 1908.
The Dec. 20, 1908, legal-size cover has not been seen in decades; the Oct. 2, 1908, cover sold in 2018 and is the used cover valued.
Numerous counterfeits exist.

322	A129	2c carmine, type II	7,000.	—
		Never hinged	15,000.	

This Government Coil Stamp should not be confused with those of the International Vending Machine Co., which are perforated 12½.
All examples of Nos. 321-322 must be accompanied by certificates of authenticity issued by recognized expertizing committees.

VALUES FOR VERY FINE STAMPS
Please note: Stamps are valued in the grade of Very Fine unless otherwise indicated.

LOUISIANA PURCHASE EXPOSITION ISSUE

Robert R. Livingston
A130

Thomas Jefferson
A131

James Monroe
A132

William McKinley
A133

Map of Louisiana Purchase
A134

1904, Apr. 30   Wmk. 191   Perf. 12

323	A130 1c green	22.50	4.75
	Never hinged	60.00	
324	A131 2c carmine	22.50	2.00
	Never hinged	60.00	
a.	Vertical pair, imperf. horiz.	25,000.	
325	A132 3c violet	65.00	27.50
	Never hinged	170.00	
326	A133 5c dark blue	70.00	22.50
	Never hinged	180.00	
327	A134 10c red brown	125.00	27.50
	Never hinged	300.00	
	Nos. 323-327 (5)	305.00	84.25
	Nos. 323-327, never hinged	770.00	

JAMESTOWN EXPOSITION ISSUE

Captain John Smith — A135

Founding of Jamestown
A136

Pocahontas
A137

1907   Wmk. 191   Perf. 12

328	A135 1c green	27.50	4.50
	Never hinged	70.00	
329	A136 2c carmine	30.00	4.00
	Never hinged	80.00	
a.	2c carmine lake	—	
330	A137 5c blue	140.00	30.00
	Never hinged	350.00	
	Nos. 328-330 (3)	197.50	38.50
	Nos. 328-330, never hinged	500.00	

Franklin A138

Washington A139

There are several types of some of the 2c and 3c stamps of this and succeeding issues. These types are described under the dates at which they first appeared.

Illustrations of Types I-VII of the 2c (A140) and Types I-IV of the 3c (A140) are reproduced by permission of H. L. Lindquist.

1908-09   Wmk. 191   Perf. 12

331	A138 1c green	6.50	.40
	Never hinged	16.50	
a.	Booklet pane of 6	150.00	700.00
	Never hinged	300.00	

No. 331 exists in horizontal pair, imperforate between, a variety resulting from booklet experiments. Not regularly issued. Value in the grade of fine, $3,750.

No. 331a used is valued with a contemporaneous cancel. A certificate of authenticity is advised.

332	A139 2c carmine	6.00	.35
	Never hinged	14.50	
a.	Booklet pane of 6	135.00	500.00
	Never hinged	240.00	
b.	2c lake	4,250.	

No. 332a used is valued with a contemporaneous cancel. A certificate of authenticity is advised.

No. 332b is valued in the grade of fine.

Washington — A140

TYPE I

THREE CENTS

Type I. The top line of the toga rope is weak and the rope shading lines are thin. The 5th line from the left is missing. The line between the lips is thin. (For descriptions of 3c types II, III and IV, see notes and illustrations preceding Nos. 484, 529-530.)

Used on both flat plate and rotary press printings.

333	A140 3c dp vio, type I	30.00	3.00
	Never hinged	75.00	
334	A140 4c org brn	35.00	1.50
	Never hinged	87.50	
335	A140 5c blue	45.00	2.25
	Never hinged	110.00	
336	A140 6c red orange	62.50	6.00
	Never hinged	145.00	
337	A140 8c olive green	45.00	2.75
	Never hinged	105.00	
338	A140 10c yellow ('09)	70.00	1.80
	Never hinged	165.00	
339	A140 13c bl grn ('09)	37.50	17.50
	Never hinged	90.00	
340	A140 15c pale ultra ('09)	67.50	6.00
	Never hinged	160.00	
341	A140 50c violet ('09)	275.00	20.00
	Never hinged	650.00	
342	A140 $1 vio brn ('09)	450.00	95.00
	Never hinged	1,050.	
	Nos. 331-342 (12)	1,130.	156.55

For listings of other perforated sheet stamps of A138, A139 and A140 see:
Nos. 357-366 Bluish paper
Nos. 374-382, 405-407 Single line wmk. Perf. 12
Nos. 423A-423C Single line wmk. Perf 12x10
Nos. 423D-423E Single line wmk. Perf 10x12
Nos. 424-430 Single line wmk. Perf. 10
Nos. 461 Single line wmk. Perf. 11
Nos. 462-469 unwmk. Perf. 10
Nos. 498-507 unwmk. Perf. 11
Nos. 519 Double line wmk. Perf. 11
Nos. 525-530 and 536 Offset printing
Nos. 538-546 Rotary press printing

Imperf

343	A138 1c green	4.50	5.00
	Never hinged	9.00	
344	A139 2c carmine	4.50	2.75
	Never hinged	9.00	
345	A140 3c dp violet, type I	9.00	20.00
	Never hinged	19.00	
346	A140 4c org brn ('09)	12.50	20.00
	Never hinged	25.00	
347	A140 5c blue ('09)	25.00	32.50
	Never hinged	50.00	
	Nos. 343-347 (5)	55.50	80.25
	Nos. 343-347, never hinged	129.00	

For listings of other imperforate stamps of designs A138, A139 and A140 see Nos. 383, 384, 408, 409 and 459 Single line wmk.
Nos. 481-485 unwmk.

Nos. 531-535 Offset printing

The values for used coil stamps are for examples with contemporaneous cancels that can be authenticated by expertizing committees. Used coils with cancels most commonly from the 1950s exist, and these and stamps with other non-contemporaneous cancels sell for less than the values shown.

COIL STAMPS

1908-10   Perf. 12 Horizontally

348	A138 1c green	40.00	60.00
	Never hinged	80.00	
349	A139 2c carmine ('09)	100.00	160.00
	Never hinged	225.00	
350	A140 4c org brn ('10)	140.00	250.00
	Never hinged	325.00	
351	A140 5c blue ('09)	140.00	300.00
	Never hinged	325.00	
	Nos. 348-351 (4)	420.00	770.00

1909   Perf. 12 Vertically

352	A138 1c green	100.00	225.00
	Never hinged	230.00	
353	A139 2c carmine	90.00	220.00
	Never hinged	200.00	
354	A140 4c org brn	200.00	275.00
	Never hinged	425.00	
355	A140 5c blue	210.00	300.00
	Never hinged	450.00	
356	A140 10c yellow	3,250.	6,000.
	Never hinged	8,000.	

For listings of other coil stamps of designs A138, A139 and A140, see #385-396, 410-413, 441-458 (single line wmk.), #486-496 (unwatermarked).

Beware of stamps offered as No. 356 which may be examples of No. 338 with perfs. trimmed at top and/or bottom. Beware also of plentiful fakes in the marketplace of Nos. 348-355, made by fraudulently perforating imperforate stamps or by fraudulently trimming perforations off fully perforated stamps. Authentication of all these coils is advised.

BLUISH PAPER

This was made with 35 percent rag stock instead of all wood pulp. The "bluish" color (actually grayish blue) goes through the paper showing clearly on the back as well as on the face.

1909   Perf. 12

357	A138 1c green	90.00	160.00
	Never hinged	190.00	
358	A139 2c carmine	80.00	150.00
	Never hinged	170.00	
359	A140 3c dp vio, type I	1,800.	12,500.
	Never hinged	4,000.	
360	A140 4c org brn	27,500.	
361	A140 5c blue	5,750.	20,000.
	Never hinged	14,500.	

Only two examples of No. 361 used off cover (three additional on cover) are recorded. Value used is for the better of the two examples, which is well-centered but has two reattached perforations.

362	A140 6c red org	1,250.	12,500.
	Never hinged	3,000.	
363	A140 8c olive green	30,000.	
	Never hinged	85,000.	
364	A140 10c yellow	1,600.	10,000.
	Never hinged	4,000.	
365	A140 13c blue green	2,600.	4,000.
	Never hinged	6,000.	
366	A140 15c pale ultra	1,300.	16,000.
	Never hinged	3,000.	

Nos. 360 and 363 were not regularly issued.
Used examples of Nos. 357-366 must bear contemporaneous cancels, and Nos. 359-366 used must be accompanied by certificates of authenticity issued by recognized expertizing committees.

LINCOLN CENTENARY OF BIRTH ISSUE

Lincoln — A141

1909, Feb. 12   Wmk. 191   *Perf. 12*
367 A141 2c carmine   4.50   1.75
    Never hinged   9.50

Imperf
368 A141 2c carmine   12.50   19.00
    Never hinged   24.00

BLUISH PAPER
Perf. 12
369 A141 2c carmine   150.00   225.00
    Never hinged   300.00

Used examples of No. 369 must bear contemporaneous cancels. Expertizing is recommended.

ALASKA-YUKON-PACIFIC EXPOSITION ISSUE

William H. Seward — A142

1909, June 1   Wmk. 191   *Perf. 12*
370 A142 2c carmine   6.75   2.00
    Never hinged   15.00
  a.   Imperf. (error), P#5209 block
    of 6   2,250.

No. 370a comes from error panes found in perforated stock. Plate 5209 was used only to print the perforated Alaska-Yukon-Pacific Exposition issue. No 370a can only be collected as a plate-number stamp or multiple. Without an attached plate number 5209, the stamps from this pane cannot be differentiated from No. 371.

Imperf
371 A142 2c carmine   14.00   21.00
    Never hinged   30.00

Seattle, Wash., June 1 to Oct. 16.

HUDSON-FULTON CELEBRATION ISSUE

"Half Moon" and Steamship A143

1909, Sept. 25   Wmk. 191   *Perf. 12*
372 A143 2c carmine   10.00   4.75
    Never hinged   21.00

Imperf
373 A143 2c carmine   20.00   27.50
    Never hinged   40.00

Tercentenary of the discovery of the Hudson River and Centenary of Robert Fulton's steamship.

DESIGNS OF 1908-09 ISSUES

1910-11   Wmk. 190   *Perf. 12*
374 A138 1c green   6.00   .25
    Never hinged   14.00
  a.   Booklet pane of 6   225.00   400.00
    Never hinged   375.00
  b.   Double impression   300.00
375 A139 2c carmine   6.00   .25
    Never hinged   14.00
  a.   Booklet pane of 6   125.00   300.00
    Never hinged   200.00
  b.   2c lake   825.00   —
    Never hinged   1,800.
  c.   As "b," booklet pane of 6   10,000.
  d.   Double impression   750.00   —
    Never hinged   1,500.
376 A140 3c dp vio, type I
    ('11)   18.00   2.00
    Never hinged   40.00
377 A140 4c brown ('11)   27.50   1.00
    Never hinged   65.00
378 A140 5c blue ('11)   27.50   .75
    Never hinged   65.00
379 A140 6c red org ('11)   37.50   1.25
    Never hinged   85.00
380 A140 8c ol grn ('11)   90.00   15.00
    Never hinged   200.00
381 A140 10c yellow ('11)   85.00   6.00
    Never hinged   200.00
382 A140 15c pale ultra
    ('11)   225.00   20.00
    Never hinged   500.00
    Nos. 374-382 (9)   522.50   46.50

1910, Dec.   *Imperf.*
383 A138 1c green   2.50   2.75
    Never hinged   5.00
384 A139 2c carmine   4.00   2.75
    Never hinged   8.00

The values for used coil stamps are for examples with contemporaneous cancels that can be authenticated by expertizing committees. Used coils with cancels most commonly from the 1950s exist, and these and stamps with other non-contemporaneous cancels sell for less than the values shown.

COIL STAMPS

1910, Nov. 1   *Perf. 12 Horizontally*
385 A138 1c green   45.00   *50.00*
    Never hinged   100.00
386 A139 2c carmine   120.00   *90.00*
    Never hinged   260.00

1910-11   *Perf. 12 Vertically*
387 A138 1c green   190.00   *140.00*
    Never hinged   400.00
388 A139 2c carmine   1,500.   *2,250.*
    Never hinged   3,500.

Stamps offered as No. 388 frequently are privately perforated examples of No. 384, or examples of No. 375 with top and/or bottom perfs trimmed.

389 A140 3c dp vio, type
    I ('11)   110,000.   *10,000.*
    Never hinged   240,000.

No. 389 is valued in the grade of fine. Stamps offered as No. 389 sometimes are examples of No. 376 with top and/or bottom perfs trimmed.
Beware also of plentiful fakes in the marketplace of Nos. 385-387.
Expertization by competent authorities is recommended.

1910   *Perf. 8½ Horizontally*
390 A138 1c green   4.50   *14.00*
    Never hinged   10.00
391 A139 2c carmine   42.50   *50.00*
    Never hinged   90.00

1910-13   *Perf. 8½ Vertically*
392 A138 1c green   27.50   *50.00*
    Never hinged   65.00
393 A139 2c carmine   45.00   *55.00*
    Never hinged   105.00
394 A140 3c dp vio, type I
    ('11)   65.00   65.00
    Never hinged   135.00
395 A140 4c brown ('12)   65.00   65.00
    Never hinged   135.00
396 A140 5c blue ('13)   65.00   65.00
    Never hinged   135.00
    Nos. 392-396 (5)   267.50   300.00

Beware also of plentiful fakes in the marketplace of Nos. 390-393.

PANAMA-PACIFIC EXPOSITION ISSUE

Vasco Nunez de Balboa — A144

Pedro Miguel Locks, Panama Canal — A145

Golden Gate — A146

Discovery of San Francisco Bay — A147

1913   Wmk. 190   *Perf. 12*
397 A144 1c green   15.00   2.00
    Never hinged   35.00
398 A145 2c carmine   16.00   1.00
    Never hinged   35.00
  a.   2c carmine lake   1,500.

  b.   2c lake   2,500.
    Never hinged   5,250.   3,000.
    Never hinged   8,500.
399 A146 5c blue   70.00   10.00
    Never hinged   160.00
400 A147 10c orange yel   115.00   20.00
    Never hinged   260.00
400A A147 10c orange   175.00   22.50
    Never hinged   390.00
    Nos. 397-400A (5)   391.00   55.50
    Nos. 397-400A, never
    hinged   850.00

1914-15   *Perf. 10*
401 A144 1c green   25.00   7.00
    Never hinged   60.00
402 A145 2c car ('15)   70.00   3.00
    Never hinged   170.00
403 A146 5c blue ('15)   160.00   17.50
    Never hinged   400.00
404 A147 10c org ('15)   675.00   70.00
    Never hinged   1,650.
    Nos. 401-404 (4)   930.00   97.50
    Nos. 401-404, never
    hinged   2,280.

1912-14   Wmk. 190   *Perf. 12*
405 A140 1c green   6.50   .25
    Never hinged   15.00
  a.   Vert. pair, imperf. horiz.   2,000.
  b.   Booklet pane of 6   65.00   90.00
    Never hinged   110.00
  c.   Double impression   5,500.

TYPE I

TWO CENTS

Type I. There is one shading line in the first curve of the ribbon above the left "2" and one in the second curve of the ribbon above the right "2."
The button of the toga has only a faint outline.
The top line of the toga rope, from the button to the front of the throat, is also very faint.
The shading lines of the face terminate in front of the ear with little or no joining, to form a lock of hair.
Used on both flat plate and rotary press printings.

406 A140 2c car, type I   6.50   .25
    Never hinged   15.00
  a.   Booklet pane of 6   65.00   90.00
    Never hinged   110.00
  b.   Double impression   1,250.   —
  c.   2c lake, type I   3,000.   6,000.
    Never hinged   5,500.
407 A140 7c black ('14)   70.00   14.00
    Never hinged   150.00
    Nos. 405-407 (3)   83.00   14.50

1912   *Imperf.*
408 A140 1c green   1.00   1.00
    Never hinged   2.00
409 A140 2c car, type I   1.20   1.20
    Never hinged   2.40

COIL STAMPS

1912   *Perf. 8½ Horizontally*
410 A140 1c green   6.00   *12.50*
    Never hinged   13.00
411 A140 2c carmine, type I   10.00   *17.50*
    Never hinged   22.50

**   *Perf. 8½ Vertically***
412 A140 1c green   25.00   *40.00*
    Never hinged   55.00
413 A140 2c carmine, type I   60.00   50.00
    Never hinged   130.00
    Nos. 410-413 (4)   101.00   120.00

Beware also of plentiful fakes in the marketplace of Nos. 410-413.

Franklin — A148

1912-14   Wmk. 190   *Perf. 12*
414 A148 8c pale ol grn   40.00   2.00
    Never hinged   100.00
415 A148 9c sal red ('14)   50.00   14.00
    Never hinged   120.00
416 A148 10c org yel   40.00   .80
    Never hinged   100.00
  a.   10c brown yellow   1,250.
    Never hinged   2,750.
417 A148 12c cl brn ('14)   40.00   5.00
    Never hinged   100.00

418 A148 15c gray   80.00   4.00
    Never hinged   190.00
419 A148 20c ultra ('14)   190.00   17.50
    Never hinged   400.00
420 A148 30c org red ('14)   115.00   17.50
    Never hinged   250.00
421 A148 50c violet ('14)   350.00   27.50
    Never hinged   775.00
    Nos. 414-421 (8)   905.00   88.30

No. 421 almost always has an offset of the frame lines on the back under the gum. No. 422 does not have this offset.

> **VALUES FOR VERY FINE STAMPS**
> **Please note:** Stamps are valued in the grade of Very Fine unless otherwise indicated.

1912, Feb. 12   Wmk. 191   *Perf. 12*
422 A148 50c violet   225.00   25.00
    Never hinged   500.00
423 A148 $1 violet brown   475.00   85.00
    Never hinged   1,000.

Perforated sheet stamps of type A148: #431-440 (single line wmk., perf. 10), #460 (double line wmk., perf. 10), #470-478 (unwmkd., perf. 10), #508-518 (unwmkd., perf. 11).

1914   Wmk. 190   *Perf. 12x10*
423A A140 1c green   12,500.   5,500.
423B A140 2c rose red,
    type I   175,000.   12,500.
423C A140 5c blue   16,000.

Nos. 423A-423C formerly were Nos. 424a, 425d and 428a, respectively.
No. 423A unused is valued in the grade of fine. Values for 423A used and 423B-423C are for fine-very fine examples.

1914   Wmk. 190   *Perf. 10x12*
423D A140 1c green   8,000.
423E A140 2c rose red,
    type I   —

Nos. 423D and 423E formerly were Nos. 424b and 425c, respectively. Only one example is recorded of No. 423E.
No. 423D is valued in the grade of fine-very fine.

1913-15   Wmk. 190   *Perf. 10*
424 A140 1c grn ('14)   2.25   .25
    Never hinged   4.75
  c.   Vert. pair, imperf.
    horiz.   3,000.   2,750.
    Never hinged   4,500.
  d.   Booklet pane of 6
    ('13)   5.25   7.50
    Never hinged   8.75
  f.   Vert. pair, imperf. between and
    straight edge at top   13,000.

For former Nos. 424a and 424b, see Nos. 423A and 423D.
The unique example of No. 424f is never hinged, and it is valued thus.

Research has proven beyond doubt that all examples of the previously listed No. 424e, booklet pane of 6, imperforate and without gum, are unissued fabrications made from an ungummed press sheet on stamp paper once undoubtedly housed in the Smithsonian philatelic collection.

425 A140 2c rose red,
    type I
    ('14)   2.25   .25
    Never hinged   5.00
  e.   Booklet pane of 6
    ('13)   17.50   *25.00*
    Never hinged   30.00

For former Nos. 425c and 425d, see Nos. 423A and 423D.

426 A140 3c dp vio,
    type I
    ('14)   15.00   1.25
    Never hinged   35.00
427 A140 4c brn ('14)   32.50   .90
    Never hinged   75.00
428 A140 5c blue ('14)   32.50   .90
    Never hinged   75.00

For former No. 428a, see No. 423C.

429 A140 6c red org
    ('14)   45.00   2.00
    Never hinged   105.00
430 A140 7c black ('14)   85.00   4.75
    Never hinged   190.00
431 A148 8c pale ol
    grn ('14)   40.00   3.00
    Never hinged   80.00
  a.   Double impression   —
432 A148 9c sal red
    ('14)   40.00   8.00
    Never hinged   95.00

433	A148 10c org yel ('14)	40.00	1.00
	Never hinged	95.00	
434	A148 11c dk grn ('15)	25.00	8.00
	Never hinged	60.00	
435	A148 12c clar brn ('14)	30.00	5.50
	Never hinged	75.00	
a.	12c copper red	30.00	6.50
	Never hinged	75.00	
437	A148 15c gray ('14)	120.00	8.00
	Never hinged	275.00	
438	A148 20c ultra ('14)	200.00	7.00
	Never hinged	450.00	
439	A148 30c org red ('14)	225.00	20.00
	Never hinged	500.00	
440	A148 50c violet ('15)	450.00	20.00
	Never hinged	1,075.	
	Nos. 424-440 (16)	1,385.	90.80

The values for used coil stamps are for examples with contemporaneous cancels that can be authenticated by expertizing committees. Used coils with cancels most commonly from the 1950s exist, and these and stamps with other non-contemporaneous cancels sell for less than the values shown.

COIL STAMPS

1914		**Perf. 10 Horizontally**	
441	A140 1c green	1.00	*1.50*
	Never hinged	2.00	
442	A140 2c carmine, type I	10.00	*45.00*
	Never hinged	22.50	

1914		**Perf. 10 Vertically**	
443	A140 1c green	30.00	*45.00*
	Never hinged	65.00	
444	A140 2c car, type I	50.00	40.00
	Never hinged	120.00	
a.	2c lake		*2,000.*
445	A140 3c violet, type I	210.00	250.00
	Never hinged	500.00	
446	A140 4c brown	130.00	150.00
	Never hinged	280.00	
447	A140 5c blue	45.00	110.00
	Never hinged	100.00	
	Nos. 443-447 (5)	465.00	595.00

Beware also of plentiful fakes in the marketplace of Nos. 441-447.

ROTARY PRESS STAMPS
The Rotary Press Stamps are printed from plates that are curved to fit around a cylinder. This curvature produces stamps that are slightly larger, either horizontally or vertically, than those printed from flat plates. Designs of stamps from flat plates measure about 18½-19mm wide by 22mm high.

When the impressions are placed sidewise on the curved plates the designs are 19½-20mm wide; when they are placed vertically the designs are 22½ to 23mm high. A line of color (not a guide line) shows where the curved plates meet or join on the press.

ROTARY PRESS COIL STAMPS
Stamp designs: 18½-19x22½mm

1915-16		**Perf. 10 Horizontally**	
448	A140 1c green	10.00	*17.50*
	Never hinged	20.00	

Type II

TWO CENTS
Type II. Shading lines in ribbons as on type I.
The toga button, rope and rope shading lines are heavy.
The shading lines of the face at the lock of hair end in a strong vertical curved line.
Used on rotary press printings only.

Type III

Type III. Two lines of shading in the curves of the ribbons.
Other characteristics similar to type II.
Used on rotary press printings only.

Fraudulently altered examples of type III (Nos. 455, 488, 492 and 540) have had one line of shading scraped off to make them resemble type II (Nos. 454, 487, 491 and 539).

449	A140 2c red, type I	2,500.	650.00
	Never hinged	5,500.	
450	A140 2c car, type III ('16)	12.50	*25.00*
	Never hinged	27.50	

1914-16		**Perf. 10 Vertically**	
Stamp designs: 19½-20x22mm			
452	A140 1c green	12.50	*17.50*
	Never hinged	25.00	
453	A140 2c car rose, type I	140.00	45.00
	Never hinged	300.00	
454	A140 2c red, type II	70.00	22.50
	Never hinged	160.00	
455	A140 2c car, type III	8.00	3.50
	Never hinged	18.00	
456	A140 3c vio, type I ('16)	225.00	170.00
	Never hinged	500.00	
457	A140 4c brown ('16)	30.00	30.00
	Never hinged	60.00	
458	A140 5c blue ('16)	32.50	30.00
	Never hinged	65.00	
	Nos. 452-458 (7)	518.00	318.50

Horizontal Coil

1914, June 30		**Imperf.**	
459	A140 2c car, type I	200.	*1,300.*
	Never hinged	300.	

When the value for a used stamp is higher than the unused value, the stamp must have a contemporaneous cancel. Valuable stamps of this type should be accompanied by certificates of authenticity issued by recognized expertizing committees. The used value for No. 459 is for an example with such a certificate.

Beware of examples of No. 453 with perforations fraudulently trimmed to resemble single examples of No. 459.

FLAT PLATE PRINTINGS

1915, Feb. 8	**Wmk. 191**	**Perf. 10**	
460	A148 $1 violet black	650.	140.
	Never hinged	1,450.	

1915, June 17	**Wmk. 190**	**Perf. 11**	
461	A140 2c pale car red, type I	150.	*375.*
	Never hinged	325.	

Beware of fraudulently perforated examples of No. 409 being offered as No. 461.
See note on used stamps following No. 459.

Unwatermarked
From 1916 onward all postage stamps except Nos. 519 and 832b are on unwatermarked paper.

1916-17	**Unwmk.**	**Perf. 10**	
462	A140 1c green	7.00	.35
	Never hinged	16.00	
a.	Booklet pane of 6	9.50	*12.50*
	Never hinged	16.00	
463	A140 2c car, type I	4.50	.40
	Never hinged	10.00	.45
a.	Booklet pane of 6	110.00	110.00
	Never hinged	180.00	

See No. 467 for P# block of 6 from plate 7942.

464	A140 3c vio, type I	65.00	17.50
	Never hinged	165.00	

Beware of fraudulently perforated examples of No. 483 being offered as No. 464.

465	A140 4c org brn	60.00	2.25
	Never hinged	125.00	
466	A140 5c blue	65.00	2.25
	Never hinged	150.00	
467	A140 5c car (error in plate of 2c, '17)	425.00	*3,250.*
	Never hinged	800.00	

No. 467 is an error caused by using a 5c transfer roll in re-entering three subjects: 7942

UL 74, 7942 UL 84, 7942 LR 18; the balance of the subjects on the plate being normal 2c entries. No. 467 imperf. is listed as No. 485. The error perf 11 on unwatermarked paper is No. 505.

468	A140 6c red orange	100.00	8.00
	Never hinged	225.00	
469	A140 7c black	120.00	13.00
	Never hinged	270.00	
470	A148 8c olive green	65.00	7.00
	Never hinged	140.00	
471	A148 9c salmon red	75.00	17.50
	Never hinged	160.00	
472	A148 10c orange yel	120.00	3.00
	Never hinged	250.00	
473	A148 11c dark green	50.00	19.00
	Never hinged	110.00	
474	A148 12c claret brn	55.00	8.00
	Never hinged	120.00	
475	A148 15c gray	170.00	15.00
	Never hinged	375.00	
476	A148 20c lt ultra	240.00	17.50
	Never hinged	500.00	
476A	A148 30c orange red	*2,000.*	
	Never hinged	*4,250.*	

No. 476A is valued in the grade of fine.

477	A148 50c lt vio ('17)	850.	80.00
	Never hinged	2,000.	
478	A148 $1 violet black	600.	27.50
	Never hinged	1,400.	
	Nos. 462-466,468-476,477-478 (16)	2,647.	238.25

TYPES OF 1902-03 ISSUE

1917, Mar. 22	**Unwmk.**	**Perf. 10**	
479	A127 $2 dark blue	210.00	40.00
	Never hinged	475.00	
480	A128 $5 light green	170.00	35.00
	Never hinged	375.00	

1916-17		**Imperf.**	
481	A140 1c green	1.25	.95
	Never hinged	1.90	

Type Ia

TWO CENTS
Type Ia. The design characteristics are similar to type I except that all of the lines of the design are stronger.
The toga button, toga rope and rope shading lines are heavy.
The latter characteristics are those of type II, which, however, occur only on impressions from rotary plates.
Used only on flat plates 10208 and 10209.

482	A140 2c car, type I	1.50	1.30
	Never hinged	2.60	
482A	A140 2c dp rose, type Ia	—	*65,000.*

No. 482A was issued imperforate but all examples were privately perforated with large oblong perforations at the sides (Schermack type III).

Type II

THREE CENTS
Type II. The top line of the toga rope is strong and the rope shading lines are heavy and complete.
The line between the lips is heavy.
Used on both flat plate and rotary press printings.

483	A140 3c vio, type I ('17)	12.00	10.00
	Never hinged	24.00	
484	A140 3c violet, type II	10.00	8.00
	Never hinged	20.00	
485	A140 5c car (error in plate of 2c) ('17)	10,000.	
	Never hinged	13,000.	

Although No. 485 is valued as a single stamp, such examples are seldom seen in the marketplace.

No. 485 usually is seen as the center stamp in a block of 9 with 8 No. 482 (value with #485 never hinged, $22,500) or as two center stamps in a block of 12 (value with both No. 485 never hinged, $42,500).

ROTARY PRESS COIL STAMPS
(See note over No. 448)

1916-18		**Perf. 10 Horizontally**	
Stamp designs: 18½-19x22½mm			
486	A140 1c green ('18)	.85	.85
	Never hinged	1.75	
487	A140 2c carmine, type II	12.50	14.00
	Never hinged	27.50	
488	A140 2c carmine, type III	3.00	*5.00*
	Never hinged	1.75	
489	A140 3c vio, type I ('17)	4.50	2.25
	Never hinged	10.00	
	Nos. 486-489 (4)	20.85	22.10

1916-22		**Perf. 10 Vertically**	
Stamp designs: 19½-20x22mm			
490	A140 1c green	.50	*.60*
	Never hinged	1.05	
491	A140 2c car, type II	2,500.	800.00
	Never hinged	5,250.	
492	A140 2c car, type III	9.00	1.00
	Never hinged	19.00	
493	A140 3c vio, type I ('17)	14.00	4.50
	Never hinged	30.00	
494	A140 3c vio, type II ('18)	10.00	2.50
	Never hinged	21.50	
495	A140 4c org brn ('17)	10.00	7.00
	Never hinged	21.50	
496	A140 5c blue ('19)	3.25	2.50
	Never hinged	7.00	
497	A148 10c org yel ('22)	17.50	17.50
	Never hinged	35.00	

Blind Perfs

Listings of imperforate-between varieties are for examples which show no trace of "blind perfs," traces of impressions from the perforating pins which do not cut into the paper.

Some unused stamps have had the gum removed to eliminate the impressions from the perforating pins. These stamps do not qualify as the listed varieties.

TYPES OF 1913-15 ISSUE
FLAT PLATE PRINTINGS
1917-19   Unwmk.   Perf. 11

498	A140 1c green	.50	.25
	Never hinged	1.00	
a.	Vertical pair, imperf. horiz.	800.00	
	Never hinged	1,600.	
b.	Horizontal pair, imperf. between	600.00	
	Never hinged	1,350.	
c.	Vertical pair, imperf. between	700.00	—
d.	Double impression	250.00	3,750.
e.	Booklet pane of 6	2.50	2.00
	Never hinged	4.25	
f.	Booklet pane of 30	1,050.	12,500.
	Never hinged	1,700.	
g.	Perf. 10 at top or bottom	15,000.	20,000.
	Never hinged	27,500.	

No. 498g used is valued in the grade of fine.

499	A140 2c rose, type I	.50	.25
	Never hinged	1.00	
a.	Vertical pair, imperf. horiz., type I	3,000.	
	Never hinged	4,250.	
b.	Horiz. pair, imperf. vert., type I	550.00	600.00
	Never hinged	1,100.	
c.	Vert. pair, imperf. btwn., type I	900.00	300.00
e.	Booklet pane of 6, type I	4.00	2.50
	Never hinged	6.75	
f.	Booklet pane of 30, type I	20,000.	—
	Never hinged	28,000.	
g.	Double impression, type I	200.00	2,000.
	Never hinged	400.00	
h.	2c lake, type I	500.00	800.00
	Never hinged	1,000.	
i.	As "e," single stamp, lake	—	—

No. 499b is valued in the grade of fine. No 499g used is valued in the grade of fine.

500	A140 2c deep rose, type Ia	260.00	240.00
	Never hinged	570.00	
501	A140 3c lt vio, type I	9.00	.40
	Never hinged	20.00	
b.	Booklet pane of 6, type I	75.00	80.00
	Never hinged	125.00	
c.	Vert. pair, imper. horiz., type I	2,100.	
	Never hinged	3,250.	
d.	Double impression	3,500.	3,500.
	Never hinged	5,000.	

No. 501d is valued in the grade of fine.

502	A140 3c dk vio, type II	12.00	.75
	Never hinged	27.50	
b.	Bklt. pane of 6, type II	60.00	75.00
	Never hinged	100.00	
c.	Vert. pair, imperf. horiz., type II	1,400.	850.00
	Never hinged	2,750.	
d.	Double impression	800.00	1,000.
	Never hinged	1,600.	
e.	Perf. 10 at top or bottom	15,000.	30,000.
	Never hinged	21,500.	
503	A140 4c brown	8.50	.40
	Never hinged	19.00	
b.	Double impression	—	
504	A140 5c blue	7.50	.35
	Never hinged	17.00	
a.	Horizontal pair, imperf. between	20,000.	—
b.	Double impression	1,750.	1,600.
505	A140 5c rose (error in plate of 2c)	325.00	600.00
	Never hinged	625.00	
506	A140 6c red orange	11.00	.40
	Never hinged	25.00	
a.	Perf. 10 at top or bottom	30,000.	8,000.
b.	Double impression, never hinged	2,000.	

No. 506a also exists as a transitional stamp gauging partly perf 10 and partly perf 11 at top. Value thus the same as normal 506a.
No. 506b is a partial double impression. Two authenticated examples are documented.

507	A140 7c black	24.00	1.25
	Never hinged	55.00	
508	A148 8c olive bister	11.00	.65
	Never hinged	25.00	
b.	Vertical pair, imperf. between	—	—
c.	Perf. 10 at top or bottom		9,000.
509	A148 9c salmon red	11.00	1.60
	Never hinged	25.00	
a.	Perf. 10 at top or bottom	37,500.	7,500.

No. 509a also exists as a transitional stamp gauging partly perf 10 and partly perf 11 at top or bottom. Value thus the same as normal 509a.

510	A148 10c org yel	15.00	.25
	Never hinged	34.00	
a.	10c brown yellow	1,400.	
	Never hinged	3,250.	

511	A148 11c lt green	7.50	2.25
	Never hinged	17.00	
a.	Perf. 10 at top or bottom	3,250.	3,250.
	Never hinged	7,000.	

No. 511a also exists as a transitional stamp gauging partly perf 10 and partly perf 11 at top or bottom. Value thus the same as normal 511a.

512	A148 12c claret brown	7.50	.40
	Never hinged	17.00	
a.	12c brown carmine	8.50	.50
	Never hinged	19.00	
b.	Perf. 10 at top or bottom	25,000.	15,000.
513	A148 13c apple grn ('19)	9.50	5.50
	Never hinged	21.00	
514	A148 15c gray	32.50	1.40
	Never hinged	75.00	
a.	Perf. 10 at bottom		10,000.
515	A148 20c lt ultra	40.00	.45
	Never hinged	85.00	
b.	Vertical pair, imperf. between	1,750.	3,250.
c.	Double impression	1,250.	
	Never hinged	2,500.	
d.	Perf. 10 at top or bottom		11,000.

No. 515b is valued in the grade of fine.
Beware of pairs with blind perforations inside the design of the top stamp that are offered as No. 515b.
No. 515c is a partial double impression.

516	A148 30c orange red	30.00	1.50
	Never hinged	70.00	
a.	Perf. 10 at top or bottom	20,000.	15,000.
	Never hinged	37,500.	
b.	Double impression		

No. 516a used is valued in the grade of fine.

517	A148 50c red violet	50.00	.75
	Never hinged	120.00	
b.	Vertical pair, imperf. between & with natural straight edge at bottom	6,000.	
c.	Perf. 10 at top or bottom		17,000.

No. 517b is valued in average condition and may be a unique used pair (precanceled). The editors would like to see authenticated evidence of an unused pair.

518	A148 $1 violet brown	37.50	1.50
	Never hinged	95.00	
b.	$1 deep brown	1,800.	1,100.
	Never hinged	4,000.	
Nos. 498-504,506-518 (20)		*584.50*	*260.30*

No. 518b is valued in the grade of fine to very fine.

TYPE OF 1908-09 ISSUE
1917, Oct. 10   Wmk. 191   Perf. 11

519	A139 2c carmine	425.00	1,800.
	Never hinged	900.00	

Beware of examples of No. 344 fraudulently perforated and offered as No. 519. Obtaining a certificate from a recognized expertizing committee is strongly recommended.

Warning: See note following No. 459 regarding used stamps.

Franklin — A149

1918, Aug.   Unwmk.   Perf. 11

523	A149 $2 org red & blk	525.	240.
	Never hinged	1,175.	
524	A149 $5 dp grn & blk	160.	35.
	Never hinged	340.	

See No. 547 for $2 carmine & black.

TYPES OF 1917-19 ISSUE
OFFSET PRINTING
1918-20   Unwmk.   Perf. 11

525	A140 1c gray green	2.50	.90
	Never hinged	6.00	
a.	1c dark green	10.00	1.75
	Never hinged	25.00	
c.	Horizontal pair, imperf. between	750.00	650.00
d.	Double impression	40.00	750.00
	Never hinged	90.00	

No. 525c is valued in the grade of fine and with natural straight edge at right, as virtually all recorded examples come thus. No. 525d used is valued in the grade of very good.

Type IV

TWO CENTS

Type IV — Top line of the toga rope is broken.
The shading lines in the toga button are so arranged that the curving of the first and last form "D (reversed) ID."
The line of color in the left "2" is very thin and usually broken.
Used on offset printings only.

Type V

Type V — Top line of the toga is complete.
There are five vertical shading lines in the toga button.
The line of color in the left "2" is very thin and usually broken.
The shading dots on the nose are as shown on the diagram.
Used on offset printings only.

Type Va

Type Va — Characteristics are the same as type V except in the shading dots of the nose. The third row of dots from the bottom has four dots instead of six. The overall height is ⅓mm shorter than the other types.
Used on offset printings only.

Type VI

Type VI — General characteristics the same as type V except that the line of color in the left "2" is very heavy.
Used on offset printings only.

TYPE VII

Type VII — The line of color in the left "2" is invariably continuous, clearly defined and heavier than in type V or Va but not as heavy as type VI.
An additional vertical row of dots has been added to the upper lip.
Numerous additional dots have been added to the hair on top of the head.
Used on offset printings only.

526	A140 2c car, type IV ('20)	25.00	4.00
	Never hinged	57.50	

527	A140 2c car, type V ('20)	18.00	1.25
	Never hinged	40.00	
a.	Double impression	100.00	—
b.	Vert. pair, imperf. horiz.	225.00	
c.	Horiz. pair, imperf. vert.	850.00	
d.	Double impression	1,000.	—
528	A140 2c car, type Va ('20)	10.00	.40
	Never hinged	22.50	
c.	Double impression	60.00	
	Never hinged	150.00	
g.	Vert. pair, imperf. between	3,250.	
528A	A140 2c car, type VI ('20)	47.50	2.00
	Never hinged	115.00	
d.	Double impression	200.00	900.00
	Never hinged	450.00	
f.	Vert. pair, imperf. horiz.		
h.	Vert. pair, imperf. between	5,000.	
528B	A140 2c car, type VII ('20)	20.00	.75
	Never hinged	50.00	
e.	Double impression	77.50	400.00

No. 528Be used is valued in the grade of very good to fine.

TYPE III

THREE CENTS
Type III — The top line of the toga rope is strong but the 5th shading line is missing as in type I.
Center shading line of the toga button consists of two dashes with a central dot.
The "P" and "O" of "POSTAGE" are separated by a line of color.
The frame line at the bottom of the vignette is complete.
Used on offset printings only.

TYPE IV

Type IV — The shading lines of the toga rope are complete.
The second and fourth shading lines in the toga button are broken in the middle and the third line is continuous with a dot in the center.
The "P" and "O" of "POSTAGE" are joined.
The frame line at the bottom of the vignette is broken.
Used on offset printings only.

529	A140 3c vio, type III	3.50	.50
	Never hinged	7.75	
a.	Double impression	50.00	800.00
	Never hinged	115.00	
b.	Printed on both sides	2,500.	

No. 529a used is valued in the grade of very good.

530	A140 3c pur, type IV	2.00	.30
	Never hinged	4.50	
a.	Double impression	40.00	800.00
	Never hinged	90.00	
b.	Printed on both sides	750.00	
	Never hinged	1,100.	
c.	Triple impression	1,750.	
Nos. 525-530 (8)		*128.50*	*10.10*

No. 530a used is valued in the grade of fine.

1918-20   Imperf.

531	A140 1c green ('19)	12.00	12.00
	Never hinged	21.00	

532	A140	2c car rose, type IV ('20)	45.00 42.50
		Never hinged	80.00
533	A140	2c car, type V ('20)	110.00 150.00
		Never hinged	175.00
534	A140	2c car, type Va ('20)	15.00 15.00
		Never hinged	26.00
534A	A140	2c car, type VI ('20)	47.50 40.00
		Never hinged	90.00
534B	A140	2c car, type VII ('20)	2,250. 1,500.
		Never hinged	3,750.
535	A140	3c vio, type IV	10.00 6.00
		Never hinged	18.00
a.		Double impression	100.00 —
		Never hinged	200.00
		Nos. 531-534A,535 (6)	239.50 265.50

1919, Aug. 12   **Perf. 12½**

536	A140	1c gray green	20.00 35.00
		Never hinged	45.00
a.		Horiz. pair, imperf. vert.	900.00
		Never hinged	1,400.

VICTORY ISSUE

"Victory" and Flags of the Allies — A150

FLAT PLATE PRINTING

1919, Mar. 3   **Engr.**   **Perf. 11**

537	A150	3c violet	10.00 3.25
		Never hinged	20.00
a.		3c deep red violet	1,250. 1,750.
		Never hinged	2,300.
b.		3c light reddish violet	150.00 50.00
		Never hinged	300.00
c.		3c red violet	200.00 60.00
		Never hinged	400.00

Victory of the Allies in World War I.
No. 537a is valued in the grade of fine.

ROTARY PRESS PRINTINGS

1919   **Perf. 11x10**
Stamp designs: 19½-20x22-22¼mm

538	A140	1c green	10.00 9.00
		Never hinged	23.00
a.		Vert. pair, imperf. horiz.	60.00 125.00
		Never hinged	125.00
539	A140	2c car rose, type II	2,700. 17,500.
		Never hinged	4,250.
540	A140	2c car rose, type III	12.00 9.50
		Never hinged	27.50
a.		Vert. pair, imperf. horiz.	60.00 140.00
		Never hinged	125.00
b.		Horiz. pair, imperf. vert.	2,750.
541	A140	3c vio, type II	40.00 37.50
		Never hinged	100.00

The part perforate varieties of Nos. 538a and 540a were issued in sheets and may be had in blocks; similar part perforate varieties, Nos. 490 and 492, are from coils and are found only in strips.
See note over No. 448 regarding No. 539.
No. 539 is valued in the grade of fine.
No. 540b is valued in the grade of fine.

1920, May 26   **Perf. 10x11**
Stamp design: 19x22½-22¾mm

542	A140	1c green	12.50 1.50
		Never hinged	30.00

1921   **Perf. 10**
Stamp design: 19x22½mm

543	A140	1c green	.70 .40
		Never hinged	1.75
a.		Horizontal pair, imperf. between	4,500.

1922   **Perf. 11**
Stamp design: 19x22½mm

544	A140	1c green	22,500. 3,500.
		Never hinged	35,000.

No. 544 is valued in the grade of fine.

1921
Stamp designs: 19½-20x22mm

545	A140	1c green	225.00 200.00
		Never hinged	550.00
546	A140	2c car rose, type III	105.00 190.00
		Never hinged	230.00
a.		Perf. 10 on left side	7,500. 17,500.

No. 546a used is valued in the grade of very good. It is unique used.

FLAT PLATE PRINTING

1920, Nov. 1   **Perf. 11**

547	A149	$2 carmine & black	125. 40.
		Never hinged	275.
a.		$2 lake & black	200. 40.
		Never hinged	425.

PILGRIM TERCENTENARY ISSUE

"Mayflower" A151

Landing of the Pilgrims — A152

Signing of the Compact — A153

1920, Dec. 21   **Perf. 11**

548	A151	1c green	3.75 2.00
		Never hinged	9.25
549	A152	2c carmine rose	5.00 1.60
		Never hinged	12.00
550	A153	5c deep blue	30.00 12.50
		Never hinged	65.00
		Nos. 548-550 (3)	38.75 16.10
		Nos. 548-550, never hinged	97.50

Tercentenary of the landing of the Pilgrims at Plymouth, Mass.

Nathan Hale A154

Franklin A155

Harding A156

Washington A157

Lincoln A158

Martha Washington A159

Theodore Roosevelt A160

Garfield A161

McKinley A162

Grant A163

Jefferson A164

Monroe A165

Rutherford B. Hayes A166

Grover Cleveland A167

American Indian A168

Statue of Liberty A169

Golden Gate — A170

Niagara Falls — A171

American Buffalo A172

Arlington Amphitheater A173

Lincoln Memorial A174

U.S. Capitol A175

Head of Freedom Statue, Capitol Dome — A176

FLAT PLATE PRINTINGS

1922-25   **Unwmk.**   **Perf. 11**

551	A154	½c ol brn ('25)	.25 .25
		Never hinged	.50
552	A155	1c dp grn ('23)	1.25 .25
		Never hinged	2.75
a.		Booklet pane of 6	7.50 4.00
		Never hinged	12.50
553	A156	1½c yel brn ('25)	2.00 .25
		Never hinged	4.10
554	A157	2c carmine ('23)	1.10 .25
		Never hinged	2.50
a.		Horiz. pair, imperf. vert.	250.00
		Never hinged	400.00
b.		Vert. pair, imperf. horiz.	6,000.
		Never hinged	10,000.
c.		Booklet pane of 6	7.00 3.00
		Never hinged	15.000.
d.		Perf. 10 at top or bottom	12,500. 8,500.
		Never hinged	15,000.
555	A158	3c violet ('23)	13.00 1.20
		Never hinged	27.50
556	A159	4c yel brn ('23)	16.00 .50
		Never hinged	35.00
a.		Vert. pair, imperf. horiz.	12,500.
b.		Perf. 10 at top or bottom	3,500. 22,500.

No. 556a is unique. It resulted from a sheet that was damaged and patched during production.
No. 556b used also exists as a transitional stamp gauging 10 at left top and 11 at right top. Value the same.

557	A160	5c dark blue	16.00 .30
		Never hinged	35.00
a.		Imperf., pair	2,000.
		Never hinged	4,000.

b.		Horiz. pair, imperf. vert.	—
c.		Perf. 10 at top or bottom	— 10,000.
558	A161	6c red orange	30.00 1.00
		Never hinged	65.00
559	A162	7c black ('23)	7.25 .75
		Never hinged	15.50
560	A163	8c ol grn ('23)	37.50 1.00
		Never hinged	80.00
561	A164	9c rose ('23)	11.00 1.25
		Never hinged	25.00
562	A165	10c orange ('23)	13.50 .35
		Never hinged	30.00
a.		Vert. pair, imperf. horiz.	2,000.
		Never hinged	3,250.
b.		Imperf., pair	1,750.
c.		Perf. 10 at top or bottom	60,000. 12,500.

No. 562a is valued in the grade of fine, with gum and without blue defacing lines. No. 562b is valued without gum and without blue pencil defacing lines. No. 562c is valued in the grade of fine.

563	A166	11c greenish blue	1.25 .60
		Never hinged	2.75
a.		11c light bluish green	1.25 .60
		Never hinged	2.75
d.		Imperf., pair	20,000.

Many other intermediate shades exist for Nos. 563 and 563a, all falling within the blue or green color families.

564	A167	12c brn vio ('23)	4.75 .35
		Never hinged	10.50
a.		Horiz. pair, imperf. vert.	3,750.
565	A168	14c blue ('23)	4.25 .90
		Never hinged	9.50
566	A169	15c gray	16.00 .30
		Never hinged	35.00
567	A170	20c car rose ('23)	16.00 .30
		Never hinged	35.00
a.		Horiz. pair, imperf. vert.	2,500.
		Never hinged	5,000.

No. 567a is valued in the grade of fine.

568	A171	25c yel grn	13.50 .75
		Never hinged	30.00
b.		Vert. pair, imperf. horiz.	3,250.
c.		Perf. 10 at one side	5,000. 11,000.
		Never hinged	7,500.

No. 568b is valued in the grade of fine. No. 568c used is valued in the grade of fine.

569	A172	30c ol brn ('23)	22.50 .60
		Never hinged	50.00
570	A173	50c lilac	32.50 .40
		Never hinged	70.00
571	A174	$1 vio brn ('23)	35.00 .80
		Never hinged	75.00
572	A175	$2 dp blue ('23)	55.00 9.00
		Never hinged	120.00
573	A176	$5 car & bl ('23)	90.00 15.00
		Never hinged	180.00
a.		$5 car lake & dk bl	180.00 30.00
		Never hinged	375.00
		Nos. 551-573 (23)	439.60 36.35
		Nos. 551-573, never hinged	940.60

No. 556a is unique. No. 554b is valued in the grade of fine. No. 562b is valued without gum and without blue pencil defacing lines. No. 568b is valued in the grade of fine.
For other listings of perforated stamps of designs A154 to A173 see:
Nos. 578 & 579, Perf. 11x10
Nos. 581-591, Perf. 10
Nos. 594-596, Perf. 11
Nos. 632-642, 653, 692-696, Perf. 11x10½
Nos. 697-701, Perf. 10½x11
This series also includes #622-623 (perf. 11), 684-687 & 720-723.

1923-25   **Imperf.**
Stamp design 19¼x22¼mm

575	A155	1c green	5.00 5.00
		Never hinged	11.00
576	A156	1½c yel brn ('25)	1.25 1.50
		Never hinged	2.70

The 1½c A156 Rotary press imperforate is listed as No. 631.

577	A157	2c carmine	1.30 1.25
		Never hinged	2.90
a.		2c carmine lake	—
		Nos. 575-577 (3)	7.55 7.75
		Nos. 575-577, never hinged	16.60

ROTARY PRESS PRINTINGS
(See note over No. 448)

1923   **Perf. 11x10**

578	A155	1c green	75.00 160.00
		Never hinged	150.00
579	A157	2c carmine	70.00 140.00
		Never hinged	140.00

Nos. 578-579 were made from coil waste of Nos. 597, 599 and measure approximately 19¾x22¼mm.

1923-26   **Perf. 10**

581	A155	1c green	10.00 .75
		Never hinged	21.00
582	A156	1½c brown ('25)	6.00 .65
		Never hinged	13.00
583	A157	2c car ('24)	3.00 .30
		Never hinged	6.25
a.		Booklet pane of 6	110.00 150.00
		Never hinged	150.00
584	A158	3c violet ('25)	27.50 3.00
		Never hinged	60.00
585	A159	4c yel brn ('25)	17.50 .65
		Never hinged	37.50

586 A160 5c blue ('25)   17.50   .40
     Never hinged   37.50
a. Horizontal pair, imperf.
     vertically   7,500.

No. 586a is unique, precanceled, with average centering and small faults, and it is valued as such.

587 A161 6c red org ('25)   9.25   .60
     Never hinged   20.00
588 A162 7c black ('26)   12.50   6.25
     Never hinged   26.00
589 A163 8c ol grn ('26)   27.50   4.50
     Never hinged   57.50
590 A164 9c rose ('26)   6.00   2.50
     Never hinged   12.50
591 A165 10c org ('25)   40.00   .50
     Never hinged   85.00
Nos. 581-591 (11)   176.75   20.10
Nos. 581-591, never
hinged   371.25

1923   *Perf. 11*
594 A155 1c green   35,000. 10,500.
     With gum   65,000.

The main listing for No. 594 unused is for an example without gum; both unused and used are valued with perforations just touching frameline on one side.

595 A157 2c carmine   240.00   375.00
     Never hinged   450.00

Nos. 594-595 were made from coil waste of Nos. 597 and 599, and measure approximately 19¾x22¼mm.

596 A155 1c green   250,000.
     Precanceled   200,000.

No. 596 was made from rotary press sheet waste and measures approximately 19¼x22¼mm. A majority of the examples carry the Bureau precancel "Kansas City, Mo." No. 596 is valued in the grade of fine.

COIL STAMPS
ROTARY PRESS
1923-29   *Perf. 10 Vertically*
Stamp designs approximately
19¾x22¼mm

597 A155 1c green   .30   .25
     Never hinged   .60
598 A156 1½c brown ('25)   .90   .25
     Never hinged   1.80

Type I

Type II

Type I   Type II

TYPE I. No line outlining forehead. No heavy hair lines at top center of head. Outline of left acanthus scroll generally faint at top and toward base at left side.
TYPE II. Thin line outlining forehead. Three heavy hair lines at top center of head; two being outstanding in the white area. Outline of left acanthus scroll very strong and clearly defined at top (under left edge of lettered panel) and at lower curve (above and to left of numeral oval). This type appears only on Nos. 599A and 634A.

599 A157 2c car, type I   .35   .25
     Never hinged   .70
b. 2c carmine lake, type I,
     never hinged   300.00   —
599A A157 2c car, type II
     ('29)   100.00 16.00
     Never hinged   200.00
600 A158 3c violet ('24)   5.25   .25
     Never hinged   10.50
601 A159 4c yel brn   3.75   .35
     Never hinged   7.50
602 A160 5c dk blue ('24)   1.75   .25
     Never hinged   3.50
603 A165 10c orange ('24)   3.50   .25
     Never hinged   7.00

The 6c design A161 coil stamp is listed as No. 723.

1923-25   *Perf. 10 Horizontally*
Stamp designs: 19¼x22½mm

604 A155 1c green ('24)   .40   .25
     Never hinged   .80
605 A156 1½c yel brn ('25)   .40   .25
     Never hinged   .80
606 A157 2c carmine   .40   .25
     Never hinged   .80
a. 2c carmine lake   75.00   —
     Never hinged   150.00
Nos. 597-599,600-606 (10)   17.00   2.60
Nos. 597-599, 600-606,
never hinged   36.00

HARDING MEMORIAL ISSUE

Warren G.
Harding — A177

FLAT PLATE PRINTING
Stamp designs: 19¼x22¼mm

1923   *Perf. 11*
610 A177 2c black   .50   .25
     Never hinged   1.00
a. Horiz. pair, imperf. vert.   2,000.
b. Imperf. (error), P#14870
     block of 6   25,000.

No. 610a is valued in the grade of fine.
No. 610b comes from left side error panes found in a normal pad of No. 610 stamps before No. 611 was issued. Two left side plate blocks and one top position plate block are recorded. Plate #14870 was not used to print No. 611. Loose stamps separated from the top and left plate blocks are indistinguishable from No. 611.

Imperf
611 A177 2c black   4.50   4.00
     Never hinged   9.00
ROTARY PRESS PRINTING
Stamp designs: 19¼x22½mm
Perf. 10
612 A177 2c black   1.00   1.75
     Never hinged   32.50
Perf. 11
613 A177 2c black   35,000.

Tribute to President Warren G. Harding, who died August 2, 1923.
No. 613 was produced from rotary press sheet waste. It is valued in the grade of fine.

HUGUENOT-WALLOON
TERCENTENARY ISSUE

"New
Netherland"
A178

Landing at
Fort Orange
A179

Monument to
Jan Ribault
at Duvall
County,
Fla. — A180

FLAT PLATE PRINTINGS
1924, May 1   *Perf. 11*
614 A178 1c dark green   2.30   3.00
     Never hinged   4.25
615 A179 2c carmine rose   3.75   2.25
     Never hinged   7.00
616 A180 5c dark blue   15.00 13.00
     Never hinged   27.50
Nos. 614-616 (3)   21.05   18.25
Nos. 614-616, never hinged   38.75

Tercentenary of the settling of the Walloons and in honor of the Huguenots.

LEXINGTON-CONCORD ISSUE

Washington
at
Cambridge
A181

"Birth of
Liberty," by
Henry
Sandham
A182

The Minute
Man, by
Daniel
Chester
French
A183

1925, Apr. 4   *Perf. 11*
617 A181 1c deep green   2.00   2.50
     Never hinged   3.75
618 A182 2c carmine rose   3.50   4.00
     Never hinged   6.50
619 A183 5c dark blue   14.00 13.00
     Never hinged   26.00
Nos. 617-619 (3)   19.50   19.50
Nos. 617-619, never hinged   36.25

150th anniv. of the Battle of Lexington-Concord.

NORSE-AMERICAN ISSUE

A184

A185

1925, May 18   *Perf. 11*
620 A184 2c carmine & black   3.00   2.75
     Never hinged   6.00
621 A185 5c dark blue & black   9.00   9.00
     Never hinged   19.00

100th anniv. of the arrival in NY on Oct. 9, 1825, of the sloop "Restaurationen" with the first group of immigrants from Norway to the U.S.

Benjamin
Harrison
A186

Woodrow
Wilson
A187

1925-26   *Perf. 11*
622 A186 13c green ('26)   9.00   .75
     Never hinged   19.00
623 A187 17c black   9.00   .30
     Never hinged   19.00

SESQUICENTENNIAL EXPOSITION
ISSUE

Liberty
Bell — A188

1926, May 10   *Perf. 11*
627 A188 2c carmine rose   2.25   .50

150th anniv. of the Declaration of Independence, Philadelphia, June 1-Dec. 1.

ERICSSON MEMORIAL ISSUE

Statue of John
Ericsson — A189

1926, May 29   *Perf. 11*
628 A189 5c gray lilac   5.00   3.25
     Never hinged   8.50

John Ericsson, builder of the "Monitor."

BATTLE OF WHITE PLAINS ISSUE

Alexander Hamilton's
Battery — A190

1926, Oct. 18   *Perf. 11*
629 A190 2c carmine rose   1.60   1.70
     Never hinged   2.75

Battle of White Plains, NY, 150th anniv.

INTERNATIONAL PHILATELIC
EXHIBITION ISSUE
Souvenir Sheet

A190a

Condition valued:
Centering: Overall centering will average very fine, but individual stamps may be better or worse.
Perforations: No folds along rows of perforations.
Gum: There may be some light gum bends but no gum creases.
Hinging: There may be hinge marks in the selvage and on up to two or three stamps, but no heavy hinging or hinge remnants (except in the ungummed portion of the wide selvage).
Margins: Top panes should have about ½ inch bottom margin and 1 inch top margin.
Bottom panes should have about ½ inch top margin and just under ¾ inch bottom margin. Both will have one wide side (usually 1 inch plus) and one narrow (½ inch) side margin. The wide margin corner will have a small diagonal notch on top panes.

1926, Oct. 18   *Perf. 11*
630 A190a 2c car rose,
     pane of 25   275.00 450.00
     Never hinged   500.00
a. Single stamp (see foot-
     note)   10.00
     Never hinged   14.00

Issued in panes measuring 158-160¼x136-146½mm containing 25 stamps with inscription "International Philatelic Exhibition, Oct. 16th to 23rd, 1926" in top margin.
No. 630a can be identified only when attached to the distinctive selvage as shown in illustration A190a. The four plate numbers used to print the White Plains souvenir sheets were distinct from the plate numbers used to print No. 629, and therefore all stamps in a plate block, for instance, are identifiable as No. 630a.

VALUES FOR VERY FINE STAMPS
Please note: Stamps are valued in the grade of Very Fine unless otherwise indicated.

TYPES OF 1922-26 ISSUE
REGULAR ISSUE
ROTARY PRESS PRINTINGS
(See note above No. 448.)

			Imperf.
1926, Aug. 27			
631	A156 1½c yellow brown	2.00	1.70
	Never hinged	3.00	

			Perf. 11x10½
1926-34			
632	A155 1c green ('27)	.25	.25
	Never hinged	.35	
a.	Booklet pane of 6	5.00	4.00
	Never hinged	8.00	
b.	Vertical pair, imperf. be-tween	3,000.	3,250.
	Never hinged	5,500.	
c.	Horiz. pair, imperf. be-tween	5,000.	

No. 632b is valued in the grade of fine. No. 632c is valued in the grade of fine and never hinged. It is possibly unique.

633	A156 1½c yel brn ('27)	1.70	.25
	Never hinged	2.60	
634	A157 2c car, type I	.25	.25
	Never hinged	.30	
b.	2c carmine lake	180.00	500.00
	Never hinged	425.00	
c.	Horiz. pair, imperf. btwn.	6,000.	
d.	Booklet pane of 6, car-mine	1.50	1.50
	Never hinged	2.50	
e.	As "d," carmine lake	400.00	1,000.
	Never hinged	750.00	

Shades of the carmine exist.
No. 634c is valued in the grade of fine.

634A	A157 2c car, type II ('28)	300.00	13.50
	Never hinged	600.00	
635	A158 3c violet ('27)	.75	.25
	Never hinged	1.20	
a.	3c bright violet ('34)	.35	.25
	Never hinged	.45	
636	A159 4c yel brn ('27)	1.90	.25
	Never hinged	3.00	
637	A160 5c dk blue ('27)	1.90	.25
	Never hinged	3.00	
638	A161 6c red org ('27)	2.00	.25
	Never hinged	3.20	
639	A162 7c black ('27)	2.00	.25
	Never hinged	3.20	
a.	Vertical pair, imperf. be-tween	550.00	400.00
	Never hinged	1,000.	
640	A163 8c ol grn ('27)	2.00	.25
	Never hinged	3.20	
641	A164 9c rose ('27)	1.90	.25
	Never hinged	3.00	
642	A165 10c org ('27)	3.25	.25
	Never hinged	5.50	
Nos. 632-634,635-642 (11)		17.90	2.75
Nos. 632-634, 635-642 never hinged		28.00	

The 1½c, 2c, 4c, 5c, 6c, 8c imperf. (dry print) are printer's waste.
For ½c, 11c-50c see Nos. 653, 692-701.

VERMONT SESQUICENTENNIAL ISSUE

Battle of Bennington, 150th anniv. and State independence.

Green Mountain Boy — A191

FLAT PLATE PRINTING

			Perf. 11
1927, Aug. 3			
643	A191 2c carmine rose	1.20	.80
	Never hinged	2.00	

BURGOYNE CAMPAIGN ISSUE

Battles of Bennington, Oriskany, Fort Stanwix and Saratoga.

"The Surrender of General Burgoyne at Saratoga," by John Trumbull A192

			Perf. 11
1927, Aug. 3			
644	A192 2c carmine rose	3.00	2.10
	Never hinged	5.25	

VALLEY FORGE ISSUE

150th anniversary of Washington's encampment at Valley Forge, Pa.

Washington at Prayer — A193

			Perf. 11
1928, May 26			
645	A193 2c carmine rose	1.15	.50
	Never hinged	1.80	
a.	2c lake	—	
	Never hinged	—	

BATTLE OF MONMOUTH ISSUE

150th anniv. of the Battle of Monmouth, N.J., and "Molly Pitcher" (Mary Ludwig Hayes), the heroine of the battle.

No. 634 Overprinted

ROTARY PRESS PRINTING

			Perf. 11x10½
1928, Oct. 20			
646	A157 2c carmine	1.00	1.00
	Never hinged	1.60	
a.	"Pitcher" only	675.00	
b.	2c carmine lake		2,500.

No. 646a is valued in the grade of fine.
Normally the overprints were placed 18mm apart vertically, but pairs exist with a space of 28mm between the overprints.

HAWAII SESQUICENTENNIAL ISSUE

Sesquicentennial Celebration of the discovery of the Hawaiian Islands.

Nos. 634 and 637 Overprinted

ROTARY PRESS PRINTING

			Perf. 11x10½
1928, Aug. 13			
647	A157 2c carmine	4.00	4.00
	Never hinged	7.25	
648	A160 5c dark blue	11.00	12.50
	Never hinged	21.50	

Nos. 647-648 were sold at post offices in Hawaii and at the Postal Agency in Washington, D.C. They were valid throughout the nation.
Normally the overprints were placed 18mm apart vertically, but pairs exist with a space of 28mm between the overprints.

AERONAUTICS CONFERENCE ISSUE

Intl. Civil Aeronautics Conf., Washington, D.C., Dec. 12 - 14, 1928, and 25th anniv. of the 1st airplane flight by the Wright Brothers, Dec. 17, 1903.

Wright Airplane A194

Globe and Airplane A195

FLAT PLATE PRINTING

			Perf. 11
1928, Dec. 12			
649	A194 2c carmine rose	1.10	.80
	Never hinged	1.75	
650	A195 5c blue	4.50	3.25
	Never hinged	7.00	

GEORGE ROGERS CLARK ISSUE

150th anniv. of the surrender of Fort Sackville, the present site of Vincennes, Ind., to Clark.

Surrender of Fort Sackville A196

			Perf. 11
1929, Feb. 25			
651	A196 2c carmine & black	.70	.50
	Never hinged	1.15	

TYPE OF 1922-26 ISSUE
ROTARY PRESS PRINTING

			Perf. 11x10½
1929, May 25			
653	A154 ½c olive brown	.25	.25
	Never hinged	.35	

ELECTRIC LIGHT'S GOLDEN JUBILEE ISSUE

Invention of the 1st incandescent electric lamp by Thomas Alva Edison, Oct. 21, 1879, 50th anniv.

Edison's First Lamp — A197

FLAT PLATE PRINTING

			Perf. 11
1929			
654	A197 2c carmine rose	.65	.65
	Never hinged	1.10	
a.	2c lake	—	

ROTARY PRESS PRINTING

			Perf. 11x10½
655	A197 2c carmine rose	.65	.25
	Never hinged	1.10	

ROTARY PRESS COIL STAMP

			Perf. 10 Vertically
656	A197 2c carmine rose	10.00	1.75
	Never hinged	20.00	

SULLIVAN EXPEDITION ISSUE

150th anniversary of the Sullivan Expedition in New York State during the Revolutionary War.

Maj. Gen. John Sullivan — A198

FLAT PLATE PRINTING

			Perf. 11
1929, June 17			
657	A198 2c carmine rose	.55	.55
	Never hinged	.95	
a.	2c lake	375.00	250.00
	Never hinged	625.00	
b.	Vert. pair, imperf. btwn.	4,000.	

The unique No. 657b resulted from a paper foldover before perfing, and it has angled errant perfs from another row of horiz. perfs through the left side of the stamps.

Nos. 632-634, 635-642 Overprinted

This special issue was authorized as a measure of preventing losses from post office burglaries. Approximately a year's supply was printed and issued to postmasters. The P.O. Dept. found it desirable to discontinue the State overprinted stamps after the initial supply was used.

ROTARY PRESS PRINTING

			Perf. 11x10½
1929, May 1			
658	A155 1c green	2.50	2.00
	Never hinged	5.00	
a.	Vertical pair, one without ovpt.	300.00	
	Never hinged	500.00	
659	A156 1½c brown	3.25	2.90
	Never hinged	6.50	
a.	Vertical pair, one without ovpt.	475.00	
660	A157 2c carmine	4.00	1.00
	Never hinged	7.50	

661	A158 3c violet	17.50	15.00
	Never hinged	35.00	
a.	Vertical pair, one without ovpt.	600.00	
	Never hinged	800.00	
662	A159 4c yellow brown	17.50	9.00
	Never hinged	35.00	
a.	Vertical pair, one without ovpt.	500.00	
663	A160 5c deep blue	12.50	9.75
	Never hinged	25.00	
664	A161 6c red orange	25.00	18.00
	Never hinged	50.00	
665	A162 7c black	25.00	27.50
	Never hinged	50.00	
666	A163 8c olive green	72.50	65.00
	Never hinged	145.00	
667	A164 9c light rose	14.00	11.50
	Never hinged	27.50	
668	A165 10c org yel	22.50	12.50
	Never hinged	45.00	
Nos. 658-668 (11)		216.25	174.15
Nos. 658-668, never hinged		431.50	

See notes following No. 679.

Overprinted

1929, May 1			
669	A155 1c green	3.25	2.25
	Never hinged	6.50	
b.	No period after "Nebr." (19338, 19339 UR 26, 36 and 19339 LR 26, 36)	50.00	
670	A156 1½c brown	3.00	2.50
	Never hinged	6.00	
671	A157 2c carmine	3.00	1.30
	Never hinged	6.00	
672	A158 3c violet	11.00	12.00
	Never hinged	22.00	
a.	Vertical pair, one without ovpt.	500.00	
673	A159 4c yellow brown	17.50	15.00
	Never hinged	35.00	
674	A160 5c deep blue	15.00	15.00
	Never hinged	30.00	
675	A161 6c red orange	35.00	24.00
	Never hinged	70.00	
676	A162 7c black	22.50	18.00
	Never hinged	45.00	
677	A163 8c olive green	30.00	25.00
	Never hinged	60.00	

678	A164	9c light rose	35.00	27.50
		Never hinged	70.00	
a.		Vertical pair, one without		
		ovpt.	800.00	
679	A165	10c org yel	90.00	22.50
		Never hinged	180.00	
		Nos. 669-679 (11)	265.25	165.05
		Nos. 669-679, never		
		hinged	530.50	

Nos. 658-661, 669-673, 677-678 are known with the overprints on vertical pairs spaced 32mm apart instead of the normal 22mm.
Important: Nos. 658-679 with original gum have either one horizontal gum breaker ridge per stamp or portions of two at the extreme top and bottom of the stamps, 21mm apart. Multiple complete gum breaker ridges indicate a fake overprint. Absence of the gum breaker ridge indicates either regumming or regumming and a fake overprint.

BATTLE OF FALLEN TIMBERS ISSUE

Memorial to Gen. Anthony Wayne and for 135th anniv. of the Battle of Fallen Timbers, Ohio.

Gen. Anthony Wayne Memorial — A199

FLAT PLATE PRINTING
1929, Sept. 14   **Perf. 11**

| 680 | A199 | 2c carmine rose | .65 | .65 |
| | | Never hinged | 1.00 | |

OHIO RIVER CANALIZATION ISSUE

Completion of the Ohio River Canalization Project, between Cairo, Ill. and Pittsburgh, Pa.

Lock No. 5, Monongahela River — A200

1929, Oct. 19   **Perf. 11**

681	A200	2c carmine rose	.55	.55
		Never hinged	.90	
a.		2c lake	425.00	—
		Never hinged	650.00	
b.		2c carmine lake, never hinged	—	

MASSACHUSETTS BAY COLONY ISSUE

300th anniversary of the founding of the Massachusetts Bay Colony.

Mass. Bay Colony Seal — A201

1930, Apr. 8   **Perf. 11**

| 682 | A201 | 2c carmine rose | .65 | .50 |
| | | Never hinged | .95 | |

CAROLINA-CHARLESTON ISSUE

260th anniv. of the founding of the Province of Carolina and the 250th anniv. of the city of Charleston, S.C.

Gov. Joseph West & Chief Shadoo, a Kiowa — A202

1930, Apr. 10   **Perf. 11**

| 683 | A202 | 2c carmine rose | 1.00 | 1.00 |
| | | Never hinged | 1.50 | |

TYPES OF 1922-26 ISSUE

Warren G. Harding A203

William H. Taft A204

ROTARY PRESS PRINTING
1930   **Perf. 11x10½**

684	A203	1½c brown	.50	.25
		Never hinged	.70	
685	A204	4c brown	.80	.25
		Never hinged	1.25	

ROTARY PRESS COIL STAMPS
Perf. 10 Vertically

686	A203	1½c brown	1.75	.25
		Never hinged	2.60	
687	A204	4c brown	3.00	.45
		Never hinged	4.50	

BRADDOCK'S FIELD ISSUE

175th anniversary of the Battle of Braddock's Field, otherwise the Battle of Monongahela.

Statue of Col. George Washington — A205

FLAT PLATE PRINTING
1930, July 9   **Perf. 11**

| 688 | A205 | 2c carmine rose | .85 | .85 |
| | | Never hinged | 1.30 | |

VON STEUBEN ISSUE

Baron Friedrich Wilhelm von Steuben (1730-1794), participant in the American Revolution.

General von Steuben — A206

FLAT PLATE PRINTING
1930, Sept. 17   **Perf. 11**

689	A206	2c carmine rose	.50	.50
		Never hinged	.75	
a.		Imperf., pair	2,000.	
		Never hinged	3,000.	
b.		2c carmine lake	950.00	

PULASKI ISSUE

150th anniversary (in 1929) of the death of Gen. Casimir Pulaski, Polish patriot and hero of the American Revolutionary War.

General Casimir Pulaski — A207

1931, Jan. 16   **Perf. 11**

| 690 | A207 | 2c carmine rose | .30 | .25 |
| | | Never hinged | .40 | |

TYPE OF 1922-26 ISSUES
ROTARY PRESS PRINTING
1931   **Perf. 11x10½**

692	A166	11c light blue	2.50	.25
		Never hinged	3.75	
693	A167	12c brown violet	5.00	.25
		Never hinged	8.00	
694	A186	13c yellow green	2.25	.25
		Never hinged	3.50	
695	A168	14c dark blue	4.00	.60
		Never hinged	6.25	
696	A169	15c gray	7.75	.25
		Never hinged	12.00	

Perf. 10½x11

697	A187	17c black	4.75	.25
		Never hinged	7.25	
698	A170	20c carmine rose	7.75	.25
		Never hinged	12.50	

699	A171	25c blue green	8.00	.25
		Never hinged	13.00	
700	A172	30c brown	12.50	.25
		Never hinged	21.00	
701	A173	50c lilac	30.00	.25
		Never hinged	50.00	
		Nos. 692-701 (10)	84.50	2.85
		Nos. 692-701, never hinged 137.25		

RED CROSS ISSUE

50th anniversary of the founding of the American Red Cross Society.

"The Greatest Mother" — A208

FLAT PLATE PRINTING
1931, May 21   **Perf. 11**

702	A208	2c black & red	.25	.25
		Never hinged	.35	
a.		Red cross missing (FO)	40,000.	

One example of No. 702a is documented; believed to be unique. Value reflects most recent sale price at auction in 1994.

YORKTOWN ISSUE

Surrender of Cornwallis at Yorktown, 1781.

Count de Rochambeau, Washington, Count de Grasse — A209

1931, Oct. 19   **Perf. 11**

703	A209	2c car rose & blk	.35	.25
		Never hinged	.50	
a.		2c lake & black	4.50	.75
		Never hinged	6.25	
b.		2c dark lake & black	400.00	
		Never hinged	750.00	
c.		Horiz. pair, imperf. vertically	7,000.	
		Never hinged	8,500.	

No. 703c is valued in the grade of fine.

WASHINGTON BICENTENNIAL ISSUE

200th anniversary of the birth of George Washington. Various Portraits of George Washington.

A210   A211

A212   A213

A214   A215

A216   A217

A218   A219

A220   A221

ROTARY PRESS PRINTINGS
1932, Jan. 1   **Perf. 11x10½**

704	A210	½c olive brown	.25	.25
		Never hinged	.35	
705	A211	1c green	.25	.25
		Never hinged	.35	
706	A212	1½c brown	.45	.25
		Never hinged	.60	
707	A213	2c carmine rose	.30	.25
		Never hinged	.45	
708	A214	3c purple	.55	.25
		Never hinged	.80	
709	A215	4c light brown	.60	.25
		Never hinged	.85	
710	A216	5c blue	1.40	.25
		Never hinged	2.25	
711	A217	6c red orange	2.75	.25
		Never hinged	4.50	
712	A218	7c black	.60	.25
		Never hinged	.85	
713	A219	8c olive bister	2.50	.50
		Never hinged	4.00	
714	A220	9c pale red	2.00	.25
		Never hinged	3.25	
715	A221	10c orange yellow	9.00	.25
		Never hinged	15.00	
		Nos. 704-715 (12)	20.65	3.25
		Nos. 704-715, never hinged 33.25		

OLYMPIC WINTER GAMES ISSUE

3rd Olympic Winter Games, held at Lake Placid, N.Y., Feb. 4-13, 1932.

Skier — A222

FLAT PLATE PRINTING
1932, Jan. 25   **Perf. 11**

716	A222	2c carmine rose	.35	.25
		Never hinged	.55	
a.		2c lake	800.00	
		Never hinged	1,250.	

No. 716a should be accompanied by a certificate of authenticity issued by a recognized exertizing committee.

ARBOR DAY ISSUE

Boy and Girl Planting Tree — A223

ROTARY PRESS PRINTING
1932, Apr. 22   **Perf. 11x10½**

| 717 | A223 | 2c carmine rose | .25 | .25 |
| | | Never hinged | .35 | |

60th anniv. of the 1st observance of Arbor Day in Nebr., April, 1872.
Birth centenary of Julius Sterling Morton, who conceived the plan and the name "Arbor Day," while a member of the Nebr. State Board of Agriculture.

OLYMPIC GAMES ISSUE

Issued in honor of the 10th Olympic Games, held at Los Angeles, Calif., July 30 to Aug. 14, 1932.

Runner at Starting Mark A224

Myron's Discobolus A225

ROTARY PRESS PRINTING
1932, June 15   *Perf. 11x10½*
718 A224 3c purple   1.50   .25
    Never hinged   2.00
719 A225 5c blue   2.25   .25
    Never hinged   2.90

Washington — A226

ROTARY PRESS PRINTING
1932, June 16   *Perf. 11x10½*
720 A226 3c purple   .35   .25
    Never hinged   .45
   b.   Booklet pane of 6   35.00   12.50
    Never hinged   60.00
   c.   Vertical pair, imperf. be-
    tween   725.00   1,750.
    Never hinged   1,450.

ROTARY PRESS COIL STAMPS
1932   *Perf. 10 Vertically*
721 A226 3c purple   2.75   .25
    Never hinged   3.50
    Perf. 10 Horizontally
722 A226 3c purple   1.50   .35
    Never hinged   2.00
   Issued: #721, 6/24; #722, 10/12.

TYPE OF 1922-26 ISSUES
1932, Aug. 18   *Perf. 10 Vertically*
723 A161 6c deep orange   11.00   .30
    Never hinged   15.00

WILLIAM PENN ISSUE
250th anniv. of the arrival in America of Penn (1644-1718), English Quaker and founder of Pennsylvania.

William Penn — A227

FLAT PLATE PRINTING
1932, Oct. 24   *Perf. 11*
724 A227 3c purple   .45   .25
    Never hinged   .60
   a.   Vert. pair, imperf. horiz.   —

DANIEL WEBSTER ISSUE

Daniel Webster — A228

FLAT PLATE PRINTING
1932, Oct. 24   *Perf. 11*
725 A228 3c purple   .45   .25
    Never hinged   .60
Daniel Webster (1782-1852), statesman.

GEORGIA BICENTENNIAL ISSUE
200th anniv. of the founding of the Colony of Georgia, and honoring Oglethorpe, who landed from England, Feb. 12, 1733, and personally supervised the establishing of the colony.

Gen. James Edward Oglethorpe — A229

FLAT PLATE PRINTING
1933, Feb. 12   *Perf. 11*
726 A229 3c purple   .50   .25
    Never hinged   .65

PEACE OF 1783 ISSUE
150th anniv. of the issuance by George Washington of the official order containing the Proclamation of Peace marking officially the ending of hostilities in the War for Independence.

Washington's Headquarters, Newburgh, NY — A230

ROTARY PRESS PRINTING
1933, Apr. 19   *Perf. 10½x11*
727 A230 3c violet   .25   .25
    Never hinged   .30
   See No. 752.

CENTURY OF PROGRESS ISSUES
"Century of Progress" Intl. Exhibition, Chicago, which opened June 1, 1933, and centenary of the incorporation of Chicago as a city.

Restoration of Fort Dearborn A231   Federal Building at Chicago, 1933 A232

ROTARY PRESS PRINTING
1933, May 25   *Perf. 10½x11*
728 A231 1c yellow green   .25   .25
    Never hinged   .30
729 A232 3c purple   .25   .25
    Never hinged   .35

AMERICAN PHILATELIC SOCIETY ISSUE
SOUVENIR SHEETS

Restoration of Fort Dearborn — A231a

Federal Building at Chicago, 1933 — A232a

FLAT PLATE PRINTING
1933, Aug. 25   *Imperf.*
Without Gum
730 A231a 1c dp yel grn, pane
    of 25   20.00   25.00
   a.   Single stamp   .70   .50
731 A232a 3c pur, pane of 25   20.00   22.50
   a.   Single stamp   .65   .50
Issued in panes measuring 134x120mm.
See Nos. 766-767.

NATIONAL RECOVERY ACT ISSUE
Issued to direct attention to and arouse the support of the nation for the National Recovery Act.

Group of Workers — A233

ROTARY PRESS PRINTING
1933, Aug. 15   *Perf. 10½x11*
732 A233 3c purple   .25   .25
    Never hinged   .30

BYRD ANTARCTIC ISSUE
Issued in connection with the Byrd Antarctic Expedition of 1933 and for use on letters mailed through the Little America Post Office established at the Base Camp of the Expedition in the territory of the South Pole.

World Map on van der Grinten's Projection — A234

FLAT PLATE PRINTING
1933, Oct. 9   *Perf. 11*
733 A234 3c dark blue   .50   .50
    Never hinged   .60
   See Nos. 735, 753.

KOSCIUSZKO ISSUE
Kosciuszko (1746-1817), Polish soldier and statesman served in the American Revolution, on the 150th anniv. of the granting to him of American citizenship.

Statue of Gen. Tadeusz Kosciuszko — A235

FLAT PLATE PRINTING
1933, Oct. 13   *Perf. 11*
734 A235 5c blue   .55   .25
    Never hinged   .65
   a.   Horiz. pair, imperf. vert.   1,750.
    Never hinged   2,750.

NATIONAL STAMP EXHIBITION ISSUE
SOUVENIR SHEET

A235a

1934, Feb. 10   *Imperf.*
Without Gum
735 A235a 3c dk blue, pane of
    6   10.00   9.00
   a.   Single stamp   1.60   1.25
   Issued in panes measuring 87x93mm.
   See No. 768.

MARYLAND TERCENTENARY ISSUE
300th anniversary of the founding of Maryland.

"The Ark" and "The Dove" — A236

FLAT PLATE PRINTING
1934, Mar. 23   *Perf. 11*
736 A236 3c carmine rose   .30   .25
    Never hinged   .40
   a.   Horizontal pair, imperf be-
    tween   4,000.
   b.   3c lake   1,000.
   c.   3c carmine lake, never hinged   —
The unique No. 736a resulted from a paper foldover before perfing, and it has angled errant perfs from another column of vert. perfs through the upper-left corner of the left stamp.

MOTHERS OF AMERICA ISSUE

Issued to commemorate Mother's Day.

Adaptation of Whistler's Portrait of his Mother
A237

ROTARY PRESS PRINTING

1934, May 2   **Perf. 11x10½**
737 A237 3c purple   .25   .25
     Never hinged   .30

FLAT PLATE PRINTING
Perf. 11

738 A237 3c purple   .25   .25
     Never hinged   .30
     See No. 754.

WISCONSIN TERCENTENARY ISSUE

Arrival of Jean Nicolet, French explorer, on the shores of Green Bay, 300th anniv. According to historical records, Nicolet was the 1st white man to reach the territory now comprising the State of Wisconsin.

Nicolet's Landing
A238

FLAT PLATE PRINTING

1934, July 7   **Perf. 11**
739 A238 3c purple   .25   .25
     Never hinged   .40
a.   Vert. pair, imperf. horiz.   575.00
     Never hinged   1,050.
b.   Horiz. pair, imperf. vert.   1,000.
     Never hinged   1,750.
     See No. 755.

NATIONAL PARKS YEAR ISSUE

El Capitan, Yosemite (California)
A239

Old Faithful, Yellowstone (Wyoming)
A243

Grand Canyon (Arizona)
A240

Mt. Rainier and Mirror Lake (Washington) — A241

Mesa Verde (Colorado)
A242

Crater Lake (Oregon)
A244

Great Head, Acadia Park (Maine)
A245

Great White Throne, Zion Park (Utah)
A246

Great Smoky Mts. (North Carolina)
A248

Mt. Rockwell (Mt. Sinopah) and Two Medicine Lake, Glacier Natl. Park (Montana)
A247

FLAT PLATE PRINTING

1934   **Unwmk.**   **Perf. 11**
740 A239 1c green   .25   .25
     Never hinged   .40
a.   Vert. pair, imperf. horiz.,
     with gum   1,750.
     Never hinged   3,000.
741 A240 2c red   .30   .25
     Never hinged   .40
a.   Vert. pair, imperf. horiz.,
     with gum   800.00
     Never hinged   1,450.
b.   Horiz. pair, imperf. vert.,
     with gum   900.00
     Never hinged   1,600.
c.   Imperf. P# 21261 block of
     20   7,500.

No. 741c is a unique bottom margin plate #21261 block of 20. This plate was not used to print the imperforate Farley special printing, No. 757. Loose stamps separated from this block or from other possible imperforate No. 741 Plate #21261 blocks are indistinguishable from gummed examples of No. 757.

742 A241 3c purple   .40   .25
     Never hinged   .50
a.   Vert. pair, imperf. horiz.,
     with gum   1,000.
     Never hinged   1,850.
743 A242 4c brown   .50   .40
     Never hinged   .70
a.   Vert. pair, imperf. horiz.,
     with gum   3,500.
     Never hinged   8,000.
744 A243 5c blue   .80   .65
     Never hinged   1.10
a.   Horiz. pair, imperf. vert.,
     with gum   1,500.
     Never hinged   4,000.
745 A244 6c dark blue   1.20   .85
     Never hinged   1.65
746 A245 7c black   .80   .75
     Never hinged   1.10
a.   Horiz. pair, imperf. vert.,
     with gum   1,250.
     Never hinged   2,000.
747 A246 8c sage green   1.75   1.50
     Never hinged   2.70
748 A247 9c red orange   1.60   .65
     Never hinged   2.40
749 A248 10c gray black   3.25   1.25
     Never hinged   5.00
     Nos. 740-749 (10)   10.85   6.80
     Nos. 740-749, never hinged   15.95

Beware of fakes of the part-perforate errors of Nos. 740-749, including those with gum (see "without gum" note before No. 752).
See Nos. 750-751, 756-765, 769-770, 797.

AMERICAN PHILATELIC SOCIETY ISSUE
SOUVENIR SHEET

A248a

1934, Aug. 28   **Imperf.**
750 A248a 3c pur, pane of 6   20.00   27.50
     Never hinged   30.00
a.   Single stamp   3.25   3.25
     Never hinged   4.00

Issued in panes measuring approximately 98x93mm.
See No. 770.

TRANS-MISSISSIPPI PHILATELIC EXPOSITION ISSUE
SOUVENIR SHEET

A248b

1934, Oct. 10   **Imperf.**
751 A248b 1c grn, pane of 6   10.00   12.50
     Never hinged   15.00
a.   Single stamp   1.65   1.60
     Never hinged   2.25

Issued in panes measuring approximately 92x99mm.
See No. 769.

SPECIAL PRINTING
(Nos. 752-771 inclusive)

"Issued for a limited time in full sheets as printed, and in blocks thereof, to meet the requirements of collectors and others who may be interested." — From Postal Bulletin No. 16614.

Issuance of the following 20 stamps in complete sheets resulted from the protest of collectors and others at the practice of presenting, to certain government officials, complete sheets of unsevered panes, imperforate (except Nos. 752 and 753) and generally ungummed.

Designs of Commemorative Issues
Without Gum

NOTE: In 1940 the P.O. Department offered to and did gum full sheets of Nos. 756-765 and 769-770 sent in by owners. No other Special Printings were accepted for gumming.

TYPE OF PEACE ISSUE
Issued in sheets of 400
ROTARY PRESS PRINTING
Perf. 10½x11

1935, Mar. 15   **Unwmk.**
752 A230 3c purple   .25   .25

TYPE OF BYRD ISSUE
Issued in sheets of 200
FLAT PLATE PRINTING
Perf. 11
753 A234 3c dark blue   .50   .45

No. 753 is similar to No. 733. Positive identification is by blocks or pairs showing guide line between stamps. These lines between stamps are found only on No. 753.

TYPE OF MOTHERS OF AMERICA ISSUE
Issued in sheets of 200
FLAT PLATE PRINTING
Imperf
754 A237 3c deep purple   .60   .60

TYPE OF WISCONSIN ISSUE
Issued in sheets of 200
FLAT PLATE PRINTING
Imperf
755 A238 3c deep purple   .60   .60

TYPES OF NATIONAL PARKS ISSUE
Issued in sheets of 200
FLAT PLATE PRINTING
Imperf
756 A239 1c green   .25   .25
757 A240 2c red   .25   .25
758 A241 3c deep purple   .50   .45
759 A242 4c brown   1.00   .95
760 A243 5c blue   1.60   1.40
761 A244 6c dark blue   2.40   2.25
762 A245 7c black   1.60   1.40
763 A246 8c sage green   1.90   1.50
764 A247 9c red orange   2.00   1.75
765 A248 10c gray black   4.00   3.50
     Nos. 756-765 (10)   15.50   13.70
     Nos. 756-765, with original
     gum, never hinged   114.35
     Nos. 756-765, P# blocks of
     6   254.75

SOUVENIR SHEETS

Note: Single items from these sheets are identical with other varieties, 766 and 730, 766a and 730a, 767 and 731, 767a and 731a, 768 and 735, 768a and 735a, 769a and 756, 770a and 758.

Positive identification is by blocks or pairs showing wide gutters between stamps. These wide gutters occur only on Nos. 766-770 and measure, horizontally, 13mm on Nos. 766-767; 16mm on No. 768, and 23mm on Nos. 769-770.

TYPE OF CENTURY OF PROGRESS ISSUE
Issued in sheets of 9 panes of 25 stamps each
FLAT PLATE PRINTING
Imperf
766 A231a 1c yel grn, pane of
     25   30.00   30.00
a.   Single stamp   .85   .50
767 A232a 3c dp pur, pane of
     25   30.00   25.00
a.   Single stamp   .85   .50

NATIONAL EXHIBITION ISSUE TYPE OF BYRD ISSUE
Issued in sheets of 25 panes of 6 stamps each
FLAT PLATE PRINTING
Imperf
768 A235a 3c dk blue, pane of
     6   20.00   15.00
a.   Single stamp   2.80   2.40

TYPES OF NATIONAL PARKS ISSUE
Issued in sheets of 20 panes of 6 stamps each
FLAT PLATE PRINTING
Imperf
769 A248b 1c grn, pane of 6   11.00   11.00
a.   Single stamp   1.85   1.80
770 A248a 3c dp pur, pane of
     6   30.00   24.00
a.   Single stamp   3.25   3.10

TYPE OF AIR POST SPECIAL DELIVERY

Issued in sheets of 200
FLAT PLATE PRINTING
Imperf
771 APSD1 16c dark blue   2.50 2.60

> Catalogue values for unused stamps in this section, from this point to the end, are for Never Hinged items.

VALUES FOR HINGED STAMPS AFTER NO. 771

This catalogue does not value unused stamps after No. 771 in hinged condition. Hinged unused stamps from No. 772 to the present are worth considerably less than the values given for unused stamps, which are for never-hinged examples.

CONNECTICUT TERCENTENARY ISSUE

300th anniv. of the settlement of Connecticut.

Charter Oak A249

ROTARY PRESS PRINTING
Perf. 11x10½
1935, Apr. 26   **Unwmk.**
772 A249 3c rose purple   .35 .25

CALIFORNIA PACIFIC EXPOSITION ISSUE

California Pacific Exposition at San Diego.

View of San Diego Exposition A250

1935, May 29   **Unwmk.**
773 A250 3c purple   .35 .25

BOULDER DAM ISSUE

Dedication of Boulder Dam.

Boulder Dam — A251

FLAT PLATE PRINTING
1935, Sept. 30   **Unwmk.**   *Perf. 11*
774 A251 3c purple   .35 .25

MICHIGAN CENTENARY ISSUE

Advance celebration of Michigan Statehood centenary.

Michigan State Seal A252

ROTARY PRESS PRINTING
1935, Nov. 1   **Unwmk.**   *Perf. 11x10½*
775 A252 3c purple   .35 .25

TEXAS CENTENNIAL ISSUE

Centennial of Texas independence.

Sam Houston, Stephen F. Austin and the Alamo A253

1936, Mar. 2   **Unwmk.**
776 A253 3c purple   .35 .25

RHODE ISLAND TERCENTENARY ISSUE

300th anniv. of the settlement of Rhode Island.

Statue of Roger Williams — A254

1936, May 4 Unwmk.   *Perf. 10½x11*
777 A254 3c purple   .35 .25

THIRD INTERNATIONAL PHILATELIC EXHIBITION ISSUE
SOUVENIR SHEET

A254a

FLAT PLATE PRINTING
1936, May 9   **Unwmk.**   *Imperf.*
778 A254a   purple, pane of 4   1.75 1.25
   a.   3c Type A249   .40   .30
   b.   3c Type A250   .40   .30
   c.   3c Type A252   .40   .30
   d.   3c Type A253   .40   .30

Issued in panes measuring 98x66mm containing four stamps, inscribed in the margins: "Printed by the Treasury Department, Bureau of Engraving and Printing, under authority of James A. Farley, Postmaster General, in compliment to the third International Philatelic Exhibition of 1936. New York, N. Y., May 9-17, 1936. Plate No. 21557."
   Also used was plate 21558. Each different plate number used is inscribed in the bottom selvage of the respective souvenir sheets.

ARKANSAS CENTENNIAL ISSUE

100th anniv. of the State of Arkansas.

Arkansas Post, Old and New State Houses A255

ROTARY PRESS PRINTING
Perf. 11x10½
1936, June 15   **Unwmk.**
782 A255 3c purple   .35 .25

OREGON TERRITORY ISSUE

Opening of the Oregon Territory, 1836, 100th anniv.

Map of Oregon Territory A256

1936, July 14   **Unwmk.**
783 A256 3c purple   .35 .25

SUSAN B. ANTHONY ISSUE

Susan Brownell Anthony (1820-1906), woman-suffrage advocate, and 16th anniv. of the ratification of the 19th Amendment which grants American women the right to vote.

Susan B. Anthony — A257

1936, Aug. 26   **Unwmk.**
784 A257 3c purple   .25 .25

ARMY ISSUE

Issued in honor of the United States Army.

George Washington, Nathanael Greene and Mount Vernon — A258

Andrew Jackson, Winfield Scott and the Hermitage A259

Generals Sherman, Grant and Sheridan A260

Generals Robert E. Lee, "Stonewall" Jackson and Stratford Hall A261

U.S. Military Academy, West Point A262

1936-37   **Unwmk.**
785 A258 1c green   .30 .25
786 A259 2c carmine ('37)   .30 .25
787 A260 3c purple ('37)   .40 .25
788 A261 4c gray ('37)   .60 .25
789 A262 5c ultra ('37)   .75 .25
   Nos. 785-789 (5)   2.35 1.25

NAVY ISSUE

Issued in honor of the United States Navy.

John Paul Jones and John Barry A263

Stephen Decatur and Thomas MacDonough — A264

Admirals David G. Farragut and David D. Porter A265

Admirals William T. Sampson, George Dewey and Winfield S. Schley A266

Seal of U.S. Naval Academy and Naval Midshipmen — A267

1936-37   **Unwmk.**
790 A263 1c green   .30 .25
791 A264 2c carmine ('37)   .30 .25
792 A265 3c purple ('37)   .40 .25
793 A266 4c gray ('37)   .60 .25
794 A267 5c ultra ('37)   .75 .25
   Nos. 790-794 (5)   2.35 1.25

ORDINANCE OF 1787 SESQUICENTENNIAL ISSUE

150th anniv. of the adoption of the Ordinance of 1787 and the creation of the Northwest Territory.

Manasseh Cutler, Rufus Putnam and Map of Northwest Territory A268

1937, July 13   **Unwmk.**
795 A268 3c rose purple   .30 .25

VIRGINIA DARE ISSUE

350th anniv. of the birth of Virginia Dare, 1st child born in America of English parents (Aug. 18, 1587), and the settlement at Roanoke Island.

Virginia Dare and Parents — A269

FLAT PLATE PRINTING
1937, Aug. 18   **Unwmk.**   *Perf. 11*
796 A269 5c gray blue   .35 .25

SOCIETY OF PHILATELIC AMERICANS ISSUE
SOUVENIR SHEET

A269a

TYPE OF NATIONAL PARKS ISSUE

1937, Aug. 26   Unwmk.   Imperf.
797 A269a 10c blue green   .60   .40

Issued in panes measuring 67x78mm.

CONSTITUTION SESQUICENTENNIAL ISSUE

150th anniversary of the signing of the Constitution on September 17, 1787.

Signing of the Constitution A270

Perf. 11x10½
1937, Sept. 17   Unwmk.
798 A270 3c brt reddsh pur   .40   .25

TERRITORIAL ISSUES
Hawaii

Statue of Kamehameha I, Honolulu — A271

Alaska

Landscape with Mt. McKinley A272

Puerto Rico

La Fortaleza, San Juan A273

Virgin Islands

Charlotte Amalie A274

1937   Unwmk.   Perf. 10½x11
799 A271 3c violet   .35   .25

Perf. 11x10½
800 A272 3c violet   .40   .25
801 A273 3c bright purple   .40   .25
802 A274 3c rose violet   .40   .25
   Nos. 799-802 (4)   1.55 1.00

PRESIDENTIAL ISSUE

Benjamin Franklin A275

George Washington A276

Martha Washington A277

John Adams A278

Thomas Jefferson A279

James Madison A280

White House A281

James Monroe A282

John Q. Adams A283

Andrew Jackson A284

Martin Van Buren A285

William H. Harrison A286

John Tyler — A287

James K. Polk — A288

Zachary Taylor A289

Millard Fillmore A290

1938   Unwmk.
803 A275 ½c deep orange   .25   .25
804 A276 1c green   .25   .25
   b.   Booklet pane of 6   2.00   .50
   c.   Horiz. pair, imperf between
         (from booklet pane)   —
805 A277 1 ½c bister brown   .25   .25
   b.   Horiz. pair, imperf. be-
         tween   100.00 20.00

No. 805b unused is not precanceled. Pre-canceled examples are considered used and

---

Franklin Pierce A291

James Buchanan A292

Abraham Lincoln A293

Andrew Johnson A294

Ulysses S. Grant A295

Rutherford B. Hayes A296

James A. Garfield A297

Chester A. Arthur A298

Grover Cleveland A299

Benjamin Harrison A300

William McKinley A301

Theodore Roosevelt A302

William Howard Taft A303

Woodrow Wilson A304

Warren G. Harding A305

Calvin Coolidge A306

---

are valued in the used column. They are valued with gum; pairs without gum are worth less.

806 A278 2c rose carmine   .25   .25
   b.   Booklet pane of 6   5.50   1.00
807 A279 3c light violet   .25   .25
   a.   Booklet pane of 6   8.50   2.00
   b.   Horiz. pair, imperf. be-
         tween   2,000.
   c.   Imperf., pair   3,500.
   d.   As "a," imperf between
         vert.   5,000.
808 A280 4c brt rose pur   .75   .25
809 A281 4½c dark gray   .40   .25
810 A282 5c bright blue   .35   .25
811 A283 6c red orange   .40   .25
812 A284 7c sepia   .40   .25
813 A285 8c olive green   .40   .25
814 A286 9c rose pink   .45   .25
815 A287 10c brown red   .40   .25
816 A288 11c ultramarine   .75   .25
817 A289 12c bright mauve   1.00   .25
818 A290 13c blue green   1.30   .25
819 A291 14c blue   1.00   .25
820 A292 15c blue gray   .80   .25
821 A293 16c black   1.50   .25
822 A294 17c rose red   1.00   .25
823 A295 18c brn car   2.25   .25
824 A296 19c bright mauve   1.30   .35
825 A297 20c brt bl grn   1.20   .25
826 A298 21c dull blue   1.30   .25
827 A299 22c vermilion   1.20   .40
828 A300 24c gray black   3.25   .25
829 A301 25c deep red lilac   1.20   .25
830 A302 30c dp ultra   3.50   .25
   a.   30c blue   20.00
   b.   30c deep blue   250.00   —
831 A303 50c mauve   5.50   .25

FLAT PLATE PRINTING

1938   Perf. 11
832 A304 $1 pur & blk   7.00   .25
   a.   Vert. pair, imperf. horiz. 1,100.
   b.   Watermarked USIR
         ('51)   200.00 65.00
   c. $1 red violet & black
         ('54)   6.00   .25
   d.   As "c," vert. pair, im-
         perf. horiz.   900.00
   e.   Vert. pair, imperf. btwn. 7,500.
   f.   As "c," vert. pair, im-
         perf. btwn.   10,000.
   g.   As "c," bright magenta
         & black   70.00 50.00
   h.   As No. 832, red violet &
         black   —   —

No. 832c is dry printed from 400-subject flat plates on thick white paper with smooth, colorless gum.
No. 832g is the far end of the color spectrum for the No. 832c stamp, trending toward a more pinkish shade, but the shade is not pink. No. 832g is known in bright magenta and in deep bright magenta; both shades qualify as No. 832g.
No. 832h is a shade variety of the wet printing (No. 832), but the shade essentially matches the red violet normally seen on the dry printing (No. 000a).

833 A305 $2 yel grn & blk   16.00   3.75
834 A306 $5 car & blk   75.00   3.00
   a. $5 red brown & black   3,000. 7,000.
   Nos. 803-834 (32)   130.85 14.50

No. 834 can be chemically altered to resemble Scott 834a. No. 834a should be purchased only with competent expert certification.

Watermarks
All stamps from No. 835 on are unwatermarked.

CONSTITUTION RATIFICATION ISSUE

150th anniversary of the ratification of the United States Constitution.

Old Court House, Williamsburg, Va. — A307

ROTARY PRESS PRINTING
1938, June 21   Perf. 11x10½
835 A307 3c deep violet   .45   .25

SWEDISH-FINNISH TERCENTENARY ISSUE

Tercentenary of the founding of the Swedish and Finnish Settlement at Wilmington, Delaware.

Landing of the Swedes and Finns — A308

FLAT PLATE PRINTING

1938, June 27   *Perf. 11*

836 A308 3c brt reddsh pur   .35   .25

NORTHWEST TERRITORY SESQUICENTENNIAL

Statue Symbolizing Colonization of the West — A309

ROTARY PRESS PRINTING

1938, July 15   *Perf. 11x10½*

837 A309 3c bright rose purple   .30   .25

IOWA TERRITORY CENTENNIAL ISSUE

Old Capitol, Iowa City A310

1938, Aug. 24

838 A310 3c violet   .40   .25

TYPES OF 1938
ROTARY PRESS COIL STAMPS

1939, Jan. 20   *Perf. 10 Vertically*

839	A276	1c green	.30	.25
840	A277	1½c bister brown	.30	.25
841	A278	2c rose carmine	.40	.25
842	A279	3c light violet	.50	.25
843	A280	4c red violet	7.50	.40
844	A281	4½c dark gray	.70	.40
845	A282	5c bright blue	5.00	2.50
846	A283	6c red orange	1.10	.55
847	A287	10c brown red	11.00	1.00

1939, Jan. 27   *Perf. 10 Horizontally*

848	A276	1c green	.85	.25
849	A277	1½c bister brown	1.25	.30
850	A278	2c rose carmine	2.50	.40
851	A279	3c light violet	2.50	.40
		Nos. 839-851 (13)	33.90	7.20

GOLDEN GATE INTL. EXPOSITION, SAN FRANCISCO

"Tower of the Sun" — A311

ROTARY PRESS PRINTING

1939, Feb. 18   *Perf. 10½x11*

852 A311 3c bright purple   .30   .25

NEW YORK WORLD'S FAIR ISSUE

Trylon and Perisphere — A312

1939, Apr. 1

853 A312 3c violet   .30   .25

WASHINGTON INAUGURATION ISSUE

Sesquicentennial of the inauguration of George Washington as First President.

George Washington Taking Oath of Office — A313

FLAT PLATE PRINTING

1939, Apr. 30   *Perf. 11*

854 A313 3c bright purple   .60   .25

BASEBALL CENTENNIAL ISSUE

Sand-lot Baseball Game A314

ROTARY PRESS PRINTING

1939, June 12   *Perf. 11x10½*

855 A314 3c violet   1.75   .25

PANAMA CANAL ISSUE

25th anniv. of the opening of the Panama Canal.

Theodore Roosevelt, Gen. George W. Goethals and Gaillard Cut — A315

FLAT PLATE PRINTING

1939, Aug. 15   *Perf. 11*

856 A315 3c reddish purple   .40   .25

PRINTING TERCENTENARY ISSUE

Issued in commemoration of the 300th anniversary of printing in Colonial America. The Stephen Daye press is in the Harvard University Museum.

Stephen Daye Press — A316

ROTARY PRESS PRINTING

1939, Sept. 25   *Perf. 10½x11*

857 A316 3c violet   .25   .25

50th ANNIVERSARY OF STATEHOOD ISSUE

Map of North and South Dakota, Montana and Washington A317

1939, Nov. 2   *Perf. 11x10½*

858 A317 3c rose purple   .35   .25

FAMOUS AMERICANS ISSUES
AMERICAN AUTHORS

Washington Irving — A318   James Fenimore Cooper — A319

Ralph Waldo Emerson A320   Louisa May Alcott A321

Samuel L. Clemens (Mark Twain) — A322

1940   *Perf. 10½x11*

859	A318	1c bright blue green	.25	.25
860	A319	2c rose carmine	.25	.25
861	A320	3c bright purple	.25	.25
862	A321	5c ultramarine	.35	.25
863	A322	10c dark brown	1.75	1.20
		Nos. 859-863 (5)	2.85	2.20

AMERICAN POETS

Henry W. Longfellow A323   John Greenleaf Whittier A324

James Russell Lowell A325   Walt Whitman A326

James Whitcomb Riley — A327

864	A323	1c bright blue green	.25	.25
865	A324	2c rose carmine	.25	.25
866	A325	3c bright purple	.25	.25
867	A326	5c ultramarine	.50	.25
868	A327	10c dark brown	1.75	1.25
		Nos. 864-868 (5)	3.00	2.25

AMERICAN EDUCATORS

Horace Mann — A328   Mark Hopkins — A329

Charles W. Eliot — A330   Frances E. Willard — A331

Booker T. Washington — A332

869	A328	1c bright blue green	.25	.25
870	A329	2c rose carmine	.25	.25
871	A330	3c bright purple	.25	.25
872	A331	5c ultramarine	.50	.25
873	A332	10c dark brown	2.25	1.10
		Nos. 869-873 (5)	3.50	2.10

AMERICAN SCIENTISTS

John James Audubon A333   Dr. Crawford W. Long A334

Luther Burbank — A335   Dr. Walter Reed — A336

Jane Addams — A337

874	A333	1c bright blue green	.25	.25
875	A334	2c rose carmine	.25	.25
876	A335	3c bright purple	.25	.25
877	A336	5c ultramarine	.50	.25
878	A337	10c dark brown	1.50	.85
		Nos. 874-878 (5)	2.75	1.85

AMERICAN COMPOSERS

Stephen Collins Foster — A338   John Philip Sousa — A339

Victor Herbert A340   Edward MacDowell A341

Ethelbert
Nevin — A342

879	A338	1c bright blue green	.25	.25
880	A339	2c rose carmine	.25	.25
881	A340	3c bright purple	.25	.25
882	A341	5c ultramarine	.50	.25
883	A342	10c dark brown	3.75	1.35
		Nos. 879-883 (5)	5.00	2.35

AMERICAN ARTISTS

Gilbert Charles
Stuart — A343

James A.
McNeill
Whistler — A344

Augustus Saint-
Gaudens
A345

Daniel Chester
French
A346

Frederic
Remington — A347

884	A343	1c bright blue green	.25	.25
885	A344	2c rose carmine	.25	.25
886	A345	3c bright purple	.30	.25
887	A346	5c ultramarine	.50	.25
888	A347	10c dark brown	1.75	1.25
		Nos. 884-888 (5)	3.05	2.25

AMERICAN INVENTORS

Eli
Whitney — A348

Samuel F. B.
Morse — A349

Cyrus Hall
McCormick
A350

Elias Howe
A351

Alexander Graham
Bell — A352

889	A348	1c brt blue grn	.25	.25
890	A349	2c rose carmine	.30	.25
891	A350	3c bright purple	.30	.25
892	A351	5c ultramarine	1.10	.30
893	A352	10c dark brown	11.00	2.00
		Nos. 889-893 (5)	12.95	3.05
		Nos. 859-893 (35)	33.10	16.05

PONY EXPRESS, 80th ANNIV. ISSUE

Pony
Express
Rider
A353

1940, Apr. 3   *Perf. 11x10½*
894 A353 3c henna brown   .50   .25

PAN AMERICAN UNION ISSUE

Founding of the Pan American Union, 50th anniv.

The Three Graces
from Botticelli's
"Spring" — A354

1940, Apr. 14   *Perf. 10½x11*
895 A354 3c bright rose purple   .30   .25

IDAHO STATEHOOD, 50th ANNIV.

Idaho
Capitol,
Boise
A355

1940, July 3   *Perf. 11x10½*
896 A355 3c bright mauve   .35   .25

WYOMING STATEHOOD, 50th ANNIV.

Wyoming State
Seal — A356

1940, July 10   *Perf. 10½x11*
897 A356 3c brown violet   .35   .25

CORONADO EXPEDITION, 400th ANNIV.

"Coronado
and His
Captains,"
painted by
Gerald
Cassidy
A357

1940, Sept. 7   *Perf. 11x10½*
898 A357 3c bright violet   .35   .25

NATIONAL DEFENSE ISSUE

Statue of
Liberty — A358

90-millimeter Anti-
aircraft Gun — A359

Torch of
Enlightenment — A360

1940, Oct. 16

899	A358	1c bright blue green	.25	.25
a.		Vertical pair, imperf. between	600.00	—
b.		Horizontal pair, imperf. between	32.50	—
900	A359	2c rose carmine	.25	.25
a.		Horizontal pair, imperf. between	37.50	—
901	A360	3c bright mauve	.25	.25
a.		Horizontal pair, imperf. between	22.50	—
		Nos. 899-901 (3)	.75	.75

THIRTEENTH AMENDMENT ISSUE

75th anniv. of the 13th Amendment to the Constitution abolishing slavery.

"Emancipation,"
Statue of Lincoln and
Slave, by Thomas
Ball — A361

1940, Oct. 20   *Perf. 10½x11*
902 A361 3c violet   .50   .25

VERMONT STATEHOOD, 150th ANNIV.

Vermont
Capitol,
Montpelier
A362

1941, Mar. 4   *Perf. 11x10½*
903 A362 3c light violet   .45   .25

KENTUCKY STATEHOOD, 150th ANNIV.

Daniel Boone and Three Frontiersmen,
from mural by Gilbert White — A363

1942, June 1
904 A363 3c purple   .30   .25

WIN THE WAR ISSUE

American
Eagle — A364

1942, July 4

905	A364	3c bright lilac	.25	.25
b.		3c reddish purple	750.00	500.00

All examples of No. 905b are precanceled either Los Angeles, Calif., Fremont, Ohio, or St. Paul, Minn. Value is for Los Angeles, which is the more common. Value of Fremont, unused, $1,500. Value of St. Paul, used (without gum), $2,500. The stamps with St. Paul precancel are slightly less reddish than Los Angeles or Fremont, but they are in the same reddish purple/purple color family.

CHINESE RESISTANCE ISSUE

Issued to commemorate the Chinese people's five years of resistance to Japanese aggression.

Lincoln,
Sun Yat-
sen & Map
A365

1942, July 7
906 A365 5c bright blue   4.00   .50

ALLIED NATIONS ISSUE

Allegory of
Victory — A366

1943, Jan. 14
907 A366 2c rose carmine   .25   .25
Bureau Precancels: Denver, Baltimore.

FOUR FREEDOMS ISSUE

A367

1943, Feb. 12
908 A367 1c bright blue green   .25 .25

OVERRUN COUNTRIES ISSUE

Flag of
Poland
A368

No. 909, Poland. No. 910, Czechoslovakia. No. 911, Norway. No. 912, Luxembourg. No. 913, Netherlands. No. 914, Belgium. No. 915, France. No. 916, Greece. No. 917, Yugoslavia. No. 918, Albania. No. 919, Austria. No. 920, Denmark. No. 921, Korea.

Printed by the American Bank Note Co.

FRAMES ENGRAVED, CENTERS
OFFSET LETTERPRESS
ROTARY PRESS PRINTING
Plates of 200 subjects in four panes of 50.

1943-44   *Perf. 12*

909	A368	5c blue vio, brt red & blk	.25	.25
a.		Double impression of "Poland"	200.00	

b.	Double impression of black flag color and red "Poland"	—
910 A368a	5c blue vio, blue, brt red & blk	.25 .25
a.	Double impression of "Czechoslovakia"	600.00
911 A368b	5c blue vio, dk rose, dp blue & blk	.25 .25
a.	Double impression of "Norway"	225.00
912 A368c	5c blue vio, dk rose, lt blue & blk	.25 .25
a.	Double impression of "Luxembourg"	—
913 A368d	5c blue vio, dk rose, blue & blk	.25 .25
914 A368e	5c blue vio, dk rose, yel & blk	.25 .25
a.	Double impression of "Belgium"	200.00
915 A368f	5c blue vio, dp blue, dk rose & blk	.25 .25
916 A368g	5c blue vio, pale blue, grnsh blue & blk	.50 .25
917 A368h	5c blue vio, blue, dk rose & blk	.40 .25
b.	Double impression of black	250.00 200.00
918 A368i	5c blue vio, dk red & blk	.25 .25
a.	Double impression of "Albania"	— 600.00
919 A368j	5c blue vio, red & blk	.30 .25
a.	Double impression of "Austria"	400.00
c.	Double impression of black	— —
920 A368k	5c blue vio, red & blk	.30 .25
b.	5c blue violet, red & gray	.30 .25
921 A368m	5c blue vio, red, lt blue & gray	.25 .25
a.	Double impression of light blue (including "Korea")	— —
c.	Double impression of red	— —
	Nos. 909-921 (13)	3.75 3.25

TRANSCONTINENTAL RAILROAD ISSUE

Completion of the 1st transcontinental railroad, 75th anniv.

"Golden Spike Ceremony" Painting by John McQuarrie A369

ENGRAVED
ROTARY PRESS PRINTING

1944, May 10   *Perf. 11x10½*
922 A369 3c violet   .25 .25

STEAMSHIP ISSUE

1st steamship to cross the Atlantic, 125th anniv.

"Savannah" A370

1944, May 22
923 A370 3c violet   .25 .25

TELEGRAPH ISSUE

1st message transmitted by telegraph, cent.

Telegraph Wires & the First Transmitted Words "What Hath God Wrought" A371

1944, May 24
924 A371 3c bright purple   .25 .25

PHILIPPINE ISSUE

Final resistance of the US and Philippine defenders on Corregidor to the Japanese invaders in 1942.

View of Corregidor A372

1944, Sept. 27
925 A372 3c deep violet   .25 .25

MOTION PICTURE, 50th ANNIV.

Motion Picture Showing for the Armed Forces in South Pacific A373

1944, Oct. 31
926 A373 3c deep violet   .25 .25

FLORIDA STATEHOOD, CENTENARY

Old Florida Seal, St. Augustine Gates and State Capitol A374

1945, Mar. 3
927 A374 3c bright red violet   .25 .25

UNITED NATIONS CONFERENCE ISSUE

United Nations Conference, San Francisco, Calif.

A375

1945, Apr. 25
928 A375 5c ultramarine   .25 .25

IWO JIMA (MARINES) ISSUE

Battle of Iwo Jima and honoring the achievements of the US Marines.

Marines Raising the Flag on Mt. Suribachi, Iwo Jima, from a Photograph by Joel Rosenthal — A376

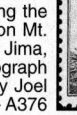

1945, July 11   *Perf. 10½x11*
929 A376 3c yellow green   .30 .25

FRANKLIN D. ROOSEVELT ISSUE

Franklin Delano Roosevelt (1882-1945).

Roosevelt and Hyde Park Home A377

Roosevelt and "Little White House," Warm Springs, Georgia A378

Roosevelt and White House A379

Roosevelt, Globe and Four Freedoms A380

1945-46   *Perf. 11x10½*
930 A377 1c blue green   .25 .25
931 A378 2c carmine rose   .25 .25
932 A379 3c purple   .25 .25
933 A380 5c bright blue   .25 .25
     Nos. 930-933 (4)   1.00 1.00

ARMY ISSUE

Achievements of the US Army in World War II.

U.S. Troops Passing Arch of Triumph, Paris A381

1945, Sept. 28
934 A381 3c olive   .25 .25

NAVY ISSUE

Achievements of the U.S. Navy in World War II.

U.S. Sailors A382

1945, Oct. 27
935 A382 3c blue   .25 .25

COAST GUARD ISSUE

Achievements of the US Coast Guard in World War II.

Coast Guard Landing Craft and Supply Ship A383

1945, Nov. 10
936 A383 3c bright blue green   .25 .25

ALFRED E. SMITH ISSUE

Alfred E. Smith — A384

1945, Nov. 26
937 A384 3c purple   .25 .25

TEXAS STATEHOOD, 100th ANNIV.

U.S. and Texas State Flags A385

1945, Dec. 29
938 A385 3c dark blue   .25 .25

MERCHANT MARINE ISSUE

Achievements of the US Merchant Marine in World War II.

Liberty Ship Unloading Cargo A386

1946, Feb. 26
939 A386 3c blue green   .25 .25

VETERANS OF WORLD WAR II ISSUE

Issued to honor all veterans of World War II.

Honorable Discharge Emblem — A387

1946, May 9
940 A387 3c dark violet   .25 .25

TENNESSEE STATEHOOD, 150th ANNIV.

Andrew Jackson, John Sevier & Tennessee Capitol A388

1946, June 1
941 A388 3c dark violet   .25 .25

IOWA STATEHOOD, 100th ANNIV.

Iowa State Flag & Map A389

1946, Aug. 3
942 A389 3c deep blue   .25 .25

SMITHSONIAN INSTITUTION ISSUE

100th anniversary of the establishment of the Smithsonian Institution, Washington, D.C.

Smithsonian Institution A390

1946, Aug. 10
943 A390 3c violet brown　　　　.25　.25

KEARNY EXPEDITION ISSUE

100th anniversary of the entry of General Stephen Watts Kearny into Santa Fe.

"Capture of Santa Fe" by Kenneth M. Chapman A391

1946, Oct. 16
944 A391 3c brown violet　　　　.25　.25

THOMAS A. EDISON ISSUE

Thomas A. Edison, Birth Centenary — A392

1947, Feb. 11　　　　**Perf. 10½x11**
945 A392 3c bright red violet　.25　.25

JOSEPH PULITZER ISSUE

Joseph Pulitzer & Statue of Liberty A393

1947, Apr. 10　　　　**Perf. 11x10½**
946 A393 3c purple　　　　.25　.25

POSTAGE STAMP CENTENARY ISSUE

Centenary of the first postage stamps issued by the United States Government

Washington & Franklin; Early and Modern Mail-carrying Vehicles — A394

1947, May 17
947 A394 3c deep blue　　　　.25　.25

CENTENARY INTERNATIONAL PHILATELIC EXHIBITION ISSUE
SOUVENIR SHEET

A395

FLAT PLATE PRINTING

1947, May 19　　　　*Imperf.*
948 A395　Pane of 2　　　　.55　.45
　a.　5c blue, type A1　　　　.25　.25
　b.　10c brown orange, type A2　.25　.25

Pane size varies: 96-98x66-68mm.

DOCTORS ISSUE

Issued to honor the physicians of America.

"The Doctor," by Sir Luke Fildes A396

ROTARY PRESS PRINTING

1947, June 9　　　　**Perf. 11x10½**
949 A396 3c brown violet　　　.25　.25

UTAH ISSUE

Centenary of the settlement of Utah.

Pioneers Entering the Valley of Great Salt Lake A397

1947, July 24
950 A397 3c dark violet　　　　.25　.25

U.S. FRIGATE CONSTITUTION ISSUE

150th anniversary of the launching of the U.S. frigate Constitution ("Old Ironsides").

Naval Architect's Drawing of Frigate Constitution A398

1947, Oct. 21
951 A398 3c blue green　　　　.25　.25

EVERGLADES NATIONAL PARK ISSUE

Dedication of the Everglades National Park, Florida, Dec. 6, 1947.

Great White Heron and Map of Florida — A399

1947, Dec. 5　　　　**Perf. 10½x11**
952 A399 3c bright green　　　.25　.25

GEORGE WASHINGTON CARVER ISSUE

5th anniversary of the death of Dr. George Washington Carver, (1864-1943), botanist.

Dr. George Washington Carver — A400

1948, Jan. 5
953 A400 3c bright red violet　.25　.25

CALIFORNIA GOLD CENTENNIAL ISSUE

Sutter's Mill, Coloma, California A401

1948, Jan. 24　　　　**Perf. 11x10½**
954 A401 3c dark violet　　　.25　.25

MISSISSIPPI TERRITORY ISSUE

Mississippi Territory establishment, 150th anniv.

Map, Seal and Gov. Winthrop Sargent A402

1948, Apr. 7
955 A402 3c brown violet　　　.25　.25

FOUR CHAPLAINS ISSUE

George L. Fox, Clark V. Poling, John P. Washington and Alexander D. Goode, the 4 chaplains who sacrificed their lives in the sinking of the S.S. Dorchester, Feb. 3, 1943.

Four Chaplains and Sinking S.S. Dorchester A403

1948, May 28
956 A403 3c gray black　　　.25　.25

WISCONSIN STATEHOOD, 100th ANNIV.

Map on Scroll & State Capitol A404

1948, May 29
957 A404 3c dark violet　　　.25　.25

SWEDISH PIONEER ISSUE

Centenary of the coming of the Swedish pioneers to the Middle West.

Swedish Pioneer with Covered Wagon Moving Westward — A405

1948, June 4
958 A405 5c deep blue　　　.25　.25

PROGRESS OF WOMEN ISSUE

Century of progress of American Women.

Elizabeth Stanton, Carrie C. Catt & Lucretia Mott A406

1948, July 19
959 A406 3c dark violet　　　.25　.25

WILLIAM ALLEN WHITE ISSUE

William Allen White, Editor and Author — A407

1948, July 31　　　　**Perf. 10½x11**
960 A407 3c bright red violet　.25　.25

UNITED STATES-CANADA FRIENDSHIP ISSUE

Century of friendship between the US and Canada.

Niagara Railway Suspension Bridge A408

1948, Aug. 2　　　　**Perf. 11x10½**
961 A408 3c blue　　　　.25　.25

FRANCIS SCOTT KEY ISSUE

Francis Scott Key (1779-1843), Maryland lawyer and author of "The Star-Spangled Banner" (1813).

Key and American Flags of 1814 and 1948 A409

1948, Aug. 9
962 A409 3c rose pink　　　.25　.25

SALUTE TO YOUTH ISSUE

Issued to honor the Youth of America and to publicize "Youth Month," September, 1948.

Girl and Boy Carrying Books A410

1948, Aug. 11
963 A410 3c deep blue　　　.25　.25

OREGON TERRITORY ISSUE

Centenary of the establishment of Oregon Territory.

John McLoughlin, Jason Lee & Wagon on Oregon Trail A411

1948, Aug. 14
964 A411 3c brown red　　　.25　.25

HARLAN F. STONE ISSUE

Chief Justice Harlan Fiske Stone — A412

1948, Aug. 25　　　　**Perf. 10½x11**
965 A412 3c bright red violet　.25　.25

PALOMAR MOUNTAIN OBSERVATORY ISSUE

Dedication, August 30, 1948.

Observatory,
Palomar Mt.,
Cal. — A413

1948, Aug. 30
966 A413 3c blue .25 .25
a. Vert. pair, imperf. between 300.00

CLARA BARTON ISSUE

Founder of
the
American
Red Cross
(1882)
A414

Designed by Charles R. Chickering.

1948, Sept. 7 *Perf. 11x10½*
967 A414 3c rose pink .25 .25

POULTRY INDUSTRY CENTENNIAL ISSUE

Light
Brahma
Rooster
A415

1948, Sept. 9
968 A415 3c sepia .25 .25

GOLD STAR MOTHERS ISSUE

Issued to honor the mothers of deceased members of the United States armed forces.

Star and Palm
Frond — A416

1948, Sept. 21 *Perf. 10½x11*
969 A416 3c orange yellow .25 .25

FORT KEARNY ISSUE

Establishment of Fort Kearny, Neb., centenary.

Fort Kearny
and Pioneer
Group
A417

1948, Sept. 22 *Perf. 11x10½*
970 A417 3c violet .25 .25

VOLUNTEER FIREMEN ISSUE

300th anniv. of the organization of the 1st volunteer firemen in America by Peter Stuyvesant.

Peter
Stuyvesant;
Early and
Modern Fire
Engines
A418

1948, Oct. 4
971 A418 3c bright rose carmine .25 .25

INDIAN CENTENNIAL ISSUE

Centenary of the arrival in Indian Territory, later Oklahoma, of the Five Civilized Indian Tribes: Cherokee, Chickasaw, Choctaw, Muscogee and Seminole.

Map of
Indian
Territory &
Seals of
Five Tribes
A419

1948, Oct. 15
972 A419 3c dark brown .25 .25

ROUGH RIDERS ISSUE

50th anniversary of the organization of the Rough Riders of the Spanish-American War.

Statue of
Capt.
William O.
(Bucky)
O'Neill
A420

1948, Oct. 27
973 A420 3c violet brown .25 .25

JULIETTE LOW ISSUE

Low (1860-1927), founder of the Girl Scouts of America. Mrs. Low organized the 1st Girl Guides troop in 1912 at Savannah. The name was changed to Girl Scouts in 1913 and headquarters moved to New York.

Low and
Girl Scout
Emblem
A421

1948, Oct. 29
974 A421 3c blue green .25 .25

WILL ROGERS ISSUE

Will Rogers — A422

1948, Nov. 4 *Perf. 10½x11*
975 A422 3c bright red violet .25 .25
Will Rogers, 1879-1935, humorist and political commentator.

FORT BLISS CENTENNIAL ISSUE

Fort Bliss and
Rocket — A423

1948, Nov. 5
976 A423 3c henna brown .25 .25

MOINA MICHAEL ISSUE

Moina Michael (1870-1944), educator who originated (1918) the Flanders Field Poppy Day idea as a memorial to the war dead.

Moina
Michael
and Poppy
Plant
A424

1948, Nov. 9 *Perf. 11x10½*
977 A424 3c rose pink .25 .25

GETTYSBURG ADDRESS ISSUE

85th anniversary of Abraham Lincoln's address at Gettysburg, Pennsylvania.

Lincoln and
Quotation
from
Gettysburg
Address
A425

1948, Nov. 19
978 A425 3c bright blue .25 .25

AMERICAN TURNERS ISSUE

Formation of the American Turners Soc., cent.

Torch and American
Turners'
Emblem — A426

1948, Nov. 20 *Perf. 10½x11*
979 A426 3c carmine .25 .25

JOEL CHANDLER HARRIS ISSUE

Joel Chandler
Harris — A427

1948, Dec. 9
980 A427 3c bright red violet .25 .25
Harris (1848-1908), editor and author.

MINNESOTA TERRITORY ISSUE

Establishment of Minnesota Territory, cent.

Pioneer and
Red River
Oxcart
A428

1949, Mar. 3 *Perf. 11x10½*
981 A428 3c blue green .25 .25

WASHINGTON AND LEE UNIVERSITY ISSUE

Bicentenary of Washington and Lee University.

George Washington, Robert E. Lee
and University Building — A429

1949, Apr. 12
982 A429 3c ultramarine .25 .25

PUERTO RICO ELECTION ISSUE

First gubernatorial election in the Territory of Puerto Rico, Nov. 2, 1948.

Puerto Rican Farmer Holding
Cogwheel and Ballot Box
A430

1949, Apr. 27
983 A430 3c green .25 .25

ANNAPOLIS TERCENTENARY ISSUE

Founding of Annapolis, Maryland, 300th anniv.

Stoddert's
1718 Map
of Regions
about
Annapolis,
Redrawn
A431

1949, May 23
984 A431 3c aquamarine .25 .25

G.A.R. ISSUE

Final encampment of the Grand Army of the Republic, Indianapolis, Aug. 28 - Sept. 1, 1949.

Union
Soldier and
GAR
Veteran of
1949
A432

1949, Aug. 29
985 A432 3c bright rose carmine .25 .25

EDGAR ALLAN POE ISSUE

Edgar Allan Poe
(1809-1849),
Poet, Story
Writer and
Editor — A433

1949, Oct. 7 *Perf. 10½x11*
986 A433 3c bright red violet .25 .25

AMERICAN BANKERS ASSOCIATION ISSUE

75th anniv. of the formation of the Association.

Coin, Symbolizing Fields of Banking
Service — A434

1950, Jan. 3 *Perf. 11x10½*
987 A434 3c yellow green .25 .25

SAMUEL GOMPERS ISSUE

Samuel Gompers
(1850-1924), Labor
Leader — A435

1950, Jan. 27 *Perf. 10½x11*
988 A435 3c bright red violet .25 .25

NATIONAL CAPITAL SESQUICENTENNIAL ISSUE

150th anniversary of the establishment of the National Capital, Washington, D.C.

Statue of Freedom on Capitol Dome — A436

Executive Mansion A437

Supreme Court Building A438

United States Capitol A439

1950   **Perf. 10½x11, 11x10½**
989 A436 3c bright blue   .25   .25
990 A437 3c deep green   .25   .25
991 A438 3c light violet   .25   .25
992 A439 3c bright red violet   .25   .25
   Nos. 989-992 (4)   1.00 1.00

RAILROAD ENGINEERS ISSUE

Issued to honor the Railroad Engineers of America. Stamp portrays John Luther (Casey) Jones (1864-1900), locomotive engineer killed in train wreck near Vaughn, Miss.

"Casey" Jones and Locomotives of 1900 and 1950 — A440

1950, Apr. 29   **Perf. 11x10½**
993 A440 3c violet brown   .25   .25

KANSAS CITY, MISSOURI, CENTENARY ISSUE

Kansas City, Missouri, incorporation.

Kansas City Skyline, 1950 and Westport Landing, 1850 A441

1950, June 3
994 A441 3c violet   .25   .25

BOY SCOUTS ISSUE

Honoring the Boy Scouts of America on the occasion of the 2nd National Jamboree, Valley Forge, Pa.

Three Boys, Statue of Liberty and Scout Badge A442

1950, June 30
995 A442 3c sepia   .25   .25

INDIANA TERRITORY ISSUE

Establishment of Indiana Territory, 150th anniv.

Gov. William Henry Harrison & First Indiana Capitol, Vincennes A443

1950, July 4
996 A443 3c bright blue   .25   .25

CALIFORNIA STATEHOOD ISSUE

Gold Miner, Pioneers and S.S. Oregon A444

1950, Sept. 9
997 A444 3c yellow orange   .25   .25

UNITED CONFEDERATE VETERANS FINAL REUNION ISSUE

Final reunion of the United Confederate Veterans, Norfolk, Virginia, May 30, 1951.

Confederate Soldier & United Confederate Veteran A445

1951, May 30
998 A445 3c gray   .25   .25

NEVADA CENTENNIAL ISSUE

Centenary of the settlement of Nevada.

Carson Valley, c. 1851 A446

Designed by Charles R. Chickering.

1951, July 14
999 A446 3c light olive green   .25   .25

LANDING OF CADILLAC ISSUE

250th anniversary of the landing of Antoine de la Mothe Cadillac at Detroit.

Detroit Skyline and Cadillac Landing A447

1951, July 24
1000 A447 3c blue   .25   .25

COLORADO STATEHOOD, 75th ANNIV.

Colorado Capitol and Mount of the Holy Cross A448

1951, Aug. 1
1001 A448 3c blue violet   .25   .25

AMERICAN CHEMICAL SOCIETY ISSUE

75th anniv. of the formation of the Society.

A.C.S. Emblem and Symbols of Chemistry A449

1951, Sept. 4
1002 A449 3c violet brown   .25   .25

BATTLE OF BROOKLYN, 175th ANNIV.

Gen. George Washington Evacuating Army A450

1951, Dec. 10
1003 A450 3c violet   .25   .25

BETSY ROSS ISSUE

200th anniv. of the birth of Betsy Ross, maker of the first American flag.

Betsy Ross Showing Flag to Gen. George Washington, Robert Morris & George Ross — A451

1952, Jan. 2
1004 A451 3c carmine rose   .25   .25

4-H CLUB ISSUE

Farm, Club Emblem, Boy and Girl — A452

1952, Jan. 15
1005 A452 3c blue green   .25   .25

B. & O. RAILROAD ISSUE

125th anniv. of the granting of a charter to the Baltimore and Ohio Railroad Company by the Maryland Legislature.

Charter and Three Stages of Rail Transportation — A453

1952, Feb. 28
1006 A453 3c bright blue   .25   .25

A. A. A. ISSUE

50th anniv. of the formation of the American Automobile Association.

School Girls and Safety Patrolman, Automobiles of 1902 and 1952 — A454

1952, Mar. 4
1007 A454 3c deep blue   .25   .25

NATO ISSUE

Signing of the North Atlantic Treaty, 3rd anniv.

Torch of Liberty and Globe — A455

1952, Apr. 4
1008 A455 3c deep violet   .25   .25

GRAND COULEE DAM ISSUE

50 years of Federal cooperation in developing the resources of rivers and streams in the West.

Spillway, Grand Coulee Dam A456

1952, May 15
1009 A456 3c blue green   .25   .25

LAFAYETTE ISSUE

175th anniversary of the arrival of Marquis de Lafayette in America.

Marquis de Lafayette, Flags, Cannon and Landing Party A457

1952, June 13
1010 A457 3c bright blue   .25   .25

MT. RUSHMORE MEMORIAL ISSUE

Dedication of the Mt. Rushmore National Memorial in the Black Hills of South Dakota, 25th anniv.

Sculptured Heads on Mt. Rushmore — A458

1952, Aug. 11   **Perf. 10½x11**
1011 A458 3c blue green   .25   .25

ENGINEERING CENTENNIAL ISSUE

American Society of Civil Engineers founding.

George Washington Bridge & Covered Bridge of 1850s A459

1952, Sept. 6   *Perf. 11x10½*
1012 A459 3c violet blue   .25 .25

SERVICE WOMEN ISSUE

Women in the United States Armed Services.

Women of the Marine Corps, Army, Navy and Air Force A460

1952, Sept. 11
1013 A460 3c deep blue   .25 .25

GUTENBERG BIBLE ISSUE

Printing of the 1st book, the Holy Bible, from movable type, by Johann Gutenberg, 500th anniv.

Gutenberg Showing Proof to the Elector of Mainz A461

1952, Sept. 30
1014 A461 3c violet   .25 .25

NEWSPAPER BOYS ISSUE

Newspaper Boy, Torch and Group of Homes A462

1952, Oct. 4
1015 A462 3c violet   .25 .25

RED CROSS ISSUE

Globe, Sun and Cross A463

1952, Nov. 21
1016 A463 3c dp blue & car   .25 .25

NATIONAL GUARD ISSUE

National Guardsman and Amphibious Landing A464

1953, Feb. 23
1017 A464 3c bright blue   .25 .25

OHIO STATEHOOD, 150th ANNIV.

Map and Ohio State Seal — A465

1953, Mar. 2
1018 A465 3c chocolate   .25 .25

WASHINGTON TERRITORY ISSUE

Organization of Washington Territory, cent.

Medallion, Pioneers and Washington Scene A466

1953, Mar. 2
1019 A466 3c green   .25 .25

LOUISIANA PURCHASE, 150th ANNIV.

Monroe, Livingston and Barbé-Marbois — A467

1953, Apr. 30
1020 A467 3c violet brown   .25 .25

OPENING OF JAPAN CENTENNIAL ISSUE

Centenary of Commodore Matthew Calbraith Perry's negotiations with Japan, which opened her doors to foreign trade.

Commodore Perry and 1st Anchorage off Tokyo Bay — A468

1953, July 14
1021 A468 5c green   .25 .25

AMERICAN BAR ASSOCIATION, 75th ANNIV.

Section of Frieze, Supreme Court Room A469

1953, Aug. 24
1022 A469 3c rose violet   .25 .25

SAGAMORE HILL ISSUE

Opening of Sagamore Hill, Theodore Roosevelt's home, as a national shrine.

Home of Theodore Roosevelt A470

1953, Sept. 14
1023 A470 3c yellow green   .25 .25

FUTURE FARMERS ISSUE

25th anniversary of the organization of Future Farmers of America.

Agricultural Scene and Future Farmer A471

1953, Oct. 13
1024 A471 3c deep blue   .25 .25

TRUCKING INDUSTRY ISSUE

50th anniv. of the Trucking Industry in the US.

Truck, Farm and Distant City A472

1953, Oct. 27
1025 A472 3c violet   .25 .25

GENERAL PATTON ISSUE

Honoring Gen. George S. Patton, Jr. (1885-1945), and the armored forces of the US Army.

Gen. George S. Patton, Jr. and Tank in Action A473

1953, Nov. 11
1026 A473 3c blue violet   .25 .25

NEW YORK CITY, 300th ANNIV.

Dutch Ship in New Amsterdam Harbor A474

1953, Nov. 20
1027 A474 3c bright red violet   .25 .25

GADSDEN PURCHASE ISSUE

Centenary of James Gadsden's purchase of territory from Mexico to adjust the US-Mexico boundary.

Map and Pioneer Group A475

1953, Dec. 30
1028 A475 3c copper brown   .25 .25

COLUMBIA UNIVERSITY, 200th ANNIV.

Low Memorial Library A476

1954, Jan. 4
1029 A476 3c blue   .25 .25

Wet and Dry Printings

In 1953 the Bureau of Engraving and Printing began experiments in printing on "dry" paper (moisture content 5-10 per cent). In previous "wet" printings the paper had a moisture content of 13-35 per cent.

The new process required a thicker, stiffer paper, special types of inks and greater pressure to force the paper into the recessed plates. The "dry" printings show whiter paper, a higher sheen on the surface, feel thicker and stiffer, and the designs stand out more clearly than on the "wet" printings.

Nos. 832c and 1041 (flat plate) were the first "dry" printings to be issued of flat-plate, regular-issue stamps. No. 1063 was the first rotary-press stamp to be produced entirely by "dry" printing. Nos. QE1a, QE2a and QE3a, RF26A and RW21 (all flat plate) were the first "dry" printings of back-of-the-book issue stamps.

All postage stamps have been printed by the "dry" process since the late 1950's.

See the Scott *Specialized Catalogue of United States Stamps* for listings of the wet and dry printings and for No. 1033 on Silkote paper.

LIBERTY ISSUE

Franklin A477   Washington A478

Palace of the Governors, Santa Fe — A478a — 1031A   Mount Vernon — A479

Thomas Jefferson A480   Bunker Hill Monument, Mass. Flag, 1776 A481

Statue of Liberty A482   Abraham Lincoln A483

The Hermitage A484   James Monroe A485

Theodore
Roosevelt
A486

Woodrow
Wilson
A487

A488

Statue of
Liberty
A489

The Alamo
A490

Independence
Hall — A491

Statue of
Liberty —
A491a

Benjamin
Harrison
A492

John Jay
A493

Monticello
A494

Paul Revere
A495

Robert E. Lee
A496

John Marshall
A497

Susan B.
Anthony
A498

Patrick Henry
A499

Alexander
Hamilton — A500

ROTARY PRESS PRINTING

1954-68   *Perf. 11x10½, 10½x11*

1030	A477	½c red org ('55)	.25	.25
1031	A478	1c dark grn	.25	.25
1031A	A478a	1¼c turq ('60)	.25	.25
1032	A479	1½c brn car ('56)	.25	.25
1033	A480	2c car rose	.25	.25
1034	A481	2½c gray blue ('59)	.25	.25
1035	A482	3c dp vio	.25	.25
a.		Booklet pane of 6, June 30, 1954	3.50	1.25
b.		Horiz. pairs, imperf. btwn in #1035a with foldover (two pairs recorded in two full panes) or miscut (three pairs from pane)	5,000.	
e.		Tagged ('66)	.35	.25
f.		Imperf., pair	3,000.	
g.		Horiz. pair, imperf. between	1,000.	

No. 1057b measures about 19½x22mm; No. 1035f, about 18¾x22½mm.

1036	A483	4c red vio	.25	.25
b.		Booklet pane of 6 ('58)	2.75	1.25
c.		As "b," imperf. horiz.	10,000.	
d.		Horiz. pair, imperf between	4,150.	
e.		Tagged ('63)	.65	.40
1037	A484	4½c blue grn ('59)	.25	.25
1038	A485	5c dp blue	.25	.25
1039	A486	6c car ('55)	.40	.25
		Pair with full vert. gutter btwn.	2,750.	
b.		Imperf, block of 4 (unique)	23,000.	
1040	A487	7c rose car ('56)	.25	.25
a.		dk rose car	.25	.25

FLAT PLATE PRINTING
Size: 22.7mm high
Perf. 11

1041	A488	8c dk vio blue & car	.25	.25
a.		Double impression of carmine	575.00	—

ROTARY PRESS PRINTING
Size: 22.9mm high

1041B	A488	8c dk vio blue & car	.40	.25

GIORI PRESS PRINTING
Redrawn design

1042	A489	8c dk vio bl & car rose ('58)	.25	.25

The 8c John J. Pershing stamp, formerly No. 1042A, is now included with the regular issue of 1961-66. See No. 1214.

ROTARY PRESS PRINTING
Perf. 10½x11

1043	A490	9c rose lil ('56)	.30	.25
a.		9c dark rose lilac	.30	.25
1044	A491	10c rose lake ('56)	.30	.25
b.		10c dark rose lake	.25	.25
d.		Tagged	2.00	1.00

GIORI PRESS PRINTING
Perf. 11

1044A	A491a	11c car & dk vio bl ('61)	.30	.25
c.		Tagged	3.00	1.60

Perf. 11x10½, 10½x11

1045	A492	12c red ('59)	.35	.25
a.		Tagged ('68)	.35	.35
1046	A493	15c rose lake ('58)	.60	.25
a.		Tagged	1.10	.80
1047	A494	20c ultra ('56)	.50	.25
a.		deep bright ultra	.50	.25

1048	A495	25c grn ('58)	1.00	.75
1049	A496	30c blk ('55)	1.20	.75
b.		30c intense black	.80	.25

No. 1049b is from later printings and is on a harder, whiter paper than No. 1049.

1050	A497	40c brn red ('55)	1.75	.25
1051	A498	50c brt pur ('55)	1.75	.25
1052	A499	$1 purple ('55)	5.00	1.00

FLAT PLATE PRINTING
Perf. 11

1053	A500	$5 black	47.50	6.75
Nos. 1030-1053 (27)			64.60	15.00

Luminescence

During 1963 quantities of certain issues (Nos. C64a, 1213b, 1213c and 1229a) were overprinted with phosphorescent coating, "tagged," for use in testing automated facing and canceling machines. Listings for tagged varieties of stamps previously issued without tagging start with Nos. 1035b and C59a.

The entire printings of Nos. 1238, 1278, 1280-1281, 1283B, 1286-1288, 1298-1305, 1323-1340, 1342-1362, 1364, and C69-C75 and all following listings, unless otherwise noted, were tagged.

Stamps tagged with zinc orthosilicate glow yellow green. Airmail stamps with calcium silicate overprint glow orange red. Both tagging overprints are activated only by shortwave ultraviolet light.

ROTARY PRESS COIL STAMPS
Perf. 10 Vert., Horiz. (1¼c, 4½c)
1954-80

1054	A478	1c dk grn	.60	.25
c.		Imperf., pair		
1054A	A478a	1¼c turq ('60)	.25	.25
d.		Imperf., pair		

All examples of No. 1054Ad are precanceled "SEATTLE/WASH." No. 1054A with large holes exists non-precanceled as well as precanceled. The values shown are for the non-precanceled variety; precanceled stamps with large holes are quite common.

1055	A480	2c car rose	.60	.25
b.		Tagged ('68)	.25	.25
c.		Imperf. pair (Bureau precanceled)	325.00	
d.		As "b," Imperf. pair	425.00	
1056	A481	2½c gray blue ('59)	.30	.25
1057	A482	3c dp vio	.35	.25
b.		Imperf., pair	1,250.	800.00
d.		Tagged ('66)	1.00	.50

No. 1057b measures about 19½x22mm; No. 1035f, about 18¾x22½mm.

1058	A483	4c red vio ('58)	.75	.25
a.		Imperf., pair	75.00	70.00
1059	A484	4½c bl grn ('59)	1.50	1.00
1059A	A495	25c grn ('65)	.50	.30
b.		Tagged	.80	.25
d.		Imperf., pair, tagged	30.00	

Value for No. 1059Ad is for fine centering.

NEBRASKA TERRITORY ISSUE

Establishment of the Nebraska Territory, centenary.

Mitchell Pass, Scotts Bluff & "The Sower," by Lee Lawrie A507

ROTARY PRESS PRINTING
1954, May 7   *Perf. 11x10½*

1060	A507	3c violet	.25	.25

KANSAS TERRITORY ISSUE

Establishment of the Kansas Territory, centenary.

Wheat Field and Pioneer Wagon Train A508

1954, May 31

1061	A508	3c brown orange	.25	.25

GEORGE EASTMAN ISSUE

George Eastman (1854-1932), Inventor & Philanthropist A509

1954, July 12   *Perf. 10½x11*

1062	A509	3c violet brown	.25	.25

LEWIS AND CLARK EXPEDITION

150th anniv. of the Lewis and Clark expedition.

Landing of Lewis and Clark A510

1954, July 28   *Perf. 11x10½*

1063	A510	3c violet brown	.25	.25

PENNSYLVANIA ACADEMY OF THE FINE ARTS ISSUE

150th anniversary of the founding of the Pennsylvania Academy of the Fine Arts, Philadelphia.

Charles Willson Peale in his Museum, Self-portrait — A511

1955, Jan. 15   *Perf. 10½x11*

1064	A511	3c rose brown	.25	.25

LAND GRANT COLLEGES ISSUE

Centenary of the founding of Michigan State College and Pennsylvania State University, first of the land grant institutions.

Open Book and Symbols of Subjects Taught A512

1955, Feb. 12   *Perf. 11x10½*

1065	A512	3c green	.25	.25

ROTARY INTERNATIONAL, 50th ANNIV.

Torch, Globe and Rotary Emblem A513

1955, Feb. 23

1066	A513	8c deep blue	.25	.25

ARMED FORCES RESERVE ISSUE

Marine, Coast Guard, Army, Navy, & Air Force Personnel
A514

1955, May 21
1067 A514 3c bright red violet .25 .25

NEW HAMPSHIRE ISSUE

Sesquicentennial of the discovery of the "Old Man of the Mountains."

Great Stone Face — A515

1955, June 21 **Perf. 10½x11**
1068 A515 3c green .25 .25

SOO LOCKS ISSUE

Centenary of the opening of the Soo Locks.

Map of Great Lakes and Two Steamers A516

1955, June 28 **Perf. 11x10½**
1069 A516 3c blue .25 .25

ATOMS FOR PEACE ISSUE

Issued to promote an Atoms for Peace policy.

Atomic Energy Encircling the Hemispheres — A517

1955, July 28
1070 A517 3c deep blue .25 .25

FORT TICONDEROGA ISSUE

Bicentenary of Fort Ticonderoga, New York.

Map of the Fort, Ethan Allen and Artillery A518

1955, Sept. 18
1071 A518 3c light brown .25 .25

ANDREW W. MELLON ISSUE

Andrew W. Mellon — A519

1955, Dec. 20 **Perf. 10½x11**
1072 A519 3c rose carmine .25 .25

Mellon, U.S. Sec. of the Treasury (1921-32), financier and art collector.

BENJAMIN FRANKLIN ISSUE

250th anniv. of the birth of Benjamin Franklin.

"Franklin Taking Electricity from the Sky," by Benjamin West — A520

1956, Jan. 17
1073 A520 3c bright carmine .25 .25

BOOKER T. WASHINGTON ISSUE

Washington (1856-1915), black educator, founder and head of Tuskegee Institute in Alabama.

Log Cabin A521

1956, Apr. 5 **Perf. 11x10½**
1074 A521 3c deep blue .25 .25

FIFTH INTERNATIONAL PHILATELIC EXHIBITION ISSUES

FIPEX, New York City, Apr. 28 - May 6, 1956.

SOUVENIR SHEET

A522

FLAT PLATE PRINTING

1956, Apr. 28 *Imperf.*
1075 A522 Pane of 2 1.20 1.50
  a. A482 3c deep violet .75 .60
  b. A488 8c dark violet blue & carmine .85 .75

No. 1075 measures 108x73mm. Nos. 1075a and 1075b measure 24x28mm. Inscriptions printed in dark violet blue; scrolls and stars in carmine.

New York Coliseum & Columbus Monument A523

ROTARY PRESS PRINTING
1956, Apr. 30 **Perf. 11x10½**
1076 A523 3c deep violet .25 .25

WILDLIFE CONSERVATION ISSUE

Issued to emphasize the importance of Wildlife Conservation in America.

Wild Turkey A524

Pronghorn Antelope A525

King Salmon A526

1956
1077 A524 3c rose lake .25 .25
1078 A525 3c brown .25 .25
1079 A526 3c blue green .25 .25
  Nos. 1077-1079 (3) .75 .75

PURE FOOD AND DRUG LAWS, 50th ANNIV.

Harvey W. Wiley — A527

1956, June 27 **Perf. 10½x11**
1080 A527 3c dark blue green .25 .25

WHEATLAND ISSUE

President Buchanan's Home, "Wheatland," Lancaster, PA — A528

1956, Aug. 5
1081 A528 3c black brown .25 .25

LABOR DAY ISSUE

Mosaic, AFL-CIO Headquarters A529

1956, Sept. 3 **Perf. 10½x11**
1082 A529 3c deep blue .25 .25

NASSAU HALL ISSUE

200th anniv. of Nassau Hall, Princeton University.

Nassau Hall, Princeton, NJ — A530

1956, Sept. 22
1083 A530 3c black, *orange* .25 .25

DEVILS TOWER ISSUE

Issued to commemorate the 50th anniversary of the Federal law providing for protection of American natural antiquities. Devils Tower National Monument, Wyoming, is an outstanding example.

Devils Tower — A531

1956, Sept. 24 **Perf. 10½x11**
1084 A531 3c violet .25 .25

CHILDREN'S ISSUE

Issued to promote friendship among the children of the world.

Children of the World A532

1956, Dec. 15 **Perf. 11x10½**
1085 A532 3c dark blue .25 .25

ALEXANDER HAMILTON (1755-1804)

Alexander Hamilton (1757-1804) and Federal Hall A533

1957, Jan. 11
1086 A533 3c rose red .25 .25

POLIO ISSUE

Honoring "those who helped fight polio," and on for 20th anniv. of the Natl. Foundation for Infantile Paralysis and the March of Dimes.

Allegory — A534

1957, Jan. 15 **Perf. 10½x11**
1087 A534 3c red lilac .25 .25

COAST AND GEODETIC SURVEY ISSUE

150th anniversary of the establishment of the Coast and Geodetic Survey.

Flag of Coast and Geodetic Survey and Ships at Sea A535

1957, Feb. 11 **Perf. 11x10½**
1088 A535 3c dark blue .25 .25

ARCHITECTS ISSUE

American Institute of Architects, centenary.

Corinthian Capital and Mushroom Type Head & Shaft A536

1957, Feb. 23
1089 A536 3c red lilac .25 .25

STEEL INDUSTRY ISSUE

Centenary of the steel industry in America.

American Eagle and Pouring Ladle — A537

1957, May 22   *Perf. 10½x11*
1090 A537 3c bright ultramarine   .25 .25

INTERNATIONAL NAVAL REVIEW ISSUE

Issued to commemorate the International Naval Review and the Jamestown Festival.

Aircraft Carrier and Jamestown Festival Emblem A538

1957, June 10   *Perf. 11x10½*
1091 A538 3c blue green   .25 .25

OKLAHOMA STATEHOOD, 50th ANNIV.

Map of Oklahoma, Arrow and Atom Diagram A539

1957, June 14
1092 A539 3c dark blue   .25 .25

SCHOOL TEACHERS ISSUE

Teacher and Pupils A540

1957, July 1
1093 A540 3c rose lake   .25 .25

FLAG ISSUE

"Old Glory" (48 Stars) A541

GIORI PRESS PRINTING
1957, July 4   *Perf. 11*
1094 A541 4c dark blue & deep carmine   .25 .25

SHIP BUILDING ISSUE

350th anniversary of shipbuilding in America.

"Virginia of Sagadahock" and Seal of Maine — A542

ROTARY PRESS PRINTING
1957, Aug. 15   *Perf. 10½x11*
1095 A542 3c deep violet   .25 .25

CHAMPION OF LIBERTY ISSUE

Magsaysay (1907-57), Pres. of the Philippines.

Ramon Magsaysay, (1907-1957), Philippines President A543

GIORI PRESS PRINTING
1957, Aug. 31   *Perf. 11*
1096 A543 8c car, ultra & ocher   .25 .25

For other Champion of Liberty issues, see Nos. 1110-1111, 1117-1118, 1125-1126, 1136-1137, 1147-1148, 1159-1160, 1165-1166, 1168-1169, 1174-1175.

LAFAYETTE BICENTENARY ISSUE

Marquis de Lafayette — A544

1957, Sept. 6   *Perf. 10½x11*
1097 A544 3c rose lake   .25 .25

WILDLIFE CONSERVATION ISSUE

Issued to emphasize the importance of Wildlife Conservation in America.

Whooping Cranes — A545

GIORI PRESS PRINTING
1957, Nov. 22   *Perf. 11*
1098 A545 3c blue, ocher & green   .25 .25

RELIGIOUS FREEDOM ISSUE

300th anniv. of the Flushing Remonstrance.

Bible, Hat and Quill Pen — A546

ROTARY PRESS PRINTING
1957, Dec. 27   *Perf. 10½x11*
1099 A546 3c black   .25 .25

GARDENING HORTICULTURE ISSUE

Issued to honor the garden clubs of America and in connection with the centenary of the birth of Liberty Hyde Bailey, horticulturist.

"Bountiful Earth" — A547

1958, Mar. 15
1100 A547 3c green   .25 .25

BRUSSELS EXHIBITION ISSUE

Issued in honor of the opening of the Universal and International Exhibition at Brussels, April 17.

U.S. Pavilion at Brussels A551

1958, Apr. 17   *Perf. 11x10½*
1104 A551 3c deep claret   .25 .25

JAMES MONROE ISSUE

James Monroe, by Gilbert Stuart — A552

1958, Apr. 28
1105 A552 3c purple   .25 .25

MINNESOTA STATEHOOD, 100th ANNIV.

Minnesota Lakes and Pines A553

1958, May 11
1106 A553 3c green   .25 .25

GEOPHYSICAL YEAR ISSUE

International Geophysical Year, 1957-58.

Solar Disc and Hands from Michelangelo's "Creation of Adam" — A554

GIORI PRESS PRINTING
1958, May 31   *Perf. 11*
1107 A554 3c black & red orange   .25 .25

GUNSTON HALL ISSUE

Issued for the bicentenary of Gunston Hall and to honor George Mason, author of the Constitution of Virginia and the Virginia Bill of Rights.

Gunston Hall, Virginia A555

ROTARY PRESS PRINTING
1958, June 12   *Perf. 11x10½*
1108 A555 3c light green   .25 .25

MACKINAC BRIDGE ISSUE

Dedication of Mackinac Bridge, Michigan.

Mackinac Bridge — A556

1958, June 25   *Perf. 10½x11*
1109 A556 3c brt greenish blue   .25 .25

CHAMPION OF LIBERTY ISSUE

Simon Bolívar, South American freedom fighter.

Simon Bolivar — A557

1958, July 24
1110 A557 4c olive bister   .25 .25

GIORI PRESS PRINTING
Perf. 11
1111 A557 8c car, ultra & ocher   .25 .25

ATLANTIC CABLE CENTENNIAL ISSUE

Centenary of the Atlantic Cable, linking the Eastern and Western hemispheres.

Neptune, Globe and Mermaid A558

ROTARY PRESS PRINTING
1958, Aug. 15   *Perf. 11x10½*
1112 A558 4c reddish purple   .25 .25

LINCOLN SESQUICENTENNIAL ISSUE

Sesquicentennial of the birth of Abraham Lincoln. No. 1114 also for the centenary of the founding of Cooper Union, New York City. No. 1115 marks the centenary of the Lincoln-Douglas Debates.

Lincoln, by George Healy — A559

Lincoln, by Gutzon Borglum — A560

Abraham Lincoln and Stephen A. Douglas Debating A561

Lincoln, by Daniel Chester French A562

1958-59   **Perf. 10½x11**
1113 A559 1c green ('59)   .25 .25
1114 A560 3c dark rose ('59)   .25 .25

Perf. 11x10½

1115 A561 4c sepia   .25 .25
1116 A562 4c dark blue ('59)   .25 .25
Nos. 1113-1116 (4)   1.00 1.00

CHAMPION OF LIBERTY ISSUE

Lajos Kossuth, Hungarian freedom fighter.

Lajos Kossuth, (1802-1892) — A563

1958, Sept. 19   **Perf. 10½x11**
1117 A563 4c green   .25 .25

GIORI PRESS PRINTING
Perf. 11
1118 A563 8c car, ultra & ocher   .25 .25

FREEDOM OF PRESS ISSUE

Honoring Journalism and freedom of the press in connection with the 50th anniv. of the 1st School of Journalism at the University of Missouri.

Early Press and Hand Holding Quill — A564

ROTARY PRESS PRINTING
1958, Sept. 22   **Perf. 10½x11**
1119 A564 4c black   .25 .25

OVERLAND MAIL ISSUE

Centenary of Overland Mail Service.

Mail Coach and Map of Southwest U.S. A565

1958, Oct. 10   **Perf. 11x10½**
1120 A565 4c crimson rose   .25 .25

NOAH WEBSTER ISSUE

Webster (1758-1843), lexicographer and author.

Noah Webster — A566

1958, Oct. 16   **Perf. 10½x11**
1121 A566 4c dark carmine rose   .25 .25

FOREST CONSERVATION ISSUE

Issued to publicize forest conservation and the protection of natural resources and to honor Theodore Roosevelt, a leading forest conservationist, on the centenary of his birth.

Forest Scene — A567

GIORI PRESS PRINTING
1958, Oct. 27   **Perf. 11**
1122 A567 4c green, yellow & brown   .25 .25

FORT DUQUESNE ISSUE

Bicentennial of Fort Duquesne (Fort Pitt) at future site of Pittsburgh.

Occupation of Fort Duquesne A568

ROTARY PRESS PRINTING
1958, Nov. 25   **Perf. 11x10½**
1123 A568 4c blue   .25 .25

OREGON STATEHOOD, 100th ANNIV.

Covered Wagon and Mt. Hood A569

1959, Feb. 14
1124 A569 4c blue green   .25 .25

CHAMPION OF LIBERTY ISSUE

San Martin, So. American soldier and statesman.

José de San Martin — A570

1959, Feb. 25   **Perf. 10½x11**
1125 A570 4c blue   .25 .25
a.   Horiz. pair, imperf. between   900.00

GIORI PRESS PRINTING
Perf. 11
1126 A570 8c car, ultra & ocher   .25 .25

NATO ISSUE

North Atlantic Treaty Organization, 10th anniv.

NATO Emblem — A571

ROTARY PRESS PRINTING
1959, Apr. 1   **Perf. 10½x11**
1127 A571 4c blue   .25 .25

ARCTIC EXPLORATIONS ISSUE

Conquest of the Arctic by land by Rear Admiral Robert Edwin Peary in 1909 and by sea by the submarine "Nautilus" in 1958.

North Pole, Dog Sled and "Nautilus" A572

1959, Apr. 6   **Perf. 11x10½**
1128 A572 4c brt grnsh blue   .25 .25

WORLD PEACE THROUGH WORLD TRADE ISSUE

Issued in conjunction with the 17th Congress of the International Chamber of Commerce, Washington, D.C., April 19-25.

Globe and Laurel A573

1959, Apr. 20
1129 A573 8c rose lake   .25 .25

SILVER CENTENNIAL ISSUE

Discovery of silver at the Comstock Lode, Nevada.

Henry Comstock at Mount Davidson Site A574

1959, June 8
1130 A574 4c black   .25 .25

ST. LAWRENCE SEAWAY ISSUE

Opening of the St. Lawrence Seaway.

Great Lakes, Maple Leaf and Eagle Emblems A575

GIORI PRESS PRINTING
1959, June 26   **Perf. 11**
1131 A575 4c red & dark blue   .25 .25
See Canada No. 387.

49-STAR FLAG ISSUE

U.S. Flag, 1959 A576

1959, July 4
1132 A576 4c ocher, dark blue & deep carmine   .25 .25

SOIL CONSERVATION ISSUE

Issued as a tribute to farmers and ranchers who use soil and water conservation measures.

Modern Farm A577

1959, Aug. 26
1133 A577 4c blue, green & ocher   .25 .25

PETROLEUM INDUSTRY ISSUE

Centenary of the completion of the nation's first oil well at Titusville, Pa.

Oil Derrick — A578

ROTARY PRESS PRINTING
1959, Aug. 27   **Perf. 10½x11**
1134 A578 4c brown   .25 .25

DENTAL HEALTH ISSUE

Issued to publicize Dental Health and for the centenary of the American Dental Association.

Children A579

1959, Sept. 14   **Perf. 11x10½**
1135 A579 4c green   .25 .25

CHAMPION OF LIBERTY ISSUE

Ernst Reuter, Mayor of Berlin, 1948-53.

Ernst Reuter — A580

1959, Sept. 29   **Perf. 10½x11**
1136 A580 4c gray   .25 .25

GIORI PRESS PRINTING
Perf. 11
1137 A580 8c car, ultra & ocher   .25 .25
a.   Ocher missing (EP)   3,000.
b.   Ultramarine missing (EP)   3,750.
c.   Ocher & ultramarine missing (EP)   4,000.
d.   All colors missing (EP)   2,000.

DR. EPHRAIM McDOWELL ISSUE

Honoring McDowell (1771-1830) on the 150th anniv. of the 1st successful ovarian operation in the US, performed at Danville, Ky., 1809.

Dr. Ephraim McDowell — A581

ROTARY PRESS PRINTING
1959, Dec. 3   **Perf. 10½x11**
1138 A581 4c rose lake   .25 .25
a.   Vert. pair, imperf. btwn.   375.00
b.   Vert. pair, imperf. horiz.   200.00

AMERICAN CREDO ISSUE

Issued to re-emphasize the ideals upon which America was founded and to honor those great Americans who wrote or uttered the credos.

Quotation from Washington's Farewell Address, 1796 — A582

Benjamin Franklin Quotation A583

Thomas Jefferson Quotation A584

Francis Scott Key Quotation A585

Abraham Lincoln Quotation A586

Patrick Henry Quotation A587

Designed by Frank Conley.

GIORI PRESS PRINTING
Plates of 200 subjects in four panes of 50.

1960-61   **Perf. 11**
1139 A582 4c dk vio bl & car   .25   .25
1140 A583 4c ol bister & grn   .25   .25
1141 A584 4c gray & vermilion   .25   .25
1142 A585 4c car & dark blue   .25   .25
1143 A586 4c magenta & green   .25   .25
1144 A587 4c green & brown   .25   .25
     Nos. 1139-1144 (6)   1.50   1.50
Issued: 1/20; 3/31; 5/8; 9/14; 11/19; 1/11/61.

BOY SCOUT JUBILEE ISSUE

50th anniv. of the Boy Scouts of America.

Boy Scout Giving Scout Sign A588

1960, Feb. 8
1145 A588 4c red, dark blue & dark bister   .25   .25

OLYMPIC WINTER GAMES ISSUE

Opening of the 8th Olympic Winter Games, Squaw Valley, Feb. 18-29, 1960.

Olympic Rings and Snowflake — A589

ROTARY PRESS PRINTING
1960, Feb. 18   **Perf. 10½x11**
1146 A589 4c dull blue   .25   .25

CHAMPION OF LIBERTY ISSUE

Issued to honor Thomas G. Masaryk, founder and president of Czechoslovakia (1918-35), on the 110th anniversary of his birth.

Thomas G. Masaryk — A590

1960, Mar. 7
1147 A590 4c blue   .25   .25
    a.   Vert. pair, imperf. between   *1,900.*

GIORI PRESS PRINTING
Perf. 11
1148 A590 8c car, ultra & ocher   .25   .25
    a.   Horiz. pair, imperf. between   —

WORLD REFUGEE YEAR ISSUE

World Refugee Year, July 1, 1959-June 30, 1960.

Refugee Family Walking Toward New Life A591

ROTARY PRESS PRINTING
1960, Apr. 7   **Perf. 11x10½**
1149 A591 4c gray black   .25   .25

WATER CONSERVATION ISSUE

Issued to stress the importance of water conservation and to commemorate the 7th Watershed Congress, Washington, D.C.

Water, from Watershed to Consumer A592

GIORI PRESS PRINTING
1960, Apr. 18   **Perf. 11**
1150 A592 4c dk bl, brn org & grn   .25   .25
    a.   Brown orange missing (EP)   *2,750.*

SEATO ISSUE

South-East Asia Treaty Organization and for the SEATO Conf., Washington, D.C., May 31-June 3.

SEATO Emblem — A593

ROTARY PRESS PRINTING
1960, May 31   **Perf. 10½x11**
1151 A593 4c blue   .25   .25
    a.   Vertical pair, imperf. between   *125.00*

AMERICAN WOMAN ISSUE

Issued to pay tribute to American women and their accomplishments in civic affairs, education, arts and industry.

Mother and Daughter A594

1960, June 2   **Perf. 11x10½**
1152 A594 4c deep violet   .25   .25

50-STAR FLAG ISSUE

U.S. Flag, 1960 — A595

GIORI PRESS PRINTING
1960, July 4   **Perf. 11**
1153 A595 4c dark blue & red   .25   .25

PONY EXPRESS CENTENNIAL ISSUE

Pony Express Rider A596

ROTARY PRESS PRINTING
1960, July 19   **Perf. 11x10½**
1154 A596 4c sepia   .25   .25

EMPLOY THE HANDICAPPED ISSUE

Promoting the employment of the physically handicapped and publicizing the 8th World Congress of the Intl. Soc. for the Welfare of Cripples, New York City.

Man in Wheelchair Operating Drill Press — A597

1960, Aug. 28   **Perf. 10½x11**
1155 A597 4c dark blue   .25   .25

WORLD FORESTRY CONGRESS ISSUE

5th World Forestry Cong., Seattle, Wash., Aug. 29-Sept. 10.

5th World Forestry Congress Seal — A598

1960, Aug. 29
1156 A598 4c green   .25   .25

MEXICAN INDEPENDENCE, 150th ANNIV.

A599

GIORI PRESS PRINTING
1960, Sept. 16   **Perf. 11**
1157 A599 4c green & rose red   .25   .25
     See Mexico No. 910.

US-JAPAN TREATY ISSUE

Centenary of the United States-Japan Treaty of Amity and Commerce.

A600

1960, Sept. 28
1158 A600 4c blue & pink   .25   .25

CHAMPION OF LIBERTY ISSUE

Jan Paderewski, Polish statesman and musician.

Ignacy Jan Paderewski — A601

ROTARY PRESS PRINTING
1960, Oct. 8   **Perf. 10½x11**
1159 A601 4c blue   .25   .25

GIORI PRESS PRINTING
Perf. 11
1160 A601 8c car, ultra & ocher   .25   .25

SENATOR TAFT MEMORIAL ISSUE

Senator Robert A. Taft (1889-1953) of Ohio.

Robert A. Taft — A602

ROTARY PRESS PRINTING
1960, Oct. 10   **Perf. 10½x11**
1161 A602 4c dull violet   .25   .25

WHEELS OF FREEDOM ISSUE

Issued to honor the automotive industry and in connection with the National Automobile Show, Detroit, Oct. 15-23.

Globe and Steering Wheel with Tractor, Car and Truck A603

1960, Oct. 15   **Perf. 11x10½**
1162 A603 4c dark blue   .25   .25

BOYS' CLUBS OF AMERICA ISSUE

Boys' Clubs of America movement, centenary.

Profile of a Boy — A604

GIORI PRESS PRINTING
1960, Oct. 18   **Perf. 11**
1163 A604 4c indigo, slate & rose red   .25   .25

FIRST AUTOMATED POST OFFICE IN THE US ISSUE

Publicizing the opening of the 1st automated post office in the US at Providence, R.I.

Architect's Sketch of New Post Office, Providence, RI — A605

1960, Oct. 20
1164 A605 4c dark blue & carmine .25 .25
a. Red missing (PS) 250.00

CHAMPION OF LIBERTY ISSUE

Baron Karl Gustaf Emil Mannerheim (1867-1951), Marshal and President of Finland.

Baron Gustaf Emil Mannerheim — A606

ROTARY PRESS PRINTING
1960, Oct. 26 *Perf. 10½x11*
1165 A606 4c blue .25 .25

GIORI PRESS PRINTING
Plates of 288 subjects in four panes of 72 each.
Perf. 11
1166 A606 8c car, ultra & ocher .25 .25

CAMP FIRE GIRLS ISSUE

50th anniv. of the Camp Fire Girls' movement and in connection with the Golden Jubilee Convention celebration of the Camp Fire Girls.

Camp Fire Girls Emblem — A607

GIORI PRESS PRINTING
1960, Nov. 1 *Perf. 11*
1167 A607 4c dark blue & bright red .25 .25

CHAMPION OF LIBERTY ISSUE

Giuseppe Garibaldi (1807-1882), Italian patriot and freedom fighter.

Giuseppe Garibaldi (1807-1882) — A608

ROTARY PRESS PRINTING
1960, Nov. 2 *Perf. 10½x11*
1168 A608 4c green .25 .25

GIORI PRESS PRINTING
Perf. 11
1169 A608 8c car, ultra & ocher .25 .25

SENATOR GEORGE MEMORIAL ISSUE

Walter F. George (1878-1957) of Georgia.

Walter F. George (1878-1957) — A609

ROTARY PRESS PRINTING
1960, Nov. 5 *Perf. 10½x11*
1170 A609 4c dull violet .25 .25

ANDREW CARNEGIE ISSUE

Carnegie (1835-1919), industrialist & philanthropist.

Andrew Carnegie — A610

1960, Nov. 25
1171 A610 4c deep claret .25 .25

JOHN FOSTER DULLES MEMORIAL ISSUE

Dulles (1888-1959), Secretary of State (1953-59).

John Foster Dulles — A611

1960, Dec. 6
1172 A611 4c dull violet .25 .25

ECHO I — COMMUNICATIONS FOR PEACE ISSUE

World's 1st communications satellite, Echo I, placed in orbit by the Natl. Aeronautics and Space Admin., Aug. 12, 1960.

Radio Waves Connecting Echo I and Earth A612

1960, Dec. 15 *Perf. 11x10½*
1173 A612 4c deep violet .25 .25

CHAMPION OF LIBERTY ISSUE

Mohandas K. Gandhi, leader in India's struggle for independence.

Mahatma Gandhi — A613

1961, Jan. 26 *Perf. 10½x11*
1174 A613 4c red orange .25 .25

GIORI PRESS PRINTING
Perf. 11
1175 A613 8c car, ultra & ocher .25 .25

RANGE CONSERVATION ISSUE

Issued to stress the importance of range conservation and to commemorate the meeting of the American Society of Range Management. "The Trail Boss" from a drawing by Charles M. Russell is the Society's emblem.

The Trail Boss and Modern Range A614

1961, Feb. 2 *Perf. 11*
1176 A614 4c blue, slate & brown orange .25 .25

HORACE GREELEY ISSUE

Horace Greeley (1811-1872), Publisher and Editor — A615

ROTARY PRESS PRINTING
1961, Feb. 3 *Perf. 10½x11*
1177 A615 4c dull violet .25 .25

CIVIL WAR CENTENNIAL ISSUE

Centenaries of the firing on Fort Sumter (No. 1178), the Battle of Shiloh (No. 1179), the Battle of Gettysburg (No. 1180), the Battle of the Wilderness (No. 1181) and the surrender at Appomattox (No. 1182).

Sea Coast Gun of 1861 A616

Rifleman at Shiloh, 1862 A617

Blue and Gray at Gettysburg, 1863 A618

Battle of the Wilderness, 1864 A619

Appomattox, 1865 — A620

1961-65 *Perf. 11x10½*
1178 A616 4c light green .25 .25
1179 A617 4c black, *peach blossom* .25 .25

GIORI PRESS PRINTING
Plates of 200 subjects in four panes of 50.
Perf. 11
1180 A618 5c gray & blue .25 .25
1181 A619 5c dk red & black .25 .25
1182 A620 5c Prus. blue & blk .30 .25
a. Horiz. pair, imperf. vert. 3,500.
Nos. 1178-1182 (5) 1.30 1.25

Issued: #1178-1182, 4/12; 4/7/62; 7/1/63; 5/5/64; 4/9/65.

KANSAS STATEHOOD, 100th ANNIV.

Sunflower, Pioneer Couple and Stockade A621

1961, May 10 *Perf. 11*
1183 A621 4c brown, dark red & green, *yellow* .25 .25

SENATOR NORRIS ISSUE

Norris and Norris Dam, Tenn. A622

ROTARY PRESS PRINTING
1961, July 11 *Perf. 11x10½*
1184 A622 4c blue green .25 .25

NAVAL AVIATION, 50th ANNIV.

Navy's First Plane (Curtiss A-1 of 1911) and Naval Air Wings A623

1961, Aug. 20
1185 A623 4c blue .25 .25

WORKMEN'S COMPENSATION ISSUE

50th anniv. of the 1st successful Workmen's Compensation Law, enacted by the Wisconsin legislature.

Scales of Justice, Factory, Worker and Family — A624

1961, Sept. 4 *Perf. 10½x11*
1186 A624 4c ultramarine, *grayish* .25 .25

FREDERIC REMINGTON ISSUE

Remington (1861-1909), artist of the West. The design is from an oil painting, Amon Carter Museum of Western Art, Fort Worth, Texas.

Remington's "Smoke Signal" — A625

GIORI PRESS PRINTING
1961, Oct. 4 *Perf. 11*
1187 A625 4c multicolored .25 .25

REPUBLIC OF CHINA ISSUE

50th anniversary of the Republic of China.

Sun Yat-sen — A626

ROTARY PRESS PRINTING

1961, Oct. 10   **Perf. 10½x11**
1188 A626 4c blue   .35 .25

NAISMITH — BASKETBALL ISSUE

Honoring basketball and James Naismith (1861-1939), Canada-born director of physical education, who invented the game in 1891 at Y.M.C.A. College, Springfield, Mass.

Basketball — A627

1961, Nov. 6
1189 A627 4c brown   .25 .25

NURSING ISSUE

Issued to honor the nursing profession.

Student Nurse Lighting Candle — A628

GIORI PRESS PRINTING

1961, Dec. 28   **Perf. 11**
1190 A628 4c bl, grn, org & blk   .25 .25

NEW MEXICO STATEHOOD, 50th ANNIV.

Shiprock A629

1962, Jan. 6
1191 A629 4c lt. blue, maroon & bister   .25 .25

ARIZONA STATEHOOD, 50th ANNIV.

Giant Saguaro Cactus — A630

1962, Feb. 14
1192 A630 4c carmine, violet blue & green   .25 .25

PROJECT MERCURY ISSUE

1st orbital flight of a US astronaut, Lt. Col. John H. Glenn, Jr., Feb. 20, 1962.

"Friendship 7" Capsule and Globe A631

1962, Feb. 20
1193 A631 4c dark blue & yellow   .25 .25
    Imperfs. are printers waste.

MALARIA ERADICATION ISSUE

World Health Organization's drive to eradicate malaria.

Great Seal of U.S. and WHO Symbol A632

1962, Mar. 30
1194 A632 4c blue & bister   .25 .25

CHARLES EVANS HUGHES ISSUE

Hughes (1862-1948), Governor of New York, Chief Justice of the US.

Charles Evans Hughes — A633

ROTARY PRESS PRINTING

1962, Apr. 11   **Perf. 10½x11**
1195 A633 4c black, *buff*   .25 .25

SEATTLE WORLD'S FAIR ISSUE

"Century 21" International Exposition, Seattle, Wash., Apr. 21-Oct. 21.

Space Needle and Monorail — A634

GIORI PRESS PRINTING

1962, Apr. 25   **Perf. 11**
1196 A634 4c red & dark blue   .25 .25

LOUISIANA STATEHOOD, 150th ANNIV.

Riverboat on the Mississippi A635

1962, Apr. 30
1197 A635 4c blue, dark slate green & red   .25 .25

HOMESTEAD ACT, CENTENARY

Sod Hut and Settlers A636

ROTARY PRESS PRINTING

1962, May 20   **Perf. 11x10½**
1198 A636 4c slate   .25 .25

GIRL SCOUTS ISSUE

50th anniversary of the Girl Scouts of America.

Senior Girl Scout & Flag A637

1962, July 24
1199 A637 4c rose red   .25 .25

SENATOR BRIEN McMAHON ISSUE

McMahon (1903-52) of Connecticut had a role in opening the way to peaceful uses of atomic energy through the Atomic Energy Act establishing the Atomic Energy Commission.

Brien McMahon & Atomic Diagram A638

1962, July 28
1200 A638 4c purple   .25 .25

APPRENTICESHIP ISSUE

National Apprenticeship Program and 25th anniv. of the National Apprenticeship Act.

Machinist Handing Micrometer to Apprentice A639

1962, Aug. 31
1201 A639 4c blk, *yellow bister*   .25 .25

SAM RAYBURN ISSUE

Sam Rayburn and Capitol — A640

GIORI PRESS PRINTING

1962, Sept. 16   **Perf. 11**
1202 A640 4c dark blue & red brown   .25 .25

DAG HAMMARSKJOLD ISSUE

UN Headquarters & Dag Hammarskjold, U.N. Sec. Gen., 1953-61 — A641

1962, Oct. 23
1203 A641 4c blk, brn & yel   .25 .25

No. 1203a can only be collected on a cover postmarked before Nov. 16, 1962 (the date the Hammarskjold Special Printing, No. 1204, was issued), or tied on dated piece (unique used pair). Covers are known machine postmarked Cuyahoga Falls, Ohio, Nov. 14, 1962, and notarized in the lower left corner by George W. Schwartz, Notary Public. Other covers are reported postmarked Oct. 26, 1962, Brooklyn, NY, Vanderveer Station. Unaddressed, uncacheted first day covers also exist. Other covers may exist. All covers must be accompanied by certificates from recognized expertizing committees. Value of first-day cover, $3,000.

An unused pane of 50 was signed in the selvage by ten well-known philatelists attesting to its genuineness. This pane was donated to the American Philatelic Society in 1987.

An unknown number of "first day covers" exist bearing Artmaster cachets. These were contrived using examples of No. 1204.

Hammarskjold Special Printing

1962, Nov. 16
1204 A641 4c black, brown & yel (yellow inverted)   .25 .25

No. 1204 was issued following discovery of No. 1203 with yellow background inverted.

CHRISTMAS ISSUE

Wreath and Candles — A642

1962, Nov. 1
1205 A642 4c green & red   .25 .25

HIGHER EDUCATION ISSUE

Higher education's role in American cultural and industrial development and the centenary celebrations of the signing of the law creating land-grant colleges and universities.

Map of U.S. and Lamp A643

1962, Nov. 14
1206 A643 4c blue green & black   .25 .25

WINSLOW HOMER ISSUE

Homer (1836-1910), painter, showing his oil, "Breezing Up," which hangs in the National Gallery, Washington, D.C.

"Breezing Up" — A644

1962, Dec. 15
1207 A644 4c multicolored   .25 .25
    a.   Horiz. pair, imperf. btwn. and at right   7,000.

FLAG ISSUE

Flag over White House — A645

1963-66
1208 A645 5c blue & red   .25 .25
    a.   Tagged ('68)   .25 .25
    b.   Horiz. pair, imperf. between, tagged   2,250.

Beware of pairs with faint blind perfs between offered as No. 1208b.

REGULAR ISSUE

Andrew Jackson A646   George Washington A650

John J. Pershing A651

ROTARY PRESS PRINTING

1961-66   **Perf. 11x10½**
1209	A646 1c green ('63)	.25	.25
a.	Tagged ('66)	.25	.25
1213	A650 5c dk gray blue	.25	.25
a.	Booklet pane of 5 + label	2.00	2.00
b.	Tagged ('63)	.50	.25
c.	As "a," tagged, ('63)	2.00	1.50
d.	Horiz. pair, imperf. between, in #1213a with foldover or miscut	1,750.	
1214	A651 8c brown ('61)	.25	.25

See Luminescence note after No. 1053.

Three different messages are found on the label in No. 1213a, and two messages on that of No. 1213c.

No. 1213d resulted from a paper foldover after perforating and before cutting into panes.

Unused catalogue numbers were left vacant for additional denominations.

COIL STAMPS
(Rotary Press)

1962-66   **Perf. 10 Vertically**
1225	A646 1c green ('63)	.40	.25
a.	Tagged ('66)	.40	.25
1229	A650 5c dk blue gray	1.50	.25
a.	Tagged ('63)	2.50	.25
b.	Imperf., pair	300.00	

CAROLINA CHARTER ISSUE

Tercentenary of the Carolina Charter granting to 8 Englishmen lands extending coast-to-coast roughly along the present border of Virginia to the north and Florida to the south. Original charter on display at Raleigh.

First Page of Carolina Charter A662

GIORI PRESS PRINTING

1963, Apr. 6   **Perf. 11**
1230	A662 5c dark carmine & brown	.25	.25

FOOD FOR PEACE-FREEDOM FROM HUNGER ISSUE

American "Food for Peace" program and the "Freedom from Hunger" campaign of the FAO.

Wheat — A663

1963, June 4
1231	A663 5c green, buff & red	.25	.25

WEST VIRGINIA STATEHOOD, 100th ANNIV.

Map of West Virginia & State Capitol A664

1963, June 20
1232	A664 5c green, red & black	.25	.25

EMANCIPATION PROCLAMATION ISSUE

Centenary of Lincoln's Emancipation Proclamation freeing about 3,000,000 slaves in 10 southern states.

Severed Chain A665

1963, Aug. 16
1233	A665 5c dark blue, black & red	.25	.25

ALLIANCE FOR PROGRESS ISSUE

2nd anniv. of the Alliance for Progress, which aims to stimulate economic growth and raise living standards in Latin America.

Alliance Emblem A666

1963, Aug. 17
1234	A666 5c ultramarine & green	.25	.25

CORDELL HULL ISSUE

Hull (1871-1955), Secretary of State (1933-44).

Cordell Hull (1871-1955), Sec. of State (1933-44) — A667

ROTARY PRESS PRINTING

1963, Oct. 5   **Perf. 10½x11**
1235	A667 5c blue green	.25	.25

ELEANOR ROOSEVELT ISSUE

Mrs. Franklin D. Roosevelt (1884-1962).

Mrs. Franklin D. Roosevelt (1884-1962) A668

1963, Oct. 11   **Perf. 11x10½**
1236	A668 5c bright purple	.25	.25

SCIENCE ISSUE

Honoring the sciences and in connection with the centenary of the Natl. Academy of Science.

"The Universe" A669

GIORI PRESS PRINTING

1963, Oct. 14   **Perf. 11**
1237	A669 5c Prussian blue & black	.25	.25

CITY MAIL DELIVERY ISSUE

Centenary of free city mail delivery.

Letter Carrier, 1863 — A670

1963, Oct. 26   **Tagged**
1238	A670 5c gray, dark blue & red	.25	.25

RED CROSS CENTENARY ISSUE

A671

1963, Oct. 29
1239	A671 5c bluish black & red	.25	.25

CHRISTMAS ISSUE

Natl. Christmas Tree & White House — A672

1963, Nov. 1
1240	A672 5c dk bl, bluish blk & red	.25	.25
a.	Tagged	.65	.50
b.	Horiz. pair, imperf between	7,500.	
c.	Red missing (PS)		

JOHN JAMES AUDUBON ISSUE

Audubon (1785-1851), ornithologist and artist. The birds pictured are actually Collie's magpie jays. See No. C71.

Columbia Jays — A673

1963, Dec. 7
1241	A673 5c dk blue & multi	.25	.25

SAM HOUSTON ISSUE

Houston (1793-1863), soldier, president of Texas, US senator.

Sam Houston — A674

ROTARY PRESS PRINTING

1964, Jan. 10   **Perf. 10½x11**
1242	A674 5c black	.25	.25

CHARLES M. RUSSELL ISSUE

Russell (1864-1926), painter. The design is from a painting, Thomas Gilcrease Institute of American History and Art, Tulsa, Okla.

"Jerked Down" A675

GIORI PRESS PRINTING

1964, Mar. 19   **Perf. 11**
1243	A675 5c multicolored	.25	.25

NEW YORK WORLD'S FAIR ISSUE

New York World's Fair, 1964-65.

Mall with Unisphere & "Rocket Thrower," by Donald De Lue — A676

ROTARY PRESS PRINTING

1964, Apr. 22   **Perf. 11x10½**
1244	A676 5c blue green	.25	.25
a.	All color omitted	—	—

On No. 1244a, a clear albino impression of the design is present.

JOHN MUIR ISSUE

Muir (1838-1914), naturalist and conservationist.

John Muir (1838-1914), naturalist and conservationist and Redwood Forest — A677

GIORI PRESS PRINTING

1964, Apr. 29   **Perf. 11**
1245	A677 5c brn, grn, yel grn & ol	.25	.25

KENNEDY MEMORIAL ISSUE

President John Fitzgerald Kennedy, (1917-1963).

Pres. John F. Kennedy (1917-63) and Eternal Flame A678

ROTARY PRESS PRINTING

1964, May 29   **Perf. 11x10½**
1246	A678 5c blue gray	.25	.25

NEW JERSEY TERCENTENARY ISSUE

300th anniv. of English colonization of New Jersey. The design is from a mural by Howard Pyle in the Essex County Courthouse, Newark, N.J.

Philip Carteret Landing at Elizabethtown & Map of New Jersey — A679

1964, June 15   **Perf. 10½x11**
1247	A679 5c brt ultramarine	.25	.25

NEVADA STATEHOOD, 100th ANNIV.

Virginia City and Map of Nevada A680

GIORI PRESS PRINTING

1964, July 22   **Perf. 11**
1248	A680 5c red, yellow & blue	.25	.25

REGISTER AND VOTE ISSUE

Campaign to draw more voters to the polls.

Flag — A681

1964, Aug. 1
1249 A681 5c dark blue & red   .25   .25

SHAKESPEARE ISSUE

William Shakespeare (1564-1616).

William Shakespeare
A682

ROTARY PRESS PRINTING

1964, Aug. 14   *Perf. 10½x11*
1250 A682 5c black brown, *tan*   .25   .25

DOCTORS MAYO ISSUE

Dr. William James Mayo (1861-1939) and his brother, Dr. Charles Horace Mayo (1865-1939), surgeons who founded the Mayo Foundation for Medical Education and Research in affiliation with the Univ. of Minnesota at Rochester. Heads on stamp are from a sculpture by James Earle Fraser.

Drs. William and Charles Mayo — A683

1964, Sept. 11
1251 A683 5c green   .25   .25

AMERICAN MUSIC ISSUE

50th anniv. of the founding of the American Society of Composers, Authors and Publishers (ASCAP).

Lute, Horn, Laurel, Oak and Music Score
A684

GIORI PRESS PRINTING

1964, Oct. 15   *Perf. 11*
Gray Paper with Blue Threads
1252 A684 5c red, black & blue   .25   .25
  a.   Blue omitted   650.00
  b.   Blue missing (PS)   500.00

Beware of examples offered as No. 1252a which have traces of blue.

HOMEMAKERS ISSUE

Honoring American women as homemakers and for the 50th anniv. of the passage of the Smith-Lever Act. By providing economic experts under an extension service of the U.S. Dept. of Agriculture, this legislation helped to improve homelife.

Farm Scene Sampler
A685

Engraved (Giori Press); Background Lithographed
1964, Oct. 26
1253 A685 5c multicolored   .25   .25

CHRISTMAS ISSUE

Holly
A686

Mistletoe
A687

Poinsettia
A688

Sprig of Conifer
A689

GIORI PRESS PRINTING

1964, Nov. 9
1254 A686 5c green, car & black   .25   .25
  a.   Tagged   .75   .50
  b.   Printed on gummed side   1,850.
  c.   All color missing (FO)   2,000.
1255 A687 5c car, green & black   .25   .25
  a.   Tagged   .75   .50
1256 A688 5c car, green & black   .25   .25
  a.   Tagged   .75   .50
1257 A689 5c black, green & car   .25   .25
  a.   Tagged   .75   .50
  b.   Block of 4, #1254-1257   1.00   1.00
  c.   Block of 4, tagged   3.00   2.25

Tagged stamps issued Nov. 10.
No. 1254b resulted from a paper foldover before printing and perforating.
No. 1254c is unique and is in a block of four with the other three stamps missing parts of the designs.

VERRAZANO-NARROWS BRIDGE ISSUE

Opening of the Verrazano-Narrows Bridge connecting Staten Island and Brooklyn.

Verrazano-Narrows Bridge and Map of NY Bay — A690

ROTARY PRESS PRINTING

1964, Nov. 21   *Perf. 10½x11*
1258 A690 5c blue green   .25   .25

FINE ARTS ISSUE

Abstract Design by Stuart Davis
A691

GIORI PRESS PRINTING

1964, Dec. 2   *Perf. 11*
1259 A691 5c ultra., black & dull red   .25   .25

AMATEUR RADIO ISSUE

Issued to honor the radio amateurs on the 50th anniversary of the American Radio Relay League.

Radio Waves and Dial — A692

ROTARY PRESS PRINTING

1964, Dec. 15   *Perf. 10½x11*
1260 A692 5c red lilac   .25   .25

BATTLE OF NEW ORLEANS ISSUE

Battle of New Orleans, Chalmette Plantation, Jan. 8-18, 1815, established 150 years of peace and friendship between the US and Great Britain.

General Andrew Jackson and Sesquicentennial Medal — A693

GIORI PRESS PRINTING

1965, Jan. 8   *Perf. 11*
1261 A693 5c deep carmine, violet blue & gray   .25   .25

PHYSICAL FITNESS-SOKOL ISSUE

Publicizing the importance of physical fitness and for the centenary of the founding of the Sokol (athletic) organization in America.

Discus Thrower — A694

1965, Feb. 15
1262 A694 5c maroon & black   .25   .25

CRUSADE AGAINST CANCER ISSUE

Issued to publicize the "Crusade Against Cancer" and to stress the importance of early diagnosis.

Microscope and Stethoscope — A695

1965, Apr. 1
1263 A695 5c black, purple & red orange   .25   .25

CHURCHILL MEMORIAL ISSUE

Sir Winston Spencer Churchill (1874-1965), British statesman and World War II leader.

Winston Churchill — A696

ROTARY PRESS PRINTING

1965, May 13   *Perf. 10½x11*
1264 A696 5c black   .25   .25

MAGNA CARTA ISSUE

750th anniversary of the Magna Carta, the basis of English and American common law.

Procession of Barons and King John's Crown
A697

GIORI PRESS PRINTING

1965, June 15   *Perf. 11*
1265 A697 5c black, yellow ocher & red lilac   .25   .25

INTERNATIONAL COOPERATION YEAR

ICY, 1965, and 20th anniv. of the UN.

ICY Emblem
A698

1965, June 26
1266 A698 5c dull blue & black   .25   .25

SALVATION ARMY ISSUE

Centenary of the founding of the Salvation Army by William Booth in London.

A699

1965, July 2
1267 A699 5c red, black & dark blue   .25   .25

DANTE ISSUE

Dante Alighieri (1265-1321), Italian poet.

A700

ROTARY PRESS PRINTING

1965, July 17   *Perf. 10½x11*
1268 A700 5c maroon, *tan*   .25   .25

HERBERT HOOVER ISSUE

President Herbert Clark Hoover, (1874-1964).

A701

1965, Aug. 10
1269 A701   5c rose red   .25   .25

ROBERT FULTON ISSUE

Fulton (1765-1815), inventor of the 1st commercial steamship.

Robert Fulton & Clermont A702

GIORI PRESS PRINTING

1965, Aug. 19   Perf. 11
1270 A702   5c black & blue   .25   .25

FLORIDA SETTLEMENT ISSUE

400th anniv. of the settlement of Florida, and the 1st permanent European settlement in the continental US, St. Augustine, Fla.

Spanish Explorer, Royal Flag of Spain and Ships — A703

1965, Aug. 28
1271 A703   5c red, yel & blk   .25   .25
   a. Yellow omitted   200.00

See Spain No. 1312.

TRAFFIC SAFETY ISSUE

Issued to publicize traffic safety and the prevention of traffic accidents.

Traffic Signal A704

1965, Sept. 3
1272 A704   5c emer, red & blk   .25   .25

JOHN SINGLETON COPLEY ISSUE

Copley (1738-1815), painter. The portrait of the artist's daughter is from the oil painting "The Copley Family," which hangs in the National Gallery of Art, Washington, D.C.

Elizabeth Clarke Copley — A705

1965, Sept. 17
1273 A705   5c blk, brn & olive   .25   .25

INTERNATIONAL TELECOMMUNICATION UNION, 100th ANNIV.

Gall Projection World Map & Radio Sine Wave A706

1965, Oct. 6
1274 A706   11c blk, car & bister   .35   .25

ADLAI STEVENSON ISSUE

Adlai Ewing Stevenson (1900-65), governor of Illinois, US ambassador to the UN.

Adlai E. Stevenson — A707

LITHOGRAPHED, ENGRAVED (Giori)
1965, Oct. 23
1275 A707   5c pale bl, blk, car & vio bl   .25   .25

CHRISTMAS ISSUE

Angel with Trumpet — A708

GIORI PRESS PRINTING
1965, Nov. 2
1276 A708   5c carmine, dark olive green & bister   .25   .25
   a. Tagged   .75   .25

PROMINENT AMERICANS ISSUE

Thomas Jefferson A710

Albert Gallatin A711

Frank Lloyd Wright & Guggenheim Museum A712

Francis Parkman A713

Lincoln A714

Washington A715

Washington (Redrawn) A715a

Franklin D. Roosevelt A716

Albert Einstein A717

Andrew Jackson — A718

Henry Ford, 1909 Model T — A718a

John F. Kennedy A719

Oliver Wendell Holmes A720

Type 3 — A720a

George Catlett Marshall A721

Frederick Douglass A722

John Dewey — A723

Thomas Paine — A724

Lucy Stone A725

Eugene O'Neill A726

John Bassett Moore — A727

Types of 15c:
I. Necktie barely touches coat at bottom; crosshatching of tie strong and complete. Flag of "5" is true horizontal. Crosshatching of "15" is colorless when visible.
II. Necktie does not touch coat at bottom; LL to UR crosshatching lines strong, UL to LR lines very faint. Flag of "5" slants down slightly at right. Crosshatching of "15" is colored and visible when magnified.
III. Used only for No. 1288B; smaller in overall size and "15¢" is ¾mm closer to head.

ROTARY PRESS PRINTING
1965-78   Perf. 11x10½, 10½x11
1278 A710   1c green, tagged   .25   .25
   a. Booklet pane of 8   1.00   .75
   b. Bklt. pane of 4+2 labels   .75   .60
   c. Untagged (Bureau pre-canceled)   6.25 1.25
1279 A711   1¼c light green   .25   .25
1280 A712   2c dk blue gray, tagged   .25   .25
   a. Bklt. pane of 5 + label   1.25   .80
   b. Untagged (Bureau pre-canceled)   1.35   .40
   c. Bklt. pane of 6   1.00   .75
1281 A713   3c violet, tagged   .25   .25
   a. Untagged (Bureau pre-canceled)   3.00   .75
1282 A714   4c black   .25   .25
   a. Tagged   .25   .25
1283 A715   5c blue   .25   .25
   a. Tagged   .25   .25
1283B A715a 5c blue, tagged   .25   .25
   d. Untagged (Bureau pre-canceled)   12.50 1.00

No. 1283B is redrawn; highlights, shadows softened.

1284 A716   6c gray brn   .25   .25
   a. Tagged   .25   .25
   b. Booklet pane of 8   1.50 1.00
   c. Bklt. pane of 5+ label   1.40 1.00
   d. Horiz. pair, imperf. between   2,250.
1285 A717   8c violet   .25   .25
   a. Tagged   .25   .25
1286 A718   10c lilac, tagged   .25   .25
   b. Untagged (Bureau pre-canceled)   55.00 1.75
1286A 718a   12c black, tagged   .25   .25
   c. Untagged (Bureau pre-canceled)   4.75 1.00
1287 A719   13c brn, tagged   .30   .25
   a. Untagged (Bureau pre-canceled)   6.00 1.00
1288 A720   15c mag, type I, tagged   .30   .25
   a. Untagged (Bureau pre-canceled)   .75   .75
   d. Type II   .55   .25

Imperforates exist from printer's waste.
Values for No. 1288a are for the bars-only precancel. Also exists with city precancels, and worth more thus.

Perf. 10 on 2 or 3 Sides
1288B A720a 15c mag, type III   .35   .25
   c. Booklet pane of 8   2.80 1.75
   e. As "c," vert. imperf. between   1,500.

No. 1288B issued in booklets only. All stamps have one or two straight edges. Plates made from redrawn die.

Perf. 11x10½, 10½x11
1289 A721   20c deep olive   .40   .25
   a. Tagged   .40   .25
   b. black olive   .50   .25
   c. As "a," double impression   500.00
1290 A722   25c rose lake   .55   .25
   a. Tagged   .45   —
   b. 25c magenta   15.00

Shades of No. 1290 rose lake exist that tend toward magenta, but are not. Competent identification is important for No. 1290b.

1291 A723   30c red lilac   .65   .25
   a. Tagged   .50   .25
1292 A724   40c blue black   .80   .25
   a. Tagged   .75   .25
1293 A725   50c rose mag   1.00   .25
   a. Tagged   .80   .25
1294 A726 $1 dull purple   2.25   .25
   a. Tagged   1.75   .25
   b. $1 black violet   100.00 350.00
1295 A727 $5 gray black   10.00 1.25
   a. Tagged   8.50 2.00
   Nos. 1278-1295 (21)   19.35 7.25

Issued (without tagging) — 1965: 4c, 11/19.
1966: 5c, 2/22; 6c, 1/29; 8c, 3/14; $5, 12/3.
1967: 1¼c, 1/30; 20c, 10/24; 25c, 2/14; $1, 10/16.
1968: 30c, 10/21; 40c, 1/29; 50c, 8/13.
Dates for tagged: 1965: 4c, 12/1.
1966: 2c, 6/8; 5c, 2/23; 6c, 12/29; 8c, 7/6.
1967: 3c, 9/16; #1283B, 11/17; #1284b, 12/28; 10c, 3/15; 13c, 5/29.
1968: 1c, #1284c, 1/12; #1280a, 1/8; 12c, 7/30; 15c, 3/8.
1973: 20c, 25c, 30c, 40c, 50c, $1, $5, 4/3.
1978: No. 1288B, 6/14.

COIL STAMPS
Perf. 10 Horizontally
1966-81   **Tagged**
1297 A713   3c violet   .25   .25
   a. Imperf., pair   22.50
   b. Untagged (Bureau pre-canceled)   .40   .25
   c. As "b," imperf. pair   8.00
1298 A716   6c gray brn   .25   .25
     Imperf., pair   1,500.

Franklin D. Roosevelt
— A727a

Perf. 10 Vertically

1299	A710	1c green	.25	.25
a.		Untagged (Bureau pre-canceled)	8.00	1.75
b.		Imperf., pair	22.50	
1303	A714	4c black	.25	.25
a.		Untagged (Bureau pre-canceled)	8.75	.75
b.		Imperf., pair	600.00	
1304	A715	5c blue	.25	.25
a.		Untagged (Bureau pre-canceled)	6.50	.65
b.		Imperf., pair	110.00	
e.		As "a," imperf., pair	250.00	
f.		Tagging omitted (not Bureau precanceled)	—	—

No. 1304b is valued in the grade of fine.
No. 1304e is precanceled Mount Pleasant, Iowa. Also exists from Chicago, Illinois; value $1,500 for pair.

1304C	A715a	5c blue	.25	.25
d.		Imperf., pair	375.00	
1305	A727a	6c gray brn	.25	.25
a.		Imperf., pair	55.00	
b.		Untagged (Bureau pre-canceled)	20.00	1.00
m.		Pair, imperf. between	250.00	
1305E	A720	15c mag, type		
		I	.25	.25
f.		Untagged (Bureau pre-canceled)	32.50	—
g.		Imperf., pair, type I	20.00	
h.		Pair, imperf. between	125.00	
i.		Type II	1.50	.25
j.		Imperf., pair, type II	55.00	
1305C	A726	$1 dull pur	3.25	.40
d.		Imperf., pair	1,250.	

Nos. 1297-1305C (9)　　5.25　2.40

Issued: 1c, 1/12/68; 3c, 11/4/75; 4c, 5/28/66; #1304, 9/8/66; 6c, #1298, 12/28/67; #1305, 2/28/68;
$1, 1/12/73; 15c, 6/14/78.

MIGRATORY BIRD TREATY ISSUE

Migratory Birds over Canada-U.S. Border — A728

GIORI PRESS PRINTING

1966, Mar. 16　　　　　**Perf. 11**
1306　A728　5c blk, crim & dk blue　.25　.25

HUMANE TREATMENT OF ANIMALS ISSUE

Issued to promote humane treatment of all animals and for the centenary of the American Society for the Prevention of Cruelty to Animals.

Mongrel
A729

LITHOGRAPHED, ENGRAVED (Giori)

1966, Apr. 9
1307　A729　5c orange brown & black　　　.25　.25

INDIANA STATEHOOD, 150th ANNIV.

Sesquicentennial
Seal — A730

GIORI PRESS PRINTING

1966, Apr. 16
1308　A730　5c ocher, brn & vio blue　　　.25　.25

AMERICAN CIRCUS ISSUE

Issued to honor the American Circus on the centenary of the birth of John Ringling.

Clown — A731

1966, May 2
1309　A731　5c multicolored　.25　.25

SIXTH INTERNATIONAL PHILATELIC EXHIBITION ISSUES

Sixth International Philatelic Exhibition (SIPEX), Washington, D.C., May 21-30.

Stamped
Cover
A732

LITHOGRAPHED, ENGRAVED (Giori)
1966
1310　A732　5c multicolored　.25　.25

Souvenir Sheet

A733

Imperf
1311　A733　5c multicolored　　.25　.25

No. 1311 measures 108x74mm.

BILL OF RIGHTS, 175th ANNIV.

"Freedom" Checking
"Tyranny" — A734

GIORI PRESS PRINTING
1966, July 1　　　　　**Perf. 11**
1312　A734　5c carmine, dark & light blue　.25　.25

POLISH MILLENNIUM ISSUE

Adoption of Christianity in Poland, 1000th anniv.

Polish Eagle and
Cross — A735

ROTARY PRESS PRINTING
1966, July 30　　　　**Perf. 10½x11**
1313　A735　5c red　　　　　.25　.25

Tagging Extended

During 1966, experimental use of tagged stamps was extended to the Cincinnati Postal Region covering offices in Indiana, Kentucky and Ohio. To supply these offices about 12 percent of the following nine issues (Nos. 1314-1322) were tagged.

NATIONAL PARK SERVICE ISSUE

50th anniv. of the Natl. Park Service of the Interior Dept. The design "Park-scape U.S.A." identifies Natl. Park Service facilities.

National
Park
Service
Emblem
A736

LITHOGRAPHED, ENGRAVED (Giori)
1966, Aug. 25　　　　　**Perf. 11**

1314	A736	5c yellow, black & green	.25	.25
a.		Tagged	.35	.35

MARINE CORPS RESERVE ISSUE

US Marine Corps Reserve founding, 50th anniv.

A737

1966, Aug. 29

1315	A737	5c black, bister, red & ultra	.25	.25
a.		Tagged	.40	.25
b.		Black & bister (engraved) missing (EP)	16,000.	

GENERAL FEDERATION OF WOMEN'S CLUBS ISSUE

75 years of service by the General Federation of Women's Clubs.

Women of
1890 and
1966
A738

GIORI PRESS PRINTING
1966, Sept. 12

1316	A738	5c black, pink & blue	.25	.25
a.		Tagged	.40	.25

AMERICAN FOLKLORE ISSUE
Johnny Appleseed

Issued to honor Johnny Appleseed (John Chapman 1774-1845), who wandered over 100,000 square miles planting apple trees, and who gave away and sold seedlings to Midwest pioneers.

Johnny
Appleseed — A739

1966, Sept. 24

1317	A739	5c green, red & black	.25	.25
a.		Tagged	.40	.25

BEAUTIFICATION OF AMERICA ISSUE

Issued to publicize President Johnson's "Plant for a more beautiful America" campaign.

Jefferson
Memorial
A740

1966, Oct. 5

1318	A740	5c emerald, pink & black	.25	.25
a.		Tagged	.40	.25

Compare with No. 4716c.

GREAT RIVER ROAD ISSUE

Issued to publicize the 5,600-mile Great River Road connecting New Orleans with Kenora, Ontario, and following the Mississippi most of the way.

Central U.S. Map
With Great River
Road — A741

LITHOGRAPHED, ENGRAVED (Giori)
1966, Oct. 21

1319	A741	5c vermilion, yellow, blue & green	.25	.25
a.		Tagged	.45	.25

SAVINGS BOND-SERVICEMEN ISSUE

25th anniv. of US Savings Bonds, and honoring American servicemen.

Statue of Liberty &
"Old Glory" — A742

1966, Oct. 26

1320	A742	5c red, dk bl, lt bl & blk	.25	.25
a.		Tagged	.40	.25
b.		Red, dark blue & black missing (EP)	3,750.	
c.		Dark blue (engr.) missing (EP)	5,000.	

CHRISTMAS ISSUE

Madonna and
Child — A743

Modeled after "Madonna and Child with Angels," by the Flemish artist Hans Memling (c.1430-1494), Mellon Collection, National Gallery of Art, Washington, D.C.

1966, Nov. 1

1321	A743	5c multicolored	.25	.25
a.		Tagged	.40	.25

MARY CASSATT ISSUE

Cassatt (1844-1926), painter. The painting "The Boating Party" is in the Natl. Gallery of Art, Washington, D.C.

"The Boating Party" A744

GIORI PRESS PRINTING
1966, Nov. 17
1322 A744 5c multicolored .25 .25
a. Tagged .40 .25

Cassatt (1844-1926), painter. The original painting is in the Natl. Gallery of Art, Washington, DC.

NATIONAL GRANGE ISSUE
Centenary of the founding of the National Grange, American farmers' organization.

Grange Poster, 1870 — A745

1967, Apr. 17
1323 A745 5c org, yel, brn, grn & blk .25 .25

Phosphor Tagging
From No. 1323 onward, all postage issues are tagged, unless otherwise noted.

Tagging Omitted
Inadvertent omissions of tagging occurred on Nos. 1238, 1278, 1281, 1298 and 1305. In addition many tagged issues from 1967 on exist with tagging unintentionally omitted. These errors are listed in the *Scott Specialized Catalogue of United States Stamps and Covers.*

CANADA CENTENARY ISSUE
Centenary of Canada's emergence as a nation.

Canadian Landscape A746

1967, May 25
1324 A746 5c lt bl, dp grn, ultra, olive & blk .25 .25

ERIE CANAL ISSUE
150th anniversary of the Erie Canal ground-breaking ceremony at Rome, N.Y. The canal links Lake Erie and New York City.

Stern of Early Canal Boat A747

LITHOGRAPHED, ENGRAVED (Giori)
1967, July 4
1325 A747 5c ultra, grnsh blue, blk & crim .25 .25

"SEARCH FOR PEACE" — LIONS ISSUE
Issued to publicize the search for peace. "Search for Peace" was the theme of an essay contest for young men and women sponsored by Lions International on its 50th anniversary.

Peace Dove A748

GIORI PRESS PRINTING
1967, July 5
Gray Paper with Blue Threads
1326 A748 5c blue, red & black .25 .25

HENRY DAVID THOREAU ISSUE

Henry David Thoreau (1817-1862), Writer — A749

1967, July 12
1327 A749 5c carmine, black & blue green .25 .25
b. Carmine missing (PS) 400.00

NEBRASKA STATEHOOD, 100th ANNIV.

Hereford Steer and Corn A750

LITHOGRAPHED, ENGRAVED (Giori)
1967, July 29
1328 A750 5c dark red brown, lemon & yellow .25 .25

VOICE OF AMERICA ISSUE
25th anniv. of the radio branch of the United States Information Agency (USIA).

Radio Transmission Tower and Waves — A751

1967, Aug. 1
1329 A751 5c red, blue, black & carmine .25 .25

AMERICAN FOLKLORE ISSUE
Davy Crockett (1786-1836), frontiersman, hunter, and congressman from Tennessee who died at the Alamo.

Davy Crockett & Scrub Pines A752

1967, Aug. 17
1330 A752 5c green, black, & yellow .25 .25
a. Vertical pair, imperf. between 7,500.
b. Green (engr.) missing (FO) —
c. Black & green (engr.) missing (FO) —

A foldover on a pane of No. 1330 resulted in one example each of Nos. 1330b-1330c. Part of the colors appear on the back of the selvage and one freak stamp. An engraved black-and-green-only impression appears on the gummed side of one almost-complete "stamp."

ACCOMPLISHMENTS IN SPACE ISSUE
US accomplishments in space. Printed with continuous design in horizontal rows of 5. In the left panes the astronaut stamp is 1st, 3rd and 5th, the spaceship 2nd and 4th. This arrangement is reversed in the right panes.

Space-Walking Astronaut — A753

Gemini 4 Capsule and Earth A754

1967, Sept. 29
1331 A753 5c multicolored .55 .25
1332 A754 5c multicolored .55 .25
b. Pair, #1331-1332 1.25 1.25

URBAN PLANNING ISSUE
Publicizing the importance of Urban Planning in connection with the Intl. Conf. of the American Institute of Planners, Washington, D.C., Oct. 1-6.

View of Model City — A755

1967, Oct. 2
1333 A755 5c dark blue, light blue & black .25 .25

FINNISH INDEPENDENCE, 50th ANNIV.

Finnish Coat of Arms — A756

ENGRAVED (Giori)
1967, Oct. 6
1334 A756 5c blue .25 .25

THOMAS EAKINS ISSUE
Eakins (1844-1916), painter and sculptor. The painting is in the Natl. Gallery of Art, Washington, D.C.

"The Biglin Brothers Racing" (Sculling on Schuylkill River, Philadelphia) — A757

Printed by Photogravure & Color Co., Moonachie, N.J.

PHOTOGRAVURE
1967, Nov. 2 **Perf. 12**
1335 A757 5c gold & multicolored .25 .25

CHRISTMAS ISSUE

Madonna and Child, by Hans Memling — A758

LITHOGRAPHED, ENGRAVED (Giori)
1967, Nov. 6 **Perf. 11**
1336 A758 5c multicolored .25 .25
See note on painting above No. 1321.

MISSISSIPPI STATEHOOD, 150th ANNIV.

Magnolia A759

GIORI PRESS PRINTING
1967, Dec. 11
1337 A759 5c brt grnsh bl, grn & red brn .25 .25

FLAG ISSUE

Flag and White House — A760

1968, Jan. 24
Size: 19x22mm
1338 A760 6c dk bl, red & grn .25 .25
k. Vert. pair, imperf. btwn. 250.00 150.00
s. Red missing (FO) —
u. Vert. pair, imperf horiz. 275.00
v. All color omitted —

No. 1338s is unique.
Beware of regumming on No. 1338u. Most examples have had the gum washed off to make it difficult or impossible to detect blind perfs. Check carefully for blind perfs. Value is for pair with original gum.
On No. 1338v, an albino impression of the engraved plate is present.

COIL STAMP
MULTICOLOR HUCK PRESS
1969, May 30 **Perf. 10 Vertically**
Size: 18¼x21mm
1338A A760 6c dk bl, red & grn .25 .25
b. Imperf., pair 350.00

MULTICOLOR HUCK PRESS
1970-71 **Perf. 11x10½**
Size: 18¼x21mm
1338D A760 6c dk bl, red & grn .25 .25
e. Horiz. pair, imperf. between 115.00
1338F A760 8c dk bl, red & slate grn ('71) .25 .25
i. Imperf., vert. pair 35.00
j. Horiz. pair, imperf. between 45.00
p. Slate green omitted 300.00
t. Horiz. pair, imperf. vertically —

Issued: #1338D, 8/7/70

COIL STAMP
MULTICOLOR HUCK PRESS
1971, May 10 **Perf. 10 Vertically**
Size: 18¼x21mm
1338G A760 8c dk bl, red & slate grn .30 .25
h. Imperf., pair 45.00

ILLINOIS STATEHOOD, 150th ANNIV.

Farm House & Fields of Ripening Grain — A761

LITHOGRAPHED, ENGRAVED (Giori)
1968, Feb. 12 **Perf. 11**
1339 A761 6c dk blue, blue, red
& ocher .25 .25

HEMISFAIR '68 ISSUE

HemisFair '68 exhibition, San Antonio, Texas, Apr. 6-Oct. 6, for the 250th anniv. of San Antonio.

Map of North & South America — A762

1968, Mar. 30
1340 A762 6c blue, rose red & white .25 .25
a. White omitted 650.00

AIRLIFT ISSUE

Eagle Holding Pennant A763

1968, Apr. 4 **Untagged**
1341 A763 $1 sepia, dk. blue, ocher & brown
1.00 1.00

Issued to pay for airlift of parcels from and to U.S. ports to servicemen overseas and in Alaska, Hawaii and P.R. Valid for all regular postage.
On Apr. 26, 1969, the POD ruled that henceforth No. 1341 "may be used toward paying the postage or fees for special services on airmail articles."

"SUPPORT OUR YOUTH" — ELKS ISSUE

Support Our Youth program, and honoring the Benevolent and Protective Order of Elks, which extended its youth service program in observance of its centennial year.

Girls & Boys A764

1968, May 1 **Tagged**
1342 A764 6c ultramarine & orange red .25 .25

LAW AND ORDER ISSUE

Publicizing the policeman as protector and friend and to encourage respect for law and order.

Policeman and Small Boy — A765

GIORI PRESS PRINTING
1968, May 17
1343 A765 6c chalky blue, black & red .25 .25

REGISTER AND VOTE ISSUE

Campaign to draw more voters to the polls. The weather vane is from an old house in the Russian Hill section of San Francisco, Cal.

Eagle Weather Vane — A766

LITHOGRAPHED, ENGRAVED (Giori)
1968, June 27
1344 A766 6c black, yellow & orange .25 .25

HISTORIC FLAG SERIES

Flags carried by American colonists and by citizens of the new United States. Printed se-tenant in vertical columns of 10. The flag sequence on the 2 upper panes is as listed. On the 2 lower panes the sequence is reversed with the Navy Jack in the 1st row and the Fort Moultrie flag in the 10th.

Ft. Moultrie, 1776 A767

Ft. McHenry, 1795-1818 A768

Washington's Cruisers, 1775 — A769

Bennington, 1777 A770

Rhode Island, 1775 A771

First Stars and Stripes, 1777 A772

Bunker Hill, 1775 A773

Grand Union, 1776 A774

Philadelphia Light Horse, 1775 — A775

First Navy Jack, 1775 A776

ENGR. (Giori) (#1345-1348, 1350);
ENGR. & LITHO. (#1349, 1351-1354)
1968, July 4
1345 A767 6c dark blue .40 .25
1346 A768 6c dark blue & red .40 .25
1347 A769 6c dark blue & olive green .30 .25
1348 A770 6c dark blue & red .30 .25
1349 A771 6c dark blue, yellow & red .30 .25
1350 A772 6c dark blue & red .30 .25
1351 A773 6c dark blue, olive green & red .30 .25
1352 A774 6c dark blue & red .30 .25
1353 A775 6c dark blue, yellow & red .30 .25
1354 A776 6c dark blue, red & yellow .30 .25
a. Strip of ten, #1345-1354 3.25 3.25
b. #1345b-1354b, any single, tagging omitted 65.00
c. As "a," imperf 4,500.

WALT DISNEY ISSUE

Walt Disney (1901-1966), cartoonist, film producer and creator of Mickey Mouse.

Disney and Children of the World — A777

Printed by Achrovure Division of Union-Camp Corp., Englewood, N.J.

PHOTOGRAVURE
1968, Sept. 11 **Perf. 12**
1355 A777 6c multicolored .40 .25
a. Ocher omitted ("Walt Disney," "6c," etc.) 300.00 —
b. Vert. pair, imperf. horiz. 575.00
c. Imperf., pair 425.00
d. Black omitted 1,750.
e. Horiz. pair, imperf. between 5,000.
f. Blue omitted 1,500.

FATHER MARQUETTE ISSUE

Father Jacques Marquette (1637-1675), French Jesuit missionary, who together with Louis Jolliet explored the Mississippi River and its tributaries.

Father Marquette and Louis Jolliet Exploring the Mississippi A778

LITHOGRAPHED, ENGRAVED (Giori)
1968, Sept. 20 **Perf. 11**
1356 A778 6c black, apple green & orange brown .25 .25

AMERICAN FOLKLORE ISSUE

Daniel Boone (1734-1820), frontiersman and trapper.

Pennsylvania Rifle, Powder Horn, Tomahawk Pipe & Knife — A779

LITHOGRAPHED, ENGRAVED (Giori)
1968, Sept. 26
1357 A779 6c yel, dp yel, mar & blk .25 .25

ARKANSAS RIVER NAVIGATION ISSUE

Opening of the Arkansas River to commercial navigation.

Ship's Wheel, Power Transmission Tower & Barge — A780

1968, Oct. 1
1358 A780 6c bright blue, dark blue & black .25 .25

LEIF ERIKSON ISSUE

Leif Erikson, 11th century Norse explorer, called the 1st European to set foot on the American continent, at a place he called Vinland. The statue by the American sculptor A. Stirling Calder is in Reykjavik, Iceland.

Leif Erikson, by Stirling Calder — A781

1968, Oct. 9
1359 A781 6c light gray brown & black brown .25 .25

The luminescent element is in the light gray brown ink of the background. The engraved parts were printed on a rotary currency press.

CHEROKEE STRIP ISSUE

75th anniversary of the opening of the Cherokee Strip to settlers, Sept. 16, 1893.

Homesteaders Racing to Cherokee Strip — A782

ROTARY PRESS PRINTING

1968, Oct. 15   *Perf. 11x10½*
1360 A782 6c brown   .25 .25

JOHN TRUMBULL ISSUE

Trumbull (1756-1843), painter. The stamp shows Lt. Thomas Grosvenor and his attendant Peter Salem. The painting hangs at Yale University.

Detail from "The Battle of Bunker's Hill" — A783

LITHOGRAPHED, ENGRAVED (Giori)

1968, Oct. 18   *Perf. 11*
1361 A783 6c multicolored   .25 .25
    b.   Black (engr.) missing (FO)   11,000. —

WATERFOWL CONSERVATION ISSUE

Wood Ducks A784

1968, Oct. 24
1362 A784 6c blk & multi   .25 .25
    a.   Vertical pair, imperf. between   250.00 —
    b.   Red & dark blue omitted   350.00 —
    c.   Red omitted   1,750.

Dangerous fakes exist of Nos. 1362b and 1362c. Authentication by experts is required.

CHRISTMAS ISSUE

"The Annunciation" by the 15th century Flemish painter Jan van Eyck is in the National Gallery of Art, Washington, D.C.

Gabriel, from van Eyck's Annunciation — A785

ENGRAVED (Multicolor Huck press)

1968, Nov. 1
1363 A785 6c multicolored   .25 .25
    a.   Untagged   .25 .25
    b.   Imperf., pair, tagged   140.00
    c.   Light yellow omitted   60.00 —
    d.   Imperf., pair, untagged   200.00

AMERICAN INDIAN ISSUE

Honoring the American Indian and to celebrate the opening of the Natl. Portrait Gallery, Washington, D.C. Chief Joseph (Indian name, Thunder Traveling over the Mountains), a leader of the Nez Percé, was born in eastern Oregon about 1840 and died at the Colville Reservation in Washington State in 1904.

Chief Joseph, by Cyrenius Hall — A786

LITHOGRAPHED, ENGRAVED (Giori)

1968, Nov. 4
1364 A786 6c black & multi   .25 .25

BEAUTIFICATION OF AMERICA ISSUE

Publicizing the Natural Beauty Campaign for more beautiful cities, parks, highways and streets. In the left panes Nos. 1365 and 1367 appear in 1st, 3rd and 5th place, Nos. 1366 and 1368 in 2nd and 4th place. This arrangement is reversed in the right panes.

Capitol, Azaleas and Tulips A787

Washington Monument, Potomac River and Daffodils A788

Poppies and Lupines along Highway A789

Blooming Crab Apples along Street A790

1969, Jan. 16   **Tagged**
1365 A787 6c multicolored   .25 .25
1366 A788 6c multicolored   .25 .25
1367 A789 6c multicolored   .25 .25
1368 A790 6c multicolored   .25 .25
    a.   Block of 4, #1365-1368   1.00 1.25

Compare with Nos. 4716a, 4716b, 4716d, 4716e.

AMERICAN LEGION, 50th ANNIV.

Eagle from Great Seal of U.S. — A791

1969, Mar. 15
1369 A791 6c red, blue & black   .25 .25

AMERICAN FOLKLORE ISSUE

Grandma Moses (Anna Mary Robertson Moses, 1860-1961), primitive painter of American life.

July Fourth, by Grandma Moses — A792

1969, May 1
1370 A792 6c multicolored   .25 .25
    a.   Horizontal pair, imperf. between   140.00
    b.   Engraved black ("6c U.S. Postage") & Prus. blue ("Grandma Moses") omitted   400.00

Beware of pairs with blind perfs. being offered as No. 1370a.

No. 1370b often comes with mottled or disturbed gum. Such stamps sell for about two-thirds as much as examples with perfect gum.

APOLLO 8 ISSUE

Apollo 8 mission, which 1st put men into orbit around the moon, Dec. 21-27, 1968. The astronauts were: Col. Frank Borman, Capt. James Lovell and Maj. William Anders.

Moon Surface and Earth — A793

LITHOGRAPHED, ENGRAVED (Giori)

1969, May 5
1371 A793 6c black, blue & ocher   .25 .25
   Imperfs. exist from printer's waste.

W.C. HANDY ISSUE

Handy (1873-1958), jazz musician and composer.

W. C. Handy (1873-1958), Jazz Musician and Composer — A794

LITHOGRAPHED, ENGRAVED (Giori)

1969, May 17
1372 A794 6c violet, deep lilac & blue   .25 .25

CALIFORNIA SETTLEMENT, 200th ANNIV.

Carmel Mission Belfry — A795

1969, July 16
1373 A795 6c orange, red, black & light blue   .25 .25
    b.   Red (engr.) missing (CM)   400.00

JOHN WESLEY POWELL ISSUE

Powell (1834-1902), geologist who explored the Green and Colorado Rivers 1869-75, and ethnologist.

Powell Exploring Colorado River A796

1969, Aug. 1
1374 A796 6c black, ocher & light blue   .25 .25

ALABAMA STATEHOOD, 150th ANNIV.

Camellia & Yellow-shafted Flicker — A797

1969, Aug. 2
1375 A797 6c mag, rose red, yel, dk, grn & brn   .25 .25

BOTANICAL CONGRESS ISSUE

11th Intl. Botanical Cong., Seattle, Wash., Aug. 24-Sept. 2. In left panes Nos. 1376 and 1378 appear in 1st, 3rd and 5th place; Nos. 1377 and 1379 in 2nd and 4th place. This arrangement is reversed in right panes.

Douglas Fir (Northwest) A798

Lady's-slipper (Northeast) — A799

Ocotillo (Southwest) A800

Franklinia (Southeast) A801

1969, Aug. 23
1376 A798 6c multicolored   .35 .25
1377 A799 6c multicolored   .35 .25
1378 A800 6c multicolored   .35 .25
1379 A801 6c multicolored   .35 .25
    a.   Block of 4, #1376-1379   1.40 1.75

DARTMOUTH COLLEGE CASE ISSUE

150th anniv. of the Dartmouth College Case, which Daniel Webster argued before the Supreme Court, reasserting the sanctity of contracts.

Daniel Webster & Dartmouth Hall — A802

ROTARY PRESS PRINTING

1969, Sept. 22   *Perf. 10½x11*
1380 A802 6c green   .25 .25

PROFESSIONAL BASEBALL, 100th ANNIV.

Batter A803

LITHOGRAPHED, ENGRAVED (Giori)

1969, Sept. 24   *Perf. 11*
1381 A803 6c yellow, red, black & green   .45 .25
    a.   Black omitted ("1869-1969, United States, 6c, Professional Baseball")   500.00
    c.   Double impression of black (engr.)   5,750.

INTERCOLLEGIATE FOOTBALL, 100th ANNIV.

Football Player & Coach
A804

1969, Sept. 26

1382	A804	6c red & green	.25	.25
b.		Vert. pair, imperf horiz.	5,750.	
c.		Double impression	2,500.	

The engraved parts were printed on a rotary currency press.
No. 1382b is unique.
Two examples of No. 1382c are recorded, with the double impression on the left part of the left stamps within a lower left plate block of 4. Value given is for the plate block.

DWIGHT D. EISENHOWER ISSUE

Dwight D. Eisenhower
A805

Designed by Robert J. Jones; photograph by Bernie Noble.

GIORI PRESS PRINTING

1969, Oct. 14

1383	A805	6c blue, black & red	.25	.25
b.		Blue ("U.S. 6c Postage") missing (PS)	600.00	

CHRISTMAS ISSUE

The painting, painted about 1870 by an unknown primitive artist, is the property of the N.Y. State Historical Association, Cooperstown, N.Y.

Winter Sunday in Norway, Maine
A806

ENGRAVED (Multicolor Huck)

1969, Nov. 3   **Perf. 11x10½**

1384	A806	6c dark green & multicolored	.25	.25
		Precancel	.60	.25
b.		Imperf., pair	700.00	
c.		Light green omitted	30.00	
d.		Light green, red & yellow omitted	600.00	—
e.		Yellow omitted	1,250.	
g.		Red & yellow omitted	2,250.	
h.		Light green and yellow omitted	500.00	
i.		Light green and red omitted	—	
j.		Vert. pair, top stamp Baltimore precancel, bottom stamp precancel missing (FO)	—	
k.		Baltimore precancel printed on gum side	175.00	
l.		Baltimore precancel, vert. pair, one stamp missing precancel, other stamp with precancel printed inverted on reverse (FO)	500.00	
m.		Inverted Baltimore precancel	225.00	
n.		Baltimore precancel printed inverted on reverse (FO)	150.00	
p.		Double impression of New Haven precancel	—	
q.		Inverted Memphis precancel	100.00	
t.		Inverted Atlanta precancel	500.00	

The precancel value applies to the least expensive of experimental precancels printed locally in four cities, on tagged stamps, with the names between lines 4½mm apart: in black or green, "ATLANTA, GA" and in green only "BALTIMORE, MD," "MEMPHIS, TN" and "NEW HAVEN, CT." They were sold freely to the public and could be used on any class of mail at all post offices during the experimental program and thereafter.
Most examples of No. 1384c show orange where the offset green was. Value is for this variety. Examples without orange sell for more.

On No. 1384i, almost all of the yellow is also omitted. Do not confuse with No. 1384d.

HOPE FOR CRIPPLED ISSUE

Issued to encourage the rehabilitation of crippled children and adults and to honor the National Society for Crippled Children and Adults (Easter Seal Society) on its 50th anniversary.

Cured Child — A807

LITHOGRAPHED, ENGRAVED (Giori)

1969, Nov. 20   **Perf. 11**

1385	A807	6c multicolored	.25	.25

WILLIAM M. HARNETT ISSUE

Harnett (1848-1892), painter. The painting hangs in the Museum of Fine Arts, Boston.

"Old Models" — A808

1969, Dec. 3

1386	A808	6c multicolored	.25	.25
a.		Red (engr.) missing (CM)	—	

NATURAL HISTORY ISSUE

Centenary of the American Museum of Natural History, New York City. Nos. 1387-1388 alternate in 1st row. Nos. 1389-1390 in 2nd row. This arrangement is repeated throughout the pane.

American Bald Eagle — A809

African Elephant Herd — A810

Tlingit Chief in Haida Ceremonial Canoe — A811

Brontosaurus, Stegosaurus & Allosaurus — A812

1970, May 6

1387	A809	6c multicolored	.25	.25
1388	A810	6c multicolored	.25	.25
1389	A811	6c multicolored	.25	.25
1390	A812	6c multicolored	.25	.25
a.		Block of 4, #1387-1390	1.00	1.00

MAINE STATEHOOD, 150th ANNIV.

The painting hangs in the Metropolitan Museum of Art, New York City.

Lighthouse at Two Lights, Maine
A813

1970, July 9   **Tagged**   **Perf. 11**

1391	A813	6c black & multi	.25	.25

WILDLIFE CONSERVATION ISSUE

American Buffalo
A814

ROTARY PRESS PRINTING

1970, July 20   **Perf. 11x10½**

1392	A814	6c black, *light brown*	.25	.25

REGULAR ISSUE
Dwight David Eisenhower

Dot between "R" and "U"
A815

No dot between "R" and "U" — A815a

Benjamin Franklin
A816

Fiorello H. LaGuardia
A817a

Dr. Elizabeth Blackwell
A818a

USPS Emblem
A817

Ernest Taylor Pyle — A818

Amadeo P. Giannini
A818b

ROTARY PRESS PRINTING

1970-74

1393	A815	6c dk blue gray	.25	.25
a.		Booklet pane of 8	2.00	2.00
b.		Booklet pane of 5 + label	1.40	1.40
c.		Untagged (Bureau precanceled)	12.75	3.00

       Perf. 10½x11

1393D	A816	7c bright blue ('73)	.25	.25
e.		Untagged (Bureau precanceled)	4.25	1.00

GIORI PRESS PRINTING
Perf. 11

1394	A815a	8c blk, red & bl gray ('71)	.25	.25
b.		Red missing (PS)	150.00	
c.		Red missing (FO)	1,250.	
d.		Red and blue gray missing (PS)	—	
e.		Red and blue gray missing (FO or preprinting paper crease)	1,000.	
f.		All colors and tagging missing (PS)	1,000.	
g.		Printed on gum side, tagged	1,000.	

No. 1394f must be collected se-tenant with No. 1394c, 1394e, or with a partially printed No. 1394.

ROTARY PRESS PRINTING
Perf. 11x10½ on 2 or 3 Sides

1395	A815	8c deep claret ('71)	.25	.25
a.		Booklet pane of 8	2.00	2.00
b.		Booklet pane of 6	1.50	1.50
c.		Booklet pane of 4 +2 ('72)	1.65	1.10
d.		Booklet pane of 7 + label ('72)	1.90	1.90
e.		Vert. pair, imperf. between, in #1395a or 1395d with foldover	750.00	

No. 1395 was issued only in booklets.
At least 4 pairs of No. 1395e are recorded from 3 panes (one No. 1395a and two 1395d) with different foldover patterns. A pane of No. 1395d also is known with a foldover resulting in a vertical pair of stamp and label, imperf between.

PHOTOGRAVURE (Andreotti)
Plates of 400 subjects in four panes of 100.
Perf. 11x10½

1396	A817	8c multi ('71)	.25	.25

ROTARY PRESS PRINTING

1397	A817a	14c gray brown ('72)	.25	.25
a.		Untagged (Bureau precanceled)	100.00	17.50
1398	A818	16c brown ('72)	.35	.25
a.		Untagged (Bureau precanceled)	22.50	5.00
1399	A818a	18c violet ('74)	.35	.25
1400	A818b	21c green ('73)	.40	.25
		Nos. 1393-1400 (9)	2.60	2.25

Issued: 6c, 8/6/70; 7c, 10/20/72; #1394-1395, 5/10/71; #1396, 7/1/71; 14c, 4/24/72; 16c, 5/7/71; 18c, 1/23/74; 21c, 6/27/73.

COIL STAMPS
ROTARY PRESS PRINTING

1970-71   **Perf. 10 Vert.**

1401	A815	6c dk blue gray	.25	.25
a.		Untagged (Bureau precanceled)	19.50	3.00
b.		Imperf., pair	2,500.	
1402	A815	8c dp claret ('71)	.25	.25
a.		Imperf., pair	37.50	
b.		Untagged (Bureau precanceled)	6.75	.75
c.		Pair, imperf. between	6,250.	

No. 1401b often found with small faults and/or without gum. Such examples sell for considerably less.
Issue dates: 6c, Aug. 6; 8c, May 10, 1971.

EDGAR LEE MASTERS ISSUE

A819

LITHOGRAPHED, ENGRAVED (Giori)
1970, Aug. 22   **Perf. 11**
1405 A819 6c black & olive bister .25 .25

WOMAN SUFFRAGE ISSUE

50th anniversary of the 19th Amendment, which gave the vote to women.

Suffragettes, 1920 & Woman Voter,
1970 — A820

GIORI PRESS PRINTING
1970, Aug. 26
1406 A820 6c blue   .25 .25

SOUTH CAROLINA ISSUE

300th anniv. of the founding of Charles Town (Charleston), the 1st permanent settlement of South Carolina. Against a background of pine wood the line drawings of the design represent the economic and historic development of South Carolina: the spire of St. Phillip's Church, Capitol, state flag, a ship, 17th century man and woman, a Fort Sumter cannon, barrels, cotton, tobacco and yellow jasmine.

Symbols of
South
Carolina
A821

LITHOGRAPHED, ENGRAVED (Giori)
1970, Sept. 12
1407 A821 6c bister, black & red .25 .25

STONE MOUNTAIN MEMORIAL ISSUE

Dedication of the Stone Mountain Confederate Memorial, Georgia, May 9, 1970.

A822

GIORI PRESS PRINTING
1970, Sept. 19
1408 A822 6c gray   .25 .25

FORT SNELLING ISSUE

150th anniv. of Fort Snelling, Minnesota, an important outpost for the opening of the Northwest.

Fort
Snelling,
Keelboat &
Tepees
A823

LITHOGRAPHED, ENGRAVED (Giori)
1970, Oct. 17
1409 A823 6c yellow & multi   .25 .25

ANTI-POLLUTION ISSUE

Issued to focus attention on the problems of pollution.

In left panes Nos. 1410 and 1412 appear in 1st, 3rd and 5th place; Nos. 1411 and 1413 in 2nd and 4th place. This arrangement is reversed in right panes.

Globe and
Wheat
A824

Globe and
City
A825

Globe and
Bluegill
A826

Globe and
Seagull
A827

PHOTOGRAVURE
1970, Oct. 28   **Perf. 11x10½**
1410 A824 6c multicolored   .25 .25
1411 A825 6c multicolored   .25 .25
1412 A826 6c multicolored   .25 .25
1413 A827 6c multicolored   .25 .25
  a.   Block of 4, #1410-1413   1.00 1.25

CHRISTMAS ISSUE

In left panes Nos. 1415 and 1417 appear in 1st, 3rd and 5th place; Nos. 1416 and 1418 in 2nd and 4th place. This arrangement is reversed in right panes.

Nativity — A828

Tin and
Cast-iron
Locomotive
A829

Toy Horse
on Wheels
A830

Mechanical
Tricycle
A831

Doll
Carriage
A832

1970, Nov. 5   **Perf. 10½x11**
1414 A828 6c multicolored   .25 .25
  a.   Precanceled   .25 .25
  b.   Black omitted   400.00

  c.   As "a," blue omitted   1,100.
  d.   Type II   .25 .25
  e.   Type II, precanceled   .25 .25

No. 1414 has a slightly blurry impression, snowflaking in the sky and no gum breaker ridges. No. 1414d has shiny surfaced paper, sharper impression, no snowflaking and vertical and horizontal gum breaker ridges.

No. 1414a has a slightly blurry impression, snowflaking in the sky, no gum breaker ridges and the precancel is grayish black. No. 1414e has sharper impression, no snowflaking, gum breaker ridges and the precancel is intense black.

Perf. 11x10½
1415 A829 6c multicolored   .30 .25
  a.   Precanceled   .65 .25
  b.   Black omitted   1,750.
1416 A830 6c multicolored   .30 .25
  a.   Precanceled   .65 .25
  b.   Black omitted   1,750.
  c.   Imperf., pair (#1416,
      1418)   2,500.
1417 A831 6c multicolored   .30 .25
  a.   Precanceled   .65 .25
  b.   Black omitted   1,750.
1418 A832 6c multicolored   .30 .25
  a.   Precanceled   .65 .25
  b.   Block of 4, #1415-1418 1.25 1.40
  c.   As "b," precanceled   3.75 3.50
  d.   Black omitted   1,750.
  e.   As "b," black omitted 8,000.
  f.   As "b," black omitted on
      #1417 & 1418   4,000.
  g.   P# block of 8, black
      omitted on #1415 &
      1416   4,000.
    Nos. 1415-1418 (4)   1.20 1.00

Nos. 1415-1418 and 1415a-1418a are known both without gum breaker ridges (common) and with gum breaker ridges (scarce).

The precanceled stamps, Nos. 1414a-1418a, were furnished to 68 cities. The plates include two straight (No. 1414a) or two wavy (Nos. 1415a-1418a) black lines that make up the precancellation. Unused values are for stamps with gum and used values are for stamps with an additional cancellation or without gum.

UNITED NATIONS, 25th ANNIV.

"UN" & UN
Emblem
A833

LITHOGRAPHED, ENGRAVED (Giori)
1970, Nov. 20   **Perf. 11**
1419 A833 6c blk, verm & ultra   .25 .25

LANDING OF THE PILGRIMS ISSUE

350th anniv. of the landing of the Mayflower.

Mayflower &
Pilgrims — A834

1970, Nov. 21
1420 A834 6c blk, org, yel,
         mag, bl & brn   .25 .25
  a.   Orange & yellow omitted 525.00

DISABLED AMERICAN VETERANS AND SERVICEMEN ISSUE

No. 1421 for the 50th anniv. of the Disabled Veterans of America Organization; No. 1422 honors the contribution of servicemen, particularly those who were prisoners of war, missing or killed in action. Nos. 1421-1422 are printed se-tenant in horizontal rows of 10.

A835

A836

1970, Nov. 24
1421 A835 6c dark blue, red &
      multicolored   .25 .25

ENGRAVED
1422 A836 6c dark blue, black &
      red   .25 .25
  a.   Pair, #1421-1422   .50 .50

AMERICAN WOOL INDUSTRY ISSUE

450th anniv. of the introduction of sheep to the North American continent and the beginning of the American wool industry.

Ewe and
Lamb — A837

Plates of 200 subjects in four panes of 50.

1971, Jan. 19
1423 A837 6c multicolored   .25 .25
  b.   Teal blue ("United States")
      missing (CM)   400.00

GEN. DOUGLAS MacARTHUR ISSUE

MacArthur (1880-1964), Chief of Staff, Supreme Commander for the Allied Powers in the Pacific Area during World War II and Supreme Commander in Japan after the war.

Douglas
MacArthur — A838

GIORI PRESS PRINTING
1971, Jan. 26
1424 A838 6c black, red & dark
      blue   — .25
  a.   Red missing (PS)   —
  c.   Blue missing (PS)   —

BLOOD DONOR ISSUE

Salute to blood donors and spur to increased participation in the blood donor program.

Giving
Blood
Saves
Lives
A839

LITHOGRAPHED, ENGRAVED (Giori)
1971, Mar. 12
1425 A839 6c bl, scarlet & ind .25 .25

MISSOURI STATEHOOD, 150th ANNIV.

The stamp design shows a Pawnee facing a hunter-trapper and a group of settlers. It is from a mural by Thomas Hart Benton in the Harry S Truman Library, Independence, Mo.

"Independence and the Opening of the
West" — A840

PHOTOGRAVURE (Andreotti)

1971, May 8   *Perf. 11x10½*
1426 A840 8c multicolored   .25   .25

See note on Andreotti printings and their color control markings in Information for Collectors under Printing, Photogravure.

WILDLIFE CONSERVATION ISSUE

Nos. 1427-1428 alternate in first row, Nos. 1429-1430 in second row. This arrangement repeated throughout pane.

Trout A841

Alligator — A842

Polar Bear, Cubs A843

California Condor — A844

LITHOGRAPHED, ENGRAVED (Giori)

1971, June 12   *Perf. 11*
1427	A841 8c multicolored	.25	.25
a.	Red omitted		1,250.
b.	Green (engr.) omitted		—
1428	A842 8c multicolored	.25	.25
1429	A843 8c multicolored	.25	.25
1430	A844 8c multicolored	.25	.25
a.	Block of 4, #1427-1430	1.00	1.00
b.	As "a," light green & dark green omitted from #1427-1428	3,250.	
c.	As "a," red omitted from #1427, 1429-1430	3,000.	

ANTARCTIC TREATY ISSUE

Map of Antarctica A845

Adapted from emblem on official documents of Consultative Meetings.

GIORI PRESS PRINTING

1971, June 23
1431 A845 8c red & dark blue   .25   .25
   b. Both colors missing (EP) 500.00

No. 1431b should be collected se-tenant with a normal stamp and/or a partially printed stamp.

AMERICAN REVOLUTION BICENTENNIAL

Bicentennial Commission Emblem — A846

LITHOGRAPHED, ENGRAVED (Giori)

1971, July 4
1432 A846 8c gray, red, blue & black   .25   .25
   a. Gray & black missing (EP) 325.00
   b. Gray ("U.S. Postage 8c") missing (EP) 650.00

JOHN SLOAN ISSUE

John Sloan (1871-1951), painter. The painting hangs in the Phillips Gallery, Washington, D.C.

The Wake of the Ferry A847

1971, Aug. 2
1433 A847 8c multicolored   .25   .25
   b. Red engr. ("John Sloan" and "8") missing (CM) 1,000.

SPACE ACHIEVEMENT DECADE ISSUE

Decade of space achievements and the Apollo 15 moon exploration mission, July 26-Aug. 7. In the left panes the earth and sun stamp is 1st, 3rd and 5th, the rover 2nd and 4th. This arrangement is reversed in the right panes.

Earth, Sun, Landing Craft on Moon A848

Lunar Rover A849

1971, Aug. 2
1434 A848 8c blk, bl, gray, yel & red   .25   .25
1435 A849 8c blk, bl, gray, yel & red   .25   .25
   b. Pair, #1434-1435 .50 .50
   d. As "b," blue & red (litho.) omitted 950.00

EMILY DICKINSON ISSUE

Emily Elizabeth Dickinson — A850

1971, Aug. 28
1436 A850 8c multi, *grnsh*   .25   .25
   a. Black & olive (engr.) omitted 500.00
   b. Pale rose missing (EP) 5,000.
   c. Red omitted

SAN JUAN ISSUE

450th anniversary of San Juan, Puerto Rico.

Sentry Box, Morro Castle, San Juan — A851

1971, Sept. 12
1437 A851 8c pale brn, blk, yel, red brn & dk brn   .25   .25
   b. Dark brown (engr.) omitted 1,500. —

VALUES FOR HINGED STAMPS AFTER NO. 771

This catalogue does not value unused stamps after No. 771 in hinged condition. Hinged unused stamps from No. 772 to the present are worth considerably less than the values given for unused stamps, which are for never-hinged examples.

PREVENT DRUG ABUSE ISSUE

Drug Abuse Prevention Week, Oct. 3-9.

Young Woman Drug Addict — A852

PHOTOGRAVURE (Andreotti)

1971, Oct. 4   *Perf. 10½x11*
1438 A852 8c blue, deep blue & black   .25   .25

CARE ISSUE

25th anniversary of CARE, a US-Canadian Cooperative for American Relief Everywhere.

Hands Reaching for CARE — A853

1971, Oct. 27
1439 A853 8c blue, blk, vio & red lilac   .25   .25
   a. Black omitted 1,100.

HISTORIC PRESERVATION ISSUE

Nos. 1440-1441 alternate in 1st row, Nos. 1442-1443 in 2nd row. This arrangement is repeated throughout pane.

Decatur House, Washington, DC — A854

Whaling Ship Charles W. Morgan, Mystic, Conn. — A855

Cable Car, San Francisco — A856

San Xavier del Bac Mission, Tucson, Ariz. — A857

LITHOGRAPHED, ENGRAVED (Giori)

1971, Oct. 29   Tagged   *Perf. 11*
1440 A854 8c blk brn & ocher, *buff*   .25   .25
1441 A855 8c blk brn & ocher, *buff*   .25   .25
1442 A856 8c blk brn & ocher, *buff*   .25   .25
1443 A857 8c blk brn & ocher, *buff*   .25   .25
   a. Block of 4, #1440-1443 1.00 1.00
   b. As "a," black brown omitted 800.00
   c. As "a," ocher omitted 2,500.

CHRISTMAS ISSUE

Adoration of the Shepherds, by Giorgione A858

Partridge in a Pear Tree, by Jamie Wyeth A859

No. 1444 after a painting by Giorgione in the National Gallery of Art, Washington D.C.

PHOTOGRAVURE (Andreotti)

1971, Nov. 10   *Perf. 10½x11*
1444 A858 8c gold & multi   .25   .25
   a. Gold omitted 350.00
1445 A859 8c dark green, red & multicolored   .25   .25

SIDNEY LANIER ISSUE

Lanier (1842-81), poet, musician, lawyer, educator.

Sidney Lanier (1842-1881) — A860

GIORI PRESS PRINTING

1972, Feb. 3   *Perf. 11*
1446 A860 8c black, brown & light blue   .25   .25

PEACE CORPS ISSUE

Peace Corps Poster, by David Battle — A861

PHOTOGRAVURE (Andreotti)
1972, Feb. 11   Perf. 10½x11
1447 A861 8c dark blue, light
             blue & red   .25   .25

NATIONAL PARKS CENTENNIAL ISSUE

Centenary of Yellowstone National Park, the 1st National Park, and of the entire National Park System. See No. C84.

Hulk of Ship A862   Cape Hatteras Lighthouse A863

Laughing Gulls on Driftwood A864   Laughing Gulls and Dune A865

Wolf Trap Farm, Vienna, Va. — A866

Old Faithful, Yellowstone A867

Mt. McKinley, Alaska A868

LITHOGRAPHED, ENGRAVED (Giori)
1972   Perf. 11
Plates of 400 subjects in 4 panes of 100 each
1448 A862 2c black & multi   .25   .25
1449 A863 2c black & multi   .25   .25
1450 A864 2c black & multi   .25   .25
1451 A865 2c black & multi   .25   .25
  a.   Block of 4, #1448-1451   .50   .50
  b.   As "a," black (litho.) omit-
          ted   1,000.
1452 A866 6c black & multi   .25   .25
1453 A867 8c blk, bl, brn &
             multi   .25   .25
1454 A868 15c black & multi   .30   .25
  b.   Yellow omitted   3,000.

FAMILY PLANNING ISSUE

Family — A869

1972, Mar. 18
1455 A869 8c blk & multi   .25   .25
  a.   Yellow omitted   300.00
  c.   Dark brown missing (FO)   9,500.

AMERICAN BICENTENNIAL ISSUE
Colonial American Craftsmen

In left panes Nos. 1456 and 1458 appear in 1st, 3rd and 5th place; Nos. 1457 and 1459 in 2nd and 4th place. This arrangement is reversed in right panes.

Glassmaker A870

Silversmith A871

Wigmaker A872

Hatter A873

ENGRAVED
1972, July 4   Perf. 11x10½
1456 A870 8c deep brown   .25   .25
1457 A871 8c deep brown   .25   .25
1458 A872 8c deep brown   .25   .25
1459 A873 8c deep brown   .25   .25
  a.   Block of 4, #1456-1459   1.00 1.00

OLYMPIC GAMES ISSUE

11th Winter Olympic Games, Sapporo, Japan, Feb. 3-13 and 20th Summer Olympic Games, Munich, Germany, Aug. 26-Sept. 11. See No. C85.

Bicycling and Olympic Rings A874

Bobsledding A875

Running A876

PHOTOGRAVURE (Andreotti)
1972, Aug. 17   Perf. 11x10½
1460 A874 6c blk, bl, red, emer
             & yel   .25   .25
1461 A875 8c blk, bl, red, emer
             & yel   .25   .25
1462 A876 15c blk, bl, red, emer
             & yel   .30   .25
       Nos. 1460-1462 (3)   .80   .75

PARENT TEACHER ASSN., 75th ANNIV.

Blackboard A877

1972, Sept. 15
1463 A877 8c yellow & black   .25   .25

WILDLIFE CONSERVATION ISSUE

Nos. 1464-1465 alternate in 1st row, Nos. 1468-1469 in 2nd row. This arrangement repeated throughout pane.

Fur Seals A878

Cardinal — A879

Brown Pelican — A880

Bighorn Sheep — A881

LITHOGRAPHED, ENGRAVED (Giori)
1972, Sept. 20   Perf. 11
1464 A878 8c multicolored   .25   .25
1465 A879 8c multicolored   .25   .25
1466 A880 8c multicolored   .25   .25
1467 A881 8c multicolored   .25   .25
  a.   Block of 4, #1464-1467   1.00 1.00
  b.   As "a," brown omitted   2,750.
  c.   As "a," green & blue omit-
          ted   2,750.
  d.   As "a," red & brown omit-
          ted   3,250.

MAIL ORDER BUSINESS ISSUE

Centenary of mail order business, originated by Aaron Montgomery Ward, Chicago. Design based on Headsville, W.Va., post office in Smithsonian Institution, Washington, D.C.

Rural Post Office Store A882

PHOTOGRAVURE (Andreotti)
1972, Sept. 27   Perf. 11x10½
1468 A882 8c multicolored   .25   .25

OSTEOPATHIC MEDICINE ISSUE

75th anniv. of the American Osteopathic Assoc., founded by Dr. Andrew T. Still (1828-1917), who developed the principles of osteopathy in 1874.

Man's Quest for Health — A883

1972, Oct. 9   Perf. 10½x11
1469 A883 8c multicolored   .25   .25

AMERICAN FOLKLORE ISSUE

Tom Sawyer, by Norman Rockwell — A884

Designed by Bradbury Thompson.

LITHOGRAPHED, ENGRAVED (Giori)
1972, Oct. 13   Perf. 11
1470 A884 8c blk, red, yel,
             tan, bl & rose
             red   .25   .25
  a.   Horiz. pair, imperf. be-
          tween   6,750.
  b.   Red & black (engr.) omit-
          ted   800.00
  c.   Yellow & tan (litho.) omit-
          ted   1,100.
  e.   Red (engr. 8c) missing
          (CM)   750.

CHRISTMAS ISSUE

Angel from "Mary, Queen of Heaven" — A885   Santa Claus — A886

No. 1471, detail from a painting by the Master of the St. Lucy Legend in the National Gallery of Art, Washington, D.C.

PHOTOGRAVURE (Andreotti)
1972, Nov. 9   Perf. 10½x11
1471 A885 8c multicolored   .25   .25
  a.   Pink omitted   100.00
  b.   Black omitted   2,500.
1472 A886 8c multicolored   .25   .25

PHARMACY ISSUE

Honoring American druggists in connection with the 120th anniversary of the American Pharmaceutical Association.

Mortar & Pestle, Bowl of Hygeia, 19th Century Medicine Bottles A887

LITHOGRAPHED, ENGRAVED (Giori)
1972, Nov. 10   **Perf. 11**
1473	A887 8c black & multi		.25	.25
a.	Blue & orange omitted	600.00		
b.	Blue omitted	1,250.		
c.	Orange omitted	1,250.		
e.	Vertical pair, imperf horiz.	2,000.		

STAMP COLLECTING ISSUE
Issued to publicize stamp collecting.

U.S. No. 1 Under Magnifying Glass A888

1972, Nov. 17
| 1474 | A888 8c multicolored | | .25 | .25 |
| a. | Black (litho.) omitted | 325.00 | | |

LOVE ISSUE

"Love," by Robert Indiana A889

PHOTOGRAVURE (Andreotti)
1973, Jan. 26   **Perf. 11x10½**
| 1475 | A889 8c red, emer & vio blue | | .25 | .25 |

AMERICAN BICENTENNIAL ISSUE
Communications in Colonial Times

Printer and Patriots Examining Pamphlet A890

Posting a Broadside A891

Postrider A892

Drummer A893

GIORI PRESS PRINTING
1973   **Perf. 11**
1476	A890 8c ultra, greenish blk & red		.25	.25
b.	Red missing (PS)	300.00		
1477	A891 8c blk, vermilion & ultra		.25	.25

LITHOGRAPHED, ENGRAVED (Giori)
1478	A892 8c bl, blk, red & grn		.25	.25
a.	Red missing (CM)	1,300.		
1479	A893 8c bl, blk, yel & red		.25	.25
a.	Blue missing (CM)	—		
b.	Red missing (CM)	—		
	Nos. 1476-1479 (4)		1.00	1.00

AMERICAN BICENTENNIAL ISSUE
Boston Tea Party

In left panes Nos. 1480 and 1482 appear in 1st, 3rd and 5th place, Nos. 1481 and 1483 appear in 2nd and 4th place. This arrangement is reversed in right panes.

British Merchantman — A894

British Three-master — A895

Boats and Ship's Hull A896

Boat and Dock A897

1973, July 4
1480	A894 8c blk & multi		.25	.25
1481	A895 8c blk & multi		.25	.25
1482	A896 8c blk & multi		.25	.25
1483	A897 8c blk & multi		.25	.25
a.	Block of 4, #1480-1483		1.00	1.00
b.	As "a," black (engraved) omitted	950.00		
c.	As "a," black (litho.) omitted	900.00		
e.	As "a," dk blue omitted	1,500.	750.00

AMERICAN ARTS ISSUE

George Gershwin (1898-1937), composer (No. 1484); Robinson Jeffers (1887-1962), poet (No. 1485); Henry Ossawa Tanner (1859-1937), black painter (No. 1486); Willa Cather (1873-1947), novelist (No. 1487).

Gershwin, Sportin' Life, Porgy & Bess A898

Robinson Jeffers, Man & Children of Carmel with Burro A899

Henry Ossawa Tanner, Palette & Rainbow A900

Willa Cather, Pioneer Family & Covered Wagon A901

PHOTOGRAVURE (Andreotti)
1973
1484	A898 8c dp grn & multi		.25	.25
a.	Vertical pair, imperf. horiz.	160.00		
1485	A899 8c Prus bl & multi		.25	.25
a.	Vertical pair, imperf. horiz.	160.00		
1486	A900 8c yel brn & multi		.25	.25
1487	A901 8c dp brn & multi		.25	.25
a.	Vertical pair, imperf. horiz.	175.00		
	Nos. 1484-1487 (4)		1.00	1.00

Honoring: No. 1484, George Gershwin (1898-1937), composer. No. 1485, Robinson Jeffers (1887-1962), poet. No. 1486, Henry Ossawa Tanner (1859-1937), black painter (portrait by Thomas Eakins). No. 1487, Willa Sibert Cather (1873-1947), novelist.
Issued: No. 1484, Feb. 28; No. 1485, Aug. 13; No. 1486, Sept. 10; No. 1487, Sept. 20.

COPERNICUS ISSUE

Nicolaus Copernicus (1473-1543), Polish Astronomer — A902

LITHOGRAPHED, ENGRAVED (Giori)
1973, Apr. 23
1488	A902 8c black & orange		.25	.25
a.	Orange omitted	400.00		
b.	Black (engraved) omitted	600.00		

The orange can be chemically removed. Expertization of No. 1488a is required.

POSTAL SERVICE EMPLOYEES ISSUE

A tribute to US Postal Service employees. Nos. 1489-1498 are printed se-tenant in horizontal rows of 10. Emerald inscription on back, printed beneath gum in water-soluble ink, includes Postal Service emblem, "People Serving You" and a statement, differing for each of the 10 stamps, about some aspect of postal service.

Each stamp in top or bottom row has a tab with blue inscription enumerating various jobs in postal service.

Stamp Counter A903

Mail Collection A904

Letter Facing on Conveyor Belt — A905

Parcel Post Sorting — A906

Mail Canceling A907

Manual Letter Routing A908

Electronic Letter Routing — A909

Loading Mail on Truck — A910

Mailman A911

Rural Mail Delivery A912

PHOTOGRAVURE (Andreotti)
1973, Apr. 30   **Perf. 10½x11**
1489	A903 8c multicolored		.25	.25
1490	A904 8c multicolored		.25	.25
1491	A905 8c multicolored		.25	.25
1492	A906 8c multicolored		.25	.25
1493	A907 8c multicolored		.25	.25
1494	A908 8c multicolored		.25	.25
1495	A909 8c multicolored		.25	.25
1496	A910 8c multicolored		.25	.25
1497	A911 8c multicolored		.25	.25
1498	A912 8c multicolored		.25	.25
a.	Strip of 10, #1489-1498		2.50	2.50

HARRY S. TRUMAN ISSUE

Harry S Truman, 33rd President (1884-1972) A913

GIORI PRESS PRINTING
1973, May 8   **Perf. 11**
| 1499 | A913 8c carmine rose, black & blue | | .25 | .25 |

ELECTRONICS PROGRESS ISSUE

Marconi's Spark Coil and Gap A914

Transistors and Printed Circuit Board A915

Microphone, Speaker, Vacuum Tube, TV Camera Tube A916

LITHOGRAPHED, ENGRAVED (Giori)
1973, July 10
1500	A914 6c lilac & multi		.25	.25
1501	A915 8c tan & multi		.25	.25
a.	Black (inscriptions & "U.S. 8c") omitted	300.00		
b.	Tan (background) & lilac omitted	600.00		

Many examples of No. 1501b are hinged. Value about one-half never hinged value.

1502	A916	15c gray green & multicolored	.30	.25
a.		Black (inscriptions & "U.S. 15c") omitted	850.00	
		Nos. 1500-1502 (3)	.80	.75

See No. C86.

LYNDON B. JOHNSON ISSUE

Lyndon B. Johnson (1908-1973), 36th President A917

PHOTOGRAVURE (Andreotti)
1973, Aug. 27

1503	A917	8c black & multi	.25	.25
a.		Horiz. pair, imperf. vert.	200.00	

RURAL AMERICA ISSUE

Centenary of the introduction of Aberdeen Angus cattle into the US (#1504); of the Chautauqua Institution (#1505); and of the introduction of hard winter wheat into Kansas by Mennonite immigrants (#1506).

Angus and Longhorn Cattle A918

Chautauqua Tent and Buggies — A919

Wheat Fields and Train A920

No. 1504 after painting by F.C. "Frank" Murphy.

LITHOGRAPHED, ENGRAVED (Giori)
1973-74

1504	A918	8c multi	.25	.25
a.		Green & red brown omitted	600.00	
b.		Vert. pair, imperf. between		5,000.
d.		Blue (engr.) missing (PS)	—	
1505	A919	10c multi	.25	.25
a.		Black (litho.) omitted		1,750.
1506	A920	10c multi	.25	.25
a.		Black and blue (engr.) omitted	450.00	
		Nos. 1504-1506 (3)	.75	.75

CHRISTMAS ISSUE

Small Cowper Madonna, by Raphael A921

Christmas Tree in Needlepoint A922

No. 1507 after painting in the National Gallery of Art, Washington, D.C.

PHOTOGRAVURE (Andreotti)
1973, Nov. 7   *Perf. 10½x11*

1507	A921	8c multicolored	.25	.25
1508	A922	8c multicolored	.25	.25
a.		Vertical pair, imperf. between	225.00	

50-Star & 13-Star Flags A923

Jefferson Memorial & Signature A924

Mail Transport A925

Liberty Bell A926

MULTICOLOR HUCK PRESS
1973-74   *Perf. 11x10½*

1509	A923	10c red & blue	.25	.25
a.		Horizontal pair, imperf. between	40.00	—
b.		Blue omitted	150.00	
c.		Imperf., vert. pair	450.00	
d.		Horiz. pair, imperf. vert.	900.00	
f.		Vert. pair, imperf. between	—	

No. 1509 exists imperf and with red omitted from printer's waste.

ROTARY PRESS PRINTING

1510	A924	10c blue	.25	.25
a.		Untagged (Bureau precanceled)	4.00	1.00
b.		Booklet pane of 5 + label	1.65	1.25
c.		Booklet pane of 8	2.00	2.00
d.		Booklet pane of 6 ('74)	5.00	1.75
e.		Vert. pair, imperf. horiz.	300.00	
f.		Vert. pair, imperf. btwn., in #1510c with miscut or with foldover	450.00	
i.		As "b," double booklet pane of 10 plus stamps with 2 horiz. pairs imperf. btwn. plus stamp and label imperf. btwn. (FO)	1,750.	

No. 1510f resulted from a paper foldover after perforating and before cutting into booklet panes.

PHOTOGRAVURE (Andreotti)

1511	A925	10c multi	.25	.25
a.		Yellow omitted	40.00	

Beware of stamps with yellow chemically removed offered as No. 1511a.

COIL STAMPS
ROTARY PRESS PRINTING
1973-74   *Perf. 10 Vert.*

1518	A926	6.3c brick red	.25	.25
a.		Untagged (Bureau precanceled)	.35	.25
b.		Imperf., pair	130.00	
c.		As "a," imperf., pair	75.00	

No. 1518c is precanceled Washington, DC. Columbus, Ohio and Garden City, N.Y. Values for Columbus pair $400, for Garden City pair $850.

MULTICOLOR HUCK PRESS

1519	A923	10c red & blue	.25	.25
a.		Imperf., pair	35.00	

Huck press printings often show parts of a joint line, but this feature is not consistent.

ROTARY PRESS PRINTING

1520	A924	10c blue	.25	.25
a.		Untagged (Bureau precanceled)	5.50	1.25
b.		Imperf., pair	30.00	

VETERANS OF FOREIGN WARS ISSUE

75th anniversary of Veterans of Spanish-American and Other Foreign Wars.

V.F.W. Emblem A928

GIORI PRESS PRINTING
1974, Mar. 11   *Perf. 11*

1525	A928	10c red & dark blue	.25	.25
b.		Blue missing (PS)		

ROBERT FROST ISSUE

Robert Frost (1874-1963), Poet — A929

1974, Mar. 26   *Perf. 10½x11*

1526	A929	10c black	.25	.25

EXPO '74 WORLD'S FAIR ISSUE

EXPO '74 World's Fair "Preserve the Environment," Spokane, Wash., May 4-Nov. 4.

"Cosmic Jumper" A930

PHOTOGRAVURE (Andreotti)
1974, Apr. 18   *Perf. 11*

1527	A930	10c multicolored	.25	.25

HORSE RACING ISSUE

Kentucky Derby, Churchill Downs, centenary.

Horses Rounding Turn A931

1974, May 4   *Perf. 11x10½*

1528	A931	10c yel & multi	.25	.25
a.		Blue ("Horse Racing") omitted	650.00	
b.		Red ("U.S. postage 10 cents") omitted	1,750.	

Beware of stamps offered as No. 1528b that have traces of red.

SKYLAB ISSUE

First anniversary of the launching of Skylab I, honoring all who participated in the Skylab project.

Skylab A932

LITHOGRAPHED, ENGRAVED (Giori)
1974, May 14   *Perf. 11*

1529	A932	10c multicolored	.25	.25
a.		Vert. pair, imperf. between	—	
c.		Vert. pair, imperf. horiz.	—	
d.		Double impression of magenta	—	

UNIVERSAL POSTAL UNION ISSUE

UPU cent. In the 1st row Nos. 1530-1537 are in sequence as listed. In the 2nd row Nos. 1534-1537 are followed by Nos. 1530-1533. Every row of 8 and every horizontal block of 8 contains all 8 designs. The letter writing designs are from famous works of art; some are details. The quotation on every second stamp, "Letters mingle souls," is from a letter by poet John Donne.

Michelangelo, from School of Athens — A933

Five Feminine Virtues — A934

Old Time Letter Rack — A935

Mlle. La Vergne — A936

Lady Writing Letter — A937

Inkwell and Quill — A938

Mrs. John
Douglas — A939

Universal
Postal Union   Goya
1874-1974   10cUS   Don Antonio
                      Noreiga — A940

PHOTOGRAVURE (Andreotti)
1974, June 6
1530 A933 10c multicolored   .25   .25
1531 A934 10c multicolored   .25   .25
1532 A935 10c multicolored   .25   .25
1533 A936 10c multicolored   .25   .25
1534 A937 10c multicolored   .25   .25
1535 A938 10c multicolored   .25   .25
1536 A939 10c multicolored   .25   .25
1537 A940 10c multicolored   .25   .25
   a.   Block or strip of 8 (#1530-
        1537)   2.00 2.00
   b.   As "a," (block), imperf.
        vert.   2,500.

MINERAL HERITAGE ISSUE
The sequence of stamps in 1st horizontal row is Nos. 1538-1541, 1538-
1539. In 2nd row Nos. 1540-1541 are
followed by Nos. 1538-1541.

Petrified
Wood
A941

Tourmaline — A942

Amethyst — A943

Rhodochrosite — A944

1974, June 13
1538 A941 10c blue & multi   .25   .25
   a.   Light blue & yellow (litho.)
        omitted   —
1539 A942 10c blue & multi   .25   .25
   a.   Light blue (litho.) omitted —
   b.   Black & purple (engr.) omit-
        ted   —
1540 A943 10c blue & multi   .25   .25
   a.   Light blue & yellow (litho.)
        omitted   —
1541 A944 10c blue & multi   .25   .25
   a.   Block or strip of 4, #1538-
        1541   1.00 1.00
   b.   As "a," light blue & yellow
        (litho.) omitted   900.00 —
   c.   Light blue (litho.) omitted —
   d.   Black & red (engr.) omitted —
   e.   Block of 4, two right stamps
        being Nos. 1539b and
        1541d   7,000.

No. 1541e is usually collected as a transition block of six or larger.

**KENTUCKY SETTLEMENT, 200th
ANNIV.
Fort Harrod, first settlement in
Kentucky.**

Fort Harrod — A945

1974, June 15
1542 A945 10c green & multi   .25   .25
   a.   Dull black (litho.) omitted 400.00
   b.   Green (engr. & litho.),
        black (engr. & litho.) &
        blue missing (EP)   1,750.
   c.   Green (engr.) missing
        (EP)   3,000.
   d.   Green (engr.) & black
        (litho.) missing (EP)   —
   f.   Blue (litho.) omitted   —

No. 1542f was caused by an occurrence
that seems to be unique for U.S. total color
omitted/missing errors. According to the BEP,
oil on the printing blanket made a small area
unreceptive to the blue ink. No blue at all was
printed on one unique error stamp.

**AMERICAN REVOLUTION
BICENTENNIAL ISSUE
First Continental Congress**
Nos. 1543-1544 alternate in 1st row,
Nos. 1545-1546 in 2nd row. This
arrangement is repeated throughout the
pane.

Carpenters'
Hall
A946

A948

Independence Hall — A949

1974, July 4
1543 A946 10c dark blue & red   .25   .25
1544 A947 10c gray, dark blue &
            red   .25   .25
1545 A948 10c gray, dark blue &
            red   .25   .25
1546 A949 10c red & dark blue   .25   .25
   a.   Block of 4, #1543-1546   1.00 1.00

ENERGY CONSERVATION ISSUE
Publicizing the importance of
conserving all forms of energy.

A950

LITHOGRAPHED, ENGRAVED (Giori)
1974, Sept. 23
1547 A950 10c multicolored   .25   .25
   a.   Blue & orange omitted   400.00
   b.   Orange & green omitted   275.00
   c.   Green omitted   400.00

**AMERICAN FOLKLORE ISSUE
Legend of Sleepy Hollow**
The Headless Horseman in pursuit of
Ichabod Crane from "Legend of Sleepy
Hollow," by Washington Irving.

Legend of
Sleepy
Hollow
A951

1974, Oct. 10
1548 A951 10c dk bl, blk, org &
            yel   .25   .25

RETARDED CHILDREN ISSUE
Retarded Children Can Be Helped,
theme of annual convention of the
National Association of Retarded
Citizens.

Retarded
Child — A952

GIORI PRESS PRINTING
1974, Oct. 12
1549 A952 10c brown red & dark
            brown   .25   .25

**WARNING ABOUT SELF-ADHESIVE
STAMPS**
**Many, though not all, self-adhesive
stamps, which first appear with No.
1552, will not separate from paper or
otherwise respond well to a standard
warm-water soak. Consult the listings in the Scott U.S. Specialized
Catalogue for information about
which self-adhesives will and which
will not soak. The editors strongly
recommend that stamps that will not
soak be collected on piece.**

Angel, from Perussis
Altarpiece,
1480 — A953

"The Road-Winter," by Currier &
Ives — A954

No. 1550, detail from the Perussis altarpiece
painted by anonymous French artist, 1480, in
Metropolitan Museum of Art, New York City.
Currier and Ives print from drawing by Otto
Knirsch

PHOTOGRAVURE (Andreotti)
1974, Oct. 23   Perf. 10½x11
1550 A953 10c multicolored   .25   .25
                   Perf.   11x10½
1551 A954 10c multicolored   .25   .25
   a.   Buff omitted   12.50

No. 1551a is difficult to identify. Competent
expertization is necessary.

Dove
Weather
Vane — A955

Die Cut, Paper Backing Rouletted
**1974, Nov. 15   Untagged
Self-adhesive; Inscribed
"Precanceled"**
1552 A955 10c multicolored   .25   .25
       Nos. 1550-1552 (3)   .75   .75

Unused value of No. 1552 is for stamp on
rouletted paper backing as issued. Used value
is for stamp on piece, with or without postmark. **Most examples are becoming discolored from the adhesive. The Catalogue
value is for discolored examples.**
Die cutting includes crossed slashes
through dove, applied to prevent removal and
re-use of the stamp. The stamp will separate
into layers if soaked.

AMERICAN ARTS ISSUE
Benjamin West (1738-1820), painter
(No. 1553); Paul Laurence Dunbar
(1872-1906), poet (No. 1554); David
(Lewelyn) Wark Griffith (1875-1948),
motion picture producer (No. 1555).

Benjamin
West — A956

Paul Laurence
Dunbar — A957

D. W.
Griffith &
Projector
A958

PHOTOGRAVURE (Andreotti)
1975   Perf. 10½x11
1553 A956 10c multicolored   .25   .25
                   Perf.   11
1554 A957 10c multicolored   .25   .25
   a.   Imperf., pair   800.00

LITHOGRAPHED, ENGRAVED (Giori)
Perf. 11

1555	A958	10c brown & multicolored	.25	.25
a.		Brown (engr.) omitted	450.00	
		Nos. 1553-1555 (3)	.75	.75

SPACE ISSUES

US space accomplishments with unmanned craft. Pioneer 10 passed within 81,000 miles of Jupiter, Dec. 10, 1973. Mariner 10 explored Venus and Mercury in 1974 and Mercury again in 1975.

Pioneer 10 Passing Jupiter A959

Mariner 10, Venus & Mercury A960

LITHOGRAPHED, ENGRAVED (Giori)
1975   **Perf. 11**

1556	A959	10c lt yel, dk yel, red, bl & 2 dk blues	.25	.25
a.		Red & dark yellow omitted	750.00	
b.		Dark blues (engr.) omitted	400.00	
d.		Dark yellow omitted	—	

Imperfs. exist from printer's waste.

1557	A960	10c blk, red, ultra & bister	.25	.25
a.		Red omitted	275.00	
b.		Ultramarine & bister omitted	850.00	
d.		Red missing (PS)	525.00	

COLLECTIVE BARGAINING ISSUE

Collective Bargaining law, enacted 1935, in Wagner Act.

"Labor and Management" — A961

PHOTOGRAVURE (Andreotti)
1975, Mar. 13

1558	A961	10c multicolored	.25	.25

Imperforates exist from printer's waste.

AMERICAN BICENTENNIAL ISSUE
Contributors to the Cause

Sybil Ludington, age 16, rallied militia, Apr. 26, 1777; Salem Poor, black freeman, fought in Battle of Bunker Hill; Haym Salomon, Jewish immigrant, raised money to finance Revolutionary War; Peter Francisco, Portuguese-French immigrant, joined Continental Army at 15. Emerald inscription on back, printed beneath gum in water-soluble ink, gives thumbnail sketch of portrayed contributor.

Sybil Ludington A962

Salem Poor A963

Haym Salomon A964

Peter Francisco A965

1975, Mar. 25   **Perf. 11x10½**

1559	A962	8c multicolored	.25	.25
a.		Back inscriptions omitted	110.00	
1560	A963	10c multicolored	.25	.25
a.		Back inscription omitted	110.00	
b.		Black missing (PS)	—	
1561	A964	10c multicolored	.25	.25
a.		Back inscription omitted	110.00	
1562	A965	18c multicolored	.35	.25
		Nos. 1559-1562 (4)	1.10	1.00

On No. 1560, two black plates were used. No. 1560b is missing the impression from one of those plates ("Salem Poor - U.S. Bicentennial symbol - Gallant Soldier") due to an upward shift of the horizontal perforations.

Dangerous fakes exist of No. 1561 with red apparently omitted. Professional authentication is mandatory in order to establish such a stamp as a genuine error.

Lexington-Concord Battle, 200th Anniv.

"Birth of Liberty," by Henry Sandham A966

1975, Apr. 19   **Perf. 11**

1563	A966	10c multicolored	.25	.25
a.		Vert. pair, imperf. horiz.	300.00	

Bunker Hill Battle, 200th Anniv.

Battle of Bunker Hill, by John Trumbull — A967

1975, June 17

1564	A967	10c multicolored	.25	.25

Military Uniforms

Bicentenary of US Military Services. Nos. 1565-1566 alternate in one row, Nos. 1567-1568 in next row.

Soldier with Flintlock Musket, Uniform Button — A968

Sailor with Grappling Hook, First Navy Jack, 1775 — A969

Marine with Musket, Full-rigged Ship — A970

Militiaman with Musket, Powder Horn — A971

1975, July 4

1565	A968	10c multicolored	.25	.25
1566	A969	10c multicolored	.25	.25
1567	A970	10c multicolored	.25	.25
1568	A971	10c multicolored	.25	.25
a.		Block of 4, #1565-1568	1.00	1.00

APOLLO SOYUZ SPACE ISSUE

Apollo Soyuz space test project, Russo-American cooperation, launched July 15; link-up, July 17. Nos. In the 1st row, No. 1569 is in 1st and 3rd space, No. 1570 is 2nd space; in the 2nd row No. 1570 is in 1st and 3rd space, No. 1569 in 2nd space, etc.

Participating US and USSR crews: Thomas P. Stafford, Donald K. Slayton, Vance D. Brand, Aleksei A. Leonov, Valery N. Kubasov.

Apollo & Soyuz After Docking, Earth — A972

Spacecraft Before Docking, Earth & Project Emblem — A973

1975, July 15

1569	A972	10c multicolored	.25	.25
1570	A973	10c multicolored	.25	.25
a.		Pair, #1569-1570	.50	.50
c.		As "a," vert. pair, imperf. horiz.	800.00	
d.		As "a," yellow omitted	900.00	

Nos. 1569-1570 totally imperforate are printer's waste.
See Russia Nos. 4339-4340.

INTERNATIONAL WOMEN'S YEAR ISSUE

International Women's Year 1975.

Worldwide Equality for Women A974

1975, Aug. 26   **Perf. 11x10½**

1571	A974	10c blue, orange & dark blue	.25	.25

US POSTAL SERVICE BICENTENNIAL ISSUE

Nos. 1572-1573 alternate in 1st row, Nos. 1574-1575 in 2nd row. This arrangement is repeated throughout the pane.

Stagecoach and Trailer Truck A975

Old and New Locomotives — A976

Early Mail Plane and Jet — A977

Satellite for Transmission of Mailgrams — A978

1975, Sept. 3

1572	A975	10c multicolored	.25	.25
1573	A976	10c multicolored	.25	.25
1574	A977	10c multicolored	.25	.25
1575	A978	10c multicolored	.25	.25
a.		Block of 4, #1572-1575	1.00	1.00
b.		As "a," red "10c" omitted, tagging omitted	—	

WORLD PEACE THROUGH LAW ISSUE

A prelude to 7th World Law Conference of the World Peace Through Law Center at Washington, D.C., Oct. 12-17.

Law Book, Olive Branch and Globe A979

GIORI PRESS PRINTING
1975, Sept. 29   **Perf. 11**

1576	A979	10c green, Prussian blue & rose brown	.25	.25
b.		Horiz. pair, imperf vert.	7,500.	
c.		All colors omitted	—	

No. 1576c is collected in a horiz. strip as two errors se-tenant with a partially printed stamp.

BANKING AND COMMERCE ISSUE

Banking and commerce in the U.S., and for the Centennial Convention of the American Bankers Association.

Engine Turning, Indian Head Penny & Morgan Silver Dollar A980

Seated Liberty Quarter, $20 Gold (Double Eagle), Engine Turning A981

LITHOGRAPHED, ENGRAVED (Giori)
1975, Oct. 6

1577	A980	10c multicolored	.25	.25
1578	A981	10c multicolored	.25	.25
a.		Pair, #1577-1578	.50	.50
b.		As "a," brown & blue (litho) omitted	1,400.	
c.		As "a," brown, blue & yellow (litho) omitted	1,750.	

CHRISTMAS ISSUE

Madonna, by Domenico Ghirlandaio A982

Christmas Card, by Louis Prang, 1878 A983

PHOTOGRAVURE (Andreotti)
1975, Oct. 14

1579	A982 (10c) multicolored	.25	.25
a.	Imperf., pair	75.00	

Perf. 11.2

1580	A983 (10c) multicolored	.25	.25
a.	Imperf., pair	85.00	
c.	Perf. 10.9	.25	.25

Perf. 10.5x11.3

1580B	A983 (10c) multicolored	.65	.25

AMERICANA ISSUE

Inkwell and Quill
A984

Speaker's Stand
A985

Early Ballot Box
A987

Books, Bookmark, Eyeglasses
A988

Dome of Capitol
A994

Contemplation of Justice
A995

Early American Printing Press — A996

Torch — A997

Liberty Bell
A998

Eagle and Shield
A999

Fort McHenry Flag
A1001

Head, Statue of Liberty
A1002

Old North Church, Boston
A1003

Fort Nisqually
A1004

Sandy Hook Lighthouse, NJ — A1005

Morris Township School No. 2, Devils Lake, ND — A1006

Iron "Betty" Lamp, 17th-18th Cent. A1007

Rush Lamp and Candle Holder A1008

Kerosene Table Lamp A1009

Railroad Conductor's Lantern, c. 1850 A1010

ROTARY PRESS PRINTING
1975-81   **Perf. 11¼x10½**

Size: 18½x22½mm

1581	A984 1c dk bl, grnish	.25	.25
a.	Untagged (Bureau precanceled)	4.50	1.50
c.	White paper, dull gum	100.00	—
1582	A985 2c red brn, grnsh	.25	.25
a.	Untagged (Bureau precanceled)	4.50	1.50
c.	Cream paper ('81)	.25	.25
1584	A987 3c olive, grnsh	.25	.25
a.	Untagged (Bureau precanceled), dull gum	.75	.50

Values for No. 1584a are for the lines-only precancel. Also known with city precancels, and valued at $50 thus.

1585	A988 4c rose mag, cream	.25	.25
a.	Untagged (Bureau precanceled)	1.00	.75

The pair with horiz. gutter between also is misperfed through the stamps horizontally.

Also known with city precancels, and valued at $100 thus.

Size: 17½x20½mm
Perf. 11x10½ on 3 Sides

1590	A994 9c slate green	.45	1.00

From bklt. pane #1623a.

Perf. 10x9¾ on 3 Sides

1590A	A994 9c slate green	12.50	12.50

From bklt. pane #1623Bc.

Size: 18½x22½mm
Perf. 11¼x10½

1591	A994 9c sl grn, gray	.25	.25
a.	Untagged (Bureau precanceled)	1.75	1.00

Values for No. 1591a are for the lines-only precancel. Also known with city precancels, and valued at $32.50 thus.

1592	A995 10c violet, gray	.25	.25
a.	Untagged (Bureau precanceled, Chicago)	9.50	5.00
1593	A996 11c orange, gray	.25	.25
1594	A997 12c red brown, beige	.25	.25

Perf. 11¼x10½ on 2 or 3 Sides

1595	A998 13c brown	.30	.25
a.	Booklet pane of 6	2.25	1.50
b.	Booklet pane of 7 + label	2.25	1.50
c.	Booklet pane of 8	2.25	1.50
d.	Booklet pane of 5 + label, Apr. 2, 1976	1.75	1.25
e.	Vert. pair, imperf. btwn., in #1595c with foldover	1,100.	
g.	Horiz. pair, imperf. btwn., in #1595d with foldover	—	

Nos. 1595e and 1595g resulted from paper foldovers after perforating and before cutting

into panes. Beware of printer's waste consisting of complete panes with perfs around all outside edges.

PHOTOGRAVURE (Andreotti)
Perf. 11¼ Bullseye

1596	A999 13c multicolored	.25	.25
a.	Imperf., pair	40.00	—
b.	Yellow omitted	75.00	

ENGRAVED (Combination Press)
Perf. 11x11¼

1597	A1001 15c gray, dk bl & red	.30	.25
b.	Gray omitted	300.00	
c.	Vert. pair, imperf btwn and with natural straight edge at bottom	350.00	
e.	Imperf., vert. pair	15.00	

ENGRAVED
Perf. 11x10½ on 2 or 3 Sides

1598	A1001 15c gray, dk bl & red	.40	.25
a.	Booklet pane of 8	3.75	1.50

Perf. 11¼x10½

1599	A1002 16c blue	.35	.25
1603	A1003 24c red, blue	.50	.25
	red, greenish blue	.50	.25
1604	A1004 28c brown, blue	.55	.25
1605	A1005 29c blue, blue	.60	.25
1606	A1006 30c green, blue	.55	.25

LITHOGRAPHED AND ENGRAVED
Perf. 11

1608	A1007 50c tan, blk & org	.85	.25
a.	Black omitted	375.00	
b.	Vert. pair, imperf. horiz.	1,200.	

Beware of examples offered as No. 1608b that have blind perfs.

1610	A1008 $1 tan, brn, org & yel	2.00	.25
a.	Brown (engraved) omitted	175.00	
b.	Tan, orange & yellow omitted	175.00	
c.	Brown (engraved) inverted	17,000.	
1611	A1009 $2 tan, dk grn, org & yel	3.75	.75
1612	A1010 $5 tan, red brn, yel & org	8.50	1.75
	Nos. 1581-1612 (23)	33.85	20.75

Nos. 1590, 1590A, 1595, 1598, 1623 and 1623b were issued only in booklets. All stamps have one or two straight edges.

Years of issue: #1591, 1595-1596, 11c, 24c, 1975. #1590, 1c-4c, 10c, 1977. #1597-1598, 16c, 28c, 29c, $2, 1978. 30c-$1, $5, 1979. 12c, 1981.

Guitar A1011

Saxhorns A1012

Drum A1013

Piano A1014

Designers: 3.1c, George Mercer. 7.7c, Susan Robb. 7.9c, Bernard Glassman. 10c, Walter Brooks. 15c, V. Jack Ruther.

COIL STAMPS
ENGRAVED
1975-79   **Perf. 10 Vertically**

1613	A1011 3.1c brown ('79)	.25	.25
a.	Untagged (Bureau precanceled, lines only)	.35	.35
b.	Imperf., pair	850.00	
1614	A1012 7.7c brown ('76)	.25	.25
a.	Untagged (Bureau precanceled)	.40	.30
b.	As "a," imperf., pair	1,250.	

No. 1614b is precanceled Washington, DC. Also exists with Marion, OH precancel; value $1,950 for pair.

1615	A1013 7.9c carmine ('76)	.25	.25
a.	Untagged (Bureau precanceled)	.40	.40
b.	Imperf., pair	300.00	
1615C	A1014 8.4c dak blue ('78)	.25	.25
d.	Untagged (Bureau precanceled)	.50	.40
e.	As "d," pair, imperf. between	45.00	
f.	As "d," imperf. pair, shiny gum	15.00	

No. 1615Ce is precanceled with lines only. No. 1615Cf is precanceled with lines only (value shown) and also exists in pairs precanceled Newark, N.J. ($25), Brownstown, Ind. ($900), Oklahoma City, Okla. ($1,500.) and Washington, DC ($900).

1616	A994 9c slate green ('75)	.25	.25
a.	Imperf., pair	125.00	
b.	Untagged (Bureau precanceled)	.75	.75
c.	As "b," imperf., pair	600.00	

Value for No. 1616b is for stamp with dull gum.

No. 1616c is precanceled Pleasantville, NY.

1617	A995 10c violet ('77)	.25	.25
a.	Untagged (Bureau precanceled)	1.35	1.35
b.	Imperf., pair	55.00	
c.	As "a," imperf pair	3,750.	

Values for No. 1617a and 1617b are for stamps with dull gum. These varieties with shiny gum are worth considerably more.

1618	A998 13c brown ('75)	.25	.25
a.	Untagged (Bureau precanceled)	.75	.75
b.	Imperf., pair	22.50	
g.	Pair, imperf. between	600.00	
h.	As "a," imperf., pair	—	

Value for No. 1618a is for stamp with dull gum.

1618C	A1001 15c gray, dk bl & red ('78)	.75	.25
d.	Imperf., pair	20.00	
e.	Pair, imperf. between	100.00	
f.	Gray omitted	30.00	
1619	A1002 16c ultra ('78)	.35	.25
	Huck Press Printing	.50	.25
	Nos. 1613-1619 (9)	2.85	2.25

No. 1619a (the B press printing) has a white background without bluish tinge, is a fraction of a millimeter smaller than No. 1619 (the Cottrell press printing) and has no joint lines.

See Nos. 1811, 1813, 1816.

13-Star Flag, Independence Hall — A1015

Flag over Capitol — A1016

1975-81   **Perf. 11x10¾**

1622	A1015 13c dk bl, red & brn red	.25	.25
a.	Horiz. pair, imperf. between	40.00	
b.	Vertical pair, imperf.	300.00	—
e.	Horiz. pair, imperf. vert.	—	

No. 1622 was printed on the Multicolored Huck Press. Plate markings are at top or bottom of pane.

Perf. 11¼

1622C	A1015 13c dk bl, red & brn red ('81)	1.00	.25
d.	Vertical pair, imperf	100.00	

No. 1622C was printed on the Combination Press. Plate markings are at sides of pane.

BOOKLET STAMPS
Perf. 11x10½ on 2 or 3 Sides
1977, Mar. 11

1623	A1016 13c blue & red	.25	.25
a.	Booklet pane, 1 #1590 + 7 #1623	2.25	2.00
d.	Pair, #1590 & #1623	.70	1.25

Perf. 10x9¾ on 2 or 3 Sides

1623B	A1016 13c blue & red	.65	.75
c.	Booklet pane, 1 #1590A + 7 #1623B	15.00	15.00
e.	Pair, #1590A & #1623B	14.00	14.00

COIL STAMP
1975, Nov. 15   **Perf. 10 Vertically**

1625	A1015 13c dk blue, red & brown red	.35	.25
a.	Imperf., pair	20.00	

AMERICAN BICENTENNIAL ISSUE
The Spirit of '76

Designed after painting by Archibald M. Willard in Abbot Hall, Marblehead, Massachusetts. Nos. 1629-1631 printed in continuous design.

Left panes contain 3 No. 1631a and one No. 1629; right panes contain one No. 1631 and 3 No. 1631a.

Drummer Boy
A1019

Old Drummer
A1020

Fifer — A1021

PHOTOGRAVURE (Andreotti)

1976, Jan. 1   *Perf. 11*

1629	A1019	13c blue violet & multi	.25	.25
a.		Imperf., vert. pair	—	
1630	A1020	13c blue violet & multi	.25	.25
1631	A1021	13c blue violet & multi	.25	.25
a.		Strip of 3, #1629-1631	.75	.75
b.		As "a," imperf.	700.00	
c.		Imperf., vert. pair, #1631	500.00	

INTERPHIL ISSUE

Interphil 76 International Philatelic Exhibition, Philadelphia, Pa., May 29-June 6.

"Interphil
76"
A1022

LITHOGRAPHED, ENGRAVED (Giori)

1976, Jan. 17

1632	A1022	13c dark blue & red (engr.), ultra. & red (litho.)	.25	.25
a.		Dark blue & red (engr.) missing (CM)	—	
c.		Red (engr,) missing (CM)	—	

State Flags
A1023

Photo.

1976, Feb. 23

1633	A1023	13c Delaware	.30	.25
1634	A1024	13c Pennsylvania	.30	.25
1635	A1025	13c New Jersey	.30	.25
1636	A1026	13c Georgia	.30	.25
1637	A1027	13c Connecticut	.30	.25
1638	A1028	13c Massachusetts	.30	.25
1639	A1029	13c Maryland	.30	.25
1640	A1030	13c South Carolina	.30	.25
1641	A1031	13c New Hampshire	.30	.25
1642	A1032	13c Virginia	.30	.25
1643	A1033	13c New York	.30	.25
1644	A1034	13c North Carolina	.30	.25
1645	A1035	13c Rhode Island	.30	.25
1646	A1036	13c Vermont	.30	.25
1647	A1037	13c Kentucky	.30	.25
1648	A1038	13c Tennessee	.30	.25
1649	A1039	13c Ohio	.30	.25
1650	A1040	13c Louisiana	.30	.25
1651	A1041	13c Indiana	.30	.25
1652	A1042	13c Mississippi	.30	.25
1653	A1043	13c Illinois	.30	.25
1654	A1044	13c Alabama	.30	.25
1655	A1045	13c Maine	.30	.25
1656	A1046	13c Missouri	.30	.25
1657	A1047	13c Arkansas	.30	.25
1658	A1048	13c Michigan	.30	.25
1659	A1049	13c Florida	.30	.25
1660	A1050	13c Texas	.30	.25
1661	A1051	13c Iowa	.30	.25
1662	A1052	13c Wisconsin	.30	.25
1663	A1053	13c California	.30	.25
1664	A1054	13c Minnesota	.30	.25
1665	A1055	13c Oregon	.30	.25
1666	A1056	13c Kansas	.30	.25
1667	A1057	13c West Virginia	.30	.25
1668	A1058	13c Nevada	.30	.25
1669	A1059	13c Nebraska	.30	.25
1670	A1060	13c Colorado	.30	.25
1671	A1061	13c North Dakota	.30	.25
1672	A1062	13c South Dakota	.30	.25
1673	A1063	13c Montana	.30	.25
1674	A1064	13c Washington	.30	.25
1675	A1065	13c Idaho	.30	.25
1676	A1066	13c Wyoming	.30	.25
1677	A1067	13c Utah	.30	.25
1678	A1068	13c Oklahoma	.30	.25
1679	A1069	13c New Mexico	.30	.25
1680	A1070	13c Arizona	.30	.25
1681	A1071	13c Alaska	.30	.25
1682	A1072	13c Hawaii	.30	.25
a.		Pane of 50	17.50	15.00

TELEPHONE CENTENNIAL ISSUE

Centenary of first telephone call by Alexander Graham Bell, March 10, 1876.

Bell's
Telephone
Patent
Application
A1073

ENGRAVED (Giori)

1976, Mar. 10

1683	A1073	13c blk, pur & red, *tan*	.25	.25
a.		Black & purple missing (EP)	450.00	
b.		Red missing (EP)	—	
c.		All colors missing (EP)	—	

On No. 1683a, the errors have only tiny traces of red present, so are best collected as a horiz. strip of 5 with 2 or 3 error stamps. No. 1683c also must be collected as a transitional strip.

COMMERCIAL AVIATION ISSUE

50th anniversary of first contract airmail flights: Dearborn, Mich. to Cleveland, Ohio, Feb. 15, 1926; and Pasco, Wash. to Elko, Nev., Apr. 6, 1926.

A1074

PHOTOGRAVURE (Andreotti)

1976, Mar. 19   **Tagged**   *Perf. 11*

1684	A1074	13c blue & multicolored	.25	.25

CHEMISTRY ISSUE

Honoring American chemists, in conjunction with the centenary of the American Chemical Society.

A1075

PHOTOGRAVURE (Andreotti)

1976, Apr. 6

1685	A1075	13c multicolored	.25	.25

AMERICAN BICENTENNIAL ISSUES
SOUVENIR SHEETS

Designs, from Left to Right, No. 1686: a, Two British officers. b, Gen. Benjamin Lincoln. c, George Washington. d, John Trumbull, Col. Cobb, von Steuben, Lafayette, Thomas Nelson. e, Alexander Hamilton, John Laurens, Walter Stewart (all vert.).

No. 1687: a, John Adams, Roger Sherman, Robert R. Livingston. b, Jefferson, Franklin. c, Thomas Nelson, Jr., Francis Lewis, John Witherspoon, Samuel Huntington. d, John Hancock, Charles Thomson. e, George Read, John Dickinson, Edward Rutledge (a, d, vert., b, c, e, horiz.).

No. 1688: a, Boatsman. b, Washington. c, Flag bearer. d, Men in boat. e, Men on shore (a, d, horiz., b, c, e, vert.).

No. 1689: a, Two officers. b, Washington. c, Officer, black horse. d, Officer, white horse. e, Three soldiers (a, c, e, horiz., b, d, vert.).

LITHOGRAPHED

1976, May 29

1686	A1076	Pane of 5	2.75	2.25
a.-e.		13c multicolored	.40	.40
f.		"USA/13c" omitted on "b," "c" & "d," imperf, tagging omitted	—	1,750.
g.		"USA/13c" omitted on "a" & "e"	500.00	300.00
h.		Imperf., tagging omitted	—	2,500.
i.		"USA/13c" omitted on "b," "c" & "d"	500.00	
j.		"USA/13c" double on "b"		
k.		"USA/13c" omitted on "c" & "d"	750.00	
l.		"USA/13c" omitted on "e"	475.00	
m.		"USA/13c" omitted, imperf., tagging omitted		
n.		As "g," imperf., tagging omitted		1,400.
o.		"USA/13c" missing on "a" (PS)	450.00	
q.		"USA/13c" omitted on "a"	750.00	
r.		Imperf., tagged		
s.		"USA/13c" missing on "b" and "d" (PS)		
1687	A1077	Pane of 5	3.75	3.25
a.-e.		18c multicolored	.50	.50
f.		Design & marginal inscriptions omitted	2,500.	
g.		"USA/18c" omitted on "a" & "e"	550.00	1,800.
h.		"USA/18c" omitted on "b," "d" & "e"	350.00	
i.		"USA/18c" omitted on "d"	425.00	475.00
j.		Black omitted in design	1,500.	
k.		"USA/18c" omitted, imperf., tagging omitted	1,500.	
m.		"USA/18c" omitted on "b" & "e"	500.00	
n.		"USA/18c" omitted on "b" & "d"	1,000.	
q.		Imperf. (tagged)	1,000.	
q.		"USA/18c" missing on "c" (CM)		
r.		Yellow omitted	5,000.	
s.		"USA/18c" missing on "a," "c" and "d" (PS)	—	
t.		"USA/18c" missing on "a" and "d" (PS)	300.00	
u.		"USA/18c" omitted on "a"	5,000.	
1688	A1078	Pane of 5	4.75	4.25
a.-e.		24c multicolored	.65	.65
f.		"USA/24c" omitted, imperf., tagging omitted	950.00	
g.		"USA/24c" omitted on "d" & "e"	400.00	400.00
h.		Design & marginal inscriptions omitted	2,500.	
i.		"USA/24c" omitted on "a," "b" & "c"	400.00	400.00
j.		Imperf., tagging omitted	1,250.	
k.		"USA/24c" of "d" & "e" inverted	12,500.	
l.		As "i," imperf, tagging omitted	3,250.	—
n.		As No. 1688, perfs inverted and reversed	7,500.	
p.		"USA/24c" missing on "d" and "e" (CM)	—	
q.		"USA/24c" omitted on "b" and "c"	—	
r.		"USA/24c" omitted on "a"	400.00	
s.		As No. 1688, imperf.	1,250.	
1689	A1079	Pane of 5	5.75	5.25
a.-e.		31c multicolored	.80	.80
f.		"USA/31c" omitted, imperf.	950.00	
g.		"USA/31c" omitted on "a" & "c"	375.00	
h.		"USA/31c" omitted on "b," "d" & "e"	450.00	—
i.		"USA/31c" omitted on "e"	375.00	
j.		Black omitted in design	1,450.	
k.		Imperf., tagging omitted		2,000.
l.		"USA/31c" omitted on "b" & "d"	300.00	
m.		"USA/31c" omitted on "a," "c" & "e"	750.00	
n.		As "m," imperf., tagging omitted		
p.		As "h," imperf., tagging omitted		1,250.
q.		As "g," imperf., tagging omitted	2,500.	
r.		"USA/31c" omitted on "d" & "e"	600.00	
s.		As "f," tagging omitted	2,000.	
t.		"USA/31c" omitted on "d"	500.00	
v.		As No. 1689, perfs and tagging inverted	10,000.	
w.		"USA/31c" missing on "a," "b," "c" and "d" (PS)	500.00	
x.		"USA/31c" missing on "e" (CM)	—	
y.		"USA/31c" omitted on "a"	—	
		Nos. 1686-1689 (4)	17.00	

Issued in connection with Interphil 76 International Philatelic Exhibition, Philadelphia, Pa., May 29-June 6. Size of panes: 203x152mm.

Benjamin Franklin

American Bicentennial: Benjamin Franklin (1706-1790), deputy postmaster general for the colonies (1753-1774) and statesman. Design based on marble bust by anonymous Italian sculptor after terra cotta bust by Jean Jacques Caffieri, 1777. Map published by R. Sayer and J. Bennett in London.

Franklin &
Map of
North
America,
1776
A1080

LITHOGRAPHED, ENGRAVED (Giori)

1976, June 1

1690	A1080	13c multicolored	.25	.25
a.		Light blue omitted	150.00	

See Canada No. 691.

American Bicentennial Issue

A1081   A1082

A1083   A1084

Declaration of Independence, by John Trumbull

PHOTOGRAVURE (Andreotti)

1976, July 4

1691	A1081	13c multicolored	.30	.25
1692	A1082	13c multicolored	.30	.25
1693	A1083	13c multicolored	.30	.25
1694	A1084	13c multicolored	.30	.25
a.		Strip of 4, #1691-1694	1.20	1.10

OLYMPIC GAMES ISSUE

12th Winter Olympic Games, Innsbruck, Austria, Feb. 4-15, and 21st Summer Olympic Games, Montreal, Canada, July 17-Aug. 1. Nos. 1695-1696 alternate in one row, Nos. 1697-1698 in other row.

A1076

The Surrender of Lord Cornwallis at Yorktown
From a Painting by John Trumbull

A1077

The Declaration of Independence, 4 July 1776 at Philadelphia
From a Painting by John Trumbull

Washington Crossing the Delaware
From a Painting by Emanuel Leutze/Eastman Johnson

A1078

Washington Reviewing His Ragged Army at Valley Forge
From a Painting by William T. Trego

A1079

Diving — A1085

Skiing — A1086

Running A1087

Skating A1088

1976, July 16

1695	A1085	13c multicolored	.30	.25
1696	A1086	13c multicolored	.30	.25
1697	A1087	13c multicolored	.30	.25
1698	A1088	13c multicolored	.30	.25
a.		Block of 4, #1695-1698	1.20	1.20
b.		As "a," imperf.	375.00	

CLARA MAASS ISSUE

Clara Louise Maass (1876-1901), volunteer in fight against yellow fever, birth centenary.

Clara Maass, Newark German Hospital Pin — A1089

1976, Aug. 18

1699	A1089	13c multicolored	.25	.25
a.		Horiz. pair, imperf. vert.	350.00	
b.		Dark blue missing (PS)	700.00	

On No. 1699, two blue plates were used. No 1699b is missing the dark blue ("She gave her life") at bottom due to an upward shift of the horizontal perforations.

ADOLPH S. OCHS ISSUE

Adolph S. Ochs, Publisher of the NY Times, 1896-1935 A1090

GIORI PRESS PRINTING
1976, Sept. 18

1700	A1090	13c black & gray	.25	.25

CHRISTMAS ISSUE

Nativity, by John Singleton Copley A1091

Winter Pastime, by Nathaniel Currier A1092

PHOTOGRAVURE (Andreotti)
1976, Oct. 27

1701	A1091	13c multicolored	.25	.25
a.		Imperf., pair	85.00	
1702	A1092	13c multi, overall tagging	.25	.25
a.		Imperf., pair	75.00	

COMBINATION PRESS

1703	A1092	13c multicolored	.25	.25
a.		Imperf., pair	75.00	
b.		Vert. pair, imperf. between	275.00	
d.		Red omitted	500.00	
e.		Yellow omitted	675.00	

No. 1702 has overall tagging. Lettering at base is black and usually ½mm below design. As a rule, no "snowflaking" in sky or pond. Pane of 50 has margins on 4 sides with slogans. Plate Nos. 37465-37478.

No. 1703 has block tagging the size of printed area. Lettering at base is gray black and usually ¾mm below design. "Snowflaking" generally in sky and pond. Plate Nos. 37617-37621 or 37634-37638.

Examples of No. 1703 are known with various amounts of red or yellow missing. Nos. 1703d-1703e are stamps with the colors totally omitted. Expertization is recommended.

AMERICAN BICENTENNIAL ISSUE
Washington at Princeton

Washington's Victory over Lord Cornwallis at Princeton, N.J., bicentenary.

Washington, Nassau Hall, Hessians, 13-Star Flag — A1093

1977, Jan. 3

1704	A1093	13c multicolored	.25	.25
a.		Horiz. pair, imperf. vert.	425.00	
b.		Black (inscriptions) missing (PS)	—	

SOUND RECORDING ISSUE

Centenary of the invention of the phonograph by Thomas Alva Edison and development of sophisticated recording industry.

Tin Foil Phonograph A1094

LITHOGRAPHED, ENGRAVED (Giori)
1977, Mar. 23

1705	A1094	13c black & multi	.25	.25

AMERICAN FOLK ART SERIES
Pueblo Pottery

Pueblo art, 1880-1920, from Museums in New Mexico, Arizona and Colorado.

Zia — A1095

San Ildefonso
A1096

Hopi — A1097

Acoma — A1098

PHOTOGRAVURE (Andreotti)
1977, Apr. 13

1706	A1095	13c multicolored	.25	.25
1707	A1096	13c multicolored	.25	.25
1708	A1097	13c multicolored	.25	.25
1709	A1098	13c multicolored	.25	.25
a.		Block or strip of 4, #1706-1709	1.00	1.00
b.		As "a," imperf. vert.	1,100.	

LINDBERGH FLIGHT ISSUE

Charles A. Lindbergh's solo transatlantic flight from New York to Paris, 50th anniversary.

Spirit of St.
Louis
A1099

1977, May 20

1710	A1099	13c multicolored	.25	.25
a.		Imperf., pair	700.00	

COLORADO STATEHOOD ISSUE

Issued to honor Colorado as the "Centennial State." It achieved statehood in 1876.

Columbine & Rocky
Mountains — A1100

1977, May 21

1711	A1100	13c multicolored	.25	.25
a.		Horiz. pair, imperf. between and with natural straight edge at right	650.00	
b.		Horiz. pair, imperf. vertically	500.00	
c.		Perf. 11.2	.75	.25

BUTTERFLY ISSUE

Nos. 1712-1713 alternate in 1st row, Nos. 1714-1715 in 2nd row. This arrangement is repeated throughout the pane. Butterflies represent different geographic US areas.

Swallowtail
A1101

Checkerspot — A1102

Dogface
A1103

Orange Tip
A1104

1977, June 6   Tagged   Perf. 11

1712	A1101	13c tan & multi	.25	.25
1713	A1102	13c tan & multi	.25	.25
1714	A1103	13c tan & multi	.25	.25
1715	A1104	13c tan & multi	.25	.25
a.		Block of 4, #1712-1715	1.00	1.00
b.		As "a," imperf. horiz.	9,500.	

AMERICAN BICENTENNIAL ISSUES
Marquis de Lafayette

200th anniversary of Lafayette's Landing on the coast of South Carolina, north of Charleston.

Marquis de
Lafayette
A1105

GIORI PRESS PRINTING
1977, June 13

1716	A1105	13c blue, black & red	.25	.25
a.		Red missing (PS)	300.00	

Skilled Hands for Independence

Nos. 1717-1718 alternate in 1st row, Nos. 1719-1720 in 2nd row. This arrangement is repeated throughout the pane.

Seamstress
A1106

Blacksmith
A1107

Wheelwright — A1108

Leatherworker — A1109

1977, July 4

1717	A1106	13c multicolored	.25	.25
1718	A1107	13c multicolored	.25	.25
1719	A1108	13c multicolored	.25	.25
1720	A1109	13c multicolored	.25	.25
a.		Block of 4, #1717-1720	1.00	1.00

PEACE BRIDGE ISSUE

50th anniversary of the Peace Bridge, connecting Buffalo (Fort Porter), N.Y. and Fort Erie, Ontario.

Peace
Bridge &
Dove
A1110

ENGRAVED
1977, Aug. 4   Perf. 11x10½

1721	A1110	13c blue	.25	.25

AMERICAN BICENTENNIAL ISSUE
Battle of Oriskany

200th anniv. of the Battle of Oriskany, American Militia led by Brig. Gen. Nicholas Herkimer (1728-77).

Herkimer at
Oriskany,
by Yohn
A1111

PHOTOGRAVURE (Andreotti)
1977, Aug. 6   Perf. 11

1722	A1111	13c multicolored	.25	.25

ENERGY ISSUE

Conservation and development of nation's energy resources. Nos. 1723-1724 se-tenant vertically.

Energy Conservation — A1112

Energy Development — A1113

1977, Oct. 20

1723	A1112	13c multicolored	.25	.25
1724	A1113	13c multicolored	.25	.25
a.		Pair, #1723-1724	.50	.50

ALTA CALIFORNIA ISSUE

Founding of El Pueblo de San José de Guadalupe, first civil settlement in Alta California, 200th anniversary.

Farm
Houses
A1114

LITHOGRAPHED, ENGRAVED (Giori)
1977, Sept. 9   Tagged   Perf. 11

1725	A1114	13c black & multi	.25	.25

AMERICAN BICENTENNIAL ISSUE
Articles of Confederation

200th anniversary of drafting the Articles of Confederation, York Town, Pa.

Members of
Continental
Congress in
Conference
A1115

ENGRAVED (Giori)
1977, Sept. 30

1726	A1115	13c red & brn, cream	.25	.25
b.		Red omitted	500.00	
c.		Red & brown omitted	300.00	

No. 1726b also has most of the brown omitted. No. 1726c must be collected as a transition multiple, certainly with No. 1726b and preferably also with No. 1726.

TALKING PICTURES, 50th ANNIV.

Movie
Projector
and
Phonograph
A1116

LITHOGRAPHED, ENGRAVED (Giori)
1977, Oct. 6

1727	A1116	13c multicolored	.25	.25

AMERICAN BICENTENNIAL ISSUE
Surrender at Saratoga

200th anniversary of Gen. John Burgoyne's surrender at Saratoga.

Surrender
of
Burgoyne,
by John
Trumbull
A1117

PHOTOGRAVURE (Andreotti)
1977, Oct. 7

1728	A1117	13c multicolored	.25	.25

CHRISTMAS ISSUE

Washington at
Valley Forge
A1118

Rural Mailbox
A1119

PHOTOGRAVURE (Combination Press)
1977, Oct. 21

1729	A1118	13c multicolored	.25	.25
a.		Imperf., pair	50.00	

See Combination Press note after No. 1703.

PHOTOGRAVURE (Andreotti)

1730	A1119	13c multicolored	.25	.25
a.		Imperf., pair	175.00	

CARL SANDBURG ISSUE

Carl Sandburg (1878-1967), poet, biographer and collector of American folk songs, birth centenary.

Carl Sandburg, by William A. Smith, 1952 — A1120

GIORI PRESS PRINTING

1978, Jan. 6

1731	A1120	13c black & brown	.25	.25
a.		Brown omitted	1,750.	
c.		All colors omitted	—	

No. 1731c is tagged and has a faint black tagging ghost. Authentication is advised.

CAPTAIN COOK ISSUE

Capt. James Cook, 200th anniversary of his arrival in Hawaii, at Waimea, Kauai, Jan. 20, 1778, and of his anchorage in Cook Inlet, near Anchorage, Alaska, June 1, 1778. Nos. 1732-1733 printed in panes of 50, containing 25 each of Nos. 1732-1733 including 5 No. 1733b.

Capt. Cook, by Nathaniel Dance, 1776 — A1121

"Resolution" and "Discovery," by John Webber — A1122

1978, Jan. 20

1732	A1121	13c dark blue	.25	.25
1733	A1122	13c green	.25	.25
a.		Vert. pair, imperf. horiz.	1,000.	
b.		Pair, #1732-1733	.50	.50
c.		As "b," imperf. between	4,000.	

Indian Head Penny, 1877 A1123

Eagle A1124

Roses — A1126

ENGRAVED (Giori)

1978

| 1734 | A1123 | 13c brown & blue green, *bister*, *Jan. 11*, *1978* | .25 | .25 |
| a. | | Horiz. pair, imperf. vert. | 175.00 | |

PHOTOGRAVURE (Andreotti)

1735	A1124	(15c) orange, *May 22, 1978*	.30	.25
a.		Imperf., pair	70.00	
b.		Vert. pair, imperf. horiz.	500.00	
c.		Perf. 11.2	.35	.25

BOOKLET STAMPS
ENGRAVED

Perf. 11x10½ on 2 or 3 Sides

1736	A1124	(15c) orange	.30	.25
a.		Booklet pane of 8, *May 22, 1978*	2.50	1.50
c.		Vert. pair, imperf. btwn., in #1736a with foldover	1,000.	

Perf. 10 on 2 or 3 Sides

1737	A1126	15c multi	.30	.25
a.		Booklet pane of 8, *July 11, 1978*	2.50	2.00
b.		Imperf, pair	450.00	
c.		As "a," imperf	2,250.	

Robertson Windmill, Williamsburg A1127

Old Windmill, Portsmouth A1128

Cape Cod Windmill, Eastham A1129

Dutch Mill, Batavia A1130

Southwestern Windmill — A1131

BOOKLET STAMPS
ENGRAVED

Perf. 11 on 2 or 3 Sides

1980, Feb. 7

1738	A1127	15c sepia, *yellow*	.30	.25
1739	A1128	15c sepia, *yellow*	.30	.25
1740	A1129	15c sepia, *yellow*	.30	.25
1741	A1130	15c sepia, *yellow*	.30	.25
1742	A1131	15c sepia, *yellow*	.30	.25
a.		Booklet pane of 10, 2 each #1738-1742	3.50	3.00
b.		Strip of 5, #1738-1742	1.50	1.40

COIL STAMP

1978, May 22   *Perf. 10 Vert.*

| 1743 | A1124 | (15c) orange | .30 | .25 |
| a. | | Imperf., pair | 65.00 | |

No. 1743a is valued in the grade of fine.

BLACK HERITAGE SERIES

Harriet Tubman (1820-1913), born a slave, helped more than 300 slaves escape to freedom.

Harriet Tubman (1820-1913), Cart Carrying Slaves — A1133

PHOTOGRAVURE (Andreotti)

1978, Feb. 1   *Perf. 10½x11*

| 1744 | A1133 | 13c multicolored | .25 | .25 |

AMERICAN FOLK ART SERIES
Quilts
Basket Design

A1134

A1135

A1136

A1137

1978, Mar. 8   *Perf. 11*

1745	A1134	13c multicolored	.25	.25
1746	A1135	13c multicolored	.25	.25
1747	A1136	13c multicolored	.25	.25
1748	A1137	13c multicolored	.25	.25
a.		Block of 4, #1745-1748	1.00	1.00

AMERICAN DANCE ISSUE

Ballet A1138

Theater A1139

Folk Dance A1140

Modern Dance A1141

1978, Apr. 26

1749	A1138	13c multicolored	.25	.25
1750	A1139	13c multicolored	.25	.25
1751	A1140	13c multicolored	.25	.25
1752	A1141	13c multicolored	.25	.25
a.		Block of 4, #1749-1752	1.00	1.00

AMERICAN BICENTENNIAL ISSUE

French Alliance, signed in Paris, Feb. 6, 1778 and ratified by Continental Congress, May 4, 1778.

Louis XVI and Franklin, Porcelain Sculpture by C. G. Sauvage A1142

GIORI PRESS PRINTING

1978, May 4

| 1753 | A1142 | 13c blue, black & red | .25 | .25 |
| a. | | Red missing (PS) | — | |

EARLY CANCER DETECTION ISSUE

George Papanicolaou, M.D. (1883-1962), cytologist and developer of Pap Test, early cancer detection in women.

Dr. George Papanicolaou (1883-1962) A1143

ENGRAVED

1978, May 18   *Perf. 10½x11*

| 1754 | A1143 | 13c brown | .25 | .25 |

PERFORMING ARTS SERIES

Jimmie Rodgers (1897-1933), the "Singing Brakeman, Father of Country Music" (No. 1755); George M. Cohan (1878-1942), actor and playwright (No. 1756).

Jimmie Rodgers and Locomotive A1144

George M. Cohan, "Yankee Doodle Dandy" and Stars A1145

PHOTOGRAVURE (Andreotti)

1978   *Perf. 11*

| 1755 | A1144 | 13c multicolored | .25 | .25 |
| 1756 | A1145 | 15c multicolored | .30 | .25 |

CAPEX ISSUE

CAPEX '78, Canadian International Philatelic Exhibition, Toronto, Ont., June 9-18.

Wildlife from Canadian-U.S. Border — A1146

LITHOGRAPHED, ENGRAVED (Giori)

1978, June 10

1757	A1146	Block of 8, multi	2.00	2.00
a.		13c Cardinal	.25	.25
b.		13c Mallard	.25	.25
c.		13c Canada goose	.25	.25

d.	13c Blue jay		.25	.25
e.	13c Moose		.25	.25
f.	13c Chipmunk		.25	.25
g.	13c Red fox		.25	.25
h.	13c Raccoon		.25	.25
i.	As No. 1757, yellow, green, red, brown, blue, black (litho) omitted		6,000.	
j.	Strip of 4 (a-d), imperf. vert.		5,000.	
k.	Strip of 4 (e-h), imperf. vert.		2,000.	
l.	As No. 1757, "d" and "h" with black (engr.) omitted		—	
m.	As No. 1757, "b" with blue missing (PS)		—	
o.	Strip of 4 (e-h), all colors except black missing on "e," "f" and "g," all colors except black and brown missing on "h" (PS)		1,250.	
p.	As No. 1757, yellow, red, brown omitted, pane of 48		—	

No. 1757k is worth more when contained in the block of 8. Value is for strip only.

PHOTOGRAPHY ISSUE

Photography's contribution to communications and understanding.

Photographic Equipment
A1147

PHOTOGRAVURE (Andreotti)

1978, June 26
1758 A1147 15c multicolored .30 .25

VIKING MISSIONS TO MARS ISSUE

Second anniv. of landing of Viking 1 on Mars.

Viking 1 Lander Scooping Up Soil on Mars
A1148

LITHOGRAPHED, ENGRAVED (Giori)

1978, July 20
1759 A1148 15c multicolored .30 .25

WILDLIFE CONSERVATION

Nos. 1760-1761 alternate in one horizontal row. Nos. 1762-1763 in the next.

Great Gray Owl — A1149

Saw-whet Owl — A1150

Barred Owl — A1151

Great Horned Owl — A1152

1978, Aug. 26
1760 A1149 15c multicolored .30 .25
1761 A1150 15c multicolored .30 .25
1762 A1151 15c multicolored .30 .25

1763 A1152 15c multicolored .30 .25
  a. Block of 4, #1760-1763 1.25 1.25
  c. As "a," yellow and orange (litho.) omitted

Two panes of No. 1763c have been reported. On one pane, the black (engr.) is shifted to the left.

AMERICAN TREES ISSUE

Giant Sequoia
A1153

White Pine
A1154

White Oak
A1155

Gray Birch
A1156

PHOTOGRAVURE (Andreotti)

1978, Oct. 9
1764 A1153 15c multicolored .30 .25
1765 A1154 15c multicolored .30 .25
1766 A1155 15c multicolored .30 .25
1767 A1156 15c multicolored .30 .25
  a. Block of 4, #1764-1767 1.25 1.25
  b. As "a," imperf. horiz. 17,500.

No. 1767b is unique.

CHRISTMAS ISSUE

Madonna and Child with Cherubim, by Andrea della Robbia
A1157

Child on Hobby-horse and Christmas Trees
A1158

No. 1768, after terra cotta sculpture in National Gallery, Washington, D.C.

1978, Oct. 18   **Perf. 11**
1768 A1157 15c blue & multi .30 .25
  a. Imperf., pair 70.00

Value for No. 1768a is for an uncreased pair.

1769 A1158 15c red & multi .30 .25
  a. Imperf., pair 75.00
  b. Vert. pair, imperf. horiz. 900.00

ROBERT F. KENNEDY ISSUE

Robert F. Kennedy (1925-68), U.S. Attorney General — A1159

ENGRAVED

1979, Jan. 12
1770 A1159 15c blue .35 .25

BLACK HERITAGE SERIES

Dr. Martin Luther King, Jr. (1929-1968), Civil Rights leader.

Dr. Martin Luther King, Jr. (1929-68), and Civil Rights Marchers — A1160

PHOTOGRAVURE (Andreotti)

1979, Jan. 13
1771 A1160 15c multicolored .40 .25
  a. Imperf., pair 800.00

INTERNATIONAL YEAR OF THE CHILD ISSUE

Children
A1161

ENGRAVED

1979, Feb. 15
1772 A1161 15c orange red .30 .25

LITERARY ARTS SERIES

John Steinbeck — A1162

1979, Feb. 27   **Perf. 10½x11**
1773 A1162 15c dark blue .30 .25

ALBERT EINSTEIN ISSUE

Albert Einstein — A1163

1979, Mar. 4
1774 A1163 15c chocolate .30 .25

AMERICAN FOLK ART SERIES

Pennsylvania Toleware, c. 1800.

Coffeepot
A1164

Tea Caddy — A1165

Sugar Bowl — A1166

Coffeepot
A1167

PHOTOGRAVURE (Andreotti)

1979, Apr. 19   **Perf. 11**
1775 A1164 15c multicolored .30 .25
1776 A1165 15c multicolored .30 .25
1777 A1166 15c multicolored .30 .25
1778 A1167 15c multicolored .30 .25
  a. Block of 4, #1775-1778 1.25 1.25
  b. As "a," imperf. horiz. 2,000.

AMERICAN ARCHITECTURE SERIES

Virginia Rotunda, by Thomas Jefferson
A1168

Baltimore Cathedral, by Benjamin Latrobe — A1169

Boston State House, by Charles Bulfinch
A1170

Philadelphia Exchange, by William Strickland
A1171

ENGRAVED (Giori)

1979, June 4
1779 A1168 15c blk & brick red .30 .25
1780 A1169 15c blk & brick red .30 .25
1781 A1170 15c blk & brick red .30 .25
1782 A1171 15c blk & brick red .30 .25
  a. Block of 4, #1779-1782 1.25 1.25

ENDANGERED FLORA ISSUE

Persistent
Trillium
A1172

Hawaiian Wild
Broadbean
A1173

Contra Costa
Wallflower
A1174

Antioch Dunes
Evening
Primrose
A1175

PHOTOGRAVURE (Andreotti)

1979, June 7

1783	A1172 15c multicolored	.30	.25
1784	A1173 15c multicolored	.30	.25
1785	A1174 15c multicolored	.30	.25
1786	A1175 15c multicolored	.30	.25
a.	Block of 4, #1783-1786	1.25	1.25
b.	As "a," imperf.	200.00	

SEEING EYE DOGS ISSUE

1st guide dog program in the US, 50th anniv.

German Shepherd Leading
Man — A1176

PHOTOGRAVURE (Combination Press)

1979, June 15

1787	A1176 15c multicolored	.30	.25
a.	Imperf., pair	325.00	

SPECIAL OLYMPICS ISSUE

Special Olympics for special children, Brockport, N.Y., Aug. 8-13.

Child Holding
Winner's
Medal — A1177

PHOTOGRAVURE (Andreotti)

1979, Aug. 9

1788	A1177 15c multicolored	.30	.25

JOHN PAUL JONES ISSUE

John Paul Jones (1747-1792), Naval Commander, American Revolution.

John Paul Jones, by
Charles Willson
Peale — A1178

PHOTOGRAVURE (Champlain)

1979, Sept. 23　　　　*Perf. 11x12*

1789	A1178 15c multi	.30	.25
c.	Vert. pair, imperf. horiz.	125.00	

Imperforates on gummed stamp paper, including gutter pairs and blocks, are proofs from the ABNCo. archives. See No. 1789P in Proofs section of the Scott United States Specialized Catalogue.

Perf. 11

1789A	A1178 15c multi	.55	.25
d.	Vertical pair, imperf. horiz.	115.00	

Perf. 12

1789B	A1178 15c multi	3,000.	3,500.

OLYMPIC GAMES ISSUE

22nd Summer Olympic Games, Moscow, July 19-Aug. 3, 1980. Nos. 1791-1792 alternate in one horizontal row, Nos. 1793-1794 in next.

Javelin — A1179

Running
A1180

Swimming
A1181

Rowing
A1182

Equestrian
A1183

PHOTOGRAVURE

1979, Sept. 5　　　　*Perf. 11*

1790	A1179 10c multicolored	.25	.25

1979, Sept. 28

1791	A1180 15c multicolored	.30	.25
1792	A1181 15c multicolored	.30	.25
1793	A1182 15c multicolored	.30	.25
1794	A1183 15c multicolored	.30	.25
a.	Block of 4, #1791-1794	1.25	1.25
b.	As "a," imperf.	900.00	

OLYMPIC GAMES ISSUE

13th Winter Olympic Games, Lake Placid, N.Y., Feb. 12-24. Nos. 1795-1796 alternate in one horizontal row, Nos. 1797-1798 in next.

Speed
Skating
A1184

Downhill
Skiing
A1185

Ski Jump
A1186

Ice Hockey
A1187

1980, Feb. 1　　　　*Perf. 11¼x10½*

1795	A1184 15c multicolored	.35	.25
1796	A1185 15c multicolored	.35	.25
1797	A1186 15c multicolored	.35	.25
1798	A1187 15c multicolored	.35	.25
b.	Block of 4, #1795-1798	1.50	1.40

Perf. 11

1795A	A1184 15c multicolored	1.00	.60
1796A	A1185 15c multicolored	1.00	.60
1797A	A1186 15c multicolored	1.00	.60
1798A	A1187 15c multicolored	1.00	.60
c.	Block of 4, #1795A-1798A	4.00	3.50

CHRISTMAS ISSUE

Virgin and
Child, by
Gerard David
A1188

Santa Claus,
Christmas
Tree
Ornament
A1189

No. 1799 is designed after a painting in National Gallery of Art, Washington, D.C.

PHOTOGRAVURE (Andreotti)

1979, Oct. 18　　　　*Perf. 11*

1799	A1188 15c multicolored	.30	.25
a.	Imperf., pair	70.00	
b.	Vert. pair, imperf. horiz.	450.00	
c.	Vert. pair, imperf. between	950.00	

Perf. 11x10½

1800	A1189 15c multicolored	.30	.25
a.	Green & yellow omitted	400.00	
b.	Green, yellow & tan omitted	400.00	
c.	Vert. se-tenant pair, #1800a & 1800b	850.00	

Nos. 1800a and 1800b always have the remaining colors misaligned.
Nos. 1800a, 1800b and 1800c are valued in the grade of fine.

VALUES FOR HINGED STAMPS AFTER NO. 771
This catalogue does not value unused stamps after No. 771 in hinged condition. Hinged unused stamps from No. 772 to the present are worth considerably less than the values given for unused stamps, which are for never-hinged examples.

PERFORMING ARTS SERIES

Will Rogers (1879-1935), Actor and Humorist — A1190

1979, Nov. 4　　Tagged　　*Perf. 11*

1801	A1190 15c multicolored	.30	.25
a.	Imperf., pair	135.00	

VIETNAM VETERANS ISSUE

A tribute to veterans of the Vietnam War.

Ribbon for
Viet Nam
Service
Medal
A1191

1979, Nov. 11

1802	A1191 15c multicolored	.30	.25

PERFORMING ARTS SERIES

W.C. Fields (1880-1946), actor and comedian.

W.C. Fields (1880-1946), Actor and Comedian — A1192

PHOTOGRAVURE

1980, Jan. 29

1803	A1192 15c multicolored	.30	.25
a.	Imperf., pair		

BLACK HERITAGE SERIES

Benjamin Banneker (1731-1806), astronomer and mathematician.

Benjamin Banneker (1731-1806), Astronomer and Mathematician, Transverse — A1193

1980, Feb. 15

1804	A1193 15c multicolored	.30	.25
a.	Horiz. pair, imperf. vert.	275.00	

Imperfs, including gutter pairs and blocks, exist from printer's waste. These have been fraudulently perforated to simulate No. 1804a. Genuine examples of No. 1804a do not have colors misregistered.

NATIONAL LETTER WRITING WEEK ISSUE

National Letter Writing Week, Feb. 24-Mar. 1. Nos. 1805-1810 are printed vertically se-tenant.

Letters Preserve
Memories
A1194

P.S. Write Soon
A1195

Letters Lift
Spirits
A1196

Letters Shape
Opinions
A1197

1980, Feb. 25
1805 A1194 15c multicolored .30 .25
1806 A1195 15c purple & multi .30 .25
1807 A1196 15c multicolored .30 .25
1808 A1195 15c green & multi .30 .25
1809 A1197 15c multicolored .30 .25
1810 A1195 15c red & multi .30 .25
  a. Vertical strip of 6, #1805-1810 1.85 2.00
  Nos. 1805-1810 (6) 1.80 1.50

AMERICANA TYPE

Weaver
Violins — A1199

COIL STAMPS
1980-81 Engr. Perf. 10 Vertically
1811 A984 1c dk blue, grnish .25 .25
  a. Imperf., pair 60.00
1813 A1199 3.5c pur, yel .25 .25
  a. Untagged (Bureau precanceled, lines only) .25 .25
  b. Imperf., pair 125.00
1816 A997 12c red brown, beige ('81) .25 .25
  a. Untagged (Bureau precanceled), red brown, beige 1.25 1.25
  b. Imperf., pair 135.00
  c. As "a," brownish red, reddish beige 1.25 1.25
  Nos. 1811-1816 (3) .75 .75

A1207

PHOTOGRAVURE
1981, Mar. 15 Tagged Perf. 11x10½
1818 A1207 (18c) violet .35 .25

BOOKLET STAMP
ENGRAVED
Perf. 10 on 2 or 3 Sides
1819 A1207 (18c) violet .40 .25
  a. Booklet pane of 8 3.50 2.25

COIL STAMP
Perf. 10 Vert.
1820 A1207 (18c) violet .40 .25
  a. Imperf., pair 75.00

FRANCES PERKINS ISSUE
Frances Perkins (1882-1965), Secretary of Labor, 1933-1945 (first woman cabinet member).

Frances
Perkins — A1208

ENGRAVED
1980, Apr. 10 Perf. 10½x11
1821 A1208 15c Prussian blue .30 .25

DOLLEY MADISON ISSUE
Dolley Madison (1768-1849), First Lady, 1809-1817.

Dolley Madison — A1209

1980, May 20 Perf. 11
1822 A1209 15c red brown & sepia .30 .25
  a. Red brown missing (PS) 575.00

EMILY BISSELL ISSUE
Emily Bissell (1861-1948), social worker; introduced Christmas seals in United States.

Emily
Bissell — A1210

1980, May 31
1823 A1210 15c black & red .30 .25
  a. Vert. pair, imperf. horiz. 250.00
  b. All colors missing (EP) —
  c. Red missing (FO) —
  d. Red omitted —

On No. 1823d, traces of black are present.

HELEN KELLER ISSUE
Helen Keller (1880-1968), blind and deaf writer and lecturer taught by Anne Sullivan (1867-1936).

Helen Keller and
Anne
Sullivan — A1211

LITHOGRAPHED AND ENGRAVED
1980, June 27
1824 A1211 15c multicolored .30 .25

VETERANS ADMINISTRATION, 50th ANNIV.

Veterans Administration
Emblem — A1212

PHOTOGRAVURE
Plates of 200 subjects in four panes of 50.

1980, July 21
1825 A1212 15c car & vio blue .30 .25
  a. Horiz. pair, imperf. vert. 375.00

BERNARDO DE GALVEZ ISSUE
Gen. Bernardo de Galvez (1746-1786), helped defeat British in Battle of Mobile, 1780.

Gen. Bernardo de
Galvez — A1213

LITHOGRAPHED & ENGRAVED
1980, July 23
1826 A1213 15c multicolored .30 .25
  a. Red, brown & blue (engr.) omitted 550.00
  b. Light yellow, red, blue & brown (litho.) omitted 550.00

CORAL REEFS ISSUE

Brain Coral, Beaugregory Fish A1214

Elkhorn Coral, Porkfish A1215

Chalice Coral, Moorish Idol Fish — A1216

Finger Coral, Sabertooth Blenny Fish — A1217

PHOTOGRAVURE
1980, Aug. 26
1827 A1214 15c multi .30 .25
1828 A1215 15c multi .30 .25
1829 A1216 15c multi .30 .25
1830 A1217 15c multi .30 .25
  a. Block of 4, #1827-1830 1.25 1.10
  b. As "a," imperf. 350.00
  c. As "a," vert. imperf. between 1,750.00
  d. As "a," imperf. vert. 2,750.00

ORGANIZED LABOR ISSUE

American Bald
Eagle — A1218

1980, Sept. 1
1831 A1218 15c multi .30 .25
  a. Imperf., pair 275.00

LITERARY ARTS SERIES
Edith Wharton (1862-1937), novelist.

Edith
Wharton — A1219

ENGRAVED
1980, Sept. 5 Perf. 10½x11
1832 A1219 15c purple .30 .25

EDUCATION ISSUE

"Homage to the Square: Glow," by Josef Albers — A1220

PHOTOGRAVURE
1980, Sept. 12 Perf. 11
1833 A1220 15c multi .30 .25
  a. Horiz. pair, imperf. vert. 150.00

AMERICAN FOLK ART SERIES
Pacific Northwest Indian Masks

Heiltsuk, Bella
Bella
Tribe — A1221

Chilkat Tlingit
Tribe — A1222

Tlingit
Tribe — A1223

Bella Coola
Tribe — A1224

1980, Sept. 25
1834 A1221 15c multi .35 .25
1835 A1222 15c multi .35 .25
1836 A1223 15c multi .35 .25
1837 A1224 15c multi .35 .25
  a. Block of 4, #1834-1837 1.50 1.25

AMERICAN ARCHITECTURE SERIES

Smithsonian Institution, by James Renwick
A1225

Trinity Church, Boston, by Henry Hobson Richardson
A1226

Pennsylvania Academy of Fine Arts, by Frank Furness — A1227

Lyndhurst, Tarrytown, NY, by Alexander Jackson Davis
A1228

ENGRAVED (Giori)

1980, Oct. 9

1838	A1225	15c black & red	.30	.25
a.		Red missing (PS)	—	
1839	A1226	15c black & red	.30	.25
1840	A1227	15c black & red	.30	.25
1841	A1228	15c black & red	.30	.25
a.		Block of 4, #1838-1841	1.25	1.25
b.		As "a," red missing on Nos. 1838, 1839 (PS)	400.00	

CHRISTMAS ISSUE

Madonna and Child
A1229

Wreath, Toys on Windowsill
A1230

Design of No. 1842 after Epiphany Window, Washington Cathedral.

PHOTOGRAVURE

1980, Oct. 31

1842	A1229	15c multi	.30	.25
a.		Imperf., pair	40.00	

PHOTOGRAVURE (Combination Press)

1843	A1230	15c multi	.30	.25
a.		Imperf., pair	45.00	
b.		Buff omitted	22.50	
c.		Vert. pair, imperf. horiz.		
d.		Horiz. pair, imperf. between	3,250.	

No. 1843b is difficult to identify and should have a competent certificate.

GREAT AMERICANS ISSUE

A1231   A1232

A1233

A1235

A1237

A1239

A1241

A1243

A1245

A1247

A1249

A1251

A1234

A1236

A1238

A1240

A1242

A1244

A1246

A1248

A1250

A1252

A1253

A1255

A1254

A1256

ENGRAVED

Perf. 11x10½, 11 (1c, 6c-11c, 14c, No. 1862, 22c, 30c, 39c, 40c, 50c)

1980-85

1844	A1231	1c black ('83)	.25	.25
a.		Imperf., pair	250.00	
b.		Vert. pair, imperf. btwn. and with natural straight edge at bottom	1,000.	
e.		Vert. pair, imperf. horiz.	1,000.	
1845	A1232	2c brn blk ('82)	.25	.25
1846	A1233	3c ol grn ('83)	.25	.25
1847	A1234	4c violet ('83)	.25	.25
1848	A1235	5c henna brn ('83)	.30	.25
1849	A1236	6c org verm ('85)	.25	.25
a.		Vert. pair, imperf. between and with natural straight edge at bottom	1,000.	
1850	A1237	7c brt car ('85)	.25	.25
1851	A1238	8c ol blk ('85)	.25	.25
1852	A1239	9c dk grn ('86)	.25	.25
1853	A1240	10c Prussian bl ('84)	.25	.25
b.		Vert. pair, imperf. between	550.00	
c.		Horiz. pair, imperf. between	1,250.	
d.		Vert. pair, imperf horiz.		

Almost all examples of No. 1853b also have a natural straight edge at bottom. At least one pair has perfs at bottom and partial perfs at top.

Completely imperforate tagged or untagged stamps are from printer's waste. Known unused and used.

1854	A1241	11c dk blue ('85)	.40	.25
1855	A1242	13c lt maroon ('82)	.40	.25
1856	A1243	14c slate grn ('85)	.30	.25
b.		Vert. pair, imperf. horiz.	90.00	
c.		Horiz. pair, imperf. between	8.00	—
d.		Vert. pair, imperf. between	1,060.	—
e.		All color omitted		

No. 1856e comes from a partially printed pane and should be collected as a vertical strip of 10, one stamp normal, one stamp transitional and 8 stamps with color omitted.

1857	A1244	17c green ('81)	.35	.25
1858	A1245	18c dk blue ('81)	.35	.25
1859	A1246	19c brown	.45	.25
1860	A1247	20c claret ('82)	.40	.25
1861	A1248	20c green ('83)	.50	.25
1862	A1249	20c black ('84)	.40	.25
1863	A1250	22c dk chalky bl ('85)	.75	.25
d.		Vert. pair, imperf. horiz.	1,300.	
f.		Horiz. pair, imperf. between	1,300.	
g.		Vert. pair, imperf. between		
1864	A1251	30c ol gray ('84)	.60	.25
b.		Perf. 11.2, overall tagging	3.75	.25
1865	A1252	35c gray ('81)	.75	.25
1866	A1253	37c blue ('82)	.80	.25
1867	A1254	39c rose lilac ('85)	1.00	.25
a.		Vert. pair, imperf. horiz.	350.00	
b.		Vert. pair, imperf. between	1,500.	
1868	A1255	40c dk green ('84)	1.00	.25
1869	A1256	50c brown ('85)	1.00	.25
		Nos. 1844-1869 (26)	12.00	6.50

EVERETT DIRKSEN (1896-1969)

Senate minority leader, 1960-1969.

A1261

ENGRAVED

1981, Jan. 4   **Perf. 11**

1874	A1261	15c gray	.30	.25
a.		All color omitted	500.00	

No. 1874a comes from a partially printed pane and may be collected as a vertical strip of 3 or 5 (1 or 3 stamps normal, one stamp transitional and one stamp with color omitted) or as a pair with one partially printed stamp.

BLACK HERITAGE SERIES

Whitney Moore Young, Jr. (1921-1971), civil rights leader.

A1262

PHOTOGRAVURE

1981, Jan. 30

1875	A1262	15c multi	.35	.25

FLOWER ISSUE

Rose USA 18c
A1263

Camellia USA 18c
A1264

Dahlia USA 18c
A1265

Lily USA 18c
A1266

1981, Apr. 23

1876	A1263	18c multicolored	.35	.25
1877	A1264	18c multicolored	.35	.25
1878	A1265	18c multicolored	.35	.25
1879	A1266	18c multicolored	.35	.25
a.		Block of 4, #1876-1879	1.40	1.25

AMERICAN WILDLIFE

A1267

A1268

A1269

A1270

A1271

A1272

A1273

A1274

A1275

A1276

No. 1880, Bighorn. No. 1881, Puma. No. 1882, Harbor seal. No. 1883, American Buffalo. No. 1884, Brown bear. No. 1885, Polar bear. No. 1886, Elk (wapiti). No. 1887, Moose. No. 1888, White-tailed deer. No. 1889, Pronghorn.

ENGRAVED
1981, May 14

1880	A1267	18c multicolored	.50	.25
1881	A1268	18c multicolored	.50	.25
1882	A1269	18c multicolored	.50	.25
1883	A1270	18c multicolored	.50	.25
1884	A1271	18c multicolored	.50	.25
1885	A1272	18c multicolored	.50	.25
1886	A1273	18c multicolored	.50	.25
1887	A1274	18c multicolored	.50	.25
1888	A1275	18c multicolored	.50	.25
1889	A1276	18c multicolored	.50	.25

a. Booklet pane of 10, #1880-1889   5.00   5.00
Nos. 1880-1889 (10)   5.00   2.50

Nos. 1880-1889 issued in booklet only. All stamps have one or two straight edges. Imperfs are from printer's waste.

FLAG AND ANTHEM ISSUE

A1277

A1278

A1279

A1280

ENGRAVED
1981, Apr. 24   *Perf. 11*

1890	A1277	18c multicolored	.35	.25

a. Imperf., pair   75.00
b. Vert. pair, imperf. horiz.   550.00
c. Vert. pair, imperf. between   550.00

Coil Stamp
Perf. 10 Vert.

1891	A1278	18c multicolored	.35	.25

a. Imperf., pair   17.50   —
b. Pair, imperf. between   1,750.

Beware of pairs offered as No. 1891b that have faint blind perfs.
Vertical pairs and blocks exist from printer's waste.

Booklet Stamps
Perf. 11x10½ on 3 Sides

1892	A1279	6c dark blue & red	.50	.25

Perf. 11x10½ on 2 or 3 Sides

1893	A1280	18c multicolored	.30	.25

a. Booklet pane of 8 (2 #1892, 6 #1893)   3.00   2.50
b. As "a," vert. imperf. between   60.00
c. Se-tenant pair, #1892 & #1893   .90   1.00

Bureau Precanceled Coils
Starting with No. 1895b, Bureau precanceled coil stamps are valued unused as well as used. The coils issued with dull gum may be difficult to distinguish.

When used normally these stamps do not receive any postal markings so that used stamps with an additional postal cancellation of any kind are worth considerably less than the values shown here.

FLAG OVER SUPREME COURT ISSUE

A1281

1981, Dec. 17   *Perf. 11*

1894	A1281	20c blk, dk bl & red	.40	.25

a. Vert. pair, imperf.   30.00
b. Vert. pair, imperf. horiz.   250.00
c. Dark blue omitted   60.00
d. Black omitted   225.00

Coil Stamp
Perf. 10 Vert.

1895	A1281	20c blk, dk bl & red	.40	.25

b. Untagged (Bureau precanceled, lines only)   .50   .50
d. Imperf., pair   8.00
e. Pair, imperf. between   6.00
f. Black omitted   45.00
g. Dark blue omitted   1,000.
h. Black field of stars instead of blue   —

BOOKLET STAMP
Perf. 11x10½ on 2 or 3 Sides

1896	A1281	20c blk, dk bl & red	.40	.25

a. Booklet pane of 6   3.00   2.25
b. Booklet pane of 10, *June 1, 1982*   5.25   3.25
    Scored perforations   7.50   5.00

TRANSPORTATION ISSUE

A1283

A1284

COIL STAMPS ENGRAVED
1981-84   *Perf. 10 Vert.*

1897	A1283	1c violet ('83)	.25	.25

b. Imperf., pair   325.00
    See No. 2225.

1897A	A1284	2c black ('82)	.25	.25

c. Imperf., pair   45.00
    See No. 2226.

A1284a

A1285

1898	A1284a	3c dk grn ('83)	.25	.25
1898A	A1285	4c reddish brn ('82)	.25	.25

b. Untagged (Bureau precanceled, Nonprofit Org.)   .25   .25
c. As "b," imperf., pair   375.00
d. As No. 1898A, imperf. pair   400.00   —
    See No. 2228.

A1286

A1287

1899	A1286	5c gray grn ('83)	.25	.25

a. Imperf., pair   1,500.

1900	A1287	5.2c car ('83)	.25	.25

a. Untagged (Bureau precanceled, lines only)   .25   .25

A1288

A1289

1901	A1288	5.9c blue ('82)	.25	.25

a. Untagged (Bureau precanceled, lines only)   .25   .25
b. As "a," imperf., pair   140.00

1902	A1289	7.4c brown ('84)	.25	.25

a. Untagged (Bureau precanceled, Blk. Rt. CAR-RT SORT)   .25   .25

A1290

A1291

1903	A1290	9.3c car rose	.30	.25

a. Untagged (Bureau precanceled, lines only)   .25   .25
b. As "a," imperf., pair   90.00

1904	A1291	10.9c pur ('82)	.30	.25

a. Untagged (Bureau precanceled, lines only)   .30   .25
b. As "a," imperf., pair   125.00

A1292

A1293

1905	A1292	11c red ('84)	.30	.25

a. Untagged *Sept. 1991*   .25   .25

Untagged stamps from plate 1 come only Bureau precanceled with lines. Untagged stamps from plate 2 come only without precancel lines.

1906	A1293	17c ultra	.35	.25

a. Untagged (Bureau precanceled, Presorted First Class)   .35   .35
b. Imperf., pair   130.00
c. As "a," imperf., pair   400.00

A1294

A1295

1907	A1294	18c dk brn	.35	.25

a. Imperf., pair   95.00

1908	A1295	20c vermilion	.35	.25

a. Imperf., pair   75.00
Nos. 1897-1908 (14)   3.95   3.50

A1296

Booklet Stamp
PHOTOGRAVURE
Perf. 10 Vert. on 1 or 2 Sides
1983, Aug. 12   **Untagged**

1909	A1296	$9.35 multicolored	19.00	15.00

a. Booklet pane of 3   57.50   —

AMERICAN RED CROSS CENTENNIAL

A1297

Plates of 200 subjects in four panes of 50.

1981, May 1   *Perf. 10½x11*

1910	A1297	18c multicolored	.35	.25

SAVINGS & LOAN SESQUICENTENNIAL

A1298

1981, May 8   *Perf. 11*

1911	A1298	18c multicolored	.35	.25

SPACE ACHIEVEMENT ISSUE

A1299

A1302

A1300

A1301

A1303

A1306

A1304

A1305

Designs: A1299, Moon walk. A1300-A1301, A1304-A1305, Columbia space shuttle. A1302, Skylab. A1303, Pioneer 11. A1306, Telescope.

1981, May 21

1912	A1299	18c multicolored	.35	.25
1913	A1300	18c multicolored	.35	.25
1914	A1301	18c multicolored	.35	.25
1915	A1302	18c multicolored	.35	.25
1916	A1303	18c multicolored	.35	.25
1917	A1304	18c multicolored	.35	.25
1918	A1305	18c multicolored	.35	.25
1919	A1306	18c multicolored	.35	.25
a.	Block of 8, #1912-1919		2.80	3.00
b.	As "a," imperf.		5,500.	
c.	As "a," imperf. vert.		2,000.	
e.	As "a," top 4 stamps part perf, bottom 4 stamps imperf		2,700.	

No. 1919c is unique and has blind horiz. perfs.

PROFESSIONAL MANAGEMENT EDUCATION CENTENARY

Joseph Wharton A1307

1981, June 18

1920	A1307	18c blue & black	.35	.25

PRESERVATION OF WILDLIFE HABITATS

A1308   A1309

A1310   A1311

1981, June 26

1921	A1308	18c multicolored	.35	.25
1922	A1309	18c multicolored	.35	.25
1923	A1310	18c multicolored	.35	.25
1924	A1311	18c multicolored	.35	.25
a.	Block of 4, #1921-1924		1.50	1.25

INTERNATIONAL YEAR OF THE DISABLED

Man Looking through Microscope A1312

1981, June 29

1925	A1312	18c multicolored	.35	.25
a.	Vert. pair, imperf. horiz.		1,500.	

EDNA ST. VINCENT MILLAY ISSUE

A1313

LITHOGRAPHED AND ENGRAVED

1981, July 10

1926	A1313	18c multicolored	.35	.25
a.	Black (engr., inscriptions) omitted		200.00	—

ALCOHOLISM

A1314

ENGRAVED

1981, Aug. 19

1927	A1314	18c blue & black	.45	.25
a.	Imperf., pair		325.00	
b.	Vert. pair, imperf. horiz.		2,000.	

AMERICAN ARCHITECTURE SERIES

New York University Library by Sanford White A1315

Biltmore House by Richard Morris Hunt A1316

Palace of the Arts by Bernard Maybeck A1317

National Farmer's Bank by Louis Sullivan A1318

1981, Aug. 28

1928	A1315	18c black & red	.40	.25
1929	A1316	18c black & red	.40	.25
a.	Red missing (PS)			
1930	A1317	18c black & red	.40	.25
b.	Red missing (PS)			
1931	A1318	18c black & red	.40	.25
a.	Block of 4, #1928-1931		1.65	1.65

SPORTS PERSONALITIES

Mildred Didrikson Zaharias A1319

Robert Tyre Jones A1320

1981, Sept. 22   *Perf. 10½x11*

1932	A1319	18c purple	.40	.25
1933	A1320	18c green	.60	.25

FREDERIC REMINGTON

Coming Through the Rye A1321

LITHOGRAPHED AND ENGRAVED

1981, Oct. 9   *Perf. 11*

1934	A1321	18c gray, olive green & brown	.35	.25
a.	Vert. pair, imperf. between		160.00	
b.	Brown omitted		190.00	

JAMES HOBAN

Irish-American Architect of White House — A1322

PHOTOGRAVURE

1981, Oct. 13

1935	A1322	18c multicolored	.35	.25
1936	A1322	20c multicolored	.35	.25

See Ireland No. 504.

AMERICAN BICENTENNIAL

Battle of Yorktown A1323

Battle of Virginia Capes A1324

LITHOGRAPHED AND ENGRAVED

1981, Oct. 16

1937	A1323	18c multicolored	.35	.25
1938	A1324	18c multicolored	.35	.25
a.	Pair, #1937-1938		.90	.75
b.	As "a," black (engr., inscriptions) omitted		275.00	
d.	As "a," black (litho.) omitted			

CHRISTMAS

Madonna and Child, Botticelli — A1325

SEASON'S GREETINGS

Felt Bear on Sled A1326

PHOTOGRAVURE

1981, Oct. 28

1939	A1325	(20c) multi	.40	.25
a.	Imperf., pair		90.00	
b.	Vert. pair, imperf. horiz.		750.00	
1940	A1326	(20c) multi	.40	.25
a.	Imperf., pair		175.00	
b.	Vert. pair, imperf. horiz.		1,750.	

JOHN HANSON

First President of Continental Congress — A1327

1981, Nov. 5

1941	A1327	20c multicolored	.40	.25

DESERT PLANTS

Barrel Cactus — A1328

Agave — A1329

Beavertail Cactus — A1330

Saguaro — A1331

LITHOGRAPHED AND ENGRAVED

1981 Dec. 11

1942	A1328	20c multicolored	.35	.25
1943	A1329	20c multicolored	.35	.25
1944	A1330	20c multicolored	.35	.25
1945	A1331	20c multicolored	.35	.25
a.	Block of 4, #1942-1945		1.50	1.25
b.	As "a," deep brown (litho.) omitted		3,000.	
c.	No. 1945 imperf., vert. pair		3,000.	
d.	As "a," dark green & dark blue (engr.) missing (EP)		—	
e.	As "a," dark green (engr.) missing on left stamp (EP)		—	

A1332   A1333

PHOTOGRAVURE

1981, Oct. 11   **Perf. 11x10½**
1946 A1332 (20c) brown   .40   .25
  b. All color omitted   425.00

No. 1946b comes from a partially printed pane with most stamps normal. It must be collected as a vertical pair or strip with normal or partially printed stamps attached.

ENGRAVED
COIL STAMP
Perf. 10 Vert.
1947 A1332 (20c) brown   .60   .25
  a. Imperf. pair   700.00

BOOKLET STAMPS
Perf. 11 on 2 or 3 Sides
1948 A1333 (20c) brown   .40   .25
  a. Booklet pane of 10   4.50   3.25

A1334

BOOKLET STAMP
ENGRAVED
Perf. 11 on 2 or 3 Sides
1982, Jan. 8
1949 A1334 20c dark blue   .50   .25
  a. Booklet pane of 10   5.00   2.50
  b. As "a," imperf. vert.   90.00
  c. Type II   1.40   .25
  d. Type II, booklet pane of 10   14.00

No. 1949 is 18¾mm wide and has overall tagging. No. 1949c is 18½mm wide and has block tagging.
See No. 1880.

FRANKLIN DELANO ROOSEVELT

A1335

1982, Jan. 30   **Perf. 11**
1950 A1335 20c blue   .40   .25

LOVE ISSUE

A1336

PHOTOGRAVURE
1982, Feb. 1   **Perf. 11¼**
1951   A1336 20c multicolored   .50   .25
  b. Imperf., pair   200.00
  c. Blue omitted   200.00
  d. Yellow omitted   600.00
  e. Purple omitted   —

No. 1951c is valued in the grade of fine.

Perf. 11¼x10½
1951A A1336 20c multicolored   .90   .25

GEORGE WASHINGTON

A1337

1982, Feb. 22   **Perf. 11**
1952 A1337 20c multicolored   .40   .25

STATE BIRDS AND FLOWERS ISSUE

A1338

1982, Apr. 14   **Perf. 10½x11¼**
1953 A1338 20c Alabama   .55   .30
1954 A1339 20c Alaska   .55   .30
1955 A1340 20c Arizona   .55   .30
1956 A1341 20c Arkansas   .55   .30
1957 A1342 20c California   .55   .30
1958 A1343 20c Colorado   .55   .30
1959 A1344 20c Connecticut   .55   .30
1960 A1345 20c Delaware   .55   .30
1961 A1346 20c Florida   .55   .30
1962 A1347 20c Georgia   .55   .30
1963 A1348 20c Hawaii   .55   .30
1964 A1349 20c Idaho   .55   .30
1965 A1350 20c Illinois   .55   .30
1966 A1351 20c Indiana   .55   .30
1967 A1352 20c Iowa   .55   .30
1968 A1353 20c Kansas   .55   .30
1969 A1354 20c Kentucky   .55   .30
1970 A1355 20c Louisiana   .55   .30
1971 A1356 20c Maine   .55   .30
1972 A1357 20c Maryland   .55   .30
1973 A1358 20c Massachu-
    setts   .55   .30
1974 A1359 20c Michigan   .55   .30
1975 A1360 20c Minnesota   .55   .30
1976 A1361 20c Mississippi   .55   .30
1977 A1362 20c Missouri   .55   .30
1978 A1363 20c Montana   .55   .30
1979 A1364 20c Nebraska   .55   .30
1980 A1365 20c Nevada   .55   .30
1981 A1366 20c New Hamp-
    shire   .55   .30
  b. Black missing (EP)   4,000.
1982 A1367 20c New Jersey   .55   .30
1983 A1368 20c New Mexico   .55   .30
1984 A1369 20c New York   .55   .30
1985 A1370 20c North Caroli-
    na   .55   .30
1986 A1371 20c North Dako-
    ta   .55   .30
1987 A1372 20c Ohio   .55   .30
1988 A1373 20c Oklahoma   .55   .30
1989 A1374 20c Oregon   .55   .30
1990 A1375 20c Pennsylvania   .55   .30
1991 A1376 20c Rhode Is-
    land   .55   .30
  b. Black missing (EP)   4,000.
1992 A1377 20c South Caro-
    lina   .55   .30
1993 A1378 20c South Dako-
    ta   .55   .30
1994 A1379 20c Tennessee   .55   .30
1995 A1380 20c Texas   .55   .30
1996 A1381 20c Utah   .55   .30
1997 A1382 20c Vermont   .55   .30
1998 A1383 20c Virginia   .55   .30
1999 A1384 20c Washington   .55   .30
2000 A1385 20c West Virgin-
    ia   .55   .30
2001 A1386 20c Wisconsin   .55   .30
  b. Black missing (EP)   4,000.
2002 A1387 20c Wyoming   .55   .30
  b. A1338-A1387 Pane of
    50, Nos. 1953-2002   27.50   20.00
  d. Pane of 50, imperf.   21,000.

Perf. 11¼x11
1953A A1338 20c Alabama   .60   .30
1954A A1339 20c Alaska   .60   .30
1955A A1340 20c Arizona   .60   .30
1956A A1341 20c Arkansas   .60   .30
1957A A1342 20c California   .60   .30
1958A A1343 20c Colorado   .60   .30
1959A A1344 20c Connecticut   .60   .30
1960A A1345 20c Delaware   .60   .30
1961A A1346 20c Florida   .60   .30
1962A A1347 20c Georgia   .60   .30
1963A A1348 20c Hawaii   .60   .30
1964A A1349 20c Idaho   .60   .30
1965A A1350 20c Illinois   .60   .30
1966A A1351 20c Indiana   .60   .30
1967A A1352 20c Iowa   .60   .30
1968A A1353 20c Kansas   .60   .30
1969A A1354 20c Kentucky   .60   .30
1970A A1355 20c Louisiana   .60   .30
1971A A1356 20c Maine   .60   .30
1972A A1357 20c Maryland   .60   .30
1973A A1358 20c Massachu-
    setts
1974A A1359 20c Michigan   .60   .30
1975A A1360 20c Minnesota   .60   .30
1976A A1361 20c Mississippi   .60   .30
1977A A1362 20c Missouri   .60   .30
1978A A1363 20c Montana   .60   .30
1979A A1364 20c Nebraska   .60   .30
1980A A1365 20c Nevada   .60   .30
1981A A1366 20c New Hamp-
    shire   .60   .30
1982A A1367 20c New Jersey   .60   .30
1983A A1368 20c New Mexico   .60   .30
1984A A1369 20c New York   .60   .30
1985A A1370 20c North Caroli-
    na   .60   .30
1986A A1371 20c North Dako-
    ta   .60   .30
1987A A1372 20c Ohio   .60   .30
1988A A1373 20c Oklahoma   .60   .30
1989A A1374 20c Oregon   .60   .30
1990A A1375 20c Penn-
    sylvania   .60   .30
1991A A1376 20c Rhode Is-
    land   .60   .30
1992A A1377 20c South Caro-
    lina   .60   .30
1993A A1378 20c South Dako-
    ta   .60   .30
1994A A1379 20c Tennessee   .60   .30
1995A A1380 20c Texas   .60   .30
1996A A1381 20c Utah   .60   .30
1997A A1382 20c Vermont   .60   .30
1998A A1383 20c Virginia   .60   .30
1999A A1384 20c Washington   .60   .30
2000A A1385 20c West Virgin-
    ia   .60   .30
2001A A1386 20c Wisconsin   .60   .30
2002A A1387 20c Wyoming   .60   .30
  c. A1338-A1387 Pane of
    50, Nos. 1953A-2002A   30.00   22.50

Nos. 1953-2002 are line perforated. The perforations do not meet perfectly at the corners of each stamp and extend into the narrow selvage margins of an intact pane. Nos. 1953A-2002A are comb perforated. The perforations meet perfectly at the corners of each stamp and do not extend into the narrow selvage margins of an intact pane.

US-NETHERLANDS

200th
Anniv. of
Diplomatic
Recognition
by the
Netherlands
A1388

1982, Apr. 20   **Perf. 11**
2003 A1388 20c multicolored   .40   .25
  a. Imperf., pair   250.00

See Netherlands Nos. 640-641.

LIBRARY OF CONGRESS

A1389

ENGRAVED
1982, Apr. 21
2004 A1389 20c red & black   .40   .25
  a. All color missing   —

No. 2004a must be collected as a right margin horiz. strip of 3, 4 or 5 with one No. 2004a, one transitional stamp and one or more normal stamps.

CONSUMER EDUCATION

A1390

Coil Stamp
1982, Apr. 27   **Perf. 10 Vert.**
2005 A1390 20c sky blue   .55   .25
  a. Imperf., pair   70.00

KNOXVILLE WORLD'S FAIR

A1391

A1392

A1393

A1394

PHOTOGRAVURE
1982, Apr. 29   **Perf. 11**
2006 A1391 20c multicolored   .45   .25
2007 A1392 20c multicolored   .45   .25
2008 A1393 20c multicolored   .45   .25
2009 A1394 20c multicolored   .45   .25
  a. Block of 4, #2006-2009   1.80   1.50

HORATIO ALGER

Frontispiece from
"Ragged
Dick" — A1395

ENGRAVED
1982, Apr. 30
2010 A1395 20c red & black, *tan*   .40   .25
  a. Red and black omitted   —

The Philatelic Foundation has issued a certificate for a pane of 50 with red and black colors omitted. Recognition of this error is by the paper and by a tiny residue of red ink from the tagging roller. The engraved plates did not strike the paper.

AGING TOGETHER

A1396

ENGRAVED
1982, May 21
2011 A1396 20c brown   .40   .25

PERFORMING ARTS SERIES

A1397

PHOTOGRAVURE
1982, June 8
2012 A1397 20c multicolored .40 .25
  a. Black missing (EP) —

John (1882-1942), Ethel (1879-1959), and Lionel (1878-1954) Barrymore, actors.

DR. MARY WALKER

A1398

1982, June 10
2013 A1398 20c multicolored .40 .25

Dr. Mary Walker (1832-1919), 1865 recipient of Medal of Honor.

INTERNATIONAL PEACE GARDEN

A1399

LITHOGRAPHED AND ENGRAVED
1982, June 30
2014 A1399 20c multicolored .45 .25
  a. Black (engr.) omitted 200.00

AMERICA'S LIBRARIES

A1400

ENGRAVED
1982, July 13
2015 A1400 20c red & black .40 .25
  a. Vert. pair, imperf. horiz. 200.00
  c. All colors missing (EP) 175.00

On No. 2015c, an albino impression of the design is present.

BLACK HERITAGE SERIES

Jackie Robinson (1919-72), baseball player.

A1401

PHOTOGRAVURE
1982, Aug. 2   **Perf. 10½x11**
2016 A1401 20c multicolored 1.00 .25

TOURO SYNAGOGUE

A1402

PHOTOGRAVURE AND ENGRAVED
1982, Aug. 22   **Perf. 11**
2017 A1402 20c multicolored .40 .25
  a. Imperf., pair 1,400.

WOLF TRAP FARM PARK

A1403

PHOTOGRAVURE
1982, Sept. 1
2018 A1403 20c multicolored .40 .25

AMERICAN ARCHITECTURE SERIES

Fallingwater, Mill Run, Pa., by Frank Lloyd Wright — A1404

Illinois Institute of Technology by Ludwig Mies van der Rohe A1405

Gropius House, Lincoln, Mass., by Walter Gropius A1406

Dulles Airport, by Eero Saarinen A1407

ENGRAVED
1982, Sept. 30
2019 A1404 20c black & brown .45 .25
  b. Red missing (PS) —
2020 A1405 20c black & brown .45 .25
  a. Red missing (PS) —
2021 A1406 20c black & brown .45 .25
2022 A1407 20c black & brown .45 .25
  a. Block of 4, #2019-2022 2.00 1.75

FRANCIS OF ASSISI

A1408

PHOTOGRAVURE
1982, Oct. 7
2023 A1408 20c multicolored .40 .25

PONCE DE LEON

A1409

PHOTOGRAVURE (Combination press)
1982, Oct. 12
2024 A1409 20c multicolored .40 .25
  a. Imperf., pair 250.00
  b. Vert. pair, imperf. between and at top 500.00

CHRISTMAS ISSUES

A1410

A1411

A1412

A1413

A1414

A1415

PHOTOGRAVURE
1982, Nov. 3
2025 A1410 13c multicolored .25 .25
  a. Imperf., pair 300.00

PHOTOGRAVURE (Combination Press)
1982, Oct. 28
2026 A1411 20c multicolored .40 .25
  a. Imperf. pair 90.00
  b. Horiz. pair, imperf. vert. 900.00
  c. Vert. pair, imperf. horiz. —

PHOTOGRAVURE
2027 A1412 20c multicolored .60 .25
2028 A1413 20c multicolored .60 .25
2029 A1414 20c multicolored .60 .25
2030 A1415 20c multicolored .60 .25
  a. Block of 4, #2027-2030 2.40 1.50
  b. As "a," imperf. 1,250.
  c. As "a," imperf. horiz. 700.00
  Nos. 2025-2030 (6) 3.05 1.50

SCIENCE & INDUSTRY

A1416

LITHOGRAPHED AND ENGRAVED
1983, Jan. 19
2031 A1416 20c multicolored .40 .25
  a. Black (engr.) omitted 750.00

BALLOONS

A1417   A1420

A1418

A1419

PHOTOGRAVURE
1983, Mar. 31 **Tagged** *Perf. 11*
2032 A1417 20c multicolored .50 .25
2033 A1418 20c multicolored .50 .25
2034 A1419 20c multicolored .50 .25
2035 A1420 20c multicolored .50 .25
  a. Block of 4, #2032-2035 2.00 1.50
  b. As "a," imperf. 2,750.
  c. As "a," right stamp perf., otherwise imperf. 2,750.

US-SWEDEN

A1421

ENGRAVED
1983, Mar. 24
2036 A1421 20c blue, blk & red brn .40 .25

See Sweden No. 1453.

CCC, 50th ANNIV.

A1422

PHOTOGRAVURE
1983, Apr. 5
2037 A1422 20c multicolored .40 .25
  a. Imperf., pair 2,250.
  b. Vert. pair, imperf. horiz. —

JOSEPH PRIESTLEY

A1423

1983, Apr. 13
2038 A1423 20c multicolored .40 .25

VOLUNTEERISM

A1424

ENGRAVED (Combination Press)
1983, Apr. 20
2039 A1424 20c red & black .40 .25
a. Imperf., pair 225.00

US-GERMANY

Concord, 1683
A1425

ENGRAVED
1983, Apr. 29
2040 A1425 20c brown .40 .25
See Germany No. 1397.

BROOKLYN BRIDGE

A1426

1983, May 17
2041 A1426 20c blue .40 .25
b. All color missing (EP) 90.00
On No. 2041b, an albino impression of part of the design is evident.

TVA

A1427

PHOTOGRAVURE AND ENGRAVED
(Combination Press)
1983, May 18
2042 A1427 20c multicolored .40 .25

A1428

PHOTOGRAVURE (Combination Press)
1983, May 14
2043 A1428 20c multicolored .40 .25

BLACK HERITAGE SERIES

A1429

PHOTOGRAVURE
1983, June 9
2044 A1429 20c multicolored .50 .25
a. Imperf., pair 300.00

MEDAL OF HONOR

A1430

LITHOGRAPHED AND ENGRAVED
1983, June 7
2045 A1430 20c multicolored .55 .25
a. Red omitted 150.00

GEORGE HERMAN RUTH (1895-1948)

A1431

ENGRAVED
1983, July 6 *Perf. 10½x11*
2046 A1431 20c blue 1.00 .25

LITERARY ARTS SERIES

Nathaniel Hawthorne (1804-1864), novelist.

A1432

PHOTOGRAVURE
1983, July 8 *Perf. 11*
2047 A1432 20c multicolored .40 .25

1984 SUMMER OLYMPICS

Discus
A1433

High Jump
A1434

Archery
A1435

Boxing
A1436

1983, July 28
2048 A1433 13c multicolored .35 .25
2049 A1434 13c multicolored .35 .25
2050 A1435 13c multicolored .35 .25
2051 A1436 13c multicolored .35 .25
a. Block of 4, #2048-2051 1.50 1.25

SIGNING OF TREATY OF PARIS

John Adams, Franklin, John Jay, David Hartley
A1437

1983, Sept. 2
2052 A1437 20c multicolored .40 .25

CIVIL SERVICE

A1438

PHOTOGRAVURE AND ENGRAVED
1983, Sept. 9
2053 A1438 20c buff, blue & red .40 .25

METROPOLITAN OPERA

A1439

LITHOGRAPHED AND ENGRAVED
1983, Sept. 14
2054 A1439 20c yellow & maroon .40 .25

AMERICAN INVENTORS

A1440

A1441

A1442

A1443

LITHOGRAPHED AND ENGRAVED
1983, Sept. 21
2055 A1440 20c multicolored .50 .25
2056 A1441 20c multicolored .50 .25
2057 A1442 20c multicolored .50 .25
2058 A1443 20c multicolored .50 .25
a. Block of 4, #2055-2058 2.00 1.50
b. As "a," black omitted 275.00

STREETCARS

A1444

First American streetcar, New York City, 1832

A1445

Early electric streetcar, Montgomery, Ala., 1886

"Bobtail" horsecar, Sulphur Rock, Ark., 1926
A1446

A1447
St. Charles streetcar, New Orleans, La., 1923

PHOTOGRAVURE AND ENGRAVED
1983, Oct. 8
2059 A1444 20c multicolored .50 .25
2060 A1445 20c multicolored .50 .25
a. Horiz. pair, black (engr.)
missing on Nos. 2059,
2060 (EP) —
2061 A1446 20c multicolored .50 .25
a. Vert. pair, black (engr.)
missing on Nos. 2059,
2061 (EP) —
2062 A1447 20c multicolored .50 .25
a. Block of 4, #2059-2062 2.00 1.50
b. As "a," black (engr.) omitted 250.00
c. As "a," black (engr.) omitted
on #2059, 2061 —

CHRISTMAS

A1448
Raphael, 1483-1983, National Gallery

A1449
Season's Greetings USA 20c

PHOTOGRAVURE
1983, Oct. 28
2063 A1448 20c multicolored .40 .25
2064 A1449 20c multicolored .40 .25
a. Imperf., pair 100.00

MARTIN LUTHER (1483-1546)

Martin Luther (1483-1546), German Religious Leader — A1450

1983, Nov. 11
2065 A1450 20c multicolored .40 .25

ALASKA STATEHOOD, 25th ANNIV.

Caribou and Alaska Pipeline — A1451

1984, Jan. 3
2066 A1451 20c multicolored .40 .25
a. Vert. pair, imperf. horiz. —

14th WINTER OLYMPIC GAMES

Ice Dancing
A1452

Downhill Skiing
A1453

Cross-country
Skiing
A1454

Hockey
A1455

1984, Jan. 6   Perf. 10½x11
2067 A1452 20c multicolored   .55 .25
2068 A1453 20c multicolored   .55 .25
2069 A1454 20c multicolored   .55 .25
2070 A1455 20c multicolored   .55 .25
   a.   Block of 4, #2067-2070   2.20 1.75

FEDERAL DEPOSIT INSURANCE CORPORATION, 50TH ANNIV.

A1456

1984, Jan. 12   Perf. 11
2071 A1456 20c multicolored   .40 .25

LOVE

A1457

PHOTOGRAVURE AND ENGRAVED
(Combination Press)
1984, Jan. 31   Perf. 11x10½
2072 A1457 20c multicolored   .40 .25
   a.   Horiz. pair, imperf. vert.   125.00

BLACK HERITAGE SERIES

Carter G. Woodson (1875-1950), Historian.

A1458

PHOTOGRAVURE
1984, Feb. 1   Perf. 11
2073 A1458 20c multicolored   .40 .25
   a.   Horiz. pair, imperf. vert.   800.00

SOIL & WATER CONSERVATION

A1459

1984, Feb. 6
2074 A1459 20c multicolored   .40 .25

50TH ANNIV. OF CREDIT UNION ACT

Dollar Sign,
Coin — A1460

1984, Feb. 10
2075 A1460 20c multicolored   .40 .25

ORCHIDS

A1461

A1462

A1463

A1464

1984, Mar. 5
2076 A1461 20c multicolored   .50 .25
2077 A1462 20c multicolored   .50 .25
2078 A1463 20c multicolored   .50 .25
2079 A1464 20c multicolored   .50 .25
   a.   Block of 4, #2076-2079   2.00 1.50

HAWAII STATEHOOD, 25th ANNIV.

Eastern Polynesian Canoe, Golden
Plover, Mauna Loa Volcano
A1465

1984, Mar. 12
2080 A1465 20c multicolored   .40 .25

50TH ANNIV., NATIONAL ARCHIVES

Abraham Lincoln,
George Washington
A1466

1984, Apr. 16
2081 A1466 20c multicolored   .40 .25

LOS ANGELES SUMMER OLYMPICS

Diving — A1467

Long
Jump — A1468

Wrestling
A1469

Kayak
A1470

1984, May 4
2082 A1467 20c multicolored   .55 .25
2083 A1468 20c multicolored   .55 .25
2084 A1469 20c multicolored   .55 .25
2085 A1470 20c multicolored   .55 .25
   a.   Block of 4, #2082-2085   2.40 1.90
   b.   As "a," imperf between
     vertically   9,500.

LOUISIANA WORLD EXPOSITION

River
Wildlife
A1471

1984, May 11
2086 A1471 20c multicolored   .50 .25

HEALTH RESEARCH

Lab
Equipment
A1472

1984, May 17
2087 A1472 20c multicolored   .40 .25

PERFORMING ARTS

A1473

PHOTOGRAVURE AND ENGRAVED
(Combination Press)
1984, May 23
2088 A1473 20c multicolored   .40 .25
   b.   Horiz. pair, imperf between   —

JIM THORPE

A1474

ENGRAVED
1984, May 24
2089 A1474 20c dark brown   .60 .25
   a.   All color omitted   —
On No. 2089a, an albino impression of the
design is evident.

PERFORMING ARTS

Tenor John
McCormack (1884-
1945)
A1475

PHOTOGRAVURE
1984, June 6
2090 A1475 20c multicolored   .40 .25
See Ireland No. 594.

ST. LAWRENCE SEAWAY, 25th ANNIV.

Aerial View
of Seaway,
Freighters
A1476

1984, June 26
2091 A1476 20c multicolored   .40 .25

WATERFOWL PRESERVATION ACT, 50TH ANNIV.

"Mallards
Dropping
In," by Jay
N. Darling
A1477

ENGRAVED
1984, July 2   Perf. 11
2092 A1477 20c blue   .50 .25
   a.   Horiz. pair, imperf. vert.   275.00

ROANOKE VOYAGES

The
Elizabeth — A1478

PHOTOGRAVURE
1984, July 13
2093 A1478 20c multicolored   .40 .25

LITERARY ARTS SERIES

Herman Melville
(1819-1891),
Author — A1479

ENGRAVED

1984, Aug. 1
2094 A1479 20c sage green .40 .25

HORACE MOSES (1862-1947), FOUNDER OF JUNIOR ACHIEVEMENT

Junior Achievement
Founder — A1480

ENGRAVED (Combination Press)

1984, Aug. 6
2095 A1480 20c org & dark brn .40 .25

SMOKEY BEAR

Smokey
Bear — A1481

LITHOGRAPHED AND ENGRAVED

1984, Aug. 13
2096 A1481 20c multicolored .40 .25
  a. Horiz. pair, imperf. btwn. 175.00
  b. Vert. pair, imperf. btwn. 150.00
  c. Block of 4, imperf. btwn.
    vert. and horiz. 2,500.
  d. Horiz. pair, imperf. vert. 450.00

ROBERTO CLEMENTE (1934-1972)

Clemente, Puerto
Rican Flag — A1482

PHOTOGRAVURE

1984, Aug. 17
2097 A1482 20c multicolored 1.00 .25
  a. Horiz. pair, imperf. vert. 1,250.

DOGS

Beagle,
Boston
Terrier
A1483

Chesapeake Bay Retriever, Cocker
Spaniel — A1484

Alaskan
Malamute,
Collie
A1485

Black & Tan
Coonhound,
American
Foxhound
A1486

1984, Sept. 7
2098 A1483 20c multicolored .50 .25
2099 A1484 20c multicolored .50 .25
2100 A1485 20c multicolored .50 .25
2101 A1486 20c multicolored .50 .25
  a. Block of 4, #2098-2101 2.00 1.90
  b. As "a," imperf horiz. 5,500.

CRIME PREVENTION

McGruff, The Crime
Dog — A1487

1984, Sept. 26
2102 A1487 20c multicolored .40 .25

HISPANIC AMERICANS

A1488

1984, Oct. 31
2103 A1488 20c multicolored .40 .25
  a. Vert. pair, imperf. horiz. 1,250.

FAMILY UNITY

A1489

PHOTOGRAVURE AND ENGRAVED (Combination Press)

1984, Oct. 1
2104 A1489 20c multicolored .40 .25
  a. Horiz. pair, imperf. vert. 325.00
  c. Vert. pair, imperf. btwn. and
    at bottom —
  d. Horiz. pair, imperf. between 900.00

ELEANOR ROOSEVELT (1884-1962)

A1490

ENGRAVED

1984, Oct. 11
2105 A1490 20c deep blue .40 .25

NATION OF READERS

Lincoln, Son
Tad — A1491

1984, Oct. 16
2106 A1491 20c brown & maroon .40 .25

CHRISTMAS

Madonna and
Child by Fra
Filippo
Lippi — A1492

Santa
Claus — A1493

PHOTOGRAVURE

1984, Oct. 30
2107 A1492 20c multicolored .40 .25
  a. Imperf., pair 1,400.
2108 A1493 20c multicolored .40 .25
  a. Horiz. pair, imperf. vert. 750.00

No. 2108a is valued in the grade of fine.

VIETNAM VETERANS MEMORIAL

Memorial Wall — A1494

ENGRAVED

1984, Nov. 10
2109 A1494 20c multicolored .50 .25

PERFORMING ARTS

Composer Jerome
Kern (1885-1945)
A1495

PHOTOGRAVURE

1985, Jan. 23
2110 A1495 22c multicolored .45 .25

A1496

A1497

PHOTOGRAVURE

1985, Feb. 1 *Perf. 11*
2111 A1496 (22c) green .60 .25
  a. Vert. pair, imperf. 35.00
  b. Vert. pair, imperf. horiz. 750.00

COIL STAMP
Perf. 10 Vert.
2112 A1496 (22c) green .60 .25
  a. Imperf., pair 45.00

BOOKLET STAMP
ENGRAVED
Perf. 11 on 2 or 3 Sides
2113 A1497 (22c) green .70 .25
  a. Booklet pane of 10 7.00 3.00
  b. As "a," Horiz. imperf. btwn. 1,850.

Two examples of No. 2113b are reported,
both in an unexploded booklet.

A1498

Flag over
Capitol
Dome
A1499

ENGRAVED

1985, Mar. 29 *Perf. 11*
2114 A1498 22c blue, red &
    black .45 .25
  a. All color missing (EP) —

No. 2114a should be collected se-tenant
with a normal or a partially printed stamp.

COIL STAMP
Perf. 10 Vert.
2115 A1498 22c blue, red &
    black .45 .25
  c. Inscribed "T" at bottom ('87) .55 .40
  d. Black field of stars instead of
    blue —
  f. Imperf., pair, wide block tag-
    ging 10.00
  g. Imperf., pair, narrow block
    tagging 10.00

BOOKLET STAMP
Perf. 10 Horiz.
2116 A1499 22c blue, red &
    black .50 .25
  a. Booklet pane of 5 2.50 1.25

BOOKLET STAMPS

Frilled
Dogwinkle
A1500

Reticulated
Helmet
A1501

New England
Neptune
A1502

Calico Scallop
A1503

Lightning
Whelk — A1504

ENGRAVED
Perf. 10 on 2 or 3 Sides
1985, Apr. 4

2117	A1500	22c black & brown	.45	.25
2118	A1501	22c black & multi	.45	.25
2119	A1502	22c black & brown	.45	.25
2120	A1503	22c black & violet	.45	.25
2121	A1504	22c black & multi	.45	.25
a.		Booklet pane of 10, 2 ea #2117-2121	4.50	3.00
b.		As "a," violet omitted on both Nos. 2120	400.00	
c.		As "a," vert. imperf. between	350.00	
d.		As "a," imperf.		
e.		Strip of 5, Nos. 2117-2121	2.00	—

Eagle and Half Moon — A1505

TYPE I: washed out, dull appearance most evident in the black of the body of the eagle, and the red in the background between the eagle's shoulder and the moon. "$10.75" appears splotchy or grainy (P# 11111).

TYPE II: brighter, more intense colors most evident in the black on the eagle's body, and red in the background. "$10.75" appears smoother, brighter, and less grainy (P# 22222).

PHOTOGRAVURE
Perf. 10 Vert. on 1 or 2 Sides
1985, Apr. 29   **Untagged**

2122	A1505	$10.75 multi, type I	20.00	7.50
a.		Booklet pane of 3	60.00	
b.		Type II, June 19, 1989	20.00	10.00
c.		As "b," booklet pane of 3	60.00	—

TRANSPORTATION ISSUE

School Bus 1920s 3.4 USA — A1506

Buckboard 1880s USA 4.9 — A1507

Star Route Truck 5.5 USA 1910s — A1508

Tricycle 1880s 6 USA — A1509

Tractor 1920s 7.1 USA — A1510

Ambulance 1860s 8.3 USA — A1511

TowTruck 1920s 8.5 USA — A1512

Oil Wagon 1890s 10.1 USA — A1513

Stutz Bearcat 1933 11 USA — A1514

Stanley Steamer 1909 USA 12 — A1515

Pushcart 1880s 12.5 — A1516

Iceboat 1880s USA 14 — A1517

Dog Sled 1920s 17 USA — A1518

Bread Wagon 1880s 25 USA — A1519

COIL STAMPS
ENGRAVED
1985-89   **Tagged**   **Perf. 10 Vert.**

2123	A1506	3.4c dk bluish green	.25	.25
a.		Untagged (Bureau precancel, Nonprofit Org. CAR-RT SORT)	.25	.25
2124	A1507	4.9c brn blk	.25	.25
a.		Untagged (Bureau precancel, Nonprofit Org.)	.25	.25
2125	A1508	5.5c dp mag ('86)	.25	.25
a.		Untagged (Bureau precancel, Nonprofit Org. CAR-RT SORT)	.25	.25
2126	A1509	6c red brn	.25	.25
a.		Untagged (Bureau precancel, Nonprofit Org.)	.25	.25
b.		As "a," imperf., pair	175.00	
2127	A1510	7.1c lake ('87)	.25	.25
a.		Untagged (Bureau precancel)	.25	.25
c.		As "a," black (precancel) omitted	—	

On. No. 2127c, an albino impression of the precancel is present.

2128	A1511	8.3c green	.25	.25
a.		Untagged (Bureau precancel, Blk. Rt. CAR-RT SORT)	.25	.25

On No. 2231 "Ambulance 1860s" is 18mm long; on No. 2128, 18 ½mm long.

2129	A1512	8.5c dk Prus grn ('87)	.25	.25
a.		Untagged (Bureau precancel, Nonprofit Org.)	.25	.25
2130	A1513	10.1c slate blue	.55	.25
a.		Untagged (Bureau precancel "Bulk Rate Carrier Route Sort" in red) ('88)	.25	.25
b.		As "a," red precancel, imperf. pair	15.00	
		As "a," black precancel, imperf. pair	70.00	
2131	A1514	11c dk green	.25	.25
2132	A1515	12c dk bl, I	.35	.25
a.		Untagged, type I (Bureau precancel, PRESORTED FIRST-CLASS), Apr. 2	.25	.25
b.		Untagged, type II (Bureau precancel, PRESORTED FIRST-CLASS) ('87)	.40	.30

Type II has "Stanley Steamer 1909" ⅛mm shorter (17⅞mm) than No. 2132 (18mm).

2133	A1516	12.5c ol grn	.35	.25
a.		Untagged (Bureau precancel, Bulk Rate)	.25	.25
b.		As "a," imperf., pair	45.00	
2134	A1517	14c sky bl, I	.30	.25
a.		Imperf., pair	75.00	
b.		Type II ('86)	.30	.25
c.		Tagging omitted, type I	35.00	—

Type II design is ¼mm narrower (17 ¼mm) than the original stamp (17 ½mm) and has block tagging. No. 2134 has overall tagging.

2135	A1518	17c brt bl ('86)	.75	.25
a.		Imperf., pair	300.00	
2136	A1519	25c org brn ('86)	.50	.25
a.		Imperf., pair	10.00	
b.		Pair, imperf. between	525.00	
		Nos. 2123-2136 (14)	4.90	3.50

See Nos. 1897-1908, 2225-2231, 2252-2266, 2451-2468.

BLACK HERITAGE SERIES

Mary McLeod Bethune (1875-1955), Educator — A1520

PHOTOGRAVURE
1985, Mar. 5   **Perf. 11**

2137	A1520	22c multicolored	.60	.25

AMERICAN FOLK ART SERIES
Duck Decoys

Broadbill A1521

Mallard A1522

Canvasback — A1523

Redhead A1524

1985, Mar. 22

2138	A1521	22c multicolored	.90	.25
2139	A1522	22c multicolored	.90	.25
2140	A1523	22c multicolored	.90	.25
2141	A1524	22c multicolored	.90	.25
a.		Block of 4, #2138-2141	3.60	2.75

WINTER SPECIAL OLYMPICS

Ice Skater, Emblem, Skier A1525

1985, Mar. 25

2142	A1525	22c multicolored	.50	.25
a.		Vert. pair, imperf. horiz.	300.00	

LOVE

A1526

1985, Apr. 17

2143	A1526	22c multicolored	.45	.25
a.		Imperf., pair	800.00	

RURAL ELECTRIFICATION ADMINISTRATION

Electrified Farm A1527

PHOTOGRAVURE & ENGRAVED
(Combination Press)
1985, May 11

2144	A1527	22c multicolored	.50	.25
a.		Vert. pair, imperf between		

AMERIPEX '86

U.S. No. 134 — A1528

LITHOGRAPHED & ENGRAVED
1985, May 25

2145	A1528	22c multicolored	.45	.25
a.		Red, black & blue (engr.) omitted	110.00	
b.		Red & black omitted	1,250.	
c.		Red omitted	1,750.	
d.		Black missing (PS)	—	

ABIGAIL ADAMS (1744-1818)

Abigail Adams (1744-1818) A1529

PHOTOGRAVURE
1985, June 14

2146	A1529	22c multicolored	.45	.25
a.		Imperf., pair	200.00	

FREDERIC AUGUSTE BARTHOLDI (1834-1904)

Frederic Auguste Bartholdi (1834-1904), Statue of Liberty — A1530

LITHOGRAPHED & ENGRAVED
1985, July 18

2147	A1530	22c multicolored	.45	.25

Examples of No. 2147 exist with most, but not all, of the engraved black omitted.

George Washington, Washington Monument A1532

Envelopes A1533

COIL STAMPS
PHOTOGRAVURE
1985   **Perf. 10 Vertically**

2149	A1532	18c multicolored	.40	.25
a.		Untagged (Bureau precancel)	.35	.35
b.		Imperf., pair	750.00	
c.		As "a," imperf., pair	575.00	
2150	A1533	21.1c multicolored	.40	.25
a.		Untagged (Bureau Precancel)	.40	.40
c.		Imperf., pair		

Precancellations on Nos. 2149a ("PRESORTED FIRST-CLASS") and 2150a ("ZIP+4") do not have lines.

KOREAN WAR VETERANS

American Troops in Korea A1535

ENGRAVED
1985, July 26   **Perf. 11**

2152	A1535	22c gray green & rose red	.45	.25

SOCIAL SECURITY ACT, 50th ANNIV.

Men, Women, Children, Corinthian Columns
A1536

PHOTOGRAVURE

1985, Aug. 14
2153 A1536 22c deep & light blue   .45   .25

WORLD WAR I VETERANS

The Battle of Marne, France, by Harvey Dunn
A1537

ENGRAVED

1985, Aug. 26
2154 A1537 22c gray green & rose red   .45   .25
   a.   Red missing (PS)   300.00

HORSES

Quarter Horse
A1538

Morgan
A1539

Saddlebred
A1540

Appaloosa
A1541

PHOTOGRAVURE

1985, Sept. 25
2155 A1538 22c multicolored   1.10   .25
2156 A1539 22c multicolored   1.10   .25
2157 A1540 22c multicolored   1.10   .25
2158 A1541 22c multicolored   1.10   .25
   a.   Block of 4, #2155-2158   4.40   4.00

PUBLIC EDUCATION IN AMERICA

Quill Pen, Apple, Spectacles, Penmanship Quiz — A1542

1985, Oct. 1
2159 A1542 22c multicolored   .45   .25

INTERNATIONAL YOUTH YEAR

YMCA Youth Camping, Cent.
A1543

Boy Scouts, 75th Anniv.
A1544

Big Brothers/Big Sisters Fed., 40th Anniv. — A1545

Camp Fire, Inc., 75th Anniv.
A1546

1985, Oct. 7
2160 A1543 22c multicolored   .70   .25
2161 A1544 22c multicolored   .70   .25
2162 A1545 22c multicolored   .70   .25
2163 A1546 22c multicolored   .70   .25
   a.   Block of 4, #2160-2163   3.00   2.25

HELP END HUNGER

Youths and the Elderly Suffering from Malnutrition
A1547

PHOTOGRAVURE

1985, Oct. 15
2164 A1547 22c multicolored   .45   .25

CHRISTMAS

Genoa Madonna, Enameled Terra-Cotta by Luca Della Robbia (1400-1482)
A1548

Poinsettia Plants
A1549

1985, Oct. 30
2165 A1548 22c multicolored   .45   .25
   a.   Imperf., pair   55.00
2166 A1549 22c multicolored   .45   .25
   a.   Imperf., pair   50.00

ARKANSAS STATEHOOD, 150th ANNIV.

Old State House, Little Rock
A1550

1986, Jan. 3
2167 A1550 22c multicolored   .65   .25
   a.   Vert. pair, imperf. horiz.   500.00

GREAT AMERICANS ISSUE

A1551

A1552

ENGRAVED
Perf. 11, 11½x11 (#2185), 11.2x11.1 (#2179)

1986-94
2168 A1551 1c brnsh ver   .25   .25
   b.   1c red brown   .30   .30
2169 A1552 2c brt bl ('87)   .25   .25
   a.   Untagged   .40   .25

A1553

A1554

2170 A1553 3c bright blue   .25   .25
   a.   Untagged ('94)   .30   .25
2171 A1554 4c blue violet   .25   .25
   a.   4c grayish violet, untagged   .25   .25
   b.   4c deep grayish blue, untagged   .35   .25
   d.   All color missing (EP)   —

No. 2171d has an albino impression, and it also may be collected with a fully or partially printed stamp.

A1555

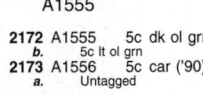

A1556

2172 A1555 5c dk ol grn   .25   .25
   b.   5c lt ol grn   .35   .25
2173 A1556 5c car ('90)   .25   .25
   a.   Untagged   .25   .25

A1557

A1558

2175 A1557 10c lake ('87)   .25   .25
   e.   10c carmine   .80   .25
   f.   All color omitted   125.00

No. 2175f may be collected se-tenant with a partially printed stamp or longer vertical strip. Stamps not se-tenant with a partially printed stamp are identified by a light setoff on the gum side.

2176 A1558 14c crimson ('87)   .30   .25

A1559

A1560

2177 A1559 15c claret ('88)   1.00   .25
   d.   All color omitted   200.00

No. 2177d resulted from partially printed panes. It must be collected se-tenant with a partially printed stamp or in a longer horizontal strip showing error stamps plus partially/completely printed stamps.

2178 A1560 17c dull bl grn   .35   .25

A1561

A1562

2179 A1561 20c red brn ('94)   .40   .25
   a.   20c orange brown   .75   .25
   b.   20c bright red brown   1.25   .25
2180 A1562 21c bl vio ('88)   .45   .25

A1563

A1564

2181 A1563 23c pur ('88)   .45   .25
2182 A1564 25c blue ('88)   .50   .25
   a.   Booklet pane of 10, perf. 11¼, May 3, 1988   5.00   3.75
   d.   Horiz. pair, imperf between   750.00
   e.   As "a," all color omitted on right stamps   1,250.
   f.   As No. 2182 (sheet stamp), vert. pair, bottom stamp all color omitted   —
   h.   As "a," all color omitted on left stamps   1,250.

No. 2182f may be collected se-tenant with a partially printed stamp or longer vertical strip. See Nos. 2197, 2197a.

A1565

A1566

2183 A1565 28c myrtle grn ('89)   .65   .35
2184 A1566 29c blue ('92)   .70   .25

A1567

A1568

2185 A1567 29c indigo ('93)   .65   .25
2186 A1568 35c black ('91)   .75   .25

A1569

A1570

2187 A1569 40c dk bl ('90)   .85   .25
2188 A1570 45c brt bl ('88)   1.00   .25
   a.   45c blue ('90)   2.75   .25

Almost all examples of No. 2188a are in the grade of fine or fine-very fine. Values are for stamps in the grade of fine-very fine.

A1571

A1572

2189 A1571 52c pur ('91)   1.10   .25
2190 A1572 56c scarlet   1.20   .25

A1573

A1574

| 2191 | A1573 | 65c dk bl ('88) | 1.30 | .25 |
| 2192 | A1574 | 75c dp mag ('92) | 1.75 | .25 |

A1575

A1576

| 2193 | A1575 | $1 dk Prus grn | 3.00 | .50 |
| a. | | All color omitted | | |

No. 2193a must be collected se-tenant vertically with partially printed stamps.

2194	A1576	$1 intense dp bl ('89)	2.25	.50
b.		$1 dp bl ('90)	2.50	.50
d.		$1 dk bl ('92)	2.50	.50
e.		$1 blue ('93)	2.75	.60

The intense deep blue of No. 2194 is much deeper than the deep blue and dark blue of the other $1 varieties.

A1577

A1578

2195	A1577	$2 brt violet	4.50	.50
2196	A1578	$5 copper red ('87)	9.00	1.00
		Nos. 2168-2196 (28)	33.90	8.60

Booklet Stamp
Perf. 10 on 2 or 3 Sides

| 2197 | A1564 | 25c blue ('88) | .55 | .25 |
| a. | | Booklet pane of 6 | 3.30 | 2.50 |

Issued: No. 2182, 1/11; No. 2172, 2/27; $2, 3/19; 17c, 6/18; 1c, 6/30; 4c, 7/14; 56c, 9/3; 3c, 9/15; No. 2193, 9/23; 14c, 2/12/87; 2c, 2/28/87; 10c, 8/15/87; $5, 8/25/87; Nos. 2182a, 2197, 5/3/88; 15c, 6/6/88; 45c, 6/17/88; 21c, 10/21/88; 23c, 11/4/88; 65c, 11/5/88; No. 2194, 6/7/89; 28c, 9/14/89; No. 2173, 2/18/90; 40c, 9/6/90; Nos. 2188a, 2194b, 1990; 35c, 4/3/91; 52c, 6/3/91; No. 2173a, 1991; 75c, 2/16/92; No. 2184, 3/9/92; No. 2194d, 1992; No. 2185, 4/13/93; Nos. 2171b, 2194e, 1993; 20c, 10/24/94; Nos. 2170a, 2175e, 1994.

UNITED STATES - SWEDEN STAMP COLLECTING

Handstamped Cover, No. 213, Philatelic Memorabilia — A1581

Boy Examining Stamp Collection A1582

No. 836 Under Magnifying Glass, Sweden Nos. 268, 271 — A1583

1986 Presidents Miniature Sheet on First Day Cover A1584

**BOOKLET STAMPS
LITHOGRAPHED & ENGRAVED**
Perf. 10 Vert. on 1 or 2 Sides
1986, Jan. 23

2198	A1581	22c multicolored	.45	.25
2199	A1582	22c multicolored	.45	.25
2200	A1583	22c multicolored	.45	.25
2201	A1584	22c multicolored	.45	.25
a.		Bklt. pane of 4, #2198-2201	2.00	1.75
b.		As "a," black omitted on Nos. 2198, 2201	50.00	
c.		As "a," blue (litho.) omitted on Nos. 2198-2200	1,500.	
d.		As "a," buff (litho.) omitted	—	

See Sweden Nos. 1585-1588.

LOVE ISSUE

A1585

PHOTOGRAVURE
1986, Jan. 30　　　*Perf. 11*

| 2202 | A1585 | 22c multicolored | .55 | .25 |

BLACK HERITAGE SERIES

Sojourner Truth (c. 1797-1883), Abolitionist — A1586

PHOTOGRAVURE
1986, Feb. 4

| 2203 | A1586 | 22c multicolored | .55 | .25 |

REPUBLIC OF TEXAS, 150th ANNIV.

San Jacinto, 1836, Texas State Flag and Silver Spur — A1587

1986, Mar. 2

2204	A1587	22c dk bl, dk red & grayish blk	.50	.25
a.		Horiz. pair, imperf. vert.	600.00	
b.		Dark red omitted	1,750.	
c.		Dark blue omitted	5,000.	

FISH

Muskellunge — A1588

Atlantic Cod A1589

Largemouth Bass — A1590

Bluefin Tuna A1591

Catfish A1592

**BOOKLET STAMPS
PHOTOGRAVURE**
Perf. 10 Horiz. on 1 or 2 Sides
1986, Mar. 21

2205	A1588	22c multicolored	1.00	.25
2206	A1589	22c multicolored	1.00	.25
2207	A1590	22c multicolored	1.00	.25
2208	A1591	22c multicolored	1.00	.25
2209	A1592	22c multicolored	1.00	.25
a.		Bklt. pane of 5, #2205-2209	5.00	2.75

The magenta used to print this issue is extremely fugitive. Dangerous fakes purported to be magenta omitted exist. No genuine examples are known. Panes apparently lacking red must be certified, and examples presently with certificates should be recertified.

PUBLIC HOSPITALS

A1593

1986, Apr. 11　　　*Perf. 11*

2210	A1593	22c multicolored	.45	.25
a.		Vert. pair, imperf. horiz.	250.00	
b.		Horiz. pair, imperf. vert.	800.00	

PERFORMING ARTS

Edward Kennedy "Duke" Ellington (1899-1974), Jazz Composer — A1594

1986, Apr. 29

| 2211 | A1594 | 22c multicolored | .45 | .25 |
| a. | | Vert. pair, imperf. horiz. | 500.00 | |

AMERIPEX '86 ISSUE
Miniature Sheets

35 Presidents — A1599a

No. 2216: a, George Washington. b, John Adams. c, Thomas Jefferson. d, James Madison. e, James Monroe. f, John Quincy Adams. g, Andrew Jackson. h, Martin Van Buren. i, William H. Harrison.

No. 2217: a, John Tyler. b, James Knox Polk. c, Zachary Taylor. d, Millard Fillmore. e, Franklin Pierce. f, James Buchanan. g, Abraham Lincoln. h, Andrew Johnson. i, Ulysses S. Grant.

No. 2218: a, Rutherford B. Hayes. b, James A. Garfield. c, Chester A. Arthur. d, Grover Cleveland. e, Benjamin Harrison. f, William McKinley. g, Theodore Roosevelt. h, William H. Taft. i, Woodrow Wilson.

No. 2219: a, Warren G. Harding. b, Calvin Coolidge. c, Herbert Hoover. d, Franklin Delano Roosevelt. e, White House. f, Harry S. Truman. g, Dwight D. Eisenhower. h, John F. Kennedy. i, Lyndon B. Johnson.

LITHOGRAPHED & ENGRAVED
1986, May 22

2216	A1599a	Pane of 9	6.50	4.00
a.-i.		22c, any single	.65	.40
j.		Blue (engr.) omitted	1,800.	
k.		Black inscription omitted	1,000.	
l.		Imperf.	10,500.	
m.		As "k," double impression of red	1,700.	
n.		Blue omitted on b-c, e-f, i	—	
q.		Double impression of red	600.00	
2217	A1599b	Pane of 9	6.50	4.00
a.-i.		22c, any single	.65	.40
j.		Black inscription omitted	1,500.	
2218	A1599c	Pane of 9	6.50	4.00
a.-i.		22c, any single	.65	.40
j.		Brown (engr.) omitted		
k.		Black inscription omitted	1,500.	
2219	A1599d	Pane of 9	6.50	4.00
a.-i.		22c, any single	.65	.40
j.		Blackish blue (engr.) inscription omitted on a-b, d-e, g-h	2,250.	
l.		Blackish blue (engr.) omitted on all stamps		
		Nos. 2216-2219 (4)	26.00	16.00

Issued in conjunction with AMERIPEX '86 Intl. Philatelic Exhibition, Chicago, IL May 22-June 1.

ARCTIC EXPLORERS

Elisha Kent Kane A1600

Adolphus W. Greely A1601

Vilhjalmur Stefansson A1602

Robert E. Peary and Matthew Alexander Henson A1603

PHOTOGRAVURE

1986, May 28

2220	A1600	22c multicolored	.65	.25
2221	A1601	22c multicolored	.65	.25
2222	A1602	22c multicolored	.65	.25
2223	A1603	22c multicolored	.65	.25
a.		Block of 4, #2220-2223	2.75	2.25
b.		As "a," black omitted	3,500.	
c.		As "a," Nos. 2220, 2221 black omitted	1,000.	
d.		As "a," Nos. 2222, 2223 black omitted	1,000.	

STATUE OF LIBERTY, 100th ANNIVERSARY

Statue of Liberty, Cent. — A1604

ENGRAVED

1986, July 4

2224	A1604	22c scar & dk bl	.45	.25
a.		Scarlet omitted	—	

On No. 2224a, virtually all of the dark blue also is omitted, so the error stamp should be collected as part of a transition strip. See France No. 2014.

TRANSPORTATION ISSUE
Types of 1982-85 and

A1604a   A1604b

COIL STAMPS
ENGRAVED

1986-90   **Perf. 10 Vert.**

2225	A1604a	1c violet	.25	.25
b.		Untagged	.25	.25
c.		Imperf., pair	1,500.	
2226	A1604b	2c black	.25	.25
a.		Untagged	.25	

REDUCED SIZE

2228	A1285	4c reddish brown	.25	.25
b.		Imperf., pair	175.00	

Untagged

2231	A1511	8.3c green (Bureau precancel)	.65	.25
	Nos. 2225-2231 (4)		1.40	1.00

Issued: 1c, 11/26; 2c, 3/6/87. Earliest known usage of 4c, 8/15/86; 8.3c, 8/29.
On No. 2228 "Stagecoach 1890s" is 17¾mm long, on No. 1898A, 19½mm long. On No. 2231 "Ambulance 1860s" is 18mm long, on No. 2128, 18½mm long.
No. 2226 inscribed "2 USA"; No. 1897A inscribed "USA 2c".

AMERICAN FOLK ART SERIES
Navajo Art

Navajo Art USA 22   Navajo Art USA 22

A1605   A1606

Navajo Art USA 22   Navajo Art USA 22

A1607   A1608

LITHOGRAPHED & ENGRAVED

1986, Sept. 4   **Perf. 11**

2235	A1605	22c multicolored	.80	.25
a.		Black (engr.) omitted	65.00	
2236	A1606	22c multicolored	.80	.25
a.		Black (engr.) omitted	65.00	
2237	A1607	22c multicolored	.80	.25
a.		Black (engr.) omitted	65.00	
2238	A1608	22c multicolored	.80	.25
a.		Black (engr.) omitted	65.00	
b.		Block of 4, #2235-2238	3.25	2.25
c.		As "b," black (engr.) omitted	275.00	

LITERARY ARTS SERIES

T. S. Eliot (1888-1965), Poet — A1609

ENGRAVED

1986, Sept. 26

2239	A1609	22c copper red	.45	.25

AMERICAN FOLK ART SERIES
Woodcarved Figurines

Highlander Figure A1610   Ship Figurehead A1611

Nautical Figure — A1612   Cigar Store Figure — A1613

PHOTOGRAVURE

1986, Oct. 1

2240	A1610	22c multicolored	.50	.25
2241	A1611	22c multicolored	.50	.25
2242	A1612	22c multicolored	.50	.25
2243	A1613	22c multicolored	.50	.25
a.		Block of 4, #2240-2243	2.00	1.50
b.		As "a," imperf. vert.	750.00	

CHRISTMAS

Madonna, by Perugino (c. 1450-1523) A1614   Village Scene A1615

1986, Oct. 24

2244	A1614	22c multicolored	.45	.25
a.		Imperf., pair	400.00	
2245	A1615	22c multicolored	.45	.25

MICHIGAN STATEHOOD, 150th ANNIV.

White Pine — A1616

1987, Jan. 26

2246	A1616	22c multicolored	.50	.25

PAN AMERICAN GAMES

Runner in Full Stride A1617

1987, Jan. 29

2247	A1617	22c multicolored	.45	.25
a.		Silver omitted	550.00	

No. 2247a is valued in the grade of fine.

LOVE ISSUE

A1618

PHOTOGRAVURE

1987, Jan. 30   **Perf. 11½x11**

2248	A1618	22c multicolored	.45	.25

BLACK HERITAGE SERIES

Jean Baptiste Pointe du Sable (c. 1750-1818), Pioneer Trader, Founder of Chicago — A1619

1987, Feb. 20   **Perf. 11**

2249	A1619	22c multicolored	.40	.25

PERFORMING ARTS SERIES

Enrico Caruso (1873-1921), Opera Tenor — A1620

PHOTOGRAVURE

1987, Feb. 27

2250	A1620	22c multicolored	.45	.25
a.		Black omitted	3,500.	

GIRL SCOUTS, 75TH ANNIVERSARY

Fourteen Achievement Badges — A1621

LITHOGRAPHED & ENGRAVED

1987, Mar. 12

2251	A1621	22c multicolored	.45	.25
a.		All litho. colors omitted	1,600.	
b.		Red & black (engr.) omitted	1,500.	

All known examples of No. 2251a have been expertized and certificate must accompany purchase. The unique pane of No. 2251b has been expertized and a certificate exists for the pane of 50.

TRANSPORTATION ISSUE

A1622   A1623

A1624   A1625

A1626   A1627

A1628   A1629

A1630   A1631

A1632   A1633

A1634   A1635

Tandem Bicycle 1890s 24.1 USA ZIP+4

A1636

COIL STAMPS
ENGRAVED

1987-88   **Perf. 10 Vert.**

2252	A1622	3c claret ('88)	.25	.25
a.		Untagged	.25	.25
b.		As "a," imperf. pair	1,350.	
2253	A1623	5c black	.25	.25
2254	A1624	5.3c black (Bureau precancel in red), untagged ('88)	.25	.25
2255	A1625	7.6c brown (Bureau precancel in red), untagged ('88)	.25	.25
2256	A1626	8.4c dp clar (Bureau precancel in red), untagged ('88)	.25	.25
a.		Imperf., pair	350.00	
2257	A1627	10c blue	.40	.25
e.		Imperf. pair	1,000.	
2258	A1628	13c black (Bureau precancel in red), untagged ('88)	.65	.25
2259	A1629	13.2c slate grn (Bureau precancel in red), untagged ('88)	.25	.25
a.		Imperf., pair	75.00	
2260	A1630	15c violet ('88)	.30	.25
c.		As "a," imperf. pair	500.00	
2261	A1631	16.7c rose (Bureau precancel in black), untagged ('88)	.30	.30
a.		Imperf., pair	125.00	

All known examples of No. 2261a are miscut top to bottom.

2262	A1632	17.5c dk vio	.75	.25
a.		Untagged (Bureau precancel in red)	.65	.30
b.		Imperf., pair	1,000.	
2263	A1633	20c blue vio ('88)	.35	.25
a.		Imperf., pair	50.00	
2264	A1634	20.5c rose (Bureau precancel in black), untagged ('88)	.75	.40
2265	A1635	21c olive grn (Bureau precancel in red), untagged ('88)	.50	.40
a.		Imperf., pair	35.00	
2266	A1636	24.1c deep ultra (Bureau precancel in red), untagged ('88)	.80	.45
		Nos. 2252-2266 (15)	6.30	4.30

5.3c, 7.6c, 8.4c, 13.2c, 16.7c, 20.5c, 21c and 24.1c only available precanceled.
See Nos. 1897-1908, 2123-2136, 2225-2231, 2451-2468.

SPECIAL OCCASIONS

Congratulations! 22 USA

A1637

Get Well!

A1638

Thank You!

A1639

Love You, Dad! USA 22

A1640

Best Wishes! USA 22   Happy Birthday! USA 22

A1641   A1642

Love You, Mother! USA 22

A1643

Keep In Touch! USA 22

A1644

BOOKLET STAMPS
PHOTOGRAVURE
Perf. 10 on 1, 2 or 3 Sides

1987, Apr. 20

2267	A1637	22c multicolored	.75	.25
2268	A1638	22c multicolored	.90	.25
2269	A1639	22c multicolored	.90	.25
2270	A1640	22c multicolored	.90	.25
2271	A1641	22c multicolored	.90	.25
2272	A1642	22c multicolored	.75	.25
2273	A1643	22c multicolored	1.50	.25
2274	A1644	22c multicolored	.90	.25
a.		Bkt. pane of 10 (#2268-2271, 2273-2274, 2 each #2267, 2272)	9.00	5.00
		Nos. 2267-2274 (8)	7.50	2.00

UNITED WAY, 100th ANNIV.

United Way 1887-1987

Six Profiles Uniting Communities USA 22
A1645

LITHOGRAPHED & ENGRAVED
1987, Apr. 28   **Perf. 11**

2275	A1645	22c multicolored	.45	.25

22 USA

A1646

E Earth Domestic USA

A1647

USA 25

A1648

Yosemite USA 25

A1649

---

25 USA

Pheasant
A1649a

25 USA

Grosbeak
A1649b

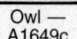

25 USA

Owl —
A1649c

25 USA

Honeybee
A1649d

Photo., Engr. (No. 2280). Litho. & Engr. (No. 2281)

1987-88   **Perf. 11**

2276	A1646	22c multi	.45	.25
a.		Booklet pane of 20, Nov. 30	9.00	—
b.		As "a," vert. pair, imperf. btwn.	1,450.	
c.		As "a," miscut and inserted upside down into booklet cover, imperf between stamps and right selvage	—	
d.		Yellow omitted	—	

All documented examples of No. 2276d show significant misregistration of the red ink.

2277	A1647	(25c) multi	.50	.25
2278	A1648	25c multi ('88)	.50	.25
		Nos. 2276-2278 (3)	1.45	.75

COIL STAMPS
Perf. 10 Vert.

2279	A1647	(25c) multi ('88)	.50	.25
a.		Imperf., pair	60.00	—
2280	A1649	25c multi ('88)	.50	.25
c.		Imperf. pair	10.00	
e.		Black trees	90.00	—
f.		Pair, imperf. between	375.00	
2281	A1649d	25c multi ('88)	.50	.25
a.		As No. 2281, imperf. pair	45.00	
c.		Black (litho. - "25 USA") omitted	500.00	
d.		Pair, imperf. between	600.00	
e.		Yellow (litho.) omitted	700.00	
		Nos. 2279-2281 (3)	1.50	.75

Beware of stamps with traces of the litho. black that are offered as No. 2281c.
Vertical pairs or blocks of No. 2281 and imperfs. with the engr. black missing are from printer's waste.

BOOKLET STAMPS
PHOTOGRAVURE
Perf. 10 on 2 or 3 Sides

2282	A1647	(25c) multi ('88)	.50	.25
a.		Booklet pane of 10	6.50	3.50

Perf. 11 on 2 or 3 Sides

2283	A1649a	25c multi ('88)	.50	.25
a.		Booklet pane of 10	6.00	3.50
b.		25c multicolored, red removed from sky	4.50	.25
c.		As "b," bkt. pane of 10	45.00	
d.		Vert. pair, imperf. btwn.	275.00	

Imperf. panes exist from printers waste, and a large number exist. No. 2283d resulted from a foldover. Non-foldover pairs and multiples are printer's waste.

Perf. 10 on 2 or 3 Sides

2284	A1649b	25c multi ('88)	.50	.25
2285	A1649c	25c multi ('88)	.50	.25
b.		Bkt. pane of 10, 5 each #2284-2285	5.00	3.50
d.		Pair, Nos. 2284-2285	1.10	.50
2285A	A1648	25c multi ('88)	.50	.25
c.		Booklet pane of 6	3.00	2.00
		Nos. 2282-2285A (5)	2.50	1.25

Issued: #2276, 5/9; #2277, 2279, 2282, 3/22; #2278, 5/6; #2280, 5/20; #2281, 9/2; #2283, 4/29; #2284-2285, 5/28; #2285A, 7/5.

NORTH AMERICAN WILDLIFE

22 USA Barn Swallow

North American Wildlife — A1650

PHOTOGRAVURE
1987, June 13   **Perf. 11**

2286	A1650	22c Barn swallow	1.00	.50
2287	A1651	22c Monarch butterfly	1.00	.50
2288	A1652	22c Bighorn sheep	1.00	.50
2289	A1653	22c Broad-tailed hummingbird	1.00	.50
2290	A1654	22c Cottontail	1.00	.50
2291	A1655	22c Osprey	1.00	.50
2292	A1656	22c Mountain lion	1.00	.50
2293	A1657	22c Luna moth	1.00	.50
2294	A1658	22c Mule deer	1.00	.50
2295	A1659	22c Gray squirrel	1.00	.50
2296	A1660	22c Armadillo	1.00	.50
2297	A1661	22c Eastern chipmunk	1.00	.50
2298	A1662	22c Moose	1.00	.50
2299	A1663	22c Black bear	1.00	.50
2300	A1664	22c Tiger swallowtail	1.00	.50
2301	A1665	22c Bobwhite	1.00	.50
2302	A1666	22c Ringtail	1.00	.50
2303	A1667	22c Red-winged blackbird	1.00	.50
2304	A1668	22c American lobster	1.00	.50
2305	A1669	22c Black-tailed jack rabbit	1.00	.50
2306	A1670	22c Scarlet tanager	1.00	.50
2307	A1671	22c Woodchuck	1.00	.50
2308	A1672	22c Roseate spoonbill	1.00	.50
2309	A1673	22c Bald eagle	1.00	.50
2310	A1674	22c Alaskan brown bear	1.00	.50
2311	A1675	22c Iiwi	1.00	.50
2312	A1676	22c Badger	1.00	.50
2313	A1677	22c Pronghorn	1.00	.50
2314	A1678	22c River otter	1.00	.50
2315	A1679	22c Ladybug	1.00	.50
2316	A1680	22c Beaver	1.00	.50
2317	A1681	22c White-tailed deer	1.00	.50
2318	A1682	22c Blue jay	1.00	.50
2319	A1683	22c Pika	1.00	.50
2320	A1684	22c Bison	1.00	.50
2321	A1685	22c Snowy egret	1.00	.50
2322	A1686	22c Gray wolf	1.00	.50
2323	A1687	22c Mountain goat	1.00	.50
2324	A1688	22c Deer mouse	1.00	.50
2325	A1689	22c Black-tailed prairie dog	1.00	.50
2326	A1690	22c Box turtle	1.00	.50
2327	A1691	22c Wolverine	1.00	.50
2328	A1692	22c American elk	1.00	.50
2329	A1693	22c California sea lion	1.00	.50
2330	A1694	22c Mockingbird	1.00	.50
2331	A1695	22c Raccoon	1.00	.50
2332	A1696	22c Bobcat	1.00	.50
2333	A1697	22c Black-footed ferret	1.00	.50
2334	A1698	22c Canada goose	1.00	.50
2335	A1699	22c Red fox	1.00	.50
a.		Pane of 50, #2286-2335	50.00	35.00
2286b-2335b		Any single, red omitted	2,000.	

RATIFICATION OF THE CONSTITUTION BICENTENNIAL

Dec 7, 1787 USA Delaware 22

A1700

22 USA Dec 12, 1787 Pennsylvania

A1701

Dec 18,1787 USA
New Jersey 22
A1702

January 2, 1788
Georgia 22
A1703

January 9,1788
Connecticut 22
A1704

Feb 6,1788
Massachusetts 22
A1705

April 28,1788 USA
Maryland 22
A1706

May 23,1788
South Carolina 25
A1707

June 21,1788
New Hampshire 25
A1708

June 25,1788 USA
Virginia 25
A1709

July 26, 1788 USA
New York 25
A1710

November 21,1789
North Carolina 25
A1711

May 29, 1790
Rhode Island 25
A1712

LITHOGRAPHED & ENGRAVED, PHOTOGRAVURE (#2337-2339, 2343-2344, 2347), ENGRAVED (#2341).

1987-90

2336	A1700	22c multi	.55	.25
2337	A1701	22c multi	.55	.25
2338	A1702	22c multi	.55	.25
a.	Black (engr.) omitted		2,750.	
2339	A1703	22c multi	.55	.25
2340	A1704	22c multi	.55	.25
2341	A1705	22c dk bl & dk red	.55	.25
2342	A1706	22c multi	.55	.25
2343	A1707	25c multi	.55	.25
a.	Strip of 3, vert. imperf btwn.		12,500.	
b.	Red missing (PS)			
2344	A1708	25c multi	.55	.25
2345	A1709	25c multi	.55	.25
2346	A1710	25c multi	.55	.25
2347	A1711	25c multi	.55	.25
2348	A1712	25c multi	.55	.25
	Nos. 2336-2348 (13)		7.15	3.25

No. 2343b resulted either from a shifting of all colors or from a shift of both the perforations and the cutting of the pane.

Issued: No. 2336, 7/4; No. 2337, 8/26; No. 2338, 9/11; No. 2339, 1/6/88; No. 2340, 1/9/88; No. 2341, 2/6/88; No. 2342, 2/15/88; No. 2343, 5/23/88; No. 2344, 6/21/88; No. 2345, 6/25/88; No. 2346, 7/26/88; No. 2347, 8/22/89; No. 2348, 5/29/90.

US-MOROCCO DIPLOMATIC RELATIONS, 200th ANNIV.

Arabesque, Dar Batha Palace, Fez — A1713

LITHOGRAPHED & ENGRAVED
1987, July 17

2349	A1713	22c scar & blk	.50	.25
a.	Black (engr.) omitted		180.00	

See Morocco No. 642.

LITERARY ARTS SERIES

William Cuthbert Faulkner (1897-1962), Novelist — A1714

ENGRAVED
1987, Aug. 3

2350	A1714	22c bright green	.50	.25

Used untagged imperfs exist from printer's waste.

AMERICAN FOLK ART SERIES
Lacemaking

Lacemaking USA 22 — A1715

Lacemaking USA 22 — A1716

Lacemaking USA 22 — A1717

Lacemaking USA 22 — A1718

LITHOGRAPHED & ENGRAVED
1987, Aug. 14

2351	A1715	22c ultra & white	.45	.25
2352	A1716	22c ultra & white	.45	.25
2353	A1717	22c ultra & white	.45	.25
2354	A1718	22c ultra & white	.45	.25
a.	Block of 4, #2351-2354		1.90	1.90
b.	As "a," white omitted		350.00	
c.	Any single stamp, white omitted		90.00	

DRAFTING OF THE CONSTITUTION BICENTENNIAL
Excerpts from the Preamble

A1719

A1720

A1721

A1722

A1723

BOOKLET STAMPS PHOTOGRAVURE
Perf. 10 Horiz. on 1 or 2 Sides
1987, Aug. 28

2355	A1719	22c multicolored	.75	.25
a.	Grayish green (background) omitted		400.00	
2356	A1720	22c multicolored	.75	.25
a.	Grayish green (background) omitted		400.00	
2357	A1721	22c multicolored	.75	.25
a.	Grayish green (background) omitted		400.00	
2358	A1722	22c multicolored	.75	.25
a.	Grayish green (background) omitted		400.00	
2359	A1723	22c multicolored	.75	.25
a.	Bklt. pane of 5, #2355-2359		3.75	2.25
b.	Grayish green (background) omitted		400.00	

SIGNING OF THE CONSTITUTION

A1724

LITHOGRAPHED & ENGRAVED
1987, Sept. 17 — Perf. 11

2360	A1724	22c multicolored	.55	.25

CERTIFIED PUBLIC ACCOUNTING

A1725

1987, Sept. 21

2361	A1725	22c multicolored	.70	.25
a.	Black (engr.) omitted		425.00	

LOCOMOTIVES

Stourbridge Lion, 1829 — A1726

Best Friend of Charleston, 1830 — A1727

John Bull, 1831 A1728

Brother Jonathan, 1832 — A1729

Gowan & Marx, 1839 A1730

BOOKLET STAMPS
Perf. 10 Horiz. on 1 or 2 Sides
1987, Oct. 1

2362	A1726	22c multi	.50	.25
a.	Red (litho.) omitted			
2363	A1727	22c multi	.50	.25
a.	Red (litho.) omitted			
2364	A1728	22c multi	.50	.25
a.	Red (litho.) omitted			
2365	A1729	22c multi	.50	.25
a.	Red omitted		1,000.	250.00
2366	A1730	22c multi	.50	.25
a.	Bklt. pane of 5, #2362-2366		2.50	2.00
b.	As No. 2366, black (engr.) omitted (single)		—	
c.	As No. 2366, blue omitted (single)		—	

CHRISTMAS

Moroni Madonna A1731 — Christmas Ornaments A1732

PHOTOGRAVURE
1987, Oct. 23 — Perf. 11

2367	A1731	22c multicolored	.45	.25
2368	A1732	22c multicolored	.45	.25

1988 WINTER OLYMPICS, CALGARY

Skiing — A1733

1988, Jan. 10

2369	A1733	22c multicolored	.50	.25

AUSTRALIA BICENTENNIAL

Caricature of Australian Koala & American Bald Eagle — A1734

1988, Jan. 26
2370 A1734 22c multicolored   .45 .25
       See Australia No. 1052.

BLACK HERITAGE SERIES

James Weldon Johnson, Author, Lyricist — A1735

1988, Feb. 2
2371 A1735 22c multicolored   .50 .25

CATS

Siamese, Exotic Shorthair A1736

Abyssinian, Himalayan A1737

Maine Coon, Burmese A1738

American Shorthair, Persian A1739

1988, Feb. 5
2372 A1736 22c multicolored   .70 .25
2373 A1737 22c multicolored   .70 .25
2374 A1738 22c multicolored   .70 .25
2375 A1739 22c multicolored   .70 .25
   a.   Block of 4, #2372-2375   2.80 1.90

AMERICAN SPORTS

Knute Rockne (1888-1931), Notre Dame football coach.

A1740

LITHOGRAPHED & ENGRAVED
1988, Mar. 9
2376 A1740 22c multicolored   .50 .25

AMERICAN SPORTS

Francis Ouimet (1893-1967), 1st amateur golfer to win the US Open championship.

A1741

PHOTOGRAVURE
1988, June 13
2377 A1741 25c multicolored   .60 .25

LOVE ISSUE (Roses)

Rose   Roses
A1742   A1743

1988
2378 A1742 25c multi   .50 .25
   a.   Imperf., pair   1,500.
2379 A1743 45c multi   .85 .25

1988 SUMMER OLYMPICS, SEOUL

Gymnastic Rings A1744

1988, Aug. 19
2380 A1744 25c multicolored   .50 .25

CLASSIC AUTOMOBILES

1928 Locomobile — A1745

1929 Pierce-Arrow A1746

1931 Cord A1747

1932 Packard A1748

1935 Duesenberg — A1749

LITHOGRAPHED & ENGRAVED
BOOKLET STAMPS
Perf. 10 Horiz. on 1 or 2 Sides
1988, Aug. 25
2381 A1745 25c multicolored   .65 .25
2382 A1746 25c multicolored   .65 .25
2383 A1747 25c multicolored   .65 .25
2384 A1748 25c multicolored   .65 .25
2385 A1749 25c multicolored   .65 .25
   a.   Bklt. pane of 5, #2381-2385   3.25 2.50

ANTARCTIC EXPLORERS

Nathaniel Palmer (1799-1877) A1750

Lt. Charles Wilkes (1798-1877) A1751

Richard E. Byrd (1888-1957) A1752

Lincoln Ellsworth (1880-1951) A1753

PHOTOGRAVURE
1988, Sept. 14   *Perf. 11*
2386 A1750 25c multicolored   .65 .25
2387 A1751 25c multicolored   .65 .25
2388 A1752 25c multicolored   .65 .25
2389 A1753 25c multicolored   .65 .25
   a.   Block of 4, #2386-2389   2.75 2.00
   b.   As "a," black omitted   750.00
   c.   As "a," imperf. horiz.   1,500.

AMERICAN FOLK ART SERIES
Carousel Animals

Deer — A1754   Horse — A1755

Camel — A1756   Goat — A1757

LITHOGRAPHED & ENGRAVED
1988, Oct. 1
2390 A1754 25c multicolored   .75 .25
2391 A1755 25c multicolored   .75 .25
2392 A1756 25c multicolored   .75 .25
2393 A1757 25c multicolored   .75 .25
   a.   Block of 4, #2390-2393   3.00 2.00
   b.   As "a," red omitted   800.00

EXPRESS MAIL RATE

Eagle in Flight — A1758

1988, Oct. 4
2394 A1758 $8.75 multicolored 16.00 8.00

SPECIAL OCCASIONS

Happy Birthday — A1759

Best Wishes — A1760

Thinking of You — A1761

Love You — A1762

BOOKLET STAMPS
PHOTOGRAVURE
Perf. 11 on 2 or 3 Sides
1988, Oct. 22
2395 A1759 25c multicolored   .50 .25
2396 A1760 25c multicolored   .50 .25
   a.   Bklt. pane of 6, 3 #2395 +
          3 #2396 with gutter be-
          tween   3.50 3.25
2397 A1761 25c multicolored   .50 .25
2398 A1762 25c multicolored   .50 .25
   a.   Bklt. pane of 6, 3 #2397 +
          3 #2398 with gutter be-
          tween   3.50 3.25
   b.   As "a," imperf. horiz. 2,250.
   c.   As "a," imperf.   —
          Nos. 2395-2398 (4)   2.00 1.00

CHRISTMAS

Madonna and Child, by Botticelli A1763

One-horse Open Sleigh & Village Scene A1764

LITHOGRAPHED & ENGRAVED (No. 2399), PHOTOGRAVURE (No. 2400)
1988, Oct. 20   *Perf. 11½*
2399 A1763 25c multicolored   .50 .25
   a.   Gold omitted   25.00
2400 A1764 25c multicolored   .50 .25

MONTANA STATEHOOD, 100th ANNIV.

C.M. Russell and Friends, by Charles M. Russell (1865-1926) A1765

LITHOGRAPHED & ENGRAVED
1989, Jan. 15   **Perf. 11**
2401	A1765	25c multicolored	.55	.25

Imperfs without gum exist from printer's waste.

BLACK HERITAGE SERIES

Asa Philip Randolph (1889-1979), Labor & Civil Rights Leader — A1766

PHOTOGRAVURE
1989, Feb. 3
2402	A1766	25c multicolored	.50	.25

NORTH DAKOTA STATEHOOD, 100th ANNIV.

Grain Elevator A1767

1989, Feb. 21
2403	A1767	25c multicolored	.50	.25

WASHINGTON STATEHOOD, 100th ANNIV.

Mt. Rainier — A1768

1989, Feb. 22
2404	A1768	25c multicolored	.50	.25

STEAMBOATS

Experiment, 1788-1790 — A1769

Phoenix, 1809 — A1770

New Orleans, 1812 — A1771

Washington, 1816 — A1772

Walk in the Water, 1818 — A1773

LITHOGRAPHED & ENGRAVED BOOKLET STAMPS
Perf. 10 Horiz. on 1 or 2 Sides
1989, Mar. 3
2405	A1769	25c multicolored	.60	.25
2406	A1770	25c multicolored	.60	.25
2407	A1771	25c multicolored	.60	.25
2408	A1772	25c multicolored	.60	.25
2409	A1773	25c multicolored	.60	.25
a.		Booklet pane of 5, #2405-2409	3.00	1.75

WORLD STAMP EXPO '89
Nov. 17-Dec. 3. Washington, D.C.

No. 122 — A1774

1989, Mar. 16   **Perf. 11**
2410	A1774	25c grayish brn, blk & car rose	.50	.25

PERFORMING ARTS

Arturo Toscanini (1867-1957), Conductor — A1775

PHOTOGRAVURE
1989, Mar. 25
2411	A1775	25c multicolored	.50	.25

CONSTITUTION BICENTENNIAL SERIES

House of Representatives A1776

Senate A1777

Executive Branch A1778

Supreme Court A1779

LITHOGRAPHED & ENGRAVED
1989-90
2412	A1776	25c multi	.50	.25
2413	A1777	25c multi	.50	.25
2414	A1778	25c multi	.50	.25
2415	A1779	25c multi	.50	.25
		Nos. 2412-2415 (4)	2.00	1.00

Issued: No. 2412, 4/4; No. 2413, 4/6; No. 2414, 4/16; No. 2415, 2/2/90.

SOUTH DAKOTA STATEHOOD, 100th ANNIV.

Pasque Flowers, Pioneer Woman and Sod House on Grasslands A1780

PHOTOGRAVURE
1989, May 3
2416	A1780	25c multicolored	.60	.25

Imperfs exist from printer's waste.

AMERICAN SPORTS

Lou Gehrig (1903-1941), New York Yankee Baseball Player — A1781

1989, June 10
2417	A1781	25c multicolored	.60	.25

LITERARY ARTS SERIES

Ernest Hemingway (1899-1961), Nobel Prize-winner for Literature, 1954 — A1782

1989, July 17
2418	A1782	25c multicolored	.50	.25
a.		Vert. pair, imperf horiz.	800.00	

Imperforates on gummed stamp paper, including gutter pairs and blocks, are proofs from the ABNCo. archives. See No. 2418P in Proofs section of the Scott U.S. Specialized Catalogue.

MOON LANDING, 20TH ANNIVERSARY

Raising the Flag on Lunar Surface, July 20, 1969 A1783

LITHOGRAPHED & ENGRAVED
1989, July 20   **Perf. 11x11½**
2419	A1783	$2.40 multi	4.75	2.00
a.		Black (engr.) omitted	1,350.	
b.		Imperf., pair	375.00	
c.		Black (litho.) omitted	1,500.	

LETTER CARRIERS

Letter Carriers A1784

PHOTOGRAVURE
2420	A1784	25c multicolored	.50	.25

CONSTITUTION BICENTENNIAL

Bill of Rights — A1785

LITHOGRAPHED & ENGRAVED
1989, Sept. 25
2421	A1785	25c multicolored	.50	.25
a.		Black (engr.) omitted	225.00	

PREHISTORIC ANIMALS

Tyrannosaurus Rex — A1786

Pteranodon A1787

Stegosaurus — A1788

Brontosaurus — A1789

1989, Oct. 1
2422	A1786	25c multicolored	.70	.25
a.		Black (engr.) omitted	80.00	—
2423	A1787	25c multicolored	.70	.25
a.		Black (engr.) omitted	80.00	
2424	A1788	25c multicolored	.70	.25
a.		Black (engr.) omitted	80.00	—
2425	A1789	25c multicolored	.70	.25
a.		Black (engr.) omitted	80.00	
b.		Block of 4, #2422-2425	2.80	2.00
c.		As "b," black (engr.) omitted	325.00	

No. 2425c is valued in the grade of fine. Very fine blocks exist and sell for approximately $600.

PRE-COLUMBIAN AMERICA ISSUE

Southwest Carved Figure, A. D. 1150-1350 — A1790

PHOTOGRAVURE

1989, Oct. 12

2426 A1790 25c multicolored   .60   .25

See No. C121.

CHRISTMAS

Madonna and Child, by Caracci A1791

Sleigh Full of Presents A1792

LITHOGRAPHED & ENGRAVED, PHOTOGRAVURE (#2428-2429)

1989, Oct. 19   *Perf. 11¼*

2427 A1791 25c multicolored   .50   .25
   a.   Booklet pane of 10   5.00   3.50
   b.   Red (litho.) omitted   400.00
   c.   As "a," imperf.   —

         Perf. 11½

2428 A1792 25c multicolored   .50   .25
   a.   Vert. pair, imperf. horiz.   500.00

BOOKLET STAMP

Perf. 11½ on 2 or 3 Sides

2429 A1792 25c multicolored   .50   .25
   a.   Booklet pane of 10   5.00   3.50
   b.   Vert. pair, imperf. btwn. (from miscut bklt pane)   500.00
   c.   As "a," horiz. imperf. between   2,250.
   d.   As "a," red omitted   3,250.
   e.   Imperf., pair   750.00

Marked differences exist between Nos. 2428 and 2429: No. 2429 was printed in four colors, No. 2428 in five colors. The runners on the sleigh in No. 2429 are twice as thick as those on No. 2428. On No. 2429 the package at the upper left in the sleigh has a red bow, whereas the same package in No. 2428 has a red and black bow; and the ribbon on the upper right package in No. 2429 is green, whereas the same ribbon in No. 2428 is black.

Eagle and Shield — A1793

PHOTOGRAVURE BOOKLET STAMP

1989, Nov. 10   *Die Cut*

Self-Adhesive

2431 A1793 25c multicolored   .50   .25
   a.   Booklet pane of 18   10.00
   b.   Vert. pair, die cutting omitted between   325.00
   c.   Die cutting omitted, pair   200.00

Panes sold for $5.
Also available in strips of 18 with stamps spaced for use in affixing machines to service first day covers. Sold for $5.
No. 2431c will include part of the margins around the stamps.
Sold only in 15 test cities (Atlanta, Chicago, Cleveland, Columbus, OH, Dallas, Denver, Houston, Indianapolis, Kansas City, MO, Los Angeles, Miami, Milwaukee, Minneapolis, Phoenix, St. Louis) and through the philatelic agency.

WORLD STAMP EXPO '89

The classic 1869 U.S. Abraham Lincoln stamp is reborn in these four larger versions commemorating World Stamp Expo '89, held in Washington, D.C. during the 20th Universal Postal Congress of the UPU. These stamps show the issued stamp and three of the trial proof color combinations.

World Stamp Expo, Washington, DC, Nov. 17-Dec. 3 — A1794

LITHOGRAPHED & ENGRAVED

1989, Nov. 17   *Imperf.*

2433 A1794 Pane of 4   16.00   14.00
   a.   90c like No. 122   4.00   3.00
   b.   90c like 132TC4j   4.00   3.00
   c.   90c like 132TC4i   4.00   3.00
   d.   90c like 132TC4d   4.00   3.00
   f.   Double impression of all 4 frames   —

20th UPU CONGRESS
Traditional Mail Delivery

Stagecoach, c. 1850 — A1795

Paddlewheel Steamer A1796

Biplane — A1797

Depot-hack Type Automobile A1798

1989, Nov. 19   *Perf. 11*

2434 A1795 25c multicolored   .50   .25
2435 A1796 25c multicolored   .50   .25
2436 A1797 25c multicolored   .50   .25
2437 A1798 25c multicolored   .50   .25
   a.   Block of 4, #2434-2437   2.00   1.75
   b.   As "a," dark blue (engr.) omitted   300.00

No. 2437b is valued in the grade of fine. Very fine blocks exist and sell for approximately $450.

Souvenir Sheet

1989, Nov. 28   *Imperf.*

2438   Sheet of 4   5.00   3.75
   a.   A1795 25c multicolored   1.25   .80
   b.   A1796 25c multicolored   1.25   .80
   c.   A1797 25c multicolored   1.25   .80
   d.   A1798 25c multicolored   1.25   .80
   e.   Dark blue & gray (engr.) omitted   4,000.

20th Universal Postal Union Congress.

VALUES FOR HINGED STAMPS AFTER NO. 771
This catalogue does not value unused stamps after No. 771 in hinged condition. Hinged unused stamps from No. 772 to the present are worth considerably less than the values given for unused stamps, which are for never-hinged examples.

IDAHO STATEHOOD, 100th ANNIV.

Mountain Bluebird, Sawtooth Mountains — A1799

PHOTOGRAVURE

1990, Jan. 6   *Perf. 11*

2439 A1799 25c multicolored   .55   .25

LOVE

A1800

PHOTOGRAVURE

1990, Jan. 18   *Perf. 12½x13*

2440 A1800 25c multi   .50   .25
   a.   Imperf., pair   550.00

BOOKLET STAMP

Perf. 11½ on 2 or 3 Sides

2441 A1800 25c multi   .50   .25
   a.   Booklet pane of 10   5.00   3.50
   b.   Bright pink omitted   80.00
   c.   As "a," bright pink omitted   950.00

No. 2441b may be obtained from booklet panes containing both normal and color-omitted stamps.

BLACK HERITAGE SERIES

Ida B. Wells (1862-1931), Journalist — A1801

1990, Feb. 1   *Perf. 11*

2442 A1801 25c multicolored   .75   .25

Beach Umbrella — A1802

BOOKLET STAMP

Perf. 11 on 2 or 3 Sides

1990, Feb. 3

2443 A1802 15c multicolored   .30   .25
   a.   Booklet pane of 10   3.00   2.50
   b.   Blue omitted   100.00
   c.   As "a," blue omitted   900.00

WYOMING STATEHOOD, 100th ANNIV.

High Mountain Meadows, by Conrad Schwiering A1803

LITHOGRAPHED & ENGRAVED

1990, Feb. 23   *Perf. 11*

2444 A1803 25c multicolored   .80   .25
   a.   Black (engr.) omitted   900.00   —

CLASSIC FILMS

Judy Garland and Toto (The Wizard of Oz) — A1804

Clark Gable & Vivien Leigh (Gone With the Wind) — A1805

Gary Cooper (Beau Geste) — A1806

John Wayne (Stagecoach) A1807

PHOTOGRAVURE

1990, Mar. 23

2445 A1804 25c multicolored   1.25   .25
2446 A1805 25c multicolored   1.25   .25
2447 A1806 25c multicolored   1.25   .25
2448 A1807 25c multicolored   1.25   .25
   a.   Block of 4, #2445-2448   5.00   3.50

LITERARY ARTS SERIES

Marianne Craig Moore (1887-1972), Poet — A1808

1990, Apr. 18

2449 A1808 25c multicolored   .55   .25
   a.   All colors missing (EP)

No. 2449a must be collected se-tenant with a partially printed stamp or in longer horizontal strips with a partially printed stamp and normal stamps.

TRANSPORTATION ISSUE

A1810

A1811

A1811a   A1812

A1816

A1822

A1823   A1825

A1827

COIL STAMPS
ENGRAVED, PHOTOGRAVURE
(#2452B, 2452D, 2454, 2458)

1990-95   **Perf. 9.8 Vert.**
Untagged (Nos. 2452B, 2452D, 2453, 2454, 2457-2458)
Bureau Precancel in Gray (#2453-2458)

2451	A1810	4c claret	.25	.25
a.		Imperf., pair	450.00	
b.		Untagged	.25	
2452	A1811	5c carmine	.25	.25
a.		Untagged, dull gum	.25	
c.		Imperf., pair	350.00	

No. 2452c is valued in the grade of fine.

2452B	A1811	5c carmine	.25	.25
2452D	A1811a	5c carmine	.25	.25
e.		Imperf., pair	115.00	
2453	A1812	5c brown	.40	.25
a.		Imperf., pair	225.00	
b.		Gray omitted	—	
2454	A1812	5c red	.45	.25
2457	A1816	10c green	.45	.25
a.		Imperf., pair	110.00	
b.		All color omitted	—	

No. 2457b must be accompanied by a 2012 certificate of authentication confirming that stamps are from the discovery coil roll that also contained normal and partially printed stamps.

2458	A1816	10c green	.55	.25
2463	A1822	20c green	.40	.25
a.		Imperf., pair	75.00	
2464	A1823	23c dark blue	.45	.25
b.		Imperf., pair	100.00	
2466	A1825	32c blue	.80	.25
a.		Imperf., pair, shiny gum	375.00	
b.		bright blue	3.00	2.25

Some specialists refer to No. 2466b as "Bronx blue," and it is considered to be an error of color.

2468	A1827	$1 bl & scar	2.25	.50
a.		Imperf., pair	1,750.	1,150.
		Nos. 2451-2468 (12)	6.75	3.25

Some mint pairs of No. 2468 appear to be imperf. but have faint blind perforations on the gum. Beware of examples with the gum removed.

Issued: $1, 4/20; No. 2452, 8/31; 4c, 1/25/91; 23c, 4/12/91; Nos. 2453, 2457, 5/25/91; No. 2454, 10/22/91; No. 2452B, 12/8/92; No. 2458, 5/25/94; Nos. 2452D, 3/20/95; 32c, 6/2/95; 20c, 6/9/95.

LIGHTHOUSES

Admiralty Head, WA — A1829

Cape Hatteras, NC — A1830

West Quoddy Head, ME — A1831

American Shoals, FL — A1832

Sandy Hook, NJ — A1833

BOOKLET STAMPS
LITHOGRAPHED & ENGRAVED
Perf. 10 Vert. on 1 or 2 Sides

1990, Apr. 26

2470	A1829	25c multicolored	1.50	.25
2471	A1830	25c multicolored	1.50	.25
2472	A1831	25c multicolored	1.50	.25
2473	A1832	25c multicolored	1.50	.25
2474	A1833	25c multicolored	1.50	.25
a.		Bklt. pane of 5, #2470-2474	7.50	2.00
b.		As "a," white ("USA 25") omitted	85.00	—

Perforations on Lighthouse booklet panes separate very easily. Careful handling is required.

FLAG

A1834

PHOTOGRAVURE

1990, May 18   Untagged   Die Cut
Self-adhesive
Printed on Plastic

2475	A1834	25c dk red & dk bl	.55	.25
a.		Pane of 12	6.60	

Sold only in panes of 12; peelable plastic backing inscribed in light ultramarine. Available for a test period of six months at 22 First National Bank automatic teller machines in Seattle.

FLORA AND FAUNA

A1840

American Kestrel A1841

Fawn A1843

Eastern Bluebird A1842

Cardinal A1844

Pumpkinseed Sunfish — A1845

Bobcat A1846

LITHOGRAPHED
Perf. 11, 11.2 (#2477)

1990-95   Untagged (1c, 3c)

2476	A1840	1c multi	.25	.25
a.		Quadruple impression of black inscriptions and denomination	850.00	
b.		Quintuple impression of black inscriptions and denomination	1,500.	
2477	A1841	1c multi	.25	.25
2478	A1842	3c multi	.25	.25
a.		Vert. pair, imperf horiz.		
b.		Double impression of all colors except yellow	200.00	
c.		Double impression of blue, triple impression of black	—	

Imperforates on gummed stamp paper, plus imperforate and perforated gutter pairs and blocks (including imperforate and perforated gutter pairs and blocks of No. 2476 se-tenant with No. 2478), are proofs from the ABNCo. archives. See Nos. 2476P and 2478P in Proofs section of the Scott U.S. Specialized Catalogue.

See Nos. 3031, 3031A, 3044. Compare design A1842 with design A2336.

PHOTOGRAVURE

2479	A1843	19c multi	.35	.25
b.		Red omitted	425.00	
c.		Imperf., pair	900.00	

On No. 2479b other colors are shifted.

2480	A1844	30c multicolored, June 22, 1991	.60	.25

LITHOGRAPHED & ENGRAVED

2481	A1845	45c multi	.90	.25
a.		Black (engr.) omitted	300.00	—
2482	A1846	$2 multi	3.50	1.25
a.		Black (engr.) omitted	200.00	
		Nos. 2476-2482 (7)	6.10	2.75

Issued: $2, 6/1; 19c, 3/11/91; No. 2476, 3c, 30c, 6/22/91; 45c, 12/2/92; No. 2477, 5/10/95.

Blue Jay — A1847

African Violets A1849

Pear A1851

Rose A1853

Wood Duck — A1848

Peach A1850

Red Squirrel A1852

Pine Cone A1854

PHOTOGRAVURE
BOOKLET STAMPS
Perf. 10.9x9.8 on 2 or 3 Sides

1991-95

2483	A1847	20c multi	.50	.25
a.		Booklet pane of 10	5.25	2.50
b.		As "a," imperf		

Perf. 10 on 2 or 3 sides

2484	A1848	29c blk & multi	.60	.25
a.		Booklet pane of 10	6.00	3.75
b.		Vert. pair, imperf. horiz.	175.00	
c.		As "b," bklt. pane of 10	875.00	
f.		Vert. pair, imperf between and with natural straight edge at top or bottom	175.00	
g.		As "f," bklt. pane of 10	875.00	

Perf. 11 on 2 or 3 Sides

2485	A1848	29c red & multi	.60	.25
a.		Booklet pane of 10	6.00	4.00
b.		Vert. pair, imperf. between	2,500.	
c.		Imperf., pair	4,500.	

Perf. 10x11 on 2 or 3 Sides

2486	A1849	29c multi	.60	.25
a.		Booklet pane of 10	6.00	4.00

Perf. 11x10 on 2 or 3 Sides

2487	A1850	32c multi	.65	.25
2488	A1851	32c multi	.65	.25
a.		Booklet pane, 5 each #2487-2488	6.50	4.25
b.		Pair, #2487-2488	1.30	.30

Issued: Nos. 2484-2485, 4/12; No. 2486, 10/8/93; 20c, 6/15/95; 32c, 7/8/95.

PHOTOGRAVURE, ENGRAVED
(#2491)

1993-95   Die Cut
Self-Adhesive
Booklet Stamps

2489	A1852	29c multi	.60	.25
a.		Booklet pane of 18	11.00	
b.		As "a," die cutting omitted		
2490	A1853	29c red, green & black	.60	.25
a.		Booklet pane of 18	11.00	
2491	A1854	29c multi	.60	.25
a.		Booklet pane of 18	11.00	
b.		Horiz. pair, die cutting omitted between	175.00	125.00
c.		Coil with plate # B1	—	6.00

Stamps without plate number from coil strips are indistinguishable from booklet stamps once they are removed from the backing paper.

Serpentine Die Cut 11.3x11.7 on 2, 3 or 4 Sides

2492	A1853	32c pink, green & black	.65	.25
a.		Booklet pane of 20 + label	13.00	
b.		Booklet pane of 15 + label	9.75	
c.		Horiz. pair, die cutting omitted between		
d.		As "a," 2 stamps and parts of 7 others printed on backing liner		
e.		Booklet pane of 14	20.00	
f.		Booklet pane of 16	20.00	
g.		Coil with plate # S111		5.50
h.		Vert. pair, die cutting omitted between (from No. 2492b)	400.00	
i.		As "a," 6 pairs plus stamp and label die cutting omitted vert. btwn. (due to miscutting)	800.00	
j.		As "f," with 2 vert. pairs at bottom die cutting omitted horiz., in full bklt. #BK178D		
k.		As "a," horiz. die cutting omitted		

Serpentine Die Cut 8.8 on 2, 3 or 4 Sides

2493	A1850	32c multi	.65	.25
2494	A1851	32c multi	.65	.25
a.		Booklet pane of 20, 10 each #2493-2494 + label	13.00	
b.		Pair, #2493-2494	1.30	
c.		As "b," die cutting omitted		

COIL STAMPS
Serpentine Die Cut 8.8 Vert.

2495	A1850	32c multi	2.00	.25
2495A	A1851	32c multi	2.00	.25
b.		Pair, #2495-2495A	4.00	

Issued: No. 2489, 6/25; No. 2490, 8/19; No. 2491, 11/5; No. 2492, 6/2/95; Nos. 2493-2495A, 7/8/95.
See Nos. 3048-3049, 3053-3054.

Values for used self-adhesive stamps are for examples either on piece or off piece.

OLYMPIANS

Jesse Owens, 1936
A1855

Ray Ewry, 1900-08
A1856

Hazel Wightman, 1924
A1857

Eddie Eagan, 1920, 1932
A1858

Helene Madison, 1932
A1859

PHOTOGRAVURE

1990, July 6   *Perf. 11*

2496	A1855	25c multicolored	.60	.25
2497	A1856	25c multicolored	.60	.25
2498	A1857	25c multicolored	.60	.25
2499	A1858	25c multicolored	.60	.25
2500	A1859	25c multicolored	.60	.25
a.		Strip of 5, #2496-2500	3.25	2.50
b.		As "a," blue omitted		

Imperforates on gummed stamp paper, including gutter pairs, strips and blocks, are proofs from the ABNCo. archives. See No. 2500aP in Proofs section of the Scott U.S. Specialized Catalogue.

INDIAN HEADDRESSES

Assiniboin
A1860

Cheyenne
A1861

Comanche
A1862

Flathead
A1863

Shoshone
A1864

LITHOGRAPHED & ENGRAVED BOOKLET STAMPS
Perf. 11 on 2 or 3 Sides

1990, Aug. 17

2501	A1860	25c multicolored	.80	.25
2502	A1861	25c multicolored	.80	.25
2503	A1862	25c multicolored	.80	.25
a.		Black (engr.) omitted	125.00	—
2504	A1863	25c multicolored	.80	.25
a.		Black (engr.) omitted	125.00	—
2505	A1864	25c multicolored	.80	.25
a.		Bklt. pane of 10, 2 each #2501-2505	8.00	6.00
b.		As "a," black (engr.) omitted	2,500.	
c.		Strip of 5, #2501-2505	4.00	2.50
d.		As "a," horiz. imperf. between	2,250.	

At least one of the examples of No. 2505d that have been reported is actually split at the booklet fold and is a block of 4 and a block of 6.

MICRONESIA & MARSHALL ISLANDS

Canoe & Federated States of Micronesia Flag
A1865

Stick Chart, Canoe & Republic of the Marshall Islands Flag
A1866

1990, Sept. 28   *Perf. 11*

2506	A1865	25c multicolored	.50	.25
2507	A1866	25c multicolored	.50	.25
a.		Pair, #2506-2507	1.00	.75
b.		As "a," black (engr.) omitted	1,400.	

See Micronesia Nos. 124-126, Marshall Islands No. 381.

SEA CREATURES

Killer Whales
A1867

Northern Sea Lions
A1868

Sea Otter
A1869

Common Dolphin
A1870

1990, Oct. 3

2508	A1867	25c multicolored	.55	.25
2509	A1868	25c multicolored	.55	.25
2510	A1869	25c multicolored	.55	.25
2511	A1870	25c multicolored	.55	.25
a.		Block of 4, #2508-2511	2.25	1.90
b.		As "a," black (engr.) omitted	250.00	

See Russia Nos. 5933-5936.

PRE-COLUMBIAN AMERICA ISSUE

Grand Canyon
A1871

PHOTOGRAVURE

1990, Oct. 12

2512	A1871	25c multicolored	.55	.25

See No. C127.

DWIGHT D. EISENHOWER, BIRTH CENTENARY

A1872

1990, Oct. 13   *Tagged*   *Perf. 11*

2513	A1872	25c multicolored	.80	.25

Imperforates on gummed stamp paper are proofs from the ABNCo. archives. See No. 2513P in Proofs section of the Scott U.S. Specialized Catalogue.

CHRISTMAS

Madonna and Child by Antonello da Messina
A1873

Christmas Tree
A1874

LITHOGRAPHED & ENGRAVED

1990, Oct. 18   *Perf. 11¼x11½*

2514	A1874	25c multi	.50	.25
b.		Booklet pane of 10	5.00	3.25

PHOTOGRAVURE
Perf. 11

2515	A1874	25c multicolored	.50	.25
a.		Vert. pair, imperf. horiz.	500.00	—
b.		All colors missing (EP)	—	

No. 2515b must be collected se-tenant with normal and/or partially printed stamp(s).

BOOKLET STAMP
Perf. 11½x11 on 2 or 3 Sides

2516	A1874	25c multicolored	.60	.25
a.		Booklet pane of 10	6.00	3.25

Marked differences exist between Nos. 2515 and 2516. The background red on No. 2515 is even while that on No. 2516 is splotchy. The bands across the tree and "Greetings" are blue green on No. 2515 and yellow green on No. 2516.

A1875   A1876

1991, Jan. 22   *Perf. 13*

2517	A1875	(29c) yel, blk, red & yel grn	.60	.25
a.		Imperf., pair	1,000.	
b.		Horiz. pair, imperf. vert.	1,000.	

See note after No. 2518.
Gutter pairs and blocks, and cross gutter blocks, all perforated, are proofs from the

---

ABNCo. archives. See No. 2517P in Proofs section of the Scott U.S. Specialized Catalogue.

No. 2517a is usually collected as a vertical pair, though No. 2517 can be distinguished from the other "F" stamp issues.

COIL STAMP
Perf. 10 Vert.

2518	A1875	(29c) yel, blk, dull red & dk yel grn	.60	.25
a.		Imperf., pair	25.00	

"For U.S. addresses only" is 17½mm long on No. 2517, 16½mm long on No. 2518. Design of No. 2517 measures 21½x17½mm, No. 2518, 21x18mm.

BOOKLET STAMPS
Perf. 11 on 2 or 3 Sides

2519	A1875	(29c) yel, blk, dull red & dk grn	.60	.25
a.		Booklet pane of 10	6.50	4.50
2520	A1875	(29c) pale yel, blk, red & brt grn	1.50	.25
a.		Booklet pane of 10	15.00	4.50
b.		As "a," imperf. horiz.		
c.		Horiz. pair, imperf btwn., in error-booklet pane of 12 stamps	450.00	
d.		Imperf. vert., pair	—	

No. 2519 has bullseye perforations that measure approximately 11.2. No. 2520 has less pronounced black lines in the leaf, which is a much brighter green than on No. 2519. No. 2520c is from a paper foldover before perforating.

LITHOGRAPHED

1991, Jan. 22   *Untagged*   *Perf. 11*

2521	A1876	(4c) bister & carmine	.25	.25
a.		Vert. pair, imperf. horiz.	70.00	
b.		Imperf., pair	60.00	

FLAG

A1877

PHOTOGRAVURE

1991, Jan. 22   *Untagged*   *Die Cut*
Self-Adhesive
Printed on Plastic

2522	A1877	(29c) blk, blue & dk red	.60	.25
a.		Pane of 12	7.25	

Sold only in panes of 12; peelable plastic backing inscribed in light ultramarine. Available during a test period at First National Bank automatic teller machines in Seattle.

Flag Over Mt. Rushmore — A1878

COIL STAMPS
ENGRAVED

1991, Mar. 29   *Tagged*   *Perf. 10 Vert.*

2523	A1878	29c bl, red & claret	.75	.25
b.		Imperf., pair	20.00	
c.		blue, red & brown	3.00	—

Specialists often call No. 2523c the "Toledo brown" variety.

PHOTOGRAVURE

1991, July 4

2523A	A1878	29c bl, red, lt brn, med brn & dk brn		
e.		Medium brown omitted	.75	.25

On No. 2523A, USA and 29 are not outlined in white and are farther from the bottom of the design.

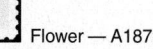

Flower — A1879

PHOTOGRAVURE

1991-92   *Perf. 11*
2524   A1879   29c dull yel,
     blk, red
     & yel grn   .60   .25

See note after No. 2527.

Perf. 13x12¾
2524A   A1879   29c dull yel,
     blk, red
     & yel grn   1.00   .25

COIL STAMPS
Rouletted 10 Vert.
2525   A1879   29c pale yel,
     blk, red
     & yel grn   .60   .25

Perf. 10 Vert.
2526   A1879   29c pale yel,
     blk, red
     & yel grn   .80   .25

BOOKLET STAMP
Perf. 11 on 2 or 3 Sides
2527   A1879   29c pale yel,
     blk, red
     & bright
     grn   .60   .25
   a.   Booklet pane of 10   6.00   3.50
   b.   Horiz. pair, imperf. be-
     tween   —   —
   c.   Horiz. pair, imperf.
     vert.   150.00
   d.   As "a," imperf. horiz.   750.00
   e.   As "a," imperf. vert.   500.00

Flower on Nos. 2524-2524A has grainy appearance, inscriptions look rougher.
Issued: Nos. 2524, 2524A, 2527, 4/5; No. 2525, 8/16; No. 2526, 3/3/92.

Flag, Olympic
Rings — A1880

BOOKLET STAMP
Perf. 11 on 2 or 3 Sides
1991, Apr. 21
2528   A1880   29c multicolored   .60   .25
   a.   Booklet pane of 10   6.00   3.50
   b.   As "a," imperf. horiz.   2,750.
   c.   Vert. pair, imperf. between,
     perfed at top and bottom   225.00
   d.   Vert. strip of 3, top or bot-
     tom pair imperf. between
   e.   Vert. pair, imperf. horiz.   650.00
   f.   As "d," two pairs in #2528a
     with foldover   —

No. 2528c comes from misperfed booklet panes. No. 2528d resulted from paper foldovers after normal perforating and before cutting into panes. Two No. 2528d are known. No. 2528e is valued in the grade of fine.

Fishing Boat — A1881

COIL STAMPS
1991, Aug. 8   *Perf. 9.8 Vert.*
2529   A1881   19c multi, type I   .40   .25
   a.   Type II ('93)   .40   .25
   b.   As "a," untagged ('93)   1.00   .40

Design on Type II stamps is created by a finer dot pattern. Vertical sides of "1" are smooth on Type II and jagged on Type I stamps.
Imperforates are from printer's waste.
Nos. 2529 and 2529a have two loops of rope tying boat to piling.

1994, June 25
2529C   A1881   19c multicolored   .50   .25

No. 2529C has one loop of rope tying boat to piling.

Balloon — A1882

BOOKLET STAMP
Perf. 10 on 2 or 3 Sides
1991, May 17
2530   A1882   19c multicolored   .40   .25
   a.   Booklet pane of 10   4.00   2.75

Flags on
Parade — A1883

1991, May 30   *Perf. 11*
2531   A1883   29c multi   .60   .25

Liberty Torch — A1884

1991, June 25   *Die Cut*
Self-Adhesive
2531A   A1884   29c blk, gold &
     grn   .60   .25
   b.   Booklet pane of 18   11.00
   c.   Die cutting omitted, pair   1,000.

Sold only in panes of 18; peelable paper backing inscribed in light blue. Available for consumer testing at First National Bank automatic teller machines in Seattle, WA.

SWITZERLAND

Switzerland, 700th Anniv. — A1887

1991, Feb. 22   *Perf. 11*
2532   A1887   50c multi   1.00   .25
   a.   Vert. pair, imperf.
     horiz.   1,400.

See Switzerland No. 888.
Imperfs exist from printer's waste.

VERMONT STATEHOOD, 200th ANNIV.

A1888

1991, Mar. 1
2533   A1888   29c multicolored   .80   .25

SAVINGS BONDS, 50TH ANNIVERSARY

A1889

1991, Apr. 30   *Perf. 11*
2534   A1889   29c multicolored   .60   .25

LOVE

A1890   A1891

1991, May 9   *Perf. 12½x13*
2535   A1890   29c multi   .60   .25
   b.   Imperf., pair   1,650.

Perf. 11
2535A   A1890   29c multi   1.00   .25

BOOKLET STAMP (#2536)
Perf. 11.1x11.3 on 2 or 3 Sides
2536   A1890   29c multi   .60   .25
   a.   Booklet pane of 10   6.00   3.50

"29" is closer to edge of design on No. 2536 than on No. 2535.

Perf. 11
2537   A1891   52c multi   .90   .25

LITERARY ARTS SERIES

William
Saroyan
A1892

1991, May 22   *Perf. 11*
2538   A1892   29c multicolored   .60   .25
   a.   All colors missing (EP)
   b.   All colors except black
     missing (EP)   11,000.

No. 2538a must be collected se-tenant with a partially printed stamp. On No. 2538b, only part of the black is present; it is unique.
See Russia No. 6002.

Eagle, Olympic
Rings — A1893

A1894

A1895

A1896

Futuristic
Space
Shuttle
A1897

Space
Shuttle
Challenger
A1898

Space
Shuttle
Endeavour
— A1898a

1991, Sept. 29
2539   A1893 $1 gold & multi   2.00   .50
   a.   Black omitted   —

LITHOGRAPHED & ENGRAVED
1991, July 7
2540   A1894 $2.90 multicolored   6.00   1.50
   a.   Vert. pair, imperf horiz.   900.00
   b.   Black (engr.) omitted   750.00

Imperforates on gummed stamp paper, including gutter pairs and blocks, are proofs from the ABNCo. archives. From the same source also come imperforate progressive proofs. See No. 2540P in Proofs section of the Scott U.S. Specialized Catalogue.

1991, June 16   **Untagged**
2541   A1895 $9.95 multicolored   20.00   6.00
   a.   Imperf., pair   —

No. 2541 exists imperf plus black (engr.) omitted from printer's waste.

1991, Aug. 31   **Untagged**
2542   A1896 $14 multicolored   25.00   15.00
   a.   Red (engr. inscriptions)
     omitted   750.00

No. 2542 exists imperf plus red omitted from printer's waste.

PHOTOGRAVURE
1993, June 3   *Perf. 11x10¾*
2543   A1897 $2.90 multicolored   6.00   1.75

Faked examples of No. 2543, unused and used, exist with red omitted due to bleaching.

1995, June 22   *Perf. 11.2*
2544   A1898 $3 multicolored,
     dated "1995"   5.75   1.75
   b.   Dated "1996"   5.75   1.75
   c.   As "b," horiz. pair, imperf
     between   1,000.
   d.   As "b," imperf pair   700.00

Imperf examples of No. 2544 with "1995" date are believed to be printer's waste.

1995, Aug. 4   *Perf. 11*
2544A   A1898a $10.75 multi   20.00   9.00

No. 2544A was printed on paper embedded with red fibers.
Imperf examples of No. 2544A are believed to be printer's waste.

FISHING FLIES

Royal Wulff
A1899

Jock Scott
A1900

Apte Tarpon
Fly
A1901

Lefty's Deceiver A1902

Muddler Minnow A1903

PHOTOGRAVURE
BOOKLET STAMPS

Perf. 11 Horiz. on 1 or 2 Sides

1991, May 31

2545	A1899	29c multicolored	1.10	.25
a.		Black omitted	—	
b.		Horiz. pair, imperf. btwn., in #2549a with foldover	2,400.	
2546	A1900	29c multicolored	1.10	.25
a.		Black omitted	—	
2547	A1901	29c multicolored	1.10	.25
a.		Black omitted	—	
2548	A1902	29c multicolored	1.10	.25
2549	A1903	29c multicolored	1.10	.25
a.		Bklt. pane of 5, #2545-2549	5.50	3.00

Horiz. pairs, imperf vert., exist from printer's waste.

No. 2545b is unique and resulted from a foldover after perfing but before cutting. Both stamps are creased.

PERFORMING ARTS

Cole Porter (1891-1964), Composer — A1904

1991, June 8 **Perf. 11**

2550	A1904	29c multicolored	.60	.25
a.		Vert. pair, imperf. horiz.	400.00	

OPERATIONS DESERT SHIELD & DESERT STORM

S. W. Asia Service Medal — A1905

1991, July 2

2551	A1905	29c multicolored	.60	.25
a.		Vert. pair, imperf. horiz.	600.00	

No. 2551 is 21mm wide.

BOOKLET STAMP

Perf. 11 Vert. on 1 or 2 Sides

2552	A1905	29c multicolored	.60	.25
a.		Booklet pane of 5	3.00	2.25

No. 2552 is 20½mm wide. Inscriptions are shorter than on No. 2551.

No. 2552 Vert. pairs, imperf horiz., are from printer's waste.

1992 SUMMER OLYMPICS, BARCELONA

Discus A1908

Women's Sprints A1909

Javelin A1910

Women's Hurdles A1911

1991, July 12 **Perf. 11**

2553	A1907	29c multicolored	.60	.25
2554	A1908	29c multicolored	.60	.25
2555	A1909	29c multicolored	.60	.25
2556	A1910	29c multicolored	.60	.25
2557	A1911	29c multicolored	.60	.25
a.		Strip of 5, #2553-2557	3.00	2.25

NUMISMATICS

1858 Flying Eagle Cent, 1907 Standing Liberty Double Eagle, Series 1875 $1 Note, Series 1902 $10 National Currency Note — A1912

LITHOGRAPHED & ENGRAVED

1991, Aug. 13

2558	A1912	29c multicolored	.60	.25

WORLD WAR II

A1913

Designs and events of 1941: a, Military vehicles (Burma Road, 717-mile lifeline to China). b, Recruits (America's first peacetime draft). c, Shipments for allies (U.S. supports allies with Lend-Lease Act). d, Franklin D. Roosevelt, Winston Churchill (Atlantic Charter sets war aims of allies). e, Tank (America becomes the "arsenal of democracy.") f, Sinking of Destoyer Reuben James, Oct. 31. g, Gas mask, helmet (Civil defense mobilizes Americans at home). h, Liberty Ship, sea gull (First Liberty ship delivered December 30). i, Sinking ships (Japanese bomb Pearl Harbor, December 7). j, Congress in session (U.S. declares war on Japan, December 8). Central label is the size of 15 stamps and shows world map, extent of axis control.

LITHOGRAPHED & ENGRAVED

1991, Sept. 3

2559	A1913	Block of 10	7.50	5.00
a.-j.		29c any single	.75	.45
k.		Black (engr.) omitted	6,500.	

No. 2559 has selvage at left and right and either top or bottom.

BASKETBALL, 100TH ANNIVERSARY

Basketball, Hoop, Players' Arms — A1914

PHOTOGRAVURE

1991, Aug. 28

2560	A1914	29c multicolored	.60	.25

DISTRICT OF COLUMBIA BICENTENNIAL

Capitol Building from Pennsylvania Avenue, Circa 1903 — A1915

LITHOGRAPHED & ENGRAVED

1991, Sept. 7

2561	A1915	29c multicolored	.60	.25
a.		Black (engr.) omitted	85.00	

COMEDIANS

Stan Laurel and Oliver Hardy A1916

Edgar Bergen and Charlie McCarthy A1917

Jack Benny A1918

Fanny Brice A1919

Bud Abbott and Lou Costello A1920

BOOKLET STAMPS

Perf. 11 on 2 or 3 Sides

1991, Aug. 29

2562	A1916	29c multicolored	1.00	.25
2563	A1917	29c multicolored	1.00	.25
2564	A1918	29c multicolored	1.00	.25
2565	A1919	29c multicolored	1.00	.25
2566	A1920	29c multicolored	1.00	.25
a.		Strip of 5, #2562-2566	5.00	2.25
b.		Bklt. pane of 10, 2 each #2562-2566	10.00	5.00
c.		As "b," scar & brt violet (engr.) omitted	350.00	

BLACK HERITAGE SERIES

Jan E. Matzeliger (1852-1889), Inventor — A1921

PHOTOGRAVURE

1991, Sept. 15 **Perf. 11**

2567	A1921	29c multicolored	.60	.25
a.		Horiz. pair, imperf. vert.	600.00	
b.		Vert. pair, imperf. horiz.	550.00	
c.		Imperf., pair	275.00	

SPACE EXPLORATION

Mercury, Mariner 10 A1922

Venus, Mariner 2 A1923

Earth, Landsat A1924

Moon, Lunar Orbiter A1925

Mars, Viking Orbiter A1926

Jupiter, Pioneer 11 A1927

Saturn, Voyager 2 A1928

Uranus, Voyager 2 A1929

Neptune, Voyager 2 A1930

Pluto
A1931

PHOTOGRAVURE
BOOKLET STAMPS
Perf. 11 on 2 or 3 Sides
1991, Oct. 1

2568	A1922	29c multicolored	.90	.25
2569	A1923	29c multicolored	.90	.25
2570	A1924	29c multicolored	.90	.25
2571	A1925	29c multicolored	.90	.25
2572	A1926	29c multicolored	.90	.25
2573	A1927	29c multicolored	.90	.25
2574	A1928	29c multicolored	.90	.25
2575	A1929	29c multicolored	.90	.25
2576	A1930	29c multicolored	.90	.25
2577	A1931	29c multicolored	.90	.25
a.		Bklt. pane of 10, #2568-2577	9.00	4.50

CHRISTMAS

Madonna and
Child by
Antoniazzo
Romano
A1933

Santa Claus in
Chimney
A1934

Santa Checking
List — A1935

Santa with
Present — A1936

Santa at Fireplace
A1937

Santa and
Sleigh — A1938

LITHOGRAPHED & ENGRAVED
1991, Oct. 17 *Perf. 11¼*

2578	A1933	(29c) multi	.60	.25
a.		Booklet pane of 10	6.00	3.25
b.		Red & black (engr.) omitted	2,250.	

PHOTOGRAVURE
Perf. 11

2579	A1934	(29c) multi	.60	.25
		P# block of 4, 3#+A	2.50	—
		Zip block of 4	2.25	—
a.		Horiz. pair, imperf. vert.	175.00	
b.		Vert. pair, imperf. horiz.	350.00	

BOOKLET STAMPS
Size: 25x18½mm
Perf. 11 on 2 or 3 Sides

2580	A1934	(29c) multi, type I	2.00	.25
2581	A1934	(29c) multi, type II	2.00	.25
a.		Pair #2580-2581	4.00	.55
b.		Bklt. pane, 2 each, #2580-2581	8.00	1.25
2582	A1935	(29c) multi	.60	.25
a.		Bklt. pane of 4	2.40	1.25
2583	A1936	(29c) multi	.60	.25
a.		Bklt. pane of 4	2.40	1.25
2584	A1937	(29c) multi	.60	.25
a.		Bklt. pane of 4	2.40	1.25
2585	A1938	(29c) multi	.60	.25
a.		Bklt. pane of 4	2.40	1.25
		Nos. 2578-2585 (8)	7.60	2.00

The far left brick from the top row of the chimney is missing from Type II, No. 2581.
Imperfs of Nos. 2581, 2583-2585 are printer's waste.

A1939   A1942

A1944

ENGRAVED
1994-95 *Perf. 11.2*

2587	A1939	32c red brown	.65	.25

Perf. 11.5

2590	A1942	$1 blue	1.90	.50
2592	A1944	$5 slate green	8.00	2.50

Issued: $2, 5/5; $5, 8/19; 32c, 11/2/95.

Flag — A1946

Eagle and
Shield — A1947

A1950

Statue of
Liberty — A1951

BOOKLET STAMPS
PHOTOGRAVURE
Perf. 10 on 2 or 3 Sides
1992, Sept. 8

2593	A1946	29c black & multi	.60	.25
a.		Booklet pane of 10	6.00	4.25
d.		Imperf, pair	500.00	

Perf. 11x10 on 2 or 3 Sides

2593B	A1946	29c blk & multi	2.50	.50
c.		Bklt. pane of 10, shiny gum	30.00	7.50

Perf. 11x10 on 2 or 3 Sides
1993, Apr. 8 (?)

2594	A1946	29c red & multi	.65	.25
a.		Booklet pane of 10	6.50	4.25

Denomination is red on #2594 and black on #2593 and 2593B.

LITHOGRAPHED & ENGRAVED
(#2595), PHOTOGRAVURE
1992, Sept. 25 *Die Cut*
Self-Adhesive

2595	A1947	29c brn & multi	.75	.25
a.		Bklt. pane of 17 + label	12.75	
b.		Die cutting omitted, pair	90.00	
c.		Brown omitted	250.00	
d.		As "a," die cutting omitted	725.00	
2596	A1947	29c grn & multi	.75	.25
a.		Bklt. pane of 17 + label	12.75	
2597	A1947	29c red & multi	.75	.25
a.		Bklt. pane of 17 + label	12.75	

Plate No. and inscription reads down on No. 2595a and up on Nos. 2596a-2597a. Design is sharper and more finely detailed on Nos. 2595, 2597.
Nos. 2595a-2597a sold for $5 each.
Nos. 2595-2597 also available in strips with stamps spaced for use in affixing machines to service first day covers.

1994 *Die Cut*
Self-Adhesive

2598	A1950	29c red, cream & blue	.60	.25
a.		Booklet pane of 18	11.00	
b.		Coil with P#111	—	5.00
c.		Die cutting omitted, pair	1,000.	
2599	A1951	29c multi	.60	.25
a.		Booklet pane of 18	11.00	
b.		Coil with P#D1111	—	5.00

Except for Nos. 2598b and 2599b with plate numbers, coil stamps of Nos. 2595-2599 are indistinguishable from booklet stamps once they are removed from the backing paper.
See Nos. 3122-3122E.
Issued: No. 2598, 2/4; No. 2599, 6/24.

Scott values for used self-adhesive stamps are for examples either on piece or off piece.

A1956   A1957

A1959   A1960

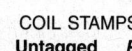

Flag Over White
House — A1961

COIL STAMPS
1991-93 Untagged *Perf. 10 Vert.*

2602	A1956	(10c) multi	.30	.25
a.		Imperf., pair	3,500.	
2603	A1957	(10c) org yel & multi	.30	.25
a.		Imperf., pair	20.00	
2604	A1957	(10c) gold & multi	.25	.25
2605	A1959	23c multi	.45	.40
a.		Imperf., pair		

Vertical pairs uncut between on gummed stamp paper are proofs from the ABNCo. archives. See No. 2605P in Proofs section of the Scott U.S. Specialized Catalogue.

2606	A1960	23c multi	.45	.40

"First-Class" is 9½mm long and "23" is 6mm long on No. 2606.

2607	A1960	23c multi	.45	.40
c.		Imperf., pair	65.00	

"First-Class" is 9mm long and "23" is 6½mm long on No. 2607.

2608	A1960	23c vio bl, red & blk	.80	.40

"First-Class" is 8½mm long and "23" is 6½mm long on No. 2608.
Nos. 2602-2608 are considered precancels by the USPS.

ENGRAVED
Tagged

2609	A1961	29c blue & red	.60	.25
a.		Imperf., pair	15.00	25.00
b.		Pair, imperf. between	60.00	
c.		Indigo blue & red	22.50	—
		Nos. 2602-2609 (8)	3.60	2.60

Beware of pairs with blind perfs sometimes offered as No. 2609b.
Issued: No. 2605, 9/27; No. 2602, 12/31; 29c, 4/23/92; No. 2606, 7/21/92; No. 2607, 10/9/92; Nos. 2603-2604, 5/29/93; No. 2608, 5/14/93.
See Nos. 2907, 3270-3271.

WINTER OLYMPICS

Hockey
A1963

Figure
Skating
A1964

Speed
Skating
A1965

Skiing
A1966

Bobsledding — A1967

PHOTOGRAVURE
1992, Jan. 11 *Perf. 11*

2611	A1963	29c multicolored	.60	.25
2612	A1964	29c multicolored	.60	.25
2613	A1965	29c multicolored	.60	.25
2614	A1966	29c multicolored	.60	.25
2615	A1967	29c multicolored	.60	.25
a.		Strip of 5, #2611-2615	3.00	2.50

WORLD COLUMBIAN STAMP EXPO

Portion of Vignette
of No. 129 — A1968

LITHOGRAPHED & ENGRAVED
1992, Jan. 24

2616	A1968	29c multicolored	.60	.25

BLACK HERITAGE SERIES

W.E.B. Du Bois
(1868-1963), Civil
Rights
Leader — A1969

1992, Jan. 31

2617	A1969	29c multicolored	.60	.25

LOVE

A1970

PHOTOGRAVURE

1992, Feb. 6

2618　A1970　29c multicolored　　　.60　.25
　　a.　Horiz. pair, imperf. vert.　300.00
　　b.　As "a," green omitted on
　　　　right stamp　　　　　　　1,250.

OLYMPIC BASEBALL

A1971

1992, Apr. 3　Tagged　Perf. 11

2619　A1971　29c multicolored　　　.60　.25

VOYAGES OF COLUMBUS

Seeking
Queen
Isabella's
Support
A1972

Crossing
the Atlantic
A1973

Approaching Land — A1974

Coming
Ashore
A1975

LITHOGRAPHED & ENGRAVED

1992, Apr. 24

2620　A1972　29c multicolored　　　.65　.25
2621　A1973　29c multicolored　　　.65　.25
2622　A1974　29c multicolored　　　.65　.25
2623　A1975　29c multicolored　　　.65　.25
　　a.　Block of 4, #2620-2623　　2.60　2.00

See Italy Nos. 1877-1880.

Souvenir Sheets

A1976

A1977

A1978

A1979

A1980

A1981

1992, May 22　　　　Perf. 10½
Tagged (15c-$5), Untagged

2624　A1976　Pane of 3　　2.25　1.50
　　a.　A71 1c deep blue　　.25　.25
　　b.　A74 4c ultramarine　　.25　.25
　　c.　A82 $1 salmon　　1.75　1.00
2625　A1977　Pane of 3　　7.50　5.00
　　a.　A72 2c brown violet　　.25　.25
　　b.　A73 3c green　　.25　.25
　　c.　A85 $4 crimson lake　　7.00　4.00
2626　A1978　Pane of 3　　1.75　1.25
　　a.　A75 5c chocolate　　.25　.25
　　b.　A80 30c orange brown　　.60　.30
　　c.　A81 50c slate blue　　.90　.50
2627　A1979　Pane of 3　　6.00　3.75
　　a.　A76 6c purple　　.25　.25
　　b.　A77 8c magenta　　.25　.25
　　c.　A84 $3 yellow green　　5.50　3.00
2628　A1980　Pane of 3　　4.25　3.00
　　a.　A78 10c black brown　　.25　.25
　　b.　A79 15c dark green　　.30　.25
　　c.　A83 $2 brown red　　3.50　2.00
2629　A1981　$5 Pane of 1　　8.75　6.00
　　a.　A86 $5 black, single stamp　8.50　5.00
　　Nos. 2624-2629 (6)　30.50　20.50

See Italy Nos. 1883-1888, Portugal Nos.
1918-1923 and Spain Nos. 2677-2682.

Imperforate souvenir sheets on gummed
stamp paper, singly or in pairs and blocks, are
proofs from the ABNCo. archives. Additionally,
one imperforate essay, with the background of
No. 2622 combined with the stamps of No.
2620, is recorded. See Nos. 2624P-2629P in
Proofs section of the Scott U.S. Specialized
Catalogue.

NEW YORK STOCK EXCHANGE BICENTENNIAL

A1982

1992, May 17　　　　Perf. 11

2630　A1982　29c green, red
　　　　　　& black　　　　.60　.25
　　a.　Black missing (EP)　　4,000.
　　b.　Black missing (CM)　　4,000.
　　c.　Center (black engr.) in-
　　　　verted　　　　　　　17,000.
　　d.　Se-tenant pair, #2630b
　　　　and #2630c　　　　22,500.

No. 2630a resulted from extraneous paper
that blocked the black from appearing on the
stamp paper. It is from a unique pane that
contained four color-missing errors plus a fifth
stamp missing half the black center.

No. 2630a must be collected se-tenant with
a normal stamp or with a stamp with half of
black engraving missing, or se-tenant with a
normal stamp and an additional 2630a.

No. 2630b may be collected alone or se-
tenant with No. 2630c.

Two panes, each containing 28 No. 2630c
and 12 No. 2630b, have been documented.

SPACE ACCOMPLISHMENTS

Cosmonaut,
U.S. Space
Shuttle
A1983

Astronaut,
Russian Space
Station
A1984

Sputnik, Vostok,
Apollo
Command &
Lunar Modules
A1985

Soyuz, Mercury
and Gemini
Spacecraft
A1986

PHOTOGRAVURE

1992, May 29

2631　A1983　29c multicolored　　.60　.25
2632　A1984　29c multicolored　　.60　.25
2633　A1985　29c multicolored　　.60　.25
2634　A1986　29c multicolored　　.60　.25
　　a.　Block of 4, #2631-2634　　2.40　2.00
　　b.　As "a," yellow omitted　　4,750.

The yellow color in Nos. 2631-2634 is easily
removed by exposure to sunlight. Expertization of No. 2634b is essential.

See Russia Nos. 6080-6083.

ALASKA HIGHWAY, 50th ANNIVERSARY

A1987

LITHOGRAPHED & ENGRAVED

1992, May 30

2635　A1987　29c multicolored　　.60　.25
　　a.　Black (engr.) omitted　　575.00

Almost half the recorded No. 2635a errors
are poorly centered. These sell for approximately $400.

KENTUCKY STATEHOOD BICENTENNIAL

A1988

PHOTOGRAVURE

1992, June 1

2636　A1988　29c multicolored　　.60　.25
　　a.　Dark blue missing (EP)　　—
　　b.　Dark blue and red missing
　　　　(EP)　　　　　　　　—
　　c.　All colors missing (EP)　　—

Nos. 2636a-2636c must be collected se-tenant with normal stamps.

SUMMER OLYMPICS

Soccer
A1989

Gymnastics
A1990

Volleyball
A1991

Boxing
A1992

Swimming
A1993

1992, June 11

2637　A1989　29c multicolored　　.60　.25
2638　A1990　29c multicolored　　.60　.25
2639　A1991　29c multicolored　　.60　.25

2640	A1992	29c multicolored		.60	.25
2641	A1993	29c multicolored		.60	.25
a.		Strip of 5, #2637-2641		3.00	2.50

HUMMINGBIRDS

Ruby-throated A1994   Broad-billed A1995

Costa's A1996   Rufous A1997

Calliope — A1998

BOOKLET STAMPS
Perf. 11 Vert. on 1 or 2 Sides
1992, June 15

2642	A1994	29c multicolored		.60	.25
2643	A1995	29c multicolored		.60	.25
2644	A1996	29c multicolored		.60	.25
2645	A1997	29c multicolored		.60	.25
2646	A1998	29c multicolored		.60	.25
a.		Bklt. pane of 5, #2642-2646		3.00	2.50

Imperforate singles, booklet panes and pane multiples or varieties on gummed stamp paper are proofs from the ABNCo. archives. From the same source also come imperforate progressive proofs. See No. 2646aP in Proofs section of the Scott U.S. Specialized Catalogue.

WILDFLOWERS

A1999

LITHOGRAPHED
1992, July 24   *Perf. 11*

2647	A1999	29c Indian paint-brush		.60	.60
2648	A2000	29c Fragrant water lily		.60	.60
2649	A2001	29c Meadow beauty		.60	.60
2650	A2002	29c Jack-in-the-pulpit		.60	.60
2651	A2003	29c California poppy		.60	.60
2652	A2004	29c Large-flowered trillium		.60	.60
2653	A2005	29c Tickseed		.60	.60
2654	A2006	29c Shooting star		.60	.60
2655	A2007	29c Stream violet		.60	.60
2656	A2008	29c Bluets		.60	.60
2657	A2009	29c Herb Robert		.60	.60
2658	A2010	29c Marsh marigold		.60	.60
2659	A2011	29c Sweet white violet		.60	.60
2660	A2012	29c Claret cup cactus		.60	.60
2661	A2013	29c White mountain avens		.60	.60
2662	A2014	29c Sessile bellwort		.60	.60
2663	A2015	29c Blue flag		.60	.60
2664	A2016	29c Harlequin lupine		.60	.60
2665	A2017	29c Twinflower		.60	.60
2666	A2018	29c Common sunflower		.60	.60
2667	A2019	29c Sego lily		.60	.60
2668	A2020	29c Virginia bluebells		.60	.60
2669	A2021	29c Ohi'a lehua		.60	.60
2670	A2022	29c Rosebud orchid		.60	.60
2671	A2023	29c Showy evening primrose		.60	.60
2672	A2024	29c Fringed gentian		.60	.60
2673	A2025	29c Yellow lady's slipper		.60	.60
2674	A2026	29c Passionflower		.60	.60
2675	A2027	29c Bunchberry		.60	.60
2676	A2028	29c Pasqueflower		.60	.60
2677	A2029	29c Round-lobed hepatica		.60	.60
2678	A2030	29c Wild columbine		.60	.60
2679	A2031	29c Fireweed		.60	.60
2680	A2032	29c Indian pond lily		.60	.60
2681	A2033	29c Turk's cap lily		.60	.60
2682	A2034	29c Dutchman's breeches		.60	.60
2683	A2035	29c Trumpet honeysuckle		.60	.60
2684	A2036	29c Jacob's ladder		.60	.60
2685	A2037	29c Plains prickly pear		.60	.60
2686	A2038	29c Moss campion		.60	.60
2687	A2039	29c Bearberry		.60	.60
2688	A2040	29c Mexican hat		.60	.60
2689	A2041	29c Harebell		.60	.60
2690	A2042	29c Desert five spot		.60	.60
2691	A2043	29c Smooth Solomon's seal		.60	.60
2692	A2044	29c Red maids		.60	.60
2693	A2045	29c Yellow skunk cabbage		.60	.60
2694	A2046	29c Rue anemone		.60	.60
2695	A2047	29c Standing cypress		.60	.60
2696	A2048	29c Wild flax		.60	.60
a.		A1999-A2048 Pane of 50, #2647-2696		30.00	—

WORLD WAR II

A2049

No. 2697 — Events of 1942: a, B-25's take off to raid Tokyo, Apr. 18. b, Ration coupons (Food and other commodities rationed). c, Divebomber and deck crewman (US wins Battle of the Coral Sea, May). d, Prisoners of war (Corregidor falls to Japanese, May 6). e, Dutch Harbor buildings on fire (Japan invades Aleutian Islands, June). f, Headphones, coded message (Allies decipher secret enemy codes). g, Yorktown lost, U.S. wins at Midway. h, Woman with drill (Millions of women join war effort). i, Marines land on Guadalcanal, Aug. 7. j, Tank in desert (Allies land in North Africa, Nov.).

Central label is the size of 15 stamps and shows world map, extent of axis control.

LITHOGRAPHED & ENGRAVED
1992, Aug. 17

2697	A2049	Block of 10	7.50	5.00
a.-j.		29c any single	.75	.30
k.		Red (litho.) omitted	4,000.	

No. 2697 has salvage at left and right and either top or bottom.

LITERARY ARTS SERIES

A2050

PHOTOGRAVURE
1992, Aug. 22

2698	A2050	29c multicolored		.60	.25

Dorothy Parker (1893-1967), author.

THEODORE VON KARMAN

A2051

1992, Aug. 31

2699	A2051	29c multicolored		.60	.25

Von Karman (1881-1963), rocket scientist.

MINERALS

Azurite — A2052

Copper — A2053

Variscite A2054

Wulfenite A2055

LITHOGRAPHED & ENGRAVED
1992, Sept. 17

2700	A2052	29c multicolored		.60	.25
2701	A2053	29c multicolored		.60	.25
2702	A2054	29c multicolored		.60	.25
2703	A2055	29c multicolored		.60	.25
a.		Block or strip of 4, #2700-2703		2.40	2.00
b.		As "a," silver (litho.) omitted	6,000.	
d.		As "a," silver omitted on two stamps	—	

JUAN RODRIGUEZ CABRILLO

Cabrillo, Ship, Map of San Diego Bay Area — A2056

1992, Sept. 28

2704	A2056	29c multicolored		.60	.25
a.		Black (engr.) omitted	1,500.	

WILD ANIMALS

Giraffe A2057

Giant Panda A2058

Flamingo A2059

King Penguins A2060

White Bengal Tiger A2061

PHOTOGRAVURE
BOOKLET STAMPS
Perf. 11 Horiz. on 1 or 2 Sides
1992, Oct. 1

2705	A2057	29c multicolored		.65	.25
2706	A2058	29c multicolored		.65	.25
2707	A2059	29c multicolored		.65	.25
2708	A2060	29c multicolored		.65	.25
2709	A2061	29c multicolored		.65	.25
a.		Booklet pane of 5, #2705-2709		3.25	2.25
b.		As "a," imperf.	2,000.	

CHRISTMAS

Madonna and Child, by Giovanni Bellini — A2062

Horse and Rider — A2063

Fire Pumper — A2064

Train Engine — A2065

Riverboat A2066

LITHOGRAPHED & ENGRAVED
1992   **Perf. 11¼**
2710	A2062	29c multicolored	.60	.25
a.		Booklet pane of 10	6.00	3.50

LITHOGRAPHED
Perf. 11¼x11
2711	A2063	29c multicolored	.75	.25
2712	A2064	29c multicolored	.75	.25
2713	A2065	29c multicolored	.75	.25
2714	A2066	29c multicolored	.75	.25
a.		Block of 4, #2711-2714	3.00	1.10

Booklet Stamps
PHOTOGRAVURE
Perf. 11 on 2 or 3 Sides
2715	A2063	29c multicolored	.90	.25
2716	A2064	29c multicolored	.90	.25
2717	A2065	29c multicolored	.90	.25
2718	A2066	29c multicolored	.90	.25
a.		Booklet pane of 4, #2715-2718	3.60	1.25

Imperforates and part-perforates on gummed stamp paper are proofs from the ABNCo. archives. From the same source come imperforates with Toys only and imperforates without denominations. See No. 2718aP in Proofs section of the Scott U.S. Specialized Catalogue.

Self-Adhesive
Die Cut
2719	A2065	29c multicolored	.65	.25
a.		Booklet pane of 18	12.00	

"Greetings" is 27mm long on Nos. 2711-2714, 25mm long on Nos. 2715-2718 and 21½mm long on No. 2719. Nos. 2715-2719 differ in color from Nos. 2711-2714.
Issued: #2710-2718, 10/22; #2719, 10/28.

CHINESE NEW YEAR

Year of the Rooster A2067

LITHOGRAPHED & ENGRAVED
1992, Dec. 30   **Perf. 11**
2720	A2067	29c multicolored	.60	.25

See Nos. 3895j, 3997j.

AMERICAN MUSIC SERIES

Elvis Presley A2068

Oklahoma! A2069

Hank Williams A2070

Elvis Presley A2071

Bill Haley A2072

Clyde McPhatter A2073

Ritchie Valens A2074

Otis Redding A2075

Buddy Holly A2076

Dinah Washington A2077

PHOTOGRAVURE
1993   **Perf. 11**
2721	A2068	29c multicolored	.60	.25
a.		Imperf, pair	—	

Perf. 10
2722	A2069	29c multicolored	.60	.25
2723	A2070	29c multicolored	.75	.25

Perf. 11.2x11.5
2723A	A2070	29c multicolored	12.00	10.00

1993, June 16   **Perf. 10**
2724	A2071	29c multicolored	.70	.25
2725	A2072	29c multicolored	.70	.25
2726	A2073	29c multicolored	.70	.25
2727	A2074	29c multicolored	.70	.25
2728	A2075	29c multicolored	.70	.25
2729	A2076	29c multicolored	.70	.25
2730	A2077	29c multicolored	.70	.25
a.		Vert. strip of 7, #2724-2730	5.50	3.00

Booklet Stamps
Perf. 11 Horiz. on 1 or 2 Sides
2731	A2071	29c multicolored	.65	.25
2732	A2072	29c multicolored	.65	.25
2733	A2073	29c multicolored	.65	.25
2734	A2074	29c multicolored	.65	.25
2735	A2075	29c multicolored	.65	.25
2736	A2076	29c multicolored	.65	.25
2737	A2077	29c multicolored	.65	.25
a.		Booklet pane, 2 #2731, 1 each #2732-2737	5.25	2.25
b.		Booklet pane, #2731, 2735-2737 + tab	2.60	1.50

Nos. 2731-2737 have smaller design sizes, brighter colors and shorter inscriptions than Nos. 2724-2730, as well as framelines around the designs and other subtle design differences.
No. 2737b without tab is indistinguishable from broken No. 2737a.
Imperforates of both No. 2737a and 2737b on gummed stamp paper are proofs from the ABNCo. archives. Perforated booklet pane multiples and varieties also exist from the same source. See Nos. 2737aP-2737bP in

Proofs section of the Scott U.S. Specialized Catalogue.
See Nos. 2769, 2771, 2775 and designs A2112-A2117.

SPACE FANTASY

A2086

A2087

A2088   A2089

A2090

BOOKLET STAMPS
1993, Jan. 25   **Perf. 11 Vert.**
2741	A2086	29c multicolored	.60	.25
2742	A2087	29c multicolored	.60	.25
2743	A2088	29c multicolored	.60	.25
2744	A2089	29c multicolored	.60	.25
2745	A2090	29c multicolored	.60	.25
a.		Booklet pane of 5, #2741-2745	3.00	2.25

BLACK HERITAGE SERIES

Percy Lavon Julian (1899-1975), Chemist — A2091

LITHOGRAPHED & ENGRAVED
1993, Jan. 29   **Perf. 11**
2746	A2091	29c multicolored	.60	.25

OREGON TRAIL

A2092

1993, Feb. 12
2747	A2092	29c multicolored	.60	.25
b.		Blue omitted	650.00	

WORLD UNIVERSITY GAMES

A2093

PHOTOGRAVURE
1993, Feb. 25
2748	A2093	29c multicolored	.60	.25

GRACE KELLY (1929-1982)

Actress, Princess of Monaco — A2094

ENGRAVED
1993, Mar. 24
2749	A2094	29c deep ultra	.60	.25

See Monaco No. 1851.

CIRCUS

Clown — A2095

Ringmaster A2096

Trapeze Artist — A2097

Elephant A2098

LITHOGRAPHED
1993, Apr. 6
2750	A2095	29c multicolored	.60	.25
2751	A2096	29c multicolored	.60	.25
2752	A2097	29c multicolored	.60	.25
2753	A2098	29c multicolored	.60	.25
a.		Block of 4, #2750-2753	2.40	1.75

CHEROKEE STRIP LAND RUN, CENTENNIAL

A2099

LITHOGRAPHED & ENGRAVED
1993, Apr. 17
2754	A2099	29c multicolored	.60	.25

Imperforates on gummed stamp paper, including gutter pairs and blocks, are proofs from the ABNCo. archives. From the same source also come perforated gutter pairs and blocks, plus imperforates missing the red text and black denomination and "USA." An approved die proof also is recorded. See No. 2754P in Proofs section of the Scott U.S. Specialized Catalogue.

DEAN ACHESON (1893-1971)

Secretary of State — A2100

ENGRAVED

1993, Apr. 21
2755 A2100 29c greenish gray .60 .25

SPORTING HORSES

Steeplechase — A2101

Thoroughbred Racing — A2102

Harness Racing A2103

Polo A2104

LITHOGRAPHED & ENGRAVED

1993, May 1   **Perf. 11x11½**
2756 A2101 29c multicolored .60 .25
2757 A2102 29c multicolored .60 .25
2758 A2103 29c multicolored .60 .25
2759 A2104 29c multicolored .60 .25
  a.   Block of 4, #2756-2759   2.40 2.00
  b.   As "a," black (engr.) omitted   500.00

GARDEN FLOWERS

Hyacinth A2105   Daffodil A2106

Tulip — A2107

Iris — A2108

Lilac — A2109

LITHOGRAPHED & ENGRAVED BOOKLET STAMPS

1993, May 15   **Perf. 11 Vert.**
2760 A2105 29c multicolored .60 .25
2761 A2106 29c multicolored .60 .25
2762 A2107 29c multicolored .60 .25
2763 A2108 29c multicolored .60 .25
2764 A2109 29c multicolored .60 .25
  a.   Booklet pane of 5, #2760-2764   3.00 2.25
  b.   As "a," black (engr.) omitted   135.00
  c.   As "a," imperf.   700.00

WORLD WAR II

A2110

Designs and events of 1943: a, Destroyers (Allied forces battle German U-boats). b, Military medics treat the wounded. c, Amphibious landing craft on beach (Sicily attacked by Allied forces, July). d, B-24s hit Ploesti refineries, August. e, V-mail delivers letters from home. f, PT boat (Italy invaded by Allies, Sept.). g, Nos. WS7, WS8, savings bonds, (Bonds and stamps help war effort). h, "Willie and Joe" keep spirits high. i, Banner in window (Gold Stars mark World War II losses). j, Marines assault Tarawa, Nov.

Central label is the size of 15 stamps and shows world map with extent of Axis control and Allied operations.

1993, May 31   **Perf. 11**
2765 A2110   Block of 10   7.50 5.00
  a.-j.   29c any single   .75 .40

No. 2765 has selvage at left and right and either top or bottom.

JOE LOUIS (1914-1981)

A2111

LITHOGRAPHED & ENGRAVED

1993, June 22
2766 A2111 29c multicolored .60 .25

AMERICAN MUSIC SERIES
Oklahoma! Type and

Show Boat A2112

Porgy & Bess A2113

My Fair Lady A2114

BOOKLET STAMPS
PHOTOGRAVURE

Perf. 11 Horiz. on 1 or 2 Sides
1993, July 14
2767 A2112 29c multicolored .60 .25
2768 A2113 29c multicolored .60 .25
2769 A2069 29c multicolored .60 .25
2770 A2114 29c multicolored .60 .25
  a.   Booklet pane of 4, #2767-2770   2.75 2.25

No. 2769 has smaller design size, brighter colors and shorter inscription than No. 2722, as well as a frameline around the design and other subtle design differences.

Imperforate booklet panes, singly or in multiples, on gummed stamp paper are proofs from the ABNCo. archives. From the same source come imperforate progressive proofs, plus imperforate proofs/essays showing slightly altered designs. See No. 2770aP in Proofs section of the Scott U.S. Specialized Catalogue.

AMERICAN MUSIC SERIES
Hank Williams Type and

Patsy Cline A2115

The Carter Family A2116

Bob Wills A2117

PHOTOGRAVURE

1993, Sept. 25   **Perf. 10**
2771 A2070 29c multicolored .75 .25
2772 A2115 29c multicolored .75 .25
2773 A2116 29c multicolored .75 .25
2774 A2117 29c multicolored .75 .25
  a.   Block or horiz. strip of 4, #2771-2774   3.00 1.75

Booklet Stamps
Perf. 11 Horiz. on one or two sides
With Black Frameline

2775 A2070 29c multicolored .60 .25
2776 A2116 29c multicolored .60 .25
2777 A2115 29c multicolored .60 .25

2778 A2117 29c multicolored .60 .25
  a.   Booklet pane of 4, #2775-2778   2.50 2.00

Inscription at left measures 27½mm on No. 2723, 27mm on No. 2771 and 22mm on No. 2775. No. 2723 shows only two tuning keys on guitar, while No. 2771 shows those two and parts of two others.

Imperforate booklet panes on gummed stamp paper, singly or in multiples, are proofs from the ABNCo. archives. From the same source come panes perfed horiz. but uncut vertically, plus imperforate progressive proofs and other die proof varieties. See No. 2778aP in Proofs section in the Scott U.S. Specialized Catalogue.

NATIONAL POSTAL MUSEUM

Independence Hall, Benjamin Franklin, Printing Press, Colonial Post Rider — A2118

Pony Express Rider, Civil War Soldier, Concord Stagecoach A2119

JN-4H Biplane, Charles Lindbergh, Railway Mail Car, 1931 Model A Ford Mail Truck A2120

California Gold Rush Miner's Letter, Nos. 39, 295, C3a, C13, Barcode & Circular Date Stamp A2121

LITHOGRAPHED AND ENGRAVED

1993, July 30   **Tagged**   **Perf. 11**
2779 A2118 29c multicolored .60 .25
2780 A2119 29c multicolored .60 .25
2781 A2120 29c multicolored .60 .25
2782 A2121 29c multicolored .60 .25
  a.   Block or strip of 4, #2779-2782   2.40 2.00
  b.   As "a," engr. maroon (USA/29) and black ("My dear...") omitted   2,500.
  c.   As "a," imperf   2,500.

AMERICAN SIGN LANGUAGE

A2122

A2123

PHOTOGRAVURE
1993, Sept. 20　　　　　*Perf. 11½*

2783	A2122	29c multicolored	.60 .25
2784	A2123	29c multicolored	.60 .25
a.		Pair, #2783-2784	1.20 .75

CLASSIC BOOKS

A2124

A2125

A2126

A2127

Designs: No. 2785, Rebecca of Sunnybrook Farm, by Kate Douglas Wiggin. No. 2786, Little House on the Prairie, by Laura Ingalls Wilder. No. 2787, The Adventures of Huckleberry Finn, by Mark Twain. No. 2788, Little Women, by Louisa May Alcott.

LITHOGRAPHED & ENGRAVED
1993, Oct. 23　　　　　*Perf. 11*

2785	A2124	29c multicolored	.60 .25
2786	A2125	29c multicolored	.60 .25
2787	A2126	29c multicolored	.60 .25
2788	A2127	29c multicolored	.60 .25
a.		Block or horiz. strip of 4, #2785-2788	2.40 2.00

Imperforates on gummed stamp paper, including gutter pairs and blocks, are proofs from the ABNCo. archives. See No. 2788aP in Proofs section of the Scott U.S. Specialized Catalogue.

CHRISTMAS

Madonna and Child in a Landscape, by Giovanni Battista Cima — A2128

Jack-in-the-Box
A2129

Red-Nosed Reindeer
A2130

Snowman
A2131

Toy Soldier Blowing Horn
A2132

1993, Oct. 21

2789	A2128	29c multicolored	.60 .25

Booklet Stamp
Size: 18x25mm
Perf. 11½x11 on 2 or 3 Sides

2790	A2128	29c multicolored	.60 .25
a.		Booklet pane of 4	2.40 1.75
b.		Imperf., pair	—
c.		As "a," imperf	—

Nos. 2789-2790 have numerous design differences.

1993　　　　　*Perf. 11½*

PHOTOGRAVURE

2791	A2129	29c multicolored	.60 .25
2792	A2130	29c multicolored	.60 .25
2793	A2131	29c multicolored	.60 .25
2794	A2132	29c multicolored	.60 .25
a.		Block or strip of 4, #2791-2794	2.40 2.00

Booklet Stamps
Size: 18x21mm
Perf. 11x10 on 2 or 3 Sides

2795	A2132	29c multicolored	.85 .25
2796	A2131	29c multicolored	.85 .25
2797	A2130	29c multicolored	.85 .25
2798	A2129	29c multicolored	.85 .25
a.		Booklet pane, 3 each #2795-2796, 2 each #2797-2798	8.50 4.00
b.		Booklet pane, 3 each #2797-2798, 2 each #2795-2796	8.50 4.00
c.		Block of 4, #2795-2798	3.40 1.75

Self-Adhesive
Size: 19½x26½mm
Die Cut

2799	A2131	29c multicolored	.75 .25
a.		Coil with plate # V1111111	— 6.00
b.		Horiz. coil strip of 4, #2799-2802	3.00
2800	A2132	29c multicolored	.75 .25
2801	A2129	29c multicolored	.75 .25
2802	A2130	29c multicolored	.75 .25
a.		Booklet pane, 3 each #2799-2802	9.00
b.		Block of 4, #2799-2802	3.00

Except for No. 2799 with plate number, coil stamps are indistinguishable from booklet stamps once they are removed from the backing paper.

Size: 17x20mm

2803	A2131	29c multicolored	.60 .25
a.		Booklet pane of 18	11.00

Snowman on Nos. 2793, 2799 has three buttons and seven snowflakes beneath nose (placement differs on both stamps). No. 2796 has two buttons and five snowflakes beneath nose. No. 2803 has two orange buttons and four snowflakes beneath nose.

Issued: #2791-2798, 10/21; #2799-2803, 10/28.

MARIANA ISLANDS

A2133

LITHOGRAPHED AND ENGRAVED
1993, Nov. 4　　　　　*Perf. 11*

2804	A2133	29c multicolored	.60 .25

COLUMBUS' LANDING IN PUERTO RICO, 500th ANNIVERSARY

A2134

PHOTOGRAVURE
1993, Nov. 19　　　　　*Perf. 11.2*

2805	A2134	29c multicolored	.60 .25

AIDS AWARENESS

A2135

1993, Dec. 1

2806	A2135	29c black & red	.60 .25
a.		Perf. 11 vert. on 1 or 2 sides, from bklt. pane	.70 .25
b.		As "a," booklet pane of 5	3.50 2.00

WINTER OLYMPICS

Slalom — A2136

Luge — A2137

Ice Dancing
A2138

Cross-Country Skiing
A2139

Ice Hockey — A2140

LITHOGRAPHED
1994, Jan. 6

2807	A2136	29c multicolored	.60 .25
2808	A2137	29c multicolored	.60 .25
2809	A2138	29c multicolored	.60 .25
2810	A2139	29c multicolored	.60 .25
2811	A2140	29c multicolored	.60 .25
a.		Strip of 5, #2807-2811	3.00 2.50

EDWARD R. MURROW, JOURNALIST (1908-65)

A2141

ENGRAVED
1994, Jan. 21

2812	A2141	29c brown	.60 .25

LOVE

A2142

A2143

A2144

Booklet Stamps
LITHOGRAPHED & ENGRAVED
1994　　　　　*Die Cut*
Self-adhesive

2813	A2142	29c multicolored	.60 .25
a.		Booklet pane of 18	11.00
b.		Coil with plate # B1	— 5.00

Except for No. 2813b with plate number, coil stamps are indistinguishable from booklet stamps once they are removed from the backing paper.

PHOTOGRAVURE
Perf. 10.9x11.1 on 2 or 3 sides

2814	A2143	29c multicolored	.60 .25
a.		Booklet pane of 10	6.00 3.50
b.		Imperf, pair	—
d.		As "a," imperf.	—

Horiz. pairs, imperf between, are printer's waste.
No. 2814 was issued in booklets only.

LITHOGRAPHED & ENGRAVED
Perf. 11.1

2814C	A2143	29c multicolored	.70 .25

Size of No. 2814C is 20x28mm. No. 2814 is 18x24½mm.

PHOTOGRAVURE & ENGRAVED
Perf. 11.2

2815	A2144	52c multicolored	1.00 .25

Issued: No. 2813, Jan. 27; Nos. 2814-2815, Feb. 14; No. 2814C, June 11.

BLACK HERITAGE SERIES

Dr. Allison Davis (1902-83), Social Anthropologist, Educator — A2145

ENGRAVED
1994, Feb. 1　　　　　*Perf. 11.2*

2816	A2145	29c red brown & brown	.60 .25

CHINESE NEW YEAR

Year of the Dog
A2146

PHOTOGRAVURE
1994, Feb. 5

2817	A2146	29c multicolored	.80 .25

See Nos. 3895k, 3997k.

BUFFALO SOLDIERS

A2147

LITHOGRAPHED & ENGRAVED
1994, Apr. 22　　　　　*Perf. 11.5x11.2*

2818	A2147	29c multicolored	.60 .25
a.		Double impression (second impression light) of red brown (engr. inscriptions)	

SILENT SCREEN STARS

Rudolph Valentino (1895-1926)
A2148

Clara Bow (1905-65)
A2149

Charlie Chaplin (1889-1977)
A2150

Lon Chaney (1883-1930)
A2151

John Gilbert (1895-1936)
A2152

Zasu Pitts (1898-1963)
A2153

Harold Lloyd (1894-1971)
A2154

Keystone Cops
A2155

Theda Bara (1885-1955)
A2156

Buster Keaton (1895-1966)
A2157

1994, Apr. 27   *Perf. 11.2*

2819	A2148	29c red, blk & brt vio	1.10	.30
2820	A2149	29c red, blk & brt vio	1.10	.30
2821	A2150	29c red, blk & brt vio	1.10	.30
2822	A2151	29c red, blk & brt vio	1.10	.30
2823	A2152	29c red, blk & brt vio	1.10	.30
2824	A2153	29c red, blk & brt vio	1.10	.30
2825	A2154	29c red, blk & brt vio	1.10	.30
2826	A2155	29c red, blk & brt vio	1.10	.30
2827	A2156	29c red, blk & brt vio	1.10	.30
2828	A2157	29c red, blk & brt vio	1.10	.30
a.		Block of 10, #2819-2828	11.00	5.00
b.		As "a," black (litho.) omitted	—	
c.		As "a," blk, red & brt vio (litho.) omitted	—	

GARDEN FLOWERS

Lily — A2158

Zinnia — A2159

Gladiola
A2160

Marigold
A2161

Rose — A2162

1994, Apr. 28   *Perf. 10.9 Vert.*
Booklet Stamps

2829	A2158	29c multicolored	.60	.25
2830	A2159	29c multicolored	.60	.25
2831	A2160	29c multicolored	.60	.25
2832	A2161	29c multicolored	.60	.25
2833	A2162	29c multicolored	.60	.25
a.		Booklet pane of 5, #2829-2833	3.00	2.25
b.		As "a," imperf	400.00	
c.		As "a," black (engr.) omitted	125.00	

1994 WORLD CUP SOCCER CHAMPIONSHIPS

A2163

A2163a

A2164

A2165

Design: 40c, Soccer player, diff.

PHOTOGRAVURE
1994, May 26   *Perf. 11.1*

2834	A2163	29c multicolored	.60	.25
2835	A2163a	40c multicolored	.80	.25
2836	A2164	50c multicolored	1.00	.25
		Nos. 2834-2836 (3)	2.40	.75

Souvenir Sheet of 3

2837	A2165	#a.-#c.	4.50	3.00

No. 2837c has a portion of the yellow map in the LR corner.

WORLD WAR II

A2166

Designs and events of 1944: a, Allied forces retake New Guinea. b, P-51s escort B-17s on bombing raids. c, Troops running from landing craft (Allies in Normandy, D-Day, June 6). d, Airborne units spearhead attacks. e, Officer at periscope (Submarines shorten war in Pacific). f, Parade (Allies free Rome, June 4; Paris, Aug. 25).

g, Soldier firing flamethrower (US troops clear Saipan bunkers). h, Red Ball Express speeds vital supplies. i, Battleship firing main battery (Battle for Leyte Gulf, Oct. 23-26). j, Soldiers in snow (Bastogne and Battle of the Bulge, Dec.).

Central label is size of 15 stamps and shows world map with extent of Axis control and Allied operations.

Illustration reduced.

LITHOGRAPHED & ENGRAVED
1994, June 6   *Perf. 10.9*

2838	A2166	Block of 10	17.00	10.00
a.-j.		29c any single	1.70	.50

No. 2838 has selvage at left and right and either top or bottom.

NORMAN ROCKWELL

A2167

A2168

1994, July 1   *Perf. 10.9x11.1*

2839	A2167	29c multicolored	.60	.25

Souvenir Sheet
LITHOGRAPHED

2840	A2168	Sheet of 4	4.50	2.75
a.		50c Freedom From Want	1.10	.65
b.		50c Freedom From Fear	1.10	.65
c.		50c Freedom of Speech	1.10	.65
d.		50c Freedom of Worship	1.10	.65

Moon Landing, 25th Anniv.

A2169

A2170

Miniature Sheet
1994, July 20   *Perf. 11.2x11.1*

2841	A2169	29c Sheet of 12	10.50	—
a.		Single stamp	.85	.60

LITHOGRAPHED & ENGRAVED
Perf. 10.7x11.1

2842	A2170	$9.95 multicolored	20.00	16.00

LOCOMOTIVES

Hudson's General
A2171

McQueen's Jupiter
A2172

Eddy's No. 242
A2173

Ely's No. 10
A2174

Buchanan's No. 999
A2175

PHOTOGRAVURE
1994, July 28   *Perf. 11 Horiz.*
Booklet Stamps

2843	A2171	29c multicolored	.75	.25
2844	A2172	29c multicolored	.75	.25
2845	A2173	29c multicolored	.75	.25
2846	A2174	29c multicolored	.75	.25
2847	A2175	29c multicolored	.75	.25
a.		Booklet pane of 5, #2843-2847	3.75	2.00
b.		As "a," imperf.	2,500.	

GEORGE MEANY, LABOR LEADER (1894-1980)

A2176

ENGRAVED
1994, Aug. 16   *Perf. 11.1x11*

2848	A2176	29c blue	.60	.25

AMERICAN MUSIC SERIES
Popular Singers

Al Jolson (1886-1950) A2177

Bing Crosby (1904-77) A2178

Ethel Waters (1896-1977) A2179

Nat "King" Cole (1919-65) A2180

Ethel Merman (1908-84) A2181

Jazz Singers

Bessie Smith (1894-1937) A2182

Muddy Waters (1915-83) A2183

Billie Holiday (1915-59) A2184

Robert Johnson (1911-38) A2185

Jimmy Rushing (1902-72) A2186

"Ma" Rainey (1886-1939) A2187

Mildred Bailey (1907-51) A2188

Howlin' Wolf (1910-76) A2189

PHOTOGRAVURE

1994, Sept. 1			**Perf. 10.1x10.2**	
2849	A2177	29c multicolored	.85	.25
2850	A2178	29c multicolored	.85	.25
2851	A2179	29c multicolored	.85	.25
2852	A2180	29c multicolored	.85	.25
2853	A2181	29c multicolored	.85	.25
a.		Vert. strip of 5, #2849-2853	4.25	2.00
b.		Pane of 20, imperf	10,000.	

1994, Sept. 17			**Perf. 11x10.8**	
2854	A2182	29c multicolored	1.50	.25
2855	A2183	29c multicolored	1.50	.25
2856	A2184	29c multicolored	1.50	.25
2857	A2185	29c multicolored	1.50	.25
2858	A2186	29c multicolored	1.50	.25
2859	A2187	29c multicolored	1.50	.25
2860	A2188	29c multicolored	1.50	.25
2861	A2189	29c multicolored	1.50	.25
a.		Block of 10, #2854-2861 +2 additional stamps	15.00	4.50

LITHOGRAPHED

(see above)

LITERARY ARTS SERIES

James Thurber (1894-1961) A2190

LITHOGRAPHED & ENGRAVED

1994, Sept. 10			**Perf. 11**	
2862	A2190	29c multicolored	.60	.25

WONDERS OF THE SEA

Diver, Motorboat A2191

Diver, Ship A2192

Diver, Ship's Wheel A2193

Diver, Coral A2194

LITHOGRAPHED

1994, Oct. 3			**Perf. 11x10.9**	
2863	A2191	29c multicolored	.75	.25
2864	A2192	29c multicolored	.75	.25
2865	A2193	29c multicolored	.75	.25
2866	A2194	29c multicolored	.75	.25
a.		Block of 4, #2863-2866	3.00	1.50
b.		As "a," imperf	450.00	

CRANES

Black-Necked A2195

Whooping A2196

LITHOGRAPHED & ENGRAVED

1994, Oct. 9			**Perf. 10.8x11**	
2867	A2195	29c multicolored	.70	.25
2868	A2196	29c multicolored	.70	.25
a.		Pair, #2867-2868	1.40	.75
b.		As "a," black & magenta (engr.) omitted	1,250.	
c.		As "a," double impression of engr. black (Birds' names and "USA") & magenta ("29")	3,000.	
d.		As "a," double impression of engr. black ("USA") & magenta ("29")	3,000.	

See People's Republic of China Nos. 2528-2529.

LEGENDS OF THE WEST

A2197

g. Bill Pickett (1870-1932) (Revised)

Designs: a, Home on the Range. b, Buffalo Bill Cody (1846-1917). c, Jim Bridger (1804-81). d, Annie Oakley (1860-1926). e, Native American Culture. f, Chief Joseph (c. 1840-1904). h, Bat Masterson (1853-1921). i, John C. Fremont (1813-90). j, Wyatt Earp (1848-1929). k, Nellie Cashman (c. 1849-1925). l, Charles Goodnight (1826-1929). m, Geronimo (1823-1909). n, Kit Carson (1809-68). o, Wild Bill Hickok (1837-76). p, Western Wildlife. q, Jim Beckwourth (c. 1798-1866). r, Bill Tilghman (1854-1924). s, Sacagawea (c. 1787-1812). t, Overland Mail.

PHOTOGRAVURE

1994, Oct. 18			**Perf. 10.1x10**	
2869	A2197	Pane of 20	15.00	10.00
a.-t.		29c any single	.75	.50
u.		As No. 2869, a.-e. imperf.		
		f.-j. part perf.	—	

LEGENDS OF THE WEST (Recalled)

g. Bill Pickett (Recalled)

Nos. 2870b-2870d, 2870f-2870o, 2870q-2870s have a frameline around the vignette that is half the width of the frameline on similar stamps in No. 2869. Other design differences may exist.

1994

2870	A2197	29c Pane of 20	125.00	—

150,000 panes of No. 2870 were made available through a drawing. Panes were delivered in an envelope. Value is for pane without envelope. Panes with envelopes sell for somewhat more.

CHRISTMAS

Madonna and Child, by Elisabetta Sirani A2200

Stocking A2201

Santa Claus A2202

Cardinal in Snow A2203

LITHOGRAPHED & ENGRAVED

1994, Oct. 20			**Perf. 11¼**	
2871	A2200	29c multi	.60	.25

BOOKLET STAMP
Perf. 9¾x11

2871A	A2200	29c multi	.60	.25
b.		Booklet pane of 10	6.25	3.50
c.		Imperf, pair	350.00	

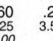

LITHOGRAPHED
Perf. 11¼

2872	A2201 29c multi		.60	.25
a.	Booklet pane of 20		12.50	6.00
b.	Imperf., pair		—	
c.	Vert. pair, imperf. horiz.		—	
d.	Quadruple impression of black, triple impression of blue, double impressions of red and yellow, green normal		900.00	
e.	Vert. pair, imperf. between		125.00	
f.	As "a," imperf.			

PHOTOGRAVURE
BOOKLET STAMPS
Self-Adhesive
Die Cut

2873	A2202 29c multi		.70	.25
a.	Booklet pane of 12		8.50	
b.	Coil with plate #V1111		—	5.75

Except for No. 2873b with plate number, coil stamps are indistinguishable from booklet stamps once they are removed from the backing paper.

2874	A2203 29c multi		.60	.25
a.	Booklet pane of 18		11.00	

BUREAU OF ENGRAVING & PRINTING
Souvenir Sheet

A2204

LITHOGRAPHED & ENGRAVED
1994, Nov. 3 — Perf. 11

2875	A2204 $2 Pane of 4		16.00	13.50
a.	Single stamp		4.00	2.00
b.	Pane of 4 with double impression of the brown lettering panel		1,200.	

The double impression is clear, but may be seen best in the scrolls at lower right.

CHINESE NEW YEAR

Year of the Boar
A2205

PHOTOGRAVURE
1994, Dec. 30 — Perf. 11.2x11.1

2876	A2205 29c multicolored		.70	.25

See Nos. 3895l, 3997l.

A2206

LITHOGRAPHED
Perf. 11x10.8
1994, Dec. 13 — Untagged

2877	A2206 (3c) tan, brt bl & red		.25	.25
a.	Imperf., pair		115.00	
b.	Double impression of red		175.00	

No. 2877 imperf and with blue omitted is known from printer's waste.

Perf. 10.8x10.9
Untagged

2878	A2206 (3c) tan, dk bl & red		.25	.25

Inscriptions on #2877 are in a thin typeface. Those on #2878 are in heavy, bold type.

A2207

PHOTOGRAVURE
Perf. 11.2x11.1

2879	A2207 (20c) black "G," yel & multi		.40	.25
a.	Imperf., pair		—	

Perf. 11x10.9

2880	A2207 (32c) red "G," yel & multi		.75	.25

A2208

Perf. 11.2x11.1

2881	A2208 (32c) black "G" & multi		1.25	.25
a.	Booklet pane of 10		12.50	5.00

Perf. 11x10.9

2882	A2208 (32c) red "G" & multi		.60	.25

Distance on #2882 from bottom of red G to top of flag immediately above is 13¾mm.

BOOKLET STAMPS
Perf. 10x9.9 on 2 or 3 Sides

2883	A2208 (32c) black "G" & multi		.65	.25
a.	Booklet pane of 10		6.50	3.75

Perf. 10.9 on 2 or 3 Sides

2284	A2208 (32c) blue "G" & multi		.65	.25
a.	Booklet pane of 10		6.50	3.75
b.	As "a," imperf		4,500.	
c.	Horiz. pair, imperf. btwn. due to miscut		—	
d.	Horiz. pair, imperf. vert.		—	

Perf. 11x10.9 on 2 or 3 Sides

2285	A2208 (32c) red "G" & multi		.90	.25
a.	Booklet pane of 10		9.00	4.50
b.	Horiz. pair, imperf vert.		750.00	
c.	Horiz. pair, imperf. btwn., in #2885a with foldover		—	

Distance on #2885 from bottom of red G to top of flag immediately above is 13½mm. See note below #2882.

No. 2885c resulted from a paper foldover after perforating and before cutting into panes.

No. 2886

No. 2887

Die Cut
Self-Adhesive

2286	A2208 (32c) gray, bl, lt bl, lt blk, red & blk		.70	.25
a.	Booklet pane of 18		12.50	
b.	Coil with plate # V11111		—	9.50

No. 2886 is printed on prephosphored paper that is opaque, thicker and brighter than that of No. 2887 and has only a small number of blue shading dots in the white stripes immediately below the flag's blue field.

Except for No. 2886b with plate number, coil stamps are indistinguishable from booklet stamps once they are removed from the backing paper.

2887	A2208 (32c) black, blue & red		.70	.25
a.	Booklet pane of 18		12.50	

No. 2887 has noticeable blue shading in the white stripes immediately below the blue field and has overall tagging. The paper is translucent, thinner and duller than No. 2886.

A2209

COIL STAMPS
Perf. 9.8 Vert.

2888	A2209 (25c) black "G"		.90	.50
2889	A2208 (32c) black "G"		1.50	.25
a.	Imperf., pair		250.00	
2890	A2208 (32c) blue "G"		.65	.25
2891	A2208 (32c) red "G"		.85	.25

Rouletted 9.8 Vert.

2892	A2208 (32c) red "G"		.75	.25

A2210

PHOTOGRAVURE
1995 — Untagged — Perf. 9.8 Vert.

2893	A2210 (5c) green & multi		.50	.25

Flag Over Porch — A2212

1995, May 19 — Perf. 10.4

2897	A2212 32c multicolored		.75	.25
a.	Imperf., vert. pair		55.00	

See Nos. 2913-2916, 2920-2921, 3133.

Butte — A2217

COIL STAMPS
1995-97 — Perf. 9.8 Vert.
Untagged (Nos. 2902-2912B)
Self-Adhesive (#2902B)

2902	A2217 (5c) yel, red & bl		.25	.25
a.	Imperf., pair		350.00	

Serpentine Die Cut 11.5 Vert.
Untagged

2902B	A2217 (5c) yel, red & bl ('96)		.35	.25

Perf. 9.8 Vert.

Mountain — A2218

Self-Adhesive (#2904A-2904B)
Untagged

2903	A2218 (5c) purple & multi ('96)		.25	.25

Letters of inscription "USA NONPROFIT ORG." outlined in purple on No. 2903. No. 2903 has purple "1996" at left bottom.

Untagged

2904	A2218 (5c) blue & multi ('96)		.25	.25
c.	Imperf., pair		250.00	

Letters of inscription have no outline on No. 2904. No. 2904 has blue "1996" at bottom left.

Serpentine Die Cut 11.2 Vert.
Untagged

2904A	A2218 (5c) purple & multi ('96)		.40	.25

Serpentine Die Cut 9.8 Vert.
Untagged

2904B	A2218 (5c) purple & multi ('97)		.25	.25

Letters of inscription outlined in purple on No. 2904B, not outlined on No. 2904A. No. 2904A has large purple "1996" at bottom left. No. 2904B has small purple "1997" at bottom left.

Auto — A2220

Self-Adhesive (#2906-2907)
Perf. 9.8 Vert.
Untagged

2905	A2220 (10c) blk, red brn & brn, small "1995" date		.25	.25
a.	Medium "1995" date		.35	.25
b.	Large "1995" date ('96)		.60	.25
c.	As "b," brown omitted, P#S33 single		400.00	

Date on 2905 is approximately 1.9mm long, on No. 2905a 2mm long, and on No. 2905b 2.1mm long.

Serpentine Die Cut 11.5 Vert.
Untagged

2906	A2220 (10c) blk, brn & red brn ('96)		.50	.25

Untagged

2907	A1957 (10c) gold & multi ('96)		.75	.25

Auto Tail Fin — A2223

Self-Adhesive (#2910)
Perf. 9.8 Vert.
Untagged

2908	A2223 (15c) dk org yel & multi		.30	.25

No. 2908 has "1995" in blue and has dark, bold colors, heavy shading lines and heavily shaded chrome.

Untagged

2909	A2223 (15c) buff & multi		.30	.30

No. 2909 has "1995" in black and has shinier chrome, more subdued colors and finer details than No. 2908.

Serpentine Die Cut 11.5 Vert.
Untagged

2910	A2223 (15c) buff & multi ('96)		.30	.30

Juke Box — A2225

Self-Adhesive (#2912A-2912B)
Perf. 9.8 Vert.
Untagged

2911	A2225 (25c) dk red, dk yel grn & multi		.50	.50
a.	Imperf, pair		400.00	

No. 2911 has dark, saturated colors and dark blue lines in the music selection board. See No. 3132.

Untagged

2912	A2225 (25c) brt org red, brt yel grn & multi		.75	.50

No. 2912 has bright colors, less shading and light blue lines in the music selection board.

Serpentine Die Cut 11.5 Vert.
Untagged

2912A	A2225 (25c) brt org red, brt yel grn & multi ('96)		.50	.50

Serpentine Die Cut 9.8 Vert.
Untagged
2912B A2225 (25c) dk red, dk yel grn & multi ('97) .75 .50

Perf. 9.8 Vert.
2913 A2212 32c bl, tan, & lt bl .65 .25
 a. Imperf., pair 30.00

No. 2913 has pronounced light blue shading in the flag and red "1995" at left bottom. See No. 3133.

2914 A2212 32c bl, yel brn, red & gray .80 .25

No. 2914 has pale gray shading in the flag and blue "1995" at left bottom.

Serpentine Die Cut 8.7 Vert.
Self-Adhesive (#2915-2915D)
2915 A2212 32c multi 1.25 .30

No. 2915 has blue "1995" at bottom left.

Serpentine Die Cut 9.8 Vert.
2915A A2212 32c dk bl, tan, brn, red & lt bl ('96) .65 .25
 h. Die cutting omitted, pair 32.50
 i. Tan omitted —
 j. Double die cutting 30.00

No. 2915A has red "1996" at left bottom. Sky on No. 3133 shows color gradation at LR not on No. 2915A.
On No. 2915Ai all other colors except brown are severely shifted.
On No. 2915Aj, the second die cutting is a different gauge than the normal 9.8.

Serpentine Die Cut 11.5 Vert.
2915B A2212 32c dk bl, tan, brn, red & lt bl ('96) 1.00 .90

Serpentine Die Cut 10.9 Vert.
2915C A2212 32c dk bl, tan, brn, red & lt bl ('96) 3.50 .40

Serpentine Die Cut 9.8 Vert.
2915D A2212 32c dk bl, tan, brn, red & lt bl ('97) 2.00 .90

Stamps on multiples of No. 2915A touch, and are on a peelable backing the same size as the stamps, while those of No. 2915D are separated on the peelable backing, which is larger than the stamps.
No. 2915D has red "1997" at left bottom, No. 2915A has red "1996" at left bottom.
Sky on No. 3133 shows color gradation at LR not on No. 2915D, and it has blue "1996" at left bottom.

BOOKLET STAMPS
Perf. 10.8x9.8 on 2 or 3 Adjacent Sides
2916 A2212 32c bl, tan, brn, red & lt bl .65 .25
 a. Booklet pane of 10 6.50 3.25
 b. As "a," imperf. 1,100.

Flag Over Field — A2230

Self-Adhesive (#2919-2921)
Die Cut
2919 A2230 32c multi .65 .25
 a. Booklet pane of 18 12.00
 b. Vert. pair, die cutting omitted btwn. —

Serpentine Die Cut 8.7 on 2, 3 or 4 Adjacent Sides
2920 A2212 32c multi, dated blue "1995" .65 .25
 a. Booklet pane of 20+label 13.00
 b. Small date 6.00 .35
 c. As "b," booklet pane of 20+label 110.00
 f. As No. 2920, pane of 15+label 9.75
 g. As "a," partial pane of 10, 3 stamps and parts of 7 stamps printed on backing liner —
 h. As No. 2920, booklet pane of 15 47.50
 i. As No. 2920, die cutting omitted, pair —
 j. Dark blue omitted (from No. 2920a) 2,100.

 k. Vert. pair, die cutting missing btwn., three examples in No. 2920a with shift in die cutting (PS) —

Date on No. 2920 is nearly twice as large as date on No. 2920b. No. 2920f comes in various configurations.
No. 2920h is a pane of 16 with one stamp removed. The missing stamp is the lower right stamp in the pane or (more rarely) the upper left stamp. No. 2920f, a pane of 15 + label. The label is located in the sixth or seventh row of the pane and is die cut. If the label is removed, an impression of the die cutting appears on the backing paper.

Serpentine Die Cut 11.3 on 3 sides
2920D A2212 32c multi, dated blue "1996" ('96) .80 .25
 e. Booklet pane of 10 8.00
 i. As "e," die cutting omitted —

Serpentine Die Cut 9.8 on 2 or 3 Adjacent Sides
2921 A2212 32c dk bl, tan, brn, red & lt bl, dated red "1996" ('96) .90 .25
 a. Booklet pane of 10, dated red "1996" 9.00
 b. As No. 2921, dated red "1997," Jan. 24, 1997 1.20 .25
 c. As "a," dated red "1997" 12.00
 d. Booklet pane of 5 + label, dated red "1997," Jan. 24, 1997 8.00
 e. As "a," die cutting omitted 200.00

Issued: #2902, 2905, 3/10/95; #2908-2909, 2911-2912, 2919, 3/17/95; #2915, 2920, 4/18/95; #2897, 2913-2914, 2916, 5/19/95; #2920d, 1/20/96; #2904B, 2912B, 2915D, 2921b-2921d, 1/24/97; #2903-2904, 3/16/96; #2915A, 5/21/97; #2907, 2921, 5/21/96; #2902B, 2904A, 2906, 2910, 2912A, 2915B, 6/15/96; #2915C, 5/21/96.
See Nos. 3132-3133.

> **Scott values for used self-adhesive stamps are for examples either on piece or off piece.**

GREAT AMERICANS ISSUE
 A2248
 A2249
 A2250
A2251
 A2253
A2255
 A2256
 A2257
A2258

ENGRAVED
1995-99
Self-Adhesive (#2941-2942)
Perf. 11.2, Serpentine Die Cut 11.7x11.5 (#2941-2942)
2933 A2248 32c brown .75 .25
2934 A2249 32c green ('96) .75 .25
2935 A2250 32c lake ('98) .65 .35
2936 A2251 32c gray blue ('98) .65 .35
 a. 32c light blue 2.00 .50
2938 A2253 46c carmine .90 .30
2940 A2255 55c green 1.15 .25
 a. Imperf, pair
2941 A2256 55c black ('99) 1.10 .25
2942 A2257 77c blue ('98) 1.50 .40
2943 A2258 78c bright violet 1.60 .25
 a. 78c dull violet 1.60 .25
 b. 78c pale violet .30 .30
 Nos. 2933-2943 (9) 9.05 2.65

The pale violet ink on No. 2943b luminesces bright pink under long-wave ultraviolet light.

LOVE
 A2263

Cherub from Sistine Madonna, by Raphael — A2264

LITHOGRAPHED & ENGRAVED
1995, Feb. 1   Perf. 11.2
2948 A2263 (32c) multi .65 .25
Self-Adhesive
Die Cut
2949 A2264 (32c) multi .65 .25
 a. Booklet pane of 20 + label 13.00
 b. Red (engr.) omitted 100.00
 c. As "a," red (engr.) omitted 2,000.
 d. Red (engr.) missing (CM) —

No. 2949d must be collected se-tenant with a normal stamp.
See Nos. 2957-2960, 3030.

FLORIDA STATEHOOD
 A2265

LITHOGRAPHED
1995, Mar. 3   Perf. 11.1
2950 A2265 32c multicolored .65 .25

EARTH DAY

Earth Clean-Up A2266

Solar Energy A2267

Tree Planting A2268

Beach Clean-Up A2269

1995, Apr. 20   Perf. 11.1x11
2951 A2266 32c multicolored .65 .25
2952 A2267 32c multicolored .65 .25
2953 A2268 32c multicolored .65 .25
2954 A2269 32c multicolored .65 .25
 a. Block of 4, #2951-2954 2.60 1.75

RICHARD M. NIXON
37th President (1913-94)

Richard M. Nixon, 37th President (1913-94) — A2270

LITHOGRAPHED & ENGRAVED
1995, Apr. 26   Perf. 11.2
2955 A2270 32c multicolored .65 .25
 a. Red (engr. missing (CM) 800.00

No. 2955 is known with red (engr. "Richard Nixon") inverted, and with red engr. omitted but only half the Nixon portrait present, both from printer's waste. No. 2955a shows a complete Nixon portrait.

BLACK HERITAGE SERIES

Bessie Coleman, Aviator — A2271

ENGRAVED
1995, Apr. 27
2956 A2271 32c red & black .85 .25

LOVE
 A2272
 A2273
 A2274

LITHOGRAPHED & ENGRAVED
1995, May 12
2957 A2272 32c multicolored .65 .25
 Compare with No. 3030.
2958 A2273 55c multicolored 1.10 .25

BOOKLET STAMPS
Perf. 9.8x10.8
2959 A2272 32c multicolored .65 .25
 a. Booklet pane of 10 6.50 3.25
 b. Imperf, pair 100.00
 c. As "a," imperf. 500.00
Self-Adhesive
Die Cut
2960 A2274 55c multicolored 1.10 .25
 a. Booklet pane of 20 + label 22.50

RECREATIONAL SPORTS

Volleyball
A2275

Softball
A2276

Bowling
A2277

Tennis
A2278

Golf
A2279

LITHOGRAPHED
1995, May 20

2961	A2275 32c multicolored	.65	.25
2962	A2276 32c multicolored	.65	.25
2963	A2277 32c multicolored	.65	.25
2964	A2278 32c multicolored	.65	.25
2965	A2279 32c multicolored	.65	.25
a.	Vert. strip of 5, #2961-2965	3.25	2.00
b.	As "a," imperf	1,750.	
c.	As "a," yellow omitted	1,600.	
d.	As "a," yellow, blue & magenta omitted	1,600.	

PRISONERS OF WAR & MISSING IN ACTION

A2280

1995, May 29

2966	A2280 32c multicolored	.65	.25

LEGENDS OF HOLLYWOOD

Marilyn Monroe
(1926-62) — A2281

PHOTOGRAVURE
1995, June 1   *Perf. 11.1*

2967	A2281 32c multicolored	.80	.25
a.	Imperf., pair	225.00	

Perforations in corner of each stamp are star-shaped.

TEXAS STATEHOOD

A2282

LITHOGRAPHED
1995, June 16   *Perf. 11.2*

2968	A2282 32c multicolored	.70	.25

GREAT LAKES LIGHTHOUSES

Split Rock, Lake
Superior
A2283

St. Joseph, Lake
Michigan
A2284

Spectacle Reef,
Lake
Huron — A2285

Marblehead,
Lake
Erie — A2286

Thirty Mile Point,
Lake
Ontario — A2287

PHOTOGRAVURE
BOOKLET STAMPS
1995, June 17   *Perf. 11.2 Vert.*

2969	A2283 32c multicolored	.90	.30
2970	A2284 32c multicolored	.90	.30
2971	A2285 32c multicolored	.90	.30
2972	A2286 32c multicolored	.90	.30
2973	A2287 32c multicolored	.90	.30
a.	Booklet pane of 5, #2969-2973	4.50	2.50
b.	As "a," two vert. pairs imperf. horiz. of #2972 and 2973, in pane of 7+ stamps in cplt. bklt. #BK230 (due to foldover)	—	

U.N., 50th ANNIV.

A2288

ENGRAVED
1995, June 26   *Perf. 11.2*

2974	A2288 32c blue	.65	.25

CIVIL WAR

A2289

Designs: a, Monitor and Virginia. b, Robert E. Lee. c, Clara Barton. d, Ulysses S. Grant. e, Battle of Shiloh. f, Jefferson Davis. g, David Farragut. h, Frederick Douglass. i, Raphael Semmes. j, Abraham Lincoln. k, Harriet Tubman. l, Stand Watie. m, Joseph E. Johnston. n, Winfield Hancock. o, Mary Chesnut. p, Battle of Chancellorsville. q, William T. Sherman. r, Phoebe Pember. s, "Stonewall" Jackson. t, Battle of Gettysburg.

PHOTOGRAVURE
1995, June 29   *Perf. 10.1*

2975	A2289 Pane of 20	32.50	17.50
a.-t.	32c any single	1.50	.60
u.	As No. 2975, a.-e. imperf, f.-j. part perf, others perf	800.00	
v.	As No. 2975, k.-t. imperf, f.-j. part perf, others perf	1,250.	
w.	As No. 2975, imperf	800.00	
x.	Block of 9 (f.-h., k.-m., p.-r.) k.-l. & p.-q. imperf. vert.	800.00	
y.	As No. 2975, a.-b. perf, c., f.-h. part perf, others imperf	800.00	
z.	As No. 2975, o. and t. imperf, j., n. & s. part perf, others perf	—	
aa.	As No. 2975, c.-e. imperf, b., g.-j. part perf, others perf	500.00	

AMERICAN FOLK ART SERIES
Carousel Horses

A2290

A2291

A2292

A2293

LITHOGRAPHED
1995, July 21   *Perf. 11*

2976	A2290 32c multicolored	.65	.25
2977	A2291 32c multicolored	.65	.25
2978	A2292 32c multicolored	.65	.25
2979	A2293 32c multicolored	.65	.25
a.	Block or strip of 4, #2976-2979	2.60	2.00

WOMAN SUFFRAGE

A2294

LITHOGRAPHED & ENGRAVED
1995, Aug. 26   *Perf. 11.1x11*

2980	A2294 32c multicolored	.65	.25
a.	Black (engr.) omitted	275.00	
b.	Imperf., pair	750.00	
c.	Vert. pair, imperf between and at bottom	500.00	

No. 2980a is valued in the grade of fine. Very fine examples exist and sell for much more.

WORLD WAR II

A2295

Designs and events of 1945: a, Marines raise flag on Iwo Jima. b, Fierce fighting frees Manila by March 3, 1945. c, Soldiers advancing (Okinawa, the last big battle). d, Destroyed bridge (US and Soviets link up at Elbe River). e, Allies liberate Holocaust survivors. f, Germany surrenders at Reims. g, Refugees (By 1945, World War II has uprooted millions). h, Truman announces Japan's surrender. i, Sailor kissing nurse (News of victory hits home). j, Hometowns honor their returning veterans.

Central label is size of 15 stamps and shows world map with extent of Axis control and Allied operations.

1995, Sept. 2   *Perf. 11.1*

2981	A2295 Block of 10	15.00	7.50
a.-j.	32c any single	1.50	.50

No. 2981 has selvage at left and right and either top or bottom.

AMERICAN MUSIC SERIES

Louis
Armstrong
A2296

Coleman
Hawkins
A2297

James P.
Johnson
A2298

Jelly Roll
Morton
A2299

Charlie
Parker
A2300

Eubie Blake
A2301

Charles
Mingus
A2302

Thelonious
Monk
A2303

John
Coltrane
A2304

Erroll
Garner
A2305

LITHOGRAPHED
Plates of 120 in six panes of 20

1995			**Perf. 11.1x11**	
2982	A2296	32c white denomination	.90	.25
a.		Imperf. pair	—	
2983	A2297	32c multicolored	2.25	.30
2984	A2296	32c black denomination	2.25	.30
2985	A2298	32c multicolored	2.25	.30
2986	A2299	32c multicolored	2.25	.30
2987	A2300	32c multicolored	2.25	.30
2988	A2301	32c multicolored	2.25	.30
2989	A2302	32c multicolored	2.25	.30
2990	A2303	32c multicolored	2.25	.30
2991	A2304	32c multicolored	2.25	.30
2992	A2305	32c multicolored	2.25	.30
a.		Vert. block of 10, #2983-2992	23.00	7.50
b.		Pane of 20, dark blue (inscriptions) omitted	—	
c.		Imperf pair of Nos. 2991-2992	5,000.	

An imperf. block of Nos. 2983-2992 is believed to be printer's waste.

GARDEN FLOWERS

A2306   A2307

A2308   A2309

A2310

LITHOGRAPHED & ENGRAVED
BOOKLET STAMPS

1995, Sept. 19			**Perf. 10.9 Vert.**	
2993	A2306	32c multi	.65	.25
2994	A2307	32c multi	.65	.25
2995	A2308	32c multi	.65	.25
2996	A2309	32c multi	.65	.25
2997	A2310	32c multi	.65	.25
a.		Booklet pane of 5, #2993-2997	3.25	2.25
b.		As "a," imperf	2,250.	
c.		As "a," black (engr.) omitted	—	

EDDIE RICKENBACKER (1890-1973), AVIATOR

A2311

PHOTOGRAVURE

1995, Sept. 25			**Perf. 11¼**	
2998	A2311	60c multi, small "1995" year date	1.40	.50
a.		Large "1995" date, Oct., 1999	2.00	.50

Date on No. 2998 is 1mm long, on No. 2998a 1½mm long.

REPUBLIC OF PALAU

A2312

LITHOGRAPHED

1995, Sept. 29			**Perf. 11.1**	
2999	A2312	32c multicolored	.65	.25

See Palau Nos. 377-378.

COMIC STRIPS

A2313

Designs: a, The Yellow Kid. b, Katzenjammer Kids. c, Little Nemo in Slumberland. d, Bringing Up Father. e, Krazy Kat. f, Rube Goldberg's Inventions. g, Toonerville Folks. h, Gasoline Alley. i, Barney Google. j, Little Orphan Annie. k, Popeye. l, Blondie. m, Dick Tracy. n, Alley Oop. o, Nancy. p, Flash Gordon. q, Li'l Abner. r, Terry and the Pirates. s, Prince Valiant. t, Brenda Starr, Reporter.

PHOTOGRAVURE

1995, Oct. 1			**Perf. 10.1**	
3000	A2313	Pane of 20	13.00	10.00
a.-t.		32c any single	.65	.50
u.		As No. 3000, m.-t. imperf., i.-l. part perf	3,250.	
v.		As No. 3000, m.-t. imperf., i.-l. part perf	3,250.	
w.		As No. 3000, a.-l. imperf.,m.-t. imperf vert.	3,250.	
x.		As No. 3000, imperf	4,250.	

U.S. NAVAL ACADEMY, 150th ANNIVERSARY

A2314

LITHOGRAPHED

1995, Oct. 10			**Perf. 10.9**	
3001	A2314	32c multicolored	.65	.25

LITERARY ARTS SERIES

Tennessee
Williams
(1911-83)
A2315

1995, Oct. 13			**Perf. 11.1**	
3002	A2315	32c multicolored	.65	.25

CHRISTMAS

Madonna and Child — A2316

LITHOGRAPHED & ENGRAVED

1995			**Perf. 11.2**	
3003	A2316	32c multi	.65	.25
c.		Black (engr., denomination) omitted	200.00	—

BOOKLET STAMP
Perf. 9.8x10.9

3003A	A2316	32c multi	.65	.25
b.		Booklet pane of 10	6.50	4.00

Santa Claus   Child Holding
Entering   Jumping Jack
Chimney   A2318
A2317

Child Holding   Santa Claus
Tree — A2319   Working on
                            Sled — A2320

LITHOGRAPHED
Perf. 11.25

3004	A2317	32c multi	.70	.25
3005	A2318	32c multi	.70	.25
3006	A2319	32c multi	.70	.25
3007	A2320	32c multi	.70	.25
a.		Block or strip of 4, #3004-3007	2.80	1.25
b.		Booklet pane of 10, 3 each #3004-3005, 2 each #3006-3007	8.00	4.00
c.		Booklet pane of 10, 2 each #3004-3005, 3 each #3006-3007	8.00	4.00
d.		As "a," imperf	325.00	
e.		As "b," miscut and inserted upside down into booklet cover, with full bottom selvage	—	

PHOTOGRAVURE
Self-Adhesive Stamps
Serpentine Die Cut 11.25 on 2, 3 or 4 sides

3008	A2320	32c multi	.95	.25
3009	A2318	32c multi	.95	.25
3010	A2317	32c multi	.95	.25
3011	A2319	32c multi	.95	.25
a.		Booklet pane of 20, 5 each #3008-3011 + label	19.00	
b.		Strip of 4, #3008-3011	3.80	

Midnight Angel   Children
A2321   Sledding
                            A2322

LITHOGRAPHED
Serpentine Die Cut 11.3x11.6 on 2, 3 or 4 sides

3012	A2321	32c multi	.65	.25
a.		Booklet pane of 20 + label	13.00	
b.		Vert. pair, die cutting omitted between	—	
c.		Booklet pane of 15 + label, 1996	12.00	
d.		Booklet pane of 16	30.00	

No. 3012a comes either with no die cutting in the label (1995 printing) or with the die cutting from the 1996 printing.

No. 3012d is a pane of 16 with one stamp removed. The missing stamp can be from either row 1, 2, 3, 7 or 8 of the pane. No. 3012d cannot be made from No. 3012c, a pane of 15 + label. The label is die cut. If the label is removed, an impression of the die cutting appears on the backing paper.

PHOTOGRAVURE
Die Cut

3013	A2322	32c multi	.65	.25
a.		Booklet pane of 18	12.00	

Self-Adhesive Coil Stamps
Serpentine Die Cut 11.2 Vert.

3014	A2320	32c multi	3.00	.30
3015	A2318	32c multi	3.00	.30
3016	A2317	32c multi	3.00	.30
3017	A2319	32c multi	3.00	.30
a.		Strip of 4, #3014-3017	12.00	

LITHOGRAPHED
Serpentine Die Cut 11.6 Vert.

3018	A2321	32c multi	1.10	.30

Nos. 3005-3006 have "USA" printed in green. It is red on the self-adhesive stamps.
Issued: #3003-3003A, 3012-3013, 3018, 10/19; #3004-3011, 3014-3017, 9/30.

ANTIQUE AUTOMOBILES

1893
Duryea
A2323

1894
Haynes
A2324

1898
Columbia
A2325

1899
Winton
A2326

1901 White
A2327

PHOTOGRAVURE

1995, Nov. 3			**Perf. 10.1x11.1**	
3019	A2323	32c multicolored	.90	.25
3020	A2324	32c multicolored	.90	.25
3021	A2325	32c multicolored	.90	.25
3022	A2326	32c multicolored	.90	.25
3023	A2327	32c multicolored	.90	.25
a.		Vert. or horiz. strip of 5, #3019-3023	4.50	2.00

Vert. and horiz. strips are all in different order.

UTAH STATEHOOD CENTENARY

Delicate Arch,
Arches Natl.
Park — A2328

LITHOGRAPHED

1996, Jan. 4   **Perf. 11.1**
3024 A2328 32c multicolored   .75 .25

GARDEN FLOWERS

Crocus   Winter Aconite
A2329   A2330

Pansy   Snowdrop
A2331   A2332

Anemone — A2333

LITHOGRAPHED & ENGRAVED
BOOKLET STAMPS

1996, Jan. 19   **Perf. 10.9 Vert.**
3025 A2329 32c multi   .65 .25
3026 A2330 32c multi   .65 .25
3027 A2331 32c multi   .65 .25
3028 A2332 32c multi   .65 .25
3029 A2333 32c multi   .65 .25
   a.   Booklet pane of 5,
        #3025-3029   3.25 2.50
   b.   As "a," imperf.   —

LOVE

Cherub from Sistine Madonna, by
Raphael — A2334

BOOKLET STAMP
Serpentine Die Cut 11.3x11.7
1996, Jan. 20
Self-Adhesive

3030 A2334 32c multicolored   .65 .25
   a.   Booklet pane of 20 + label   13.00
   b.   Booklet pane of 15 + label   9.75
   c.   Red (engr. "Love") omitted   75.00
   d.   Red (engr. "Love") missing
        (CM)   —
   e.   Double impression of red
        (engr. "Love")   450.00
   f.   Die cutting omitted, pair   225.00
   g.   As "a," stamps 1-5 double
        impression of red (engr.
        "LOVE")   1,000.

---

   h.   As "a," red (engr. "LOVE")
        omitted   1,200.
   i.   As "a," die cutting omitted   —
   j.   As "e," two examples in
        booklet pane of 20 (No.
        3030a)   1,000.
   k.   As "d," three examples in
        booklet pane of 20 (No.
        3030a)   310.00

No. 3030d must be collected se-tenant with
a stamp bearing the red engraving.

FLORA AND FAUNA SERIES
Kestrel, Blue Jay and Rose Types of 1993-95 and

Red-headed   Eastern
Woodpecker   Bluebird
A2335   A2336

Serpentine Die Cut 10½
1996-2002   **Untagged**
Self-Adhesive (#3031, 3031A)

3031 A1841 1c multicolored   .25 .25
   c.   Die cutting omitted, pair   —

Serpentine Die Cut 11¼
Untagged

3031A A1841 1c multicolored   .25 .25
   b.   Die cutting omitted, pane
        of 50   325.00

No. 3031A has blue inscription and year.
See No. 2477.

Perf. 11
Untagged

3032 A2335 2c multicolored   .25 .25
3033 A2336 3c multicolored   .25 .25

Red Fox — A2339

Serpentine Die Cut 11½x11¼
Self-Adhesive

3036 A2339 $1 multicolored   6.00 .50
   a.   Serpentine die cut
        11¾x11 ('02)   6.50 .50

Beginning with Nos. 3036 and 3036a,
hidden 3-D images can be seen on
some stamps when they are viewed
with a special "Stamp Decoder" lens
sold by the USPS. See the *Scott Specialized Catalogue of U.S. Stamps and
Covers* for descriptions of these
images. Stamps with 3-D images are
3036-3036a, 3167, 3168-3172, 3178,
3206, 3230-3234, 3238-3242, 3261-
3262, 3321-3324, 3472-3473, 3647-
3648, 3651, 3771, 3787-3791, 3808-
3811, 3838 and 3862.

COIL STAMPS
Untagged
Perf. 9¾ Vert.

3044 A1841 1c multicolored,
        small date   .25 .25
   a.   Large date   .25 .25

Date on No. 3044 is 1mm long, on No.
3044a 1.5mm long.

Untagged

3045 A2335 2c multicolored   .25 .25

Issued: #3032, 2/2/96; #3033, 4/3/96;
#3044, 1/20/96; #3036, 8/14/98; #3045,
6/22/99; #3031, 11/19/99; #3031A, 10/00.

BOOKLET STAMPS
PHOTOGRAVURE
Serpentine Die Cut 10.4x10.8 on 3 Sides
Tagged
Self-Adhesive

3048 A1847 20c multi   .40 .25
   a.   Booklet pane of 10   4.00
   b.   Booklet pane of 4   70.00
   c.   Booklet pane of 6   100.00

Nos. 3048b-3048c are from the vending
machine booklet No. BK237 that has a glue
strip at the top edge of the top pane, the peelable strip removed and the rouletting line 2mm
lower than on No. 3048a on some booklets,
when the panes are compared with bottoms

---

aligned. Vending booklets with plate #S2222
always have gauge 8½ rouletting on booklet
covers. Convertible booklets (No. 3048a) with
plate #S2222 always have gauge 12½ rouletting on booklet covers. Vending booklets with
plate #S1111 can have either 8½ or 12½
gauge rouletting on booklet cover, and it may
be impossible to tell a vending booklet with
12½ gauge rouletting and plate #S1111 from a
convertible booklet with peelable strip
removed.

Serpentine Die Cut 11.3x11.7 on 2, 3 or 4 Sides

3049 A1853 32c yel, org, grn
        & blk   .65 .25
   a.   Booklet pane of 20 + label   13.00
   b.   Booklet pane of 4   2.60
   c.   Booklet pane of 5 + label   3.50
   d.   Booklet pane of 6   4.00

Ring-necked
Pheasant — A2350

Serpentine Die Cut 11.2 on 3 Sides

3050 A2350 20c multi   .65 .25
   a.   Booklet pane of 10, all
        stamps upright   6.50
   b.   Serpentine die cut 11   3.25 .25
   c.   As "b," booklet pane of 10,
        all stamps upright   35.00

Serpentine Die Cut 10½x11 on 3 Sides

3051 A2350 20c multi   .75 .25

Serpentine Die Cut 10.6x10.4 on 3 Sides

3051A A2350 20c multicolored   7.00 .50
   b.   Booklet pane of 5, 4
        #3051, 1 #3051A turned
        sideways at top   10.00
   c.   Booklet pane of 5, 4
        #3051, 1 #3051A turned
        sideways at bottom   10.00

No. 3051 represents the eight upright
stamps on the booklet panes Nos. 3051Ab
and 3051Ac. The two stamps turned sideways
on those panes are No. 3051A.

Coral Pink Rose — A2351

Serpentine Die Cut 11½x11¼ on 2, 3 or 4 Sides

3052 A2351 33c multi   .90 .25
   a.   Booklet pane of 4   3.60
   b.   Booklet pane of 5 + label   4.50
   c.   Booklet pane of 6   5.50
   d.   Booklet pane of 20 + label   17.50
   j.   Die cutting omitted, pair   —
   k.   As "d," die cutting omitted   5,500.

Serpentine Die Cut 10¾x10½ on 2 or 3 sides

3052E A2351 33c multi   .75 .25
   f.   Booklet pane of 20   15.00
   g.   Black ("33 USA," etc.) omit-
        ted   350.00
   h.   As "f," all 12 stamps on
        one side with black omit-
        ted   —
   i.   Horiz. pair, die cutting
        missing between due to
        miscutting of the pane   —
   j.   As "f," vert. die cutting
        missing between due to
        miscutting of the pane   —

No. 3052Ef is a double-sided booklet pane
with 12 stamps on one side and 8 stamps plus
label on the other side.

COIL STAMPS
Serpentine Die Cut 11½ Vert.

3053 A1847 20c multi   .50 .25
   a.   Die cutting omitted, pair   2,100.

Yellow Rose, Ring-necked Pheasant Types of 1996-98
LITHOGRAPHED
Self-Adhesive

3054 A1858 32c yel, mag,
        blk & grn   .65 .25
   a.   Die cutting omitted,
        pair   85.00
   b.   Black, yellow & green
        omitted   —
   c.   Black, yellow & green
        omitted, die cutting
        omitted, pair   —
   d.   Black omitted   250.00
   e.   Black omitted, die-cut-
        ting omitted, pair   550.00
   f.   All colors omitted, die
        cutting omitted   —

---

   g.   Pair, die cutting omit-
        ted, containing one
        stamp each of "c"
        and "e"   —

Nos. 3054b and 3054d also are miscut and
with shifted die cuttings.
No. 3054f must be collected se-tenant with
a partially printed stamp(s).

3055 A2350 20c multi   .40 .25
   a.   Die cutting omitted,
        pair   125.00

No. 3055a exists miscut. It is more common
in this form and is valued thus.

Issued: #3048, 3053, 8/2/96; #3049,
10/24/96; #3054, 8/1/97; #3050, 3055,
7/31/98; #3051, 7/99; #3052, 8/13/99;
#3052E, 4/7/00.

BLACK HERITAGE SERIES

Ernest E. Just
(1883-1941), Marine
Biologist — A2358

LITHOGRAPHED

1996, Feb. 1   **Perf. 11.1**
3058 A2358 32c gray & black   .65 .25

SMITHSONIAN INSTITUTION, 150TH ANNIVERSARY

A2359

1996, Feb. 7
3059 A2359 32c multicolored   .65 .25

CHINESE NEW YEAR

Year of the Rat — A2360

PHOTOGRAVURE

1996, Feb. 8
3060 A2360 32c multicolored   .90 .25
   a.   Imperf., pair   550.00

See Nos. 3895a, 3997a.

PIONEERS OF COMMUNICATION

Eadweard
Muybridge
A2361

Ottmar Mergenthaler — A2362

Frederic E.
Ives
A2363

William
Dickson
A2364

LITHOGRAPHED

1996, Feb. 22   **Perf. 11.1x11**

3061	A2361	32c multicolored	.65	.25
3062	A2362	32c multicolored	.65	.25
3063	A2363	32c multicolored	.65	.25
3064	A2364	32c multicolored	.65	.25
a.		Block or strip of 4, #3061-3064	2.60	2.00

Muybridge (1830-1904), Photographer; Mergenthaler (1854-99), Inventor of Linotype; Ives (1856-1937), Developer of Halftone Process; Dickson (1860-1935), Co-developer of Kinetoscope.

FULBRIGHT SCHOLARSHIPS, 50th ANNIVERSARY

A2365

LITHOGRAPHED & ENGRAVED

1996, Feb. 28   **Perf. 11.1**

3065	A2365	32c multicolored	.75	.25

JACQUELINE COCHRAN (1910-80), PILOT

A2366

1996, Mar. 9

3066	A2366	50c multicolored	1.00	.40
a.		Black (engr.) omitted	45.00	

MARATHON

A2367

LITHOGRAPHED

1996, Apr. 11

3067	A2367	32c multicolored	.65	.25

1996 SUMMER OLYMPIC GAMES

A2368

Designs: a, Decathlon (javelin). b, Men's canoeing. c, Women's running. d, Women's diving. e, Men's cycling. f, Freestyle wrestling. g, Women's gymnastics. h, Women's sailboarding. i, Men's shot put. j, Women's soccer. k, Beach volleyball. l, Men's rowing. m, Men's sprints. n, Women's swimming. o, Women's softball. p, Men's hurdles. q, Men's swimming. r, Men's gymnastics (pommel horse). s, Equestrian. t, Men's basketball.

PHOTOGRAVURE

1996, May 2   **Perf. 10.1**

3068	A2368	Pane of 20	14.00	10.00
a.-t.		32c any single	.70	.50
u.		As No. 3068, imperf	700.00	
v.		As No. 3068, back inscriptions omitted on a., f., k. & p., incorrect back inscriptions on others	—	
w.		As No. 3068, e. imperf, d., i.-j. part perf, all others perf	750.00	

GEORGIA O'KEEFFE (1887-1986)

A2369

PHOTOGRAVURE

1996, May 23   **Perf. 11.6x11.4**

3069	A2369	32c multicolored	.85	.25
a.		Imperf., pair	110.00	

TENNESSEE STATEHOOD BICENTENNIAL

A2370

1996, May 31   **Perf. 11.1**

3070	A2370	32c multicolored	.65	.25
a.		Imperf., pair		

One pane of 3070 containing 3069a is known. Some stamps on that pane have blind horizontal perforations.

Booklet Stamp
Self-Adhesive
Serpentine Die Cut 9.9x10.8

3071	A2370	32c multicolored	.65	.30
a.		Booklet pane of 20, #S11111	13.00	
b.		Horiz. pair, die cutting omitted btwn.	300.00	—
c.		Die cutting omitted, pair	—	
d.		Horiz. pair, die cutting omitted vert.	—	

AMERICAN INDIAN DANCES

A2371   A2372

A2373   A2374

A2375

LITHOGRAPHED

1996, June 7   **Perf. 11.1**

3072	A2371	32c Fancy	1.20	.25
3073	A2372	32c Butterfly	1.20	.25
3074	A2373	32c Traditional	1.20	.25
3075	A2374	32c Raven	1.20	.25
3076	A2375	32c Hoop	1.20	.25
a.		Strip of 5, #3072-3076	6.00	2.50

PREHISTORIC ANIMALS

A2376

A2377

A2378

A2379

1996, June 8   **Perf. 11.1x11**

3077	A2376	32c Eohippus	.65	.25
3078	A2377	32c Woolly Mammoth	.65	.25
3079	A2378	32c Mastodon	.65	.25
3080	A2379	32c Saber-tooth Cat	.65	.25
a.		Block or strip of 4, #3077-3080	2.60	2.00

BREAST CANCER AWARENESS

A2380

1996, June 15   **Perf. 11.1**

3081	A2380	32c multicolored	.65	.25

LEGENDS OF HOLLYWOOD

A2381

PHOTOGRAVURE

1996, June 24

3082	A2381	32c multicolored	.65	.25
a.		Imperf., pair	100.00	
b.		As "a," red (USA 32c) missing (CM) and tan (JAMES DEAN) omitted	—	
c.		As "a," tan (JAMES DEAN) omitted	—	
d.		As "a," top stamp red missing (CM) and tan (JAMES DEAN) omitted, bottom stamp tan omitted	—	
e.		As No. 3082 pane of 20, right two columns perf, left three columns imperf	1,750.	

Perforations in corner of each stamp are star-shaped. No. 3082 was also available on the first day of issue in at least 127 Warner Bros. Studio stores.

Nos. 3082b-3082d come from the same error pane. The top row is No. 3082b; rows 2-4 are No. 3082c. No. 3082d is a vertical pair with one stamp from No. 3082b at top and one stamp from No. 3082c at bottom.

FOLK HEROES

A2382   A2383

A2384   A2385

LITHOGRAPHED

1996, July 11   **Perf. 11.1x11**

3083	A2382	32c multicolored	.65	.25
3084	A2383	32c multicolored	.65	.25
3085	A2384	32c multicolored	.65	.25
3086	A2385	32c multicolored	.65	.25
a.		Block or strip of 4, #3083-3086	2.60	2.00

CENTENNIAL OLYMPIC GAMES

Myron's
Discobolus — A2386

ENGRAVED

1996, July 19   **Tagged**   **Perf. 11.1**

3087	A2386	32c brown	.75	.25

Sheet margin of the pane of 20 is lithographed.

IOWA STATEHOOD, 150TH ANNIVERSARY

Young Corn, by
Grant
Wood — A2387

LITHOGRAPHED

1996, Aug. 1

3088	A2387	32c multicolored	.80	.25

BOOKLET STAMP
Self-Adhesive
Serpentine Die Cut 11.6x11.4

3089 A2387 32c multicolored .65 .30
a. Booklet pane of 20 13.00

RURAL FREE DELIVERY, CENT.

A2388

LITHOGRAPHED & ENGRAVED
1996, Aug. 7   *Perf. 11.2x11*
3090 A2388 32c multicolored .80 .25

RIVERBOATS

Robt. E. Lee A2389

Sylvan Dell A2390

Far West A2391

Rebecca Everingham A2392

Bailey Gatzert A2393

PHOTOGRAVURE
Serpentine Die Cut 11x11.1
1996, Aug. 22
Self-Adhesive
3091 A2389 32c multicolored .65 .40
3092 A2390 32c multicolored .65 .40
3093 A2391 32c multicolored .65 .40
3094 A2392 32c multicolored .65 .40
3095 A2393 32c multicolored .65 .40
a. Vert. strip of 5, #3091-3095 3.25
b. Strip of 5, #3091-3095, with special die cutting, die cut 11¼ 45.00 45.00

The serpentine die cutting runs through the peelable backing to which Nos. 3091-3095 are affixed. No. 3095a exists with stamps in different sequences.

On the long side of each stamp in No. 3095b, the die cutting is missing 3 "perforations" between the stamps, one near each end and one in the middle. This allows a complete strip to be removed from the backing paper for use on a first day cover.

AMERICAN MUSIC SERIES
Big Band Leaders

Count Basie A2394

Tommy & Jimmy Dorsey A2395

Glenn Miller A2396

Benny Goodman A2397

Songwriters

Harold Arlen A2398

Johnny Mercer A2399

Dorothy Fields A2400

Hoagy Carmichael A2401

LITHOGRAPHED
1996, Sept. 11   *Perf. 11.1x11*
3096 A2394 32c multicolored .75 .25
3097 A2395 32c multicolored .75 .25
3098 A2396 32c multicolored .75 .25
3099 A2397 32c multicolored .75 .25
a. Block or strip of 4, #3096-3099 3.00 2.00
3100 A2398 32c multicolored .75 .25
3101 A2399 32c multicolored .75 .25
3102 A2400 32c multicolored .75 .25
3103 A2401 32c multicolored .75 .25
a. Block or strip of 4, #3100-3103 3.00 2.00

LITERARY ARTS SERIES

F. Scott Fitzgerald (1896-1940) A2402

PHOTOGRAVURE
1996, Sept. 27   *Perf. 11.1*
3104 A2402 23c multicolored .55 .25

ENDANGERED SPECIES

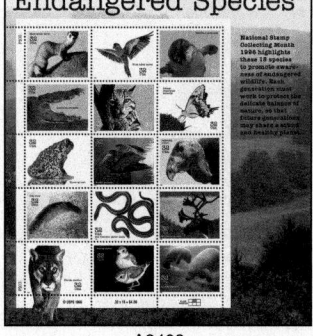
A2403

Designs: a, Black-footed ferret. b, Thick-billed parrot. c, Hawaiian monk seal. d, American crocodile. e, Ocelot. f, Schaus swallowtail butterfly. g, Wyoming toad. h, Brown pelican. i, California condor. j, Gila trout. k, San Francisco garter snake. l, Woodland caribou. m, Florida panther. n, Piping plover. o, Florida manatee.

LITHOGRAPHED
1996, Oct. 2   *Perf. 11.1x11*
3105 A2403 Pane of 15 12.00 8.00
a.-o. 32c any single .80 .50
See Mexico No. 1995.

COMPUTER TECHNOLOGY

A2404

LITHOGRAPHED & ENGRAVED
1996, Oct. 8   *Perf. 10.9x11.1*
3106 A2404 32c multicolored .65 .25

CHRISTMAS

Madonna and Child from Adoration of the Shepherds, by Paolo de Matteis — A2405

Family at Fireplace A2406

Decorating Tree A2407

Dreaming of Santa Claus A2408

Holiday Shopping A2409

LITHOGRAPHED & ENGRAVED
1996   *Perf. 11.1x11.2*
3107 A2405 32c multicolored .65 .25
a. Black (engr.) omitted at bottom 600.00
On No. 3107a, an albino impression of the lettering at bottom is present, but there is no trace of black ink.

No. 3107b is missing the black lettering at bottom due to a small upward shift of the horizontal perforations. This lettering is the only engraved black on the stamp.

LITHOGRAPHED
Perf. 11.3
3108 A2406 32c multicolored .65 .25
3109 A2407 32c multicolored .65 .25
3110 A2408 32c multicolored .65 .25
3111 A2409 32c multicolored .65 .25
a. Block or strip of 4, #3108-3111 2.60 1.75
b. Strip of 4, #3110-3111, 3108-3109, with #3109 imperf., #3108 imperf. at right 1,000.
c. Strip of 4, #3108-3111, with #3111 imperf, #3110 imperf at right 1,000.

BOOKLET STAMPS
Self-Adhesive
LITHOGRAPHED & ENGRAVED
Serpentine Die Cut 10 on 2, 3 or 4 Sides
3112 A2405 32c multicolored .75 .25
a. Booklet pane of 20 + label 15.00
b. Die cutting omitted, pair 40.00
c. As "a," die cutting omitted 400.00
d. As "a," top seven stamps with black (engr.) missing (PS) —

No. 3112d is missing the black lettering at bottom due to a small upward shift of the horizontal perforations. This lettering is the only engraved black on the stamp.

LITHOGRAPHED
Serpentine Die Cut 11.8x11.5 on 2, 3 or 4 Sides
3113 A2406 32c multicolored .65 .25
3114 A2407 32c multicolored .65 .25
3115 A2408 32c multicolored .65 .25
3116 A2409 32c multicolored .65 .25
a. Booklet pane of 20, 5 ea #3113-3116 13.00
b. Strip of 4, #3113-3116 2.60
c. As "a," die cutting omitted 1,250.
d. As "b," die cutting omitted 500.00
e. Block of 6, die cutting omitted 700.00

Skaters — A2410

PHOTOGRAVURE
Die Cut
3117 A2410 32c multicolored .65 .25
a. Booklet pane of 18 12.00
Issued: #3108-3111, 3113-3117, 10/8; #3107, 3112, 11/1.

HANUKKAH

A2411

Serpentine Die Cut 11.1
1996, Oct. 22
Self-Adhesive
3118 A2411 32c multicolored .65 .25
See Nos. 3352, 3547, 3672, Israel No. 1289. For booklet see No. BK258.

CYCLING
Souvenir Sheet

A2412

1996, Nov. 1   *Perf. 11x11.1*
3119 A2412 Sheet of 2 2.75 2.00
a. 50c orange & multi 1.30 1.00
b. 50c blue green & multi 1.30 1.00

No. 3119 exists overprinted in gold and in silver for the Tour of China '96. This overprint is a private production. Value, set of 2 sheets $12.50.

CHINESE NEW YEAR

Year of the Ox A2413

1997, Jan. 5   *Perf. 11.2*
3120 A2413 32c multicolored   .80   .25
See Nos. 3895b, 3997b.

BLACK HERITAGE SERIES

Brig. Gen. Benjamin O. Davis, Sr. (1880-1970) A2414

LITHOGRAPHED
Serpentine Die Cut 11.4
1997, Jan. 28
Self-Adhesive
3121 A2414 32c multicolored   .70   .25

Statue of Liberty Type of 1994
PHOTOGRAVURE
Serpentine Die Cut 11 on 2, 3 or 4 Sides
1997, Feb. 1
Self-Adhesive

3122 A1951 32c red, lt bl, dk bl & yel   .70   .25
  a.   Booklet pane of 20 + label   14.00
  b.   Booklet pane of 4   2.80
  c.   Booklet pane of 5 + label   3.75
  d.   Booklet pane of 6   4.25
  h.   As "a," die cutting omitted   —

Serpentine Die Cut 11.5x11.8 on 2, 3 or 4 Sides
1997
Self-Adhesive

3122E A1951 32c red, lt bl, dk bl & yel   1.50   .25
  f.   Booklet pane of 20 + label   40.00
  g.   Booklet pane of 6   9.00

LOVE

A2415   Swans — A2416

LITHOGRAPHED
Serpentine Die Cut 11.8x11.6 on 2, 3 or 4 Sides
1997, Feb. 4
Self-Adhesive

3123 A2415 32c multicolored   .65   .25
  a.   Booklet pane of 20 + label   13.00
  b.   Die cutting omitted, pair   100.00
  c.   As "a," die cutting omitted   675.00
  d.   As "a," black omitted   —

Serpentine Die Cut 11.6x11.8 on 2, 3 or 4 Sides

3124 A2416 55c multicolored   1.10   .25
  a.   Booklet pane of 20 + label   22.00

HELPING CHILDREN LEARN

A2417

PHOTOGRAVURE
Serpentine Die Cut 11.6x11.7
1997, Feb. 18
Self-Adhesive
3125 A2417 32c multicolored   .65   .25

MERIAN BOTANICAL PRINTS

Citron, Moth, Larvae, Pupa, Beetle A2418   Flowering Pineapple, Cockroaches A2419

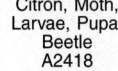

No. 3128 (r), No. 3129 (l), No. 3128a below

Serpentine Die Cut 10.9x10.2 on 2, 3 or 4 Sides
1997, Mar. 3
Self-Adhesive
3126 A2418 32c multicolored   .65   .25
3127 A2419 32c multicolored   .65   .25
  a.   Booklet pane, 10 ea #3126-3127 + label   13.00
  b.   Pair, #3126-3127   1.30
  c.   Vert. pair, die cutting omitted between   350.00

Size: 18.5x24mm
Serpentine Die Cut 11.2x10.8 on 2 or 3 Sides
3128 A2418 32c multicolored   1.00   .25
  a.   See footnote   2.50   .25
  b.   Booklet pane, 2 ea #3128-3129, 1 #3128a   6.50
3129 A2419 32c multicolored   1.00   .25
  a.   See footnote   4.50   .35
  b.   Booklet pane, 2 ea #3128-3129, 1 #3129a   8.50
  c.   Pair, #3128-3129   2.00

Nos. 3128a-3129a are placed sideways on the pane and are serpentine die cut 11.2 on top and bottom, 10.8 on left side. One of the two No. 3128a per pane has a straight edge at left. The right side is 11.2 broken by a sloping die cut where the stamp meets the vertical die cutting of the two stamps above it. See illustration above.

PACIFIC 97

Sailing Ship — A2420

[Stagecoach]

Stagecoach — A2421

ENGRAVED
1997, Mar. 13   Tagged   *Perf. 11.2*
3130 A2420 32c blue   .65   .30
3131 A2421 32c red   .65   .30
  a.   Pair, #3130-3131   1.30   .75

Juke Box — A2225a

PHOTOGRAVURE
COIL STAMPS
1997, Mar. 14   Untagged   *Imperf.*
Self-Adhesive
3132 A2225a (25c) brt org red, brt yel grn & multi   1.50   .50
Tagged
Serpentine Die Cut 9.9 Vert.
3133 A2212 32c dk bl, tan, brn, red & lt bl   1.75   .25

Nos. 3132-3133 were issued without backing paper. No. 3132 has simulated perforations ending in black bars at the top and bottom edges of the stamp. Sky on No. 3133 shows color gradation at LR not on Nos. 2915A or 2915D, and it has blue "1996" at left bottom.
See Nos. 2897, 2913-2916, 2920-2921.

LITERARY ARTS SERIES

Thornton Wilder (1897-1975) A2422

LITHOGRAPHED
1997, Apr. 17   *Perf. 11.1*
3134 A2422 32c multicolored   .65   .25

RAOUL WALLENBERG (1912-47)

Wallenberg and Jewish Refugees A2423

1997, Apr. 24
3135 A2423 32c multicolored   .65   .25

DINOSAURS

A2424

Designs: a, Ceratosaurus. b, Camptosaurus. c, Camarasaurus. d, Brachiosaurus. e, Goniopholis. f, Stegosaurus. g, Allosaurus. h, Opisthias. i, Edmontonia. j, Einiosaurus. k, Daspletosaurus. l, Palaeosaniwa. m, Corythosaurus. n, Ornithomimus. o, Parasaurolophus.

1997, May 1   *Perf. 11x11.1*
3136 A2424 Sheet of 15   10.00 8.00
  a.-o.   32c any single   .65   .50
  p.   As No. 3136, bottom 7 stamps imperf.   2,500.
  q.   As No. 3136, top 8 stamps imperf.   2,500.
  r.   As No. 3136, all colors and tagging missing (EP)   —

No. 3136r resulted from double sheeting in the sheet-fed press. It is properly gummed and perforated.
No. 3136 completely imperf. is believed to be printer's waste.

BUGS BUNNY

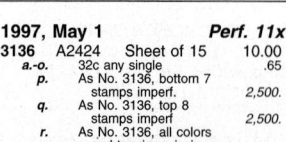

A2425

PHOTOGRAVURE
1997, May 22   *Serpentine Die Cut 11*
Self-Adhesive
3137   Pane of 10 #3137a   6.75
  a.   A2425 32c single   .65   .25
  b.   Pane of 9 #3137a   6.00
  c.   Pane of 1 #3137a   .65

Die cutting on #3137 does not extend through the backing paper.

3138   Pane of 10, #3138c, 9 #3138a   130.00
  a.   A2425 32c single   2.75
  b.   Pane of 9 #3138a   20.00
  c.   Pane of 1, no die cutting   100.00

Die cutting on No. 3138b extends through the backing paper.
An untagged promotional piece similar to No. 3137c exists on the same backing paper as the pane, with the same design image, but without Bugs' signature and the single stamp. Replacing the stamp is an enlarged "32 / USA" in the same style as used on the stamp. This promotional piece was not valid for postage.

PACIFIC 97

Franklin A2426   Washington A2427

LITHOGRAPHED & ENGRAVED
1997   *Perf. 10.5x10.4*
3139   Pane of 12   12.00 9.00
  a.   A2426 50c single   1.00   .50
3140   Pane of 12   14.50 11.00
  a.   A2427 60c single   1.20   .60

Selvage on Nos. 3139-3140 is lithographed.
Issued: No. 3139, 5/29; No. 3140, 5/30.

MARSHALL PLAN, 50TH ANNIV.

Gen. George C. Marshall, Map of Europe — A2428

1997, June 4   *Perf. 11.1*
3141 A2428 32c multicolored   .65   .25

CLASSIC AMERICAN AIRCRAFT

A2429

Designs: a, Mustang. b, Model B. c, Cub. d, Vega. e, Alpha. f, B-10. g, Corsair. h, Stratojet. i, GeeBee. j, Staggerwing. k, Flying Fortress. l, Stearman. m, Constellation. n, Lightning. o, Peashooter. p, Tri-Motor. q, DC-3. r, 314 Clipper. s, Jenny. t, Wildcat.

PHOTOGRAVURE

				Perf. 10.1
1997, July 19				
3142	A2429	Pane of 20	13.00	10.00
a.-t.		32c any single	.65	.50

FOOTBALL COACHES

Bear Bryant
A2430

Pop Warner
A2431

Vince Lombardi
A2432

George Halas
A2433

LITHOGRAPHED

			Perf. 11.2
1997			
3143	A2430	32c multicolored	.65	.25
3144	A2431	32c multicolored	.65	.25
3145	A2432	32c multicolored	.65	.25
3146	A2433	32c multicolored	.65	.25
a.		Block or strip of 4, #3143-3146	2.60	1.50

With Red Bar Above Coach's Name
Perf. 11

3147	A2432	32c multicolored	.65	.45
3148	A2430	32c multicolored	.65	.45
3149	A2431	32c multicolored	.65	.45
3150	A2433	32c multicolored	.65	.45

Issued: #3143-3146, 7/25; #3147, 8/5; #3148, 8/7; #3149, 8/8; #3150, 8/16.

AMERICAN DOLLS

A2434

Designs: a, "Alabama Baby," and doll by Martha Chase. b, "Columbian Doll." c, Johnny Gruelle's "Raggedy Ann." d, Doll by Martha Chase. e, "American Child." f, "Baby Coos." g, Plains Indian. h, Doll by Izannah Walker. i, "Babyland Rag." j, "Scootles." k, Doll by Ludwig Greiner. l, "Betsy McCall." m, Percy Crosby's "Skippy." n, "Maggie Mix-up." o, Dolls by Albert Schoenhut.

			Perf. 10.9x11.1
1997, July 28			
3151	A2434	Pane of 15	13.50	—
a.-o.		32c any single	.90	.60

LEGENDS OF HOLLYWOOD
Humphrey Bogart (1899-1957).

A2435

PHOTOGRAVURE

			Perf. 11.1
1997, July 31			
3152	A2435	32c multicolored	.85	.25

Perforations in corner of each stamp are star-shaped.

"THE STARS AND STRIPES FOREVER!"

A2436

1997, Aug. 21				
3153	A2436	32c multicolored	.65	.25

AMERICAN MUSIC SERIES
Opera Singers

Lily Pons
A2437

Richard Tucker
A2438

Lawrence Tibbett
A2439

Rosa Ponselle
A2440

LITHOGRAPHED

			Perf. 11
1997, Sept. 10			
3154	A2437	32c multicolored	.75	.25
3155	A2438	32c multicolored	.75	.25
3156	A2439	32c multicolored	.75	.25
3157	A2440	32c multicolored	.75	.25
a.		Block or strip of 4, #3154-3157	3.00	2.00

AMERICAN MUSIC SERIES
Classical Composers & Conductors

Leopold Stokowski
A2441

Arthur Fiedler
A2442

George Szell
A2443

Eugene Ormandy
A2444

Samuel Barber
A2445

Ferde Grofé
A2446

Charles Ives
A2447

Louis Moreau Gottschalk
A2448

LITHOGRAPHED

			Perf. 11
1997, Sept. 12			
3158	A2441	32c multicolored	1.50	.25
3159	A2442	32c multicolored	1.50	.25
3160	A2443	32c multicolored	1.50	.25
3161	A2444	32c multicolored	1.50	.25
3162	A2445	32c multicolored	1.50	.25
3163	A2446	32c multicolored	1.50	.25
3164	A2447	32c multicolored	1.50	.25
3165	A2448	32c multicolored	1.50	.25
a.		Block of 8, #3158-3165	12.00	4.00

PADRE FÉLIX VARELA (1788-1853)

A2449

			Perf. 11.2
1997, Sept. 15			
3166	A2449	32c purple	.65	.25

DEPARTMENT OF THE AIR FORCE, 50TH ANNIV.

Thunderbirds Aerial Demonstration Squadron — A2450

			Perf. 11.2x11.1
1997, Sept. 18			
3167	A2450	32c multicolored	.65	.25

CLASSIC MOVIE MONSTERS

A2451

A2452

A2453

A2454

A2455

PHOTOGRAVURE

1997, Sept. 30   *Perf. 10.2*

3168	A2451	32c multicolored	.75	.25
3169	A2452	32c multicolored	.75	.25
3170	A2453	32c multicolored	.75	.25
3171	A2454	32c multicolored	.75	.25
3172	A2455	32c multicolored	.75	.25
a.		Strip of 5, #3168-3172	3.75	2.25

FIRST SUPERSONIC FLIGHT, 50TH ANNIV.

A2456

LITHOGRAPHED
Serpentine Die Cut 11.4
1997, Oct. 14
Self-Adhesive

3173	A2456	32c multicolored	.65	.25

WOMEN IN MILITARY SERVICE

A2457

1997, Oct. 18   *Perf. 11.1*

3174	A2457	32c multicolored	.65	.25

KWANZAA

A2458

PHOTOGRAVURE

1997, Oct. 22 Serpentine Die Cut 11
Self-Adhesive

3175	A2458	32c multicolored	.65	.25
		See Nos. 3368, 3548, 3673.		

CHRISTMAS

Madonna and   Holly
Child   A2460
A2459

LITHOGRAPHED
Serpentine Die Cut 9.9 on 2, 3 or 4 Sides
1997
Booklet Stamps
Self-Adhesive

3176	A2459	32c multicolored	.65	.25
a.		Booklet pane of 20 + label	13.00	

Serpentine Die Cut 11.2x11.6 on 2, 3 or 4 Sides

3177	A2460	32c multicolored	.65	.25
a.		Booklet pane of 20 + label	13.00	
b.		Booklet pane of 4	2.60	
c.		Booklet pane of 5 + label	3.25	
d.		Booklet pane of 6	3.90	

Madonna and Child, by Sano di Pietro.
Issued: No. 3176, 10/27; No. 3177, 10/30.

MARS PATHFINDER
Souvenir Sheet

Mars Rover Sojourner — A2461

PHOTOGRAVURE

1997, Dec. 10 Tagged *Perf. 11x11.1*

3178	A2461	$3 multicolored	6.00	4.00
a.		$3, single stamp	5.50	3.00
b.		Single souvenir sheet from sheet of 18	7.50	—
c.		As No. 3178, imperf.		

The perforations at the bottom of the stamp contain the letters "USA." Vertical rouletting extends from the vertical perforations of the stamp to the bottom of the souvenir sheet.
Sheet of 18 has vertical perforations separating the three columns of souvenir sheets. These were cut away when No. 3178 was produced. Thus, the souvenir sheet from the sheet of 18 is wider and has vertical perforations on one or two sides.

CHINESE NEW YEAR

Year of the Tiger — A2462

1998, Jan. 5   *Perf. 11.2*

3179	A2462	32c multicolored	.80	.25
		See Nos. 3895c, 3997c.		

ALPINE SKIING

A2463

LITHOGRAPHED

1998, Jan. 22   *Perf. 11.2*

3180	A2463	32c multicolored	.75	.25

BLACK HERITAGE SERIES

A2464

Serpentine Die Cut 11.6x11.3
1998, Jan. 28
Self-Adhesive

3181	A2464	32c sepia & black	.70	.25

CELEBRATE THE CENTURY

1900s — A2465

No. 3182: a, Model T Ford. b, Theodore Roosevelt. c, Motion picture "The Great Train Robbery," 1903. d, Crayola Crayons introduced, 1903. e, St. Louis World's Fair, 1904. f, Design used on Hunt's Remedy stamp (#RS56), Pure Food & Drug Act, 1906. g, Wright Brothers first flight, Kitty Hawk, 1903. h, Boxing match shown in painting "Stag at Sharkey's," by George Bellows of the Ash Can School. i, Immigrants arrive. j, John Muir, preservationist. k, "Teddy" Bear created. l, W.E.B. Du Bois, social activist. m, Gibson Girl. n, First baseball World Series, 1903. o, Robie House, Chicago, designed by Frank Lloyd Wright.

1910s — A2466

No. 3183: a, Charlie Chaplin as the Little Tramp. b, Federal Reserve System created, 1913. c, George Washington Carver. d, Avant-garde art introduced at Armory Show, 1913. e, First transcontinental telephone line, 1914. f, Panama Canal opens, 1914. g, Jim Thorpe wins decathlon at Stockholm Olympics, 1912. h, Grand Canyon National Park, 1919. i, U.S. enters World War I. j, Boy Scouts started in 1910, Girl Scouts formed in 1912. k, Woodrow Wilson. l, First crossword puzzle published, 1913. m, Jack Dempsey wins heavyweight title, 1919. n, Construction toys. o, Child labor reform.

1920s — A2467

No. 3184: a, Babe Ruth. b, The Gatsby style. c, Prohibition enforced. d, Electric toy trains. e, 19th Amendment (woman voting). f, Emily Post's Etiquette. g, Margaret Mead, anthropologist. h, Flappers do the Charleston.

i, Radio entertains America. j, Art Deco style (Chrysler Building). k, Jazz flourishes. l, Four Horsemen of Notre Dame. m, Lindbergh flies the Atlantic. n, American realism (Automat, by Edward Hopper). o, Stock Market crash, 1929.

1930s — A2468

No. 3185: a, Franklin D. Roosevelt. b, The Empire State Building. c, 1st Issue of Life Magazine, 1936. d, Eleanor Roosevelt. e, FDR's New Deal. f, Superman arrives, 1938. g, Household conveniences. h, "Snow White and the Seven Dwarfs," 1937. i, "Gone with the Wind," 1936. j, Jesse Owens. k, Streamline design. l, Golden Gate Bridge. m, America survives the Depression. n, Bobby Jones wins golf Grand Slam, 1938. o, The Monopoly Game.

1940s — A2469

No. 3186: a, World War II. b, Antibiotics save lives. c, Jackie Robinson. d, Harry S Truman. e, Women support war effort. f, TV entertains America. g, Jitterbug sweeps nation. h, Jackson Pollock, Abstract Expressionism. i, GI Bill, 1944. j, Big Band Sound. k, Intl. style of architecture (UN Headquarters). l, Postwar baby boom. m, Slinky, 1945. n, "A Streetcar Named Desire," 1947. o, Orson Welles' "Citizen Kane."

1950s — A2470

No. 3187: a, Polio vaccine developed. b, Teen fashions. c, The "Shot Heard 'Round the World." d, US launches satellites. e, Korean War. f, Desegregating public schools. g, Tail-fins, chrome. h, Dr. Seuss' "The Cat in the Hat." i, Drive-in movies. j, World Series rivals. k, Rocky Marciano, undefeated boxer. l, "I Love Lucy." m, Rock 'n Roll. n, Stock car racing. o, Movies go 3-D.

1960s — A2471

No. 3188: a, Martin Luther King, Jr., "I Have a Dream." b, Woodstock. c, Man walks on the moon. d, Green Bay Packers. e, Star Trek. f, The Peace Corps. g, Viet Nam War. h, Ford Mustang. i, Barbie Doll. j, Integrated circuit. k, Lasers. l, Super Bowl I. m, Peace symbol. n, Roger Maris, 61 in '61. o, The Beatles "Yellow Submarine."

1970s — A2472

No. 3189: a, Earth Day celebrated. b, "All in the Family" television series. c, "Sesame Street" television series character, Big Bird. d, Disco music. e, Pittsburgh Steelers win four Super Bowls. f, US Celebrates 200th birthday. g, Secretariat wins Triple Crown. h, VCRs transform entertainment. i, Pioneer 10. j, Women's rights movement. k, 1970s fashions. l, "Monday Night Football." m, Smiley face buttons. n, Jumbo jets. o, Medical imaging.

1980s — A2473

No. 3190: a, Space shuttle program. b, "Cats" Broadway show. c, San Francisco 49ers. d, Hostages in Iran come home. e, Figure skating. f, Cable TV. g, Vietnam Veterans Memorial. h, Compact discs. i, Cabbage Patch Kids. j, "The Cosby Show" television series. k, Fall of the Berlin Wall. l, Video games. m, "E. T. The Extra-Terrestrial" movie. n, Personal computers. o, Hip-hop culture.

1990s — A2474

No. 3191: a, New baseball records. b, Gulf War. c, "Seinfeld" television series. d, Extreme sports. e, Improving education. f, Computer art and graphics. g, Recovering species. h, Return to space. i, Special Olympics. j, Virtual reality. k, Movie "Jurassic Park." l, Movie "Titanic." m, Sport utility vehicles. n, World Wide Web. o, Cellular phones.

LITHOGRAPHED, ENGRAVED
(#3182m, 3183f, 3184m, 3185b, 3186k, 3187a, 3188c, 3189h)

1998-2000			Perf. 11½	
3182	A2465	Pane of 15	10.00	8.50
a.-o.		32c any single	.75	.65
p.		Engr. red (No. 3182m, Gibson girl) omitted, in pane of 15	3,000.	
3183	A2466	Pane of 15	10.00	8.50
a.-o.		32c any single	.75	.65
p.		Nos. 3183g, 3183 l-3183o imperf, in pane of 15	7,000.	
3184	A2467	Pane of 15	12.50	8.50
a.-o.		32c any single	.80	.65
3185	A2468	Pane of 15	12.50	8.50
a.-o.		32c any single	.80	.65
3186	A2469	Pane of 15	13.00	8.50
a.-o.		33c any single	.85	.65
3187	A2470	Pane of 15	13.00	8.50
a.-o.		33c any single	.85	.65
3188	A2471	Pane of 15	13.00	8.50
a.-o.		33c any single	.85	.65
3189	A2472	Pane of 15	13.00	8.50
a.-o.		33c any single	.85	.65
3190	A2473	Pane of 15	13.00	8.50
a.-o.		33c any single	.85	.65
3191	A2474	Pane of 15	13.00	8.50
a.-o.		33c any single	.85	.65
		Nos. 3182-3191 (10)	123.00	85.00

Issued: #3182-3183, 2/3; #3184, 5/28; #3185, 9/10; #3186, 2/18/99; #3187, 5/26/99; #3188, 9/17/99; #3189, 11/18/99; #3190, 1/12/00; #3191, 5/2/00.

"REMEMBER THE MAINE"

A2475

LITHOGRAPHED & ENGRAVED
1998, Feb. 15			Perf. 11.2x11	
3192	A2475	32c red & black	.70	.25

FLOWERING TREES

Southern Magnolia A2476

Blue Paloverde A2477

Yellow Poplar — A2478

Prairie Crab Apple — A2479

Pacific Dogwood A2480

LITHOGRAPHED
1998, Mar. 19   Die Cut Perf 11.3
Self-Adhesive

3193	A2476	32c multicolored	1.50	.40
3194	A2477	32c multicolored	1.50	.40
3195	A2478	32c multicolored	1.50	.40
3196	A2479	32c multicolored	1.50	.40
3197	A2480	32c multicolored	1.50	.40
a.		Strip of 5, #3193-3197	7.50	
b.		As "a," die cutting omitted		

ALEXANDER CALDER (1898-1976), SCULPTOR

Black Cascade, 13 Verticals, 1959 — A2481

Untitled, 1965 — A2482

Rearing Stallion, 1928 — A2483

Portrait of a Young Man, c. 1945 — A2484

Un Effet du Japonais, 1945 — A2485

PHOTOGRAVURE
1998, Mar. 25			Perf. 10.2	
3198	A2481	32c multicolored	.65	.25
3199	A2482	32c multicolored	.65	.25
3200	A2483	32c multicolored	.65	.25
3201	A2484	32c multicolored	.65	.25
3202	A2485	32c multicolored	.65	.25
a.		Strip of 5, #3198-3202	3.25	2.25

CINCO DE MAYO

A2486

Serpentine Die Cut 11.7x10.9
1998, Apr. 16
Self-Adhesive

3203	A2486	32c multicolored	.65	.25

See Mexico No. 2066. For 33c version, see No. 3309.

SYLVESTER & TWEETY

A2487

Serpentine Die Cut 11.1
1998, Apr. 27
Self-Adhesive

3204		Pane of 10 #3204a	6.75	
		A2487 32c single	.65	.25
a.		A2487 32c single	.65	
b.		Pane of 9 #3204a	6.00	
c.		Pane of 1 #3204a	.65	

Die cutting on No. 3204b does not extend through the backing paper.

3205		Pane of 10, #3205c, 9 #3205a	11.00	
a.		A2487 32c single	.90	
b.		Pane of 9 #3205a	7.00	
c.		Pane of 1, no die cutting	3.00	

Die cutting on #3205a extends through the backing paper.

WISCONSIN STATEHOOD

A2488

Serpentine Die Cut 10.8x10.9
1998, May 29
Self-Adhesive

3206	A2488	32c multicolored	.65	.30

Wetlands
A2489

Diner
A2490

COIL STAMPS

1998   **Untagged**   *Perf. 10 Vert.*
3207 A2489 (5c) multicolored .25 .25

Serpentine Die Cut 9.8 Vert.
Self-adhesive
Untagged
3207A A2489 (5c) multicolored,
            small date .25 .25
    b.   Large date .30 .25
   Date on No. 3207A is approximately 1.4mm long, on No. 3207Ab approx. 1.6mm long.

Perf. 10 Vert.
Untagged
3208 A2490 (25c) multicolored .50 .50

Serpentine Die Cut 9.8 Vert.
Self-Adhesive
Untagged
3208A A2490 (25c) multicolored .50 .50
   Issued: #3207-3208, 6/5; #3208A, 9/30; #3207A, 12/14.

1898 TRANS-MISSISSIPPI STAMPS, CENT.

A2491

LITHOGRAPHED & ENGRAVED

1998, June 18   *Perf. 12x12.4*
3209 A2491   Pane of 9   9.50 7.00
  a.   A100 1c green & black .25 .25
  b.   A108 2c red brown & black .25 .25
  c.   A102 4c orange & black .25 .25
  d.   A103 5c blue & black .25 .25
  e.   A104 8c dark lilac & black .25 .25
  f.   A105 10c purple & black .25 .25
  g.   A106 50c green & black 1.25 .60
  h.   A107 $1 red & black 2.50 1.25
  i.   A101 $2 red brown & black 4.25 2.50

Vignettes on Nos. 3209b and 3209i are reversed in comparison to the original issue.

3210 A107 $1 Pane of 9
        #3209h   22.50 —

BERLIN AIRLIFT, 50th ANNIV.

A2492

PHOTOGRAVURE

1998, June 26   *Perf. 11.2*
3211 A2492 32c multicolored .65 .25

AMERICAN MUSIC SERIES
Folk Singers

Huddie
"Leadbelly"
Ledbetter
A2493

Woody
Guthrie
A2494

Sonny Terry
A2495

Josh White
A2496

1998, June 26   *Perf. 10.1x10.2*
3212 A2493 32c multicolored .90 .25
3213 A2494 32c multicolored .90 .25
3214 A2495 32c multicolored .90 .25
3215 A2496 32c multicolored .90 .25
  a.   Block or strip of 4, #3212-
       3215   3.60 2.00

AMERICAN MUSIC SERIES
Gospel Singers

Mahalia
Jackson
A2497

Roberta
Martin
A2498

Clara Ward
A2499

Sister
Rosetta
Tharpe
A2500

1998, July 15   *Perf. 10.1x10.3*
3216 A2497 32c multicolored 1.00 .25
3217 A2498 32c multicolored 1.00 .25
3218 A2499 32c multicolored 1.00 .25
3219 A2500 32c multicolored 1.00 .25
  a.   Block or strip of 4, #3216-
       3219   4.00 2.00

SPANISH SETTLEMENT OF THE SOUTHWEST

La Mision de San Miguel de San
Gabriel, Española, NM — A2501

LITHOGRAPHED
1998, July 11   *Perf. 11.2*
3220 A2501 32c multicolored .65 .25

LITERARY ARTS SERIES

Stephen Vincent Benét — A2502

1998, July 22   *Perf. 11.2*
3221 A2502 32c multicolored .65 .25

TROPICAL BIRDS

Antillean Euphonia — A2503

Green-throated Carib — A2504

Crested Honeycreeper — A2505

Cardinal
Honeyeater
A2506

1998, July 29
3222 A2503 32c multicolored .65 .25
3223 A2504 32c multicolored .65 .25
3224 A2505 32c multicolored .65 .25
3225 A2506 32c multicolored .65 .25
  a.   Block or strip of 4, #3222-
       3225   2.60 2.00

LEGENDS OF HOLLYWOOD

A2507

PHOTOGRAVURE
1998, Aug. 3   *Perf. 11.1*
3226 A2507 32c multicolored .75 .25
   Perforations in corner of each stamp are star-shaped.

ORGAN & TISSUE DONATION

A2508

Serpentine Die Cut 11.7
1998, Aug. 5
Self-Adhesive
3227 A2508 32c multicolored .65 .25

MODERN BICYCLE

A2509

COIL STAMP
Serpentine Die Cut 9.8 Vert.
1998, Aug. 14   **Untagged**
Self-Adhesive (#3228)
3228 A2509 (10c) multicolored,
        small "1998"
        year date .25 .25
  a.   Large date .35 .25
  Date on No. 3228a is approximately 1 ½mm; on No. 3228 approximately 1mm.

Untagged
Perf. 9.9 Vert.
3229 A2509 (10c) multicolored .25 .25
  Date on No. 3229 is approximately 2mm wide.

BRIGHT EYES

Dog
A2510

Fish
A2511

Cat
A2512

Parakeet
A2513

Hamster
A2514

Serpentine Die Cut 9.9
1998, Aug. 20
Self-Adhesive
3230 A2510 32c multicolored .75 .40
3231 A2511 32c multicolored .75 .40
3232 A2512 32c multicolored .75 .40
3233 A2513 32c multicolored .75 .40
3234 A2514 32c multicolored .75 .40
  a.   Strip of 5, #3230-3234   3.75

KLONDIKE GOLD RUSH, CENTENNIAL

A2515

LITHOGRAPHED
1998, Aug. 21   *Perf. 11.1*
3235 A2515 32c multicolored .65 .25

AMERICAN ART

A2516

Paintings: a, "Portrait of Richard Mather," by John Foster. b, "Mrs. Elizabeth Freake and Baby Mary," by The Freake Limner. c, "Girl in Red Dress with Cat and Dog," by Ammi Phillips. d, "Rubens Peale with a Geranium," by Rembrandt Peale. e, "Long-billed Curlew, Numenius Longrostris," by John James Audubon. f, "Boatmen on the Missouri," by George Caleb Bingham. g, "Kindred Sprits," by Asher B. Durand. h, "The Westwood Children," by Joshua Johnson. i, "Music and Literature," by William Harnett. j, "The Fog Warning," by Winslow Homer. k, "The White Cloud, Head Chief of the Iowas," by George Catlin. l, "Cliffs of Green River," by Thomas Moran. m, "The Last of the Buffalo," by Alfred Bierstadt. n, "Niagara," by Frederic Edwin Church. o, "Breakfast in Bed," by Mary Cassatt. p, "Nighthawks," by Edward Hopper. q, "American Gothic," by Grant Wood. r, "Two Against the White," by Charles Sheeler. s, "Mahoning," by Franz Kline. t, "No. 12," by Mark Rothko.

PHOTOGRAVURE

			1998, Aug. 27		**Perf. 10.2**
3236	A2516		Pane of 20	18.00	10.00
a.-t.			32c any single	.90	.60

AMERICAN BALLET

A2517

LITHOGRAPHED

			1998, Sept. 16	**Perf. 10.9x11.1**	
3237	A2517	32c multicolored		.65	.25

SPACE DISCOVERY

A2518   A2519

A2520   A2521

A2522

PHOTOGRAVURE

			1998, Oct. 1		**Perf. 11.1**
3238	A2518	32c multicolored		.65	.25
3239	A2519	32c multicolored		.65	.25
3240	A2520	32c multicolored		.65	.25
3241	A2521	32c multicolored		.65	.25
3242	A2522	32c multicolored		.65	.25
a.			Strip of 5, #3238-3242	3.25	2.25

GIVING AND SHARING

A2523

PHOTOGRAVURE

Serpentine Die Cut 11.1

1998, Oct. 7

Self-Adhesive

3243	A2523	32c multicolored		.65	.25

CHRISTMAS

Madonna and Child, Florence, 15th Cent. — A2524

Evergreen   Victorian
A2525   A2526

Chili Pepper   Tropical
A2527   A2528

LITHOGRAPHED

Serpentine Die Cut 10.1x9.9 on 2, 3 or 4 Sides

1998, Oct. 15

Self-Adhesive

Booklet Stamps

3244	A2524	32c multicolored		.65	.25
a.			Booklet pane of 20 + label	13.00	
b.			Die cutting omitted, pair		

Size: 22x25mm

Serpentine Die Cut 11.3x11.7 on 2 or 3 Sides

3245	A2525	32c multicolored		3.25	.25
3246	A2526	32c multicolored		3.25	.25
3247	A2527	32c multicolored		3.25	.25
3248	A2528	32c multicolored		3.75	.25
a.			Booklet pane of 4, #3245-3248	13.00	
b.			Booklet pane of 5, #3245-3246, 3248, 2 #3247 + label	16.25	
c.			Booklet pane of 6, #3247-3248, 2 each #3245-3246	19.50	
d.			As "a," die cutting omitted	—	
e.			As "b," die cutting omitted	—	
f.			As "c," die cutting omitted	—	
g.			Block of 4, #3245-3248	13.00	

Size: 23x30mm

Serpentine Die Cut 11.4x11.5 on 2, 3, or 4 Sides

3249	A2525	32c multicolored		1.35	.25
a.			Serp. die cut 11.7x11.6 on 2, 3, or 4 sides	1.75	.25
3250	A2526	32c multicolored		1.35	.25
a.			Serp. die cut 11.7x11.6 on 3 or 4 sides	1.75	.25
3251	A2527	32c multicolored		1.35	.25
a.			Serp. die cut 11.7x11.6 on 3 or 4 sides	1.75	.25
3252	A2528	32c multi + label		1.35	.25
a.			Serp. die cut 11.7x11.6 on 2, 3, or 4 sides	1.75	.25
b.			Block or strip of 4, #3249-3252	5.40	
c.			Booklet pane of 20, 5 each #3249-3252 + label	30.00	
d.			Block or strip of 4, #3249a-3252a	7.00	
e.			Booklet pane of 20, 5 each #3249a-3252a + label	35.00	
f.			Block or strip of 4, #3249-3252, red ("Greetings 32 USA" and "1998") omitted on #3249, 3252	625.00	
g.			Block or strip of 4, #3249-3252, red ("Greetings 32 USA" and "1998") omitted on #3250, 3252; green (same) omitted on #3250, 3251		
h.			As "b," die cutting omitted	—	
i.			As "c," die cutting omitted	4,500.	

Dedicated printing plates were used to print the red and green denominations, salutations and dates. Red and green appearing in the wreaths come from other plates and, therefore, are not part of the color omissions.

Weather Vane — A2529

LITHOGRAPHED

		1998	**Untagged**		**Perf. 11.2**
3257	A2529		(1c) multi	.25	.25
a.			Black omitted	125.00	
b.			Horiz. pair, imperf. vert. and at top		

Untagged

3258	A2529		(1c) multi	.25	.25
a.			Black missing (PS)		

No. 3257 is 18mm high, has thin letters, white USA, and black 1998. No. 3258 is 17mm high, has thick letters, pale blue USA and blue 1998.

Uncle Sam — A2530   Uncle Sam's Hat — A2531

PHOTOGRAVURE

Serpentine Die Cut 10.8

Self-Adhesive (#3259, 3261-3263, 3265-3269)

3259	A2530	22c multi		.45	.25
a.			Die cut 10.8x10.5	2.50	.25
b.			Vert. pair, No. 3259 + 3259a	3.50	

See No. 3353.

Perf. 11.2

3260	A2531	(33c) multi		.65	.25

Space Shuttle Landing — A2532

Piggyback Space Shuttle — A2533

LITHOGRAPHED

Sheets of 120 in six panes of 20 (#3261-3262)

Serpentine Die Cut 11.5

3261	A2532	$3.20 multi		6.00	1.50
3262	A2533	$11.75 multi		22.50	10.00

Hidden 3-D images (ENTERPRISE/COLUMBIA/CHALLENGER/ATLANTIS/ENDEAVOR/DISCOVERY) can be seen on Nos. 3261 and 3262 when viewed with a special "Stamp Decoder" lens sold by the USPS.

COIL STAMPS

PHOTOGRAVURE

Serpentine Die Cut 9.9 Vert.

3263	A2530	22c multi		.45	.25
a.			Die cutting omitted, pair	600.00	

See No. 3353.

Perf. 9.8 Vert.

3264	A2531	(33c) multi		.65	.25
a.			Imperf, pair	325.00	

Serpentine Die Cut 9.9 Vert.

3265	A2531	(33c) multi		.80	.25
a.			Die cutting omitted, pair	65.00	—
b.			Red omitted	300.00	
c.			Black omitted	1,400.	
d.			Black omitted, die cutting omitted, pair	700.00	
e.			Red omitted, die cutting omitted, pair	500.00	
f.			Blue omitted		

Unused examples of No. 3265 are on backing paper the same size as the stamps. Corners of the stamp are 90 degree angles.

On No. 3265b, the blue and gray colors are shifted down and to the right.

On No. 3265f, the red is misregistered to right by 10½ stamps and gray by 3mm.

Serpentine Die Cut 9.9 Vert.

3266	A2531	(33c) multi		2.25	.25

Unused examples of No. 3266 are on backing paper larger than the stamps, and the stamps are spaced approximately 2mm. apart. Corners of stamps are rounded.

BOOKLET STAMPS

Serpentine Die Cut 9.9 on 2 or 3 Sides

3267	A2531	(33c) multi		.75	.25
a.			Booklet pane of 10	7.50	

Serpentine Die Cut 11¼ on 3 Sides (#3268, 3268a) or 11 on 2, 3 or 4 sides (#3268b, 3268c)

3268	A2531	(33c) multi		.75	.25
a.			Booklet pane of 10	7.50	
b.			Serpentine die cut 11	.75	.25
c.			As "b," booklet pane of 20 + label	15.00	

Die Cut 8 on 2, 3 or 4 Sides

3269	A2531	(33c) multi		.65	.25
a.			Booklet pane of 18	12.00	

Issued: No. 3262, 11/19; others, 11/9.

Unused and used examples of an "H" nondenominated stamp inscribed "Postcard Rate" exist in the marketplace. There is no evidence that these stamps were ever officially issued. Values: unused $2,400; used $1,750.

A2534

PHOTOGRAVURE

COIL STAMPS

Perf. 9.8 Vert.

		1998, Dec. 14			**Untagged**
3270	A2534	(10c) multi, small date		.25	.25
a.			Large date	.45	.25

Self-Adhesive
Untagged
Serpentine Die Cut 9.9 Vert.

3271	A2534 (10c) multi, small date	.25	.25
a.	Large date	1.00	.25

Dates on Nos. 3270a and 3271a are approximately 1¾mm; on Nos. 3270-3271 approximately 1¼mm.

Compare to Nos. 2602-2604, 2907.

> Scott values for used self-adhesive stamps are for examples either on piece or off piece.

CHINESE NEW YEAR

Year of the Rabbit — A2535

1999, Jan. 5   *Perf. 11.2*
3272	A2535 33c multicolored	.80	.25

See Nos. 3895a, 3997d.

BLACK HERITAGE SERIES

Malcolm X — A2536

LITHOGRAPHED
Serpentine Die Cut 11.4
1999, Jan. 20
Self-Adhesive
3273	A2536 33c multicolored	.85	.25

VICTORIAN LOVE

A2537   A2538

PHOTOGRAVURE
1999, Jan. 28   *Die Cut*
Booklet Stamp
Self-Adhesive
3274	A2537 33c multicolored	.65	.25
a.	Booklet pane of 20	13.00	
b.	Die cutting omitted, pair	100.00	
c.	As "a," die cutting omitted	800.00	
3275	A2538 55c multicolored	1.10	.25

HOSPICE CARE

A2539

LITHOGRAPHED
Serpentine Die Cut 11.4
1999, Feb. 9
3276	A2539 33c multicolored	.65	.25
a.	Horiz. pair, vert. die cutting omitted	—	

Flag & City — A2540

PHOTOGRAVURE
1999, Feb. 25   *Perf. 11.2*
Self-Adhesive (#3278, 3278F, 3279, 3281-3282)
3277	A2540 33c multi	.70	.25

No. 3277 has red date.

Serpentine Die Cut 11 on 2, 3 or 4 Sides
3278	A2540 33c multi	.65	.25
a.	Booklet pane of 4	2.60	
b.	Booklet pane of 5 + label	3.25	
c.	Booklet pane of 6	3.90	
d.	Booklet pane of 10	13.00	
e.	Booklet pane of 20 + label	17.00	
h.	As "e," die cutting omitted	—	
i.	Serpentine die cut 11¼	.90	.25
j.	As "i," booklet pane of 10	9.00	

No. 3278 has black date.

BOOKLET STAMPS
Serpentine Die Cut 11½x11¾ on 2, 3 or 4 Sides
3278F	A2540b 33c multi	1.40	.25
g.	Booklet pane of 20 + label	28.00	

No. 3278F has black date.

Serpentine Die Cut 9.8 on 2 or 3 Sides
3279	A2540 33c multi	.85	.25
a.	Booklet pane of 10	8.50	

No. 3279 has red date.

COIL STAMPS
Perf. 9.9 Vert.
3280	A2540 33c multi, small "1999" year date	.65	.25
a.	Large date	2.00	.25
b.	As No. 3280, imperf pair	125.00	150.00

Serpentine Die Cut 9.8 Vert.

Two types of No. 3281: Type I, Long vertical feature at left and right of tallest building consists of 3 separate lines; Type II, Same features consist of solid color.

3281	A2540 33c multi, type I, large "1999" year date	.65	.25
a.	As No. 3281, die cutting omitted, pair	30.00	
b.	Light blue and yellow omitted	275.00	
c.	Small date, type II	.65	.25
d.	Small date, type I	5.00	.30
e.	As "c," die cutting omitted, pair	—	

Corners are square on No. 3281. Unused examples are on backing paper the same size as the stamps, and the stamps are adjoining.

Date on Nos. 3280a and 3281 is approximately 1¾mm; on Nos. 3280, 3281c and 3281d approximately 1¼mm.

3282	A2540 33c multi	.65	.25

Corners are rounded on #3282. Unused examples are on backing paper larger than the stamps, and the stamps are spaced approximately 2mm. apart.

Flag & Chalkboard — A2541

Printed by Avery Dennison.

PHOTOGRAVURE
Serpentine Die Cut 7.9 on 2, 3 or 4 Sides
1999, Mar. 13
Self-Adhesive
BOOKLET STAMP
3283	A2541 33c multicolored	.65	.25
a.	Booklet pane of 18	12.00	
b.	Die cutting omitted, pair	—	

IRISH IMMIGRATION

A2542

LITHOGRAPHED
1999, Feb. 26   *Perf. 11.2*
3286	A2542 33c multicolored	.65	.25

See Ireland No. 1168.

PERFORMING ARTS SERIES
Alfred Lunt (1892-1977), Lynn Fontanne (1887-1983), Actors

A2543

LITHOGRAPHED
1999, Mar. 2   *Perf. 11.2*
3287	A2543 33c multicolored	.65	.25

ARCTIC ANIMALS

A2544

A2545

A2546

A2547

A2548

LITHOGRAPHED
1999, Mar. 12   *Perf. 11*
3288	A2544 33c Arctic Hare	.85	.25
3289	A2545 33c Arctic Fox	.85	.25
3290	A2546 33c Snowy Owl	.85	.25

3291	A2547 33c Polar Bear	.85	.25
3292	A2548 33c Gray Wolf	.85	.25
a.	Strip of 5, #3288-3292	4.25	—

SONORAN DESERT

A2549

Designs: a, Cactus wren, brittlebush, teddy bear cholla. b, Desert tortoise. c, White-winged dove, prickly pear. d, Gambel quail. e, Saguaro cactus. f, Desert mule deer. g, Desert cottontail, hedgehog cactus. h, Gila monster. i, Western diamondback rattlesnake, cactus mouse. j, Gila woodpecker.

LITHOGRAPHED
Serpentine Die Cut Perf 11.2
1999, Apr. 6
Self-Adhesive
3293	A2549 Pane of 10	8.00	
a.-j.	33c any single	.80	.50

BERRIES

Blueberries   Raspberries
A2550   A2551

Strawberries   Blackberries
A2552   A2553

PHOTOGRAVURE
Serpentine Die Cut 11¼x11½ on 2, 3 or 4 Sides (Nos. 3294-3297), or 2 or 3 sides (Nos. 3294a-3297a)
1999, Apr. 10
Self-Adhesive
3294	A2550 33c multicolored	.85	.25
a.	Dated "2000"	1.25	.25
3295	A2551 33c multicolored	.85	.25
a.	Dated "2000"	1.25	.25
3296	A2552 33c multicolored	.85	.25
a.	Dated "2000"	1.25	.25
3297	A2553 33c multicolored	.85	.25
a.	Dated "2000"	1.25	.25
b.	Booklet pane of 20, 5 each #3294-3297 + label	17.50	
c.	Block or strip of 4, #3294-3297	3.50	
d.	Booklet pane of 20, 5 #3297e + label	25.00	
e.	Block of 4, #3294a-3297a	4.00	

No. 3297d is a double-sided booklet pane, with 12 stamps on one side and eight stamps plus label on the other side.

Serpentine Die Cut 9½x10 on 2 or 3 Sides
3298	A2550 33c multicolored	1.00	.25
3299	A2552 33c multicolored	1.00	.25
3300	A2551 33c multicolored	1.00	.25
3301	A2553 33c multicolored	1.00	.25
a.	Booklet pane of 4, #3298-3301	4.00	
b.	Booklet pane of 5, #3298, 3299, 3301, 2 #3300 + label	5.00	
c.	Booklet pane of 6, #3300, 3301, 2 #3298, 3299	6.00	
d.	Block of 4, #3298-3301	4.00	

COIL STAMPS
Serpentine Die Cut 8.5 Vert.
3302	A2550 33c multicolored	2.25	.25
3303	A2551 33c multicolored	2.25	.25
3304	A2553 33c multicolored	2.25	.25
3305	A2552 33c multicolored	2.25	.25
a.	Strip of 4, #3302-3305	9.00	

See Nos. 3404-3407.

DAFFY DUCK

A2554

PHOTOGRAVURE

Serpentine Die Cut 11.1

1999, Apr. 16

Self-Adhesive

3306   Pane of 10 #3306a   6.75
a.   A2554 33c single   .65   .25
b.   Pane of 9 #3306a   6.00
c.   Pane of 1 #3306a   .65

Die cutting on #3306b does not extend through the backing paper.

3307   Pane of 10, #3307c, 9
    #3307a   13.00
a.   A2554 33c single   1.10
b.   Pane of 9 #3307a   10.00
c.   Pane of 1, no die cutting   2.75
d.   As "a," vert. pair, die cutting omitted btwn. pos. 6 and 9 (unique)   4,250.

Die cutting on #3307b extends through the backing paper.

LITERARY ARTS SERIES

Ayn Rand (1905-82) — A2555

LITHOGRAPHED

1999, Apr. 22   **Perf. 11.2**
3308 A2555 33c multicolored   .65   .25

Cinco De Mayo Type of 1998
LITHOGRAPHED
Serpentine Die Cut 11.6x11.3
1999, Apr. 27
Self-Adhesive
3309 A2486 33c multicolored   .70   .25

TROPICAL FLOWERS

Bird of Paradise A2556

Royal Poinciana A2557

Gloriosa Lily A2558

Chinese Hibiscus A2559

PHOTOGRAVURE
BOOKLET STAMPS
Serpentine Die Cut 10.9 on 2 or 1 Sides
1999, May 1
Self-Adhesive
3310 A2556 33c multicolored   .65   .30
3311 A2557 33c multicolored   .65   .30
3312 A2558 33c multicolored   .65   .30
3313 A2559 33c multicolored   .65   .30
a.   Block of 4, #3310-3313   2.60
b.   Booklet pane, 5 each #3313a   13.00

No. 3313b is a double-sided booklet pane with 12 stamps on one side and 8 stamps plus label on the other side.

JOHN (1699-1777) & WILLIAM (1739-1823) BARTRAM, BOTANISTS

A2560

LITHOGRAPHED
Serpentine Die Cut 11½
1999, May 18
Self-Adhesive
3314 A2560 33c multicolored   .65   .25

PROSTATE CANCER AWARENESS

A2561

PHOTOGRAVURE
1999, May 28   *Serpentine Die Cut 11*
Self-Adhesive
3315 A2561 33c multicolored   .65   .25

CALIFORNIA GOLD RUSH, 150TH ANNIV.

A2562

LITHOGRAPHED
1999, June 18   **Perf. 11¼**
3316 A2562 33c multicolored   .65   .25

AQUARIUM FISH

A2563

A2564

A2565

Reef Fish A2566

Designs: No. 3317, Yellow fish, red fish, cleaner shrimp. No. 3318, Fish, thermometer. No. 3319, Red fish, blue & yellow fish. No. 3320, Fish, heater/aerator.

LITHOGRAPHED
Serpentine Die Cut 11½
1999, June 24
Self-Adhesive
3317 A2563 33c multicolored   .65   .30
3318 A2564 33c multicolored   .65   .30
3319 A2565 33c multicolored   .65   .30
3320 A2566 33c multicolored   .65   .30
b.   Strip of 4, #3317-3320   2.60

EXTREME SPORTS

A2567

A2568

A2569

A2570

PHOTOGRAVURE
Serpentine Die Cut 11
1999, June 25
Self-Adhesive
3321 A2567 33c multicolored   .75   .30
3322 A2568 33c multicolored   .75   .30
3323 A2569 33c multicolored   .75   .30
3324 A2570 33c multicolored   .75   .30
a.   Block or strip of 4, #3321-3324   3.00

AMERICAN GLASS

Free-Blown Glass — A2571

Mold-Blown Glass — A2572

Pressed Glass — A2573

Art Glass — A2574

LITHOGRAPHED
1999, June 29   **Perf. 11**
3325 A2571 33c multicolored   1.90   .25
3326 A2572 33c multicolored   1.90   .25
3327 A2573 33c multicolored   1.90   .25
3328 A2574 33c multicolored   1.90   .25
a.   Strip or block of 4, #3325-3328   7.75   3.00

LEGENDS OF HOLLYWOOD

James Cagney (1899-1986) A2575

PHOTOGRAVURE
1999, July 22   **Perf. 11**
3329 A2575 33c multicolored   .80   .25

Perforations in corner of each stamp are star-shaped.

GEN. WILLIAM "BILLY" L. MITCHELL (1879-1936), AVIATION PIONEER

A2576

Serpentine Die Cut 9¾x10
1999, July 30
Self-Adhesive
3330 A2576 55c multicolored   1.10   .30

HONORING THOSE WHO SERVED

A2577

Serpentine Die Cut 11
1999, Aug. 16
Self-Adhesive
3331 A2577 33c black, blue & red   .65   .25

UNIVERSAL POSTAL UNION

A2578

LITHOGRAPHED
1999, Aug. 25   **Perf. 11**
3332 A2578 45c multicolored   1.00   .45

FAMOUS TRAINS

Daylight
A2579

Congressional — A2580

20th
Century
Limited
A2581

Hiawatha
A2582

Super Chief
A2583

1999, Aug. 26

3333	A2579	33c multicolored	.75	.25
3334	A2580	33c multicolored	.75	.25
3335	A2581	33c multicolored	.75	.25
3336	A2582	33c multicolored	.75	.25
3337	A2583	33c multicolored	.75	.25
a.		Strip of 5, #3333-3337	3.75	—

Stamps in No. 3337a are arranged in four different orders.

FREDERICK LAW OLMSTED (1822-1903), LANDSCAPE ARCHITECT

A2584

1999, Sept. 12

3338	A2584	33c multicolored	.65	.25

AMERICAN MUSIC SERIES
Hollywood Composers

Max Steiner
(1888-1971)
A2585

Dimitri
Tiomkin
(1894-1975)
A2586

Bernard
Herrmann
(1911-75)
A2587

Franz
Waxman
(1906-67)
A2588

Alfred
Newman
(1907-70)
A2589

Erich
Wolfgang
Korngold
(1897-1957)
A2590

1999, Sept. 16   **Perf. 11**

3339	A2585	33c multicolored	1.40	.25
3340	A2586	33c multicolored	1.40	.25
3341	A2587	33c multicolored	1.40	.25
3342	A2588	33c multicolored	1.40	.25
3343	A2589	33c multicolored	1.40	.25
3344	A2590	33c multicolored	1.40	.25
a.		Block of 6, #3339-3344	8.50	4.50

AMERICAN MUSIC SERIES
Broadway Songwriters

Ira (1896-1983) &
George (1898-1937)
Gershwin
A2591

Alan Jay
Lerner
(1918-86) &
Frederick
Loewe
(1901-88)
A2592

Lorenz Hart
(1895-1943)
A2593

Richard Rodgers (1902-79) & Oscar
Hammerstein II (1895-1960) — A2594

Meredith
Willson
(1902-84)
A2595

Frank
Loesser
(1910-69)
A2596

1999, Sept. 21

3345	A2591	33c multicolored	1.25	.25
3346	A2592	33c multicolored	1.25	.25
3347	A2593	33c multicolored	1.25	.25
3348	A2594	33c multicolored	1.25	.25
3349	A2595	33c multicolored	1.25	.25
3350	A2596	33c multicolored	1.25	.25
a.		Block of 6, #3345-3350	7.50	4.50

INSECTS & SPIDERS

A2597

Designs: a, Black widow. b, Elderberry long-horn. c, Lady beetle. d, Yellow garden spider. e, Dogbane beetle. f, Flower fly. g, Assassin bug. h, Ebony jewelwing. i, Velvet ant. j, Monarch caterpillar. k, Monarch butterfly. l, Eastern Hercules beetle. m, Bombardier beetle. n, Dung beetle. o, Spotted water beetle. p, True katydid. q, Spinybacked spider. r, Periodical cicada. s, Scorpionfly. t, Jumping spider.

1999, Oct. 1   **Perf. 11**

3351	A2597	Pane of 20	14.00	10.00
a.-t.		33c any single	.70	.50

Hanukkah Type of 1996
PHOTOGRAVURE

1999, Oct. 8   *Serpentine Die Cut 11*
Self-Adhesive

3352	A2411	33c multicolored	.65	.25

See Nos. 3352, 3547, 3672, Israel No. 1289.

Uncle Sam Type of 1998
COIL STAMP

1999, Oct. 8   **Perf. 9¾ Vert.**

3353	A2530	22c multicolored	.45	.25

See Nos. 3259, 3263.

NATO, 50TH ANNIV.

A2598

LITHOGRAPHED

1999, Oct. 13   **Perf. 11¼**

3354	A2598	33c multicolored	.65	.25

CHRISTMAS

Madonna and Child,
by Bartolomeo
Vivarini — A2599

Serpentine Die Cut 11¼ on 2 or 3 sides

1999, Oct. 20
Booklet Stamp
Self-Adhesive

3355	A2599	33c multicolored	.90	.25
a.		Booklet pane of 20	18.00	

Deer — A2600

Serpentine Die Cut 11¼

3356	A2600	33c gold & red	2.25	.25
3357	A2260	33c gold & blue	2.25	.25
3358	A2260	33c gold & purple	2.25	.25
3359	A2260	33c gold & green	2.25	.25
a.		Block or strip of 4, #3356-3359	9.00	

Booklet Stamps
Serpentine Die Cut 11¼ on 2, 3 or 4 sides

3360	A2260	33c gold & red	1.10	.25
3361	A2260	33c gold & blue	1.10	.25
3362	A2260	33c gold & purple	1.10	.25
3363	A2600	33c gold & green	1.10	.25
a.		Booklet pane of 20, 5 each #3360-3363	22.50	
b.		Block or strip of 4, #3360-3363	4.40	
c.		As "b," die cutting omitted	100.00	
d.		As "a," die cutting omitted	500.00	

Size: 21x19mm
Serpentine Die Cut 11½x11¼ on 2 or 3 sides

3364	A2260	33c gold & red	1.35	.25
3365	A2260	33c gold & blue	1.35	.25
3366	A2260	33c gold & purple	1.35	.25
3367	A2260	33c gold & green	1.35	.25
a.		Booklet pane of 4, #3364-3367	5.50	
b.		Booklet pane of 5, #3364, 3366, 3367, 2 #3365 + label	7.00	
c.		Booklet pane of 6, #3365, 3367, 2 each #3364 & 3366	8.00	
d.		Block of 4, #3364-3367	5.50	

The frame on Nos. 3356-3359 is narrow and the space between it and the hoof is a hairline. The frame on Nos. 3360-3363 is much thicker, and the space between it and the hoof is wider.

Kwanzaa Type of 1997
PHOTOGRAVURE

1999, Oct. 29   *Serpentine Die Cut 11*
Self-Adhesive

3368	A2458	33c multicolored	.65	.25

See Nos. 3175, 3548, 3673.

YEAR 2000

Baby New
Year — A2601

LITHOGRAPHED
Serpentine Die Cut 11¼
1999, Dec. 27
Self-Adhesive

3369	A2601	33c multicolored	.65	.25

CHINESE NEW YEAR

Year of the Dragon — A2602

2000, Jan. 6   *Perf. 11¼*
3370 A2602 33c multicolored   .80   .25
     See Nos. 3895e, 3997e.

BLACK HERITAGE SERIES

Patricia Roberts
Harris — A2603

Serpentine Die Cut 11½x11¼
2000, Jan. 27
Self-Adhesive
3371 A2603 33c indigo   .65   .25

SUBMARINES

S Class
A2604

Los
Angeles
Class
A2605

Ohio Class
A2606

USS
Holland
A2607

Gato Class — A2608

2000, Mar. 27   *Perf. 11*
3372 A2605 33c **multi,** with
     microprinted
     "USPS" at
     base of sail   .75   .25

BOOKLET STAMPS
3373 A2604 22c multicolored   .75   .75
3374 A2605 33c **multi,** no
     microprint-
     ing   1.00   1.00
3375 A2606 55c multicolored   1.50   1.25
3376 A2607 60c multicolored   1.75   1.50
3377 A2608 $3.20 multicolored   10.00   5.00
    a.   Booklet pane of 5, #3373-
         3377   15.00

    No. 3377a was issued with two types of text
in the selvage.

PACIFIC COAST RAIN FOREST

A2609

Designs: a, Harlequin duck. b, Dwarf
oregongrape, snail-eating ground beetle. c,
American dipper, horiz. d, Cutthroat trout,
horiz. e, Roosevelt elk. f, Winter wren. g,
Pacific giant salamander, Rough-skinned
newt. h, Western tiger swallowtail, horiz. i,
Douglas squirrel, foliose lichen. j, Foliose
lichen, banana slug.

*Serpentine Die Cut 11¼x11½, 11½
(horiz. stamps)*
2000, Mar. 29
Self-Adhesive
3378 A2609   Pane of 10   10.00
  a.-j.   33c any single   1.00   .50

LOUISE NEVELSON (1899-1988), SCULPTOR

Silent Music
I — A2610

Royal Tide
I — A2611

Black
Chord — A2612

Nightsphere-Light — A2613

Dawn's Wedding
Chapel
I — A2614

2000, Apr. 6   *Perf. 11x11¼*
3379 A2610 33c multicolored   .65   .25
3380 A2611 33c multicolored   .65   .25
3381 A2612 33c multicolored   .65   .25
3382 A2613 33c multicolored   .65   .25
3383 A2614 33c multicolored   .65   .25
   a.   Strip of 5, #3379-3383   3.25   —

HUBBLE SPACE TELESCOPE IMAGES

Eagle
Nebula — A2615

Ring
Nebula — A2616

Lagoon
Nebula — A2617

Egg
Nebula — A2618

Galaxy NGC 1316 — A2619

PHOTOGRAVURE
2000, Apr. 10   *Perf. 11*
3384 A2615 33c multicolored   .65   .25
3385 A2616 33c multicolored   .65   .25
3386 A2617 33c multicolored   .65   .25
3387 A2618 33c multicolored   .65   .25
3388 A2619 33c multicolored   .65   .25
   a.   Strip of 5, #3384-3388   3.25   2.00
   b.   As "a," imperf   900.00

AMERICAN SAMOA

Samoan
Double
Canoe
A2620

LITHOGRAPHED
2000, Apr. 17
3389 A2620 33c multicolored   .85   .25

LIBRARY OF CONGRESS

A2621

2000, Apr. 24
3390 A2621 33c multicolored   .65   .25

ROAD RUNNER & WILE E. COYOTE

A2622

Serpentine Die Cut 11
2000, Apr. 26
Self-Adhesive
3391   Pane of 10 #3391a   10.00
  a.   A2622 33c single   .85   .25
  b.   Pane of 9 #3391a   8.00
  c.   Pane of 1 #3391a   1.50
  d.   All die cutting omitted, pane
       of 10   2,250.

   Die cutting on #3391b does not extend
through the backing paper.

3392   Pane of 10, #3392c,
      9 #3392a   30.00
  a.   A2622 33c single   2.75
  b.   Pane of 9 #3392a   25.00
  c.   Pane of 1, no die cutting   5.00

   Die cutting on #3392a extends through the
backing paper. Used examples of No. 3392a
are identical to those of No. 3391a.
   Nos. 3391b-3391c and 3392b-3392c are
separated by a vertical line of
microperforations.

DISTINGUISHED SOLDIERS

A2623

A2624

A2625

A2626

Designs: No. 3393, Maj. Gen. John L.
Hines. No. 3394, Gen. Omar N. Bradley. No.
3395, Sgt. Alvin C. York. No. 3396, Second Lt.
Audie L. Murphy.

2000, May 3   *Perf. 11*
3393 A2623 33c multicolored   .70   .25
3394 A2624 33c multicolored   .70   .25
3395 A2625 33c multicolored   .70   .25
3396 A2626 33c multicolored   .70   .25
   a.   Block or strip of 4, #3393-
       3396   2.80   1.50

SUMMER SPORTS

Runners
A2627

2000, May 5
3397 A2627 33c multicolored   .65   .25

ADOPTION

Stick
Figures — A2628

Serpentine Die Cut 11½
2000, May 10
Self-Adhesive
3398   A2628   33c multicolored   .65   .25
  a.   Die cutting omitted, pair   2,500.

See note after No. 1549.

YOUTH TEAM SPORTS

A2629

A2630

A2631

A2632

2000, May 27   **Perf. 11**
3399   A2629   33c Basketball   .70   .25
3400   A2630   33c Football   .70   .25
3401   A2631   33c Soccer   .70   .25
3402   A2632   33c Baseball   .70   .25
  a.   Block or strip of 4, #3399-
          3402   2.80 1.75

THE STARS AND STRIPES

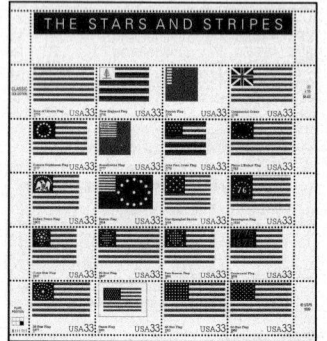

A2633

Designs: a, Sons of Liberty Flag, 1775. b,
New England Flag, 1775. c, Forster Flag,
1775. d, Continental Colors, 1776. e, Francis
Hopkinson Flag, 1777. f, Brandywine Flag,
1777. g, John Paul Jones Flag, 1779. h, Pierre
L'Enfant Flag, 1783. i, Indian Peace Flag,
1803. j, Easton Flag, 1814. k, Star-Spangled
Banner, 1814. l, Bennington Flag, c. 1820. m,
Great Star Flag, 1837. n, 29-Star Flag, 1847.
o, Fort Sumter Flag, 1861. p, Centennial Flag,
1876. q, 38-Star Flag, 1877. r, Peace Flag,
1891. s, 48-Star Flag, 1912. t, 50-Star Flag,
1960.

2000, June 14   **Perf. 10½x11**
3403   A2633   Pane of 20   15.00 11.00
  a.-t.   33c any single   .75   .50

BERRIES

Blueberries
A2634

Strawberries
A2635

Blackberries
A2636

Raspberries
A2637

See designs A2550-A2553.

PHOTOGRAVURE
COIL STAMPS
Serpentine Die Cut 8½ Horiz.
2000, June 16   **Tagged**
Self-Adhesive
3404   A2634   33c multicolored   3.50   .25
3405   A2635   33c multicolored   3.50   .25
3406   A2636   33c multicolored   3.50   .25
3407   A2637   33c multicolored   3.50   .25
  a.   Strip of 4, #3404-3407   15.00

Nos. 3404-3407 are linerless coils issued
without backing paper. The adhesive is strong
and can remove the ink from stamps in the roll.

LEGENDS OF BASEBALL

A2638

Designs: a, Jackie Robinson. b, Eddie Col-
lins. c, Christy Mathewson. d, Ty Cobb. e,
George Sisler. f, Rogers Hornsby. g, Mickey
Cochrane. h, Babe Ruth. i, Walter Johnson. j,
Roberto Clemente. k, Lefty Grove. l, Tris
Speaker. m, Cy Young. n, Jimmie Foxx. o, Pie
Traynor. p, Satchel Paige. q, Honus Wagner. r,
Josh Gibson. s, Dizzy Dean. t, Lou Gehrig.

LITHOGRAPHED
Serpentine Die Cut 11¼
2000, July 6
Self-Adhesive
3408   A2638   Pane of 20   15.00
  a.-t.   33c any single   .75   .50

SPACE
Souvenir Sheets

A2639

A2640

A2641

A2642

A2643

Designs: No. 3409: a, Hubble Space Telescope. b, Radio interferometer very large
array, New Mexico. c, Optical and infrared
telescopes, Keck Observatory, Hawaii. d, Optical telescopes, Cerro Tololo Observatory,
Chile. e, Optical telescope, Mount Wilson
Observatory, California. f, Radio telescope,
Arecibo Observatory, Puerto Rico.
  No. 3410: a, Sun and corona. b, Cross-section of sun. c, Sun and earth. d, Sun and solar
flare. e, Sun and clouds.
  No. 3411: a, Space Shuttle and Space Station. b, Astronauts working in space.

PHOTOGRAVURE
2000   **Perf. 10½x11**
3409   A2639   Sheet of 6   15.00   7.00
  a.-f.   60c any single   2.25   1.00
                                  Perf. 10¾
3410   A2640   Sheet of 5 +
               label   17.50 10.00
  a.-e. $1 any single   3.00   1.75
  f.   As No. 3410, imperf   2,000.
  g.   As No. 3410, with ho-
            logram from No.
            3411b applied   1,500.
Untagged
Photogravure with Hologram
Affixed
Perf. 10½, 10¾ (#3412)
3411   A2641   Sheet of 2   22.50 10.00
  a.-b. $3.20 any single   10.00   4.00
  c.   Hologram omitted on
            right stamp
3412   A2642   multicolored   40.00 17.50
  a. $11.75 single   35.00 15.00
  b.   Hologram omitted
  c.   Hologram omitted on
            No. 3412 in uncut
            sheet of 5 panes
3413   A2643   multicolored   40.00 17.50
  a. $11.75 single   35.00 15.00
  b.   Double hologram   3,000.
  c.   Double hologram on No.
            3413 in uncut sheet of
            5 panes
  d.   Hologram omitted on
            No. 3413 in uncut
            sheet of 5 panes
        Nos. 3409-3413 (5)   135.00 62.00

Issued: No. 3409, 7/10; No. 3410, 7/11; No.
3411, 7/9; No. 3412, 7/7; No. 3413, 7/8.
The holograms on Nos. 3411-3413 scratch
easily. Values are for examples with minimal
scratches. Examples without scratches are
worth more.
Warning: Soaking in water may affect
holographic images.

STAMPIN' THE FUTURE
CHILDREN'S STAMP DESIGN
CONTEST WINNERS

by Zachary
Canter
A2644

by Sarah
Lipsey
A2645

by Morgan
Hill
A2646

by Ashley
Young
A2647

LITHOGRAPHED
Serpentine Die Cut 11¼
2000, July 13
Self-Adhesive

3414	A2644	33c multicolored	.65	.30
3415	A2645	33c multicolored	.65	.30
3416	A2646	33c multicolored	.65	.30
3417	A2647	33c multicolored	.65	.30
a.		Horiz. strip of 4, #3414-3417	2.60	

DISTINGUISHED AMERICANS

Gen. Joseph W. Stilwell A2650

Wilma Rudolph (1940-94), Athlete A2652

Sen. Claude Pepper A2656

Sen. Margaret Chase Smith (1897-1995) A2657

James A. Michener (1907-97), Author — A2657a

Dr. Jonas Salk (1914-95), Polio Vaccine Pioneer A2658

Harriet Beecher Stowe (1811-96), Author A2660

Sen. Hattie Caraway (1878-1950) — A2661

Edward Trudeau (1848-1915), Phthisiologist — A2661a

Mary Lasker (1900-94), Philanthropist — A2661b

Edna Ferber (1887-1968), Writer A2662

Edna Ferber (With Curving Shoulder) A2663

Dr. Albert Sabin (1906-93), Polio Vaccine Pioneer — A2664

LITHOGRAPHED & ENGRAVED, LITHOGRAPHED (#3427A, 3432A, 3432B)
Perf. 11 (#3420, 3426), Serpentine Die Cut 11¼x10¾ (#3422, 3430, 3432B), 11¼x11 (#3427A, 3428, 3432A, 3435), 11 (#3427, 3431), 11½x11 (#3432), 11x11¾ (#3433), 11¼ (#3434)

2000-09
Self-Adhesive (All Except #3420, 3426)

3420	A2650	10c red & blk	.25	.25
a.		Imperf, pair	200.00	
3422	A2652	23c red & blk	.45	.25
a.		Imperf, pair	800.00	
3426	A2656	33c red & blk	.65	.25
3427	A2657	58c red & blk	1.25	.25
b.		Black (engr.) omitted	350.00	
3427A	A2657a	59c multi	1.30	.25
c.		Blue, magenta and yellow omitted	1,500.	
d.		Blue and yellow omitted		

On No. 3427Ad, traces of magenta, where it would not normally appear, are present.

3428	A2658	63c red & blk	1.25	.25
a.		Black (litho.) omitted	275.00	
3430	A2660	75c red & blk	1.50	.25
3431	A2661	76c red & blk	1.50	.25
3432	A2661	76c red & blk	4.00	2.00
3432A	A2661a	76c multi	2.00	.25
3432B	A2661b	78c multi	1.60	.25
3433	A2662	83c red & blk	1.70	.30
3434	A2663	83c red & blk	1.60	.30
3435	A2664	87c red & blk	1.75	.30

LITHOGRAPHED
BOOKLET STAMP
Serpentine Die Cut 11¼x10¾ on 3 Sides
Self-Adhesive

3436	A2652	23c red & blk	.45	.25
a.		Booklet pane of 4	1.80	
b.		Booklet pane of 6	2.70	
c.		As "a" & "b" in cplt booklet of 10 (No. BK279A), die cutting omitted and peel strip intact, P#P44	—	
d.		Booklet pane of 10	4.50	
e.		As "d," die cutting omitted	—	—

The backing on No. 3436b has a different product number (672900) than that found on the lower portion of No. 3436d (673000).

Issued: 10c, 8/24; 33c, 9/7; No. 3432, 2/21/01; No. 3433, 7/29/02; No. 3434, Aug. 2003; 23c, 7/14/04; 63c, 87c, 3/2/06; 58c, 75c, 6/13/07; 59c, No. 3432A, 5/12/08; No. 3432B, 5/15/09.

CALIFORNIA STATEHOOD, 150TH ANNIV.

Big Sur and Iceplant — A2668

PHOTOGRAVURE
2000, Sept. 8 *Serpentine Die Cut 11*
Self-Adhesive

3438	A2668	33c multicolored	.75	.25

DEEP SEA CREATURES

Fanfin Anglerfish A2669

Sea Cucumber A2670

Fangtooth A2671

Amphipod A2672

Medusa A2673

3439	A2669	33c multicolored	.75	.25
3440	A2670	33c multicolored	.75	.25
3441	A2671	33c multicolored	.75	.25
3442	A2672	33c multicolored	.75	.25
3443	A2673	33c multicolored	.75	.25
a.		Vert. strip of 5, #3439-3443	3.75	2.00

2000, Oct. 2   Tagged   Perf. 10x10¼

LITERARY ARTS SERIES

Thomas Wolfe (1900-38), Novelist — A2674

LITHOGRAPHED
2000, Oct. 3   Perf. 11

3444	A2674	33c multicolored	.65	.25

WHITE HOUSE, 200TH ANNIV.

A2675

Serpentine Die Cut 11¼
2000, Oct. 18
Self-Adhesive

3445	A2675	33c multicolored	1.00	.25

LEGENDS OF HOLLYWOOD

Edward G. Robinson (1893-1973), Actor — A2676

PHOTOGRAVURE
2000, Oct. 24   Perf. 11

3446	A2676	33c multicolored	1.60	.25

Perforations in corner of each stamp are star-shaped.

New York Public Library Lion — A2677

PHOTOGRAVURE
COIL STAMP
Serpentine Die Cut 11½ Vert.
2000, Nov. 9   Untagged
Self-Adhesive

3447	A2677	(10c) multi, "2000" year date	.25	.25
a.		"2003" year date	.25	.25

See No. 3769.

Flag Over Farm — A2678

LITHOGRAPHED (#3448-3449), PHOTOGRAVURE (#3450)
2000, Dec. 15   Perf. 11¼

3448	A2678	(34c) multicolored	1.00	.25

Serpentine Die Cut 11¼

3449	A2678	(34c) multicolored	1.00	.25

Booklet Stamp
Self-Adhesive
Serpentine Die Cut 8 on 2, 3 or 4 Sides

3450	A2678	(34c) multicolored	.85	.25
a.		Booklet pane of 18	16.00	
b.		Die cutting omitted, pair		

A2679

PHOTOGRAVURE
Serpentine Die Cut 11 on 2, 3 or 4 Sides
2000, Dec. 15
Self-Adhesive
Booklet Stamp

3451	A2679	(34c) multicolored	1.10	.25
a.		Booklet pane of 20	22.00	
b.		Booklet pane of 4	4.40	
c.		Booklet pane of 6	6.60	
d.		As "a," die cutting omitted		

Statue of Liberty — A2680

Coil Stamps
Perf. 9¾ Vert.

3452	A2680	(34c) multicolored	1.10	.25

Serpentine Die Cut 10 Vert.
Self-Adhesive

3453	A2680	(34c) multi, small date	.70	.25
a.		Die cutting omitted, pair	300.00	
b.		Large date	.75	.25

The date on No. 3453 is 1.4mm long, on No. 3453b 1.55mm long and darker in color.

A2681

A2682

A2683

Flowers — A2684

PHOTOGRAVURE
Serpentine Die Cut 10½x10¾ on 2 or 3 Sides
2000, Dec. 15
Booklet Stamps
Self-Adhesive

3454	A2681	(34c) purple & multi	1.10	.25
3455	A2682	(34c) tan & multi	1.10	.25
3456	A2683	(34c) green & multi	1.10	.25
3457	A2684	(34c) red & multi	1.10	.25
a.		Block of 4, #3454-3457	4.40	
b.		Booklet pane of 4, #3454-3457	4.40	
c.		Booklet pane of 6, #3456, 3457, 2 each #3454-3455	7.00	
d.		Booklet pane of 6, #3454, 3455, 2 each #3456-3457	7.00	
e.		Booklet pane of 20, 5 each #3454-3457 + label	22.50	

No. 3457e is a double-sided booklet pane, with 12 stamps on one side and eight stamps plus label on the other side.

Serpentine Die Cut 11½x11¾ on 2 or 3 Sides

3458	A2681	(34c) purple & multi	5.00	.25
3459	A2682	(34c) tan & multi	5.00	.25
3460	A2683	(34c) green & multi	5.00	.25
3461	A2684	(34c) red & multi	5.00	.25
a.		Block of 4, #3458-3461	20.00	
b.		Booklet pane of 20, 2 each #3461a, 3 each #3457a	55.00	
c.		Booklet pane of 20, 2 each #3457a, 3 each #3461a	90.00	

Nos. 3461b and 3461c are double-sided booklet panes, with 12 stamps on one side and eight stamps plus label on the other side.

Coil Stamps
Serpentine Die Cut 8½ Vert.

3462	A2683	(34c) green & multi	4.50	.25
3463	A2684	(34c) red & multi	4.50	.25
3464	A2682	(34c) tan & multi	4.50	.25
3465	A2681	(34c) purple & multi	4.50	.25
a.		Strip of 4, #3462-3465	20.00	

Lettering on No. 3462 has black outline not found on No. 3456. Zeroes of "2000" are rounder on Nos. 3454-3457 than on Nos. 3462-3465.

Statue of Liberty — A2685

Serpentine Die Cut 9¾ Vert.
2001, Jan. 7
Coil Stamp
Self-Adhesive

3466	A2685	34c multi	.70	.25

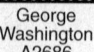

George Washington A2686   American Buffalo A2687

Designed by Carl Herrman (#3467, 3468), Richard Sheaff (#3468A).

Printed by Sterling Sommer for Ashton-Potter (USA) Ltd. (#3467), Avery Dennison (#3468), Banknote Corporation of America (#3468A).

Sheets of 400 in four panes of 100 (#3467), Sheets of 200 in 10 panes of 20 (#3468), Sheets of 120 in six panes of 20 (#3468A)

Self-Adhesive (#3468-3468A)
2001   **Perf. 11¼x11**

3467	A2687	21c multi	.50	.25

Serpentine Die Cut 11

3468	A2687	21c multi	.50	.25

Litho.
Serpentine Die Cut 11¼x11¾

3468A	A2686	23c green	.50	.25

Flag Over Farm — A2688

Photo.
Perf. 11¼

3469	A2688	34c multi	.75	.25

Serpentine Die Cut 11¼

3470	A2688	34c multi	1.00	.25

Eagle — A2696

Serpentine Die Cut 10¾

3471	A2696	55c multi	1.10	.25
3471A	A2696	57c multi	1.10	.25

Capitol Dome — A2697

Washington Monument A2698

Serpentine Die Cut 11¼x11½
Litho.
Self-Adhesive (#3473)

3472	A2697	$3.50 multi	7.00	2.00
a.		Die cutting omitted, pair	500.00	
3473	A2698	$12.25 multi	22.50	10.00

COIL STAMPS
Self-Adhesive (#3475-3475A, 3477-3481)
Photo.
Serpentine Die Cut 8½ Vert.

3475	A2687	21c multi	.50	.25
3475A	A2686	23c green	.75	.25

Compare No. 3475A ("2001" date at lower left) with No. 3617 ("2002" date at lower left).

Perf. 9¾ Vert.

3476	A2685	34c multi	.90	.25

Serpentine Die Cut 9¾ Vert.

3477	A2685	34c multi	.80	.25
a.		Die cutting omitted, pair	65.00	

No. 3477 has right angle corners and backing paper as high as the stamp. No. 3466 has rounded corners and is on backing paper larger than the stamp.

A2690   A2691

A2692

Flowers — A2693

Serpentine Die Cut 8½ Vert.

3478	A2690	34c green & multi	1.50	.25
3479	A2691	34c red & multi	1.50	.25
3480	A2692	34c tan & multi	1.50	.25
3481	A2693	34c purple & multi	1.50	.25
a.		Strip of 4, #3478-3481	6.00	

BOOKLET STAMPS
Litho.
Self-Adhesive
Serpentine Die Cut 11¼x11 on 3 Sides

3482	A2686	20c dk car	.55	.25
a.		Booklet pane of 10	5.50	
b.		Booklet pane of 4	2.20	
c.		Booklet pane of 6	3.30	

Serpentine Die Cut 10½x11 on 3 Sides

3483	A2686	20c dk car	5.50	1.25
a.		Booklet pane of 4, 2 #3482 at L, 2 #3483 at R	12.50	
b.		Booklet pane of 6, 3 #3482 at L, 3 #3483 at R	20.00	
c.		Booklet pane of 10, 5 #3482 at L, 5 #3483 at R	30.00	
d.		Booklet pane of 4, 2 #3483 at L, 2 #3482 at R	12.50	
e.		Booklet pane of 6, 3 #3483 at L, 3 #3482 at R	20.00	
f.		Booklet pane of 10, 5 #3483 at L, 5 #3482 at R	30.00	
g.		Pair, #3482 at L, #3483 at R	6.00	
h.		Pair, #3483 at L, #3482 at R	6.00	

Serpentine Die Cut 11¼ on 3 Sides

3484	A2687	21c multi	.60	.25
b.		Booklet pane of 4	2.40	
c.		Booklet pane of 6	3.60	
d.		Booklet pane of 10	6.00	

Serpentine Die Cut 10½x11¼

3484A	A2687	21c multi	5.50	1.50
e.		Booklet pane of 4, 2 #3484 at L, 2 #3484A at R	12.50	
f.		Booklet pane of 6, 3 #3484 at L, 3 #3484A at R	20.00	
g.		Booklet pane of 10, 5 #3484 at L, 5 #3484A at R	30.00	
h.		Booklet pane of 4, 2 #3484A at L, 2 #3484 at R	12.50	
i.		Booklet pane of 6, 3 #3484A at L, 3 #3484 at R	20.00	
j.		Booklet pane of 10, 5 #3484A at L, 5 #3484 at R	30.00	
k.		Pair, #3484 at L, #3484A at R	6.00	
l.		Pair, #3484A at L, #3484 at R	6.00	

Statue of Liberty — A2689

Photo.
Serpentine Die Cut 11 on 2, 3 or 4 Sides

3485	A2689	34c multi	.70	.25
a.		Booklet pane of 10	7.00	
b.		Booklet pane of 20	14.00	
c.		Booklet pane of 4	3.00	
d.		Booklet pane of 6	4.50	
e.		Die cutting omitted, pair (from No. 3485b)	—	
f.		As "e," booklet pane of 20	—	

Serpentine Die Cut 10½x10¾ on 2 or 3 Sides

3487	A2693	34c purple & multi	.85	.25
3488	A2692	34c tan & multi	.85	.25
3489	A2690	34c green & multi	.85	.25
3490	A2691	34c red & multi	.85	.25
a.		Block of 4, #3487-3490	3.50	
b.		Booklet pane of 4, #3487-3490	3.50	
c.		Booklet pane of 6, #3489-3490, 2 each #3487-3488	5.00	

---

d.	Booklet pane of 6, #3487-3488, 2 each #3489-3490	5.00	
e.	Booklet pane of 20, 5 each #3490a + label	20.00	

No. 3490e is a double-sided booklet pane, with 12 stamps on one side and eight stamps plus label on the other side.

Apple A2694   Orange A2695

Litho.
Serpentine Die Cut 11¼ on 2, 3 or 4 Sides

3491	A2694	34c multi	.70	.25
3492	A2695	34c multi	.70	.25
b.		Pair, #3491-3492	1.40	
c.		Booklet pane, 10 each #3491-3492	14.00	
c.		As "a," black ("34 USA") omitted	—	
d.		As "a," die cutting omitted	1,100.	
e.		As "b," die cutting omitted	5,500.	
f.		As "b," right four stamps yellow omitted	3,500.	

Serpentine Die Cut 11½x10¾ on 2 or 3 Sides

3493	A2694	34c multi	1.05	.25
3494	A2695	34c multi	1.05	.25
a.		Pair, #3493-3494	2.10	
b.		Booklet pane, 2 each #3493-3494	4.20	
c.		Booklet pane, 3 each #3493-3494, #3493 at UL	6.30	
d.		Booklet pane, 3 each #3493-3494, #3494 at UL	6.30	

Serpentine Die Cut 8 on 2, 3, or 4 Sides

3495	A2688b	34c multi	1.10	.25
a.		Booklet pane of 18	18.00	

Issued: Nos. 3472-3473, 1/29; Nos. 3469, 3476-3481, 3485, 3487-3490, 2/7; Nos. 3468, 3471, 3475, 3482, 3483, 2/22; Nos. 3470, 3491-3492, 3/6; Nos. 3493-3494, May; Nos. 3467, 3468A, 3471A, 3475A, 3483, 3484A, 9/20; No. 3495, 12/17.

See Nos. 3616-3619.

LOVE

Rose, Apr. 20, 1763 Love Letter by John Adams A2699   Rose, Apr. 20, 1763 Love Letter by John Adams A2700

Rose, Aug. 11, 1763 Love Letter by Abigail Smith (Abigail Adams in 1764) — A2701

LITHOGRAPHED
Serpentine Die Cut 11¼ on 2, 3 or 4 Sides
2001
Self-Adhesive
Booklet Stamps (Nos. 3496-3498)

3496	A2699	(34c) multi	1.10	.25
a.		Booklet pane of 20	22.00	
b.		Vert. pair, die cutting omitted between	—	

Serpentine Die Cut 11¼ on 2, 3 or 4 Sides

3497	A2700	34c multi	.90	.25
a.		Booklet pane of 20	18.00	
b.		Vertical pair, die cutting omitted between	—	

Size: 18x21mm
Serpentine Die Cut 11½x10¾ on 2 or 3 Sides

3498	A2700	34c multi	.85	.25
a.		Booklet pane of 4	3.50	

b. Booklet pane of 6   5.10
Serpentine Die Cut 11¼
3499 A2701   55c multi   1.10   .25
     Issued: No. 3496, 1/19; others, 2/14.
     See No. 3551.

CHINESE NEW YEAR

Year of
the Snake
A2702

2001, Jan. 20   ***Perf. 11¼***
3500 A2702   34c multicolored   .75   .25
     See Nos. 3895f, 3997f.

BLACK HERITAGE SERIES

Roy Wilkins (1901-
81), Civil Rights
Leader — A2703

Serpentine Die Cut 11½x11¼
2001, Jan. 24
     Self-Adhesive
3501 A2703   34c blue   .70   .25

AMERICAN ILLUSTRATORS

A2704

No. 3502: a, Marine Corps poster "First in
the Fight, Always Faithful," by James Montgomery Flagg. b, "Interlude (The Lute Players)," by Maxfield Parrish. c, Advertisement for
Arrow Collars and Shirts, by J. C. Leyen-
decker. d, Advertisement for Carrier Corp.
Refrigeration, by Robert Fawcett. e, Advertisement for Luxite Hosiery, by Coles Phillips. f,
Illustration for correspondence school lesson,
by Al Parker. g, "Br'er Rabbit," by A. B. Frost.
h, "An Attack on a Galleon," by Howard Pyle. i,
Kewpie and Kewpie Doodle Dog, by Rose
O'Neill. j, Illustration for cover of True Magazine, by Dean Cornwell. k, "Galahad's Departure," by Edwin Austin Abbey. l, "The First Lesson," by Jessie Willcox Smith. m, Illustration
for cover of McCall's Magazine, by Neysa
McMein. n, "Back Home For Keeps," by Jon
Whitcomb. o, "Something for Supper," by Harvey Dunn. p, "A Dash for the Timber," by Frederic Remington. q, Illustration for "Moby
Dick," by Rockwell Kent. r, "Captain Bill
Bones," by N. C. Wyeth. s, Illustration for cover
of The Saturday Evening Post, by Norman
Rockwell. t, "The Girl He Left Behind," by John
Held, Jr.

PHOTOGRAVURE
Serpentine Die Cut 11¼
2001, Feb. 1
     Self-Adhesive
3502 A2704   Pane of 20   19.00
a.-t.   34c any single   .90   .60

DIABETES AWARENESS

A2705

LITHOGRAPHED
Serpentine Die Cut 11¼x11½
2001, Mar. 16
     Self-Adhesive
3503 A2705   34c multicolored   .65   .25

NOBEL PRIZE CENTENARY

Alfred
Nobel and
Obverse
of Medals
A2706

LITHOGRAPHED & ENGRAVED
2001, Mar. 22   ***Perf. 11***
3504 A2706   34c multicolored   .70   .25
     a.   Imperf, pair   500.00
     See Sweden No. 2415.

PAN-AMERICAN EXPOSITION INVERT STAMPS, CENT.

A2707

No. 3505: Reproductions (dated 2001) of: a,
#294a. b, #295a. c, #296a. d, Commemora-
tive "cinderella" stamp depicting a buffalo.

LITHOGRAPHED (#3505d), ENGRAVED (others)
Perf. 12 (#3505d), 12½x12 (others)
2001, Mar. 29
Tagged (#3505d), Untagged (others)
3505 A2707   Pane of 7,
      #3505a-3505c, 4
      #3505d   10.00   7.00
a.   A109 1c green & black   .75   .25
b.   A110 2c carmine & black   .75   .25
c.   A111 4c deep red brown &
     black   .75   .25
d.   80c red & blue   1.90   .35
e.   As #3505, all colors except
     black (vignettes) missing
     on a.-c. (CM)   15,000.

On No. 3505e, the green, carmine and deep
red brown frames appear 4mm above Nos.
3505a-3505c on the pane.

GREAT PLAINS PRAIRIE

A2708

No. 3506 — Wildlife and flowers: a,
Pronghorns, Canada geese. b, Burrowing
owls, American buffalos. c, American buffalo,
Black-tailed prairie dogs, wild alfalfa, horiz. d,
Black-tailed prairie dog, American buffalos,. e,

Painted lady butterfly, American buffalo, prairie coneflowers, prairie wild roses, horiz. f,
Western meadowlark, camel cricket, prairie
coneflowers, prairie wild roses. g, Badger, harvester ants. h, Eastern short-horned lizard,
plains pocket gopher. i, Plains spadefoot, dung
beetle, prairie wild roses, horiz. j, Two-striped
grasshopper, Ord's kangaroo rat.

LITHOGRAPHED
Serpentine Die Cut 10
2001, Apr. 19
     Self-Adhesive
3506 A2708   Pane of 10   10.00
a.-j.   34c Any single   1.00   .50

PEANUTS COMIC STRIP

Snoopy
A2709

Serpentine Die Cut 11¼x11½
2001, May 17
     Self-Adhesive
3507 A2709   34c multicolored   .80   .25

HONORING VETERANS

A2710

2001, May 23
     Self-Adhesive
3508 A2710   34c multicolored   .80   .25

FRIDA KAHLO (1907-54), PAINTER

Self-portrait
A2711

2001, June 21   ***Perf. 11¼***
3509 A2711   34c multicolored   .70   .25

LEGENDARY PLAYING FIELDS

Ebbets
Field
A2712

Tiger
Stadium
A2713

Crosley
Field
A2714

Yankee
Stadium
A2715

Polo
Grounds
A2716

Forbes
Field
A2717

Fenway
Park
A2718

Comiskey
Park
A2719

Shibe
Park
A2720

Wrigley
Field
A2721

PHOTOGRAVURE
Serpentine Die Cut 11¼x11½
2001, June 27   **Self-Adhesive**
3510 A2712   34c multicolored   .90   .60
3511 A2713   34c multicolored   .90   .60
3512 A2714   34c multicolored   .90   .60
3513 A2715   34c multicolored   .90   .60
3514 A2716   34c multicolored   .90   .60
3515 A2717   34c multicolored   .90   .60
3516 A2718   34c multicolored   .90   .60
3517 A2719   34c multicolored   .90   .60
3518 A2720   34c multicolored   .90   .60
3519 A2721   34c multicolored   .90   .60
     a.   Block of 10, #3510-3519   9.00

ATLAS STATUE, NEW YORK CITY

A2722

COIL STAMP
Serpentine Die Cut 8½ Vert.
2001, June 29   **Untagged**
     Self-Adhesive
3520 A2722   (10c) multicolored   .25   .25
     No. 3520 is dated 2001. See No. 3770.
     No. 3520 is known with extremely faint tag-
ging, most likely from contamination in the
paper-making process.

LEONARD BERNSTEIN (1918-90), CONDUCTOR

A2723

LITHOGRAPHED

2001, July 10 *Perf. 11¼*

3521 A2723 34c multicolored .70 .25

WOODY WAGON

A2724

PHOTOGRAVURE
COIL STAMP

Serpentine Die Cut 11½ Vert.

2001, Aug. 3 **Untagged**

Self-Adhesive

3522 A2724 (15c) multicolored .30 .25

LEGENDS OF HOLLYWOOD

Lucille Ball (1911-89) — A2725

LITHOGRAPHED

2001, Aug. 6 ***Serpentine Die Cut 11***

Self-Adhesive

3523 A2725 34c multicolored 1.00 .25
a. Die cutting omitted, pair 700.00

AMERICAN TREASURES SERIES
Amish Quilts

Diamond in the Square, c. 1920 — A2726

Lone Star, c. 1920 — A2727

Sunshine and Shadow, c. 1910 — A2728

Double Ninepatch Variation A2729

Serpentine Die Cut 11¼x11½

2001, Aug. 9

Self-Adhesive

3524 A2726 34c multicolored .70 .30
3525 A2727 34c multicolored .70 .30
3526 A2728 34c multicolored .70 .30
3527 A2729 34c multicolored .70 .30
a. Block or strip of 4, #3524-3527 2.80

CARNIVOROUS PLANTS

Venus Flytrap A2730

Yellow Trumpet A2731

Cobra Lily — A2732

English Sundew — A2733

PHOTOGRAVURE

Serpentine Die Cut 11½

2001, Aug. 23

Self-Adhesive

3528 A2730 34c multicolored .70 .25
3529 A2731 34c multicolored .70 .25
3530 A2732 34c multicolored .70 .25
3531 A2733 34c multicolored .70 .25
a. Block or strip of 4, #3528-3531 2.80

EID

"Eid Mubarak" — A2734

Serpentine Die Cut 11¼

2001, Sept. 1

Self-Adhesive

3532 A2734 34c multicolored .70 .25

See Nos. 3674, 4117, 4202, 4351, 4416.

ENRICO FERMI (1901-54), PHYSICIST

A2735

LITHOGRAPHED

2001, Sept. 29 ***Perf. 11***

3533 A2735 34c multicolored .70 .25

THAT'S ALL FOLKS!

Porky Pig at Mailbox — A2736

PHOTOGRAVURE

2001, Oct. 1 ***Serpentine Die Cut 11***

Self-Adhesive

3534 Pane of 10 #3534a 7.00
a. A2736 34c single .70 .25
b. Pane of 9 #3534a 6.25
c. Pane of 1 #3534a .70

Die cutting on No. 3534b does not extend through the backing paper.

3535 Pane of 10, #3535c, 9 #3535a 50.00
a. A2736 34c single 2.75
b. Pane of 9 #3535a 25.00
c. Pane of 1, no die cutting 25.00

Die cutting on No. 3535a extends through backing paper.

Nos. 3534b-3534c and 3535b-3535c are separated by a vertical line of microperforations.

CHRISTMAS

Virgin and Child, by Lorenzo Costa — A2737

Serpentine Die Cut 11½ on 2, 3 or 4 Sides

2001, Oct. 10

Self-Adhesive

Booklet Stamps (#3536, 3537a-3540a, 3537b, 3538b, 3539b, 3540e, 3541-3544)

3536 A2737 34c multicolored .75 .25
a. Booklet pane of 20 15.00

A2738

A2739

A2740

19th Century Chromolithographs of Santa Claus — A2741

Serpentine Die Cut 10¾x11

Black Inscriptions

3537 A2738 34c multi, large date .70 .25
a. Small date (from booklet pane) .90 .25
b. Large date (from booklet pane) 2.00 .25
3538 A2739 34c multi, large date .70 .25
a. Small date (from booklet pane) .90 .25
b. Large date (from booklet pane) 2.00 .25
3539 A2740 34c multi, large date .70 .25
a. Small date (from booklet pane) .90 .25
b. Large date (from booklet pane) 2.00 .25
3540 A2741 34c multi, large date .70 .25
a. Small date (from booklet pane) .90 .25
b. Block or strip of 4, #3537-3540 2.80
c. Block of 4, small date, #3537a-3540a 3.60
d. Booklet pane of 20, 5 #3540c + label 18.00
e. Large date (from booklet pane) 2.00 .25
f. Block of 4, large date, #3537b-3539b, 3540e 8.00
g. Booklet pane of 20, 5 #3540f + label 40.00

Nos. 3540d and 3540g are double-sided booklet panes, with 12 stamps on one side and eight stamps plus label on the other side.

Numerals "3" and "4" are distinctly separate on Nos. 3537-3540, and touching or separated by a slight hairline on the booklet pane stamps.

Designs of booklet stamps Nos. 3537a-3539a and 3537b-3539b are slightly taller than Nos. 3537-3539. Nos. 3540a and 3540e measure the same as No. 3540.

Serpentine Die Cut 11 on 2 or 3 Sides

Size: 21x18½mm

Green and Red Inscriptions

3541 A2738 34c multicolored .90 .25
3542 A2739 34c multicolored .90 .25
3543 A2740 34c multicolored .90 .25
3544 A2741 34c multicolored .90 .25
a. Block of 4, #3541-3544 3.60
b. Booklet pane of 4, #3541-3544 3.60
c. Booklet pane of 6, #3543-3544, 2 #3541-3542 5.40
d. Booklet pane of 6, #3541-3542, 2 #3543-3544 5.40
Nos. 3536-3544 (9) 7.15 2.25

JAMES MADISON (1751-1836)

Madison and His Home, Montpelier A2742

LITHOGRAPHED & ENGRAVED

2001, Oct. 18 ***Perf. 11x11¼***

3545 A2742 34c green & black .70 .25

THANKSGIVING

Cornucopia A2743

LITHOGRAPHED

Serpentine Die Cut 11¼

2001, Oct. 19

Self-Adhesive

3546 A2743 34c multicolored .70 .25

Hanukkah Type of 1996

PHOTOGRAVURE

2001, Oct. 21 ***Serpentine Die Cut 11***

Self-Adhesive

3547 A2411 34c multicolored .70 .25

Kwanzaa Type of 1997

2001, Oct. 21

Self-Adhesive

3548 A2458 34c multicolored .70 .25

UNITED WE STAND

A2744

LITHOGRAPHED
BOOKLET STAMPS

Serpentine Die Cut 11¼ on 2, 3, or 4 Sides

2001, Oct. 24
Self-Adhesive

3549	A2744	34c multicolored	.75	.25
a.		Booklet pane of 20	15.00	

PHOTOGRAVURE

Serpentine Die Cut 10½x10¾ on 2 or 3 Sides

2002, Jan.
Self-Adhesive

3549B	A2744	34c multicolored	.85	.25
c.		Booklet pane of 4	3.40	
d.		Booklet pane of 6	5.10	
e.		Booklet pane of 20	18.00	

No. 3549Be is a double-sided booklet pane, with 12 stamps on one side and eight stamps plus label on the other side.

"First day covers" of No. 3549B are dated Oct. 24, 2001.

COIL STAMPS Self-Adhesive

Serpentine Die Cut 9¾ Vert.

2001, Oct. 24

3550	A2744	34c multicolored	1.25	.25
3550A	A2744	34c multicolored	1.75	.25

No. 3550 has right angle corners and backing paper as high as the stamp. No. 3550A has rounded corners, the backing paper larger than the stamp, and the stamps are spaced approximately 2mm apart.

Love Letters Type of 2001
LITHOGRAPHED

Serpentine Die Cut 11¼

2001, Nov. 19
Self-Adhesive

3551	A2701	57c multicolored	1.10	.25

WINTER OLYMPICS

Ski Jumping
A2745

Snowboarding — A2746

Ice Hockey
A2747

Figure Skating
A2748

PHOTOGRAVURE

Serpentine Die Cut 11½x10¾

2002, Jan. 8
Self-Adhesive

3552	A2745	34c multicolored	.70	.35
3553	A2746	34c multicolored	.70	.35
3554	A2747	34c multicolored	.70	.35
3555	A2748	34c multicolored	.70	.35
a.		Block or strip of 4, #3552-3555	2.80	
b.		Die cutting inverted, pane of 20	100.00	
c.		Die cutting omitted, block of 4	825.00	

MENTORING A CHILD

Child and Adult
A2749

Serpentine Die Cut 11x10¾

2002, Jan. 10
Self-Adhesive

3556	A2749	34c multicolored	.70	.25

BLACK HERITAGE SERIES

Langston Hughes (1902-67),
Writer — A2750

LITHOGRAPHED

Serpentine Die Cut 10¼x10½

2002, Feb. 1
Self-Adhesive

3557	A2750	34c multicolored	.70	.25
a.		Die cutting omitted, pair	725.00	

Beware of pairs/panes with extremely faint die cutting offered as imperf errors.

HAPPY BIRTHDAY

A2751

PHOTOGRAVURE

2002, Feb. 8 *Serpentine Die Cut 11*
Self-Adhesive

3558	A2751	34c multicolored	.75	.25

See Nos. 3695, 4079.

CHINESE NEW YEAR

Year of the Horse
A2752

LITHOGRAPHED

Serpentine Die Cut 10½x10¼

2002, Feb. 11
Self-Adhesive

3559	A2752	34c multicolored	.75	.25
a.		Horiz. pair, vert. die cutting omitted	5,000.	

See Nos. 3895g, 3997g.

U.S. MILITARY ACADEMY, BICENT.

Military Academy Coat of Arms — A2753

PHOTOGRAVURE

Serpentine Die Cut 10½x11

2002, Mar. 16
Self-Adhesive

3560	A2753	34c multicolored	.75	.25

GREETINGS FROM AMERICA

Alabama
A2754

Serpentine Die Cut 10¾

2002, Apr. 4
Self-Adhesive

3561	A2754	34c Alabama	.70	.60
3562	A2755	34c Alaska	.70	.60
3563	A2756	34c Arizona	.70	.60
3564	A2757	34c Arkansas	.70	.60
3565	A2758	34c California	.70	.60
3566	A2759	34c Colorado	.70	.60
3567	A2760	34c Connecticut	.70	.60
3568	A2761	34c Delaware	.70	.60
3569	A2762	34c Florida	.70	.60
3570	A2763	34c Georgia	.70	.60
3571	A2764	34c Hawaii	.70	.60
3572	A2765	34c Idaho	.70	.60
3573	A2766	34c Illinois	.70	.60
3574	A2767	34c Indiana	.70	.60
3575	A2768	34c Iowa	.70	.60
3576	A2769	34c Kansas	.70	.60
3577	A2770	34c Kentucky	.70	.60
3578	A2771	34c Louisiana	.70	.60
3579	A2772	34c Maine	.70	.60
3580	A2773	34c Maryland	.70	.60
3581	A2774	34c Massachusetts	.70	.60
3582	A2775	34c Michigan	.70	.60
3583	A2776	34c Minnesota	.70	.60
3584	A2777	34c Mississippi	.70	.60
3585	A2778	34c Missouri	.70	.60
3586	A2779	34c Montana	.70	.60
3587	A2780	34c Nebraska	.70	.60
3588	A2781	34c Nevada	.70	.60
3589	A2782	34c New Hampshire	.70	.60
3590	A2783	34c New Jersey	.70	.60
3591	A2784	34c New Mexico	.70	.60
3592	A2785	34c New York	.70	.60
3593	A2786	34c North Carolina	.70	.60
3594	A2787	34c North Dakota	.70	.60
3595	A2788	34c Ohio	.70	.60
3596	A2789	34c Oklahoma	.70	.60
3597	A2790	34c Oregon	.70	.60
3598	A2791	34c Pennsylvania	.70	.60
3599	A2792	34c Rhode Island	.70	.60
3600	A2793	34c South Carolina	.70	.60
3601	A2794	34c South Dakota	.70	.60
3602	A2795	34c Tennessee	.70	.60
3603	A2796	34c Texas	.70	.60
3604	A2797	34c Utah	.70	.60
3605	A2798	34c Vermont	.70	.60
3606	A2799	34c Virginia	.70	.60
3607	A2800	34c Washington	.70	.60
3608	A2801	34c West Virginia	.70	.60
3609	A2802	34c Wisconsin	.70	.60
3610	A2803	34c Wyoming	.70	.60
a.		Pane of 50, #3561-3610	35.00	

See Nos. 3696-3745.

LONGLEAF PINE FOREST

A2804

No. 3611 — Wildlife and flowers: a, Bachman's sparrow. b, Northern bobwhite, yellow pitcher plants. c, Fox squirrel, red-bellied woodpecker. d, Brown-headed nuthatch. e, Broadhead skink, yellow pitcher plants, pipeworts. f, Eastern towhee, yellow pitcher plants, Savannah meadow beauties, toothache grass. g, Gray fox, gopher tortoise, horiz. h, Blind click beetle, sweetbay, pine woods treefrog. i, Rosebud orchid, pipeworts, southern toad, yellow pitcher plants. j, Grass-pink orchid, yellow-sided skimmer, pipeworts, yellow pitcher plants, horiz.

Serpentine Die Cut 10½x10¾, 10¾x10½

2002, Apr. 26
Self-Adhesive

3611	A2804	Pane of 10	19.00	
a.-j.		34c Any single	1.90	.50
k.		As No. 3611, die cutting omitted	2,500.	

AMERICAN DESIGN SERIES

Toleware Coffeepot — A2805

PHOTOGRAVURE
COIL STAMP

Perf. 9¾ Vert.

2002, May 31 Untagged

3612	A2805	5c multicolored	.25	.25
a.		Imperf, pair	—	

No. 3612a is valued with disturbed gum. It is also known without gum and is valued only slightly less thus.

See Nos. 3756-3756A.

Star — A2806

LITHOGRAPHED

Serpentine Die Cut 11

2002, June 7 Untagged
Self-Adhesive (#3613-3614)
Year at Lower Left

3613	A2806	3c red, blue & black	.25	.25
a.		Die cutting omitted, pair	—	

PHOTOGRAVURE

Serpentine Die Cut 10
Year at Lower Right
Untagged

3614	A2806	3c red, blue & black	.25	.25

Coil Stamp

Perf. 9¾ Vert.
Year at Lower Left
Untagged

3615	A2806	3c red, blue & black	.25	.25

Washington Type of 2001
LITHOGRAPHED, PHOTOGRAVURE
(#3617)

2002, June 7 *Perf. 11¼*

3616	A2686	23c green	.50	.25

Self-Adhesive
Coil Stamp

Serpentine Die Cut 8½ Vert.

3617	A2686	23c gray green	.45	.25
a.		Die cutting omitted, pair	—	

Compare No. 3617 ("2002" date at lower left) with No. 3475A ("2001" date at lower left).

LITHOGRAPHED
Booklet Stamps

Serpentine Die Cut 11¼x11 on 3 Sides

3618	A2686	23c green	.50	.25
a.		Booklet pane of 4	2.00	
b.		Booklet pane of 6	3.00	
c.		Booklet pane of 10	5.00	
d.		Nos. 3619c and 3619d, in bklt. of 10 (#BK289A), imperf. vert. btwn. on both panes	1,100.	

Serpentine Die Cut 10½x11 on 3 Sides

3619	A2686	23c green	4.50	1.75
a.		Booklet pane of 4, 2 #3619 at L, 2 #3618 at R	10.00	
b.		Booklet pane of 6, 3 #3619 at L, 3 #3618 at R	15.00	
c.		Booklet pane of 4, 2 #3618 at L, 2 #3619 at R	10.00	
d.		Booklet pane of 6, 3 #3618 at L, 3 #3619 at R	15.00	
e.		Booklet pane of 10, 5 #3619 at L, 5#3618 at R	27.50	
f.		Booklet pane of 10, 5 #3618 at L, 5 #3619 at R	27.50	
g.		Pair, #3619 at L, #3618 at R	5.00	
h.		Pair, #3618 at L, #3619 at R	5.00	

See Nos. 3468A, 3475A, 3482-3483, 3819.

Flag — A2807

LITHOGRAPHED

2002, June 7   **Perf. 11¼x11**
3620 A2807 (37c) multicolored   1.10   .25

LITHOGRAPHED, PHOTOGRAVURE (#3622)

Self-Adhesive

Serpentine Die Cut 11¼x11
3621 A2807 (37c) multicolored   1.10   .25

Coil Stamp

Serpentine Die Cut 10 Vert.
3622 A2807 (37c) multicolored   1.10   .25
  a.   Die cutting omitted, pair   475.00
  b.   Yellow omitted   —

Booklet Stamps

Serpentine Die Cut 11¼ on 2, 3 or 4 Sides
3623 A2807 (37c) multicolored   1.10   .25
  a.   Booklet pane of 20   22.00

No. 3623 has "USPS" microprinted in the top red stripe of the flag.

Serpentine Die Cut 10½x10¾ on 2 or 3 Sides
3624 A2807 (37c) multicolored   1.10   .25
  a.   Booklet pane of 4   4.40
  b.   Booklet pane of 6   6.60
  c.   Booklet pane of 20   22.00

No. 3624 does not have a microprinted "USPS."

Serpentine Die Cut 8 on 2, 3 or 4 Sides
3825 A2807e(37c) multicolored   1.10   .25
  a.   Booklet pane of 18   19.00

Toy Mail Wagon   Toy Locomotive
A2808   A2809

Toy Taxicab   Toy Fire
A2810   Pumper
                   A2811

PHOTOGRAVURE

Serpentine Die Cut 11 on 2, 3 or 4 Sides

2002, June 7

Booklet Stamps

Self-Adhesive
3626 A2808 (37c) multicolored   1.10   .25
3627 A2809 (37c) multicolored   1.10   .25
3628 A2810 (37c) multicolored   1.10   .25
3629 A2811 (37c) multicolored   1.10   .25
  a.   Block or strip of 4, #3626-3629   4.40
  b.   Booklet pane of 4, #3626-3629   4.40
  c.   Booklet pane of 6, #3627, 3629, 2 each #3626, 3628   6.60
  d.   Booklet pane of 6, #3626, 3628, 2 each #3627, 3629   6.60
  e.   Booklet pane of 20, 5 each #3626-3629   22.00

Flag — A2812

LITHOGRAPHED

2002-05   **Perf. 11¼**
3629F A2812 37c multi   .90   .25
  g.   Imperf, pair   100.00

No. 3629F has microprinted "USA" in top red stripe of flag.

Serpentine Die Cut 11¼x11
Self-Adhesive (#3630, 3632-3637)
3630 A2812 37c multi   .90   .25

No. 3630 has microprinted "USA" in top red stripe of the flag.

COIL STAMPS

Perf. 9¾ Vert.
3631 A2812 37c multi   .75   .25

Serpentine Die Cut 9¾ Vert.
3632 A2812 37c multi   .75   .25
  b.   Die cutting omitted, pair 55.00 55.00

Serpentine Die Cut 10¼ Vert.
3632A A2812 37c multi   .75   .25
  f.   Die cutting omitted, pair 250.00
  g.   Vert. pair, horiz. die-cut slits omitted   750.00

No. 3632A lacks points of stars at margin at left top, and was printed in "logs" of adjacent coil rolls that are connected at the top or bottom, wherein each roll could be separated from an adjacent roll as needed.
No. 3632 has "2002" date at left bottom. No. 3632A has "2003" date at left bottom.

Serpentine Die Cut 11¾ Vert.
3632C A2812 37c multi   1.50   .25

No. 3632C is the only 37c Flag coil stamp with a "2004" date at left bottom.

LITHOGRAPHED, PHOTOGRAVURE (#3633)

Serpentine Die Cut 8½ Vert.
3633   A2812 37c multi   .75   .25
3633A A2812 37c multi   2.25   .25

No. 3633A has right angle corners and backing paper as high as the stamp, and is dated "2003." No. 3633 is dated "2002," has rounded corners, the backing paper larger than the stamp, and the stamps are spaced approximately 2mm apart.

Serpentine Die Cut 9½ Vert.
3633B A2812 37c multi   .90   .25

No. 3633B has microprinted "USA" in top red stripe of flag, and has "2005" date at bottom left.

LITHOGRAPHED, PHOTOGRAVURE (#3634, 3636, 3636D)

Booklet Stamps

Serpentine Die Cut 11.1 on 3 Sides (#3634)
3634   A2812 37c multi, large "2002" year date   .75   .25
  a.   Booklet pane of 10   7.50
  b.   Small "2003" date, die cut 11   .75   .25
  c.   Booklet pane, 4 #3634b   3.00
  d.   Booklet pane, 6 #3634b   4.50
  e.   As #3634, die cut 11.3   1.00   .25
  f.   As "e," booklet pane of 10   10.00

Serpentine Die Cut 11.3 on 2, 3 or 4 Sides
3635   A2812 37c multi   .75   .25
  a.   Booklet pane of 20   15.00
  b.   Black omitted   3,000.

No. 3635 has "USPS" microprinted in the top red flag stripe and has a small "2002" year date.

Serpentine Die Cut 10½x10¾ on 2 or 3 Sides
3636   A2812 37c multi   .75   .25
  a.   Booklet pane of 4   3.00
  b.   Booklet pane of 6   4.50
  c.   Booklet pane of 20   15.00
  f.   As "c," 11 stamps and part of 12th stamp on reverse printed on backing liner, the 8 stamps on front side die cutting omitted   —

No. 3636c is a double-sided booklet pane, with 12 stamps on one side and eight stamps plus label on the other side.

Serpentine Die Cut 11¼x11 on 2 or 3 Sides
3636D A2812 37c multi   1.25   .25
  e.   Booklet pane of 20   25.00

No. 3636D lacks points of stars at margin at UL. No. 3636D is the only 37c Flag booklet stamp with a "2004" date at left bottom. No. 3636De is a double-sided booklet pane with 12 stamps on one side and eight stamps plus label on the other side.

LITHOGRAPHED

Serpentine Die Cut 8 on 2, 3 or 4 Sides
3637   A2812 37c multi   .75   .25
  a.   Booklet pane of 18   13.50

Issued: Nos. 3630-3632, 3633, 3634, 3635-3636, 6/7; No. 3637, 2/4/03; No. 3633A, Apr. 2003; No. 3632A, 8/7/03; No. 3634b, 10/23/03; No. 3629F, 11/24/03; No. 3636D, July 2004; No. 3632C, 2004; No. 3633B, 6/7/05.

Toy Locomotive   Toy Mail Wagon
A2813   A2814

Toy Fire   Toy Taxicab
Pumper   A2816
A2815

PHOTOGRAVURE

Serpentine Die Cut 8½ Horiz.

2002-03

Self-Adhesive

Coil Stamps
3638 A2813 37c multi   1.50   .25
3639 A2814 37c multi   1.50   .25
3640 A2815 37c multi   1.50   .25
3641 A2816 37c multi   1.50   .25
  a.   Strip of 4, #3638-3641   6.00

Serpentine Die Cut 11 on 2, 3 or 4 Sides

Booklet Stamps
3642 A2814 37c multi, "2002" year date   .75   .25
  a.   Serpentine die cut 11x11¼ on 2 or 3 sides, dated "2003"   .75   .25
3643 A2813 37c multi, "2002" year date   .75   .25
  a.   Serpentine die cut 11x11¼ on 2 or 3 sides, dated "2003"   .75   .25
3644 A2816 37c multi, "2002" year date   .75   .25
  a.   Serpentine die cut 11x11¼ on 2 or 3 sides, dated "2003"   .75   .25
3645 A2815 37c multi, "2002" year date   .75   .25
  a.   Block or strip of 4, #3642-3645   3.00
  b.   Booklet pane of 4, #3642-3645   3.00
  c.   Booklet pane of 6, #3643, 3645, 2 each #3642, 3644   4.50
  d.   Booklet pane of 6, #3642, 3644, 2 each #3643, 3645   4.50
  e.   Booklet pane of 20, 5 each #3642-3645   15.00
  f.   Serpentine die cut 11x11¼ on 2 or 3 sides, dated "2003"   .75   .25
  g.   Block of 4, #3642a, 3643a, 3644a, 3645f   3.00
  h.   Booklet pane of 20, 5 #3645g   15.00

No. 3645h is a double-sided booklet with 12 stamps on one side and 8 stamps plus label (booklet cover) on the other side. Nos. 3642a, 3643a, 3644a and 3645f have slightly narrower designs than Nos. 3642-3645.
Issued: Nos. 3638-3645, 7/26; Nos. 3642a, 3643a, 3644a, 3645f, 9/3/03.

Coverlet
Eagle — A2817

LITHOGRAPHED

Serpentine Die Cut 11x11¼

2002, July 12

Self-Adhesive
3646 A2817 60c multicolored   1.25   .25

Jefferson
Memorial
A2818

Capitol
Dome — A2819

Serpentine Die Cut 11¼ (#3647, 3648), 11x10¾ (#3647A)

2002-03   **Tagged**

Self-Adhesive
3647   A2818 $3.85 multi   7.50   2.00
3647A A2818 $3.85 multi   9.00   2.00
3648   A2819 $13.65 multi   27.50 10.00

No. 3647 is dated 2002, and No. 3647A is dated 2003.

MASTERS OF AMERICAN PHOTOGRAPHY

A2820

No. 3649: a, Portrait of Daniel Webster, by Albert Sands Southworth and Josiah Johnson Hawes. b, Gen. Ulysses S. Grant and Officers, by Timothy H. O'Sullivan. c, "Cape Horn, Columbia River," by Carleton E. Watkins. d, "Blessed Art Thou Among Women," by Gertrude Käsebier. e, "Looking for Lost Luggage, Ellis Island," by Lewis W. Hine. f, "The Octopus," by Alvin Langdon Coburn. g, "Lotus, Mount Kisco, New York," by Edward Steichen. h, "Hands and Thimble," by Alfred Stieglitz. i, "Rayograph," by Man Ray. j, "Two Shells," by Edward Weston. k, "My Corsage," by James VanDerZee. l, "Ditched, Stalled, and Stranded, San Joaquin Valley, California," by Dorothea Lange. m, "Washroom and Dining Area of Floyd Burroughs' Home, Hale County, Alabama," by Walker Evans. n, "Frontline Soldier with Canteen, Saipan," by W. Eugene Smith. o, "Steeple," by Paul Strand. p, "Sand Dunes, Sunrise," by Ansel Adams. q, "Age and Its Symbols," by Imogen Cunningham. r, New York cityscape, by André Kertész. s, Photograph of pedestrians, by Garry Winogrand. t, "Bristol, Vermont," by Minor White.

PHOTOGRAVURE

Serpentine Die Cut 10½x10¾

2002, June 13

Self-Adhesive
3649   A2820   Pane of 20   22.50
  a.-t. 37c Any single   1.00   .50
  u.   As No. 3649, die cutting omitted   —

AMERICAN TREASURES SERIES

Scarlet and
Louisiana Tanagers,
by John James
Audubon — A2821

Serpentine Die Cut 10¾

2002, June 27

Self-Adhesive
3650   A2821 37c multicolored   1.00   .25

HARRY HOUDINI (1874-1926), MAGICIAN

A2822

LITHOGRAPHED
Serpentine Die Cut 11¼
2002, July 3
Self-Adhesive

3651 A2822 37c multicolored .75 .25

ANDY WARHOL (1928-87), ARTIST

Self-Portrait
A2823

PHOTOGRAVURE
Serpentine Die Cut 10½x10¾
2002, Aug. 9
Self-Adhesive

3652 A2823 37c multicolored .75 .25

TEDDY BEARS, CENTENNIAL

Bruin Bear, c.
1907 — A2824

"Stick" Bear,
1920s — A2825

Gund Bear, c.
1948 — A2826

Ideal Bear, c.
1905 — A2827

Serpentine Die Cut 10½
2002, Aug. 15
Self-Adhesive

3653 A2824 37c multicolored 1.00 .30
3654 A2825 37c multicolored 1.00 .30
3655 A2826 37c multicolored 1.00 .30
3656 A2827 37c multicolored 1.00 .30
a. Block or vert. strip of 4,
#3653-3656 4.00

LOVE

A2828

A2829

LITHOGRAPHED (#3657),
PHOTOGRAVURE
Serpentine Die Cut 11 on 2, 3 or 4 Sides
2002, Aug. 16
Booklet Stamp (#3657)
Self-Adhesive

3657 A2828 37c multicolored .75 .25
a. Booklet pane of 20 15.00
b. As "a," silver ("Love 37
USA") missing on top five
stamps (CM) 750.00
c. Strip of 5, silver ("Love 37
USA") omitted on one
stamp 1,000.

Serpentine Die Cut 11

3658 A2829 60c multicolored 1.25 .25

Beware of examples of No. 3658 with gold ink fraudulently removed.

LITERARY ARTS

Ogden
Nash (1902-
71), Poet
A2830

PHOTOGRAVURE
Serpentine Die Cut 11
2002, Aug. 19
Self-Adhesive

3659 A2830 37c multicolored .75 .25

DUKE KAHANAMOKU (1890-1968), "FATHER OF SURFING" AND OLYMPIC SWIMMER

Kahanamoku
and Surfers at
Waikiki
Beach — A2831

PHOTOGRAVURE
Serpentine Die Cut 11½x11¾
2002, Aug. 24
Self-Adhesive

3660 A2831 37c multicolored .75 .25

AMERICAN BATS

Red Bat
A2832

Leaf-nosed
Bat
A2833

Pallid Bat
A2834

Spotted Bat
A2835

Serpentine Die Cut 10¾
2002, Sept. 13
Self-Adhesive

3661 A2832 37c multicolored .75 .30
3662 A2833 37c multicolored .75 .30
3663 A2834 37c multicolored .75 .30
3664 A2835 37c multicolored .75 .30
a. Block or strip of 4, #3661-
3664 3.00

WOMEN IN JOURNALISM

Nellie Bly (1864-1922) — A2836

Ida M. Tarbell (1857-1944) — A2837

Ethel L.
Payne
(1911-91)
A2838

Marguerite
Higgins
(1920-66)
A2839

Serpentine Die Cut 11x10½
2002, Sept. 14
Self-Adhesive

3665 A2836 37c multicolored 1.25 .35
3666 A2837 37c multicolored 1.25 .35
3667 A2838 37c multicolored 1.25 .35
3668 A2839 37c multicolored 1.25 .35
a. Block or horiz. strip of 4,
#3665-3668 5.00

IRVING BERLIN (1888-1989), COMPOSER

Berlin and Score of
"God Bless
America" — A2840

Serpentine Die Cut 11
2002, Sept. 15
Self-Adhesive

3669 A2840 37c multicolored .75 .25

NEUTER AND SPAY

Kitten
A2841

Puppy
A2842

Serpentine Die Cut 10¾x10½
2002, Sept. 20
Self-Adhesive

3670 A2841 37c multicolored 1.00 .25
3671 A2842 37c multicolored 1.00 .25
a. Horiz. or vert. pair, #3670-
3671 2.00

Hanukkah Type of 1996
2002, Oct. 10 *Serpentine Die Cut 11*
Self-Adhesive

3672 A2411 37c multicolored .75 .25

Kwanzaa Type of 1997
2002, Oct. 10 *Serpentine Die Cut 11*
Self-Adhesive

3673 A2458 37c multicolored .75 .25

Eid Type of 2001
2002, Oct. 10 *Serpentine Die Cut 11*
Self-Adhesive

3674 A2734 37c multicolored .75 .25

CHRISTMAS

Madonna and Child,
by Jan
Gossaert — A2843

LITHOGRAPHED
Serpentine Die Cut 11x11¼ on 2, 3 or 4 Sides
2002, Oct. 10
Self-Adhesive
Booklet Stamp
Design size: 19x27mm

3675 A2843 37c multicolored .75 .25
a. Booklet pane of 20 15.00

Compare to No. 3820, which measures 19½x28mm.
See No. 3820.

CHRISTMAS

Snowman with
Red and
Green Plaid
Scarf — A2844

Snowman with
Blue Plaid
Scarf — A2845

Snowman with
Pipe — A2846

Snowman with
Top
Hat — A2847

PHOTOGRAVURE
Serpentine Die Cut 11
2002, Oct. 28   Tagged
Self-Adhesive

3676	A2844 37c multicolored	.90	.25
3677	A2845 37c multicolored	.90	.25
3678	A2846 37c multicolored	.90	.25
3679	A2847 37c multicolored	.90	.25
a.	Block or vert. strip of 4, #3676-3679	3.75	

Snowman with Blue Plaid Scarf — A2848

Snowman with Pipe — A2849

Snowman with Top Hat — A2850

Snowman with Red and Green Plaid Scarf — A2851

COIL STAMPS
Serpentine Die Cut 8½ Vert.

3680	A2848 37c multicolored	3.25	.25
3681	A2849 37c multicolored	3.25	.25
3682	A2850 37c multicolored	3.25	.25
3683	A2851 37c multicolored	3.25	.25
a.	Strip of 4, #3680-3683	13.00	

BOOKLET STAMPS
Serpentine Die Cut 10¾x11 on 2 or 3 Sides

3684	A2844 37c multicolored	1.25	.25
3685	A2845 37c multicolored	1.25	.25
3686	A2846 37c multicolored	1.25	.25
3687	A2847 37c multicolored	1.25	.25
a.	Block of 4, #3684-3687	5.00	
b.	Booklet pane of 20, 5 #3687a + label	25.00	

No. 3687b is a double-sided booklet pane with 12 stamps on one side and eight stamps plus label on the other side.
Colors of Nos. 3684-3687 are deeper and designs are slightly smaller than those found on Nos. 3676-3679.

Serpentine Die Cut 11 on 2 or 3 Sides

3688	A2851 37c multicolored	1.15	.25
3689	A2848 37c multicolored	1.15	.25
3690	A2849 37c multicolored	1.15	.25
3691	A2850 37c multicolored	1.15	.25
a.	Block of 4, #3688-3691	4.60	
b.	Booklet pane of 4, #3688-3691	4.60	
c.	Booklet pane of 6, #3690-3691, 2 each #3688-3689	7.00	
d.	Booklet pane of 6, #3688-3689, 2 each #3690-3691	7.00	
	Nos. 3676-3691 (16)	26.20	4.00

LEGENDS OF HOLLYWOOD

Cary Grant (1904-86), Actor — A2852

Serpentine Die Cut 10¾
2002, Oct. 15
Self-Adhesive

3692	A2852 37c multicolored	1.25	.25

Sea Coast — A2853

PHOTOGRAVURE
COIL STAMP
Serpentine Die Cut 8½ Vert.
2002, Oct. 21
Self-Adhesive

3693	A2853 (5c) multicolored	.25	.25

See Nos. 3775, 3785, 3864, 3874-3875, 4348.

HAWAIIAN MISSIONARY STAMPS

A2854

No. 3694: a, 2c stamp of 1851 (Hawaii Scott 1). b, 5c stamp of 1851 (Hawaii Scott 2) c, 13c stamp of 1851 (Hawaii Scott 3). d, 13c stamp of 1852 (Hawaii Scott 4).

LITHOGRAPHED
2002, Oct. 24   Tagged   Perf. 11

3694	A2854 Pane of 4	5.00	2.50
a.-d.	37c Any single	1.25	.50

Happy Birthday Type of 2002
PHOTOGRAVURE
2002, Oct. 25 *Serpentine Die Cut 11*
Self-Adhesive

3695	A2751 37c multicolored	.75	.25

GREETINGS FROM AMERICA TYPE OF 2002
Serpentine Die Cut 10¾
2002, Oct. 25
Self-Adhesive

3696	A2754 37c Alabama	.75	.60
3697	A2755 37c Alaska	.75	.60
3698	A2756 37c Arizona	.75	.60
3699	A2757 37c Arkansas	.75	.60
3700	A2758 37c California	.75	.60
3701	A2759 37c Colorado	.75	.60
3702	A2760 37c Connecticut	.75	.60
3703	A2761 37c Delaware	.75	.60
3704	A2762 37c Florida	.75	.60
3705	A2763 37c Georgia	.75	.60
3706	A2764 37c Hawaii	.75	.60
3707	A2765 37c Idaho	.75	.60
3708	A2766 37c Illinois	.75	.60
3709	A2767 37c Indiana	.75	.60
3710	A2768 37c Iowa	.75	.60
3711	A2769 37c Kansas	.75	.60
3712	A2770 37c Kentucky	.75	.60
3713	A2771 37c Louisiana	.75	.60
3714	A2772 37c Maine	.75	.60
3715	A2773 37c Maryland	.75	.60
3716	A2774 37c Massachusetts	.75	.60
3717	A2775 37c Michigan	.75	.60
3718	A2776 37c Minnesota	.75	.60
3719	A2777 37c Mississippi	.75	.60
3720	A2778 37c Missouri	.75	.60
3721	A2779 37c Montana	.75	.60
3722	A2780 37c Nebraska	.75	.60
3723	A2781 37c Nevada	.75	.60
3724	A2782 37c New Hampshire	.75	.60
3725	A2783 37c New Jersey	.75	.60
3726	A2784 37c New Mexico	.75	.60
3727	A2785 37c New York	.75	.60
3728	A2786 37c North Carolina	.75	.60
3729	A2787 37c North Dakota	.75	.60
3730	A2788 37c Ohio	.75	.60
3731	A2789 37c Oklahoma	.75	.60
3732	A2790 37c Oregon	.75	.60
3733	A2791 37c Pennsylvania	.75	.60
3734	A2792 37c Rhode Island	.75	.60
3735	A2793 37c South Carolina	.75	.60
3736	A2794 37c South Dakota	.75	.60
3737	A2795 37c Tennessee	.75	.60
3738	A2796 37c Texas	.75	.60
3739	A2797 37c Utah	.75	.60
3740	A2798 37c Vermont	.75	.60
3741	A2799 37c Virginia	.75	.60
3742	A2800 37c Washington	.75	.60
3743	A2801 37c West Virginia	.75	.60
3744	A2802 37c Wisconsin	.75	.60
3745	A2803 37c Wyoming	.75	.60
a.	Pane of 50, #3696-3745	37.50	

See Nos. 3561-3610.

BLACK HERITAGE SERIES

Thurgood Marshall (1908-93), Supreme Court Justice — A2855

LITHOGRAPHED
Serpentine Die Cut 11½
2003, Jan. 7
Self-Adhesive

3746	A2855 37c black & gray	.75	.25

CHINESE NEW YEAR

Year of the Ram A2856

Serpentine Die Cut 11½
2003, Jan. 15
Self-Adhesive

3747	A2856 37c multicolored	.75	.25

See Nos. 3895h, 3997h.

LITERARY ARTS

Zora Neale Hurston (1891-1960), Writer — A2857

PHOTOGRAVURE
Serpentine Die Cut 10¾
2003, Jan. 24
Self-Adhesive

3748	A2857 37c multicolored	.90	.25

AMERICAN DESIGN SERIES
Toleware Coffeepot Type of 2002 and

Navajo Necklace A2858

Tiffany Lamp A2866

LITHOGRAPHED, PHOTOGRAVURE (#3750, 3751)
Self-Adhesive (#3749-3757)
2003-14 *Serpentine Die Cut 11¼x11*

3749	A2866 1c multi	.25	.25
3749A	A2866 1c multi	.25	.25

No. 3749A has "USPS" microprinted on a white field high on the lamp stand, just below the shade and is dated "2008." No. 3749 has "USPS" microprinted lower on the lamp stand and not on a white field and is dated "2007."

Serpentine Die Cut 11

3750	A2858 2c multi	.25	.25

A reprinting of No. 3750 shows the borders in a much brighter deep turquoise blue shade.

Serpentine Die Cut 11¼x11

3751	A2858 2c multi	1.00	.25

Serpentine Die Cut 11¼x11
With "USPS" Microprinting

3752	A2858 2c multi	.25	.25

Serpentine Die Cut 11¼x10¾

3753	A2858 2c multi	.25	.25

Silver Coffeepot — A2868

LITHOGRAPHED
Serpentine Die Cut 11¼x11

3754	A2868 3c multi	.25	.25

Microprinted "USPS" on No. 3752 is found on top silver appendage next to and below the middle turquoise stone on the right side of the necklace. Microprinting on No. 3753 is found on the top silver appendage next to and below the lower turquoise stone on the left side of the necklace. Nos. 3751 and 3752 are dated "2006." No. 3753 is dated "2007."

Chippendale Chair — A2859

LITHOGRAPHED
Serpentine Die Cut 10¾x10¼

3755	A2859 4c multi	.25	.25

LITHOGRAPHED, PHOTOGRAVURE (#3756)
Serpentine Die Cut 11¼x11¾

3756	A2805 5c multi	.25	.25

Serpentine Die Cut 11¼x10¾

3756A	A2805 5c multi	.25	.25
b.	Die cutting omitted, pair	400.00	

No. 3756A has microprinting on the lower part of the coffeepot handle and is dated "2007." No. 3756 has no microprinting and is dated "2004." Existence of No. 3756A was reported in Aug. 2008.
No. 3756A is known printed with non-reactive cream-colored background ink and also with luminescent cream-colored ink that glows orange under both shortwave and longwave ultraviolet light.

American Clock — A2860

LITHOGRAPHED

3757	A2860 10c multi	.25	.25
a.	Die cutting omitted, pair	—	

PHOTOGRAVURE
Perf. 9¾ Vert.
COIL STAMPS

3758	A2866 1c multi	.25	.25
3758A	A2866 1c multi	.25	.25
3758B	A2858 2c multi	.25	.25
3759	A2868 3c multi	.25	.25
3761	A2859 4c multi, dated "2007" at LL	.25	.25
3761A	A2859 4c multi, dated "2013" at UL	.25	.25

On plate number singles, the plate number is at the lower right on No. 3761 and centered at bottom on No. 3761A.

LITHOGRAPHED, PHOTOGRAVURE (#3762)

3762	A2860 10c multi	.25	.25
3763	A2860 10c multi	.25	.25

No. 3763 is dated "2008," has a microprinted "USPS" as the middle "I" in "VIII," and has a network of beige dots on clock face. No. 3762 is dated "2006," lacks microprinting, and has network of gray dots on clock face.

Issued: No. 3757, 1/24; No. 3758, 3/1; No. 3755, 3/5/04; No. 3756, 6/25/04; No. 3750, 8/20/04; No. 3759, 9/16/05; Nos. 3751-3752, 12/8/05; No. 3762, 8/4/06; Nos. 3749, 3754, 3/16/07; No. 3753, 5/12/07; No. 3761, 7/19/07; No. 3749A, 3/7/08; No. 3758A, 6/7/08; No. 3758B, 2/12/11; No. 3763, 7/15/08; No. 3756A, Aug. 2008.

This is an ongoing set. Numbers may change.
See No. 3612.

AMERICAN CULTURE SERIES

Wisdom, Rockefeller
Center, New York
City — A2875

LITHOGRAPHED
Serpentine Die Cut 11¼x11
2003, Feb. 28
Self-Adhesive

3766	A2875	$1 multicolored	2.00	.40
a.		Dated "2008"	2.00	.40

New York Public Library Lion Type of 2000
PHOTOGRAVURE
COIL STAMP
Perf. 9¾ Vert.
2003, Feb. 4   **Untagged**

3769	A2677	(10c) multicolored	.25	.25

Atlas Statue Type of 2001
PHOTOGRAVURE
Serpentine Die Cut 11 Vert.
2003, Oct.   **Untagged**
Coil Stamp
Self-Adhesive

3770	A2722	(10c) multicolored	.25	.25

No. 3770 is dated 2003.
See No. 3520.

SPECIAL OLYMPICS

Athlete with
Medal — A2879

Serpentine Die Cut 11
2003, Feb. 13
Self-Adhesive

3771	A2879	80c multicolored	1.60	.35

AMERICAN FILMMAKING: BEHIND THE SCENES

A2880

No. 3772: a, Screenwriting (segment of
script from *Gone With the Wind*). b, Directing
(John Cassavetes). c, Costume design (Edith
Head). d, Music (Max Steiner working on
score). e, Makeup (Jack Pierce working on
Boris Karloff's makeup for *Frankenstein*). f, Art
direction (Perry Ferguson working on sketch
for *Citizen Kane*). g, Cinematography (Paul
Hill, assistant cameraman for *Nagana*). h, Film
editing (J. Watson Webb editing *The Razor's
Edge*). i, Special effects (Mark Siegel working
on model for *E.T. The Extra-Terrestrial*). j,
Sound (Gary Summers works on control
panel).

Serpentine Die Cut 11 Horiz.
2003, Feb. 25
Self-Adhesive

3772	A2880	Pane of 10	12.00	
a.-j.		37c Any single	1.20	.50

OHIO STATEHOOD BICENTENNIAL

Aerial View of Farm
Near
Marietta — A2881

LITHOGRAPHED
Serpentine Die Cut 11¾x11½
2003, Mar. 1
Self-Adhesive

3773	A2881	37c multicolored	.75	.25

PELICAN ISLAND NATIONAL WILDLIFE REFUGE, CENT.

Brown
Pelican — A2882

Serpentine Die Cut 12x11½
2003, Mar. 14
Self-Adhesive

3774	A2882	37c multicolored	.75	.25

Sea Coast Type of 2002
PHOTOGRAVURE
COIL STAMP
Perf. 9¾ Vert.
2003, Mar. 19   **Untagged**

3775	A2853	(5c) multicolored	.25	.25

See No. 3864. No. 3775 has "2003" year
date in blue, dots that run together in surf
area, and a distinct small orange cloud. No.
3864 has "2004" year date in black, rows of
distinctly separated dots in surf area, and the
small orange cloud is indistinct.
See Nos. 3693, 3785, 3864, 3874-3875,
4348.

OLD GLORY

Uncle Sam on
Bicycle with
Liberty Flag,
20th
Cent. — A2883

1888
Presidential
Campaign
Badge — A2884

1893 Silk
Bookmark
A2885

Modern Hand
Fan
A2886

Carving of Woman
with Flag and Sword,
19th Cent. — A2887

LITHOGRAPHED
BOOKLET STAMPS
Serpentine Die Cut 10x9¾
2003, Apr. 3
Self-Adhesive

3776	A2883	37c multicolored	.75	.50
3777	A2884	37c multicolored	.75	.50
3778	A2885	37c multicolored	.75	.50
3779	A2886	37c multicolored	.75	.50
3780	A2887	37c multicolored	.75	.50
a.		Horiz. strip of 5, #3776-3780	3.75	
b.		Booklet pane, 2 #3780a	7.50	

Nos. 3776-3780 were issued in booklets
containing two No. 3780b, each with a different backing.

CESAR E. CHAVEZ (1927-93), LABOR ORGANIZER

A2888

Serpentine Die Cut 11¾x11½
2003, Apr. 23
Self-Adhesive

3781	A2888	37c multicolored	.75	.25

LOUISIANA PURCHASE, BICENTENNIAL

English Translation of
Treaty, Map of U.S.,
Treaty
Signers — A2889

PHOTOGRAVURE
Serpentine Die Cut 10¾
2003, Apr. 30
Self-Adhesive

3782	A2889	37c multicolored	.95	.40

FIRST FLIGHT OF WRIGHT BROTHERS, CENT.

Orville
Wright
Piloting
1903
Wright
Flyer
A2890

2003, May 22   *Serpentine Die Cut 11*
Self-Adhesive

3783		Pane of 10	9.00	
a.	A2890	37c single	.90	.40
b.		Pane of 9 #3783a	8.00	
c.		Pane of 1 #3783a	.90	

PURPLE HEART

A2891

LITHOGRAPHED
2003   *Serpentine Die Cut 11¼x10¾*
Self-Adhesive

3784	A2891	37c multi	.75	.25
b.		Printed on back of backing paper	—	
d.		Die cutting omitted, pair	—	

Serpentine Die Cut 10¾x10¼

3784A	A2891	37c multi	.75	.25
e.		Die cutting omitted, pair	150.00	

See Nos. 4032, 4164, 4263-4264, 4390.

Sea Coast Type of 2002
COIL STAMP
PHOTOGRAVURE
Serpentine Die Cut 9½x10
2003, June   **Untagged**
Self-Adhesive

3785	A2853	(5c) multicolored	.25	.25
a.		Serp. die cut 9¼x10	.25	.25

On No. 3785, the stamps are spaced on
backing paper that is taller than the stamps.
One printing of No. 3785 has more of a
scarlet shade in the sky than do other examples of Nos. 3785 and 3785a. Nos. 3785 and
3785a have black "2003" year date.
See Nos. 3693, 3775, 3864, 3874-3875,
4348.

LEGENDS OF HOLLYWOOD

Audrey Hepburn
(1929-93),
Actress — A2892

Serpentine Die Cut 10¾
2003, June 11
Self-Adhesive

3786	A2892	37c multicolored	1.25	1.00

SOUTHEASTERN LIGHTHOUSES

Old Cape
Henry, Virginia
A2893

Cape Lookout,
North Carolina
A2894

Morris Island,
South Carolina
A2895

Tybee Island,
Georgia
A2896

Hillsboro Inlet,
Florida — A2897

Serpentine Die Cut 10¾
2003, June 13
Self-Adhesive

3787	A2893	37c multicolored	1.10	.30
3788	A2894	37c multicolored	1.10	.30
a.		Bottom of "USA" even with top of upper half-diamond of lighthouse (pos. 2)	4.00	2.50

3789	A2895	37c	multicolored	1.10	.30
3790	A2896	37c	multicolored	1.10	.30
3791	A2897	37c	multicolored	1.10	.30
a.	Strip of 5, #3787-3791			5.50	
b.	Strip of 5, #3787, 3788a, 3789-3791			9.50	

Eagle in Gold on Colored Background
A2898

Colored Eagle on Gold Background
A2899

COIL STAMPS
Dated "2003"

Serpentine Die Cut 11¾ Vert.

2003, June 26   Untagged

Self-Adhesive

3792	A2898	(25c)	gray & gold	.50	.25
3793	A2899	(25c)	gold & red	.50	.25
3794	A2898	(25c)	dull blue & gold	.50	.25
3795	A2899	(25c)	gold & Prussian blue	.50	.25
3796	A2898	(25c)	green & gold	.50	.25
3797	A2899	(25c)	gold & gray	.50	.25
3798	A2898	(25c)	Prussian blue & gold	.50	.25
3799	A2899	(25c)	gold & dull blue	.50	.25
3800	A2898	(25c)	red & gold	.50	.25
3801	A2899	(25c)	gold & green	.50	.25
b.	Strip of 10, #3792-3801			5.00	

Dated "2005"

Serpentine Die Cut 11½ Vert.

2005, Aug. 5   Untagged

3792d	A2898	(25c)	gray & gold	.50	.25
3793d	A2899	(25c)	gold & red	.50	.25
3794d	A2898	(25c)	dull blue & gold	.50	.25
3795d	A2899	(25c)	gold & Prussian blue	.50	.25
3796d	A2898	(25c)	green & gold	.50	.25
3797d	A2899	(25c)	gold & gray	.50	.25
3798d	A2898	(25c)	Prussian blue & gold	.50	.25
3799d	A2899	(25c)	gold & dull blue	.50	.25
3800d	A2898	(25c)	red & gold	.50	.25
3801d	A2899	(25c)	gold & green	.50	.25
e.	Strip of 10, #3792d-3801d			5.00	

See Nos. 3844-3853.

ARCTIC TUNDRA

A2900

No. 3802 — Wildlife and vegetation: a, Gyrfalcon. b, Gray wolf, vert. c, Common raven, vert. d, Musk oxen and caribou, vert. e, Grizzly bears, caribou. f, Caribou, willow ptarmigans. g, Arctic ground squirrel, vert. h, Willow ptarmigan, bearberry. i, Arctic grayling. j, Singing vole, thin-legged wolf spider, lingonberry, Labrador tea.

LITHOGRAPHED

Serpentine Die Cut 10¾x10½, 10½x10¾

2003, July 2

Self-Adhesive

3802	A2900	Pane of 10	8.50	
a.-j.		37c Any single	.85	.50

KOREAN WAR VETERANS MEMORIAL

Memorial in Snow
A2901

Serpentine Die Cut 11½x11¾

2003, July 27

Self-Adhesive

3803	A2901	37c	multicolored	.75	.25

MARY CASSATT PAINTINGS

Young Mother, 1888 — A2902

Children Playing on the Beach, 1884 — A2903

On a Balcony, 1878-79
A2904

Child in a Straw Hat, c. 1886
A2905

PHOTOGRAVURE

Serpentine Die Cut 10¾ on 2 or 3 Sides

2003, Aug. 7

Self-Adhesive

Booklet Stamps

3804	A2902	37c	multicolored	.75	.30
3805	A2903	37c	multicolored	.75	.30
3806	A2904	37c	multicolored	.75	.30
3807	A2905	37c	multicolored	.75	.30
a.	Block of 4, #3804-3807			3.00	
b.	Booklet pane of 20, 5 #3807a			15.00	

No. 3807b is a double-sided booklet with 12 stamps on one side and 8 stamps plus label (booklet cover) on the other side.

EARLY FOOTBALL HEROES

Bronko Nagurski (1908-90)
A2906

Ernie Nevers (1903-76)
A2907

Walter Camp (1859-1925)
A2908

Red Grange (1903-91)
A2909

Serpentine Die Cut 11½x11¾

2003, Aug. 8

Self-Adhesive

3808	A2906	37c	multicolored	.75	.35
3809	A2907	37c	multicolored	.75	.35
3810	A2908	37c	multicolored	.75	.35
3811	A2909	37c	multicolored	.75	.35
a.	Block or strip of 4, #3808-3811			3.00	

ROY ACUFF

Acuff (1903-92), Country Music Artist, and Fiddle — A2910

Serpentine Die Cut 11

2003, Sept. 13

Self-Adhesive

3812	A2910	37c	multicolored	.75	.25

DISTRICT OF COLUMBIA

Map, National Mall, Row Houses and Cherry Blossoms — A2911

2003, Sept. 23

Self-Adhesive

3813	A2911	37c	multicolored	.80	.25

REPTILES AND AMPHIBIANS

Scarlet Kingsnake
A2912

Blue-Spotted Salamander — A2913

Reticulate Collared Lizard
A2914

Ornate Chorus Frog
A2915

Ornate Box Turtle
A2916

2003, Oct. 7

Self-Adhesive

3814	A2912	37c	multicolored	.80	.40
3815	A2913	37c	multicolored	.80	.40
3816	A2914	37c	multicolored	.80	.40
3817	A2915	37c	multicolored	.80	.40
3818	A2916	37c	multicolored	.80	.40
a.	Vert. strip of 5, #3814-3818			4.00	

Washington Type of 2002
PHOTOGRAVURE

2003, Oct.   Serpentine Die Cut 11

Self-Adhesive

3819	A2686	23c	gray green	2.00	.25

Christmas Type of 2002
LITHOGRAPHED

Serpentine Die Cut 11¼ on 2 or 3 Sides

2003, Oct. 23

Self-Adhesive

Booklet Stamp

Size: 19½x28mm

3820	A2843	37c	multicolored	.75	.25
a.	Booklet pane of 20			16.00	
b.	Die cutting omitted, pair			—	

See No. 3675.

No. 3820a is a double-sided booklet with 12 stamps on one side and 8 stamps plus label (booklet cover) on the other side.
Compare to No. 3675, which measures 19x27mm.

CHRISTMAS

Reindeer with Pan Pipes
A2917

Santa Claus with Drum
A2918

Santa Claus with Trumpet
A2919

Reindeer with Horn
A2920

Reindeer with
Pan Pipes
A2921

Santa Claus
with Drum
A2922

Santa Claus
with Trumpet
A2923

Reindeer with
Horn
A2924

PHOTOGRAVURE
Serpentine Die Cut 11¾x11
2003, Oct. 23
Self-Adhesive

3821	A2917	37c multicolored	1.00	.25
3822	A2918	37c multicolored	1.00	.25
3823	A2919	37c multicolored	1.00	.25
3824	A2920	37c multicolored	1.00	.25
a.		Block or strip of 4, #3821-3824	4.00	
b.		Booklet pane of 20, 5 each #3821-3824	20.00	

No. 3824b is a double-sided booklet with 12 stamps on one side and 8 stamps plus label (booklet cover) on the other side.

BOOKLET STAMPS
Serpentine Die Cut 10½x10¾ on 2 or 3 Sides

3825	A2921	37c multicolored	1.00	.25
3826	A2922	37c multicolored	1.00	.25
3827	A2923	37c multicolored	1.00	.25
3828	A2924	37c multicolored	1.00	.25
a.		Block of 4, #3825-3828	4.00	
b.		Booklet pane of 4, #3825-3828	4.00	
c.		Booklet pane of 6, #3827-3828, 2 each #3825-3826	6.00	
d.		Booklet pane of 6, #3825-3826, 2 each #3827-3828	6.00	

Snowy Egret — A2925

COIL STAMPS
PHOTOGRAVURE
Serpentine Die Cut 8½ Vert.
2003-04   Tagged
Self-Adhesive

3829	A2925	37c multi	.75	.25
b.		Black omitted	—	—

LITHOGRAPHED
Serpentine Die Cut 9½ Vert.

3829A	A2925	37c multi	.85	.25

Serpentine Die Cut 11½x11 on 2, 3 or 4 Sides
Booklet Stamps
PHOTOGRAVURE

3830	A2925	37c multi	.75	.25
a.		Booklet pane of 20	15.00	
b.		As "a," die cutting omitted	250.00	

With "USPS" Microprinted on Bird's Breast
Litho.

3830D	A2925	37c multi	5.00	.25
e.		Booklet pane of 20	100.00	
f.		Die cutting omitted, pair	150.00	
g.		As "e," die cutting omitted	1,200.	

Issued: No. 3829, 10/24; No. 3830, 1/30/04; No. 3829A, Mar. 2004; No. 3830D, 2004.
Nos 3829, 3829A, 3830 and 3830D all have "2003" year dates even though some were issued in 2004.

PACIFIC CORAL REEF

A2926

No. 3831 — Marine life: a, Emperor angelfish, blue coral, mound coral, vert. b, Humphead wrasse, Moorish idol. c, Bumphead parrotfish, vert. d, Black-spotted puffer, threadfin butterflyfish, staghorn coral. e, Hawksbill turtle, palette surgeonfish. f, Pink anemonefish, magnificent sea anemone, vert. g, Snowflake moray eel, Spanish dancer. h, Lionfish, vert. i, Triton's trumpet. j, Oriental sweetlips, bluestreak cleaner wrasse, mushroom coral, vert.

PHOTOGRAVURE
Serpentine Die Cut 10¾
2004, Jan. 2
Self-Adhesive

3831	A2926	Pane of 10	9.00	
a.-j.		37c Any single	.90	.40

CHINESE NEW YEAR

Year of the
Monkey
A2927

Serpentine Die Cut 10¾
2004, Jan. 13
Self-Adhesive

3832	A2927	37c multicolored	.75	.25
a.		Yellow omitted	—	

See Nos. 3895i, 3997i.

LOVE

Candy
Hearts — A2928

BOOKLET STAMP
Serpentine Die Cut 10¾ on 2, 3 or 4 Sides
2004, Jan. 14
Self-Adhesive

3833	A2928	37c multicolored	.75	.25
a.		Booklet pane of 20	15.00	

BLACK HERITAGE SERIES

Paul Robeson (1898-1976), Actor, Singer, Athlete and Activist — A2929

PHOTOGRAVURE
Serpentine Die Cut 10¾
2004, Jan. 20
Self-Adhesive

3834	A2929	37c multicolored	.85	.25

THEODOR SEUSS GEISEL (DR. SEUSS)

Dr. Seuss (1904-91), Children's Book Writer, and Book Characters A2930

PHOTOGRAVURE
Serpentine Die Cut 10¾x10½
2004, Mar. 2
Self-Adhesive

3835	A2930	37c multicolored	.85	.25
a.		Die cutting omitted, pair	1,400.	

FLOWERS

White Lilacs and Pink Roses A2931

Five Varieties of Pink Roses A2932

LITHOGRAPHED (#3836),
PHOTOGRAVURE
BOOKLET STAMP (#3836)
Serpentine Die Cut 10¾ on 2, 3 or 4 Sides
2004, Mar. 4
Self-Adhesive

3836	A2931	37c multicolored	.75	.25
a.		Booklet pane of 20	15.00	

Serpentine Die Cut 11½x11

3837	A2932	60c multicolored	2.00	.25

UNITED STATES AIR FORCE ACADEMY, 50TH ANNIV.

Cadet Chapel A2933

PHOTOGRAVURE
Serpentine Die Cut 10¾
2004, Apr. 1
Self-Adhesive

3838	A2933	37c multicolored	.75	.25

HENRY MANCINI

Henry Mancini (1924-94), Composer, and Pink Panther A2934

2004, Apr. 13
Self-Adhesive

3839	A2934	37c multicolored	.75	.25

AMERICAN CHOREOGRAPHERS

Martha Graham (1893-1991) — A2935

Alvin Ailey (1931-89), and Dancers A2936

Agnes de Mille (1909-93), and Dancers A2937

George Balanchine (1904-83), and Dancers A2938

LITHOGRAPHED
2004, May 4
Self-Adhesive

3840	A2935	37c multicolored	.75	.35
3841	A2936	37c multicolored	.75	.35
3842	A2937	37c multicolored	.75	.35
3843	A2938	37c multicolored	.75	.35
a.		Horiz. strip of 4, #3840-3843	3.00	
b.		Strip of 4, die cutting omitted	300.00	
c.		Pane of 20 misprinted and miscut to show 5 #3843 and half of 5 #3842 at left, lower center plate position diagram at center, and 10 blank stamps at right.	—	

Eagle Types of 2003
PHOTOGRAVURE
COIL STAMPS
Perf. 9¾ Vert.
2004, May 12   Untagged

3844	A2898	(25c) gray & gold	.95	.25
3845	A2899	(25c) gold & green	.95	.25
3846	A2898	(25c) red & gold	.95	.25
3847	A2899	(25c) gold & dull blue	.95	.25
3848	A2898	(25c) Prussian blue & gold	.95	.25
3849	A2899	(25c) gold & gray	.95	.50
3850	A2898	(25c) green & gold	.95	.25
3851	A2899	(25c) gold & Prussian blue	.95	.25
3852	A2898	(25c) dull blue & gold	.95	.25
3853	A2899	(25c) gold & red	.95	.25
a.		Strip of 10, #3844-3853	9.50	—

LEWIS & CLARK EXPEDITION, BICENTENNIAL

Meriwether Lewis (1774-1809) and William Clark (1770-1838) On Hill — A2939

Lewis — A2940

Clark — A2941

LITHOGRAPHED & ENGRAVED
Serpentine Die Cut 10¾
2004, May 14
Self-Adhesive

3854	A2939	37c green & multi	1.10	.25

Booklet Stamps
Serpentine Die Cut 10½x10¾
3855	A2940 37c blue & multi	.90	.45
3856	A2941 37c red & multi	.90	.45
a.	Horiz. or vert. pair, #3855-3856	1.80	
b.	Booklet pane, 5 each #3855-3856	9.00	

Nos. 3855-3856 were issued in booklets containing two No. 3856b, each with a different backing. The booklets sold for $8.95.

ISAMU NOGUCHI (1904-88), SCULPTOR

Akari 25N — A2942

Margaret La Farge Osborn A2943

Black Sun — A2944

Mother and Child — A2945

Figure (Detail) — A2946

LITHOGRAPHED
Serpentine Die Cut 10½x10¾
2004, May 18
Self-Adhesive
3857	A2942 37c black	.90	.40
3858	A2943 37c black	.90	.40
3859	A2944 37c black	.90	.40
3860	A2945 37c black	.90	.40
3861	A2946 37c black	.90	.40
a.	Horiz. strip of 5, #3857-3861	4.50	

NATIONAL WORLD WAR II MEMORIAL

A2947

Serpentine Die Cut 10¾
2004, May 29
Self-Adhesive
3862	A2947 37c multicolored	.75	.25

Scott values for used self-adhesive stamps are for examples either on piece or off piece.

OLYMPIC GAMES, ATHENS, GREECE

Stylized Runner A2948

2004, June 9
Self-Adhesive
3863	A2948 37c multicolored	.75	.25

Sea Coast Type of 2002
PHOTOGRAVURE
COIL STAMP
Perf. 9¾ Vert.
2004, June 11   Untagged
3864	A2853 (5c) multicolored	.25	.25

No. 3864 has "2004" year date in black, rows of distinctly separated dots in surf area, and the small orange cloud is indistinct.
No. 3775 has "2003" year date in blue, dots that run together in surf area, and a distinct small orange cloud.
See Nos. 3693, 3775, 3785, 3874-3875, 4348.

THE ART OF DISNEY: FRIENDSHIP

Goofy, Mickey Mouse, Donald Duck — A2949

Bambi, Thumper A2950

Mufasa, Simba — A2951

Jiminy Cricket, Pinocchio A2952

LITHOGRAPHED
Serpentine Die Cut 10½x10¾
2004, June 23
Self-Adhesive
3865	A2949 37c multicolored	1.00	.30
3866	A2950 37c multicolored	1.00	.30
3867	A2951 37c multicolored	1.00	.30
3868	A2952 37c multicolored	1.00	.30
a.	Block or vert. strip of 4, #3865-3868	4.00	

U.S.S. CONSTELLATION

A2953

ENGRAVED
Serpentine Die Cut 10½
2004, June 30
Self-Adhesive
3869	A2953 37c brown	.75	.25

R. BUCKMINSTER FULLER (1895-1983), ENGINEER

Time Magazine Cover Depicting Fuller, by Boris Artzybasheff A2954

LITHOGRAPHED
Serpentine Die Cut 10½x10¾
2004, July 12
Self-Adhesive
3870	A2954 37c multicolored	.75	.25

LITERARY ARTS

James Baldwin (1924-87), Writer A2955

Serpentine Die Cut 10¾
2004, July 23
Self-Adhesive
3871	A2955 37c multicolored	.75	.25
a.	Die cutting omitted, pair	750.00	

AMERICAN TREASURES SERIES

Giant Magnolias on a Blue Velvet Cloth, by Martin Johnson Heade A2956

PHOTOGRAVURE
BOOKLET STAMP
Serpentine Die Cut 10¾ on 2 or 3 Sides
2004, Aug. 12
Self-Adhesive
3872	A2956 37c multicolored	.70	.25
a.	Booklet pane of 20	15.00	
b.	Die cutting omitted, pair, in #3872a with foldover	—	

No. 3872a is a double-sided booklet pane with 12 stamps on one side and eight stamps plus label on the other side.

ART OF THE AMERICAN INDIAN

A2957

No. 3878: a, Mimbres bowl. b, Kutenai parfleche. c, Tlingit sculptures. d, Ho-Chunk bag. e, Seminole doll. f, Mississippian effigy. g, Acoma pot. h, Navajo weaving. i, Seneca carving. j, Luiseño basket.

Serpentine Die Cut 10¾x11
2004, Aug. 21
Self-Adhesive
3873	A2957 Pane of 10	25.00	
a.-j.	37c Any single	2.50	.40

Sea Coast Type of 2002
PHOTOGRAVURE
COIL STAMPS
Serpentine Die Cut 10 Vert.
2004-05   Untagged
Self-Adhesive
3874	A2853 (5c) multi, large "2003" year date	.25	.25
a.	Small "2003" year date ('05)	.25	.25

Serpentine Die Cut 11½ Vert.
Untagged
3875	A2853 (5c) multi, "2004" year date	.25	.25

On Nos. 3874, 3874a and 3875, the stamps are spaced on backing paper that is taller than the stamps.
See Nos. 3693, 3775, 3785, 3864, 4348.

LEGENDS OF HOLLYWOOD

John Wayne (1907-79), Actor — A2958

Serpentine Die Cut 10¾
2004, Sept. 9
Self-Adhesive
3876	A2958 37c multicolored	.85	.25

SICKLE CELL DISEASE AWARENESS

Mother and Child — A2959

Serpentine Die Cut 11
2004, Sept. 29
Self-Adhesive
3877	A2959 37c multicolored	.75	.25

CLOUDSCAPES

A2960

No. 3878 — Clouds: a, Cirrus radiatus. b, Cirrostratus fibratus. c, Cirrocumulus undulatus. d, Cumulonimbus mammatus. e, Cumulonimbus incus. f, Altocumulus stratiformis. g, Altostratus translucidus. h, Altocumulus undulatus. i, Altocumulus castellanus. j, Altocumulus lenticularis. k, Stratocumulus undulatus. l, Stratus opacus. m, Cumulus humilis. n, Cumulus congestus. o, Cumulonimbus with tornado.

2004, Oct. 4
Self-Adhesive

3878	A2960	Pane of 15	15.00	
a.-o.		37c Any single	1.00	.50

CHRISTMAS

Madonna and Child,
by Lorenzo
Monaco — A2961

LITHOGRAPHED
BOOKLET STAMP
Serpentine Die Cut 10¾x11 on 2 or 3 Sides
2004, Oct. 14
Self-Adhesive

3879	A2961	37c multicolored	.75	.25
a.		Booklet pane of 20	15.00	
b.		As "a," die cutting omitted	—	

No. 3879a is a double-sided booklet pane with 12 stamps on one side and eight stamps plus label that serves as a booklet cover on the other side.

HANUKKAH

Dreidel — A2962

Serpentine Die Cut 10¾
2004, Oct. 15
Self-Adhesive

3880	A2962	37c multicolored	.75	.25
a.		Die cuts applied to wrong sides of stamp (hyphenhole die cuts and wavy line on face, die cut 10¾ on reverse)	—	—

See Nos. 4118, 4219, 4372.

KWANZAA

People in
Robes — A2963

Serpentine Die Cut 10¾
2004, Oct. 16
Self-Adhesive

3881	A2963	37c multicolored	.75	.25

See Nos. 4119, 4220, 4373.

LITERARY ARTS

Moss Hart
(1904-61),
Playwright
A2964

PHOTOGRAVURE
2004, Oct. 25 *Serpentine Die Cut 11*
Self-Adhesive

3882	A2964	37c multicolored	.75	.25

CHRISTMAS

Purple Santa
Ornament
A2965

Green Santa
Ornament
A2966

Blue Santa
Ornament
A2967

Red Santa
Ornament
A2968

Serpentine Die Cut 11½x11
2004, Nov. 16
Self-Adhesive

3883	A2965	37c purple & multi	1.00	.25
3884	A2966	37c green & multi	1.00	.25
3885	A2967	37c blue & multi	1.00	.25
3886	A2968	37c red & multi	1.00	.25
a.		Block or strip of 4, #3883-3886	4.00	
b.		Booklet pane of 20, 5 #3886a blocks	20.00	

Purple Santa
Ornament
A2969

Green Santa
Ornament
A2970

Blue Santa
Ornament
A2971

Red Santa
Ornament
A2972

Booklet Stamps
Serpentine Die Cut 10¼x10¾ on 2 or 3 Sides

3887	A2969	37c purple & multi	.90	.25
3888	A2970	37c green & multi	.90	.25
3889	A2971	37c blue & multi	.90	.25
3890	A2972	37c red & multi	.90	.25
a.		Block of 4, #3887-3890	3.60	
b.		Booklet pane of 4, #3887-3890	3.60	
c.		Booklet pane of 6, #3889-3890, 2 each #3887-3888	5.50	
d.		Booklet pane of 6, #3887-3888, 2 each #3889-3890	5.50	

Serpentine Die Cut 8 on 2, 3 or 4 Sides

3891	A2970	37c green & multi	2.00	.25
3892	A2969	37c purple & multi	2.00	.25
3893	A2972	37c red & multi	2.00	.25
3894	A2971	37c blue & multi	2.00	.25
a.		Block of 4, #3891-3894	8.00	
b.		Booklet pane of 18, 6 each #3891, 3893, 3 each # 3892, 3894	36.00	
		Nos. 3883-3894 (12)	15.60	3.00

No. 3886b is a double-sided booklet with 12 stamps on one side and 8 stamps plus label that serves as a booklet cover on the other side.

The design of No. 3894b shows ornaments in a wooden box. The pattern of the wooden box dividers creates three types of each design. Rows 1 and 4 are Type 1, with a top horizontal strip of frame extending from edge to edge while the bottom strip of frame stops at the design's width. Rows 2 and 5 are Type 2, with both top and bottom strips of frame stopping at the design's width. Rows 3 and 6 are Type 3, with the top strip of frame stopping at design's width while the bottom strip of frame extends from edge to edge. Each variety is equally common.

Chinese New Year Types of 1992-2004
PHOTOGRAVURE
Serpentine Die Cut 10¾
2005, Jan. 6
Self-Adhesive

3895		Double sided pane of 24, 2 each #a-l	18.00	
a.	A2360	37c Rat	.75	.40
b.	A2413	37c Ox	.75	.40
c.	A2462	37c Tiger	.75	.40
d.	A2535	37c Rabbit	.75	.40
e.	A2602	37c Dragon	.75	.40
f.	A2702	37c Snake	.75	.40
g.	A2752	37c Horse	.75	.40
h.	A2856	37c Ram	.75	.40
i.	A2927	37c Monkey	.75	.40
j.	A2067	37c Rooster	.75	.40
k.	A2146	37c Dog	.75	.40
l.	A2205	37c Boar	.75	.40
m.		As No. 3895, die cutting missing on "a," "b," and "c" on reverse side (PS)	900.00	

No. 3895h has "2005" year date and is photogravure while No. 3747 has "2003" year date and is lithographed.

Stamps are on the right side of the front and on the left side of the reverse.

See Nos. 2720, 2817, 2876, 3060, 3120, 3179, 3272, 3370, 3500, 3559, 3747, 3832, 3997.

BLACK HERITAGE SERIES

Marian Anderson
(1897-1993),
Singer — A2973

2005, Jan. 27
Self-Adhesive

3896	A2973	37c multicolored	.85	.25

RONALD REAGAN

Ronald Reagan
(1911-2004), 40th
President — A2974

2005, Feb. 9
Self-Adhesive

3897	A2974	37c multicolored	.75	.25

See No. 4078.

LOVE

Hand and Flower
Bouquet — A2975

BOOKLET STAMP
Serpentine Die Cut 10¾x11 on 2, 3 or 4 Sides
2005, Feb. 18
Self-Adhesive

3898	A2975	37c multicolored	.75	.25
a.		Booklet pane of 20	15.00	

NORTHEAST DECIDUOUS FOREST

A2976

No. 3899 — Wildlife: a, Eastern buckmoth, vert. b, Red-shouldered hawk. c, Eastern red bat. d, White-tailed deer. e, Black bear. f, Long-tailed weasel, vert. g, Wild turkey, vert. h, Ovenbird, vert. i, Red eft. j, Eastern chipmunk.

Serpentine Die Cut 10¾
2005, Mar. 3
Self-Adhesive

3899	A2976	Pane of 10	8.50	
a.-j.		37c Any single	.85	.40

SPRING FLOWERS

Hyacinth
A2977

Daffodil
A2978

Tulip — A2979

Iris — A2980

LITHOGRAPHED
BOOKLET STAMPS
Serpentine Die Cut 10¾ on 2 or 3 Sides
2005, Mar. 15
Self-Adhesive

3900	A2977	37c multicolored	.85	.30
3901	A2978	37c multicolored	.85	.30
3902	A2979	37c multicolored	.85	.30
3903	A2980	37c multicolored	.85	.30
a.		Block of 4, #3900-3903	3.40	
b.		Booklet pane of 20, 5 each #3900-3903	17.00	
c.		As "b," die cutting omitted on side with 8 stamps	—	

No. 3903b is a double-sided booklet with 12 stamps on one side and 8 stamps plus label (booklet cover) on the other side.

LITERARY ARTS

Robert
Penn
Warren
(1905-89),
Writer
A2981

PHOTOGRAVURE
Serpentine Die Cut 10¾
2005, Apr. 22
Self-Adhesive

3904	A2981	37c multicolored	.75	.25

EDGAR Y. "YIP" HARBURG

Harburg (1896-1981), Lyricist — A2982

LITHOGRAPHED
2005, Apr. 28
Self-Adhesive

3905 A2982 37c multicolored   .75 .25

AMERICAN SCIENTISTS

Barbara McClintock (1902-92), Geneticist A2983

Josiah Willard Gibbs (1839-1903), Thermodynamicist — A2984

John von Neumann (1903-57), Mathematician — A2985

Richard Feynman (1918-88), Physicist A2986

2005, May 4
Self-Adhesive

3906 A2983 37c multicolored   1.00 .35
3907 A2984 37c multicolored   1.00 .35
3908 A2985 37c multicolored   1.00 .35
  a. Vert. pair, die cutting omitted,
    #3906 & 3908   —
3909 A2986 37c multicolored   1.00 .35
  a. Block or horiz. strip of 4,
    #3906-3909   4.00
  b. All colors omitted, tagging
    omitted, pane of 20   —
  c. As "a," printing on back of
    stamps omitted   —
  d. Vert. pair, die cutting omitted,
    #3907 & 3909   —

On No. 3909b, the printing on the back of the pane and all die cutting is normal.

MODERN AMERICAN ARCHITECTURE

A2987

No. 3910 — Buildings: a, Guggenheim Museum, New York. b, Chrysler Building, New York. c, Vanna Venturi House, Philadelphia. d, TWA Terminal, New York. e, Walt Disney Concert Hall, Los Angeles. f, 860-880 Lake Shore Drive, Chicago. g, National Gallery of Art, Washington, DC. h, Glass House, New Canaan, CT. i, Yale Art and Architecture Building, New Haven, CT. j, High Museum of Art, Atlanta. k, Exeter Academy Library, Exeter, NH. l, Hancock Center, Chicago.

Serpentine Die Cut 10¾x11
2005, May 19
Self-Adhesive

3910 A2987 Pane of 12   11.00
  a.-l. 37c Any single   .90 .50
  m. As No. 3910, orange yel-
    low omitted   400.00 —

LEGENDS OF HOLLYWOOD

Henry Fonda (1905-82), Actor — A2988

Sheets of 180 in nine panes of 20
Serpentine Die Cut 11x10¾
2005, May 20
Self-Adhesive

3911 A2988 37c multicolored   .90 .25

THE ART OF DISNEY: CELEBRATION

Pluto, Mickey Mouse — A2989

Mad Hatter, Alice — A2990

Flounder, Ariel — A2991

Snow White, Dopey — A2992

Serpentine Die Cut 10½x10¾
2005, June 30
Self-Adhesive

3912 A2989 37c multi   .85 .30
3913 A2990 37c multi   .85 .30
3914 A2991 37c multi   .85 .30
3915 A2992 37c multi   .85 .30
  a. Block or vert. strip of
    4, #3912-3915   3.40
  b. Die cutting omitted,
    pane of 20   5,500. 1,400.
  c. Printed on backing
    paper, pane of 20

On the unique used pane of No. 3915b, the outer selvage was removed by cutting.

ADVANCES IN AVIATION

Boeing 247 A2993

Consolidated PBY Catalina — A2994

Grumman F6F Hellcat A2995

Republic P-47 Thunderbolt A2996

Engineering and Research Corporation Ercoupe 415 A2997

Lockheed P-80 Shooting Star A2998

Consolidated B-24 Liberator — A2999

Boeing B-29 Superfortress — A3000

Beechcraft 35 Bonanza A3001

Northrop YB-49 Flying Wing A3002

Serpentine Die Cut 10¾x10½
2005, July 29
Self-Adhesive

3916 A2993 37c multicolored   .80 .40
3917 A2994 37c multicolored   .80 .40
3918 A2995 37c multicolored   .80 .40
3919 A2996 37c multicolored   .80 .40
3920 A2997 37c multicolored   .80 .40
3921 A2998 37c multicolored   .80 .40
3922 A2999 37c multicolored   .80 .40
3923 A3000 37c multicolored   .80 .40
3924 A3001 37c multicolored   .80 .40
3925 A3002 37c multicolored   .80 .40
  a. Block of 10, #3916-3925   8.00

RIO GRANDE BLANKETS

A3003   A3004

A3005   A3006

LITHOGRAPHED BOOKLET STAMPS
Serpentine Die Cut 10¾ on 2 or 3 Sides
2005, July 30
Self-Adhesive

3926 A3003 37c multicolored   .75 .30
3927 A3004 37c multicolored   .75 .30
3928 A3005 37c multicolored   .75 .30
3929 A3006 37c multicolored   .75 .30
  a. Block of 4, #3926-3929   3.00
  b. Booklet pane, 5 each #3926-
    3929   15.00

No. 3929b is a double-sided booklet with 12 stamps on one side and 8 stamps plus label (booklet cover) on the other side.

PRESIDENTIAL LIBRARIES ACT, 50th ANNIV.

Presidential Seal — A3007

Serpentine Die Cut 10¾
2005, Aug. 4
Self-Adhesive

3930 A3007 37c multicolored   .80 .25

SPORTY CARS OF THE 1950S

1953 Studebaker Starliner A3008

1954 Kaiser Darrin A3009

1953 Chevrolet Corvette A3010

1952 Nash Healey A3011

1955 Ford Thunderbird — A3012

BOOKLET STAMPS

Serpentine Die Cut 10¾ on 2 or 3 Sides

			Tagged
2005, Aug. 20			
Self-Adhesive			
3931	A3008 37c multicolored	1.60	.40
3932	A3009 37c multicolored	1.60	.40
3933	A3010 37c multicolored	1.60	.40
3934	A3011 37c multicolored	1.60	.40
3935	A3012 37c multicolored	1.60	.40
a.	Vert. strip of 5, #3931-3935	8.00	
b.	Booklet pane, 4 each #3931-3935	32.00	

Stamps in No. 3935a are not adjacent, as rows of selvage are between stamps one and two, and between stamps three and four.

No. 3935b is a double-sided booklet pane with 12 stamps on one side (2 each #3931, 3933, 3935, and 3 each #3932, 3934) and eight stamps (1 each #3932, 3934, and 2 each #3931, 3933, 3935) plus label on the other side.

ARTHUR ASHE

Arthur Ashe (1943-93), Tennis Player — A3013

Serpentine Die Cut 10¾
2005, Aug. 27
Self-Adhesive

3936	A3013 37c multicolored	.75	.25

TO FORM A MORE PERFECT UNION

A3014

No. 3937 — Inscriptions and artwork: a, 1948 Executive Order 9981 (Training for War, by William H. Johnson). b, 1965 Voting Rights Act (Youths on the Selma March, 1965, photograph by Bruce Davidson). c, 1960 Lunch Counter Sit-ins (National Civil Rights Museum exhibits, by StudioEIS). d, 1957 Little Rock Nine (America Cares, by George Hunt). e, 1955 Montgomery Bus Boycott (Walking, by Charles Alston). f, 1961 Freedom Riders (Freedom Riders, by May Stevens). g, 1964 Civil Rights Act (Dixie Café, by Jacob Lawrence). h, 1963 March on Washington (March on Washington, by Alma Thomas). i, 1965 Selma March (Selma March, by Bernice Sims). j, 1954 Brown v. Board of Education (The Lamp, by Romare Bearden).

Serpentine Die Cut 10¾x10½
2005, Aug. 30
Self-Adhesive

3937	A3014	Pane of 10	11.00	
a.-j.		37c Any single	1.10	.40

CHILD HEALTH

Child and Doctor — A3015

PHOTOGRAVURE
Serpentine Die Cut 10½x11
2005, Sept. 7
Self-Adhesive

3938	A3015 37c multicolored	.75	.25

LET'S DANCE

Merengue A3016

Salsa — A3017

Cha Cha Cha — A3018

Mambo — A3019

Serpentine Die Cut 10¾
2005, Sept. 17
Self-Adhesive

3939	A3016 37c multicolored	1.00	.35
3940	A3017 37c multicolored	1.00	.35
3941	A3018 37c multicolored	1.00	.35
3942	A3019 37c multicolored	1.00	.35
a.	Vert. strip of 4, #3939-3942	4.00	

Stamps in the vertical strip are not adjacent as rows of selvage are between the stamps. The backing paper of stamps from the 2nd and 4th columns have Spanish inscriptions, while the other columns have English inscriptions.

GRETA GARBO

Garbo (1905-90), Actress A3020

ENGRAVED
2005, Sept. 23
Self-Adhesive

3943	A3020 37c black	.75	.25

See Sweden No. 2517.

JIM HENSON AND THE MUPPETS

A3021

No. 3944: a, Kermit the Frog. b, Fozzie Bear. c, Sam the Eagle and flag. d, Miss Piggy. e, Statler and Waldorf. f, The Swedish Chef and fruit. g, Animal. h, Dr. Bunsen Honeydew and Beaker. i, Rowlf the Dog. j, The Great Gonzo and Camilla the Chicken. k, Jim Henson.

Nos. 3944a-3944j are 30x30mm; No. 3944k, 28x37mm.

PHOTOGRAVURE
Serpentine Die Cut 10½, 10½x10¾ (#3944k)
2005, Sept. 28
Self-Adhesive

3944	A3021	Pane of 11	9.00	
a.-k.		37c Any single	.80	.50

CONSTELLATIONS

Leo — A3022   Orion — A3023

Lyra A3024   Pegasus A3025

LITHOGRAPHED
Serpentine Die Cut 10¾
2005, Oct. 3
Self-Adhesive

3945	A3022 37c multicolored	.85	.35
3946	A3023 37c multicolored	.85	.35
3947	A3024 37c multicolored	.85	.35
3948	A3025 37c multicolored	.85	.35
a.	Block or vert. strip of 4, #3945-3948	3.40	
b.	As "a," die cutting omitted	750.00	

CHRISTMAS COOKIES

Santa Claus A3026   Snowmen A3027

Angel — A3028   Elves — A3029

LITHOGRAPHED
Serpentine Die Cut 10¾x11
2005, Oct. 20
Self-Adhesive
Design Size: 19x26mm

3949	A3026 37c multicolored	.85	.25
3950	A3027 37c multicolored	.85	.25
3951	A3028 37c multicolored	.85	.25
3952	A3029 37c multicolored	.85	.25
a.	Block or vert. strip of 4, #3949-3952	3.50	

Booklet Stamps
Serpentine Die Cut 10¾x11 on 2 or 3 Sides
Design Size: 19½x27mm

3953	A3026 37c multicolored	1.00	.25
3954	A3027 37c multicolored	1.00	.25
3955	A3028 37c multicolored	1.00	.25
3956	A3029 37c multicolored	1.00	.25
a.	Block of 4, #3953-3956	4.00	
b.	Booklet pane of 20, 5 #3956a	20.00	

Santa Claus A3030   Snowmen A3031

Angel A3032   Elves A3033

Serpentine Die Cut 10½x10¾

3957	A3030 37c multicolored	1.10	.25
3958	A3031 37c multicolored	1.10	.25
3959	A3032 37c multicolored	1.10	.25
3960	A3033 37c multicolored	1.10	.25
a.	Block of 4, #3957-3960	4.50	
b.	Booklet pane of 4, #3957-3960	4.50	
c.	Booklet pane of 6, #3959-3960, 2 each #3957-3958	7.00	
d.	Booklet pane of 6, #3957-3958, 2 each #3959-3960	7.00	

No. 3956b is a double-sided booklet pane with 12 stamps on one side and eight stamps plus label that serves as a booklet cover on the other side. Nos. 3949-3952 have a small "2005" year date, while Nos. 3953-3956 have a large year date. Other design differences caused by different cropping of the images can be found, with Nos. 3953-3956 showing slightly more design features on one or more sides.

DISTINGUISHED MARINES

Lt. Gen. John A. Lejeune (1867-1942), 2nd Infantry Division Insignia — A3034

Lt. Gen. Lewis B. Puller (1898-1971), 1st Marine Division Insignia — A3035

Sgt. John
Basilone
(1916-45),
5th Marine
Division
Insignia
A3036

Sgt. Major Daniel J. Daly (1873-1937),
73rd Machine Gun Company, 6th
Marine Regiment Insignia — A3037

LITHOGRAPHED
Serpentine Die Cut 11x10½
2005, Nov. 10
Self-Adhesive

3961	A3034	37c multicolored	1.00	.35
3962	A3035	37c multicolored	1.00	.35
3963	A3036	37c multicolored	1.00	.35
3964	A3037	37c multicolored	1.00	.35
a.		Block or horiz. strip of 4, #3961-3964	4.00	

Flag and Statue of
Liberty — A3038

LITHOGRAPHED
2005, Dec. 8   *Perf. 11¼*

3965	A3038	(39c) multicolored	1.10	.25

Self-Adhesive (#3966, 3968-3975)
Serpentine Die Cut 11¼x10¾

3966	A3038	(39c) multicolored	1.10	.25
a.		Booklet pane of 20	22.00	
b.		As "a," die cutting omitted	375.00	

LITHOGRAPHED (#3970),
PHOTOGRAVURE
COIL STAMPS
Perf. 9¾ Vert.

3967	A3038	(39c) multicolored	1.10	.25

Serpentine Die Cut 8½ Vert.

3968	A3038	(39c) multicolored	1.10	.25

Serpentine Die Cut 10¼ Vert.

3969	A3038	(39c) multicolored	1.50	.25

Serpentine Die Cut 9½ Vert.

3970	A3038	(39c) multicolored	3.50	.25

LITHOGRAPHED (#3974),
PHOTOGRAVURE
BOOKLET STAMPS
Serpentine Die Cut 11¼x10¾ on 2
or 3 Sides

3972	A3038	(39c) multicolored	1.10	.25
a.		Booklet pane of 20	22.00	

Serpentine Die Cut 10½x10¾ on 2
or 3 Sides

3973	A3038	(39c) multicolored	1.10	.25
a.		Booklet pane of 20	22.00	

On both Nos. 3972 and 3973, the sky immediately above the date is bright blue and extends from the left side to beyond the "6" in the date, the left arm of the star at upper left barely touches the frame line and is without the "USPS" microprinting. They are distinguishable by the die cutting. Nos. 3872a and 3973a are double-sided booklet panes with 12 stamps on one side and eight stamps plus label that serves as a booklet cover on the other side.

No. 3973 was not available until January 2006.

Serpentine Die Cut 11¼x10¾ on 2
or 3 Sides

3974	A3038	(39c) multicolored	1.10	.25
a.		Booklet pane of 4	4.40	
b.		Booklet pane of 6	6.60	

Serpentine Die Cut 8 on 2, 3 or 4
Sides

3975	A3038	(39c) multicolored	1.10	.25
a.		Booklet pane of 18	20.00	
		Nos. 3965-3975 (10)	13.80	2.50

Nos. 3965-3975 are dated "2006."
On No. 3966, the sky immediately above the date is bright blue and extends from the left side to beyond the "6" in the date, the left arm of the star at upper left is clear of the top

frame, and "USPS" is microprinted on the top red flag stripe.

On No. 3974, the sky immediately above the date is dark blue and extends from the left side to the second "0" in the date, the left arm of the star at upper left touches the top frame, and lacks the microprinting found on No. 3966.

Nos. 3965 and 3970 also have "USPS" microprinted on the top red flag stripe.

Nos. 3966a and 3972a are double-sided booklet panes with 12 stamps on one side and eight stamps plus label that serves as a booklet cover on the other side. On No. 3966a, the stamps on one side are upside-down with relation to the stamps on the other side. On No. 3972a the stamps are all aligned the same on both sides.

LOVE

Birds — A3039

PHOTOGRAVURE
Serpentine Die Cut 11 on 2, 3, or 4
Sides
2006, Jan. 3
BOOKLET STAMP
Self-Adhesive

3976	A3039	(39c) multicolored	1.10	.25
a.		Booklet pane of 20	22.00	

See No. 4029.

Flag and Statue of
Liberty — A3040

LITHOGRAPHED
2006   *Serpentine Die Cut 11¼x10¾*
Self-Adhesive (#3978, 3980-3985)

3978	A3040	39c multi	.85	.25
a.		Booklet pane of 10	8.50	
b.		Booklet pane of 20	17.00	
c.		As "b," die cutting omitted on side with 8 stamps	—	

No. 3978 has "USPS" microprinted on top red flag stripe.

No. 3978b is a double-sided booklet with 12 stamps on one side and 8 stamps plus label (booklet cover) on the other side.

LITHOGRAPHED (#3981),
PHOTOGRAVURE (#3979-3980, 3982-3983)
COIL STAMPS
Perf. 9¾ Vert.

3979	A3040	39c multi	1.00	.25

Serpentine Die Cut 11 Vert.

3980	A3040b	39c multi	.80	.25

No. 3980 has rounded corners and lacks microprinting. Unused examples are on backing paper taller than the stamp, and the stamps are spaced approximately 3mm apart.

Serpentine Die Cut 9½ Vert.

3981	A3040	39c multi	1.40	.25
a.		Die cutting omitted, pair	150.00	

No. 3981 has "USPS" microprinted on top red flag stripe.

Serpentine Die Cut 10¼ Vert.

3982	A3040	39c multi	1.25	.25
a.		Vert. pair, unslit between	500.00	

Serpentine Die Cut 8½ Vert.

3983	A3040	39c multi	.80	.25

PHOTOGRAVURE
BOOKLET STAMP
Serpentine Die Cut 11¼x10¾ on 2
or 3 Sides

3985	A3040	39c multi	.80	.25
a.		Booklet pane of 20	16.00	
b.		Serpentine die cut 11.1 on 2 or 3 sides	.80	.25
c.		Booklet pane of 4 #3985b	3.20	
d.		Booklet pane of 6 #3985b	4.80	

Nos. 3983 and 3985 lack the microprinting found on Nos. 3978 and 3981. No. 3982 was not made available until June, despite the official first day of issue. No. 3983 was not made available until July and No. 3985 was not made available until August, despite the official first day of issue. No. 3985a is a double-sided booklet with 12 stamps on one side and 8 stamps plus label (booklet cover) on the other side.

Issued: No. 3980, 1/9; No. 3979, 3/8; Nos. 3978, 3981, 3982, 3985, 4/8.

CHILDREN'S BOOK ANIMALS

The Very
Hungry
Caterpillar,
from *The Very
Hungry
Caterpillar,* by
Eric Carle
A3041

Wilbur, from
*Charlotte's
Web,* by E. B.
White
A3042

Fox in Socks,
from *Fox in
Socks,* by Dr.
Seuss
A3043

Maisy, from
Maisy's ABC,
by Lucy
Cousins
A3044

Wild Thing,
from *Where
the Wild
Things Are,* by
Maurice
Sendak
A3045

Curious
George, from
*Curious
George,* by
Margaret and
H. A.
Rey — A3046

Olivia, from
Olivia, by Ian
Falconer
A3047

Frederick,
from
Frederick, by
Leo Lionni
A3048

PHOTOGRAVURE
Serpentine Die Cut 10¾
2006, Jan. 10
Self-Adhesive

3987	A3041	39c multicolored	.80	.40
3988	A3042	39c multicolored	.80	.40
3989	A3043	39c multicolored	.80	.40
3990	A3044	39c multicolored	.80	.40
3991	A3045	39c multicolored	.80	.40
3992	A3046	39c multicolored	.80	.40

3993	A3047	39c multicolored	.80	.40
3994	A3048	39c multicolored	.80	.40
a.		Block of 8, #3987-3994	6.50	

See Great Britain Nos. 2340-2341.

2006 WINTER OLYMPICS, TURIN, ITALY

Skier
A3049

LITHOGRAPHED
2006, Jan. 11
Self-Adhesive

3995	A3049	39c multicolored	.80	.25

BLACK HERITAGE SERIES

Hattie McDaniel
(1895-1952),
Actress — A3050

2006, Jan. 25
Self-Adhesive

3996	A3050	39c multicolored	.80	.25

Chinese New Year Types of 1992-2004
2006, Jan. 29
Self-Adhesive

3997		Pane of 12	12.00	
a.	A2360	39c Rat	1.00	.50
b.	A2413	39c Ox	1.00	.50
c.	A2462	39c Tiger	1.00	.50
d.	A2535	39c Rabbit	1.00	.50
e.	A2602	39c Dragon	1.00	.50
f.	A2702	39c Snake	1.00	.50
g.	A2752	39c Horse	1.00	.50
h.	A2856	39c Ram	1.00	.50
i.	A2927	39c Monkey	1.00	.50
j.	A2067	39c Rooster	1.00	.50
k.	A2146	39c Dog	1.00	.50
l.	A2205	39c Boar	1.00	.50

See Nos. 2720, 2817, 2876, 3060, 3120, 3179, 3272, 3370, 3500, 3559, 3747, 3832, 3895.

WEDDING DOVES

Dove Facing
Left — A3051

Dove Facing
Right — A3052

BOOKLET STAMPS
Serpentine Die Cut 10¾x11 on 2, 3
or 4 Sides
2006, Mar. 1
Self-Adhesive

3998	A3051	39c pale lilac	.80	.25
a.		Booklet pane of 20	16.00	
b.		As "a," die cutting omitted	—	

Serpentine Die Cut 10¾x11

3999	A3052	63c pale yellow green	1.40	.50
a.		Booklet pane, 20 each #3998-3999	45.00	
b.		Horiz. pair, #3998-3999 with vertical gutter between	2.25	1.50

Common Buckeye
Butterfly — A3053

LITHOGRAPHED (#4000),
PHOTOGRAVURE (#4001-4002)
2006, Mar. 8   *Perf. 11¼*

4000	A3053	24c multicolored	.50	.25

Self-Adhesive
Serpentine Die Cut 11

4001	A3053	24c multicolored	.55	.25
a.		Serpentine die cut 10¾x11¼ on 3 sides (from booklet panes)	.50	.25
b.		Booklet pane of 10 #4001a	5.00	
c.		Booklet pane of 4 #4001a	2.00	
d.		Booklet pane of 6 #4001a	3.00	

No. 4001b is a convertible booklet that was sold flat. It has a self-adhesive panel that covers the rouletting on the inside of the booklet cover. Nos. 4001c and 4001d are component panes of a vending machine booklet, which was sold pre-folded and sealed, and which does not have the self-adhesive panel covering the rouletting on the inside of the booklet cover.

COIL STAMP
Serpentine Die Cut 8½ Horiz.

4002	A3053	24c multicolored	.50	.25

CROPS OF THE AMERICAS

Chili Peppers A3054

Beans A3055

Sunflower and Seeds A3056

Squashes A3057

Corn — A3058

PHOTOGRAVURE
Serpentine Die Cut 10¼ Horiz.
2006, Mar. 16
Self-Adhesive
Coil Stamps

4003	A3054	39c multicolored	2.40	.35
4004	A3055	39c multicolored	2.40	.35
4005	A3056	39c multicolored	2.40	.35
4006	A3057	39c multicolored	2.40	.35
4007	A3058	39c multicolored	2.40	.35
a.		Strip of 5, #4003-4007	12.00	

Booklet Stamps
Serpentine Die Cut 10¾x10½ on 2 or 3 Sides

4008	A3058	39c multicolored	1.25	.35
4009	A3057	39c multicolored	1.25	.35
4010	A3056	39c multicolored	1.25	.35
4011	A3055	39c multicolored	1.25	.35
4012	A3054	39c multicolored	1.25	.35
a.		Horiz. strip of 5, #4008-4012	6.25	
b.		Booklet pane, 4 each #4008-4012	25.00	

LITHOGRAPHED
Serpentine Die Cut 10¾x11¼ on 2 or 3 Sides

4013	A3054	39c multicolored	1.10	.35
4014	A3058	39c multicolored	1.10	.35
4015	A3057	39c multicolored	1.10	.35
4016	A3056	39c multicolored	1.10	.35
a.		Booklet pane of 4, #4013-4016	4.50	
4017	A3055	39c multicolored	1.10	.35
a.		Horiz. strip of 5, #4013-4017	5.50	
b.		Booklet pane of 4 #4013-4015, 4017	4.50	
c.		Booklet pane of 6, #4013-4016, 2 #4017	6.75	
d.		Booklet pane of 6, #4013-4015, 4017, 2 #4016	6.75	

Stamps in Nos. 4012a and 4017a are not adjacent, as one or two rows of selvage is between stamps (or a blank space where selvage was removed by the manufacturer).

No. 4012b is a double-sided booklet with 12 stamps on one side and 8 stamps plus label (booklet cover) on the other side.

"USA" is at right of "39" on No. 4004, at left of "39" on Nos. 4011, 4017. Top of "USA" is aligned with top of "39" on No. 4013, with bottom of "39" on Nos. 4003, 4012.

X-PLANES

A3059

A3060

LITHOGRAPHED WITH HOLOGRAM AFFIXED
Serpentine Die Cut 10¾x10½
2006, Mar. 17   Self-Adhesive

4018	A3059	$4.05 multi	8.00	5.00
a.		Silver foil ("X") omitted		
4019	A3060	$14.40 multi	27.50	15.00

Beware of Nos. 4018 and 4019 with "X" hologram chemically removed. Certification is strongly recommended.

SUGAR RAY ROBINSON (1921-89), BOXER

A3061

PHOTOGRAVURE
2006, Apr. 7   Serpentine Die Cut 11
Self-Adhesive

4020	A3061	39c red & blue	.80	.25

BENJAMIN FRANKLIN (1706-90)

Statesman A3062

Scientist A3063

Printer A3064

Postmaster A3065

2006, Apr. 7

4021	A3062	39c multicolored	1.25	.35
4022	A3063	39c multicolored	1.25	.35
4023	A3064	39c multicolored	1.25	.35
4024	A3065	39c multicolored	1.25	.35
a.		Block or horiz. strip of 4	5.00	

THE ART OF DISNEY: ROMANCE

Mickey and Minnie Mouse — A3066

Cinderella and Prince Charming A3067

Beauty and the Beast — A3068

Lady and Tramp — A3069

LITHOGRAPHED
Serpentine Die Cut 10½x10¾
2006, Apr. 21
Self-Adhesive

4025	A3066	39c multicolored	.80	.30
4026	A3067	39c multicolored	.80	.30
4027	A3068	39c multicolored	.80	.30
4028	A3069	39c multicolored	.80	.30
a.		Block or vert. strip of 4, #4025-4028	3.20	

LOVE

Birds — A3070

PHOTOGRAVURE
Serpentine Die Cut 11 on 2, 3 or 4 Sides
2006, May 1
Self-Adhesive
Booklet Stamp

4029	A3070	39c multicolored	.95	.25
a.		Booklet pane of 20	19.00	

See No. 3976.

LITERARY ARTS

Katherine Anne Porter (1890-1980), Author — A3071

LITHOGRAPHED
Serpentine Die Cut 10¾
2006, May 15
Self-Adhesive

4030	A3071	39c multicolored	.80	.25

AMBER ALERT

Mother and Child A3072

PHOTOGRAVURE
Serpentine Die Cut 10¾
2006, May 25
Self-Adhesive

4031	A3072	39c multicolored	.80	.25

Purple Heart Type of 2003
LITHOGRAPHED
Serpentine Die Cut 11¼x11
2006, May 26
Self-Adhesive

4032	A2891	39c multicolored	.80	.25

See Nos. 3784-3784A, 4164, 4263-4264, 4390.

WONDERS OF AMERICA

American Alligator — A3073

Designs: No. 4033, American alligator, largest reptile. No. 4034, Moloka'i, highest sea cliffs. No. 4035, Saguaro, tallest cactus. No. 4036, Bering Glacier, largest glacier. No. 4037, Great Sand Dunes, tallest dunes. No. 4038, Chesapeake Bay, largest estuary. No. 4039, Cliff Palace, largest cliff dwelling. No. 4040, Crater Lake, deepest lake. No. 4041, American bison, largest land mammal. No. 4042, Off the Florida Keys, longest reef. No. 4043, Pacific Crest Trail, longest hiking trail. No. 4044, Gateway Arch, tallest man-made monument. No. 4045, Appalachians, oldest mountains. No. 4046, American lotus, largest flower. No. 4047, Lake Superior, largest lake. No. 4048, Pronghorn, fastest land animal. No. 4049, Bristlecone pines, oldest trees. No. 4050, Yosemite Falls, tallest waterfall. No. 4051, Great Basin, largest desert. No. 4052, Verrazano-Narrows Bridge, longest span. No. 4053, Mount Washington, windiest place. No. 4054, Grand Canyon, largest canyon. No. 4055, American bullfrog, largest frog. No. 4056, Oroville Dam, tallest dam. No. 4057, Peregrine falcon, fastest bird. No. 4058, Mississippi River Delta, largest delta. No. 4059, Steamboat, tallest geyser. No. 4060, Rainbow Bridge, largest natural bridge. No. 4061, White sturgeon, largest freshwater fish. No. 4062, Rocky Mountains, longest mountain chain. No. 4063, Coast redwoods, tallest trees. No. 4064, American beaver, largest rodent. No. 4065, Mississippi-Missouri, longest river system. No. 4066, Mount Wai'ale'ale, rainiest spot. No. 4067, Kilauea, most active volcano. No. 4068, Mammoth Cave, longest cave. No. 4069, Blue whale, loudest animal. No. 4070, Death Valley, hottest spot. No. 4071, Cornish-Windsor Bridge, longest covered bridge. No. 4072, Quaking aspen, largest plant.

PHOTOGRAVURE
Serpentine Die Cut 10¾
2006, May 27
Self-Adhesive

4033	A3073	39c multicolored	.80	.60
4034	A3074	39c multicolored	.80	.60
4035	A3075	39c multicolored	.80	.60
4036	A3076	39c multicolored	.80	.60
4037	A3077	39c multicolored	.80	.60
4038	A3078	39c multicolored	.80	.60
4039	A3079	39c multicolored	.80	.60
4040	A3080	39c multicolored	.80	.60
4041	A3081	39c multicolored	.80	.60
4042	A3082	39c multicolored	.80	.60
4043	A3083	39c multicolored	.80	.60
4044	A3084	39c multicolored	.80	.60
4045	A3085	39c multicolored	.80	.60
4046	A3086	39c multicolored	.80	.60
4047	A3087	39c multicolored	.80	.60
4048	A3088	39c multicolored	.80	.60
4049	A3089	39c multicolored	.80	.60
4050	A3090	39c multicolored	.80	.60
4051	A3091	39c multicolored	.80	.60
4052	A3092	39c multicolored	.80	.60
4053	A3093	39c multicolored	.80	.60
4054	A3094	39c multicolored	.80	.60

4055	A3095 39c multicolored	.80	.60
4056	A3096 39c multicolored	.80	.60
4057	A3097 39c multicolored	.80	.60
4058	A3098 39c multicolored	.80	.60
4059	A3099 39c multicolored	.80	.60
4060	A3100 39c multicolored	.80	.60
4061	A3101 39c multicolored	.80	.60
4062	A3102 39c multicolored	.80	.60
4063	A3103 39c multicolored	.80	.60
4064	A3104 39c multicolored	.80	.60
4065	A3105 39c multicolored	.80	.60
4066	A3106 39c multicolored	.80	.60
4067	A3107 39c multicolored	.80	.60
4068	A3108 39c multicolored	.80	.60
4069	A3109 39c multicolored	.80	.60
4070	A3110 39c multicolored	.80	.60
4071	A3111 39c multicolored	.80	.60
4072	A3112 39c multicolored	.80	.60
a.	Pane of 40, #4033-4072	32.00	

EXPLORATION OF EAST COAST BY SAMUEL DE CHAMPLAIN, 400TH ANNIV.

Ship and Map — A3113

A3114

LITHOGRAPHED & ENGRAVED
Serpentine Die Cut 10¾
2006, May 28
Self-Adhesive (#4073)

4073	A3113 39c multicolored	.85	.25

Souvenir Sheet
Perf. 11

4074	A3114	Pane of 4, 2 each #4074a,	
		Canada #2156a	8.50 8.50
a.	A3113 39c multicolored	2.00 .25

Washington 2006 World Philatelic Exhibition (#4074). Canada No. 2156, which was sold only by Canada Post, has a bar code in the lower left margin of the pane. No. 4074, which was sold only by the United States Postal Service for $1.75, lacks this bar code.

WASHINGTON 2006 WORLD PHILATELIC EXHIBITION
Souvenir Sheet

A3115

LITHOGRAPHED (MARGIN) & ENGRAVED
2006, May 29   *Perf. 10¾x10½*

4075	A3115	Pane of 3	16.00 6.00
a.	A174 $1 violet brown	2.00	.50
b.	A175 $2 deep blue	4.00	1.00
c.	A176 $5 carmine & blue	10.00	2.50

DISTINGUISHED AMERICAN DIPLOMATS
Souvenir Sheet

A3116

No. 4076: a, Robert D. Murphy (1894-1978). b, Frances E. Willis (1899-1983). c, Hiram Bingham IV (1903-88). d, Philip C. Habib (1920-92). e, Charles E. Bohlen (1904-74). f, Clifton R. Wharton, Sr. (1899-1990).

PHOTOGRAVURE
Serpentine Die Cut 10¾
2006, May 29
Self-Adhesive

4076	A3116	Pane of 6	6.00
a.-f.	39c any single	1.00	.40

LEGENDS OF HOLLYWOOD

Judy Garland (1922-69), Actress — A3117

LITHOGRAPHED
2006, June 10
Self-Adhesive

4077	A3117 39c multicolored	1.00	.25
a.	Pair, die cutting omitted	—	

Ronald Reagan Type of 2005
PHOTOGRAVURE
2006, June 14
Self-Adhesive

4078	A2974 39c multicolored	.90	.25
	See No. 3897.		

Happy Birthday Type of 2002
Serpentine Die Cut 11
2006, June 23
Self-Adhesive

4079	A2751 39c multicolored	.80	.25
	See Nos. 3558, 3695.		

BASEBALL SLUGGERS

Roy Campanella (1921-93) A3118 | Hank Greenberg (1911-86) A3119

Mel Ott (1909-58) A3120 | Mickey Mantle (1931-95) A3121

Serpentine Die Cut 10¾
2006, July 15
Self-Adhesive

4080	A3118 39c multicolored	.80	.30
4081	A3119 39c multicolored	.80	.30
4082	A3120 39c multicolored	.80	.30
4083	A3121 39c multicolored	.80	.30
a.	Block or vert. strip of 4, #4080-4083	3.20	

DC COMICS SUPERHEROES

A3122

No. 4084: a, Superman. b, Green Lantern. c, Wonder Woman. d, Green Arrow. e, Batman. f, The Flash. g, Plastic Man. h, Aquaman. i, Supergirl. j, Hawkman. k, Cover of *Superman #11*. l, Cover of *Green Lantern #4*. m, Cover of *Wonder Woman #22 (Second Series)*. n, Cover of *Green Arrow #15*. o, Cover of *Batman #1*. p, Cover of *The Flash #111*. q, Cover of *Plastic Man #4*. r, Cover of *Aquaman #5 (of 5)*. s, Cover of *The Daring New Adventures of Supergirl #1*. t, Cover of *The Brave and the Bold Presents Hawkman #36*.

Serpentine Die Cut 10½x10¾
2006, July 20
Self-Adhesive

4084	A3122	Pane of 20	16.00
a.-t.	39c Any single	.80	.50
u.	As No. 4084, all inscriptions omitted on reverse	2,000.	

MOTORCYCLES

1940 Indian Four A3123

1918 Cleveland A3124

Generic "Chopper," c. 1970 A3125

1965 Harley-Davidson Electra-Glide — A3126

Serpentine Die Cut 10¾x10½
2006, Aug. 7
Self-Adhesive

4085	A3123 39c multicolored	1.00	.35
4086	A3124 39c multicolored	1.00	.35
4087	A3125 39c multicolored	1.00	.35

4088	A3126 39c multicolored	1.00	.35
a.	Block or horiz. strip of 4, #4085-4088	4.00	

AMERICAN TREASURES SERIES
Quilts of Gee's Bend, Alabama

Housetop Variation, by Mary Lee Bendolph A3127 | Pig in a Pen Medallion, by Minnie Sue Coleman A3128

Nine Patch, by Ruth P. Mosely A3129 | Housetop Four Block Half Log Cabin Variation, by Lottie Mooney A3130

Roman Stripes Variation, by Loretta Pettway A3131 | Chinese Coins Variation, by Arlonzia Pettway A3132

Blocks and Strips, by Annie Mae Young A3133 | Medallion, by Loretta Pettway A3134

Bars and String-pieced Columns, by Jessie T. Pettway A3135 | Medallion With Checkerboard Center, by Patty Ann Williams A3136

BOOKLET STAMPS
Serpentine Die Cut 10¾ on 2 or 3 Sides
2006, Aug. 24
Self-Adhesive

4089	A3127 39c multicolored	1.10	.40
4090	A3128 39c multicolored	1.10	.40
4091	A3129 39c multicolored	1.10	.40

4092	A3130	39c multicolored	1.10	.40
4093	A3131	39c multicolored	1.10	.40
4094	A3132	39c multicolored	1.10	.40
4095	A3133	39c multicolored	1.10	.40
4096	A3134	39c multicolored	1.10	.40
4097	A3135	39c multicolored	1.10	.40
4098	A3136	39c multicolored	1.10	.40
a.		Block of 10, #4089-4098	11.00	
b.		Booklet pane of 20, 2 each #4089-4098	22.50	

No. 4098b is a double-sided booklet pane with 12 stamps on one side (1 each #4090-4093, 4095-4098, and 2 each #4089, 4094) and eight stamps (1 each #4090-4093, 4095-4098) plus label (booklet cover) on the other side.

SOUTHERN FLORIDA WETLAND

A3137

No. 4099 — Wildlife: a, Snail kite. b, Wood storks. c, Florida panther. d, Bald eagle, horiz. e, American crocodile, horiz. f, Roseate spoonbills, horiz. g, Everglades mink. h, Cape Sable seaside sparrow, horiz. i, American alligator, horiz. j, White ibis.

Serpentine Die Cut 10¾
2006, Oct. 4
Self-Adhesive

4099	A3137	Pane of 10	9.00	
a.-j.		39c any single	.90	.40

CHRISTMAS

Madonna and Child with Bird, by Ignacio Chacón A3138

Snowflake A3139

Snowflake A3140

Snowflake A3141

Snowflake — A3142

LITHOGRAPHED
Serpentine Die Cut 10¾x11 on 2 or 3 Sides
2006
Self-Adhesive
Booklet Stamps (#4100, 4105-4116)

4100	A3138	39c multi	.80	.25
a.		Booklet pane of 20	16.00	

Base of Denomination Higher Than Year Date
Serpentine Die Cut 11¼x11

4101	A3139	39c multi	.90	.25
4102	A3140	39c multi	.90	.25
4103	A3141	39c multi	.90	.25
4104	A3142	39c multi	.90	.25
a.		Block or vert. strip of 4, #4101-4104	3.60	

Base of Denominations Even With Year Date
Serpentine Die Cut 11¼x11½ on 2 or 3 Sides

4105	A3139	39c multi	.90	.25
a.		Red missing (PS)	—	
4106	A3140a	39c multi	.90	—
a.		Red missing (PS)	—	
4107	A3141	39c multi	.90	.25
4108	A3142	39c multi	.90	.25
a.		Block of 4, #4105-4108	3.60	
b.		Booklet pane of 20, 5 #4108a	18.00	
c.		As "a," red ("USA") and green ("39") omitted	—	

Serpentine Die Cut 11¼x10¾ on 2 or 3 Sides

4109	A3139	39c multi	1.00	.25
4110	A3140	39c multi	1.00	.25
4111	A3141	39c multi	1.00	.25
4112	A3142	39c multi	1.00	.25
a.		Block of 4, #4109-4112	4.00	
b.		Booklet pane of 4, #4109-4112	4.00	
c.		Booklet pane of 6, #4111-4112, 2 each #4109-4110	6.00	
d.		Booklet pane of 6, #4111-4110, 2 each #4111-4112	6.00	

Serpentine Die Cut 8 on 2, 3 or 4 Sides

PHOTOGRAVURE

4113	A3139	39c multi	1.50	.35
a.		Red and green missing (PS)	—	
4114	A3141	39c multi	1.50	.35
4115	A3140	39c multi	1.50	.35
4116	A3142	39c multi	1.50	.35
a.		Block or strip of 4, #4113-4116	6.00	
b.		Booklet pane of 18, 4 each #4114, 4116, 5 each #4113, 4115	27.00	
		Nos. 4100-4116 (17)	18.00	4.65

No. 4108b is a double-sided booklet pane with 12 stamps on one side and eight stamps plus label that serves as a booklet cover on the other side. Snowflakes on Nos. 4101-4104 are slightly smaller than those on Nos. 4105-4116.

Issued: No. 4100, 10/17, Nos. 4101-4116, 10/5.

Eid Type of 2001
PHOTOGRAVURE
2006, Oct. 6 *Serpentine Die Cut 11*
Self-Adhesive

4117	A2734	39c multicolored	.80	.25

See Nos. 3532, 3674, 4202, 4351, 4416.

Hanukkah Type of 2004
LITHOGRAPHED
Serpentine Die Cut 10¾x11
2006, Oct. 6
Self-Adhesive

4118	A2962	39c multicolored	.80	.25
a.		Die cutting omitted, pane of 20	—	

See Nos. 3880, 4219, 4372.

Kwanzaa Type of 2004
Serpentine Die Cut 11x10¾
2006, Oct. 6
Self-Adhesive

4119	A2963	39c multicolored	.80	.25

See Nos. 3881, 4220, 4373.

BLACK HERITAGE SERIES

Ella Fitzgerald (1917-96), Singer — A3143

Serpentine Die Cut 11
2007, Jan. 10
Self-Adhesive

4120	A3143	39c multicolored	.80	.25

OKLAHOMA STATEHOOD, 100TH ANNIV.

Cimarron River A3144

2007, Jan. 11
Self-Adhesive

4121	A3144	39c multicolored	.80	.25

LOVE

Hershey's Kiss — A3145

PHOTOGRAVURE
Serpentine Die Cut 10¾x11 on 2, 3 or 4 Sides
2007, Jan. 13
BOOKLET STAMP
Self-Adhesive

4122	A3145	39c multicolored	.80	.25
a.		Booklet pane of 20	16.00	

INTERNATIONAL POLAR YEAR
Souvenir Sheet

A3146

No. 4123: a, Aurora borealis. b, Aurora australis.

LITHOGRAPHED
Serpentine Die Cut 10¾
2007, Feb. 21
Self-Adhesive

4123	A3146	Pane of 2	4.00	
a.-b.		84c Either single	2.00	.50

LITERARY ARTS

Henry Wadsworth Longfellow (1807-82), Poet A3147

2007, Mar. 15
Self-Adhesive

4124	A3147	39c multicolored	.80	.25

Beginning with No. 4125, the United States Postal Service began issuing "Forever" stamps that satisfy the domestic 1-ounce first-class letter rate and the 1-ounce international letter rate regardless of future rate increases. The denomination in parentheses in the catalogue listing represents the face value at the time of issue. The face value increases to the new letter rate whenever rates change.

"FOREVER" STAMP

Liberty Bell — A3148

Large Microprinting (#4125, 4128)   Small Microprinting (#4126)

Medium Microprinting (#4127)

PHOTOGRAVURE
Serpentine Die Cut 11¼x10¾ on 2 or 3 Sides
2007-09
Booklet Stamps
Self-Adhesive
Large Microprinting, Bell 16mm Wide

4125	A3148	(41c) multi, dated "2007," Apr. 12	1.10	.25
a.		Booklet pane of 20	22.00	
b.		(42c) Dated "2008"	1.10	.25
c.		Booklet pane of 20 #4125b	22.00	
d.		As "c," copper ("FOREVER") omitted	1,000.	
e.		As "c," copper ("FOREVER") omitted on side with 12 stamps, copper splatters on side with 8 stamps	—	
f.		(44c) Dated "2009" ('09)	1.10	.25
g.		Booklet pane of 20 #4125f	22.00	
h.		As No. 4125, copper ("FOREVER") omitted	—	
i.		As No. 4125, die cutting missing, horiz. pair (PS)	—	
j.		As "b," copper ("FOREVER") omitted	—	

LITHOGRAPHED
Small Microprinting, Bell 16mm Wide

4126	A3148	(41c) multi, dated "2007"	1.10	.25
a.		Booklet pane of 20	22.00	
b.		(42c) Dated "2008" ('08)	1.10	.25
c.		Booklet pane of 20 #4126b	22.00	
d.		(44c) Dated "2009" in copper ('09)	1.10	.25
e.		Booklet pane of 20 #4126d	22.00	
f.		As "b," copper ("FOREVER") omitted	1,400.	
g.		As "c," die cutting omitted		

Medium Microprinting, Bell 15mm Wide

4127	A3148	(41c) multi, dated "2007" ('07)	1.10	.25
a.		Booklet pane of 20	22.00	
b.		Booklet pane of 4	4.40	
c.		Booklet pane of 6	6.60	
d.		(42c) Dated "2008" ('08)	1.10	.25
e.		As "d," booklet pane of 20	22.00	
f.		(42c) Dated "2008," date in smaller type ('08)	1.10	.25
g.		As "f," booklet pane of 4	4.40	
h.		As "f," booklet pane of 6	6.60	
i.		(44c) Dated "2009" in copper ('09)	1.10	.25
j.		As "i," booklet pane of 20	22.00	
k.		As "i," die cutting omitted, pair		
l.		As No. 4127, copper ("FOREVER") and "USA FIRST-CLASS" missing (PS)	—	
m.		As "e," die cutting omitted	650.00	

PHOTOGRAVURE
Large Microprinting, Bell 16mm Wide
Serpentine Die Cut 8 on 2, 3 or 4 Sides

4128	A3148	(41c) multi, dated "2007"	1.10	.25
a.		Booklet pane of 18	20.00	
b.		(42c) Dated "2009" ('09)	1.10	.25
c.		As "b," booklet pane of 18	20.00	
		Nos. 4125-4128 (4)	4.40	1.00

Nos. 4125-4128 were sold for 41c on the day of issue and will be valid for the one ounce first class postage rate after any new rates go into effect. As of May 12, 2008, any "Forever" stamp (Nos. 4125-4128 and 4127d) in stock was sold for 42c. As of May 15, 2009, all "Forever" stamps in stock were sold for 44c, etc.

Nos. 4125a, 4125c, 4126a, 4126c, 4127a, 4127e and 4127j are double-sided booklet panes, with 12 stamps on one side and eight stamps plus a label that serves as a booklet cover on the other side.

Nos. 4127b and 4127c exist with rouletting on backing paper of either gauge 9½ or 13.

See No. 4437.

Flag — A3149

LITHOGRAPHED

2007, Apr. 12		**Perf. 11¼**	
4129 A3149	(41c) multicolored	.90	.40

Self-Adhesive
Serpentine Die Cut 11¼x10¾

4130 A3149	(41c) multicolored	1.10	.25

COIL STAMPS
Perf. 9¾ Vert.

4131 A3149	(41c) multicolored	1.10	.40

Self-Adhesive (#4132-4135)
With Perpendicular Corners
Serpentine Die Cut 9½ Vert.

4132 A3149	(41c) multicolored	1.20	.25

Serpentine Die Cut 11 Vert.

4133 A3149	(41c) multicolored	1.20	.25
a.	Die cutting omitted, pair	1,250.	

Serpentine Die Cut 8½ Vert.

PHOTOGRAVURE

4134 A3149	(41c) multicolored, overall tagging	1.10	.25

With Rounded Corners
Serpentine Die Cut 11 Vert.

4135 A3149	(41c) multicolored	1.25	.75
	Nos. 4129-4135 (7)	7.85	2.55

Nos. 4132-4134 are on backing paper as high as the stamp. No. 4135 is on backing paper that is larger than the stamp.

SETTLEMENT OF JAMESTOWN, 400TH ANNIV.

Ships Susan Constant, Godspeed and Discovery — A3150

LITHOGRAPHED
Serpentine Die Cut 10½x10½x10¾
2007, May 11
Self-Adhesive

4136 A3150	41c multicolored	1.10	.25

WILDLIFE

Bighorn Sheep
A3151

Florida Panther
A3152

LITHOGRAPHED, PHOTOGRAVURE
(#4138, 4142)

2007		**Perf. 11¼x11**	
4137 A3152	26c multi	.60	.25

Self-Adhesive
Serpentine Die Cut 11

4138 A3151	17c multi	.35	.25

Serpentine Die Cut 11¼x11

4139 A3152	26c multi	.55	.25

Coil Stamps
Serpentine Die Cut 11 Vert.

4140 A3151	17c multi	.35	.25
4141 A3152	26c multi	.75	.25
a.	Die cutting omitted, pair	400.00	

Booklet Stamp
Serpentine Die Cut 11¼x11 on 3 Sides

4142 A3152	26c multi	.55	.25
a.	Booklet pane of 10	5.50	

Nos. 4137 and 4139 have microprinted "USPS" to the left and above the lower left whisker. No. 4140 has microprinted "USPS" on right horn. No. 4141 has microprinted "USPS" along the right edge of the stamp just above the panther. Nos. 4138 and 4142 lack microprinting.
Issued: Nos. 4137, 4139, 4141, 4142, 5/12; No. 4138, 5/14; No. 4140, 5/21.

PREMIERE OF MOVIE "STAR WARS," 30TH ANNIVERSARY

A3153

No. 4143: a, Darth Vader (40x53mm). b, Millennium Falcon (47x25mm). c, Emperor Palpatine (41x26mm). d, Anakin Skywalker and Obi-Wan Kenobi (41x33mm). e, Luke Skywalker (31x41mm). f, Princess Leia and R2-D2 (41x33mm). g, C-3PO (21x65mm). h, Queen Padmé Amidala (26x48mm). i, Obi-Wan Kenobi (31x48mm). j, Boba Fett (32x40mm). k, Darth Maul (26x41mm). l, Chewbacca and Han Solo (48x31mm). m, X-wing Starfighter (41x26mm). n, Yoda (31x48mm). o, Stormtroopers (41x31mm).

LITHOGRAPHED
2007, May 25 *Serpentine Die Cut 11*
Self-Adhesive

4143 A3153	Pane of 15	15.00	
a.-o.	41c Any single	1.00	.50

PRESIDENTIAL AIRCRAFT

Air Force One
A3154

Marine One
A3155

LITHOGRAPHED & ENGRAVED
(#4144), LITHOGRAPHED (#4145)
Serpentine Die Cut 10¾
2007, June 13
Self-Adhesive

4144 A3154	$4.60 multi	9.25	5.00
a.	Black (engr.) omitted	250.00	
4145 A3155	$16.25 multi	30.00	16.00

PACIFIC LIGHTHOUSES

Diamond Head Lighthouse, Hawaii — A3156

Five Finger Lighthouse, Alaska — A3157

Grays Harbor Lighthouse, Washington
A3158

Umpqua River Lighthouse, Oregon
A3159

St. George Reef Lighthouse, California — A3160

PHOTOGRAVURE
Serpentine Die Cut 11
2007, June 21
Self-Adhesive

4146 A3156	41c multicolored	1.20	.40
4147 A3157	41c multicolored	1.20	.40
4148 A3158	41c multicolored	1.20	.40
4149 A3159	41c multicolored	1.20	.40
4150 A3160	41c multicolored	1.20	.40
a.	Horiz. strip of 5, #4146-4150	6.00	

WEDDING HEARTS

Heart With Lilac Background
A3161

Heart With Pink Background
A3162

LITHOGRAPHED (#4151),
PHOTOGRAVURE (#4152)
BOOKLET STAMP (#4151)
Serpentine Die Cut 10¾ on 2, 3 or 4 Sides
2007, June 27
Self-Adhesive

4151 A3161	41c multicolored	1.00	.25
a.	Booklet pane of 20	20.00	

Serpentine Die Cut 10¾x11

4152 A3162	58c multicolored	1.25	.25

POLLINATION

Purple Nightshade, Morrison's Bumblebee
A3163

Hummingbird Trumpet, Calliope Hummingbird — A3164

Saguaro, Lesser Long-nosed Bat
A3165

Prairie Ironweed, Southern Dogface Butterfly
A3166

No. 4153: Type I, Tip of bird wing is directly under center of "U" in "USA," straight edge at left. Type II, Tip of bird wing is directly under the right line of the "U" in "USA," straight edge at right.
No. 4154: Type I, Tip of bird wing is even with the top of the denomination, straight edge at right. Type II, Tip of bird wing is well above denomination, straight edge at left.
No. 4155: Type I, Top of "USA" is even with the lower portion of the nearest unopened green saguaro flower bud, straight edge at left. Type II, Top of "USA" is even with the point where the flower and unopened green saguaro bud meet, straight edge at right.
No. 4156: Type I, Bottom of denomination is even with top point of the white triangle found between the bottom of the purple flower and the green leaf below it, straight edge at right. Type II, Bottom of denomination is even with the lower point of the white triangle found between the bottom of the purple flower and the green leaf below it, straight edge at left.

LITHOGRAPHED
Serpentine Die Cut 11 on 2, 3 or 4 Sides

2007, June 29			**Tagged**

Self-Adhesive
Booklet Stamps

4153 A3163	41c multi, Type I	.85	.30
a.	Type II	.85	.30
4154 A3164	41c multi, Type I	.85	.30
a.	Type II	.85	.30
4155 A3165	41c multi, Type I	.85	.30
a.	Type II	.85	.30
4156 A3166	41c multi, Type I	.85	.30
a.	Type II	.85	.30
b.	Block of 4, #4153-4156	3.40	
c.	Block of 4, #4153a-4156a	3.40	
d.	Booklet pane of 20, 3 each #4153-4156, 2 each #4153a-4156a	17.00	

No. 4156d is a double-sided booklet with 12 stamps (2 each #4153-4156, 1 each #4153a-4156a) on one side and 8 stamps plus label (booklet cover) on the other side.

Patriotic Banner — A3167

PHOTOGRAVURE (#4157),
LITHOGRAPHED (#4158)
Serpentine Die Cut 11 Vert.

2007, July 4			**Untagged**

Coil Stamps
Self-Adhesive

4157 A3167	(10c) red, gold & blue	.25	.25

Serpentine Die Cut 11¾ Vert.

4158 A3167	(10c) red, gold & blue	.25	.25

See No. 4385.

MARVEL COMICS SUPERHEROES

A3168

No. 4159: a, Spider-man. b, The Hulk. c, Sub-Mariner. d, The Thing. e, Captain America. f, Silver Surfer. g, Spider-Woman. h, Iron Man. i, Elektra. j, Wolverine. k, Cover of *The Amazing Spider-Man #1.* l, Cover of *The*

Incredible Hulk #1. m, Cover of *Sub-Mariner #1*. n, Cover of *The Fantastic Four #3*. o, Cover of *Captain America #100*. p, Cover of *The Silver Surfer #1*. q, Cover of *Marvel Spotlight on The Spider-Woman #32*. r, Cover of *Iron Man #1*. s, Cover of *Daredevil #176 Featuring Elektra*. t, Cover of *The X-Men #1*.

PHOTOGRAVURE
Serpentine Die Cut 10½x10¾
2007, July 26
Self-Adhesive

4159	A3168	Pane of 20	20.00	
a.-t.		41c Any single	1.00	.50

VINTAGE MAHOGANY SPEEDBOATS

1915 Hutchinson A3169

1954 Chris-Craft A3170

1939 Hacker-Craft A3171

1931 Gar Wood — A3172

LITHOGRAPHED
Serpentine Die Cut 10½
2007, Aug. 4
Self-Adhesive

4160	A3169	41c multicolored	.85	.35
4161	A3170	41c multicolored	.85	.35
4162	A3171	41c multicolored	.85	.35
4163	A3172	41c multicolored	.85	.35
a.		Horiz. strip of 4, #4160-4163	3.40	

Purple Heart Type of 2003
LITHOGRAPHED
Serpentine Die Cut 11¼x10¾
2007, Aug. 7
Self-Adhesive

4164	A2891	41c multicolored	.85	.25

See Nos. 3784-3784A, 4032, 4263-4264, 4390.

AMERICAN TREASURES SERIES

Magnolia and Irises, Stained Glass by Louis Comfort Tiffany — A3173

BOOKLET STAMP
Serpentine Die Cut 10¾ on 2 or 3 Sides
2007, Aug. 9
Self-Adhesive

4165	A3173	41c multicolored	.85	.25
a.		Booklet pane of 20	17.00	

No. 4165a is a double-sided booklet pane with 12 stamps on one side and eight stamps plus label (booklet cover) on the other side.

FLOWERS

Iris — A3174

Dahlia — A3175

Magnolia A3176

Red Gerbera Daisy A3177

Coneflower A3178

Tulip A3179

Water Lily — A3180

Poppy — A3181

Chrysanthemum A3182

Orange Gerbera Daisy A3183

LITHOGRAPHED
Serpentine Die Cut 9½ Vert.
2007, Aug. 10
COIL STAMPS
Self-Adhesive

4166	A3174	41c multicolored	2.00	.35
4167	A3175	41c multicolored	2.00	.35
4168	A3176	41c multicolored	2.00	.35
4169	A3177	41c multicolored	2.00	.35
4170	A3178	41c multicolored	2.00	.35
4171	A3179	41c multicolored	2.00	.35
4172	A3180	41c multicolored	2.00	.35
4173	A3181	41c multicolored	2.00	.35
4174	A3182	41c multicolored	2.00	.35
4175	A3183	41c multicolored	2.00	.35
a.		Strip of 10, #4166-4175	20.00	

PHOTOGRAVURE
BOOKLET STAMPS
Serpentine Die Cut 11¼x11½ on 2 or 3 Sides

4176	A3182	41c multicolored	1.25	.35
4177	A3183	41c multicolored	1.25	.35
4178	A3174	41c multicolored	1.25	.35
4179	A3175	41c multicolored	1.25	.35
4180	A3176	41c multicolored	1.25	.35
4181	A3177	41c multicolored	1.25	.35
4182	A3180	41c multicolored	1.25	.35
4183	A3181	41c multicolored	1.25	.35
4184	A3178	41c multicolored	1.25	.35
4185	A3179	41c multicolored	1.25	.35
a.		Booklet pane of 20, 2 each #4176-4185	25.00	
b.		As "a," die cutting missing on Nos. 4178 & 4183 on side with 8 stamps (PS)	1,000.	

No. 4185a is a double-sided booklet pane with 12 stamps on one side (2 each #4176-4177, 1 each #4178-4185) and eight stamps

(#4178-4185) plus label (booklet cover) on the other side.

Flag — A3184

LITHOGRAPHED
Serpentine Die Cut 9½ Vert.
2007, Aug. 15
COIL STAMPS
Self-Adhesive
With "USPS" Microprinted on Right Side of Flagpole
With Perpendicular Corners

4186	A3184	41c multicolored	1.20	.25

With "USPS" Microprinted on Left Side of Flagpole
Serpentine Die Cut 11 Vert.

4187	A3184	41c multicolored	1.20	.25

PHOTOGRAVURE
Without "USPS" Microprinting on Flagpole
Serpentine Die Cut 8½ Vert.

4188	A3184	41c multicolored	.85	.25

Serpentine Die Cut 11 Vert.
With Rounded Corners

4189	A3184	41c multicolored	.85	.25

No. 4188 is on backing paper as high as the stamp. No. 4189 is on backing paper that is larger than the stamp.

LITHOGRAPHED
BOOKLET STAMPS
Serpentine Die Cut 11¼x10¾ on 3 Sides
With "USPS" Microprinted on Right Side of Flagpole

4190	A3184	41c multicolored	.85	.25
a.		Booklet pane of 10	8.50	

With "USPS" Microprinted on Left Side of Flagpole
Serpentine Die Cut 11¼x10¾ on 2 or 3 Sides

4191	A3184	41c multicolored	.85	.25
a.		Booklet pane of 20	17.00	

The microprinting on Nos. 4190 and 4191 is under the ball of the flagpole. The flagpole is light gray on No. 4190 and dark gray on No. 4191. No. 4191a is a double-sided booklet with 12 stamps on one side of the peelable backing and 8 stamps plus label (booklet cover) on the other side.

THE ART OF DISNEY: MAGIC

Mickey Mouse A3185

Peter Pan and Tinker Bell — A3186

Dumbo and Timothy Mouse A3187

Aladdin and Genie — A3188

PHOTOGRAVURE
Serpentine Die Cut 10½x10¾
2007, Aug. 16
Self-Adhesive

4192	A3185	41c multicolored	.85	.30
4193	A3186	41c multicolored	.85	.30
4194	A3187	41c multicolored	.85	.30
4195	A3188	41c multicolored	.85	.30
a.		Block or strip of 4, #4192-4195	3.40	

CELEBRATE

A3189

LITHOGRAPHED
Serpentine Die Cut 10¾
2007, Aug. 17
Self-Adhesive

4196	A3189	41c multicolored	.85	.25

See Nos. 4335, 4407.

LEGENDS OF HOLLYWOOD

James Stewart (1908-97), Actor — A3190

2007, Aug. 17
Self-Adhesive

4197	A3190	41c multicolored	1.00	.25

ALPINE TUNDRA

A3191

No. 4198 — Wildlife: a, Elk. b, Golden eagle, horiz. c, Yellow-bellied marmot. d, American pika. e, Bighorn sheep. f, Magdalena alpine butterfly. g, White-tailed ptarmigan. h, Rocky Mountain parnassian butterfly. i, Melissa arctic butterfly, horiz. j, Brown-capped rosy-finch, horiz.

PHOTOGRAVURE
2007, Aug. 28
Self-Adhesive

4198	A3191	Pane of 10	8.50	
a.-j.		41c any single	.85	.40

GERALD R. FORD

Gerald R. Ford (1913-2006), 38th President — A3192

LITHOGRAPHED
Serpentine Die Cut 11
2007, Aug. 31
Self-Adhesive
4199 A3192 41c multicolored   .85   .25

JURY DUTY

Twelve Jurors — A3193

Serpentine Die Cut 10½
2007, Sept. 12
Self-Adhesive
4200 A3193 41c multicolored   .85   .25

MENDEZ v. WESTMINSTER, 60th ANNIV.

A3194

LITHOGRAPHED
Serpentine Die Cut 11
2007, Sept. 14
Self-Adhesive
4201 A3194 41c multicolored   .85   .25

Eid Type of 2001
PHOTOGRAVURE
Serpentine Die Cut 11
2007, Sept. 28
Self-Adhesive
4202 A2734 41c multicolored   .90   .25
See Nos. 3532, 3674, 4117, 4351, 4416.

AURORAS

Aurora Borealis A3195

Aurora Australis A3196

LITHOGRAPHED
Serpentine Die Cut 10¾
2007, Oct. 1
Self-Adhesive
4203 A3195 41c multicolored   1.25   .30
4204 A3196 41c multicolored   1.25   .30
   a.   Horiz. or vert. pair, #4203-4204   2.50

YODA

A3197

Serpentine Die Cut 10½x10¾
2007, Oct. 25
Self-Adhesive
4205 A3197 41c multicolored   1.00   .25

CHRISTMAS

Madonna of the Carnation, by Bernardino Luini — A3198

LITHOGRAPHED
Serpentine Die Cut 10¾x11 on 2 or 3 Sides
2007, Oct. 25
Self-Adhesive
Booklet Stamps (#4206, 4210b, 4211-4218)
4206 A3198 41c multicolored   .85   .25
   a.   Booklet pane of 20   17.00
No. 4206a is a double-sided booklet pane with 12 stamps on one side and eight stamps plus label that serves as a booklet cover on the other side.

Knit Reindeer A3199

Knit Christmas Tree A3200

Knit Snowman A3201

Knit Bear A3202

Serpentine Die Cut 10¾ on 2, 3 or 4 Sides
4207 A3199 41c multicolored   .85   .25
4208 A3200 41c multicolored   .85   .25
4209 A3201 41c multicolored   .85   .25
4210 A3202 41c multicolored, overall tagging   .85   .25
   b.   Block or vert. strip of 4, #4207-4210   3.40
   d.   Booklet pane of 20   17.00
No. 4210d is a double-sided booklet pane with 12 stamps on one side and eight stamps plus label that serves as a booklet cover on the other side.

Knit Reindeer A3203

Knit Christmas Tree A3204

Knit Snowman A3205

Knit Bear A3206

Serpentine Die Cut 11¼x11 on 2 or 3 Sides
4211 A3203 41c multicolored   1.25   .25
4212 A3204 41c multicolored   1.25   .25
4213 A3205 41c multicolored   1.25   .25
4214 A3206 41c multicolored   1.25   .25
   a.   Block of 4, #4211-4214   5.00
   b.   Booklet pane of 4, #4211-4214   5.00
   c.   Booklet pane of 6, #4213-4214, 2 each #4211-4212   7.50
   d.   Booklet pane of 6, #4211-4212, 2 each #4213-4214   7.50

PHOTOGRAVURE
Serpentine Die Cut 8 on 2, 3 or 4 Sides
4215 A3203 41c multicolored   1.30   .25
4216 A3204 41c multicolored   1.30   .25
4217 A3205 41c multicolored   1.30   .25
4218 A3206 41c multicolored   1.30   .25
   a.   Block or strip of 4, #4215-4218   5.20
   b.   Booklet pane of 18, 4 each #4215, 4218, 5 each #4216, 4217   23.50
   Nos. 4206-4218 (13)   14.45   3.25

Hanukkah Type of 2004
LITHOGRAPHED
Serpentine Die Cut 10¾x11
2007, Oct. 26
Self-Adhesive
4219 A2962 41c multicolored   .85   .25
   See Nos. 3880, 4118, 4372.

Kwanzaa Type of 2004
LITHOGRAPHED
Serpentine Die Cut 11x10¾
2007, Oct. 26
Self-Adhesive
4220 A2963 41c multicolored   .85   .25
   See Nos. 3881, 4119, 4373.

CHINESE NEW YEAR

Year of the Rat A3207

PHOTOGRAVURE
Serpentine Die Cut 10¾
2008, Jan. 9   **Self-Adhesive**
4221 A3207 41c multicolored   .85   .25

BLACK HERITAGE SERIES

Charles W. Chesnutt (1858-1932), Writer — A3208

Serpentine Die Cut 11
2008, Jan. 31   **Self-Adhesive**
4222 A3208 41c multicolored   .85   .25

LITERARY ARTS SERIES

Marjorie Kinnan Rawlings (1896-1953), Writer — A3209

Serpentine Die Cut 11
2008, Feb. 21
Self-Adhesive
4223 A3209 41c multicolored   .85   .25

AMERICAN SCIENTISTS

Gerty Cori (1896-1957), Biochemist — A3210

Linus Pauling (1901-94), Structural Chemist A3211

Edwin Hubble (1889-1953), Astronomer — A3212

John Bardeen (1908-91), Theoretical Physicist A3213

2008, Mar. 6
Self-Adhesive
4224 A3210 41c multicolored   1.00   .35
4225 A3211 41c multicolored   1.00   .35
4226 A3212 41c multicolored   1.00   .35
4227 A3213 41c multicolored   1.00   .35
   a.   Horiz. strip of 4, #4224-4227   4.00

Flag at Dusk — A3214

Flag at Night — A3215

Flag at Dawn A3216

Flag at Midday A3217

PHOTOGRAVURE
2008, Apr. 18   *Perf. 9¾ Vert.*
COIL STAMPS
4228 A3214 42c multicolored   2.50   .40
4229 A3215 42c multicolored   2.50   .40
4230 A3216 42c multicolored   2.50   .40
4231 A3217 42c multicolored   2.50   .40
   a.   Horiz. strip of 4, #4228-4231   10.00   1.60
Self-Adhesive
With Perpendicular Corners
Serpentine Die Cut 9½ Vert.
4232 A3214 42c multicolored   2.25   .25
4233 A3215 42c multicolored   2.25   .25
4234 A3216 42c multicolored   2.25   .25
4235 A3217 42c multicolored   2.25   .25
   a.   Horiz. strip of 4, #4232-4235   9.00
Serpentine Die Cut 11 Vert.
4236 A3214 42c multicolored   2.50   .25
4237 A3215 42c multicolored   2.50   .25
4238 A3216 42c multicolored   2.50   .25
4239 A3217 42c multicolored   2.50   .25
   a.   Horiz. strip of 4, #4236-4239   10.00
Serpentine Die Cut 8½ Vert.
4240 A3214 42c multicolored   2.00   .25
4241 A3215 42c multicolored   2.00   .25
4242 A3216 42c multicolored   2.00   .25

4243	A3217	42c multicolored	2.00	.25
a.		Horiz. strip of 4, #4240-4243	8.00	

Serpentine Die Cut 11 Vert.
With Rounded Corners

4244	A3214	42c multicolored	1.25	.30
4245	A3215	42c multicolored	1.25	.30
4246	A3216	42c multicolored	1.25	.30
4247	A3217	42c multicolored	1.25	.30
a.		Horiz. strip of 4, #4244-4247	6.00	
		Nos. 4228-4247 (20)	42.00	5.80

Nos. 4232-4243 are on backing paper as high as the stamp. Nos. 4244-4247 are on backing paper that is larger than the stamp. Nos. 4232-4235 have "USPS" microprinted on the right side of a white flag stripe. Nos. 4236-4239 have "USPS" micoprinted on red flag stripes. On Nos. 4244-4247, the paper, vignette size and "2008" year date are slightly larger than those features on Nos. 4236-4239.

AMERICAN JOURNALISTS

Martha Gellhorn (1908-98) A3218

John Hersey (1914-93) A3219

George Polk (1913-48) A3220

Ruben Salazar (1928-70) A3221

Eric Sevareid (1912-92) A3222

LITHOGRAPHED
Serpentine Die Cut 10¾x10½
2008, Apr. 22
Self-Adhesive

4248	A3218	42c multicolored	1.40	.40
4249	A3219	42c multicolored	1.40	.40
4250	A3220	42c multicolored	1.40	.40
4251	A3221	42c multicolored	1.40	.40
4252	A3222	42c multicolored	1.40	.40
a.		Vert. strip of 5, #4248-4252	7.00	

TROPICAL FRUIT

Pomegranate A3223

Star Fruit A3224

Kiwi A3225

Papaya A3226

Guava — A3227

LITHOGRAPHED
Serpentine Die Cut 11¼x10¾
2008, Apr. 25
Self-Adhesive

4253	A3223	27c multicolored	.90	.25
4254	A3224	27c multicolored	.90	.25
4255	A3225	27c multicolored	.90	.25
4256	A3226	27c multicolored	.90	.25
4257	A3227	27c multicolored	.90	.25
a.		Horiz. strip of 5, #4253-4257	4.50	

PHOTOGRAVURE
COIL STAMPS
Serpentine Die Cut 8½ Vert.

4258	A3226	27c multicolored	1.80	.25
4259	A3227	27c multicolored	1.80	.25
4260	A3223	27c multicolored	1.80	.25
4261	A3224	27c multicolored	1.80	.25
4262	A3225	27c multicolored	1.80	.25
a.		Strip of 5, #4258-4262	9.00	
b.		As No. 4262, light green ("27 USA," "Kiwi" and year date) omitted	—	
		Nos. 4253-4262 (10)	13.50	2.50

Purple Heart Type of 2003
LITHOGRAPHED

2008, Apr. 30			*Perf. 11¼*	
4263	A2891	42c multicolored	.90	.25

Self-Adhesive
Serpentine Die Cut 11¼x10¾

4264	A2891	42c multicolored	.85	.25

See Nos. 4032, 4164, 4390.

FRANK SINATRA

Frank Sinatra (1915-98), Singer and Actor — A3228

Serpentine Die Cut 10¾
2008, May 13
Self-Adhesive

4265	A3228	42c multicolored	.85	.25

MINNESOTA STATEHOOD, 150th ANNIV.

Bridge Over Mississippi River Near Winona — A3229

Serpentine Die Cut 10¾
2008, May 17
Self-Adhesive

4266	A3229	42c multicolored	.85	.25

WILDLIFE

Dragonfly — A3230

LITHOGRAPHED
Serpentine Die Cut 11¼x11
2008, May 19
Self-Adhesive

4267	A3230	62c multicolored	2.50	.25

AMERICAN LANDMARKS

Mount Rushmore A3231

Hoover Dam A3232

2008   *Serpentine Die Cut 10¾x10½*
Self-Adhesive

4268	A3231	$4.80 multi	12.00	5.00
4269	A3232	$16.50 multi	35.00	17.00

Issued: $4.80, 6/6; $16.50, 6/20.

LOVE

Man Carrying Heart — A3233

PHOTOGRAVURE
Serpentine Die Cut 10¾ on 2, 3, or 4 Sides
2008, June 10
Booklet Stamp
Self-Adhesive

4270	A3233	42c multicolored	.95	.25
a.		Booklet pane of 20	19.00	

WEDDING HEARTS

Heart With Light Green Background A3234

Heart With Buff Background A3235

LITHOGRAPHED (#4271), PHOTOGRAVURE (#4272) BOOKLET STAMP (#4271)
Serpentine Die Cut 10¾ on 2, 3 or 4 Sides
2008, June 10
Self-Adhesive

4271	A3234	42c multicolored	.90	.25
a.		Booklet pane of 20	18.00	

Serpentine Die Cut 10¾

4272	A3235	59c multicolored	1.25	.25

FLAGS OF OUR NATION

American Flag and Clouds — A3236

Alabama Flag and Shrimp Boat — A3237

Alaska Flag and Humpback Whale — A3238

American Samoa Flag and Island Peaks and Trees — A3239

Arizona Flag and Saguaro Cacti A3240

Arkansas Flag and Wood Duck — A3241

California Flag and Coast — A3242

Colorado Flag and Mountain — A3243

Connecticut Flag, Sailboats and Buoy — A3244

Delaware Flag and Beach — A3245

PHOTOGRAVURE
Serpentine Die Cut 11 Vert.
2008, June 14
Self-Adhesive
Coil Stamps

4273	A3236	42c multicolored	1.00	.30
4274	A3237	42c multicolored	1.00	.30
4275	A3238	42c multicolored	1.00	.30
4276	A3239	42c multicolored	1.00	.30
4277	A3240	42c multicolored	1.00	.30
a.		Strip of 5, #4273-4277	5.00	
4278	A3241	42c multicolored	1.00	.30
4279	A3242	42c multicolored	1.00	.30
4280	A3243	42c multicolored	1.00	.30
4281	A3244	42c multicolored	1.00	.30
4282	A3245	42c multicolored	1.00	.30
a.		Strip of 5, #4278-4282	5.00	
b.		P # set of 10, #4277a + 4282a	10.00	

No. 4273 always has a plate number. No. 4282b may be collected as one continuous strip, but the item will not fit in any standard album.

District of Columbia Flag and Cherry Tree — A3246

Florida Flag and Anhinga A3247

Georgia Flag, Fence and Lamppost — A3248

Guam Flag, Fish and Tropicbird — A3249

Hawaii Flag and Ohia Lehua Flowers A3250

Idaho Flag and Rainbow Trout — A3251

Illinois Flag and Windmill A3252

Indiana Flag and Tractor A3253

Iowa Flag, Farm Field and Cornstalks — A3254

Kansas Flag and Farm Buildings — A3255

2008, Sept. 2
Self-Adhesive
Coil Stamps

4283	A3246	42c multicolored	1.00	.30
4284	A3247	42c multicolored	1.00	.30
4285	A3248	42c multicolored	1.00	.30
4286	A3249	42c multicolored	1.00	.30
4287	A3250	42c multicolored	1.00	.30
a.		Strip of 5, #4283-4287	5.00	
4288	A3251	42c multicolored	1.00	.30
4289	A3252	42c multicolored	1.00	.30
4290	A3253	42c multicolored	1.00	.30
4291	A3254	42c multicolored	1.00	.30
4292	A3255	42c multicolored	1.00	.30
a.		Strip of 5, #4288-4292	5.00	
b.		P # set of 10, #4287a + 4192a	10.00	

No. 4283 always has a plate number. No. 4292b may be collected as one continuous strip, but the item will not fit in any standard album.

Kentucky Flag, Fence and Horses — A3256

Louisiana Flag and Brown Pelicans — A3257

Maine Flag and Moose A3258

Maryland Flag and Red-winged Blackbird — A3259

Massachusetts Flag, Sea Birds and Sailboats — A3260

Michigan Flag and Great Lakes Ships — A3261

Minnesota Flag, Swans and Grain Elevator — A3262

Mississippi Flag and Black Bears — A3263

Missouri Flag and Paddle Wheeler A3264

American Flag and Wheat — A3265

2009, Aug. 6
Self-Adhesive
Coil Stamps

4293	A3256	44c multicolored	1.00	.30
4294	A3257	44c multicolored	1.00	.30
4295	A3258	44c multicolored	1.00	.30
4296	A3259	44c multicolored	1.00	.30
4297	A3260	44c multicolored	1.00	.30
a.		Strip of 5, #4293-4297	5.00	
4298	A3261	44c multicolored	1.00	.30
4299	A3262	44c multicolored	1.00	.30
4300	A3263	44c multicolored	1.00	.30
4301	A3264	44c multicolored	1.00	.30
4302	A3265	44c multicolored	1.00	.30
a.		Strip of 5, #4298-4302	5.00	
b.		P # set of 10, #4297a + 4302a	10.00	

No. 4293 always has a plate number. No. 4302b may be collected as one continuous strip, but the item will not fit in any standard album.

American Flag and Mountains — A3266

Montana Flag and Mountain Lion — A3267

Nebraska Flag and Central-pivot Irrigation System — A3268

Nevada Flag, Mountains and Ocotillos — A3269

New Hampshire Flag and Loon — A3270

New Jersey Flag and Sand Castle A3271

New Mexico Flag, Mountains and Hot Air Balloons — A3272

New York Flag, Fireboats and City Skyline — A3273

North Carolina Flag, Great Blue Heron and Cape Hatteras Lighthouse — A3274

North Dakota Flag and Elk A3275

2010, Apr. 16
Self-Adhesive
Coil Stamps

4303	A3266	44c multicolored	1.00	.30
4304	A3267	44c multicolored	1.00	.30
4305	A3268	44c multicolored	1.00	.30
4306	A3269	44c multicolored	1.00	.30
4307	A3270	44c multicolored	1.00	.30
a.		Strip of 5, #4303-4307	5.00	
4308	A3271	44c multicolored	1.00	.30
4309	A3272	44c multicolored	1.00	.30
4310	A3273	44c multicolored	1.00	.30
4311	A3274	44c multicolored	1.00	.30
4312	A3275	44c multicolored	1.00	.30
a.		Strip of 5, #4308-4312	5.00	
b.		P # set of 10, #4307a + 4312a	10.00	

No. 4303 always has a plate number. No. 4312b may be collected as one continuous strip, but the item will not fit in any standard album.

Northern Marianas Flag, Beach and Palm Trees — A3276

Ohio Flag, Butterfly, Milkweed Flowers and River — A3277

Oklahoma Flag and Oil Pumps — A3278

Oregon Flag, Mount Hood and Camas Lilies A3279

Pennsylvania Flag and White-tailed Deer — A3280

Puerto Rico Flag and Puerto Rican Tody Bird A3281

Rhode Island Flag and Sailboat A3282

South Carolina Flag, Marsh and Gazebo A3283

South Dakota Flag and Bison A3284

Tennessee Flag and Scarlet Tanagers — A3285

PHOTOGRAVURE
Serpentine Die Cut 11 Vert.
2011, Aug. 11
Self-Adhesive
Coil Stamps

4313	A3276	(44c) multicolored	1.25	.30
4314	A3277	(44c) multicolored	1.25	.30
4315	A3278	(44c) multicolored	1.25	.30
4316	A3279	(44c) multicolored	1.25	.30
4317	A3280	(44c) multicolored	1.25	.30
a.		Strip of 5, #4313-4317	6.25	
4318	A3281	(44c) multicolored	1.25	.30
4319	A3282	(44c) multicolored	1.25	.30
4320	A3283	(44c) multicolored	1.25	.30
4321	A3284	(44c) multicolored	1.25	.30
4322	A3285	(44c) multicolored	1.25	.30
a.		Strip of 5, #4318-4322	6.25	
b.		P# set of 10, #4317a + 4322a	12.50	

Alternating examples of the five examples of No. 4313 in the roll have a plate number. No. 4322b may be collected as one continuous strip, but the item will not fit in any standard album.

Texas Flag, Cotton Plant and Field A3286

Utah Flag, Cactus and Rock Arch A3287

Vermont Flag and Owls A3288

Virgin Islands Flag, Sailfish and Boat A3289

Virginia Flag and Replicas of Ships that Carried Settlers to Jamestown — A3290

Washington Flag and Evergreen Forest — A3291

West Virginia Flag and Wild Turkeys A3292

Wisconsin Flag and Dairy Cows — A3293

Wyoming Flag and Bighorn Sheep — A3294

American Flag and Fruited Plain — A3295

PHOTOGRAVURE
Serpentine Die Cut 11 Vert.
2012, Aug. 16
Self-Adhesive
Coil Stamps

4323	A3286	(45c) multicolored	2.00	.30
4324	A3287	(45c) multicolored	2.00	.30
4325	A3288	(45c) multicolored	2.00	.30
4326	A3289	(45c) multicolored	2.00	.30
4327	A3290	(45c) multicolored	2.00	.30
a.		Strip of 5, #4323-4327	10.00	
4328	A3291	(45c) multicolored	2.00	.30
4329	A3292	(45c) multicolored	2.00	.30
4330	A3293	(45c) multicolored	2.00	.30
4331	A3294	(45c) multicolored	2.00	.30
4332	A3295	(45c) multicolored	2.00	.30
a.		Strip of 5, #4328-4332	10.00	
b.		P# set of 10, #4327a + 4332a	20.00	

Alternating examples of the five examples of No. 4323 in the roll have a plate number. No. 4332b may be collected as one continuous strip, but the item will not fit in any standard album.

CHARLES (1907-78) AND RAY (1912-88) EAMES, DESIGNERS

A3296

No. 4333: a, Christmas card depicting Charles and Ray Eames. b, "Crosspatch" fabric design. c, Stacking chairs. d, Case Study House #8, Pacific Palisades, CA. e, Wire-base table. f, Lounge chair and ottoman. g, Hang-it-all. h, La Chaise. i, Scene from film, "Tops." j, Wire mesh chair. k, Cover of May 1943 edition of *California Arts & Architecture* Magazine. l, House of Cards. m, Molded plywood sculpture. n, Eames Storage Unit. o, Aluminum group chair. p, Molded plywood chair.

PHOTOGRAVURE
Serpentine Die Cut 10¾x10½
2008, June 17
Self-Adhesive

4333	A3296	Pane of 16 + label	18.00	
a.-p.		42c Any single	1.10	.50

SUMMER OLYMPIC GAMES, BEIJING, CHINA

Gymnast A3297

LITHOGRAPHED
Serpentine Die Cut 10¾
2008, June 19
Self-Adhesive

4334	A3297	42c multicolored	.85	.25

Celebrate Type of 2007
Serpentine Die Cut 10¾
2008, July 10
Self-Adhesive

4335	A3189	42c multicolored	.85	.25

VINTAGE BLACK CINEMA

Poster for "Black and Tan" — A3298

Poster for "The Sport of the Gods" — A3299

Poster for "Prinsesse Tam-Tam" A3300

Poster for "Caldonia" A3301

Poster for "Hallelujah" — A3302

Serpentine Die Cut 10¾
2008, July 16   **Tagged**
Self-Adhesive

4336	A3298	42c multicolored	.95	.45
4337	A3299	42c multicolored	.95	.45
4338	A3300	42c multicolored	.95	.45
4339	A3301	42c multicolored	.95	.45
4340	A3302	42c multicolored	.95	.45
a.		Horiz. strip of 5, #4336-4340	4.75	

"TAKE ME OUT TO THE BALLGAME," CENT.

Baseball Players and First Six Notes of Song — A3303

PHOTOGRAVURE
Serpentine Die Cut 11
2008, July 16
Self-Adhesive

4341	A3303	42c multicolored	.85	.25

THE ART OF DISNEY: IMAGINATION

Pongo and Pup — A3304

Steamboat Willie — A3305

Princess
Aurora, Flora,
Fauna and
Merryweather
A3306

Mowgli and
Baloo — A3307

Serpentine Die Cut 10½x10¾
2008, Aug. 7
Self-Adhesive

4342	A3304	42c multicolored	.85	.30
4343	A3305	42c multicolored	.85	.30
4344	A3306	42c multicolored	.85	.30
4345	A3307	42c multicolored	.85	.30
a.		Block or strip of 4, #4342-4345	3.40	

AMERICAN TREASURES SERIES

Valley of
the
Yosemite,
by Albert
Bierstadt
A3308

LITHOGRAPHED
BOOKLET STAMP
Serpentine Die Cut 11 on 2 or 3 Sides
2008, Aug. 14
Self-Adhesive

4346	A3308	42c multicolored	.85	.25
a.		Booklet pane of 20	17.00	

No. 4346a is a double-sided booklet pane with 12 stamps on one side and eight stamps plus label (booklet cover) on the other side.

Sunflower — A3309

BOOKLET STAMP
Serpentine Die Cut 11¼x10¾ on 2 or 3 Sides
2008, Aug. 15
Self-Adhesive

4347	A3309	42c multicolored	.85	.25
a.		Booklet pane of 20	17.00	

No. 4347a is a double-sided booklet pane with 12 stamps on one side and eight stamps plus label (booklet cover) on the other side.

Sea Coast Type of 2002
LITHOGRAPHED
COIL STAMP
Perf. 9¾ Vert.
2008, Sept. 5　　　　　　Untagged

4348	A2853	(5c) multicolored	.25	.25

No. 4348 has "2008" year date in black, and microprinted "USPS" at the end of the purple rock to the right of the crashing wave.
See Nos. 3693, 3775, 3785, 3864, 3874-3875.

LATIN JAZZ

Musicians
A3310

PHOTOGRAVURE
Serpentine Die Cut 11x10¾
2008, Sept. 8
Self-Adhesive

4349	A3310	42c multicolored	.85	.25

LEGENDS OF HOLLYWOOD

Bette Davis (1908-89), Actress — A3311

LITHOGRAPHED
Serpentine Die Cut 10¾
2008, Sept. 18
Self-Adhesive

4350	A3311	42c multicolored	1.00	.25

Eid Type of 2001
PHOTOGRAVURE
Serpentine Die Cut 11
2008, Sept. 23
Self-Adhesive

4351	A2734	42c multicolored	.85	.25

GREAT LAKES DUNES

A3312

No. 4352 — Wildlife: a, Vesper sparrow. b, Red fox, vert. c, Piping plover. d, Eastern hognose snake. e, Common mergansers. f, Spotted sandpiper, vert. g, Tiger beetle, vert. h, White-footed mouse, vert. i, Piping plover nestlings. j, Red admiral butterfly, vert.

Serpentine Die Cut 10¾
2008, Oct. 2
Self-Adhesive

4352	A3312	Pane of 10	10.00	
a.-j.		42c Any single	1.00	.40

AUTOMOBILES OF THE 1950s

1959
Cadillac
Eldorado
A3313

1957
Studebaker
Golden
Hawk
A3314

1957
Pontiac
Safari
A3315

1957
Lincoln
Premiere
A3316

1957
Chrysler
300C
A3317

LITHOGRAPHED
2008, Oct. 3
Self-Adhesive

4353	A3313	42c multicolored	.85	.45
4354	A3314	42c multicolored	.85	.45
4355	A3315	42c multicolored	.85	.45
4356	A3316	42c multicolored	.85	.45
4357	A3317	42c multicolored	.85	.45
a.		Vert. strip of 5, #4353-4357	4.25	

ALZHEIMER'S DISEASE AWARENESS

A3318

PHOTOGRAVURE
Serpentine Die Cut 10¾
2008, Oct. 17
Self-Adhesive

4358	A3318	42c multicolored	.85	.25

CHRISTMAS

Virgin and Child with the Young John the Baptist, by Sandro Botticelli
A3319

Drummer Nutcracker
A3320

Santa Claus Nutcracker
A3321

King Nutcracker
A3322

Soldier Nutcracker — A3323

LITHOGRAPHED
Serpentine Die Cut 10¾x11 on 2 or 3 Sides
2008, Oct. 23
Self-Adhesive
Booklet Stamps

4359	A3319	42c multicolored	.85	.25
a.		Booklet pane of 20	17.00	
b.		Die cutting omitted, pair		

4360	A3320	42c multicolored	1.00	.25
4361	A3321	42c multicolored	1.00	.25
4362	A3322	42c multicolored	1.00	.25
4363	A3323	42c multicolored	1.00	.25
a.		Block of 4, #4360-4363	4.00	
b.		Booklet pane of 20, 5 each #4360-4363	20.00	

No. 4359a is a double-sided booklet pane with 12 stamps on one side and eight stamps plus label that serves as a booklet cover on the other side. No. 4363b is a double-sided booklet pane with 12 stamps on one side (3 each of Nos. 4360-4363) and eight stamps (2 each of Nos. 4360-4363) plus label that serves as a booklet cover on the other side.

Drummer
Nutcracker
A3324

Santa Claus
Nutcracker
A3325

King
Nutcracker
A3326

Soldier
Nutcracker
A3327

Serpentine Die Cut 11¼x11 on 2 or 3 Sides

4364	A3324	42c multicolored	1.25	.25
4365	A3325	42c multicolored	1.25	.25
4366	A3326	42c multicolored	1.25	.25
4367	A3327	42c multicolored	1.25	.25
a.		Block of 4, #4364-4367	5.00	
b.		Booklet pane of 4, #4364-4367	5.00	
c.		Booklet pane of 6, #4366-4367, 2 each #4364-4365	7.50	
d.		Booklet pane of 6, #4364-4365, 2 each #4366-4367	7.50	

Serpentine Die Cut 8 on 2, 3 or 4 Sides
PHOTOGRAVURE

4368	A3324	42c multicolored	1.25	.25
4369	A3325	42c multicolored	1.25	.25
4370	A3326	42c multicolored	1.25	.25
4371	A3327	42c multicolored	1.25	.25
a.		Block or strip of 4, #4368-4371	5.00	
b.		Booklet pane of 10, 5 each #4368-4369, 4 each #4370-4371	22.50	
		Nos. 4359-4371 (13)	14.85	3.25

Hanukkah Type of 2004
LITHOGRAPHED
Serpentine Die Cut 10¾x11
2008, Oct. 24
Self-Adhesive

4372	A2962	42c multicolored	.85	.25

Kwanzaa Type of 2004
Serpentine Die Cut 11x10¾
2008, Oct. 24
Self-Adhesive

4373	A2963	42c multicolored	.85	.25

ALASKA STATEHOOD, 50TH ANNIV.

Dogsledder
Near Rainy
Pass
A3328

Serpentine Die Cut 10¾
2009, Jan. 3
Self-Adhesive

4374	A3328	42c multicolored	.85	.25

CHINESE NEW YEAR

Year of the
Ox
A3329

2009, Jan. 8
Self-Adhesive
4375 A3329 42c multicolored .85 .25

OREGON STATEHOOD, 150TH ANNIV.

Pacific Coast of Oregon A3330

2009, Jan. 14
Self-Adhesive
4376 A3330 42c multicolored .85 .25

EDGAR ALLAN POE

Edgar Allan Poe (1809-49), Writer — A3331

PHOTOGRAVURE
2009, Jan. 16
Self-Adhesive
4377 A3331 42c multicolored .90 .25

AMERICAN LANDMARKS

Redwood Forest A3332

Old Faithful A3333

LITHOGRAPHED
Serpentine Die Cut 10¾x10½
2009, Jan. 16
Self-Adhesive
4378 A3332 $4.95 multi 11.00 5.00
4379 A3333 $17.50 multi 40.00 20.00

ABRAHAM LINCOLN (1809-65), 16TH PRESIDENT

Lincoln as Rail-splitter A3334

Lincoln as Lawyer A3335

Lincoln as Politician A3336

Lincoln as President A3337

Serpentine Die Cut 10¾
2009, Feb. 9
Self-Adhesive
4380 A3334 42c multicolored 1.50 .35
4381 A3335 42c multicolored 1.50 .35
4382 A3336 42c multicolored 1.50 .35
4383 A3337 42c multicolored 1.50 .35
a. Horiz. strip of 4, #4380-4383 6.00

CIVIL RIGHTS PIONEERS

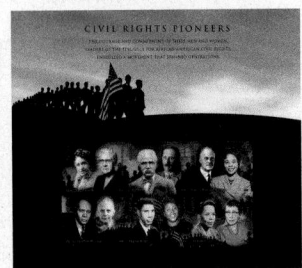

A3338

No. 4384: a, Mary Church Terrell (1863-1954), writer, Mary White Ovington (1865-1951), journalist. b, J. R. Clifford (1848-1933), attorney, Joel Elias Spingarn (1875-1939), educator. c, Oswald Garrison Villard (1872-1949), co-founder of National Association for the Advancement of Colored People (NAACP), Daisy Gatson Bates (1914-99), mentor of black Little Rock Central High School students. d, Charles Hamilton Houston (1895-1950), lawyer, Walter White (1893-1955), chief secretary of NAACP. e, Medgar Evers (1925-63), assassinated Mississippi NAACP field secretary, Fannie Lou Hamer (1917-77), voting rights activist. f, Ella Baker (1903-86), activist, Ruby Hurley (1909-80), NAACP Southeast Regional Director.

PHOTOGRAVURE
2009, Feb. 21
Self-Adhesive
4384 A3338 Pane of 6 9.00
a.-f. 42c Any single 1.50 .40

Patriotic Banner Type of 2007
LITHOGRAPHED
COIL STAMP
Perf. 9¾ Vert.
2009, Feb. 24 **Untagged**
4385 A3167 (10c) multicolored .25 .25
See Nos. 4157-4158.

LITERARY ARTS

Richard Wright (1908-60), Author A3339

Serpentine Die Cut 10¾
2009, Apr. 9
Self-Adhesive
4386 A3339 61c multicolored 1.25 .25

WILDLIFE

Polar Bear A3340

Dolphin A3341

LITHOGRAPHED (#4387), PHOTOGRAVURE
2009 *Serpentine Die Cut 11¼x11*
Self-Adhesive
4387 A3340 28c multi .75 .25
a. Die cutting omitted, pane of 20 7,250.
Serpentine Die Cut 11
4388 A3341 64c multi 1.40 .25
COIL STAMP
Serpentine Die Cut 8½ Vert.
4389 A3340 28c multi .60 .25
Issued: Nos. 4387, 4389, 4/16; No. 4388, 6/12.

Purple Heart Type of 2003
LITHOGRAPHED
Serpentine Die Cut 11¼x10¾
2009, Apr. 28
Self-Adhesive
4390 A2891 44c multicolored .90 .25
See Nos. 3784-3784A, 4032, 4164, 4263-4264.

Flag — A3342

LITHOGRAPHED
2009 *Perf. 9¾ Vert.*
COIL STAMPS
4391 A3342 44c multi 1.00 1.00
Self-Adhesive
Serpentine Die Cut 11 Vert.
With Pointed Corners
4392 A3342 44c multi 2.00 .25
a. Die cutting omitted, pair 350.00
Serpentine Die Cut 9½ Vert.
4393 A3342 44c multi 1.50 .25
Serpentine Die Cut 8½ Vert.
PHOTOGRAVURE
4394 A3342 44c multi 1.50 .25
Serpentine Die Cut 11 Vert.
With Rounded Corners
4395 A3342 44c multi 1.25 .25
BOOKLET STAMP
Serpentine Die Cut 11¼x10¾ on 3 Sides
4396 A3342 44c multi .90 .25
a. Booklet pane of 10 9.00
Nos. 4392-4394 are on backing paper as high as the stamp. No. 4395 is on backing paper that is taller than the stamp. No. 4393 has microprinted "USPS" on white stripe below the blue field.
Issued: Nos. 4391, 4395, 5/1; Nos. 4392-4394, 5/8, No. 4396, 6/5.

WEDDINGS

Wedding Rings — A3343

Wedding Cake — A3344

LITHOGRAPHED, PHOTOGRAVURE (#4398)
Serpentine Die Cut 10¾
2009, May 1
Self-Adhesive
4397 A3343 44c multicolored .90 .25
4398 A3344 61c multicolored 1.25 .25
See Nos. 4521, 4602, 4735, 4867, 5000.

THE SIMPSONS TELEVISION SHOW, 20TH ANNIV.

Homer Simpson A3345

Marge Simpson A3346

Bart Simpson A3347

Lisa Simpson A3348

Maggie Simpson — A3349

LITHOGRAPHED
BOOKLET STAMPS
Serpentine Die Cut 10¾ on 2, 3 or 4 Sides
2009, May 7
Self-Adhesive
4399 A3345 44c multicolored 1.15 .40
4400 A3346 44c multicolored 1.15 .40
4401 A3347 44c multicolored 1.15 .40
4402 A3348 44c multicolored 1.15 .40
4403 A3349 44c multicolored 1.15 .40
a. Horiz. strip of 5, #4399-4403 5.75
b. Booklet pane of 20, 4 each #4399-4403 23.00

LOVE

King of Hearts A3350

Queen of Hearts A3351

PHOTOGRAVURE
BOOKLET STAMPS
Serpentine Die Cut 10¾ on 2, 3 or 4 Sides
2009, May 8
Self-Adhesive
4404 A3350 44c multicolored 1.15 .25
4405 A3351 44c multicolored 1.15 .25
a. Horiz. or vert. pair, #4404-4405 2.30
b. Booklet pane of 20, 10 each #4404-4405 23.00

BOB HOPE

Bob Hope (1903-2003), Actor, Comedian — A3352

LITHOGRAPHED
Serpentine Die Cut 10¾
2009, May 29
Self-Adhesive
4406 A3352 44c multicolored 1.00 .25

Celebrate Type of 2007
2009, June 10
Self-Adhesive

4407	A3189	44c multicolored	.90	.25
a.		Die cutting omitted, pair	—	

See Nos. 4196, 4335.

BLACK HERITAGE

Anna Julia Cooper
(c. 1858-1964),
Educator — A3353

2009, June 11
Self-Adhesive

4408	A3353	44c multicolored	.90	.25

GULF COAST LIGHTHOUSES

Matagorda Island
Lighthouse,
Texas
A3354

Sabine Pass
Lighthouse,
Louisiana
A3355

Biloxi
Lighthouse,
Mississippi
A3356

Sand Island
Lighthouse,
Alabama
A3357

Fort Jefferson
Lighthouse,
Florida — A3358

Serpentine Die Cut 11x10¾
2009, July 23
Self-Adhesive

4409	A3354	44c multicolored	.90	.40
4410	A3355	44c multicolored	.90	.40
4411	A3356	44c multicolored	.90	.40
4412	A3357	44c multicolored	.90	.40
4413	A3358	44c multicolored	.90	.40
a.		Horiz. strip of 5, #4409-4413	4.50	

EARLY TV MEMORIES

A3359

No. 4414: a, Milton Berle in "Texaco Star Theater." b, Lucille Ball and Vivian Vance in "I Love Lucy." c, Red Skelton in "The Red Skelton Show." d, Marionette Howdy Doody in "Howdy Doody." e, Jack Webb in "Dragnet." f, Lassie in "Lassie." g, William Boyd and horse, Topper, in "Hopalong Cassidy." h, Groucho Marx in "You Bet Your Life." i, Dinah Shore in "The Dinah Shore Show." j, Ed Sullivan in "The Ed Sullivan Show." k, Fran Allison and puppets, Kukla and Ollie in "Kukla, Fran and Ollie." l, Phil Silvers in "The Phil Silvers Show." m, Clayton Moore and horse, Silver, in "The Lone Ranger." n, Raymond Burr and William Talman in "Perry Mason." o, Alfred Hitchcock in "Alfred Hitchcock Presents." p, George Burns and Gracie Allen in "Burns and Allen." q, Ozzie and Harriet Nelson in "Ozzie and Harriet." r, Steve Allen in "The Tonight Show." s, Rod Serling in "The Twilight Zone." t, Jackie Gleason and Art Carney in "The Honeymooners."

Serpentine Die Cut 10¾x10½
2009, Aug. 11
Self-Adhesive

4414	A3359	Pane of 20	20.00	
a.-t.		44c Any single	1.00	.50

HAWAII STATEHOOD, 50TH ANNIV.

Surfer and
Outrigger
Canoe
A3360

PHOTOGRAVURE
Serpentine Die Cut 11
2009, Aug. 21
Self-Adhesive

4415	A3360	44c multicolored	1.25	.25

Eid Type of 2001
PHOTOGRAVURE
2009, Sept. 3
Self-Adhesive

4416	A2734	44c multicolored	.90	.25

See Nos. 3532, 3674, 4117, 4202, 4351.

THANKSGIVING DAY PARADE

Crowd,
Street
Sign, Bear
Balloon
A3361

Drum
Major,
Musicians
A3362

Musicians,
Balloon,
Horse
A3363

Cowboy, Turkey Balloon, Crowd,
Television Cameraman — A3364

Serpentine Die Cut 11x10¾
2009, Sept. 9
Self-Adhesive

4417	A3361	44c multicolored	.90	.35
4418	A3362	44c multicolored	.90	.35
4419	A3363	44c multicolored	.90	.35
4420	A3364	44c multicolored	.90	.35
a.		Horiz. strip of 4, #4417-4420	3.60	

LEGENDS OF HOLLYWOOD

Gary Cooper (1901-
61), Actor — A3365

Serpentine Die Cut 11
2009, Sept. 10
Self-Adhesive

4421	A3365	44c multicolored	1.00	.25

SUPREME COURT JUSTICES
Souvenir Sheet

A3366

No. 4422: a, Felix Frankfurter (1882-1965). b, William J. Brennan, Jr. (1906-97). c, Louis D. Brandeis (1856-1941). d, Joseph Story (1779-1845).

LITHOGRAPHED
Serpentine Die Cut 11x10½
2009, Sept. 22
Self-Adhesive

4422	A3366	Pane of 4	4.00	
a.-d.		44c Any single	1.00	.30

KELP FOREST

A3367

Wildlife: a, Brown pelican. b, Western gull, southern sea otters, red sea urchin. c, Harbor seal. d, Lion's mane nudibranch, vert. e, Yellowtail rockfish, white-spotted rose anemone. f, Vermilion rockfish. g, Copper rockfish. h, Pacific rock crab, jeweled top snail. i, Northern kelp crab, vert. j, Treefish, Monterey turban snail, brooding sea anemones.

PHOTOGRAVURE
Serpentine Die Cut 10¾
2009, Oct. 1
Self-Adhesive

4423	A3367	Pane of 10	11.00	
a.-j.		44c Any single	1.10	.40

CHRISTMAS

Madonna and
Sleeping Child, by
Sassoferrato (Giovanni
Battista Salvi)
A3368

Reindeer
A3369

Snowman
A3370

Gingerbread
Man
A3371

Toy Soldier
A3372

Reindeer
A3373

Snowman
A3374

Gingerbread
Man
A3375

Toy Soldier — A3376

LITHOGRAPHED, PHOTOGRAVURE
(#4429-4432)
Serpentine Die Cut 10¾x11 on 2 or 3 Sides
2009
Self-Adhesive
Booklet Stamps

4424	A3368	44c multicolored	.90	.25
a.		Booklet pane of 20	18.00	
4425	A3369	44c multicolored	1.10	.25
4426	A3370	44c multicolored	1.10	.25
4427	A3371	44c multicolored	1.10	.25
4428	A3372	44c multicolored	1.10	.25
a.		Block of 4, #4425-4428	4.40	
b.		Booklet pane of 20, 5 each #4425-4428	22.00	
c.		As "b," die cutting omitted on side with 12 stamps	—	
d.		As "b," die cutting omitted on side with 8 stamps	—	
e.		As "a," die cutting omitted	375.00	

Serpentine Die Cut 8 on 2, 3 or 4 Sides

4429	A3373	44c multicolored	1.10	.25
4430	A3374	44c multicolored	1.10	.25
4431	A3375	44c multicolored	1.10	.25
4432	A3376	44c multicolored	1.10	.25
a.		Block or strip of 4, #4429-4432	4.40	
b.		Booklet pane of 18, 5 each #4429, 4431, 4 each #4430, 4432	20.00	
		Nos. 4424-4432 (9)	9.70	2.25

No. 4424a is a double-sided booklet pane with 12 stamps on one side and eight stamps plus label that serves as a booklet cover on the other side. No. 4428b is a double-sided booklet pane with 12 stamps on one side (3 each of Nos. 4425-4428) and eight stamps (2 each of Nos. 4425-4428) plus label that serves as a booklet cover on the other side.

HANUKKAH

Menorah — A3377

LITHOGRAPHED
Serpentine Die Cut 10¾x11
2009, Oct. 9
Self-Adhesive

4433 A3377 44c multicolored .90 .25

KWANZAA

Family — A3378

2009, Oct. 9
Self-Adhesive

4434 A3378 44c multicolored .90 .25

CHINESE NEW YEAR

Year of the Tiger A3379

PHOTOGRAVURE
Serpentine Die Cut 11
2010, Jan. 14   **Tagged**
Self-Adhesive

4435 A3379 44c multicolored 1.10 .25

2010 WINTER OLYMPICS, VANCOUVER

Snowboarder A3380

PHOTOGRAVURE
Serpentine Die Cut 11
2010, Jan. 22   **Tagged**
Self-Adhesive

4436 A3380 44c multicolored .90 .25

"Forever" Liberty Bell Type of 2007
Serpentine Die Cut 11¼x10¾ on 2, 3 or 4 Sides
2010, Feb. 3 Self-Adhesive Litho.
Booklet Stamp
Medium Microprinting, Bell 16mm Wide
Dated "2009" in Copper

4437 A3148 (44c) multicolored 1.10 .25
 a.   Booklet pane of 18   20.00

On No. 4437, the "2009" date is smaller than that on No. 4127i, which has a 15mm wide bell. The bell on No. 4437 is also 17mm tall while No. 4127i is 16mm tall. The microprinted "Forever" is on a dotted background on No. 4437 and on a white background on No. 4127i.

See also Nos. 4125, 4128c.

AMERICAN LANDMARKS

Mackinac Bridge, Michigan A3381

Bixby Creek Bridge, California A3382

PHOTOGRAVURE
Serpentine Die Cut 10¾x10½
2010, Feb. 3   **Tagged**
Self-Adhesive

4438 A3381 $4.90 multi 11.00 5.00
4439 A3382 $18.30 multi 45.00 18.00

DISTINGUISHED SAILORS

Admiral William S. Sims (1858-1936), Emblem of USS W.S. Sims — A3383

Admiral Arleigh A. Burke (1901-96), Emblem of USS Arleigh Burke A3384

Lieutenant Commander John McCloy (1876-1945), Emblem of USS McCloy — A3385

Petty Officer 3rd Class Doris Miller (1919-43), Emblem of USS Miller A3386

PHOTOGRAVURE
Serpentine Die Cut 10¾x10½
2010, Feb. 4   **Tagged**
Self-Adhesive

4440 A3383 44c multicolored .90 .40
4441 A3384 44c multicolored .90 .40
4442 A3385 44c multicolored .90 .40
4443 A3386 44c multicolored .90 .40
 a.   Block or horiz. strip of 4, #4440-4443   3.60

ABSTRACT EXPRESSIONISTS

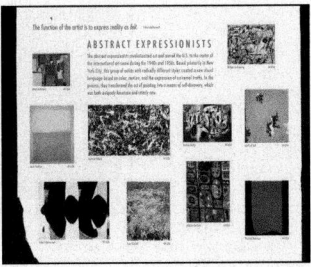

A3387

No. 4444: a, The Golden Wall, by Hans Hofmann (30x30mm). b, Asheville, by Willem de Kooning (38x38mm). c, Orange and Yellow, by Mark Rothko (35x49mm). d, Convergence, by Jackson Pollock (63x43mm). e, The Liver Is the Cock's Comb, by Arshile Gorky (39x32mm). f, 1948-C, by Clyfford Still (35x49mm). g, Elegy to the Spanish Republic No. 34, by Robert Motherwell (54x49mm). h, La Grande Vallée 0, by Joan Mitchell (35x49mm). i, Romanesque Façade, by Adolph Gottlieb (35x49mm). j, Achilles, by Barnett Newman (35x49mm).

LITHOGRAPHED
Serpentine Die Cut 10¾x11, 10¾ (#4444a, 4444b, 4444e), 11x10¾ (#4444d)
2010, Mar. 11   **Tagged**
Self-Adhesive

4444 A3387   Pane of 10   12.50
 a.-j.   44c Any single   1.25 .40

BILL MAULDIN (1921-2003), CARTOONIST

A3388

LITHOGRAPHED
Serpentine Die Cut 10¾
2010, Mar. 31   **Tagged**
Self-Adhesive

4445 A3388 44c multicolored .90 .25

COWBOYS OF THE SILVER SCREEN

Roy Rogers (1911-98) A3389

Tom Mix (1880-1940) A3390

William S. Hart (1864-1946) A3391

Gene Autry (1907-98) A3392

LITHOGRAPHED
Serpentine Die Cut 10½x10¾
2010, Apr. 17
Self-Adhesive

4446 A3389 44c multicolored 1.25 .35
4447 A3390 44c multicolored 1.25 .35
4448 A3391 44c multicolored 1.25 .35
4449 A3392 44c multicolored 1.25 .35
 a.   Block or strip of 4, #4446-4449   5.00

LOVE

Pansies in a Basket — A3393

PHOTOGRAVURE
Serpentine Die Cut 10¾
2010, Apr. 22
Self-Adhesive

4450 A3393 44c multicolored .90 .25

ANIMAL RESCUE

Wire-haired Jack Russell Terrier — A3394

Maltese — A3395

Calico — A3396

Yellow Labrador Retriever A3397

Golden Retriever A3398

Gray, White and Tan Cat — A3399

Black, White and Tan Cat — A3400

Australian Shepherd A3401

Boston Terrier — A3402

Orange Tabby — A3403

LITHOGRAPHED
Serpentine Die Cut 10¾
2010, Apr. 30
Self-Adhesive

4451	A3394	44c multicolored	1.25	.40
4452	A3395	44c multicolored	1.25	.40
4453	A3396	44c multicolored	1.25	.40
4454	A3397	44c multicolored	1.25	.40
4455	A3398	44c multicolored	1.25	.40
4456	A3399	44c multicolored	1.25	.40
4457	A3400	44c multicolored	1.25	.40
4458	A3401	44c multicolored	1.25	.40
4459	A3402	44c multicolored	1.25	.40
4460	A3403	44c multicolored	1.25	.40
a.		Block of 10, #4451-4460	12.50	

LEGENDS OF HOLLYWOOD

Katharine Hepburn (1907-2003), Actress — A3404

PHOTOGRAVURE
Serpentine Die Cut 10¾
2010, May 12
Self-Adhesive

4461	A3404	44c black	1.00	.25

MONARCH BUTTERFLY

A3405

PHOTOGRAVURE
Serpentine Die Cut 10½
2010, May 17
Self-Adhesive

4462	A3405	64c multicolored	1.50	.25

KATE SMITH

Kate Smith (1907-86), Singer — A3406

PHOTOGRAVURE
2010, May 27   *Serpentine Die Cut 11*
Self-Adhesive

4463	A3406	44c multicolored	.90	.25

BLACK HERITAGE

Oscar Micheaux (1884-1951), Film Director — A3407

Serpentine Die Cut 11
2010, June 22
Self-Adhesive

4464	A3407	44c multicolored	.90	.25

NEGRO LEAGUES BASEBALL

Play at the Plate A3408

Andrew "Rube" Foster (1879-1930), Founder of Negro National League — A3409

PHOTOGRAVURE
Serpentine Die Cut 11
2010, July 15
Self-Adhesive

4465	A3408	44c multicolored	.90	.30
4466	A3409	44c multicolored	.90	.30
a.		Horiz. pair, #4465-4466	1.80	

SUNDAY FUNNIES

Beetle Bailey — A3410

Calvin and Hobbes A3411

Archie — A3412

Garfield A3413

Dennis the Menace A3414

LITHOGRAPHED
Serpentine Die Cut 10½x10¾
2010, July 16
Self-Adhesive

4467	A3410	44c multicolored	1.00	.30
4468	A3411	44c multicolored	1.00	.30
4469	A3412	44c multicolored	1.00	.30
4470	A3413	44c multicolored	1.00	.30
4471	A3414	44c multicolored	1.00	.30
a.		Horiz. strip of 5, #4467-4471	5.00	

BOY SCOUTS OF AMERICA, CENTENNIAL

Boy Scouts — A3415

PHOTOGRAVURE
Serpentine Die Cut 11
2010, July 27
Self-Adhesive

4472	A3415	44c multicolored	.90	.25

Boys in a Pasture, by Winslow Homer (1836-1910) — A3416

Serpentine Die Cut 10¾
2010, Aug. 12
Self-Adhesive

4473	A3416	44c multicolored	1.00	.25

HAWAIIAN RAIN FOREST

A3417

No. 4474: a, Hawaii 'amakihi, Hawaii 'elepaio, ohi'a lehua. b, 'Akepa, 'ope'ape'a, vert. c, 'I'iwi, haha. d, 'Oma'o, kanawao, 'ohelo kau la'au, vert. e, 'Oha, vert. f, Pulelehua butterfly, kolea lau nui, 'ilihia. g, Koele Mountain damselfly, 'akala, vert. h, 'Apapane, Hawaiian mint, vert. i, Jewel orchid, vert. j, Happyface spider, 'ala'ala wai nui, vert.

LITHOGRAPHED
Serpentine Die Cut 10¾
2010, Sept. 1
Self-Adhesive

4474	A3417	Pane of 10	10.00	
a.-j.		44c Any single	1.00	.40

MOTHER TERESA

Mother Teresa (1910-97), Humanitarian, 1979 Nobel Peace Laureate — A3418

PHOTOGRAVURE
2010, Sept. 5   *Serpentine Die Cut 11*
Self-Adhesive

4475	A3418	44c multicolored	.90	.25

LITERARY ARTS

Julia de Burgos (1914-53), Poet A3419

PHOTOGRAVURE
Serpentine Die Cut 11
2010, Sept. 14
Self-Adhesive

4476	A3419	44c multicolored	.90	.25

CHRISTMAS

Angel with Lute, Detail of Fresco by Melozzo da Forli — A3420

PHOTOGRAVURE (#4477), LITHOGRAPHED
Serpentine Die Cut 10¾
2010, Oct. 21   **Tagged**
Self-Adhesive

4477	A3420	44c multi	1.00	.25

Ponderosa Pine A3421

Eastern Red Cedar A3422

Balsam Fir A3423

Blue Spruce A3424

Booklet Stamps
Serpentine Die Cut 11 on 2 or 3 Sides

4478	A3421	(44c) multi	1.50	.25
4479	A3422	(44c) multi	1.50	.25
4480	A3423	(44c) multi	1.50	.25
4481	A3424	(44c) multi	1.50	.25
a.		Block of 4, #4478-4481	6.00	
b.		Booklet pane of 20, 5 each #4478-4481	30.00	
c.		As "a," die cutting omitted	—	500.00
d.		As "b," die cutting omitted on side with 12 stamps	600.00	
e.		As "b," die cutting omitted on side with 8 stamps	700.00	
f.		As "b," die cutting omitted on side with 12 stamps, die cutting omitted on bottom 4 stamps on side with 8 stamps	—	

Ponderosa Pine
A3425

Eastern Red Cedar
A3426

Balsam Fir
A3427

Blue Spruce
A3428

Serpentine Die Cut 11¼x10¾ on 2, 3 or 4 Sides

4482	A3425 (44c) multi	2.50	.25
4483	A3426 (44c) multi	2.50	.25
4484	A3427 (44c) multi	2.50	.25
4485	A3428 (44c) multi	2.50	.25
a.	Block or strip of 4, #4482-4485	10.00	
b.	Booklet pane of 18, 5 each #4482, 4484, 4 each #4483, 4485	37.50	
	Nos. 4477-4485 (9)	17.00	2.25

No. 4481b is a double-sided booklet pane with 12 stamps on one side (3 each of Nos. 4478-4481) and eight stamps (2 each of Nos. 4478-4481) plus label that serves as a booklet cover on the other side.

Statue of Liberty
A3429

Flag
A3430

LITHOGRAPHED (#4486-4489)
Serpentine Die Cut 9½ Vert.
2010, Dec. 1
COIL STAMPS
Self-Adhesive

4486	A3429 (44c) multicolored	1.50	.25
4487	A3430 (44c) multicolored	1.50	.25
a.	Pair, #4486-4487	3.00	

Serpentine Die Cut 11 Vert.

4488	A3429 (44c) multicolored	1.50	.25
a.	Vert. pair, horiz. unslit btwn.	—	
4489	A3430 (44c) multicolored	1.50	.25
a.	Pair, #4488-4489	3.00	
b.	Block of 4 (one pair each from two different coil rolls), horiz. unslit btwn.	600.00	

Serpentine Die Cut 8½ Vert.

4490	A3429 (44c) multicolored	1.50	.25
4491	A3430 (44c) multicolored	1.50	.25
a.	Pair, #4490-4491	3.00	
	Nos. 4486-4491 (6)	9.00	1.50

Microprinting reads "4evR" on Nos. 4486-4487, "4evr" on Nos. 4488-4489, and "4EVR" on Nos. 4490-4491. The microprinting is found above the Statue of Liberty's hair, and at the bottom of the lowest red stripe of the flag.
See Nos. 4518-4519, 4559-4564.

CHINESE NEW YEAR

Year of the Rabbit
A3431

PHOTOGRAVURE
Serpentine Die Cut 11
2011, Jan. 22
Self-Adhesive

4492	A3431 (44c) multicolored	1.10	.25

KANSAS STATEHOOD, 150TH ANNIV.

Windmill and Wind Turbines
A3432

LITHOGRAPHED
Serpentine Die Cut 11
2011, Jan. 27
Self-Adhesive

4493	A3432 (44c) multicolored	1.10	.25

PRES. RONALD REAGAN (1911-2004)

Pres. Ronald Reagan
A3433

PHOTOGRAVURE
Serpentine Die Cut 10½
2011, Feb. 10
Self-Adhesive

4494	A3433 (44c) multicolored	1.10	.25

Art Deco Bird — A3434

LITHOGRAPHED
Serpentine Die Cut 10 Vert.
2011, Feb. 11 Untagged
COIL STAMP
Self-Adhesive

4495	A3434 (5c) multicolored	.25	.25

Quill and Inkwell — A3435

LITHOGRAPHED
Serpentine Die Cut 11¾ Vert.
2011, Feb. 14
COIL STAMP
Self-Adhesive

4496	A3435 44c multicolored	.95	.25

LATIN MUSIC LEGENDS

Tito Puente (1923-2000)
A3436

Carmen Miranda (1909-55)
A3437

Selena (1971-95)
A3438

Carlos Gardel (1890-1935)
A3439

Celia Cruz (1925-2003)
A3440

PHOTOGRAVURE
Serpentine Die Cut 10¾
2011, Mar. 16
Self-Adhesive

4497	A3436 (44c) multicolored	1.10	.40
4498	A3437 (44c) multicolored	1.10	.40
4499	A3438 (44c) multicolored	1.10	.40
4500	A3439 (44c) multicolored	1.10	.40
4501	A3440 (44c) multicolored	1.10	.40
a.	Horiz. strip of 5, #4497-4501	5.50	

CELEBRATE

A3441

PHOTOGRAVURE
Serpentine Die Cut 11x11½
2011, Mar. 25
Self-Adhesive

4502	A3441 (44c) multicolored	1.10	.25

Compare with type A3855.

JAZZ

Musicians
A3442

PHOTOGRAVURE
Serpentine Die Cut 10¾
2011, Mar. 26
Self-Adhesive

4503	A3442 (44c) multicolored	1.10	.25

Statue of Liberty and Flag Types of 2010 and

George Washington — A3443

LITHOGRAPHED (#4504, 4518-4519)
2011 *Serpentine Die Cut 11¼x10¾*
Self-Adhesive

4504	A3443 20c multicolored	.40	.25

Oregano
A3444

Flax
A3445

Foxglove
A3446

Lavender
A3447

Sage — A3448

Oveta Culp Hobby (1905-95), First Health, Education and Welfare Department Secretary — A3449

PHOTOGRAVURE (#4505-4510)
Serpentine Die Cut 11

4505	A3444 29c multicolored	1.50	.25
4506	A3445 29c multicolored	1.50	.25
4507	A3446 29c multicolored	1.50	.25
4508	A3447 29c multicolored	1.50	.25
4509	A3448 29c multicolored	1.50	.25
a.	Horiz. strip of 5, #4505-4509	7.50	
4510	A3449 84c multicolored	1.75	.35

New River Gorge Bridge, West Virginia — A3450

LITHOGRAPHED (#4511)
Serpentine Die Cut 10¾x10½

4511	A3450 $4.95 multicolored	10.00	5.00
	Nos. 4504-4511 (7)	17.90	6.50

LITHOGRAPHED (#4512)
Coil Stamps
Serpentine Die Cut 9½ Vert.

4512	A3443 20c multicolored	.40	.25

No. 4512a is recorded only on a single cover bearing a strip of 9 and three strips of 10. The editors would welcome reports of unused examples.

LITHOGRAPHED (#4512)
Serpentine Die Cut 8½ Vert.

4513	A3446 29c multicolored	1.50	.25
4514	A3447 29c multicolored	1.50	.25
4515	A3448 29c multicolored	1.50	.25
4516	A3444 29c multicolored	1.50	.25
4517	A3445 29c multicolored	1.50	.25
a.	Horiz. strip of 5, #4513-4517	7.50	
	Nos. 4512-4517 (6)	7.90	1.50

LITHOGRAPHED (#4518-4519)
Booklet Stamps
Thin Paper
Serpentine Die Cut 11¼x10¾ on 2, 3, or 4 Sides

4518	A3429 (44c) multicolored	1.10	.25
4519	A3430 (44c) multicolored	1.10	.25
a.	Pair, #4518-4519	2.20	
b.	Booklet pane of 18, 9 each #4518-4519	20.00	

Issued: Nos. 4504, 4511, 4512, 4/11; Nos. 4505-4509, 4513-4517, 4/7; No. 4510, 4/15; Nos. 4518-4519. 4/8.

Wedding Cake Type of 2009 With "USA" in Serifed Type and

Wedding Roses — A3450i

LITHOGRAPHED (#4520),
PHOTOGRAVURE (#4521)

2011   *Serpentine Die Cut 11*
Self-Adhesive

4520	A3450i	(44c) multicolored	2.25	.25
a.		Die cutting omitted, pair	250.00	
4521	A3344	64c multicolored	2.50	.25

CIVIL WAR SESQUICENTENNIAL

Battle of Fort Sumter — A3451

First Battle of Bull Run — A3452

LITHOGRAPHED
Serpentine Die Cut 11
2011, Apr. 12
Self-Adhesive

4522	A3451	(44c) multicolored	1.10	.30
4523	A3452	(44c) multicolored	1.10	.30
a.		Pair, #4522-4523	2.20	

GO GREEN

A3453

No. 4524 — Messages: a, Buy local produce, reuse bags. b, Fix water leaks. c, Share rides. d, Turn off lights not in use. e, Choose to walk. f, Go Green, reduce our environmental footprint step by step. g, Compost. h, Let nature do the work. i, Recycle more. j, Ride a bike. k, Plant trees. l, Insulate the home. m, Use public transportation. n, Use efficient light bulbs. o, Adjust the thermostat. p, Maintain tire pressure.

PHOTOGRAVURE
Serpentine Die Cut 10¾
2011, Apr. 14
Self-Adhesive

4524	A3453	Pane of 16	17.50	
a.-p.		(44c) Any single	1.10	.50

HELEN HAYES

Helen Hayes (1900-93), Actress — A3454

Serpentine Die Cut 11
2011, Apr. 25   **Tagged**
Self-Adhesive

4525	A3454	(44c) multicolored	1.10	.25

LEGENDS OF HOLLYWOOD

Gregory Peck (1916-2003), Actor — A3455

Serpentine Die Cut 10¾
2011, Apr. 28
Self-Adhesive

4526	A3455	(44c) black	1.25	.25

SPACE FIRSTS

Alan B. Shepard, Jr. (1923-98), First American in Space A3456

Messenger, First Spacecraft to Orbit Mercury — A3457

LITHOGRAPHED
2011, May 4   *Serpentine Die Cut 11*
Self-Adhesive

4527	A3456	(44c) multicolored	1.10	.30
4528	A3457	(44c) multicolored	1.10	.30
a.		Horiz. pair, #4527-4528	2.20	

Purple Heart and Ribbon — A3458

Serpentine Die Cut 11¼x10¾
2011, May 5
Self-Adhesive

4529	A3458	(44c) multicolored	1.10	.25

INDIANAPOLIS 500, CENT.

Ray Harroun Driving Marmon Wasp A3459

LITHOGRAPHED
Serpentine Die Cut 10¾
2011, May 20
Self-Adhesive

4530	A3459	(44c) multicolored	1.10	.25

GARDEN OF LOVE

Pink Flower A3460   Red Flower A3461

Blue Flowers A3462   Butterfly A3463

Green Vine Leaves A3464   Blue Flower A3465

Doves A3466   Orange Red Flowers A3467

Strawberry A3468   Yellow Orange Flowers A3469

Designed by Derry Noyes. Printed by Avery Dennison.

PHOTOGRAVURE
Serpentine Die Cut 10¾
2011, May 23
Self-Adhesive

4531	A3460	(44c) multicolored	2.00	.40
4532	A3461	(44c) multicolored	2.00	.40
4533	A3462	(44c) multicolored	2.00	.40
4534	A3463	(44c) multicolored	2.00	.40
4535	A3464	(44c) multicolored	2.00	.40
4536	A3465	(44c) multicolored	2.00	.40
4537	A3466	(44c) multicolored	2.00	.40
4538	A3467	(44c) multicolored	2.00	.40
4539	A3468	(44c) multicolored	2.00	.40
4540	A3469	(44c) multicolored	2.00	.40
a.		Block of 10, #4531-4540	20.00	
		Nos. 4531-4540 (10)	20.00	4.00

The two blocks of 10 on the pane are separated by a gutter.

AMERICAN SCIENTISTS

Melvin Calvin (1911-97), Chemist A3470

Asa Gray (1810-88), Botanist A3471

Maria Goeppert Mayer (1906-72), Physicist A3472

Severo Ochoa (1905-93), Biochemist A3473

LITHOGRAPHED
Serpentine Die Cut 11
2011, June 16
Self-Adhesive

4541	A3470	(44c) multicolored	1.10	.50
4542	A3471	(44c) multicolored	1.10	.50
4543	A3472	(44c) multicolored	1.10	.50
4544	A3473	(44c) multicolored	1.10	.50
a.		Horiz. strip of 4, #4541-4544	4.40	
b.		Horiz. strip of 4, die cutting missing on backing paper (from misaligned die-cutting mat)	375.00	

LITERARY ARTS

Mark Twain (Samuel L. Clemens) (1835-1910), Writer — A3474

PHOTOGRAVURE
Serpentine Die Cut 11
2011, June 25
Self-Adhesive

4545	A3474	(44c) multicolored	1.10	.25

PIONEERS OF AMERICAN INDUSTRIAL DESIGN

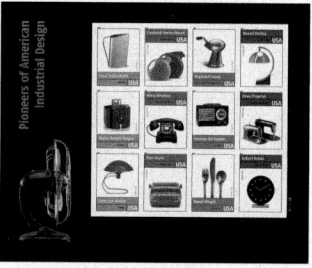

A3475

No. 4546: a, "Normandie" pitcher, designed by Peter Müller-Munk (1904-67). b, Fiesta dinnerware, designed by Frederick Hurten Rhead (1880-1942). c, Streamlined pencil sharpener, designed by Raymond Loewy (1893-1986). d, Table lamp, designed by Donald Deskey (1894-1989). e, Kodak "Baby Brownie" camera, designed by Walter Dorwin Teague (1883-1960). f, Model 302 Bell telephone, designed by Henry Dreyfuss (1904-72). g, Emerson "Patriot" radio, designed by Norman Bel Geddes (1893-1958). h, Streamlined sewing machines, designed by Dave Chapman (1909-78). i, "Anywhere" lamp, designed by Greta von Nessen (1900-74). j, IBM "Selectric" typewriter, designed by Eliot Noyes (1910-77). k, "Highlight/Pinch" flatware, designed by Russel Wright (1904-76). l, Herman Miller electric clock, designed by Gilbert Rohde (1894-1944).

PHOTOGRAVURE
Serpentine Die Cut 10¾
2011, June 29
Self-Adhesive

4546	A3475	Pane of 12	13.25	
a.-l.		(44c) Any single	1.10	.50

OWNEY, THE POSTAL DOG

Owney, His Medals and Tags A3476

PHOTOGRAVURE
Serpentine Die Cut 11
2011, July 27
Self-Adhesive

4547	A3476	(44c) multicolored	1.50	.25

U.S. MERCHANT MARINE

Clipper Ship A3477

Auxiliary Steamship A3478

Liberty Ship A3479

Container Ship A3480

PHOTOGRAVURE
Serpentine Die Cut 11
2011, July 28
Self-Adhesive

4548	A3477	(44c) multicolored	1.10	.35
4549	A3478	(44c) multicolored	1.10	.35
4550	A3479	(44c) multicolored	1.10	.35
4551	A3480	(44c) multicolored	1.10	.35
a.		Block or horiz. strip of 4, #4548-4551	4.40	

EID

"Eid Mubarak" — A3481

PHOTOGRAVURE
Serpentine Die Cut 11¼
2011, Aug. 12
Self-Adhesive

4552	A3481	(44c) mar, gray & gold	1.10	.25

CHARACTERS FROM DISNEY-PIXAR FILMS
Send a Hello

Lightning McQueen and Mater from *Cars* — A3482

Remy the Rat and Linguini from *Ratatouille* A3483

Buzz Lightyear and Aliens from *Toy Story* — A3484

Carl Fredricksen and Dug the Dog from *Up* — A3485

WALL-E from *WALL-E* A3486

PHOTOGRAVURE
Serpentine Die Cut 10½
2011, Aug. 19
Self-Adhesive

4553	A3482	(44c) multicolored	1.10	.40
4554	A3483	(44c) multicolored	1.10	.40
4555	A3484	(44c) multicolored	1.10	.40
4556	A3485	(44c) multicolored	1.10	.40
4557	A3486	(44c) multicolored	1.10	.40
a.		Horiz. strip of 5, #4553-4557	5.50	

Adjacent horizontal or vertical stamps will have selvage between the stamps.

AMERICAN TREASURES SERIES

The Long Leg, by Edward Hopper (1882-1967) — A3487

PHOTOGRAVURE
Serpentine Die Cut 11
2011, Aug. 24
Self-Adhesive

4558	A3487	(44c) multicolored	1.10	.25

Statue of Liberty and Flag Types of 2010
LITHOGRAPHED (#4559-4562), PHOTOGRAVURE
Serpentine Die Cut 11¼x11 on 2 or 3 Sides
2011, Sept. 14
BOOKLET STAMPS
Self-Adhesive

4559	A3429	(44c) multicolored	1.25	.25
4560	A3430	(44c) multicolored	1.25	.25
a.		Pair, #4559-4560	2.50	
b.		Booklet pane of 20, 10 each #4559-4560	25.00	

4561	A3429	(44c) multicolored	1.10	.25
4562	A3430	(44c) multicolored	1.10	.25
a.		Pair, #4561-4562	2.20	
b.		Booklet pane of 20, 10 each #4561-4562	22.00	

Serpentine Die Cut 11¼x11½ on 2 or 3 Sides

4563	A3429	(44c) multicolored	1.10	.25
4564	A3430	(44c) multicolored	1.10	.25
a.		Pair, #4563-4564	2.20	
b.		Booklet pane of 20, 10 each #4563-4564	22.00	
		Nos. 4559-4564 (6)	6.90	1.50

Microprinting reads "4evR" on Nos. 4559-4560, "4evr" on Nos. 4561-4562, and "4EVR" on Nos. 4563-4564. The microprinting is found above the Statue of Liberty's hair, and at the bottom of the lowest red stripe of the flag. Nos. 4560b, 4562b and 4564b are double-sided booklet panes with 12 stamps one one side (6 each of types A3429-A3430) and 8 stamps (4 each of types A3429-A3430) on the other side. The paper used on Nos. 4561-4562 is thicker than that used on Nos. 4518-4519.

BLACK HERITAGE

Barbara Jordan (1936-96), Congresswoman A3488

LITHOGRAPHED
Serpentine Die Cut 10¾
2011, Sept. 16
Self-Adhesive

4565	A3488	(44c) multicolored	1.10	.25

ART OF ROMARE BEARDEN (1911-88)

Conjunction A3489

Odysseus: Poseidon, The Sea God - Enemy of Odysseus A3490

Prevalence of Ritual: Conjur Woman A3491

Falling Star — A3492

PHOTOGRAVURE
Serpentine Die Cut 10¾
2011, Sept. 28
Self-Adhesive

4566	A3489	(44c) multicolored	1.10	.40
4567	A3490	(44c) multicolored	1.10	.40
4568	A3491	(44c) multicolored	1.10	.40
4569	A3492	(44c) multicolored	1.10	.40
a.		Horiz. strip of 4, #4566-4569	4.40	

CHRISTMAS

Madonna of the Candelabra, by Raphael — A3493

A3494 A3495

A3496 A3497

LITHOGRAPHED
Serpentine Die Cut 10¾x 11 on 2 or 3 Sides
2011, Oct. 13
Booklet Stamps
Self-Adhesive

4570	A3493	(44c) multicolored	1.10	.25
a.		Booklet pane of 20	22.00	

With "USPS" Microprinted on Collar of Ornament

4571	A3494	(44c) multicolored	1.50	.25
4572	A3495	(44c) multicolored	1.50	.25
4573	A3496	(44c) multicolored	1.50	.25
4574	A3497	(44c) multicolored	1.50	.25
a.		Block of 4, #4571-4574	6.00	
b.		Booklet pane of 20, 5 each #4571-4574	30.00	

Microprinted "USPS" in Places Other Than Collar of Ornament

4575	A3494	(44c) multicolored	1.50	.25
4576	A3495	(44c) multicolored	1.50	.25
4577	A3496	(44c) multicolored	1.50	.25
4578	A3497	(44c) multicolored	1.50	.25
a.		Block of 4, #4575-4578	6.00	
b.		Booklet pane of 20, 5 each #4575-4578	30.00	

A3498 A3499

Ornaments
A3500 A3501

Serpentine Die Cut 11¼x11 on 2, 3 or 4 Sides

4579	A3498	(44c) multicolored	1.50	.25
4580	A3499	(44c) multicolored	1.50	.25
4581	A3500	(44c) multicolored	1.50	.25
4582	A3501	(44c) multicolored	1.50	.25
a.		Block or strip of 4, #4579-4582	6.00	
b.		Booklet pane of 18, 5 each #4579, 4582, 4 each #4580-4581	27.50	
		Nos. 4570-4582 (13)	19.10	3.25

The microprinted "USPS" is to the left of the third stripe on Nos. 4575 and 4579, on the left side of the bottom ribbon of the ribbon cluster above the ornament collar on Nos. 4576 and 4578, below the bottom stripe near the bottom tip on No. 4577, on the vertical ribbon on No. 4580, on a curved ribbon above the collar on No. 4581, and on the left side of the ornament, below the curve, on No. 4582.

No. 4570a is a double-sided booklet with 12 stamps on one side and eight stamps plus a label that serves as a booklet cover on the other side. Nos. 4574b and 4578b are double sided booklets with 12 stamps (3 each of types A3494-A3497) on one side and eight

stamps (2 each of types A3494-A3497) plus a
label that serves as a booklet cover on the
other side.

HANUKKAH

A3502

Serpentine Die Cut 11x10¾
2011, Oct. 14
Self-Adhesive

4583 A3502 (44c) multicolored 1.10 .25

KWANZAA

Family — A3503

Serpentine Die Cut 10¾x11
2011, Oct. 14
Self-Adhesive

4584 A3503 (44c) multicolored 1.10 .25

Eagle — A3504

PHOTOGRAVURE
Serpentine Die Cut 11 Vert.
2012, Jan. 3
Coil Stamps
Self-Adhesive
Color Behind "USA"

4585	A3504	(25c) green	.50	.25
4586	A3504	(25c) blue green	.50	.25
4587	A3504	(25c) blue	.50	.25
4588	A3504	(25c) red violet	.50	.25
4589	A3504	(25c) brown orange	.50	.25
4590	A3504	(25c) yellow orange	.50	.25
a.		Strip of 6, #4585-4590	3.00	

NEW MEXICO STATEHOOD CENTENNIAL

Sanctuary
II, Painting
by Doug
West
A3505

PHOTOGRAVURE
2012, Jan. 6 *Serpentine Die Cut 11*
Self-Adhesive

4591 A3505 (44c) multicolored 1.10 .25

ALOHA SHIRTS

Surfers and
Palm Trees
A3506

Surfers
A3507

Bird of
Paradise
Flowers
A3508

Kilauea
Volcano
A3509

Fossil Fish, Shells
and Starfish — A3510

PHOTOGRAVURE
Serpentine Die Cut 11
2012, Jan. 19
Self-Adhesive

4592	A3506	32c multicolored	2.00	.30
4593	A3507	32c multicolored	2.00	.30
4594	A3508	32c multicolored	2.00	.30
4595	A3509	32c multicolored	2.00	.30
4596	A3510	32c multicolored	2.00	.30
a.		Horiz. strip of 5, #4592-4596	10.00	

LITHOGRAPHED
Coil Stamps
Serpentine Die Cut 11 Vert.

4597	A3510	32c multicolored	2.00	.30
4598	A3506	32c multicolored	2.00	.30
4599	A3507	32c multicolored	2.00	.30
4600	A3508	32c multicolored	2.00	.30
4601	A3509	32c multicolored	2.00	.30
a.		Strip of 5, #4597-4601	10.00	
b.		As "a," die cutting omitted	125.00	
		Nos. 4592-4601 (10)	20.00	3.00

On Nos. 4592-4596, the top of the shirt collars are all higher than the cross line of the "A"
in "USA," and on Nos. 4597-4601, they are
even with or slightly below the cross line.
See Nos. 4682-4686.

Wedding Cake Type of 2009
LITHOGRAPHED
Serpentine Die Cut 10¾
2012, Jan. 20
Self-Adhesive

4602 A3344 65c multicolored 1.35 .25

See Nos. 4398, 4521, 4735, 4867, 5000.

BALTIMORE CHECKERSPOT BUTTERFLY

A3511

PHOTOGRAVURE
Serpentine Die Cut 10¾
2012, Jan. 20
Self-Adhesive

4603 A3511 65c multicolored 1.50 .25

DOGS AT WORK

Seeing Eye
Dog — A3512

Therapy
Dog — A3513

Military
Dog — A3514

Rescue
Dog — A3515

PHOTOGRAVURE
Serpentine Die Cut 10¾
2012, Jan. 20
Self-Adhesive

4604	A3512	65c multicolored	1.30	.30
4605	A3513	65c multicolored	1.30	.30
4606	A3514	65c multicolored	1.30	.30
4607	A3515	65c multicolored	1.30	.30
a.		Block or vert. strip of 4, #4604-4607	5.20	

BIRDS OF PREY

Northern
Goshawk
A3516

Peregrine
Falcon
A3517

Golden Eagle
A3518

Osprey
A3519

Northern
Harrier — A3520

LITHOGRAPHED
Serpentine Die Cut 11¼x10¾
2012, Jan. 20
Self-Adhesive

4608	A3516	85c multicolored	1.75	.35
4609	A3517	85c multicolored	1.75	.35
4610	A3518	85c multicolored	1.75	.35
4611	A3519	85c multicolored	1.75	.35
4612	A3520	85c multicolored	1.75	.35
a.		Horiz. strip of 5, #4608-4612	8.75	

WEATHER VANES

Rooster With
Perch — A3521

Cow — A3522

Eagle — A3523

Rooster
Without
Perch — A3524

Centaur — A3525

LITHOGRAPHED
Serpentine Die Cut 11¾ Vert.
2012, Jan. 20
Coil Stamps
Self-Adhesive

4613	A3521	45c multicolored	1.50	.30
4614	A3522	45c multicolored	1.50	.30
4615	A3523	45c multicolored	1.50	.30
4616	A3524	45c multicolored	1.50	.30
4617	A3525	45c multicolored	1.50	.30
a.		Strip of 5, #4613-4617	7.50	

BONSAI

Sierra
Juniper — A3526

Black
Pine — A3527

Banyan — A3528

Trident
Maple — A3529

Azalea — A3530

LITHOGRAPHED
Serpentine Die Cut 11x10¾ on 2 or 3 Sides
2012, Jan. 23
Booklet Stamps
Self-Adhesive

4618	A3526	(45c) multicolored	2.00	.40
4619	A3527	(45c) multicolored	2.00	.40
4620	A3528	(45c) multicolored	2.00	.40
4621	A3529	(45c) multicolored	2.00	.40
4622	A3530	(45c) multicolored	2.00	.40
a.		Vert. strip of 5, #4618-4622	10.00	
b.		Booklet pane of 20, 4 each #4618-4622	40.00	

Stamps in No. 4622a are not adjacent, as
rows of selvage are between stamps two and
three, and between stamps four and five.

No. 4622b is a double-sided booklet with 12
stamps on one side (3 each #4618, 4621, 2
each #4619, 4620, 4622) and eight stamps
(#4618, 4621, 2 each #4619, 4620, 4622) plus
label that serves as a booklet cover on the
other side.

CHINESE NEW YEAR

Year of the
Dragon
A3531

PHOTOGRAVURE
Serpentine Die Cut 11x10¾
2012, Jan. 23
Self-Adhesive

4623 A3531 (45c) multicolored 1.15 .25

BLACK HERITAGE

John H. Johnson
(1918-2005),
Magazine
Publisher — A3532

LITHOGRAPHED
Serpentine Die Cut 10¾
2012, Jan. 31
Self-Adhesive

4624 A3532 (45c) multicolored 1.10 .25

HEART HEALTH

Tree, Man, Sun and
Apple — A3533

PHOTOGRAVURE
Serpentine Die Cut 11
2012, Feb. 9
Self-Adhesive

4625	A3533	(45c) multicolored	1.10	.25

LOVE

Ribbons
A3534

LITHOGRAPHED
Serpentine Die Cut 10¾
2012, Feb. 14
Self-Adhesive

4626	A3534	(45c) red	1.10	.25
a.	Die cutting omitted, pair		—	

Postal Service officials declared on Feb. 2 that No. 4626 could be sold in post offices as of that date to make the stamp available to customers before St. Valentine's Day, but the first day ceremony for the stamp was held Feb. 14 in Colorado Springs, CO. Official first day covers have that date and city.

ARIZONA STATEHOOD CENTENNIAL

Cathedral
Rock
A3535

PHOTOGRAVURE
Serpentine Die Cut 11
2012, Feb. 14
Self-Adhesive

4627	A3535	(45c) multicolored	1.10	.25

DANNY THOMAS

Thomas (1912-91), Comedian, and St. Jude's Children's Research Hospital, Memphis
A3536

LITHOGRAPHED
Serpentine Die Cut 10¾x10½
2012, Feb. 16
Self-Adhesive

4628	A3536	(45c) multicolored	1.10	.25

Flag and   Flag and
"Equality"   "Justice"
A3537   A3538

 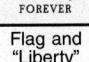

Flag and   Flag and
"Freedom"   "Liberty"
A3539   A3540

PHOTOGRAVURE
Serpentine Die Cut 8½ Vert.
2012, Feb. 22
Coil Stamps
Self-Adhesive

4629	A3537	(45c) multicolored	1.50	.25
4630	A3538	(45c) multicolored	1.50	.25
4631	A3539	(45c) multicolored	1.50	.25
4632	A3540	(45c) multicolored	1.50	.25
a.	Strip of 4, #4629-4632		6.00	

LITHOGRAPHED (#4633-4648)
Serpentine Die Cut 9½ Vert.

4633	A3537	(45c) multicolored	1.10	.25
4634	A3538	(45c) multicolored	1.10	.25
4635	A3539	(45c) multicolored	1.10	.25
4636	A3540	(45c) multicolored	1.10	.25
b.	Strip of 4, #4633-4636		4.40	

Serpentine Die Cut 11 Vert.

4637	A3537	(45c) multicolored	1.50	.25
4638	A3538	(45c) multicolored	1.50	.25
4639	A3539	(45c) multicolored	1.50	.25
4640	A3540	(45c) multicolored	1.50	.25
a.	Strip of 4, #4637-4640		6.00	
b.	As "a," die cutting omitted		450.00	
	Nos. 4629-4640 (12)		16.40	3.00

Booklet Stamps
Colored Dots in Stars
18½mm From Lower Left to Lower Right Corners of Flag
Serpentine Die Cut 11¼x10¾ on 2 or 3 Sides

4641	A3539	(45c) multicolored	1.25	.25
4642	A3540	(45c) multicolored	1.25	.25
4643	A3537	(45c) multicolored	1.25	.25
4644	A3538	(45c) multicolored	1.25	.25
b.	Block of 4, #4641-4644		5.00	
c.	Booklet pane of 20, 5 each #4641-4644		25.00	

Dark Dots Only in Stars
19mm from Lower Left to Lower Right Corners of Flag

4645	A3539	(45c) multicolored	1.50	.25
4646	A3540	(45c) multicolored	1.50	.25
4647	A3537	(45c) multicolored	1.50	.25
4648	A3538	(45c) multicolored	1.50	.25
a.	Block of 4, #4645-4648		6.00	
b.	Booklet pane of 20, 5 each #4645-4648		30.00	
	Nos. 4641-4648 (8)		11.00	2.00

On Nos. 4641-4644, the blue canton of the flag is made up of blue and red inks. The paper is tagged over each block of 4, with no tagging on the paper between the blocks. The tagging is a dull yellow green under ultraviolet light. The words are slightly longer than those on Nos. 4645-4648.

On Nos. 4645-4648, the blue canton is made up of blue and dull blue inks. The paper is prephosphored with the tagging appearing bright yellow green under ultraviolet light. The words are slightly shorter than those on Nos. 4641-4644.

No. 4644b is a double-sided booklet with 12 stamps on one side (3 each #4641-4644) and eight stamps (2 each #4641-4644) plus label that serves as a booklet cover on the other side.

No. 4648b is a double-sided booklet with 12 stamps on one side (3 each #4645-4648) and eight stamps (2 each #4645-4648) plus label that serves as a booklet cover on the other side.

See Nos. 4673-4676.

AMERICAN LANDMARKS ISSUE

Sunshine
Skyway
Bridge,
Florida
A3541

Carmel
Mission,
Carmel,
CA
A3542

LITHOGRAPHED
Serpentine Die Cut 10¾x10½
2012, Feb. 28
Self-Adhesive

4649	A3541	$5.15 multi	11.00	5.75
4650	A3542	$18.95 multi	42.50	19.00

CHERRY BLOSSOM CENTENNIAL

Cherry Blossoms and Washington
Monument — A3543

Cherry
Blossoms
and
Jefferson
Memorial
A3544

LITHOGRAPHED
Serpentine Die Cut 10¾
2012, Mar. 24   **Tagged**
Self-Adhesive

4651	A3543	(45c) multicolored	1.10	.25
4652	A3544	(45c) multicolored	1.10	.25
a.	Horiz. pair, #4651-4652		2.20	

See Japan No. 3413.

AMERICAN TREASURES SERIES

Flowers, by William
H. Johnson (1901-
70) — A3545

PHOTOGRAVURE
Serpentine Die Cut 10¾
2012, Apr. 11   **Tagged**
Self-Adhesive

4653	A3545	(45c) multicolored	1.15	.35

TWENTIETH CENTURY POETS

Joseph Brodsky
(1940-96)
A3546

Gwendolyn
Brooks (1917-
2000)
A3547

William Carlos
Williams (1883-
1963)
A3548

Robert Hayden
(1913-80)
A3549

Sylvia Plath
(1932-63)
A3550

Elizabeth
Bishop (1911-
79)
A3551

Wallace
Stevens (1879-
1955)
A3552

Denise Levertov
(1923-97)
A3553

E. E.
Cummings
(1894-1962)
A3554

Theodore
Roethke (1908-
63)
A3555

LITHOGRAPHED
Sheets of 160 in eight panes of 20
Serpentine Die Cut 10¾x11
2012, Apr. 21   **Tagged**
Self-Adhesive

4654	A3546	(45c) multicolored	2.00	.50
4655	A3547	(45c) multicolored	2.00	.50
4656	A3548	(45c) multicolored	2.00	.50
4657	A3549	(45c) multicolored	2.00	.50
4658	A3550	(45c) multicolored	2.00	.50
4659	A3551	(45c) multicolored	2.00	.50
4660	A3552	(45c) multicolored	2.00	.50
4661	A3553	(45c) multicolored	2.00	.50
4662	A3554	(45c) multicolored	2.00	.50
4663	A3555	(45c) multicolored	2.00	.50
a.	Block of 10, #4654-4663		20.00	
	Nos. 4654-4663 (10)		20.00	5.00

CIVIL WAR SESQUICENTENNIAL

Battle of New Orleans — A3556

Battle of Antietam — A3557

LITHOGRAPHED
Serpentine Die Cut 11
2012, Apr. 24   **Tagged**
Self-Adhesive

4664	A3556	(45c) multicolored	1.10	.30
4665	A3557	(45c) multicolored	1.10	.30
a.	Pair, #4664-4665		2.20	

DISTINGUISHED AMERICANS

José Ferrer (1912-92), Actor — A3558

LITHOGRAPHED
Serpentine Die Cut 10¾x11
2012, Apr. 26   **Tagged**
Self-Adhesive

4666 A3558 (45c) multicolored   1.10   .25

LOUISIANA STATEHOOD BICENTENNIAL

Sunset Over Flat Lake — A3559

PHOTOGRAVURE
Serpentine Die Cut 11
2012, Apr. 30   **Tagged**
Self-Adhesive

4667 A3559 (45c) multicolored   1.10   .25

GREAT FILM DIRECTORS

John Ford (1894-1973), Scene From *The Searchers,* Starring John Wayne — A3560

Frank Capra (1897-1991), Scene From *It Happened One Night,* Starring Clark Gable and Claudette Colbert — A3561

Billy Wilder (1906-2002), Scene From *Some Like It Hot,* Starring Marilyn Monroe — A3562

John Huston (1906-87), Scene From *The Maltese Falcon,* Starring Humphrey Bogart A3563

PHOTOGRAVURE
Serpentine Die Cut 10¾
2012, May 23
Self-Adhesive

4668	A3560	(45c) multicolored	1.10	.40
4669	A3561	(45c) multicolored	1.10	.40
4670	A3562	(45c) multicolored	1.10	.40
4671	A3563	(45c) multicolored	1.10	.40
a.	Block or horiz. strip of 4, #4668-4671		4.40	

WILDLIFE

Bobcat — A3564

LITHOGRAPHED
Serpentine Die Cut 10 Vert.
2012, June 1
Coil Stamp
Self-Adhesive

4672 A3564 1c multicolored   .25   .25
   a.   Dated "2015"   .25   .25

Issued: No. 4672a, 2/21/15. Microprinting is on bobcat's ear on No. 4672 and on the bobcat's leg on No. 4672a.
See No. 4802.

Flags Type of 2012
PHOTOGRAVURE
Serpentine Die Cut 11¼x10¾ on 3 Sides
2012, June 1   **Tagged**
Booklet Stamps
Self-Adhesive
Colored Dots in Stars
19¼mm From Lower Left to Lower Right Corners of Flag

4673	A3539	(45c) multicolored	1.10	.25
4674	A3540	(45c) multicolored	1.10	.25
4675	A3537	(45c) multicolored	1.10	.25
4676	A3538	(45c) multicolored	1.10	.25
a.	Block of 4, #4673-4676		4.40	
b.	Booklet pane of 10, 3 each #4673-4674, 2 each #4675-4676		11.00	

Nos. 4673 and No. 4675 have straight edge on left side only. Nos. 4674 and 4676 have straight edge on right side only. Nos. 4641-4648 each have a straight edge at top or bottom. The letters in the "USPS" microprinting on Nos. 4673-4676, found at the right side of the bottom white flag stripe, are printed in a distinct curve, with the tops of the middle letters, "SP," being below the tops of the outside letters, "U" and "S," and the letters can be difficult to distinguish against the shading on the stripe. The letters in the microprinting on Nos. 4641-4648, found in the same place on the stamp, are printed in a straight line, and are printed boldly, making them easily distinguishable from the shading. The lettering on Nos. 4673-4767 has a fuzzier, less distinct appearance under magnification than the lettering on Nos. 4641-4648, which is most evident in the year "2012."

CHARACTERS FROM DISNEY-PIXAR FILMS
Mail a Smile

Flik and Dot From *A Bug's Life* — A3565

Bob Parr and Dashiell Parr From *The Incredibles* A3566

Nemo and Squirt From *Finding Nemo* — A3567

Jessie, Woody and Bullseye From *Toy Story 2* — A3568

Boo, Mike Wazowski and James P. "Sulley" Sullivan From *Monsters, Inc.* — A3569

PHOTOGRAVURE
Serpentine Die Cut 10½
2012, June 1
Self-Adhesive

4677	A3565	(45c) multicolored	1.20	.40
4678	A3566	(45c) multicolored	1.20	.40
4679	A3567	(45c) multicolored	1.20	.40
4680	A3568	(45c) multicolored	1.20	.40
4681	A3569	(45c) multicolored	1.20	.40
a.	Horiz. strip of 5, #4677-4681		6.00	

Adjacent horizontal or vertical stamps will have selvage between the stamps.

Aloha Shirts Type of 2012
LITHOGRAPHED
Tagged
Serpentine Die Cut 11¼x10¾ on 3 Sides
2012, June 2
Booklet Stamps
Self-Adhesive

4682	A3506	32c multicolored	6.00	.30
4683	A3508	32c multicolored	6.00	.30
4684	A3510	32c multicolored	6.00	.30
4685	A3507	32c multicolored	6.00	.30
4686	A3509	32c multicolored	6.00	.30
a.	Vert. strip of 5, #4682-4686		30.00	
b.	Booklet pane of 10, 2 each #4682-4686		60.00	

Stamps in No. 4686a are not adjacent, as a row of selvage is between stamps two and three.
See Nos. 4592-4601.

BICYCLING

Child on Bicycle with Training Wheels A3570

Commuter on Bicycle with Panniers A3571

Road Racer A3572

BMX Rider A3573

LITHOGRAPHED
Serpentine Die Cut 10¾
2012, June 7
Self-Adhesive

4687	A3570	(45c) multicolored	1.10	.35
4688	A3571	(45c) multicolored	1.10	.35
4689	A3572	(45c) multicolored	1.10	.35
4690	A3573	(45c) multicolored	1.10	.35
a.	Horiz. strip of 4, #4687-4690		4.40	

GIRL SCOUTS OF AMERICA, CENT.

Girl Scouts — A3574

LITHOGRAPHED
Serpentine Die Cut 10¾
2012, June 9
Self-Adhesive

4691 A3574 (45c) multicolored   1.10   .25
   a.   Die cutting omitted, pair   —

MUSICIANS

Edith Piaf (1915-63), Singer — A3575

Miles Davis (1926-91), Jazz Trumpet Player — A3576

PHOTOGRAVURE
Serpentine Die Cut 10¾x11
2012, June 12
Self-Adhesive

4692	A3575	(45c) multicolored	1.20	.30
4693	A3576	(45c) multicolored	1.20	.30
a.	Pair, #4692-4693		2.40	

See France Nos. 4256-4257.

Imperforate Uncut Press Sheets Beginning with Nos. 4694-4697, the United States Postal Service made available for sale imperforate uncut press sheets of selected commemorative and definitive issues. These sheets, along with their corresponding multiples, are described and valued in footnotes following each issue in the Scott *Specialized Catalogue of United States Stamps and Covers.* For descriptions and illustrations of typical press-sheet multiples, see the note after No. 2868 in the Scott U.S. Specialized catalogue.

MAJOR LEAGUE BASEBALL ALL-STARS

Ted Williams (1918-2002) — A3577

Larry Doby (1923-2003) — A3578

Willie Stargell (1940-2001) — A3579

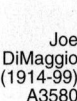

Joe DiMaggio (1914-99) A3580

PHOTOGRAVURE
Serpentine Die Cut 10¾x11
2012, July 20
Self-Adhesive

4694	A3577	(45c) multicolored	1.10	.30
a.		Imperforate	2.50	
4695	A3578	(45c) multicolored	1.10	.30
a.		Imperforate	2.50	
4696	A3579	(45c) multicolored	1.10	.30
a.		Imperforate	2.50	
4697	A3580	(45c) multicolored	1.10	.30
a.		Imperforate	2.50	
b.		Horiz. strip or block of 4, #4694-4697	4.40	
c.		Imperf. horiz. strip or block of 4, #4694a-4697a	14.00	—

Panes containing 20 of the same stamp were issued on July 21 in Boston, MA (for No. 4694), Cleveland, OH (for No. 4695), Pittsburgh, PA (for No. 4696) and New York, NY (for No. 4697).

INNOVATIVE CHOREOGRAPHERS

Isadora Duncan (1877-1927) A3581

José Limón (1908-72) A3582

Katherine Dunham (1909-2006) A3583

Bob Fosse (1927-87) A3584

LITHOGRAPHED
Serpentine Die Cut 10¾x11
2012, July 28
Self-Adhesive

4698	A3581	(45c) multicolored	1.10	.35
4699	A3582	(45c) multicolored	1.10	.35
4700	A3583	(45c) multicolored	1.10	.35
4701	A3584	(45c) multicolored	1.10	.35
a.		Vert. strip of 4, #4698-4701	4.40	

EDGAR RICE BURROUGHS

Edgar Rice Burroughs (1875-1950), Writer, and Tarzan — A3585

LITHOGRAPHED
Serpentine Die Cut 10¾
2012, Aug. 17
Self-Adhesive

4702	A3585	(45c) multicolored	1.10	.25

WAR OF 1812 BICENTENNIAL

Painting of U.S.S. Constitution, by Michele Felice Corné — A3586

PHOTOGRAVURE
Serpentine Die Cut 10¾x10½
2012, Aug. 18
Self-Adhesive

4703	A3586	(45c) multicolored	1.75	.25
a.		Imperforate	2.75	

Purple Heart and Ribbon

Purple Heart and Ribbon — A3587

PHOTOGRAVURE
2012, Sept. 4 *Serpentine Die Cut 11*
Self-Adhesive

4704	A3587	(45c) multicolored	1.10	.25
a.		Imperforate	2.50	
b.		Dated "2014"	1.10	.25

Compare with Type A3458.

LITERARY ARTS

O. Henry (William S. Porter) (1862-1910), New York City Buildings and Elevated Trains — A3588

PHOTOGRAVURE
Serpentine Die Cut 11
2012, Sept. 11
Self-Adhesive

4705	A3588	(45c) multicolored	1.10	.25

Flags Type of 2012
LITHOGRAPHED
Serpentine Die Cut 11¼x10¾ on 2, 3 or 4 Sides
2012, Sept. 22
Booklet Stamps
Self-Adhesive
Colored Dots in Stars
18½mm From Lower Left to Lower Right Corners of Flag
Thin Paper

4706	A3539	(45c) multicolored	1.10	.25
4707	A3540	(45c) multicolored	1.10	.25
4708	A3537	(45c) multicolored	1.10	.25
4709	A3538	(45c) multicolored	1.10	.25
a.		Block or strip of 4, #4706-4709	4.40	
b.		Booklet pane of 18, 5 each #4706-4707, 4 each #4708-4709	20.00	
		Nos. 4706-4709 (4)	4.40	1.00

The overall-tagged paper used for Nos. 4706-4709 is glossier than that used on Nos. 4641-4644.The blue canton of the flag on Nos. 4706-4709 is made up of blue and red inks, similar to Nos. 4641-4644.

EARTHSCAPES

A3589

No. 4710: a, Glacier and icebergs. b, Volcanic crater. c, Geothermal spring. d, Butte in early morning fog. e, Inland marsh. f, Salt evaporation ponds. g, Log rafts on way to sawmill. h, Center-pivot irrigation. i, Cherry orchard. j, Cranberry harvest. k, Residential subdivision. l, Barge fleeting. m, Railroad roundhouse. n, Skyscraper apartments. o, Highway interchange.

LITHOGRAPHED
Serpentine Die Cut 10¾
2012, Oct. 1
Self-Adhesive

4710	A3589	Pane of 15	25.00	
a.-o.		(45c) Any single	1.65	.50
p.		Imperforate pane of 15	75.00	

CHRISTMAS

Holy Family and Donkey A3590

Reindeer in Flight, Moon A3591

Santa Claus and Sleigh — A3592

Reindeer Over Roof — A3593

Snow-covered Buildings A3594

LITHOGRAPHED
Serpentine Die Cut 11 on 2 or 3 Sides
2012
Booklet Stamps
Self-Adhesive

4711	A3590	(45c) multi	1.10	.25
a.		Booklet pane of 20	22.00	
b.		Imperforate	1.75	—
c.		Imperforate booklet pane of 20	35.00	

Serpentine Die Cut 11x10¾ on 2 or 3 sides

4712	A3591	(45c) multi	1.50	.25
4713	A3592	(45c) multi	1.50	.25
4714	A3593	(45c) multi	1.50	.25
4715	A3594	(45c) multi	1.50	.25
a.		Block of 4, #4712-4715	6.00	
b.		Booklet pane of 20, 5 each #4712-4715	30.00	
c.		Imperforate block of 4	8.00	
d.		Imperforate booklet pane of 20	40.00	
		Nos. 4711-4715 (5)	4.50	1.25

Issued: No. 4711, Oct. 10, Nos. 4712-4715, Oct. 13.

No. 4711a is a double-sided booklet with 12 stamps on one side plus a label that serves as a booklet cover on the other side. No. 4715b is a double-sided booklet with 12 stamps on one side (3 each of Nos. 4712-4715) and eight stamps (2 each of Nos. 4712-4715) plus a label that serves as a booklet cover on the other side.

See No. 4813.

LADY BIRD JOHNSON

A3595

No. 4716: a, Blooming crab apples lining avenue (Plant for more Beautiful Streets). b, Washington Monument, Potomac River and daffodils (Plant for more Beautiful Parks). c, Jefferson Memorial, Tidal Basin and cherry blossoms (Plant for a more Beautiful America). d, Poppies and lupines along highway (Plant for more Beautiful Highways). e, Capitol, azaleas and tulips (Plant for more Beautiful Cities). f, Lady Bird Johnson (1912-2007), First Lady, vert.

LITHOGRAPHED
Serpentine Die Cut 10¾
2012, Nov. 30
Self-Adhesive

4716	A3595	Pane of 6	6.60	
a.-f.		(45c) Any single	1.10	.40
g.		Imperforate pane of 6	25.00	

WAVES OF COLOR

A3596

A3597

A3598

A3599

LITHOGRAPHED & ENGRAVED
Serpentine Die Cut 11, 10¾ (#4719)
2012, Dec. 1
Self-Adhesive

4717	A3596	$1 multi	4.50	.50
4718	A3597	$2 multi	4.50	1.25
4719	A3598	$5 multi	8.75	2.50
4720	A3599	$10 multi	17.50	9.00
		Nos. 4717-4720 (4)	35.25	13.25

Adjacent horizontal or vertical stamps have selvage between the stamps. Plate blocks have sheet margins on the top or bottom and both sides.

EMANCIPATION PROCLAMATION, 150th ANNIV.

A3600

PHOTOGRAVURE

2013, Jan. 1   *Serpentine Die Cut 11*

Self-Adhesive

4721	A3600	(45c) multicolored	1.10	.25
a.		Imperforate	2.00	—

KALEIDOSCOPE FLOWERS

A3601   A3602

A3603   A3604

LITHOGRAPHED
Serpentine Die Cut 11 Vert.

2013, Jan. 14

Coil Stamps
Self-Adhesive
Color of Large Outer Leaves

4722	A3601	46c yellow orange	1.25	.25
4723	A3602	46c yellow green	1.25	.25
4724	A3603	46c red violet	1.25	.25
4725	A3604	46c red	1.25	.25
a.		Strip of 4, #4722-4725	5.00	
		Nos. 4722-4725 (4)	5.00	1.00

CHINESE NEW YEAR

Year of the
Snake
A3605

PHOTOGRAVURE
Serpentine Die Cut 11

2013, Jan. 16

Self-Adhesive

4726	A3605	(45c) multicolored	1.10	.25
a.		Imperforate	2.00	—

APPLES

Northern Spy   Golden
Apple   Delicious
A3606   Apple
                            A3607

Granny Smith   Baldwin Apple
Apple   A3609
A3608

LITHOGRAPHED
Serpentine Die Cut 11¼x10¾

2013, Jan. 17

Self-Adhesive

4727	A3606	33c multicolored	1.25	.25
4728	A3607	33c multicolored	1.25	.25
4729	A3608	33c multicolored	1.25	.25
4730	A3609	33c multicolored	1.25	.25
a.		Block or strip of 4, #4727-4730	5.00	
b.		Imperforate block or strip of 4	6.50	—

Coil Stamps
Serpentine Die Cut 11 Vert.

4731	A3609	33c multicolored	1.50	.25
4732	A3606	33c multicolored	1.50	.25
4733	A3607	33c multicolored	1.50	.25
4734	A3608	33c multicolored	1.50	.25
a.		Strip of 4, #4731-4734	6.00	
		Nos. 4727-4734 (8)	11.00	2.00

Wedding Cake Type of 2009
LITHOGRAPHED
Serpentine Die Cut 10¾

2013, Jan. 18

Self-Adhesive

4735	A3344	66c multicolored	1.40	.25
a.		Imperforate	3.50	—

See Nos. 4398, 4521, 4602, 4867, 5000.

SPICEBUSH SWALLOWTAIL BUTTERFLY

A3610

PHOTOGRAVURE
Serpentine Die Cut 10¾

2013, Jan. 23

Self-Adhesive

4736	A3610	66c multicolored	1.40	.25
a.		Imperforate	3.00	—

TUFTED PUFFINS

A3611

LITHOGRAPHED
Serpentine Die Cut 11¼x10¾

2013, Jan. 23
"2013" in Orange Red
Solid Color in "Tufted Puffins" and "86"

Self-Adhesive

4737	A3611	86c multicolored	1.80	.35
b.		Imperforate	4.00	—

"2013" in Black
With Dots in "Tufted Puffins" and "86"

4737A	A3611	86c multi	2.50	.35

AMERICAN LANDMARKS ISSUE

Arlington
Green
Bridge,
Vermont
A3612

Grand
Central
Terminal,
New York
City
A3613

PHOTOGRAVURE

2013   *Serpentine Die Cut 10¾x10½*

4738	A3612	$5.60 multi	11.00	6.25
4739	A3613	$19.95 multi	40.00	21.00

Earth
A3614

PHOTOGRAVURE

2013, Jan. 28   *Serpentine Die Cut*

Self-Adhesive

4740	A3614	($1.10) multi	2.25	.50
a.		Imperforate	5.00	—

Unused values are for stamps with surrounding selvage. Adjacent stamps are separated by rouletting.

LOVE

Envelope With
Wax
Seal — A3615

PHOTOGRAVURE
Serpentine Die Cut 10¾

2013, Jan. 30

Self-Adhesive

4741	A3615	(46c) multicolored	1.10	.25
a.		Imperforate	2.00	—

ROSA PARKS

Parks (1913-2005),
Civil Rights
Pioneer — A3616

PHOTOGRAVURE
Serpentine Die Cut 10¾

2013, Feb. 4

Self-Adhesive

4742	A3616	(46c) multicolored	1.10	.25
a.		Imperforate	2.00	—

MUSCLE CARS

1969
Dodge
Charger
Daytona
A3617

1966
Pontiac
GTO
A3618

1967 Ford
Mustang
Shelby GT
500
A3619

1970
Chevrolet
Chevelle
SS
A3620

1970
Plymouth
Hemi
Barracuda
A3621

PHOTOGRAVURE
Serpentine Die Cut 10¾

2013, Feb. 22   Tagged

Self-Adhesive

4743	A3617	(46c) multicolored	1.10	.30
4744	A3618	(46c) multicolored	1.10	.30
4745	A3619	(46c) multicolored	1.10	.30
4746	A3620	(46c) multicolored	1.10	.30
4747	A3621	(46c) multicolored	1.10	.30
a.		Vert. strip of 5, #4743-4747	5.50	
		Vert. P# block of 10, 5# + V	11.00	
		Horiz. P# block of 8, 2 sets of 5# + V	8.80	
b.		Imperforate vert. strip of 5	10.00	—
		Nos. 4743-4747 (5)	5.50	1.50

MODERN ART IN AMERICA

A3622

No. 4748: a, I Saw the Figure 5 in Gold, by Charles Demuth (37x51mm). b, Sunset, Maine Coast, by John Marin (43x43mm). c, House and Street, by Stuart Davis (51x41mm). d, Painting, Number 5, by Marsden Hartley (37x51mm). e, Black Mesa Landscape, New Mexico/Out Back of Marie's II, by Georgia O'Keeffe (51x41mm). f, Noire et Blanche, by Man Ray (43x41mm). g, The Prodigal Son, by Aaron Douglas (34x51mm). h, American Landscape, by Charles Sheeler (43x41mm). i, Brooklyn Bridge, by Joseph Stella (38x47mm). j, Razor, by Gerald Murphy (43x43mm). k, Nude Descending a Staircase, No. 2, by Marcel Duchamp (34x58mm). l, Fog Horns, by Arthur Dove (43x37mm).

PHOTOGRAVURE
Serpentine Die Cut 10½

2013, Mar. 7

Self-Adhesive

4748	A3622	Pane of 12	13.25	
a.-l.		(46c) Any single	1.10	.50
m.		Imperforate pane of 12	70.00	—

Armory Show, cent.

Patriotic Star — A3623

LITHOGRAPHED
Serpentine Die Cut 10¾ Vert.

2013, Mar. 19

Coil Stamp
Self-Adhesive

4749	A3623	46c multicolored	1.10	.25

LA FLORIDA

A3624   A3625

A3626   A3627

PHOTOGRAVURE
Serpentine Die Cut 10½
2013, Apr. 3
Self-Adhesive

4750	A3624	(46c) multicolored	1.25	.25
4751	A3625	(46c) multicolored	1.25	.25
4752	A3626	(46c) multicolored	1.25	.25
4753	A3627	(46c) multicolored	1.25	.25
a.	Block of 4, #4750-4753		5.00	
b.	Imperforate block of 4		10.00	
	Nos. 4750-4753 (4)		5.00	1.00

Naming of Florida, 500th anniv.

VINTAGE SEED PACKETS

Phlox   Calendula
A3628   A3629

Digitalis   Linum
A3630   A3631

Alyssum   Zinnias
A3632   A3633

Pinks   Cosmos
A3634   A3635

Aster   Primrose
A3636   A3637

PHOTOGRAVURE
Serpentine Die Cut 10¾ on 2 or 3 Sides
2013, Apr. 5
Booklet Stamps
Self-Adhesive

4754	A3628	(46c) multicolored	2.50	.25
4755	A3629	(46c) multicolored	2.50	.25
4756	A3630	(46c) multicolored	2.50	.25
4757	A3631	(46c) multicolored	2.50	.25
4758	A3632	(46c) multicolored	2.50	.25
4759	A3633	(46c) multicolored	2.50	.25
4760	A3634	(46c) multicolored	2.50	.25
4761	A3635	(46c) multicolored	2.50	.25
4762	A3636	(46c) multicolored	2.50	.25
4763	A3637	(46c) multicolored	2.50	.25
a.	Block of 10, #4754-4763		25.00	
b.	Booklet pane of 20, 2 each #4754-4763		50.00	
	Nos. 4754-4763 (10)		25.00	2.50

No. 4763b is a double-sided booklet pane with 12 stamps on one side (2 each #4754, 4759, 1 each #4755-4758, 4760-4763), and eight stamps (1 each #4755-4758, 4760-4763) plus label (booklet cover) on the other side.

WEDDING FLOWERS

Flowers — A3638

Flowers and "Yes I Do" A3639

LITHOGRAPHED
Serpentine Die Cut 10¾
2013, Apr. 11
Self-Adhesive

4764	A3638	(46c) multicolored	1.10	.25
a.	Dated "2014"		1.10	
b.	Imperforate		2.50	—
4765	A3639	66c multicolored	1.40	.30
a.	Imperforate		3.00	

Flag in Autumn   Flag in Winter
A3640   A3641

Flag in Spring   Flag in Summer
A3642   A3643

PHOTOGRAVURE
2013 *Serpentine Die Cut 8½ Vert.*
Coil Stamps
Self-Adhesive

4766	A3640	(46c) multicolored	2.25	.25
4767	A3641	(46c) multicolored	2.25	.25
4768	A3642	(46c) multicolored	2.25	.25
4769	A3643	(46c) multicolored	2.25	.25
a.	Strip of 4, #4766-4769		9.00	

LITHOGRAPHED (#4770-4785)
Serpentine Die Cut 9½ Vert.

4770	A3640	(46c) multicolored	2.25	.25
4771	A3641	(46c) multicolored	2.25	.25
4772	A3642	(46c) multicolored	2.25	.25
4773	A3643	(46c) multicolored	2.25	.25
a.	Strip of 4, #4770-4773		9.00	

Serpentine Die Cut 11 Vert.

4774	A3641	(46c) multicolored	3.00	.25
4775	A3642	(46c) multicolored	3.00	.25
4776	A3643	(46c) multicolored	3.00	.25
4777	A3640	(46c) multicolored	3.00	.25
a.	Strip of 4, #4774-4777		12.00	
b.	Block of 28 (4x7), #4774-4777, with no horiz. slits		—	
	Nos. 4766-4777 (12)		30.00	3.00

Booklet Stamps
With Microprinted "USPS" at Lower Left Corner of Flag
Serpentine Die Cut 11¼x10¾ on 2 or 3 Sides

4778	A3642	(46c) multicolored	1.25	.25
4779	A3643	(46c) multicolored	1.25	.25
4780	A3640	(46c) multicolored	1.25	.25
4781	A3641	(46c) multicolored	1.25	.25
a.	Block of 4, #4778-4781		6.00	
b.	Booklet pane of 20, 5 each #4778-4781		30.00	

With Microprinted "USPS" Near Top of Pole or at Lower Left Corner Near Rope (#4783, 4783b)
Pre-phosphored Paper

4782	A3642	(46c) multicolored	1.10	.25
b.	As #4782, dated "2014"		1.10	
4783	A3643	(46c) multicolored	1.10	.25
b.	As #4783, dated "2014"		1.10	
4784	A3640	(46c) multicolored	1.10	.25
b.	As #4784, dated "2014"		1.10	
c.	Tagging omitted		30.00	
4785	A3641	(46c) multicolored	1.10	.25
b.	As #4785, dated "2014"		1.10	
c.	Block of 4, #4782-4785		4.40	
d.	Booklet pane of 20, 5 each #4782-4785		22.00	
f.	Booklet pane of 10, 3 each #4782a, 4783a, 2 each #4784a, 4785a		11.00	
g.	Block of 4, #4782b, 4783b, 4784b, 4785b		4.40	
h.	Booklet pane of 20, 5 each #4782b, 4783b, 4784b, 4785b		22.00	
i.	As "h," die cutting omitted on side with 8 stamps and 3 pairs on side with 12 stamps		—	
	Nos. 4778-4785 (8)		9.40	2.00

Issued: Nos. 4766-4777, 5/3; Nos. 4778-4785, 5/17. No. 4781b is a double-sided booklet with 12 stamps on one side (3 each #4778-4781) and eight stamps (2 each #4778-4781) plus label that serves as a booklet cover on the other side.

No. 4785c is a double-sided booklet with 12 stamps on one side (3 each #4782-4785) and eight stamps (2 each #4782-4785) plus label that serves as a booklet cover on the other side.

A microprinted "USPS" is found on tree trunk to the left of the "F" in "Forever" on No. 4766, on tree trunk near lower left corner of flag on No. 4767, on white flag stripe at lower right on No. 4768, and on the top of the flagpole below the ball on No. 4769. Nos. 4770-4773 are microprinted "USPS" in the same places as on Nos. 4778-4781. Nos. 4774-4777 are microprinted "USPS" in the same places as on Nos. 4782-4785.

No. 4785e comprises stamps printed on paper with overall tagging. For detailed listings, see the *Scott Specialized Catalogue of United States Stamps and Covers.*

See Nos. 4796-4799.

Issued: Nos. 4782b, 4783b, 4784b, 4785b, 3/17/14. Nos. 4782b, 4783b, 4784b and 4785b each sold for 49c on day of issue.

MUSIC ICONS

Lydia Mendoza (1916-2007), Tejano Music Recording Artist — A3644

PHOTOGRAVURE
Serpentine Die Cut 10¾
2013, May 15
Self-Adhesive

4786	A3644	(46c) multicolored	1.10	.25
a.	Imperforate		1.75	—

Adjacent horizontal or vertical stamps have selvage between the stamps.

CIVIL WAR SESQUICENTENNIAL

Battle of Vicksburg — A3645

Battle of Gettysburg — A3646

LITHOGRAPHED
2013, May 23 *Serpentine Die Cut 11*
Self-Adhesive

4787	A3645	(46c) multicolored	1.10	.30
4788	A3646	(46c) multicolored	1.10	.30
a.	Pair, #4787-4788		2.20	
b.	Imperforate pair, #4787-4788		5.50	—

MUSIC ICONS

Johnny Cash (1932-2003), Country Music Recording Artist — A3647

PHOTOGRAVURE
Serpentine Die Cut 10¾
2013, June 5
Self-Adhesive

4789	A3647	(46c) multicolored	1.10	.25
a.	Imperforate		1.75	

WEST VIRGINIA STATEHOOD, 150th ANNIV.

Hills in Monongahela National Forest — A3648

PHOTOGRAVURE
Serpentine Die Cut 11
2013, June 20
Self-Adhesive

4790	A3648	(46c) multicolored	1.10	.25
a.	Imperforate		1.75	

NEW ENGLAND COASTAL LIGHTHOUSES

Portland Head Lighthouse, Maine A3649   Portsmouth Harbor Lighthouse, New Hampshire A3650

Boston Harbor Lighthouse, Massachusetts A3651   Point Judith Lighthouse, Rhode Island A3652

New London Harbor Lighthouse, Connecticut A3653

Original

"FOREVER" and "USA" 1mm higher than original

LITHOGRAPHED
Serpentine Die Cut 11x10¾
2013, July 13
Self-Adhesive

4791	A3649 (46c) multicolored		1.10	.40
a.	"FOREVER" and "USA" 1mm higher than normal (pos. 1)		2.00	1.00
b.	Horiz. strip of 5, #4791a, 4792-4795		6.50	
4792	A3650 (46c) multicolored		1.10	.40
4793	A3651 (46c) multicolored		1.10	.40
4794	A3652 (46c) multicolored		1.10	.40
4795	A3653 (46c) multicolored		1.10	.40
a.	Horiz. strip of 5, #4791-4795		5.50	
b.	Imperforate horiz. strip of 5		11.00	—
c.	Imperforate horiz. strip of 5, pos. 1 as No. 4791a		13.00	—
	Nos. 4791-4795 (5)		5.50	2.00

Flag Types of 2013
PHOTOGRAVURE
Serpentine Die Cut 11¼x11½ on 2 or 3 Sides
2013, Aug. 8
Booklet Stamps
Self-Adhesive

4796	A3642 (46c) multicolored		1.50	.25
4797	A3643 (46c) multicolored		1.50	.25
4798	A3640 (46c) multicolored		1.50	.25
4799	A3641 (46c) multicolored		1.50	.25
a.	Block of 4, #4796-4799		6.00	
b.	Booklet pane of 20, 5 each #4796-4799		30.00	
	Nos. 4796-4799 (4)		6.00	1.00

No. 4799b is a double-sided booklet with 12 stamps on one side (3 each #4796-4799) and eight stamps (2 each #4796-4799) plus label that serves as a booklet cover on the other side. Nos. 4796-4799 are microprinted "USPS" in the same places as Nos. 4766-4769.

EID

"Eid Mubarak" — A3654

LITHOGRAPHED
2013, Aug. 8   *Serpentine Die Cut 11*
Self-Adhesive

4800	A3654 (46c) dk grn, gray & gold		1.10	.25
a.	Imperforate		2.00	—

BUILDING A NATION

Airplane Mechanic, Photograph by Lewis Hine — A3655

Derrick Man on Empire State Building, Photograph by Lewis Hine — A3656

Millinery Apprentice, Photograph by Lewis Hine — A3657

Man on Hoisting Ball on Empire State Building, Photograph by Lewis Hine — A3658

Linotype Operator, Photograph by Lewis Hine — A3659

Welder on Empire State Building, Photograph by Lewis Hine — A3660

Coal Miner, by Anonymous Photographer A3661

Riveters on Empire State Building, Photograph by Lewis Hine — A3662

Powerhouse Mechanic, Photograph by Lewis Hine — A3663

Railroad Track Walker, Photograph by Lewis Hine — A3664

Textile Worker, Photograph by Lewis Hine — A3665

Man Guiding Beam on Empire State Building, Photograph by Lewis Hine — A3666

PHOTOGRAVURE
Serpentine Die Cut 10½x10¾
2013, Aug. 8
Self-Adhesive

4801	Pane of 12		15.00	
a.	A3655 (46c) black & gray		1.25	.50
b.	A3656 (46c) black & gray		1.25	.50
c.	A3657 (46c) black & gray		1.25	.50
d.	A3658 (46c) black & gray		1.25	.50
e.	A3659 (46c) black & gray		1.25	.50
f.	A3660 (46c) black & gray		1.25	.50
g.	A3661 (46c) black & gray		1.25	.50
h.	A3662 (46c) black & gray		1.25	.50
i.	A3663 (46c) black & gray		1.25	.50
j.	A3664 (46c) black & gray		1.25	.50
k.	A3665 (46c) black & gray		1.25	.50
l.	A3666 (46c) black & gray		1.25	.50
m.	Imperforate pane of 12		70.00	

No. 4801 was printed with five different sheet margins depicting coal miner from No. 4801g, man on hoisting ball on Empire State Building, man measuring bearings in large gearwheel, man on cable at Empire State Building, and woman welder. Value is for sheet with any margin.

Bobcat Type of 2012
LITHOGRAPHED
2013, Aug. 9   *Perf. 9¾ Vert.*
Coil Stamp

4802	A3564 1c multicolored		.25	.25
	See No. 4672.			

BLACK HERITAGE

Althea Gibson (1927-2003), Tennis Player — A3667

PHOTOGRAVURE
Serpentine Die Cut 11
2013, Aug. 23
Self-Adhesive

4803	A3667 (46c) multicolored		1.25	.25
a.	Imperforate		1.75	—

MARCH ON WASHINGTON, 50th ANNIV.

Marchers and Washington Monument — A3668

PHOTOGRAVURE
Serpentine Die Cut 10¾
2013, Aug. 23
Self-Adhesive

4804	A3668 (46c) multicolored		1.10	.25
a.	Imperforate		1.75	—

WAR OF 1812 BICENTENNIAL

Painting of Battle of Lake Erie, by William Henry Powell A3669

LITHOGRAPHED
Serpentine Die Cut 10¾
2013, Sept. 10
Self-Adhesive

4805	A3669 (46c) multicolored		1.10	.25
a.	Imperforate		1.75	—

INVERTED JENNY
Miniature Sheet

A3670

LITHOGRAPHED & ENGRAVED
Serpentine Die Cut 10½x11¼
2013, Sept. 22
Self-Adhesive

4806	A3670 multicolored		24.00	
a.	$2 Single stamp		4.00	1.25
b.	Imperforate pane of 6		72.50	
c.	As "b," single stamp		12.00	
d.	Pane of 6, airplane right-side up		70,000.	
e.	As "d," single stamp		13,500.	

No. 4806, along with a piece of white cardboard backing, was placed in a sealed envelope. The envelope, along with a piece of gray cardboard backing, was inside a sealed plastic outerwrap. One hundred panes were produced that contain the airplane right-side up. These panes were included in the same envelope and outerwrap and were distributed randomly. No returns or refunds were offered for any opened packages. Values for No. 4806 are for panes removed from the envelope.

A book containing an unused and a first-day canceled example of No. 4806, along with items that are termed "proofs" and "die wipes" sold for $200.

MUSIC ICONS

Ray Charles (1930-2004), Recording Artist — A3671

LITHOGRAPHED
Serpentine Die Cut 10½
2013, Sept. 23
Self-Adhesive

4807	A3671	(46c) multicolored	1.10	.25
a.		Imperforate	1.75	—

Adjacent horizontal or vertical stamps have selvage between the stamps.

SNOWFLAKES

A3672   A3673

A3674   A3675

A3676

PHOTOGRAVURE
Serpentine Die Cut 11 Vert.
2013, Oct. 1
Coil Stamps
Self-Adhesive

4808	A3672	(10c) lt bl & multi	.25	.25
4809	A3673	(10c) pale bl & multi	.25	.25
4810	A3674	(10c) lt bl & multi	.25	.25
4811	A3675	(10c) pale bl & multi	.25	.25
4812	A3676	(10c) lil & multi	.25	.25
a.		Strip of 5, #4808-4812	1.25	
		Nos. 4808-4812 (5)	1.25	1.25

Holy Family and Donkey Type of 2012 Dated "2013" and

Wreath
A3677

Virgin and Child, by Jan Gossaert
A3678

Poinsettia
A3679

Gingerbread House With Red Door — A3680

Gingerbread House With Blue Door — A3681

Gingerbread House With Green Door — A3682

Gingerbread House With Orange Door — A3683

Poinsettia — A3684

LITHOGRAPHED, PHOTOGRAVURE (#4821)

2013   *Serpentine Die Cut 11*
Self-Adhesive

4813	A3590	(46c) multicolored	1.10	.25
a.		Imperforate	1.75	

Serpentine Die Cut

4814	A3677	($1.10) multicolored	2.25	.50
a.		Imperforate	4.00	

Booklet Stamps
Serpentine Die Cut 11 on 2 or 3 Sides

4815	A3678	(46c) multicolored	1.10	.25
a.		Booklet pane of 20	22.00	
b.		Imperforate	1.75	—
c.		Imperforate booklet pane of 20	35.00	
4816	A3679	(46c) multicolored	1.10	.25
a.		Booklet pane of 20	22.00	
b.		Dated "2014"	1.10	.25
c.		As #4816a, dated "2014"	22.00	
d.		Imperforate, dated "2013"	1.75	—
e.		Imperforate booklet pane of 20	35.00	
4817	A3680	(46c) multicolored	1.10	.25
4818	A3681	(46c) multicolored	1.10	.25
4819	A3682	(46c) multicolored	1.10	.25
4820	A3683	(46c) multicolored	1.10	.25
b.		Block of 4, #4817-4820	4.40	
c.		Booklet pane of 20, 5 each #4817-4820	22.00	
f.		Imperforate block of 4	8.00	—
g.		Imperforate booklet pane of 20	40.00	

Serpentine Die Cut 8 on 2, 3 or 4 Sides

4821	A3684	(46c) multicolored	1.10	.25
a.		Booklet pane of 18	18.00	
		Nos. 4815-4821 (7)	7.70	1.75

Issued: Nos. 4813, 4815, 10/11; No. 4814, 10/24; Nos. 4816, 4821, 10/10; Nos. 4817-4820, 11/6.

MEDALS OF HONOR

Navy Medal of Honor — A3685

Army Medal of Honor — A3686

LITHOGRAPHED
Serpentine Die Cut 11
2013, Nov. 11
Self-Adhesive

4822	A3685	(46c) multicolored	1.10	.30
a.		Dated "2014"	1.10	.30
b.		Dated "2015"	1.10	.30
4823	A3686	(46c) multicolored	1.10	.30
a.		Dated "2014"	1.10	.30
b.		Dated "2015"	1.10	.30
c.		Pair, #4822-4823	2.20	
d.		Pair, #4822a-4823a	2.20	

---

e.		Pair, 4822b-4823b	2.20	
f.		Imperf. pair, #4822-4823	4.50	—
g.		Imperf. pair, #4822a-4823a	4.50	—

Issued: Nos. 4822a, 4823a, 7/26/14. Nos. 4822a, 4822b, 4823a and 4823b sold for 49c on day of issue. Folios containing Nos. 4822a and 4823a have different images of Medal of Honor recipients, product numbers (on folio margins) and text on the paper backing than that found on the folios with Nos. 4822 and 4823. Nos. 4822b and 4823b were in a folio with No. 4988.

HANUKKAH

Menorah
A3687

LITHOGRAPHED
Serpentine Die Cut 11
2013, Nov. 19
Self-Adhesive

4824	A3687	(46c) multicolored	1.10	.25
a.		Imperforate	1.75	—

Postal Service officials declared on Nov. 8 that No. 4824 could be sold in post offices on Nov. 9, but the first day ceremony was held on Nov. 19 in New York, NY. Official first day covers have that date and city.

SCENES FROM HARRY POTTER MOVIES

Harry Potter — A3688

Harry Potter and Ron Weasley
A3689

Harry Potter, Ron Weasley, Hermione Granger
A3690

Hermione Granger — A3691

Harry Potter and Fawkes the Phoenix
A3692

Hedwig the Owl — A3693

Dobby the House Elf — A3694

Harry Potter and Buckbeak the Hippogriff
A3695

Headmaster Albus Dumbledore
A3696

Professor Severus Snape
A3697

Rubeus Hagrid
A3698

Professor Minerva McGonagall
A3699

Harry Potter, Ron Weasley, Hermione Granger
A3700

Luna Lovegood
A3701

Fred and George Weasley
A3702

Ginny Weasley
A3703

Draco
Malfoy — A3704

Harry
Potter
A3705

Lord
Voldemort
A3706

Bellatrix
Lestrange — A3707

LITHOGRAPHED
Serpentine Die Cut 11
2013, Nov. 19
Booklet Stamps
Self-Adhesive

4825	A3688	(46c) multicolored	2.00	.30
4826	A3689	(46c) multicolored	2.00	.30
4827	A3690	(46c) multicolored	2.00	.30
4828	A3691	(46c) multicolored	2.00	.30
a.		Booklet pane of 4, #4825-4828, + central label	8.00	
b.		Imperf. booklet pane of 4	12.50	—
4829	A3692	(46c) multicolored	2.00	.30
4830	A3693	(46c) multicolored	2.00	.30
4831	A3694	(46c) multicolored	2.00	.30
4832	A3695	(46c) multicolored	2.00	.30
a.		Booklet pane of 4, #4829-4832, + central label	8.00	
b.		Imperf. booklet pane of 4	12.50	—
4833	A3696	(46c) multicolored	2.00	.30
4834	A3697	(46c) multicolored	2.00	.30
4835	A3698	(46c) multicolored	2.00	.30
4836	A3699	(46c) multicolored	2.00	.30
a.		Booklet pane of 4, #4833-4836, + central label	8.00	
b.		Imperf. booklet pane of 4	12.50	—
4837	A3700	(46c) multicolored	2.00	.30
4838	A3701	(46c) multicolored	2.00	.30
4839	A3702	(46c) multicolored	2.00	.30
4840	A3703	(46c) multicolored	2.00	.30
a.		Booklet pane of 4, #4837-4840, + central label	8.00	
b.		Imperf. booklet pane of 4	12.50	—
4841	A3704	(46c) multicolored	2.00	.30
4842	A3705	(46c) multicolored	2.00	.30
4843	A3706	(46c) multicolored	2.00	.30
4844	A3707	(46c) multicolored	2.00	.30
a.		Booklet pane of 4, #4841-4844, + central label	8.00	
b.		Imperf. booklet pane of 4	12.50	—
		Nos. 4825-4844 (20)	40.00	6.00

KWANZAA

People, Candles and
Book — A3708

LITHOGRAPHED
Serpentine Die Cut 11
2013, Nov. 26
Self-Adhesive

4845	A3708	(46c) multicolored	1.10	.25
a.		Imperforate	1.75	—

CHINESE NEW YEAR

Year of the
Horse
A3709

PHOTOGRAVURE
Serpentine Die Cut 11
2014, Jan. 15
Self-Adhesive

4846	A3709	(46c) multicolored	1.10	.25
a.		Imperforate	2.00	—

LOVE

Heart — A3710

PHOTOGRAVURE
Serpentine Die Cut 10¾
2014, Jan. 21
Self-Adhesive

4847	A3710	(46c) multicolored	1.25	.25
a.		Imperforate	2.00	—

FERNS

Fortune's Holly
Fern — A3711

Soft Shield
Fern — A3712

Autumn
Fern — A3713

Goldie's Wood
Fern — A3714

Painted Fern — A3715

PHOTOGRAVURE
Serpentine Die Cut 11 Vert.
2014, Jan. 27
Coil Stamps
Self-Adhesive

4848	A3711	49c multicolored	1.50	.25
4849	A3712	49c multicolored	1.50	.25
4850	A3713	49c multicolored	1.50	.25
4851	A3714	49c multicolored	1.50	.25
4852	A3715	49c multicolored	1.50	.25
a.		Strip of 5, #4848-4852	7.50	
		Nos. 4848-4852 (5)	7.50	1.25

Fort McHenry Flag
and
Fireworks — A3716

PHOTOGRAVURE
Serpentine Die Cut 8½ Vert.
2014, Jan. 28
Coil Stamps
Self-Adhesive

4853	A3716	(49c) multicolored	1.10	.25
		Pair	2.20	

LITHOGRAPHED (#4854-4855)
Serpentine Die Cut 9½ Vert.

4854	A3716	(49c) multicolored	1.10	.25
		Pair	2.20	
a.		Die cutting omitted, pair	150.00	

Booklet Stamp
Serpentine Die Cut 11¼x10¾ on 2 or 3 Sides

4855	A3716	(49c) multicolored	1.10	.25
a.		Booklet pane of 20	22.00	

No. 4855a is a double-sided booklet with 12 stamps on one side and eight stamps plus a label that serves as the booklet cover on the other side.

Nos. 4854 and 4855 each have a microprinted "USPS" on the right side of the lowest white stripe of the flag.

See Nos. 4868-4871.

BLACK HERITAGE

Shirley Chisholm
(1924-2005),
Congresswoman
A3717

PHOTOGRAVURE
Serpentine Die Cut 11
2014, Jan. 31
Self-Adhesive

4856	A3717	(49c) multicolored	1.10	.25
a.		Imperforate	2.00	—

WILDLIFE ISSUE

Hummingbird
A3718

LITHOGRAPHED
Serpentine Die Cut 11¼x10¾
2014, Feb. 7
Self-Adhesive

4857	A3718	34c multicolored	.70	.25

Coil Stamp
Serpentine Die Cut 9½ Vert.

4858	A3718	34c multicolored	.70	.25
a.		Overall tagging	.70	.25
b.		As "a," die cutting omitted, pair	—	

**GREAT SPANGLED FRITILLARY
BUTTERFLY**

A3719

PHOTOGRAVURE
Serpentine Die Cut 10¾
2014, Feb. 10
Self-Adhesive

4859	A3719	70c multicolored	1.40	.25
a.		Imperforate	3.25	—

Statue of Abraham
Lincoln in Lincoln
Memorial — A3720

PHOTOGRAVURE
Serpentine Die Cut 11
2014, Feb. 12
Self-Adhesive

4860	A3720	21c multicolored	.45	.25
a.		Imperforate	1.25	

Coil Stamp
Serpentine Die Cut 8½ Vert.

4861	A3720	21c multicolored	.45	.25

WINTER FLOWERS

Amaryllis
A3721

Cyclamen
A3722

Paperwhite
A3723

Christmas
Cactus
A3724

LITHOGRAPHED
Serpentine Die Cut 11 on 2 or 3 Sides
2014, Feb. 14
Booklet Stamps
Self-Adhesive

4862	A3721	(49c) multicolored	1.50	.30
4863	A3722	(49c) multicolored	1.50	.30
4864	A3723	(49c) multicolored	1.50	.30
4865	A3724	(49c) multicolored	1.50	.30
a.		Block of 4, #4862-4865	6.00	
b.		Booklet pane of 20, 5 each #4862-4865	30.00	
c.		Imperforate block of 4	7.00	—
d.		Imperforate booklet pane of 20	35.00	
		Nos. 4862-4865 (4)	6.00	1.20

No. 4865b is a double-sided booklet pane with 12 stamps on one side (3 each #4862-4865), and eight stamps (2 each #4862-4865) plus label (booklet cover) on the other side.

LITERARY ARTS

Ralph
Ellison
(1913-94),
Buildings in
Harlem
A3725

PHOTOGRAVURE
Serpentine Die Cut 11
2014, Feb. 18
Self-Adhesive

4866	A3725	91c multicolored	1.90	.45
a.		Imperforate	4.00	

Wedding Cake Type of 2009
LITHOGRAPHED
Serpentine Die Cut 10¾
2014, Feb. 22
Self-Adhesive

4867	A3344	70c multicolored	1.40	.25

See Nos. 4398, 4521, 4602, 4735, 5000.

**Fort McHenry Flag and Fireworks
Type of 2014**
LITHOGRAPHED
**Coil Stamp Self-Adhesive With
"USPS" Microprinted in Fireworks
Above Flagpole**
Serpentine Die Cut 11 Vert.
2014, Mar. 3

4868	A3716	(49c) multicolored	1.10	.25
a.		Vert. strip of 3 (one single each from three different coil rolls), horiz. unslit between	60.00	
b.		Pair, die cutting omitted		

PHOTOGRAVURE (#4869), LITHO-
GRAPHED (#4870-4871)
**Booklet Stamps
Without Microprinted "USPS"**
*Serpentine Die Cut 11¼x11½ on 2
or 3 Sides*

4869	A3716	(49c) multicolored	1.10	.25
a.		Booklet pane of 20	22.00	

With "USPS" Microprinted in Fireworks Above Flagpole

Serpentine Die Cut 11¼x10¾ on 2 or 3 Sides

4870	A3716	(49c) multicolored	1.10	.25
a.		Booklet pane of 20	22.00	

The actual design images on Nos. 4855, 4869 and 4870 differ slightly in size. This is easiest seen by measuring the height of the flagpole: No. 4855 is 13mm, No. 4869 is 14mm, and No. 4870 is 12mm.

Thin Paper

Serpentine Die Cut 11¼x11 on 2, 3 or 4 Sides

4871	A3716	(49c) multicolored	1.10	.25
a.		Booklet pane of 18	20.00	

Nos. 4869a and 4870a are double-sided booklets with 12 stamps on one side and eight stamps plus a label that serves as the booklet cover on the other side.

AMERICAN LANDMARKS ISSUE

Verrazano-Narrows Bridge, New York — A3726

USS Arizona Memorial, Hawaii A3727

LITHOGRAPHED

2014 *Serpentine Die Cut 10¾x10½*
Self-Adhesive

4872	A3726	$5.60 multi	11.00	6.25
4873	A3727	$19.99 multi	40.00	21.00
a.		Imperforate	55.00	

Issued: $5.60, 3/4; $19.99, 3/13.

FERNS

Fortune's Holly Fern — A3728

Soft Shield Fern — A3729

Autumn Fern — A3730

Goldie's Wood Fern — A3731

Painted Fern — A3732

PHOTOGRAVURE

Serpentine Die Cut 11 Vert.
2014, Mar. 6
Coil Stamps
Self-Adhesive

4874	A3728	(49c) multicolored	2.00	.25
4875	A3729	(49c) multicolored	2.00	.25
4876	A3730	(49c) multicolored	2.00	.25
4877	A3731	(49c) multicolored	2.00	.25
4878	A3732	(49c) multicolored	2.00	.25
a.		Strip of 5, #4874-4878	10.00	
Nos. 4874-4878 (5)			10.00	1.25

DISTINGUISHED AMERICANS

C. Alfred "Chief" Anderson (1907-96), Aviator — A3733

LITHOGRAPHED

Serpentine Die Cut 10¾x11
2014, Mar. 13
Self-Adhesive

4879	A3733	70c multicolored	1.40	.30
a.		Imperforate	3.00	—

MUSIC ICONS

Jimi Hendrix (1942-70), Rock Guitarist A3734

PHOTOGRAVURE

2014, Mar. 13   **Tagged**
Self-Adhesive

4880	A3734	(49c) multicolored	1.10	.25
a.		Imperforate	1.75	—

Adjacent horizontal or vertical stamps have selvage between the stamps. Any stamp on the pane is rotated 90 degrees with respect to any adjacent stamp, so that any block of four has stamps oriented in each of the four directions.
See No. 4765.

Flowers and "Yes I Do" Type of 2013

LITHOGRAPHED

Serpentine Die Cut 10¾
2014, Mar. 21
Self-Adhesive

4881	A3639	70c multicolored	1.40	.30

See Nos. 4765, 5001.

SONGBIRDS

Western Meadowlark A3735

Mountain Bluebird A3736

Western Tanager A3737

Painted Bunting A3738

Baltimore Oriole A3739

Evening Grosbeak A3740

Scarlet Tanager A3741

Rose-breasted Grosbeak A3742

American Goldfinch A3743

White-throated Sparrow A3744

LITHOGRAPHED

Serpentine Die Cut 10¾ on 2 or 3 Sides
2014, Apr. 5
Booklet Stamps
Self-Adhesive

4882	A3735	(49c) multicolored	1.50	.40
4883	A3736	(49c) multicolored	1.50	.40
4884	A3737	(49c) multicolored	1.50	.40
4885	A3738	(49c) multicolored	1.50	.40
4886	A3739	(49c) multicolored	1.50	.40
4887	A3740	(49c) multicolored	1.50	.40
4888	A3741	(49c) multicolored	1.50	.40
4889	A3742	(49c) multicolored	1.50	.40
4890	A3743	(49c) multicolored	1.50	.40
4891	A3744	(49c) multicolored	1.50	.40
a.		Block of 10, #4882-4891	15.00	
b.		Booklet pane of 20, 2 each #4882-4891	30.00	
c.		Imperforate block of 10	20.00	—
d.		Imperforate booklet pane of 20	40.00	
Nos. 4882-4891 (10)			15.00	4.00

No. 4891b is a double-sided booklet pane with 12 stamps on one side (Nos. 4883-4886, 4888-4891, 2 each Nos. 4882, 4887) and eight stamps (Nos. 4883-4886, 4888-4891) plus label (booklet cover) on the other side.

LEGENDS OF HOLLYWOOD

Charlton Heston (1923-2008), Actor — A3745

LITHOGRAPHED

Serpentine Die Cut 11
2014, Apr. 11
Self-Adhesive

4892	A3745	(49c) multicolored	1.10	.25
a.		Imperforate	1.75	—

Map of Sea Surface Temperatures A3746

LITHOGRAPHED

2014, Apr. 22 *Serpentine Die Cut*
Self-Adhesive

4893	A3746	($1.15) multi	2.40	.50
a.		Imperforate	3.50	—

Unused values are for stamps with surrounding selvage. Adjacent stamps are separated by rouletting.

FLAGS

Flag With 5 Full and 3 Partial Stars — A3747

Flag With 3 Full Stars — A3748

Flag With 4 Full and 2 Partial Stars — A3749

Flag With 2 Full and 2 Partial Stars — A3750

PHOTOGRAVURE

Serpentine Die Cut 11 Vert.
2014, Apr. 25
Coil Stamps
Self-Adhesive

4894	A3747	(49c) blue & red	1.10	.25
4895	A3748	(49c) blue & red	1.10	.25
4896	A3749	(49c) blue & red	1.10	.25
4897	A3750	(49c) blue & red	1.10	.25
a.		Strip of 4, #4894-4897	4.40	
Nos. 4894-4897 (4)			4.40	1.00

CIRCUS POSTERS

Barnum and Bailey Circus Poster With Clown — A3751

Sells-Floto Circus Poster — A3752

Ringling Bros. Barnum and Bailey Circus Poster With Dainty Miss Leitzel — A3753

Al G. Barnes Wild Animal Circus Poster — A3754

Ringling Bros. Shows Poster With Hillary Long — A3755

Barnum and Bailey Circus Poster With Tiger — A3756

Ringling Bros. Barnum and Bailey Circus Poster With Elephant — A3757

Carl Hagenbeck-Wallace Circus Poster — A3758

A3758a

LITHOGRAPHED, ENGRAVED (50c), SHEET MARGIN (#4905b) LITHOGRAPHED WITH FOIL APPLICATION

2014, May 5   Serpentine Die Cut 11
Self-Adhesive

4898	A3751	(49c)	multicolored	1.10	.45
4899	A3752	(49c)	multicolored	1.10	.45
4900	A3753	(49c)	multicolored	1.10	.45
4901	A3754	(49c)	multicolored	1.10	.45
4902	A3755	(49c)	multicolored	1.10	.45
4903	A3756	(49c)	multicolored	1.10	.45
4904	A3757	(49c)	multicolored	1.10	.45
4905	A3758	(49c)	multicolored	1.10	.45
a.	Block of 8, #4898-4905			8.80
b.	Imperforate block of 8			16.00
c.	A3758a Imperforate souvenir sheet of 3, #4905d, 2 #4905c			9.00	—
d.	A1811 50c red, imperforate			2.25	—
e.	$1 multicolored (57x48mm stamp similar to #4898), imperforate			4.50	—
f.	As "c," gold omitted in sheet margin			
	Nos. 4898-4905 (8)			8.80	3.60

No. 4905c was printed only in press sheets containing 12 souvenir sheets. No. 4905c has die cutting around the souvenir sheet margin, but values for unused examples are for souvenir sheets having the white press sheet margin surrounding the die cutting. Examples of No. 4905c with serpentine die cutting around the three stamps were sold only with the USPS 2014 Stamp Yearbook, which sold for $64.95. The souvenir sheets sold with the yearbook are punched out from the press sheets and lack the white press sheet margin.

HARVEY MILK

Harvey Milk (1930-78), Homosexual Rights Advocate and Politician — A3759

LITHOGRAPHED
Sheets of 240 in 12 panes of 20
Serpentine Die Cut 10¾
2014, May 22
Self-Adhesive

4906	A3759	(49c)	multicolored	1.10	.25
a.	Imperforate			1.75	—

NEVADA STATEHOOD, 150th ANNIV.

Fire Canyon
A3760

LITHOGRAPHED
Serpentine Die Cut 10¾
2014, May 29
Self-Adhesive

4907	A3760	(49c)	multicolored	1.10	.25
a.	Imperforate			1.75	—

HOT RODS

Rear of 1932 Ford "Deuce" Roadster
A3761

Front of 1932 Ford "Deuce" Roadster
A3762

PHOTOGRAVURE
Serpentine Die Cut 11¾x11¼ on 2 or 3 Sides
2014, June 6
Booklet Stamps
Self-Adhesive

4908	A3761	(49c)	multicolored	1.10	.25
4909	A3762	(49c)	multicolored	1.10	.25
a.	Pair, #4908-4909			2.20
b.	Booklet pane of 20, 10 each #4908-4909			22.00
c.	Imperforate pair			4.00	—
d.	Imperforate booklet pane of 20			40.00

No. 4909b is a double-sided booklet pane with 12 stamps on one side (6 each Nos. 4908-4909) and eight stamps (4 each Nos. 4908-4909) plus label (booklet cover) on the other side.

CIVIL WAR SESQUICENTENNIAL

Battle of Petersburg — A3763

Battle of Mobile Bay — A3764

LITHOGRAPHED
Serpentine Die Cut 11
2014, July 30
Self-Adhesive

4910	A3763	(49c)	multicolored	1.10	.35
4911	A3764	(49c)	multicolored	1.10	.35
a.	Pair, #4910-4911			2.20
b.	Imperforate pair			5.00	—

FARMERS MARKETS

Breads
A3765

Fruits and Vegetables
A3766

Flowers
A3767

Plants
A3768

LITHOGRAPHED
Serpentine Die Cut 10¾
2014, Aug. 7
Self-Adhesive

4912	A3765	(49c)	multicolored	1.10	.30
4913	A3766	(49c)	multicolored	1.10	.30
4914	A3767	(49c)	multicolored	1.10	.30
4915	A3768	(49c)	multicolored	1.10	.30
a.	Horiz. strip of 4, #4912-4915			4.40
b.	Imperf. horiz. strip of 4			9.00	—
	Nos. 4912-4915 (4)			4.40	1.20

MUSIC ICONS

Janis Joplin (1943-70), Rock Singer — A3769

LITHOGRAPHED
Serpentine Die Cut 10½
2014, Aug. 8
Self-Adhesive

4916	A3769	(49c)	multicolored	1.10	.25
a.	Imperforate			1.75	—

HUDSON RIVER SCHOOL PAINTINGS

Grand Canyon, by Thomas Moran (1837-1926) — A3770

Summer Afternoon, by Asher B. Durand (1796-1886) A3771

Sunset, by Frederic Edwin Church (1826-1900) — A3772

Distant View of Niagara Falls, by Thomas Cole (1801-48) A3773

PHOTOGRAVURE
Serpentine Die Cut 10¾ on 2 or 3 Sides
2014, Aug. 21
Booklet Stamps
Self-Adhesive

4917	A3770	(49c)	multicolored	1.50	.30
4918	A3771	(49c)	multicolored	1.50	.30
4919	A3772	(49c)	multicolored	1.50	.30
4920	A3773	(49c)	multicolored	1.50	.30
a.	Block of 4, #4917-4920			6.00
b.	Booklet pane of 20, 5 each #4917-4920			30.00
c.	Imperforate block of 4			8.00	—
d.	Imperforate booklet pane of 20			40.00
	Nos. 4917-4920 (4)			6.00	1.20

No. 4920b is a double-sided booklet pane with 12 stamps on one side (3 each #4917-4920) and eight stamps (2 each #4917-4920) plus label (booklet cover) on the other side.

WAR OF 1812 BICENTENNIAL

Bombardment of Fort McHenry — A3774

PHOTOGRAVURE
Serpentine Die Cut 10¾x10½
2014, Sept. 13
Self-Adhesive

4921	A3774	(49c)	multicolored	1.10	.25
	Pane of 20			22.00
a.	Imperforate			1.75	—

CELEBRITY CHEFS

Edna Lewis (1916-2006)
A3775

Felipe Rojas-Lombardi (1946-91)
A3776

Joyce Chen (1917-94)
A3777

James Beard (1903-85)
A3778

Julia Child (1912-2004)
A3779

LITHOGRAPHED
Serpentine Die Cut 11x10¾
2014, Sept. 26
Self-Adhesive

4922	A3775	(49c) multicolored	1.20	.45
4923	A3776	(49c) multicolored	1.20	.45
4924	A3777	(49c) multicolored	1.20	.45
4925	A3778	(49c) multicolored	1.20	.45
4926	A3779	(49c) multicolored	1.20	.45
a.		Horiz. strip of 5, #4922-4926	6.00	
b.		Imperf. horiz. strip of 5	8.00	—
		Nos. 4922-4926 (5)	6.00	2.25

The gray shading of the inner curve of the dinner plate shown in the margin of the pane continues into the white frames surrounding some of the stamps in the pane's outer rows and columns.

AMERICAN LANDMARKS ISSUE

Glade Creek Grist Mill, West Virginia
A3780

LITHOGRAPHED
Serpentine Die Cut 10¾x10½
2014, Sept. 29
Self-Adhesive

4927	A3780	$5.75 multi	11.50	6.50
a.		Imperforate	15.00	—

BATMAN

Bat Signal — A3781   Bat Signal — A3782

Bat Signal — A3783   Bat Signal — A3784

Batman A3785   Batman and Bat Signal A3786

Batman and Rope A3787   Batman A3788

LITHOGRAPHED
2014, Oct. 9   *Serpentine Die Cut*
Self-Adhesive

4928	A3781	(49c) multicolored	2.50	.40
4929	A3782	(49c) multicolored	2.50	.40
4930	A3783	(49c) multicolored	2.50	.40
4931	A3784	(49c) multicolored	2.50	.40

Serpentine Die Cut 11x10¾

4932	A3785	(49c) multicolored	1.25	.40
4933	A3786	(49c) multicolored	1.25	.40
4934	A3787	(49c) multicolored	1.25	.40

4935	A3788	(49c) multicolored	1.25	.40
a.		Vert. block of 8, #4928-4935	15.00	
b.		Imperf. vert. block of 8	20.00	—
		Nos. 4928-4935 (8)	15.00	3.20

Silver Bells Wreath
A3789

LITHOGRAPHED
2014, Oct. 23   *Serpentine Die Cut*
Self-Adhesive

4936	A3789	($1.15) multicolored	2.50	.50
a.		Imperforate	4.00	—

Unused values are for stamps with surrounding selvage. Adjacent stamps are separated by rouletting.

WINTER FUN

Skaters A3790   Child Making Snowman A3791

Cardinal A3792   Child Making Snow Angel A3793

PHOTOGRAVURE
Serpentine Die Cut 10¾x11 on 2 or 3 Sides
2014, Oct. 23
Booklet Stamps
Self-Adhesive

4937	A3790	(49c) multicolored	1.25	.30
4938	A3791	(49c) multicolored	1.25	.30
4939	A3792	(49c) multicolored	1.25	.30
4940	A3793	(49c) multicolored	1.25	.30
a.		Block of 4, #4937-4940	5.00	
b.		Booklet pane of 20, 5 each #4937-4940	25.00	
c.		Imperforate block of 4	7.00	
d.		Imperf. booklet pane of 20	35.00	

Skaters A3794   Child Making Snowman A3795

Cardinal A3796   Child Making Snow Angel A3797

LITHOGRAPHED
Serpentine Die Cut 11¼x11 on 2, 3 or 4 Sides
Thin Paper

4941	A3794	(49c) multicolored	2.00	.30
4942	A3795	(49c) multicolored	2.00	.30
4943	A3796	(49c) multicolored	2.00	.30
4944	A3797	(49c) multicolored	2.00	.30
a.		Block or strip of 4, #4941-4944	8.00	

---

b.		Booklet pane of 18, 5 each #4941-4942, 4 each #4943-4944	36.00	
		Nos. 4937-4944 (8)	13.00	2.40

CHRISTMAS

Magi — A3798   Rudolph, the Red-Nosed Reindeer — A3799

Hermey and Rudolph — A3800

Santa Claus — A3801

Bumble — A3802

LITHOGRAPHED (#4945), PHOTOGRAVURE
Serpentine Die Cut 10¾x11 on 2 or 3 Sides
2014
Booklet Stamps
Self-Adhesive

4945	A3798	(49c) multi	1.10	.25
a.		Booklet pane of 20	22.00	
b.		Imperforate	1.75	—
c.		Imperf. booklet pane of 20	35.00	

Serpentine Die Cut 11x10¾ on 2 or 3 sides

4946	A3799	(49c) multi	1.20	.30
4947	A3800	(49c) multi	1.20	.30
4948	A3801	(49c) multi	1.20	.30
4949	A3802	(49c) multi	1.20	.30
a.		Block of 4, #4946-4949	4.80	
b.		Booklet pane of 20, 5 each #4946-4949	24.00	
c.		Imperf. block of 4	7.50	—
d.		Imperf. booklet pane of 20	37.50	
		Nos. 4945-4949 (5)	5.90	1.45

Issued: No. 4945, 11/19; Nos. 4946-4949, 11/6.

Premiere of *Rudolph, the Red-Nosed Reindeer* animated television show, 50th anniv.

No. 4945a is a double-sided booklet with 12 stamps on one side and eight stamps plus a label that serves as a booklet cover on the other side. No. 4949b is a double-sided booklet with 12 stamps on one side (3 each of Nos. 4946-4949) and eight stamps (2 each of Nos. 4946-4949) plus a label that serves as a booklet cover on the other side.

WILT CHAMBERLAIN (1936-99), BASKETBALL PLAYER

Chamberlain in Philadelphia Warriors Uniform A3803   Chamberlain in Los Angeles Lakers Uniform A3804

LITHOGRAPHED
Serpentine Die Cut 11x10¾
2014, Dec. 5
Self-Adhesive

4950	A3803	(49c) multicolored	1.10	.25
4951	A3804	(49c) multicolored	1.10	.25
a.		Pair, #4950-4951	2.20	
b.		Imperforate pair	3.50	

WAR OF 1812 BICENTENNIAL

Battle of New Orleans A3805

PHOTOGRAVURE
Serpentine Die Cut 10¾x10½
2015, Jan. 8
Self-Adhesive

4952	A3805	(49c) multicolored	1.10	.25
a.		Imperforate	1.75	

PATRIOTIC WAVES

A3806

A3807

LITHOGRAPHED
Serpentine Die Cut 11
2015   **Tagged**
Self-Adhesive

4953	A3806	$1 multicolored	2.00	.50
a.		Imperforate	3.00	
4954	A3807	$2 multicolored	4.00	1.00
a.		Imperforate	5.00	

LOVE

A3808   A3809

LITHOGRAPHED
Serpentine Die Cut 11
2015, Jan. 22   **Tagged**
Self-Adhesive

4955	A3808	(49c) red	1.10	.25
4956	A3809	(49c) red & gray	1.10	.25
a.		Pair, #4955-4956	2.20	
b.		Imperforate pair	3.50	—

CHINESE NEW YEAR

Year of the Ram A3810

LITHOGRAPHED
2015, Feb. 7   *Serpentine Die Cut 11*
Self-Adhesive

4957	A3810	(49c) multicolored	1.25	.25
a.		Imperforate	1.75	

BLACK HERITAGE

Robert Robinson Taylor (1868-1942), Architect — A3811

LITHOGRAPHED
Serpentine Die Cut 11
2015, Feb. 12
Self-Adhesive

4958	A3811	(49c) multicolored	1.10	.25
a.		Imperforate	2.25	

FLOWERS

Rose and Heart — A3812

Tulip and Heart — A3813

ENGRAVED
Serpentine Die Cut 10¾x 11
2015, Feb. 14
Self-Adhesive

4959	A3812	(49c) red & black	1.50	.25
a.		Imperforate	1.75	
4960	A3813	70c black & red	1.50	.30
a.		Imperforate	2.50	

See No. 5002.

FLAGS

Stripes at Left, Stars at Right A3814

Stars and White Stripe A3815

Stars at Left, Stripes at Right — A3816

LITHOGRAPHED
Serpentine Die Cut 11 Vert.
2015, Feb. 27
Coil Stamps
Self-Adhesive

4961	A3814	(10c) multicolored	.25	.25
4962	A3815	(10c) multicolored	.25	.25
4963	A3816	(10c) multicolored	.25	.25
a.		Strip of 3, #4961-4963	.75	
		Nos. 4961-4963 (3)	.75	.75

WATER LILIES

Pale Pink Water Lily — A3817

Red Water Lily — A3818

Purple Water Lily — A3819

White Water Lily — A3820

LITHOGRAPHED
Serpentine Die Cut 11x11¼ on 2 or 3 Sides
2015, Mar. 20
Booklet Stamps
Self-Adhesive

4964	A3817	(49c) multicolored	1.50	.25
4965	A3818	(49c) multicolored	1.50	.25
4966	A3819	(49c) multicolored	1.50	.25
4967	A3820	(49c) multicolored	1.50	.25
a.		Block of 4, #4964-4967	6.00	
b.		Booklet pane of 20, 5 each #4964-4967	30.00	
c.		Imperf. block of 4	7.00	
d.		Imperf. booklet pane of 20	35.00	
		Nos. 4964-4967 (4)	6.00	1.00

No. 4967b is a double-sided booklet pane with 12 stamps on one side (3 each Nos. 4964-4967) and eight stamps (2 each Nos. 4964-4967) plus label (booklet cover) on the other side.

ART BY MARTIN RAMIREZ (1895-1963)

Untitled (Horse and Rider With Trees), 1954 — A3821

Untitled (Man Riding Donkey), c. 1960-63 A3822

Untitled (Trains on Inclined Tracks), c. 1960-63 A3823

Untitled (Deer), c. 1960-63 A3824

Untitled (Tunnel with Cars and Buses), 1954 — A3825

LITHOGRAPHED
Serpentine Die Cut 10¾
2015, Mar. 26
Self-Adhesive

4968	A3821	(49c) multicolored	1.10	.40
4969	A3822	(49c) multicolored	1.10	.40
4970	A3823	(49c) multicolored	1.10	.40
4971	A3824	(49c) multicolored	1.10	.40
4972	A3825	(49c) multicolored	1.10	.40
a.		Vert. strip of 5, #4968-4972	5.50	
b.		Imperf. vert. strip of 5	7.50	—

Ferns Type of 2014
LITHOGRAPHED
Serpentine Die Cut 11 Vert.
2015, Mar. 27
Coil Stamps
Self-Adhesive
With Microprinted "USPS"
Dated "2014"

4973	A3729	(49c) multicolored	1.10	.25
a.		Dated "2015"	1.10	
4974	A3730	(49c) multicolored	1.10	.25
a.		Dated "2015"	1.10	
4975	A3731	(49c) multicolored	1.10	.25
a.		Dated "2015"	1.10	
4976	A3732	(49c) multicolored	1.10	.25
a.		Dated "2015"	1.10	.25

4977	A3728	(49c) multicolored	1.10	.25
a.		Dated "2015"	1.10	.25
b.		Strip of 5, #4973-4977	5.50	
c.		Strip of 5, #4973a-4977a	5.50	
		Nos. 4973-4977 (5)	5.50	1.25

Nos. 4973a-4977a are from coil rolls containing 3,000 stamps. Nos. 4973-4977 are from coil rolls containing 10,000 stamps. Microprinted "USPS" is near the end of the upper left fern branch on No. 4973 and near the base of the fern's stem on Nos. 4974-4977. Nos. 4973a-4977a have same microprinting locations as Nos. 4973-4977. Nos. 4874-4878 lack microprinted "USPS."

FROM ME TO YOU

A3826

LITHOGRAPHED
Sheets of 120 in six panes of 20
2015, Apr. 1 *Serpentine Die Cut 11*
Self-Adhesive

4978	A3826	(49c) multicolored	1.25	.25
a.		Imperforate	2.00	

MAYA ANGELOU (1928-2014), WRITER

Angelou and Quotation A3827

LITHOGRAPHED
2015, Apr. 7 *Serpentine Die Cut 11*
Self-Adhesive

4979	A3827	(49c) multicolored	1.10	.25
a.		Imperforate	1.75	—

The quotation on the stamp is not Angelou's but is similar to a quote by Joan Walsh Anglund.

CIVIL WAR SESQUICENTENNIAL

Battle of Five Forks — A3828

Surrender at Appomattox Court House — A3829

LITHOGRAPHED
Double-sided sheets of 72 in six panes of 12 (60 on one side, 12 on other side)
2015, Apr. 9 *Serpentine Die Cut 11*
Self-Adhesive

4980	A3828	(49c) multicolored	1.10	.30
4981	A3829	(49c) multicolored	1.10	.30
a.		Pair, #4980-4981	2.20	
b.		Imperforate pair	27.50	—

GIFTS OF FRIENDSHIP

Lincoln Memorial and Cherry Blossoms A3830

U.S. Capitol and Dogwood Blossoms A3831

Japanese Diet, Tokyo, and Cherry Blossoms A3832

Clock Tower, Tokyo, and Dogwood Blossoms A3833

LITHOGRAPHED
Sheets of 72 in six panes of 12
Serpentine Die Cut 11
2015, Apr. 10
Self-Adhesive

4982	A3830	(49c) multicolored	1.10	.30
4983	A3831	(49c) multicolored	1.10	.30
a.		Horiz. pair, #4982-4983	2.20	
b.		Imperforate pair	4.50	—
4984	A3832	(49c) multicolored	5.00	.30
4985	A3833	(49c) multicolored	5.00	.30
a.		Horiz. pair, #4984-4985	10.00	
b.		Imperforate pair	12.50	—
		Nos. 4982-4985 (4)	12.20	1.20

See Japan No. 3814.

SPECIAL OLYMPICS WORLD GAMES

Emblem — A3834

LITHOGRAPHED
Serpentine Die Cut 10¾
2015, May 9
Self-Adhesive

4986	A3834	(49c) multicolored	1.10	.25
a.		Imperforate	1.75	—

HELP FIND MISSING CHILDREN

Forget-me-nots — A3835

LITHOGRAPHED
Serpentine Die Cut 10¾
2015, May 18
Self-Adhesive

4987	A3835	(49c) multicolored	1.10	.25
a.		Imperforate	1.75	—

MEDAL OF HONOR

Air Force Medal of Honor — A3836

LITHOGRAPHED
2015, May 25 *Serpentine Die Cut 11*
Self-Adhesive

4988	A3836	(49c) multicolored	1.10	.25
a.		Horiz. strip of 3, #4822b, 4823b, 4988	3.30	
b.		Imperforate strip of 3	6.00	—

WILDLIFE ISSUE

Emperor Penguins — A3837

LITHOGRAPHED
Serpentine Die Cut 11¼x11
2015, June 1
Self-Adhesive

4989	A3837	(22c) multicolored	.45	.25
a.		Imperforate	1.00	—

Coil Stamp
Serpentine Die Cut 11 Vert.

4990	A3837	(22c) multicolored	.45	.25

COASTAL BIRDS

Red Knot — A3838

King Eider — A3839

Spoonbill A3840

Frigatebird A3841

LITHOGRAPHED
Serpentine Die Cut 11¼x11
2015, June 1
Self-Adhesive

4991	A3838	(35c) multicolored	.70	.25
4992	A3839	(35c) multicolored	.70	.25
4993	A3840	(35c) multicolored	.70	.25
4994	A3841	(35c) multicolored	.70	.25
a.		Block or vert. strip of 4, #4991-4994	2.80	
b.		Imperforate block or vert. strip of 4	4.50	—

Coil Stamps
Serpentine Die Cut 9½ Vert.

4995	A3840	(35c) multicolored	.70	.25
4996	A3841	(35c) multicolored	.70	.25
4997	A3838	(35c) multicolored	.70	.25
4998	A3839	(35c) multicolored	.70	.25
a.		Horiz. strip of 4, #4995-4998	2.80	

EASTERN TIGER SWALLOWTAIL BUTTERFLY

A3842

LITHOGRAPHED
Serpentine Die Cut 10½
2015, June 1
Self-Adhesive

4999	A3842	(71c) multicolored	1.50	.25
a.		Imperforate	2.50	—

Wedding Cake — A3843

LITHOGRAPHED
Serpentine Die Cut 10¾
2015, June 1
Self-Adhesive

5000	A3843	(71c) multicolored	1.50	.25

Flowers and "Yes, I Do" A3844

LITHOGRAPHED
Serpentine Die Cut 10¾
2015, June 1   **Tagged**
Self-Adhesive

5001	A3844	(71c) multicolored	2.00	.25

See Nos. 4765, 4881.

Tulip and Heart — A3845

ENGRAVED
2015, June 1 *Serpentine Die Cut 11*
Self-Adhesive

5002	A3845	(71c) black & red	1.50	.25

See No. 4960.

LITERARY ARTS

Flannery O'Connor (1925-64), Novelist A3846

LITHOGRAPHED
Serpentine Die Cut 10¾
2015, June 5
Self-Adhesive

5003	A3846	(93c) multicolored	1.90	.30
a.		Imperforate	2.50	

SUMMER HARVEST

Watermelon A3847

Sweet Corn A3848

Cantaloupes A3849

Tomatoes A3850

LITHOGRAPHED
Serpentine Die Cut 11¼x10¾ on 2 or 3 Sides
2015, July 11
Booklet Stamps
Self-Adhesive

5004	A3847	(49c) multicolored	1.50	.30
5005	A3848	(49c) multicolored	1.50	.30
5006	A3849	(49c) multicolored	1.50	.30
5007	A3850	(49c) multicolored	1.50	.30
a.		Block of 4, #5004-5007	6.00	
b.		Booklet pane of 20, 5 each #5004-5007	30.00	
c.		As "a," imperforate	7.00	—
d.		As "b," imperforate	35.00	—
		Nos. 5004-5007 (4)	6.00	1.20

No. 5007b is a double-sided booklet pane with 12 stamps on one side (3 each #5004-5007), and eight stamps (2 each #5004-5007) plus label (booklet cover) on the other side.

COAST GUARD

MH-65 Dolphin Helicopter and Cutter *Eagle* A3851

LITHOGRAPHED
Serpentine Die Cut 10¾
2015, Aug. 4   **Tagged**
Self-Adhesive

5008	A3851	(49c) multicolored	1.10	.25
a.		Imperforate	1.75	—

MUSIC ICONS

Elvis Presley (1935-77), Singer — A3852

LITHOGRAPHED
Serpentine Die Cut 10½
2015, Aug. 12
Self-Adhesive

5009	A3852	(49c) multicolored	1.10	.25
a.		Imperforate	1.75	—

2016 WORLD STAMP SHOW, NEW YORK CITY

Star — A3853

LITHOGRAPHED
Serpentine Die Cut 11
2015, Aug. 20
Self-Adhesive

5010	A3853	(49c) red	1.10	.25
5011	A3853	(49c) blue	1.10	.25
a.		Pair, #5010-5011	2.20	
b.		As "a," imperforate	4.00	—

LEGENDS OF HOLLYWOOD

Ingrid Bergman (1915-82), Actress — A3854

LITHOGRAPHED
Serpentine Die Cut 11
2015, Aug. 20
Self-Adhesive

5012	A3854	(49c) multicolored	1.50	.25
a.		Imperforate	1.75	—

See Sweden Nos. 2756-2758.

Eagle Type of 2012
LITHOGRAPHED
Serpentine Die Cut 10¼ Vert.
2015, Sept. 2
Coil Stamps
Self-Adhesive
Color Behind "USA"

5013	A3504	(25c) green	.50	.25
5014	A3504	(25c) blue green	.50	.25
5015	A3504	(25c) blue	.50	.25
5016	A3504	(25c) red violet	.50	.25
5017	A3504	(25c) orange	.50	.25
5018	A3504	(25c) yellow orange	.50	.25
a.		Strip of 6, #5013-5018	3.00	
		Nos. 5013-5018 (6)	3.00	1.50

See Nos. 4585-4590.

CELEBRATE

A3855

LITHOGRAPHED
Serpentine Die Cut 10¾
2015, Sept. 9
Self-Adhesive

5019	A3855	(49c) multicolored	1.10	.25

Compare with type A3441.

PAUL NEWMAN (1925-2008), ACTOR AND PHILANTHROPIST

A3856

LITHOGRAPHED
Serpentine Die Cut 10¾
2015, Sept. 18
Self-Adhesive

5020	A3856	(49c) multicolored	1.10	.25
a.		Imperforate	1.75	—

CHRISTMAS

Charlie Brown Carrying Christmas Tree — A3857

Charlie Brown, Pigpen and Dirty Snowman A3858

Snoopy, Lucy, Violet, Sally and Schroeder Skating — A3859

Characters, Dog House and Christmas Tree — A3860

Linus and Christmas Tree — A3861

Charlie Brown Looking in Mailbox — A3862

Charlie Brown and Linus Behind Brick Wall — A3863

Charlie Brown, Linus and Christmas Tree — A3864

Charlie Brown Screaming, Snoopy Decorating Dog House — A3865

Charlie Brown Hanging Ornament on Christmas Tree — A3866

LITHOGRAPHED
Serpentine Die Cut 10¾ on 2 or 3 Sides
2015, Oct. 1
Booklet Stamps
Self-Adhesive

5021	A3857	(49c) multicolored	2.00	.40
5022	A3858	(49c) multicolored	2.00	.40
5023	A3859	(49c) multicolored	2.00	.40
5024	A3860	(49c) multicolored	2.00	.40
5025	A3861	(49c) multicolored	2.00	.40
5026	A3862	(49c) multicolored	2.00	.40
5027	A3863	(49c) multicolored	2.00	.40
5028	A3864	(49c) multicolored	2.00	.40
5029	A3865	(49c) multicolored	2.00	.40
5030	A3866	(49c) multicolored	2.00	.40
a.		Block of 10, #5021-5030	20.00	
b.		Booklet pane of 20, 2 each #5021-5030	40.00	
c.		As "a," imperforate	17.50	—
d.		As "b," imperforate	35.00	
		Nos. 5021-5030 (10)	20.00	4.00

Premiere of *A Charlie Brown Christmas* animated television show, 50th anniv.
No. 5030b is a double-sided booklet pane with 12 stamps on one side (Nos. 5023-5030, 2 each Nos. 5021-5022) and eight stamps (Nos. 5023-5030) plus label (booklet cover) on the other side.

GEOMETRIC SNOWFLAKES

A3867

A3868

A3869

A3870

LITHOGRAPHED
Serpentine Die Cut 11¼x10¾ on 2 or 3 Sides
2015, Oct. 23
Booklet Stamps
Self-Adhesive
Snowflake Colors

5031	A3867	(49c) purple & lilac	1.25	.30
5032	A3868	(49c) dark blue & blue	1.25	.30
5033	A3869	(49c) dark green & green	1.25	.30
5034	A3870	(49c) crimson & pink	1.25	.30
a.		Block of 4, #5031-5034	5.00	
b.		Booklet pane of 20, 5 each #5031-5034	25.00	
c.		As "a," imperforate	7.00	—
d.		As "b," imperforate	35.00	
		Nos. 5031-5034 (4)	5.00	1.20

No. 5034b is a double-sided booklet pane with 12 stamps on one side (3 each Nos. 5031-5034), and eight stamps (2 each Nos. 5031-5034) plus label (booklet cover) on the other side.

Purple Heart and Ribbon Type of 2012
LITHOGRAPHED
2015, Oct. *Serpentine Die Cut .11*
Self-Adhesive
With "USPS" Microprinted At Left of Ribbon

5035	A3587	(49c) multicolored	1.10	.25

See Nos. 4529, 4704.

LOVE

Quilled Paper Heart — A3871

LITHOGRAPHED
Serpentine Die Cut 10¾
2016, Jan. 12
Self-Adhesive

5036	A3871	(49c) multicolored	1.10	.25
a.		Imperforate	1.75	—
b.		Die cutting omitted, P#B11111 block of 4	100.00	

No. 5036b was printed from P#B11111 only and may also be collected in plate blocks of 6, half panes of 10 and full panes of 20. Pairs or other multiples without P#B11111 selvage attached cannot be distinguished from No. 5036a, which was printed only from P#S11111.

FRUIT

Albemarle Pippin Apples A3872

Pinot Noir Grapes A3873

Red Pears — A3874

LITHOGRAPHED
Serpentine Die Cut 10 Vert.
2016
Self-Adhesive
Coil Stamps

5037	A3872	1c multicolored	.25	.25
5038	A3873	5c multicolored	.25	.25

Serpentine Die Cut 10¾ Vert.

5039	A3874	10c multicolored	.25	.25

See Nos. 5177-5178 for sheet versions of Nos. 5038-5039, also see No. 5201, 5256.

AMERICAN LANDMARKS ISSUE

La Cueva del Indio, Puerto Rico A3875

Columbia River Gorge A3876

LITHOGRAPHED
Serpentine Die Cut 10¾x10½
2016, Jan. 17
Self-Adhesive

5040	A3875	$6.45 multi	13.00	7.50
a.		Imperforate	17.50	
5041	A3876	$22.95 multi	45.00	24.00
a.		Imperforate	150.00	—

BOTANICAL ART

Corn Lilies A3877

Tulips A3878

Tulips A3879

Dahlias A3880

Stocks A3881

Roses A3882

Japanese Irises — A3883

Tulips — A3884

Petunias A3885

Jonquils A3886

LITHOGRAPHED
Serpentine Die Cut 10¾ on 2 or 3 Sides
2016, Jan. 29
Booklet Stamps
Self-Adhesive

5042	A3877	(49c) multicolored	2.00	.40
5043	A3878	(49c) multicolored	2.00	.40
5044	A3879	(49c) multicolored	2.00	.40
5045	A3880	(49c) multicolored	2.00	.40
5046	A3881	(49c) multicolored	2.00	.40
5047	A3882	(49c) multicolored	2.00	.40
5048	A3883	(49c) multicolored	2.00	.40
5049	A3884	(49c) multicolored	2.00	.40
5050	A3885	(49c) multicolored	2.00	.40
5051	A3886	(49c) multicolored	2.00	.40
a.		Block of 10, #5042-5051	20.00	
b.		Booklet pane of 10, #5042-5051	20.00	
c.		Booklet pane of 20, 2 each #5042-5051	40.00	
d.		Imperforate block of 10	90.00	—
e.		Imperforate booklet pane of 20	150.00	
f.		As "c," horiz. die cutting missing between all stamps front and reverse	—	
		Nos. 5042-5051 (10)	20.00	4.00

No. 5051c is a double-sided booklet pane with 12 stamps on one side (Nos. 5042-5049, 2 each Nos. 5050-5051) and eight stamps (Nos. 5042-5049) plus label (booklet cover) on the other side.
No. 5051f resulted from a misregistration of the die cutting/pane cutting and the printed

web. The horizontal rows are reversed from their normal positions, and horizontal die cutting appears at the top and bottom of the pane.

Flag — A3887

LITHOGRAPHED
Serpentine Die Cut 11 Vert.
2016, Jan. 29
Coil Stamps
Self-Adhesive
Microprinted "USPS" To Right of Pole Under Flag

5052	A3887	(49c) multicolored	1.10	.25
a.		Die cutting omitted, pair	—	
b.		As "a," grayish blue (inscription and date) omitted	—	

Serpentine Die Cut 9½ Vert.
Microprinted "USPS" on Second White Flag Stripe

5053	A3887	(49c) multicolored	1.10	.25

Booklet Stamps
Microprinted "USPS" To Right of Pole Under Flag
Serpentine Die Cut 11¼x10¾ on 2 or 3 Sides

5054	A3887	(49c) multicolored	1.10	.25
a.		Booklet pane of 10	11.00	
b.		Booklet pane of 20	22.00	
c.		As "b," horiz. die cutting omitted on side with 12 stamps	—	

Microprinted "USPS" on Second White Flag Stripe

5055	A3887	(49c) multicolored	1.10	.25
a.		Booklet pane of 20	22.00	

Nos. 5054b and 5055a are double-sided booklets with 12 stamps on one side and eight stamps plus a label that serves as the booklet cover on the other side.

BLACK HERITAGE

Richard Allen (1760-1831), Founder of African Methodist Episcopal Church — A3888

LITHOGRAPHED
Serpentine Die Cut 10¾
2016, Feb. 2
Self-Adhesive

5056	A3888	(49c) multicolored	1.10	.25
a.		Imperforate	2.75	

CHINESE NEW YEAR

Year of the Monkey A3889

LITHOGRAPHED
Serpentine Die Cut 10¾
2016, Feb. 5
Self-Adhesive

5057	A3889	(49c) multicolored	1.10	.25
a.		Imperforate	1.50	

Moon A3890

LITHOGRAPHED
2016, Feb. 22 *Serpentine Die Cut*
Self-Adhesive
5058 A3890 ($1.20) multicolored 2.40 .50

Unused values are for stamps with surrounding selvage. Adjacent stamps are separated by rouletting.

MUSIC ICONS

Sarah Vaughan
(1924-90),
Singer — A3891

LITHOGRAPHED
Serpentine Die Cut 10½
2016, Mar. 29
Self-Adhesive
5059 A3891 (49c) multicolored 1.10 .25

LEGENDS OF HOLLYWOOD

Shirley Temple
(1928-2014),
Actress and
Diplomat — A3892

LITHOGRAPHED
Serpentine Die Cut 10¾
2016, Apr. 18
Self-Adhesive
5060 A3892 (47c) multicolored 1.10 .25

"USA" and
Star — A3893

LITHOGRAPHED
Serpentine Die Cut 10 Vert.
2016, Apr. 28
COIL STAMP
Self-Adhesive
5061 A3893 (5c) multicolored .25 .25
See No. 5172.

2016 WORLD STAMP SHOW, NEW YORK CITY

Star — A3894

ENGRAVED
Serpentine Die Cut 10¾
2016, May 28
Self-Adhesive
5062 A3894 (47c) blue 1.10 .25
5063 A3894 (47c) red 1.10 .25
  a. Pair, #5062-5063 2.20

REPEAL OF THE STAMP ACT, 250TH ANNIV.

Man Posting of
Notice of Repeal
on
Tree — A3895

LITHOGRAPHED
Serpentine Die Cut 10¾
2016, May 29
Self-Adhesive
5064 A3895 (47c) multicolored 1.10 .25

SERVICE CROSS MEDALS

Distinguished
Service
Cross — A3896

Navy
Cross — A3897

Air Force
Cross — A3898

Coast Guard
Cross — A3899

LITHOGRAPHED
Serpentine Die Cut 10¾
2016, May 30
Self-Adhesive
5065 A3896 (47c) multicolored 1.10 .30
5066 A3897 (47c) multicolored 1.10 .30
5067 A3898 (47c) multicolored 1.10 .30
5068 A3899 (47c) multicolored 1.10 .30
  a. Block or horiz. strip of 4,
      #5065-5068 4.40
  Nos. 5065-5068 (4) 4.40 1.20

VIEWS OF OUR PLANETS

Mercury
A3900

Venus — A3901

Earth — A3902

Mars — A3903

Jupiter — A3904

Saturn — A3905

Uranus — A3906

Neptune
A3907

LITHOGRAPHED
Serpentine Die Cut 10½
2016, May 31
Self-Adhesive
5069 A3900 (47c) multicolored 1.50 :40
5070 A3901 (47c) multicolored 1.50 .40
5071 A3902 (47c) multicolored 1.50 .40
5072 A3903 (47c) multicolored 1.50 .40
5073 A3904 (47c) multicolored 1.50 .40
5074 A3905 (47c) multicolored 1.50 .40
5075 A3906 (47c) multicolored 1.50 .40
5076 A3907 (47c) multicolored 1.50 .40
  a. Block of 8, #5069-5076 12.00
  Nos. 5069-5076 (8) 12.00 3.20

PLUTO EXPLORED

Pluto — A3908

New Horizons
Probe — A3909

LITHOGRAPHED
Serpentine Die Cut 10½
2016, May 31
Self-Adhesive
5077 A3908 (47c) multicolored 1.10 .25
5078 A3909 (47c) multicolored 1.10 .25
  a. Pair, #5077-5078 2.20

CLASSICS FOREVER

A3910

No. 5079: a, George Washington (redrawn type A16). b, Benjamin Franklin (redrawn type A5). c, Washington (redrawn type A17). d, Washington (redrawn type A19). e, Abraham Lincoln (redrawn type A33). f, Franklin (redrawn type A24).

LITHOGRAPHED & ENGRAVED
Serpentine Die Cut 10¾
2016, June 1
Self-Adhesive
5079 A3910 Pane of 6 6.60
  a. (47c) tan & black 1.10 .40
  b. (47c) tan & blue 1.10 .40
  c. (47c) tan & black 1.10 .40
  d. (47c) tan & blue 1.10 .40
  e. (47c) tan & black 1.10 .40
  f. (47c) tan & blue 1.10 .40

NATIONAL PARK SERVICE, CENT.

A3911

No. 5080: a, Iceberg in Glacier Bay National Park and Preserve, Alaska (48x31mm). b, Mount Rainier National Park (48x31mm). c, *Scenery in the Grand Tetons,* painting by Albert Bierstadt, at Marsh-Billings-Rockefeller National Historic Park, Vermont (24x31mm). d, Bass Harbor Head Lighthouse, Acadia National Park, Maine (48x31mm). e, *The Grand Canyon of Arizona,* painting by Thomas Moran, at Grand Canyon National Park, Arizona (48x31mm). f, Horses at Assateague Island National Seashore, Virginia and Maryland (48x31mm). g, Ship *Balclutha,* at San Francisco Maritime National Historic Park, California (24x31mm). h, Stone arch at Arches National Park, Utah (24x31mm). i, Aerial view of Theodore Roosevelt National Park, North Dakota (24x31mm). j, Water lily at Kenilworth Park and Aquatic Gardens, Washington, D.C. (24x31mm). k, *Administration Building at Frijoles Canyon,* drawing by Helmuth Naumer, Sr., at Bandelier National Monument, New Mexico (48x31mm). l, Everglades National Park, Florida (48x31mm). m, Rainbow at Haleakala National Park, Hawaii (48x31mm). n, Bison at Yellowstone National Park, Idaho, Montana and Wyoming (48x31mm). o, Carlsbad Caverns National Park, New Mexico (48x31mm). p, Heron at Gulf Islands National Seashore, Florida and Mississippi (24x31mm).

LITHOGRAPHED
Serpentine Die Cut 10½x10¾
2016, June 2 **Self-Adhesive**
5080 A3911 Pane of 16 + label 17.50
  a.-p. (47c) Any single 1.10 .50

COLORFUL CELEBRATIONS

Bird and Flowers — A3912

Birds and Flowers A3913

Flowers — A3914

Flowers A3915

Flowers — A3916

Flowers A3917

Birds and Flower — A3918

Bird and Flower — A3919

Flowers — A3920

Birds and Flower — A3921

LITHOGRAPHED
Serpentine Die Cut 11 on 2 or 3 Sides
2016, June 3
Booklet Stamps
Self-Adhesive

5081	A3912	(47c)	lt blue	1.50	.40
5082	A3913	(47c)	orange	1.50	.40
5083	A3914	(47c)	violet	1.50	.40
5084	A3915	(47c)	magneta	1.50	.40
5085	A3916	(47c)	lt blue	1.50	.40
5086	A3917	(47c)	orange	1.50	.40
5087	A3918	(47c)	violet	1.50	.40
5088	A3919	(47c)	magneta	1.50	.40
5089	A3920	(47c)	magneta	1.50	.40
5090	A3921	(47c)	violet	1.50	.40

a.   Block of 10, #5081-5090   15.00
b.   Booklet pane of 20, 2 each
     #5081-5090   30.00
Nos. 5081-5090 (10)   15.00   4.00

No. 5090b is a double-sided booklet pane with 12 stamps on one side (Nos. 5083-5090,

2 each Nos. 5081-5082) and eight stamps (Nos. 5083-5090) plus label (booklet cover) on the other side.

INDIANA STATEHOOD, 200th ANNIV.

Corn Field Near Milford A3922

LITHOGRAPHED
Serpentine Die Cut 10¾
2016, June 7
Self-Adhesive
5091 A3922 (47c) multicolored   1.10   .25

EID

"Eidukum Mubarak" A3923

LITHOGRAPHED
Serpentine Die Cut 11
2016, June 10
Self-Adhesive
5092 A3923 (47c) multicolored   1.10   .25

SODA FOUNTAIN FAVORITES

Ice Cream Cone A3924   Egg Cream A3925

Banana Split — A3926

Root Beer Float A3927   Hot Fudge Sundae A3928

No. 5095   No. 5095a

LITHOGRAPHED
Serpentine Die Cut 10¾
2016, June 30
Booklet Stamps
Self-Adhesive

5093	A3924	(47c)	multicolored	1.10	.40
5094	A3925	(47c)	multicolored	1.10	.40
5095	A3926	(47c)	multicolored (long sloping die cut at bottom)	1.10	.40

a.   Long sloping die cut at top   1.10   .40
5096 A3927 (47c) multicolored   1.10   .40
5097 A3928 (47c) multicolored   1.10   .40
a.   Horiz. strip of 5, #5093-5097   5.50
b.   Horiz. strip of 5, #5093-5094, 5095a, 5096-5097   5.50

c.   Booklet pane of 20, 4 each #5093-5094, 5096-5097, 2 each #5095, 5095a   22.00
Nos. 5093-5097 (5)   5.50   2.00

STAR QUILTS

A3929   A3930

LITHOGRAPHED
Serpentine Die Cut 11 Vert.
2016, July 6
Coil Stamps
Self-Adhesive
5098 A3929 (25c) multicolored   .50   .25
5099 A3930 (25c) multicolored   .50   .25
a.   Pair, #5098-5099   1.00

JAIME ESCALANTE

Jaime Escalante (1930-2010), High School Calculus Teacher — A3931

LITHOGRAPHED
Serpentine Die Cut 10¾
2016, July 13
Self-Adhesive
5100 A3931 (47c) multicolored   1.10   .25
Adjacent horizontal or vertical stamps have selvage between the stamps.

PICKUP TRUCKS

1938 International Harvester D-2 — A3932

1953 Chevrolet A3933

1948 Ford F-1 — A3934

1965 Ford F-100 — A3935

LITHOGRAPHED
Serpentine Die Cut 11 on 2 or 3 Sides
2016, July 15
Booklet Stamps
Self-Adhesive

5101	A3932	(47c)	multicolored	1.10	.30
5102	A3933	(47c)	multicolored	1.10	.30
5103	A3934	(47c)	multicolored	1.10	.30
5104	A3935	(47c)	multicolored	1.10	.30

a.   Block of 4, #5101-5104   4.40
b.   Booklet pane of 20, 5 each #5101-5104   22.00
Nos. 5101-5104 (4)   4.40   1.20

No. 5104b is a double-sided booklet pane with 12 stamps on one side (3 each Nos. 5101-5104) and eight stamps (2 each Nos. 5101-5104) plus label (booklet cover) on the other side.

LITERARY ARTS

Henry James (1843-1916), Novelist — A3936

LITHOGRAPHED
Serpentine Die Cut 11
2016, July 31
Self-Adhesive
5105 A3936 (89c) multicolored   1.90   .30

PETS

Puppy — A3937

Betta Fish — A3938

Iguana — A3939

Hamster A3940

Goldfish — A3941

Kitten — A3942

Rabbit — A3943

Tortoise — A3944

Guinea Pig — A3945

Parrot — A3946

Corn
Snake — A3947

Mouse — A3948

Hermit
Crab — A3949

Chinchilla
A3950

Gerbil — A3951

Gecko — A3952

Cat — A3953

Horse — A3954

Parakeets
A3955

Dog — A3956

LITHOGRAPHED
Serpentine Die Cut 11 on 2 or 3 Sides

2016, Aug. 2
Booklet Stamps
Self-Adhesive

5106	A3937	(47c) multicolored	1.10	.50
5107	A3938	(47c) multicolored	1.10	.50
5108	A3939	(47c) multicolored	1.10	.50
5109	A3940	(47c) multicolored	1.10	.50
5110	A3941	(47c) multicolored	1.10	.50
5111	A3942	(47c) multicolored	1.10	.50
5112	A3943	(47c) multicolored	1.10	.50
5113	A3944	(47c) multicolored	1.10	.50
5114	A3945	(47c) multicolored	1.10	.50
5115	A3946	(47c) multicolored	1.10	.50
5116	A3947	(47c) multicolored	1.10	.50
5117	A3948	(47c) multicolored	1.10	.50
5118	A3949	(47c) multicolored	1.10	.50
5119	A3950	(47c) multicolored	1.10	.50
5120	A3951	(47c) multicolored	1.10	.50
5121	A3952	(47c) multicolored	1.10	.50
5122	A3953	(47c) multicolored	1.10	.50
5123	A3954	(47c) multicolored	1.10	.50

5124	A3955	(47c) multicolored	1.10	.50
5125	A3956	(47c) multicolored	1.10	.50
a.		Booklet pane of 20, #5106-5125	22.00	
		Nos. 5106-5125 (20)	22.00	10.00

No. 5125a is a double-sided booklet pane with 12 stamps on one side (Nos. 5106-5117) and eight stamps (Nos. 5118-5125) plus label (booklet cover) on the other side.

SONGBIRDS IN SNOW

Golden-crowned
Kinglets
A3957

Cedar Waxwing
A3958

Northern
Cardinal
A3959

Red-breasted
Nuthatches
A3960

LITHOGRAPHED
Serpentine Die Cut 10¾ on 2 or 3 Sides

2016, Aug. 4
Booklet Stamps
Self-Adhesive

5126	A3957	(47c) multicolored	1.10	.30
5127	A3958	(47c) multicolored	1.10	.30
5128	A3959	(47c) multicolored	1.10	.30
5129	A3960	(47c) multicolored	1.10	.30
a.		Block of 4, #5126-5129	4.40	
b.		Booklet pane of 20, 5 each #5126-5129	22.00	
		Nos. 5126-5129 (4)	4.40	1.20

No. 5129b is a double-sided booklet pane with 12 stamps on one side (3 each Nos. 5126-5129) and eight stamps (2 each Nos. 5126-5129) plus label (booklet cover) on the other side.

PATRIOTIC SPIRAL

Stars — A3961

LITHOGRAPHED
Serpentine Die Cut 10 Vert.
2016, Aug. 19
Coil Stamp
Self-Adhesive

5130	A3961	(47c) multicolored	1.10	.25

Booklet Stamp
Serpentine Die Cut 11 on 2 or 3 Sides

5131	A3961	(47c) multicolored	1.10	.25
a.		Booklet pane of 10	11.00	

STAR TREK TELEVISION SHOW, 50TH ANNIV

Starship
Enterprise and
Starfleet Insignia
A3962

Crewman in
Transporter
A3963

Starship
Enterprise and
Planet — A3964

Starship
Enterprise,
Planet, Vulcan
Hand
Salute — A3965

LITHOGRAPHED
2016, Sept. 2 *Serpentine Die Cut 11*
Self-Adhesive

5132	A3962	(47c) multicolored	1.10	.30
5133	A3963	(47c) multicolored	1.10	.30
5134	A3964	(47c) multicolored	1.10	.30
5135	A3965	(47c) multicolored	1.10	.30
a.		Block or vert. strip of 4, #5132-5135	4.40	
		Nos. 5132-5135 (4)	4.40	1.20

EASTERN TAILED-BLUE BUTTERFLY

A3966

LITHOGRAPHED
Serpentine Die Cut 10½
2016, Sept. 24
Self-Adhesive

5136	A3966	(68c) multicolored	1.40	.25

JACK-O'-LANTERNS

Four Teeth
A3967

Five Teeth
A3968

Three Teeth
A3969

Nine Teeth
A3970

LITHOGRAPHED
Serpentine Die Cut 11x10¾ on 2 or 3 Sides
2016, Sept. 29
Booklet Stamps
Self-Adhesive

5137	A3967	(47c) multicolored	1.10	.30
5138	A3968	(47c) multicolored	1.10	.30
5139	A3969	(47c) multicolored	1.10	.30

5140	A3970	(47c) multicolored	1.10	.30
a.		Block of 4, #5137-5140	4.40	
b.		Booklet pane of 20, 5 each #5137-5140	22.00	
		Nos. 5137-5140 (4)	4.40	1.20

No. 5140b is a double-sided booklet pane with 12 stamps on one side (3 each Nos. 5137-5140) and eight stamps (2 each Nos. 5137-5140) plus label (booklet cover) on the other side.

KWANZAA

Woman, Fruits and
Vegetables — A3971

LITHOGRAPHED
2016, Oct. 1 *Serpentine Die Cut 11*
Self-Adhesive

5141	A3971	(47c) multicolored	1.10	.25

DIWALI

Diya — A3972

LITHOGRAPHED
2016, Oct. 5 *Serpentine Die Cut 11*
Self-Adhesive

5142	A3972	(47c) multicolored	1.10	.25

CHRISTMAS

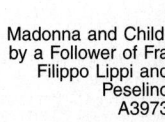

Madonna and Child,
by a Follower of Fra
Filippo Lippi and
Peselino
A3973

Nativity
A3974

Candle in
Window
A3975

Wreath in
Window
A3976

Star in Window
A3977

Christmas Tree
in Window
A3978

LITHOGRAPHED
Serpentine Die Cut 10¾x11 on 2 or 3 Sides
2016
Booklet Stamps
Self-Adhesive

5143	A3973	(47c) multicolored	1.10	.25
a.		Booklet pane of 20	22.00	
5144	A3974	(47c) multicolored	1.10	.25
a.		Booklet pane of 20	22.00	

5145	A3975 (47c) multicolored	1.10	.25
5146	A3976 (47c) multicolored	1.10	.25
5147	A3977 (47c) multicolored	1.10	.25
5148	A3978 (47c) multicolored	1.10	.25
a.	Block of 4, #5145-5148	4.40	
b.	Booklet pane of 20, 5 each #5145-5148	22.00	
	Nos. 5143-5148 (6)	6.60	1.50

Issued: No. 5143, 10/18; No. 5144, 11/3; Nos. 5145-5148, 10/6. Nos. 5143a and 5144a are double-sided booklet panes with 12 stamps on one side and eight stamps plus label (booklet cover) on the other side. No. 5148b is a double-sided booklet pane with 12 stamps on one side (3 each Nos. 5145-5148) and eight stamps (2 each Nos. 5145-5148) plus label (booklet cover) on the other side.

WONDER WOMAN, 75TH ANNIVERSARY

Modern Age Wonder Woman A3979 — Bronze Age Wonder Woman A3980

Silver Age Wonder Woman A3981 — Golden Age Wonder Woman A3982

LITHOGRAPHED
2016, Oct. 7   Serpentine Die Cut 11
Self-Adhesive

5149	A3979 (47c) multicolored	1.10	.30
5150	A3980 (47c) multicolored	1.10	.30
5151	A3981 (47c) multicolored	1.10	.30
5152	A3982 (47c) multicolored	1.10	.30
a.	Vert. strip of 4, #5149-5152	4.40	
	Nos. 5149-5152 (4)	4.40	1.20

HANUKKAH

Menorah A3983

LITHOGRAPHED
2016, Nov. 1   Serpentine Die Cut 11
Self-Adhesive

5153	A3983 (47c) multicolored	1.10	.25

CHINESE NEW YEAR

Year of the Rooster A3984

LITHOGRAPHED
Serpentine Die Cut 10¾
2017, Jan. 5
Self-Adhesive

5154	A3984 (47c) multicolored	1.10	.25

LOVE

Airplane and Skywriting A3985

LITHOGRAPHED
Serpentine Die Cut 11x10¾
2017, Jan. 7
Self-Adhesive

5155	A3985 (47c) light blue	1.25	.25

AMERICAN LANDMARKS ISSUE

Lili'uokalani Gardens, Hilo, Hawaii A3986

Gateway Arch, St. Louis, Missouri A3987

LITHOGRAPHED
Serpentine Die Cut 10¾x10½
2017, Jan. 22
Self-Adhesive

5156	A3986 $6.65 multi	13.50	7.75
5157	A3987 $23.75 multi	47.50	25.00

Flag — A3988

LITHOGRAPHED
Serpentine Die Cut 11 Vert.
2017, Jan. 27
Coil Stamps
Self-Adhesive
Microprinted "USPS" On Right End of Fourth Red Stripe

5158	A3988 (49c) multicolored	1.10	.25
a.	Die cutting omitted, pair	—	
b.	Vert. pair, unslit between	—	

Serpentine Die Cut 9½ Vert.
Microprinted "USPS" on Right End of Second White Flag Stripe

5159	A3988 (49c) multicolored	1.10	.25

Booklet Stamps
Microprinted "USPS" on Right End of Fourth Red Stripe
Serpentine Die Cut 11¼x10¾ on 2 or 3 Sides

5160	A3988 (49c) multicolored	1.10	.25
a.	Booklet pane of 10	11.00	
b.	Booklet pane of 20	22.00	

Microprinted "USPS" on Right End of Second White Flag Stripe

5161	A3988c (49c) multicolored	1.10	.25
a.	Booklet pane of 20	22.00	

Microprinted "USPS" on Left End of Second White Flag Stripe Near Blue Field
Thin Paper
Serpentine Die Cut 11¼x10¾ on 2, 3 or 4 Sides

5162	A3988 (49c) multicolored	2.75	.25
a.	Booklet pane of 18	50.00	
	Nos. 5160-5162 (3)	4.95	.75

Nos. 5160b and 5161a are double-sided booklets with 12 stamps on one side and eight stamps plus a label that serves as the booklet cover on the other side.

SHELLS

Queen Conch A3989 — Pacific Calico Scallop A3990

Alphabet Cone A3991 — Zebra Nerite A3992

LITHOGRAPHED
Serpentine Die Cut 11¼x10¾
2017, Jan. 28
Self-Adhesive

5163	A3989 (34c) multicolored	.70	.25
5164	A3990 (34c) multicolored	.70	.25
5165	A3991 (34c) multicolored	.70	.25
5166	A3992 (34c) multicolored	.70	.25
a.	Horiz. or vert. strip of 4, #5163-5166	2.80	
	Nos. 5163-5166 (4)	2.80	1.00

Coil Stamps
Serpentine Die Cut 9¾ Vert.

5167	A3991 (34c) multicolored	.70	.25
5168	A3992 (34c) multicolored	.70	.25
5169	A3989 (34c) multicolored	.70	.25
5170	A3990 (34c) multicolored	.70	.25
a.	Horiz. strip of 4, #5167-5170	2.80	
	Nos. 5167-5170 (4)	2.80	1.00

BLACK HERITAGE

Dorothy Height (1912-2010), President of National Council of Negro Women — A3993

LITHOGRAPHED
2017, Feb. 1   Serpentine Die Cut 11
Self-Adhesive

5171	A3993 (49c) multicolored	1.10	.25

"USA" and Star With Blue Frame — A3994

LITHOGRAPHED
Serpentine Die Cut 10 Vert.
2017, Feb. 10
COIL STAMP
Self-Adhesive

5172	A3994 (5c) multicolored	.25	.25
a.	Red omitted		

The discovery example of No. 5172a is on piece, uncanceled.

OSCAR DE LA RENTA

Oscar de la Renta (1932-2014), Fashion Designer — A3995

A3996

A3997

A3998

A3999

A4000

A4001

A4002

A4003

A4004

A4005

LITHOGRAPHED

Serpentine Die Cut 11x10¾ (No. 5173a), 10¾x11

2017, Feb. 16

Self-Adhesive

5173		Pane of 11	12.00	
a.	A3995	(49c) multicolored	1.10	.50
b.	A3996	(49c) multicolored	1.10	.50
c.	A3997	(49c) multicolored	1.10	.50
d.	A3998	(49c) multicolored	1.10	.50
e.	A3999	(49c) multicolored	1.10	.50
f.	A4000	(49c) multicolored	1.10	.50
g.	A4001	(49c) multicolored	1.10	.50
h.	A4002	(49c) multicolored	1.10	.50
i.	A4003	(49c) multicolored	1.10	.50
j.	A4004	(49c) multicolored	1.10	.50
k.	A4005	(49c) multicolored	1.10	.50

People Wearing Uncle Sam Hats — A4006

LITHOGRAPHED

Serpentine Die Cut 11¼x11

2017, Feb. 18

Self-Adhesive

5174	A4006	(21c) multicolored	.45	.25

See No. 5341.

PRES. JOHN F. KENNEDY (1917-63)

Pres. John F. Kennedy
A4007

LITHOGRAPHED

Serpentine Die Cut 10¾

2017, Feb. 20

Self-Adhesive

5175	A4007	(49c) brown	1.10	.25

Fruits Type of 2016

Designs: 5c, Pinot Noir Grapes. 10c, Red Pears.

LITHOGRAPHED

2017   *Serpentine Die Cut 11¼x11*

Self-Adhesive

5177	A3873	5c multicolored	.25	.25

See Nos. 5038, 5039.

5178	A3874	10c multicolored	.25	.25

Issued: 5c, 2/24; 10c, 3/23.
See Nos. 5038-5039, 5201, 5256.

NEBRASKA STATEHOOD, 150th ANNIV.

Sandhill Cranes Flying Over Platte River
A4008

LITHOGRAPHED

Serpentine Die Cut 10¾

2017, Mar. 1

Self-Adhesive

5179	A4008	(49c) multicolored	1.10	.25

WORKS PROGRESS ADMINISTRATION (WORK PROJECTS ADMINISTRATION) POSTERS

See America Welcome to Montana Poster — A4009

Work Pays America Poster — A4010

Field Day Poster — A4011

Discover Puerto Rico Poster — A4012

City of New York Municipal Airports Poster — A4013

Foreign Trade Zone Poster — A4014

Visit the Zoo Poster — A4015

Work with Care Poster — A4016

The National Parks Preserve Wild Life Poster — A4017

Hiking Poster — A4018

LITHOGRAPHED

Serpentine Die Cut 11 on 2 or 3 Sides

2017, Mar. 7

Booklet Stamps

Self-Adhesive

5180	A4009	(49c) multicolored	1.10	.40
5181	A4010	(49c) multicolored	1.10	.40
5182	A4011	(49c) multicolored	1.10	.40
5183	A4012	(49c) multicolored	1.10	.40
5184	A4013	(49c) multicolored	1.10	.40
5185	A4014	(49c) multicolored	1.10	.40
5186	A4015	(49c) multicolored	1.10	.40
5187	A4016	(49c) multicolored	1.10	.40
5188	A4017	(49c) multicolored	1.10	.40

5189	A4018	(49c) multicolored	1.10	.40
a.		Block of 10, #5180-5189	11.00	
b.		Booklet pane of 20, 2 each #5180-5189	22.00	
		Nos. 5180-5189 (10)	11.00	4.00

No. 5189b is a double-sided booklet pane with 12 stamps on one side (Nos. 5181-5184, 5186-5189, 2 each Nos. 5180, 5185) and eight stamps (Nos. 5181-5184, 5186-5189) plus label (booklet cover) on the other side.

MISSISSIPPI STATEHOOD, 200th ANNIV.

Guitarist
A4019

LITHOGRAPHED

Serpentine Die Cut 10¾

2017, Mar. 31

Self-Adhesive

5190	A4019	(49c) multicolored	1.10	.25

DISTINGUISHED AMERICANS

Robert Panara (1920-2014), Educator of the Deaf — A4020

LITHOGRAPHED

Serpentine Die Cut 10¾

2017, Apr. 11   **Tagged**

Self-Adhesive

5191	A4020	(70c) multicolored	1.40	.25

Adjacent horizontal or vertical stamps have selvage between the stamps.

DELICIOSO (LATIN AMERICAN DISHES)

Tamales
A4021

Flan — A4022

Sancocho
A4023

Empanadas
A4024

Chile Relleno — A4025

Ceviche — A4026

LITHOGRAPHED

Serpentine Die Cut 11 on 2 or 3 Sides

2017, Apr. 20   **Tagged**

Booklet Stamps

Self-Adhesive

5192	A4021	(49c) multicolored	1.10	.40
5193	A4022	(49c) multicolored	1.10	.40
5194	A4023	(49c) multicolored	1.10	.40
5195	A4024	(49c) multicolored	1.10	.40
5196	A4025	(49c) multicolored	1.10	.40
5197	A4026	(49c) multicolored	1.10	.40
a.		Block of 6, #5192-5197	6.60	
b.		Booklet pane of 20, 4 each #5192-5193, 3 each #5194-5197	22.00	
		Nos. 5192-5197 (6)	6.60	2.40

No. 5197b is a double-sided booklet pane with 12 stamps on one side (2 each Nos. 5192-5197) and eight stamps (Nos. 5194-5197, 2 each Nos. 5192-5193) plus label (booklet cover) on the other side.

Echeveria
A4027

LITHOGRAPHED

Serpentine Die Cut

2017, Apr. 28   **Tagged**

Self-Adhesive

5198	A4027	($1.15) multicolored	2.40	.50

Unused values are for stamps with surrounding selvage. Adjacent stamps are separated by rouletting.

CELEBRATION FLOWERS

Boutonniere
A4028

Corsage
A4029

LITHOGRAPHED

Serpentine Die Cut 10¾

2017, May 2   **Tagged**

Self-Adhesive

5199	A4028	(49c) multicolored	1.10	.25
5200	A4029	(70c) multicolored	1.40	.25

FRUIT

Strawberries — A4030

LITHOGRAPHED

Serpentine Die Cut 10 Vert.

2017, May 5

Coil Stamps

Self-Adhesive

5201	A4030	3c multicolored	.25	.25

HENRY DAVID THOREAU

Henry David Thoreau (1817-62), Writer, and Sumac Leaves
A4031

LITHOGRAPHED
Serpentine Die Cut 10¾
2017, May 23
Self-Adhesive
5202 A4031 (49c) multicolored 1.10 .25

SPORTS BALLS

Football
A4032

Volleyball
A4033

Soccer
Ball — A4034

Golf
Ball — A4035

Baseball
A4036

Basketball
A4037

Tennis
Ball — A4038

Kickball
A4039

LITHOGRAPHED & TYPOGRAPHED
2017, June 14 *Serpentine Die Cut*
Self-Adhesive

5203 A4032 (49c) multicolored 1.10 .40
5204 A4033 (49c) multicolored 1.10 .40
5205 A4034 (49c) multicolored 1.10 .40
5206 A4035 (49c) multicolored 1.10 .40
5207 A4036 (49c) multicolored 1.10 .40
5208 A4037 (49c) multicolored 1.10 .40

5209 A4038 (49c) multicolored 1.10 .40
5210 A4039 (49c) multicolored 1.10 .40
a. Block of 8, #5203-5210 8.80
Nos. 5203-5210 (8) 8.80 3.20

The typographed printing imitates the texture of the ball.

AUGUST 21, 2017, TOTAL SOLAR ECLIPSE

Total Solar
Eclipse — A4040

LITHOGRAPHED
Serpentine Die Cut 10½
2017, June 20
Self-Adhesive
5211 A4040 (49c) multicolored 1.10 .25

The moon is covered with a circle of thermochromic ink, which when warmed, allows the moon and the corona of the sun around the moon to be seen.

PAINTINGS BY ANDREW WYETH (1917-2009)

Wind from the Sea, 1947
A4041

Big Room, 1988
A4042

Christina's World, 1948
A4043

Alvaro and Christina, 1968
A4044

Frostbitten, 1962
A4045

Sailor's Valentine, 1985
A4046

Soaring, 1942-50
A4047

North Light, 1984
A4048

Spring Fed, 1967
A4049

The Carry, 2003
A4050

Young Bull, 1960
A4051

My Studio, 1974
A4052

LITHOGRAPHED
Serpentine Die Cut 10¾x10½
2017, July 12
Self-Adhesive
5212 Pane of 12 13.00
a. A4041 (49c) multicolored 1.10 .50
b. A4042 (49c) multicolored 1.10 .50
c. A4043 (49c) multicolored 1.10 .50
d. A4044 (49c) multicolored 1.10 .50
e. A4045 (49c) multicolored 1.10 .50
f. A4046 (49c) multicolored 1.10 .50
g. A4047 (49c) multicolored 1.10 .50
h. A4048 (49c) multicolored 1.10 .50
i. A4049 (49c) multicolored 1.10 .50
j. A4050 (49c) multicolored 1.10 .50
k. A4051 (49c) multicolored 1.10 .50
l. A4052 (49c) multicolored 1.10 .50

DISNEY VILLAINS

The Queen from *Snow White and the Seven Dwarfs* — A4053

Honest John from *Pinocchio*
A4054

Lady Tremaine from *Cinderella*
A4055

Queen of Hearts from *Alice in Wonderland*
A4056

Captain Hook from *Peter Pan* — A4057

Maleficent from *Sleeping Beauty* — A4058

Cruella De Vil from *One Hundred and One Dalmatians*
A4059

Ursula from *The Little Mermaid*
A4060

Gaston from *Beauty and the Beast* — A4061

Scar from *The Lion King* — A4062

LITHOGRAPHED
Serpentine Die Cut 10½x10¾
2017, July 15   **Self-Adhesive**

5213	A4053	(49c) multicolored	1.10	.40
5214	A4054	(49c) multicolored	1.10	.40
5215	A4055	(49c) multicolored	1.10	.40
5216	A4056	(49c) multicolored	1.10	.40
5217	A4057	(49c) multicolored	1.10	.40
5218	A4058	(49c) multicolored	1.10	.40
5219	A4059	(49c) multicolored	1.10	.40
5220	A4060	(49c) multicolored	1.10	.40
5221	A4061	(49c) multicolored	1.10	.40
5222	A4062	(49c) multicolored	1.10	.40
a.		Block of 10, #5213-5222	11.00	
		Nos. 5213-5222 (10)	11.00	4.00

SHARKS

Mako Shark A4063

Whale Shark A4064

Thresher Shark A4065

Hammerhead Shark — A4066

Great White Shark A4067

LITHOGRAPHED
Serpentine Die Cut 10¾
2017, July 26   **Self-Adhesive**

5223	A4063	(49c) multicolored	1.10	.40
5224	A4064	(49c) multicolored	1.10	.40
5225	A4065	(49c) multicolored	1.10	.40
5226	A4066	(49c) multicolored	1.10	.40
5227	A4067	(49c) multicolored	1.10	.40
a.		Vert. strip of 5, #5223-5227	5.50	
		Nos. 5223-5227 (5)	5.50	2.00

PROTECT POLLINATORS

Monarch Butterfly on Purple Coneflower A4068

Western Honeybee on Golden Ragwort A4069

Monarch Butterfly on Red Zinnia A4070

Western Honeybee on Purple New England Aster A4071

Monarch Butterfly on Goldenrod A4072

LITHOGRAPHED
Serpentine Die Cut 10¾
2017, Aug. 3   **Self-Adhesive**

5228	A4068	(49c) multicolored	1.10	.40
5229	A4069	(49c) multicolored	1.10	.40
5230	A4070	(49c) multicolored	1.10	.40
5231	A4071	(49c) multicolored	1.10	.40
5232	A4072	(49c) multicolored	1.10	.40
a.		Vert. strip of 5, #5228-5232	5.50	
		Nos. 5228-5232 (5)	5.50	2.00

FLOWERS FROM THE GARDEN

Red Camellias and Yellow Forsythia in Yellow Pitcher A4073

White Peonies and Pink Tree Peonies in Clear Vase A4074

Blue Hydrangeas in Blue Pot — A4075

Assorted Flowers in White Vase — A4076

Red Camellias and Yellow Forsythia in Yellow Pitcher A4077

Assorted Flowers in White Vase A4078

White Peonies and Pink Tree Peonies in Clear Vase — A4079

Blue Hydrangeas in Blue Pot — A4080

LITHOGRAPHED
Serpentine Die Cut 10¾ Vert.
2017, Aug. 16   **Coil Stamps**   **Self-Adhesive**

5233	A4073	(49c) multicolored	1.10	.30
5234	A4074	(49c) multicolored	1.10	.30
5235	A4075	(49c) multicolored	1.10	.30
5236	A4076	(49c) multicolored	1.10	.30
a.		Strip of 4, #5233-5236	4.40	
		Nos. 5233-5236 (4)	4.40	1.20

Booklet Stamps
Serpentine Die Cut 11 on 2 or 3 Sides

5237	A4077	(49c) multicolored	1.25	.30
5238	A4078	(49c) multicolored	1.25	.30
5239	A4079	(49c) multicolored	1.25	.30
5240	A4080	(49c) multicolored	1.25	.30
a.		Block of 4, #5237-5240	5.00	
b.		Booklet pane of 20, 5 each #5237-5240	25.00	
		Nos. 5237-5240 (4)	5.00	1.20

No. 5240b is a double-sided booklet pane with 12 stamps on one side (3 each Nos. 5237-5240) and eight stamps (2 each Nos. 5237-5240) plus label (booklet cover) on the other side.

FATHER THEODORE ("TED") HESBURGH

Hesburgh (1917-2015), President of University of Notre Dame — A4081

LITHOGRAPHED
Serpentine Die Cut 11
2017, Sept. 1   **Tagged**
Self-Adhesive

5241	A4081	(49c) multicolored	1.10	.25

Coil Stamp
Serpentine Die Cut 9½ Horiz.

5242	A4081	(49c) multicolored	1.10	.25

"THE SNOWY DAY," BY EZRA JACK KEATS

Peter Making Snowball A4082

Peter Sliding Down Mountain of Snow A4083

Peter Making Snow Angel — A4084

Peter Leaving Footprints in Snow — A4085

LITHOGRAPHED
Serpentine Die Cut 10¾ on 2 or 3 Sides
2017, Oct. 4   **Booklet Stamps**   **Self-Adhesive**

5243	A4082	(49c) multicolored	1.10	.30
5244	A4083	(49c) multicolored	1.10	.30
5245	A4084	(49c) multicolored	1.10	.30
5246	A4085	(49c) multicolored	1.10	.30
a.		Block of 4, #5243-5246	4.40	
b.		Booklet pane of 20, 5 each #5243-5246	22.00	
		Nos. 5243-5246 (4)	4.40	1.20

No. 5246b is a double-sided booklet pane with 12 stamps on one side (3 each Nos. 5243-5246), and eight stamps (2 each Nos. 5243-5246) plus label (booklet cover) on the other side.

CHRISTMAS CAROLS

Christmas Lights, Cookies, and Line From "Deck the Halls" — A4086

Star of Bethlehem, Lamb, and Line From "Silent Night" — A4087

Snowflakes, Horse, and Line From "Jingle Bells" — A4088

Child, Santa Claus, and Line From "Jolly Old St. Nicholas" A4089

LITHOGRAPHED
Serpentine Die Cut 10¾ on 2 or 3 Sides
2017, Oct. 5   **Booklet Stamps**   **Self-Adhesive**

5247	A4086	(49c) multicolored	1.10	.30
5248	A4087	(49c) multicolored	1.10	.30
5249	A4088	(49c) multicolored	1.10	.30
5250	A4089	(49c) multicolored	1.10	.30
a.		Block of 4, #5247-5250	4.40	
b.		Booklet pane of 20, 5 each #5247-5250	22.00	
		Nos. 5247-5250 (4)	4.40	1.20

No. 5250b is a double-sided booklet pane with 12 stamps on one side (3 each Nos. 5247-5250), and eight stamps (2 each Nos. 5247-5250) plus label (booklet cover) on the other side.

NATIONAL MUSEUM OF AFRICAN AMERICAN HISTORY AND CULTURE

Museum Building, Washington, D.C. — A4090

LITHOGRAPHED
Serpentine Die Cut 10¾x10½
2017, Oct. 13   **Tagged**
Self-Adhesive

5251	A4090	(49c) multicolored	1.10	.25

HISTORY OF ICE HOCKEY

Player Wearing Helmet and Protective Gear — A4091

Player Wearing Hat and Scarf — A4092

LITHOGRAPHED
2017, Oct. 20   *Serpentine Die Cut 11*
Self-Adhesive

5252	A4091	(49c) multicolored	1.10	.25
a.		As No. 5252, matte-finish stamp	1.10	.25

5253 A4092 (49c) multicolored　1.10　.25
a.　As No. 5253, matte-finish
　　stamp　1.10　.25
b.　Vert. pair, #5252-5253　2.20
c.　Souvenir sheet of 2,
　　#5252a-5253a　2.20

On Nos. 5253b and 5253c, stamps are printed tete-beche. Stamps from No. 5253b have a glossier finish than those on No. 5253c. Adjacent horizontal stamps have selvage between them.
See Canada Nos. 3039-3041.

CHINESE NEW YEAR

Year of the Dog A4093

LITHOGRAPHED
Serpentine Die Cut 10¾
2018, Jan. 11
Self-Adhesive
5254 A4093 (49c) multicolored　1.10　.25

LOVE

Flowers — A4094

LITHOGRAPHED
Serpentine Die Cut 11x10¾
2018, Jan. 18
Self-Adhesive
5255 A4094 (49c) multicolored　1.10　.25

FRUIT

Meyer Lemons — A4095

LITHOGRAPHED
Serpentine Die Cut 10¾ Vert.
2018, Jan. 19
Coil Stamp
Self-Adhesive
5256 A4095　2c multicolored　.25　.25

AMERICAN LANDMARKS ISSUE

Byodo-In Temple, Kaneohe, Hawaii A4096

Sleeping Bear Dunes, Michigan A4097

LITHOGRAPHED
Serpentine Die Cut 10¾x10½
2018, Jan. 21
Self-Adhesive
5257 A4096　$6.70 multi　13.50　7.75
5258 A4097　$24.70 multi　50.00　25.00

BLACK HERITAGE

Lena Horne (1917-2010), Singer — A4098

LITHOGRAPHED
Serpentine Die Cut 10¾
2018, Jan. 30
Self-Adhesive
5259 A4098 (50c) multicolored　1.10　.25

Flag — A4099

LITHOGRAPHED
Serpentine Die Cut 9½ Vert.
2018, Feb. 9
Coil Stamps
Self-Adhesive
Microprinted "USPS" at Left of Flag Fold on Fourth White Stripe
5260 A4099 (50c) multicolored　1.10　.25
Serpentine Die Cut 11 Vert.
Microprinted "USPS" at Right of Flag Fold on Fifth White Stripe
5261 A4099 (50c) multicolored　1.10　.25
Booklet Stamps Microprinted "USPS" at Left of Flag Fold on Fourth Red Stripe
Serpentine Die Cut 11¼x10¾ on 2 or 3 Sides
5262 A4099b(50c) multicolored　1.10　.25
a.　Booklet pane of 20　22.00
Microprinted "USPS" at Right of Flag Fold on Fifth White Stripe
5263 A4099 (50c) multicolored　1.10　.25
a.　Booklet pane of 20　22.00

Nos. 5262a and 5263a are double-sided booklets with 12 stamps on one side and eight stamps plus a label that serves as the booklet cover on the other side.

BIOLUMINESCENT LIFE

Octopus A4100

Jellyfish A4101

Comb Jelly A4102

Mushrooms A4103

Firefly A4104

Bamboo Coral A4105

Marine Worm A4106

Crown Jellyfish A4107

Marine Worm A4108

Sea Pen A4109

LITHOGRAPHED
Serpentine Die Cut 11
2018, Feb. 22
Self-Adhesive
5264 A4100 (50c) multicolored　1.10　.40
5265 A4101 (50c) multicolored　1.10　.40
5266 A4102 (50c) multicolored　1.10　.40
5267 A4103 (50c) multicolored　1.10　.40
5268 A4104 (50c) multicolored　1.10　.40
5269 A4105 (50c) multicolored　1.10　.40
5270 A4106 (50c) multicolored　1.10　.40
5271 A4107 (50c) multicolored　1.10　.40
5272 A4108 (50c) multicolored　1.10　.40
5273 A4109 (50c) multicolored　1.10　.40
a.　Block of 10, #5264-5273　11.00
　　Nos. 5264-5273 (10)　11.00　4.00

ILLINOIS STATEHOOD, 200TH ANNIV.

Map of Illinois and Sun Rays — A4110

LITHOGRAPHED
2018, Mar. 5　*Serpentine Die Cut 11*
Self-Adhesive
5274 A4110 (50c) multicolored　1.10　.25

MISTER ROGERS

Fred Rogers (1928-2003), Host of Children's Television Show, *Mister Rogers*, and Puppet, King Friday XIII — A4111

LITHOGRAPHED
Serpentine Die Cut 11
2018, Mar. 23
Self-Adhesive
5275 A4111 (50c) multicolored　1.10　.25

SCIENCE, TECHNOLOGY, ENGINEERING AND MATHEMATICS (STEM) EDUCATION

Head and Symbols of Science Education A4112

Head and Symbols of Technology Education A4113

Head and Symbols of Engineering Education A4114

Head and Symbols of Mathematics Education A4115

LITHOGRAPHED
2018, Apr. 6　*Serpentine Die Cut 11*
Self-Adhesive
5276 A4112 (50c) multicolored　1.10　.30
5277 A4113 (50c) multicolored　1.10　.30
5278 A4114 (50c) multicolored　1.10　.30
5279 A4115 (50c) multicolored　1.10　.30
a.　Vert. strip of 4, #5276-5279　4.40
　　Nos. 5276-5279 (4)　4.40　1.20

Peace Rose — A4116

LITHOGRAPHED
Serpentine Die Cut 11¼x10¾ on 2 or 3 Sides
2018, Apr. 21
Booklet Stamp
Self-Adhesive
5280 A4116 (50c) multicolored　1.10　.25
a.　Booklet pane of 20　22.00

No. 5280a is a double-sided booklet with 12 stamps on one side and eight stamps plus a label that serves as the booklet cover on the other side.
See note after No. 1549.

AIR MAIL, CENT.

Curtiss JN-4H "Jenny" Biplane A4117

ENGRAVED
2018　*Serpentine Die Cut 10¾*
Self-Adhesive
5281 A4117 (50c) blue　1.10　.25
5282 A4117 (50c) carmine lake　1.10　.25

Issued: No. 5281, 5/1. No. 5282, 8/11.

SALLY RIDE

Sally Ride (1951-2012), First American Woman in Space, and Space Shuttle Launch — A4118

LITHOGRAPHED
Serpentine Die Cut 10½x10¾
2018, May 23
Self-Adhesive

5283 A4118 (50c) multicolored   1.10   .25

FLAG ACT OF 1818, BICENT.

20-Star Flag — A4119

LITHOGRAPHED
Serpentine Die Cut 10¾
2018, June 9
Self-Adhesive

5284 A4119 (50c) multicolored   1.10   .25

FROZEN TREATS

A4120   A4121

A4122   A4123

A4124   A4125

A4126   A4127

A4128   A4129

LITHOGRAPHED
Serpentine Die Cut 11¼x10¾ on 2 or 3 Sides
2018, June 20
Booklet Stamps
Self-Adhesive

5285	A4120 (50c) multicolored	1.10	.40
5286	A4121 (50c) multicolored	1.10	.40
5287	A4122 (50c) multicolored	1.10	.40
5288	A4123 (50c) multicolored	1.10	.40
5289	A4124 (50c) multicolored	1.10	.40
5290	A4125 (50c) multicolored	1.10	.40
5291	A4126 (50c) multicolored	1.10	.40
5292	A4127 (50c) multicolored	1.10	.40
5293	A4128 (50c) multicolored	1.10	.40

5294	A4129 (50c) multicolored	1.10	.40
a.	Block of 10, #5285-5294	11.00	
b.	Booklet pane of 20, 2 each #5285-5294	22.00	
	Nos. 5285-5294 (10)	11.00	4.00

Nos. 5294b has a scratch-and-sniff coating with a fruity aroma, and is a double-sided booklet with 12 stamps on one side (Nos. 5286-5289, 5291-5294, 2 each Nos 5285, 5290), and eight stamps (Nos. 5286-5289, 5291-5294) plus a label that serves as the booklet cover on the other side.

STATUE OF FREEDOM

Head of Statue of Freedom on U.S. Capitol Dome — A4130

LITHOGRAPHED & ENGRAVED
Serpentine Die Cut 10¾x10½
2018, June 27
Self-Adhesive

5295	A4130 $1 emer, reddsh pink & blk	2.00	.50
5296	A4130 $2 indigo, reddsh pink & blk	4.00	1.00
5297	A4130 $5 brk red, reddsh pink & blk	10.00	2.50
	Nos. 5295-5297 (3)	16.00	4.00

Optically-variable ink was used for the numerals in the denominations.

O BEAUTIFUL

Death Valley National Park, California and Nevada — A4131

Three Fingers Mountain, Washington — A4132

Double Rainbow Over Field, Kansas — A4133

Great Smoky Mountains National Park, North Carolina and Tennessee — A4134

Field of Wheat, Wisconsin — A4135

Plowed Wheat Fields, Palouse Hills, Washington — A4136

Grasslands Wildlife Management Area, Merced County, California — A4137

Field of Wheat, Montana — A4138

Yosemite National Park, California — A4139

Crater Lake National Park, Oregon — A4140

Monument Valley Navajo Tribal Park, Arizona and Utah — A4141

Maroon Bells, Colorado — A4142

Sunrise Near Orinda, California — A4143

Pigeon Point, Near Pescadero, California — A4144

Edna Valley, San Luis Obispo County, California — A4145

Livermore, California — A4146

Napali Coast State Wilderness Park, Hawaii — A4147

Lone Ranch Beach, Oregon — A4148

Canaveral National Seashore, Florida — A4149

Bailey Island, Maine — A4150

LITHOGRAPHED
Serpentine Die Cut 10½
2018, July 4
Self-Adhesive

5298		Pane of 20	22.00	
a.	A4131	(50c) multicolored	1.10	.50
b.	A4132	(50c) multicolored	1.10	.50
c.	A4133	(50c) multicolored	1.10	.50
d.	A4134	(50c) multicolored	1.10	.50
e.	A4135	(50c) multicolored	1.10	.50
f.	A4136	(50c) multicolored	1.10	.50
g.	A4137	(50c) multicolored	1.10	.50
h.	A4138	(50c) multicolored	1.10	.50
i.	A4139	(50c) multicolored	1.10	.50
j.	A4140	(50c) multicolored	1.10	.50
k.	A4141	(50c) multicolored	1.10	.50
l.	A4142	(50c) multicolored	1.10	.50
m.	A4143	(50c) multicolored	1.10	.50
n.	A4144	(50c) multicolored	1.10	.50
o.	A4145	(50c) multicolored	1.10	.50
p.	A4146	(50c) multicolored	1.10	.50
q.	A4147	(50c) multicolored	1.10	.50
r.	A4148	(50c) multicolored	1.10	.50
s.	A4149	(50c) multicolored	1.10	.50
t.	A4150	(50c) multicolored	1.10	.50

SCOOBY-DOO

Cartoon Character Scooby-Doo Watering Plant — A4151

LITHOGRAPHED
Serpentine Die Cut 10¾x10½
2018, July 14
Self-Adhesive

5299 A4151 (50c) multicolored   1.10   .25

WORLD WAR I, CENT.

Member of American Expeditionary Force Holding Flag — A4152

LITHOGRAPHED
Serpentine Die Cut 10¾
2018, July 27
Self-Adhesive

5300 A4152 (50c) multicolored   1.10   .25

THE ART OF MAGIC

Rabbit in
Hat — A4153

Fortune Teller
and Crystal
Ball — A4154

Levitating
Woman and
Hoop — A4155

Empty Bird
Cage — A4156

Bird Emerging
From
Flower — A4157

LITHOGRAPHED (Nos. 5301-5305),
TYPOGRAPHED WITH LENTICULAR
LENS AFFIXED (No. 5306)
Serpentine Die Cut 10½x10¾
2018, Aug. 7
Self-Adhesive

5301 A4153 (50c) multicolored   1.10   .40
5302 A4154 (50c) multicolored   1.10   .40
5303 A4155 (50c) multicolored   1.10   .40
5304 A4156 (50c) multicolored   1.10   .40
5305 A4157 (50c) multicolored   1.10   .40
   a. Horiz. strip of 5, #5301-5305   5.50
     Nos. 5301-5305 (5)   5.50 2.00
Souvenir Sheet
5306 A4153 Sheet of 3
     #5306a   3.30
   a. (50c) Single stamp   1.10   .30
   b. As No. 5306, die cutting
     omitted   900.00

The printing method used on No. 5306a
makes the rabbit in the vignette appear and
disappear when the stamp is tilted.

DRAGONS

Green Dragon   Purple Dragon
and   and
Castle — A4158   Castle — A4159

Black Dragon   Orange Dragon
and Ship   and Pagoda
A4160   A4161

**LITHOGRAPHED WITH FOIL
APPLICATION**
Serpentine Die Cut 10¾
2018, Aug. 9
Self-Adhesive

5307 A4158 (50c) multicolored   1.10   .30
5308 A4159 (50c) multicolored   1.10   .30
5309 A4160 (50c) multicolored   1.10   .30
5310 A4161 (50c) multicolored   1.10   .30
   a. Strip or block of 4, #5307-
     5310   4.40
   b. Horiz. strip of 4, #5307-
     5310, with die cutting
     missing (PS)   400.00
     Nos. 5307-5310 (4)   4.40 1.20

Poinsettia
A4162

LITHOGRAPHED
2018, Aug. 26 *Serpentine Die Cut*
Self-Adhesive

5311 A4162 ($1.15) multicolored   2.40   .50

Unused values are for stamps with surrounding selvage. Adjacent stamps are separated by rouletting.

MUSIC ICONS

John Lennon
(1940-80), Rock
Musician
A4163

LITHOGRAPHED
Serpentine Die Cut 10¾
2018, Sept. 7
Self-Adhesive
Color of Shoulders

5312 A4163 (50c) red   1.10   .30
5313 A4163 (50c) red lilac   1.10   .30
5314 A4163 (50c) dark violet   1.10   .30
5315 A4163 (50c) blue   1.10   .30
   a. Vert. strip of 4, #5312-5315 4.40
   b. As "a," die cutting omitted
     Nos. 5312-5315 (4)   4.40 1.20

Adjacent horizontal or vertical stamps have
selvage between the stamps.

FIRST RESPONDERS

Firefighter, Paramedic, and Law
Enforcement Officer — A4164

LITHOGRAPHED
Serpentine Die Cut 11
2018, Sept. 13
Self-Adhesive

5316 A4164 (50c) multicolored   1.10   .25

BIRDS IN WINTER

Black-capped   Northern
Chickadee   Cardinal
A4165   A4166

Red-bellied   Blue Jay
Woodpecker   A4168
A4167

LITHOGRAPHED
*Serpentine Die Cut 10¾ on 2 or 3
Sides*
2018, Sept. 22
Booklet Stamps
Self-Adhesive

5317 A4165 (50c) multicolored   1.10   .30
5318 A4166 (50c) multicolored   1.10   .30
5319 A4167 (50c) multicolored   1.10   .30
5320 A4168 (50c) multicolored   1.10   .30
   a. Block of 4, #5317-5320   4.40
   b. Booklet pane of 20, 5 each
     #5317-5320   22.00
     Nos. 5317-5320 (4)   4.40 1.20

No. 5320b is a double-sided booklet pane
with 12 stamps on one side (3 each Nos.
5317-5320), and eight stamps (2 each Nos.
5317-5320) plus label (booklet cover) on the
other side.

HOT WHEELS TOY CARS, 50TH
ANNIV.

Purple
Passion
A4169

Rocket-Bye-Baby — A4170

Rigor
Motor
A4171

Rodger
Dodger
A4172

Mach
Speeder
A4173

Twin Mill
A4174

Bone
Shaker
A4175

HW40
A4176

Deora
II — A4177

Sharkruiser
A4178

LITHOGRAPHED
Serpentine Die Cut 10¾
2018, Sept. 29
Self-Adhesive

5321 A4169 (50c) multicolored   1.10   .40
5322 A4170 (50c) multicolored   1.10   .40
5323 A4171 (50c) multicolored   1.10   .40
5324 A4172 (50c) multicolored   1.10   .40
5325 A4173 (50c) multicolored   1.10   .40
5326 A4174 (50c) multicolored   1.10   .40
5327 A4175 (50c) multicolored   1.10   .40
5328 A4176 (50c) multicolored   1.10   .40
5329 A4177 (50c) multicolored   1.10   .40
5330 A4178 (50c) multicolored   1.10   .40
     Nos. 5321-5330 (10)   11.00 4.00

CHRISTMAS

Madonna and   Head of Santa
Child, by   Claus, by
Bachiacca   Haddon
A4179   Sundblom
                     A4180

Santa Claus and Wreath, by Sundblom
A4181

Santa Claus and Book, by Sundblom
A4182

Santa Claus and Card, by Sundblom — A4183

Santa Claus and Book, by Sundblom — A4184

LITHOGRAPHED
Serpentine Die Cut 10¾x11 on 2 or 3 Sides

2018

Booklet Stamps
Self-Adhesive

5331	A4179 (50c) multicolored	1.10	.25
a.	Booklet pane of 20	22.00	
5332	A4180 (50c) multicolored	1.10	.30
5333	A4181 (50c) multicolored	1.10	.30
5334	A4182 (50c) multicolored	1.10	.30
5335	A4183 (50c) multicolored	1.10	.30
a.	Block of 4, #5332-5335	4.40	
b.	Booklet pane of 20, 5 each #5332-5335	22.00	
c.	As "a," die cutting omitted	—	
	Nos. 5331-5335 (5)	5.50	1.45

Souvenir Sheet
Serpentine Die Cut 10¾

5336	A4184 (50c) multicolored	1.10	.30
a.	Single stamp	1.10	.30

Issued: No. 5331, 10/3; Nos. 5332-5336, 10/11.

No. 5331a is a double-sided booklet panes with 12 stamps on one side and eight stamps plus label (booklet cover) on the other side.
No. 5335b is a double-sided booklet pane with 12 stamps on one side (3 each Nos. 5332-5335) and eight stamps (2 each Nos. 5332-5335) plus label (booklet cover) on the other side.

The three examples of No. 5335c are from a booklet pane missing the stamps on the 8-stamp side.

KWANZAA

Family and Kinara — A4185

LITHOGRAPHED
Serpentine Die Cut 10¾

2018, Oct. 10

Self-Adhesive

5337	A4185 (50c) multicolored	1.10	.25

HANUKKAH

Menorah — A4186

LITHOGRAPHED
Serpentine Die Cut 10¾

2018, Oct. 16

Self-Adhesive

5338	A4186 (50c) multicolored	1.10	.25

See Israel No. 2200.

LOVE

Hearts — A4187

LITHOGRAPHED
Serpentine Die Cut 10¾x11

2019, Jan. 10

Self-Adhesive

5339	A4187 (50c) multicolored	1.10	.25

CHINESE NEW YEAR

Year of the Boar
A4188

LITHOGRAPHED
Serpentine Die Cut 10¾

2019, Jan. 17

Self-Adhesive

5340	A4188 (50c) multicolored	1.10	.25

People Wearing Uncle Sam Hats Type of 2017

LITHOGRAPHED
Serpentine Die Cut 11 Vert.

2019, Jan. 27   **Tagged**

Coil Stamp
Self-Adhesive

5341	A4006 (15c) multicolored	.30	.25

See No. 5174.

Flag — A4189

LITHOGRAPHED
Serpentine Die Cut 9½ Horiz.

2019, Jan. 27

Coil Stamps
Self-Adhesive
Microprinted "USPS" at Lower Flag Grommet

5342	A4189 (55c) multicolored	1.10	.25

Serpentine Die Cut 11 Horiz.

Microprinted "USPS" to Right of Sixth Red Flag Stripe

5343	A4189 (55c) multicolored	1.10	.25
a.	Die cutting omitted, pair		

Booklet Stamps
Microprinted "USPS" at Upper Left Corner of Flag
Serpentine Die Cut 10¾x11¼ on 2 or 3 Sides

5344	A4189 (55c) multicolored	1.10	.25
a.	Booklet pane of 20	22.00	

Microprinted "USPS" to Right of Sixth Red Flag Stripe

5345	A4189 (55c) multicolored	1.10	.25
a.	Booklet pane of 20	22.00	

Nos. 5344a and 5345a are double-sided booklets with 12 stamps on one side and eight stamps plus a label that serves as the booklet cover on the other side.

CALIFORNIA DOGFACE BUTTERFLY

A4190

LITHOGRAPHED
Serpentine Die Cut 10½

2019, Jan. 27

Self-Adhesive

5346	A4190 (70c) multicolored	1.40	.25

AMERICAN LANDMARKS ISSUE

Joshua Tree
A4191

Bethesda Fountain, Central Park, New York City
A4192

LITHOGRAPHED
Serpentine Die Cut 10¾x10½

2019, Jan. 27

Self-Adhesive

5347	A4191 $7.35 multi	15.00	7.50
5348	A4192 $25.50 multi	50.00	25.00

BLACK HERITAGE

Gregory Hines (1946-2003), Tap Dancer — A4193

LITHOGRAPHED
Serpentine Die Cut 10¾

2019, Jan. 28

Self-Adhesive

5349	A4193 (55c) multicolored	1.10	.25

CACTUS FLOWERS

Opuntia Engelmannii
A4194

Rebutia Minuscula
A4195

Echinocereus Dasyacanthus
A4196

Echinocereus Poselgeri
A4197

Echinocereus Coccineus
A4198

Pelecyphora Aselliformis
A4199

Parodia Microsperma
A4200

Echinocactus Horizonthalonius
A4201

Thelocactus Heterochromus
A4202

Parodia Scopa — A4203

LITHOGRAPHED
Serpentine Die Cut 11 on 2 or 3 Sides

2019, Feb. 15

Booklet Stamps
Self-Adhesive

5350	A4194 (55c) multicolored	1.50	.40
5351	A4195 (55c) multicolored	1.50	.40
5352	A4196 (55c) multicolored	1.50	.40
5353	A4197 (55c) multicolored	1.50	.40
5354	A4198 (55c) multicolored	1.50	.40
5355	A4199 (55c) multicolored	1.50	.40
5356	A4200 (55c) multicolored	1.50	.40
5357	A4201 (55c) multicolored	1.50	.40
5358	A4202 (55c) multicolored	1.50	.40
5359	A4203 (55c) multicolored	1.50	.40
a.	Block of 10, #5350-5359	15.00	
b.	Booklet pane of 20, 2 each #5350-5359	25.00	
	Nos. 5350-5359 (10)	15.00	4.00

No. 5359b is a double-sided booklet pane with 12 stamps on one side (Nos. 5352-5359, 2 each Nos. 5350-5351), and eight stamps (Nos. 5352-5359) plus label (booklet cover) on the other side.

ALABAMA STATEHOOD, BICENT.

Pulpit Rock, Cheaha State Park
A4204

LITHOGRAPHED
Serpentine Die Cut 11x10¾
2019, Feb. 23
Self-Adhesive

5360 A4204 (55c) multicolored 1.10 .25

Star Ribbon — A4205

LITHOGRAPHED
Serpentine Die Cut 11¼x10¾
2019, Mar. 22
Self-Adhesive

5361 A4205 (55c) multicolored 1.10 .25

Coil Stamp
Serpentine Die Cut 10¾ Vert.

5362 A4205 (55c) multicolored 1.10 .25

CORAL REEFS

Elkhorn Coral and French Angelfish A4206

Brain Coral and Spotted Moray Eel A4207

Pillar Coral, Coney Grouper and Neon Gobies A4208

Staghorn Coral and Blue-striped Grunts A4209

LITHOGRAPHED
Serpentine Die Cut 11¼x10¾
2019, Mar. 29
Self-Adhesive

5363 A4206 (35c) multicolored .70 .25
5364 A4207 (35c) multicolored .70 .25
5365 A4208 (35c) multicolored .70 .25
5366 A4209 (35c) multicolored .70 .25
  a. Horiz. or vert. strip of 4, #5363-5366 2.80
  Nos. 5363-5366 (4) 2.80 1.00

Coil Stamps
Serpentine Die Cut 9½ Vert.

5367 A4208 (35c) multicolored .70 .25
5368 A4209 (35c) multicolored .70 .25
5369 A4206 (35c) multicolored .70 .25
5370 A4207 (35c) multicolored .70 .25
  a. Horiz. strip of 4, #5367-5370 2.80
  Nos. 5367-5370 (4) 2.80 1.00

MUSIC ICONS

Marvin Gaye (1939-84), Singer — A4210

LITHOGRAPHED
Serpentine Die Cut 10½
2019, Apr. 2
Self-Adhesive

5371 A4210 (55c) multicolored 1.10 .25

POST OFFICE MURALS

Piggott, Arkansas Mural *Air Mail,* by Daniel Rhodes — A4211

Florence, Colorado Mural, *Antelope,* by Olive Rush — A4212

Rockville, Maryland Mural, *Sugarloaf Mountain,* by Judson Smith — A4213

Anadarko, Oklahoma Mural, *Kiowas Moving Camp,* by Stephen Mopope, James Auchiah, and Spencer Asah — A4214

Deming, New Mexico Mural, *Mountains and Yucca,* by Kenneth Miller Adams — A4215

LITHOGRAPHED
Serpentine Die Cut 11½x11
2019, Apr. 10
Self-Adhesive

5372 A4211 (55c) multicolored 1.10 .40
5373 A4212 (55c) multicolored 1.10 .40
5374 A4213 (55c) multicolored 1.10 .40
5375 A4214 (55c) multicolored 1.10 .40
5376 A4215 (55c) multicolored 1.10 .40
  a. Vert. strip of 5, #5372-5376 5.50
  Nos. 5372-5376 (5) 5.50 2.00

MAUREEN CONNOLLY BRINKER

Maureen "Little Mo" Connolly Brinker (1934-69), Tennis Player — A4216

LITHOGRAPHED
Serpentine Die Cut 10¾
2019, Apr. 23
Self-Adhesive

5377 A4216 (55c) multicolored 1.10 .25

TRANSCONTINENTAL RAILROAD, 150TH ANNIV.

Jupiter Locomotive — A4217

Golden Spike — A4218

No. 119 Locomotive — A4219

LITHOGRAPHED WITH FOIL APPLICATION
Serpentine Die Cut 10¾x10½
2019, May 10
Self-Adhesive

5378 A4217 (55c) multicolored 1.10 .30
5379 A4218 (55c) multicolored 1.10 .30
5380 A4219 (55c) multicolored 1.10 .30
  a. Horiz. strip of 3, #5378-5380 3.30
  Nos. 5378-5380 (3) 3.30 .90

WILD AND SCENIC RIVERS

A4220

No. 5381: a, Merced River. b, Owyhee River. c, Koyukuk River. d, Niobrara River. e, Snake River. f, Flathead River. g, Missouri River. h, Skagit River. i, Deschutes River. j, Tlikakila River. k, Ontonagon River. l, Clarion River.

LITHOGRAPHED
Serpentine Die Cut 10¾x10½
2019, May 21
Self-Adhesive

5381 A4220 Pane of 12 13.50
  a.-l. (55c) Any single 1.10 .50

ART OF ELLSWORTH KELLY (1923-2015)

Yellow White, 1961 — A4221

Colors for a Large Wall, 1951 — A4222

Blue Red Rocker, 1963 — A4223

Spectrum I, 1953 — A4224

South Ferry, 1956 — A4225

Blue Green, 1962 — A4226

Orange Red Relief (for Delphine Seyrig), 1990 — A4227

Meschers, 1951 — A4228

Red Blue, 1964 — A4229

Gaza, 1956 — A4230

LITHOGRAPHED
Serpentine Die Cut 10½x10¾
2019, May 31
Self-Adhesive

5382	A4221	(55c) multicolored	1.10	.40
5383	A4222	(55c) multicolored	1.10	.40
5384	A4223	(55c) multicolored	1.10	.40
5385	A4224	(55c) multicolored	1.10	.40
5386	A4225	(55c) multicolored	1.10	.40
5387	A4226	(55c) multicolored	1.10	.40
5388	A4227	(55c) multicolored	1.10	.40
5389	A4228	(55c) multicolored	1.10	.40
5390	A4229	(55c) multicolored	1.10	.40
5391	A4230	(55c) multicolored	1.10	.40
a.		Block of 10, #5382-5391	11.00	
		Nos. 5382-5391 (10)	11.00	4.00

COMMISSIONING OF U.S.S. MISSOURI, 75TH ANNIV.

U.S.S. Missouri — A4231

LITHOGRAPHED
Serpentine Die Cut 10¾
2019, June 11   **Tagged**
Self-Adhesive

5392	A4231	(55c) multicolored	1.10	.25
a.		Die cutting omitted, pair		

GEORGE HERBERT WALKER BUSH

George Herbert Walker Bush (1924-2018), 41st President — A4232

LITHOGRAPHED
Serpentine Die Cut 10¾
2019, June 12   **Tagged**
Self-Adhesive

5393	A4232	(55c) multicolored	1.10	.25
a.		Die cutting omitted, pair	500.00	

SESAME STREET CHILDREN'S TELEVISION SHOW, 50TH ANNIV.

Muppet Characters — A4233

No. 5394: a, Big Bird. b, Ernie. c, Bert. d, Cookie Monster. e, Rosita. f, The Count. g, Oscar the Grouch. h, Abby Cadabby. i, Herry Monster. j, Julia. k, Guy Smiley. l, Snuffleupagus. m, Elmo. n, Telly. o, Grover. p, Zoe.

LITHOGRAPHED
Serpentine Die Cut 10¾
2019, June 22   **Tagged**
Self-Adhesive

5394	A4233	Pane of 16	18.00	
a.-p.		(55c) Any single	1.10	.50

FROGS

Pacific Tree Frog — A4234

Northern Leopard Frog — A4235

American Green Tree Frog — A4236

Squirrel Tree Frog — A4237

LITHOGRAPHED
Serpentine Die Cut 11x10¾ on 2 or 3 Sides
2019, July 9   **Tagged**
Booklet Stamps
Self-Adhesive

5395	A4234	(55c) multicolored	1.10	.30
5396	A4235	(55c) multicolored	1.10	.30
5397	A4236	(55c) multicolored	1.10	.30
5398	A4237	(55c) multicolored	1.10	.30
a.		Block of 4, #5395-5398	4.40	
b.		Booklet pane of 20, 5 each #5395-5398	22.00	
		Nos. 5395-5398 (4)	4.40	1.20

FIRST MOON LANDING, 50TH ANNIV.

Astronaut Edwin E. "Buzz" Aldrin, Jr. on Moon A4238

Moon with Landing Site Highlighted A4239

LITHOGRAPHED
Serpentine Die Cut 10¾
2019, July 19
Self-Adhesive

5399	A4238	(55c) multicolored	1.10	.25
5400	A4239	(55c) multicolored	1.10	.25
a.		Pair, #5399-5400	2.20	

Adjacent horizontal or vertical stamps have selvage between the stamps.

STATE AND COUNTY FAIRS

Farmers Unloading Large Fruits and Vegetables A4240

Girl and Farm Animals A4241

Parents and Children A4242

Child Buying Candy Apple A4243

LITHOGRAPHED
Serpentine Die Cut 10½x10¾
2019, July 25
Self-Adhesive

5401	A4240	(55c) multicolored	1.10	.30
5402	A4241	(55c) multicolored	1.10	.30
5403	A4242	(55c) multicolored	1.10	.30
5404	A4243	(55c) multicolored	1.10	.30
a.		Horiz. strip of 4, #5401-5404	4.40	
		Nos. 5401-5404 (4)	4.40	1.20

Adjacent vertical stamps have selvage between the stamps.

MILITARY WORKING DOGS

German Shepherd A4244

Labrador Retriever A4245

Belgian Malinois A4246

Dutch Shepherd A4247

LITHOGRAPHED
Serpentine Die Cut 10¾x10½ (Nos. 5405, 5408), 10½x10¾ (Nos. 5406-5407)
2019, Aug. 1
Booklet Stamps
Self-Adhesive

5405	A4244	(55c) multicolored	1.10	.30
5406	A4245	(55c) multicolored	1.10	.30
5407	A4246	(55c) multicolored	1.10	.30
5408	A4247	(55c) multicolored	1.10	.30
a.		Block of 4, #5405-5408	4.40	
b.		Booklet pane of 20, 5 each #5405-5408	22.00	
		Nos. 5405-5408 (4)	4.40	1.20

Adjacent horizontal and vertical stamps have selvage between the stamps. No. 5408b is a double-sided booklet pane with 12 stamps on one side (3 each Nos. 5405-5408), and eight stamps (2 each Nos. 5405-5408) plus label (booklet cover) on the other side.

WOODSTOCK MUSIC FESTIVAL, 50TH ANNIV.

Dove — A4248

TYPOGRAPHED
Serpentine Die Cut 10¾
2019, Aug. 8
Self-Adhesive

5409	A4248	(55c) multicolored	1.10	.25

TYRANNOSAURUS REX

Juvenile Tyrannosaurus Rex, Egg, and Insect — A4249

Adult Tyrannosaurus Rex — A4250

Young Adult Tyrannosaurus Rex and Juvenile Triceratops — A4251

Juvenile Tyrannosaurus Rex Chasing Mammal — A4252

TYPOGRAPHED WITH LENTICULAR LENS AFFIXED
Serpentine Die Cut 10¾x10½
2019, Aug. 29
Self-Adhesive

5410	A4249	(55c) multicolored	1.10	.30
5411	A4250	(55c) multicolored	1.10	.30
5412	A4251	(55c) multicolored	1.10	.30
5413	A4252	(55c) multicolored	1.10	.30
a.		Block of 4, #5410-5413	4.40	
		Nos. 5410-5413 (4)	4.40	1.20

Adjacent stamps have selvage between them. Only Nos. 5411 and 5412 show movement in the design when viewed from different positions.

LITERARY ARTS

Walt Whitman (1819-92), Poet A4253

LITHOGRAPHED
Serpentine Die Cut 10¾
2019, Sept. 12
Self-Adhesive
5414 A4253 (85c) multicolored   1.75   .30

WINTER BERRIES

Winterberry
A4254

Juniper Berry
A4255

Beautyberry
A4256

Soapberry
A4257

LITHOGRAPHED
Serpentine Die Cut 11¼x10¾ on 2 or 3 Sides
2019, Sept. 17
Booklet Stamps
Self-Adhesive
5415 A4254 (55c) multicolored   1.10   .30
5416 A4255 (55c) multicolored   1.10   .30
5417 A4256 (55c) multicolored   1.10   .30
5418 A4257 (55c) multicolored   1.10   .30
  a. Block of 4, #5415-5418   4.40
  b. Booklet pane of 20, 5 each
      #5415-5418   22.00
      Nos. 5415-5418 (4)   4.40 1.20

No. 5398b is a double-sided booklet pane with 12 stamps on one side (3 each Nos. 5395-5398), and eight stamps (2 each Nos. 5395-5398) plus label (booklet cover) on the other side.

Purple Heart and
Ribbon With
Frame — A4258

LITHOGRAPHED
Serpentine Die Cut 11¼x10¾
2019, Oct. 4
Self-Adhesive
5419 A4258 (55c) multicolored   1.10   .25

SPOOKY SILHOUETTES

Cat and Raven
A4259

Ghosts
A4260

Spider and
Web — A4261

Bats — A4262

TYPOGRAPHED WITH FOIL APPLICATION
Serpentine Die Cut 10¾
2019, Oct. 11
Self-Adhesive
Color of Foil
5420 A4259 (55c) silver   1.10   .30
5421 A4260 (55c) orange   1.10   .30
5422 A4261 (55c) red   1.10   .30
5423 A4262 (55c) violet   1.10   .30
  a. Block of 4, #5420-5423   4.40
      Nos. 5420-5423 (4)   4.40 1.20

CHRISTMAS WREATHS

Aspidistra Leaf
Wreath
A4263

Wreath Made
of Gilded Pine
Cones and
Magnolia Pods
A4264

Wreath Made
of Gilded
Hydrangea,
Eucalyptus,
Nandina and
Ribbon
A4265

Wreath Made
of Woodland
Bush Ivy and
Red
Winterberry
A4266

LITHOGRAPHED
Serpentine Die Cut 11¼x10¾ on 2 or 3 Sides
2019, Oct. 25
Booklet Stamps
Self-Adhesive
5424 A4263 (55c) multicolored   1.10   .30
5425 A4264 (55c) multicolored   1.10   .30
5426 A4265 (55c) multicolored   1.10   .30
5427 A4266 (55c) multicolored   1.10   .30
  a. Block of 4, #5424-5427   4.40
  b. Booklet pane of 20, 5 each
      #5424-5427   22.00
      Nos. 5424-5427 (4)   4.40 1.20

No. 5398b is a double-sided booklet pane with 12 stamps on one side (3 each Nos. 5395-5398), and eight stamps (2 each Nos. 5395-5398) plus label (booklet cover) on the other side.

CHINESE NEW YEAR

Year of the
Rat — A4267

LITHOGRAPHED WITH FOIL APPLICATION
Serpentine Die Cut 10¾
2020, Jan. 11
Self-Adhesive
5428 A4267 (55c) multicolored   1.10   .25

AMERICAN LANDMARKS ISSUE

Big Bend
National
Park,
Texas
A4268

Grand
Island Ice
Caves,
Michigan
A4269

LITHOGRAPHED
Serpentine Die Cut 10¾x10½
2020, Jan. 18
Self-Adhesive
5429 A4268 $7.75 multi   15.50   7.75
5430 A4269 $26.35 multi   53.00 26.50

LOVE

Hearts — A4270

LITHOGRAPHED
Serpentine Die Cut 10¾
2020, Jan. 23
Self-Adhesive
5431 A4270 (55c) multicolored   1.10   .25

BLACK HERITAGE

Gwen Ifill (1955-2016), Television Newscaster
A4271

LITHOGRAPHED
Serpentine Die Cut 10¾
2020, Jan. 30
Self-Adhesive
5432 A4271 (55c) multicolored   1.10   .25

Star and
Stripes — A4272

LITHOGRAPHED
Serpentine Die Cut 10¾ Vert.
2020, Feb. 3
COIL STAMP
Self-Adhesive
5433 A4272 (10c) multicolored   .25   .25

CELEBRATE

A4273

LITHOGRAPHED WITH FOIL APPLICATION
Serpentine Die Cut 10¾
2020, Feb. 14
Self-Adhesive
5434 A4273 (55c) multicolored   1.10   .25

WILD ORCHIDS

Platanthera
Grandiflora
A4274

Cyrtopodium
Polyphyllum
A4275

Calopogon
Tuberosus
A4276

Spiranthes
Odorata
A4277

Triphora
Trianthophoros
A4278

Cypripedium
Californicum
A4279

Hexalectris
Spicata
A4280

Cypripedium
Reginae
A4281

Platanthera
Leucophaea
A4282

Triphora
Trianthophoros
A4283

Triphora
Trianthophoros
A4284

Cypripedium
Californicum
A4285

Hexalectris
Spicata
A4286

Cypripedium
Reginae
A4287

Spiranthes
Odorata
A4288

Platanthera
Leucophaea
A4289

Triphora
Trianthophoros
A4290

Platanthera
Grandiflora
A4291

Cyrtopodium
Polyphyllum
A4292

Calopogon
Tuberosus
A4293

LITHOGRAPHED
Serpentine Die Cut 10¾ Vert.
2020, Feb. 21
Coil Stamps
Self-Adhesive

5435	A4274	(55c) multicolored	1.10	.40
5436	A4275	(55c) multicolored	1.10	.40
5437	A4276	(55c) multicolored	1.10	.40
5438	A4277	(55c) multicolored	1.10	.40
5439	A4278	(55c) multicolored	1.10	.40
5440	A4279	(55c) multicolored	1.10	.40
5441	A4280	(55c) multicolored	1.10	.40
5442	A4281	(55c) multicolored	1.10	.40
5443	A4282	(55c) multicolored	1.10	.40
5444	A4283	(55c) multicolored	1.10	.40
a.		Horiz. strip of 10, #5435-5444	11.00	
	Nos. 5435-5444 (10)		11.00	4.00

Booklet Stamps
Serpentine Die Cut 10¾x11 on 2 or 3 Sides

5445	A4284	(55c) multicolored	1.10	.40
5446	A4285	(55c) multicolored	1.10	.40
5447	A4286	(55c) multicolored	1.10	.40
5448	A4287	(55c) multicolored	1.10	.40
5449	A4288	(55c) multicolored	1.10	.40
5450	A4289	(55c) multicolored	1.10	.40
5451	A4290	(55c) multicolored	1.10	.40
5452	A4291	(55c) multicolored	1.10	.40
5453	A4292	(55c) multicolored	1.10	.40
5454	A4293	(55c) multicolored	1.10	.40
a.		Block of 10, #5445-5454	11.00	
b.		Booklet pane of 20, 2 each #5445-5454	22.00	
	Nos. 5445-5454 (10)		11.00	4.00

Nos. 5454b is a double-sided booklet with 12 stamps on one side (Nos. 5446-5449, 5451-5454, 2 each Nos 5445, 5450), and eight stamps (Nos. 5446-5449, 5451-5454) plus a label that serves as the booklet cover on the other side.

ARNOLD PALMER

Arnold Palmer
(1929-2016),
Professional
Golfer — A4294

LITHOGRAPHED
Serpentine Die Cut 10¾
2020, Mar. 4
Self-Adhesive

5455	A4294	(55c) multicolored	1.10	.25

MAINE STATEHOOD BICENTENARY

Sea at Ogunquit, by Edward Hopper
(1882-1967) — A4295

LITHOGRAPHED
Serpentine Die Cut 10¾
2020, Mar. 15
Self-Adhesive

5456	A4295	(55c) multicolored	1.10	.25

Boutonniere
A4296

Corsage
A4297

LITHOGRAPHED
Serpentine Die Cut 10¾x11
2020, Apr. 2
Self-Adhesive

5457	A4296	(55c) multicolored	1.10	.25

Perf. 11x10¾

5458	A4297	(70c) multicolored	1.40	.25

EARTH DAY, 50th ANNIV.

Stylized
Globe — A4298

LITHOGRAPHED
Serpentine Die Cut 11x10¾ on 2 or 3 Sides
2020, Apr. 18
Booklet Stamp
Self-Adhesive

5459	A4298	(55c) multicolored	1.10	.25
a.		Booklet pane of 20	22.00	

No. 5459a is a double-sided booklet with 12 stamps on one side and eight stamps plus a label that serves as the booklet cover on the other side.

Chrysanthemum — A4299

LITHOGRAPHED
Sheets of 90 in nine panes of 10
Serpentine Die Cut
2020, Apr. 24   **Tagged**
Self-Adhesive

5460	A4299	($1.20) multicolored	2.40	.50

Unused values are for stamps with surrounding selvage. Adjacent stamps are separated by rouletting.

AMERICAN GARDENS

Brooklyn
Botanic
Garden,
New York
A4300

Stan Hywet
Hall and
Gardens,
Ohio
A4301

Dumbarton
Oaks,
District of
Columbia
A4302

Coastal
Maine
Botanical
Gardens,
Maine
A4303

Chicago
Botanic
Garden,
Illinois
A4304

Winterthur
Garden,
Delaware
A4305

Biltmore
Estate
Gardens,
North
Carolina
A4306

Alfred B.
Maclay
Gardens
State Park,
Florida
A4307

The
Huntington
Botanical
Gardens,
California
A4308

Norfolk
Botanical
Garden,
Virginia
A4309

LITHOGRAPHED
Serpentine Die Cut 10¾x10½
2020, May 13
Self-Adhesive

5461	A4300	(55c) multicolored	1.10	.40
5462	A4301	(55c) multicolored	1.10	.40
5463	A4302	(55c) multicolored	1.10	.40
5464	A4303	(55c) multicolored	1.10	.40
5465	A4304	(55c) multicolored	1.10	.40
5466	A4305	(55c) multicolored	1.10	.40
5467	A4306	(55c) multicolored	1.10	.40
5468	A4307	(55c) multicolored	1.10	.40
5469	A4308	(55c) multicolored	1.10	.40
5470	A4309	(55c) multicolored	1.10	.40
a.		Block of 10, #5461-5470	11.00	
	Nos. 5461-5470 (10)		11.00	4.00

Die cut uncut press sheets of Nos. 5461-5470 were made available for sale. Values: cross gutter block of 10, $18; pairs with gutters between, $4.25 each. See note after No. 4693.

See note after No. 1549.

VOICES OF THE HARLEM RENAISSANCE

Nella Larsen
(1891-1964),
Novelist
A4310

Arturo
Schomburg
(1874-1938),
Historian
A4311

Anne Spencer
(1882-1975),
Poet — A4312

Alain Locke
(1885-1954),
Writer — A4313

LITHOGRAPHED
Serpentine Die Cut 10¾
2020, May 21
Self-Adhesive

5471	A4310	(55c) multicolored	1.10	.30
5472	A4311	(55c) multicolored	1.10	.30
5473	A4312	(55c) multicolored	1.10	.30
5474	A4313	(55c) multicolored	1.10	.30
a.		Horiz. or vert. strip of 4, #5471-5474	4.40	
	Nos. 5471-5474 (4)		4.40	1.20

Die cut uncut press sheets of Nos. 5471-5474 were made available for sale. Values: cross gutter block of 8, $16; pairs with gutters between, $4.25 each. See note after No. 4693.

See note after No. 1549.

ENJOY THE GREAT OUTDOORS

Child
Building
Sandcastle
A4314

Canoeing
A4315

Hiking
A4316

Bicycling
A4317

Cross-country Skiing — A4318

LITHOGRAPHED
Serpentine Die Cut 10¾
2020, June 13
Self-Adhesive

5475	A4314	(55c) multicolored	1.10	.40
5476	A4315	(55c) multicolored	1.10	.40
5477	A4316	(55c) multicolored	1.10	.40
5478	A4317	(55c) multicolored	1.10	.40
5479	A4318	(55c) multicolored	1.10	.40
a.		Vert. strip of 5, #5475-5479	5.50	
	Nos. 5475-5479 (5)		5.50	2.00

HIP HOP

MC With
Microphone
Rapping
A4319

B-Boy Dancing
A4320

Graffiti Art
A4321

DJ at Turntable
A4322

LITHOGRAPHED
Serpentine Die Cut 10¾
2020, July 1
Self-Adhesive

5480	A4319	(55c)	multicolored	1.10	.30
5481	A4320	(55c)	multicolored	1.10	.30
5482	A4321	(55c)	multicolored	1.10	.30
5483	A4322	(55c)	multicolored	1.10	.30
a.	Block or vert. strip of 4,				
	#5480-5483			4.40	
	Nos. 5480-5483 (4)			4.40	1.20

FRUITS AND VEGETABLES

Red and Black
Plums
A4323

Heirloom and
Cherry
Tomatoes
A4324

Carrots
A4325

Lemons
A4326

Blueberries
A4327

Red and Green
Grapes
A4328

Lettuce
A4329

Strawberries
A4330

Eggplants
A4331

Figs
A4332

LITHOGRAPHED
Serpentine Die Cut 10¾x11 on 2 or 3 Sides
2020, July 17
Booklet Stamps
Self-Adhesive

5484	A4323	(55c)	multicolored	1.10	.40
5485	A4324	(55c)	multicolored	1.10	.40
5486	A4325	(55c)	multicolored	1.10	.40
5487	A4326	(55c)	multicolored	1.10	.40
5488	A4327	(55c)	multicolored	1.10	.40
5489	A4328	(55c)	multicolored	1.10	.40
5490	A4329	(55c)	multicolored	1.10	.40
5491	A4330	(55c)	multicolored	1.10	.40
5492	A4331	(55c)	multicolored	1.10	.40
5493	A4332	(55c)	multicolored	1.10	.40
a.	Block of 10, #5484-5493			11.00	
b.	Booklet pane of 20, 2 each				
	#5484-5493			22.00	
	Nos. 5484-5493 (10)			11.00	4.00

Nos. 5493b is a double-sided booklet pane with 12 stamps on one side (Nos. 5485-5488, 5490-5493, 2 each Nos. 5484, 5489) and eight stamps (Nos. 5485-5488, 5490-5493) plus label (booklet cover) on the other side.

BUGS BUNNY, 80th ANNIV.

Bugs Bunny as
Barber, From
Rabbit of Seville,
1950 — A4333

Bugs Bunny as
Basketball
Player, From
Space Jam,
1996 — A4334

Bugs Bunny as
Hollywood
Celebrity, From
*A Hare Grows in
Manhattan,*
1947 — A4335

Bugs Bunny as
Court Jester,
From *Knighty
Knight Bugs,*
1958 — A4336

Bugs Bunny as
Brunhilde, From
*What's Opera,
Doc?,*
1957 — A4337

Bugs Bunny as
Mermaid, From
Hare Ribbin',
1944 — A4338

Bugs Bunny as
Piano Player,
From *Rhapsody
Rabbit,*
1946 — A4339

Bugs Bunny as
Super-Rabbit,
From *Super-
Rabbit,*
1943 — A4340

Bugs Bunny as
Baseball Player,
From *Baseball
Bugs,*
1946 — A4341

Bugs Bunny as
Soldier, From
World War II
Poster — A4342

LITHOGRAPHED
Serpentine Die Cut 10½x10¾
2020, July 27
Self-Adhesive

5494	A4333	(55c)	multicolored	1.10	.40
5495	A4334	(55c)	multicolored	1.10	.40
5496	A4335	(55c)	multicolored	1.10	.40
5497	A4336	(55c)	multicolored	1.10	.40
5498	A4337	(55c)	multicolored	1.10	.40
5499	A4338	(55c)	multicolored	1.10	.40
5500	A4339	(55c)	multicolored	1.10	.40
5501	A4340	(55c)	multicolored	1.10	.40
5502	A4341	(55c)	multicolored	1.10	.40
5503	A4342	(55c)	multicolored	1.10	.40
a.	Block of 10, #5494-5503			11.00	
	Nos. 5494-5503 (10)			11.00	4.00

WIRE SCULPTURES BY RUTH ASAWA (1926-2013)

Three Untitled
Sculptures From
1958, 1978 and
1959 — A4343

Untitled
Sculpture From
1959 — A4344

Untitled
Sculpture From
1958 — A4345

Untitled
Sculpture From
1955 — A4346

Untitled
Sculpture From
1955 — A4347

Untitled
Sculpture From
1980 — A4348

Untitled
Sculpture From
1978 — A4349

Untitled
Sculpture From
1952 — A4350

Untitled
Sculpture From
1954 — A4351

Six Untitled
Sculptures From
Various
Years — A4352

LITHOGRAPHED
Serpentine Die Cut 10¾
2020, Aug. 13
Self-Adhesive

5504	A4343	(55c)	multicolored	1.10	.40
5505	A4344	(55c)	multicolored	1.10	.40
5506	A4345	(55c)	multicolored	1.10	.40
5507	A4346	(55c)	multicolored	1.10	.40
5508	A4347	(55c)	multicolored	1.10	.40
5509	A4348	(55c)	multicolored	1.10	.40
5510	A4349	(55c)	multicolored	1.10	.40
5511	A4350	(55c)	multicolored	1.10	.40
5512	A4351	(55c)	multicolored	1.10	.40
5513	A4352	(55c)	multicolored	1.10	.40
a.	Block of 10, #5504-5513			11.00	

INNOVATION

Computing
A4353

Biomedicine
A4354

Genome
Sequencing
A4355

Robotics
A4356

Solar Technology
A4357

**LITHOGRAPHED WITH FOIL
APPLICATION**
Sheets of 120 in six panes of 20
Serpentine Die Cut 10¾
2020, Aug. 20
Self-Adhesive

5514	A4353	(55c) multicolored	1.10	.40
5515	A4354	(55c) multicolored	1.10	.40
5516	A4355	(55c) multicolored	1.10	.40
5517	A4356	(55c) multicolored	1.10	.40
5518	A4357	(55c) multicolored	1.10	.40
a.		Horiz. strip of 5, #5514-5518	5.50	
	Nos. 5514-5518 (5)		5.50	2.00

THANK YOU

A4358

A4359

A4360

A4361

**TYPOGRAPHED WITH FOIL
APPLICATION**
Serpentine Die Cut 10¾
2020, Aug. 21
Self-Adhesive

5519	A4358	(55c) rose brown & gold	1.10	.40
5520	A4359	(55c) olive & gold	1.10	.40
5521	A4360	(55c) slate blue & gold	1.10	.40
5522	A4361	(55c) violet & gold	1.10	.40
a.		Block of 4, #5519-5522	4.40	
	Nos. 5519-5522 (4)		4.40	1.60

WOMAN SUFFRAGE CENTENARY

Suffragists Marching
for Passage of 19th
Amendment
A4362

LITHOGRAPHED
Serpentine Die Cut 10¾
2020, Aug. 22
Self-Adhesive

5523	A4362	(55c) multicolored	1.10	.25

**MAYFLOWER IN PLYMOUTH
HARBOR, 400th ANNIV.**

The
Mayflower
in Plymouth
Harbor and
Mayflower
A4363

LITHOGRAPHED & ENGRAVED
Serpentine Die Cut 10¾
2020, Sept. 17
Self-Adhesive

5524	A4363	(55c) multicolored	1.10	.25

A pane of No. 5524, imperforate panes of
single-color progressive proofs in cyan,
magenta, yellow, and lithographed black, a
commemorative book, and a numbered certificate were produced in a quantity of 2500 and
sold as a unit for $59.95.

CHRISTMAS

Our Lady of
Guápulo, by
Unknown 18th
Century
Peruvian Artist
A4364

Ornament
A4365

Christmas Tree
A4366

Christmas
Stocking
A4367

Reindeer — A4368

LITHOGRAPHED
*Serpentine Die Cut 10¾ on 2 or 3
Sides*
2020
Booklet Stamps
Self-Adhesive

5525	A4364	(55c) multicolored	1.10	.25
a.		Booklet pane of 20	22.00	
5526	A4365	(55c) multicolored	1.10	.30
5527	A4366	(55c) multicolored	1.10	.30
5528	A4367	(55c) multicolored	1.10	.30
5529	A4368	(55c) multicolored	1.10	.30
a.		Block of 4, #5526-5529	4.40	
b.		Booklet pane of 20, 5 each #5526-5529	22.00	
	Nos. 5525-5529 (5)		5.50	1.45

No. 5529b is a double-sided booklet pane
with 12 stamps on one side (3 each Nos.
5526-5529), and eight stamps (2 each Nos.
5526-55290) plus label (booklet cover) on the
other side.

HANUKKAH

Children and
Menorah
A4369

LITHOGRAPHED
Serpentine Die Cut 10¾
2020, Oct. 6
Self-Adhesive

5530	A4369	(55c) multicolored	1.10	.25

KWANZAA

Woman and
Kinara — A4370

LITHOGRAPHED
Serpentine Die Cut 10¾
2020, Oct. 13
Self-Adhesive

5531	A4370	(55c) multicolored	1.10	.25

WINTER SCENES

Two Deer,
Photograph by
Lisa Carter
A4371

Cardinal,
Photograph by
Gerald A.
DeBoer
A4372

Snowy Morning
at Sunrise,
Photograph by
Lisa Lacasse
A4373

Red Barn with
Wreath,
Photograph by
Lisa Lacasse
A4374

Barred Owl,
Photograph by
Malachi
Ives — A4375

Blue Jay,
Photograph by
Edgar Lee
Espe — A4376

Mackenzie
Barn,
Woodstock,
Vermont,
Photograph by
Lisa Lacasse
A4377

Rabbit,
Photograph by
Melani Wright
A4378

After the
Snowfall,
Photograph by
Lisa Lacasse
A4379

Mike and Burt,
the Belgian
Draft Horses,
Photograph by
Lisa Lacasse
A4380

LITHOGRAPHED
*Serpentine Die Cut 10¾ on 2 or 3
Sides*
2020, Oct. 16
Booklet Stamps
Self-Adhesive

5532	A4371	(55c) multicolored	1.10	.40
5533	A4372	(55c) multicolored	1.10	.40
5534	A4373	(55c) multicolored	1.10	.40
5535	A4374	(55c) multicolored	1.10	.40
5536	A4375	(55c) multicolored	1.10	.40
5537	A4376	(55c) multicolored	1.10	.40
5538	A4377	(55c) multicolored	1.10	.40
5539	A4378	(55c) multicolored	1.10	.40
5540	A4379	(55c) multicolored	1.10	.40
5541	A4380	(55c) multicolored	1.10	.40
a.		Block of 10, #5532-5541	11.00	
b.		Booklet pane of 20, 2 each #5532-5541	22.00	
	Nos. 5532-5541 (10)		11.00	4.00

Nos. 5541b is a double-sided booklet with
12 stamps on one side (Nos. 5533-5536,
5538-5541, 2 each Nos 5532, 5537), and eight
stamps (Nos. 5533-5536, 5538-5541) plus a
label that serves as the booklet cover on the
other side.

DRUG FREE USA

Star and
Stripes — A4381

LITHOGRAPHED
Serpentine Die Cut 10¾
2020, Oct. 27
Self-Adhesive

5542	A4381	(55c) multicolored	1.10	.25

UNITED STATES

SEMI-POSTAL STAMPS

BREAST CANCER RESEARCH

SP1

PHOTOGRAVURE
Serpentine Die Cut 11
1998, July 29
Self-Adhesive

B1 SP1 (32c+8c) multicolored   1.10   .25

HEROES OF 2001

Firemen Atop
World Trade
Center
Rubble — SP2

LITHOGRAPHED
Serpentine Die Cut 11¼
2002, June 7
Self-Adhesive

B2 SP2 (34c+11c) multicolored   1.10   .35

STOP FAMILY VIOLENCE

SP3

PHOTOGRAVURE
2003, Oct. 8   *Serpentine Die Cut 11*
Self-Adhesive

B3 SP3 (37c+8c) multicolored   1.10   .45

SAVE VANISHING SPECIES

Amur Tiger
Cub — SP4

PHOTOGRAVURE
Serpentine Die Cut 10¾
2011, Sept. 20
Self-Adhesive

B4 SP4 (44c+11c) multicolored   1.10   .50

The 11c surtax was for the Multinational Species Conservation Funds of the U.S. Fish and Wildlife Service.

Breast Cancer Awareness Type of 1998

LITHOGRAPHED
Design Size: 20x35mm
Serpentine Die Cut 11x10¾
2014, Sept. 30
Dated 2014
Self-Adhesive

B5 SP1 (49c+11c) multicolored   1.10   .50
 a. Imperforate (from uncut press
     sheet)   2.25   —
 b. Imperf., pair (error, see foot-
     note)   —

Imperforates from imperforate uncut press sheets (No. B5a) do not have die cutting on either the front or the reverse. On the imperforate error (No. B5b), there is die cutting on the reverse.

ALZHEIMER'S DISEASE AWARENESS

SP5

LITHOGRAPHED
Serpentine Die Cut 10½x10¾
2017, Nov. 30
Self-Adhesive

B6 SP5 (49c+11c) multicolored   1.10   .60

The 11c surtax was for the National Institutes of Health.

HEALING POST-TRAUMATIC STRESS DISORDER

Plant Sprout and
Fallen
Leaves — SP6

LITHOGRAPHED
Serpentine Die Cut 10¾
2019, Dec. 2   **Tagged**
Self-Adhesive

B7 SP6 (55c+10c) multicolored   1.10   .60

The 10c surtax was for the National Center for Post-traumatic Stress Disorder of the Department of Veterans Affairs to assist in treatment of those impacted by post-traumatic stress disorder.

AIR POST STAMPS

Curtiss Jenny — AP1

FLAT PLATE PRINTINGS

1918	**Unwmk.**	**Engr.**	**Perf. 11**	
C1	AP1 6c orange		55.	30.
	Never hinged		110.	
C2	AP1 16c green		60.	35.
	Never hinged		120.	
C3	AP1 24c car rose & blue		65.	35.
	Never hinged		130.	
a.	Center inverted		450,000.	
	Never hinged		850,000.	
	Nos. C1-C3 (3)		180.00	100.00
	Nos. C1-C3, never hinged		360.00	

Wooden   Emblem of Air
Propeller and   Service — AP3
Radiator — AP2

De Havilland
Biplane — AP4

1923

C4	AP2 8c dark green	17.50	15.00
	Never hinged	35.00	
C5	AP3 16c dark blue	60.00	30.00
	Never hinged	120.00	
C6	AP4 24c carmine	65.00	30.00
	Never hinged	130.00	
	Nos. C4-C6 (3)	142.50	75.00
	Nos. C4-C6, never hinged	285.00	

Map of U.S. and Two Mail
Planes — AP5

1926-27

C7	AP5 10c dark blue	2.25	.35
	Never hinged	4.00	
C8	AP5 15c olive brown	2.50	2.50
	Never hinged	4.75	
C9	AP5 20c yellow green	6.50	2.00
	Never hinged	12.50	
	Nos. C7-C9 (3)	11.25	4.85
	Nos. C7-C9, never hinged	21.25	

Lindbergh's Airplane "Spirit of St.
Louis" — AP6

1927, June 18

C10	AP6 10c dark blue	7.00	2.50
	Never hinged	12.50	
a.	Booklet pane of 3	70.00	65.00
	Never hinged	115.00	
b.	Double impression		16,500.

Singles from No. C10a are imperf. at sides or imperf. at sides and bottom.
Only one example is recorded of No. C10b.

Beacon on
Rocky
Mountains
AP7

1928, July 25

C11	AP7 5c carmine and blue	5.50	.85
	Never hinged	10.00	
a.	Vert. pair, imperf. between		7,000.

No. C11a is unique. It is torn and valued thus.

Winged Globe — AP8

1930, Feb. 10
Stamp design: 46½x19mm

C12	AP8 5c violet	9.50	.50
	Never hinged	17.50	
a.	Horiz. pair, imperf. between		4,500.

See Nos. C16-C17, C19.

GRAF ZEPPELIN ISSUE

Zeppelin over Atlantic Ocean — AP9

Zeppelin between Continents — AP10

Zeppelin Passing Globe — AP11

1930, Apr. 19

C13	AP9 65c green	180.	160.
	Never hinged	250.	
C14	AP10 $1.30 brown	375.	360.
	Never hinged	575.	
C15	AP11 $2.60 blue	525.	550.
	Never hinged	850.	
	Nos. C13-C15 (3)	1,080.	1,070.
	Nos. C13-C15, never hinged	1,675.	

ROTARY PRESS PRINTING
1931-32   *Perf. 10½x11*
Stamp design: 47½x19mm

C16	AP8 5c violet	4.75	.60
	Never hinged	8.50	
C17	AP8 8c olive bister ('32)	2.25	.40
	Never hinged	3.75	

CENTURY OF PROGRESS ISSUE

Airship "Graf Zeppelin" — AP12

FLAT PLATE PRINTING
1933, Oct. 2   *Perf. 11*

C18	AP12 50c green	45.00	47.50
	Never hinged	75.00	

Catalogue values for unused stamps in this section, from this point to the end, are for Never Hinged items.

Type of 1930 Issue
ROTARY PRESS PRINTING
1934, June 30   *Perf. 10½x11*

C19	AP8 6c dull orange	3.50	.25

TRANSPACIFIC ISSUES

The "China
Clipper"
over the
Pacific
AP13

FLAT PLATE PRINTING
1935, Nov. 22   *Perf. 11*

C20	AP13 25c blue	1.40	1.00

The "China
Clipper"
over the
Pacific
AP14

1937, Feb. 15

C21	AP14 20c green	10.00	1.75
C22	AP14 50c carmine	10.00	5.00

Eagle
Holding
Shield, Olive
Branch and
Arrows
AP15

1938, May 14

C23	AP15 6c dark blue & carmine	.70	.25
a.	Vert. pair, imperf. horiz.	300.00	300.00
b.	Horiz. pair, imperf. vert.	12,500.	
c.	6c ultra & car	240.00	2,000.
	On cover		2,250.

TRANSATLANTIC ISSUE

Winged Globe — AP16

1939, May 16
C24 AP16 30c dull blue   11.00   1.50

Twin-Motored Transport Plane — AP17

ROTARY PRESS PRINTING
1941-44   *Perf. 11x10½*
C25 AP17 6c carmine   .25   .25
  a. Booklet pane of 3   3.50   1.50
  b. Horiz. pair, imperf. between   2,250.

Singles from No. C25a are imperf. at sides
or at sides and bottom.
Value of No. C25b is for pair without blue
crayon P. O. rejection mark on front. Very fine
pairs with crayon mark sell for about $1,500.

C26 AP17 8c olive green   .25   —
  a. All color omitted

No. C26a has an albino impression and
exists as a pair of stamps within a double-
paper spliced strip of six stamps.

C27 AP17 10c violet   1.10   .25
C28 AP17 15c brown carmine   2.10   .25
C29 AP17 20c bright green   2.10   .30
C30 AP17 30c blue   2.10   .35
C31 AP17 50c orange   11.00 3.25
    Nos. C25-C31 (7)   18.90 5.00

DC-4
Skymaster
AP18

1946, Sept. 25   *Perf. 11x10½*
C32 AP18 5c carmine   .25   .25

DC-4
Skymaster — AP19

1947, Mar. 26   *Perf. 10½x11*
C33 AP19 5c carmine   .25   .25

Pan American Union Building,
Washington, DC — AP20

Statue of
Liberty &
New York
Skyline
AP21

Plane over San Francisco-Oakland
Bay Bridge — AP22

1947   *Perf. 11x10½*
C34 AP20 10c black   .25   .25
  a. Dry printing   .40   .25

C35 AP21 15c bright blue
    green   .35   .25
  a. Horiz. pair, imperf. between 1,500.
  b. Dry printing   .55   .25
C36 AP22 25c blue   .90   .25
  a. Dry printing   1.20 .25
    Nos. C34-C36 (3)   1.50 .75

See note on wet and dry printings following
No. 1029.
No. C35a is valued in the grade of fine.

Type of 1947
ROTARY PRESS COIL STAMP
1948, Jan. 15   Perf. 10 Horizontally
C37 AP19 5c carmine   1.00   .80

NEW YORK CITY ISSUE

Map of Five Boroughs,
Circular Band &
Planes — AP23

50th anniv. of the consolidation of the five
boroughs of New York City.

ROTARY PRESS PRINTING
1948, July 31   *Perf. 11x10½*
C38 AP23 5c bright carmine   .25   .25

Type of 1947
1949   *Perf. 10½x11*
C39 AP19 6c carmine   .25   .25
  a. Booklet pane of 6   12.00 5.00
  b. Dry printing   .50   .25
  c. As "a," dry printing   25.00   —

See note on wet and dry printings following
No. 1029.

ALEXANDRIA BICENTENNIAL ISSUE

Home of John Carlyle, Alexandria Seal
& Gadsby's Tavern
AP24

200th anniv. of the founding of Alexandria,
Va.

1949, May 11   *Perf. 11x10½*
C40 AP24 6c carmine   .25   .25

Type of 1947
ROTARY PRESS COIL STAMP
1949, Aug. 25   Perf. 10 Horizontally
C41 AP19 6c carmine   3.00   .25

UNIVERSAL POSTAL UNION ISSUE

Post Office
Department
Building
AP25

Globe &
Doves
Carrying
Messages
AP26

Boeing Stratocruiser & Globe — AP27

ROTARY PRESS PRINTING
1949   *Perf. 11x10½*
C42 AP25 10c violet   .25   .25
C43 AP26 15c ultramarine   .30   .25
C44 AP27 25c rose carmine   .60   .40
    Nos. C42-C44 (3)   1.15 .90

WRIGHT BROTHERS ISSUE

Wilbur &
Orville
Wright and
their Plane
AP28

1949, Dec. 17
C45 AP28 6c magenta   .25   .25

Diamond
Head,
Honolulu,
Hawaii
AP29

1952, Mar. 26
C46 AP29 80c bright red violet   4.50 1.25

POWERED FLIGHT, 50th ANNIV.

First Plane
and Modern
Plane
AP30

1953, May 29
C47 AP30 6c carmine   .25   .25

Eagle in Flight — AP31

Issued primarily for use on domestic post
cards.

1954, Sept. 3
C48 AP31 4c bright blue   .25   .25

AIR FORCE, 50th ANNIV.

B-52 Stratofortress and F-104
Starfighters — AP32

1957, Aug. 1
C49 AP32 6c blue   .25   .25

Type of 1954
1958, July 31
C50 AP31 5c red   .25   .25

Silhouette of Jet
Airliner — AP33

1958, July 31   *Perf. 10½x11*
C51 AP33 7c blue   .25   .25
  a. Booklet pane of 6   6.50 5.00
  b. Vert. pair, imperf. between
    (from booklet pane)   4,000.

No. C51b resulted from a paper foldover
after perforating and before cutting into panes.
Two or three pairs are believed to exist.

ROTARY PRESS COIL STAMP
Perf. 10 Horizontally
C52 AP33 7c blue   2.00   .25

ALASKA STATEHOOD ISSUE

Big Dipper,
North Star
& Map of
Alaska
AP34

ROTARY PRESS PRINTING
1959, Jan. 3   *Perf. 11x10½*
C53 AP34 7c dark blue   .25   .25

BALLOON JUPITER ISSUE

Balloon &
Crowd — AP35

Centenary of the carrying of mail by the balloon Jupiter from Lafayette to Crawfordsville,
Ind.

GIORI PRESS PRINTING
1959, Aug. 17   *Perf. 11*
C54 AP35 7c dark blue & red   .30   .25

HAWAII STATEHOOD ISSUE

Alii Warrior,
Map of
Hawaii &
Star of
Statehood
AP36

ROTARY PRESS PRINTING
1959, Aug. 21   *Perf. 11x10½*
C55 AP36 7c rose red   .25   .25

PAN AMERICAN GAMES ISSUE

Runner Holding
Torch — AP37

3rd Pan American Games, Chicago, Aug.
27-Sept. 7, 1959.

GIORI PRESS PRINTING
1959, Aug. 27   *Perf. 11*
C56 AP37 10c red, white & blue   .25   .25

Liberty Bell
AP38

Statue of
Liberty
AP39

Abraham
Lincoln
AP40

1959-66
C57 AP38 10c black & green
    ('60)   1.00   .70
C58 AP39 15c black & orange   .35   .25

C59 AP40 25c black & maroon
('60)   .50   .25
   a.   Tagged ('66)   .60   .30
     Nos. C57-C59 (3)   1.85   1.20

Airmail stamps starting with No. C69 are tagged unless otherwise noted.

Type of 1958
ROTARY PRESS PRINTING
1960, Aug. 12   **Perf. 10½x11**
C60 AP33 7c carmine   .25   .25
   a.   Booklet pane of 6   7.00   6.00
   b.   Vert. pair, imperf between
      (from booklet pane)   5,500.

No. C60b resulted from a paper foldover after perforating and before cutting into panes. Two pairs are known.

Type of 1958
ROTARY PRESS COIL STAMP
1960, Oct. 22   **Perf. 10 Horizontally**
C61 AP33 7c carmine   4.00   .25

Type of 1959-60 and

Statue of Liberty AP41

GIORI PRESS PRINTING
1961-67   **Perf. 11**
C62 AP38 13c black & red   .40   .25
   a.   Tagged ('67)   .75   .50
C63 AP41 15c black & orange   .30   .25
   a.   Tagged ('67)   .35   .25
   b.   As "a," horiz. pair, imperf.
      vert.   15,000.
   c.   As "a," horiz. pair, imperf
      between and at left   2,750.
   d.   All color omitted   100.00

On No. C63d, there is a clear albino plate impression.

Jet Airliner Over Capitol — AP42

ROTARY PRESS PRINTING
1962, Dec. 5   **Perf. 10½x11**
C64 AP42 8c carmine   .25   .25
   a.   Tagged ('63)   .25   .25
   b.   Booklet pane of 5 + label   6.00   3.00
   c.   As "b," tagged ('64)   1.75   .75

Nos. C64a and C64c were made by overprinting Nos. C64 and C64b with phosphorescent ink. No. C64a was first issued at Dayton, Ohio, for experiments in high speed mail sorting. The tagging is visible in shortwave ultraviolet light.

COIL STAMP; ROTARY PRESS
Perf. 10 Horizontally
C65 AP42 8c carmine   .40   .25
   a.   Tagged ('64)   .35   .25

MONTGOMERY BLAIR ISSUE

Montgomery Blair — AP43

Montgomery Blair (1813-83), Postmaster General (1861-64), who called the 1st Intl. Postal Conf., Paris, 1863, forerunner of the UPU.

GIORI PRESS PRINTING
1963, May 3   **Perf. 11**
C66 AP43 15c dull red, dark
brown & blue   .55   .50

Bald Eagle — AP44

Issued primarily for use on domestic post cards.

ROTARY PRESS PRINTING
1963, July 12   **Perf. 11x10½**
C67 AP44 6c red   .25   .25
   a.   Tagged ('67)   4.00   3.00

AMELIA EARHART ISSUE

Amelia Earhart & Lockheed Electra — AP45

GIORI PRESS PRINTING
1963, July 24   **Perf. 11**
C68 AP45 8c carmine & maroon   .25   .25

ROBERT H. GODDARD ISSUE

Robert H. Goddard, Atlas Rocket & Launching Tower, Cape Kennedy AP46

1964, Oct. 5
C69 AP46 8c blue, red & bister   .35   .25

Luminescence
Air Post stamps issued after mid-1964 are tagged.

ALASKA PURCHASE ISSUE

Tlingit Totem, Southern Alaska — AP47

1967, Mar. 30
C70 AP47 8c brown   .25   .25

"Columbia Jays," by Audubon — AP48

1967, Apr. 26
C71 AP48 20c multicolored   .75   .25
See note over No. 1241.

50-Star Runway — AP49

ROTARY PRESS PRINTING
1968, Jan. 5   **Perf. 11x10½**
C72 AP49 10c carmine   .25   .25
   b.   Booklet pane of 8   2.25   2.00
   c.   Booklet pane of 5 + label   3.50   1.25
   d.   Vert. pair, imperf. btwn., in
      #C72b with foldover   5,000.

No. C72d resulted from a paper foldover after perforating and before cutting into panes. Two pairs are recorded from different panes.

ROTARY PRESS COIL STAMP
Perf. 10 Vertically
C73 AP49 10c carmine   .30   .25
   a.   Imperf., pair   450.00

The $1 Airlift stamp is listed as No. 1341.

50th ANNIVERSARY OF AIR MAIL ISSUE

Curtiss Jenny AP50

50th anniv. of regularly scheduled air mail service.

LITHOGRAPHED, ENGRAVED (GIORI)
1968, May 15   **Perf. 11**
C74 AP50 10c blue, black & red   .25   .25

USA and Jet — AP51

1968, Nov. 22
C75 AP51 20c red, blue & black   .35   .25
See No. C81.

MOON LANDING ISSUE

First Man on the Moon AP52

1969, Sept. 9
C76 AP52 10c multicolored   .25   .25
   a.   Rose red (litho.) omitted   500.00

On No. C76a, the lithographed rose red is missing from the entire vignette-the dots on top of the yellow areas as well as the flag shoulder patch.

Silhouette of Delta Wing Plane AP53

Silhouette of Jet Airliner AP54

Winged Airmail Envelope — AP55

Statue of Liberty AP56

ROTARY PRESS PRINTING
1971-73   **Perf. 10½x11**
C77 AP53 9c red   .25   .25

No. C77 issued primarily for use on domestic post cards.

Perf. 11x10½
C78 AP54 11c carmine   .25   .25
   a.   Booklet pane of 4 + 2 labels   1.25   1.00
   b.   Untagged (Bureau precanceled)   .85   .85
C79 AP55 13c carmine ('73)   .25   .25
   a.   Booklet pane of 5 + label
      ('73)   1.50   1.00
   b.   Untagged (Bureau precanceled)   .85   .85
   c.   Green instead of red tagging (single from booklet pane)   —

No. C78b Bureau precanceled "WASHINGTON D.C." (or "DC" - more valuable thus), No. C79b "WASHINGTON DC" only; both for use of Congressmen, but available to any permit holder.

GIORI PRESS PRINTING
Perf. 11
C80 AP56 17c bluish black, red, & dark green   .35   .25

"USA" & Jet Type of 1968
LITHOGRAPHED, ENGRAVED (GIORI)
C81 AP51 21c red, blue & black   .40   .25
   b.   Black (engr.) missing (FO)   2,750.

The two recorded examples of No. C81b are in a single full pane. Catalogue value is for both errors.

COIL STAMPS
ROTARY PRESS PRINTING
1971-73   **Perf. 10 Vertically**
C82 AP54 11c carmine   .25   .25
   a.   Imperf., pair   180.00
C83 AP55 13c carmine ('73)   .30   .25
   a.   Imperf., pair   60.00

NATIONAL PARKS CENTENNIAL ISSUE
City of Refuge, Hawaii

Kii Statue & Temple, City of Refuge, Hawaii — AP57

LITHOGRAPHED, ENGRAVED (GIORI)
1972, May 3   **Perf. 11**
C84 AP57 11c orange & multicolored   .25   .25
   a.   Blue & green (litho.) omitted   450.00   900.00

OLYMPIC GAMES ISSUE

Skiing & Olympic Rings AP58

11th Winter Olympic Games, Sapporo, Japan, Feb. 3-13, and 20th Summer Olympic Games, Munich, Germany, Aug. 26-Sept. 11.

PHOTOGRAVURE (Andreotti)
1972, Aug. 17   **Perf. 11x10½**
C85 AP58 11c black, blue, red, emerald & yellow   .25   .25

ELECTRONICS PROGRESS ISSUE

De Forest Audions AP59

188 UNITED STATES

LITHOGRAPHED, ENGRAVED (GIORI)

1973, July 10   *Perf. 11*
C86 AP59 11c multicolored .30 .25
  a. Vermilion & olive (litho.) omitted 700.00
  c. Olive omitted 1,000.

Statue of Liberty AP60

Mt. Rushmore National Memorial AP61

GIORI PRESS PRINTING

1974
C87 AP60 18c carmine, black & ultramarine .35 .30
C88 AP61 26c ultramarine, black & carmine .60 .25

Plane & Globes AP62

Plane, Globes & Flag AP63

1976, Jan. 2
C89 AP62 25c red, blue & black .50 .25
C90 AP63 31c red, blue & black .60 .25
  b. All colors omitted

On No. C90b, there is a colorless embossed image and a tagging ghost plane visible under UV light.

WRIGHT BROTHERS ISSUE

Orville and Wilbur Wright, Flyer A AP64

Wright Brothers, Flyer A and Shed AP65

LITHOGRAPHED, ENGRAVED (GIORI)

1978, Sept. 23
C91 AP64 31c ultra & multi .65 .30
C92 AP65 31c ultra & multi .65 .30
  a. Vert. pair, #C91-C92 1.30 1.20
  b. As "a", ultra. & black (engr.) omitted 475.00
  c. As "a," black (engr.) omitted 1,750.
  d. As "a," black, yellow, magenta, blue & brown (litho.) omitted 1,750.

OCTAVE CHANUTE ISSUE

Chanute & Biplane Hangglider AP66

Biplane Hanggliders & Chanute AP67

1979, Mar. 29
C93 AP66 21c blue & multi .70 .35
C94 AP67 21c blue & multi .70 .35
  a. Vert. pair, #C93-C94 1.40 1.20
  b. As "a," ultra & black (engr.) omitted 4,000.

WILEY POST ISSUE

Wiley Post & "Winnie Mae" AP68

NR-105 W, Post in Pressurized Suit, Portrait AP69

1979, Nov. 20
C95 AP68 25c blue &multi .90 .45
C96 AP69 25c blue &multi .90 .45
  a. Vert. pair, #C95-C96 1.80 1.50

OLYMPIC GAMES ISSUE

High Jump AP70

PHOTOGRAVURE

1979, Nov. 1
C97 AP70 31c multicolored .70 .30

PHILIP MAZZEI (1730-1816)

Philip Mazzei (1730-1816), Italian-born Political Writer — AP71

1980, Oct. 13
C98 AP71 40c multicolored .80 .25
  b. Imperf., pair 2,250.

1982   *Perf. 10½x11¼*
C98A AP71 40c multicolored 5.00 1.50
  c. Horiz. pair, imperf. vert. 3,250.

BLANCHE STUART SCOTT

Blanche Stuart Scott (1886-1970) AP72

1980, Dec. 30   *Perf. 11*
C99 AP72 28c multicolored .60 .25
  a. Imperf., pair 2,000.

GLENN CURTISS

Glenn Curtiss (1878-1930) — AP73

1980, Dec. 30
C100 AP73 35c multicolored .65 .25
  a. Light blue (background) omitted 2,000.

SUMMER OLYMPICS 1984

Women's Gymnastics AP74

Hurdles AP75

Women's Basketball AP76

Soccer AP77

1983, June 17
C101 AP74 28c multicolored 1.00 .30
C102 AP75 28c multicolored 1.00 .30
C103 AP76 28c multicolored 1.00 .30
C104 AP77 28c multicolored 1.00 .30
  a. Block of 4, #C101-C104 4.25 2.50
  b. As "a," imperf. vert. 5,000.

Shot Put — AP78

Men's Gymnastics AP79

Women's Swimming AP80

Weight Lifting AP81

1983, Apr. 8   *Perf. 11.2 Bullseye*
C105 AP78 40c multicolored .90 .40
C106 AP79 40c multicolored .90 .40
C107 AP80 40c multicolored .90 .40
C108 AP81 40c multicolored .90 .40
  b. Block of 4, #C105-C108 4.25 3.00
  d. Block of 4, imperf. 650.00

Women's Fencing AP82

Cycling AP83

Women's Volleyball AP84

Pole Vaulting AP85

1983, Nov. 4   *Perf. 11*
C109 AP82 35c multicolored .90 .55
C110 AP83 35c multicolored .90 .55
C111 AP84 35c multicolored .90 .55
C112 AP85 35c multicolored .90 .55
  a. Block of 4, #C109-C112 4.00 3.25

AVIATION PIONEERS

Alfred V. Verville AP86

Lawrence & Elmer Sperry AP87

1985, Feb. 13   **Tagged**   *Perf. 11*
C113 AP86 33c multicolored .65 .25
  a. Imperf., pair 550.00
C114 AP87 39c multicolored .80 .25
  a. Imperf., pair 1,250.

TRANSPACIFIC AIRMAIL
50th Anniversary

Transpacific Airmail AP88

1985, Feb. 15
C115 AP88 44c multicolored .85 .25
  a. Imperf., pair 600.00

FR. JUNIPERO SERRA (1713-1784)
California Missionary

Outline Map of Southern California, Portrait, San Gabriel Mission AP89

1985, Aug. 22
C116 AP89 44c multicolored 1.00 .35
  a. Imperf., pair 950.00

SETTLING OF NEW SWEDEN, 350th ANNIV.

Settling of New Sweden, 350th Anniv. AP90

LITHOGRAPHED AND ENGRAVED
1988, Mar. 29
C117 AP90 44c multicolored 1.00 .25
See Sweden No. 1672 and Finland No. 768.

SAMUEL P. LANGLEY (1834-1906)

Langley and Unmanned Aerodrome No. 5 AP91

1988, May 14
C118 AP91 45c multicolored   1.00 .25

IGOR SIKORSKY (1889-1972)

Sikorsky and VS300 Helicopter, 1939 AP92

PHOTOGRAVURE AND ENGRAVED
1988, June 23
C119 AP92 36c multicolored   .70 .25
  a. Red, dk blue & black (en-
      graved) omitted   1,000.

Beware of examples with traces of engraved red offered as "red omitted" varieties.

FRENCH REVOLUTION BICENTENNIAL

Liberty, Equality and Fraternity — AP93

LITHOGRAPHED AND ENGRAVED
1989, July 14   *Perf. 11½x11*
C120 AP93 45c multicolored   .95 .25
    See France Nos. 2143-2145a.

PRE-COLUMBIAN AMERICA ISSUE

UPAE Emblem & *Key Marco Cat* — AP94

PHOTOGRAVURE
1989, Oct. 12   *Perf. 11*
C121 AP94 45c multicolored   .90 .25

20th UPU CONGRESS
Futuristic Mail Delivery

Spacecraft AP95

Air-suspended Hover Car — AP96

Moon Rover — AP97

Space Shuttle — AP98

LITHOGRAPHED & ENGRAVED
1989, Nov. 27
C122 AP95 45c multicolored   1.00 .50
C123 AP96 45c multicolored   1.00 .50
C124 AP97 45c multicolored   1.00 .50
C125 AP98 45c multicolored   1.00 .50
  a. Block of 4, #C122-C125   4.00 3.00
  b. As "a," light blue (engr.)
      omitted   500.00

Souvenir Sheet
LITHOGRAPHED & ENGRAVED
1989, Nov. 24   *Imperf.*
C126   Sheet of 4   5.00 4.00
  a. AP95 45c multicolored   1.25 .50
  b. AP96 45c multicolored   1.25 .50
  c. AP97 45c multicolored   1.25 .50
  d. AP98 45c multicolored   1.25 .50

PRE-COLUMBIAN AMERICA ISSUE

Tropical Coast AP99

PHOTOGRAVURE
1990, Oct. 12   *Perf. 11*
C127 AP99 45c multicolored   .90 .25

HARRIET QUIMBY, 1ST AMERICAN WOMAN PILOT

Harriet Quimby, Bleriot Aircraft AP100

1991, Apr. 27
C128 AP100 50c multicolored   1.00 .25
  a. Vert. pair, imperf. horiz. 850.00
  b. Perf. 11.2 bullseye,
      prephosphored uncoated
      paper ('93)   1.25 .25

WILLIAM T. PIPER, AIRCRAFT MANUFACTURER

William T. Piper, Piper Cub AP101

1991, May 17
C129 AP101 40c multicolored   .80 .25

Blue sky is plainly visible all the way across stamp above Piper's head.
See No. C132.

ANTARCTIC TREATY, 30TH ANNIVERSARY

Antarctic Treaty, 30th Anniv. AP102

1991, June 21
C130 AP102 50c multicolored   1.00 .35

PRE-COLUMBIAN AMERICA ISSUE

First Americans Crossed Over From Asia AP103

1991, Oct. 12
C131 AP103 50c multicolored   1.00 .35

Piper Type of 1991
1993   **Perf. 11.2 Bullseye**
C132 AP101 40c multicolored   3.50 .65

Piper's hair touches top edge of design. No selvage inscriptions.

"All LC (Letters and Cards) mail receives First-Class Mail service in the United States, is dispatched by the fastest transportation available, and travels by airmail or priority service in the destination country. All LC mail should be marked 'AIRMAIL' or 'PAR AVION.'" (U.S. Postal Service, Pub. 51).

No. C133 listed below was issued to meet the LC rate to Canada and Mexico and is inscribed with the silhouette of a jet plane next to the denomination indicating the need for airmail service. This is unlike No. 2998, which met the LC rate to other countries, but contained no indication that it was intended for that use.

Future issues that meet a specific international airmail rate and contain the airplane silhouette will be treated by Scott as Air Post stamps. Stamps similar to No. 2998 will be listed in the Postage section.

SCENIC AMERICAN LANDSCAPES

Niagara Falls AP104

1999, May 12 *Serpentine Die Cut 11*
Self-Adhesive
C133 AP104 48c multicolored   .95 .25

Rio Grande AP105

1999, July 30
Self-Adhesive
C134 AP105 40c multicolored   .80 .60

Grand Canyon AP106

LITHOGRAPHED
Serpentine Die Cut 11¼x11½
2000, Jan. 20
Self-Adhesive
C135 AP106 60c multi   1.25 .25
  a. Die cutting omitted, pair 1,250.
  b. Vert. pair, die cutting
      omitted horiz.   —
  c. Horiz. pair, die cutting
      omitted between   —
  d. Horiz. pair, die cutting
      omitted vert.   —

Nine-Mile Prairie, Nebraska AP107

LITHOGRAPHED
2001, Mar. 6
Self-Adhesive
C136 AP107 70c multi   1.40 .30

Mt. McKinley AP108

PHOTOGRAVURE
Serpentine Die Cut 11
2001, Apr. 17
Self-Adhesive
C137 AP108 80c multi   1.60 .35

Acadia National Park AP109

LITHOGRAPHED
Serpentine Die Cut 11.25x11.5
2001-05
Self-Adhesive
C138 AP109 60c multi   1.25 .25
  a. Serpentine die cut
      11½x11¾   1.25 .25
  b. As "a," with "2005" year
      date   1.25 .25
  c. As "b," printed on back
      of backing paper   —

Bryce Canyon National Park AP110

Great Smoky Mountains National Park AP111

LITHOGRAPHED
Serpentine Die Cut 10¾
2006, Feb. 24
Self-Adhesive
C139 AP110 63c multicolored   1.25 .25
  a. Die cutting omitted, pair 450.00
C140 AP111 75c multicolored   1.50 .35
  a. Die cutting omitted, pair 500.00

Yosemite National Park AP112

PHOTOGRAVURE
Serpentine Die Cut 11
C141 AP112 84c multicolored   1.75 .35
    Nos. C139-C141 (3)   4.50 .95

Okefenokee Swamp, Georgia and Florida AP113

Hagatña Bay, Guam AP114

LITHOGRAPHED (#C142),
PHOTOGRAVURE (#C143)
Serpentine Die Cut 10¾
2007, June 1
Self-Adhesive

C142	AP113	69c multicolored	1.40 .30

Serpentine Die Cut 11

C143	AP114	90c multicolored	1.80 .40

13-Mile Woods, New Hampshire AP115

Trunk Bay, St. John, Virgin Islands AP116

LITHOGRAPHED (#C144),
PHOTOGRAVURE (#C145)
Serpentine Die Cut 10¾
2008, May 16
Self-Adhesive

C144	AP115	72c multicolored	1.50 .30

Serpentine Die Cut 11

C145	AP116	94c multicolored	1.90 .45

AP117

AP118

LITHOGRAPHED, PHOTOGRAVURE
(#C147)
Serpentine Die Cut 10¾
2009, June 28
Self-Adhesive

C146	AP117	79c multicolored	1.75 .35

Serpentine Die Cut 11

C147	AP118	98c multicolored	2.00 .45

Voyageurs National Park, Minnesota AP119

LITHOGRAPHED
Serpentine Die Cut 10¾
2011, Apr. 11
Self-Adhesive

C148	AP119	80c multicolored	1.60 .25

See note after No. 1549.

Glacier National Park, Montana — AP120

Amish Horse and Buggy on Road, Lancaster County, Pennsylvania — AP121

LITHOGRAPHED
2012　　*Serpentine Die Cut 10¾*
Self-Adhesive

C149	AP120	85c multicolored	1.75 .35
a.		Die cutting omitted on front, pair	500.00
b.		Silver (airplane silhouette) missing (PS)	—

Issued: 85c, 1/19; $1.05, 1/20.

AIR POST SPECIAL DELIVERY STAMPS

To provide for the payment of both the postage and the special delivery fee in one stamp.

Great Seal of United States APSD1

1934, Aug. 30　　Unwmk.　　*Perf. 11*

CE1	APSD1	16c dark blue	.70 .80
		Never hinged	.90

For imperforate variety see No. 771.

Great Seal of United States APSD2

1936, Feb. 10

CE2	APSD2	16c red & blue	.45 .35
		Never hinged	.65
a.		Horiz. pair, imperf. vert.	4,250.
		Never hinged	5,250.

SPECIAL DELIVERY STAMPS

When affixed to any letter or article of mailable matter, secured immediate delivery, between 7 A. M. and midnight, at any post office.

Messenger Running — SD1

Flat Plate Printing
1885　　　Unwmk.　　*Perf. 12*

E1	SD1	10c blue	550.00 80.00
		Never hinged	1,250.

Messenger Running SD2

1888, Sept. 6

E2	SD2	10c blue	500.00 45.00
		Never hinged	1,150.

COLUMBIAN EXPOSITION ISSUE

Though not issued expressly for the Exposition, No. E3 is considered to be part of that issue.

1893, Jan. 24

E3	SD2	10c orange	300.00 50.00
		Never hinged	650.00

Messenger Running SD3

1894, Oct. 10
Line under "TEN CENTS"

E4	SD3	10c blue	850.00 110.00
		Never hinged	2,000.

No. E5a

1895, Aug. 16　　　　Wmk. 191

E5	SD3	10c blue	210.00 12.50
		Never hinged	475.00
a.		Dots in curved frame above messenger (Pl. 882)	400.00 50.00
		Never hinged	800.00
b.		Printed on both sides	—

Messenger on Bicycle SD4

1902, Dec. 9

E6	SD4	10c ultramarine	230.00 10.00
		Never hinged	500.00
a.		10c blue	300.00 12.50
		Never hinged	750.00

Helmet of Mercury and Olive Branch — SD5

1908, Dec. 12

E7	SD5	10c green	65.00 50.00
		Never hinged	140.00

1911, Jan.　　Wmk. 190　　*Perf. 12*

E8	SD4	10c ultramarine	120.00 10.00
		Never hinged	250.00
b.		10c violet blue	160.00 14.00
		Never hinged	350.00

1914, Sept.　　　　　*Perf. 10*

E9	SD4	10c ultramarine	190.00 12.00
		Never hinged	425.00
a.		10c blue	260.00 15.00
		Never hinged	575.00

1916, Oct. 19　　Unwmk.　　*Perf. 10*

E10	SD4	10c pale ultramarine	320.00 50.00
		Never hinged	700.00
a.		10c blue	375.00 50.00
		Never hinged	800.00

1917, May 2　　　　　*Perf. 11*

E11	SD4	10c ultramarine	20.00 .75
		Never hinged	45.00
b.		10c gray violet	35.00 3.00
		Never hinged	75.00
c.		10c blue	100.00 5.00
		Never hinged	210.00
d.		Perf. 10 at left	—

Postman and Motorcycle SD6

1922, July 12

E12	SD6	10c gray violet	45.00 3.00
		Never hinged	95.00
a.		10c deep ultramarine	55.00 3.50
		Never hinged	130.00

Post Office Truck SD7

1925

E13	SD6	15c deep orange	40.00 3.75
		Never hinged	75.00
E14	SD7	20c black	2.00 1.00
		Never hinged	4.00
		Nos. E12-E14 (3)	87.00 7.75

Motorcycle Type of 1922
ROTARY PRESS PRINTING

1927-31　　　　　*Perf. 11x10½*

E15	SD6	10c gray violet	1.00 .25
		Never hinged	1.75
		On cover	.50
a.		10c red lilac	.80 .25
		Never hinged	1.40
b.		10c gray lilac	.90 .25
		Never hinged	1.60
c.		Horiz. pair, imperf. btwn., red lilac shade	350.00
		Never hinged	575.00
E16	SD6	15c orange ('31)	.60 .25
		Never hinged	.90

> **Catalogue values for unused stamps in this section, from this point to the end, are for Never Hinged items.**

1944-51

E17	SD6	13c blue	.60 .25
E18	SD6	17c orange yellow	3.50 2.50
E19	SD7	20c black ('51)	1.20 .25

Special Delivery Letter, Hand to Hand SD8

1954, Oct. 13　　　　*Perf. 11x10½*

E20	SD8	20c deep blue	.40 .25

1957, Sept. 3

E21	SD8	30c lake	.50 .25

Arrows SD9

GIORI PRESS PRINTING

1969, Nov. 21　　　　*Perf. 11*

E22	SD9	45c car & vio blue	1.20 .25

1971, May 10

E23	SD9	60c vio blue & car	1.25 .25

From 1885 to the present, special delivery stamps have not been and are not valid for the payment of postage of any description, nor for registry fees.

REGISTRATION STAMP

Issued for the prepayment of registry fees; not usable for postage.

Eagle — RS1

1911, Dec. 1   Wmk. 190   *Perf. 12*
F1	RS1 10c ultramarine		75.00	14.00
	Never hinged		160.00	

CERTIFIED MAIL STAMP

For use on first-class mail for which no indemnity value is claimed, but for which proof of mailing and proof of delivery are available at less cost than registered mail.

> **Catalogue value for the unused stamp in this section is for a Never Hinged item.**

Letter Carrier — CM1

ROTARY PRESS PRINTING
1955, June 6   Unwmk.   *Perf. 10½x11*
FA1	CM1 15c red		.75	.75

POSTAGE DUE STAMPS

For affixing, by a postal clerk to any piece of mailable matter, to denote the amount to be collected from the addressee because of insufficient pre-payment of postage.

D1

Printed by the American Bank Note Co.

Plates of 200 subjects in two panes of 100 each.

1879   Unwmk.   Engr.   *Perf. 12*
J1	D1 1c brown		90.00	14.00
	Never hinged		260.00	
J2	D1 2c brown		425.00	25.00
	Never hinged		1,050.	
J3	D1 3c brown		100.00	6.00
	Never hinged		280.00	
J4	D1 5c brown		800.00	70.00
	Never hinged		1,950.	
J5	D1 10c brown		900.00	70.00
	Never hinged		2,500.	
a.	Imperf., pair		2,500.	
J6	D1 30c brown		400.00	65.00
	Never hinged		900.00	
J7	D1 50c brown		650.00	90.00
	Never hinged		1,600.	
	Nos. J1-J7 (7)		3,365.	340.00

Special Printing
J8	D1 1c deep brown		16,000.	
	Never hinged		—	
	No gum		6,400.	
J9	D1 2c deep brown		15,000.	
	No gum		6,000.	
J10	D1 3c deep brown		20,000.	
	No gum		8,000.	
J11	D1 5c deep brown		13,000.	
	No gum		5,250.	
J12	D1 10c deep brown		6,500.	
	No gum		2,750.	

J13	D1 30c deep brown		*7,000.*	
	No gum		*3,000.*	
J14	D1 50c deep brown		*7,000.*	
	No gum		*3,000.*	

1884
J15	D1 1c red brown		70.00	7.00
	Never hinged		190.00	
J16	D1 2c red brown		80.00	6.00
	Never hinged		225.00	
J17	D1 3c red brown		1,050.	350.00
	Never hinged		2,500.	
J18	D1 5c red brown		550.00	50.00
	Never hinged		1,300.	
J19	D1 10c red brown		550.00	35.00
	Never hinged		1,300.	
J20	D1 30c red brown		225.00	70.00
	Never hinged		550.00	
J21	D1 50c red brown		1,800.	250.00
	Never hinged		3,750.	
	Nos. J15-J21 (7)		4,325.	768.00

1891
J22	D1 1c bright claret		30.00	2.00
	Never hinged		85.00	
J23	D1 2c bright claret		32.50	2.00
	Never hinged		90.00	
J24	D1 3c bright claret		67.50	16.00
	Never hinged		180.00	
J25	D1 5c bright claret		100.00	16.00
	Never hinged		290.00	
J26	D1 10c bright claret		165.00	30.00
	Never hinged		500.00	
J27	D1 30c bright claret		575.00	225.00
	Never hinged		1,700.	
J28	D1 50c bright claret		625.00	225.00
	Never hinged		1,750.	
	Nos. J22-J28 (7)		1,595.	516.00

Nos. J22-J28 fluoresce orange under longwave ultraviolet light. Nos. J15-J21 do not.

See Die and Plate Proofs in the Scott U.S. Specialized catalog for imperfs. on stamp paper.

> **The color on Nos. J29-J44 will run when immersed in water. Extreme caution is advised.**

D2

Printed by the Bureau of Engraving and Printing.

1894
J29	D2 1c vermilion		2,250.	750.
	Never hinged		*5,750.*	
J30	D2 2c vermilion		775.	350.
	Never hinged		1,900.	

1894-95
J31	D2 1c deep claret		72.50	12.00
	Never hinged		260.00	
b.	Vertical pair, imperf. horiz.		—	
J32	D2 2c deep claret		62.50	10.00
	Never hinged		240.00	
J33	D2 3c deep claret ('95)		200.00	50.00
	Never hinged		575.00	
J34	D2 5c deep claret ('95)		300.00	55.00
	Never hinged		850.00	
J35	D2 10c deep claret ('95)		350.00	40.00
	Never hinged		1,000.	
J36	D2 30c deep claret ('95)		550.00	250.00
	Never hinged		1,250.	
a.	30c carmine		675.00	275.00
	Never hinged		1,600.	
b.	30c pale rose		450.00	200.00
	Never hinged		1,100.	
J37	D2 50c deep claret ('95)		1,800.	800.00
	Never hinged		4,250.	
a.	50c pale rose		1,600.	725.00
	Never hinged		3,750.	
	Nos. J31-J37 (7)		3,335.	1,217.

Shades are numerous in the 1894 and later issues.
See Die and Plate Proofs in the Scott U.S. Specialized catalog for imperfs. on stamp paper.

1895-97   Wmk. 191
J38	D2 1c deep claret		13.50	1.00
	Never hinged		40.00	
J39	D2 2c deep claret		13.50	1.00
	Never hinged		40.00	
J40	D2 3c deep claret		100.00	5.00
	Never hinged		225.00	
J41	D2 5c deep claret		110.00	5.00
	Never hinged		280.00	
J42	D2 10c deep claret		110.00	7.50
	Never hinged		280.00	
J43	D2 30c deep claret ('97)		600.00	75.00
	Never hinged		1,500.	
J44	D2 50c deep claret ('96)		375.00	60.00
	Never hinged		925.00	
	Nos. J38-J44 (7)		1,322.	154.50

1910-12   Wmk. 190
J45	D2 1c deep claret		40.00	5.00
	Never hinged		115.00	
a.	1c rose carmine		35.00	5.00
	Never hinged		105.00	
J46	D2 2c deep claret		40.00	2.00
	Never hinged		115.00	
a.	2c rose carmine		35.00	2.00
	Never hinged		105.00	
J47	D2 3c deep claret		625.00	60.00
	Never hinged		1,600.	
J48	D2 5c deep claret		120.00	12.00
	Never hinged		275.00	
a.	5c rose carmine		120.00	12.00
	Never hinged		275.00	
J49	D2 10c deep claret		125.00	20.00
	Never hinged		280.00	
a.	10c rose carmine		125.00	20.00
	Never hinged		280.00	
J50	D2 50c deep claret ('12)		1,100.	200.00
	Never hinged		2,900.	
a.	50c rose carmine		1,150.	190.00
	Never hinged		3,000.	
	Nos. J45-J50 (6)		2,050.	299.00

1914   *Perf. 10*
J52	D2 1c carmine lake		80.00	15.00
	Never hinged		220.00	
a.	1c dull rose		85.00	15.00
	Never hinged		230.00	
J53	D2 2c carmine lake		62.50	1.00
	Never hinged		170.00	
a.	2c dull rose		67.50	2.00
	Never hinged		180.00	
b.	2c vermilion		67.50	2.00
	Never hinged		180.00	
J54	D2 3c carmine lake		1,050.	75.00
	Never hinged		3,000.	
a.	3c dull rose		1,000.	75.00
	Never hinged		2,900.	
J55	D2 5c carmine lake		50.00	6.00
	Never hinged		140.00	
a.	5c dull rose		45.00	4.00
	Never hinged		130.00	
J56	D2 10c carmine lake		75.00	4.00
	Never hinged		200.00	
a.	10c dull rose		80.00	5.00
	Never hinged		210.00	
J57	D2 30c carmine lake		225.00	55.00
	Never hinged		525.00	
J58	D2 50c carmine lake		*11,500.*	1,700.
	Never hinged		*21,000.*	
	Nos. J52-J58 (7)		13,043.	1,856.

No. J58 unused is valued in the grade of fine to very fine.

1916   Unwmk.   *Perf. 10*
J59	D2 1c rose		4,000.	750.00
	Never hinged		9,000.	
J60	D2 2c rose		250.00	75.00
	Never hinged		625.00	

1917   *Perf. 11*
J61	D2 1c carmine rose		2.75	.25
	Never hinged		9.00	
	Never hinged		15.00	
a.	1c rose red		2.75	.25
	Never hinged		9.00	
b.	1c deep claret		2.75	.25
	Never hinged		9.00	
J62	D2 2c carmine rose		2.75	.25
	Never hinged		9.00	
a.	2c rose red		2.75	.25
	Never hinged		9.00	
b.	2c deep claret		2.75	.25
	Never hinged		9.00	
J63	D2 3c carmine rose		13.50	.80
	Never hinged		35.00	
a.	3c rose red		13.50	.80
	Never hinged		35.00	
b.	3c deep claret		13.50	.80
	Never hinged		35.00	
J64	D2 5c carmine		11.00	.80
	Never hinged		32.50	
a.	5c rose red		11.00	.80
	Never hinged		32.50	
b.	5c deep claret		11.00	.80
	Never hinged		32.50	

J65	D2 10c carmine rose		22.50	1.00
	Never hinged		65.00	
a.	10c rose red		22.50	1.00
	Never hinged		65.00	
b.	10c deep claret		22.50	1.00
	Never hinged		65.00	
J66	D2 30c carmine rose		80.00	2.00
	Never hinged		220.00	
a.	30c deep claret		80.00	2.00
	Never hinged		220.00	
b.	As "a," perf 10 at top, precanceled			*21,000.*

No. J66b is valued with small faults and fine centering, as the two recorded examples are in this condition and grade.

J67	D2 50c carmine rose		140.00	1.00
	Never hinged		325.00	
a.	50c rose red		140.00	1.00
	Never hinged		325.00	
b.	50c deep claret		140.00	1.00
	Never hinged		325.00	
	Nos. J61-J67 (7)		272.50	6.10

1925
J68	D2 ½c dull red		1.00	.25
	Never hinged		1.75	

D3   D4

1930   *Perf. 11*
J69	D3 ½c carmine		4.25	1.90
	Never hinged		9.50	
J70	D3 1c carmine		2.75	.35
	Never hinged		6.25	
J71	D3 2c carmine		3.75	.35
	Never hinged		8.50	
J72	D3 3c carmine		20.00	2.75
	Never hinged		47.50	
J73	D3 5c carmine		18.00	5.00
	Never hinged		42.50	
J74	D3 10c carmine		42.50	2.00
	Never hinged		95.00	
J75	D3 30c carmine		125.00	4.00
	Never hinged		275.00	
J76	D3 50c carmine		175.00	2.00
	Never hinged		375.00	
J77	D4 $1 carmine		32.50	.35
	Never hinged		65.00	
a.	$1 scarlet		27.50	.35
	Never hinged		55.00	
J78	D4 $5 dull carmine		37.50	.35
	Never hinged		85.00	
a.	scarlet		32.50	.35
	Never hinged		70.00	

Type of 1930-31 Issue
Rotary Press Printing
1931   *Perf. 11x10½*
J79	D3 ½c dull carmine		.90	.25
	Never hinged		1.30	
a.	½c scarlet		.90	.25
	Never hinged		1.30	
J80	D3 1c dull carmine		.25	.25
	Never hinged		.30	
a.	scarlet		.25	.25
	Never hinged		.30	
J81	D3 2c dull carmine		.25	.25
	Never hinged		.30	
a.	scarlet		.25	.25
	Never hinged		.30	

J82	D3	3c dull carmine	.25	.25
		Never hinged	.40	
a.		scarlet	.30	.25
		Never hinged	.45	
J83	D3	5c dull carmine	.40	.25
		Never hinged	.60	
a.		scarlet	.50	.25
		Never hinged	.75	
J84	D3	10c dull carmine	1.10	.25
		Never hinged	1.80	
a.		scarlet	1.25	.25
		Never hinged	1.90	
J85	D3	30c dull carmine	7.50	.25
		Never hinged	11.50	
a.		30c scarlet	7.50	.25
		Never hinged	11.50	
J86	D3	50c dull carmine	9.00	.25
		Never hinged	15.00	
a.		50c scarlet	9.00	.25
		Never hinged	15.00	

Design measures 22½x19mm

1956   Perf. 10½x11

J87	D4	$1 scarlet	30.00	.25
		Never hinged	52.50	
		Nos. J79-J87 (9)	49.65	2.25

For listings of other color shades and printing varieties see the *Scott Specialized Catalogue of United States Stamps and Covers.*

> **Catalogue values for unused stamps in this section, from this point to the end, are for Never Hinged items.**

 D5

Denominations added in black by rubber plates in an operation similar to precanceling.

Rotary Press Printing
Perf. 11x10½
1959, June 19   Unwmk.
Denomination in Black

J88	D5	½c carmine rose	1.50	1.10
J89	D5	1c carmine rose	.25	.25
a.		Denomination omitted	150.00	
b.		Pair, one without "1 CENT"	350.00	
J90	D5	2c carmine rose	.25	.25
J91	D5	3c carmine rose	.25	.25
a.		Pair, one without "3 CENTS"	550.00	
J92	D5	4c carmine rose	.25	.25
J93	D5	5c carmine rose	.25	.25
a.		Pair, one without "5 CENTS"	1,500.	
J94	D5	6c carmine rose	.25	.25
a.		Pair, one without "6 CENTS"	700.00	
J95	D5	7c carmine rose	.25	.25
J96	D5	8c carmine rose	.25	.25
a.		Pair, one without "8 CENTS"	750.00	
J97	D5	10c carmine rose	.25	.25
J98	D5	30c carmine rose	.70	.25
J99	D5	50c carmine rose	1.10	.25

Straight Numeral Outlined in Black

J100	D5	$1 carmine rose	2.00	.25
J101	D5	$5 carmine rose	9.00	.25
		Nos. J88-J101 (14)	16.55	4.35

All single stamps with denomination omitted are catalogued as No. J89a.

1978-85   Denomination in Black

J102	D5	11c carmine rose	.25	.25
J103	D5	13c carmine rose	.25	.25
J104	D5	17c carmine rose ('85)	.40	.35

UNITED STATES OFFICES IN CHINA

Issued for sale by the postal agency at Shanghai, at their surcharged value in local currency. Valid to the amount of their original values for the prepayment of postage on mail dispatched from the U.S. postal agency at Shanghai to addresses in the U.S.

Nos. 498-499, 502-504, 506-510, 512, 514-518 Surcharged

1919   Unwmk.   Perf. 11

K1	A140	2c on 1c green	22.50	70.00
		Never hinged	67.50	

K2	A140	4c on 2c rose, type I	22.50	70.00
		Never hinged	67.50	
K3	A140	6c on 3c vio, type II	55.00	140.00
		Never hinged	140.00	
K4	A140	8c on 4c brown	55.00	140.00
		Never hinged	140.00	
K5	A140	10c on 5c blue	60.00	140.00
		Never hinged	160.00	
K6	A140	12c on 6c red org	80.00	210.00
		Never hinged	210.00	
K7	A140	14c on 7c black	82.50	210.00
		Never hinged	215.00	
K8	A148	16c on 8c ol bis	65.00	160.00
		Never hinged	170.00	
a.		16c on 8c ol grn	55.00	140.00
		Never hinged	150.00	
K9	A148	18c on 9c sal red	60.00	175.00
		Never hinged	150.00	
K10	A148	20c on 10c org yel	55.00	140.00
		Never hinged	140.00	
K11	A148	24c on 12c brn car	75.00	160.00
		Never hinged	190.00	
a.		24c on 12c cl brn	110.00	240.00
		Never hinged	275.00	
K12	A148	30c on 15c gray	82.50	230.00
		Never hinged	200.00	
K13	A148	40c on 20c deep ultra	120.00	325.00
		Never hinged	300.00	
K14	A148	60c on 30c org red	110.00	275.00
		Never hinged	260.00	
K15	A148	$1 on 50c lt vio	550.00	1,000.
		Never hinged	1,200.	
K16	A148	$2 on $1 vio brn	425.00	750.00
		Never hinged	925.00	
a.		Double surcharge	10,500.	12,500.
		Never hinged	17,500.	
		Nos. K1-K16 (16)	1,920.	4,195.

Fake surcharges exist, but most are rather crudely made.

Nos. 498 and 528B Surcharged

1922, July 3

K17	A140	2c on 1c green	100.00	225.00
		Never hinged	225.00	
K18	A140	4c on 2c car, type VII	90.00	200.00
		Never hinged	210.00	
a.		"SHANGHAI" omitted	7,500.	
b.		"CHINA" only	15,000.	

OFFICIAL STAMPS

The franking privilege having been abolished, as of July 1, 1873, these stamps were provided for each of the departments of Government for the prepayment of postage on official matter.

Penalty franks were first authorized in 1877, and their expanded use after 1879 reduced the need for official stamps, the use of which was finally abolished on July 5, 1884.

Designs, except Post Office, resemble those illustrated but are not identical. Each bears the name of Department. Portraits are as follows: 1c, Franklin; 2c, Jackson; 3c, Washington; 6c, Lincoln; 7c, Stanton; 10c, Jefferson; 12c, Clay; 15c, Webster; 24c, Scott; 30c, Hamilton; 90c, Perry.

> **Special printings overprinted "SPECIMEN" follow No. O120.**

Printed by the Continental Bank Note Co.

O1

Thin Hard Paper
AGRICULTURE

1873   Engr.   Unwmk.   Perf. 12

O1	O1	1c yellow	300.00	200.00
		Never hinged	1,000.	
		No gum	170.00	
O2	O1	2c yellow	275.00	100.00
		Never hinged	575.00	
		No gum	130.00	
O3	O1	3c yellow	225.00	17.50
		Never hinged	450.00	
		No gum	105.00	
O4	O1	6c yellow	275.00	60.00
		Never hinged	575.00	
		No gum	130.00	
O5	O1	10c yellow	525.00	200.00
		Never hinged	1,150.	
		No gum	240.00	
O6	O1	12c yellow	450.00	260.00
		Never hinged	1,000.	
		No gum	250.00	
O7	O1	15c yellow	425.00	230.00
		Never hinged	950.00	
		No gum	225.00	
O8	O1	24c yellow	425.00	250.00
		Never hinged	950.00	
		No gum	225.00	
O9	O1	30c yellow	550.00	280.00
		Never hinged	1,200.	
		No gum	275.00	
		Nos. O1-O9 (9)	3,450.	1,598.

EXECUTIVE

Franklin—O2

1873

O10	O2	1c carmine	900.00	550.00
		Never hinged	3,500.	
		No gum	450.00	
O11	O2	2c carmine	575.00	260.00
		Never hinged	1,400.	
		No gum	260.00	
O12	O2	3c carmine	700.00	225.00
		Never hinged	1,600.	
		No gum	325.00	
a.		3c violet rose	1,000.	275.00
		Never hinged	2,250.	
		No gum	450.00	
		On cover	—	
O13	O2	6c carmine	900.00	600.00
		Never hinged	—	
		No gum	425.00	
O14	O2	10c carmine	1,200.	1,000.
		Never hinged	2,500.	
		No gum	600.00	
		Nos. O10-O14 (5)	4,275.	2,635.

INTERIOR

O3

1873

O15	O3	1c vermilion	75.00	10.00
		Never hinged	170.00	
		No gum	35.00	
O16	O3	2c vermilion	70.00	12.00
		Never hinged	160.00	
		No gum	30.00	
O17	O3	3c vermilion	80.00	6.00
		Never hinged	175.00	
		No gum	40.00	
O18	O3	6c vermilion	70.00	10.00
		Never hinged	160.00	
		No gum	30.00	
O19	O3	10c vermilion	70.00	20.00
		Never hinged	160.00	
		No gum	30.00	
O20	O3	12c vermilion	90.00	12.00
		Never hinged	200.00	
		No gum	45.00	
O21	O3	15c vermilion	200.00	25.00
		Never hinged	450.00	
		No gum	90.00	
O22	O3	24c vermilion	180.00	20.00
		Never hinged	400.00	
		No gum	85.00	
a.		Double impression	—	
O23	O3	30c vermilion	290.00	20.00
		Never hinged	625.00	
		No gum	130.00	
O24	O3	90c vermilion	325.00	50.00
		Never hinged	700.00	
		No gum	140.00	
		Nos. O15-O24 (10)	1,450.	185.00

JUSTICE

O4

1873

O25	O4	1c purple	250.00	100.00
		Never hinged	550.00	
		No gum	120.00	
O26	O4	2c purple	310.00	110.00
		Never hinged	700.00	
		No gum	135.00	
O27	O4	3c purple	300.00	35.00
		Never hinged	700.00	
		No gum	135.00	
O28	O4	6c purple	310.00	45.00
		Never hinged	700.00	
		No gum	135.00	
O29	O4	10c purple	310.00	100.00
		Never hinged	1,250.	
		No gum	135.00	
O30	O4	12c purple	260.00	75.00
		Never hinged	1,500.	
		No gum	125.00	
O31	O4	15c purple	500.00	200.00
		Never hinged	1,500.	
		No gum	240.00	
O32	O4	24c purple	1,250.	425.00
		Never hinged	4,250.	
		No gum	600.00	
O33	O4	30c purple	1,300.	350.00
		Never hinged	—	
		No gum	625.00	
O34	O4	90c purple	1,900.	900.00
		Never hinged	4,000.	
		No gum	900.00	
		Nos. O25-O34 (10)	6,690.	2,340.

NAVY

O5

1873

O35	O5	1c ultramarine	160.00	50.00
		Never hinged	350.00	
		No gum	75.00	
a.		1c dull blue	175.00	50.00
		Never hinged	375.00	
		No gum	82.50	
O36	O5	2c ultramarine	160.00	25.00
		Never hinged	350.00	
		No gum	75.00	
a.		2c dull blue	175.00	25.00
		Never hinged	385.00	
		No gum	82.50	
O37	O5	3c ultramarine	170.00	15.00
		Never hinged	1,750.	
		No gum	80.00	
a.		3c dull blue	175.00	15.00
		Never hinged	385.00	
		No gum	85.00	
O38	O5	6c ultramarine	150.00	25.00
		Never hinged	450.00	
		No gum	70.00	
a.		6c dull blue	175.00	25.00
		Never hinged	385.00	
		No gum	82.50	
O39	O5	7c ultramarine	700.00	230.00
		Never hinged		
		No gum	325.00	
a.		7c dull blue	750.00	230.00
		Never hinged	—	
		No gum	325.00	
O40	O5	10c ultramarine	210.00	45.00
		Never hinged	1,000.	
		No gum	95.00	
a.		10c dull blue	225.00	45.00
		Never hinged	1,000.	
		No gum	110.00	
O41	O5	12c ultramarine	240.00	45.00
		Never hinged	900.00	
		No gum	115.00	
O42	O5	15c ultramarine	425.00	75.00
		Never hinged	1,750.	
		No gum	200.00	
O43	O5	24c ultramarine	425.00	85.00
		Never hinged	1,750.	
		No gum	200.00	
a.		24c dull blue	425.00	80.00
		Never hinged	—	
		No gum	200.00	
O44	O5	30c ultramarine	350.00	50.00
		Never hinged	3,000.	
		No gum	160.00	
O45	O5	90c ultramarine	1,050.	375.00
		Never hinged	6,000.	
		No gum	500.00	
a.		Double impression		20,000.
		Nos. O35-O45 (11)	4,040.	1,020.

POST OFFICE

Stamps of the Post Office Department are often on paper with a gray surface. This is essentially a wiping problem, caused by an over-milled carbon black pigment that released acid and etched the plates. There is no premium for stamps on paper with a gray surface.

O6

1873

O47	O6 1c black	25.00	12.00
	Never hinged	60.00	
	No gum	12.00	
O48	O6 2c black	30.00	10.00
	Never hinged	75.00	
	No gum	14.00	
a.	Double impression	1,000.	600.00
O49	O6 3c black	10.00	2.00
	Never hinged	25.00	
	No gum	4.50	
a.	Printed on both sides		7,500.
O50	O6 6c black	30.00	8.00
	Never hinged	75.00	
	No gum	14.00	
a.	Diagonal half used as 3c on cover		5,000.
b.	Double impression		3,000.
O51	O6 10c black	140.00	55.00
	Never hinged	325.00	
	No gum	65.00	
O52	O6 12c black	120.00	12.00
	Never hinged	275.00	
	No gum	55.00	
O53	O6 15c black	140.00	20.00
	Never hinged	325.00	
	No gum	65.00	
O54	O6 24c black	225.00	25.00
	Never hinged	500.00	
	No gum	105.00	
O55	O6 30c black	200.00	25.00
	Never hinged	450.00	
	No gum	90.00	
O56	O6 90c black	220.00	25.00
	Never hinged	500.00	
	No gum	105.00	
	Nos. O47-O56 (10)	1,140.	194.00

STATE

Franklin — O7   Seward — O8

1873

O57	O7 1c dark green	260.00	75.00
	Never hinged	575.00	
	No gum	125.00	
O58	O7 2c dark green	310.00	100.00
	Never hinged	—	
	No gum	150.00	
O59	O7 3c dark green	220.00	25.00
	Never hinged	500.00	
	No gum	105.00	
O60	O7 6c dark green	250.00	30.00
	Never hinged	550.00	
	No gum	120.00	
O61	O7 7c dark green	290.00	65.00
	Never hinged	650.00	
	No gum	140.00	
O62	O7 10c dark green	250.00	55.00
	Never hinged	575.00	
	No gum	120.00	
O63	O7 12c dark green	310.00	125.00
	Never hinged	700.00	
	No gum	150.00	
O64	O7 15c dark green	350.00	90.00
	Never hinged	775.00	
	No gum	170.00	
O65	O7 24c dark green	550.00	230.00
	Never hinged	—	
	No gum	275.00	
O66	O7 30c dark green	525.00	180.00
	Never hinged	—	
	No gum	260.00	
O67	O7 90c dark green	1,100.	325.00
	Never hinged	—	
	No gum	525.00	
O68	O8 $2 green & black	1,800.	3,000.
	Never hinged	3,750.	
	No gum	850.00	
O69	O8 $5 green & black	8,000.	13,000.
	Never hinged	—	
	No gum	3,750.	
O70	O8 $10 green & black	4,500.	7,500.
	Never hinged	10,500.	
	No gum	2,500.	
O71	O8 $20 green & black	5,000.	5,500.
	Never hinged	11,500.	
	No gum	2,500.	

No. O71 used is valued with a blue or red handstamp favor cancel. Nos. O68-O71 with pen cancels sell for approximately 25-40% of the values shown.

TREASURY

O9

1873

O72	O9 1c brown	120.00	10.00
	Never hinged	250.00	
	No gum	55.00	

O73	O9 2c brown	125.00	8.00
	Never hinged	275.00	
	No gum	57.50	
O74	O9 3c brown	110.00	2.00
	Never hinged	230.00	
	No gum	50.00	
a.	Double impression		5,000.
O75	O9 6c brown	120.00	4.00
	Never hinged	250.00	
	No gum	55.00	
O76	O9 7c brown	250.00	35.00
	Never hinged	550.00	
	No gum	120.00	
O77	O9 10c brown	240.00	12.00
	Never hinged	525.00	
	No gum	110.00	
O78	O9 12c brown	350.00	10.00
	Never hinged	750.00	
	No gum	160.00	
O79	O9 15c brown	300.00	12.00
	Never hinged	650.00	
	No gum	140.00	
O80	O9 24c brown	725.00	100.00
	Never hinged	—	
	No gum	325.00	
O81	O9 30c brown	400.00	12.00
	Never hinged	—	
	No gum	180.00	
O82	O9 90c brown	475.00	15.00
	Never hinged	—	
	No gum	225.00	
	Nos. O72-O82 (11)	3,215.	220.00

WAR

O10

1873

O83	O10 1c rose	240.00	15.00
	Never hinged	850.00	
	No gum	115.00	
O84	O10 2c rose	260.00	15.00
	Never hinged	1,200.	
	No gum	125.00	
O85	O10 3c rose	275.00	5.00
	Never hinged	650.00	
	No gum	135.00	
O86	O10 6c rose	675.00	10.00
	Never hinged	1,450.	
	No gum	325.00	

Examples of Nos. O114-O117 which bear Continental Bank Note Co. imprints are often mistaken for/offered as Nos. O83-O86. If there are doubts, expert opinions should be requested.

O87	O10 7c rose	175.00	90.00
	Never hinged	600.00	
	No gum	90.00	
O88	O10 10c rose	140.00	25.00
	Never hinged	375.00	
	No gum	65.00	
O89	O10 12c rose	275.00	12.00
	Never hinged	700.00	
	No gum	130.00	
O90	O10 15c rose	85.00	15.00
	Never hinged	260.00	
	No gum	40.00	
O91	O10 24c rose	85.00	12.00
	Never hinged	190.00	
	No gum	40.00	
O92	O10 30c rose	130.00	12.00
	Never hinged	375.00	
	No gum	65.00	
O93	O10 90c rose	225.00	60.00
	Never hinged	80.00	
	No gum	110.00	
	Nos. O83-O93 (11)	2,565.	271.00

Printed by the American Bank Note Co.

1879
Soft Porous Paper
AGRICULTURE

O94	O1 1c yel, no gum	5,500.	
O95	O1 3c yellow	550.00	150.00
	Never hinged	1,250.	
	No gum	260.00	

INTERIOR

O96	O3 1c vermilion	300.00	400.00
	Never hinged	550.00	
	No gum	150.00	
O97	O3 2c vermilion	10.00	3.00
	Never hinged	17.50	
	No gum	4.50	
O98	O3 3c vermilion	10.00	3.00
	Never hinged	22.50	
	No gum	4.50	
O99	O3 6c vermilion	10.00	12.50
	Never hinged	17.50	
	No gum	4.50	
O100	O3 10c vermilion	110.00	75.00
	Never hinged	250.00	
	No gum	55.00	
O101	O3 12c vermilion	230.00	115.00
	Never hinged	525.00	
	No gum	115.00	
O102	O3 15c pale vermilion	400.00	500.00
	Never hinged	900.00	
	No gum	200.00	

O103	O3 24c pale vermilion	4,500.	6,250.
	Never hinged	10,000.	
	No gum	2,200.	
	Nos. O96-O103 (8)	5,570.	7,359.

JUSTICE

O106	O4 3c bluish pur	250.00	125.00
	Never hinged	575.00	
	No gum	120.00	
O107	O4 6c bluish pur	475.00	300.00
	Never hinged	1,050.	
	No gum	250.00	

POST OFFICE

O108	O6 3c black	30.00	10.00
	Never hinged	70.00	
	No gum	14.00	

TREASURY

O109	O9 3c brown	80.00	10.00
	Never hinged	175.00	
	No gum	35.00	
O110	O9 6c brown	200.00	50.00
	Never hinged	450.00	
	No gum	90.00	
O111	O9 10c brown	275.00	80.00
	Never hinged	650.00	
	No gum	130.00	
O112	O9 30c brown	2,400.	550.00
	Never hinged	—	
	No gum	1,200.	
O113	O9 90c brown	10,000.	750.00
	Never hinged	—	
	No gum	5,000.	
	Nos. O109-O113 (5)	12,955.	1,440.

WAR

O114	O10 1c rose red	7.50	4.00
	Never hinged	15.00	
	No gum	3.50	
O115	O10 2c rose red	15.00	4.00
	Never hinged	30.00	
	No gum	7.00	
O116	O10 3c rose red	10.00	2.00
	Never hinged	20.00	
	No gum	3.25	
a.	Imperf., pair	5,000.	
b.	Double impression	7,500.	
O117	O10 6c rose red	12.50	3.00
	Never hinged	25.00	
	No gum	6.00	
O118	O10 10c rose red	75.00	50.00
	Never hinged	150.00	
	No gum	35.00	
O119	O10 12c rose red	70.00	14.00
	Never hinged	140.00	
	No gum	35.00	
O120	O10 30c rose red	225.00	100.00
	Never hinged	500.00	
	No gum	110.00	
	Nos. O114-O120 (7)	415.00	177.00

SPECIAL PRINTINGS

Special printings of Official stamps were made in 1875 at the time the other Reprints, Re-issues and Special Printings were printed. They are ungummed.

Although perforated, these stamps were sometimes (but not always) cut apart with scissors. As a result the perforations may be mutilated and the design damaged. Values are for very fine stamps with intact perforations.

All values exist imperforate.

Printed by the Continental Bank Note Co.
Similar to Type D, without period, 11mm long
AGRICULTURE

Overprinted in Block Letters

Thin, hard white paper
Carmine Overprint

1875			Perf. 12
O1S	D 1c yellow	32.50	
a.	"Sepcimen" error	2,500.	
b.	Horiz. ribbed paper	37.50	
c.	As "b," small dotted "i" in "Specimen"	500.00	
O2S	D 2c yellow	55.00	
a.	"Sepcimen" error	3,000.	
O3S	D 3c yellow	400.00	
a.	"Sepcimen" error	19,000.	
O4S	D 6c yellow	400.00	
a.	"Sepcimen" error	22,500.	
O5S	D 10c yellow	400.00	
	P# strip of 5, Impt.	—	
a.	"Sepcimen" error	19,000.	
O6S	D 12c yellow	400.00	
a.	"Sepcimen" error	15,000.	
O7S	D 15c yellow	400.00	
a.	"Sepcimen" error	12,500.	
O8S	D 24c yellow	400.00	
a.	"Sepcimen" error	12,500.	
O9S	D 30c yellow	400.00	
a.	"Sepcimen" error	13,500.	
	Nos. O1S-O9S (9)	2,888.	

EXECUTIVE
Blue Overprint

O10S	D 1c carmine	32.50	
a.	Horiz. ribbed paper	40.00	
b.	As "a," small dotted "i" in "Specimen"	500.00	
O11S	D 2c carmine	55.00	
O12S	D 3c carmine	67.50	
O13S	D 6c carmine	67.50	
O14S	D 10c carmine	67.50	
	Nos. O10S-O14S (5)	290.00	

INTERIOR
Blue Overprint

O15S	D 1c vermilion	60.00	
O16S	D 2c vermilion	140.00	
a.	"Sepcimen" error	—	

The existence of a genuine example of No. O16Sa has been questioned by specialists. The editors would like to see authenticated evidence of the existence of the single reported example.

O17S	D 3c vermilion	2,500.	
O18S	D 6c vermilion	2,500.	
O19S	D 10c vermilion	2,500.	
O20S	D 12c vermilion	2,500.	
O21S	D 15c vermilion	2,500.	
O22S	D 24c vermilion	2,500.	
O23S	D 30c vermilion	2,500.	
O24S	D 90c vermilion	2,500.	
	Nos. O15S-O24S (10)	20,200.	

JUSTICE
Blue Overprint

O25S	D 1c purple	32.50	
a.	"Sepcimen" error	2,500.	
b.	Horiz. ribbed paper	35.00	
c.	As "b," small dotted "i" in "Specimen"	500.00	
O26S	D 2c purple	55.00	
a.	"Sepcimen" error	3,500.	
O27S	D 3c purple	1,250.	
a.	"Sepcimen" error	11,000.	
O28S	D 6c purple	1,250.	
O29S	D 10c purple	1,250.	
O30S	D 12c purple	1,250.	
a.	"Sepcimen" error	19,000.	
O31S	D 15c purple	1,250.	
a.	"Sepcimen" error	25,000.	
O32S	D 24c purple	1,250.	
a.	"Sepcimen" error	20,000.	
O33S	D 30c purple	1,250.	
a.	"Sepcimen" error	15,000.	
O34S	D 90c purple	1,250.	
	Nos. O25S-O34S (10)	10,088.	

NAVY
Carmine Overprint

O35S	D 1c ultramarine	35.00	
a.	"Sepcimen" error	2,750.	
b.	Double "Specimen" overprint	1,900.	
O36S	D 2c ultramarine	75.00	
a.	"Sepcimen" error	4,500.	
O37S	D 3c ultramarine	1,750.	
O38S	D 6c ultramarine	1,750.	
O39S	D 7c ultramarine	550.00	
a.	"Sepcimen" error	10,000.	
O40S	D 10c ultramarine	1,750.	
a.	"Sepcimen" error	17,500.	
O41S	D 12c ultramarine	1,750.	
a.	"Sepcimen" error	21,000.	
O42S	D 15c ultramarine	1,750.	
a.	"Sepcimen" error	16,000.	
O43S	D 24c ultramarine	1,750.	
a.	"Sepcimen" error	15,000.	
O44S	D 30c ultramarine	1,750.	
a.	"Sepcimen" error	17,500.	
O45S	D 90c ultramarine	1,750.	
	Nos. O35S-O45S (11)	14,660.	

POST OFFICE
Carmine Overprint

O47S	D 1c black	45.00	
a.	"Sepcimen" error	3,250.	
b.	Inverted overprint	2,500.	
O48S	D 2c black	325.00	
a.	"Sepcimen" error	15,000.	
O49S	D 3c black	1,600.	
a.	"Sepcimen" error	37,500.	
O50S	D 6c black	1,600.	
O51S	D 10c black	1,000.	
a.	"Sepcimen" error	15,000.	
O52S	D 12c black	1,600.	
O53S	D 15c black	1,600.	
a.	"Sepcimen" error	26,000.	
O54S	D 24c black	1,600.	
a.	"Sepcimen" error	22,000.	
O55S	D 30c black	1,600.	
O56S	D 90c black	1,600.	
a.	"Sepcimen" error	25,000.	
	Nos. O47S-O56S (10)	12,570.	

STATE
Carmine Overprint

O57S	D 1c bluish green	32.50	
a.	"Sepcimen" error	2,500.	
b.	Horiz. ribbed paper	35.00	
c.	As "b," small dotted "i" in "Specimen"	650.00	
d.	Double "Specimen" overprint	3,850.	
O58S	D 2c bluish green	90.00	
a.	"Sepcimen" error	2,500.	
O59S	D 3c bluish green	140.00	
a.	"Sepcimen" error	7,000.	
O60S	D 6c bluish green	350.00	
a.	"Sepcimen" error	12,500.	
O61S	D 7c bluish green	175.00	
a.	"Sepcimen" error	9,000.	
O62S	D 10c bluish green	550.00	
a.	"Sepcimen" error	27,500.	

O63S	D	12c bluish green	550.00
a.		"Sepcimen" error	*19,000.*
O64S	D	15c bluish green	600.00
O65S	D	24c bluish green	600.00
a.		"Sepcimen" error	*25,000.*
O66S	D	30c bluish green	600.00
a.		"Sepcimen" error	*27,500.*
O67S	D	90c bluish green	600.00
a.		"Sepcimen" error	*27,500.*
O68S	D	$2 green & blk	19,000.
O69S	D	$5 green & blk	50,000.
O70S	D	$10 green & blk	110,000.
O71S	D	$20 green & blk	160,000.
		Nos. O57S-O67S (11)	*4,288.*

TREASURY
Blue Overprint

O72S	D	1c dark brown	80.00
O73S	D	2c dark brown	450.00
O74S	D	3c dark brown	1,600.
O75S	D	6c dark brown	1,600.
O76S	D	7c dark brown	950.00
O77S	D	10c dark brown	1,600.
O78S	D	12c dark brown	1,600.
O79S	D	15c dark brown	1,600.
O80S	D	24c dark brown	1,600.
O81S	D	30c dark brown	1,600.
O82S	D	90c dark brown	1,650.
		Nos. O72S-O82S (11)	*14,330.*

WAR
Blue Overprint

O83S	D	1c deep rose	35.00
a.		"Sepcimen" error	*3,000.*
O84S	D	2c deep rose	125.00
a.		"Sepcimen" error	*3,500.*
O85S	D	3c deep rose	1,400.
a.		"Sepcimen" error	*30,000.*
O86S	D	6c deep rose	1,400.
a.		"Sepcimen" error	*32,000.*
O87S	D	7c deep rose	425.00
a.		"Sepcimen" error	*17,500.*
O88S	D	10c deep rose	1,400.
a.		"Sepcimen" error	*27,500.*
O89S	D	12c deep rose	1,400.
a.		"Sepcimen" error	*32,000.*
O90S	D	15c deep rose	1,400.
a.		"Sepcimen" error	*30,000.*
O91S	D	24c deep rose	1,400.
a.		"Sepcimen" error	*30,000.*
O92S	D	30c deep rose	1,400.
a.		"Sepcimen" error	*30,000.*
O93S	D	90c deep rose	1,400.
a.		"Sepcimen" error	*30,000.*
		Nos. O83S-O93S (11)	*11,785.*

EXECUTIVE
Printed by the American Bank Note Co.
Soft Porous Paper

1881		**Blue Overprint**
O10xS D 1c violet rose		95.00

NAVY
Carmine Overprint

O35xS D 1c gray blue		100.00
a. Double overprint		*1,200.*

STATE

O57xS D 1c yellow green		180.00

OFFICIAL POSTAL SAVINGS MAIL

These stamps were used to prepay postage on official correspondence of the Postal Savings Division of the POD. Discontinued Sept. 23, 1914.

O11

Printed by the Bureau of Engraving & Printing

1910-11		**Engr.**	**Wmk. 191**	
O121	O11	2c black	17.50	2.00
		Never hinged	40.00	
O122	O11	50c dark green	175.00	60.00
		Never hinged	425.00	
O123	O11	$1 ultramarine	200.00	15.00
		Never hinged	450.00	

			Wmk. 190	
O124	O11	1c dark violet	10.00	2.00
		Never hinged	22.50	
O125	O11	2c black	65.00	7.00
		Never hinged	150.00	

O126	O11	10c carmine	20.00	2.00
		Never hinged	50.00	
		Nos. O121-O126 (6)	*487.50*	*88.00*

> **Catalogue values for unused stamps in this section, from this point to the end, are for Never Hinged items.**

Catalogue values for used stamps are for regularly used examples, not for examples removed from first day covers.

From No. O127 onward, all official stamps are tagged unless noted.

OFFICIAL MAIL

O12

Engraved
Unwmk.

1983, Jan. 12-1985			**Perf. 11**	
O127	O12	1c red, blue & black	.25	.25
O128	O12	4c red, blue & black	.25	.25
O129	O12	13c red, blue & black	.50	15.00
O129A	O12	14c red, blue & black	.45	.50
O130	O12	17c red, blue & black	.55	.40
O132	O12	$1 red, blue & black	2.25	1.00
O133	O12	$5 red, blue & black	9.50	20.00
		Nos. O127-O133 (7)	*13.75*	*37.40*

No. O129A does not have a "c" after the "14."

COIL STAMPS
Perf. 10 Vert.

O135	O12	20c red, blue & black	1.75	2.00
a.		Imperf., pair	*800.00*	
O136	O12	22c red, blue & blk ('85)	1.00	*2.00*
b.		Imperf, pair		*1,750.*

Inscribed: Postal Card Rate D

1985, Feb. 4			**Perf. 11**	
O138	O12	(14c) red, blue & black	5.00	15.00

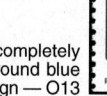

Frame line completely around blue design — O13

Inscribed: No. O139, Domestic Letter Rate D; No. O140, Domestic Mail E.

COIL STAMPS
Litho., Engr. (#O139)

1985-88			**Perf. 10 Vert.**	
O138A	O13	15c red, blue & blk	.50	.50
O138B	O13	20c red, blue & blk	.50	.30
O139	O12	(22c) red, blue & blk	5.25	20.00
O140	O13	(25c) red, blue & blk	.75	2.00
O141	O13	25c red, blue & blk	.65	.50
a.		Imperf., pair	*800.00*	—
		Nos. O138A-O141 (5)	*7.65*	*23.30*

Issue dates: 1985; E, Mar. 22, 1988; 15c, June 11; 20c, May 19; 25c, June 11.
See Nos. O143, O145-O151, O153-O156.

Plates of 400 in four panes of 100.

1989, July 5		**Litho.**	**Perf. 11**	
O143	O13	1c red, blue & black	.25	.25

On No. O143, the denomination is shown as "1". See No. O154.

Type of 1985 and

O14

COIL STAMPS

1991		**Litho.**	**Perf. 10 Vert.**	
O144	O14	(29c) red, blue & blk	.80	.50
O145	O13	29c red, blue & blk	.70	.30

Plates of 400 in four panes of 100.

1991-93		**Litho.**	**Perf. 11**	
O146	O13	4c red, blue & blk	.25	.30
O146A	O13	10c red, blue & blk	.30	.30
O147	O13	19c red, blue & blk	.40	.50
O148	O13	23c red, blue & blk	.50	.30
			Perf. 11¼	
O151	O13	$1 red, blue & blk	5.00	.75
		Nos. O146-O151 (5)	*6.45*	*2.15*

Nos. O146A, O151 have a line of microscopic printing below eagle.
See No. O156 for 23c with microscopic text below eagle.
Imperfs of No. O148 are printer's waste.
Issued: No. O146, 4/6; Nos. O147-O148, 5/24; 10c, 10/19/93; No. O151, 9/1993.

COIL STAMPS

Inscribed: No. O152, For U.S. addresses only G.

			Perf. 9.8 Vert.	
O152	O14	(32c) red, blue & blk	.65	.50
O153	O13	32c red, blue & blk	1.50	.50

Nos. O146A, O151, O153 have a line of microscopic text below the eagle.

1995, May 9		**Untagged**	**Perf. 11.2**	
O154	O13	1c red, blue & black	.25	.50

Denomination on No. O154 has a cent sign. See No. O143.

O155	O13	20c red, blue & black	.55	.50
O156	O13	23c red, blue & black	.60	.50

COIL STAMP

1000, Oct. 0			**Perf. 9¾ Vert.**	
O157	O13	33c red, blue & black	2.25	—

Type of 1985
COIL STAMP

2001, Feb. 27			**Perf. 9¾ Vert.**	
O158	O13	34c red, blue & black	2.25	.50

Nos. O154-O158 have a line of microscopic text below the eagle.

Type of 1985
COIL STAMP

2002, Aug. 2	**Photo.**		**Perf. 10 Vert.**	
O159	O13	37c red, blue & black	.75	.50

Type of 1985
COIL STAMP

2006, Mar. 8			**Perf. 10 Vert.**	
O160	O13	39c red, blue & black	1.00	*1.00*

Type of 1988
LITHOGRAPHED

2006, Sept. 29			**Perf. 11¼**	
O161	O13	$1 red, blue & black	5.00	*1.25*

No. O161 has a solid blue background. No. O151 has a background of crosshatched lines.

Type of 1985
COIL STAMP

2007, June 25			**Perf. 9¾**	
O162	O13	41c red, blue & black	1.00	*1.00*

Nos. O159-O162 have solid blue backgrounds. Nos. O138A-O158 have a background of crosshatched lines.

Type of 1985
Serpentine Die Cut 11½x10¾

2009, Feb. 24			**Untagged**	
		Self-Adhesive		
O163	O13	1c red, blue & black	.25	*.40*

NEWSPAPER STAMPS

For the prepayment of postage on bulk shipments of newspapers and periodicals. From 1875 on, the stamps were affixed to pages of receipt books, sometimes canceled and retained by the post office. Discontinued on July 1, 1898.

Virtually all used stamps of Nos. PR1-PR4 are canceled by blue brush strokes. All are rare. Most used stamps of Nos. PR9-PR32, PR57-PR79 and PR81-PR89 are pen canceled (or uncanceled), with some of Nos. PR9-PR32 also known canceled by a thick blue brush stroke.

Handstamp cancellations on any of these issues are rare and sell for much more than catalogue values which are for pen-canceled examples.

Used values for Nos. PR90-PR125 are for stamps with handstamp cancellations.

Washington — N1

Franklin — N2

Lincoln — N3

Values for Nos. PR1-PR8 are for examples with perforations on all four sides. Examples with natural straight edges sell for somewhat less. Some panes were fully perforated, while others have natural straight edges either at top or bottom affecting five stamps in the pane of ten.

Printed by the National Bank Note Co.
Thin hard paper, without gum
Size of design: 51x95mm
Typographed and Embossed
1865   Unwmk.   Perf. 12
Colored Border

PR1	N1	5c dark blue	750.00	2,000.
a.		5c light blue	1,350.	4,250.
PR2	N2	10c blue green	300.00	2,000.
a.		10c green	300.00	2,000.
b.		Pelure paper	400.00	2,000.
PR3	N3	25c orange red	400.00	2,500.
a.		25c carmine red	475.00	2,500.
b.		Pelure paper	500.00	

Nos. PR1-PR3 used are valued with faults.

White Border
Yellowish paper

PR4	N1	5c light blue	850.00	5,000.
a.		5c dark blue	850.00	—
b.		Pelure paper	950.00	—
		Nos. PR1-PR4 (4)	2,300.	

No. PR4 used is valued with faults.

REPRINTS of 1865 ISSUE
Printed by the Continental Bank Note Co. using the original National Bank Note Co. plates
1875
Hard white paper, without gum
5c White Border, 10c and 25c Colored Border

PR5	N1	5c dull blue	225.00	
a.		Printed on both sides	5,750.	
PR6	N2	10c dark bluish green	250.00	
a.		Printed on both sides	4,250.	
PR7	N3	25c dark carmine	300.00	
		Nos. PR5-PR7 (3)	775.00	

The 5c has white border, 10c and 25c have colored borders.
Many fakes exist of Nos. PR1-PR7, some of high quality. Certification is highly recommended.
The Continental Bank Note Co. made another special printing from new plates, which did not have the colored border. These exist imperforate and perforated, but they were not regularly issued. Value, imperf. set $3,250.

Printed by the American Bank Note Co.
Soft porous paper, without gum
1881   **White Border**
PR8   N1 5c dark blue   650.00

Statue of Freedom — N4

"Justice" — N5

Ceres — N6

"Victory" — N7

Clio — N8

Minerva — N9

Vesta — N10

"Peace" N11

"Commerce" N12

Hebe — N13

Indian Maiden — N14

Values for used examples of Nos. PR9-PR113 are for fine-very fine examples for denominations to $3, and fine for denominations of $5 or higher. Used examples of some Scott numbers might not exist without faults.

Printed by the Continental Bank Note Co.
Size of design: 24x35mm

1875, Jan. 1				Engr.
PR9	N4	2c black	300.00	45.00
		No gum	120.00	
PR10	N4	3c black	300.00	50.00
		No gum	120.00	
PR11	N4	4c black	300.00	45.00
		No gum	120.00	
PR12	N4	6c black	300.00	50.00
		No gum	120.00	
PR13	N4	8c black	350.00	75.00
		No gum	135.00	

PR14	N4	9c black	600.00	140.00
		No gum	225.00	
PR15	N4	10c black	375.00	67.50
		No gum	135.00	
PR16	N5	12c rose	800.00	110.00
		No gum	325.00	
PR17	N5	24c rose	850.00	175.00
		No gum	350.00	
PR18	N5	36c rose	850.00	200.00
		No gum	350.00	
PR19	N5	48c rose	1,250.	500.00
		No gum	450.00	
PR20	N5	60c rose	1,250.	125.00
		No gum	450.00	
PR21	N5	72c rose	1,500.	450.00
		No gum	550.00	
PR22	N5	84c rose	1,850.	450.00
		No gum	650.00	
PR23	N5	96c rose	2,000.	300.00
		No gum	775.00	
PR24	N6	$1.92 dk brn	1,750.	300.00
		No gum	700.00	
PR25	N7	$3 ver	2,500.	600.00
		No gum	975.00	
PR26	N8	$6 ultra	4,000.	650.00
		No gum	1,600.	
PR27	N9	$9 yel org	4,500.	2,400.
		No gum	1,750.	
PR28	N10	$12 bl grn	4,750.	1,250.
		No gum	1,850.	
PR29	N11	$24 dk gray vio	4,750.	1,400.
		No gum	1,850.	
PR30	N12	$36 brn rose	5,000.	1,600.
		No gum	2,000.	
PR31	N13	$48 red brn	7,000.	1,800.
		No gum	2,600.	
PR32	N14	$60 violet	6,500.	2,000.
		No gum	2,400.	

SPECIAL PRINTING of 1875 ISSUE
Printed by the Continental Bank Note Co.
Hard white paper, without gum
1875

PR33	N4	2c gray black	700.00	
a.	Horiz. ribbed paper		500.00	
PR34	N4	3c gray black	700.00	
a.	Horiz. ribbed paper		550.00	
PR35	N4	4c gray black	700.00	
	Horiz. ribbed paper		1,000.	
PR36	N4	6c gray black	900.00	
PR37	N4	8c gray black	975.00	
PR38	N4	9c gray black	1,050.	
PR39	N4	10c gray black	1,400.	
PR40	N5	12c pale rose	1,500.	
PR41	N5	24c pale rose	2,100.	
PR42	N5	36c pale rose	2,800.	
PR43	N5	48c pale rose	3,750.	
PR44	N5	60c pale rose	4,750.	
PR45	N5	72c pale rose	4,500.	
PR46	N5	84c pale rose	5,250.	
PR47	N5	96c pale rose	8,500.	
PR48	N6	$1.92 dk brn	20,000.	
PR49	N7	$3 vermilion	45,000.	
PR50	N8	$6 ultra	80,000.	
PR51	N9	$9 yellow org	350,000.	
PR52	N10	$12 blue green	175,000.	
PR53	N11	$24 dk gray vio	500,000.	
PR54	N12	$36 brn rose	400,000.	
PR55	N13	$48 red brown	—	
PR56	N14	$60 violet	—	

Nos. PR50 and PR52 are valued in the grade of fine.
Although four examples of No. PR51 were sold, only one is currently documented.
No. PR54 is valued in the grade of fine. Although two stamps were sold, only one is currently documented.
All values of this issue, Nos. PR33 to PR56, exist imperforate but were not regularly issued thus. Value, set $60,000.

Printed by the American Bank Note Co.
Soft porous paper
1879

PR57	N4	2c black	75.00	17.50
		No gum	30.00	
PR58	N4	3c black	85.00	22.50
		No gum	35.00	
PR59	N4	4c black	85.00	22.50
a.		Double paper	—	
PR60	N4	6c black	125.00	40.00
		No gum	50.00	
PR61	N4	8c black	135.00	40.00
		No gum	55.00	
PR62	N4	10c black	135.00	40.00
		No gum	55.00	
PR63	N5	12c red	500.00	140.00
		No gum	210.00	
PR64	N5	24c red	500.00	140.00
		No gum	210.00	
PR65	N5	36c red	1,000.	375.00
		No gum	475.00	
PR66	N5	48c red	1,000.	350.00
		No gum	450.00	
PR67	N5	60c red	1,250.	325.00
		No gum	550.00	
a.		Imperf., pair	4,000.	
PR68	N5	72c red	1,500.	475.00
		No gum	700.00	
PR69	N5	84c red	1,250.	400.00
		No gum	575.00	
PR70	N5	96c red	1,250.	325.00
		No gum	550.00	

PR71	N6	$1.92 pale brn	550.00	200.00
		No gum	225.00	
PR72	N7	$3 red ver	625.00	230.00
		No gum	250.00	
PR73	N8	$6 blue	1,050.	350.00
		No gum	400.00	
PR74	N9	$9 orange	800.00	260.00
		No gum	325.00	
PR75	N10	$12 yel grn	850.00	260.00
		No gum	325.00	
PR76	N11	$24 dk vio	800.00	350.00
		No gum	300.00	
PR77	N12	$36 Indian red	850.00	400.00
		No gum	350.00	
PR78	N13	$48 yel brn	900.00	525.00
		No gum	350.00	
PR79	N14	$60 purple	850.00	450.00
		No gum	350.00	
		Nos. PR57-PR70 (14)	8,890.	2,713.

See the Scott U.S. Specialized Catalogue Die and Plate Proof section for imperforates.

SPECIAL PRINTING of 1879 ISSUE
Printed by the American Bank Note Co.
Without gum
1883
PR80 N4 2c intense black   1,750.

REGULAR ISSUE
With gum
1885

PR81	N4	1c black, July 1, 1885	95.00	14.00
		Never hinged	225.00	
		No gum	42.50	
PR82	N5	12c carmine	200.00	35.00
		Never hinged	450.00	
		No gum	85.00	
PR83	N5	24c carmine	225.00	35.00
		Never hinged	500.00	
		No gum	95.00	
PR84	N5	36c carmine	350.00	65.00
		Never hinged	800.00	
		No gum	145.00	
PR85	N5	48c carmine	425.00	85.00
		Never hinged	975.00	
		No gum	180.00	
PR86	N5	60c carmine	600.00	120.00
		No gum	260.00	
PR87	N5	72c carmine	600.00	130.00
		No gum	260.00	
PR88	N5	84c carmine	900.00	290.00
		No gum	350.00	
PR89	N5	96c carmine	750.00	225.00
		Never hinged	1,750.	
		Nos. PR81-PR89 (9)	4,145.	999.00

See the Scott U.S. Specialized Catalogue Die and Plate Proof section for imperforates.

Printed by the Bureau of Engraving and Printing
1894
Soft wove paper, with pale, whitish gum

PR90	N4	1c intense blk	400.00	5,000.
		Never hinged	900.00	
		No gum	160.00	
PR91	N4	2c intense blk	450.00	—
		Never hinged	1,075.	
		No gum	190.00	
PR92	N4	4c intense blk	550.00	13,500.
		Never hinged	1,275.	
		No gum	210.00	
PR93	N4	6c intense blk	4,500.	
		Never hinged	11,500.	
		No gum	1,900.	
PR94	N4	10c intense blk	1,300.	
		Never hinged	2,400.	
		No gum	525.00	
PR95	N5	12c pink	2,400.	4,500.
		Never hinged	3,500.	
		No gum	1,100.	
PR96	N5	24c pink	3,750.	8,000.
		Never hinged	7,500.	
		No gum	1,850.	
PR97	N5	36c pink	50,000.	
PR98	N5	60c pink	40,000.	16,000.
PR99	N5	96c pink	50,000.	
PR100	N7	$3 scarlet	50,000.	
PR101	N8	$6 pale blue	50,000.	—
		No gum	25,000.	

Nos. PR90, PR95-PR98 used are valued with fine centering and small faults.
No. PR97 unused is valued in the grade of very good to fine. No. PR98 unused is valued in the grade of fine. Nos. PR99-PR100 unused are valued in the grade of fine-very fine.

Statue of Freedom N15   "Justice" N16

"Victory" — N17   Clio — N18

Vesta — N19   "Peace" — N20

"Commerce" N21   Indian Maiden N22

Size of designs: 1c-50c, 21x34mm; $2-$100, 24x35mm.

1895, Feb. 1

PR102	N15	1c black	230.00	125.00
		Never hinged	500.00	
		No gum	90.00	
PR103	N15	2c black	230.00	125.00
		Never hinged	500.00	
		No gum	90.00	
PR104	N15	5c black	300.00	300.00
		Never hinged	650.00	
		No gum	125.00	
PR105	N15	10c black	600.00	600.00
		Never hinged	1,300.	
		No gum	240.00	
PR106	N16	25c car	750.00	650.00
		Never hinged	1,650.	
		No gum	300.00	
PR107	N16	50c car	2,750.00	800.00
		Never hinged	6,250.	
		No gum	875.00	
PR108	N17	$2 scarlet	2,250.	1,100.
		Never hinged	5,000.	
		No gum	850.00	
PR109	N18	$5 ultra	2,100.	1,750.
		No gum	800.00	
PR110	N19	$10 green	2,500.	2,000.
		No gum	900.00	
PR111	N20	$20 slate	3,250.	2,500.
		No gum	1,200.	
PR112	N21	$50 dull rose	2,750.	950.00
		Never hinged	6,250.	
		No gum	1,050.	
PR113	N22	$100 purple	3,500.	7,000.
		No gum	1,400.	
Nos. PR102-PR113 (12)			21,210.	17,900.

1895-97   **Wmk. 191**

PR114	N15	1c black	8.00	25.00
		Never hinged	20.00	
		No gum	2.75	
PR115	N15	2c black	8.00	25.00
		Never hinged	20.00	
		No gum	2.75	
PR116	N15	5c black	13.00	40.00
		Never hinged	27.50	
		No gum	4.25	
PR117	N15	10c black	13.00	25.00
		Never hinged	27.50	
		No gum	4.25	
PR118	N16	25c carmine	20.00	65.00
		Never hinged	45.00	
		No gum	7.00	
PR119	N16	50c carmine	25.00	75.00
		Never hinged	55.00	
		No gum	8.50	

PR120	N17	$2 scarlet	30.00	110.00
		Never hinged	75.00	
		No gum	10.00	
PR121	N18	$5 dark bl	40.00	175.00
		Never hinged	100.00	
		No gum	13.50	
a.		$5 light blue	200.00	500.00
		Never hinged	500.00	
		No gum	67.50	
PR122	N19	$10 green	42.50	175.00
		Never hinged	105.00	
		No gum	14.00	
PR123	N20	$20 slate	45.00	200.00
		Never hinged	110.00	
		No gum	15.00	
PR124	N21	$50 dull rose	75.00	400.00
		Never hinged	170.00	
		No gum	27.50	
PR125	N22	$100 purple	65.00	300.00
		Never hinged	150.00	
		No gum	22.50	
Nos. PR114-PR125 (12)			384.50	1,615.
Nos. PR114-PR125, never hinged			905.00	

In 1899 the Government sold 26,989 sets of these stamps, but, as the stock of high values was not sufficient to make up the required number, an additional printing was made of the $5, $10, $20, $50 and $100. These are virtually indistinguishable from earlier printings.

For overprints, see Nos. R159-R160.

PARCEL POST STAMPS

Issued for the prepayment of postage on parcel post packages only.

Post Office Clerk — PP1

City Carrier PP2

Railway Postal Clerk — PP3

Rural Carrier PP4

Mail Train — PP5

Steamship and Mail Tender PP6

Automobile Service PP7

Airplane Carrying Mail — PP8

Manufacturing — PP9

Dairying PP10

Harvesting PP11

Fruit Growing PP12

1913   **Wmk. 190**   **Engr.**   **Perf. 12**

Q1	PP1	1c carmine rose	4.25	1.60
		Never hinged	12.00	
Q2	PP2	2c carmine rose	5.00	1.25
		Never hinged	12.50	
a.		2c lake	3,750.	
b.		2c carmine lake	350.00	

No. Q2a is valued in the grade of fine to very fine.

Q3	PP3	3c carmine	9.00	6.00
		Never hinged	24.00	
Q4	PP4	4c carmine rose	27.50	3.00
		Never hinged	77.50	
Q5	PP5	5c carmine rose	22.50	2.25
		Never hinged	62.50	
Q6	PP6	10c carmine rose	40.00	3.00
		Never hinged	90.00	
Q7	PP7	15c carmine rose	60.00	13.50
		Never hinged	170.00	
Q8	PP8	20c carmine rose	110.00	25.00
		Never hinged	260.00	
Q9	PP9	25c carmine rose	52.50	8.00
		Never hinged	145.00	
Q10	PP10	50c carmine rose	200.00	45.00
		Never hinged	500.00	
Q11	PP11	75c carmine rose	90.00	80.00
		Never hinged	180.00	
Q12	PP12	$1 carmine rose	250.00	40.00
		Never hinged	600.00	
Nos. Q1-Q12 (12)			860.75	183.60
Nos. Q1-Q12, never hinged			2,218.	

PARCEL POST POSTAGE DUE STAMPS

For affixing by a postal clerk to any parcel post package, to denote the amount to be collected from the addressee because of insufficient prepayment of postage.

PPD1

1913   **Wmk. 190**   **Engr.**   **Perf. 12**

JQ1	PPD1	1c dark green	8.00	4.00
		Never hinged	22.50	
JQ2	PPD1	2c dark green	60.00	16.00
		Never hinged	160.00	
JQ3	PPD1	5c dark green	9.00	4.50
		Never hinged	24.00	
JQ4	PPD1	10c dark green	110.00	40.00
		Never hinged	290.00	
JQ5	PPD1	25c dark green	70.00	4.50
		Never hinged	185.00	
Nos. JQ1-JQ5 (5)			257.00	69.00
Nos. JQ1-JQ5, never hinged			642.50	

SPECIAL HANDLING STAMPS

For use on fourth-class mail to secure the same expeditious handling accorded to first-class mail matter.

PP13

1925-28 **Engr.** **Unwmk.** *Perf. 11*

QE1	PP13	10c yellow green, wet printing, printed on "special" booklet paper, *1928* (see note before #551)	3.00	1.50
		Never hinged	5.25	
QE2	PP13	15c yellow green, wet printing, printed on "special" booklet paper, *1928* (see note before #551)	3.25	1.50
		Never hinged	5.75	
QE3	PP13	20c yellow green, wet printing, printed on "special" booklet paper, *1928* (see note before #551)	4.75	2.50
		Never hinged	8.75	
QE4	PP13	25c dp grn ('25)	20.00	4.00
		Never hinged	37.50	
a.		yel grn ('28)	16.50	22.50
		Never hinged	30.00	
Nos. QE1-QE4 (4)			31.00	9.50
Nos. QE1-QE4, never hinged			57.25	

COMPUTER VENDED POSTAGE

CVP1

CVP2

1989, Aug. 23 Tagged *Guillotined* **Self-Adhesive**
Washington, DC, Machine 82
Date Other Than First Day

CVP1	CVP1	25c First Class	6.00
a.		First day dated, serial Nos. 12501-15500	5.00
b.		First day dated, serial Nos. 00001-12500	5.00
c.		First day dated, over No. 27500	—
CVP2	CVP1	$1 Third Class	—
a.		First day dated, serial Nos. 24501-27500	—
b.		First day dated, over No. 27500	—
CVP3	CVP2	$1.69 Parcel Post	—
a.		First day dated, serial Nos. 21501-24500	—
b.		First day dated, over No. 27500	—
CVP4	CVP1	$2.40 Priority Mail	—
a.		First day dated, serial Nos. 18501-21500	—
b.		Priority Mail , with bar code (CVP2)	100.00
c.		First day dated, over No. 27500	—
CVP5	CVP1	$8.75 Express Mail	—
a.		First day dated, serial Nos. 15501-18500	—
b.		First day dated, over No. 27500	—

Washington, DC, Machine 83
Date Other Than First Day

CVP6	CVP1	25c First Class	6.00	—
a.	First day dated, serial Nos. 12501-15500		5.00	
b.	First day dated, serial Nos. 00001-12500		5.00	
c.	First day dated, over No. 27500		—	—
CVP7	CVP1	$1 Third Class	—	—
a.	First day dated, serial Nos. 24501-27500		—	
b.	First day dated, over No. 27500		—	
CVP8	CVP2	$1.69 Parcel Post		
a.	First day dated, serial Nos. 21501-24500		—	
b.	First day dated, over No. 27500		—	
CVP9	CVP1	$2.40 Priority Mail		
a.	First day dated, serial Nos. 18501-21500		—	
b.	First day dated, over No. 27500		—	

A Priority Mail $3.25 value also exists unused. A Priority Mail stamp exists on cover with error date 11/17/90 exists, and an unused stamp with error date 11/18/90 exists.

c.	Priority Mail , with bar code (CVP2)	100.00	

Error date 11/18/90 exists.

CVP10	CVP1	$8.75 Express Mail		
a.	First day dated, serial Nos. 15501-18500		—	—
b.	First day dated, over No. 27500		—	—

Error date 11/17/90 exists.

1989, Sept. 1
Kensington, MD, Machine 82
Date Other Than First Day

CVP11	CVP1	25c First Class	6.00	—
a.	First day dated, serial Nos. 12501-15500		5.00	
b.	First day dated, serial Nos. 00001-12500		5.00	
c.	First day dated, over No. 27500		—	—
CVP12	CVP1	$1 Third Class		
a.	First day dated, serial Nos. 24501-27500		—	
b.	First day dated, over No. 27500		—	
CVP13	CVP2	$1.69 Parcel Post		
a.	First day dated, serial Nos. 21501-24500		—	
b.	First day dated, over No. 27500		—	
CVP14	CVP1	$2.40 Priority Mail		
a.	First day dated, serial Nos. 18501-21500		—	
b.	First day dated, over No. 27500		—	
c.	Priority Mail , with bar code (CVP2)		100.00	
CVP15	CVP1	$8.75 Express Mail		
a.	First day dated, serial Nos. 15501-18500		—	—
b.	First day dated, over No. 27500		—	—

Kensington, MD, Machine 83
Date Other Than First Day

CVP16	CVP1	25c First Class	6.00	—
a.	First day dated, serial Nos. 12501-15500		5.00	
b.	First day dated, serial Nos. 00001-12500		5.00	
c.	First day dated, over No. 27500		—	—
CVP17	CVP1	$1 Third Class		
a.	First day dated, serial Nos. 24501-27500		—	
b.	First day dated, over No. 27500		—	
CVP18	CVP2	$1.69 Parcel Post	—	12.50
a.	First day dated, serial Nos. 21501-24500		—	
b.	First day dated, over No. 27500		—	
CVP19	CVP1	$2.40 Priority Mail		
a.	First day dated, serial Nos. 18501-21500		—	
b.	First day dated, over No. 27500		—	
c.	Priority Mail , with bar code (CVP2)		100.00	
CVP20	CVP1	$8.75 Express Mail		
a.	First day dated, serial Nos. 15501-18500		—	—
b.	First day dated, over No. 27500		—	—

1989, Nov.
Washington, DC, Machine 11

CVP21	CVP1	25c First Class	150.00	
a.	First day dated, with bar code (CVP2)		—	

Stamps in CVP1 design with $1.10 denomination exist (certified first class) dated 11/20/89. Value, unused, $650. A 45c denomination exists unused (dated 11/22/89) on cover to Europe and on Certificate of Mailing.

CVP22	CVP1	$1 Third Class	500.00	
CVP23	CVP2	$1.69 Parcel Post	500.00	
CVP24	CVP1	$2.40 Priority Mail	500.00	
a.	Priority Mail , with bar code (CVP2)		—	
CVP25	CVP1	$8.75 Express Mail	500.00	

Washington, DC, Machine 12

CVP26	CVP1	25c First Class	200.00	

No. CVP26, dated 12/13/89 is known on cover. $1.10 Certified First Class stamps dated 11/20/89 exist on covers.

CVP27	CVP1	$1 Third Class	600.00	

A $1.40 Third Class stamp of type CVP2, dated Dec. 1 is known on a Dec. 2 cover.

CVP28	CVP2	$1.65 Parcel Post	600.00	
CVP29	CVP1	$2.40 Priority Mail	600.00	
a.	Priority Mail with bar code (CVP2)		—	
CVP30	CVP1	$8.75 Express Mail	600.00	

An $8.50 Express Mail stamp, dated Dec. 2, exists on cover.

 CVP3 — Type 1

 CVP3 — Type II

1992, Aug. 20 Engr. *Perf. 10 Horiz.*
Coil Stamp

CVP31	CVP3	29c red & blue, type I	.75	.25
c.	32c Type II ('94)		1.25	.40

No. CVP31 was available in all denominations from 1c to $99.99.
The listing is for the first class rate. Other denominations, se-tenant combinations, or "errors" are not listed.
Type II denomination has large sans-serif numerals preceded by an asterisk measuring 2mm across. No. CVP31 has small numerals with serifs preceded by an asterisk 1½mm across.

 CVP4

1994, Feb. 19 Photo. *Perf. 9.9 Vert.*

CVP32	CVP4	29c dark red & dark blue	.75	.35

No. CVP32 was available in all denominations from 19c to $99.99.
The listing is for the first class rate at time of issue. Other denominations, se-tenant combinations, or "errors" will not be listed.

1996, Jan. 26

CVP33	CVP4	32c brt red & blue, "1996" below design	.75	.25

Letters in "USA" on No. CVP33 are thicker than on No. CVP32. Numerous other design differences exist in the moire pattern and in the bunting. No. CVP33 has "1996" in the lower left corner; No. CVP32 has no date.
For No. CVP33, the 32c value has been listed because it was the first class rate in effect at the time the stamp was issued.

 CVP5

1999, June Tagged *Die Cut*
Self-Adhesive

CVP34	CVP5	33c black	50.00	—
a.	"Priority Mail" under encryption at LL		—	
b.	"Express Mail" under encryption at LL		—	

No. CVP34 was available from 15 NCR Automated Postal Center machines located in

central Florida. Machines could produce values in any denomination required. The backing paper is taller and wider than the stamp.
Sales of No. CVP34 were discontinued in 2000 or 2001.

 CVP6

1999, May 7 Tagged *Die Cut*
Self-Adhesive
Size: 77½x39mm
Microprinting Above Red Orange Line

CVP35	CVP6	33c blk & red org, control numbers only at LL, round corners	20.00	—
a.	"Priority Mail" at LL, square corners		150.00	—
b.	"Priority Mail AS" and text string at LL, square corners		150.00	—

No Microprinting Above Red Orange Line

CVP36	CVP6	33c blk & red org, control numbers only at LL, round corners	9.00	—
a.	"Priority Mail" at LL, square corners		125.00	—
b.	"Priority Mail AS" and text string at LL, square corners		125.00	—

Size: 73½x42mm

CVP37	CVP6	33c blk & pink, control numbers only at LL	3.75	—
a.	"Priority Mail" at LL		5.00	—
b.	"Priority Mail AS" and text string at LL		5.00	—

Nos. CVP35-CVP37 were available from 18 IBM Neopost machines located in central Florida, and at least one machine in the Washington, DC area (Merrifield, VA Automated Postal Center). The backing paper is taller than the stamp. Any denomination could be printed up to $99.99.

 Simplypostage.com — CVP8

Serpentine Die Cut 8 at Right
2001 Self-Adhesive
Eagle and Stars Background

CVP39	CVP8	34c blk, blue & org, *2001*	—	—
CVP40	CVP8	34c blk, blue & org, with control number at UL, *2001*	—	—

Flag Background

CVP41	CVP8	34c blk, blue & org, with control number at UL, *2001*	—	—
CVP42	CVP8	34c blk, blue & org, with control number at LL, *2001*	—	20.00

 Large Flag Design

The item shown was produced by Neopost. It was found that the large flag image hampered the barcode from being scanned. It is believed no examples were actually sold to the public. Five panes of four are believed to exist.

Neopostage.com — CVP9

Serpentine Die Cut 8¾ at Right
2002, June Self-Adhesive

CVP43	CVP9	21c blk, blue & org	—	
a.	Booklet pane of 10		—	
CVP44	CVP9	23c blk, blue & org	—	
a.	Booklet pane of 10		90.00	
CVP45	CVP9	34c blk, blue & org	—	
a.	Booklet pane of 10		60.00	
CVP46	CVP9	37c blk, blue & org	—	
a.	Booklet pane of 10		—	
CVP47	CVP9	50c blk, blue & org	—	
a.	Booklet pane of 10		180.00	
CVP47B	CVP9	57c blk, blue & org	—	
a.	Booklet pane of 10		—	
CVP48	CVP9	60c blk, blue & org	—	
a.	Booklet pane of 10		160.00	
CVP49	CVP9	70c blk, blue & org	—	
a.	Booklet pane of 10		180.00	
CVP50	CVP9	80c blk, blue & org	—	
a.	Booklet pane of 10		180.00	
CVP51	CVP9	$3.50 blk, blue & org	—	
a.	Booklet pane of 1		—	
b.	Booklet pane of 2		—	
c.	Booklet pane of 5		—	
d.	Booklet pane of 10		—	
CVP52	CVP9	$3.85 blk, blue & org	—	
a.	Booklet pane of 1		—	
b.	Booklet pane of 2		—	
c.	Booklet pane of 5		—	
d.	Booklet pane of 10		—	
CVP52E	CVP9	$12.45 blk, blue & org	—	
a.	Booklet pane of 1		—	
CVP53	CVP9	$13.65 blk, blue & org	—	
a.	Booklet pane of 1		—	
b.	Booklet pane of 2		—	
c.	Booklet pane of 5		—	
d.	Booklet pane of 10		—	

Nos. CVP43-CVP53 were printed only with the stated values.
Denominations of 34c, 57c, $3.50 and perhaps others exist with a ICNOVA kiosk location designation. These were produced during pre-issue testing at a location not publicly accessible and are not considered to be valid postage. Stamps from the ICNOVA location have much smaller 2-D bar code squares. The denominations listed above come from other publicly accessible kiosk locations from June 20, 2002, forward. Official sales of these stamps began on June 20, 2002, or later for some denominations.
The 21c, 34c, 57c, $3.50 and $12.45 denominations were only sold from June 21 to June 29, 2002. They are all scarce, and some are rare. The 37c, $3.85 and $13.65 denominations were not sold until June 30, 2002, when the rate change took effect.
While the name on Nos. CVP39-CVP42 reads simplypostage.com and the name on Nos. CVP43-CVP53 reads neopostage.com, both were products of Neopost.
Issued: Nos. CVP43-CVP49, CVP51-CVP53, 6/2002; No. CVP50, 7/2002.

Earliest documented use: Nos. CVP43, CVP47, CVP51-CVP52, not known used; Nos. CVP44, CVP46, CVP48-CVP49, CVP53, 6/30; No. CVP45, 6/21; No. CVP50, 7/3.

CVP10

IBM Pitney Bowes — CVP11

2004, Apr. 14   *Die Cut*
Self-Adhesive

CVP54	CVP10	37c black & pink	5.00	—
a.	"First Class Mail" under encryption at LL		2.50	—
b.	"Priority Mail" under encryption at LL		2.50	—
c.	"Parcel Post" under encryption at LL		2.50	—
d.	"International" under encryption at LL		2.50	—
CVP55	CVP11	37c black, "US Postage" under encryption at LL	5.00	—
a.	"First Class Mail" under encryption at LL		2.50	—
b.	"Priority Mail" under encryption at LL		2.50	—
c.	"Parcel Post" under encryption at LL		2.50	—
d.	"International" under encryption at LL		2.50	—

Nos. CVP54-CVP55 could be printed in any denomination up to $99.99. Catalogue values for Nos. CVP54-CVP54d and CVP55 are for stamps with low denominations. Stamps with denominations appropriate to the service described are valued correspondingly higher.

CVP12

IBM Pitney Bowes — CVP13

2004, Nov. 19   *Die Cut*
Self-Adhesive
Serial Number Under Encryption
APC

CVP56	CVP12	37c black	2.50	.45
CVP57	CVP13	37c black & pink	1.25	.45

Nos. CVP56-CVP57 could be printed in any denomination. No. CVP56 could be printed with three different rate inscriptions under the denomination. No. CVP57 could be printed with 18 different rate inscriptions and/or service indicators under the denomination, and with at least 27 different rate inscriptions and or/service indicators under the denomination on stamps with a four-digit code after the zip code.

Blank Under Denomination
"IM" and Numbers Under
Encryption

CVP58	CVP13	60c black & pink	3.00	.50
CVP59	CVP13	80c black & pink	3.75	.50

"PM" and Numbers Under
Encryption

CVP60	CVP13	$3.85 black & pink	15.00	.50

"EM" and Numbers Under
Encryption

CVP61	CVP13	$13.65 black & pink	42.50	1.00

"IB" and Numbers Under
Encryption

CVP62	CVP13	$1 black & pink	4.00	.25

Nos. CVP58-CVP61 could only be printed in denominations listed. No. CVP62 could be printed in any denomination above 99c. As of May 12, 2008, it was possible to create stamps with "IB" and numbers under encryption in any denomination. The computer software was later changed to once again only permit stamps of certain denominations to be created with "IB" and numbers under the encryption.

IBM Pitney Bowes Type of 2004
2006   **Self-Adhesive**   *Die Cut*
Blank Under Denomination
"IM" and Numbers Under
Encryption

CVP63	CVP13	48c black & pink	1.50	.40
CVP64	CVP13	63c black & pink	1.75	.50
CVP65	CVP13	84c black & pink	2.25	.50

"PM" and Numbers Under
Encryption

CVP66	CVP13	$4.05 black & pink	11.00	.50
CVP66A	CVP13	$8.10 black & pink	30.00	1.00

"EM" and Numbers Under
Encryption

CVP67	CVP13	$14.40 black & pink	32.50	1.00

Nos. CVP63-CVP67 could only be printed in denominations listed.

IBM Pitney Bowes — CVP14

2006   **Self-Adhesive**   *Die Cut*
No Inscription Under Encryption
Serial Number to Right of "APC"
"Ship To:" Above Destination City

CVP69	CVP14	39c black	2.25	.25

Nos. CVP69 could be printed in any denomination, with 14 different rate inscriptions

and/or service indicators under the denomination on stamps having "Ship To:" at the left and no code below the weight, and at least 29 different rate inscriptions and/or service indicators under the denomination on stamps having a four-digit code at the right that is even with the words "Ship To:" and below the weight.

IBM Pitney Bowes Type of 2004
2006(?)-07   **Self-Adhesive**   *Die Cut*
Blank Under Denomination
"IB" and Numbers Under
Encryption

CVP70	CVP13	39c black & pink	1.00	.50
CVP71	CVP13	41c black & pink	1.75	.50
CVP72	CVP13	69c black & pink	2.50	.70

"IM" and Numbers Under
Encryption

CVP73	CVP13	61c black & pink	2.25	.50
CVP74	CVP13	90c black & pink	3.50	.95

Nos. CVP70-CVP74 could only be printed in the denominations listed.

Nos. CVP71-CVP74 issued May, 2007. No. CVP70 was issued before the May rate change. As of May 12, 2008, it was possible to create stamps with "IB" and numbers under encryption in any denomination. The computer software was later changed to once again only permit stamps of certain denominations to be created with "IB" and numbers under the encryption. No. CVP70 was available for sale from Nov. 2006 to May 13, 2007. Nos. CVP71-CVP72 were available for sale from May 14, 2007 to May 11, 2008.

Pitney Bowes With Eagle at
Right — CVP15

2006, Dec.   **Self-Adhesive**   *Die Cut*

CVP75	CVP15	41c blk & pink, no inscription below sold date	—	—
a.	"Mailed From Zip Code ..." on bottom line		—	—
b.	"Postcard" on bottom line		—	—
c.	"First-Class Mail" on bottom line		—	—
d.	"First-Class Mail Intl" on bottom line		—	—
e.	"Priority" on bottom line		—	—
f.	"Priority Envelope" on bottom line		—	—
g.	"Priority Box" on bottom line		—	—
h.	"Express Mail" on bottom line		—	—
i.	"Express Envelope" on bottom line		—	—
j.	"Parcel Post" on bottom line		—	—
k.	"Priority Tube" on bottom line		—	—
l.	"First Class" on bottom line		—	—

No. CVP75 was put into service at large companies and universities in Dec. 2006, with the majority of the machines not being available to the general public. Information about this stamp was not made available until 2007. Other rates and inscriptions might be available.

Nos. CVP75a could be printed in any denomination. Nos. CVP75b-CVP75f could be printed only in pre-programmed denominations based on the current rates for the service, or in any denominations at or above the minimum rates for the service. Values are for stamps with low denominations. A stamp with "Priority - Irregular Shape" on the bottom line has been reported to exist but has not been seen by the editors. Inscriptions generated by the software may vary from machine to machine depending on when the software was installed.

Two distinctly different colors of phosphor stripes on labels used in Mail & Go machines are known, with many Mail & Go adhesives appearing in both versions.

Private sector operators of Pitney Bowes "Mail & Go" machines are not bound to use only label paper supplied by Pitney Bowes. Competing label paper producers make and sell labels in the formats required for the machines that dispense Nos. CVP75 and CVP84. Thus, Nos. CVP75 and CVP84 without the Pitney Bowes logo on the reverse are not errors.

IBM Pitney Bowes Type of 2004
2008, May   **Self-Adhesive**   *Die Cut*
Blank Under Denomination
"IM" and Numbers Under
Encryption

CVP76	CVP13	94c black & pink	3.00	.60
CVP77	CVP13	$1.20 black & pink	3.75	1.25

Nos. CVP76-CVP77 could only be printed in the denominations listed.

IBM — CVP16

Die Cut With Rounded Corners
2008, June 4   **Self-Adhesive**

CVP78	CVP16	42c black & pink	4.25	
a.	Without "date of sale" inscription, 2009		—	—

Die Cut With Perpendicular Corners

CVP79	CVP16	42c black & pink	4.25	—
a.	Without "date of sale" inscription, 2009		—	—

Nos. CVP78-CVP79 were made available during a pilot study to evaluate a new IBM kiosk at Schaumburg, IL. No. CVP78 could be printed in any denomination from 1c to $25. Each kiosk transaction was limited to $100. Individual panes with 6, 7, 8, 9 or 10 stamps could be purchased as long as the total face value of the pane did not exceed $100. The pane of 10 exists with the vertical pink tagging stripe along the left side of the stamps. The pane of 10 could only be bought with stamps denominated from 1c to $10. Stamps denominated from $10.01 to $16.66 could only be purchased in panes containing fewer than 10 stamps. Stamps denominated from $16.67 to $25 could only be purchased as a single stamp.

IBM Pitney Bowes Type of 2004
2009   **Self-Adhesive**   *Die Cut*
Blank Under Denomination
"IM" and Numbers Under
Encryption

CVP80	CVP13	98c black & pink	2.00	.60
CVP81	CVP13	$1.24 black & pink	2.50	1.25

Nos. CVP80-CVP81 could only be printed in denominations listed.

IBM (Statue of Liberty) — CVP17

Illustration reduced.

Die Cut With Rounded Corners
2009, June 5   **Self-Adhesive**

CVP82	CVP17	44c black & pink	7.50	
a.	Without "date of sale" inscription, 2009		—	—

Die Cut With Perpendicular Corners

CVP83	CVP17	44c black & pink	7.50	—
a.	Without "date of sale" inscription, 2009		—	—

No. CVP82 could be printed in any denomination from 1c to $25. Nos. CVP82-CVP83 were made available during a pilot study to evaluate a new IBM kiosk at Schaumburg, IL. The machine study at Schaumburg was scheduled to end on July 31, 2009. No. CVP82 was created for purchases of one to five individual stamps or any extra stamps beyond multiples of 10 ending in numerals 1 to 5.

INVERTS

Labels used to produce stamps in the dimensions of many items of CVP54 and similar later issues in this format were packaged in a fanfolded strip two labels wide and packaged in boxes that are stored in the machines from which the labels are fed to printers as purchases occur. Nothing prevents the labels from being fed in reverse, which results in inverted paper "errors." Such "inverts" (with phosphor stripe appearing on the opposite edge of the stamp than the intended edge) can be deliberately produced, and therefore are not listed.

SERVICE-INSCRIBED STAMPS

Listings of small label stamps from CVP84 reveal that various service-related abbreviations appear under the denominations of some stamps. From CVP84 onward (including the FOLD HERE varieties), all denominated stamps may be purchased that include service-specific indicators under the denominations (e.g., EXPRESS for a clearly identifiable service as well as abbreviations that are less clear such as EM HFPU FRB). When a machine asks a mailer if any postage is already affixed to an item, the mailer can indicate that all postage but one cent or more is affixed. A customer stating that almost all required postage is already affixed will result in the stamp vending machine dispensing a stamp with a service-specific indicator that has a face value as low as one cent. For this reason, listings no longer include small format vended stamps with service-specific indicators beyond No. CVP84, because the stamps can be produced to show any face value, use not being restricted to the class indicated, and all types may be used on any mail matter.

Flag
CVP18

Serpentine Die Cut 13¼x12½
2011, Oct. 18   **Self-Adhesive**
CVP84 CVP18 44c multi, date
                sold only on
                bottom line   —   —
  a.   Date sold and "Postcard"
        on bottom line   —   —
  b.   Date sold and "First-Class"
        on bottom line   —   —

No. CVP84 was issued in panes of 10. It was made available at Mail & Go postal stations in Super Target stores in the Dallas, TX area. Panes could be purchased in any denomination from 29c to $9.99. Serpentine die cut 9 examples of No. CVP84 with dates earlier than Oct. 18 were produced at Pitney Bowes facilities. This serpentine die cut 9 sticker stock is not known to have been sent out for use in machines that were available for use by the general public. No. CVP84 was made available in 2013 with dozens of images other than the flag shown. These optional images are for various holidays and events, as well as social causes, such as support for breast cancer, education and recycling. One image, for bridal showers, has been made available in two different types.

Pitney Bowes With Eagle at Left — CVP18a

Pitney Bowes Without Eagle — CVP18b

Die Cut With Perpendicular Corners
2011, Oct. 18   **Self-Adhesive**
CVP84C CVP18a 46c black &
                pink, no
                inscription
                below
                sold date   5.00   —
  d.   CVP18b 46c With eagle
        emblem omitted   —   —
  e.   "Mailed From Zip Code
        ..." on bottom line   —   —
  f.   "Postcard" on bottom line 7.50   —
  g.   "First-Class Mail" on bot-
        tom line   5.00   —
  h.   "First-Class Mail Intl" on
        bottom line   —   —
  i.   "Priority Mail" on bottom
        line   —   —
  j.   "Priority Envelope" on
        bottom line   —   —
  k.   "Priority Box" on bottom
        line   —   —
  l.   "Priority Tube" on bottom
        line   —   —
  m.   "Priority - Irregular
        Shape" on bottom line   —   —
  n.   "Express Mail" on bottom
        line   —   —

No. CVP84C was made available at Mail & Go postal stations in Super Target stores in the Dallas, TX area, and presumably could be printed in any denomination.

In 2013, twelve Mail & Go machines vending No. CVP84C and the holiday and social cause designs noted under No. CVP84 were installed and operated at thirteen Rite Aid drug stores in central California along the Highway 1 corridor. The machines were installed by the LePages Company (a USPS-licensed manufacturer and wholesaler of USPS-brand mailing supplies). They were placed under the jurisdiction of the Oakland, CA region of the USPS throughout most of 2014-15. Postmasters in the towns supported the machines officially with Priority Mail containers, postal labels and daily mail collection. The locations were listed by the USPS in its online Internet database of self-service post office locations. The machines appear to have been removed between Oct. 2015 and Jan. 2016.

The stamps vended by these machines were officially approved by the USPS and are no different than stamps sold from the same models of machines installed at colleges and universities across the nation. Locations of about 40 other privately supported Mail & Go machines have been recorded. These other machines are installed and operated by Pitney Bowes employees who manage mail rooms the company operates under contracts. At those locations, the mail room staff takes the daily mail to the local post officce, and there is no USPS logistical support.

The USPS regulations classify Mail & Go machines as "third party kiosks." No. CVP84Cd is an error that Pitney Bowes technicians could not explain. It appeared for a short time on a machine in Illinois and at the U.S. Department of Defense Medical HQ facility mailroom in Annandale, Va., and other unidentified locations.

Thermal prints generated by vending machines with too little electrically generated heat tend to fade very quickly.

APC With Vertical Coding at Right of Date — CVP19

Die Cut With Rounded Corners
2012, Apr. 12   **Self-Adhesive**
CVP85 CVP19 black & pink   1.50   —
  a.   Die cut with perpendicular
        corners, colored bar at
        left, "Fold Here" at
        center, 100x38mm   —   —

No. CVP85 has "APC" reading upwards at right. No. CVP78 has "IBM" reading upwards at right. No. CVP85 was available during a nationwide test of machines, and could be printed in any denomination from 1c to $99.99.

No. CVP85a was produced on label stock normally used for No. CVP87 when machines ran out of label stock to produce orders for Nos. CVP85, CVP85B, and varieties of CVP86.

APC With Vertical Coding At Left of Date — CVP19a

Die Cut With Rounded Corners
2012   **Self-Adhesive**
CVP85B CVP19a black & pink   2.00   —
  c.   Die cut with perpendicu-
        lar corners, colored
        bar at left, "FOLD
        HERE" at center,
        100x38mm   2.00   —

No. CVP85Bc was produced on label stock normally used for No. CVP87 when machines ran out of stock to produce orders for Nos. CVP85, CVP85B, and varieties of CVP86.

APC Variable Vignette Stamp — CVP20

Die Cut With Rounded Corners
2012, Apr. 12   **Self-Adhesive**
CVP86 CVP20 (45c) black & pink   2.50   —
  a.   Die cut with perpendicular
        corners, colored bar at
        left, 100x38mm   3.00   —

No. CVP86 was available during a nationwide test of machines, and could be printed only as "Forever" stamps. The vignette portion of the stamp at left could be chosen from a gallery of six images (Mr. Zip, Heart, Flowers, Flag, Eagle, and Balloons and "Celebrate!", which is depicted). Values are for any vignette, or for any other vignette that may be programmed into the machine at a later date. Each vignette design could be purchased in a quantities ranging from 1 stamp to 100 stamps, but because a $1 minimum purchase was required, at least three examples of the first stamp chosen had to be purchased. A maximum of ten stamps could be printed on a sheet. Sales of stamps that are not in multiples of 10 were printed in strips, smaller-sized sheets containing an even number of stamps, or in sheets having one label inscribed "This Block Is Not Valid Postage" when the sheet contained an odd number of stamps.

No. CVP86a was produced on wide-label stock normally used for No. CVP87 when the small-label printer was defective or the machine had run out of small-label stock.

Examples of No. CVP86 without a printed image at left are the result of machines having their image-printing capability shut off so preprinted label stock for producing No. CVP88 could be substituted for the blank label stock used for Nos. CVP85 and CVP86. See footnote under No. CVP88 for information about examples of No. CVP86 with date of purchase inscriptions to right of "Forever."

APC With Vertical Coding to Right of Date — CVP21

Die Cut With Perpendicular Corners
2012, Apr. 12   **Self-Adhesive**
CVP87 CVP21 black & pink   —   —

No. CVP87 was available during a nationwide test of machines, and could be printed in any denomination from 1c to $99.99. Stamps can be inscribed with a variety of different service inscriptions.

APC With Vertical Coding to Left of Date — CVP21a

Die Cut With Perpendicular Corners
2012   **Self-Adhesive**
CVP87A CVP21a black & pink   —   —

Labels of type CVP21a with postage indicia inscribed FCM LETTER below the denomination have only a bar code and the Zip code of the destination at the bottom third rather than a USPS TRACKING NUMBER. Labels for which a Certified Mail fee has been paid have a CERTIFIED MAIL bar code. Express Mail labels have POSTAL USE ONLY form at the bottom.

On Nov. 7, 2013, the USPS had distributed and had begun requiring the use of "signalling label" stock with a clear phosphor stripe. The clear stripe appears positioned vertically along the left margin of the labels. Labels with pink stripes along the right margin continued to be used until stocks were exhausted or labels with pre-printed vignettes were issued for use in some machines on Apr. 1, 2014 (CVP90-CVP91).

APC With Vertical Coding at Left of Date And Clear Phosphor Stripe Along Left Margin — CVP21b

Die Cut With Rounded Corners
2013, Nov. 7   **Self-Adhesive**
CVP87B CVP21b black   5.00   —
  c.   Die cut with perpendicu-
        lar corners, colored
        bar at left, "Fold Here"
        at center, 100x38mm   8.50   —

The Scheduled Delivery and Expected Delivery inscriptions, date and times seen on Nos. CVP89B and CVP89C replaced "THIS BLOCK IS NOT VALID FOR POSTAGE" on labels normally found adjacent to Nos, CVP87B and CVP92A when sold for other than Priority Mail.

Mailbox
CVP22

Die Cut With Rounded Corners
2012, Oct. 31   **Self-Adhesive**
CVP88 CVP22 (45c) multicolored 3.50 —

The mailbox vignette is preprinted on No. CVP88. This preprinted stock was placed in machines in November 2012 and was to be removed from machines on December 31, 2012. The earliest known date of sale is Nov. 10, 2012.

Examples of No. CVP88 with the mailbox design covered by images used for Nos. CVP85 and CVP86 were the result of machines having their blank label stock replaced with the pre-printed label stock while the machine's image-printing capability was not shut off to accommodate the preprinted stock.

On No. CVP88, the number of the month and last two digits of the year in which the stamp was purchased, separated by an asterisk, appear to the right of "Forever." If the operator of the machine programmed it to sell No. CVP88 but failed to turn off the vignettes available as No. CVP86 and did not load the preprinted Christmas Mailbox label stock, the resulting vended product would be No. CVP86 with the month and year appearing to the right of "FOREVER."

Labels inscribed "This Block Is Not Valid For Postage" differ from similar labels created with No. CVP86. Various sizes of "Void" overprints on these labels exist.

USPS Emblem — CVP22a

Die Cut With Rounded Corners
2013, Oct. 31   **Self-Adhesive**
CVP88A CVP22a (46c) black & pink 3.00 —
   b.   Die cut with perpendicular corners, colored bar at left, "Fold Here" at center, 100x38mm   7.50 —

This design was first placed in a few machines in the Washington, DC and Merrifield, VA area on Oct. 31, 2013. Stamps vended with encoded dates prior to Nov. 7, 2013 were test stamps. On Nov. 6, 2013, the USPS declared the test to be successful and the image was released for general use as a fall-back design.

No. CVP88Ab was produced on wide-label stock normally used to produce No. CVP87 when the small-label printer was either defective or machines ran out of stock to produce orders for No. CVP88A. The earliest known sale date of No. CVP88Ab is Nov. 2, 2013.

Examples of CVP88A lacking the eagle vignette could be made if the machine had blank label stock in the feeder but was set to print on pre-printed labels such as No. CVP89. When the machine has pre-printed labels (starting with No. CVP89) in the feeder and is set to print on blank labels, the Eagle vignette will print on top of the preprinted image.

Reindeer — CVP23

Die Cut With Rounded Corners
2013, Nov. 7   **Self-Adhesive**
CVP89 CVP23 (46c) multicolored 3.00 2.00

The reindeer vignette is preprinted on No. CVP89. The issue date is the earliest documented sale date.

USPS Emblem With Clear Phosphor Stripe Along Left Margin — CVP23a

Die Cut With Rounded Corners
2014, Jan. 8   **Self-Adhesive**
CVP89A CVP23a (46c) black 3.00 —
   d.   (50c) Vertical serial number with no leading letter, 2018   2.50 —

Examples of CVP89A lacking the eagle vignette could be made if the machine had blank label stock in the feeder but was set to print on pre-printed labels such as No. CVP89. When the machine has pre-printed labels (starting with No. CVP89) in the feeder and is set to print on blank labels, the Eagle vignette will print on top of the preprinted image. Examples known include 2018-generation stamps with serial number with no leading letter.

APC With Scheduled Delivery — CVP23b

Die Cut With Perpendicular Corners
2014, Jan.   **Self-Adhesive**
CVP89B CVP23b black & pink — —

No. CVP89B is generated when the mailer answers a machine-system prompt with a "no" answer when asked if the full-length label (Type CVP21) will fit on the mailer's item. This is vended only when pre-printed labels are installed in the machine or the small-label printer is defective.

For selected mail service the USPS doesn't track, the field to the right of "FOLD HERE" remains blank (in effect creating No. CVP87Bc).

APC With Expected Delivery — CVP23c

Die Cut With Perpendicular Corners
2014, Jan.   **Self-Adhesive**
CVP89C CVP23c black & pink — —

See note after No. CVP89B.

Spiderman — CVP24

Die Cut With Rounded Corners
2014, Apr. 1   **Self-Adhesive**
CVP90 CVP24 (49c) multicolored 2.50 2.00

The Spiderman vignette is preprinted on No. CVP90.

Flag CVP25

Die Cut With Rounded Corners
2014, Apr. 1   **Self-Adhesive**
CVP91 CVP25 (49c) multicolored 3.00 1.25
   a.   "FOREVER" (only) missing — —
   b.   (50c) With vertical serial number with no leading letter, 2018   3.00 1.50

The flag vignette is preprinted on No. CVP91.

Examples of No. CVP91b exist with the USPS Eagle emblem (see illustration at design CVP23a) printed on top of the preprinted flag design label; value, $5. It is theoretically possible that blank labels without a preprinted flag or other preprinted design could be inserted in the new machine, and (likely) be printed without the operator having turned on the thermal-printed USPS logo that machines can produce on-site, leaving an indicia and value printed on a stamp without any pictorial element. Such varieties are products of local operator error that has occurred on all

issues from No. CVP88 in 2013 and can be manufactured through illicit cooperation of postal officials.

Rudolph, the Red-Nosed Reindeer — CVP26

Die Cut With Rounded Corners
2014, Nov. 6   **Self-Adhesive**
CVP92 CVP26 (49c) multicolored 4.00 1.75

The Rudolph vignette is preprinted on No. CVP92.

From Nov. 14, 2014, Automated Postal Centers (APC) vending machines were renamed by the USPS to be Self Service Kiosks (SSK), and the machines were changed to issue stamps inscribed "SSK" rather than "APC."

SSK With Vertical Coding at Left of Date CVP27

Die Cut With Rounded Corners
2014, Nov. 14   **Self-Adhesive**
CVP93 CVP27 black & pink — —
   a.   Black, with vertical transparent stripe at left 1.00 —

No. CVP93 was available at machines that had not yet retired the pink-striped labels.

It was not intended by the USPS that indicia inscribed with SSK would be printed on pink-striped labels. The design was shifted to appear farther to the right, to insure the bar code would remain uncompromised and at a safe distance from the clear phosphor stripe on the newer labels. Almost all examples of this issue will have SSK appearing within the pink stripe.

Value of No. CVP93a is for 49c denomination, current at the time. Other denominations pro-rata.

SSK With Vertical Coding to Left of Date — CVP28

Die Cut With Perpendicular Corners
2014, Nov. 14   **Self-Adhesive**
CVP94 CVP28 black & pink 2.50 —
   a.   Indicia at upper right with no leading letter, various service level indicators, 2018   2.50 —

Like No. CVP87A, No. CVP94 exists in other denominations inscribed with various mail service inscriptions or with blackened square in place of letters such as "F," above.

SSK With Blank Area at Right of "Fold Here" — CVP29

Die Cut With Perpendicular Corners
2014, Nov. 14   **Self-Adhesive**
CVP95 CVP29 black & pink 5.00 —
   a.   black, vertical serial number with no leading letter, clear phosphor stripe, 2018   2.50 —

See note below No. CVP89B.

SSK With "Expected Delivery" at Right of "Fold Here" — CVP30

Die Cut With Perpendicular Corners
2014, Nov. 14   **Self-Adhesive**
CVP96 CVP30 black & pink — —
   a.   black, vertical serial number with no leading letter, various service level indicators, clear phosphor stripe, 2018   2.50 —

See note below No. CVP89B.

SSK With "Scheduled Delivery" at Right of "Fold Here" — CVP31

Die Cut With Perpendicular Corners
2014, Nov. 14   **Self-Adhesive**
CVP97 CVP31 black & pink — —
   a.   black, vertical serial number with no leading letter, various service level indicators, clear phosphor stripe, 2018   1.50 —

See note below No. CVP89B.

Charlie Brown Looking in Mailbox — CVP32

Die Cut With Rounded Corners
2015, Oct. 20   **Self-Adhesive**
CVP98 CVP32 (49c) multicolored 2.50 1.00

The Charlie Brown vignette is preprinted on No. CVP98. Issue date is earliest recorded sale date. Post offices were authorized to place the labels in machines at the close of business on Oct. 20, which many did prior to the SSK system-wide date change that occurs daily prior to midnight.

mPOS — CVP33

Die Cut With Rounded Corners
2015   **Self-Adhesive**
CVP99 CVP33 black — —

No. CVP99 is generated by a mobile hand-held point-of-sale vending machine with integrated thermal postage printer and embedded credit/debit card acceptance processor. Possible denominations are limited to the postage prices applicable to each available pre-printed type of Priority and Express Mail flat rate envelopes and packages (rate determined by scanning the bar code on the package the customer needs). While this indicia is intended to be affixed to mail matter at the time it is presented, postage can be generated and sold in quantities to take away for later use. Labels are generated from vertical coils with blank labels.

Wreath in Window — CVP34

Die Cut With Rounded Corners
2016, Oct. 27   **Self-Adhesive**
CVP100 CVP34 (47c) multi   3.00 1.00

The wreath in window vignette is preprinted on No. CVP100. Issue date is earliest recorded sale date.

Christmas Cookies — CVP35

Die Cut With Rounded Corners
2017, Oct. 17   **Self-Adhesive**
CVP101 CVP35 (49c) multi   3.00 1.00
     a.   On 2018-generation stamp with serial number with no leading letter

The Christmas cookies vignette is preprinted on No. CVP101. Issue date is earliest recorded sale date.

Flag
CVP36

Die Cut With Rounded Corners
2018, Aug. 23   **Self-Adhesive**
CVP108 CVP36 (50c) multi   3.00 1.00

The flag vignette is preprinted on No. CVP108. Issue date is earliest recorded sale date.

Santa Claus CVP37

Die Cut With Rounded Corners
2018, Oct. 21   **Self-Adhesive**
CVP109 CVP37 (50c) multi   2.50 1.00

The Santa Claus vignette is preprinted on No. CVP109. Issue date is earliest recorded sale date.

Christmas Stocking — CVP38

Die Cut With Rounded Corners
2020, Nov. 16   **Self-Adhesive**
CVP110 CVP38 (55c) multi   2.50 1.00

The Christmas stocking vignette is preprinted on No. CVP110.

PERSONAL COMPUTER POSTAGE

Personal computer postage, approved by the US Postal Service, was created by subscribing to Stamps.com, an Internet website. Customers ordered self-adhesive labels showing vignettes, but lacking any franking value. The franking value indicia of the stamps could be printed at the customer's convenience at any computer with an Internet connection, using the customer's access codes. Any postage printed would be charged against the customer's account.

Neopost

CVPA1

2000   **Serpentine Die Cut 8**
Self-Adhesive
1CVP1 CVPA1 33c black, yellow
             & pink

Stamps.com

Flag and Star
— CVPA1a

Serpentine Die Cut 5¾ at Left
2002, July
"Stamps.com" in Lower Case Letters
Identification Code Below Zip Code
No Mail Class Inscribed
1CVP2   CVPA1a 37c black,
              blue &
              orange   7.00 3.00

Identification Code Above Zip Code
Inscribed "US Postage" only
1CVP2A   CVPA1a 37c black,
              blue &
              orange   4.00 3.00
  a.   "First Class" below "US Postage"   2.75 2.00
  b.   "Priority" below "US Postage"   8.25 2.50
  c.   "Express" below "US Postage"   25.00 5.00
  d.   "Media Mail" below "US Postage"   7.75 2.50
  e.   "Parcel Post" below "US Postage"   7.75 2.50
  f.   "Bound Printed Matter" below "US Postage"   7.75 2.50
  g.   "BPM" below "US Postage"   7.75 2.50

See Nos. 1CVP9, 1CVP21.

No. 1CVP2 apparently could be printed in denominations up to and including 37c. The 37c denomination comes with "FIRST-CLASS" between the Zip code and the identification code. Later versions of the Stamps.com software allow any denomination to be printed, as well as additional or different mail-class inscriptions, on any basic stamp except for No. 1CVP2.

Values for Nos. 1CVP2A and 1CVP3-1CVP42 are for items appropriate to the service described. Stamps with denominations far lower than those appropriate to the service are valued correspondingly lower.

The software changes allow Nos. 1CVP2A and 1CVP3-1CVP37 to be printed with the mail-class inscriptions described for Nos. 1CVP38f-1CVP38p.

Later software changes allow Nos. 1CVP2A, 1CVP3-1CVP42 and 1CVP51-1CVP58 to be printed with mail-class inscriptions "Library Mail," "Intl. First Class," "Intl Priority," "Intl Express," and "M-Bag" with any denomination.

Love — CVPA2

2002   **Serpentine Die Cut 5¾ at Left**
1CVP3   CVPA2 37c black, blue
           & orange   4.00 4.00
  a.   "First Class" below "US Postage"   2.75 2.00
  b.   "Priority" below "US Postage"   8.25 2.50
  c.   "Express" below "US Postage"   25.00 5.00
  d.   "Media Mail" below "US Postage"   7.75 2.50
  e.   "Parcel Post" below "US Postage"   7.75 2.50
  f.   "Bound Printed Matter" below "US Postage"   7.75 2.50
  g.   "BPM" below "US Postage"   7.75 2.50

Statue of Liberty and Flag — CVPA3

Liberty Bell and Flag — CVPA4

Eagle and Flag — CVPA5

George Washington and Flag — CVPA6

Capitol Building and Flag — CVPA7

Serpentine Die Cut 5¾ at Left
2003, June
1CVP4   CVPA3 37c black, blue
           & orange   3.50 2.00
  a.   "First Class" below "US Postage"   3.25 2.00
  b.   "Priority" below "US Postage"   8.00 1.00
  c.   "Express" below "US Postage"   25.00 3.00
  d.   "Media Mail" below "US Postage"   7.50 1.00
  e.   "Parcel Post" below "US Postage"   7.50 1.00
  f.   "Bound Printed Matter" below "US Postage"   7.50 1.00
  g.   "BPM" below "US Postage"   7.50 1.00
1CVP5   CVPA4 37c black, blue
           & orange   3.50 2.00
  a.   "First Class" below "US Postage"   3.25 2.00
  b.   "Priority" below "US Postage"   8.00 1.00
  c.   "Express" below "US Postage"   25.00 3.00
  d.   "Media Mail" below "US Postage"   7.50 1.00
  e.   "Parcel Post" below "US Postage"   7.50 1.00
  f.   "Bound Printed Matter" below "US Postage"   7.50 1.00
  g.   "BPM" below "US Postage"   7.50 1.00
1CVP6   CVPA5 37c black, blue
           & orange   3.50 2.00
  a.   "First Class" below "US Postage"   3.25 2.00
  b.   "Priority" below "US Postage"   8.00 1.00
  c.   "Express" below "US Postage"   25.00 3.00
  d.   "Media Mail" below "US Postage"   7.50 1.00
  e.   "Parcel Post" below "US Postage"   7.50 1.00
  f.   "Bound Printed Matter" below "US Postage"   7.50 1.00
  g.   "BPM" below "US Postage"   7.50 1.00
1CVP7   CVPA6 37c black, blue
           & orange   3.50 2.00
  a.   "First Class" below "US Postage"   3.25 .25
  b.   "Priority" below "US Postage"   8.00 1.00
  c.   "Express" below "US Postage"   25.00 3.00
  d.   "Media Mail" below "US Postage"   7.50 1.00
  e.   "Parcel Post" below "US Postage"   7.50 1.00
  f.   "Bound Printed Matter" below "US Postage"   7.50 1.00
  g.   "BPM" below "US Postage"   7.50 1.00
1CVP8   CVPA7 37c black, blue
           & orange   3.50 2.00
  a.   "First Class" below "US Postage"   3.25 .45
  b.   "Priority" below "US Postage"   8.00 1.00
  c.   "Express" below "US Postage"   25.00 3.00
  d.   "Media Mail" below "US Postage"   7.50 1.00
  e.   "Parcel Post" below "US Postage"   7.50 1.00
  f.   "Bound Printed Matter" below "US Postage"   7.50 1.00
  g.   "BPM" below "US Postage"   7.50 1.00
  h.   Strip of 5, #1CVP4-1CVP8   17.50

Flag and Star Type of 2002 Redrawn With "Stamps.com" in Upper Case Letters
Serpentine Die Cut 5¾ at Left
2003, June
Identification Code Above Zip Code

1CVP9 CVPA1a 37c black, blue & orange, "US Postage" only — 3.00 1.50
- a. "First Class" below "US Postage" — 2.00 .45
- b. "Priority" below "US Postage" — 8.00 1.00
- c. "Express" below "US Postage" — 25.00 3.00
- d. "Media Mail" below "US Postage" — 7.50 1.00
- e. "Parcel Post" below "US Postage" — 7.50 1.00
- f. "Bound Printed Matter" below "US Postage" — 7.50 1.00
- g. "BPM" below "US Postage" — 7.50 1.00

Snowman
CVPA8

Snowflakes
CVPA9

Holly
CVPA10

Dove
CVPA11

Gingerbread Man and Candy
CVPA12

Serpentine Die Cut 4½ at Left
2003, Dec.

1CVP10 CVPA8 37c black, blue & orange — 3.00 1.50
- a. "First Class" below "US Postage" — 2.00 1.00
- b. "Priority" below "US Postage" — 8.00 1.00
- c. "Express" below "US Postage" — 25.00 3.00
- d. "Media Mail" below "US Postage" — 7.50 1.00

- e. "Parcel Post" below "US Postage" — 7.50 1.00
- f. "Bound Printed Matter" below "US Postage" — 7.50 1.00
- g. "BPM" below "US Postage" — 7.50 1.00

1CVP11 CVPA9 37c black, blue & orange — 3.00 1.50
- a. "First Class" below "US Postage" — 2.00 1.00
- b. "Priority" below "US Postage" — 8.00 1.00
- c. "Express" below "US Postage" — 25.00 3.00
- d. "Media Mail" below "US Postage" — 7.50 1.00
- e. "Parcel Post" below "US Postage" — 7.50 1.00
- f. "Bound Printed Matter" below "US Postage" — 7.50 1.00
- g. "BPM" below "US Postage" — 7.50 1.00

1CVP12 CVPA10 37c black, blue & orange — 3.00 1.50
- a. "First Class" below "US Postage" — 2.00 1.00
- b. "Priority" below "US Postage" — 8.00 1.00
- c. "Express" below "US Postage" — 25.00 3.00
- d. "Media Mail" below "US Postage" — 7.50 1.00
- e. "Parcel Post" below "US Postage" — 7.50 1.00
- f. "Bound Printed Matter" below "US Postage" — 7.50 1.00
- g. "BPM" below "US Postage" — 7.50 1.00

1CVP13 CVPA11 37c black, blue & orange — 3.00 1.50
- a. "First Class" below "US Postage" — 2.00 1.00
- b. "Priority" below "US Postage" — 8.00 1.00
- c. "Express" below "US Postage" — 25.00 3.00
- d. "Media Mail" below "US Postage" — 7.50 1.00
- e. "Parcel Post" below "US Postage" — 7.50 1.00
- f. "Bound Printed Matter" below "US Postage" — 7.50 1.00
- g. "BPM" below "US Postage" — 7.50 1.00

1CVP14 CVPA12 37c black, blue & orange — 3.00 1.50
- a. "First Class" below "US Postage" — 2.00 1.00
- b. "Priority" below "US Postage" — 8.00 1.00
- c. "Express" below "US Postage" — 25.00 3.00
- d. "Media Mail" below "US Postage" — 7.50 1.00
- e. "Parcel Post" below "US Postage" — 7.50 1.00
- f. "Bound Printed Matter" below "US Postage" — 7.50 1.00
- g. "BPM" below "US Postage" — 7.50 1.00
- h. Strip of 5, #1CVP10-1CVP14 — 12.50

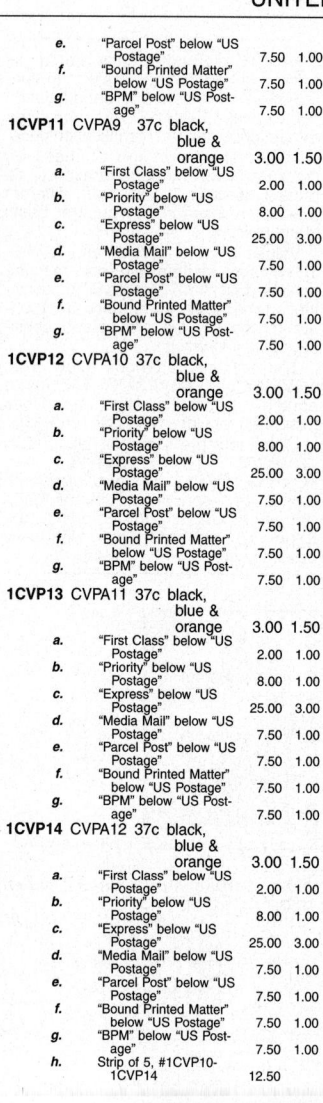

Mailbox
CVPA13

Serpentine Die Cut 6½ at Left
2004, Mar.

1CVP15 CVPA13 37c black, blue & orange — 25.00 15.00
- a. "First Class" below "US Postage" — 25.00 15.00
- b. "Priority" below "US Postage" — —
- c. "Express" below "US Postage" — —
- d. "Media Mail" below "US Postage" — —
- e. "Parcel Post" below "US Postage" — —
- f. "Bound Printed Matter" below "US Postage" — —
- g. "BPM" below "US Postage" — —

Blank sheets of No. 1CVP15 were sent free of charge to those who responded to special Stamps.com promotions which offered a fixed amount of free postage as an enticement to new subscribers. The franking portion of the stamps could only be applied after subscribing.

George Washington
CVPA14

Thomas Jefferson
CVPA15

Abraham Lincoln
CVPA16

Theodore Roosevelt
CVPA17

John F. Kennedy
CVPA18

Serpentine Die Cut 6½ at Left
2004, Apr.

1CVP16 CVPA14 37c black, blue & orange — 2.00 1.00
- a. "First Class" below "US Postage" — 1.10 .75
- b. "Priority" below "US Postage" — 5.00 2.50
- c. "Express" below "US Postage" — 20.00 5.00
- d. "Media Mail" below "US Postage" — 5.00 2.50
- e. "Parcel Post" below "US Postage" — 5.00 2.50
- f. "Bound Printed Matter" below "US Postage" — 5.00 2.50
- g. "BPM" below "US Postage" — 5.00 2.50

1CVP17 CVPA15 37c black, blue & orange — 2.00 1.00
- a. "First Class" below "US Postage" — 1.10 .75
- b. "Priority" below "US Postage" — 5.00 2.50
- c. "Express" below "US Postage" — 20.00 5.00
- d. "Media Mail" below "US Postage" — 5.00 2.50
- e. "Parcel Post" below "US Postage" — 5.00 2.50
- f. "Bound Printed Matter" below "US Postage" — 5.00 2.50
- g. "BPM" below "US Postage" — 5.00 2.50

1CVP18 CVPA16 37c black, blue & orange — 2.00 1.00
- a. "First Class" below "US Postage" — 1.10 .75
- b. "Priority" below "US Postage" — 5.00 2.50

- c. "Express" below "US Postage" — 20.00 5.00
- d. "Media Mail" below "US Postage" — 5.00 2.50
- e. "Parcel Post" below "US Postage" — 5.00 2.50
- f. "Bound Printed Matter" below "US Postage" — 5.00 2.50
- g. "BPM" below "US Postage" — 5.00 2.50

1CVP19 CVPA17 37c black, blue & orange — 2.00 1.00
- a. "First Class" below "US Postage" — 1.10 .75
- b. "Priority" below "US Postage" — 5.00 2.50
- c. "Express" below "US Postage" — 20.00 5.00
- d. "Media Mail" below "US Postage" — 5.00 2.50
- e. "Parcel Post" below "US Postage" — 5.00 2.50
- f. "Bound Printed Matter" below "US Postage" — 5.00 2.50
- g. "BPM" below "US Postage" — 5.00 2.50

1CVP20 CVPA18 37c black, blue & orange — 2.00 1.00
- a. "First Class" below "US Postage" — 1.10 .75
- b. "Priority" below "US Postage" — 5.00 2.50
- c. "Express" below "US Postage" — 20.00 5.00
- d. "Media Mail" below "US Postage" — 5.00 2.50
- e. "Parcel Post" below "US Postage" — 5.00 2.50
- f. "Bound Printed Matter" below "US Postage" — 5.00 2.50
- g. "BPM" below "US Postage" — 5.00 2.50
- h. Horiz. strip of 5, #1CVP16-1CVP20 — 10.00

Flag and Star Type of 2002 Redrawn With Orange Stars and Text at Left
Serpentine Die Cut 6½ at Left
2004, Apr.
"Stamps.com" in Upper Case Letters
Identification Code Above Zip Code

1CVP21 CVPA1a 37c black, blue & orange — 2.00 1.00
- a. "First Class" below "US Postage" — 1.35 .75
- b. "Priority" below "US Postage" — 6.00 2.50
- c. "Express" below "US Postage" — 22.50 5.00
- d. "Media Mail" below "US Postage" — 6.00 2.50
- e. "Parcel Post" below "US Postage" — 6.00 2.50
- f. "Bound Printed Matter" below "US Postage" — 6.00 2.50
- g. "BPM" below "US Postage" — 6.00 2.50

Bicycling
CVPA19

Running
CVPA20

Swimming
CVPA21

UNITED STATES

Boxing
CVPA22

Equestrian
CVPA23

Basketball
CVPA24

Judo
CVPA25

Soccer
CVPA26

Gymnastics
CVPA27

Tennis
CVPA28

Serpentine Die Cut 6½ at Left
2004, Apr.

1CVP22 CVPA19 37c black, blue & orange — 3.00 2.00
a. "First Class" below "US Postage" — 2.50 1.50
b. "Priority" below "US Postage" — 8.00 1.00
c. "Express" below "US Postage" — 25.00 3.00
d. "Media Mail" below "US Postage" — 7.50 1.00
e. "Parcel Post" below "US Postage" — 7.50 1.00
f. "Bound Printed Matter" below "US Postage" — 7.50 1.00
g. "BPM" below "US Postage" — 7.50 1.00

1CVP23 CVPA20 37c black, blue & orange — 3.00 2.00
a. "First Class" below "US Postage" — 2.50 1.50
b. "Priority" below "US Postage" — 8.00 1.00
c. "Express" below "US Postage" — 25.00 3.00
d. "Media Mail" below "US Postage" — 7.50 1.00
e. "Parcel Post" below "US Postage" — 7.50 1.00
f. "Bound Printed Matter" below "US Postage" — 7.50 1.00
g. "BPM" below "US Postage" — 7.50 1.00

1CVP24 CVPA21 37c black, blue & orange — 3.00 2.00
a. "First Class" below "US Postage" — 2.50 1.50
b. "Priority" below "US Postage" — 8.00 1.00
c. "Express" below "US Postage" — 25.00 3.00
d. "Media Mail" below "US Postage" — 7.50 1.00
e. "Parcel Post" below "US Postage" — 7.50 1.00
f. "Bound Printed Matter" below "US Postage" — 7.50 1.00
g. "BPM" below "US Postage" — 7.50 1.00

1CVP25 CVPA22 37c black, blue & orange — 3.00 2.00
a. "First Class" below "US Postage" — 2.50 1.50
b. "Priority" below "US Postage" — 8.00 1.00
c. "Express" below "US Postage" — 25.00 3.00
d. "Media Mail" below "US Postage" — 7.50 1.00
e. "Parcel Post" below "US Postage" — 7.50 1.00
f. "Bound Printed Matter" below "US Postage" — 7.50 1.00
g. "BPM" below "US Postage" — 7.50 1.00

1CVP26 CVPA23 37c black, blue & orange — 3.00 2.00
a. "First Class" below "US Postage" — 2.50 1.50
b. "Priority" below "US Postage" — 8.00 1.00
c. "Express" below "US Postage" — 25.00 3.00
d. "Media Mail" below "US Postage" — 7.50 1.00
e. "Parcel Post" below "US Postage" — 7.50 1.00
f. "Bound Printed Matter" below "US Postage" — 7.50 1.00
g. "BPM" below "US Postage" — 7.50 1.00
h. Horiz. strip of 5, #1CVP22-1CVP26 — 15.00

1CVP27 CVPA24 37c black, blue & orange — 3.00 2.00
a. "First Class" below "US Postage" — 2.50 1.50
b. "Priority" below "US Postage" — 8.00 1.00
c. "Express" below "US Postage" — 25.00 3.00
d. "Media Mail" below "US Postage" — 7.50 1.00
e. "Parcel Post" below "US Postage" — 7.50 1.00
f. "Bound Printed Matter" below "US Postage" — 7.50 1.00
g. "BPM" below "US Postage" — 7.50 1.00

1CVP28 CVPA25 37c black, blue & orange — 3.00 2.00
a. "First Class" below "US Postage" — 2.50 1.50
b. "Priority" below "US Postage" — 8.00 1.00
c. "Express" below "US Postage" — 25.00 3.00
d. "Media Mail" below "US Postage" — 7.50 1.00
e. "Parcel Post" below "US Postage" — 7.50 1.00
f. "Bound Printed Matter" below "US Postage" — 7.50 1.00
g. "BPM" below "US Postage" — 7.50 1.00

1CVP29 CVPA26 37c black, blue & orange — 3.00 2.00
a. "First Class" below "US Postage" — 2.50 1.50
b. "Priority" below "US Postage" — 8.00 1.00
c. "Express" below "US Postage" — 25.00 3.00
d. "Media Mail" below "US Postage" — 7.50 1.00
e. "Parcel Post" below "US Postage" — 7.50 1.00

f. "Bound Printed Matter" below "US Postage" — 7.50 1.00
g. "BPM" below "US Postage" — 7.50 1.00

1CVP30 CVPA27 37c black, blue & orange — 3.00 2.00
a. "First Class" below "US Postage" — 2.50 1.50
b. "Priority" below "US Postage" — 8.00 1.00
c. "Express" below "US Postage" — 25.00 3.00
d. "Media Mail" below "US Postage" — 7.50 1.00
e. "Parcel Post" below "US Postage" — 7.50 1.00
f. "Bound Printed Matter" below "US Postage" — 7.50 1.00
g. "BPM" below "US Postage" — 7.50 1.00

1CVP31 CVPA28 37c black, blue & orange — 3.00 2.00
a. "First Class" below "US Postage" — 2.50 1.50
b. "Priority" below "US Postage" — 8.00 1.00
c. "Express" below "US Postage" — 25.00 3.00
d. "Media Mail" below "US Postage" — 7.50 1.00
e. "Parcel Post" below "US Postage" — 7.50 1.00
f. "Bound Printed Matter" below "US Postage" — 7.50 1.00
g. "BPM" below "US Postage" — 7.50 1.00
h. Horiz. strip of 5, #1CVP27-1CVP31 — 15.00

The item pictured above was produced by Stamps.com for a special promotional mailing of its own and was not made available unused to customers.

Leaning Tower of Pisa — CVPA29

Sphinx and Pyramids
CVPA30

Sydney Opera House
CVPA31

Mayan Pyramid
CVPA32

Asian Temple
CVPA33

Serpentine Die Cut 6½ at Left
2004, July

1CVP32 CVPA29 37c black, blue & orange — 3.00 2.00
a. "First Class" below "US Postage" — 2.30 1.50
b. "Priority" below "US Postage" — 8.00 1.00
c. "Express" below "US Postage" — 25.00 3.00
d. "Media Mail" below "US Postage" — 7.50 1.00
e. "Parcel Post" below "US Postage" — 7.50 1.00
f. "Bound Printed Matter" below "US Postage" — 7.50 1.00
g. "BPM" below "US Postage" — 7.50 1.00

1CVP33 CVPA30 37c black, blue & orange — 3.00 2.00
a. "First Class" below "US Postage" — 2.30 1.50
b. "Priority" below "US Postage" — 8.00 1.00
c. "Express" below "US Postage" — 25.00 3.00
d. "Media Mail" below "US Postage" — 7.50 1.00
e. "Parcel Post" below "US Postage" — 7.50 1.00
f. "Bound Printed Matter" below "US Postage" — 7.50 1.00
g. "BPM" below "US Postage" — 7.50 1.00

1CVP34 CVPA31 37c black, blue & orange — 3.00 2.00
a. "First Class" below "US Postage" — 2.30 1.50
b. "Priority" below "US Postage" — 8.00 1.00
c. "Express" below "US Postage" — 25.00 3.00
d. "Media Mail" below "US Postage" — 7.50 1.00
e. "Parcel Post" below "US Postage" — 7.50 1.00
f. "Bound Printed Matter" below "US Postage" — 7.50 1.00
g. "BPM" below "US Postage" — 7.50 1.00

1CVP35 CVPA32 37c black, blue & orange — 3.00 2.00
a. "First Class" below "US Postage" — 2.30 1.50
b. "Priority" below "US Postage" — 8.00 1.00
c. "Express" below "US Postage" — 25.00 3.00
d. "Media Mail" below "US Postage" — 7.50 1.00
e. "Parcel Post" below "US Postage" — 7.50 1.00
f. "Bound Printed Matter" below "US Postage" — 7.50 1.00
g. "BPM" below "US Postage" — 7.50 1.00

1CVP36 CVPA33 37c black, blue & orange — 3.00 2.00
a. "First Class" below "US Postage" — 2.30 1.50
b. "Priority" below "US Postage" — 8.00 1.00
c. "Express" below "US Postage" — 25.00 3.00
d. "Media Mail" below "US Postage" — 7.50 1.00
e. "Parcel Post" below "US Postage" — 7.50 1.00
f. "Bound Printed Matter" below "US Postage" — 7.50 1.00
g. "BPM" below "US Postage" — 7.50 1.00
h. Strip of 5, #1CVP32-1CVP36 — 15.00

Computer and Letters CVPA34

Serpentine Die Cut 6½ at Left

2005, Mar.

1CVP37 CVPA34 37c black, blue & orange 25.00 15.00

a.	"First Class" below "US Postage"	25.00	15.00
b.	"Priority" below "US Postage"	—	—
c.	"Express" below "US Postage"	—	—
d.	"Media Mail" below "US Postage"	—	—
e.	"Parcel Post" below "US Postage"	—	—
f.	"Bound Printed Matter" below "US Postage"	—	—
g.	"BPM" below "US Postage"	—	—

Blank sheets of No. 1CVP37 were sent free of charge to those who responded to special Stamps.com promotions which offered a fixed amount of free postage as an enticement to new subscribers. The franking portion of the stamps could only be applied after subscribing.

Logo CVPA35

2005, Aug.   Die Cut Perf. 6½ at Left

1CVP38 CVPA35 37c black, blue & orange 1.00 .45

a.	"Priority" below "US Postage"	8.00	1.00
b.	"Express" below "US Postage"	25.00	3.00
c.	"Media Mail" below "US Postage"	7.50	1.00
d.	"Parcel Post" below "US Postage"	7.50	1.00
e.	"BPM" below "US Postage"	7.50	1.00
f.	"Aerogramme" below "US Postage"	1.40	1.00
g.	"Intl Air Letter" below "US Postage"	1.25	1.00
h.	"Intl Eco Letter" (Economy Letter Mail) below "US Postage"	5.50	1.00
i.	"GXG" (Global Express Guaranteed) below "US Postage"	50.00	6.00
j.	"EMS" (Global Express Mail) below "US Postage"	32.50	4.00
k.	"GPM" (Global Priority Mail) below "US Postage"	8.00	1.00
l.	"Intl Air Parcel" (Air Parcel Post) below "US Postage"	26.00	3.00
m.	"Intl Eco Parcel" (Economy Parcel Post) below "US Postage"	32.50	4.00
n.	"M-Bag (Air)" below "US Postage"	35.00	5.00
o.	"M-Bag (Economy)" below "US Postage"	18.00	3.00
p.	"Mat for Blind" below "US Postage"	1.25	—
q.	"Library Mail"	5.00	1.00

Values for lettered varieties on Nos. 1CVP38 are based on the prices set as the minimum values for each service classification in the software available at the time the stamps were issued. In mid-December 2005, the software was changed to allow for a 1c minimum value for any of these lettered varieties.

In 2006, No. 1CVP38 was made available on a coil roll. Value, $1.40.

Snowman — CVPA36

Candy Cane — CVPA37

Dove — CVPA38

Stylized Christmas Tree and Window — CVPA39

2005, Nov.   Die Cut Perf. 6 at Right

1CVP39 CVPA36 37c multi 1.60 1.00

a.	"Priority" below "US Postage"	8.00	1.00
b.	"Express" below "US Postage"	25.00	3.00
c.	"Media Mail" below "US Postage"	7.50	1.00
d.	"Parcel Post" below "US Postage"	7.50	1.00
e.	"BPM" below "US Postage"	7.50	1.00
f.	"Aerogramme" below "US Postage"	1.40	1.00
g.	"Intl Air Letter" below "US Postage"	1.25	1.00
h.	"Intl Eco Letter" (Economy Letter Mail) below "US Postage"	5.50	1.00
i.	"GXG" (Global Express Guaranteed) below "US Postage"	50.00	6.00
j.	"EMS" (Global Express Mail) below "US Postage"	32.50	4.00
k.	"GPM" (Global Priority Mail) below "US Postage"	8.00	1.00
l.	"Intl Air Parcel" (Air Parcel Post) below "US Postage"	26.00	3.00
m.	"Intl Eco Parcel" (Economy Parcel Post) below "US Postage"	32.50	4.00
n.	"M-Bag (Air)" below "US Postage"	35.00	5.00
o.	"M-Bag (Economy)" below "US Postage"	18.00	3.00
p.	"Mat for Blind" below "US Postage"	.25	—

1CVP40 CVPA37 37c multi 1.60 1.00

a.	"Priority" below "US Postage"	8.00	1.00
b.	"Express" below "US Postage"	25.00	3.00
c.	"Media Mail" below "US Postage"	7.50	1.00
d.	"Parcel Post" below "US Postage"	7.50	1.00
e.	"BPM" below "US Postage"	7.50	1.00
f.	"Aerogramme" below "US Postage"	1.40	1.00
g.	"Intl Air Letter" below "US Postage"	1.25	1.00
h.	"Intl Eco Letter" (Economy Letter Mail) below "US Postage"	5.50	1.00
i.	"GXG" (Global Express Guaranteed) below "US Postage"	50.00	6.00
j.	"EMS" (Global Express Mail) below "US Postage"	32.50	4.00
k.	"GPM" (Global Priority Mail) below "US Postage"	8.00	1.00
l.	"Intl Air Parcel" (Air Parcel Post) below "US Postage"	26.00	3.00
m.	"Intl Eco Parcel" (Economy Parcel Post) below "US Postage"	32.50	4.00
n.	"M-Bag (Air)" below "US Postage"	35.00	5.00
o.	"M-Bag (Economy)" below "US Postage"	18.00	3.00
p.	"Mat for Blind" below "US Postage"	.45	—

1CVP41 CVPA38 37c multi 1.60 1.00

a.	"Priority" below "US Postage"	8.00	1.00
b.	"Express" below "US Postage"	25.00	3.00
c.	"Media Mail" below "US Postage"	7.50	1.00
d.	"Parcel Post" below "US Postage"	7.50	1.00
e.	"BPM" below "US Postage"	7.50	1.00
f.	"Aerogramme" below "US Postage"	1.40	1.00
g.	"Intl Air Letter" below "US Postage"	1.25	1.00
h.	"Intl Eco Letter" (Economy Letter Mail) below "US Postage"	5.50	1.00
i.	"GXG" (Global Express Guaranteed) below "US Postage"	50.00	6.00
j.	"EMS" (Global Express Mail) below "US Postage"	32.50	4.00
k.	"GPM" (Global Priority Mail) below "US Postage"	8.00	1.00
l.	"Intl Air Parcel" (Air Parcel Post) below "US Postage"	26.00	3.00
m.	"Intl Eco Parcel" (Economy Parcel Post) below "US Postage"	32.50	4.00
n.	"M-Bag (Air)" below "US Postage"	35.00	5.00
o.	"M-Bag (Economy)" below "US Postage"	18.00	3.00
p.	"Mat for Blind" below "US Postage"	.45	—

1CVP42 CVPA39 37c multi 1.60 1.00

a.	"Priority" below "US Postage"	8.00	1.00
b.	"Express" below "US Postage"	25.00	3.00
c.	"Media Mail" below "US Postage"	7.50	1.00
d.	"Parcel Post" below "US Postage"	7.50	1.00
e.	"BPM" below "US Postage"	7.50	1.00
f.	"Aerogramme" below "US Postage"	1.40	1.00
g.	"Intl Air Letter" below "US Postage"	1.25	1.00
h.	"Intl Eco Letter" (Economy Letter Mail) below "US Postage"	5.50	1.00
i.	"GXG" (Global Express Guaranteed) below "US Postage"	50.00	6.00
j.	"EMS" (Global Express Mail) below "US Postage"	32.50	4.00
k.	"GPM" (Global Priority Mail) below "US Postage"	8.00	1.00
l.	"Intl Air Parcel" (Air Parcel Post) below "US Postage"	26.00	3.00
m.	"Intl Eco Parcel" (Economy Parcel Post) below "US Postage"	32.50	4.00
n.	"M-Bag (Air)" below "US Postage"	35.00	5.00
o.	"M-Bag (Economy)" below "US Postage"	18.00	3.00
p.	"Mat for Blind" below "US Postage"	.45	—
q.	Vert. strip, 2 each #1CVP39-1CVP42	6.00	

Values for lettered varieties on Nos. 1CVP39-1CVP42 are based on the prices set as the minimum values for each service classification in the software available at the time the stamps were issued. In mid-December 2005, the software was changed to allow for a 1c minimum value for any of these lettered varieties.

Endicia.com

CVPA40

CVPA41

2005-06   Serpentine Die Cut 10¼

1CVP43 CVPA40 24c black & bright rose 10.00 4.00

a.	39c "First Class" under "US Postage"	2.00	.50
b.	63c "Intl. Mail" under "US Postage"	3.25	2.50
c.	$4.05 "Priority Mail" under "US Postage"	12.00	2.50

Coil Stamps

Serpentine Die Cut 10½x10¼ on 2 Sides

1CVP44 CVPA41 24c black & pink 11.00 4.00

a.	39c "First Class" under "US Postage"	2.25	.50
b.	63c "Intl. Mail" under "US Postage"	3.50	2.50
c.	$4.05 "Priority Mail" under "US Postage"	12.50	2.50

Issued: Nos. 1CVP43, Nov. 2005; Nos. 1CVP44, Jan. 2006.

Originally, face values of 2c, 52c, 63c, 87c, $1.11, $1.35, $1.59, $1.83, $2.07, $2.31, $2.55, $2.79, $3.03, and $3.27 could also be printed on stamps with the "First class" inscription. Additionally, an 84c face value could be printed on stamps with the "Intl. Mail" inscription, and a $8.10 face value could be printed on stamps with the "Priority Mail" inscription. Values for Nos. 1CVP43-1CVP44 are for stamps with the listed face values and mail-class inscription. Values for stamps with lower or higher face values are correspondingly lower or higher.

In 2007, software changes permitted Nos. 1CVP43 and 1CVP44 to be printed with mail class inscriptions "Media Mail," "BPM," "Parcel Post," "Library Mail," and "Express Mail," as well as any face value for any mail-class inscription.

Nos. 1CVP43 and 1CVP44 printed after the software changes are inscribed "First Class" under "US Postage" and sell for considerably less than the values shown. Stamps printed before the software changes are inscribed "Postcard" under "US Postage," as shown in the illustrations.

Stamps.com

Flag and Mount Rushmore — CVPA42

Flag and Eagle — CVPA43

Flag and Statue of Liberty — CVPA44

Flag and Liberty Bell — CVPA45

2006, Mar.   Die Cut Perf. 6 at Right

1CVP51 CVPA42 39c multi 1.25 1.00
1CVP52 CVPA43 39c multi 1.25 1.00
1CVP53 CVPA44 39c multi 1.25 1.00
1CVP54 CVPA45 39c multi 1.25 1.00

a.	Vert. strip of 8, 2 each #1CVP51-1CVP54	8.00

Other service inscriptions with any possible face value can be printed on Nos. 1CVP51-1CVP54.

Stamps.com

Leaning Tower of Pisa — CVPA46

UNITED STATES

Taj Mahal — CVPA47

Eiffel Tower — CVPA48

Parthenon — CVPA49

2006   *Die Cut Perf 6 at Right*
1CVP55   CVPA46 39c multi   1.25   1.00
1CVP56   CVPA47 39c multi   1.25   1.00
1CVP57   CVPA48 39c multi   1.25   1.00
1CVP58   CVPA49 39c multi   1.25   1.00
   a.   Vert. strip, 2 each
     #1CVP55-1CVP58   8.00

With the introduction of the new software in December 2005, any stamp could have any denomination 1c and above, and any service classification.

Pitney Bowes Stamp Expressions

CVPA50

2006   *Die Cut Perf. 6 Horiz.*
Inscribed "pitneybowes.com/se" at Right

1CVP59   CVPA50 39c black + label   1.35   .80

The stamp and label are separated by vertical roulettes. Users could create their own label images on the Pitney Bowes Stamp Expressions website (which required approval of the image from Pitney Bowes before it could be used), or download various pre-approved label images from the website into their personal computers. Stamps could be printed without label images. Stamps were printed on rolls of tagged thermal paper from a device that could be operated without a direct connection to the personal computer. See No. 1CVT1.

Stamps.com

CVPA51

Personalizable Images — CVPA52

2006, Sept.   *Die Cut Perf. 6 at Right*
1CVP60   CVPA51 39c multi   1.50   .95
   a.   Numerals in denomination 2½mm high, thicker text   1.50   .95

   Perf. Die Cut Perf. 6 at Top
1CVP61   CVPA52 39c multi   1.50   .95
   a.   Numerals in denomination 2½mm high, thicker text   1.50   .95

Users could requisition sheets of Nos. 1CVP60 and 1CVP61 with images of their choice from Stamps.com at $4.99 per sheet of 24. Priority and Express service classifications could also be printed on Nos. 1CVP60-1CVP61 with any denomination. The denomination type shown on Nos. 1CVP60-1CVP61 can be placed on label types CVPA36-CVPA39, CVPA42-CVPA49, CVPA53-CVPA60 and any later stamps.com labels of this size.

Numerals in denomination are 3mm tall on Nos. 1CVP60-1CVP61. Serial numbers on Nos. 1CPVP60-1CVP61 lack periods and have small bank-check style numerals.

Autumn Leaves — CVPA53

Pumpkins — CVPA54

Basket of Apples, Sheaf of Wheat, Falling Leaves and Pumpkins — CVPA55

Leaves and Carved Pumpkin — CVPA56

2006   *Die Cut Perf. 6 at Right*
1CVP62   CVPA53 39c multi   1.25   1.00
1CVP63   CVPA54 39c multi   1.25   1.00
1CVP64   CVPA55 39c multi   1.25   1.00
1CVP65   CVPA56 39c multi   1.25   1.00
   a.   Vert. strip, 2 each
     #1CVP62-1CVP65   10.00
See note after No. 1CVP58.

"Season's Greetings" — CVPA57

Christmas Trees — CVPA58

Snowman — CVPA59

Dove — CVPA60

2006   *Die Cut Perf. 6 at Right*
1CVP66   CVPA57 39c multi   1.25   .45
1CVP67   CVPA58 39c multi   1.25   .45
1CVP68   CVPA59 39c multi   1.25   .45
1CVP69   CVPA60 39c multi   1.25   .45
   a.   Vert. strip, 2 each
     #1CVP66-1CVP69   10.00
See note after No. 1CVP58.

Flag — CVPA61

Statue of Liberty and Flag — CVPA62

Bald Eagle and Flag — CVPA63

Flag Painted on Building — CVPA64

2008   *Die Cut Perf. 5½ at Right*
Serial Number With Period, Large Letters and Numerals
1CVP70   CVPA61 42c multi   1.25   1.00
1CVP71   CVPA62 42c multi   1.25   1.00
1CVP72   CVPA63 42c multi   1.25   1.00
1CVP73   CVPA64 42c multi   1.25   1.00

On Nos. 1CVP70-1CVP105, and perhaps on other stamps, placement of the stamp serial number and the stamps.com logo might differ on various printings of the label stock. Descriptive text outside the frame might also vary or not be present on these various printings.

Autumn — CVPA65

Designs: No. 1CVP74, Oak leaves. No. 1CVP75, Pumpkin patch. No. 1CVP76, Autumn reflection. No. 1CVP77, Pumpkins and gourds.

2008
Serial Number With Period, Large Letters and Numerals
1CVP74   CVPA65 42c multi   2.00   1.00
1CVP75   CVPA65 42c multi   2.00   1.00
1CVP76   CVPA65 42c multi   2.00   1.00
1CVP77   CVPA65 42c multi   2.00   1.00

Flowers — CVPA66

Designs: No. 1CVP78, Sunflowers. No. 1CVP79, Daisies. No. 1CVP80, Sunflower sky. No. 1CVP81, Treasure flowers.

2008
Serial Number With Period, Large Letters and Numerals
1CVP78   CVPA66 42c multi   1.25   1.00
1CVP79   CVPA66 42c multi   1.25   1.00
1CVP80   CVPA66 42c multi   1.25   1.00
1CVP81   CVPA66 42c multi   1.25   1.00

Endangered Animals — CVPA67

Designs: No. 1CVP82, Bengal tiger. No. 1CVP83, Hawksbill turtle. No. 1CVP84, Panda. No. 1CVP85, African rhino.

2008
Serial Number With Period, Large Letters and Numerals
1CVP82   CVPA67 42c multi   2.00   1.00
1CVP83   CVPA67 42c multi   2.00   1.00
1CVP84   CVPA67 42c multi   2.00   1.00
1CVP85   CVPA67 42c multi   2.00   1.00

Parks — CVPA68

Designs: No. 1CVP86, Grand Canyon National Park, Arizona. No. 1CVP87, Yosemite National Park, California. No. 1CVP88, Niagara Falls. No. 1CVP89, Arches National Park, Utah.

2008
Serial Number With Period, Large Letters and Numerals

1CVP86	CVPA68	42c multi	1.25	1.00
1CVP87	CVPA68	42c multi	1.25	1.00
1CVP88	CVPA68	42c multi	1.25	1.00
1CVP89	CVPA68	42c multi	1.25	1.00

City Skylines — CVPA69

Designs: No. 1CVP90, New York City. No. 1CVP91, St. Louis. No. 1CVP92, Chicago. No. 1CVP93, San Francisco.

2008
Serial Number With Period, Large Letters and Numerals

1CVP90	CVPA69	42c multi	2.00	1.00
1CVP91	CVPA69	42c multi	2.00	1.00
1CVP92	CVPA69	42c multi	2.00	1.00
1CVP93	CVPA69	42c multi	2.00	1.00

Presidential Memorials — CVPA70

Designs: No. 1CVP94, Washington Monument. No. 1CVP95, Lincoln Memorial. No. 1CVP96, Jefferson Memorial. No. 1CVP97, Mount Rushmore.

2008
Serial Number With Period, Large Letters and Numerals

1CVP94	CVPA70	42c multi	1.25	1.00
1CVP95	CVPA70	42c multi	1.25	1.00
1CVP96	CVPA70	42c multi	1.25	1.00
1CVP97	CVPA70	42c multi	1.25	1.00

Christmas — CVPA71

Designs: No. 1CVP98, Ornament, "Happy Holidays." No. 1CVP99, Gingerbread men, "Season's Greetings." No. 1CVP100, Snowflake, "Happy Holidays." No. 1CVP101, Christmas tree, "Season's Greetings."

2008
Serial Number With Period, Large Letters and Numerals
Without Year or Text at Left

1CVP98	CVPA71	42c multi	2.00	1.00
1CVP99	CVPA71	42c multi	2.00	1.00
1CVP100	CVPA71	42c multi	2.00	1.00
1CVP101	CVPA71	42c multi	2.00	1.00

Love — CVPA72

"Love" and: No. 1CVP102, Rose. No. 1CVP103, Small hearts. No. 1CVP104, Large heart. No. 1CVP105, Hearts on curtain.

2009
Serial Number With Period, Large Letters and Numerals
Without Year or Text at Left

1CVP102	CVPA72	42c multi	1.25	1.00
1CVP103	CVPA72	42c multi	1.25	1.00
1CVP104	CVPA72	42c multi	1.25	1.00
1CVP105	CVPA72	42c multi	1.25	1.00

Wavy Lines
CVPA73

2009 — Die Cut Perf 6½ at Right

1CVP106	CVPA73	44c multi	1.25	.45

Endicia.com

Globe
CVPA74

Globe —
CVPA74a

2009 — Serpentine Die Cut 10¼x10½

1CVP107	CVPA74	44c org & blk	1.25	.45
1CVP107A	CVPA74a	45c org & blk	—	—

Software allowed for six other inscriptions below "US Postage" (Priority Mail, Media Mail, Parcel Post, Library Mail, Express Mail and Intl Mail) and any face value for any mail-class inscription.

No. 1CVP107 with space between denomination and "US POSTAGE". No. 1CVP107A with no space between denomination and "US POSTAGE".

Stamps.com

Thank You For Your Business — CVPA75

Text: No. 1CVP108, On billboard. No. 1CVP109, And building. No. 1CVP110, On red background. No. 1CVP111, And two people shaking hands.

2009 — Die Cut Perf. 5½ at Right
Serial Number With Period, Large Letters and Numerals
Without Year or Text at Left

1CVP108	CVPA75	44c multi	1.25	1.00
1CVP109	CVPA75	44c multi	1.25	1.00
1CVP110	CVPA75	44c multi	1.25	1.00
1CVP111	CVPA75	44c multi	1.25	1.00

We're Moving — CVPA76

Text: No. 1CVP112, Stack of three boxes, green background. No. 1CVP113, Eleven boxes, orange background. No. 1CVP114, Four boxes, green background. No. 1CVP115, Four boxes, red background.

2009
Serial Number With Period, Large Letters and Numerals
Without Year or Text at Left

1CVP112	CVPA76	44c multi	1.25	1.00
1CVP113	CVPA76	44c multi	1.25	1.00
1CVP114	CVPA76	44c multi	1.25	1.00
1CVP115	CVPA76	44c multi	1.25	1.00

Special Invitation — CVPA77

Text: No. 1CVP116, And pen nib. No. 1CVP117, And circled "15" on calendar. No. 1CVP118, On card on envelope. No. 1CVP119, On wax seal.

2009
Serial Number With Period, Large Letters and Numerals
Without Year or Text at Left

1CVP116	CVPA77	44c multi	1.25	1.00
1CVP117	CVPA77	44c multi	1.25	1.00
1CVP118	CVPA77	44c multi	1.25	1.00
1CVP119	CVPA77	44c multi	1.25	1.00

US Flag — CVPA78

Flag: No. 1CVP120, On flagpole. No. 1CVP121, Behind Statue of Liberty. No. 1CVP122, Behind bald eagle. No. 1CVP123, On United States map.

2009
Serial Number With Period, Large Letters and Numerals
Without Year or Text at Left

1CVP120	CVPA78	44c multi	2.00	1.00
1CVP121	CVPA78	44c multi	2.00	1.00
1CVP122	CVPA78	44c multi	2.00	1.00
1CVP123	CVPA78	44c multi	2.00	1.00

Patriotic Symbols — CVPA79

Designs: No. 1CVP124, Statue of Liberty. No. 1CVP125, Flag. No. 1CVP126, Bald eagle.

2010 — Die Cut Perf. 5½ Vert.

1CVP124	CVPA79	44c multi	1.25	1.00
1CVP125	CVPA79	44c multi	1.25	1.00
1CVP126	CVPA79	44c multi	1.25	1.00

Jewish Symbols — CVPA80

Designs: No. 1CVP127, Menorah. No. 1CVP125, Dreidel. No. 1CVP126, Star of David.

2010 — Die Cut Perf. 5½ Vert.

1CVP127	CVPA80	44c multi	1.25	1.00
1CVP128	CVPA80	44c multi	1.25	1.00
1CVP129	CVPA80	44c multi	1.25	1.00

Christmas — CVPA81

Designs: No. 1CVP130, Christmas stocking. No. 1CVP131, Christmas tree. No. 1CVP132, Santa Claus.

2010 — Die Cut Perf. 5½ Vert.

1CVP130	CVPA81	44c multi	1.25	1.00
1CVP131	CVPA81	44c multi	1.25	1.00
1CVP132	CVPA81	44c multi	1.25	1.00

Valentine's Day — CVPA82

Designs: No. 1CVP133, Hearts. No. 1CVP134, Rose. No. 1CVP135, Candy hearts.

2011 — Die Cut Perf. 5½ Vert.

1CVP133	CVPA82	44c multi	2.00	1.00
1CVP134	CVPA82	44c multi	2.00	1.00
1CVP135	CVPA82	44c multi	2.00	1.00

Christian Symbols — CVPA83

Designs: No. 1CVP136, Cross. No. 1CVP137, Fish. No. 1CVP138, Rosary beads.

2011 — Die Cut Perf. 5½ Vert.

1CVP136	CVPA83	44c multi	1.25	1.00
1CVP137	CVPA83	44c multi	1.25	1.00
1CVP138	CVPA83	44c multi	1.25	1.00

OFFICAL STAMPS PRINTED TO ORDER

1CVPO1

1CVPO2

2002-06 Serpentine Die Cut 10.6
Self-Adhesive

1CVPO1 1CVPO1 37c blk, red & bluish gray, no denomination below vignette — —

1CVPO2 1CVPO2 37c blk, red & blue, denomination below vignette — —

1CVPO3 1CVPO2 39c blk, red & blue, denomination below vignette — —

1CVPO5 1CVPO2 $4.05 blk, red & blue, denomination below vignette — —

Endicia filled federal agency orders for stamps to be limited for use by government officials. Nos. 1CVPO1 and 1CVPO2 were printed in sheets of 10. 39c and 41c denominations are thought to exist.

NON-PERSONALIZABLE POSTAGE

Stamps.com

These stamps, approved by the USPS, were non-personalizable stamps that could be purchased directly from private manufacturers, which shipped them to the customer. Other non-personalizable stamps have been created by a variety of companies, all sold at excessive amounts over face value as "collectibles". Such items are not listed here. Most items created that sold for excessive amounts over face value have vignettes that are licensed images, usually depicting sport team emblems or other sports-related themes, or celebrities.

Personalized postage stamps, first available in 2004, created by a variety of different companies, and heretofore listed with Scott numbers having a "2CVP" prefix, are no longer listed. Personalized stamps, though valid for postage, are not sold at any U.S. Postal

Service post office. They are available only by on-line ordering through the company's website. Stamps are only available from the companies in full panes of 20. Each pane is sold at a significant premium above the stated face value to cover the costs of personalization, shipping and handling.

In recent years, there has been a steadily increasing number of private companies, either directly licensed by the USPS or created as spinoff companies of these licensees, creating distinctly different personalized stamps. None of the companies has issued fewer than seven stamps for each rate change, with one issuing as many as 42 different stamps. Because mailing rates set by the USPS are expected to change yearly, the collective output of distinctly different, rate-based stamps from these various companies likely will increase. There are no restrictions in place to prevent more firms from bringing personalized stamps to the marketplace, or to keep stamp producers from offering even more customer options. Some personalized stamps do not differ in any appreciable manner from some of the non-personalizable stamps sold as collectibles and not listed here.

CVPC1

CVPC2

2007, May Die Cut
Self-Adhesive

3CVP1 CVPC1 2c black & gray green .50 .50
  a. Inscribed "US Postag"

Die Cut Perf. 5¼ at Right
3CVP2 CVPC2 2c multicolored .50 .50
  a. Tagged 2.00 2.00

2008 Die Cut
Self-Adhesive
3CVP3 CVPC1 1c black & gray .50 .50

No. 3CVP1 was printed in sheets of 40 stamps. Stamps with serial numbers ending in "06" are No. 3CVP1a. Sheets were sold for face value plus a shipping charge and were obtainable through the stamps.com website.

No. 3CVP2 was printed in sheets of 20. Full sheets were given free of charge to first-time stamps.com customers, but the full sheets were available for sale to other customers at face value plus a shipping charge through the stamps.com website.

Stamps.com Type of 2007
2019 Die Cut
Self-Adhesive
3CVP4 CVPC1 5c black & gray .50 .50

No. 3CVP4 was printed in sheets of 40 stamps that were sold for face value plus a shipping charge and were obtainable through the stamps.com website.

CARRIERS' STAMPS

GENERAL ISSUE CARRIER STAMPS

Issued by the U.S. Government to facilitate payment of fees for delivering and collecting letters.

Franklin — OC1

1851 Engr. Unwmk. Imperf.
LO1 OC1 (1c) dull blue, rose 7,000. 8,000.

U.S.P.O. Despatch

Eagle — OC2

1851
LO2 OC2 1c blue (shades) 50.00 80.00

1875 Imperf.
LO3 OC1 (1c) blue, rose 60.
Perf. 12
LO4 OC1 (1c) blue 16,000.

No. LO4 is valued in the grade of average to fine.

Eagle Reprints
Imperf.
LO5 OC2 1c blue 25.
Perf. 12
LO6 OC2 1c blue 175.

Reprints of the Franklin Carrier are printed in dark blue, instead of the dull blue or deep blue of the originals. Two reprintings of 10,000 each were made in 1875 on the same rose paper as the originals. A third reprinting of 5,000 in 1881 is on soft wove paper.

The first two reprintings of 10,000 each of the Eagle carrier are on hard white paper, ungummed and sometimes perforated. A third reprinting of 10,000 stamps in 1881 is on soft wove paper. Originals are on yellowish paper with brown gum.

No. LO6 is valued with the perfs cutting slightly into the design.

CITY CARRIER DEPARTMENT STAMPS

Issued by officials or employees of the U.S. Government for the purpose of securing or indicating payment of carriers' fees.

All are imperforate.
Baltimore, Md.

C1

1850-55 Typo.
Settings of 10 (2x5) varieties
1LB1 C1 1c red, bluish 180. 160.
1LB2 C1 1c blue, bluish 200. 150.
  a. Bluish laid paper
1LB3 C1 1c blue 160. 100.
  a. Laid paper 200. 150.
  b. Block of 14 containing three tete-beche gutter pairs (unique) 6,250.
1LB4 C1 1c green — 1,000.
1LB5 C1 1c red 2,250. 1,750.

C2

1856 Typo.
1LB6 C2 1c blue (shades) 130. 90.
1LB7 C2 1c red (shades) 130. 90.

C3

The sheet consisted of at least four panes of 10 placed horizontally, the two center panes tete beche. This makes possible five horizontal tete beche gutter pairs.

Plate of 10 (2x5); 10 Varieties

1857
1LB8 C3 1c black (shades) 65. 50.
  a. "SENT" 100. 75.
  b. Short rays 100. 75.
1LB9 C3 1c red 100. 90.
  a. "SENT" 140. 110.
  b. Short rays 140. 110.
  c. As "b," double impression 800.

Boston, Mass.

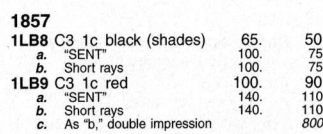

C6

Several Varieties
1849-50 Pelure Paper Typeset
3LB1 C6 1c blue 375. 180.
  a. Wrong ornament at left 400.

C7

Several Varieties
1851
Wove Paper Colored Through
3LB2 C7 1c blue (shades), slate 190. 100.

Charleston, S. C.
Honour's City Express

C8

1849 Typo.
Wove Paper Colored Through
4LB1 C8 2c blk, brn rose 10,000.
  Cut to shape 4,000. 4,000.
4LB2 C8 2c blk, yel, cut to shape —

No. 4LB1 unused is a unique uncanceled stamp on piece. The used cut-to-shape stamp is also unique. In addition two covers exist bearing No. 4LB1.

No. 4LB2 unused (uncanceled) off cover is unique; three known on cover.

See the Scott U.S. Specialized Catalogue.

4LB2A C8 2c blk, bl gray, on cover, cut to shape —

No. 4LB2A is unique.

C10

1854 Wove Paper Typeset
4LB3 C10 2c black 1,500.

C11

Several Varieties
1849-50
Wove Paper Colored Through
4LB5 C11 2c black, bluish, pelure 750. 500.
  a. "Ceuts" 5,750.
4LB7 C11 2c black, yellow 750. 1,000.
  a. "Ccnts," ms. tied on cover 14,500.

No. 4LB5a is unique. It is without gum and is valued thus. No. 4LB7a also is unique.

C13

C14

C15

Several varieties of each type

1851-58
Wove Paper Colored Through
4LB8	C13	2c black, *bluish*	350.	175.
a.		Period after "PAID"	500.	250.
b.		"Cens"	700.	900.
c.		"Conours" and "Bents"		—

The No. 4LB8 with No. 2 combination cover is unique. It is a cover front only and is valued thus.
No. 4LB8a on cover with 5c No. 1 is unique.

4LB9	C13	2c black, *bluish*, pelure	850.	950.
4LB10	C13	2c black, *pink*, pelure, on cover		7,000.
4LB11	C14	(2c) black, *bluish*	—	375.
4LB12	C14	(2c) black, *bluish*, pelure		
4LB13	C15	(2c) black, *bluish* ('58)	750.	400.
a.		Comma after "PAID"	1,100.	
b.		No period after "Post"	1,400.	

Kingman's City Post

C16   C17

Several varieties of each
Wove Paper Colored Through
1851(?)-58(?)
4LB14	C16	2c black, *bluish*	1,400.	900.
a.		"Kingman's" erased		5,000.
4LB15	C17	2c black, *bluish*	800.	800.
a.		"Kingman's" erased, on cover with 3c #11, tied by pen cancel (unique)		4,500.

Martin's City Post

C18

Several Varieties
1858   Typeset
Wove Paper Colored Through
4LB16	C18	2c black, *bluish*	8,000.

Beckman's City Post
Same as C19, but inscribed: "Beckmann's City Post."
1860
4LB17	C19	2c black, on cover	—

No. 4LB17 is unique.

Steinmeyer's City Post

C19   C20

Several varieties of Type C19
Type C20 printed from plate of 10 (2x5) varieties
1859   Typeset
Wove Paper Colored Through
4LB18	C19	2c black, *bluish*	21,000.	
4LB19	C20	2c black, *bluish*	4,500.	—
4LB20	C20	2c black, *pink*	200.	—
4LB21	C20	2c black, *yellow*	200.	

Cincinnati, Ohio
Williams' City Post

C20a

1854   Wove Paper   Litho.
9LB1	C20a	2c brown	—	4,000.

Cleveland, Ohio
Bishop's City Post

C20b   C20c

1854   Wove Paper   Litho.
10LB1	C20b	2c black, *bluish*	5,000.	4,000.

Vertically Laid Paper
10LB2	C20c	2c black, *bluish*	4,000.	6,000.

No. 10LB2 unused is unique. It is cut in at bottom and without gum, and is valued thus.

Louisville, Ky.
Wharton's U.S.P.O. Despatch

C21

1857   Lithographed
5LB1	C21	(2c) bluish green (shades)	125.

Brown & McGill's U. S. P. O. Despatch

C22

1858, Nov.-1860   Lithographed
5LB2	C22	(2c) blue (shades)	250.	750.

1858, Feb.-Aug.
5LB3	C22	(2c) black	4,500.	15,000.
		On cover, not tied, with 3c #26		17,500.

The value for No. 5LB3 used refers to the finer of the two known used (canceled) examples; it is extremely fine and on a piece with a 3c #26.

New York, N. Y.
United States City Despatch Post

C23

Wove Paper Colored Through
1842   Engr.
6LB1	C23	3c black, *grayish*	2,000.

Used examples are Carriers' stamps only when canceled with the regular government cancellation "U.S." in octagonal frame (see illustration), "U.S.CITY DESPATCH POST," or New York circular postmark.

When canceled "FREE" in frame they were used as local stamps. See No. 40L1 in the Scott Specialized Catalogue of United States Stamps.

C24

Wove Paper (unsurfaced) Colored Through
1842-45
6LB2	C24	3c black, *rosy buff*	5,000.	
6LB3	C24	3c black, *light blue*	1,500.	750.
6LB4	C24	3c black, *green*	11,500.	
a.		3c black, *apple green*		—

Some authorities consider No. 6LB2 to be an essay, and No. 6LB4 a color changeling. No. 6LB2 unused is valued without gum.

Glazed Paper, Surface Colored
6LB5	C24	3c black, *blue green* (shades)	200.	175.
a.		Double impression		1,500.
		On cover		4,500.
b.		3c black, *blue*	650.	
c.		As "b," double impression		1,000.
d.		3c black, *green*	1,250.	750.
		black, *apple green*		2,000.
		Pair		2,750.
e.		As "d," double impression		—
6LB6	C24	3c black, *pink*, on cover front		14,500.

No. 6LB6 is unique.

No. 6LB5 Surcharged in Red

1846
6LB7	C24	2c on 3c black, *bluish grn*, on cover	14,000.
		On cover, not tied, with certificate	70,000.

The City Despatch 2c red is listed in the Scott U.S. Specialized Catalogue as a Local stamp.

U.S. MAIL

C27

1849   Typo.
Wove Paper, Colored Through
6LB9	C27	1c black, *rose*	100.	100.

1849-50   Glazed Surface Paper
6LB10	C27	1c black, *yellow*	100.	100.
6LB11	C27	1c black, *buff*	100.	100.
a.		Pair, one stamp sideways		2,850.

Philadelphia, Pa.

C28

Several Varieties
Thick Wove Paper Colored Through
1849-50   Typeset
7LB1	C28	1c black, *rose* (with "L P")	450.	
7LB2	C28	1c black, *rose* (with "S")	3,000.	
7LB3	C28	1c black, *rose* (with "H")	275.	
7LB4	C28	1c black, *rose* (with "L S")	400.	500.
7LB5	C28	1c black, *rose* (with "J J")		7,500.

The used No. 7LB5 also is unique and is an uncanceled stamp on a cover front.

C29

Several Varieties
7LB6	C29	1c black, *rose*	300.	250.
7LB7	C29	1c black, *blue*, glazed		1,000.
7LB8	C29	1c blk, *ver*, glazed	700.	
7LB9	C29	1c blk, *yel*, glazed	2,750.	2,250.

Cancellations on Nos. 7LB1-7LB9: Normally these stamps were left uncanceled on the letter, but occasionally were accidentally tied by

---

the Philadelphia town postmark which was normally struck in blue ink.
A 1c black on buff (unglazed) of type C29 is believed to be a color changeling.

C30

Settings of 25 (5x5) varieties (Five basic types)
1850-52   Litho.
7LB11	C30	1c gold, *black*, glazed	175.	110.
7LB12	C30	1c blue	400.	275.
7LB13	C30	1c black	750.	550.

25 varieties of C30.

C31

Handstamped
7LB14	C31	1c blue, *buff*	3,250.

1855(?)
7LB16	C31	1c black	5,000.

C32

1856(?)   Handstamped
7LB18	C32	1c black	1,250.	2,000.

Labels of these designs are believed by most specialists not to be carrier stamps. Those seen are uncanceled, either off cover or affixed to stampless covers of the early 1850s. Some students believe they should be given carrier status.

St. Louis, Mo.

C36   C37

Illustrations enlarged to show details of the two types (note upper corners especially). Sizes of actual designs are 17 1/2x22mm.

1849   White Wove Paper   Litho.
Two Types
8LB1	C36	2c black	7,000.	3,000.
8LB2	C37	2c black	6,000.	—

Cancellation on Nos. 8LB1-8LB2: Black town.

C38

1857   **Litho.**
8LB3 C38 2c blue   22,500.

The used example off cover is unique. Five covers are recorded.

Cancellations on No. 8LB3: Black boxed "1ct," "Paid" in arc, black pen.

STAMPED ENVELOPES & WRAPPERS

VALUES

Unless otherwise noted, values are for cut squares in a grade of very fine.

Very fine cut squares will have the design well centered within moderately large margins. Precanceled cut squares must include the entire precancellation.

Values for unused entires are for those without printed or manuscript address. Values for letter sheets are for folded entires. Unfolded examples sell for more. A "full corner" includes back and side flaps and commands a premium.

Entire envelopes and wrappers are listed in the Scott U.S. Specialized Catalogue.

Wrappers are listed with envelopes of corresponding designs, and indicated by prefix letter "W" instead of "U."

An ALBINO impression is where two or more envelope blanks are fed into the printing press. The one adjacent to the printing die receives the color and the embossing, while the others are embossed only. Albinos are printing errors and are sometimes worth more than normal, inked impressions. Because of the nature of the printing process, many albinos were produced, and most collectors will not pay much, or any, premium for most of them. Albinos of earlier issues, canceled while current, are scarce.

The papers of these issues vary greatly in texture, and in color from yellowish to bluish white and from amber to dark buff.

"+" Some authorities claim that Nos. U37, U48, U49, U110, U124, U125, U130, U133A, U137A, U137B, U137C, W138, U145, U162, U178A, U185, U220, U285, U286, U298, U299, UO3, UO32, UO38, UO45 and UO45A (each with "+" before number) were not regularly issued and are not known to have been used.

U1

"THREE" in short label with curved ends; 13mm wide at top. Twelve varieties.

Washington — U2

"THREE" in short label with straight ends; 15½mm wide at top. Three varieties.

U3

"THREE" in short label with octagonal ends. Two varieties.

U4

"THREE" in wide label with straight ends; 20mm wide at top.

U5

"THREE" in medium wide label with curved ends; 14½mm wide at top. Ten varieties. A sub-variety shows curved lines at either end of label omitted; both T's have longer cross stroke; R is smaller (20 varieties).

U6

Four varieties.

U7

"TEN" in short label; 15½mm wide at top.

U8

"TEN" in wide label; 20mm wide at top.

1853-55
On Diagonally Laid Paper (Early printings of No. U1 on Horizontally Laid Paper)

U1	U1	3c red	350.00	35.00
U2	U1	3c red, *buff*	90.00	30.00
U3	U2	3c red	950.00	50.00
U4	U2	3c red, *buff*	425.00	45.00
U5	U3	3c red ('54)	5,750.	500.00
U6	U3	3c red, *buff* ('54)	3,750.	100.00
U7	U4	3c red	5,000.	150.00
U8	U4	3c red, *buff*	8,250.	175.00
U9	U5	3c red ('54)	40.00	4.00
U10	U5	3c red, *buff* ('54)	20.00	4.00
U11	U6	6c red	275.00	90.00
U12	U6	6c red, *buff*	145.00	90.00
U13	U6	6c green	260.00	150.00
U14	U6	6c green, *buff*	200.00	125.00
U15	U7	10c green ('55)	400.00	100.00
U16	U7	10c green, *buff* ('55)	175.00	90.00
a.		10c pale green, *buff*	135.00	70.00
U17	U8	10c green ('55)	375.00	140.00
a.		10c pale green	275.00	125.00
U18	U8	10c green, *buff* ('55)	375.00	100.00
a.		10c pale green, *buff*	350.00	100.00

Earliest documented uses: No. U1, July 6, 1853; No. U2, July 12, 1853 (Nesbitt seal); No.

U3, July 7, 1853 (Nesbitt seal); No. U4, July 7, 1853 (flap missing); No. U5, Feb. 18, 1854; No. U6, Feb. 24, 1854; No. U7, Oct. 6, 1853; No. U8, Nov. 9, 1853; No. U9, May 30, 1854; No. U10, Mar. 24, 1854; No. U11, Mar. 25, 1855; No. U12, Feb. 22, 1855; No. U13, Nov. 29, 1853; No. U14, Nov. 10, 1853; No. U15, Oct. 15, 1856; No. U16, May 15, 1857 (cut square), June 15, 1857 (entire); No. U16a, Dec. 19, 1856 (cut square), June 4, 1857 (entire); No. U17, no dates documented; No. U17a, Nov. 14, 1855; No. U18, June 1, 1855; No. U18a, Sept. 4, 1855.

Nos. U9, U10, U11, U12, U13, U14, U17, and U18 have been reprinted on white and buff papers, wove or vertically laid, and are not known entire. The originals are on diagonally laid paper. Value, set of 8 reprints on laid, $225. Reprints on wove sell for more.

The first printings of Nos. U1, U2, U3, U4 and U7 have G.F. Nesbitt crests printed on the envelope flaps. These sell for a premium. Such examples of Nos. U1-U4 with 1853 year-dated cancels sell for a very large premium.

No. U1 with watermark having a space between lines and on horizontally laid paper sells for a substantial premium.

U9

Period after "POSTAGE." (Eleven varieties.)

Franklin, Period after "POSTAGE." — U10

Bust touches inner frame-line at front and back.

No period after "POSTAGE" — U11

No period after "POSTAGE." (Two varieties.)

Washington — U12

Nine varieties of type U12.

Envelopes are on diagonally laid paper.
Wrappers on vertically or horizontally laid paper, or on unwatermarked wove paper (Nos. U21A, W22, W25)

1860-61

W18B	U9	1c blue ('61)	5,500.	
U19	U9	1c blue, *buff*	35.00	12.50
W20	U9	1c bl, *buff* ('61)	65.00	50.00
W21	U9	1c bl, *man* ('61)	55.00	45.00
U21A	U9	1c bl, *org*	950.00	325.00
W22	U9	1c bl, *org* ('61)	3,000.	
U23	U10	1c bl, *org*	500.00	350.00
U24	U11	1c bl, *amb*	350.00	110.00
W25	U11	1c bl, *man* ('61)	6,750.	1,500.
U26	U12	3c red	25.00	17.50
U27	U12	3c red, *buff*	22.50	12.50
U28	U12+U9	3c +1c red & bl	250.00	225.00
U29	U12+U9	3c +1c red & bl, *buff*	250.00	250.00
U30	U12	6c red	1,800.	1,500.
U31	U12	6c red, *buff*	3,500.	1,450.
U32	U12	10c green	1,250.	450.00
U33	U12	10c green, *buff*	1,250.	400.00

Nos. U26, U27, U30 to U33 have been reprinted on the same vertically laid paper as the reprints of the 1853-55 issue, and are not known entire. Value, Nos. U26-U27, $75 each; Nos. U30-U33, $75 each.

U13

U14   U15

Washington U16

Envelopes are on diagonally laid paper.

U36 and U45 come on vertically or horizontally laid paper.

1861

U34	U13	3c pink	27.50	5.00
U35	U13	3c pink, *buff*	32.50	6.00
U36	U13	3c pink, *blue* (Letter Sheet)	65.00	65.00
+U37	U13	3c pink, *orange*	2,750.	
U38	U14	6c pink	100.00	80.00
U39	U14	6c pink, *buff*	60.00	60.00
U40	U15	10c yellow green	40.00	30.00
a.		10c blue green	40.00	30.00
U41	U15	10c yel grn, *buff*	40.00	30.00
a.		10c blue green, *buff*	40.00	30.00
U42	U16	12c red & brn, *buff*	180.00	180.00
a.		12c lake & brown, *buff*	1,250.	
U43	U16	20c red & bl, *buff*	250.00	225.00
U44	U16	24c red & grn, *buff*	225.00	225.00
a.		24c lake & green, *salmon*	275.00	225.00
U45	U16	40c blk & red, *buff*	325.00	400.00

Nos. U38 and U39 have been reprinted on the same papers as the reprints of the 1853-55 issue, and are not known entire. Value, set of 2 reprints, $60.

Jackson — U17

"U.S. POSTAGE" above. Downstroke and tail of "2" unite near the point (seven varieties).

Jackson — U18

"U.S. POSTAGE" above. The downstroke and tail of the "2" touch but do not merge.

Jackson — U19

"U.S. POST" above. Stamp 24-25mm wide (Sixteen varieties).

Jackson — U20

"U.S. POST" above. Stamp 25½-26¼mm wide. (Twenty-five varieties.)

Envelopes are on diagonally laid paper. Wrappers on vertically or horizontally laid paper.

Envelopes are on diagonally laid paper. Wrappers on vertically or horizontally laid paper.

1863-64

U46	U17	2c black, *buff*	50.00	24.00
W47	U17	2c black, *dark manila*	75.00	65.00
+U48	U18	2c black, *buff*	2,250.	
+U49	U18	2c black, *orange*	1,750.	
U50	U19	2c black, *buff* ('64)	17.50	11.00
W51	U19	2c black, *buff* ('64)	425.00	275.00
U52	U19	2c black, *orange* ('64)	20.00	11.00
W53	U19	2c black, *dark manila* ('64)	42.50	40.00
U54	U20	2c black, *buff* ('64)	17.50	9.50
W55	U20	2c black, *buff* ('64)	95.00	65.00

U56	U20	2c black, *orange* ('64)	17.50	10.00
W57	U20	2c black, *light manila* ('64)	22.50	14.00

Washington — U21

79 varieties for Nos. U58-U61; 2 varieties for Nos. U63-U65.

Washington U22

1864-65

U58	U21	3c pink	8.00	1.60
U59	U21	3c pink, *buff*	7.50	1.25
U60	U21	3c brown ('65)	60.00	40.00
U61	U21	3c brown, *buff* ('65)	50.00	30.00
U62	U21	6c pink	75.00	29.00
U63	U21	6c pink, *buff*	35.00	27.50
U64	U21	6c purple ('65)	50.00	26.00
U65	U21	6c purple, *buff* ('65)	40.00	20.00
U66	U22	9c lemon, *buff*	375.00	250.00
U67	U22	9c orange, *buff* ('65)	125.00	90.00
a.		9c orange yellow, *buff*	150.00	90.00
U68	U22	12c brown, *buff* ('65)	275.00	275.00
U69	U22	12c red brown, *buff* ('65)	125.00	55.00
U70	U22	18c red, *buff* ('65)	70.00	95.00
U71	U22	24c blue, *buff* ('65)	70.00	95.00
U72	U22	30c green, *buff* ('65)	80.00	80.00
a.		30c yellow green, *buff*	75.00	75.00
U73	U22	40c rose, *buff* ('65)	80.00	*250.00*

Printed by George H. Reay, Brooklyn, N. Y.

The engravings in this issue are finely executed.

Franklin — U23

Bust points to the end of the "N" of "ONE."

Jackson — U24

Bust narrow at back. Small, thick figures of value.

Washington — U25

Queue projects below bust.

Lincoln — U26

Neck very long at the back.

Stanton — U27

Bust pointed at the back; figures "7" are normal.

Jefferson — U28

Queue forms straight line with the bust.

Clay — U29

Ear partly concealed by hair, mouth large, chin prominent.

Webster — U30

Has side whiskers.

Scott — U31

Straggling locks of hair at top of head; ornaments around the inner oval end in squares.

Hamilton — U32

Back of bust very narrow, chin almost straight; labels containing figures of value are exactly parallel.

Perry — U33

Front of bust very narrow and pointed; inner lines of shields project very slightly beyond the oval.

1870-71

U74	U23	1c blue	32.50	30.00
a.		1c ultramarine	60.00	35.00
U75	U23	1c blue, *amber*	25.00	27.50
a.		1c ultramarine, *amber*	55.00	30.00
U76	U23	1c blue, *orange*	17.00	15.00
W77	U23	1c blue, *manila*	35.00	35.00
U78	U24	2c brown	35.00	16.00
U79	U24	2c brown, *amber*	14.00	10.00

U80	U24	2c brown, *orange*	8.00	6.50
W81	U24	2c brown, *manila*	25.00	20.00
U82	U25	3c green	7.00	1.00
a.		3c brown (error), entire	9,000.	
U83	U25	3c green, *amber*	6.00	2.00
U84	U25	3c green, *cream*	8.00	4.50
U85	U26	6c dark red	17.50	16.00
a.		6c vermilion	17.50	16.00
U86	U26	6c dark red, *amber*	30.00	20.00
a.		6c vermilion, *amber*	30.00	20.00
U87	U26	6c dark red, *cream*	30.00	25.00
a.		6c vermilion, *cream*	25.00	20.00
U88	U27	7c vermilion, *amber* ('71)	55.00	175.00
U89	U28	10c olive black	650.00	900.00
U90	U28	10c olive black, *amber*	625.00	900.00
U91	U28	10c brown	82.50	70.00
U92	U28	10c brown, *amber*	85.00	52.50
a.		10c dark brown, *amber*	85.00	75.00
U93	U29	12c plum	100.00	82.50
U94	U29	12c plum, *amber*	110.00	100.00
U95	U29	12c plum, *cream*	225.00	200.00
U96	U30	15c red orange	75.00	75.00
a.		15c orange	75.00	
U97	U30	15c red orange, *amber*	160.00	275.00
a.		15c orange, *amber*	170.00	
U98	U30	15c red orange, *cream*	325.00	375.00
a.		15c orange, *cream*	325.00	
U99	U31	24c purple	110.00	125.00
U100	U31	24c purple, *amber*	180.00	300.00
U101	U31	24c purple, *cream*	225.00	450.00
U102	U32	30c black	60.00	120.00
U103	U32	30c black, *amber*	180.00	450.00
U104	U32	30c black, *cream*	150.00	450.00
U105	U33	90c carmine	125.00	300.00
U106	U33	90c carmine, *amber*	350.00	900.00
U107	U33	90c carmine, *cream*	175.00	*2,250.*

Printed by Plimpton Manufacturing Co.

The profiles in this issue are inferior to the fine engraving of the Reay issue.

U34

Bust forms an angle at the back near the frame. Lettering poorly executed. Distinct circle in "O" of "Postage."

U35

Lower part of bust points to the end of the "E" in "ONE." Head inclined downward.

U36

Bust narrow at back. Thin numerals. Head of "P" narrow. Bust broad at front, ending in sharp corners.

U37

Bust broad. Figures of value in long ovals.

U38

Similar to U37 but the figure "2" at the left touches the oval.

U39

Similar to U37 but the "O" of "TWO" has the center netted instead of plain and the "G" of "POSTAGE" and the "C" of "CENTS" have diagonal crossline.

U40

Bust broad: numerals in ovals short and thick.

U41

Similar to U40 but the ovals containing the numerals are much heavier. A diagonal line runs from the upper part of the "U" to the white frame-line.

U42

Similar to U40 but the middle stroke of "N" in "CENTS" is as thin as the vertical strokes.

U43

Bottom of bust cut almost semi-circularly.

U44

Thin lettering, long thin figures of value.

U45

Thick lettering, well-formed figures of value, queue does not project below bust.

U46

Top of head egg-shaped; knot of queue well marked and projects triangularly.

Taylor — U47

Die 1- Figures of value with thick, curved tops

Die 2- Figures of value with long, thin tops

U48

Neck short at back.

U49

Figures of value turned up at the ends.

U50

Very large head.

U51

Knot of queue stands out prominently.

U52

Ear prominent, chin receding.

U53

No side whiskers, forelock projects above head.

U54

Hair does not project; ornaments around the inner oval end in points.

U55

Back of bust rather broad, chin slopes considerably; labels containing figures of value are not exactly parallel.

U56

Front of bust sloping; inner lines of shields project considerably into the inner oval.

1874-86			
Design U34			
U108	1c dark blue	175.00	60.00
a.	1c light blue	175.00	60.00
U109	1c dk bl, amb	150.00	75.00
+U110	1c dk blue, cr	1,000.	
U111	1c dk blue,org	15.00	15.00
a.	dk blue, org	12.50	12.50
W112	1c dk blue, man	62.50	40.00
Design U35			
U113	1c light blue	2.25	1.00
a.	1c dark blue	6.50	6.50
U114	1c lt blue, amb	3.25	3.25
a.	dk blue, amb	17.50	10.00
U115	1c blue, cr	4.25	4.25
a.	dk blue, cr	17.50	8.50
U116	1c lt blue, org	.75	.40
a.	dk blue, org	4.00	2.50
U117	1c lt bl, *bl* ('80)	6.50	5.00
U118	1c lt bl, *fawn* ('79)	7.00	5.00
U119	1c lt bl, *man* ('86)	8.00	3.25
W120	1c lt bl, *man*	1.25	1.10
a.	dk bl, *man*	8.00	7.00
U121	1c lt bl, *amb man*	17.50	10.00
Design U36			
U122	2c brown	140.00	65.00
U123	2c brown, *amb*	67.50	40.00
+U124	2c brn, *crm*	1,000.	
+U125	2c brn, *org*	18,000.	
W126	2c brn, *man*	125.00	85.00
W127	2c ver, *man*	2,500.	500.00
Design U37			
U128	2c brown	60.00	35.00
U129	2c brn, *amb*	80.00	45.00
+U130	2c brn, *cr*	35,000.	
W131	2c brn, *man*	17.50	15.00

Design U38			
U132	2c brown	70.00	27.50
U133	2c brn, *amb*	325.00	70.00
+U133A	2c brn, *cr*	70,000.	
Design U39			
U134	2c brown	800.00	160.00
U135	2c brn, *amb*	425.00	150.00
U136	2c brn, *org*	50.00	27.50
W137	2c brn, *man*	75.00	40.00
+U137A	2c ver	32,500.	
+U137B	2c ver, *amb*	30,000.	
+U137C	2c ver, *org*	70,000.	
+W138	2c ver, *man*	25,000.	
Design U40			
U139	2c brn ('75)	57.50	37.50
U140	2c brn,*amb* ('75)	85.00	62.50
+U140A	2c reddish brn, *org* ('75)	17,500.	
W141	2c brn, *man* ('75)	32.50	25.00
U142	2c ver ('75)	8.00	5.00
a.	2c pink	8.00	5.00
U143	2c ver, *amb* ('75)	9.00	5.00
U144	2c ver, *cr* ('75)	17.50	7.00
+U145	2c ver, *org* ('75)	35,000.	
U146	2c ver, *bl* ('80)	110.00	40.00
U147	2c ver, *fawn* ('75)	7.00	5.00
W148	2c ver, *man* ('75)	4.00	3.50
Design U41			
U149	2c ver ('78)	45.00	25.00
a.	2c pink	52.50	27.00
U150	2c ver, *amb* ('78)	45.00	15.00
U151	2c ver, *bl* ('80)	10.00	8.00
a.	2c pink, *blue*	11.00	8.00
U152	2c ver, *fawn* ('78)	10.00	4.00
Design U42			
U153	2c ver ('76)	75.00	30.00
U154	2c ver, *amb* ('76)	300.00	90.00
W155	2c ver, *man* ('76)	20.00	10.00
Design U43			
U156	2c ver ('81)	1,250.	175.00
U157	2c ver, *amb* ('81)	42,500.	27,500.
W158	2c ver, *man* ('81)	90.00	55.00
Design U44			
U159	3c green	35.00	10.00
U160	3c grn, *amb*	35.00	10.00
U161	3c grn, *cr*	35.00	12.00
+U162	3c grn, *bl*	75,000.	
Design U45			
U163	3c green	1.40	.30
U164	3c grn, *amb*	1.50	.70
U165	3c grn, *cr*	8.50	6.50
U166	3c grn, *bl*	7.50	6.00
U167	3c grn, *fawn* ('75)	4.75	3.50
Design U46			
U168	3c grn ('81)	1,000.	80.00
U169	3c grn, *amb*	450.00	140.00
U170	3c grn, *bl* ('81)	11,500.	2,750.
U171	3c grn, *fawn* ('81)	40,000.	2,750.
Design U47			
U172	5c bl, die I ('75)	10.00	10.00
U173	5c bl, die I, *amb* ('75)	12.50	11.00
U174	5c bl, die I, *cr* ('75)	95.00	45.00
U175	5c bl, die I, *bl* ('75)	22.50	17.50
U176	5c bl, die I, *fawn* ('75)	150.00	65.00
U177	5c bl, die 2 ('75)	11.00	9.00
U178	5c bl, die 2, *amb* ('75)	8.00	8.00
+U178A	5c bl, die 2, *cr* ('76)	10,000.	
U179	5c bl, die 2, *bl* ('75)	20.00	12.50
U180	5c bl, die 2, *fawn* ('75)	125.00	50.00
Design U48			
U181	6c red	8.00	6.50
a.	6c vermilion	8.00	6.50
U182	6c red, amber	12.50	6.50
a.	6c ver, amb	8.00	6.50
U183	6c red, cream	50.00	17.50
a.	6c ver, cr	45.00	15.00
U184	6c ver, *fawn* ('75)	17.50	12.50
Design U49			
+U185	7c vermilion	1,200.	
U186	7c ver, *amb*	125.00	75.00
Design U50			
U187	10c brown	40.00	20.00
U188	10c brn, *amb*	75.00	35.00

Design U51

U189	10c choc ('75)	6.00	4.00
a.	10c bister brown	7.00	5.00
b.	10c yellow ocher	3,000.	
U190	10c choc, *amb*	7.00	6.00
a.	10c bis brn, *amb*	7.00	6.00
b.	10c yel ocher, *amb*	3,000.	
U191	10c brn, *oriental buff* ('86)	12.50	8.75
U192	10c brn, *bl* ('86)	12.50	8.00
a.	10c gray blk, *bl*	12.50	7.50
b.	10c red brn, *bl*	12.50	7.50
U193	10c brn, *man* ('86)	12.50	10.00
a.	10c red brn, *man*	12.50	10.00
U194	10c brn, *amb man* ('86)	17.50	9.00
a.	10c red brn, *amb man*	17.50	9.00

Design U52

U195	12c plum	250.00	100.00
U196	12c plum, *amb*	200.00	160.00
U197	12c plum, *cr*	200.00	130.00

Design U53

U198	15c orange	50.00	35.00
U199	15c org, *amb*	140.00	130.00
U200	15c org, *cr*	450.00	300.00

Design U54

U201	24c purple	175.00	150.00
U202	24c pur, *amb*	180.00	100.00
U203	24c pur, *cr*	200.00	100.00

Design U55

U204	30c black	55.00	25.00
U205	30c blk, *amb*	70.00	60.00
U206	30c blk, *cr* ('75)	300.00	325.00
U207	30c blk, *oriental buff* ('81)	90.00	80.00
U208	30c blk, *bl* ('81)	90.00	80.00
U209	30c blk, *man* ('81)	80.00	70.00
U210	30c blk, *amb man* ('86)	190.00	100.00

Design U56

U211	90c car ('75)	80.00	75.00
U212	90c car, *amb* ('75)	175.00	250.00
U213	90c car, *cr* ('75)	1,000.	
U214	90c car, *oriental buff* ('86)	140.00	250.00
U215	90c car, *bl* ('86)	160.00	250.00
U216	90c car, *man* ('86)	120.00	225.00
U217	90c car, *amb man* ('86)	140.00	200.00

Note: No. U206 has watermark #2; No. U207 watermark #6 or #7. No U213 has watermark #2; No. U214 watermark #7. These envelopes cannot be positively identified except by the watermark.

Single line under "POSTAGE" U57

Double line under "POSTAGE" U58

1876

U218	U57	3c red	30.00	25.00
U219	U57	3c green	30.00	17.50
+U220	U58	3c red	27,500.	
U221	U58	3c green	30.00	25.00

Cent. of the U.S., and the World's Fair at Philadelphia.
Used examples of Nos. U218-U221 with exposition cancels and/or typed addresses sell for a premium.
See No. U582.

Garfield — U59

1882-86

U222	U59	5c brown	5.00	3.00
U223	U59	5c brn, *amb*	5.25	3.50
+U224	U59	5c brn, *oriental buff* ('86)	130.00	
+U225	U59	5c brn, *bl*	75.00	
U226	U59	5c brn, *fawn*	300.00	

Washington — U60

1883, October

U227	U60	2c red	5.50	2.25
a.		2c brown (error), entire	3,000.	
U228	U60	2c red, *amb*	6.50	2.75
U229	U60	2c red, *blue*	8.00	5.00
U230	U60	2c red, *fawn*	9.00	5.25

Wavy lines fine and clear — U61

1883, November
Four Wavy Lines in Oval

U231	U61	2c red	5.00	2.50
U232	U61	2c red, *amb*	6.00	3.75
U233	U61	2c red, *blue*	10.00	7.50
U234	U61	2c red, *fawn*	7.50	4.75
W235	U61	2c red, *man*	18.00	6.25

Wavy lines thick and blurred — U62

Retouched die.

1884, June

U236	U62	2c red	15.00	4.00
U237	U62	2c red, *amber*	20.00	10.00
U238	U62	2c red, *blue*	29.00	12.00
U239	U62	2c red, *fawn*	20.00	11.00

See Nos. U260-W269.

3½ links over left "2" — U63

U240	U63	2c red	90.00	45.00
U241	U63	2c red, *amb*	550.00	300.00
U242	U63	2c red, *fawn*	25,000.	

2 links below right "2" — U64

U243	U64	2c red	110.00	75.00
U244	U64	2c red, *amb*	250.00	100.00
U245	U64	2c red, *blue*	275.00	125.00
U246	U64	2c red, *fawn*	275.00	175.00

Round "O" in "TWO." White lines above "WO" of "TWO" joined to form thick white dash. — U65

U247	U65	2c red	1,500.	400.00
U248	U65	2c red, *amb*	2,500.	750.00
U249	U65	2c red, *fawn*	750.00	500.00

See Nos. U270-U276.

Jackson — U66

Die 1- Numeral at left is 2 ¾ mm wide

Die 2- Numeral at left is 3 ¼ mm wide

1883-86

U250	U66	4c green, die 1	4.00	3.50
U251	U66	4c grn, die 1, *amb*	5.00	3.50
U252	U66	4c grn, die 1, *oriental buff* ('86)	13.00	9.00
U253	U66	4c green, die 1, *blue* ('86)	11.00	6.50
U254	U66	4c grn, die 1, *man* ('86)	16.00	7.50
U255	U66	4c grn, die 1, *amb man* ('86)	22.50	10.00
U256	U66	4c green, die 2	8.00	5.00
U257	U66	4c grn, die 2, *amb*	12.50	7.00
U258	U66	4c grn, die 2, *man* ('86)	12.50	7.50
U259	U66	4c grn, die 2, *amb man* ('86)	12.50	7.50

1884, May

U260	U61	2c brown	17.50	5.75
U261	U61	2c brown, *amber*	17.50	6.50
U262	U61	2c brown, *blue*	17.50	10.00
U263	U61	2c brown, *fawn*	15.00	9.25
W264	U61	2c brown, *manila*	15.00	11.50

1884, June
Retouched Die

U265	U62	2c brown	15.00	6.50
U266	U62	2c brn, *amb*	60.00	40.00
U267	U62	2c brown, *blue*	22.50	9.00
U268	U62	2c brown, *fawn*	15.00	11.00
W269	U62	2c brn, *man*	25.00	15.00

2 Links Below Right "2"

U270	U64	2c brown	115.00	50.00
U271	U64	2c brn, *amb*	425.00	125.00
U272	U64	2c brown, *fawn*	7,000.	2,000.

Round "O" in "Two"

U273	U65	2c brown	225.00	100.00
U274	U65	2c brn, *amb*	225.00	100.00
U275	U65	2c brown, *blue*		10,000.
U276	U65	2c brown, *fawn*	700.00	750.00

U67

Extremity of bust below the queue forms a point.

Washington — U68

Extremity of bust is rounded.

Similar to U61
Two wavy lines in oval

1884-86

U277	U67	2c brown	.50	.25
a.		2c brown lake, die 1	22.50	21.00
U278	U67	2c brn, *amb*	.65	.50
a.		2c brown lake, amber	35.00	25.00
U279	U67	2c brn, *oriental buff* ('86)	6.00	2.10
U280	U67	2c brown, *blue*	3.00	2.10
U281	U67	2c brown, *fawn*	3.75	2.40
U282	U67	2c brown, *man* ('86)	12.00	4.00
W283	U67	2c brn, *man*	8.00	5.00
U284	U67	2c brn, *amb man* ('86)	7.00	5.75
+U285	U67	2c red	600.00	
+U286	U67	2c red, *blue*	225.00	
W287	U67	2c red, *manila*	150.00	
U288	U68	2c brown	325.00	50.00
U289	U68	2c brn, *amb*	20.00	13.00
U290	U68	2c brown, *blue*	850.00	325.00
U291	U68	2c brown, *fawn*	25.00	25.00
W292	U68	2c brn, *man*	30.00	19.00

Gen. U.S. Grant — US1

Letter Sheet, 160x271mm

1886   Creamy White Paper
U293	US1	2c green, entire	30.00	20.00

See the Scott U.S. Specialized Catalogue for perforation and inscription varieties.

Franklin — U69   Washington U70

Bust points between third and fourth notches of inner oval "G" of "POSTAGE" has no bar.

U71

Bust points between second and third notches of inner oval; "G" of "POSTAGE" has a bar; ear is indicated by one heavy line; one vertical line at corner of mouth.

U72

Frame same as U71; upper part of head more rounded; ear indicated by two curved lines with two locks of hair in front; two vertical lines at corner of mouth.

Jackson — U73   Grant — U74

There is a space between the beard and the collar of the coat. A button is on the collar.

U75

The collar touches the beard and there is no button.

1887-94		Design U69	
U294	1c blue	.55	.25
U295	1c dk bl ('94)	6.50	2.50
U296	1c bl, *amb*	3.25	1.25
U297	1c dk bl, *amb* ('94)	40.00	22.50
+U298	1c bl, *oriental buff*	7,000.	—
+U299	1c bl, *bl*	10,000.	
U300	1c bl, *man*	.65	.35
W301	1c bl, *man*	.45	.30
U302	1c dk bl, *man* ('94)	27.50	12.50
W303	1c DK bl, *man* ('94)	12.50	10.00
U304	1c bl, *amb man*	12.50	5.00
	Design U70		
U305	2c green	15.00	10.00
U306	2c grn, *amb*	40.00	17.50
U307	2c grn, *oriental buff*	80.00	40.00
U308	2c grn, *bl*	12,500.	4,250.
U309	2c grn, *man*	10,000.	1,000.
U310	2c grn, *amb man*	28,000.	4,000.
	Design U71		
U311	2c green	.30	.25
a.	2c dark green ('94)	.45	.30
b.	Double impression, entire	375.00	
U312	2c grn, *amb*	.40	.25
a.	Double impression	90.00	
b.	2c dk grn, *amb* ('94)	.55	.35
U313	2c grn, *oriental buff*	.55	.25
a.	2c dk grn, *oriental buff* ('94)	2.00	1.00
b.	Double impression	150.00	
U314	2c grn, *bl*	.60	.30
a.	2c dk grn, *bl* ('94)	.80	.40
U315	2c grn, *man*	2.00	.50
a.	2c dk grn, *man* ('94)	2.75	.75
W316	2c grn, *man*	3.50	2.50
U317	2c grn, *amb man*	2.50	1.90
a.	2c dk grn, *amb man* ('94)	3.50	3.00
	Design U72		
U318	2c green	110.00	12.50
U319	2c grn, *amb*	160.00	27.50
U320	2c grn, *oriental buff*	125.00	40.00
U321	2c grn, *bl*	150.00	70.00
U322	2c grn, *man*	225.00	70.00
U323	2c grn, *amb man*	400.00	100.00
	Design U73		
U324	4c carmine	3.25	2.00
a.	4c lake	3.50	2.00
b.	4c scarlet ('94)	3.50	2.00
U325	4c car, *amb*	3.50	3.50
a.	4c lake, *amber*	3.50	3.50
b.	4c scarlet, *amber* ('94)	4.00	3.75
U326	4c car, *oriental buff*	6.00	3.50
a.	4c lake, *oriental buff*	7.00	3.50
U327	4c car, *bl*	5.50	4.00
a.	4c lake, *blue*	6.00	4.00
U328	4c car, *man*	8.00	7.00
a.	4c lake, *manila*	8.00	6.00
b.	4c pink, *manila*	15.00	10.00
U329	4c car, *amb man*	6.00	3.25
a.	4c lake, *amb man*	6.00	3.25
b.	4c pink, *amb man*	15.00	10.00
	Design U74		
U330	5c blue	3.75	4.00
U331	5c bl, *amb*	6.00	2.50
a.	Double impression, entire	—	
U332	5c bl, *oriental buff*	6.50	4.00
U333	5c blue, *blue*	7.00	6.00
	Design U75		
U334	5c blue ('94)	20.00	12.50
U335	5c bl, *amb* ('94)	11.00	7.50
	Design U55		
U336	30c red brn	40.00	45.00
a.	30c yellow brown	40.00	45.00
b.	30c chocolate	40.00	45.00
U337	30c red brn, *amb*	40.00	45.00
a.	30c yel brn, *amb*	40.00	45.00
b.	30c choc, *amb*	40.00	45.00
U338	30c red brn, *oriental buff*	40.00	45.00
a.	30c yel brn, *oriental buff*	40.00	45.00
U339	30c red brn, *bl*	40.00	45.00
a.	30c yel brn, *bl*	40.00	45.00
U340	30c red brn, *man*	40.00	45.00
a.	30c brown, *manila*	40.00	45.00
U341	30c red brn, *amb man*	40.00	45.00
a.	30c yel brn, *amb man*	40.00	45.00
	Design U56		
U342	90c purple	55.00	85.00
U343	90c pur, *amb*	70.00	85.00
U344	90c pur, *oriental buff*	75.00	85.00
U345	90c pur, *bl*	75.00	85.00
U346	90c pur, *man*	80.00	85.00
U347	90c pur, *amb man*	80.00	85.00

Columbus and Liberty — U76

1893				
U348	U76	1c deep blue	2.00	1.25
U349	U76	2c violet	1.50	.50
a.		2c dark slate (error)	1,500.	
U350	U76	5c chocolate	6.50	7.00
a.		5c slate brown (error)	700.00	1,400.
U351	U76	10c slate brown	25.00	27.50
		Nos. U348-U351 (4)	35.00	36.25

Franklin — U77

Bust points to fourth notch of inner circle.

Washington — U78

Bust points to first notch of inner oval and is only slightly concave below.

U79

Bust points to middle of second notch of inner oval and is quite hollow below. Queue has ribbon around it.

U80

Same as die 2, but hair flowing. No ribbon on queue.

Lincoln — U81

Bust pointed but not draped.

U82

Bust broad and draped.

U83

Head larger, inner oval has no notches.

Grant — U84

Similar to design of 1887-95 but smaller.

1899				
U352	U77	1c green	2.75	.25
U353	U77	1c green, *amber*	5.00	1.50
U354	U77	1c green, *oriental buff*	10.00	2.75
U355	U77	1c green, *blue*	10.00	7.50
U356	U77	1c green, *manila*	2.50	.95
W357	U77	1c green, *manila*	2.75	1.10
U358	U78	2c carmine	3.00	1.75
U359	U78	2c car, *amb*	15.00	12.50
U360	U78	2c carmine, *oriental buff*	17.50	11.00
U361	U78	2c carmine, *blue*	55.00	35.00
U362	U79	2c carmine	.35	.25
a.		2c dark lake	30.00	30.00
U363	U79	2c car, *amb*	1.75	.25
U364	U79	2c carmine, *oriental buff*	1.20	.25
U365	U79	2c carmine, *blue*	1.50	.55
W366	U79	2c car, *man*	9.00	3.25
U367	U80	2c carmine	5.00	2.75
U368	U80	2c car, *amb*	8.00	6.50
U369	U80	2c carmine, *oriental buff*	17.50	12.50
U370	U80	2c carmine, *blue*	11.00	10.00
U371	U81	4c brown	15.00	12.50
U372	U81	4c brown, *amber*	15.00	12.50
U373	U82	4c brown	6,500.	1,000.
U374	U83	4c brown	10.00	8.00
U375	U83	4c brown, *amber*	60.00	25.00
W376	U83	4c brown, *manila*	12.50	12.50
U377	U84	5c blue	9.00	9.00
U378	U84	5c blue, *amber*	10.00	10.00

Franklin — U85

Washington — U86

"D" of "UNITED" contains vertical line at right that parallels the left vertical line. One short and two long vertical lines at the right of "CENTS."

Grant — U87

Lincoln — U88

1903				
U379	U85	1c green	.75	.25
U380	U85	1c green, *amber*	10.00	2.00
U381	U85	1c green, *oriental buff*	12.50	2.50
U382	U85	1c green, *blue*	15.00	2.50
U383	U85	1c green, *manila*	3.50	.90
W384	U85	1c green, *manila*	2.50	.40
a.		Double impression, entire letter sheet	275.00	
U385	U86	2c carmine	.40	.25
a.		2c pink	2.00	1.50
b.		2c red	2.00	1.50
U386	U86	2c carmine, *amber*	2.00	.50
a.		2c pink, *amber*	5.50	3.00
b.		2c red, *amber*	12.50	7.00
U387	U86	2c carmine, *oriental buff*	2.00	.30
a.		2c pink, *oriental buff*	3.50	2.00
b.		2c red, *oriental buff*	4.00	2.25
U388	U86	2c carmine, *blue*	1.75	.50
a.		2c pink, *blue*	17.50	14.00
b.		2c red, *blue*	17.50	14.00
W389	U86	2c carmine, *manila*	15.00	9.00
U390	U87	4c choc	17.50	11.00
U391	U87	4c choc, *amber*	17.50	11.00
W392	U87	4c choc, *manila*	20.00	12.50
U393	U88	5c blue	15.00	11.00
U394	U88	5c blue, *amber*	15.00	11.00

U89

Re-cut die — "D" of "UNITED" is well rounded at right. The three lines at the right of "CENTS" and at the left of "TWO" are usually all short; the lettering is heavier and the ends of the ribbons slightly changed.

1904			**Re-cut Die**	
U395	U89	2c carmine	.75	.25
a.		2c pink	5.00	2.50
U396	U89	2c carmine, *amber*	7.50	1.00
a.		2c pink, *amber*	8.50	3.00
U397	U89	2c carmine, *oriental buff*	5.00	1.10
a.		2c pink, *oriental buff*	6.50	2.75
U398	U89	2c carmine, *blue*	3.75	.90
a.		2c pink, *blue*	5.00	2.50
W399	U89	2c carmine, *manila*	12.50	8.00
a.		2c pink, *manila*	25.00	17.50
b.		Double impression, entire	375.00	

Franklin — U90

Die 1

Die 2

Die 3

Die 4

Die 1 — Wide "D" in "UNITED."
Die 2 — Narrow "D" in "UNITED."
Die 3 — Wide "S-S" in "STATES" (1910).
Die 4 — Sharp angle at back of bust, "N" and "E" of "ONE" are parallel (1912).

1907-16			**Die 1**	
U400	U90	1c green	.35	.25
a.		Die 2	.85	.25
b.		Die 3	.85	.55
c.		Die 4	.85	.25

U401	U90 1c green, *amber*	2.00	.40
a.	Die 2	2.50	1.00
b.	Die 3	3.25	3.00
c.	Die 4	2.00	1.00
U402	U90 1c green, *oriental buff*	9.00	.75
a.	Die 2	12.50	1.50
b.	Die 3	14.00	1.50
c.	Die 4	3.50	.75
U403	U90 1c green, *blue*	9.00	.75
a.	Die 2	12.50	3.00
b.	Die 3	11.50	3.00
c.	Die 4	.75	.65
U404	U90 1c green, *manila*	2.00	1.90
a.	Die 3	4.50	3.00
W405	U90 1c green, *manila*	.65	.25
a.	Die 2	60.00	25.00
b.	Die 3	11.00	4.00

Washington — U91 — brown red

Die 1, Washington — U91 — carmine

Die 2

Die 3

Die 4

Die 5

Die 6

Die 7

Die 8

Die 1 — Oval "O" in "TWO" and "C" in "CENTS." Front of bust broad.
Die 2 — Similar to 1 but hair re-cut in two distinct locks at top of head.
Die 3 — Round "O" in "TWO" and "C" in "CENTS," coarse lettering.
Die 4 — Similar to 3 but lettering fine and clear, hair lines clearly embossed. Inner oval thin and clear.
Die 5 — All "S's" wide (1910).
Die 6 — Similar to 1 but front of bust narrow (1913).
Die 7 — Similar to 6 but upper corner of front of bust cut away (1916).
Die 8 — Similar to 7 but lower stroke of "S" in "CENTS" is a straight line. Hair as in Die 2 (1916).

Die 1

U406	U91 2c brown red	.90	.25
a.	Die 2	40.00	7.00
b.	Die 3	.80	.25
U407	U91 2c brown red, *amber*	6.50	2.00
a.	Die 2	350.00	65.00
b.	Die 3	4.50	1.25
U408	U91 2c brown red, *oriental buff*	8.75	1.50
a.	Die 2	275.00	125.00
b.	Die 3	7.50	2.50
U409	U91 2c brn red, *blue*	5.75	2.00
a.	Die 2	375.00	200.00
b.	Die 3	5.75	1.75
W410	U91 2c brn red, *man*	35.00	35.00
U411	U91 2c carmine	.35	.25
a.	Die 2	.75	.25
b.	Die 3	.75	.25
c.	Die 4	.65	.25
d.	Die 5	.65	.30
e.	Die 6	.60	.25
f.	Die 7	3.00	3.00
g.	Die 8	37.50	25.00
h.	#U411 with added impression of #U400, entire	475.00	
i.	#U411 with added impression of #U416a, entire	475.00	
k.	As No. U411, double impression, entire	175.00	
U412	U91 2c carmine, *amb*	.50	.25
a.	Die 2	1.00	.25
b.	Die 3	2.25	2.00
c.	Die 4	.55	.25
d.	Die 5	.90	.35
e.	Die 6	.70	.25
f.	Die 7	35.00	25.00
U413	U91 2c car, *oriental buff*	.55	.25
a.	Die 2	2.00	.45
b.	Die 3	9.00	3.00
c.	Die 4	.55	1.00
d.	Die 5	3.50	1.25
e.	Die 6	1.00	.70
f.	Die 7	100.00	45.00
g.	Die 8	25.00	17.50
U414	U91 2c carmine, *blue*	.55	.25
a.	Die 2	1.00	1.00
b.	Die 3	2.75	2.00
c.	Die 4	.50	.50
d.	Die 5	1.00	.45
e.	Die 6	.65	.30
f.	Die 7	37.50	25.00
g.	Die 8	37.50	25.00
W415	U91 2c car, *manila*	5.00	2.00
a.	Die 2	5.50	1.25
b.	Die 3	5.50	2.50
c.	Die 7	120.00	97.50

U90 4c Die 1   U90 4c Die 2

Die 1 — "F" close to (1mm) left "4."

Die 2 — "F" far from (1¾mm) left "4."

U416	U90 4c black, die 2, laid paper	2.00	1.50
a.	Die 1	1.50	2.00
U417	U90 4c black, *amb*, die 2	7.50	2.50
a.	Die 1	.75	2.00

Die 1 — Tall "F" in "FIVE"   Die 2 — Short "F" in "FIVE"

U418	U91 5c Die 2	1.50	1.50
a.	Die 1	7.00	2.25
b.	5c blue, *buff*, die 2 (error)	3,250.	
c.	5c blue, *blue*, die 2 (error)	3,000.	
d.	As "c," die 1 (error), entire	6,250.	
U419	U91 5c blue, *amber*, die 2, laid paper	1.00	.75
a.	Die 1	15.00	12.00

Franklin — U92

Die 1   Die 2

Die 3   Die 4   Die 5

(The 1c and 4c dies are the same except for figures of value.)
Die 1 — UNITED nearer inner circle than outer circle.
Die 2 — Large U; large NT closely spaced.
Die 3 — Knob of hair at back of neck. Large NT widely spaced.
Die 4 — UNITED nearer outer circle than inner circle.
Die 5 — Narrow oval C, (also O and G).

1915-32   **Die 1**

U420	U92 1c green ('17)	.25	.25
a.	Die 2	100.00	55.00
b.	Die 3	.35	.25
c.	Die 4	.55	.40
d.	Die 5	.45	.35
U421	U92 1c grn, *amber* ('17)	.55	.30
a.	Die 2	400.00	175.00
b.	Die 3	1.40	.65
c.	Die 4	1.90	.85
d.	Die 5	1.10	.55
U422	U92 1c grn, *oriental buff* ('17)	2.40	.90
a.	Die 4	5.50	1.25
U423	U92 1c grn, *bl* ('17)	.50	.35
a.	Die 3	.80	.45
b.	Die 4	1.40	.65
c.	Die 5	.85	.35
U424	U92 1c grn, *manila* (unglazed) ('16)	6.50	4.00
W425	U92 1c grn, *manila* (unglazed) ('16)	.30	.25
a.	Die 3	175.00	125.00
U426	U92 1c grn, *brown* (glazed) ('20)	45.00	16.00
W427	U92 1c grn, *brown* (glazed) ('20)	65.00	35.00
a.	Printed on unglazed side	400.00	
	Entire	750.00	
b.	Unglazed on both sides		150.00
U428	U92 1c grn, *brown* (unglazed) ('20)		
W428A	U92 1c grn, *brown* (unglazed) ('20)	12.50	7.50
		3,000.	

Washington — U93

Die 1

Die 2

Die 3

Die 4

Die 5

Die 6

Die 7

Die 8

Die 9

(The 1½c, 2c, 3c, 5c, and 6c dies are the same except for figures of value.)

Die 1 — Letters broad. Numerals vertical. Large head (9¼mm). from tip of nose to back of neck. E closer to inner circle than N of cents.

Die 2 — Similar to 1; but U far from left circle.

Die 3 — Similar to 2; but all inner circles very thin (Rejected die).

Die 4 — Large head as in Die 1. C of CENTS close to circle. Baseline of right numeral "2" slants downward to right. Left numeral "2" is larger.

Die 5 — Small head (8¾mm) from tip of nose to back of neck. T and S of CENTS close at bottom.

Die 6 — Similar to 5; but T and S of CENTS far apart at bottom. Left numeral slopes to right.

Die 7 — Large head. Both numerals slope to right. Clean cut lettering. All letters T have short top strokes.

Die 8 — Similar to 7; but all letters T have long top strokes.

Die 9 — Narrow oval C (also O and G).

1915-32 **Die 1**

U429	U93 2c carmine	.25	.25
a.	Die 2	15.00	7.00
b.	Die 3	40.00	50.00
c.	Die 4	25.00	15.00
d.	Die 5	.55	.35
e.	Die 6	.65	.30
f.	Die 7	.70	.25
g.	Die 8	.50	.25
h.	Die 9	.50	.25
i.	2c green (error), die 1, entire	12,500.	
j.	#U429 with added impression of #U420	600.00	
k.	#U429 with added impression of #U416a, entire	3,500.	
l.	#U429 with added impression of #U400, entire	950.00	
m.	#U429, double impression, entire	1,500.	
n.	As "f," double impression, entire	750.00	
o.	As "e," triple impression	—	
p.	As "m," second impression on side flap, entire		250.00
U430	U93 2c car, amber ('16)	.30	.25
a.	Die 2	20.00	12.50
b.	Die 4	50.00	25.00
c.	Die 5	1.60	.35
d.	Die 6	1.25	.40
e.	Die 7	.75	.35
f.	Die 8	.70	.30
g.	Die 9	.65	.25
h.	As No. U430, with added impression of 4c black (#U416a), entire	600.00	
i.	As "g," with added impression of 2c car. die 1 on side flap, entire	—	
U431	U93 2c car, oriental buff ('16)	2.25	.65
a.	Die 2	180.00	75.00
b.	Die 4	75.00	60.00
c.	Die 5	3.50	2.00
d.	Die 6	3.50	2.00
e.	Die 7	3.50	2.00
U432	U93 2c car, blue ('16)	.30	.25
b.	Die 2	35.00	25.00
c.	Die 3	130.00	90.00
d.	Die 4	60.00	50.00
e.	Die 5	1.10	.30
f.	Die 6	1.10	.40
g.	Die 7	.85	.35
h.	Die 8	.65	.25
i.	Die 9	1.00	.30
j.	2c purple (error), die 9	—	
k.	Double impression	650.00	
U432A	U93 2c car, manila, die 7, entire	50,000.	
W433	U93 2c car, manila, ('16)	.25	.25
W434	U93 2c car, brn (glazed) ('20)	70.00	45.00
W435	U93 2c car, brn (unglazed) ('20)	90.00	60.00
U436	U93 3c purple ('32)	.30	.25
a.	3c dark violet, die 1 ('17)	.60	.25
b.	3c dark violet, die 5 ('17)	1.75	.75
c.	3c dark violet, die 6 ('17)	2.10	1.40
d.	3c dark violet, die 7 ('17)	1.50	.95
e.	3c purple, die 7 ('32)	.70	.30
f.	3c purple, die 9 ('32)	.45	.25
g.	3c carmine (error), die 1	35.00	35.00
h.	3c carmine (error), die 5	27.50	—
i.	#U436 with added impression of #U420, entire	900.00	
j.	#U436 with added impression of #U429, entire	900.00	950.00
k.	As "f," double impression, preprinted, entire	600.00	
U437	U93 3c purple, amb ('32)	.35	.25
a.	3c dk vio, die 1 ('17)	5.50	1.25
b.	3c dk vio, die 5 ('17)	8.50	2.50
c.	3c dk vio, die 6 ('17)	8.50	2.50
d.	3c dk vio, die 7 ('17)	8.50	2.25
e.	3c pur, die 7 ('32)	.75	.25
f.	3c pur, die 9 ('32)	.55	.25
g.	3c carmine (error), die 5	375.00	400.00
h.	3c black (error), die 1	190.00	—
U438	U93 3c dk vio, *oriental buff* ('17)	22.50	5.50
a.	Die 5	22.50	5.50
b.	Die 6	30.00	8.00
c.	Die 7	30.00	10.00
U439	U93 3c purple, *bl* ('32)	.35	.25
a.	3c dark violet, die 1 ('17)	7.00	2.00
b.	3c dark violet, die 5 ('17)	7.50	6.00
c.	3c dark violet, die 6 ('17)	7.50	6.00
d.	3c dark violet, die 7 ('17)	10.00	6.00
e.	3c purple, die 7 ('32)	.75	.25
f.	3c purple, die 9 ('32)	.60	.25
g.	3c carmine (error), die 5	225.00	300.00
U440	U92 4c black ('18)	1.75	.60
a.	With added impression of 2c carmine (#U429), die 1, entire	450.00	
U441	U92 4c black, *amb* ('18)	3.00	.85
a.	4c black, *amb*, with added impression of 2c car (#U429), die 1	175.00	
U442	U92 4c blk, *bl* ('21)	3.25	.85
U443	U93 5c blue ('18)	3.25	2.75
U444	U93 5c blue, *amber* ('18)	4.00	1.60
U445	U93 5c bl, *blue* ('21)	3.25	3.25

For 1½c and 6c see Nos. U481-W485, U529-U531.

Double or triple surcharge listings of 1920-25 are for examples with surcharge directly or partly upon the stamp.

Surcharged on 1874-1920 Envelopes indicated by Numbers in Parentheses

Type 1

1920-21 **Surcharged in Black**

U446	U93 2c on 3c dark vio (U436a, die 1)	11.00	10.00
a.	On No. U436b (die 5)	11.00	10.00
a.	As U446, double surcharge	140.00	

Surcharged

Type 2

Rose Surcharge

U447	U93 2c on 3c dark vio (U436a)	8.00	7.50
b.	On No. U436c (die 6)	10.00	8.50

Black Surcharge

U447A	U92 2c on 1c green (U420, die 1) Entire	3,000.	
U447C	U93 2c on 2c carmine (U429, die 1)	—	
U447D	U93 2c on 2c car, amb (U430, die 1)	12,000.	
U448	U93 2c on 3c dark vio (U436a, die 1)	2.75	2.00
a.	On No. U436b (die 5)	2.75	2.00
b.	On No. U436c (die 6)	3.50	2.00
c.	On No. U436d (die 7)	2.75	2.00
U449	U93 2c on 3c dk vio, amb (U437a, die 1)	6.50	6.00
a.	On No. U437b (die 5)	13.00	7.50
b.	On No. U437c (die 6)	9.50	6.00
c.	On No. U437d (die 7)	8.50	6.50
U450	U93 2c on 3c dk vio, *oriental buff* (U438, die 1)	12.50	15.00
a.	On No. U438a (die 5)	15.00	15.00
b.	On No. U438b (die 6)	15.00	15.00
c.	On No. U438c (die 7)	130.00	90.00
U451	U93 2c on 3c dk vio, *blue* (U439a, die 1)	11.00	10.50
b.	On No. U439b (die 5)	11.00	10.50
c.	On No. U439c (die 6)	11.00	10.50
d.	On No. U439d (die 7)	22.50	22.50

Surcharged

Type 3

Bars 2mm apart, 25 to 26mm in length from outer edges of end bars

U451A	U90 2c on 1c green (U400, die 1)	25,000.	
U452	U92 2c on 1c green (U420, die 1)	1,750.	
a.	On No. U420b (die 3)	3,000.	
b.	As No. U452, double surcharge	3,750.	
U453	U91 2c on 2c car (U411b, die 3)	3,500.	
a.	On No. U411 (die 1)	3,250.	
U453B	U91 2c on 2c car, *bl* (U414e, die 6)	1,250.	750.00
U453C	U91 2c on 2c car, *oriental buff* (U413e, die 6)	1,400.	750.00
d.	On No. U413 (die 1)	1,400.	
U454	U93 2c on 2c car (U429e, die 6)	125.00	
a.	On No. U429 (die 1)	300.00	
b.	On No. U429d (die 6)	500.00	
c.	On No. U429f (die 7)	125.00	
U455	U93 2c on 2c car, *amb* (U430, die 1)	1,250.	
a.	On No. U430d (die 6)	1,500.	
b.	On No. U430e (die 7)	1,500.	
U456	U93 2c on 2c car, *oriental buff* (U431a, die 2)	225.00	
a.	On No. U431c (die 5)	225.00	
b.	On No. U431e (die 7)	800.00	
c.	As No. U456, double surcharge	700.00	
U457	U93 2c on 2c car, *bl* (U432f, die 6)	325.00	
a.	On No. U432e (die 5)	275.00	
b.	On No. U432g (die 7)	650.00	
U458	U93 2c on 3c dark vio (U436a, die 1)	.50	.35
a.	On No. U436b (die 5)	.50	.40
b.	On No. U436c (die 6)	.50	.35
c.	On No. U436d (die 7)	.50	.35
d.	As #U458, double surcharge	25.00	7.50
e.	As #U458, triple surcharge	90.00	
f.	As #U458, dbl. surch. 1 in magenta	90.00	
g.	As #U458, dbl. surch., types 2 & 3	140.00	
h.	As "a," double surcharge	27.50	15.00
i.	As "a," triple surcharge	110.00	
j.	As "a," double surch., both magenta	110.00	
k.	As "b," double surcharge	25.00	8.00
l.	As "c," double surcharge	25.00	8.00
m.	As "c," triple surcharge	110.00	
n.	Double impression of indicia, single surcharge, entire	450.00	
U459	U93 2c on 3c dk vio, *amb* (U437c, die 6)	3.00	1.00
a.	On No. U437a (die 1)	4.00	1.00
b.	On No. U437b (die 5)	4.00	1.00
c.	On No. U437d (die 7)	3.00	1.00
d.	As #U459, double surcharge	35.00	
e.	As "a," double surcharge	35.00	
f.	As "b," double surcharge	35.00	
g.	As "b," double surcharge, types 2 & 3	125.00	
h.	As "c," double surcharge	35.00	
U460	U93 2c on 3c dk vio, *oriental buff* (U438a, die 5)	3.50	2.00
a.	On No. U438 (die 1)	3.50	2.00
b.	On No. U438b (die 6)	4.00	2.00
c.	As #U460, double surcharge	20.00	
d.	As "a," double surcharge	20.00	
e.	As "b," double surcharge	20.00	
f.	As "b," triple surcharge	150.00	
U461	U93 2c on 3c dk vio, *bl* (U439a, die 1)	6.00	1.00
a.	On No. U439b (die 5)	6.00	1.00
b.	On No. U439c (die 6)	6.00	2.50
c.	On No. U439d (die 7)	12.50	7.50
d.	As #U461, double surcharge	17.50	
e.	As "a," double surcharge	17.50	
f.	As "b," double surcharge	17.50	
g.	As "c," double surcharge	17.50	
U462	U87 2c on 4c choc (U390)	475.00	260.00
U463	U87 2c on 4c choc, *amb* (U391)	750.00	350.00
U463A	U90 2c on 4c black (U416, die 2)	800.00	400.00
U464	U93 2c on 5c blue (U443)	850.00	

Surcharged

Type 4

Bars 1 mm apart, 21 to 23 mm in length from outer edges of end bars

U465	U92 2c on 1c green (U420, die 1)	900.00	
a.	On No. U420b (die 3)	1,100.	
U466	U91 2c on 2c car (U411e, die 6), entire	22,500.	
U466A	U93 2c on 2c carmine (U429, die 1)	700.00	
c.	On No. U429d (die 6)	900.00	
d.	On No. U429e (die 6)	900.00	
f.	On No. U429f (die 7)	750.00	
U466B	U93 2c on 2c car, *amb* (U430)	15,000.	
U466C	U93 2c on 2c car, *oriental buff* (U431), entire	15,000.	
U466D	U25 2c on 3c green, die 2 (U82)	7,500.	
U467	U45 2c on 3c green, die 2 (U163)	325.00	
U468	U93 2c on 3c dark vio (U436a, die 1)	.70	.45
a.	On No. U436b (die 5)	.70	.50
b.	On No. U436c (die 6)	.70	.50
c.	On No. U436d (die 7)	.70	.50
d.	As #U468, double surcharge	20.00	
e.	As #U468, triple surcharge	90.00	
f.	As #U468, dbl. surch., types 2 & 4	125.00	
g.	As "a," double surcharge	20.00	
h.	As "b," double surcharge	20.00	
i.	As "c," double surcharge	20.00	

j.	As "c," triple surcharge	100.00	
k.	As "c," inverted surcharge	75.00	
l.	2c on 3c carmine (error), (U436h)	600.00	
m.	As #U468, triple surcharge, one inverted, entire		700.00

U469 U93 2c on 3c dk vio, *amb* (U437a, die 1) — 3.75 / 2.25
a.	On No. U437c (die 5)	3.75	2.25
b.	On No. U437c (die 6)	3.75	2.25
c.	On No. U437d (die 7)	3.75	2.25
d.	As #U469, double surcharge	30.00	
e.	As "a," double surcharge	30.00	
f.	As "a," double surcharge, types 2 & 4	100.00	
g.	As "b," double surcharge	30.00	
h.	As "c," double surcharge	30.00	

U470 U93 2c on 3c dk vio, *oriental buff* (U438, die 1) — 6.00 / 2.50
a.	On No. U438a (die 5)	6.00	2.50
b.	On No. U438b (die 6)	6.00	2.50
c.	On No. U438c (die 7)	42.50	32.50
d.	As #U470, double surcharge	25.00	
e.	As #U470, double surch., types 2 & 4	80.00	
f.	As "a," double surcharge	25.00	
g.	As "b," double surcharge	25.00	

U471 U93 2c on 3c dk vio, *bl* (U439a, die 1) — 6.00 / 1.75
a.	On No. U439b (die 5)	7.00	1.75
b.	On No. U439c (die 6)	7.00	1.75
c.	On No. U439d (die 7)	10.00	10.00
d.	As #U471, double surcharge	25.00	
e.	As #U471, double surch., types 2 & 4	160.00	
f.	As "a," double surcharge	25.00	
g.	As "b," double surcharge	25.00	

U471A U83 2c on 4c brown, (U374), entire — 625.00

U472 U87 2c on 4c choc (U390) — 11.00 / 11.00
a.	Double surcharge	150.00	

U473 U87 2c on 4c choc, *amb* (U391) — 17.00 / 10.00

Surcharged

Double Surcharge, Type 4 and 1c as above

U474 U93 2c on 1c on 3c dark violet (U436a, die 1) — 175. / 500.
a.	On No. U436b (die 5)	200.	
b.	On No. U436d (die 7)	850.	

U475 U93 2c on 1c on 3c dk vio, *amb* (U437a, die 1) — 150.

Surcharged

Type 5

U476 U93 2c on 3c dk vio, *amb* (U437a, die 1) — 200.
a.	On No. U437c (die 6)	700.	
b.	As #U476, double surcharge	—	

Surcharged

Type 6

U477 U93 2c on 3c dark vio (U436a, die 1) — 120.
a.	On No. U436b (die 5)	250.	
b.	On No. U436c (die 6)	250.	
c.	On No. U436d (die 7)	250.	

U478 U93 2c on 3c dk vio, *amb* (U437a, die 1) — 250.

Handstamped Surcharge in Black or Violet — Type 7

U479 U93 2c on 3c dark violet (Bk) (U436a, die 1) — 240. / —
a.	On No. U436b (die 5)	625.	
b.	On No. U436d (die 7)	425.	

U480 U93 2c on 3c dark violet (V) (U436d, die 7) — *4,500.*
a.	Double overprint	—	

Expertization by competent authorities is required for Nos. U476-U480.

Type of 1916-32 Issue

1925-34			**Die 1**
U481	U93 1½c brown	.25	.25
a.	Die 8	.70	.25
b.	1½c purple, die 1 (error) ('34)	55.00	
U482	U93 1½c brown, *amber*	.90	.40
a.	Die 8	1.75	.75
U483	U93 1½c brown, *bl*	1.60	.95
a.	Die 8	2.40	1.25
U484	U93 1½c brown, *manila*	5.00	3.00
W485	U93 1½c brown, *manila*	.85	.25
a.	With added impression of #W433	120.00	—

Surcharged Type 8

1925	**On Envelopes of 1887**		
U486	U71 1½c on 2c grn (U311)	500.00	
U487	U71 1½c on 2c green, *amb* (U312)	900.00	
U488	U77 1½c on 1c green (U352)	500.00	
U489	U77 1½c on 1c grn, *amb* (U353)	110.00	60.
U490	U90 1½c on 1c green (U400, die 1)	6.25	3.50
a.	On No. U400a (die 2)	15.00	9.00
b.	On No. U400b (die 3)	35.00	17.50
c.	On No. U400c (die 4)	9.00	2.50
U491	U90 1½c on 1c grn, *amb* (U401c, die 4)	7.00	3.00
a.	On No. U401 (die 1)	12.50	3.50
b.	On No. U401a (die 2)	110.00	70.00
c.	On No. U401b (die 3)	60.00	50.00
U492	U90 1½c on 1c grn, *oriental buff* (U402a, die 2)	500.00	150.00
a.	On No. U402c (die 4)	700.00	250.00
U493	U90 1½c on 1c grn, *bl* (U403c, die 4)	100.00	65.00
a.	On No. U403a (die 2)	100.00	67.50
U494	U90 1½c on 1c grn, *man* (U404, die 1)	250.00	100.00
a.	On No. U404a (die 3)	950.00	
U495	U92 1½c on 1c green (U420, die 1)	.80	.25
a.	On No. U420a (die 2)	80.00	52.50
b.	On No. U420b (die 3)	2.10	.70
c.	On No. U420c (die 4)	2.10	.85

d.	As #U495, double surcharge	10.00	3.00
e.	As "b," double surcharge	10.00	3.00
f.	As "c," double surcharge	10.00	3.00

U496 U92 1½c on 1c grn, *amb* (U421, die 1) — 15.00 / 12.50
a.	On No. U421b (die 3)	725.00	
b.	On No. U421c (die 4)	15.00	12.50

U497 U92 1½c on 1c grn, *oriental buff* (U422, die 1) — 3.75 / 1.90
a.	On No. U422b (die 4)	67.50	

U498 U92 1½c on 1c grn, *bl* (U423c, die 4) — 1.40 / .75
a.	On No. U423 (die 1)	2.40	1.50
b.	On No. U423b (die 3)	1.75	1.50

U499 U92 1½c on 1c grn, *man* (U424) — 8.00 / 6.00

U500 U92 1½c on 1c grn, *brn* (unglazed) (U428) — 60.00 / 30.00

U501 U92 1½c on 1c grn, *brn* (glazed) (U426) — 65.00 / 30.00

U502 U93 1½c on 2c car (U429, die 1) — 200.00 / —
a.	On No. U429d (die 5)	250.00	
b.	On No. U429f (die 7)	250.00	
c.	On No. U429e (die 6)	325.00	
d.	On No. U429g (die 8)	450.00	

U503 U93 1½c on 2c car, *oriental buff* (U431c, die 5) — 200.00 / —
a.	Double surcharge	200.00	—
b.	Double surcharge, one inverted	700.00	

U504 U93 1½c on 2c car, *bl* (U432, die 1) — 300.00 / —
a.	On No. U432g (die 7)	300.00	
b.	As "a," double surcharge, entire	350.00	
c.	On No. U432f (die 6), entire	400.00	

U505 U93 1½c on 1½c brn (U481, die 1) — 300.00 / —
a.	On No. U481a (die 8)	300.00	
b.	As No. U505, double surcharge, entire	2,000.	

U506 U93 1½c on 1½c brn, *bl* (U483a, die 8) — 200.00 / —
a.	On No. U483 (die 1)	300.00	

The paper of No. U500 is not glazed and appears to be the same as that used for the wrappers of 1900.

Surcharged Type 9

Black Surcharge

U507 U69 1½c on 1c blue (U294) — 1,750.

U507B U69 1½c on 1c blue, *manila* (U300) — 4,750.

U508 U77 1½c on 1c grn, *amb* (U353) — 55.00

U508A U85 1½c on 1c grn (U379) — 2,750.

U509 U85 1½c on 1c grn, *amb* (U380) — 12.50 / 10.00
a.	Double surcharge	75.00	

U509B U85 1½c on 1c green, *oriental buff* (U381) — 40.00 / 40.00

U510 U90 1½c on 1c green (U400, die 1) — 2.75 / 1.25
b.	On No. U400a (die 2)	9.00	4.00
c.	On No. U400b (die 3)	37.50	8.00
d.	On No. U400c (die 4)	3.50	1.25
e.	As No. U510, double surcharge	25.00	

U511 U90 1½c on 1c grn, *amb* (U401, die 1) — 200.00 / 100.00

U512 U90 1½c on 1c grn, *oriental buff* (U402, die 1) — 7.00 / 4.00
a.	On No. U402c (die 4)	21.00	14.00

U513 U90 1½c on 1c grn, *bl* (U403, die 1) — 6.00 / 4.00
a.	On No. U403c (die 4)	6.00	4.00

U514 U90 1½c on 1c grn, *man* (U404, die 1) — 30.00 / 9.00
a.	On No. U404a (die 3)	77.50	40.00

U515 U92 1½c on 1c green (U420, die 1) — .40 / .25
a.	On No. U420a (die 2)	15.00	15.00
b.	On No. U420b (die 3)	.40	.25
c.	On No. U420c (die 4)	.40	.25
d.	As #U515, double surcharge	10.00	
e.	As #U515, inverted surcharge	15.00	
f.	As #U515, triple surcharge	15.00	
g.	As #U515, dbl. surch., one invtd., entire	—	
h.	As "b," double surcharge	10.00	
i.	As "b," inverted surcharge	15.00	
j.	As "b," triple surcharge	25.00	
k.	As "c," double surcharge	10.00	
l.	As "c," inverted surcharge	15.00	

U516 U92 1½c on 1c grn, *amb* (U421c, die 4) — 50.00 / 27.50
a.	On No. U421 (die 1)	55.00	32.50

U517 U92 1½c on 1c grn, *oriental buff* (U422, die 1) — 6.25 / 1.25
a.	On No. U422a (die 4)	7.25	1.50

U518 U92 1½c on 1c grn, *bl* (U423b, die 4) — 5.00 / 1.50
a.	On No. U423 (die 1)	8.25	4.50
b.	On No. U423a (die 3)	27.50	7.50
c.	As "a," double surcharge	30.00	

U519 U92 1½c on 1c grn, *man* (U424, die 1) — 25.00 / 12.00
a.	Double surcharge	100.00	

U520 U93 1½c on 2c car (U429, die 1) — 300.00 / —
a.	On No. U429d (die 5)	275.00	
b.	On No. U429e (die 6)	275.00	
c.	On No. U429f (die 7)	275.00	

U520D U93 1½c on 2c car, *amber* (U430c, die 5), entire — —

U520E U92 1½c on 4c black (U440, die 1), entire — —

Magenta Surcharge

U521 U92 1½c on 1c grn (U420b, die 3) — 4.25 / 3.50
a.	Double surcharge	75.00	

Sesquicentennial Exposition Issue

150th anniversary of the Declaration of Independence.

Liberty Bell — U94

Die 1. The center bar of "E" of "postage" is shorter than top bar.

Die 2. The center bar of "E" of "postage" is of same length as top bar.

1926, July 27

U522 U94 2c carmine, die 1 — 1.00 / .50
a.	Die 2	5.50	3.75

Washington Bicentennial Issue

200th anniversary of the birth of George Washington.

Mount Vernon — U95

2c Die 1 — "S" of "Postage" normal.
2c Die 2 — "S" of "Postage" raised.

1932

U523	U95	1c olive green	1.00	.80
U524	U95	1½c chocolate	2.00	1.50
U525	U95	2c car, die 1	.40	.25
a.		2c carmine, die 2	60.00	20.00
b.		2c carmine, *blue,* die 1 (error) entire	30,000.	
U526	U95	3c violet	1.75	.35
U527	U95	4c black	15.00	17.50
U528	U95	5c dark blue	3.50	3.50
	Nos. U523-U528 (6)		23.65	23.90

Type of 1916-32 Issue

1932, Aug. 18

U529	U93	6c orange, die 7	6.00	4.00
U530	U93	6c orange, *amber,* die 7	10.00	10.00
U531	U93	6c orange, *blue,* die 7	10.00	10.00

Franklin — U96

Die 1   Die 2

Die 3

Die 1 — Short (3½mm) and thick "I" in thick circle.
Die 2 — Tall (4½mm) and thin "1" in thin circle; upper and lower bars of E in ONE long and 1mm from circle.
Die 3 — As in Die 2, but E normal and 1½mm from circle.

1950

U532	U96	1c green, die 1	5.00	1.75
a.		Die 2	6.50	3.00
b.		Die 3	6.50	3.00
		Precanceled, die 3		1.25

Washington — U97

Die 1   Die 2

Die 3   Die 4

Die 1 — Thick "2" in thick circle; toe of "2" is acute angle.
Die 2 — Thin "2" in thin circle; toe of "2" is almost right angle; line through left stand of "N" in UNITED and stand of "E" in POSTAGE goes considerably below tip of chin; "N" of UNITED is tall; "O" of TWO is high.
Die 3 — Figure "2" as in Die 2. Short UN in UNITED thin crossbar in A of STATES.
Die 4 — Tall UN in UNITED; thick crossbar in A of STATES; otherwise like Die 3.

U533	U97	2c carmine, die 3	.70	.25
a.		Die 1	.80	.30
b.		Die 2	1.40	.85
c.		Die 4	1.30	.60

Die 1   Die 2

Die 3

Die 4   Die 5

Die 1 — Thick and tall (4½mm) "3" in thick circle; long top bars and short stems in T's of STATES.
Die 2 — Thin and tall (4½mm) "3" in medium circle; short top bars and long stems in T's of STATES.
Die 3 — Thin and short (4mm) "3" in thin circle; lettering wider than Dies 1 and 2; line from left stand of N to stand of E is distinctly below tip of chin.
Die 4 — Figure and letters as in Die 3. Line hits tip of chin; short N in UNITED and thin crossbar in A of STATES.
Die 5 — Figure, letter and chin line as in Die 4; but tall N in UNITED and thick crossbar in A of STATES.

U534	U97	3c dark violet, die 4	.35	.25
a.		Die 1	1.90	.70
b.		Die 2	.75	.50
c.		Die 3	.55	.25
d.		Die 5	.75	.45
e.		As "c," double impression	300.00	

Washington — U98

1952

U535	U98	1½c brown	4.50	3.50
		Precanceled		1.25

Die 1   Die 2

Die 3

Die 1 — Head high in oval (2mm below T of STATES). Circle near (1mm) bottom of colored oval.
Die 2 — Head low in oval (3mm). Circle 1½mm from edge of oval. Right leg of A in POSTAGE shorter than left. Short leg on P.
Die 3 — Head centered in oval (2½mm). Circle as in Die 2. Legs of A of POSTAGE about equal. Long leg on P.

1958

U536	U96	4c red violet, die 1	.75	.25
a.		Die 2	.90	.25
b.		Die 3	.90	.25

Nos. U429, U429f, U429h, U533, U533a-U533c Surcharged in Red at Left of Stamp

1958

U537	U93	2c + 2c carmine, die 1	3.25	1.50
a.		Die 7	10.00	7.00
b.		Die 9	4.75	5.00
U538	U97	2c + 2c carmine, die 1	.70	.80
a.		Die 2	.90	1.00
b.		Die 3	.70	.70
c.		Die 4	.70	1.00

Nos. U436a, U436e-U436f, U534, U534b-U534d Surcharged in Green at Left of Stamp

U539	U93	3c + 1c purple, die 1	12.50	9.00
a.		Die 7	11.00	7.50
b.		Die 9	17.50	15.00
U540	U97	3c + 1c dark violet, die 3	.40	1.00
a.		Die 2, entire	3,500.	—
b.		Die 4	.65	1.00
c.		Die 5	.70	1.00

Benjamin Franklin — U99

George Washington U100

Die 1

Die 2

Dies of 1¼c
Die 1 — The "4" is 3mm high. Upper leaf in left cluster is 2mm from "U."
Die 2 — The "4" is 3½mm high. Leaf clusters are larger. Upper leaf at left is 1mm from "U."

1960

U541	U99	1¼c turquoise, die 1	.65	.50
		Die 1, precanceled		.25
a.		Die 2, precanceled		1.25
U542	U100	2½c dull blue	.80	.50
		Precanceled		.25

Precanceled cut squares

Precanceled envelopes do not normally receive another cancellation. Since the lack of a cancellation makes it impossible to distinguish between cut squares from used and unused envelopes, they are valued here as used only.

Pony Express Centennial Issue

Pony Express Rider — U101

Envelope White Outside, Blue Inside.

1960

U543	U101	4c brown	.55	.30

Abraham Lincoln — U102   Die 1

Die 2

Die 3

Die 1 — Center bar of E of POSTAGE is above the middle. Center bar of E of STATES slants slightly upward. Nose sharper, more pointed. No offset ink specks inside envelope on back of die impression.

Die 2 — Center bar of E of POSTAGE in middle. P of POSTAGE has short stem. Ink specks on back of die impression.

Die 3 — FI of FIVE closer than Die 1 or 2. Second T of STATES seems taller than ES. Ink specks on back of die impression.

1962

U544	U102 5c dark blue, die 2	.80	.25
a.	Die 1	.80	.25
b.	Die 3	.85	.35
c.	Die 2 with albino impression of 4c (#U536)	50.00	—
d.	Die 3 with albino impression of 4c (#U536), entire	125.00	—
e.	Die 3 on complete impression of 4c (#U536), cut square	125.00	

No. U536 Surcharged in Green at left of Stamp

Two types of surcharge:

Type I — "U.S. POSTAGE" 18½mm high. Serifs on cross of T both diagonal. Two lines of shading in C of CENT.

Type II — "U.S. POSTAGE" 17½mm high. Right serif on cross of T is vertical. Three shading lines in C.

1962

U545	U96 4c + 1c red vio, die 1, type I	1.25	1.10
a.	Type II	1.25	1.10

Values for used envelopes are for examples used within the period of issue. Envelopes used much later sell at substantially reduced prices.

New York World's Fair Issue

Issued to publicize the New York World's Fair, 1964-65.

Globe with Satellite Orbit — U103

1964

U546	U103 5c maroon	.55	.40

Liberty Bell — U104

Old Ironsides U105

Eagle — U106

Head of Statue of Liberty — U107

1965-69

U547	U104 1¼c brown	.50	
U548	U104 1⁴⁄₁₀c brown ('68)	.50	
U548A	U104 1⁶⁄₁₀c orange ('69)	.50	
b.	1⁶⁄₁₀c brown (error), entire	5,000.	
U549	U105 4c bright blue	.90	.25
U550	U106 5c bright purple	.75	.25
a.	Bar tagged ('67)	3.00	1.00

Tagged

U551	U107 6c lt green ('68)	.70	.25
a.	6c dark gray green, entire	200.00	—

Nos. U549-U550 Surcharged in Red or Green at Left of Stamp

1968, Feb. 5

U552	U105 4c + 2c bright blue (R)	3.25	2.00
U553	U106 5c + 1c bright purple (G)	3.00	2.75
a.	Tagged	3.00	2.75
b.	With 2c surcharge type "b" (error)	400.00	

Tagged

Envelopes from No. U554 onward are tagged, except for bulk-rate and non-profit envelopes, which are untagged. The tagging element is in the ink through No. 608 unless otherwise noted. From No. 611 on, envelopes have bar or block tagging unless otherwise noted.

Herman Melville Issue

Issued to honor Herman Melville (1819-1891), writer, and the whaling industry.

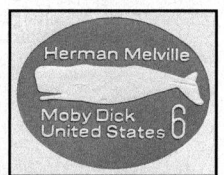

Moby Dick U108

1970, Mar. 7

U554	U108 6c blue	.50	.25

Youth Conference Issue

Issued to publicize the White House Conference on Youth, Estes Park, Colo., Apr. 18-22.

Youth Conference Emblem — U109

1971, Feb. 24

U555	U109 6c light blue	.70	1.00

Liberty Bell Type of 1965 and

Eagle — U110

1971

U556	U104 1⁷⁄₁₀c deep lilac, untagged	.35	
U557	U110 8c ultramarine	.40	.25

Nos. U551 and U555 Surcharged in Green at Left of Stamp

1971, May 16

U561	U107 6c + (2c) light green	.90	1.25
a.	Inverted surcharge, entire	225.00	
U562	U109 6c + (2c) light blue	2.00	2.50
a.	Inverted surcharge printed on reverse, entire	—	

Bowling Issue

Issued as a salute to bowling and in connection with the 7th World Tournament of the International Bowling Federation, Milwaukee, Wis.

Bowling Ball and Pin U111

1971, Aug. 21

U563	U111 8c rose red	.60	.25

Aging Conference Issue

White House Conference on Aging, Washington, D.C., Nov. 28-Dec. 2, 1971.

Conference Symbol U112

1971, Nov. 15

U564	U112 8c light blue	.50	.25

International Transportation Exhibition Issue

U.S. International Transportation Exhibition, Dulles International Airport, Washington, D.C., May 27-June 4.

Transportation Exhibition Emblem — U113

1972, May 2

U565	U113 8c ultramarine & rose red	.50	.25

No. U557 Surcharged in Ultramarine at Left of Stamp

1973, Dec. 1

U566	U110 8c + 2c brt. ultramarine	.40	1.25

Liberty Bell — U114

1973, Dec. 5

U567	U114 10c emerald	.40	.25

"Volunteer Yourself" U115

1974, Aug. 23

Untagged

U568	U115 1⁸⁄₁₀c blue green		.25

Tennis Centenary Issue

Centenary of tennis in the United States.

Tennis Racquet — U116

1974, Aug. 31 **Block Tagged**

U569	U116 10c yellow, brt. blue & light green	.55	.25

Bicentennial Era Issue

The Seafaring Tradition — Compass Rose — U118

The American Homemaker — Quilt Pattern — U119

The American Farmer — Sheaf of Wheat — U120

The American Doctor — U121

The American Craftsman — Tools, c. 1750 — U122

Designs (in brown on left side of envelope): 10c, Norwegian sloop Restaurationen. No. U572, Spinning wheel. No. U573, Plow. No. U574, Colonial era medical instruments and bottle. No. U575, Shaker rocking chair.

1975-76   **Embossed**
Light Brown Diagonally Laid Paper
U571 U118 10c brown & blue   .30   .25
  a. Brown ("10c/USA," etc.)
    omitted, entire   125.00
U572 U119 13c brown & blue
    green   .35   .25
  a. Brown ("13c/USA," etc.)
    omitted, entire   125.00
U573 U120 13c brown & bright
    green   .35   .25
  a. Brown ("13c/USA," etc.)
    omitted, entire   125.00
U574 U121 13c brown & or-
    ange   .35   .25
  a. Brown ("13c/USA," etc.)
    omitted, entire   125.00
U575 U122 13c brown & car-
    mine   .35   .25
  a. Brown ("13c/USA," etc.)
    omitted, entire   125.00
    Nos. U571-U575 (5)   1.70 1.25

Liberty Tree, Boston, 1646 U123

1975, Nov. 8   **Embossed**
U576 U123 13c orange brown   .30   .25

Star and Pinwheel U124

U125

U126

Eagle U127

"Uncle Sam" — U128

1976-78   **Embossed**
U577 U124 2c red, untagged   .25
U578 U125 2.1c green, untag-
    ged   .25
U579 U126 2.7c green, untag-
    ged   .25
U580 U127 (15c) orange   .40   .25
U581 U128 15c red, ink tagged   .40   .25
  a. Bar tagged   7.00 7.00
  For No. U581 with surcharge, see No. U586b.

Bicentennial Issue

Centennial Envelope, 1876 — U129

1976, Oct. 15   **Embossed**
U582 U129 13c emerald   .35   .25

Golf Issue

Golf Club in Motion and Golf Ball — U130

Photogravure and Embossed
1977, Apr. 7
U583 U130 13c black, blue &
    yellow green   .65   .25
  a. Black omitted, entire   500.00
  b. Black & blue omitted, entire 500.00
  c. Black, blue & yellow green
    omitted, entire   500.00
On No. U583c, the embossing is present.

Energy Issue
Conservation and development of national resources.

Energy Conservation U131

Energy Development U132

1977, Oct. 20   **Photo.**
    Bar Tagged
U584 U131 13c black, red &
    yellow   .45   .25
  a. Red, yellow & tagging omit-
    ted, entire   190.00
  b. Yellow & tagging omitted,
    entire   150.00
  c. Black omitted, entire   135.00
  d. Black & red omitted, entire 350.00
U585 U132 13c black, red &
    yellow   .45   .25

Olive Branch and Star — U133

1978, July 28   **Embossed**
    Black Surcharge
U586 U133 15c on 16c
    blue   .40   .25
  a. Surcharge omitted, en-
    tire   225.00 1,000.
  b. Surcharge on No.
    U581, entire   260.00
  c. As "a," with surcharge
    printed on envelope
    flap   175.00   —
  d. Surcharge inverted (in
    lower left corner), en-
    tire   200.00   —

Auto Racing Issue

Indianapolis 500 Racing Car — U134

1978, Sept. 2   **Embossed**
U587 U134 15c red, blue &
    black   .45   .25
  a. Black omitted, entire   100.00
  b. Black & blue omitted, entire 170.00
  c. Red & tagging omitted, en-
    tire   100.00
  d. Red, blue & tagging omit-
    ted, entire   170.00
  e. Tagging bar inverted at LL,
    entire   100.00
  f. Tagging bar on reverse, en-
    tire   —

No. U576 Surcharged

1978, Nov. 28   **Embossed**
U588 U123 15c on 13c orange
    brown   .40   .25
  a. Surcharge inverted (in lower
    left corner), entire   —

U135

    Embossed
1979, May 18   **Untagged**
U589 U135 3.1c ultramarine   .35

Weaver Violins — U136

1980, June 23   **Untagged**
U590 U136 3.5c purple   .35
  a. 3.5c violet, tagged (in
    ink), error of color and
    tagging using ink in-
    tended for No. U592,
    entire   300.00 500.00

U137

1982, Feb. 17   **Untagged**
U591 U137 5.9c brown   .35

Eagle — U138

1981, Mar. 15
U592 U138 (18c) violet   .45   .25

Star — U139

1981, Apr. 2
U593 U139 18c dark blue   .45   .25

Eagle U140

1981, Oct. 11
U594 U140 (20c) brown   .45   .25

Veterinary Medicine Issue

Seal of Veterinarians — U141

Design at left side of envelope shows 5 animals and bird in brown, "Veterinary Medicine" in gray.

1979, July 24
U595 U141 15c brown & gray   .50   .25
  a. Gray omitted, entire   425.00
  b. Brown omitted, entire   500.00
  c. Gray & brown omitted, tag-
    ging omitted, entire   325.00
On No. U595c, the embossing of the seal is present.

Olympic Games Issue
22nd Olympic Games, Moscow, July 19-Aug. 3, 1980.

U142

Design (multicolored on left side of envelope) shows two soccer players with ball.

1979, Dec. 10
U596 U142 15c red, green &
    black   .60   .25
  a. Red & green omitted, tag-
    ging omitted, entire   150.00
  b. Black omitted, tagging omit-
    ted, entire   150.00
  c. Black & green omitted, en-
    tire   150.00

d.	Red omitted, tagging omitted, entire	*325.00*	
e.	All colors omitted	*250.00*	
f.	Tagging omitted, entire	*125.00*	
g.	Black omitted, tagged, entire	*—*	

No. U596c exists with a portion of the green present in the Olympics 1980 design at the lower left corner of the envelope.

On No. U596e, the blind embossing of "USA 15c" remains.

Highwheeler Bicycle — U143

Design (blue on left side of envelope) shows racing bicycle.

1980, May 16
U597 U143 15c blue & rose claret .40 .25
a. Blue ("15c USA") omitted, entire 100.00

Racing Yacht — U144

1980, Sept. 15
U598 U144 15c blue & red .40 .25

Italian Honeybee and Orange Blossoms U145

Bee and petals colorless embossed.

Photogravure and Embossed
1980, Oct. 10
U599 U145 15c brown, green & yellow .35 .25
a. Brown ("USA 15c") omitted, entire 100.00
b. Green omitted, entire 100.00

No. U599b also has almost all of the brown color missing.

Remember the Blinded Veteran

U146

Hand and braille colorless embossed.

1981, Aug. 13   **Embossed**
U600 U146 18c blue & red .45 .25
a. Blue omitted, entire 300.00
b. Red omitted, entire 210.00

Capitol Dome U147

1981, Nov. 13
U601 U147 20c deep magenta, ink tagged .45 .25
a. Bar tagged 4.50 1.50

U148

1982, June 15
U602 U148 20c dark blue, black & magenta .45 .25
a. Dark blue omitted, entire 175.00
b. Dark blue & magenta omitted, entire 175.00
c. All colors omitted, entire 175.00

On No. 602c, the colorless embossed impression of the Great Seal is present.

U149

1982, Aug. 6
U603 U149 20c purple & black .75 .25
a. Black omitted, entire 80.00
b. Purple omitted, entire 200.00

U150

1983, Mar. 21   **Untagged**
U604 U150 5.2c orange .90

U151

1983, Aug. 3
U605 U151 20c red, blue & black .45 .25
a. Red omitted, entire 260.00
b. Blue omitted, entire 260.00
c. Red & black omitted, entire 125.00
d. Blue & black omitted, entire 125.00
e. Black omitted, entire 230.00

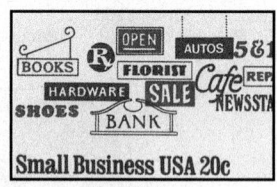

U152

Design shows storefronts at lower left. Stamp and design continue on back of envelope.

1984, May 7   **Photo.**
U606 U152 20c multi .50 .25

U153

1985, Feb. 1   **Embossed**
U607 U153 (22c) deep green .55 .30

American Buffalo U154

1985, Feb. 25
U608 U154 22c violet brown, ink tagged .55 .25
a. Untagged, 3 blue precancel lines, unwmk'd ('86) .25
b. Bar tagged 2.00 1.00

Frigate U.S.S. Constitution, "Old Ironsides" U155

1985, May 3   **Untagged**
U609 U155 6c green blue .35

Mayflower — U156

1986, Dec. 4   **Untagged**
Precanceled
U610 U156 8.5c black & gray .65

Stars U157

1988, Mar. 26   **Typo. & Embossed**
U611 U157 25c dark red & deep blue .60 .25
a. Dark red omitted, tagging omitted 50.00 —
c. Dark red omitted, tagging not omitted 60.00

Sea Gulls, Frigate USS Constellation — U158

1988, Apr. 12   **Untagged**
Precanceled
U612 U158 8.4c black & bright blue .65
a. Black omitted, entire 500.00

Snowflake — U159

"Holiday Greetings!" inscribed in lower left.

1988, Sept. 8   **Typo.**
U613 U159 25c dark red & green 1.25 *20.00*

Stars and "*Philatelic Mail*" Continuous in Dark Red Below Vignette — U160

"Philatelic Mail" and asterisks in dark red below vignette; continuous across envelope face and partly on reverse.

1989, Mar. 10
U614 U160 25c dark red & deep blue .50 .25
b. Red omitted, entire 125.00

"USA" and Stars — U161

1989, July 10   **Unwmk.**
U615 U161 25c dark red & deep blue .50 .25
a. Dark red omitted, entire *425.00*

Lined with a blue design to provide security for enclosures.

Love — U162

Litho. & Typo.
1989, Sept. 22   **Unwmk.**
U616 U162 25c dark red & bright blue .50 .75
a. Dark red and bright blue omitted, entire 150.00
b. Bright blue omitted, entire 150.00

No. U616 has light blue lines printed diagonally over the entire surface of the envelope.

Shuttle Docking at Space Station — U163

1989, Dec. 3   **Typo.**   **Unwmk.**
Die Cut
U617 U163 25c ultramarine .90 .60
a. Ultramarine omitted, entire *400.00*

A hologram, visible through the die cut window to the right of "USA 25," is affixed to the inside of the envelope.

See Nos. U625, U639.

Vince Lombardi Trophy, Football
Players — U164

1990, Sept. 9   Unwmk.   *Die Cut*
U618 U164 25c vermilion   .90   .60

A hologram, visible through the die cut window to the right of "USA 25," is affixed to the inside of the envelope.

Star — U165

Typo. & Embossed
1991, Jan. 24   Wmk.
U619 U165 29c ultramarine &
        rose   .60   .30
a.   Ultramarine omitted, entire   300.00
b.   Rose omitted, tagged, en-
        tire   250.00
c.   Rose omitted, tagging omit-
        ted, entire   275.00

See No. U623.

Birds — U166

Stamp and design continue on back of envelope.

1991, May 3   Typo.   Wmk.
Untagged, Precanceled
U620 U166 11.1c blue & red   —   .90
a.   Blue omitted, entire

Love — U167

1991, May 9   Litho.   Unwmk.
U621 U167 29c light blue, pur-
        ple & bright
        rose   .60   .60
a.   Bright rose omitted, entire   200.00
b.   Purple omitted, entire   400.00

Magazine Industry, 250th
Anniv. — U168

Photo. & Typo.
1991, Oct. 7   Unwmk.
U622 U168 29c multicolored   .70   1.00

The photogravure vignette, visible through the die cut window to the right of "USA 29", is affixed to the inside of the envelope.

Star
U169

Stamp and design continue on back of envelope.

1991, July 20   Typo.   Unwmk.
U623 U169 29c ultra & rose   .60   .30
a.   Ultra omitted, entire   350.00
b.   Rose omitted, entire   200.00

Lined with a blue design to provide security for enclosures.

Country
Geese
U170

1991, Nov. 8   Litho. & Typo.   Wmk.
U624 U170 29c blue gray & yel-
        low   .60   .60

Space Shuttle Type of 1989
Unwmk.
1992, Jan. 21   Typo.   *Die Cut*
U625 U163 29c yellow green   .80   .50

A hologram, visible through the die cut window to the right of "USA 29," is affixed to the inside of the envelope.

U171

Typo. & Litho.
1992, Apr. 10   *Die Cut*
U626 U171 29c multicolored   .60   1.00

The lithographed vignette, visible through the die cut window to the right of "USA 29," is affixed to the inside of the envelope.

Hillebrandia — U172

1992, Apr. 22
U627 U172 29c multicolored   .65   1.00

The lithographed vignette, visible through the die cut window to the right of "29 USA," is affixed to the inside of the envelope.

U173

Typo. & Embossed
1992, May 19   Precanceled
Untagged
U628 U173 19.8c red & blue   .40

U174

1992, July 22   Typo.
U629 U174 29c red & blue   .60   .30

U175

1993, Oct. 2 Typo. & Litho. *Die Cut*
U630 U175 29c multicolored   1.10   1.10

The lithographed vignette, visible through the die cut window to the right of "USA 29," is affixed to the inside of the envelope.

U176

Typo. & Embossed
1994, Sept. 17
U631 U176 29c brown &
        black   .70   1.25
a.   Black ("29/USA") omitted,
        entire   325.00

Liberty Bell — U177

1995, Jan. 3   Typo. & Embossed
U632 U177 32c greenish
        blue &
        blue   .65   .30
a.   Greenish blue omitted   120.00
b.   Blue ("USA 32") omitted   90.00
c.   All colors omitted, entire   —

A colorless embossed design is present on No. U632c.
See No. U638.

U178

Design sizes: 49x38mm (#U633), 53x44mm (U634). Stamp and design continue on back of envelope.

1995   Typo.
U633 U178 (32c) blue & red   1.25   2.00
U634 U178 (32c) blue & red   1.25   2.00
a.   Red & tagging omitted,
        entire   325.00
b.   Blue omitted, entire   325.00

Originally, Nos. U633-U634 were only available through the Philatelic Fullfillment Center after their announcement 1/12/95.

U179

Stamp and design continue on back of envelope.

1995, Mar. 10
Precanceled, Untagged
U635 U179 (5c) green & red
        brown   .40

Graphic Eagle — U180

1995, Mar. 10
Precanceled, Untagged
U636 U180 (10c) dark carmine
        & blue   1.50

Spiral Heart — U181

1995, May 12
U637 U181 32c red, *light
        blue*   .65   .30
a.   Red omitted, entire   200.00

Liberty Bell Type of 1995
1995, May 16
U638 U177 32c greenish blue
        & blue   .70   .30
a.   Greenish blue omitted, en-
        tire   175.00

Space Shuttle Type of 1989
1995, Sept. 22   *Die Cut*
U639 U163 32c carmine rose   .75   .35

A hologram, visible through the die cut window to the right of "USA 32," is affixed to the inside of the envelope.

U182

Typo. & Litho.
1996, Apr. 20   *Die Cut*
U640 U182 32c multicolored   .70   .30

The lithographed vignette, visible through the die cut window to the right of "USA 32c," is affixed to the inside of the envelope.

1996 ATLANTA
PARALYMPIC GAMES
USA 32

U183

1996, May 2
U641 U183 32c multicolored .70 .30
a. Blue & red omitted, entire 260.00
b. Blue & gold omitted, entire 550.00
c. Red omitted, entire 260.00
d. Black & red omitted, entire 450.00
e. Blue omitted, entire 300.00

USA 33

U184

USA 33

U184a

1999, Jan. 11   Typo. & Embossed
U642 U184 33c yellow, blue & red, tagging bar to left of design 1.00 .30
a. Tagging bar to right of design 7.50 3.00
b. As "a," blue omitted, entire 200.00
c. As "a," yellow omitted, entire 175.00
d. As "a," yellow and blue omitted, entire 175.00
e. As "a," blue and red omitted, entire 175.00
f. As "a," all colors omitted, entire 175.00
g. As No. U642, red omitted, entire 450.00
h. As No. U642, yellow and red omitted, entire —
i. As No. U642, blue and red omitted, entire —
j. Tagging omitted —

On No. U642f, the distinctive tagging bar is present. Expertization is required.

1999, Jan. 11   Typo.
U643 U184a 33c blue & red 1.00 .30
a. Tagging bar to right of design 10.00 5.00

Love
USA 33

U185

1999, Jan. 28   Litho.
U644 U185 33c violet .65 .30
a. Tagging bar to right of design .65 .30

Lincoln — U186

1999, June 5   Typo. & Litho.
U645 U186 33c blue & black .65 .30

USA 34

Eagle
U187

2001, Jan. 7   Typo.
U646 U187 34c blue gray & gray .70 .30
a. Blue gray omitted 175.00

Many color shades known.

34 USA

Lovebirds — U188

2001, Feb. 14   Litho.
U647 U188 34c rose & dull violet .70 .30

COMMUNITY COLLEGES
USA 34

Community Colleges, Cent. — U189

2001, Feb. 20   Typo.
U648 U189 34c dark blue & orange brown .70 .30

USA 37

Ribbon Star — U190

2002, June 7
U649 U190 37c red, blue & gray .75 .35
a. Gray omitted, entire —
b. Blue and gray omitted, entire —

All No. U649 were printed on recycled paper. It was also produced using a different blue-gray recycled paper starting in 2002.

Type of 1995 Inscribed "USA / Presorted / Standard"

2002, Aug. 8   Untagged
Precanceled
U650 U180 (10c) dark carmine & blue .25

37 USA

Nurturing Love — U191

2003, Jan. 25
U651 U191 37c olive green & yellow orange .80 .35

Jefferson Memorial Type
2003, Dec. 29
U652 A2818 $3.85 multicolored 12.50 6.25

On No. U652, the stamp indicia is printed on the flap of the envelope.

Disney Type of 2004
2004, June 23   Letter Sheet   Litho.
U653 A2949 37c multicolored 2.50 2.25
U654 A2950 37c multicolored 2.50 2.25
U655 A2951 37c multicolored 2.50 2.25
a. All color missing on reverse, entire
U656 A2952 37c multicolored 2.50 2.25
a. Booklet of 12 letter sheets, 3 each #U653-U656 30.00

No. U656a sold for $14.95.

White Lilacs and Pink Roses Type of 2004
2005, Mar. 3   Letter Sheet
U657 A2931 37c multicolored 3.00 2.50

No. U657 was sold in pads of 12 for $14.95.

USA $4.05

Computer-generated Study of an X-Plane — U192

2006, Jan. 5   Typo.
U658 U192 $4.05 multicolored 10.00 9.00

Benjamin Franklin — U193

2006, Jan. 9
U659 U193 39c blue green & black .80 .40
a. All color omitted, entire —
b. Tagging omitted, entire 45.00

On No. 659a, the tagging bar and the blue green printing on the reverse are present.

AIR FORCE ONE   USA $4.60

Air Force One
U194

2007, May 6
U660 U194 $4.60 multicolored 12.50 10.00

MARINE ONE   USA $16.25

Marine One
U195

2007, May 6
U661 U195 $16.25 multicolored 35.00 20.00

USA 41

Horses — U196

2007, May 12
U662 U196 41c reddish brown & black .85 .40

USA 42

Elk
U197

2008, May 2
U663 U197 42c green & black, tagging bar 20mm tall .85 .40
a. Tagging bar 26mm tall .85 .40
b. As No. U663, litho., tagging bar 19mm tall .85 .40

No. U663 was printed by National Envelope for Ashton-Potter (USA) Ltd. No. U663a was printed by Westvaco.

No. U663b was printed by Ashton-Potter (USA) Ltd. The lithographed impressions of No. U663b are slightly sharper (some tree branches are slightly thinner and more distinct) than the typographed impressions on Nos. U663 and U663a, but because of the nature of the design are nonetheless difficult to distinguish without measuring the tagging bar.

USA $4.80
MOUNT RUSHMORE

Mount Rushmore — U198

2008, May 12
U664 U198 $4.80 multicolored 12.50 10.00

Sunflower Type of 2008
Letter Sheet
2008, Aug. 15   Litho.
U665 A3309 42c multicolored 4.00 3.00

No. U665 was sold in packs of 10 for $14.95.

Redwood Forest Type of 2009
2009, Jan. 16   Typo.
U666 A3332 $4.95 multicolored 10.00 7.50

USA
FIRST-CLASS
FOREVER

U199

2009-11   Litho.
U667 U199 (44c) multicolored .90 .90
a. As #U667, typographed .90 .45
b. As #U667, dated "2011," "FOREVER" multicolored (with color dots) .90 .90
c. As #U667b, "FOREVER" in brown (solid color) .90 .90

Issued: No. U667, 5/11; No. U667a, 8/16; Nos. U667b, U667c, 1/3/11.

No. U667 had a franking value of 44c on the day of issue and will be valid for the one ounce first class postage rate after any new rates go into effect.

The typographed version (No. U667a) can be distinguished from No. U667 by the position of the recycle logo on the back. On the litho. version it is to the right of the recycle text; on the typo. version it is to the left of the text.

USA 44
SEABISCUIT

U200

2009, May 11
U668 U200 44c multicolored .90 .45
a. As #U668, typographed .90 .45
b. As No. U668, triple impression of black, entire —

On No. U668a, the screened blue dots cover the entire area between the "S" and the "C" on No. U668, but appear more random on No. U668a. The pattern of blue dots running towards the shoulder under the head and neck of the horse is long and distinct on No. U668, but barely noticeable, with only a few dots showing, on No. U668a.

See second paragraph of No. U667 footnote, which also applies to Nos. U668 and U668a.

Gulf Coast Lighthouses Type of 2009

2009, July 23   **Litho.**

U669	A3354	44c multicolored	3.25	3.00
U670	A3355	44c multicolored	3.25	3.00
U671	A3356	44c multicolored	3.25	3.00
U672	A3357	44c multicolored	3.25	3.00
U673	A3358	44c multicolored	3.25	3.00
	Nos. U669-U673 (5)		16.25	15.00

Pack of ten, containing two of each letter sheet, sold for $15.95.

Mackinac Bridge U201

2010, Jan. 4   **Typo.**   **Unwmk.**
U674 U201 $4.90 multicolored   12.50   10.00

No. U674 was sold only in packs of 5.

New River Gorge Bridge, West Virginia U202

2011, Jan. 3   **Typo.**   **Unwmk.**
U675 U202 $4.95 multicolored   12.50   10.00

No. U675 was sold only in packs of 5.

Sunshine Skyway Bridge, Florida U203

2012, Jan. 3   **Typo.**   **Unwmk.**
U676 U203 $5.15 multicolored   12.50   10.00

No. U676 was sold only in packs of 5.

Purple Martin — U204

Design Size: 48x33mm
U677 U204 (45c) multicolored   .95   .50
Design Size: 50x35mm
U678 U204 (45c) multicolored   .95   .50

No. U677 was from No. 6¾ size envelopes only. No. U678 was from No. 9 and No. 10 size envelopes.

No. U678 was reprinted in June 2012 without the 'Cradle to Cradle' recycling logo on the back.

Arlington Green Bridge Type of 2013

2013, Jan. 25   **Typo.**   **Unwmk.**
U679 A3612 $5.60 multicolored   11.00   8.00

No. U679 was sold only in packs of 5.

Bank Swallows U205

2013, Mar. 1   **Litho.**   **Unwmk.**
Design Size: 38x35mm
U680 U205 (46c) multicolored   .95   .50
Design Size: 41x38mm
U681 U205 (46c) multicolored   .95   .50

No. U680 is from No. 6¾ size envelopes only. No. U681 is from No. 9 and No. 10 size envelopes.

Eagle, Shield and Flags U206

2013, Aug. 9   **Litho.**   **Unwmk.**
U682 U206 (46c) multicolored   .95   .50
    a.   Double impression of magenta, entire   —
    b.   Triple impression of light blue, entire   —

Verrazano-Narrows Bridge Type of 2014

2014, Mar. 4   **Typo.**   **Unwmk.**
U683 A3726 $5.60 multicolored   12.50   8.00

No. U683 was sold only in packs of 5, 10 or 25.

Poinsettia — U207

Snowflake U208

Snowflake U209

Cardinal U210

Child Making Snowman U211

2014, Oct. 1   **Litho.**   **Unwmk.**

U684	U207	(49c) multicolored	2.00	1.50
U685	U208	(49c) multicolored	2.00	1.50
U686	U209	(49c) multicolored	2.00	1.50
U687	U210	(49c) multicolored	2.00	1.50
U688	U211	(49c) multicolored	2.00	1.50
	Nos. U684-U688 (5)		10.00	7.50

Packs of 10 No. U684 and 10 self-adhesive stickers sold for $9.95. Packs containing 5 each of Nos. U685 and U686 and 10 self-adhesive stickers sold for $9.95. Packs containing 5 each of Nos. U687 and U688 and 10 self-adhesive stickers sold for $9.95. Nos. U684-U688 were available only as No. 10 size envelopes.

Glade Creek Grist Mill Type of 2014

2015, Jan. 12   **Typo.**   **Unwmk.**
U689 A3780 $5.75 multicolored   11.50   8.25

No. U689 was sold only in packs of 5.

Red Water Lily — U212

White Water Lily — U213

2015, Apr. 17   **Litho.**   **Unwmk.**
U690 U212 (49c) multicolored   2.00   1.75
U691 U213 (49c) multicolored   2.00   1.75

Nos. U690 and U691 were only sold in packets of 10 containing five of each envelope and 10 stickers for $9.95. Nos. U690 and U691 were only available in #10 size with self-adhesive flap.

Forget-me-nots — U214

2015, May 18   **Litho.**   **Unwmk.**
U692 U214 (49c) multicolored   2.00   1.75

No. U692 was sold only in packets of 10 + 10 stickers for $9.95. It was only available in #10 size with self-adhesive flap.

La Cueva del Indio Type of 2016

2016, Jan. 17   **Typo.**   **Unwmk.**
U693 A3875 $6.45 multicolored   13.00   9.50

No. U693 was sold only in packs of 5.

Northern Cardinal U215

Designed by Derry Noyes.

2016, Nov. 3   **Litho.**   **Unwmk.**
U694 U215 (47c) multicolored   1.75   1.75

No. U694 was sold only in packets of 12 + 12 stickers for $9.95. It was only available in #10 size with self-adhesive flap. Packets of No. U694 were sold in post offices in Ohio and Puerto Rico (and perhaps elsewhere) in late December, prior to the acknowledgement of the existence of the envelope by USPS Stamp Services. The packets were not offered for sale by USPS Stamp Fulfillment Services until Jan. 4, 2017. In late January, the packet was made available for direct order on the USPS Stamp Fulfillment Services website, which then noted that the day of issue was Jan. 8, 2017, even though the packets could be ordered on Jan. 4. The official first day of issue

was announced as Nov. 3, 2016 in the Feb. 16, 2017 *Postal Bulletin*, but no indication was given that any first day cancels would be made available for this issue. The earliest documented use is postmarked Jan. 3, 2017.

Lili'uokalani Gardens Type of 2017

2017, Jan. 22   **Litho.**   **Unwmk.**
U695 A3986 $6.65 multicolored   13.50   9.75

No. U695 was sold only in packs of 5.

Barn Swallows — U216

2017, Mar. 3   **Litho.**   **Unwmk.**
U696 U216 (49c) multicolored   1.25   .50

Byodo-In Temple Type of 2018

2018, Jan. 21   **Typo.**   **Unwmk.**
U697 A4096 $6.70 multicolored   13.50   9.75

No. U697 was sold only in packs of 5.

Joshua Tree Type of 2019

2019, Jan. 27   **Typo.**   **Unwmk.**
U698 A4191 $7.35 multicolored   15.00   10.00

No. U698 was sold only in packs of 5 or 10.

Big Bend National Park Type of 2020

Designed by Greg Breeding.

2020, Jan. 18   **Typo.**   **Unwmk.**
U699 A4268 $7.75 multicolored   15.50   10.50

No. U699 was sold only in packs of 5 or 10.

Flag and Stars U217

2020, June 15   **Litho.**   **Unwmk.**
U700 U217 (55c) multicolored   1.40   .50

AIR POST STAMPED ENVELOPES & AIR LETTER SHEETS

UC1

5c — Vertical rudder is not semi-circular but slopes down to the left. The tail of the plane projects into the G of POSTAGE.

UC2

Die 2 (5c and 8c): Vertical rudder is semi-circular. The tail of the plane touches but does not project into the G of POSTAGE.
Die 2 (6c) — Same as UC2 except three types of numeral.
2a — The numeral "6" is 6½mm wide.
2b — The numeral "6" is 6mm wide.
2c — The numeral "6" is 5½mm wide.
Die 3 (6c): Vertical rudder leans forward. S closer to O than to T of POSTAGE. E of

POSTAGE has short center bar. Border types b and d, also without border.

1929-44

UC1	UC1	5c blue	3.00	2.00
a.		Orange and blue border, type b	375.00	450.00
UC2	UC2	5c blue, die 2	9.00	5.00
UC3	UC2	6c orange, die 2a ('34)	1.25	.40
a.		With added impression of 3c purple (#U436a), entire without border	4,000.	
b.		Double impression of indicium, entire, with bicolored border	—	
UC4	UC2	6c orange, die 2b ('42)	3.00	2.00
		Entire, without border	4.50	2.50
UC5	UC2	6c orange, die 2c ('44)	.70	.30
UC6	UC2	6c orange, die 3 ('42)	1.00	.35
a.		6c orange, blue, die 3 (error) Entire, without border	15,000.	10,000.
b.		Double impression, entire	400.00	
UC7	UC2	8c olive green, die 2 ('32)	10.00	3.50

Surcharged in Black on Envelopes Indicated by Number in Parenthesis

1945

UC8	U93	6c on 2c carmine (U429, die 1)	1.25	.65
a.		On U429f, die 7	2.25	1.50
b.		On U429g, die 8	1.90	1.10
c.		On U429h, die 9	8.00	7.50
d.		6c on 1c green (error) (U420)	1,750.	
e.		6c on 3c dk violet (error) (U436a)	2,000.	
f.		6c on 3c dk violet (error), amber (U437a)	3,000.	
g.		6c on 3c violet (error) (U526)	3,000.	
UC9	U95	6c on 2c carmine (U525)	40.00	35.00

Surcharged in Black

Surcharged on 6c orange air post envelopes without borders.

1946

UC10	UC2	5c on 6c orange, die 2a	2.75	1.50
a.		Double surcharge	75.00	
UC11	UC2	5c on 6c orange, die 2b	8.00	5.50
UC12	UC2	5c on 6c orange, die 2c	.75	.50
a.		Double surcharge	75.00	900.00
UC13	UC2	5c on 6c orange, die 3	.70	.60
a.		Double surcharge	75.00	50.00
c.		Double surcharge, one on reverse		
UC13B	U93	5c on 6c (UC8a), entire	—	

The 6c borderless envelopes and the revalued envelopes were issued primarily for use to and from members of the armed forces. The 5c rate came into effect Oct. 1, 1946.

DC-4 Skymaster UC3

Die 1 — The end of the wing at the right is a smooth curve. The juncture of the front end of the plane and the engine forms an acute angle. The first T of STATES and the E's of UNITED STATES lean to the left.
Die 2 — The end of the wing at the right is a straight line. The juncture of the front end of the plane and the engine is wide open. The

first T of STATES and the E's of UNITED STATES lean to the right.

1946

UC14	UC3	5c carmine, die 1	.75	.25
UC15	UC3	5c carmine, die 2	.75	.25

See Nos. UC18, UC26.

DC-4 Skymaster — UC4

1947-55 Typo.
Letter Sheets for Foreign Postage

UC16	UC4	10c brt red, pale bl, entire	8.50	7.00
e.		Blue omitted, entire	400.00	
f.		Overlay omitted front & back, entire	100.00	
g.		Overlay omitted from front only, entire	500.00	
a.		"Air Letter" on face, 4-line inscription on back ('51), entire	17.50	10.00
b.		As "a", 10c chocolate, pale bl, entire	450.00	
c.		"Air Letter" and "Aerogramme" on face, 4-line inscription on back ('53), entire	45.00	12.50
d.		As "c", 3-line inscription on back ('55), entire	9.00	8.00

Postage Stamp Centenary Issue

Centenary of the first postage stamps issued by the United States Government.

Washington & Franklin, Early and Modern Mail-carrying Vehicles UC5

Two dies: Rotary, design measures 22¼mm high; and flat bed press, design 21¾mm high.

Embossed, Rotary Press Printing
1947, May 21
For Domestic Postage

UC17	UC5	5c carmine (rotary)	.50	.30
a.		Flat plate printing	.50	.30

Type of 1946

Type I: 6's lean to right.
Type II: 6's upright.

1950 , Sept. 22

UC18	UC3	6c carmine, type I	.75	.25
a.		Type II	.90	.25

Several other types differ slightly from the two listed.

Nos. UC14, UC15, UC18 Surcharged in Red Left of Stamp

1951

UC19	UC3	6c on 5c carmine, die 1	.85	1.50
a.		Surcharge inverted at lower left, entire	—	
UC20	UC3	6c on 5c carmine, die 2	.85	1.50
a.		6c on 6c carmine (error) entire	1,500.	
b.		Double surcharge	975.00	—

To qualify as No. UC20b, both surcharges must be to the left of the indicia.

Nos. UC14-UC15 Surcharged in Red at Left of Stamp

1952

UC21	UC3	6c on 5c carmine, die 1	25.00	20.00
a.		Double surcharge, entire	600.00	
UC22	UC3	6c on 5c carmine, die 2	3.75	2.50
a.		Double surcharge	250.00	
b.		Triple surcharge, entire	275.00	

To qualify as Nos. UC22a or UC22b, all surcharges must be to the left of the indicia.

No. UC17 Surcharged in Red

UC23	UC5	6c on 5c carmine	850.

The 6c on 4c black (No. U440) is believed to be a favor printing.

Fifth International Philatelic Exhibition Issue

FIPEX, the Fifth International Philatelic Exhibition, New York, N.Y., Apr. 28-May 6, 1956.

Eagle in Flight — UC6

1956, May 2

UC25	UC6	6c red	.75	.50

Two types exist, differing slightly in the clouds at top.

Skymaster Type of 1946
1958, July 31

UC26	UC3	7c blue	.65	.50

Nos. UC3-UC5, UC18 and UC25 Surcharged in Green at Left of Stamp

1958

UC27	UC2	6c + 1c orange, die 2a	250.00	300.00
UC28	UC2	6c + 1c orange, die 2b	65.00	80.00
UC29	UC2	6c + 1c orange, die 2c	30.00	55.00
UC30	UC3	6c + 1c carmine, type I	1.00	.50
a.		Type II	1.00	.50
UC31	UC6	6c + 1c red	1.00	.50

Jet Airliner — UC7

Type I: Back inscription in 3 lines.
Type II: Back inscription in 2 lines.

Letter Sheet for Foreign Postage
Typographed, Without Embossing
1958-59

UC32	UC7	10c blue & red, blue, II ('59), entire	6.00	5.00
a.		Type I ('58), entire	10.00	5.00
b.		Red omitted, II, entire	625.00	
c.		Blue omitted, II, entire	600.00	
d.		Red omitted, I, entire	700.00	

Silhouette of Jet Airliner — UC8

1958, Nov. 21 **Embossed**

UC33	UC8	7c blue	.60	.25

1960, Aug. 18

UC34	UC8	7c carmine	.60	.25

Jet Plane and Globe UC9

Letter Sheet for Foreign Postage
Typographed, Without Embossing
1961, June 16

UC35	UC9	11c red & blue, blue, entire	3.00	3.50
a.		Red omitted, entire	750.00	
b.		Blue omitted, entire	950.00	

UC10

1962, Nov. 17 **Embossed**

UC36	UC10	8c red	.55	.25

UC11

1965-67

UC37	UC11	8c red	.45	.25
a.		Tagged	3.50	.30

No. UC37a has a 8x24mm panel at left of stamp that glows orange red under ultraviolet light.

Pres. John F. Kennedy and Jet Plane UC12

Letter Sheets for Foreign Postage
Typographed, Without Embossing
1965, May 29

UC38	UC12	11c red & dark blue, blue, entire	3.75	4.00

1967, May 29

UC39	UC12	13c red & dark blue, blue, entire	3.25	4.00
a.		Red omitted, entire	600.00	
b.		Dark blue omitted, entire	500.00	

UC13

1968, Jan. 8 **Tagged** **Embossed**

UC40	UC13	10c red	.50	.25

No. UC37 Surcharged in Red at Left of Stamp

1968, Feb. 5
UC41 UC11 8c + 2c red   .65 .25

Tagging
Envelopes and Letter Sheets from No. UC42 onward are tagged unless otherwise noted.

Human Rights Year Issue
Issued for International Human Rights Year, and to commemorate the 20th anniversary of the United Nations' Declaration of Human Rights.

Globes and Flock of Birds — UC14

Letter Sheet for Foreign Postage

1968, Dec. 3		**Photo.**
UC42 UC14 13c gray, brown, orange & black, *blue*, entire		8.00 7.50
a. Orange omitted, entire		800.00
b. Brown omitted, entire		375.00
c. Black omitted, entire		700.00
d. Gray and black omitted, entire		—
e. Tagging omitted, entire		50.00

No. UC42 has a luminescent panel ⅜x1 inch on the right globe. The panel glows orange red under ultraviolet light.

UC15

1971, May 6   Embossed (Plane)
UC43 UC15 11c red & blue   .50 *1.75*

Birds in Flight and "usa" — UC16

Letter Sheet for Foreign Postage

1971		**Photo.**
UC44 UC16 15c gray, red, white & blue, *blue,* entire		1.50 *7.50*
a. "AEROGRAMME" added to inscription, entire		1.50 *7.50*
b. As #UC44, red omitted, entire		300.00
c. As "a," red omitted, entire		—

Folding instructions (2 steps) in capitals on No. C44; (4 steps) in upper and lower case on No. UC44a.

On Nos. UC44-UC44a the white rhomboid background of "USA postage 15c" is luminescent. No. UC44 is inscribed: "VIA AIR MAIL-PAR AVION". "postage 15c" is in gray. See No. UC46.

No. UC40 Surcharged in Green at Left of Stamp

1971, June 28   Embossed
UC45 UC13 10c + (1c) red   1.50 .75

HOT AIR BALLOONING CHAMPIONSHIPS ISSUE
Hot Air Ballooning World Championships, Albuquerque, N.M., Feb. 10-17, 1973.

"usa" Type of 1971
Design: Three balloons and cloud at left in address section; no birds beside stamp. Inscribed "INTERNATIONAL HOT AIR BALLOONING." "postage 15c" in blue.

Letter Sheet for Foreign Postage

1973, Feb. 10
UC46 UC16 15c red, white & blue, *blue,* entire   1.00 *7.50*

Folding instructions as on No. UC44a. See notes after No. UC44.

Bird in Flight
UC17

1973, Dec. 1   Luminescent Ink
UC47 UC17 13c rose red   .30 .25

Beginning with No. UC48, all listings are letter sheets for foreign postage.

UC18

1974, Jan. 4		**Photo.**
UC48 UC18 18c red & blue, *blue,* entire		1.00 *6.00*
a. Red omitted, entire		200.00

25TH ANNIVERSARY OF NATO ISSUE

UC19

Design: "NATO" and NATO emblem at left in address section.

1974, Apr. 4		
UC49 UC19 18c red & blue, *blue,* entire		1.00 *6.00*
Die cutting reversed, entire		100.00

UC20

1976, Jan. 16		
UC50 UC20 22c red & blue, *blue,* entire		1.00 *6.00*
a. Red color missing due to foldover and die cutting		—

UC21

1978, Nov. 3
UC51 UC21 22c blue, *blue,* entire 1.00 *3.00*

22nd OLYMPIC GAMES, MOSCOW, JULY 19-AUG. 3, 1980.

UC22

Design (multicolored in bottom left corner) shows discus thrower.

1979, Dec. 5
UC52 UC22 22c red, black & green, *bluish,* entire   1.50 *6.00*

UC23

Design (brown on No. UC53, green and brown on No. UC54): lower left, Statue of Liberty. Inscribed "Tour the United States." Folding area shows tourist attractions.

1980, Dec. 29		
UC53 UC23 30c blue, red & brown, *blue,* entire		.85 *6.00*
a. Red omitted, entire		70.00

1981, Sept. 21		
UC54 UC23 30c yellow, magenta, blue & black, *blue,* entire		.65 *6.00*

UC24

Design: "Made in USA . . . world's best buys!" on flap, ship, tractor in lower left. Reverse folding area shows chemicals, jet silhouette, wheat, typewriter and computer tape disks.

1982, Sept. 16
UC55 UC24 30c multi, *blue,* entire   .80 *6.00*

WORLD COMMUNICATIONS YEAR

World Map Showing Locations of Satellite Tracking Stations — UC25

Design: Reverse folding area shows satellite, tracking station.

1983, Jan. 7
UC56 UC25 30c multi, *blue,* entire   .90 *8.00*

1984 OLYMPICS

UC26

Indicia in black, multicolor design of woman equestrian at lower left with montage of competitive events on reverse folding area.

1983, Oct. 14
UC57 UC26 30c black & multi, *light blue,* entire   .85 *8.00*

WEATHER SATELLITES, 25TH ANNIV.

UC27

Design: Landsat orbiting the earth at lower left with three Landsat photographs on reverse folding area. Inscribed: "Landsat views the Earth."

1985, Feb. 14
UC58 UC27 36c multi, *blue,* entire   1.25 *12.50*

NATIONAL TOURISM WEEK

Urban Skyline
UC28

Design: Inscribed "Celebrate America" at lower left and "Travel. . . the perfect freedom" on folding area. Skier, Indian chief, cowboy, jazz trumpeter and pilgrims on reverse folding area.

1985, May 21		
UC59 UC28 36c multi, *blue,* entire		1.25 *12.50*
a. Black omitted, entire		600.00

MARK TWAIN AND HALLEY'S COMET

Comet Tail Viewed from Space — UC29

Design: Portrait of Twain at lower left and inscribed "I came in with Halley's Comet in 1835. It is coming again next year, and I expect to go out with it. It will be the greatest disappointment of my life if I don't go out with Halley's Comet." "1835 . Mark Twain . 1910 . Halley's Comet . 1985" and Twain, Huckleberry Finn, steamboat and comet on reverse folding areas.

1985, Dec. 4
UC60 UC29 36c multi, entire   2.00 *12.50*

USA 39 — UC30

1988, May 9   **Litho.**
UC61 UC30 39c multi, entire   1.25 *12.50*
  a.   Tagging bar to left of design
      ('89)   1.25   *1.50*
   On No. UC61, the tagging bar is between
"USA" and "39."

MONTGOMERY BLAIR, POSTMASTER GENERAL 1861-64

USA 39

Montgomery Blair and Pres.
Lincoln — UC31

   Design: Mail bags and "Free city delivery,"
"Railway mail service" and "Money order system" at lower left. Globe, locomotive, bust of
Blair, UPU emblem and "The Paris conference
of 1863, initiated by Postmaster General Blair,
led, in 1874, to the founding of the Universal
Postal Union" contained on reverse folding
area.

1989, Nov. 20
UC62 UC31 39c multicolored,
            entire   1.40 *16.00*
  a.   Double impression   —
  b.   Triple impression   —
  c.   Quadruple impression   —

USA 45 — UC32

1991, May 17
UC63 UC32 45c gray, red &
        blue, *blue,* en-
        tire   1.40 *16.00*
  a.   White paper, entire   1.00 *16.00*

USA 50

Thaddeus Lowe (1832-1913),
Balloonist — UC33

1995, Sept. 23
UC64 UC33 50c multicolored,
       blue, entire   1.50 *20.00*

Voyageurs
Natl. Park,
Minnesota
UC34   USA 60

1999, May 15
UC65 UC34 60c multicolored,
       blue, entire   1.75 *12.50*
   No. UC65 used is often found with addi-
tional postage affixed.

OFFICIAL STAMPED ENVELOPES

   By the Act of Congress, January 31,
1873, the franking privilege of officials
was abolished as of July 1, 1873 and
the Postmaster General was authorized
to prepare official envelopes. At the
same time official stamps were prepared for all Departments. Department
envelopes became obsolete July 5,
1884. After that, government offices
began to use franked envelopes of
varied design. These indicate no
denomination and lie beyond the scope
of this Catalogue.

Post Office Department

"2" 9mm high — UO1

"3" 9mm high — UO2

"6" 9½mm
high — UO3

1873
UO1	UO1	2c black, *lemon*	22.50	10.00
UO2	UO2	3c black, *lemon*	12.50	6.50
+UO3	UO2	3c black	*17,500.*	
UO4	UO3	6c black, *lemon*	25.00	17.50

"2" 9¼mm
high — UO4

"3" 9¼mm
high — UO5

"6" 10½mm
high — UO6

1874-79
UO5	UO4	2c black, *lemon*	8.00	4.25
UO6	UO4	2c black	120.00	37.50
UO7	UO5	3c black, *lemon*	2.75	.85
UO8	UO5	3c black	1,750.	1,200.
UO9	UO5	3c black, *amber*	120.00	37.50
UO10	UO5	3c black, *blue*	—	

UO11	UO5	3c blue, *blue* ('75)	*20,000.*	
UO12	UO6	6c black, *lemon*	12.50	6.50
UO13	UO6	6c black	1,250.	1,750.

   Fakes exist of Nos. UO3, UO8 and UO13.

Postal Service

UO7

1877
UO14	UO7	black	6.00	4.50
UO15	UO7	black, *amber*	125.00	42.50
UO16	UO7	blue, *amber*	125.00	40.00
UO17	UO7	blue, *blue*	7.50	6.75

War Department

Franklin — UO8

Bust points to the end of "N" of "ONE".

Jackson — UO9

Bust narrow at the back.

Washington — UO10

Queue projects below the bust.

Lincoln — UO11

Neck very long at the back.

Jefferson — UO12

Queue forms straight line with bust.

Clay — UO13

Ear partly concealed by hair, mouth large,
chin prominent.

Webster — UO14

Has side whiskers.

Scott
UO15

Hamilton
UO16

   Back of bust very narrow; chin almost
straight; the labels containing the letters "U S"
are exactly parallel.

Reay Issue

1873
UO18	UO8	1c dk red	350.00	200.00
WO18A	UO8	1c dk red, *man,* entire	—	
UO19	UO9	2c dk red	1,000.	—
UO20	UO10	3c dk red	12.50	30.00
UO21	UO10	3c dk red, *amb*	*27,500.*	
UO22	UO10	3c dk red, *cr*	500.00	250.00
UO23	UO11	6c dk red	250.00	100.00
UO24	UO11	6c dk red, *cr*	4,000.	425.00
UO25	UO12	10c dk red	7,500.	2,250.
UO26	UO13	12c dk red	90.00	50.00
UO27	UO14	15c dk red	125.00	55.00
UO28	UO15	24c dk red	100.00	40.00
UO29	UO16	30c dk red	250.00	150.00
UO30	UO8	1c ver	200.00	
WO31	UO8	1c ver, *man*	17.50	14.00
+UO32	UO9	2c ver	400.00	
WO33	UO9	2c ver, *man*	250.00	
UO34	UO10	3c ver	75.00	40.00
UO35	UO10	3c ver, *amb*	85.00	40.00
UO36	UO10	3c ver, *cr*	12.50	12.50
UO37	UO11	6c ver	75.00	
+UO38	UO11	6c ver, *cr*	400.00	
UO39	UO12	10c ver	300.00	
UO40	UO13	12c ver	130.00	
UO41	UO14	15c ver	200.00	
UO42	UO15	24c ver	300.00	
UO43	UO16	30c ver	250.00	

UO17

Bottom serif on "S" is thick and short; bust at
bottom below hair forms a sharp point.

UO18

Bottom serif on "S" is thick and short; front
part of bust is rounded.

UO19

Bottom serif on "S" is short; queue does not
project below bust.

UO20

Neck very short at the back.

UO21

Knot of queue stands out prominently.

UO22

Ear prominent, chin receding. No "dot" uner "T" of "Dept."

UO23

Has no side whiskers; forelock projects above head.

UO24

Back of bust rather broad; chin slopes considerably; the label containing letters "U S" are not exactly parallel.

Plimpton Issue

1875

UO44	UO17	1c red	175.00	85.00
+UO45	UO17	1c red, *amb*	600.00	
+UO45A	UO17	1c red, *org*	32,500.	
WO46	UO17	1c red, *man*	4.50	2.75
UO47	UO18	2c red	90.00	—
UO48	UO18	2c red, *amber*	12.50	17.50
UO49	UO18	2c red, *orange*	12.50	17.50
WO50	UO18	2c red, *manila*	90.00	40.00
UO51	UO19	3c red	11.00	10.00
UO52	UO19	3c red, *amber*	12.50	10.00
UO53	UO19	3c red, *cream*	5.00	3.75
UO54	UO19	3c red, *blue*	3.00	2.00
UO55	UO19	3c red, *fawn*	6.00	2.75
UO56	UO20	6c red	45.00	30.00
UO57	UO20	6c red, *amber*	65.00	40.00
UO58	UO20	6c red, *cream*	175.00	85.00
UO59	UO21	10c red	180.00	80.00
UO60	UO21	10c red, *amber*	650.00	
UO61	UO22	12c red	25.00	25.00
UO62	UO22	12c red, *amber*	400.00	
UO63	UO22	12c red, *cream*	450.00	
UO64	UO23	15c red	200.00	125.00
UO65	UO23	15c red, *amber*	650.00	
UO66	UO23	15c red, *cream*	525.00	
UO67	UO24	30c red	150.00	140.00
UO68	UO24	30c red, *amber*	550.00	
UO69	UO24	30c red, *cream*	675.00	

POSTAL SAVINGS ENVELOPES

UO25

1911

UO70	UO25	1c green	75.00	25.00
UO71	UO25	1c green, *oriental buff*	175.00	85.00
UO72	UO25	2c carmine	12.50	4.00
a.		2c carmine, *manila* (error)	1,200.	1,000.

Used Values

Catalogue values for regularly used entires. Those with first-day cancels generally sell for much less.

Tagged
Envelopes from No. UO73 onward are tagged unless otherwise noted.

OFFICIAL MAIL

UO26

1983, Jan. 12   Typo. & Embossed
UO73 UO26 20c blue, entire 1.00 *10.00*

UO27

1985, Feb. 26   Typo. & Embossed
UO74 UO27 22c blue, entire .90 *5.00*

UO28

1987, Mar. 2   Typo.
UO75 UO28 22c blue, entire 1.50 *25.00*

Used exclusively to mail U.S. Savings Bonds.

UO29

1988, Mar. 22
UO76 UO29 (25c) black & blue, entire 1.25 *10.00*

Used exclusively to mail U.S. Savings Bonds.

UO30

UO31

UO31

1988, Apr. 11   Typo. & Embossed
UO77 UO30 25c black & blue, entire .85 *6.00*
a.   Denomination & lettering as on No. UO78, entire 5.00 *6.00*

Nos. UO77 and UO77a used to mail U.S. Savings Bonds and also occasionally used by the director of admissions at the U.S. Air Force Academy and by Air Force recruiting stations for intra-agency correspondence.

Typo.
UO78 UO31 25c black & blue, entire 1.00 *35.00*
a.   Denomination & lettering as on No. UO77, entire 1.00 *35.00*

Used to mail U.S. Savings Bonds. Also used by the Department of Agriculture.

Used Values

Postally used examples of Nos. UO79-UO94 seldom appear in the marketplace and thus cannot be valued with as much certainty as the editors would like. They must show evidence of postal usage. Clear cancels are valued even higher. The editors would like to have records of sales of examples of these used envelopes. If a value exists, it is based on a known transaction(s) or consultation with experts.

1990, Mar. 17

Stars and "E Pluribus Unum" illegible. "Official" is 13mm, "USA" is 16mm long.

UO79 UO31 45c black & blue, entire 1.25 *80.00*
UO80 UO31 65c black & blue, entire 1.75 *100.00*

Used exclusively to mail U.S. passports.

UO32

Stars and "E Pluribus Unum" clear and sharply printed. "Official" is 14½mm, "USA" is 17mm long.

1990, Aug. 10   Litho.
UO81 UO32 45c black & blue, entire 1.25 *80.00*
UO82 UO32 65c black & blue, entire 1.75 *50.00*

Used exclusively to mail U.S. passports.

UO33

1991, Jan. 22   Typo.   Wmk.
UO83 UO33 (29c) black & blue, entire 1.00 *20.00*

Used exclusively to mail U.S. Savings Bonds.

UO34

Litho. & Embossed
1991, Apr. 6   Wmk.
UO84 UO34 29c black & blue, entire .70 *5.00*
a.   Unwatermarked paper, entire 7.50 *4.00*

No. UO84a has a "recycled" imprint under the flap.

UO35

1991, Apr. 17   Wmk.
UO85 UO35 29c black & blue, entire .70 *20.00*

Used exclusively to mail U.S. Savings Bonds.

Consular Service, Bicent.
UO36

1992, July 10   Litho.   Unwmk.
UO86 UO36 52c blue & red, entire 6.00 *20.00*
a.   52c blue & red, *blue-white*, entire 1.50 *20.00*
UO87 UO36 75c blue & red, entire 11.00 *30.00*
a.   75c blue & red, *blue-white*, entire 2.50 *30.00*

Used exclusively to mail U.S. passports. Available only in 4⅜ inch x 8⅞ inch size with self-adhesive flap.

UO37

1995-99   Typo. & Embossed
UO88 UO37 32c blue & red, entire .90 *7.00*
UO89 UO37 33c blue & red, entire .90 *8.00*

Type of 1995
2001, Feb. 27
UO90 UO37 34c blue & red, entire 1.00 *10.00*

Type of 1995
2002, Aug. 2
UO91 UO37 37c blue & red, type I, entire 1.00 *15.00*
a.   Type II, entire 1.00 *35.00*

Type I has 29x28mm blue panel, top of "USA" even with the bottom of the eagle's neck and is made with "100% recycled paper" as noted on reverse. Type II has a 27½x27½mm blue panel, top of "USA" even with the highest arrow, and has no mention of "100% recycled paper" on reverse.

Type of 1995
2006, Jan. 9
UO92 UO37 39c blue & red, entire 2.00 *10.00*

Type of 1995
2007, May 12
UO93 UO37 41c blue & red, entire 2.00 *15.00*

Type of 1995
2008, June 20   Typo.
UO94 UO37 42c blue & red, entire 2.00 *15.00*

REVENUE STAMPS

Nos. R1-R102 were used to pay taxes on documents and proprietary articles including playing cards. Until Dec. 25, 1862, the law stated that a revenue stamp could be used only for payment of the tax upon the particular instrument or article specified on its face. After that date stamps, except the Proprietary, could be used indiscriminately.

Values quoted are for pen-canceled stamps. Stamps with handstamped cancellations sell at higher prices. Stamps canceled with cuts, punches or holes sell for less. See the Scott U.S. Specialized Catalogue.

General Issue
First Issue

Head of Washington in Oval. Various Frames as Illustrated.

Nos. R1b to R42b, part perforate, occur perforated sometimes at sides only and sometimes at top and bottom only. The higher values, part perforate, are perforated at sides only. Imperforate and part perforate revenues often bring much more in pairs or blocks than as single stamps. Part perforate revenues with an asterisk (*) after the value exist imperforate horizontally or vertically.

The experimental silk paper is a variety of the old paper and has only a very few minute fragments of fiber.

Some of the stamps were in use eight years and were printed several times. Many color variations occurred, particularly when unstable pigments were used and the color was intended to be purple or violet, such as the 4c Proprietary, 30c and $2.50 stamps. Before 1868 dull colors predominate on these and the early red stamps. In later printings of the 4c Proprietary, 30c and $2.50 stamps, red predominates in the mixture, and on the dollar values the red is brighter. The early $1.90 stamp is dull purple, imperf. or perforated. In a later printing, perforated only, the purple is darker.

R1

George Washington — R2

Old Paper

1862-71		Engr.	Perf. 12
R1	R1	1c Express, red	
a.		Imperf.	120.00
b.		Part perf.	60.00*
c.		Perf.	1.50
d.		As No. R1c, silk paper	350.00
e.		As No. R1c, vertical pair, imperf. between	200.00
f.		As "c," foreign entry of 2c, pos. 210	—
R2	R1	1c Playing Cards, red	
a.		Imperf.	4,500.
b.		Part perf.	2,500.
c.		Perf.	210.00
R3	R1	1c Proprietary, red	
a.		Imperf.	1,250.
b.		Part perf.	300.00*
c.		Perf.	.50
d.		As No. R3c, silk paper	60.00
R4	R1	1c Telegraph, red	
a.		Imperf.	900.00
c.		Perf.	20.00
R5	R2	2c Bank Check, blue	
a.		Imperf.	1.50
b.		Part perf.	5.50*
c.		Perf.	.50
e.		As No. R5c, Double impression	1,000.
f.		As No. R5c, pair imperf between	500.00
R6	R2	2c Bank Check, orange	
b.		Part perf.	60.00*
c.		Perf.	.45
d.		As No. R6c, silk paper	275.00
e.		As No. R6c, orange, green	900.00
R7	R2	2c Certificate, blue	
a.		Imperf.	17.50
c.		Perf.	32.50
R8	R2	2c Certificate, orange	
c.		Perf.	45.00
R9	R2	2c Express, blue	
a.		Imperf.	15.00
b.		Part perf.	35.00*
c.		Perf.	.40

R10	R2	2c Express, orange	
a.		Imperf.	3,250.
c.		Perf.	14.00
d.		As No. R10c, silk paper	200.00
R11	R2	2c Playing Cards, blue	
a.		Imperf.	1,750.
b.		Part perf.	325.00
c.		Perf.	4.50
R12	R2	2c Playing Cards, org	
c.		Perf.	55.00
R13	R2	2c Proprietary, blue	
a.		Imperf.	1,350.
b.		Part perf.	300.
c.		Perf.	.40
d.		As No. R13c, silk paper	250.00
		Double transfer (T13a)	350.00
		ultramarine	400.00
R14	R2	2c Proprietary, orange	
c.		Perf.	65.00
R15	R2	2c U.S. Internal Revenue, orange ('64)	
a.		Imperf	—
b.		Part perf.	—
c.		Perf.	.25
d.		As No. R15c, silk paper	1.00
e.		As No. R15c, orange, green	2,250.

R3

R16	R3	3c Foreign Exchange, green	
b.		Part perf.	1,500.
c.		Perf.	5.00
d.		As No. R16c, silk paper	200.00
R17	R3	3c Playing Cards, green ('63)	
a.		Imperf.	40,000.
c.		Perf.	200.00
R18	R3	3c Proprietary, green	
b.		Part perf.	1,250.
c.		Perf.	9.00
d.		As No. R18c, silk paper	250.00
e.		As No. R18c, double impression	1,500.
f.		As No. R18c, printed on both sides	4,000.
R19	R3	3c Telegraph, green	
a.		Imperf.	100.00
b.		Part perf.	30.00
c.		Perf.	3.00
R20	R3	4c Inland Exchange, brown ('63)	
c.		Perf.	2.25
d.		As No. R20c, silk paper	190.00
R21	R3	4c Playing Cards, slate ('63)	
c.		Perf.	750.00
R22	R3	4c Proprietary, purple	
a.		Imperf.	—
b.		Part perf.	600.00
c.		Perf.	8.50
d.		As No. R22c, silk paper	300.00

There are shade and color variations of Nos. R21-R22.

R23	R3	5c Agreement, red	
c.		Perf.	.50
d.		As No. R23c, silk paper	4.50
R24	R3	5c Certificate, red	
a.		Imperf.	4.00
b.		Part perf.	15.00
c.		Perf.	.50
d.		As No. R24c, silk paper	1.10
f.		As No. R24d, impression of No. R3 on back	3,000.
R25	R3	5c Express, red	
a.		Imperf.	8.00
b.		Part perf.	8.00*
c.		Perf.	.40
R26	R3	5c Foreign Exchange, red	
b.		Part perf.	2,000.
c.		Perf.	.50
d.		As No. R26c, silk paper	750.00
R27	R3	5c Inland Exchange, red	
a.		Imperf.	10.00
b.		Part perf.	6.75
c.		Perf.	.60
d.		As No. R27c, silk paper	17.50
e.		As No. R27c, double impression	3,500.
R28	R3	5c Playing Cards, red ('63)	
c.		Perf.	40.00
e.		Double impression	2,000.
R29	R3	5c Proprietary, red ('64)	
c.		Perf.	30.00
d.		As No. R29c, silk paper	375.00
R30	R3	6c Inland Exchange, orange ('63)	
b.		Part perf. (imperf. vert.), on document	—
c.		Perf.	2.25
d.		As No. R30c, silk paper	290.00
R31	R3	6c Proprietary, orange ('71)	
c.		Perf.	1,600.

Nearly all examples of No. R31 are faulty or repaired and poorly centered. The catalogue value is for a fine centered stamp with minor faults which do not detract from its appearance.

R32	R3	10c Bill of Lading, blue	
a.		Imperf.	90.00
b.		Part perf.	600.00
c.		Perf.	1.75

R33	R3	10c Certificate, blue	
a.		Imperf.	400.00
b.		Part perf.	850.00*
c.		Perf.	.35
d.		As No. R33c, silk paper	6.00
R34	R3	10c Contract, blue	
a.		Imperf.	625.00
be.		As No. R34b, ultramarine	1,000.
c.		Perf.	.50
ce.		As No. R34c, ultramarine	1.00
d.		As No. R34c, silk paper	4.25
R35	R3	10c Foreign Exchange, blue	
c.		Perf.	14.00
d.		As No. R35c, silk paper	
e.		As No. R35c, ultramarine	20.00
R36	R3	10c Inland Exchange, blue	
a.		Imperf.	500.00
b.		Part perf.	4.50*
c.		Perf.	.30
d.		As No. R36c, silk paper	125.00
R37	R3	10c Power of Attorney, blue	
a.		Imperf.	1,000.
b.		Part perf.	30.00
c.		Perf.	1.00
R38	R3	10c Proprietary, blue ('64)	
c.		Perf.	19.00
R39	R3	15c Foreign Exchange, brown ('63)	
c.		Perf.	17.00
e.		Double impression	1,500.
R40	R3	15c Inland Exchange, brown	
a.		Imperf.	45.00
b.		Part perf.	14.00
c.		Perf.	2.00
e.		As No. R40b, double impression	2,250.
f.		As No. R40c, double impression	950.00
R41	R3	20c Foreign Exchange, red	
a.		Imperf.	100.00
c.		Perf.	80.00
d.		As No. R41c, silk paper	500.00
R42	R3	20c Inland Exchange, red	
a.		Imperf.	17.00
b.		Part perf.	22.50
c.		Perf.	.45
d.		As No. R42c, silk paper	—

R4   R5

R43	R4	25c Bond, red	
a.		Imperf.	300.00
b.		Part perf.	6.75
c.		Perf.	3.75
R44	R4	25c Certificate, red	
a.		Imperf.	11.00
b.		Part perf.	6.75*
c.		Perf.	.50
d.		As No. R44c, silk paper	2.75
e.		As No. R44c, printed on both sides	3,500.
f.		As No. R44c, impression of No. R48 on back	6,000.
R45	R4	25c Entry of Goods, red	
a.		Imperf.	22.50
b.		Part perf.	400.00
c.		Perf.	1.50
d.		As No. R45c, silk paper	150.00
R46	R4	25c Insurance, red	
a.		Imperf.	12.50
b.		Part perf.	19.00
c.		Perf.	.30
d.		As No. R46c, silk paper	7.00
e.		As No. R46c, double impression	750.00
R47	R4	25c Life Insurance, red	
a.		Imperf.	50.00
b.		Part perf.	1,250.
c.		Perf.	11.00
R48	R4	25c Power of Attorney, red	
a.		Imperf.	10.00
b.		Part perf.	45.00
c.		Perf.	1.00
d.		As No. R48c, silk paper	1,750.
R49	R4	25c Protest, red	
a.		Imperf.	35.00
b.		Part perf.	1,000.
c.		Perf.	10.00
R50	R4	25c Warehouse Receipt, red	
a.		Imperf.	55.00
b.		Part perf.	1,300.
c.		Perf.	45.00
R51	R4	30c Foreign Exchange, lilac	
a.		Imperf.	200.00
b.		Part perf.	11,000.
c.		Perf.	60.00
d.		As No. R51c, silk paper	675.00
R52	R4	30c Inland Exchange, lilac	
a.		Imperf.	75.00
b.		Part perf.	90.00
c.		Perf.	8.50
d.		As No. R52c, silk paper	1,500.

R53	R4	40c Inland Exchange, brown	
a.		Imperf.	2,500.
b.		Part perf.	9.00
c.		Perf.	8.00
d.		As No. R53c, silk paper	425.00
f.		As No. R53c, double impression	
R54	R5	50c Conveyance, blue	
a.		Imperf.	20.00
b.		Part perf.	3.50
c.		Perf.	.35
ce.		As No. R54c, ultramarine	.50
d.		As No. R54c, silk paper, blue	3.00
de.		As No. R54d, ultramarine	
R55	R5	50c Entry of Goods, blue	
b.		Part perf.	17.50
c.		Perf.	.60
d.		As No. R55c, silk paper	150.00
R56	R5	50c Foreign Exchange, blue	
a.		Imperf.	75.00
b.		Part perf.	125.00
c.		Perf.	7.50
d.		As No. R56c, double impression	750.00
R57	R5	50c Lease, blue	
a.		Imperf.	35.00
b.		Part perf.	250.00
c.		Perf.	10.00
R58	R5	50c Life Insurance, blue	
a.		Imperf.	45.00
b.		Part perf.	200.00
c.		Perf.	1.75
d.		As No. R58c, double impression	1,100.
R59	R5	50c Mortgage, blue	
a.		Imperf.	22.50
b.		Part perf.	5.00
c.		Perf.	.70
d.		As No. R59c, silk paper	
e.		As No. R59a, double impression	—
f.		As No. R59c, double impression	
R60	R5	50c Original Process, blue	
a.		Imperf.	5.50
b.		Part perf.	4,000.
c.		Perf.	1.00
d.		As No. R60c, silk paper	7.50
R61	R5	50c Passage Ticket, blue	
a.		Imperf.	140.00
b.		Part perf.	575.00
c.		Perf.	2.25
R62	R5	50c Probate of Will, blue	
a.		Imperf.	55.00
b.		Part perf.	250.00
c.		Perf.	22.50
R63	R5	50c Surety Bond, blue	
a.		Imperf.	400.00
b.		Part perf.	2.75
c.		Perf.	.30
e.		As No. R63c, ultramarine	.75
R64	R5	60c Inland Exchange, orange	
a.		Imperf.	120.00
b.		Part perf.	82.50
c.		Perf.	9.00
d.		As No. R64c, silk paper	85.00
R65	R5	70c Foreign Exchange, green	
a.		Imperf.	750.00
b.		Part perf.	200.00
c.		Perf.	14.00
d.		As No. R65c, silk paper	75.00

R6   R7

R66	R6	$1 Conveyance, red	
a.		Imperf.	27.50
b.		Part perf.	5,500.
c.		Perf.	27.50
d.		As No. R66c, silk paper	200.00
R67	R6	$1 Entry of Goods, red	
a.		Imperf.	50.00
c.		Perf.	2.75
d.		As No. R67c, silk paper	180.00
R68	R6	$1 Foreign Exchange, red	
a.		Imperf.	90.00
c.		Perf.	.75
d.		As No. R68c, silk paper	150.00
R69	R6	$1 Inland Exchange, red	
a.		Imperf.	17.00
b.		Part perf.	6,000.*
c.		Perf.	.70
d.		As No. R69c, silk paper	6.00
e.		As No. R69c, horiz. pair, imperf. vert.	—

No. R69e is an error from a pane of stamps that was intended to be issued fully perforated. It can be differentiated from No. R69b by the color, paper and date of cancel. Expertization is strongly recommended.

R70	R6	$1 Lease, red	
a.		Imperf.	50.00
c.		Perf.	4.50

R71 R6 $1 Life Insurance, red
  a. Imperf. — 300.00
  c. Perf. — 10.00
  d. As No. R71c, silk paper — 750.00
R72 R6 $1 Manifest, red
  a. Imperf. — 47.50
  c. Perf. — 40.00
R73 R6 $1 Mortgage, red
  a. Imperf. — 27.50
  c. Perf. — 300.00
R74 R6 $1 Passage Ticket, red
  a. Imperf. — 350.00
  c. Perf. — 350.00
R75 R6 $1 Power of Attorney, red
  a. Imperf. — 100.00
  c. Perf. — 2.75
R76 R6 $1 Probate of Will, red
  a. Imperf. — 100.00
  c. Perf. — 55.00
R77 R7 $1.30 Foreign Exchange, orange ('63)
  a. Imperf. — *11,000.*
  c. Perf. — 120.00
R78 R7 $1.50 Inland Exchange, blue
  a. Imperf. — 32.50
  c. Perf. — 7.00
R79 R7 $1.60 Foreign Exchange, green ('63)
  a. Imperf. — 1,400.
  c. Perf. — 180.00
R80 R7 $1.90 Foreign Exchange, purple ('63)
  a. Imperf. — *12,500.*
  c. Perf. — 200.00
  d. As No. R80c, silk paper — 450.00

R8

R81 R8 $2 Conveyance, red
  a. Imperf. — 250.00
  b. Part perf. — 3,250.
  c. Perf. — 4.00
  d. As No. R81c, silk paper — 40.00
R82 R8 $2 Mortgage, red
  a. Imperf. — 200.00
  c. Perf. — 7.00
  d. As No. R82c, silk paper — 60.00
R83 R8 $2 Probate of Will, red ('63)
  a. Imperf. — 7,000.
  c. Perf. — 90.00
R84 R8 $2.50 Inland Exchange, purple ('63)
  a. Imperf. — *12,000.*
  c. Perf. — 22.50
  d. As No. R84c, silk paper — 40.00
  e. As No. R84c, double impression — 2,000.

There are many shade and color variations of Nos. R84c and R84d.

R85 R8 $3 Charter Party, green
  a. Imperf. — 250.00
  c. Perf. — 11.00
  d. As No. R85c, silk paper — 175.00
  e. As No. R85c, printed on both sides — 7,000.
  g. As No. R85c, impression of No. RS208 on back — 17,000.
R86 R8 $3 Manifest, green
  a. Imperf. — 250.00
  c. Perf. — 55.00
R87 R8 $3.50 Inland Exchange, blue ('63)
  a. Imperf. — *10,000.*
  c. Perf. — 70.00
  e. As No. R87c, printed on both sides — 4,000.

The $3.50 has stars in upper corners.

R9

R10

R88 R9 $5 Charter Party, red
  a. Imperf. — 300.00
  c. Perf. — 10.00
  d. As No. R88c, silk paper — 170.00
R89 R9 $5 Conveyance, red
  a. Imperf. — 50.00
  c. Perf. — 11.00
  d. As No. R89c, silk paper — 160.00
R90 R9 $5 Manifest, red
  a. Imperf. — 250.00
  c. Perf. — 120.00
R91 R9 $5 Mortgage, red
  a. Imperf. — 200.00
  c. Perf. — 25.00
R92 R9 $5 Probate of Will, red
  a. Imperf. — 750.00
  c. Perf. — 27.50
R93 R9 $10 Charter Party, green
  a. Imperf. — 900.00
  c. Perf. — 37.50
R94 R9 $10 Conveyance, green
  a. Imperf. — 175.00
  c. Perf. — 77.50
R95 R9 $10 Mortgage, green
  a. Imperf. — 900.00
  c. Perf. — 40.00
R96 R9 $10 Probate of Will, green
  a. Imperf. — 4,000.
  c. Perf. — 45.00
R97 R10 $15 Mortgage, blue
  a. Imperf. — 4,500.
  c. Perf. — 300.00
  e. As No. R97c, ultramarine — 500.00
  f. As No. R97c, milky blue — 525.00
R98 R10 $20 Conveyance, orange
  a. Imperf. — 175.00
  c. Perf. — 125.00
  d. As No. R98c, silk paper — 175.00
R99 R10 $20 Probate of Will, orange
  a. Imperf. — 3,500.
  c. Perf. — 3,000.
R100 R10 $25 Mortgage, red ('63)
  a. Imperf. — 3,250.
  c. Perf. — 250.00
  d. As No. R100c, silk paper — 300.00
  e. As No. R100c, horiz. pair, imperf. between — 3,500.
R101 R10 $50 U.S. Internal Revenue, green ('63)
  a. Imperf. — 325.00
  c. Perf. — 210.00

R11

R102 R11 $200 U.S. Int. Rev., green & red ('64)
  a. Imperf. — 2,500.
  c. Perf. — 850.00

DOCUMENTARY STAMPS
Second Issue

After release of the First Issue revenue stamps, the Bureau of Internal Revenue received many reports of fraudulent cleaning and re-use. The Bureau ordered a Second Issue with new designs and colors, using a patented "chameleon" paper which is usually violet or pinkish, with silk fibers.

While designs are different from those of the first issue, stamp sizes and make up of the plates are the same as for corresponding denominations.

R12

R12a

George Washington
Various Frames and Numeral Arrangements

1871   **Perf. 12**
R103 R12 1c blue & black — 100.00
  Cut cancel — 40.00
  a. Inverted center — 1,600.
  Cut cancel — 750.00
R104 R12 2c blue & black — 2.75
  Cut cancel — .30
  a. Inverted center — 5,000.
  Cut cancel — 3,500.
R105 R12a 3c blue & black — 75.00
  Cut cancel — 30.00
R106 R12a 4c blue & black — 160.00
  Cut cancel — 65.00
R107 R12a 5c blue & black — 2.00
  Cut cancel — .50
  a. Inverted center — 4,000.
  Cut cancel — 2,500.
R108 R12a 6c blue & black — 300.00
  Cut cancel — 100.00
R109 R12a 10c blue & black — 1.50
  Cut cancel — .30
  a. Inverted center — 2,000.
  Cut cancel — 1,250.
  b. Double impression of center — —

No. R109a is valued in the grade of fine.

R110 R12a 15c blue & black — 100.00
  Cut cancel — 35.00
R111 R12a 20c blue & black — 10.00
  Cut cancel — 4.00
  a. Inverted center — 8,000.

No. R111a is valued in the grade of fine and with small faults, as almost all examples have faults.

R13

R13a

R112 R13 25c blue & black — 1.50
  Cut cancel — .30
  a. Inverted center — 13,000.
  Cut cancel — 6,500.
  b. Imperf. — —
R113 R13 30c blue & black — 175.00
  Cut cancel — 70.00
R114 R13 40c blue & black — 150.00
  Cut cancel — 50.00
R115 R13a 50c blue & black — 1.40
  Cut cancel — .35
  a. Inverted center — 1,050.
  Cut cancel — 650.00
  Punch cancel — 275.00
R116 R13a 60c blue & black — 250.00
  Cut cancel — 80.00
R117 R13a 70c blue & black — 100.00
  Cut cancel — 35.00
  a. Inverted center — 4,000.
  Cut cancel — 1,250.

R13b

R118 R13b $1 blue & black — 10.00
  Cut cancel — 2.25
  a. Inverted center — 6,000.
  Cut cancel — 1,500.
  Punch cancel — 1,000.
R119 R13b $1.30 blue & black — 750.00
  Cut cancel — 175.00
R120 R13b $1.50 blue & black — 22.50
  Cut cancel — 9.00
R121 R13b $1.60 blue & black — 750.00
  Cut cancel — 325.00
R122 R13b $1.90 blue & black — 500.00
  Cut cancel — 150.00

R13c

R123 R13c $2 blue & black — 25.00
  Cut cancel — 10.00
R124 R13c $2.50 blue & black — 60.00
  Cut cancel — 30.00
R125 R13c $3 blue & black — 75.00
  Cut cancel — 35.00
R126 R13c $3.50 blue & black — 500.00
  Cut cancel — 250.00

R13d

R127 R13d $5 blue & black — 40.00
  Cut cancel — 15.00
  a. Inverted center — 3,000.
  Cut cancel — 1,500.
  Punch cancel — 1,100.
R128 R13d $10 blue & black — 260.00
  Cut cancel — 90.00

R13e

R129 R13e $20 blue & black — 900.00
  Cut cancel — 275.00
R130 R13e $25 blue & black — 850.00
  Cut cancel — 275.00
R131 R13e $50 blue & black — 1,050.
  Cut cancel — 325.00

R13f

R132 R13f $200 red, blue & black — 8,500.
　Cut cancel — 3,250.
　Printed in sheets of one.

R13g

R133 R13g $500 red org, grn & blk — 16,500.
　Cut cancel — 7,500.
　Printed in sheets of one.

Value for No. R133 is for a very fine appearing example with a light circular cut cancel or with minor flaws.

Inverted Centers: Fraudulently produced inverted centers exist, some excellently made.

Confusion resulting from the fact that all 1c through $50 denominations of the Second Issue were uniform in color, caused the ordering of a new printing with values in distinctive colors.

Plates used were those of the preceding issue.

Third Issue
Various Frames and Numeral Arrangements.
Violet "Chameleon" Paper with Silk Fibers.

1871-72　　　　　　**Perf. 12**

R134 R12 1c claret & black ('72) — 65.00
　Cut cancel — 30.00
R135 R12 2c orange & black — .40
　Cut cancel — .25
　a. 2c vermilion & black (error) — 900.00
　b. Inverted center — 425.00
　　Cut cancel — 300.00
　c. Imperf., pair
　d. As No. R135, double impression of frame — 2,500.
　e. As No. R135, frame printed on both sides — 1,800.
　f. As No. R135, double impression of frame — 150.00
R136 R12a 4c brown & black ('72) — 110.00
　Cut cancel — 45.00
R137 R12a 5c orange & black — .35
　Cut cancel — .25
　a. Inverted center — 5,000.
　　Cut cancel — 3,750.

No. R137a is valued in the grade of fine.

R138 R12a 6c orange & black ('72) — 125.00
　Cut cancel — 50.00
R139 R12a 15c brown & black ('72) — 27.50
　Cut cancel — 10.00
　a. Inverted center — 16,000.
　　Cut cancel — 9,000.
R140 R13 30c orange & black ('72) — 50.00
　Cut cancel — 15.00
　a. Inverted center — 3,500.
　　Cut cancel — 1,750.
R141 R13 40c brown & black ('72) — 110.00
　Cut cancel — 35.00
R142 R13a 60c orange & black ('72) — 140.00
　Cut cancel — 55.00
R143 R13a 70c green & black ('72) — 90.00
　Cut cancel — 30.00
R144 R13b $1 green & black ('72) — 3.00
　Cut cancel — .80
　a. Inverted center — 12,500.
　　Cut cancel — 10,000.

No. R144a is valued in the grade of fine.

R145 R13c $2 vermilion & black ('72) — 55.00
　Cut cancel — 25.00
R146 R13c $2.50 claret & black ('72) — 110.00
　Cut cancel — 35.00
　a. Inverted center — 25,000.
　　Cut cancel — 17,000.
R147 R13c $3 green & black ('72) — 110.00
　Cut cancel — 35.00
R148 R13d $5 vermilion & black ('72) — 50.00
　Cut cancel — 20.00
R149 R13d $10 green & black ('72) — 400.00
　Cut cancel — 85.00
R150 R13e $20 orange & black ('72) — 900.00
　Cut cancel — 350.00
　$20 vermilion & black (error) — 1,250.
　　Cut cancel — 700.00

See note on Inverted Centers after No. R133.

1874　　　　　　**Perf. 12**
R151 R12 2c orange & black, *green* — .25
　Cut cancel — .25
　a. Inverted center — 800.00
　　Cut cancel — 375.00

Liberty — R14

1875-78　　　　　　**Perf. 12**
R152 R14 2c blue, *blue*
　a. silk paper — 3.00 .45
　b. Wmk. 191R ('78) — 2.00 .35
　c. Wmk. 191R, rouletted 6 — 90.00 32.50
　d. As "a," vert. pair, imperf. horiz. — 525.00
　e. As "b," imperf., pair — 350.00
　f. As "b," vert. pair, imperf. horiz. — 350.00

The watermarked paper came into use in 1878. The rouletted stamps probably were introduced in 1881.

Nos. 279, 267a, 267, 279Bg, 279B, 272-274 Overprinted in Red or Blue

a　　　　　　b

1898　　**Wmk. 191**　　**Perf. 12**
For Nos. R153-R160, values in the first column are for unused examples, values in the second column are for used.

R153 A87(a) 1c deep grn (R) — 5.00 2.75
R154 A87(b) 1c green (R) — .35 .35
　a. Overprint inverted — 35.00 22.50
　b. Overprint on back instead of face, inverted — 4,000.
　c. Pair, one without overprint — 10,000.
R155 A88(b) 2c pink, III (Bl) — .30 .25
　b. 2c carmine, type III (Bl) — .35 .25
　c. As No. R155, overprint inverted — 6.50 4.50

---

　d. Vertical pair, one without overprint — 1,750.
　e. Horiz. pair, one without overprint — —
　f. As No. R155, overprint on back instead of face, inverted — 350.00
　i. Double ovt., one split — 850.00
R155A A88(b) 2c pink, IV (Bl) — .25 .25
　g. 2c carmine, type IV (Bl) — .25 .25
　h. As No. R155A, overprint inverted — 2.75 2.00

Handstamped Type "b" or Type "c" in Magenta

c

R156 A93(b) 8c violet brown — 5,250.
R157 A94(b) 10c dark green — 4,000.
　a. As No. R157, handstamped type "c" — —
R158 A95(b) 15c dark blue — 6,250.

Nos. R156-R158 were emergency provisionals, privately prepared, not officially issued.

Privately Prepared Provisionals

No. 285 Overprinted in Red

1898　**Wmk. 191**　**Perf. 12**
R158A A100 1c dark yellow green — 15,000. 12,500.

No. R158A is valued in sound condition and in the grade of fine to very fine. Most examples have faults, and such examples sell for less.

No. 285 Ovptd. "I.R./P.I.D. & Son" in Red

R158B A100 1c dark yellow green — 25,000. 30,000.

No. R158B is valued with small faults as each of the four recorded examples have faults.

Nos. R158A-R158B were overprinted with federal government permission by the Purvis Printing Co. upon order of Capt. L. H. Chapman of the Chapman Steamboat Line. Both the Chapman Line and P. I. Daprix & Son operated freight-carrying steamboats on the Erie Canal. The Chapman Line touched at Syracuse, Utica, Little Falls and Fort Plain; the Daprix boat ran between Utica and Rome. Overprintings of 250 of each stamp were made.

Dr. Kilmer & Co. provisional overprints and St. Louis provisional proprietary stamps are listed under "Private Die Medicine Stamps" in the Scott U.S. Specialized Catalogue.

Newspaper Stamp No. PR121 Srchd. Vertically in Red

1898　　　　　　**Perf. 12**
R159 N18 $5 dark blue, surcharge reading down — 550.00 325.00

R160 N18 $5 dark blue, surcharge reading up — 150.00 140.00

Battleship — R15

Inscribed: "Series of 1898" and "Documentary."

There are 2 styles of rouletting for the 1898 proprietary and documentary stamps, an ordinary roulette 5½ and one where small rectangles of the paper are cut out, called hyphen hole perf. 7.

1898　**Wmk. 191R**　**Rouletted 5½**
R161 R15 ½c orange — 5.00 25.00
R162 R15 ½c dark gray — .30 .25
　a. Vert. pair, imperf. horiz. — 125.00
R163 R15 1c pale blue — .25 .25
　a. Vert. pair, imperf. horiz. — 8.00
　b. Imperf., pair — 600.00
R164 R15 2c car rose — .30 .30
　a. Vert. pair, imperf. horiz. — 125.00
　b. Imperf., pair — 400.00
　c. Horiz. pair, imperf. vert. — 375.00
R165 R15 3c dark blue — 3.50 .35
R166 R15 4c pale rose — 2.50 .35
　a. Vert. pair, imperf. horiz. — 250.00
R167 R15 5c lilac — .65 .35
　a. Pair, imperf. horiz. or vert. — 350.00 175.00
　b. Horiz. pair, imperf. btwn. — 650.00
R168 R15 10c dark brown — 2.00 .25
　a. Vert. pair, imperf. horiz. — 40.00 35.00
　b. Horiz. pair, imperf. vert.
R169 R15 25c pur brown — 7.50 .50
R170 R15 40c blue lilac — 125.00 1.50
　Cut cancellation — .35
R171 R15 50c slate violet — 35.00 .25
　a. Imperf., pair — 450.00
　b. Horiz. pair, imperf. btwn. — 550.00
R172 R15 80c bister — 125.00 .50
　Cut cancellation — .25

No. R167b may not be genuine.

Hyphen Hole Perf. 7
R163p 1c — .30 .25
R164p 2c — .35 .25
R165p 3c — 40.00 1.40
R166p 4c — 17.50 1.60
R167p 5c — 17.50 .35
R168p 10c — 10.00 .25
R169p 25c — 20.00 .50
R170p 40c — 210.00 35.00
　Cut cancellation — 12.50
R171p 50c — 75.00 1.00
　b. Horiz. pair, imperf. btwn. — 250.00
R172p 80c — 250.00 60.00
　Cut cancellation — 20.00

Commerce — R16

1898　　　　　　**Rouletted 5½**
R173 R16 $1 dark green — 30.00 .25
　a. Vert. pair, imperf. vert. — 800.00
　b. Horiz. pair, imperf. vert. — 325.00
　p. Hyphen hole perf. 7 — 37.50 2.00
　Cut cancel — .75
R174 R16 $3 dark brown — 55.00 1.25
　Cut cancellation — .30
　a. Horiz. pair, imperf. vert. — 500.00
　p. Hyphen hole perf. 7 — 110.00 3.50
　Cut cancellation — .40
R175 R16 $5 orange red — 100.00 2.00
　Cut cancellation — .30
R176 R16 $10 black — 175.00 3.50
　Cut cancellation — .65
　a. Horiz. pair, imperf. vert.
R177 R16 $30 red — 600.00 175.00
　Cut cancellation — 47.50
R178 R16 $50 gray brown — 350.00 7.00
　Cut cancellation — 2.50

See Nos. R182-R183.

John Marshall — R17

Alexander
Hamilton — R18

James
Madison — R19

1899
Without Gum *Imperf.*

R179	R17	$100 yel brn & blk	350.00	40.00
		Cut cancel		22.50
R180	R18	$500 car lake & blk	2,500.	800.00
		Cut cancel		350.00
R181	R19	$1000 grn & blk	1,750.	350.00
		Cut cancel		150.00

1900
Hyphen-hole perf. 7
Allegorical Figure of Commerce

R182	R16	$1 carmine	55.00	.55
		Cut cancel		.30
R183	R16	$3 lake (fugitive ink)	350.00	60.00
		Cut cancel		10.00

Warning: The ink on No. R183 will run in water.

a

Surcharged type "a"

1900

R184	R16	$1 gray	45.00	.40
		Cut cancel		.30
a.		Horiz. pair, imperf. vert	—	
b.		Surcharge omitted	140.00	
		As "b," cut cancel		82.50
R185	R16	$2 gray	45.00	.40
				.25
R186	R16	$3 gray	190.00	15.00
				6.00
R187	R16	$5 gray	100.00	11.00
				1.60
R188	R16	$10 gray	250.00	25.00
				4.50
R189	R16	$50 gray	2,250.	575.00
				140.00

b

Surcharged type "b"

Warning: If Nos. R190-R194 are soaked, the center part of the surcharged numeral may wash off. Before the surcharging, a square of soluble varnish was applied to the middle of some stamps.

1902

R190	R16	$1 green	60.00	3.50
				.30
a.		Inverted surcharge		190.00
R191	R16	$2 green	60.00	2.50
		Cut cancel		.45
a.		Surcharged as No. R185	150.00	90.00
b.		Surcharged as No. R185, in violet	2,000.	—

c.		As "a," double surcharge	150.00	
d.		As "a," triple surcharge	2,500.	
e.		Pair, Nos. R191c and R191d	5,000.	
R192	R16	$5 green	275.00	42.50
		Cut cancel		5.00
a.		Surcharge omitted	300.00	
b.		Pair, one without surcharge	600.00	
R193	R16	$10 green	525.00	225.00
				80.00
R194	R16	$50 green	3,000.	1,250.
		Cut cancel		400.00

R20

Inscribed "Series of 1914"
Offset Printing

1914		Wmk. 190	*Perf. 10*	
R195	R20	½c rose	16.00	5.00
R196	R20	1c rose	3.50	.30
R197	R20	2c rose	5.00	.30
R198	R20	3c rose	125.00	40.00
R199	R20	4c rose	35.00	2.50
R200	R20	5c rose	12.00	.40
R201	R20	10c rose	10.00	.25
R202	R20	25c rose	60.00	.60
R203	R20	40c rose	40.00	3.00
R204	R20	50c rose	15.00	.35
R205	R20	80c rose	250.00	17.00
	Nos. R195-R205 (11)		571.50	69.70

Wmk. 191R

R206	R20	½c rose	1.60	.50
R207	R20	1c rose	.25	.25
R208	R20	2c rose	.30	.25
R209	R20	3c rose	1.50	.25
R210	R20	4c rose	4.50	.50
R211	R20	5c rose	2.00	.35
R212	R20	10c rose	.80	.25
R213	R20	25c rose	10.00	1.50
R214	R20	40c rose	150.00	15.00
		Cut cancel		.50
R215	R20	50c rose	35.00	.40
		Cut cancel		.25
R216	R20	80c rose	225.00	35.00
		Cut cancel		1.25
	Nos. R206-R216 (11)		430.95	54.25

Liberty — R21

Inscribed "Series 1914"
Engr.

R217	R21	$1 green	85.00	.55
		Cut cancel		.25
a.		$1 yellow green	85.00	.25
		Cut cancel		.25
R218	R21	$2 carmine	150.00	1.00
		Cut cancel		.25
R219	R21	$3 purple	175.00	5.00
		Cut cancel		.80
R220	R21	$5 blue	120.00	4.50
		Cut cancel		.65
R221	R21	$10 yel org	375.00	7.50
		Cut cancel		1.10
R222	R21	$30 vermilion	900.00	21.00
		Cut cancel		2.25
R223	R21	$50 violet	2,000.	1,000.
		Cut cancel		450.00

See Nos. R240-R245, R257-R259, R276-R281.

Portrait Types of 1899 Inscribed "Series of 1915" (#R224), or "Series of 1914"

1914-15		Without Gum	*Perf. 12*	
R224	R19	$60 brown (Lincoln)	250.00	150.00
		Cut cancel		70.00
R225	R17	$100 green (Washington)	77.50	45.00
		Cut cancel		16.00
R226	R18	$500 blue (Hamilton)	—	650.00
		Cut cancel		275.00
R227	R19	$1000 orange (Madison)	—	750.00
		Cut cancel		325.00

The stamps of types R17, R18 and R19 in this and subsequent issues were issued in vertical strips of 4 which are imperforate at the top, bottom and right side; therefore, single stamps are always imperforate on one or two sides.

R22

Offset Printing

1917		Wmk. 191R	*Perf. 11*	
R228	R22	1c carmine rose	.35	.25
R229	R22	2c carmine rose	.25	.25
R230	R22	3c carmine rose	1.75	.40
R231	R22	4c carmine rose	.75	.25
R232	R22	5c carmine rose	.30	.25
R233	R22	8c carmine rose	3.00	.35
R234	R22	10c carmine rose	.40	.25
R235	R22	20c carmine rose	.75	.25
R236	R22	25c carmine rose	1.75	.25
R237	R22	40c carmine rose	2.25	.50
R238	R22	50c carmine rose	2.50	.25
R239	R22	80c carmine rose	9.00	.35
	Nos. R228-R239 (12)		23.05	3.60

Liberty Type of 1914 without "Series 1914"

1917-33			Engr.	
R240	R21	$1 yellow green	12.50	.30
a.		$1 green	9.50	.25
R241	R21	$2 rose	20.00	.25
R242	R21	$3 violet	75.00	1.50
		Cut cancel		.30
R243	R21	$4 yellow brown ('33)	50.00	2.00
		Cut cancel		.30
R244	R21	$5 dark blue	35.00	.35
				.25
R245	R21	$10 orange	75.00	1.40
		Cut cancel		.25

Portrait Types of 1899 without "Series of" and Date
Portraits: $30, Grant. $60, Lincoln. $100, Washington. $500, Hamilton. $1,000, Madison.

1917		Without Gum	*Perf. 12*	
R246	R17	$30 dp org, green numerals	55.00	13.00
		Cut cancel		2.25
a.		As "b," imperf. pair		1,000.
b.		Numerals in blue	125.00	3.50
				1.50
R247	R19	$60 brown	65.00	8.00
				.85
R248	R17	$100 green	45.00	2.00
		Cut cancel		.50
R249	R18	$500 blue, red numerals	350.00	50.00
		Cut cancel		15.00
a.		Numerals in orange	425.00	65.00
		Cut cancel		20.00
R250	R19	$1000 orange	175.00	20.00
				7.50
a.		Imperf., pair		2,000.

See note after No. R227.

1928-29		Offset Printing	*Perf. 10*	
R251	R22	1c carmine rose	2.10	1.60
R252	R22	2c carmine rose	.60	.30
R253	R22	4c carmine rose	7.00	4.00
R254	R22	5c carmine rose	1.75	.55
R255	R22	10c carmine rose	2.75	1.25
R256	R22	20c carmine rose	6.00	4.50

Engr.

R257	R21	$1 green	200.00	45.00
		Cut cancel		5.00
R258	R21	$2 rose	90.00	5.00
R259	R21	$10 orange	325.00	75.00
		Cut cancel		30.00

1929		Offset Printing	*Perf. 11x10*	
R260	R22	2c carmine rose ('30)	3.00	2.75
R261	R22	5c carmine rose ('30)	2.00	1.90
R262	R22	10c carmine rose	9.25	6.75
R263	R22	20c carmine rose	15.00	8.25

Used values for Nos. R264-R734 are for stamps which are neither cut nor perforated with initials. Examples with cut cancellations or perforated initials are valued in the Scott U. S. Specialized Catalogue.

Types of 1917-33 Overprinted in Black
SERIES 1940

Offset Printing

1940		Wmk. 191R	*Perf. 11*	
R264	R22	1c rose pink	3.75	2.40
R265	R22	2c rose pink	5.00	2.25
R266	R22	3c rose pink	11.00	5.00
R267	R22	4c rose pink	5.00	.80
R268	R22	5c rose pink	5.00	1.25
R269	R22	8c rose pink	22.50	17.00
R270	R22	10c rose pink	2.50	.65

R271	R22	20c rose pink	3.25	.80
R272	R22	25c rose pink	8.00	1.50
R273	R22	40c rose pink	6.75	.90
R274	R22	50c rose pink	11.00	.55
R275	R22	80c rose pink	14.00	1.75

Engr.

R276	R21	$1 green	80.00	1.25
R277	R21	$2 rose	80.00	2.00
R278	R21	$3 violet	115.00	37.50
b.		Vert. pair, imperf. horiz.		750.00

Only one example of No. R278b is recorded. It is thinned and is valued thus.

R279	R21	$4 yellow brown	210.00	35.00
R280	R21	$5 dark blue	100.00	20.00
R281	R21	$10 orange	275.00	50.00

Types of 1917 Handstamped "Series 1940" like R264-R281

1940		Wmk. 191R	*Perf. 12*	
		Without Gum		
R282	R17	$30 vermilion (B, G)		1,250.
a.		With black 2-line handstamp in larger type		25,000.
R283	R19	$60 brown (B, G)		2,400.
a.		As #R282a, cut cancel		12,500.
R284	R17	$100 green (B)		4,500.
R285	R18	$500 blue (V)		3,000.
a.		As #R282a	3,250.	4,000.
R286	R19	$1000 orange (B, G)		1,250.
b.		Double overprint, cut cancel		—

Types of 1917 Handstamped with black 2-line "Series 1941" in larger type.

1941				
R287	R17	$30 vermilion		35,000.
R287A	R19	$60 brown		35,000.

Alexander
Hamilton
R23

Levi Woodbury
R24

Overprinted in Black   **SERIES 1940**

Various Portraits: 2c, Oliver Wolcott, Jr. 3c, Samuel Dexter. 4c, Albert Gallatin. 5c, G. W. Campbell. 8c, Alexander Dallas. 10c, William H. Crawford. 20c, Richard Rush. 25c, S. D. Ingham. 40c, Louis McLane. 50c, William J. Duane. 80c, Roger B. Taney. $2, Thomas Ewing. $3, Walter Forward. $4, J. C. Spencer. $5, G. M. Bibb. $10, R. J. Walker. $20, William M. Meredith.

1940	Engr.	Wmk. 191R	*Perf. 11*	
R288	R23	1c carmine	5.75	4.50
a.		Imperf. pair, without gum	250.00	
R289	R23	2c carmine	8.50	4.00
a.		Imperf. pair, without gum	250.00	
R290	R23	3c carmine	30.00	12.00
a.		Imperf. pair, without gum	250.00	
R291	R23	4c carmine	62.50	27.50
a.		Imperf. pair, without gum	250.00	
R292	R23	5c carmine	4.75	.80
a.		Imperf. pair, without gum	250.00	
R293	R23	8c carmine	85.00	60.00
a.		Imperf. pair, without gum	250.00	
R294	R23	10c carmine	4.25	.60
a.		Imperf. pair, without gum	250.00	
R295	R23	20c carmine	5.50	4.25
a.		Imperf. pair, without gum	250.00	
R296	R23	25c carmine	5.00	.75
a.		Imperf. pair, without gum	250.00	
R297	R23	40c carmine	75.00	30.00
a.		Imperf. pair, without gum	250.00	
R298	R23	50c carmine	8.00	.60
a.		Imperf. pair, without gum	250.00	
R299	R23	80c carmine	200.00	110.00
a.		Imperf. pair, without gum	475.00	
R300	R24	$1 carmine	50.00	.60
a.		Imperf. pair, without gum	250.00	
R301	R24	$2 carmine	100.00	.90
a.		Imperf. pair, without gum	—	

No.	Type	Denom	Unused	Used
R302	R24	$3 carmine	190.00	95.00
a.		Imperf, pair, without gum	1,400.	
R303	R24	$4 carmine	150.00	50.00
a.		Imperf, pair, without gum	—	
R304	R24	$5 carmine	85.00	3.00
a.		Imperf, pair, without gum	—	
R305	R24	$10 carmine	150.00	10.00
R305A	R24	$20 carmine	3,000.	1,400.
b.		Imperf, pair, without gum	700.00	

Thomas Corwin — R25

Various Frames and Portraits: $50, James Guthrie. $60, Howell Cobb. $100, P. F. Thomas. $500, J. A. Dix, $1,000, S. P. Chase.

Perf. 12
Without Gum

No.	Type	Denom	Unused	Used
R306	R25	$30 car	230.00	75.00
R306A	R25	$50 car	—	8,500.
R307	R25	$60 car	450.00	80.00
a.		Vert. pair, imperf. btwn.	2,750.	1,500.
R308	R25	$100 car	375.00	100.00
R309	R25	$500 car	—	5,000.
R310	R25	$1000 car	—	650.00

The $30 to $1,000 denominations in this and following similar issues, and the $2,500, $5,000 and $10,000 stamps of 1952-58 have straight edges on one or two sides. They were issued without gum through No. R723.

Nos. R288-R310 Overprinted
SERIES 1941

1941		Wmk. 191R		Perf. 11
R311	R23	1c carmine	5.00	2.75
R312	R23	2c carmine	5.25	1.10
R313	R23	3c carmine	10.00	4.25
R314	R23	4c carmine	7.50	1.75
R315	R23	5c carmine	1.50	.40
R316	R23	8c carmine	21.00	8.50
R317	R23	10c carmine	2.00	.35
R318	R23	20c carmine	1.75	.55
R319	R23	25c carmine	2.40	.65
R320	R23	40c carmine	16.00	3.25
R321	R23	50c carmine	3.50	.30
R322	R23	80c carmine	65.00	12.00
R323	R24	$1 carmine	15.00	.30
R324	R24	$2 carmine	20.00	.50
R325	R24	$3 carmine	32.50	3.50
R326	R24	$4 carmine	47.50	27.50
R327	R24	$5 carmine	60.00	1.10
R328	R24	$10 carmine	100.00	6.00
R329	R24	$20 carmine	850.00	400.00

Perf. 12
Without Gum

No.	Type	Denom	Unused	Used
R330	R25	$30 car	275.00	55.00
R331	R25	$50 car	1,500.	1,000.
R332	R25	$60 car	275.00	87.50
R333	R25	$100 car	140.00	37.50
R334	R25	$500 car	—	375.00
R335	R25	$1000 car	1,500.	225.00

Nos. R288-R310 Overprinted
SERIES 1942

1942		Wmk. 191R		Perf. 11
R336	R23	1c carmine	.65	.60
R337	R23	2c carmine	.60	.60
R338	R23	3c carmine	.90	.80
R339	R23	4c carmine	1.75	1.10
R340	R23	5c carmine	.60	.35
R341	R23	8c carmine	9.50	4.75
R342	R23	10c carmine	1.75	.35
R343	R23	20c carmine	1.75	.60
R344	R23	25c carmine	3.00	.55
R345	R23	40c carmine	6.50	1.75
R346	R23	50c carmine	4.00	.35
R347	R23	80c carmine	27.50	13.00
R348	R24	$1 carmine	12.50	.25
R349	R24	$2 carmine	15.00	.30
R350	R24	$3 carmine	27.50	3.25
R351	R24	$4 carmine	35.00	7.50
R352	R24	$5 carmine	37.50	1.50
R353	R24	$10 carmine	85.00	3.75
R354	R24	$20 carmine	300.00	45.00
a.		Imperf., perf. initials	—	

Perf. 12
Without Gum

No.	Type	Denom	Unused	Used
R355	R25	$30 carmine	125.00	42.50
R356	R25	$50 carmine	2,250.	1,400.
R357	R25	$60 carmine	5,000.	1,500.
R358	R25	$100 carmine	325.00	175.00
R359	R25	$500 carmine	2,000.	275.00
R360	R25	$1000 carmine	6,500.	175.00

Nos. R288-R310 Overprinted
SERIES 1943

1943		Wmk. 191R		Perf. 11
R361	R23	1c carmine	.80	.65
R362	R23	2c carmine	.65	.55
R363	R23	3c carmine	3.75	3.50
R364	R23	4c carmine	1.60	1.50
R365	R23	5c carmine	.70	.45
R366	R23	8c carmine	6.00	4.00
R367	R23	10c carmine	.85	.30
R368	R23	20c carmine	2.50	.80
R369	R23	25c carmine	2.75	.30
R370	R23	40c carmine	7.50	4.00
R371	R23	50c carmine	2.00	.30
R372	R23	80c carmine	27.50	8.00
R373	R24	$1 carmine	9.00	.35
R374	R24	$2 carmine	18.00	.35
R375	R24	$3 carmine	30.00	3.00
R376	R24	$4 carmine	55.00	10.00
R377	R24	$5 carmine	52.50	.75
R378	R24	$10 carmine	85.00	5.00
R379	R24	$20 carmine	275.00	60.00

Perf. 12
Without Gum

No.	Type	Denom	Unused	Used
R380	R25	$30 carmine	150.00	25.00
R381	R25	$50 carmine	250.00	75.00
R382	R25	$60 carmine	375.00	125.00
R383	R25	$100 carmine	50.00	22.50
R384	R25	$500 carmine	800.00	325.00
R385	R25	$1000 carmine	800.00	200.00

Nos. R288-R310 Overprinted
Series 1944

1944		Wmk. 191R		Perf. 11
R386	R23	1c carmine	.50	.45
R387	R23	2c carmine	.65	.55
R388	R23	3c carmine	.65	.40
R389	R23	4c carmine	.75	.65
R390	R23	5c carmine	.40	.25
R391	R23	8c carmine	2.25	1.75
R392	R23	10c carmine	.50	.25
R393	R23	20c carmine	1.10	.35
R394	R23	25c carmine	2.00	.30
R395	R23	40c carmine	3.75	.80
R396	R23	50c carmine	4.00	.35
R397	R23	80c carmine	21.00	5.50
R398	R24	$1 carmine	10.00	.30
R399	R24	$2 carmine	15.00	.45
R400	R24	$3 carmine	25.00	2.40
R401	R24	$4 carmine	32.50	11.50
R402	R24	$5 carmine	32.50	.50
R403	R24	$10 carmine	65.00	1.60
R404	R24	$20 carmine	275.00	19.00

Perf. 12
Without Gum

No.	Type	Denom	Unused	Used
R405	R25	$30 carmine	110.00	35.00
R406	R25	$50 carmine	50.00	22.50
R407	R25	$60 carmine	350.00	75.00
R408	R25	$100 carmine	70.00	12.50
R409	R25	$500 carmine	—	3,250.
R410	R25	$1000 carmine	4,000.	500.00

Nos. R288-R310 Overprinted
Series 1945

1945		Wmk. 191R		Perf. 11
R411	R23	1c carmine	.40	.30
R412	R23	2c carmine	.40	.30
R413	R23	3c carmine	.75	.50
R414	R23	4c carmine	.45	.35
R415	R23	5c carmine	.45	.30
R416	R23	8c carmine	6.25	2.75
R417	R23	10c carmine	1.25	.25
R418	R23	20c carmine	8.00	1.50
R419	R23	25c carmine	1.75	.30
R420	R23	40c carmine	9.00	1.25
R421	R23	50c carmine	4.00	.25
R422	R23	80c carmine	26.00	14.00
R423	R24	$1 carmine	13.50	.30
R424	R24	$2 carmine	13.50	.40
R425	R24	$3 carmine	27.50	3.00
R426	R24	$4 carmine	35.00	4.25
R427	R24	$5 carmine	35.00	.50
R428	R24	$10 carmine	65.00	2.50
R429	R24	$20 carmine	200.00	16.00

Perf. 12
Without Gum

No.	Type	Denom	Unused	Used
R430	R25	$30 carmine	200.00	40.00
R431	R25	$50 carmine	230.00	45.00
R432	R25	$60 carmine	450.00	80.00
R433	R25	$100 carmine	50.00	20.00
R434	R25	$500 carmine	750.00	325.00
R435	R25	$1000 carmine	500.00	125.00

Nos. R288-R310 Overprinted
Series 1946

1946		Wmk. 191R		Perf. 11
R436	R23	1c carmine	.30	.30
R437	R23	2c carmine	.45	.35
R438	R23	3c carmine	.55	.40
R439	R23	4c carmine	.80	.65
R440	R23	5c carmine	.45	.30
R441	R23	8c carmine	2.50	2.00
R442	R23	10c carmine	1.10	.30
R443	R23	20c carmine	1.75	.50
R444	R23	25c carmine	6.00	.35
R445	R23	40c carmine	4.50	.85
R446	R23	50c carmine	6.00	.30
R447	R23	80c carmine	17.50	5.00
R448	R24	$1 carmine	16.00	.30
R449	R24	$2 carmine	19.00	.30
R450	R24	$3 carmine	27.50	5.00
R451	R24	$4 carmine	60.00	20.00
R452	R24	$5 carmine	40.00	.50
R453	R24	$10 carmine	72.50	1.75
R454	R24	$20 carmine	200.00	16.00

Perf. 12
Without Gum

No.	Type	Denom	Unused	Used
R455	R25	$30 carmine	75.00	17.50
R456	R25	$50 carmine	65.00	12.50
R457	R25	$60 carmine	110.00	22.50
R458	R25	$100 carmine	90.00	12.50
R459	R25	$500 carmine	1,750.	150.00
R460	R25	$1000 carmine	750.00	160.00

Nos. R288-R310 Overprinted
Series 1947

1947		Wmk. 191R		Perf. 11
R461	R23	1c carmine	.85	.55
R462	R23	2c carmine	.75	.55
R463	R23	3c carmine	.85	.55
R464	R23	4c carmine	.90	.75
R465	R23	5c carmine	.55	.40
R466	R23	8c carmine	1.75	.80
R467	R23	10c carmine	1.40	.30
R468	R23	20c carmine	2.25	.55
R469	R23	25c carmine	3.00	.70
R470	R23	40c carmine	5.50	1.10
R471	R23	50c carmine	3.75	.40
R472	R23	80c carmine	12.00	8.00
R473	R24	$1 carmine	8.25	.35
R474	R24	$2 carmine	14.00	.65
R475	R24	$3 carmine	17.50	6.00
R476	R24	$4 carmine	19.00	5.00
R477	R24	$5 carmine	27.50	.60
R478	R24	$10 carmine	57.00	.60
R479	R24	$20 carmine	110.00	14.00

Perf. 12
Without Gum

No.	Type	Denom	Unused	Used
R480	R25	$30 carmine	180.00	27.50
R481	R25	$50 carmine	90.00	17.50
R482	R25	$60 carmine	210.00	60.00
R483	R25	$100 carmine	85.00	15.00
R484	R25	$500 carmine	900.00	250.00
R485	R25	$1000 carmine	550.00	100.00

Nos. R288-R310 Overprinted
Series 1948

1948		Wmk. 191R		Perf. 11
R486	R23	1c carmine	.35	.30
R487	R23	2c carmine	.50	.45
R488	R23	3c carmine	.60	.40
R489	R23	4c carmine	.55	.40
R490	R23	5c carmine	.50	.25
R491	R23	8c carmine	1.00	.50
R492	R23	10c carmine	1.00	.25
R493	R23	20c carmine	2.50	.40
R494	R23	25c carmine	2.25	.30
R495	R23	40c carmine	7.00	1.75
R496	R23	50c carmine	2.50	.30
R497	R23	80c carmine	12.00	8.00
R498	R24	$1 carmine	10.50	.30
R499	R24	$2 carmine	18.00	.40
R500	R24	$3 carmine	24.00	3.50
R501	R24	$4 carmine	35.00	4.00
R502	R24	$5 carmine	30.00	.50
R503	R24	$10 carmine	70.00	1.50
a.		Pair, one dated "1946"	—	
R504	R24	$20 carmine	400.00	18.00

Perf. 12
Without Gum

No.	Type	Denom	Unused	Used
R505	R25	$30 carmine	150.00	35.00
R506	R25	$50 carmine	180.00	27.50
a.		Vert. pair, imperf. btwn.	2,500.	
R507	R25	$60 carmine	300.00	75.00
a.		Vert. pair, imperf. btwn.	2,500.	
R508	R25	$100 carmine	140.00	20.00
a.		Vert. pair, imperf. btwn.	2,000.	

No. R508a is known as four used singles, all four positions from a single pane of four, clearly imperf. horiz. before being separated.

No.	Type	Denom	Unused	Used
R509	R25	$500 carmine	1,500.	200.00
R510	R25	$1000 carmine	450.00	125.00

Nos. R288-R310 Overprinted
Series 1949

1949		Wmk. 191R		Perf. 11
R511	R23	1c carmine	.40	.35
R512	R23	2c carmine	.75	.45
R513	R23	3c carmine	.60	.50
R514	R23	4c carmine	.80	.60
R515	R23	5c carmine	.55	.30
R516	R23	8c carmine	1.00	.70
R517	R23	10c carmine	.60	.35
R518	R23	20c carmine	1.75	.75
R519	R23	25c carmine	2.25	.85
R520	R23	40c carmine	6.50	2.75
R521	R23	50c carmine	5.00	.40
R522	R23	80c carmine	15.00	7.50
R523	R24	$1 carmine	13.50	.85
R524	R24	$2 carmine	17.00	2.50
R525	R24	$3 carmine	27.50	8.00
R526	R24	$4 carmine	30.00	8.00
R527	R24	$5 carmine	32.50	4.25
R528	R24	$10 carmine	72.50	5.25
R529	R24	$20 carmine	150.00	15.00

Perf. 12
Without Gum

No.	Type	Denom	Unused	Used
R530	R25	$30 carmine	200.00	35.00
R531	R25	$50 carmine	210.00	60.00
R532	R25	$60 carmine	350.00	70.00
R533	R25	$100 carmine	100.00	21.00
R534	R25	$500 carmine	1,250.	260.00
R535	R25	$1000 carmine	1,000.	160.00

Nos. R288-R310 Overprinted
Series 1950

1950		Wmk. 191R		Perf. 11
R536	R23	1c carmine	.40	.25
R537	R23	2c carmine	.40	.35
R538	R23	3c carmine	.50	.40
R539	R23	4c carmine	.70	.50
R540	R23	5c carmine	.45	.35
R541	R23	8c carmine	1.75	.80
R542	R23	10c carmine	.80	.30
R543	R23	20c carmine	1.40	.45
R544	R23	25c carmine	2.00	.45
R545	R23	40c carmine	6.00	2.10
R546	R23	50c carmine	8.00	.35
R547	R23	80c carmine	15.00	8.50
R548	R24	$1 carmine	15.00	.40
R549	R24	$2 carmine	17.50	2.75
R550	R24	$3 carmine	20.00	6.00
R551	R24	$4 carmine	27.50	7.50
R552	R24	$5 carmine	35.00	1.00
R553	R24	$10 carmine	70.00	10.00
R554	R24	$20 carmine	150.00	15.00

Perf. 12
Without Gum

No.	Type	Denom	Unused	Used
R555	R25	$30 carmine	150.00	70.00
R556	R25	$50 carmine	125.00	22.50
a.		Vert. pair, imperf. horiz.		
R557	R25	$60 carmine	260.00	75.00
R558	R25	$100 carmine	100.00	22.50
R559	R25	$500 carmine	1,250.	125.00
R560	R25	$1000 carmine	900.00	95.00

Nos. R288-R310 Overprinted
Series 1951

1951		Wmk. 191R		Perf. 11
R561	R23	1c carmine	.30	.25
R562	R23	2c carmine	.30	.35
R563	R23	3c carmine	.30	.35
R564	R23	4c carmine	.30	.35
R565	R23	5c carmine	.30	.35
R566	R23	8c carmine	1.25	.45
R567	R23	10c carmine	.30	.35
R568	R23	20c carmine	.30	.55
R569	R23	25c carmine	.30	.50
R570	R23	40c carmine	3.75	1.60
R571	R23	50c carmine	3.00	.60
R572	R23	80c carmine	10.00	3.25
R573	R24	$1 carmine	16.00	.30
R574	R24	$2 carmine	21.00	.55
R575	R24	$3 carmine	16.00	8.00
R576	R24	$4 carmine	20.00	12.50
R577	R24	$5 carmine	10.00	.70
R578	R24	$10 carmine	18.00	2.50
R579	R24	$20 carmine	55.00	16.00

Perf. 12
Without Gum

No.	Type	Denom	Unused	Used
R580	R25	$30 carmine	150.00	25.00
a.		Imperf., pair	2,500.	2,000.

R581	R25	$50 carmine	250.00	45.00
R582	R25	$60 carmine	300.00	75.00
R583	R25	$100 carmine	90.00	25.00
R584	R25	$500 carmine	900.00	175.00
R585	R25	$1000 carmine	750.00	150.00

No. R583 is known imperf horizontally. It exists as a reconstructed used vertical strip of 4 that was separated into single stamps.

Documentary Stamps and Types of 1940 Overprinted in Black
Series 1952

Designs: 55c, $1.10, $1.65, $2.20, $2.75, $3.30, L. J. Gage; $2500, William Windom; $5000, C. J. Folger; $10,000, W. Q. Gresham.

1952 Wmk. 191R Perf. 11

R586	R23	1c carmine	.35	.30
R587	R23	2c carmine	.50	.35
R588	R23	3c carmine	.40	.35
R589	R23	4c carmine	.45	.30
R590	R23	5c carmine	.35	.30
R591	R23	8c carmine	.90	.60
R592	R23	10c carmine	.50	.30
R593	R23	20c carmine	1.25	.40
R594	R23	25c carmine	2.50	.45
R595	R23	40c carmine	6.00	1.75
R596	R23	50c carmine	3.50	.30
R597	R23	55c carmine	.60	15.00
R598	R23	80c carmine	19.00	4.00
R599	R24	$1 carmine	7.00	1.50
R600	R24	$1.10 carmine	25.00	30.00
R601	R24	$1.65 carmine	175.00	62.50
R602	R24	$2 carmine	17.00	.90
R603	R24	$2.20 carmine	160.00	70.00
R604	R24	$2.75 carmine	190.00	70.00
R605	R24	$3 carmine	32.50	6.00
a.		Horiz. pair, imperf. btwn.	1,300.	
R606	R24	$3.30 carmine	225.00	90.00
R607	R24	$4 carmine	37.50	6.00
R608	R24	$5 carmine	32.50	1.25
R609	R24	$10 carmine	60.00	1.25
R610	R24	$20 carmine	92.50	16.00

Perf. 12
Without Gum

R611	R25	$30 carmine	90.00	27.50
R612	R25	$50 carmine	95.00	35.00
R613	R25	$60 carmine	600.00	70.00
R614	R25	$100 carmine	110.00	10.00
R615	R25	$500 carmine	750.00	160.00
R616	R25	$1000 carmine	325.00	75.00
R617	R25	$2500 carmine	1,250.	275.00
R618	R25	$5000 carmine	—	5,000.
R619	R25	$10,000 carmine	1,750.	1,400.

Documentary Stamps and Types of 1940 Overprinted in Black
Series 1953

1953 Wmk. 191R Perf. 11

R620	R23	1c carmine	.40	.35
R621	R23	2c carmine	.40	.30
R622	R23	3c carmine	.45	.35
R623	R23	4c carmine	.60	.45
R624	R23	5c carmine	.50	.30
a.		Vert. pair, imperf. horiz.	1,150.	
R625	R23	8c carmine	1.10	.85
R626	R23	10c carmine	.65	.35
R627	R23	20c carmine	1.50	.50
R628	R23	25c carmine	1.75	.65
R629	R23	40c carmine	2.50	.90
R630	R23	50c carmine	3.00	.35
R631	R23	55c carmine	7.00	2.00
a.		Horiz. pair, imperf. vert.	550.00	
R632	R23	80c carmine	10.00	2.10
R633	R24	$1 carmine	5.25	.35
R634	R24	$1.10 carmine	12.00	2.50
a.		Horiz. pair, imperf. vert.	700.00	
b.		Imperf. pair	850.00	
R635	R24	$1.65 carmine	12.00	4.50
R636	R24	$2 carmine	9.00	.75
R637	R24	$2.20 carmine	20.00	6.00
R638	R24	$2.75 carmine	1.75	7.00
R639	R24	$3 carmine	17.00	4.00
R640	R24	$3.30 carmine	50.00	17.50
R641	R24	$4 carmine	40.00	15.00
R642	R24	$5 carmine	27.50	1.25
R643	R24	$10 carmine	60.00	2.25
R644	R24	$20 carmine	140.00	22.50

Perf. 12
Without Gum

R645	R25	$30 car	125.00	20.00
R646	R25	$50 car	175.00	42.50
R647	R25	$60 car	1,000.	425.00
R648	R25	$100 car	70.00	15.00
R649	R25	$500 car	3,500.	175.00
R650	R25	$1000 car	800.00	80.00
R651	R25	$2500 car	2,000.	1,750.
R652	R25	$5000 car	—	7,500.
R653	R25	$10,000 car	—	4,250.

In 1955, the BEP began printing flat plate documentary stamps Nos. R654-R681 using the dry-printing method. This method used paper with a 5-10% moisture content versus the 15-35% moisture content for the wet printing. The dry-printed stamps from the same plates are .25-.75mm larger than the wet-printed examples. Four sub-varieties are known: (1) wet printing with ridged yellow gum, (2) wet printing with smooth yellow gum, (3) dry printing with smooth white gum, and (4) dry printing with smooth white gum.

Types of 1940
Without Overprint

1954 Wmk. 191R Perf. 11

R654	R23	1c carmine	.25	.25
a.		Horiz. pair, imperf. vert.	1,500.	
R655	R23	2c carmine	.25	.30
R656	R23	3c carmine	.25	.30
R657	R23	4c carmine	.25	.30
R658	R23	5c carmine	.25	.25
a.		Vert. pair, imperf. horiz.	—	
R659	R23	8c carmine	.25	.25
R660	R23	10c carmine	.25	.25
R661	R23	20c carmine	.30	.40
R662	R23	25c carmine	.35	.45
R663	R23	40c carmine	.75	.60
R664	R23	50c carmine	1.00	.25
a.		Horiz. pair, imperf. vert.	900.00	
R665	R23	55c carmine	.90	1.25
R666	R23	80c carmine	1.50	1.90
R667	R23	$1 carmine	.90	.35
R668	R24	$1.10 carmine	2.00	2.50
R669	R24	$1.65 carmine	25.00	7.50
R670	R24	$2 carmine	1.00	.45
R671	R24	$2.20 carmine	2.25	3.75
R672	R24	$2.75 carmine	25.00	55.00
R673	R24	$3 carmine	2.00	2.00
R674	R24	$3.30 carmine	3.50	5.00
R675	R24	$4 carmine	2.75	4.00
R676	R24	$5 carmine	3.25	.50
R677	R24	$10 carmine	5.00	1.50
R678	R24	$20 carmine	10.00	6.50

Documentary Stamps & Type of 1940 Ovptd. in Black

1954 Wmk. 191R Perf. 12
Without Gum

R679	R25	$30 carmine	55.00	17.50
a.		Booklet pane of 4	225.00	
R680	R25	$50 carmine	55.00	29.00
a.		Booklet pane of 4	225.00	
R681	R25	$60 carmine	55.00	30.00
a.		Booklet pane of 4	225.00	
R682	R25	$100 carmine	55.00	7.50
a.		Booklet pane of 4	225.00	
R683	R25	$500 carmine	150.00	87.50
a.		Booklet pane of 4	600.00	
R684	R25	$1000 carmine	300.00	90.00
a.		Booklet pane of 4	1,200.	
R685	R25	$2500 carmine	350.00	350.00
a.		Booklet pane of 4	1,400.	
R686	R25	$5000 carmine	2,500.	2,000.
a.		Booklet pane of 4	7,000.	
R687	R25	$10,000 carmine	1,750.	2,250.
a.		Booklet pane of 4	7,000.	

Documentary Stamps and Type of 1940 Overprinted in Black
Series 1955

1955 Wmk. 191R Perf. 12
Without Gum

R688	R25	$30 carmine	110.00	17.50
R689	R25	$50 carmine	125.00	30.00
R690	R25	$60 carmine	200.00	45.00
R691	R25	$100 carmine	160.00	20.00
R692	R25	$500 carmine	1,250.	200.00
R693	R25	$1000 carmine	1,500.	80.00
R694	R25	$2500 carmine	1,250.	275.00
R695	R25	$5000 carmine	4,000.	2,000.
R696	R25	$10,000 carmine	—	1,250.

Documentary Stamps and Type of 1940 Overprinted "Series 1956"

1956 Wmk. 191R Perf. 12
Without Gum

R697	R25	$30 carmine	180.00	20.00
R698	R25	$50 carmine	300.00	27.50
R699	R25	$60 carmine	250.00	60.00
R700	R25	$100 carmine	125.00	15.00
R701	R25	$500 carmine	1,500.	150.00
R702	R25	$1000 carmine	1,750.	100.00
R703	R25	$2500 carmine	—	750.00
R704	R25	$5000 carmine	—	1,700.
R705	R25	$10,000 carmine	—	750.00

Documentary Stamps and Type of 1940 Overprinted "Series 1957"

1957 Wmk. 191R Perf. 12
Without Gum

R706	R25	$30 carmine	275.00	60.00
R707	R25	$50 carmine	160.00	47.50
R708	R25	$60 carmine	1,500.	400.00
R709	R25	$100 carmine	140.00	20.00
R710	R25	$500 carmine	900.00	200.00
R711	R25	$1000 carmine	4,000.	100.00
R712	R25	$2500 carmine	—	1,200.
R713	R25	$5000 carmine	4,250.	1,800.
R714	R25	$10,000 carmine	—	650.00

Documentary Stamps and Type of 1940 Overprinted in Black "Series 1958"

1958 Wmk. 191R Perf. 12
Without Gum

R715	R25	$30 carmine	140.00	27.50
R716	R25	$50 carmine	190.00	35.00
R717	R25	$60 carmine	210.00	42.50
R718	R25	$100 carmine	225.00	15.00
R719	R25	$500 carmine	600.00	125.00
R720	R25	$1000 carmine	2,750.	90.00
R721	R25	$2500 carmine	—	1,500.
R722	R25	$5000 carmine	—	4,250.
R723	R25	$10,000 carmine	—	2,750.

Documentary Stamps and Type of 1940 Without Overprint

1958 Wmk. 191R Perf. 12
With Gum

R724	R25	$30 carmine	11.00	7.00
a.		Booklet pane of 4	57.50	
b.		Vert. pair, imperf. horiz.	3,000.	
R725	R25	$50 carmine	12.00	7.00
a.		Booklet pane of 4	60.00	
b.		Vert. pair, imperf. horiz.	3,500.	
R726	R25	$60 carmine	17.50	21.00
a.		Booklet pane of 4	90.00	
R727	R25	$100 carmine	13.00	4.75
a.		Booklet pane of 4	65.00	
R728	R25	$500 carmine	17.50	26.00
a.		Booklet pane of 4	90.00	
R729	R25	$1000 carmine	16.00	21.00
a.		Booklet pane of 4	80.00	
b.		Vert. pair, imperf. horiz.	1,750.	
c.		Vert. pair, imperf. btwn.	1,500.	
R730	R25	$2500 carmine	175.00	175.00
a.		Booklet pane of 4	800.00	
R731	R25	$5000 carmine	275.00	175.00
a.		Booklet pane of 4	1,200.	
R732	R25	$10,000 carmine	275.00	140.00
a.		Booklet pane of 4	1,200.	

Internal Revenue Building, Washington, DC — R26

Centenary of the Internal Revenue Service.

Giori Press Printing
1962, July 2 Unwmk. Perf. 11

R733	R26	10c violet blue & bright green	1.00	.40
		Never hinged	1.25	

1963
"Established 1862" Removed

R734	R26	10c violet blue & bright green	3.00	.70
		Never hinged	5.00	

Documentary revenue stamps were no longer required after Dec. 31, 1967.

PROPRIETARY STAMPS

Stamps for use on proprietary articles were included in the first general issue of 1862-71. They are Nos. R3, R13-R14, R18, R22, R29, R31, R38.

Washington — RB1

RB1a

Various Frame Designs
1871-74 Engr. Perf. 12

RB1	RB1	1c grn & blk	
a.		Violet paper ('71)	8.00
b.		Green paper ('74)	14.00
c.		As "a," Imperf.	80.00
d.		As "a." Inverted center	5,250.
RB2	RB1	2c grn & blk	
a.		Violet paper ('71)	8.75
b.		Green paper ('74)	30.00
c.		As "a," Invtd. center	40,000.
d.		As "b," Invtd. center	8,000.
e.		As "b," vert. half used as 1c on document	—

Only three examples recorded of the inverted center on violet paper, No. RB2c. Value is for example with very good to fine centering and very small faults.
RB2d is valued with fine centering and small faults.

RB3	RB1a	3c grn & blk	
a.		Violet paper ('71)	32.50
b.		Green paper ('74)	67.50
c.		As "a," privately perforated, sewing machine perfs	800.00
d.		As "a," inverted center	14,000.

No. RB3d is valued with small faults because all of the 8 recorded examples have faults.

RB4	RB1a	4c grn & blk	
a.		Violet paper ('71)	16.00
b.		Green paper ('74)	25.00
c.		As "a." inverted center	15,000.
d.		As "b," vert. half used as 2c on document	—

No. RB4c is valued with small faults as all seven of the recorded examples have faults.

RB5	RB1a	5c grn & blk	
a.		Violet paper ('71)	175.00
b.		Green paper ('74)	250.00
c.		As "a," inverted center	155,000.

No. RB5c is unique. Value represents price realized in 2000 auction sale.

RB6	RB1a	6c grn & blk	
a.		Violet paper ('71)	57.50
b.		Green paper ('74)	140.00
RB7	RB1a	10c grn & blk ('73)	
a.		Violet paper ('71)	300.00
b.		Green paper ('74)	65.00

RB1b

RB8	RB1b	50c grn & blk ('73)	
a.		Violet paper ('71)	1,000.
b.		Green paper ('74)	850.00
RB9	RB1b	$1 grn & blk ('73)	
a.		Violet paper ('71)	3,500.
b.		Green paper ('74)	12,500.

RB1c

RB10 RB1c $5 grn & blk ('73)
a.	Violet paper ('71)	11,000.
b.	Green paper ('74)	75,000.

No. RB10b is valued with small faults.

Washington — RB2

RB2a

Various Frame Designs
Green Paper

1875-81   **Perf.**
Unmwkd. (Silk Paper), Wmk 191R

RB11	RB2	1c green	
a.		Silk paper	2.25
b.		Wmk 191R	.50
c.		Rouletted 6	175.00
d.		As No. RB11b, vert. pair, imperf. btwn.	400.00
RB12	RB2	2c brown	
a.		Silk paper	3.25
b.		Wmk 191R	2.00
c.		Rouletted 6	190.00
RB13	RB2a	3c orange	
a.		Silk paper	14.00
b.		Wmk 191R	4.00
c.		Rouletted 6	160.00
d.		As No. RB13c, horiz. pair, imperf. between	2,500.
e.		As No. RB13c, vert. pair, imperf. between	2,500.
f.		Privately perforated, sewing machine perfs	—
RB14	RB2a	4c red brown	
a.		Silk paper	10.00
b.		Wmk 191R	9.00
c.		Rouletted 6	22,000.
RB15	RB2a	4c red	
b.		Wmk 191R	6.00
c.		Rouletted 6	450.00
RB16	RB2a	5c black	
a.		Silk paper	200.00
b.		Wmk 191R	125.00
c.		Rouletted 6	1,850.
RB17	RB2a	6c violet blue	
a.		Silk paper	35.00
b.		Wmk 191R	25.00
c.		Rouletted 6	1,100.
RB18	RB2a	6c violet	
b.		Wmk 191R	35.00
c.		Rouletted 6	2,500.
RB19	RB2a	10c blue ('81)	
b.		Wmk 191R	400.00

Many fraudulent roulettes exist.

Battleship — RB3

Inscribed "Series of 1898." and "Proprietary."
See note on rouletting preceding No. R161.

Rouletted 5½
1898   **Wmk. 191R**   **Engr.**

RB20	RB3	⅛c yel grn	.25	.25
a.		Vert. pair, imperf. horiz.	.25	
b.		Vert. pair, imperf. btwn.	1,100.	
RB21	RB3	¼c brown	.25	.25
a.		¼c red brown	.25	.25
b.		¼c yellow brown	.25	.25
c.		¼c orange brown	.25	.25
d.		¼c bister	.25	.25
e.		Vert. pair, imperf. horiz.	—	
f.		Printed on both sides	—	
RB22	RB3	⅜c dp org	.30	.30
a.		Horiz. pair, imperf. vert.	12.50	
b.		Vert. pair, imperf. horiz.		
RB23	RB3	⅜c deep ultra	.25	.25
a.		Horiz. pair, imperf. horiz.	85.00	—
b.		Horiz. pair, imperf. btwn.	450.00	400.00
RB24	RB3	1c dark green	2.25	.50
a.		Vert. pair, imperf. horiz.	600.00	
RB25	RB3	1¼c violet	.35	.25
b.		1¼c brown violet	.25	.25
RB26	RB3	1⅞c dull blue	15.00	2.00
RB27	RB3	2c violet brown	1.40	.35
a.		Horiz. pair, imperf. vert.	60.00	
RB28	RB3	2½c lake	5.00	.35
a.		Vert. pair, imperf. horiz.	—	
RB29	RB3	3¾c olive gray	42.50	15.00
RB30	RB3	4c purple	16.00	1.50
RB31	RB3	5c brn org	15.00	1.50
a.		Vert. pair, imperf. horiz.	—	400.00
b.		Horiz. pair, imperf. btwn.	—	750.00
		Nos. RB20-RB31 (12)	98.55	22.50

Hyphen Hole Perf. 7

RB20p		⅛c	.30	.25
RB21p		¼c	.25	.25
b.		¼c yellow brown	.25	.25
c.		¼c orange brown	.25	.25
d.		¼c bister	.25	.25
RB22p		⅜c	.50	.35
RB23p		⅜c	.30	.25
RB24p		1c	30.00	15.00
RB25p		1¼c	.30	.30
a.		1¼c brown violet	.25	.25
RB26p		1⅞c	40.00	9.00
RB27p		2c	10.00	1.00
RB28p		2½c	7.50	.40
RB29p		3¾c	100.00	27.50
RB30p		4c	70.00	22.50
RB31p		5c	85.00	25.00

See note before No. R161.

RB4

Inscribed "Series of 1914"

Offset Printing
1914   **Wmk. 190**   **Perf. 10**

RB32	RB4	⅛c black	.25	.35
RB33	RB4	¼c black	4.00	1.50
RB34	RB4	⅜c black	.35	.35
RB35	RB4	⅝c black	10.00	3.00
RB36	RB4	1¼c black	7.50	1.75
RB37	RB4	1⅞c black	80.00	22.50
RB38	RB4	2½c black	19.00	3.50
RB39	RB4	3⅛c black	230.00	67.50
RB40	RB4	3¾c black	75.00	27.50
RB41	RB4	4c black	110.00	45.00
RB42	RB4	4⅜c black	3,000.	
RB43	RB4	5c black	200.00	110.00
		Nos. RB32-RB41,RB43 (11)	736.10	282.95

Wmk. 191R

RB44	RB4	⅛c black	.35	.30
RB45	RB4	¼c black	.25	.25
RB46	RB4	⅜c black	.75	.45
RB47	RB4	½c black	4.25	3.75
RB48	RB4	⅝c black	.30	.25
RB49	RB4	1c black	5.50	5.50
RB50	RB4	1¼c black	.65	.40
RB51	RB4	1½c black	4.25	3.00
RB52	RB4	1⅞c black	1.35	.90
RB53	RB4	2c black	7.50	6.00
RB54	RB4	2½c black	2.00	1.40
RB55	RB4	3c black	6.00	4.00
RB56	RB4	3⅛c black	10.00	5.00
RB57	RB4	3¾c black	22.50	11.00
RB58	RB4	4c black	.50	.30
RB59	RB4	4⅜c black	22.50	11.00
RB60	RB4	5c black	6.00	3.75
RB61	RB4	6c black	90.00	52.50
RB62	RB4	8c black	30.00	16.00
RB63	RB4	10c black	20.00	11.00
RB64	RB4	20c black	40.00	24.00
		Nos. RB44-RB64 (21)	274.65	160.75

RB5

1919   **Offset Printing**   **Perf. 11**

RB65	RB5	1c dark blue	.25	.25
RB66	RB5	2c dark blue	.35	.25
RB67	RB5	3c dark blue	1.50	.75
RB68	RB5	4c dark blue	2.25	.75
RB69	RB5	5c dark blue	3.00	1.25
RB70	RB5	8c dark blue	27.50	20.00
RB71	RB5	10c dark blue	12.50	5.00
RB72	RB5	20c dark blue	20.00	7.50
RB73	RB5	40c dark blue	75.00	25.00
		Nos. RB65-RB73 (9)	142.35	60.75

FUTURE DELIVERY STAMPS

Issued to facilitate the collection of a tax upon each sale, agreement of sale or agreement to sell any products or merchandise at any exchange or board of trade, or other similar place for future delivery.

Documentary Stamps of 1917 Overprinted in Black or Red

Documentary Stamps Nos. R228-R250 Overprinted in Black or Red

Offset Printing
1918-34   **Wmk. 191R**   **Perf. 11**
Overprint Horizontal (Lines 8mm apart)
Left Value — Unused With Gum
Right Value — Used

RC1	R22	2c carmine rose	8.75	.25
RC2	R22	3c carmine rose ('34)	47.50	37.50
		Cut cancel		20.00
RC3	R22	4c carmine rose	17.50	.25
b.		Double impression of stamp		10.00
RC3A	R22	5c carmine rose ('33)	100.00	7.50
RC4	R22	10c carmine rose	24.00	.35
a.		Double overprint	—	5.25
b.		"FUTURE" omitted	—	500.00
c.		"DELIVERY FUTURE"		37.50
RC5	R22	20c carmine rose	40.00	.25
a.		Double overprint		21.00
RC6	R22	25c carmine rose	85.00	.60
		Cut cancel		.30
RC7	R22	40c carmine rose	110.00	1.25
		Cut cancel		.35
RC8	R22	50c carmine rose	27.50	.35
a.		"DELIVERY" omitted	—	110.00
RC9	R22	80c carmine rose	190.00	15.00
		Cut cancel		4.00
a.		Double overprint		37.50

Engr.
Overprint Vertical, Reading Up (Lines 2mm apart)

RC10	R21	$1 green (R)	75.00	.35
		Cut cancel		.25
a.		Overprint reading down		450.00
b.		Black overprint		
		Cut cancel		125.00
RC11	R21	$2 rose	85.00	.45
		Cut cancel		.25
RC12	R21	$3 violet (R)	270.00	3.50
		Cut cancel		.30
a.		Overprint reading down	—	52.50
RC13	R21	$5 dark blue (R)	150.00	.60
		Cut cancel		.25
RC14	R21	$10 orange	180.00	1.35
		Cut cancel		.30
a.		"DELIVERY FUTURE"		110.00
RC15	R21	$20 olive bister	450.00	9.00
		Cut cancel		.80

Overprint Horizontal (Lines 11⅝mm apart)
Perf. 12
Without Gum

RC16	R17	$30 vermilion, green numerals	150.00	5.50
		Cut cancel		1.75
a.		Numerals in blue	160.00	4.75
		Cut cancel		2.00
b.		Imperf., blue numerals		150.00
RC17	R19	$50 olive green (Cleveland)	125.00	3.00
		Cut cancel		.90
a.		$50 olive bister	125.00	2.75
		Cut cancel		.25
RC18	R19	$60 brown	160.00	9.00
		Cut cancel		1.20
a.		Vert. pair, imperf. horiz.		950.00
RC19	R17	$100 yellow green ('34)	260.00	37.50
		Cut cancel		9.00

RC20	R18	$500 blue, red numerals (R)	325.00	25.00
		Cut cancel		9.00
a.		Numerals in orange	—	70.00
		Cut cancel		20.00
RC21	R19	$1000 orange	230.00	7.50
		Cut cancel		2.00
a.		Vert. pair, imperf. horiz.		1,350.

See note after No. R227.

1923-24   **Offset Printing**   **Perf. 11**
Overprint Horizontal (Lines 2mm apart)

RC22	R22	1c carmine rose	1.25	.25
RC23	R22	80c carmine rose	200.00	3.50
		Cut cancel		.70

Documentary Stamps of 1917 Overprinted in Black or Red

1925-34   **Engr.**

RC25	R21	$1 green (R)	100.00	2.00
		Cut cancel		.45
RC26	R21	$10 orange (Bk) ('34)	260.00	29.00
		Cut cancel		18.00

Overprint Type I
1928-29   **Offset Printing**   **Perf. 10**

RC27	R22	10c carmine rose	5,000.	
RC28	R22	20c carmine rose	5,000.	

Some specialists have questioned the status of No. RC28, believing known examples to be either fraudulently reperforated examples of No. RC5, or examples of No. R256 with fake overprints applied. The editors would like to see authenticated evidence of the existence of No. RC28.

STOCK TRANSFER STAMPS

Issued to facilitate the collection of a tax on all sales or agreements to sell, or memoranda of sales or delivery of, or transfers of legal title to shares or certificates of stock.

Documentary Stamps Nos. R228-R259 Overprinted in Black or Red

Offset Printing
1918-22   **Wmk. 191R**   **Perf. 11**
Overprint Horizontal (Lines 8mm apart)

RD1	R22	1c carmine rose	1.00	.25
a.		Double overprint	—	.25
RD2	R22	2c carmine rose	.25	.25
a.		Double overprint	—	15.00
		Double overprint, cut cancel		7.50
RD3	R22	4c carmine rose	.25	.25
a.		Double overprint	—	4.25
		Double overprint, cut cancel		2.10
b.		"STOCK" omitted	—	10.50
d.		Ovpt. lines 10mm apart	—	
RD4	R22	5c carmine rose	.30	.25
RD5	R22	10c carmine rose	.30	.25
a.		Double overprint	—	5.25
		Double overprint, cut cancel		2.75
b.		"STOCK" omitted	—	
RD6	R22	20c carmine rose	.55	.25
a.		Double overprint	—	6.25
		"STOCK" double		—
RD7	R22	25c carmine rose	2.25	.30
		Cut cancel		.25
RD8	R22	40c carmine rose ('22)	2.25	.25
RD9	R22	50c carmine rose	.80	.25
a.		Double overprint	—	
RD10	R22	80c carmine rose	10.00	.45
		Cut cancel		.25

Engr.
Overprint Vertical, Reading Up
(Lines 2mm apart)

RD11	R21	$1 green (R)	225.00	40.00
		Cut cancel		10.00
a.		Overprint reading down	300.00	60.00
		Overprint reading down, cut cancel		20.00
RD12	R21	$1 green (Bk)	3.00	.30
a.		Pair, one without overprint	—	180.00
b.		Overprinted on back instead of face, inverted	—	150.00
c.		Overprint reading down	—	7.50
d.		$1 yellow green	3.00	.25
RD13	R21	$2 rose	3.00	.25
a.		Overprint reading down		11.50
		Overprint reading down, cut cancel		1.50
b.		Vert. pair, imperf. horiz.	800.00	
RD14	R21	$3 violet (R)	35.00	6.00
		Cut cancel		.30
RD15	R21	$4 yellow brown	15.00	.30
		Cut cancel		.25
RD16	R21	$5 dark blue (R)	10.00	.30
		Cut cancel		.25
a.		Overprint reading down	42.50	1.35
		Overprint reading down, cut cancel		.25
RD17	R21	$10 orange	37.50	.45
		Cut cancel		.25
RD18	R21	$20 olive bister ('21)	150.00	18.00
		Cut cancel		4.50
a.		Overprint reading down		

Overprint Horizontal (Lines 11½mm apart)

1918   Without Gum   Perf. 12

RD19	R17	$30 grn, grn numerals	55.00	6.50
		Cut cancel		2.25
a.		Numerals in blue	200.00	75.00
RD20	R19	$50 ol grn, Cleveland	160.00	70.00
		Cut cancel		27.50
RD21	R19	$60 brown	350.00	30.00
		Cut cancel		12.00
RD22	R17	$100 green	50.00	7.50
		Cut cancel		3.00
RD23	R18	$500 blue (R)	550.00	160.00
		Cut cancel		75.00
a.		Numerals in orange		175.00
RD24	R19	$1,000 orange	425.00	110.00
		Cut cancel		35.00

See note after No. R227.

1928   Offset Printing   Perf. 10
Overprint Horizontal (Lines 8mm apart)

RD25	R22	2c carmine rose	5.50	.30
RD26	R22	4c carmine rose	5.50	.30
RD27	R22	10c carmine rose	5.50	.30
b.		Inverted overprint		1,400.
c.		Ovpt. lines 9½mm apart		
RD28	R22	20c carmine rose	6.50	.35
RD29	R22	50c carmine rose	10.00	.50

Engr.
Overprint Vertical, Reading Up
(Lines 2mm apart)

RD30	R21	$1 green	60.00	.35
a.		$1 yellow green		.50
RD31	R21	$2 carmine rose	55.00	.35
a.		Pair, one without overprint	225.00	190.00
RD32	R21	$10 orange	60.00	.50

Overprinted Horiz. in Black

1920   Offset Printing   Perf. 11

RD33	R22	2c carmine rose	12.50	1.00
RD34	R22	10c carmine rose	3.00	.35
b.		Inverted overprint	2,250.	1,250.
RD35	R22	20c carmine rose	5.75	.25
b.		Horiz. pair, one without overprint	210.00	
d.		Inverted overprint (perf. initials)		—
RD36	R22	50c carmine rose	5.00	.30

Engr.

RD37	R21	$1 green	85.00	17.50
RD38	R21	$2 rose	100.00	17.50

Offset Printing
Perf. 10

RD39	R22	2c carmine rose	13.00	1.10
RD40	R22	10c carmine rose	5.25	.55
RD41	R22	20c carmine rose	6.00	.25

Used values for Nos. RD42-RD372 are for stamps which are neither cut nor perforated with initials. Stamps with cut cancellations or perforated initials are valued in the Scott U.S. Specialized Catalogue.

Documentary Stamps of 1917-33 Overprinted in Black

1940   Perf. 11

RD42	R22	1c rose pink	4.50	.65
a.		"Series 1940" inverted (pos. 31LR)	1,000.	600.00

No. RD42a always comes with a natural straight edge at left.

RD43	R22	2c rose pink	6.00	.65
RD45	R22	4c rose pink	7.50	.35
RD46	R22	5c rose pink	8.00	.25
RD48	R22	10c rose pink	14.00	.35
RD49	R22	20c rose pink	17.00	.35
RD50	R22	25c rose pink	17.00	1.10
RD51	R22	40c rose pink	11.00	1.00
RD52	R22	50c rose pink	12.50	.35
RD53	R22	80c rose pink	280.00	110.00

Engr.

RD54	R21	$1 green	50.00	.60
RD55	R21	$2 rose	55.00	1.00
RD56	R21	$3 violet	350.00	18.00
RD57	R21	$4 yellow brown	125.00	1.60
RD58	R21	$5 dark blue	100.00	2.00
RD59	R21	$10 orange	275.00	10.00
RD60	R21	$20 olive bister	500.00	150.00

Nos. RD19-RD24 Handstamped in Blue "Series 1940"

1940   Perf. 12
Without Gum

RD61	R17	$30 ver	2,000.	1,500.
RD62	R19	$50 ol grn	2,500.	2,500.
a.		Double ovpt., perf. initial		1,400.
RD63	R19	$60 brown	5,500.	3,000.
RD64	R17	$100 green	5,000.	850.00
RD65	R18	$500 blue		4,250.
RD66	R19	$1,000 orange		
		Cut cancel		5,000.

Alexander Hamilton ST1

Levi Woodbury ST2

Overprinted in Black   SERIES 1940

Same Portraits as Nos. R288-R310.

1940   Engr.   Perf. 11

RD67	ST1	1c brt grn	17.50	3.25
a.		Imperf, pair, without gum	250.00	
RD68	ST1	2c brt grn	10.00	1.75
a.		Imperf, pair, without gum	250.00	
RD70	ST1	4c brt grn	19.00	4.50
a.		Imperf, pair, without gum	250.00	
RD71	ST1	5c brt grn	12.00	1.75
a.		Imperf, pair, without gum	250.00	
b.		Without overprint, cut cancel		850.00
RD73	ST1	10c brt grn	16.00	2.10
a.		Imperf, pair, without gum	250.00	
RD74	ST1	20c brt grn	19.00	2.40
a.		Imperf, pair, without gum	250.00	
RD75	ST1	25c brt grn	60.00	10.50
a.		Imperf, pair, without gum	250.00	
RD76	ST1	40c brt grn	125.00	50.00
a.		Imperf, pair, without gum	250.00	
RD77	ST1	50c brt grn	16.00	2.10
a.		Imperf, pair, without gum	250.00	
RD78	ST1	80c brt grn	180.00	75.00
a.		Imperf, pair, without gum	250.00	
RD79	ST2	$1 brt grn	75.00	4.25
a.		Without overprint, perf. initial		750.00

RD80	ST2	$2 brt grn	75.00	12.00
a.		Imperf, pair, without gum	250.00	
RD81	ST2	$3 brt grn	110.00	15.00
a.		Imperf, pair, without gum	250.00	
RD82	ST2	$4 brt grn	900.00	300.00
a.		Imperf, pair, without gum	250.00	
RD83	ST2	$5 brt grn	110.00	16.00
a.		Imperf, pair, without gum	250.00	
RD84	ST2	$10 brt grn	250.00	60.00
a.		Imperf, pair, without gum	250.00	
RD85	ST2	$20 brt grn	1,250.	125.00
a.		Imperf, pair, without gum	250.00	

Nos. RD67-RD85 exist imperforate, without overprint. Value, set of pairs, $750.

Thomas Corwin — ST3

Overprinted "SERIES 1940"
Various frames and portraits as Nos. R306-R310.

Perf. 12
Without Gum

RD86	ST3	$30 brt grn	6,000.	200.00
RD87	ST3	$50 brt grn	3,250.	900.00
RD88	ST3	$60 brt grn	5,000.	2,250.
RD89	ST3	$100 brt grn	3,000.	450.00
RD90	ST3	$500 brt grn		—
RD91	ST3	$1,000 brt grn		4,000.

Nos. RD86-RD91 exist as unfinished imperforates with complete receipt tabs, without overprints or serial numbers. Known in singles, pairs (Nos. RD86-RD88 and Nos. RD90-RD91, value $300 per pair; No. RD89, value $150 per pair), panes of four with plate number, uncut sheets of four panes (with two plate numbers), cross gutter blocks of eight, and blocks of four with vertical gutter between and plate number.

Stock Transfer Stamps and Type of 1940 Overprinted in Black
Nos. RD67-RD91 Overprinted Instead: SERIES 1941

1941   Perf. 11

RD92	ST1	1c brt grn	.80	.55
RD93	ST1	2c brt grn	.60	.30
RD95	ST1	4c brt grn	.65	.25
RD96	ST1	5c brt grn	.60	.25
RD98	ST1	10c brt grn	1.10	.25
RD99	ST1	20c brt grn	2.40	.30
RD100	ST1	25c brt grn	2.40	.45
RD101	ST1	40c brt grn	3.75	.75
RD102	ST1	50c brt grn	5.00	.35
RD103	ST1	80c brt grn	35.00	10.00
RD104	ST2	$1 brt grn	25.00	.25
RD105	ST2	$2 brt grn	27.50	.30
RD106	ST2	$3 brt grn	40.00	1.50
RD107	ST2	$4 brt grn	65.00	8.50
RD108	ST2	$5 brt grn	65.00	.65
RD109	ST2	$10 brt grn	140.00	5.50
RD110	ST2	$20 brt grn	500.00	110.00

Perf. 12
Without Gum

RD111	ST3	$30 brt grn	2,250.	500.00
RD112	ST3	$50 brt grn	1,250.	750.00
RD113	ST3	$60 brt grn	2,500.	1,000.
RD114	ST3	$100 brt grn	500.00	210.00
RD115	ST3	$500 brt grn	4,000.	3,500.
RD116	ST3	$1,000 brt grn	—	4,000.

Stock Transfer Stamps and Type of 1940 Overprinted in Black
Nos. RD67-RD91 overprinted instead: SERIES 1942

1942   Perf. 11

RD117	ST1	1c brt grn	.75	.30
RD118	ST1	2c brt grn	.65	.35
RD119	ST1	4c brt grn	3.50	1.10
RD120	ST1	5c brt grn	.70	.25
a.		Overprint inverted		1,000.
RD121	ST1	10c brt grn	2.25	.25
RD122	ST1	20c brt grn	2.75	.25
RD123	ST1	25c brt grn	2.50	.25

RD124	ST1	40c brt grn	5.75	.40
RD125	ST1	50c brt grn	6.50	.25
RD126	ST1	80c brt grn	30.00	6.00
RD127	ST2	$1 brt grn	27.50	.40
RD128	ST2	$2 brt grn	45.00	.40
RD129	ST2	$3 brt grn	50.00	1.10
RD130	ST2	$4 brt grn	65.00	24.00
RD131	ST2	$5 brt grn	60.00	.40
a.		Double overprint, perf. initial		2,500.
RD132	ST2	$10 brt grn	125.00	9.50
RD133	ST2	$20 brt grn	350.00	65.00

Perf. 12
Without Gum

RD134	ST3	$30 brt grn	900.00	100.00
RD135	ST3	$50 brt grn	950.00	200.00
RD136	ST3	$60 brt grn	2,500.	275.00
RD137	ST3	$100 brt grn	900.00	110.00
RD138	ST3	$500 brt grn		15,000.
RD139	ST3	$1,000 brt grn	—	2,750.

Stock Transfer Stamps and Type of 1940 Overprinted in Black
Nos. RD67-RD91 overprinted instead   SERIES 1943

1943   Perf. 11

RD140	ST1	1c brt grn	.55	.30
RD141	ST1	2c brt grn	.60	.40
RD142	ST1	4c brt grn	2.10	.25
RD143	ST1	5c brt grn	.60	.25
RD144	ST1	10c brt grn	1.50	.25
RD145	ST1	20c brt grn	2.25	.25
RD146	ST1	25c brt grn	6.75	.35
RD147	ST1	40c brt grn	6.25	.30
RD148	ST1	50c brt grn	5.75	.30
RD149	ST1	80c brt grn	35.00	7.50
RD150	ST2	$1 brt grn	27.50	.25
RD151	ST2	$2 brt grn	30.00	.50
RD152	ST2	$3 brt grn	35.00	2.50
RD153	ST2	$4 brt grn	85.00	30.00
RD154	ST2	$5 brt grn	90.00	.60
RD155	ST2	$10 brt grn	140.00	7.50
RD156	ST2	$20 brt grn	450.00	90.00

Perf. 12
Without Gum

RD157	ST3	$30 brt grn	2,500.	750.00
RD158	ST3	$50 brt grn	2,500.	250.00
RD159	ST3	$60 brt grn	4,000.	2,750.
RD160	ST3	$100 brt grn	225.00	90.00
RD161	ST3	$500 brt grn	—	2,250.
RD162	ST3	$1,000 brt grn	2,500.	2,000.

Stock Transfer Stamps and Type of 1940 Overprinted in Black
Series 1944

1944   Perf. 11

RD163	ST1	1c brt grn	.90	.75
RD164	ST1	2c brt grn	.70	.25
RD165	ST1	4c brt grn	.70	.35
RD166	ST1	5c brt grn	.65	.25
RD167	ST1	10c brt grn	1.00	.30
RD168	ST1	20c brt grn	2.25	.25
RD169	ST1	25c brt grn	3.25	.90
RD170	ST1	40c brt grn	17.50	8.00
RD171	ST1	50c brt grn	5.50	.30
RD172	ST1	80c brt grn	17.50	6.25
RD173	ST2	$1 brt grn	17.50	.50
RD174	ST2	$2 brt grn	60.00	.75
RD175	ST2	$3 brt grn	55.00	2.00
RD176	ST2	$4 brt grn	95.00	17.50
RD177	ST2	$5 brt grn	65.00	3.50

RD178	ST2	$10 brt grn	150.00	7.25
RD179	ST2	$20 brt grn	350.00	25.00

Perf. 12
Without Gum

Designs: $2,500, William Windom. $5,000,
C. J. Folger. $10,000, W. Q. Gresham.

RD180	ST3	$30 brt grn	850.00	125.00
RD181	ST3	$50 brt	1,000.	150.00
RD182	ST3	$60 brt grn	4,750.	750.00
RD183	ST3	$100 brt	3,250.	100.00
RD184	ST3	$500 brt grn	2,500.	2,250.
RD185	ST3	$1,000 brt		
		grn	3,000.	2,500.
RD185A	ST3	$2,500 brt		
		grn		—
RD185B	ST3	$5,000 brt		
		grn	65,000.	
RD185C	ST3	$10,000 brt		
		grn,		
		cut		
		cancel	45,000.	
		Perf. initial	35,000.	

Stock Transfer Stamps and Type of
1940 Overprinted in Black
Series 1945

1945				Perf. 11
RD186	ST1	1c brt grn	.45	.25
RD187	ST1	2c brt grn	.45	.35
RD188	ST1	4c brt grn	.50	.35
RD189	ST1	5c brt grn	.45	.25
RD190	ST1	10c brt grn	1.25	.35
RD191	ST1	20c brt grn	2.25	.45
RD192	ST1	25c brt grn	3.50	.40
RD193	ST1	40c brt grn	5.00	.25
RD194	ST1	50c brt grn	11.00	.45
RD195	ST1	80c brt grn	17.50	4.75
RD196	ST2	$1 brt grn	20.00	.30
RD197	ST2	$2 brt grn	37.50	.90
RD198	ST2	$3 brt grn	65.00	1.75
RD199	ST2	$4 brt grn	65.00	4.25
RD200	ST2	$5 brt grn	40.00	
RD201	ST2	$10 brt grn	95.00	12.00
RD202	ST2	$20 brt grn	375.00	25.00

Perf. 12
Without Gum

RD203	ST3	$30 brt		
		grn	300.00	90.00
RD204	ST3	$50 brt		
		grn	275.00	70.00
RD205	ST3	$60 brt		
		grn	1,750.	500.00
RD206	ST3	$100 brt		
		grn	600.00	75.00
RD207	ST3	$500 brt		
		grn	—	1,400.
RD208	ST3	$1,000 brt		
		grn	3,250.	2,250.
RD208A	ST3	$2,500 brt		
		grn,		
		perf.		
		initial	20,000.	
RD208B	ST3	$5,000 brt		
		grn,		
		cut		
		cancel	45,000.	
RD208C	ST3	$10,000 brt		
		grn,		
		cut		
		cancel	45,000.	

Stock Transfer Stamps and Type of
1940 Overprinted in Black
Series 1946

1946				Perf. 11
RD209	ST1	1c brt grn	.50	.35
a.		Pair, one dated "1945"	850.00	
RD210	ST1	2c brt grn	.50	.25
RD211	ST1	4c brt grn	.50	.25
RD212	ST1	5c brt grn	.55	.25
RD213	ST1	10c brt grn	1.25	.25
RD214	ST1	20c brt grn	2.50	.30
RD215	ST1	25c brt grn	3.00	.40
RD216	ST1	40c brt grn	6.50	1.25
RD217	ST1	50c brt grn	6.75	.25
RD218	ST1	80c brt grn	24.00	9.50
RD219	ST2	$1 brt grn	17.50	.90
RD220	ST2	$2 brt grn	19.00	1.00
RD221	ST2	$3 brt grn	35.00	2.25
RD222	ST2	$4 brt grn	35.00	9.00
RD223	ST2	$5 brt grn	60.00	2.25
RD224	ST2	$10 brt grn	100.00	4.25
RD225	ST2	$20 brt grn	550.00	75.00

Perf. 12
Without Gum

RD226	ST3	$30 brt		
		grn	350.00	62.50
RD227	ST3	$50 brt		
		grn	450.00	75.00
RD228	ST3	$60 brt		
		grn	1,250.	250.00
RD229	ST3	$100 brt		
		grn	225.00	90.00

RD230	ST3	$500 brt		
		grn	2,500.	350.00
RD231	ST3	$1,000 brt		
		grn	2,000.	300.00
RD232	ST3	$2,500 brt		
		grn		25,000.
RD233	ST3	$5,000 brt		
		grn,		
		cut		
		can-		
		cel		17,500.
RD234	ST3	$10,000 brt		
		grn,		
		cut		
		can-		
		cel		22,500.

Stock Transfer Stamps and Type of
1940 Overprinted in Black
Series 1947

1947				Perf. 11
RD235	ST1	1c bright green	2.75	.90
RD236	ST1	2c bright green	2.75	.90
RD237	ST1	4c bright green	2.00	.70
RD238	ST1	5c bright green	2.00	.60
RD239	ST1	10c bright green	2.00	.90
RD240	ST1	20c bright green	3.75	.90
RD241	ST1	25c bright green	6.00	.90
RD242	ST1	40c bright green	6.00	1.40
RD243	ST1	50c bright green	7.50	.35
RD244	ST1	80c bright green	32.50	14.00
RD245	ST2	$1 bright green	25.00	1.00
RD246	ST2	$2 bright green	35.00	1.25
RD247	ST2	$3 bright green	50.00	2.50
RD248	ST2	$4 bright green	70.00	9.50
RD249	ST2	$5 bright green	50.00	3.25
RD250	ST2	$10 bright green	225.00	11.00
RD251	ST2	$20 bright green	300.00	50.00

Perf. 12
Without Gum

RD252	ST3	$30 brt grn	2,000.	85.00
RD253	ST3	$50 brt grn	1,500.	275.00
RD254	ST3	$60 brt grn	2,750.	250.00
RD255	ST3	$100 brt grn	175.00	70.00
RD256	ST3	$500 brt grn	2,500.	850.00
RD257	ST3	$1,000 brt grn	2,500.	140.00
RD258	ST3	$2,500 brt grn	3,000.	
		Cut cancel		400.00
RD259	ST3	$5,000 brt grn	2,500.	
		Cut cancel		600.00
RD260	ST3	$10,000 brt grn	—	
		Cut cancel		75.00
a.		Vert. pair, imperf.		
		horiz., cut cancel		—

Stock Transfer Stamps and Type of
1940 Overprinted in Black
Series 1948

1948				Perf. 11
RD261	ST1	1c bright green	.45	.35
RD262	ST1	2c bright green	.45	.35
RD263	ST1	4c bright green	.80	.45
RD264	ST1	5c bright green	.45	.25
RD265	ST1	10c bright green	.55	.35
RD266	ST1	20c bright green	1.60	.40
RD267	ST1	25c bright green	1.90	.55
RD268	ST1	40c bright green	5.00	1.00
RD269	ST1	50c bright green	7.00	.45
RD270	ST1	80c bright green	30.00	9.50
RD271	ST2	$1 bright green	17.50	.50
RD272	ST2	$2 bright green	35.00	1.00
RD273	ST2	$3 bright green	60.00	10.00
RD274	ST2	$4 bright green	70.00	20.00
RD275	ST2	$5 bright green	80.00	5.00
RD276	ST2	$10 bright green	90.00	7.25
RD277	ST2	$20 bright green	275.00	30.00

Perf. 12
Without Gum

RD278	ST3	$30 brt grn	350.00	100.00
RD279	ST3	$50 brt grn	225.00	95.00
RD280	ST3	$60 brt grn	2,000.	250.00
RD281	ST3	$100 brt grn	175.00	30.00
RD282	ST3	$500 brt grn	2,500.	375.00
RD283	ST3	$1,000 brt grn	2,500.	125.00
RD284	ST3	$2,500 brt grn	2,500.	1,750.
RD285	ST3	$5,000 brt grn	2,500.	1,750.
RD286	ST3	$10,000 brt grn		

Stock Transfer Stamps and Type of
1940 Overprinted in Black
Series 1949

1949				Perf. 11
RD287	ST1	1c bright green	2.25	.70
RD288	ST1	2c bright green	2.25	.75
RD289	ST1	4c bright green	2.50	.75
RD290	ST1	5c bright green	3.00	.75
RD291	ST1	10c bright green	7.50	1.00
RD292	ST1	20c bright green	12.00	1.00
RD293	ST1	25c bright green	13.00	1.25
RD294	ST1	50c bright green	30.00	3.25
RD295	ST1	50c bright green	35.00	.45
RD296	ST1	80c bright green	45.00	10.00
RD297	ST2	$1 bright green	32.50	1.00
RD298	ST2	$2 bright green	60.00	1.75

RD299	ST2	$3 bright green	110.00	10.00
RD300	ST2	$4 bright green	110.00	20.00
RD301	ST2	$5 bright green	85.00	3.00
RD302	ST2	$10 bright green	150.00	12.50
RD303	ST2	$20 bright green	325.00	22.50

Perf. 12
Without Gum

RD304	ST3	$30 brt		
		grn	2,000.	150.00
RD305	ST3	$50 brt		
		grn	2,250.	300.00
RD306	ST3	$60 brt		
		grn	2,500.	400.00
RD307	ST3	$100 brt		
		grn	225.00	70.00
RD308	ST3	$500 brt		
		grn	1,500.	300.00
RD309	ST3	$1,000 brt		
		grn	1,500.	85.00
RD310	ST3	$2,500 brt		
RD311	ST3	$5,000 brt		
RD312	ST3	$10,000 brt		
			475.00	
a.		Pair, one without ovpt., cut cancel	8,000.	

No. RD312a is unique.

Stock Transfer Stamps and Type of
1940 Overprinted in Black
Series 1950

1950				Perf. 11
RD313	ST1	1c bright green	.80	.70
RD314	ST1	2c bright green	.70	.35
RD315	ST1	4c bright green	.65	.40
RD316	ST1	5c bright green	.75	.25
RD317	ST1	10c bright green	3.25	.30
RD318	ST1	20c bright green	5.00	.80
RD319	ST1	25c bright green	10.00	1.00
RD320	ST1	40c bright green	15.00	1.50
RD321	ST1	50c bright green	19.00	.50
RD322	ST1	80c bright green	27.50	7.25
RD323	ST2	$1 bright green	27.50	.55
RD324	ST2	$2 bright green	40.00	1.25
RD325	ST2	$3 bright green	70.00	8.50
RD326	ST2	$4 bright green	85.00	20.00
RD327	ST2	$5 bright green	70.00	3.25
RD328	ST2	$10 bright green	210.00	12.50
RD329	ST2	$20 bright green	250.00	60.00

Perf. 12
Without Gum

RD330	ST3	$30 brt		
		grn	600.00	190.00
a.		Booklet pane of 4	3,300.	
RD331	ST3	$50 brt		
		grn	800.00	225.00
a.		Booklet pane of 4	3,300.	
RD332	ST3	$60 brt		
		grn	1,000.	250.00
a.		Booklet pane of 4	4,750.	
RD333	ST3	$100 brt		
		grn	150.00	55.00
a.		Vert. pair, imperf. btwn.	2,000.	1,750.
RD334	ST3	$500 brt		
		grn	—	350.00
RD335	ST3	$1,000 brt		
		grn	275.00	85.00
RD336	ST3	$2,500 brt		
		grn	5,500.	2,500.
a.		Booklet pane of 4	10,000.	
RD337	ST3	$5,000 brt		
		grn	5,500.	2,500.
a.		Booklet pane of 4	10,000.	
RD338	ST3	$10,000 brt		
		grn	5,500.	1,500.
a.		Booklet pane of 4	10,000.	

Stock Transfer Stamps and Type of
1940 Overprinted in Black
Series 1951

1951				Perf. 11
RD339	ST1	1c bright green	3.00	.75
RD340	ST1	2c bright green	2.50	.50
RD341	ST1	4c bright green	3.00	.75
RD342	ST1	5c bright green	2.25	.55
RD343	ST1	10c bright green	3.00	.35
RD344	ST1	20c bright green	10.00	1.25
RD345	ST1	25c bright green	12.00	1.50
RD346	ST1	40c bright green	50.00	12.50
RD347	ST1	50c bright green	20.00	1.50
RD348	ST1	80c bright green	40.00	14.00
RD349	ST2	$1 bright green	40.00	1.25
RD350	ST2	$2 bright green	55.00	1.75
RD351	ST2	$3 bright green	70.00	14.00
RD352	ST2	$4 bright green	350.00	25.00
RD353	ST2	$5 bright green	90.00	4.00
RD354	ST2	$10 bright green	170.00	11.00
RD355	ST2	$20 bright green	300.00	35.00

Perf. 12
Without Gum

RD356	ST3	$30 brt		
		grn	2,500.	200.00
RD357	ST3	$50 brt		
		grn	2,500.	125.00

RD358	ST3	$60 brt		
		grn	2,500.	1,600.
RD359	ST3	$100 brt		
		grn	250.00	100.00
RD360	ST3	$500 brt		
		grn	2,500.	550.00
RD361	ST3	$1,000 brt		
		grn	275.00	125.00
RD362	ST3	$2,500 brt		
		grn		4,250.
RD363	ST3	$5,000 brt		
		grn	—	3,250.
RD364	ST3	$10,000 brt		
		grn	2,000.	250.00

Stock Transfer Stamps and Type of
1940 Overprinted in Black
Series 1952

1952				Perf. 11
RD365	ST1	1c brt grn	42.50	27.50
RD366	ST1	10c brt grn	45.00	27.50
RD367	ST1	20c brt grn	400.00	—
RD368	ST1	25c brt grn	550.00	—
RD369	ST1	40c brt grn	140.00	55.00
RD370	ST2	$4 brt grn	1,500.	1,250.
RD371	ST2	$10 brt grn	3,500.	—
RD372	ST2	$20 brt grn	6,000.	—

Stock Transfer Stamps were discontinued in 1952.

> Catalogue values for all unused stamps in this section are for stamps with never-hinged original gum. Minor natural gum skips and bends are normal on Nos. RW1-RW20. No-gum stamps are without signature or other cancel.

HUNTING PERMIT STAMPS

> Catalogue values for all unused stamps in this section are for stamps with never-hinged original gum. Hinged examples from No. RW13 to present usually sell for 40%-60% of the values of never-hinged examples. Minor natural gum skips and bends are normal on Nos. RW1-RW20. No-gum stamps are without signature or other cancel.
>
> Nos. RW1-RW12 were issued in panes of 28, of which 10 stamps have a straight edge on one or two sides. Such examples sell for 20%-30% less than the values shown.

Department of Agriculture
Various Designs Inscribed
"U. S. Department of Agriculture"

Mallards Alighting — HP1

Engraved: Flat Plate Printing

1934		Unwmk.		Perf. 11

Inscribed "Void after June 30, 1935"

RW1	HP1	$1 blue	750.	175.
		Hinged	300.	
		No gum	175.	

Used value is for stamp with handstamp or manuscript cancel.

It is almost certain that examples of No. RW1 offered as imperforate vertical pairs or as vertical pairs imperforate horizontally are from printer's waste. Additionally, it is almost certain that all imperforate vertical pairs are pairs imperforate horizontally that have had the vertical perforations trimmed off. No horizontal imperforate pairs are known. All recorded pairs are vertical, with narrow side margins. Most examples exist without gum and with faults. Some pairs have gum on the front (which in some cases appears to have been removed).

The stamps imperforate horizontally are recorded as a unique vertical block of eight, with the other recorded varieties being the manufactured imperforate vertical pairs.

Canvasbacks Taking to Flight — HP2

1935
Inscribed "Void after June 30, 1936"
RW2 HP2 $1 rose lake 750. 160.
deep rose lake —
Hinged 375.
No gum 175.

Canada Geese in Flight — HP3

1936
Inscribed "Void after June 30, 1937"
RW3 HP3 $1 brown black 325. 100.
Hinged 150.
No gum 90.

Scaup Ducks Taking to Flight HP4

1937
Inscribed "Void after June 30, 1938"
RW4 HP4 $1 light green 300. 65.
Hinged 140.
No gum 85.

Pintail Drake and Hen Alighting — HP5

1938
Inscribed "Void after June 30, 1939"
RW5 HP5 $1 light violet 425. 75.
Hinged 200.
No gum 85.

Department of the Interior
Various Designs Inscribed
"U. S. Department of the Interior"

Green-Winged Teal — HP6

1939
Inscribed "Void after June 30, 1940"
RW6 HP6 $1 chocolate 250. 50.
Hinged 115.
No gum 60.

Black Mallards — HP7

1940
Inscribed "Void after June 30, 1941"
RW7 HP7 $1 sepia 250. 50.
Hinged 115.
No gum 60.

1941
Inscribed "Void after June 30, 1942"
RW8 HP8 $1 brown carmine 225. 50.
Hinged 95.
No gum 45.

1942
Inscribed "Void after June 30, 1943"
RW9 HP9 $1 violet brown 225. 45.
Hinged 95.
No gum 45.

1943
Inscribed "Void After June 30, 1944"
RW10 HP10 $1 deep rose 120. 35.
Hinged 55.
No gum 35.

1944
Inscribed "Void after June 30, 1945"
RW11 HP11 $1 red orange 125. 35.
Hinged 45.
No gum 35.

1945
Inscribed "Void after June 30, 1946"
RW12 HP12 $1 black 100. 25.
Hinged 45.
No gum 35.

1946
Inscribed "Void after June 30, 1947"
RW13 HP13 $1 red brown 50.00 12.50

The previously listed No. RW13a in a bright rose pink shade has been determined to be a chemically induced changeling.

1947
Inscribed "Void after June 30, 1948"
RW14 HP14 $1 black 55.00 15.00
No gum 18.00

1948
Inscribed "Void after June 30, 1949"
RW15 HP15 $1 bright blue 60.00 12.00
No gum 15.00

Goldeneye Ducks — HP16

1949
Inscribed "Void after June 30, 1950"
RW16 HP16 $2 bright green 70.00 15.00
No gum 20.00

1950
Inscribed "Void after June 30, 1951"
RW17 HP17 $2 violet 90.00 15.00
No gum 20.00

1951
Inscribed "Void after June 30, 1952"
RW18 HP18 $2 gray black 90.00 15.00
No gum 20.00

1952
Inscribed "Void after June 30, 1953"
RW19 HP19 $2 dp ultra 90.00 15.00
No gum 20.00

1953
Inscribed "Void after June 30, 1954"
RW20 HP20 $2 dp rose brn 90.00 15.00
No gum 20.00

No. RW21 and following issues are printed on dry, pregummed paper and the back inscription is printed on top of the gum, except for the self-adhesive stamp issues starting in 1998.

1954
Inscribed "Void after June 30, 1955"
RW21 HP21 $2 black 85.00 15.00
No gum 20.00

1955
Inscribed "Void after June 30, 1956"
RW22 HP22 $2 dark blue 85.00 12.50
No gum 20.00
a. Back inscription inverted 5,500. 4,500.

1956
Inscribed "Void after June 30, 1957"
RW23 HP23 $2 black 85.00 12.50
No gum 20.00

1957
Inscribed "Void After June 30, 1958"
RW24 HP24 $2 emerald 85.00 12.50
No gum 20.00
a. Back inscription inverted 7,500.

1958
Inscribed "Void after June 30, 1959"
RW25 HP25 $2 black 85.00 12.50
No gum 20.00
a. Back inscription inverted

Labrador Retriever Carrying Mallard Drake — HP26

Giori Press Printing

1959
Inscribed "Void after June 30, 1960"
RW26 HP26 $3 multi 130.00 12.50
No gum 45.00
a. Back inscription inverted 15,000. 12,500.

Redhead Ducks — HP27

1960
Inscribed "Void after June 30, 1961"
RW27 HP27 $3 multi 95.00 12.50
No gum 30.00

1961
Inscribed "Void after June 30, 1962"
RW28 HP28 $3 multicolored 95.00 12.50
No gum 30.00

Pintail Drakes — HP29

1962
Inscribed "Void after June 30, 1963"
RW29 HP29 $3 multicolored 110.00 12.50
No gum 35.00
a. Back inscription omitted —

1963
Inscribed "Void after June 30, 1964"
RW30 HP30 $3 multicolored 100.00 12.50
No gum 35.00

1964
Inscribed "Void after June 30, 1965"
RW31 HP31 $3 multicolored 100.00 12.50
No gum 35.00

1965
Inscribed "Void after June 30, 1966"
RW32 HP32 $3 multicolored 100.00 12.50
No gum 40.00

Whistling Swans — HP33

1966
Inscribed "Void after June 30, 1967"
RW33 HP33 $3 multi 100.00 12.50
No gum 40.00

1967
Inscribed "Void after June 30, 1968"
RW34 HP34 $3 multicolored 100.00 12.50
No gum 40.00

1968
Inscribed "Void after June 30, 1969"
RW35 HP35 $3 multicolored 65.00 12.50
No gum 20.00
a. Back inscription omitted —

White-winged Scoters — HP36

1969
Inscribed "Void after June 30, 1970"
RW36 HP36 $3 multi   65.00   8.00
    No gum   20.00

1970   **Engraved & Lithographed**
Inscribed "Void after June 30, 1971"
RW37 HP37 $3 multi   65.00   8.00
    No gum   20.00

1971
Inscribed "Void after June 30, 1972"
RW38 HP38 $3 multi   42.50   8.00
    No gum   15.00

1972
Inscribed "Void after June 30, 1973"
RW39 HP39 $5 multi   30.00   6.00
    No gum   8.00

1973
Inscribed "Void after June 30, 1974"
RW40 HP40 $5 multi   18.00   6.00
    No gum   7.00

1974
Inscribed "Void after June 30, 1975"
RW41 HP41 $5 multi   18.00   5.00
    No gum   6.00
a.   Back inscription missing,
     but printed vertically on
     face of stamp and
     selvage, from foldover   4,750.

1975
Inscribed "Void after June 30, 1976"
RW42 HP42 $5 multi   15.00   5.00
    No gum   7.00

1976   **Engr.**
Inscribed "Void after June 30, 1977"
RW43 HP43 $5 grn & blk   12.50   5.00

1977   **Litho. & Engr.**
Inscribed "Void after June 30, 1978"
RW44 HP44 $5 multi   10.00   5.00
    No gum   7.00

Hooded Merganser — HP45

1978
Inscribed "Void after June 30, 1979"
RW45 HP45 $5 multicolored   10.00   5.00
    No gum   7.00

1979
Inscribed "Void after June 30, 1980"
RW46 HP46 $7.50 multi   12.50   6.00
    No gum   8.00

1980
Inscribed "Void after June 30, 1981"
RW47 HP47 $7.50 multi   12.50   6.00
    No gum   8.00

1981
Inscribed "Void after June 30, 1982"
RW48 HP48 $7.50 multi   12.50   6.00
    No gum   8.00

1982
Inscribed "Void after June 30, 1983"
RW49 HP49 $7.50 multi   15.00   7.00
    No gum   9.00
a.   Orange and violet omit-
     ted   10,000.

A certificate from a recognized expertization committee is required for No. RW49a.

1983
Inscribed "Void after June 30, 1984"
RW50 HP50 $7.50 multi   15.00   7.00
    No gum   7.00

1984
Inscribed "Void after June 30, 1985"
RW51 HP51 $7.50 multi   12.50   7.00
    No gum   7.00

1985
Inscribed "Void after June 30, 1986"
RW52 HP52 $7.50 multi   15.00   8.00
    No gum   7.00
a.   Light blue (litho.)
     omitted   20,000.

The omitted color on No. RW52a coincides with a double paper splice affecting the top row of five stamps from the sheet and top ⅓ of stamps in the second row. There is also a color changeling of the brownish red ducks and their reflections in the water to yellow and yellow orange, respectively, on the error stamps. This error currently exists as three vertical strips of 6 (top stamp the error) and a plate number block of 12 (2x6, top two stamps the error).

1986
Inscribed "Void after June 30, 1987"
RW53 HP53 $7.50 multi   15.00   8.00
    No gum   9.00
a.   Black omitted   1,450.

1987   **Perf. 11½x11**
Inscribed "Void after June 30, 1988"
RW54 HP54 $10 multi   17.50   8.00
    No gum   8.00

1988
Inscribed "Void after June 30, 1989"
RW55 HP55 $10 multicolored   17.50   8.00
    No gum   8.00

1989
Inscribed "Void after June 30, 1990"
RW56 HP56 $12.50 multi   21.50   8.00
    No gum   9.00

1990
Inscribed "Void after June 30, 1991"
RW57 HP57 $12.50 multi   20.00   8.00
    No gum   9.00
a.   Back inscription omitted   300.00
b.   Black inscription printed
     on the stamp paper
     rather than the gum
     of stamp   —

The back inscription is normally on top of the gum so beware of examples with gum removed offered as No. RW57a. Full original gum must be intact on No. RW57a. Used examples of No. RW57a cannot exist.

Some philatelic researchers have questioned the existence of No. RW57b as a genuine error. There appears to be evidence that the inscriptions printed on the gum on the back can leach through to the paper on one of the types of gums used on these stamps. Further research is ongoing.

King Eiders — HP58

1991
Inscribed "Void after June 30, 1992"
RW58 HP58 $15 multi   30.00   8.00
    No gum   15.00
a.   Black (engr.) omitted   20,000.

1992
Inscribed "Void after June 30, 1993"
RW59 HP59 $15 multi   30.00   10.00
    No gum   15.00

1993
Inscribed "Void after June 30, 1994"
RW60 HP60 $15 multi   27.50   9.00
    No gum   15.00
a.   Black (engr.) omitted   1,750.   1,500.

1994   **Perf. 11¼x11**
Inscribed "Void after June 30, 1995"
RW61 HP61 $15 multi   27.50   10.00
    No gum   15.00

1995
Inscribed "Void after June 30, 1996"
RW62 HP62 $15 multi   32.50   12.00
    No gum   15.00

1996
Inscribed "Void after June 30, 1997"
RW63 HP63 $15 multi   32.50   12.00
    No gum   12.50

1997
Inscribed "Void after June 30, 1998"
RW64 HP64 $15 multi   27.50   12.00
    No gum   15.00

1998   **Perf. 11¼**
Inscribed "Void after June 30, 1999"
RW65 HP65 $15 multi   45.00 22.50
    No gum   22.50

Self-Adhesive
Die Cut Perf. 10

RW65A HP65 $15 multi   30.00 15.00
    No gum   15.00

> Nos. RW65 and later issues were sold in panes of 30 (RW65 and RW66) or 20 (RW67 and later issues), with four plate numbers per pane. The self-adhesives starting with No. RW65A were sold in panes of 1. The self-adhesives are valued unused as complete panes and used as single stamps.

1999   **Perf. 11¼**
Inscribed "Void after June 30, 2000"
RW66 HP66 $15 multi   40.00 20.00
    No gum   22.50

Self-Adhesive
Die Cut Perf. 10

RW66A HP66 $15 multi   30.00 12.00
    No gum   15.00

2000   **Perf. 11¼**
Inscribed "Void after June 30, 2001"
RW67 HP67 $15 multi   35.00
    No gum   17.50

Self-Adhesive
Die Cut Perf. 10

RW67A HP67 $15 multi   30.00 14.00
    No gum   17.50

2001   **Perf. 11¼**
Inscribed "Void after June 30, 2002"
RW68 HP68 $15 multi   35.00 18.00
    No gum   17.50

Self-Adhesive
Die Cut Perf. 10

RW68A HP68 $15 multi   30.00 14.00
    No gum   15.00

2002   **Perf. 11¼**
Inscribed "Void after June 30, 2003"
RW69 HP69 $15 multi   35.00 16.00
    No gum   17.50

Self-Adhesive
Serpentine Die Cut 11x10¾

RW69A HP69 $15 multi   30.00 12.00
    No gum   15.00

2003   **Perf. 11**
Inscribed "Void after June 30, 2004"
RW70 HP70 $15 multi   35.00 16.00
    No gum   17.50
b.   Imperf, pair   5,000.
c.   Back inscription omit-
     ted   4,500.

Self-Adhesive
Serpentine Die Cut 11x10¾

RW70A HP70 $15 multi   30.00 12.00
    No gum   15.00

2004   **Perf. 11**
Inscribed "Void after June 30, 2005"
RW71 HP71 $15 multicolored 35.00 16.00
    No gum   17.00

Self-Adhesive
Serpentine Die Cut 11x10¾

RW71A HP71 $15 multicolored 30.00 12.00
    No gum   15.00

2005   **Litho. & Engr.**   **Perf. 11**
Inscribed "Void after June 30, 2006".
RW72 HP72 $15 multi,
           type I   30.00 16.00
b.   Souvenir sheet of 1   1,950.
c.   Type II   30.00 16.00
     No gum   16.00

d.   As "b," without art-
     ist's signature (er-
     ror)   3,250.

There are two types of RW72: type I has no frame lines; type II has gray frame lines at top, right and bottom edges of design. No. RW72c, the type II stamp, is any stamp from the right two panes of the sheet of four panes. No. RW72, the Type I stamp, is any stamp from the left two panes.

No. RW72b sold for $20. 1,000 No. RW72b were issued. Approximately 750 were signed by the artist in black, value $1,950 as shown. Approximately 150 were signed in blue ink, value $2,500. Approximately 100 were signed in gold ink, value $3,000. Most examples of No. RW72b are in the grade of F-VF. Catalogue values are for Very Fine examples.

The Duck Stamp Office never announced the existence of No. RW72b to the public through a press release or a website announcement during the time the sheet was on sale, apparently because it was not clear beforehand that the souvenir sheet could be produced successfully and on time. No. RW72b sold out before a public announcement of the item's existence could be made.

Self-Adhesive
Litho. & Debossed
Serpentine Die Cut 11x10¾

RW72A HP72 $15 multi   27.50 11.00
    No gum   15.00

Ross's Goose — HP73

2006   **Litho. & Engr.**   **Perf. 11**
Inscribed "Void after June 30, 2007"
RW73   HP73 $15 multi   25.00 11.00
    No gum   15.00
b.   Souvenir sheet of 1   95.00   —
c.   As "b," without art-
     ist's signature (er-
     ror)   2,500.

No. RW73b sold for $25. All examples of No. RW73b have a black signature of the artist on a designated line in the sheet margin. Ten thousand were issued.

The sheet margin has a line designated for the signature of the engraver, Piotr Naszarkowski, but no sheets were sold with his signature. Naszarkowski signed approximately 2,500 sheets during three days at the Washington 2006 World Philatelic Exhibition, and he signed another 2,500 or more after the conclusion of the exhibition. Value $150.

Self-Adhesive
Serpentine Die Cut 11x10¾

RW73A HP73 $15 multi   25.00 11.00
    No gum   15.00

Ring-necked Ducks — HP74

2007   **Litho.**   **Perf. 11**
Inscribed "Void after June 30, 2008"
RW74   HP74 $15 multi   35.00 11.00
    No gum   16.00
b.   Souvenir sheet of 1   140.00
c.   As "b," without art-
     ist's signature (er-
     ror)   2,750.

No. RW74b sold for $25 plus a shipping fee. The artist signed No. RW74b on a designated line in the sheet margin. Ten thousand were issued. There is no back inscription on No. RW74b.

Self-Adhesive
Serpentine Die Cut 11x10¾

RW74A HP74 $15 multi   25.00 11.00
    No gum   15.00

Northern Pintails — HP75

2008   **Litho.**   **Perf. 13¼**
Inscribed "Void after June 30, 2009"
RW75   HP75 $15 multi   35.00   11.00
    No gum   16.00
    b.   Souvenir sheet of 1   70.00   —
    c.   As "b," without artist's
       signature (error)   *500.00*

Self-Adhesive
Serpentine Die Cut 10¾
RW75A   HP75 $15 multi   32.50   11.00
    No gum   25.00

2009   **Litho.**   **Perf. 13¼**
Inscribed "Void after June 30, 2010"
RW76   HP76 $15 multi   30.00   11.00
    No gum   16.00
    b.   Souvenir sheet of 1   60.00
    c.   As "b," without artist's
       signature (error)   *400.00*

No. RW76b sold for $30 plus a shipping fee. The artist signed No. RW76b on a designated line in the sheet margin. Ten thousand were prepared.

Self-Adhesive
Serpentine Die Cut 11x10¾
RW76A   HP76 $15 multi   27.50   11.00
    No gum   20.00

2010   **Litho.**   **Perf. 11¼x11**
Inscribed "Void after June 30, 2011"
RW77   HP77 $15 multi   27.50   11.00
    No gum   16.00
    b.   Souvenir sheet of 1,
       perf. 13¼   55.00
    c.   As "b," without artist's
       signature (error)   *225.00*

No. RW77b was sold for $30 plus a shipping fee. The artist signed No. RW77b on a designated line in the sheet margin. Ten thousand were prepared. There is no back inscription on No. RW77b, and the stamp on the sheet is tagged.

Self-Adhesive
Serpentine Die Cut 11x10¾
RW77A   HP77 $15 multi   27.50   11.00
    No gum   20.00

White-fronted Geese — HP78

2011   **Litho.**   **Perf. 13¼**
Inscribed "Void after June 30, 2012"
RW78   HP78 $15 multi   37.50   11.00
    No gum   16.00
    b.   Souvenir sheet of 1   60.00
    c.   As "b," without artist's
       signature (error)   *175.00*

No. RW78b was sold for $25 plus a shipping fee. The artist signed No. RW78b on a designated line in the sheet margin. Ten thousand were prepared.

Self-Adhesive
Serpentine Die Cut 11x10¾
RW78A   HP78 $15 multi   27.50   11.00
    No gum   20.00

Wood Duck — HP79

2012   **Litho.**   **Perf. 13¼**
Inscribed "Void after June 30, 2013"
RW79   HP79 $15 multi   37.50   11.00
    No gum   16.00
    b.   Souvenir sheet of 1   60.00
    c.   As "b," without artist's
       signature (error)   *1,750.*

No. RW79b was sold for $25 plus a shipping fee. The artist signed No. RW79b on a designated line in the sheet margin. There is a back inscription on No. RW79b. Five thousand were prepared.

One No. RW79b was signed in red ink as a "surprise" for a random buyer. This was not authorized.

Self-Adhesive
Serpentine Die Cut 11x10¾
RW79A   HP79 $15 multi   32.50   11.00
    No gum   20.00

Common Goldeneye — HP80

2013   **Litho.**   **Perf. 13¼**
Inscribed "Void after June 30, 2014"
RW80   HP80 $15 multi   37.50   11.00
    No gum   16.00
    b.   Souvenir sheet of 1   80.00
    c.   As "b," without artist's
       signature (error)   *1,250.*

No. RW80b was sold for $25 plus a shipping fee. The artist signed No. RW80b on a designated line in the sheet margin. There is a back inscription on No. RW80b. Five thousand were prepared.

Self-Adhesive
Serpentine Die Cut 11x10¾
RW80A   HP80 $15 multi   30.00   11.00
    No gum   20.00

Canvasbacks — HP81

2014   **Litho.**   **Perf. 13¼**
Inscribed "Void after June 30, 2015"
RW81   HP81 $15 multi   35.00   11.00
    No gum   16.00

Self-Adhesive
Serpentine Die Cut 11x10¾
RW81A   HP81 $15 multi   30.00   12.50
    No gum   20.00

Ruddy Ducks — HP82

2015   **Litho.**   **Perf. 13¼**
Inscribed "Void after June 30, 2016"
RW82   HP82 $25 multi   50.00   12.00
    No gum   25.00

Self-Adhesive
Serpentine Die Cut 11x10¾
RW82A   HP82 $25 multi   50.00   12.50
    No gum   32.50

Trumpeter Swans — HP83

2016   **Litho.**   **Perf. 13¼**
Inscribed "Void after June 30, 2017"
RW83   HP83 $25 multi   70.00   15.00
    No gum   40.00

Self-Adhesive
Serpentine Die Cut 11x10¾
RW83A   HP83 $25 multi   55.00   12.50
    No gum   32.50

Canada Geese — HP84

2017   **Litho.**   **Perf. 13¼**
Inscribed "Void after June 30, 2018"
RW84   HP84 $25 multi   42.50   12.50
    No gum   25.00

Self-Adhesive
Serpentine Die Cut 11x10¾
RW84A   HP84 $25 multi   40.00   12.50
    No gum   32.50

Mallards — HP85

Serpentine Die Cut 11x10¾
2018   **Litho.**
Inscribed "Void after June 30, 2019"
Self-Adhesive
RW85   HP85 $25 multi   50.00   12.50
    No gum   25.00
    b.   Souvenir sheet of 4   200.00

Sheet of 1
RW85A   HP85 $25 multi   45.00   12.50
    No gum   32.50

Inscriptions on the backing paper differ for Nos. RW85, RW85A, and RW85b. Once removed from the backing paper, used examples are considered to be No. RW85.

Wood Duck and Decoy — HP86

Serpentine Die Cut 11x10¾
2019   **Litho.**
Inscribed "Void after June 30, 2020"
Self-Adhesive
RW86   HP86 $25 multi   40.00   12.50
    No gum   25.00

Sheet of 1
RW86A   HP86 $25 multi   40.00   12.50
    No gum   32.50

Inscriptions on the backing paper differ for Nos. RW86 and RW86A. Once removed from the backing paper, used examples are considered to be No. RW86.

Black-bellied Whistling Ducks — HP87

Serpentine Die Cut 11x10¾
2020   **Litho.**
Inscribed "Void after June 30, 2021"
Self-Adhesive
RW87   HP87 $25 multi   37.50   12.50
    No gum   25.00

Sheet of 1
RW87A   HP87 $25 multi   37.50   12.50
    No gum   32.50

Inscriptions on the backing paper differ for Nos. RW87 and RW87A. Once removed from the backing paper, used examples are considered to be No. RW87.

CONFEDERATE STATES OF AMERICA

3¢ 1861 POSTMASTERS' PROVISIONALS

With the secession of South Carolina from the Union on Dec. 20, 1860, a new era began in U.S. history as well as its postal history. Other Southern states quickly followed South Carolina's lead, which in turn led to the formation of the provisional government of the Confederate States of America on Feb. 4, 1861.

President Jefferson Davis' cabinet was completed Mar. 6, 1861, with the acceptance of the position of Postmaster General by John H. Reagan of Texas. The provisional government had already passed regulations that required payment for postage in cash and that effectively carried over the U.S. 3c rate until the new Confederate Post Office Department took over control of the system.

Soon after entering on his duties, Reagan directed the postmasters in the Confederate States and in the newly seceded states to "continue the performance of their duties as such, and render all accounts and pay all moneys (sic) to the order of the Government of the U.S. as they have heretofore done, until the Government of the Confederate States shall be prepared to assume control of its postal affairs."

As coinage was becoming scarce, postal patrons began having problems buying individual stamps or paying for letters individually, especially as stamp stocks started to run short in certain areas. Even though the U.S. Post Office Department was technically in control of the postal system and southern postmasters were operating under Federal authority, the U.S.P.O. was hesitant in re-supplying seceded states with additional stamps and stamped envelopes.

The U.S. government had made the issuance of postmasters' provisionals illegal many years before, but the southern postmasters had to do what they felt was necessary to allow patrons to pay for postage and make the system work. Therefore, a few postmasters took it upon themselves to issue provisional stamps in the 3c rate then in effect.

Interestingly, these were stamps and envelopes that the U.S. government did not recognize as legal, but they did do postal duty unchallenged in the Confederate States. Yet the proceeds were to be remitted to the U.S. government in Washington! Six authenticated postmasters' provisionals in the 3c rate have been recorded.

On May 13, 1861, Postmaster General Reagan issued his proclamation "assuming control and direction of postal service within the limits of the Confederate States of America on and after the first day of June," with new postage rates and regulations.

The Federal government suspended operations in the Confederate States (except for western Virginia and the seceding state of Tennessee) by a proclamation issued by Postmaster General Montgomery Blair on May 27, 1861, effective from May 31, 1861, and June 10 for western and middle Tennessee.

As Tennessee did not join the Confederacy until July 2, 1861, the unissued 3c Nashville provisional was produced in a state that was in the process of seceding, while the other provisionals were used in the Confederacy before the June 1 assumption of control of postal service by the Confederate States of America.

Illustrations are reduced in size.

XU numbers are envelope entires.

DARLINGTON C.H., S. C.

E1

Handstamped Envelope
8AXU1 E1 3c black   3,500.
One example of No. 8AXU1 is recorded, used under a pair of C.S.A. No. 7. To be a provisional, the 3¢ marking must be unused or used under Confederate stamps.

FORT VALLEY, GA.

E1

E2

Handstamped Envelope
7AXU1 E1 3c black   —

HILLSBORO, N.C.

A1

Handstamped Adhesive
1AX1 A1 3c bluish black,
                  on cover   —
No. 1AX1 is unique. This is the same hand stamp as used for No. 39X1. 3c usage is determined from the May 27, 1861 circular date stamp.

JACKSON, MISS.

E1

Handstamped Envelope
2AXU1 E1 3c black   3,000.
See Nos. 43XU1-43XU4.
No. 2AXU1 is unique. It is on a southern patriotic cover.

MADISON COURT HOUSE, FLA.

A1

"CNETS"

Typeset Adhesive
3AX1 A1 3c gold   —   20,000.
   a. "CNETS"   22,500.
No. 3AX1a is unique.

See No. 137XU1.

NASHVILLE, TENN.

A1

Typeset Adhesive (5 varieties)
4AX1 A1 3c carmine   400.

For more than 150 years, it has been believed that No. 4AX1 was prepared by Postmaster McNish with the U.S. rate, but it was not issued. Recent research and historical evidence indicate that this "stamp" most likely is a fantasy rather than a genuine stamp.
See Nos. 61X2-61XU2.

SELMA, ALA.

E1

Handstamped Envelope
5AXU1 E1 3c black   1,950.
See Nos. 77XU1-77XU3.

TUSCUMBIA, ALA.

E1

Handstamped Envelope, impression at upper right
6AXU1 E1 3c dull red,
                  buff   30,000.
Dangerous forgeries exist of No. 6AXU1.
See Nos. 84XU1-84XU3.

For later additions, listed out of numerical sequence, see:
#7AXU1, Fort Valley, Ga.
#8AXU1, Darlington, C.H., S.C.

POSTMASTERS' PROVISIONAL ISSUES

These stamps and envelopes were issued by individual postmasters generally between June 1, 1861, when the use of U.S. stamps stopped in the Confederacy, and Oct. 16, 1861, when the 1st Confederate Government stamps were issued.

They were occasionally issued at later periods, especially in Texas, when regular issues of Government stamps were unavailable.

Canceling stamps of the post offices were often used to produce envelopes, some of which were supplied in advance by private citizens.

These envelopes and other stationery therefore may be found in a wide variety of papers, colors, sizes & shapes, including patriotic and semi-official types.

It is often difficult to determine whether the impression made by the canceling stamp indicates provisional usage or merely postage paid at the time the letter was deposited in the post office. Occasionally the same mark was used for both purposes.

The *press-printed* provisional envelopes are in a different category. They were produced in quantity, using envelopes procured in advance by the postmaster, such as those of Charleston, Lynchburg, Memphis, etc.

The press-printed envelopes are listed and valued on all known papers.

The handstamped provisional envelopes are listed and valued according to type and variety of handstamp, but not according to paper. Many exist on such a variety of papers that they defy accurate, complete listing.

The value of a handstamped provisional envelope is determined *primarily* by the clarity of the markings and its overall condition and attractiveness, rather than type of paper.

All handstamped provisional envelopes, when used, should also show the postmark of the town of issue.

Most handstamps are impressed at top right, although they exist from some towns in other positions.

Illustrations in this section are reduced in size.

XU numbers are envelope entires.

ABERDEEN, MISS.

E1

Handstamped Envelopes

1XU1	E1	5c black		5,500.
a.		10c (ms.) on 5c black		9,000.

No. 1XU1a is unique.

ABINGDON, VA.

E1

Handstamped Envelopes

2XU1	E1	2c black		12,500.
a.		5c (ms.) on 2c black		15,000.
2XU2	E1	5c black		1,500.
2XU3	E1	10c black	2,200.	3,500.

No. 2XU1 is unique. No. 2XU3 unused and used are each unique.

ALBANY, GA.

E1

E2

E3

E4

Handstamped Envelopes

3XU1	E1	5c greenish blue	1,000.
3XU2	E2	10c greenish blue	1,750.
a.		10c on 5c greenish blue	3,500.
3XU5	E3	5c greenish blue	—
3XU6	E4	10c greenish blue	3,500.

Only one example each recorded of Nos. 3XU2, 3XU2a and 3XU6. No. 3XU2 is a cover front only and is valued as such. No. 3XU2a is the unique Confederate example of one provisional marking revaluing another.

The existence of No. 3XU5 is in question. The editors would like to see an authenticated example of this marking.

ANDERSON COURT HOUSE, S.C.

E1

E2

E3

Handstamped Envelopes

4XU1	E1	5c black	1,000.	2,750.
4XU2	E2	10c (ms.) black		2,500.
4XU3	E3	(2c) black, denomination omitted (circular rate)		2,250.

ATHENS, GA

A1 — Type I

A1 — Type II

E1

Typographed Adhesives
(from woodcuts of two types)

Pairs, both horizontal and vertical, always show one of each type.

5X1	A1	5c purple (shades)	1,000.	1,400.
a.		Tete beche pair (vertical)		7,500.
5X2	A1	5c red, type II	5,750.	3,000.

The colorless ornaments in the four corners of No. 5X2 were recut making them wider than those in No. 5X1.

Dangerous fakes exist of Nos. 5X1 and 5X2. Certificates of authenticity from recognized committees are strongly recommended. No. 5X2 is unique.

Handstamped Envelopes

5XU1	E1	10c black, on patriotic cover	2,500.

The markings on No. 5XU1 are the same as those used on stampless envelopes. On the unique listed example of No. 5XU1, there is a handwritten note on the inside of the flap: 'Andrew had these envelopes stamped & I am obliged to use them or loose the postage.' Two or more similar covers from the same correspondence are known, but without the note under the flap. While these also may be provisional use, it cannot be proven, and these covers are considered handstamp paid covers.

ATLANTA, GA.

E1

E2

E2

Handstamped Envelopes

6XU1	E1	5c red		5,000.
6XU2	E1	5c black	160.	700.
a.		10c on 5c black		2,500.
6XU4	E3	2c black		2,750.
6XU5	E3	5c black		1,250.
a.		10c on 5c black		2,500.
6XU6	E3	10c black		500.

Only one example recorded of No. 6XU1.

E3

Handstamped Envelopes

6XU8	E3	5c black	3,500.
6XU9	E3	10c black ("10" upright)	3,000.

Only one example recorded of No. 6XU8.

AUSTIN, MISS.

E1

Press-printed Envelope (typeset)

8XU1	E1	5c red, *amber*	75,000.

One example recorded.

AUSTIN, TEX.

E1a

Handstamped Adhesive

9X1	E1a	10c black, *white* or *buff*	—

Handstamped Envelope

9XU1	E1a	10c black	2,500.

AUTAUGAVILLE, ALA.

E1

E2

Handstamped Envelopes

10XU1	E1	5c black	20,000.
10XU2	E2	5c black	20,000.

No. 10XU2 is unique.

BALCONY FALLS, VA.

E1

Handstamped Envelope

122XU1	E1	10c blue	2,000.

The use of No. 122XU1 as a provisional marking is in question. The editors would like to see authenticated evidence of its use as a provisional.

BARNWELL COURT HOUSE, S. C.

E1

Handstamped Envelope

123XU1	E1	5c black	3,000.

These are two separate handstamps. All recorded uses are on addressed covers without postmarks.

BATON ROUGE, LA.

A1

A2

Typeset Adhesives
Ten varieties of each
11X1 A1   2c green   8,250.   5,000.
   a.   "McCcrmick"   35,000.   35,000.
11X2 A2   5c **green &**
       carmine   1,500.   1,400.
   a.   "McCcrmick"   10,000.   3,500.

Only one example each is recorded of No. 11X1a unused, used and on cover.

A3

A4

Ten varieties of each
11X3 A3   5c green &
       carmine   10,000.   4,000.
   a.   "McCcrmick"   32,500.
11X4 A4   10c blue   50,000.

BEAUFORT, S. C.

E1

Handstamped Envelope
150XU1 E1 5c black   —   3,500.

To be the No. 150XU1 provisional, the cover must be unused, used under a Confederate stamp, or used from another town. Two examples are recorded.

BEAUMONT, TEX.

A1

A2

Typeset Adhesives
Several varieties of each
12X1 A1 10c black, *yellow*   65,000.
12X2 A1 10c black, *pink*   30,000.
12X3 A2 10c black, *yellow*,
       on cover   250,000.

One example recorded of No. 12X3. Value represents auction realization in 2019.

BLUFFTON, S. C.

E1

Handstamped Envelope
124XU1 E1 5c black   4,750.
Only one example recorded of No. 124XU1.

BRIDGEVILLE, ALA.

A1

Handstamped Adhesive in black within red pen-ruled squares
13X1 A1 5c black & red,
     pair on cover   20,000.

CAMDEN, S. C.

E1

E2

Handstamped Envelopes
125XU1 E1 5c black   2,500.
125XU2 E2 10c black   750.

No. 125XU2 unused was privately carried and is addressed but has no postal markings. No. 125XU2 is indistinguishable from a handstamp paid cover when used.

CANTON, MISS.

E1

"P" in star is initial of Postmaster William Priestly.

Handstamped Envelopes
14XU1 E1   5c black   3,500.
   a.   10c (ms.) on 5c black   5,000.

CAROLINA CITY, N. C.

E1

Handstamped Envelope
118XU1 E1   5c black   5,000.

CARTERSVILLE, GA.

E1

Handstamped Envelope
126XU1 E1   (5c) red   1,500.

CHAPEL HILL, N. C.

E1

Handstamped Envelope
15XU1 E1 5c black   4,500.

CHARLESTON, S. C.

A1

E1

E2

Lithographed Adhesive
16X1   A1   5c blue   1,400.   800.

Values are for stamps showing parts of the outer frame lines on at least 3 sides. The vast majority of this stamp small faults and are valued thus. Completely sound examples are scarce and sell for more.

Press-printed Envelopes
(typographed from woodcut)
16XU1 E1   5c blue   1,250.   1,750.
16XU2 E1   5c blue, *amber*   1,250.   2,250.
16XU3 E1   5c blue, *orange*   1,250.   2,250.
16XU4 E1   5c blue, *buff*   1,250.   1,500.
16XU5 E1   5c blue, *blue*   1,250.   2,250.
16XU6 E2 10c blue, *orange*   80,000.

The No. 16XU6 used entire is unique; value based on 1997 auction sale.
Beware of fakes of the E1 design.

Handstamped Cut Square
16XU7 E2 10c black   2,000.

There is only one example of No. 16XU7. It is a cutout, not an entire. It may not have been mailed from Charleston, and it may not have paid postage.

CHARLOTTE, N. C.

E1

146XU1   E1 5c blue, "5" in
      circle and
      straight line
      "PAID"   8,500.

CHARLOTTESVILLE, VA.

E1

Control

Handstamped Envelopes, Manuscript Initials "WmMK"
127XU1 E1   5c blue   2,250.
127XU2 E1 10c blue   2,250.

The control initials appear at the upper right on the front of the envelope.

CHATTANOOGA, TENN.

E1

E2

Handstamped Envelopes
17XU2 E1   5c black   1,900.
17XU3 E2   5c on 2c black   5,000.
     No. 17XU3 is unique.

CHRISTIANSBURG, VA.

E1

Handstamped Envelopes
Impressed at top right
99XU1 E1   5c black   2,250.
99XU2 E1   5c blue   2,000.
99XU4 E1   5c green on U.S.
      envelope No.
      U27   4,250.
99XU5 E1 10c blue   3,500.

The absence of 5c and 10c handstamped paid markings from this town suggests that Nos. 99XU1-99XU5 were used as both provisional and handstamped paid markings.

COLAPARCHEE, GA.

E1

Control

Handstamped Envelope
119XU1 E1   5c black   3,500.

There are only two recorded examples of No. 119XU1, and both are used from Savannah with a general issue stamp.
The control appears on the front of the envelope.

COLUMBIA, S. C.

Oval Control

Circular Control

E1

E2

E3

E4

E5

E6

E7

E8

Handstamped Envelopes

18XU1	E1	5c blue	550.	800.
a.		10c on 5c blue		3,500.
18XU4	E2	5c blue, oval control on front		2,500.
a.		Oval control on back		1,250.
18XU7	E3	5c blue, oval control on back		1,000.
18XU8	E4	5c blue oval control on back		1,000.
a.		Circular control on back		2,000.
18XU9	E4	10c blue oval control on back		1,250.
18XU10	E5	10c blue oval control on back		1,500.
18XU11	E6	5c blue oval control on front		2,500.
18XU12	E6	10c blue oval control on back		1,250.
18XU13	E7	5c blue oval control on back		1,000.
a.		Circular control on back		1,500.
18XU14	E8	5c blue oval control on back		1,000.
a.		No control (unused)		—

COLUMBIA, TENN.

E1

Handstamped Envelope

113XU1	E1	5c red	6,000.

One example recorded.

COLUMBUS, GA.

E1

Handstamped Envelopes

19XU1	E1	5c blue	900.
19XU2	E1	10c red	3,250.

COURTLAND, ALA.

E1

Handstamped Envelopes (from woodcut)

103XU1	E1	5c red	32,500.

One example recorded.

CUTHBERT, GA

E1

Handstamped Envelope

95XU1	E1	10c black	1,000.

The unique example of No. 95XU1 was used by having a C.S.A. 10c #12c placed over it.

DALTON, GA

E1

Handstamped Envelopes

20XU1	E1	5c black	750.
a.		Denomination omitted (5c rate)	875.
b.		10c (ms.) on 5c black	1,500.
c.		20c (ms.) on 5c black	1,250.
20XU2	E1	10c black	1,250.

DANVILLE, VA.

A1

Design measures 60x37mm — E1

E2

E3

E4

E5

E6

Typeset Adhesive
Wove Paper

21X1	A1	5c red	7,500.

Two varieties known.

Laid Paper

21X2	A1	5c red	10,000.

No. 21X2 is unique.

Press-printed Envelopes (typographed)

Two types: "SOUTHERN" in straight or curved line
Impressed (usually) at top left

21XU1	E1	5c black	6,000.
21XU2	E1	5c black, *light yellowish*	6,000.
21XU3	E1	5c black, *dark buff*	6,000.

Unissued 10c envelopes (type E1, in red) are known. All recorded examples are envelopes that show evidence of added stamps being torn off.
Dangerous forgeries exist of No. 21XU1.

Handstamped Envelopes

21XU3A	E2	5c black (ms "WBP" initials)	1,000.
21XU3B	E3	5c black (ms "WPB" initials)	8,500.
21XU4	E4	10c black	2,500.
21XU6	E5	10c black	2,750.
21XU7	E6	10c black (ms "WBP" initials)	—

Types E4 and E5 both exist on one cover. On No. 21XU3B, the "PAID 5 Cents" handstamp is to the left, and the "PAID" and ms. "5" are toward the right. It is unique.

DEMOPOLIS, ALA.

E1

Handstamped Envelopes, Signature in ms.

22XU1	E1	5c black ("Jno. Y. Hall")	3,500.
22XU2	E1	5c black ("J. Y. Hall")	3,500.
22XU3	E1	5c (ms.) black ("J. Y. Hall")	4,000.

EATONTON, GA.

E1

E2

Handstamped Envelopes

23XU1	E1	5c black	3,000.
a.		10 (ms) on 5c black	—
23XU2	E2	5c + 5c black	5,500.

EMORY, VA.

A1

Handstamped Adhesives ("PAID" and "5" in circle on selvage of U.S. 1c 1857 issue)
Perf. 15 on three sides

24X1	A1	5c blue, on cover, tied	27,500.
		On cover, not tied	22,500.

Also known with "5" above "PAID."

E1

E2

Handstamped Envelopes

24XU1	E1	5c black	4,000.
24XU2	E2	10c blue	5,000.

One example each recorded of Nos. 24XU1 and 24XU2.

FINCASTLE, VA.

E1

Press-printed Envelope (typeset)
Impressed at top right

104XU1	E1	10c black	20,000.

One example recorded of No. 104XU1.

FORSYTH, GA.

E2

E1

Handstamped Envelope

120XU1	E1	10c black	2,000.
120XU2	E2	10c black	1,250.

Only one example each recorded of Nos. 120XU1 and 120XU2.

FORT VALLEY, GA.

E2

E1

Handstamped Envelope

148XU1	E1	5c on 3c black	3,250.

Black circle control on front of envelope. Unique.

FRANKLIN, N. C.

E1

E2

Press-printed Envelope (typeset) (No. 25XU1)
Impressed at top right

25XU1	E1	5c blue, *buff*	30,000.
25XU2	E2	5c black, large "5" woodcut in 31mm circular town mark	2,500.

The one known No. 25XU1 envelope shows black circular Franklin postmark with manuscript date.

FRAZIERSVILLE, S. C.

E1

Handstamped Envelope, "5" manuscript

128XU1	E1	5c black	5,000.

Only one example recorded of No. 128XU1.

FREDERICKSBURG, VA.

A1

Sheets of 20, two panes of 10 varieties each

Typeset Adhesives
Thin bluish paper

26X1	A1	5c blue, *bluish*	750.	1,500.
26X2	A1	10c red (shades), *bluish*		2,250.

GAINESVILLE, ALA.

E1   E2

E3

Handstamped Envelopes

27XU1	E1	5c black	4,500.
27XU2	E2	5c black	5,000.
27XU3	E3	10c ("01") black	12,000.

GALVESTON, TEX.

E1

Handstamped Envelopes

98XU1	E1	5c black	500.	1,500.
98XU2	E1	10c black		2,500.

E2

E3

Handstamped Envelopes

98XU3	E2	10c black	550.	2,750.
98XU4	E2	20c black		3,500.
98XU5	E3	5c black		4,500.

GASTON, N. C.

E1

Handstamped Envelope

129XU1	E1	5c black	6,000.

Only one example recorded of No. 129XU1.

GEORGETOWN, S. C.

E1

Control

E2

Handstamped Envelopes

28XU1	E1	5c black	900.
28XU2	E2	5c black, separate "5" and straightline "PAID" handstamps, control on reverse	—	1,750.

GOLIAD, TEX.

A1

A2

Typeset Adhesives

29X1	A1	5c black	16,500.
29X2	A1	5c black, *gray*	11,500.
29X3	A1	5c black, *rose*	12,000.
29X4	A1	10c black	—	25,000.
29X5	A1	10c black, *rose*	12,000.

Type A1 stamps are signed "Clarke-P.M." vertically in black or red.

29X6	A2	5c black, *gray*	22,500.
a.		"GOILAD"	12,000.
29X7	A2	10c black, *buff*	12,000.
a.		"GOILAD"	15,000.
29X8	A2	5c black, *dark blue,* on cover	18,000.
29X9	A2	10c black, *dark blue*	27,500.

GONZALES, TEX.

Colman & Law were booksellers when John B. Law (of the firm) was appointed Postmaster. The firm used a small lithographed label on drugs and on the front or inside of books they sold.

A1

Lithographed Adhesives
on colored glazed paper

30X1	A1	(5c) gold, *dark blue,* pair on cover, 1861	15,000.
30X2	A1	(10c) gold, *garnet,* on cover, 1864	80,000.
30X3	A1	(10c) gold, *black,* on cover, 1865	50,000.

No. 30X1 must bear double-circle town cancel as validating control. The control was applied to the labels in the sheet before their sale as stamps. When used, the stamps bear an additional Gonzales double-circle postmark.

GREENSBORO, ALA.

E1

E2

E3

Handstamped Envelopes

31XU1	E1	5c black	3,250.
31XU2	E1	10c black	3,750.
31XU3	E2	10c black	6,000.
31XU4	E3	10c on 5c black	3,000.

GREENSBORO, N. C.

E1

Handstamped Envelope

32XU1	E1	10c red	1,250.

GREENVILLE, ALA.

A1

A2

Typeset Adhesives
On pinkish surface-colored glazed paper

33X1	A1	5c blue & red	28,000.
33X2	A2	10c red & blue, on cover	47,500.

Two used examples each are known of Nos. 33X1-33X2, and all are on covers. Covers bear a postmark but it was not used to cancel the stamps.

The former No. 33X1a has been identified as a fake.

GREENVILLE, TENN.

E1

144XU1	E1	5c black	5,000.

Only one example of No. 144XU1 is recorded.

GREENVILLE COURT HOUSE, S. C.

E1

E2

Control A

Control B

Control C

Handstamped Envelopes (Several types)

34XU1	E1	5c black	2,000.
34XU2	E2	10c black	2,000.
a.		20c (ms.) on 10c black	3,000.

Envelopes must bear one of three different postmark controls on the back. When the control postmark is dated, the date must be the same or prior to the date of the postmark on the front of the envelope.

GREENWOOD DEPOT, VA.

A1

"PAID" Handstamped Adhesive ("PAID" with value and signature in ms.)
Laid Paper

35X1	A1	10c black, *gray blue,* on cover	40,000.

GRIFFIN, GA.

E1

Handstamped Envelopes
102XU1 E1 5c black 2,000.
102XU2 E1 10c black 5,000.

No. 102XU2 is on a large piece of an envelope with July 25 postmark at left. It is unique.

GROVE HILL, ALA.

A1

Handstamped Adhesive (from woodcut)
36X1 A1 5c black 125,000.

Two examples are recorded. One is on cover tied by the postmark. The other is canceled by magenta pen on a cover front. Value is for the complete cover.

HALLETTSVILLE, TEX.

A1

Handstamped Adhesive Ruled Letter Paper
37X1 A1 10c black, gray blue, on cover 10,000.

One example known.

HAMBURGH, S. C.

E1

Handstamped Envelope
112XU1 E1 5c black 8,000.

HARRISBURGH (Harrisburg), TEX.

E1

E2

Handstamped Envelope
130XU1 E1 5c black 5,500.
130XU2 E2 10c black —

The unused 5c entire is the only example recorded of No. 130XU1

HELENA, TEX.

A1

Typeset Adhesives
Several varieties
38X1 A1 5c black, buff 22,500. 20,000.
38X2 A1 10c black, gray 40,000.

On 10c "Helena" is in upper and lower case italics.
Used examples are valued with small faults or repairs, as all recorded have faults.

HILLSBORO, N. C.

A1

Handstamped Adhesive
39X1 A1 5c black, on cover 12,500.
See 3c 1861 Postmaster's Provisional No. 1AX1.
No. 39X1 is unique.

Ms./Handstamped Envelope
39XU1 E1 10c "paid 10" in manuscript with undated blue town cancel as control on face 2,250.

No. 39XU1 is unique.

HOLLANDALE, TEX.

E1

Handstamped Envelope
132XU1 E1 5c black —

HOUSTON, TEX.

E1

No. 40XU1a

Handstamped Envelopes
40XU1 E1 5c red — 800.
   a. 10c (ms.) on 5c red 6,500.
40XU2 E1 10c red — 2,000.
40XU3 E1 10c black 6,750.
40XU4 E1 5c +10c red 2,500.
40XU5 E1 10c +10c red 2,500.

Nos. 40XU2-40XU5 show "TEX" instead of "TXS."

HUNTSVILLE, TEX.

E1

Control

Handstamped Envelope
92XU1 E1 5c black 5,000.

No. 92XU1 exists with "5" outside or within control circle.

INDEPENDENCE, TEX.

A1

A2

Handstamped Adhesives
41X1 A1 10c black, buff, on cover, uncanceled, cut to shape 20,000.
41X2 A1 10c black, dull rose, on cover —

With small "10" and "Pd" in manuscript
41X3 A2 10c black, buff, on cover, uncanceled, cut to shape 20,000.

No. 41X1 is unique.
All known examples of Nos. 41X1-41X3 are uncanceled on covers with black "INDEPENDANCE TEX." (sic) postmark.
The existence of No. 41X2 has been questioned by specialists. The editors would like to see authenticated evidence of the existence of this item.

ISABELLA, GA.

E1

Handstamped Envelope, Manuscript "5"
133XU1 E1 5c black 5,000.
Only one example recorded of No. 133XU1.

IUKA, MISS.

E1

Handstamped Envelope
42XU1 E1 5c black 1,750.

JACKSON, MISS.

E1

Handstamped Envelopes
Two types of numeral
43XU1 E1 5c black 750.
   a. 10c on 5c black 2,750.
43XU2 E1 10c black 2,000.
   a. 5c on 10c black 3,750.
43XU4 E1 10c on 5c blue 2,750.

The 5c also exists on a lettersheet.
See 3c 1861 Postmaster's Provisional No. 2AXU1.

JACKSONVILLE, ALA.

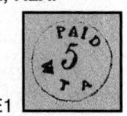

E1

Handstamped Envelope
110XU1 E1 5c black — 3,000.

JACKSONVILLE, FLA.

E1

Control

Handstamped Envelope
134XU1 E1 5c black 4,000.

Undated double circle postmark control on reverse. No. 134XU1 is unique.

JETERSVILLE, VA.

A1

**Handstamped Adhesive
("5" with ms. "AHA." initials)
Laid Paper**
44X1 A1 5c black, vertical pair on cover, uncanceled 16,000.

JONESBORO, TENN.

E1

Handstamped Envelopes
45XU1 E1 5c black 6,000.
45XU2 E1 5c dark blue 5,000.

KINGSTON, GA.

E1

E2

E3

E4

Typeset Envelopes

(design types E1-E2, E4 are handstamps; typeset design E3 probably impressed by hand but possibly press printed)

46XU1	E1	5c black	3,000.
46XU2	E2	5c black	3,250.
46XU4	E3	5c black	12,500.
46XU5	E4	5c black	2,000.

There is only one recorded example of No. 46XU4.

KNOXVILLE, TENN.

A1

Typographed Adhesives
(stereotype from woodcut)
Grayish Laid Paper

47X1	A1	5c brick red	1,750.	1,400.
47X2	A1	5c carmine	2,750.	2,250.
47X3	A1	10c green, on cover		57,750.

The #47X3 cover is unique. Value is based on 1997 auction sale.

E1   E2

Press-printed Envelopes
(typographed)

47XU1	E1	5c blue	2,500.
47XU2	E1	5c blue, orange	5,000.
47XU3	E1	10c red (cut to shape)	7,500.
47XU4	E1	10c red, orange (cut to shape)	7,500.

Only one example each recorded of Nos. 47XU3 and 47XU4.
Dangerous fakes exist of Nos. 47XU1 and 47XU2.

Handstamped Envelopes

47XU5	E2	5c black	1,400.
a.		10c on 5c black	3,500.

Type E2 exists with "5" above or below "PAID."

LA GRANGE, TEX.

E1

Handstamped Envelopes

48XU1	E1	5c black	—	3,250.
48XU2	E1	10c black		3,250.

LAKE CITY, FLA.

E1   Control Type A

Control Type B

Handstamped Envelope

96XU1	E1	10c black	3,500.

Envelopes have black circle control mark, or printed name of E. R. Ives, postmaster, on back.

LAURENS COURT HOUSE, S. C.

E1

E2

Control

Handstamped Envelopes

116XU1	E1	5c black	2,000.
116XU2	E2	5c black	2,000.

Envelopes have a 25mm undated control mark on reverse. No. 116XU1 is unique.

LENOIR, N. C.

A1   E1

Handstamped Adhesive (from woodcut)
White wove paper with cross-ruled orange lines

49X1	A1	5c blue & orange	7,250.	6,750.

Handstamped Envelopes

49XU1	A1	5c blue	4,000.
49XU2	A1	10c (5c+5c) blue	25,000.
49XU3	E1	5c blue	4,500.
49XU4	E1	5c black	4,500.

No. 49XU2 is unique.

LEXINGTON, MISS.

E1

Handstamped Envelopes

50XU1	E1	5c black	3,750.
50XU2	E1	10c black	5,000.

Only one example is recorded of No. 50XU2.

LEXINGTON, VA.

E1

Handstamped Envelopes

135XU1	E1	5c blue	350.
135XU2	E1	10c blue	350.

Nos. 135XU1-135XU2 by themselves are indistinguishable from stampless covers when used.

LIBERTY, VA. (and Salem, Va.)

A1

Typeset Adhesive (probably impressed by hand)
Laid Paper

74X1	A1	5c black, on cover, un-canceled		25,000.

Two known on covers with Liberty, Va. postmark; one cover known with the nearby Salem, Va. office postmark.

LIMESTONE SPRINGS, S. C.

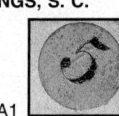

A1

Handstamped Adhesive

121X1	A1	5c black, light blue, on cover		10,000.
121X2	A1	5c black, white, two on cover		32,500.

Stamps are cut round or rectangular. Covers are not postmarked. The No. 121X2 cover bears the only two recorded examples of this stamp.

LIVINGSTON, ALA.

A1

Lithographed Adhesive

51X1	A1	5c blue	10,000.

LYNCHBURG, VA.

A1   E1

Typographed Adhesive
(stereotype from woodcut)

52X1	A1	5c blue (shades)	1,800.	1,500.

Press-printed Envelopes
(typographed)
Impressed at top right or left

52XU1	E1	5c black	700.00	3,000.
52XU2	E1	5c black, amber		3,000.
52XU3	E1	5c black, buff		3,000.
52XU4	E1	5c black, brown		3,000.

MACON, GA.

A1   A2

A3   A4

Typeset Adhesives
Several varieties of type A1, 10 of A2, 5 of A3
Wove Paper

53X1	A1	5c black, light blue green (shades)	1,250.	1,000.

Warning: Dangerous forgeries exist of the normal variety and the Comma after "OFFICE" variety. Certificates of authenticity from recognized committees are strongly recommended.

53X3	A2	5c black, yellow	2,500.	1,250.
53X4	A3	5c black, yellow (shades)	3,000.	3,000.
a.		Vertical tête bêche pair, on cover		60,000.
53X5	A4	2c black, gray green		—

Laid Paper

53X6	A2	5c black, yellow	6,000.	6,000.
53X7	A3	5c black, yellow	6,000.	
53X8	A1	5c black, light blue green	1,750.	2,250.

No. 53X4a is unique.

E1

Handstamped Envelope
Two types: "PAID" over "5," "5" over "PAID"

53XU1	E1	5c black	250.	650.

Values are for "PAID" over "5" variety. "5" over "PAID" is much scarcer.

MADISON, GA.

E1

Handstamped Envelope

136XU1	E1	5c red	600.

No. 136XU1 is indistinguishable from a handstamp paid cover when used.

MADISON COURT HOUSE, FLA.

E1

Typeset Envelope

137XU1 E1 5c black, *yellow*   35,000.

No. 137XU1 is unique.
See 3c 1861 Postmaster's Provisional No. 3AX1.

MARIETTA, GA.

E1

Control

E2

Handstamped Envelopes

54XU1 E1 5c black   500.
   a.   10c on 5c black   1,750.

With Double Circle Control

54XU3 E1 10c black
54XU4 E2 5c black   2,000.

The existence of No. 54XU3 has been questioned by specialists. The editors would like to see authenticated evidence that verifies this listing.

MARION, VA.

A1

Adhesives with Typeset frame and Handstamped numeral in center

55X1 A1 5c black   7,500.
55X2 A1 10c black   16,500.   10,000.
55X3 A1 5c black, *bluish, laid paper*   —   —
55X4 A1 5c black, *bluish, tied on cover*   6,000.

The 2c, 3c, 15c and 20c are believed to be bogus items printed later using the original typeset frame.

MARS BLUFF, S. C.

E1

145XU1 E1 5c black   2,000.

The No. 145XU1 marking is a provisional only when unused, used from another town or used under a general issue.

MEMPHIS, TENN.

A1   56X1a
            Partial Print

A2

Typographed Adhesives (stereotyped from woodcut)

56X1 A1 2c blue (shades)   100.   1,250.
   a.   Partial print   250.
56X2 A2 5c red (shades)   150.   250.
   a.   Tête bêche pair   1,500.
   b.   Pair, one sideways   2,500.   —
   c.   Pelure paper

Press-printed Envelopes (typographed)

56XU1 A2 5c red   3,000.
            (shades)   3,000.
56XU2 A2 5c red, *amber*   3,000.
56XU3 A2 5c red, *orange*   2,500.
56XU4 A2 5c red, *cream*   5,750.

Only one example of No. 56XU4 is recorded. It is on a cover on which a C.S.A. No. 11 is affixed over the provisional to pay the postage.

MICANOPY, FLA.

E1

Handstamped Envelope

105XU1 E1 5c black   11,500.

One example recorded.

MILLEDGEVILLE, GA.

E1

E2   E3

Handstamped Envelopes

Two types of No. 57XU5: Type I, tall, thin "1" and "0" of "10"; Type II, short, fat "1" and "0" of "10."

57XU1 E1 5c black   500.
   a.   Wide spacing between "I" and "D" of "PAID"   600.
   b.   10c on 5c black   1,000.
57XU2 E1 5c blue   800.
57XU4 E2 10c black   375.   1,200.
   a.   Wide spacing between "I" and "D" of "PAID"   1,200.
57XU5 E3 10c black, type I   450.   800.
   a.   Type II   1,500.

On No. 57XU4, the "PAID/10" virtually always falls outside the Milledgeville control marking (as in illustration E1).
The existence of No. 57XU2 as a provisional has been questioned by specialists. The editors would like to see authenticated evidence of provisional use of this marking.

MILTON, N. C.

E1

Handstamped Envelope, "5" Manuscript

138XU1 E1 5c black   3,750.

MOBILE, ALA.

A1

Lithographed Adhesives

58X1 A1 2c black   2,250.   1,200.
58X2 A1 5c blue   350.   450.

MONTGOMERY, ALA.

E1   E1a

Handstamped Envelopes

59XU1 E1 5c red   1,000.
   a.   10c on 5c red   2,750.
59XU2 E1 5c blue   400.   1,000.
59XU3 E1a 10c red   900.
59XU4 E1a 10c blue   1,250.
59XU5 E1a 10c black   850.

E2   E3

59XU7 E2 2c red   2,500.
59XU7A E2 2c blue   3,500.
59XU8 E2 5c black   2,000.
59XU9 E3 10c black   2,000.
59XU10 E3 10c red   1,750.

The existence of No. 59XU10 is in question. The editors would like to see an authenticated example of this marking.

MOUNT LEBANON, LA.

A1

Woodcut Adhesive (mirror image of design)

60X1 A1 5c red brown, on cover   255,000.

One example known. Value represents sale price at 2009 auction.

MOUNT PLEASANT, N. C.

E1

Handstamped Envelope

151XU1 E1 10c blue   3,500.

One example of No. 151XU1 is recorded, posted in January 1866 and covered by a U.S. 3¢ stamp subsequently removed to reveal the provisional.

NASHVILLE, TENN.

A2   E1

Typographed Adhesives (stereotyped from woodcut)
Gray Blue Ribbed Paper

61X2 A2 5c carmine (shades)   1,000.   800.
   a.   Vertical tête bêche pair   4,000.
61X3 A2 5c brick red (shades)   900.   850.
61X4 A2 5c gray (shades)   1,250.   1,500.
61X5 A2 5c violet brown (shades)   1,250.   750.
   a.   Vertical tete beche pair   5,000.   7,500.
61X6 A2 10c green   —   3,750.

Handstamped Envelopes

61XU1 E1 5c blue   900.
61XU2 E1 10c on 5c blue   2,750.

See 3c Postmaster's Provisional No. 4AX1.

NEW ORLEANS, LA.

A1   A2

Typographed Adhesives (stereotyped from woodcut)

62X1 A1 2c blue   225.   800.
   a.   Printed on both sides, on cover   10,500.
62X2 A1 2c red (shades)   190.   1,000.
62X3 A2 5c brown, *white*   300.   275.
   a.   Printed on both sides   3,750.
   b.   5c ocher   700.   625.
62X4 A2 5c red brn, *bluish*   325.   200.
   a.   Printed on both sides   3,250.
62X5 A2 5c yel brn, *off-white*   160.   250.
62X6 A2 5c red (shades)   —   14,000.
62X7 A2 5c red (shades), *bluish*   15,000.

E1

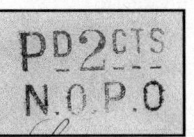

E2

Handstamped Envelopes

62XU1 E1 5c black   4,500.
62XU2 E1 10c black   11,500.

"J. L. RIDDELL, P. M." omitted

62XU3 E2 2c black   8,500.

Some authorities question the use of No. 62XU3 as a provisional.

NEW SMYRNA, FLA.

A1

Handstamped Adhesive
On white paper with blue ruled lines
63X1 A1 10c ("O1") on 5c
black   50,000.

One example known. It is uncanceled on a postmarked patriotic cover.

NORFOLK, VA.

E1   E2

Manuscript Signature

Handstamped Envelopes
Ms Signature on Back
139XU1 E1 5c blue   1,000. *1,750.*
139XU2 E2 10c blue   *1,750.*

OAKWAY, S. C.

A1

Handstamped Adhesive (from woodcut)
115X1 A1 5c black, on
cover   60,000.

Two used examples of No. 115X1 are recorded, both on cover. Value represents 2012 auction realization for the cover on which the stamp is tied by manuscript "Paid."

OXFORD, N. C.

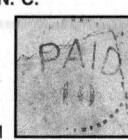

E1

Handstamped Envelope
152XU1 E1 10c black   3,500.

One example of No. 152XU1 is recorded, covered by a C.S.A. 10¢ No. 12 that paid the postage.

PATTERSON, N. C.

E1   E2

Control

Handstamped Envelopes
149XU1 E1 5c black   750.
149XU2 E2 10c black   2,500.

Nos. 149XU1 and 149XU2 must have an undated postmark on the cover as a control.

PENSACOLA, FLA.

E1

Handstamped Envelopes
106XU1 E1 5c black   5,000.
   a. 10c (ms.) on 5c black   5,250.

PETERSBURG, VA.

A1

Typeset Adhesive
Ten varieties
65X1 A1 5c red
(shades)   2,250.   500.

PITTSYLVANIA COURT HOUSE, VA.

A1

Typeset Adhesives
66X1 A1 5c dull red,
wove pa-
per   7,500.   9,000.
66X2 A1 5c dull red, laid
paper   5,500.

PLAINS OF DURA, GA.

E1

Handstamped Envelopes, Ms. Initials
140XU1 E1 5c black   —
140XU2 E1 10c black   5,000.

No. 140XU2 is unique.

PLEASANT SHADE, VA.

A1

Typeset Adhesive
Five varieties
67X1 A1 5c blue   8,000.   15,000.

PLUM CREEK, TEX.

E1

Manuscript Adhesive
141X1 E1 10c black, *blue,*
on cover   6,500.

The stamps have ruled lines with the value "10" in manuscript. Size and shape vary.

PORT GIBSON, MISS.

E1

Manuscript Signature

Handstamped Envelope, Ms Signature
142XU1 E1 5c black   —

PORT LAVACA, TEX.

A1

Typeset Adhesive
107X1 A1 10c black, on cover   27,000.

One example known. It is uncanceled on a postmarked cover.

RALEIGH, N. C.

E1

Handstamped Envelopes
68XU1 E1 5c red   500.
68XU2 E1 5c blue   3,500.

RHEATOWN, TENN.

A1

Typeset Adhesive
Three varieties
69X1 A1 5c red   6,000.   6,500.

RICHMOND, TEX.

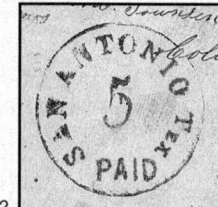

E1

Handstamped Envelopes or Letter Sheets
70XU1 E1 5c red   2,250.
   a. 10c on 5c red   11,750.
70XU2 E1 10c red   2,000.
   a. 15c (ms.) on 10c red   5,000.

RINGGOLD, GA.

E1

Handstamped Envelope
71XU1 E1 5c blue black   8,500.

RUTHERFORDTON, N. C.

A1

Handstamped Adhesive, Ms. "Paid 5cts"
72X1 A1 5c black, cut
round, on
cover (un-
canceled)   60,000.

No. 72X1 is unique.

SALEM, N. C.

"Paid 5" in Ms.   "Paid 5"
— E1   Handstamped —
              E2

Handstamped Envelopes
73XU1 E1 5c black   1,500.
73XU2 E1 10c black   3,500.
73XU3 E2 5c black   2,250.
   a. 10c on 5c black   2,800.

Reprints exist on various papers. They either lack the "Paid" and value or have them counterfeited.

Salem, Va.
See No. 74X1 under Liberty, Va.

SALISBURY, N. C.

E1

Press-printed Envelope (typeset)
Impressed at top left
75XU1 E1 5c black,
greenish   15,000.

One example known. Part of the envelope was torn away (now repaired), leaving part of design missing.

SAN ANTONIO, TEX.

E1

E2

Control

Handstamped Envelopes

76XU1	E1	10c black	500.	2,000.
76XU1A	E2	5c black		13,000.
76XU2	E2	10c black		2,500.

Black circle control mark is on front or back. One example of No. 76XU1A is recorded.

SAVANNAH, GA.

E1   Control

E2

Handstamped Envelopes

101XU1	E1	5c black	400.
a.		10c on 5c black	1,500.
101XU2	E2	5c black	600.
a.		20c on 5c black	2,000.
101XU3	E1	10c black	750.
101XU4	E2	10c black	750.

Envelopes must have octagonal control mark. One example is known of No.101XU2a.

SELMA, ALA.

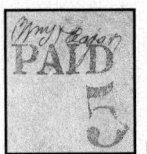

E1

Handstamped Envelopes; Signature in Ms.

77XU1	E1	5c black	1,250.
a.		10c on 5c black	3,000.
77XU2	E1	10c black	2,500.

Signature is that of Postmaster William H. Eagar.
See 3c 1861 Postmaster's Provisional No. 5AX1.

SPARTA, GA.

E1

Handstamped Envelopes

93XU1	E1	5c red	—	2,250.
93XU2	E1	10c red		5,000.

Only one example recorded of No. 93XU2.

SPARTANBURG, S. C.

A1

A2

Handstamped Adhesives
(on ruled or plain wove paper)

78X1	A1	5c black, cut to shape	—
a.		"Paid" instead of denomination, revalued to 5c with "PAID" and "5" in small circle handstamps, on cover	6,000.
78X2	A2	5c black, *bluish*, on cover	10,000.
78X3	A2	5c black, *brown*	4,000.

Most examples of Nos. 78X1-78X3 are cut round. Cut square examples in sound condition are worth much more.
No. 78X1a is unique. Also, only one example of No. 78X2 is recorded; part of the stamp is missing, and the cover is valued thus.

E1   Control

Handstamped Envelopes

78XU1	E1	10c black (control on reverse)	5,000.

STATESVILLE, N. C.

E1

Handstamped Envelopes

79XU1	E1	5c black	1,500.
a.		10c on 5c black, handstamped "10"	3,000.

Unused examples of No. 79XU1 are reprints.

SUMTER, S. C.

E1

Handstamped Envelopes

80XU1	E1	5c black	500.
a.		10c on 5c black	900.
80XU2	E1	10c black	600.
a.		2c (ms.) on 10c black	1,100.

Used examples of Nos. 80XU1-80XU2 are indistinguishable from handstamped "Paid" covers.

TALBOTTON, GA.

E1

Handstamped Envelopes

94XU1	E1	5c black	900.
a.		10c on 5c black	2,000.
94XU2	E1	10c black	1,000.

TALLADEGA, ALA.

E1

Handstamped Envelopes

143XU1	E1	5c black	1,500.	—
143XU2	E1	10c black	1,500.	—

These same markings were used on handstamped "Paid" covers.

TELLICO PLAINS, TENN.

A1

Typeset Adhesives
Laid Paper

81X1	A1	5c red	2,500.	10,000.
81X2	A1	10c red	4,500.	

THOMASVILLE, GA.

E1

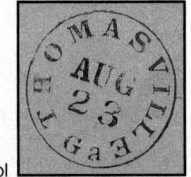

Control

Handstamped Envelopes

82XU1	E1	5c black	750.

On No. 82XU1, the control is on the reverse of the cover. The dated control is known with five different dates, including June 1, June 13, June 21, and August 23. The patriotic envelope is unique.

E2

82XU2	E2	5c black	1,000.

TULLAHOMA, TENN.

E1   Control

Handstamped Envelope

111XU1	E1	10c black	5,500.

The control appears either on the front or the back of the envelope.

TUSCALOOSA, ALA.

E1

Handstamped Envelopes

83XU1	E1	5c black	250.
83XU2	E1	10c black	250.

Used examples of Nos. 83XU1-83XU2 are indistinguishable from handstamped "Paid" covers.

TUSCUMBIA, ALA.

E1

Handstamped Envelopes

84XU1	E1	5c black	2,750.
84XU2	E1	5c red	5,000.
84XU3	E1	10c black	5,250.

See 3c 1861 Postmaster's Provisional No. 6AXU1.

UNIONTOWN, ALA.

A1

Typeset Adhesives
(settings of 4 (2x2), 4 varieties of each value)
Laid Paper

86X1	A1	2c dark blue, *gray blue*, on cover		65,000.
86X2	A1	2c dark blue, sheet of 4	60,000.	
86X3	A1	5c green, *gray blue*	4,000.	3,250.
86X4	A1	5c green	4,000.	3,250.
86X5	A1	10c red, *gray blue*		10,000.

Two examples known of No. 86X1, both on cover (drop letters), one uncanceled and one pen canceled.
The only recorded examples of No. 86X2 are in a unique sheet of 4.
The item listed as No. 86X5 used is an uncanceled stamp on a large piece with part of addressee's name in manuscript. The value is for the cover with the pen-canceled stamp.

UNIONVILLE, S. C.

A1

Handstamped Adhesive
"PAID" and "5" applied separately
Paper with Blue Ruled Lines

87X1	A1	5c black, *grayish*	3,500.

VALDOSTA, GA.

E1   Control

E2

Handstamped Envelopes

100XU1	E1	10c black	9,000.
100XU2	E2	5c +5c black	—

The black circle control must appear on front of the No. 100XU2 envelope and on the back of the No. 100XU1 envelope.

There is one recorded cover each of Nos. 100XU1-100XU2.

VICTORIA, TEX.

A1

A2

Typeset Adhesives
Surface colored paper

88X1	A1	5c red brown, green		17,500.
88X2	A1	10c red brown, green		22,500.
88X3	A2	10c red brown, green, pelure paper	32,500.	30,000.

WALTERBOROUGH, S. C.

E1

Handstamped Envelopes

108XU1	E1	10c black, *buff*	—
108XU2	E1	10c carmine	4,000.

The existence of No. 108XU1 is in question. The editors would like to see authenticated evidence of its existence.

WARRENTON, GA.

E1

Handstamped Envelopes

89XU1	E1	5c black	1,500.
a.		10c (ms.) on 5c black	900.

Fakes of the Warrenton provisional marking based on the illustration shown are known on addressed but postally unused covers.

WASHINGTON, GA.

E1

Handstamped Envelope

117XU1	E1	10c black	2,000.

Envelopes must have black circle postmark control on the back. Examples with the undated control on the front are not considered provisional unless a dated postmark is also present.

WEATHERFORD, TEX.

E1

Handstamped Envelopes
(woodcut with "PAID" inserted in type)

109XU1	E1	5c black	2,000.
109XU2	E1	5c +5c black	11,000.

One example is known of No. 109XU2.

WILKESBORO, N. C.

E1

Handstamped Envelope

147XU1	E1	5c black, revalued to 10c	3,500.

No. 147XU1 is unique.

WILLISTON, S.C.

E1

Handstamped Envelopes

153XU1	E1	10c brown	1,000.

No. 153XU1 is unique. Value is based on 2020 auction sale. This cover must be either unused (as the one recorded example is) or *cancelled by a C.D.S. stamp.*

WINNSBOROUGH, S. C.

E1

E2

Control

Handstamped Envelopes

97XU1	E1	5c black		2,000.
97XU2	E2	10c black	1,000.	2,500.

Envelopes must have black circle control on front or back.

WYTHEVILLE, VA.

E1

Control

Handstamped Envelope

114XU1	E1	5c black	900.

For later additions, listed out of numerical sequence, see:

#74X1, Liberty, Va.
#92XU1, Huntsville, Tex.
#93XU1, Sparta, Ga.
#94XU1, Talbotton, Ga.
#95XU1, Cuthbert, GA
#96XU1, Lake City, Fla.
#97XU1, Winnsborough, S.C.
#98XU1, Galveston, Tex.
#99XU1, Christiansburg, Va.
#100XU1, Valdosta, Ga.
#101XU1, Savannah, Ga.
#102XU1, Griffin, Ga.
#103XU1, Courtland, Ala.
#104XU1, Fincastle, Va.
#105XU1, Micanopy, Fla.
#106XU1, Pensacola, Fla.
#107X1, Port Lavaca, Tex.
#108XU1, Walterborough, S.C.
#109XU1, Weatherford, Tex.
#110XU1, Jacksonville, Ala.
#111XU1, Tullahoma, Tenn.
#112XU1, Hamburgh, S.C.
#113XU1, Columbia, Tenn.
#114XU1, Wytheville, Va.
#115X1, Oakway, S.C.
#116XU1, Laurens Court House, S.C.
#117XU1, Washington, Ga.
#118XU1, Carolina City, N.C.
#119XU1, Colaparchee, Ga.
#120XU1, Forsyth, Ga.
#121XU1, Limestone Springs, S.C.
#122XU1, Balcony Falls, Va.
#123XU1, Barnwell Court House, S.C.
#124XU1, Bluffton, S.C.
#125XU1, Camden, S.C.
#126XU1, Cartersville, Ga.
#127XU1, Charlottesville, Va.
#128XU1, Fraziersville, S.C.
#129XU1, Gaston, N.C.
#130XU1, Harrisburgh, Tex.
#132XU1, Hollandale, Tex.
#133XU1, Isabella, Ga.
#134XU1, Jacksonville, Fla.
#135XU1, Lexington, Va.
#136XU1, Madison, Ga.
#137XU1, Madison Court House, Fla.
#138XU1, Milton, N.C.
#139XU1, Norfolk, Va.
#140XU1, Plains of Dura, Ga.
#141X1, Plum Creek, Tex.
#142XU1, Port Gibson, Miss.
#143XU1, Talladega, Ala.
#144XU1, Greenville, Ga.
#145XU1, Mars Bluff, S.C.
#146XU1, Charlotte, N.C.
#147XU1, Wilkesboro, N.C.
#148XU1, Fort Valley, Ga.
#149XU1, Patterson, N.C.
#150XU1, Beaufort, S.C.
#151XU1, Mount Pleasant, N.C.
#152XU1, Oxford, N.C.
#153XU1, Williston, S.C.

GENERAL ISSUES

Due to its tendency to damage the paper and color of the stamps, the gum on most (but not all) Confederate States stamps very often is removed. Except for the De La Rue-printed Nos. 6 and 14, which are valued both with original gum and without gum, unused values for all Confederate States stamps are for stamps without gum. Stamps with original gum sell for about the same prices, if the gum has not deteriorated and damaged the paper or stamp color.

Jefferson Davis — A1

1861   Unwmk.   Litho.   *Imperf.*
Soft Porous Paper

1	A1	5c green (shades)	300.	175.
a.		5c light green	275.	175.
b.		5c dark green	375.	250.
c.		5c olive green	425.	250.

Thomas Jefferson — A2

1861-62

2	A2	10c blue	275.	180.
a.		10c light blue	300.	200.
b.		10c dark blue	700.	300.
c.		10c indigo	5,000.	7,500.
d.		Printed on both sides		1,750.
e.		light milky blue	1,250.	325.

Specialists have questioned the existence of No. 2bd, the Hoyer & Ludwig printed on both sides. The editors would like to see authenticated evidence of its existence.

The earliest printings of No. 2 were made by Hoyer & Ludwig, the later ones by J. T. Paterson & Co.

Stamps of the later printings usually have a small colored dash below the lowest point of the upper left spandrel.

Andrew Jackson — A3

1862

3	A3	2c green	1,000.	750.
a.		2c bright yellow green	2,000.	
4	A1	5c blue	225.	125.
a.		5c dark blue	275.	175.
b.		5c light milky blue	350.	200.
5	A2	10c rose (shades)	2,400.	400.
a.		10c carmine	3,750.	1,900.

Jefferson Davis — A4

Typo.

6	A4	5c light blue	20.	30.
		No gum	10.	
7	A4	5c blue (De La Rue thin paper)	22.	22.
a.		5c deep blue	28.	35.
b.		Printed on both sides	2,500.	1,400.

No. 6 has fine, clear impression. No. 7 has coarser impression and the color is duller and often blurred.

Both 2c and 10c stamps, types A4 and A10, were privately printed in various colors.

Andrew Jackson — A5

1863   Engr.

8	A5	2c brown red	75.	350.
a.		2c pale red	90.	450.

A6

Thick or Thin Paper

9	A6	10c blue	950.	500.
a.		10c milky blue (first printing)	1,050.	550.
b.		10c gray blue	1,050.	600.

Jefferson Davis — A6a

10	A6a	10c blue (with dividing lines)	5,500.	2,100.
a.		10c milky blue	5,500.	2,100.
b.		10c greenish blue	6,000.	2,100.
c.		10c dark blue	6,000.	2,100.

Values of Nos. 10, 10a, 10b and 10c are for examples showing parts of lines on at least three sides. Used stamps showing 4 complete lines sell for approximately 3 to 4 times the values given. Unused stamps showing 4 complete lines are exceedingly rare (only two recorded), and the one sound example is valued at $35,000.

A7

There are many slight differences between A7 and A8, the most noticeable being the additional line outside the ornaments at the four corners of A8.

1863-64

11	A7	10c blue	18.	20.
a.		10c milky blue	55.	60.
b.		10c dark blue	25.	30.
c.		10c greenish blue	30.	50.
d.		10c green	100.	80.
e.		Officially perforated 12½ (Archer & Daly printing)	450.	350.

A8

12	A8	10c blue	22.	25.
a.		10c milky blue	55.	60.
b.		10c light blue	21.	22.
c.		10c greenish blue	40.	50.
d.		10c dark blue	24.	25.
e.		10c green	150.	140.
f.		Officially perforated 12½ (Archer & Daly printing)	450.	375.

The paper of Nos. 11 and 12 varies from thin hard to thick soft. The stamp that sometimes is offered as "laid paper" is actually normal paper with thick, streaky gum.

George Washington — A9

1863

13	A9	20c green	45.	400.
a.		20c yellow green	80.	450.
b.		20c dark green	65.	500.
c.		20c bluish green	100.	
d.		Diagonal half used as 10c on cover		1,400.
e.		Horizontal half used as 10c on cover		2,500.

John C. Calhoun — A10

1862   Typo.

14	A10	1c orange	110.
		No gum	60.
a.		1c deep orange	145.
		No gum	85.

No. 14 was never put in use.

CANAL ZONE

kə-'nal 'zōn

LOCATION — A strip of land 10 miles wide, extending through the Republic of Panama, between the Atlantic and Pacific Oceans.
GOVT. — From 1904-79 a U.S. Government Reservation; from 1979-99 under joint control of the Republic of Panama and the U.S.
AREA — 552.8 sq. mi.
POP. — 41,800 (est. 1976)

The Canal Zone, site of the Panama Canal, was leased in perpetuity to the U.S. for a cash payment of $10,000,000 and a yearly rental. Treaties between the two countries provided for joint jurisdiction by the U.S. and Panama, 1979-1999, with Panama handling postal service. At the end of 1999, the canal, in its entirety, reverted to Panama.

100 Centavos = 1 Peso
100 Centesimos = 1 Balboa
100 Cents = 1 Dollar

> **Catalogue values for unused stamps in this country are for Never Hinged items, beginning with Scott 118 in the regular postage section and Scott C6 in the air post section.**

Watermarks

Wmk. 190 — "USPS" in Single-lined Capitals

Wmk. 191 — Double-lined "USPS" in Capitals

Map of Panama — A1

Violet to Violet-Blue Handstamp on Panama Nos. 72, 72a-72c, 78, 79.

On the 2c "PANAMA" is normally 13mm long. On the 5c and 10c it measures about 15mm.
On the 2c, "PANAMA" reads up on the upper half of the sheet and down on the lower half. On the 5c and 10c, "PANAMA" reads up at left and down at right on each stamp.
On the 2c only, varieties exist with inverted "V" for "A," accent on "A," inverted "N," etc., in "PANAMA."

Unwmk.

1904, June 24   Engr.   Perf. 12

1	A1	2c rose, both "PANAMA" reading up or down	650.	400.
a.		"CANAL ZONE" inverted	1,000.	850.
b.		"CANAL ZONE" double	4,250.	2,000.
c.		"CANAL ZONE" double, both inverted	20,000.	
d.		"PANAMA" reading down and up	750.	650.
e.		As "d," "CANAL ZONE" invtd.	9,000.	9,000.
f.		Vert. pair, "PANAMA" reading up on top 2c, down on other	2,100.	2,100.
g.		As "f," "CANAL ZONE" inverted	20,000.	
2	A1	5c blue	300.	190.
a.		"CANAL ZONE" inverted	775.	600.
b.		"CANAL ZONE" double	2,250.	1,500.

---

c.		Pair, one without "CANAL ZONE" overprint	5,000.	5,000.
d.		"CANAL ZONE" overprint diagonal, reading down to right	800.	700.
3	A1	10c yellow	400.	210.
a.		"CANAL ZONE" inverted	775.	600.
b.		"CANAL ZONE" double		14,000.
c.		Pair, one without "CANAL ZONE" overprint	6,000.	5,000.
		Nos. 1-3 (3)	1,350.	800.00

Cancellations consist of town and/or bars in magenta or black, or a mixture of both colors. Nos. 1-3 were withdrawn July 17, 1904. Forgeries of the "Canal Zone" overprint and cancellations are numerous.

United States Nos. 300, 319, 304, 306 & 307 Ovptd. in Black

1904, July 18   Wmk. 191

4	A115	1c blue green	35.00	22.50
5	A129	2c carmine	25.00	25.00
a.		2c scarlet	32.50	30.00
6	A119	5c blue	85.00	60.00
7	A121	8c violet black	130.00	85.00
8	A122	10c pale red brown	120.00	80.00
		Nos. 4-8 (5)	395.00	272.50

Beware of fake overprints.

A2

A3

CANAL ZONE Regular Type	CANAL ZONE Antique Type

1904-06   Unwmk.

Black Overprint on Stamps of Panama

9	A2	1c green	2.50	2.00
a.		"CANAL" in antique type	90.00	90.00
b.		"ZONE" in antique type	60.00	60.00
c.		Inverted overprint	7,500.	6,000.
d.		Double overprint	2,750.	2,000.
10	A2	2c rose	4.00	2.50
a.		Inverted overprint	225.00	275.00
b.		"L" of "CANAL" sideways	2,000.	2,250.

"PANAMA" (15mm long) reading up at left, down at right
Overprint "CANAL ZONE" in Black, "PANAMA" and Bar in Red

11	A3	2c rose	6.50	4.50
a.		"ZONE" in antique type	175.00	175.00
b.		"PANAMA" overprint inverted, bar at bottom	600.00	675.00
12	A3	5c blue	7.50	2.75
a.		"CANAL" in antique type	75.00	65.00
b.		"ZONE" in antique type	75.00	65.00
c.		"CANAL ZONE" double	800.00	800.00
d.		"PANAMA" double	1,100.	1,000.
e.		"PANAMA" inverted, bar at bottom	1,000.	1,250.
f.		"PANAAM" at right	950.00	850.00
13	A3	10c yellow	17.00	12.00
a.		"CANAL" in antique type	180.00	180.00
b.		"ZONE" in antique type	175.00	160.00
c.		"PANAMA" ovpt. double	650.00	650.00
d.		"PANAMA" overprint in red brown	27.50	22.50
		Nos. 11-13 (3)	31.00	19.25

With Added Surcharge in Red

a

14	A3	8c on 50c bister brown	25.00	25.00
a.		"ZONE" in antique type	1,150.	1,150.
b.		"CANAL ZONE" inverted	450.00	425.00
c.		"PANAMA" overprint in rose brown	35.00	35.00
d.		As "c," "CANAL" in antique type	1,750.	850.00

---

e.		As "c," "ZONE" in antique type	1,750.	
f.		As "c," "8 cts" double	1,100.	
g.		As "c," "8" omitted	4,500.	
h.		As "c," "cts 8"		

Nos. 11-14 are overprinted or surcharged on Panama Nos. 77, 77e, 78, 78c, 78d, 78f, 78g, 78h, 79 79c, 79e, 79g and 81 respectively.
On No. 14 with original gum, the gum is almost always disturbed. Unused stamps are valued thus.

Panama No. 74a, 74b Overprinted "CANAL ZONE" in Regular Type in Black and Surcharged Type "a" in Red Both "PANAMA" (13mm long) Reading Up

15	A3(a)	8c on 50c bister brown	2,000.	4,750.
a.		"PANAMA" reading down and up	6,000.	

On No. 15 with original gum, the gum is almost always disturbed. Unused stamps are valued thus.

Map of Panama — A4

Panama Nos. 19 and 21 Surcharged in Black

a	PANAMA CANAL ZONE 1 ct. PANAMA
b	PANAMA CANAL ZONE 1 ct. PANAMA
c	CANAL ZONE 1 ct.
d	PANAMA CANAL ZONE 2 cts. PANAMA
e	CANAL ZONE 2 cts. PANAMA
f	PANAMA CANAL ZONE 2 cts. PANAMA

There were three printings of each denomination, differing principally in the relative position of the various parts of the surcharges. Varieties occur with inverted "V" for the final "A" in "PANAMA," "CA" spaced, "ZO" spaced,

"2c" spaced, accents in various positions, and with bars shifted so that two bars appear on top or bottom of the stamp (either with or without the corresponding bar on top or bottom) and sometimes with only one bar at top or bottom.

1906

16	A4	1c on 20c violet, type a	1.90	1.60
a.		Type b	1.90	1.60
b.		Type c	1.90	1.50
c.		As No. 16, double surcharge		2,000.
17	A4	2c on 1p lake, type d	2.25	2.25
a.		Type e	2.25	2.25
b.		Type f	20.00	20.00

Panama Nos. 74, 74a and 74b Overprinted "CANAL ZONE" in Regular Type in Black and Surcharged in Red

b　　　　　　c

1905-06
Both "PANAMA" Reading Up

18	A3(b)	8c on 50c bister brown	45.00	45.00
a.		"ZONE" in antique type	200.00	180.00
b.		"PANAMA" reading down and up	160.00	150.00
19	A3(c)	8c on 50c bister brown	45.00	37.50
a.		"CANAL" in antique type	210.00	180.00
b.		"ZONE" in antique type	210.00	180.00
c.		"8 cts" double	1,100.	1,100.
d.		"PANAMA" reading down and up	110.00	90.00

On Nos. 18-19 with original gum, the gum is usually disturbed. Unused stamps are valued thus.

Panama No. 81 Overprinted "CANAL ZONE" in Regular Type in Black and Surcharged in Red Type "c" plus Period
"PANAMA" reading up and down

20	A3(c)	8c on 50c bister brown	35.00	37.50
a.		"CANAL" antique type	200.00	180.00
b.		"ZONE" in antique type	200.00	180.00
c.		"8 cts" omitted	800.00	800.00
d.		"8 cts" double	1,500.	
e.		"cts R"		

Nos. 14 and 18-20 exist without CANAL ZONE overprint but were not regularly issued and are considered printer's waste. Forgeries of the overprint varieties of Nos. 9-15 and 18-20 are known.

On No. 20 with original gum, the gum is usually disturbed. Unused stamps are valued thus.

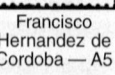

Francisco Hernández de Cordoba — A5　　　Vasco Nunez de Balboa — A6

Fernández de Córdoba A7　　　Justo Arosemena A8

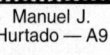

Manuel J. Hurtado — A9　　Jose de Obaldia — A10

Stamps of Panama Overprinted in Black

1906-07　　　　　　Perf. 12
Overprint Reading Up

21	A5	2c red & black	25.00	25.00
a.		"CANAL" only		4,000.

Overprint Reading Down

22	A6	1c green & black	2.00	.90
a.		Horiz. pair, imperf. btwn.	1,100.	1,100.
b.		Vert. pair, imperf. btwn.	2,000.	2,000.
c.		Vert. pair, imperf. horiz.	2,250.	1,750.
d.		Inverted overprint reading up	550.00	550.00
e.		Double overprint	275.00	275.00
f.		Double overprint, one inverted	1,750.	1,600.
g.		Invtd. center, ovpt. reading up	3,500.	4,500.
h.		Horiz. pair, imperf vert.	5,000.	
23	A7	2c red & black	3.00	1.00
a.		Horizontal pair, imperf. between	2,000.	2,000.
b.		Vertical pair, one without overprint	2,500.	2,500.
c.		Double overprint	600.00	700.00
d.		Double overprint, one diagonal	800.00	800.00
e.		Double overprint, one diagonal, in pair with normal	2,500.	
f.		2c carmine red & black	5.00	2.75
g.		As "f," inverted center and overprint reading up		14,000.
h.		As "d," one "ZONE CANAL"	4,000.	
i.		"CANAL" double	6,500.	
24	A8	5c ultramarine & black	5.75	2.00
c.		Double overprint	500.00	400.00
d.		"CANAL" only	7,000.	
e.		"ZONE CANAL"	5,000.	
25	A9	8c purple & black	20.00	8.00
a.		Horizontal pair, imperf. between and at left margin	1,600.	4,000.
26	A10	10c violet & black	20.00	7.00
a.		Dbl. ovpt., one reading up	5,000.	
b.		Overprint reading up	5,500.	
		Nos. 22-26 (5)	50.75	18.90

Nos. 22-25 occur with "CA" of "CANAL" spaced ½mm further apart on position No. 50 of the setting.
The used pair of No. 25a is unique.

Cordoba A11　　　　Arosemena A12

Hurtado — A13　　　Jose de Obaldia — A14

1909
Overprint Reading Down

27	A11	2c vermilion & black	12.00	5.00
a.		Horizontal pair, one without overprint	2,500.	
b.		Vert. pair, one without ovpt.	3,250.	
28	A12	5c deep blue & black	40.00	12.50
29	A13	8c violet & black	37.50	14.00
30	A14	10c violet & black	40.00	14.00
a.		Horizontal pair, one with "ZONE" omitted	3,000.	
b.		Vertical pair, one without overprint	4,000.	
		Nos. 27-30 (4)	129.50	45.50

Nos. 27-30 occur with "CA" spaced (position 50).
Do not confuse No. 27 with Nos. 39d or 53a.
On No. 30a, the stamp with "ZONE" omitted is also missing most of "CANAL."
For designs A11-A14 with overprints reading up, see Nos. 32-35, 39-41, 47-48, 53-54, 56-57.

Black Overprint Reading Up

Vasco Nunez de Balboa — A15

Type I

Type I Overprint: "C" with serifs both top and bottom. "L," "Z" and "E" with slanting serifs.
Compare Type I overprint with Types II to V illustrated before Nos. 38, 46, 52 and 55.

1909-10

31	A15	1c dark green & black	4.25	1.25
a.		Inverted center and overprint reading down		22,500.
c.		Bklt. pane of 6, handmade, perf. margins	500.00	
32	A11	2c vermilion & black	4.50	1.25
a.		Vert. pair, imperf. horiz.	1,000.	1,000.
b.		Bklt. pane of 6, handmade, perf. margins	800.00	
d.		Double overprint (I)		6,000.
33	A12	5c deep blue & black	17.00	3.50
a.		Double overprint	375.00	375.00
34	A13	8c violet & black	11.00	5.00
a.		Vertical pair, one without overprint	1,750.	
35	A14	10c violet & black	47.50	20.00
		Nos. 31-35 (5)	84.25	31.00

No. 32d is unique and has small faults.
See Nos. 38, 46, 52, 55.

A16　　　　　A17

Black Surcharge
1911, Jan. 14

36	A16	10c on 13c gray	6.00	2.00
a.		"10 cts" inverted	325.00	325.00
b.		"10 cts" omitted	300.00	

Many used stamps offered as No. 36b are merely No. 36 from which the surcharge has been chemically removed.

1914, Jan. 6

37	A17	10c gray	47.50	11.00

Black Overprint Reading Up

Type II: "C" with serif at top only. "L" and "E" with vertical serifs. "O" tilts to left

1912-16

38	A15	1c green & black	10.00	3.00
a.		Vertical pair, one without overprint	1,750.	1,750.
b.		Booklet pane of 6, imperf. margins	575.00	
c.		Booklet pane of 6, handmade, perf. margins	1,000.	
39	A11	2c vermilion & black	8.00	1.10
a.		Horiz. pair, right stamp without overprint	1,250.	
b.		Horiz. pair, left stamp without overprint	1,500.	
c.		Booklet pane of 6, imperf. margins	550.00	
d.		Overprint reading down	200.00	
e.		As "d," inverted center	600.00	750.00
f.		As "e," booklet pane of 6, handmade, perf. margins	8,000.	
g.		As "c," handmade, perf. margins	900.00	800.00
h.		As No. 39, "CANAL" only		2,500.
40	A12	5c deep blue & black	20.00	2.50
a.		With Cordoba portrait of 2c		12,500.
41	A14	10c violet & black	60.00	7.50
		Nos. 38-41 (4)	98.00	14.10

Map of Panama Canal A18

Balboa Takes Possession of the Pacific Ocean A19

Gatun Locks — A20

Culebra Cut — A21

1915, Mar. 1
Blue Overprint, Type II

42	A18	1c dark green & black	8.75	6.50
43	A19	2c carmine & black	12.00	4.25
44	A20	5c blue & black	10.00	5.75
45	A21	10c orange & black	19.00	11.00
		Nos. 42-45 (4)	49.75	27.50

Black Overprint Reading Up

Type III Overprint: Similar to Type I but letters appear thinner, particularly the lower bar of "L," "Z" and "E." Impressions are often light, rough and irregular, and not centered.

1915-20

46	A15	1c green & black	175.00	125.00
a.		Overprint reading down	375.00	
b.		Double overprint	225.00	
c.		"ZONE" omitted	6,500.	
d.		Double overprint, one reads "ZONE CANAL"	2,000.	
47	A11	2c orange vermilion & black	8,750.	60.00
48	A12	5c deep blue & black	425.00	130.00
		Nos. 46-48 (3)	3,350.	315.00

Spacing between words of overprint on Nos. 46-48 is 9¼mm; spacing varieties are not known. This should not be confused with a fairly common 9¼mm spacing of the 2c value of type I, nor with an uncommon 9¼mm spacing variety of the 5c of type I.

S.S. "Panama" in Culebra Cut — A22

S.S. "Panama" in Culebra Cut — A23

S.S. "Cristobal" in Gatun Locks — A24

1917, Jan. 23
Blue Overprint, Type II

49	A22	12c purple & black	17.50	5.25
50	A23	15c bright blue & black	50.00	17.50

51 A24 24c yellow brown &
black 35.00 13.00
Nos. 49-51 (3) 102.50 35.75

Black Overprint Reading Up

Type IV: "C" thick at
bottom, "E" with
center bar same
length as top and
bottom bars

1918-20
52 A15 1c green & black 32.50 10.00
a. Overprint reading down 175.00
b. Booklet pane of 6 600.00
c. Booklet pane of 6, left vertical
row of 3 without overprint 7,500.
d. Booklet pane of 6, right vertical row of 3 with double
overprint 7,500.
e. Horiz. bklt. pair, left stamp
without overprint 3,000.
f. Horiz. bklt. pair, right stamp
with double overprint 3,000.
g. Double overprint, booklet single 3,000.
53 A11 2c vermilion & black 110.00 6.00
a. Overprint reading up 150.00 150.00
b. Horiz. pair, right stamp without
ovpt. (from misregistered
overprints) 2,000.
c. Booklet pane of 6 1,050.
d. Booklet pane of 6, left vertical
row of 3 without overprint 15,000.
e. Horiz. bklt. pair, left stamp
without overprint 3,000.
f. Horiz. sheet pair, left stamp
without overprint 1,750.
54 A12 5c deep blue & black 150.00 32.50
Nos. 52-54 (3) 292.50 48.50

No. 53e used is unique and is on cover.

Black Overprint Reading Up

Type V: Smaller
block type 1¾mm
high. "A" with flat top

1920-21
55 A15 1c light green &
black 22.50 3.25
a. Overprint reading down 300.00 225.00
b. Horiz. pair, right stamp without
ovpt. 1,750.
c. Horiz. pair, left stamp without
ovpt. 1,100.
d. "ZONE" only 4,000. —
e. Booklet pane of 6 2,250.
f. As No. 55, "CANAL" double 1,750.
g. Vert. pair, one without overprint 3,000.
h. Vert. pair, one "ZONE" only,
one without overprint 4,000.
56 A11 2c orange vermilion
& black 8.50 1.75
a. Double overprint 500.00
b. Double overprint, one reading
down 600.00
c. Horiz. pair, right stamp without
overprint 1,400.
d. Horiz. pair, left stamp without
overprint 1,000.
e. Vertical pair, one without overprint 1,500.
f. "ZONE" double 900.00
g. Booklet pane of 6 900.00
h. As No. 56, "CANAL" double 800.00
57 A12 5c deep blue & black 300.00 45.00
a. Horiz. pair, right stamp without
overprint 2,000.
b. Horiz. pair, left stamp without
overprint 2,000.
Nos. 55-57 (3) 331.00 50.00

Drydock at
Balboa
A25

Ship in Pedro
Miguel
Locks — A26

1920, Sept.
Black Overprint Type V
58 A25 50c orange & black 250.00 160.00
59 A26 1b dark violet &
black 175.00 50.00

Jose
Vallarino — A27

The "Land
Gate" — A28

Bolivar's
Tribute — A29

Municipal
Building in 1821
and 1921 — A30

Statue of
Balboa — A31

Tomas
Herrera — A32

Jose de
Fabrega — A33

Type V overprint in black, reading
up, on all values except the 5c
which is overprinted with larger
type in red

1921, Nov. 13
60 A27 1c green 3.75 1.50
a. "CANAL" double 1,900.
b. Booklet pane of 6 900.00
61 A28 2c carmine 2.75 1.00
a. Overprint reading down 200.00 225.00
b. Double overprint 900.00
c. Vertical pair, one without
overprint 3,500.
d. "CANAL" double 1,900.
e. "ZONE" only 4,000.
f. Booklet pane of 6 2,000.
62 A29 5c blue (R) 10.00 3.00
a. Overprint reading down (R) 65.00
63 A30 10c violet 18.00 7.50
a. Overprint, reading down 90.00
64 A31 15c light blue 47.50 17.50
65 A32 24c black brown 67.50 22.50
66 A33 50c black 145.00 85.00
Nos. 60-66 (7) 294.50 138.00

Experts question the status of the 5c with a
small type V overprint in red or black.

Type III overprint in black, reading up

1924, Jan. 28
67 A27 1c green 500. 200.
a. "ZONE CANAL" reading
down 800.
b. "ZONE" only, reading down 1,900.
c. Se-tenant pair, #67a and 67b 2,750.

Coat of Arms — A34

1924, Feb.
68 A34 1c dark green 10.00 4.50
69 A34 2c carmine 7.00 2.75

The 5c to 1b values were prepared but never
issued. See listing in the Scott U.S. specialized catalogue.

United States Nos. 551-554, 557,
562, 564-566, 569, 570 and 571
Overprinted in Red (No. 70) or
Black (all others)

Type A: Letters "A" with
Flat Tops

Type A
Letters "A" with Flat Tops

1924-25 Unwmk. Perf. 11
70 A154 ½c olive brown .25 .70
Never hinged .40
71 A155 1c deep green 1.40 1.00
Never hinged 2.50
a. Inverted overprint 500.00 500.00
b. "ZONE" inverted 350.00 325.00
c. "CANAL" only 1,150.
d. "ZONE CANAL" 400.00
e. Booklet pane of 6 80.00 —
f. Se-tenant pair, #71c and
71d 1,750.
72 A156 1½c yellow brown 2.00 1.70
Never hinged 3.25
73 A157 2c carmine 6.75 1.70
Never hinged 10.50
a. Booklet pane of 6 175.00
74 A160 5c dark blue 16.00 7.00
Never hinged 25.00
75 A165 10c orange 40.00 20.00
Never hinged 65.00
76 A167 12c brown violet 32.50 30.00
Never hinged 62.50
a. "ZONE" inverted 3,750. 3,000.
77 A168 14c dark blue 27.50 22.50
Never hinged 45.00
78 A169 15c gray 45.00 37.50
Never hinged 70.00
79 A172 30c olive brown 32.50 20.00
Never hinged 52.50
80 A173 50c lilac 75.00 45.00
Never hinged 150.00
81 A174 $1 violet brown 225.00 95.00
Never hinged 400.00
Nos. 70-81 (12) 503.90 282.10

Normal spacing between words of the overprint is 9¼mm. Minor spacing variations are
known.

All examples of Nos. 71b and 76a have a
natural straight edge at right.

Type B: Letters "A"
with Sharp Pointed
Tops

Type B

1925-28
84 A157 2c carmine 27.50 8.00
Never hinged 45.00
a. "CANAL" only 2,250.
b. "ZONE CANAL" 425.00
c. Horizontal pair, one
without overprint 3,500.
d. Booklet pane of 6 175.00
e. Se-tenant pair, #84a and
84b 3,000.
85 A158 3c violet 3.75 3.00
Never hinged 6.00
a. "ZONE" inverted 550.00 550.00
86 A160 5c dark blue 3.50 2.75
Never hinged 6.00
a. "ZONE ZONE" (LR18) 1,000.
b. "CANAL" inverted (LR7) 950.00
c. Inverted overprint 500.00
d. Horizontal pair, one
without overprint 3,250.
e. Overprinted "ZONE CA-
NAL" 350.00
f. "ZONE" only 2,000.
g. Vertical pair, one without
overprint, other over-
print inverted 2,000.
h. "CANAL" only 2,000.
i. Se-tenant pair, #86e and
86f 2,500.
87 A165 10c orange 35.00 12.00
Never hinged 52.50
a. "ZONE ZONE" (LR18) 3,000.
b. "ZONE" only 4,000.
88 A167 12c brown violet 20.00 12.50
Never hinged 34.00
a. "ZONE ZONE" (LR18) 5,000.
89 A168 14c dark blue 27.50 15.00
Never hinged 45.00
90 A169 15c gray 7.50 4.50
Never hinged 12.00
a. "ZONE ZONE" (LR18) 5,500.
91 A187 17c black 4.50 2.75
Never hinged 7.50
a. "ZONE" only 1,000.
b. "CANAL" only 1,900.
c. "ZONE CANAL" 275.00
d. Se-tenant pair, #91a and
91c 1,400.
92 A170 20c carmine
rose 7.25 3.25
Never hinged 12.00
a. "CANAL" inverted
(UR48) 6,500.
b. "ZONE" inverted (LL76) 4,750.
c. "ZONE CANAL" (LL91) 4,750.
93 A172 30c olive brown 5.75 3.75
Never hinged 9.00

94 A173 50c lilac 230.00 165.00
Never hinged 400.00
95 A174 $1 violet brown 120.00 55.00
Never hinged 250.00
Nos. 84-95 (12) 492.25 287.50

Overprint Type B on U.S. Sesquicentennial Stamp No. 627

1926
96 A188 2c carmine rose 4.50 3.75
Never hinged 7.00

On this stamp there is a space of 5mm
instead of 9mm between the two words of the
overprint.

Overprint Type B in Black on U.S. Nos. 583, 584, 591

1926-27 Perf. 10
97 A157 2c carmine 45.00 11.00
Never hinged 75.00
a. Pair, one without overprint 2,250.
b. Booklet pane of 6 500.00
c. "CANAL" only 2,000.
d. "ZONE" only 2,750.
98 A158 3c violet 7.50 4.25
Never hinged 11.00
99 A165 10c orange 18.00 7.50
Never hinged 27.50
Nos. 97-99 (3) 70.50 22.75

No. 97d is valued in the grade of fine. Very
fine examples are not known.

Overprint Type B in Black on U.S. Nos. 632, 634 (Type I), 635, 637, 642

1927-31 Perf. 11x10½
100 A155 1c green 1.75 1.40
Never hinged 2.60
a. Vertical pair, one without
overprint 3,250.
101 A157 2c carmine 1.75 1.00
Never hinged 2.50
a. Booklet pane of 6 200.00
102 A158 3c violet 4.25 2.75
Never hinged 6.25
a. Booklet pane of 6, handmade, perf. margins 6,500.
103 A160 5c dark blue 25.00 10.00
Never hinged 45.00
104 A165 10c orange 17.50 10.00
Never hinged 26.00
Nos. 100-104 (5) 50.25 25.15

Wet and Dry Printings

Canal Zone stamps printed by both
the "wet" and "dry" process are Nos.
105, 108-109, 111-114, 117, 138-
140, C21-C24, C26, J25, J27. Starting with Nos. 147 and C27, the
Bureau of Engraving and Printing
used the "dry" method exclusively.
Late dry printings of Nos. 105, 108,
112-114, 117, 138 and 152 also exist
with dull gum.

See note on Wet and Dry Printings
following U.S. No. 1029.

Maj. Gen.
William
Crawford
Gorgas
A35

Maj. Gen.
George
Washington
Goethals
A36

Gaillard
Cut — A37

Maj. Gen.
Harry Foote
Hodges
A38

Lt. Col. David
DuB. Gaillard
A39

Maj. Gen.
William L.
Sibert — A40

Jackson
Smith — A41

Rear Adm.
Harry H.
Rousseau
A42

Col. Sydney
B. Williamson
A43

J.C.S.
Blackburn — A44

1928-40   Perf. 11

105	A35	1c green	.25	.25
		Never hinged	.25	
106	A36	2c carmine	.25	.25
		Never hinged	.30	
a.		Booklet pane of 6	15.00	20.00
		Never hinged	22.50	
107	A37	5c blue	1.00	.40
		Never hinged	1.30	
108	A38	10c orange	.25	.25
		Never hinged	.25	
109	A39	12c brown violet	.75	.60
		Never hinged	1.00	
110	A40	14c blue	.85	.85
		Never hinged	1.20	
111	A41	15c gray black	.40	.35
		Never hinged	.55	
112	A42	20c dark brown	.60	.25
		Never hinged	.80	
113	A43	30c black	.80	.70
		Never hinged	1.10	
114	A44	50c rose lilac	1.50	.65
		Never hinged	2.00	
		Nos. 105-114 (10)	6.65	4.55

For surcharges and overprints, see Nos.
J21-J24, O1-O8.
Coils are listed as Nos. 160-161.

United States Nos. 720
and 695 Overprinted
type B

1933, Jan. 14   Perf. 11x10½

115	A226	3c deep violet	2.75	.25
		Never hinged	4.00	
b.		"CANAL" only	2,600.	
c.		Booklet pane of 6, hand-made, perf. margins	80.00	—
d.		Vertical pair, one without overprint		
116	A168	14c dark blue	4.50	3.50
		Never hinged	7.00	
a.		"ZONE CANAL"	1,500.	

Gen. George Washington
Goethals — A45

20th anniversary of the opening of the Panama Canal.

1934   Perf. 11

117	A45	3c red violet	.25	.25
		Never hinged	.30	
a.		Booklet pane of 6	12.50	32.50
b.		As "a," handmade, perf. margins	160.00	

Coil is listed as No. 153.

> **Catalogue values for unused stamps in this section, from this point to the end, are for Never Hinged items.**

United States Nos. 803
and 805 Overprinted in
Black

1939, Sept. 1   Perf. 11x10½

118	A275	½c red orange	.25	.25
119	A277	1½c bister brown	.25	.25

Panama Canal Anniversary Issue

Balboa-Before — A46

Balboa-After — A47

Gaillard
Cut-Before
A48

Gaillard
Cut-After
A49

Bas Obispo-Before — A50

Bas Obispo-
After
A51

Gatun Locks-Before — A52

Gatun
Locks-After
A53

Canal
Channel-
Before
A54

Canal Channel-After — A55

Gamboa-
Before
A56

Gamboa-After — A57

Pedro Miguel Locks-Before — A58

Pedro
Miguel
Locks-After
A59

Gatun
Spillway-
Before
A60

Gatun Spillway-After — A61

25th anniversary of the opening of the Panama Canal.

1939, Aug. 15

120	A46	1c yellow green	.60	.30
121	A47	2c rose carmine	.70	.35
122	A48	3c purple	.70	.25
123	A49	5c dark blue	2.00	1.25
124	A50	6c red orange	4.50	3.00
125	A51	7c black	4.75	3.00
126	A52	8c green	7.00	3.25
127	A53	10c ultramarine	5.50	5.00
128	A54	11c blue green	11.00	8.00
129	A55	12c brown carmine	11.00	7.50
130	A56	14c dark violet	11.00	8.00
131	A57	15c olive green	14.00	5.75
132	A58	18c rose pink	15.00	8.50
133	A59	20c brown	17.50	7.00
134	A60	25c orange	27.50	15.00
135	A61	50c violet brown	30.00	6.00
		Nos. 120-135 (16)	162.75	81.15

Maj. Gen.
George W.
Davis
A62

Gov. Charles
E. Magoon
A63

Theodore
Roosevelt
A64

John F.
Stevens
A65

John F.
Wallace — A66

1946-49   Size: 19x22mm

136	A62	½c bright red	.40	.25
137	A63	1½c chocolate	.40	.25
138	A64	2c light rose carmine	.25	.25
139	A65	5c dark blue	.35	.25
140	A66	25c green	.85	.55
		Nos. 136-140 (5)	2.25	1.55

See Nos. 155, 162, 164. For overprint, see
No. O9.

Map of Biological Area and Coati-
Mundi — A67

25th anniversary of the establishment of the
Canal Zone Biological Area on Barro Colorado
Island.

1948, Apr. 17

141	A67	10c black	1.75	1.00

"Forty-niners"
Arriving at
Chagres
A68

Journey by
"Bungo" to Las
Cruces
A69

Las Cruces
Trail to
Panama
A70

Departure for
San Francisco
A71

Centenary of the California Gold Rush.

1949, June 1

142	A68	3c blue	.65	.25
143	A69	6c violet	.65	.30
144	A70	12c bright blue green	1.75	.90
145	A71	18c deep red lilac	2.00	1.50
		Nos. 142-145 (4)	5.05	2.95

Workers in Culebra
Cut — A72

Contribution of West Indian laborers in the
construction of the Panama Canal.

1951, Aug. 15

146	A72	10c carmine	3.50	1.50

Centenary of the completion of the Panama
Railroad and the first transcontinental railroad
trip in the Americas.

Early Railroad
Scene — A73

1955, Jan. 28

147	A73	3c violet	1.00	.60

Gorgas Hospital and Ancon Hill — A74

75th anniversary of Gorgas Hospital.

1957, Nov. 17
148 A74 3c black, *dull blue grn* .45 .35

S.S. Ancon A75

1958, Aug. 30
149 A75 4c greenish blue .40 .30

Roosevelt Medal and Map — A76

Centenary of the birth of Theodore Roosevelt (1858-1919).

1958, Nov. 15
150 A76 4c brown .60 .30

Boy Scout Badge — A77

50th anniversary of the Boy Scouts of America.

1960, Feb. 8   Giori Press Printing
151 A77 4c dark blue, red & bister .55 .40

Administration Building — A78

1960, Nov. 1
152 A78 4c rose lilac .25 .25

Types of 1934, 1960 and 1946 Coil Stamps
1960-62 Unwmk. Perf. 10 Vertically
153 A45 3c deep violet .25 .25
Perf. 10 Horizontally
154 A78 4c dull rose lilac .25 .25
Perf. 10 Vertically
155 A65 5c deep blue .25 .25
Nos. 153-155 (3) .75 .75

Girl Scout Badge and Camp at Gatun Lake A79

50th anniversary of the Girl Scouts.

Giori Press Printing
1962, Mar. 12   Perf. 11
156 A79 4c blue, dark green & bister .40 .30

Thatcher Ferry Bridge and Map of Western Hemisphere A80

Opening of the Thatcher Ferry Bridge, spanning the Panama Canal.

Giori Press Printing
1962, Oct. 12
157 A80 4c black & silver .35 .25
a. Silver (bridge) omitted (50) 8,000.
Hinged 6,000.

Goethals Memorial, Balboa A81

Fort San Lorenzo A82

1968-71   Giori Press Printing
158 A81 6c green & ultra. .30 .30
159 A82 8c slate green, blue, dark brown & ocher .35 .25

Types of 1928, 1932 and 1948 Coil Stamps
1975, Feb. 14   Perf. 10 Vertically
160 A35 1c green .25 .25
161 A38 10c orange .70 .40
162 A66 25c yellow green 2.75 2.75
Nos. 160-162 (3) 3.70 3.40

Dredge Cascadas A83

Giori Press Printing
1976, Feb. 23
163 A83 13c multicolored .35 .25
a. Booklet pane of 4 3.00 —

No. 163a exists with and without staple holes in selvage tab.

Stevens Type of 1946
1977   Perf. 11x10½
Size: 19x22½mm
164 A65 5c deep blue .60 .85
a. Tagged, dull gum 12.00 15.00

No. 164 exists with both shiny gum and dull gum. Stamps with dull gum exist with and without tagging.
No. 164a exists even though there was no equipment in the Canal Zone to detect tagging.

Towing Locomotive, Ship in Lock — A84

1978, Oct. 25   Perf. 11
165 A84 15c dp grn & bl grn .35 .25

AIR POST STAMPS

Nos. 105-106 Surcharged in Dark Blue

Type I - Flag of "Five" pointing up

Type II - Flag of "5" curved

1929-31   Engr.   Unwmk.   Perf. 11
C1 A35 15c on 1c green, type I 7.50 4.75
   Never hinged 11.50
C2 A35 15c on 1c yellow green, type II 60.00 47.50
   Never hinged 120.00
C3 A36 25c on 2c carmine 3.50 2.00
   Never hinged 5.25
   Nos. C1-C3 (3) 71.00 54.25

Nos. 114 and 106 Surcharged

1929, Dec. 31
C4 A44 10c on 50c lilac 8.00 5.75
   Never hinged 12.00
C5 A36 20c on 2c carmine 4.50 1.25
   Never hinged 7.50
   a. Dropped "2" in surcharge 85.00 60.00

Catalogue values for unused stamps in this section, from this point to the end, are for Never Hinged items.

Gaillard Cut — AP1

1931-49
C6 AP1 4c red violet .75 .65
C7 AP1 5c yellow green .60 .30
C8 AP1 6c yellow brown .75 .35
C9 AP1 10c orange 1.00 .35
C10 AP1 15c blue 1.25 .30
C11 AP1 20c red violet 2.00 .25
C12 AP1 30c rose lake 7.50 1.50
C13 AP1 40c yellow 3.50 1.10
C14 AP1 $1 black 10.00 1.60
   Nos. C6-C14 (9) 27.35 6.40

For overprints, see Nos. CO1-CO14.

Douglas Plane over Sosa Hill — AP2

Planes and Map of Central America AP3

Pan American Clipper and Scene near Fort Amador AP4

Pan American Clipper at Cristobal Harbor AP5

Pan American Clipper over Gaillard Cut — AP6

Pan American Clipper Landing AP7

10th anniversary of Air Mail service and the 25th anniversary of the opening of the Panama Canal.

1939, July 15
C15 AP2 5c greenish black 3.75 2.25
C16 AP3 10c dull violet 3.50 3.00
C17 AP4 15c light brown 5.00 1.00
C18 AP5 25c blue 17.50 8.00
C19 AP6 30c rose carmine 17.50 6.00
C20 AP7 $1 green 45.00 27.50
   Nos. C15-C20 (6) 92.25 47.75

Globe and Wing — AP8

1951, July 16
C21 AP8 4c lt red violet .75 .35
C22 AP8 6c lt brown .50 .25
C23 AP8 10c lt red orange .90 .35
C24 AP8 21c lt blue 8.00 4.00
C25 AP8 31c cerise 9.50 3.75
   a. Horiz. pair, imperf. vert. 1,250.
C26 AP8 80c lt gray black 6.00 1.50
   Nos. C21-C26 (6) 25.65 10.20

Flat Plate Printing
1958, Aug. 16   Unwmk.   Perf. 11
C27 AP8 5c yellow green 1.00 .60
C28 AP8 7c olive 1.00 .45
C29 AP8 15c brown violet 4.50 2.75
C30 AP8 25c orange yellow 12.50 2.75
C31 AP8 35c dark blue 9.00 2.75
   Nos. C27-C31 (5) 28.00 9.30
   Nos. C21-C31 (11) 53.65 19.50

See No. C34.

Emblem of U.S. Army Caribbean School AP9

US Army Caribbean School for Latin America at Fort Gulick.

1961, Nov. 21
C32 AP9 15c red & blue 1.60 .75

Malaria Eradication Emblem and Mosquito AP10

World Health Organization drive to eradicate malaria.

1962, Sept. 24
C33 AP10 7c yellow & black .50 .40

Globe-Wing Type of 1951
1963, Jan. 7   Perf. 10½x11
C34 AP8 8c carmine .75 .30

Alliance Emblem AP11

2nd anniv. of the Alliance for Progress, which aims to stimulate economic growth and raise living standards in Latin America.

1963, Aug. 17   *Perf. 11*
C35 AP11 15c gray, grn & dk
ultra   1.50   .85

Jet over
Canal Zone
Views
AP12

50th anniversary of the opening of the Panama Canal.

Designs: 6c, Cristobal. 8c, Gatun Locks. 15c, Madden Dam. 20c, Gaillard Cut. 30c, Miraflores Locks. 80c, Balboa.

1964, Aug. 15
C36 AP12 6c green & black   .60   .35
C37 AP12 8c rose red &
    black   .60   .35
C38 AP12 15c blue & black   1.25   .75
C39 AP12 20c rose lilac &
    black   1.60   1.00
C40 AP12 30c reddish brown
    & black   2.75   2.25
C41 AP12 80c olive bister &
    black   4.75   3.00
    Nos. C36-C41 (6)   11.55   7.70

Seal and
Jet Plane
AP13

1965, July 15
C42 AP13 6c green & black   .50   .30
C43 AP13 8c rose red &
    black   .45   .25
C44 AP13 15c blue & black   .75   .25
C45 AP13 20c lilac & black   .80   .30
C46 AP13 30c redsh brn & blk   1.10   .30
    On cover, single franking, to
    Australasia, Asia or sub-
    Sahara Africa   25.00
C47 AP13 80c bister & black   2.50   .75
    Nos. C42-C47 (6)   6.10   2.15

1968-76
C48 AP13 10c dull orange &
    black   .35   .25
   a.   Booklet pane of 4   4.25   —
C49 AP13 11c olive & black   .35   .25
   a.   Booklet pane of 4   3.50   —
C50 AP13 13c emerald & black   .85   .25
   a.   Booklet pane of 4   6.00   —
C51 AP13 22c vio & blk   1.10   2.00
C52 AP13 25c pale yellow
    green & black   .80   .70
C53 AP13 35c salmon & black   1.25   2.00
    Nos. C48-C53 (6)   4.70   5.45

AIR POST OFFICIAL STAMPS

Beginning in March 1915, stamps for use on official mail were identified by a large "P" perforated through each stamp. These were replaced by overprinted issues in 1941. The use of official stamps was discontinued December 31, 1951. During their currency, they were not for sale in mint condition and were sold to the public only when canceled with a parcel post rotary canceler reading "Balboa Heights, Canal Zone" between two wavy lines.

After having been withdrawn from use, mint stamps (except Nos. CO8-CO12 and O3, O8) were made available to the public at face value for three months beginning Jan. 2, 1952. **Values for used examples of Nos. CO1-CO7, CO14, O1-O2, O4-O9, are for canceled-to-order stamps with original gum, postally used stamps being worth more.**

Nos. C7,
C9-C14
Overprinted
in Black

Two types of overprint
Type I — "PANAMA CANAL" 19-20mm long

1941-42   **Unwmk.**   *Perf. 11*
CO1 AP1 5c yellow green   6.50   1.50
CO2 AP1 10c orange   8.50   1.75
CO3 AP1 15c blue   11.00   1.75
CO4 AP1 20c red violet   13.00   4.00
CO5 AP1 30c rose lake   17.50   5.00
CO6 AP1 40c yellow   17.50   7.50
CO7 AP1 $1 black   20.00   10.00
    Nos. CO1-CO7 (7)   94.00   31.50

Overprint varieties occur on Nos. CO1-CO7 and CO14: "O" of "OFFICIAL" over "N" of "PANAMA" (entire third row). "O" of "OFFICIAL" broken at top (position 31). "O" of "OFFICIAL" over second "A" of "PANAMA" (position 45). First "F" of "OFFICIAL" over second "A" of "PANAMA" (position 50).

Type II — "PANAMA CANAL" 17mm long

1941, Sept. 22
CO8 AP1 5c yellow
    green   —   150.00
CO9 AP1 10c orange   *1,100.*   260.00
CO10 AP1 20c red violet   —   160.00
CO11 AP1 30c rose lake   *900.*   60.00
CO12 AP1 40c yellow   —   170.00
    Nos. CO8-CO12 (5)   800.00

Type I — "PANAMA CANAL" 19-20mm long

1947, Nov.
CO14 AP1 6c yellow brown   13.00   5.50
   a.   Inverted overprint   2,000.

POSTAGE DUE STAMPS

Prior to 1914, many of the postal issues were handstamped "Postage Due" and used as postage due stamps.

Postage Due Stamps of the U.S. Nos. J45a, J46a and J49a Overprinted in Black

1914, Mar.   **Wmk. 190**   *Perf. 12*
J1 D2 1c rose carmine   85.00   15.00
J2 D2 2c rose carmine   250.00   42.50
J3 D2 10c rose carmine   900.00   40.00
    Nos. J1-J3 (3)   1,235.   97.50

Castle Gate
(See
footnote) — D1

Statue of
Columbus
D2   Pedro J. Sosa
D3

1915, Mar.   **Unwmk.**
Blue Overprint, Type II, on Postage Due Stamps of Panama
J4 D1 1c olive brown   11.00   5.00
J5 D2 2c olive brown   225.00   17.50
J6 D3 10c olive brown   50.00   10.00
    Nos. J4-J6 (3)   286.00   32.50

Type D1 was intended to show a gate of San Lorenzo Castle, Chagres, and is so labeled. By error the stamp actually shows the main gate of San Geronimo Castle, Portobelo.

Surcharged in Red

1915, Nov.
J7 D1 1c on 1c olive
    brown   110.00   14.00
J8 D2 2c on 2c olive
    brown   22.50   7.50
J9 D3 10c on 10c olive
    brown   22.50   5.00
    Nos. J7-J9 (3)   155.00   26.50

Columbus
Statue — D4   Capitol, Panama
City — D5

1919, Dec.
Surcharged in Carmine by Panama Canal Press, Mount Hope, C. Z. "Canal Zone" Type III
J10 D4 2c on 2c olive
    brown   30.00   11.00
J11 D5 4c on 4c olive
    brown   35.00   12.50
   a.   "ZONE" omitted   9,250.
   b.   "4" omitted   8,500.

Blue Overprint, Type V, on Postage Due Stamp of Panama

1922
J11C D1 1c dark olive
    brown   —   5.00
   d.   "CANAL ZONE" reading
     down   200.00

United States Postage
Due Stamps Nos. J61,
J62b and J65b
Overprinted

Type A
Letters "A" with Flat Tops

1924, July 1   *Perf. 11*
J12 D2 1c carmine rose   110.00   27.50
J13 D2 2c deep claret   55.00   15.00
J14 D2 10c deep claret   250.00   50.00
    Nos. J12-J14 (3)   415.00   92.50

U.S. Postage Stamps
Nos. 552, 554 and 562
Overprinted Type A
and additional
Overprint in Red or
Blue

1925, Feb.
J15 A155 1c deep green (R)   90.00   15.00
J16 A157 2c carmine (Bl)   22.50   7.00
J17 A165 10c orange (R)   55.00   11.00
   a.   "POSTAGE DUE" double   800.00
   b.   "E" of "POSTAGE" omitted   750.00
   c.   As "b," "POSTAGE DUE"
     double   3,250.
    Nos. J15-J17 (3)   167.50   33.00

Overprinted Type B
Letters "A" with Sharp Pointed Tops
On U.S. Postage Due Stamps Nos. J61, J62, J65, J65a

1925, June 24
J18 D2 1c carmine rose   8.00   2.75
   a.   "ZONE ZONE" (LR18)   1,500.
J19 D2 2c carmine rose   15.00   2.75
   a.   "ZONE ZONE" (LR18)   1,500.
J20 D2 10c carmine rose   150.00   20.00
   a.   Vert. pair, one without ovpt.   3,000.
   b.   10c rose red   250.00   150.00
   c.   As "b," double overprint   450.00   —
    Nos. J18-J20 (3)   173.00   25.50

Regular Issue of 1928-29 Surcharged

1929-30
J21 A37 1c on 5c blue   3.75   1.75
    Never hinged   7.50
   a.   "POSTAGE DUE" missing   5,500.
J22 A37 2c on 5c blue   6.50   2.50
    Never hinged   13.00
J23 A37 5c on 5c blue   6.50   2.75
    Never hinged   13.00
J24 A37 10c on 5c blue   6.50   2.75
    Never hinged   13.00
    Nos. J21-J24 (4)   23.25   9.75

On No. J23 the three short horizontal bars in the lower corners of the surcharge are omitted.

Canal Zone Seal — D6

1932-41
J25 D6 1c claret   .25   .25
    Never hinged   .30
J26 D6 2c claret   .25   .25
    Never hinged   .30
J27 D6 5c claret   .35   .25
    Never hinged   .50
J28 D6 10c claret   1.75   1.50
    Never hinged   2.25
J29 D6 15c claret   1.25   1.00
    Never hinged   1.60
    Nos. J25-J29 (5)   3.85   3.25

OFFICIAL STAMPS

See note at beginning of Air Post Official Stamps

Regular Issues of 1928-34 Overprinted in Black

Type 1

Type 2

Type 1 — "PANAMA" 10mm long
Type 2 — "PANAMA" 9mm long

Unwmk.
1941, Mar. 31   **Engr.**   *Perf. 11*
O1 A35 1c yellow green,
    type 1   2.00   .40
O2 A45 3c deep violet,
    type 1   3.75   .75
O3 A37 5c blue, type 2   *1,000.*   25.00
O4 A38 10c orange, type 1   7.50   1.90
O5 A41 15c gray black,
    type 1   15.00   2.25
O6 A42 20c olive brown,
    type 1   17.50   2.75
O7 A44 50c lilac, type 1   42.50   5.50
O8 A44 50c rose lilac, type
    1a   550.00
    Nos. O1-O2, O4-O7 (6)   88.25   13.55

No. 139 Overprinted in Black

1947, Feb.
O9 A65 5c deep blue,
    type 1   12.50   3.75

CUBA

ˈkyü-bə

LOCATION — The largest island of the West Indies; south of Florida.
GOVT. — socialist; under US military governor 1899-1902 and US provisional governor 1906-1909.
AREA — 44,206 sq. mi.
POP. — 9,710,000 (1981)
CAPITAL — Havana

Formerly a Spanish possession, Cuba's attempts to gain freedom led to US intervention in 1898. Under Treaty of Paris of that year, Spain relinquished the island to US trust. In 1902, a republic was established and Cuban Congress took over government from US military authorities.

100 Cents = 1 Dollar

Watermark

Wmk. 191 — Double-lined "USPS" in Capitals

The basic stamps used for overprinting at Puerto Principe are normally poorly centered. Values for Nos. 176-220 are for stamps with fine centering, as typically found. Furthermore, values are for stamps accompanied by certificates issued by competent experts. Convincing fakes and counterfeits are plentiful.

Values for Nos. 221-J4 are for very fine examples.

Issued under Administration of the United States
Puerto Principe Issue
Issues of Cuba of 1898 and 1896 Surcharged

a   b

Black Surcharge on Nos. 156-158, 160

Types a, c, d, e, f, g and h are 17½mm high, the others are 19½mm high.

1898-99

176	A19 (a) 1c on 1m org brn	100.00	60.00
177	A19 (b) 1c on 1m org brn	600.00	115.00
a.	Broken figure "1"	3,000.	275.00
b.	Inverted surcharge		500.00
d.	As "a," inverted		1,500.

c   d

178	A19 (c) 2c on 2m org brn	65.00	62.50
a.	Inverted surcharge	500.00	
179	A19 (d) 2c on 2m org brn	82.50	77.50
a.	Inverted surcharge	—	500.00

k   l

179B	A19 (k) 3c on 1m org brn	300.	175.
c.	Double surcharge		3,000.

An unused example is known with "cents" omitted.

179D	A19 (l) 3c on 1m org brn	1,350.	675.00

e   f

179F	A19 (e) 3c on 2m org brn		1,500.

Value is for examples with minor faults.

179G	A19 (f) 3c on 2m org brn	—	2,000.

Value is for examples with minor faults.

180	A19 (e) 3c on 3m	150.	100.
a.	Inverted surcharge		375.
181	A19 (f) 3c on 3m org brn	600.	400.
a.	Inverted surcharge		750.

g   h

i   j

182	A19 (g) 5c on 1m org brn	1,000.	165.
a.	Inverted surcharge	—	1,000.
183	A19 (h) 5c on 1m org brn	1,500.	1,000.
a.	Inverted surcharge	1,500.	1,500.
184	A19 (g) 5c on 2m org brn	1,000.	275.
185	A19 (h) 5c on 2m org brn	1,500.	600.
186	A19 (g) 5c on 3m org brn	1,500.	350.
a.	Inverted surcharge	1,200.	700.
187	A19 (h) 5c on 3m org brn	—	1,000.
a.	Inverted surcharge	—	1,000.
188	A19 (g) 5c on 5m org brn	145.	230.
a.	Inverted surcharge	—	750.
b.	Double surcharge	—	—
189	A19 (h) 5c on 5m org brn	3,000.	425.
a.	Inverted surcharge	3,000.	900.
b.	Double surcharge		

The 2nd printing of Nos. 188-189 has shiny ink. Values are for the 1st printing.

189C	A19 (i) 5c on 5m org brn		7,500.

No. 191

Black Surcharge on No. P25

190	N2 (g) 5c on ½m bl grn	375.	115.
a.	Inverted surcharge	1,000.	210.
b.	Pair, one without surcharge		500.

Value for 190b is for pair with unsurcharged stamp at right. Also exists with unsurcharged stamp at left.

191	N2 (h) 5c on ½m bl grn	1,000.	275.
a.	Inverted surcharge		1,000.
192	N2 (i) 5c on ½m bl grn	3,000.	100.
a.	Dbl. surch., one diagonal	3,500.	—
193	N2 (j) 5c on ½m bl grn	900.	500.

Red Surcharge on No. 161

196	A19 (k) 3c on 1c blk vio	150.	125.
a.	Inverted surcharge		500.
197	A19 (l) 3c on 1c blk vio	250.	200.
a.	Inverted surcharge		1,500.
198	A19 (i) 5c on 1c blk vio	92.50	72.50
a.	Surcharge vert. reading up		500.
c.	Double surcharge	600.	—
d.	Double invtd. surch.	—	2,750.

Value for No. 198b is for surcharge reading up. One example is known with surcharge reading down.

199	A19 (j) 5c on 1c blk vio	150.	115.
a.	Inverted surcharge		3,000.
b.	Vertical surcharge		—
c.	Double surcharge	3,000.	3,000.

m

200	A19 10c on 1c blk (m) vio	62.50	92.50
a.	Broken figure "1"	160.00	225.00

Black Surcharge on Nos. P26-P30

201	N2 (k) 3c on 1m bl grn	350.	350.
a.	Inverted surcharge		450.
b.	"EENTS"	600.	450.
c.	As "b," inverted		850.
202	N2 (l) 3c on 1m bl grn	1,000.	400.
a.	"EENTS"		850.
203	N2 (k) 3c on 2m bl grn	1,650.	400.
a.	"EENTS"	1,650.	500.
b.	Inverted surcharge		1,500.
c.	As "a," inverted		2,750.
204	N2 (l) 3c on 2m bl grn	2,750.	600.
a.	Inverted surcharge		1,500.
205	N2 (k) 3c on 3m bl grn	900.	400.
a.	Inverted surcharge		750.
b.	"EENTS"	1,250.	450.
c.	As "b," inverted		2,750.
206	N2 (l) 3c on 3m bl grn	1,500.	550.
a.	Inverted surcharge		1,000.
211	N2 (i) 5c on 1m bl grn		1,800.
a.	"EENTS"		3,000.
212	N2 (j) 5c on 1m bl grn	—	2,250.
213	N2 (i) 5c on 2m bl grn	3,000.	1,800.
a.	"EENTS"	3,000.	3,000.
214	N2 (j) 5c on 2m bl grn	3,250.	1,750.
215	N2 (i) 5c on 3m bl grn		550.
a.	"EENTS"		1,000.
216	N2 (j) 5c on 3m bl grn	3,000.	1,000.
217	N2 (i) 5c on 4m bl grn	3,000.	900.
a.	"EENTS"	3,000.	1,500.
b.	Inverted surcharge		2,000.
c.	As "a," inverted		3,000.
218	N2 (j) 5c on 4m bl grn	3,000.	1,500.
a.	Inverted surcharge		2,000.
219	N2 (i) 5c on 8m bl grn	2,500.	1,250.
a.	Inverted surcharge		1,500.
b.	"EENTS"	3,000.	2,750.
c.	As "b," inverted		2,500.
220	N2 (j) 5c on 8m bl grn		2,000.
a.	Inverted surcharge		2,500.

Beware of forgeries of the Puerto Principe issue. Obtaining expert opinions is recommended.

United States Stamps Nos. 279, 267, 267b, 279Bf, 279Bh, 268, 281, 282C and 283 Surcharged in Black

1899   Wmk. 191   Perf. 12

221	A87 1c on 1c yel grn	4.50	.40
	Never hinged	11.50	

222	A88 2c on 2c reddish car, III	10.00	.75
	Never hinged	25.00	
b.	2c on 2c vermilion, type III	10.00	.75
222A	A88 2c on 2c reddish car, IV	6.00	.40
	Never hinged	15.00	
c.	2c on 2c vermilion, IV	6.00	.40
d.	As No. 222A, inverted surcharge	5,500.	4,000.
223	A88 2½c on 2c reddish car, III	6.00	.80
	Never hinged	15.00	
b.	2½c on 2c vermilion, III	6.00	.80
223A	A88 2½c on 2c reddish car, IV	3.50	.50
	Never hinged	8.75	
c.	2½c on 2c vermilion, IV	3.50	.50
224	A89 3c on 3c purple	12.00	1.75
	Never hinged	30.00	
a.	Period between "B" and "A"	40.00	35.00
225	A91 5c on 5c blue	12.50	2.00
	Never hinged	30.00	
226	A94 10c on 10c brn, I	25.00	6.00
	Never hinged	70.00	
b.	"CUBA" omitted	7,000.	4,000.
226A	A94 10c on 10c brn, II	6,000.	
	Nos. 221-226 (8)	79.50	12.60

The 2½c was sold and used as a 2c stamp. Excellent counterfeits of this and the preceding issue exist, especially inverted and double surcharges.

Issues of the Republic under US Military Rule

Statue of Columbus A20   Royal Palms A21

"Cuba" — A22   Ocean Liner — A23

Cane Field — A24

1899   Wmk. US-C (191C)   Perf. 12

227	A20 1c yellow green	3.50	.25
	Never hinged	8.75	
228	A21 2c carmine	3.50	.25
	Never hinged	8.75	
a.	scarlet	3.50	.25
b.	Booklet pane of 6	5,500.	
229	A22 3c purple	3.50	.30
	Never hinged	8.75	
230	A23 5c blue	4.50	.30
	Never hinged	11.00	
231	A24 10c brown	11.00	.80
	Never hinged	27.50	
	Nos. 227-231 (5)	26.00	1.90

No. 228b was issued by the Republic. See Nos. 233-237. For surcharge see No. 232.

SPECIAL DELIVERY STAMPS

Issued under Administration of the United States

US No. E5 Surcharged in Red

1899   Wmk. 191   Perf. 12

E1	SD3 10c blue	130.	100.
	Never hinged	300.	
a.	No period after "CUBA"	575.	400.

Issue of the Republic under US Military Rule

Special Delivery Messenger SD2

Printed by the US Bureau of Engraving and Printing

1899   Wmk. US-C (191C)
Inscribed: "Immediata"

E2	SD2 10c orange	52.50	15.00
	Never hinged	120.00	

POSTAGE DUE STAMPS

Issued under Administration of the United States

Postage Due Stamps of the United States Nos. J38, J39, J41 and J42 Srchd. in Black Like Nos. 221-226A

1899   Wmk. 191   Perf. 12

J1	D2 1c dp claret	45.00	5.25
	Never hinged	110.00	
J2	D2 2c dp claret	45.00	5.25
	Never hinged	110.00	
a.	Inverted surcharge		4,000.
J3	D2 5c dp claret	42.50	5.25
	Never hinged	105.00	
J4	D2 10c dp claret	25.00	2.50
	Never hinged	60.00	
	Nos. J1-J4 (4)	157.50	18.25

DANISH WEST INDIES AND UNITED STATES VIRGIN ISLANDS

'dā-nish 'west 'in-dēs

LOCATION — Group of Islands in the West Indies, lying east of Puerto Rico
GOVT. — Danish colony
AREA — 132 sq. mi.
POP. — 27,086 (1911)
CAPITAL — Charlotte Amalie

The US bought these islands in 1917 and they became the US Virgin Islands, using US stamps and currency.

100 Cents = 1 Dollar
100 Bit = 1 Franc (1905)

Wmk. 111 — Small Crown   Wmk. 112 — Crown

Wmk. 113 — Crown   Wmk. 114 — Multiple Crosses

Coat of Arms — A1

Yellowish Paper
Yellow Wavy-line Burelage, UL to LR

1856   Typo.   Wmk. 111   Imperf.

1	A1 3c dark carmine, brown gum	200.	275.
a.	3c dark carmine, yellow gum	225.	275.
b.	3c carmine, white gum	4,250.	—

The brown and yellow gums were applied locally.
Reprint: 1981, carmine, back-printed across two stamps ("Reprint by Dansk Post og Telegrafmuseum 1978"), value, pair, $10.

White Paper

1866
Yellow Wavy-line Burelage UR to LL

2	A1 3c rose	40.	65.

No. 2 reprints, unwatermarked: 1930, carmine, value $100. 1942, rose carmine, back-printed across each row ("Nytryk 1942 G. A. Hagemann Danmark og Dansk Vestindiens Frimaerker Bind 2"), value $50.

1872   Perf. 12½

3	A1 3c rose	100.	275.

1873   Without Burelage

4	A1 4c dull blue	250.	475.
a.	Imperf., pair	775.	
b.	Horiz. pair, imperf. vert.	575.	

The 1930 reprint of No. 4 is ultramarine, unwatermarked and imperf., value $100. The 1942 4c reprint is blue, unwatermarked, imperf. and has printing on back (see note below No. 2), value $60.

A2

Normal Frame   Inverted Frame

The arabesques in the corners have a main stem and a branch. When the frame is in normal position, in the upper left corner the branch leaves the main stem half way between two little leaflets. In the lower right corner the branch starts at the foot of the second leaflet. When the frame is inverted the corner designs are, of course, transposed.
Values for inverted frames, covers and blocks are for the cheapest variety.

White Wove Paper
Varying from Thin to Thick

1874-79   Wmk. 112   Perf. 14x13½

5	A2 1c green & brown red	22.50	30.00
a.	1c green & rose lilac, thin paper	80.00	125.00
b.	1c green & red violet, medium paper	45.00	65.00
c.	1c green & claret, thick paper	20.00	30.00
e.	As "c," inverted frame	25.00	32.50
f.	As "a," inverted frame	475.00	

No. 5 exists with a surcharge similar to the surcharge on No. 15, with 10 CENTS value and 1895 date. This stamp is an essay.

6	A2 3c blue & carmine	27.50	20.00
a.	3c light blue & rose carmine, thin paper	65.00	50.00
b.	3c deep blue & dark carmine, medium paper	40.00	17.00
c.	3c greenish blue & lake, thick paper	32.50	17.00
d.	Imperf., pair	375.00	—
e.	Inverted frame, thick paper	30.00	20.00
f.	As "a," inverted frame	350.00	
7	A2 4c brown & dull blue	16.00	19.00
b.	4c brown & ultramarine, thin paper	225.00	225.00
c.	Diagonal half used as 2c on cover		140.00
d.	As "b," inverted frame	900.00	1,400.
8	A2 5c grn & gray ('76)	30.00	20.00
a.	5c yellow green & dark gray, thin paper	55.00	32.50
b.	Inverted frame, thick paper	30.00	20.00
9	A2 7c lilac & orange	35.00	95.00
a.	7c lilac & yellow	90.00	100.00
b.	Inverted frame	65.00	150.00
10	A2 10c blue & brn ('76)	30.00	25.00
a.	10c dark blue & black brown, thin paper	70.00	40.00
b.	Period between "t" & "s" of "cents"	35.00	25.00
c.	Inverted frame	27.50	32.50
11	A2 12c red lil & yel grn ('77)	42.50	175.00
a.	12c lilac & deep green	160.00	200.00
12	A2 14c lilac & green	650.00	1,250.
a.	Inverted frame	2,500.	3,500.
13	A2 50c vio, thin paper ('79)	190.00	300.00
a.	50c gray violet, thick paper	300.00	375.00
	Nos. 5-13 (9)	1,044.	1,934.

The central element in the fan-shaped scrollwork at the outside of the lower left corner of Nos. 5a and 7b looks like an elongated diamond.
See Nos. 16-20. For surcharges see Nos. 14-15, 23-28, 40.

No. 9 Surcharged in Black

a

1887

14	A2 (a) 1c on 7c lilac & orange	100.00	200.00
a.	1c on 7c lilac & yellow	120.00	225.00
b.	Double surcharge	250.00	500.00
c.	Inverted frame	110.00	350.00

No. 13 Surcharged in Black

b

1895

15	A2 (b) 10c on 50c violet, thin paper	42.50	67.50

The "b" surcharge also exists on No. 5, with "10" found in two sizes. These are essays.

Type of 1874-79

1896-1901   Perf. 13

16	A2 1c grn & red vio, inverted frame ('98)	15.00	22.50
a.	Normal frame	300.00	450.00
17	A2 3c blue & lake, inverted frame ('98)	12.00	17.50
a.	Normal frame	250.00	425.00
18	A2 4c bister & dull blue ('01)	17.50	11.00
a.	Diagonal half used as 2c on cover		100.00
b.	Inverted frame	60.00	80.00
c.	As "b," diagonal half used as 2c on cover		350.00
19	A2 5c green & gray, inverted frame	35.00	35.00
a.	Normal frame	800.00	1,200.
20	A2 10c blue & brn ('01)	80.00	150.00
a.	Inverted frame	1,000.	2,000.
b.	Period between "t" and "s" of "cents"	170.00	160.00
	Nos. 16-20 (5)	159.50	236.00

Arms — A5

1900

21	A5 1c light green	3.00	3.00
22	A5 5c light blue	17.50	25.00

See Nos. 29-30. For surcharges see Nos. 41-42.

Nos. 6, 17, 20 Surcharged
c

Surcharge "c" in Black

1902   Perf. 14x13½

23	A2 2c on 3c blue & carmine, inverted frame	700.00	900.00
a.	"2" in date with straight tail	750.00	950.00
b.	Normal frame	—	

Perf. 13

24	A2 2c on 3c blue & lake, inverted frame	10.00	27.50
a.	"2" in date with straight tail	12.00	32.50
b.	Dated "1901"	750.00	750.00
c.	Normal frame	175.00	300.00
d.	Dark green surcharge	2,750.	
e.	As "d" & "a"	—	—
f.	As "d" & "c"	—	

The overprint on No. 24b exists in two types: with "1901" measuring 2.5 mm or 2.2 mm high.
Only one example of No. 24f can exist.

25	A2 8c on 10c blue & brown	25.00	42.50
a.	"2" with straight tail	30.00	45.00
b.	On No. 20b	32.50	45.00
c.	Inverted frame	250.00	425.00

d

Surcharge "d" in Black

1902   Perf. 13

27	A2 2c on 3c blue & lake, inverted frame	12.00	32.50
a.	Normal frame	240.00	425.00

28	A2	8c on 10c blue & brown		12.00	12.00
a.		On No. 20b		18.50	25.00
b.		Inverted frame		225.00	400.00
		Nos. 23-28 (5)		759.00	1,015.

1903   **Wmk. 113**

29	A5	2c carmine		8.00	22.50
30	A5	8c brown		27.50	35.00

King Christian IX — A8   St. Thomas Harbor — A9

1905   **Typo.**   **Perf. 13**

31	A8	5b green		3.75	3.25
32	A8	10b red		3.75	3.25
33	A8	20b green & blue		8.75	8.75
34	A8	25b ultramarine		8.75	10.50
35	A8	40b red & gray		8.25	9.50
36	A8	50b yellow & gray		10.00	10.00

Perf. 12
Wmk. Two Crowns (113)
Frame Typographed, Center Engraved

37	A9	1fr green & blue		17.50	40.00
38	A9	2fr orange red & brown		30.00	55.00
39	A9	5fr yellow & brown		77.50	275.00
		Nos. 31-39 (9)		168.25	415.25

Favor cancels exist on Nos. 37-39. Value 25% less.

Nos. 18, 22 and 30 Surcharged in Black

1905   **Wmk. 112**

40	A2	5b on 4c bister & dull blue		16.00	50.00
a.		Inverted frame		45.00	90.00
41	A5	5b on 5c light blue		10.00	47.50

Wmk. 113

42	A5	5b on 8c brown		12.50	50.00
		Nos. 40-42 (3)		38.50	147.50

Favor cancels exist on Nos. 40-42. Value 25% less.

Frederik VIII — A10

Frame Typographed, Center Engraved

1908

43	A10	5b green		1.90	1.90
44	A10	10b red		1.90	1.90
45	A10	15b violet & brown		3.75	4.50
46	A10	20b green & blue		30.00	27.50
47	A10	25b blue & dark blue		1.90	2.50
48	A10	30b claret & slate		50.00	52.50
49	A10	40b vermilion & gray		5.75	9.50
50	A10	50b yellow & brown		5.75	14.00
		Nos. 43-50 (8)		100.95	114.30

Christian X — A11

1915   **Wmk. 114**   **Perf. 14x14½**

51	A11	5b yellow green		4.00	5.50
52	A11	10b red		4.00	55.00
53	A11	15b lilac & red brown		4.00	55.00
54	A11	20b green & blue		4.00	55.00
55	A11	25b blue & dark blue		4.00	17.50
56	A11	30b claret & black		4.00	100.00
57	A11	40b orange & black		4.00	100.00
58	A11	50b yellow & brown		3.75	100.00
		Nos. 51-58 (8)		31.75	488.00

Forged and favor cancellations exist.

POSTAGE DUE STAMPS

Royal Cipher, "Christian 9 Rex" D1

1902   **Litho.**   **Unwmk.**   **Perf. 11½**

J1	D1	1c dark blue		5.00	17.50
J2	D1	4c dark blue		12.50	22.50
J3	D1	6c dark blue		22.50	60.00
J4	D1	10c dark blue		20.00	65.00
		Nos. J1-J4 (4)		60.00	165.00

There are five types of each value. On the 4c they may be distinguished by differences in the figure "4"; on the other values differences are minute.

Used values of Nos. J1-J4 are for canceled stamps. Uncanceled stamps without gum have probably been used. Value 60% of unused.

Excellent counterfeits of Nos. J1-J4 exist.

Numeral of value — D2

1905-13   **Perf. 13**

J5	D2	5b red & gray		4.50	6.75
J6	D2	20b red & gray		7.50	14.00
J7	D2	30b red & gray		6.75	14.00
J8	D2	50b red & gray		6.00	30.00
a.		Perf. 14x14½ ('13)		90.00	375.00
b.		Perf. 11½		375.00	
		Nos. J5-J8 (4)		24.75	64.75

All values of this issue are known imperforate, but were not regularly issued.

Used values of Nos. J5-J8 are for canceled stamps. Uncanceled examples without gum have probably been used. Value 60% of unused.

No. J8b is valued in the grade of fine.

Counterfeits of Nos. J5-J8 exist.

Danish West Indies stamps were replaced by those of the U.S. in 1917, after the U.S. bought the islands.

GUAM

'gwäm

LOCATION — One of the Mariana Islands in the Pacific Ocean, about 1450 miles east of the Philippines.
GOVT. — United States Possession
AREA — 206 sq. mi.
POP. — 9,000 (est. 1899)
CAPITAL — Agaña

Formerly a Spanish possession, Guam was ceded to the United States in 1898 following the Spanish-American War. Stamps overprinted "Guam" were superseded by the regular postage stamps of the United States in 1901.

100 Cents = 1 Dollar

United States Nos. 279, 279B, 279Bc, 268, 280a, 281, 282, 272, 282C, 283, 284, 275, 275a, 276 and 276A Overprinted

1899   **Wmk. 191**   **Perf. 12**
Black Overprint

1	A87	1c deep green		20.00	25.00
		Never hinged		40.00	

A bogus inverted overprint exists.

2	A88	2c red, type IV		17.50	25.00
		Never hinged		35.00	
a.		rose carmine, type IV		30.00	30.00
		Never hinged		60.00	
3	A89	3c purple		140.00	175.00
		Never hinged		275.00	
4	A90	4c lilac brown		125.00	175.00
		Never hinged		250.00	
5	A91	5c blue		32.50	45.00
		Never hinged		65.00	
6	A92	6c lake		125.00	190.00
		Never hinged		250.00	
7	A93	8c violet brown		125.00	160.00
		Never hinged		275.00	
8	A94	10c brown, type I		45.00	55.00
		Never hinged		90.00	
9	A94	10c brown, type II		2,750.	—
		Never hinged		5,500.	
10	A95	15c olive green		150.00	140.00
		Never hinged		300.00	
11	A96	50c orange		350.00	400.00
		Never hinged		700.00	
a.		50c red orange		550.00	
		Never hinged		1,100.	

Red Overprint

12	A97	$1 black, type I		350.00	400.00
		Never hinged		700.00	
13	A97	$1 black, type II		3,750.	
		Never hinged			
		Nos. 1-8,10-12 (11)		1,480.	1,790.

Counterfeits of the overprint exist.
No. 13 exists only in the special printing.

SPECIAL DELIVERY STAMP

United States No. E5 Overprinted in Red

1899   **Wmk. 191**   **Perf. 12**

E1	SD3	10c blue		150.	200.00
		Never hinged		275.	
a.		Dots in curved frame above messenger (Plate 882)		200.	
		Never hinged		400.	

Counterfeits of the overprint exist.
The special stamps for Guam were replaced by the regular issues of the United States. Guam Guard Mail stamps of 1930 are listed in the Scott U.S. specialized catalogue.

HAWAII

hə-'wä-yē

LOCATION — Group of 20 islands in the Pacific Ocean, about 2,000 miles southwest of San Francisco.
GOVT. — Former Kingdom and Republic
AREA — 6,435 sq. mi.
POP. — 150,000 (est. 1899)
CAPITAL — Honolulu

Until 1893 an independent kingdom, from 1893 to 1898 a republic, the Hawaiian Islands were annexed to the US in 1898. The Territory of Hawaii achieved statehood in 1959.

100 Cents = 1 Dollar

Values for Nos. 1-4 are for examples with minor damage that has been skillfully repaired.

Values of Hawaii stamps vary considerably according to condition. For Nos. 1-4, values are for examples with minor damage that has been skillfully repaired.

A1   A2

A3

1851-52   **Unwmk.**   **Typeset**   *Imperf.*
Pelure Paper

1	A1	2c blue	625,000.	250,000.
2	A1	5c blue	55,000.	45,000.
3	A2	13c blue	37,000.	32,500.
4	A3	13c blue	52,500.	42,500.

Nos. 1-4 are known as the "Missionaries."
Two varieties of each. Nos. 1-4, off cover, are almost invariably damaged.
No. 1 unused is unique.

Values for Nos. 5-82 are for very fine examples. Extremely fine to superb stamps sell at much higher prices, and inferior or poor stamps sell at reduced prices, depending on the condition of the individual example.

King Kamehameha III

A4   A5

Printed in Sheets of 20 (4x5)

1853   **Engr.**
Thick White Wove Paper

5	A4	5c blue	1,900.	1,900.
a.		Line through "Honolulu" (Pos. 2)	3,000.	3,000.
6	A5	13c dark red	900.	1,700.

See Nos. 8-11.

A6

1857

7	A6	5c on 13c dark red	7,000.	10,000.

Beware of fake manuscript surcharges. Expertization is strongly recommended.

1857   **Thin White Wove Paper**

8	A4	5c blue	700.	750.
a.		Line through "Honolulu" (Pos. 2)	1,350.	1,350.
b.		Double impression	4,250.	4,750.

1861   **Thin Bluish Wove Paper**

9	A4	5c blue	400.	400.
a.		Line through "Honolulu" (Pos. 2)	950.	1,000.

RE-ISSUE

1868   **Ordinary White Wove Paper**

10	A4	5c blue		27.50
a.		Line through "Honolulu"		80.
11	A5	13c dull rose		325.

Remainders of Nos. 10 and 11 were overprinted "SPECIMEN." See Nos. 10S-11Sb in the Scott U.S. Specialized Catalogue.

Nos. 10 and 11 were never placed in use but stamps (both with and without overprint) were sold at face value at the Honolulu post office.

REPRINTS (Official Imitations)

Original   Reprint

Original   Reprint

5c — *Originals have two small dots near the left side of the square in the upper right corner. These dots are missing in the reprints.*

13c — *The bottom of the 3 of 13 in the upper left corner is flattened in the originals and rounded in the reprints. The "t" of "Cts" on the left side is as tall as the "C" in the reprints, but shorter in the originals.*

1889

10R	A4	5c blue	65.
11R	A5	13c orange red	300.

On August 19, 1892, the remaining supply of reprints was overprinted in black "REPRINT." The reprints (both with and without overprint) were sold at face value. See the Scott U.S. Specialized Catalogue.

Values for the Numeral stamps, Nos. 12-26, are for examples with four reasonably large margins. Unused values are for stamps without gum.

A7   A8

A9

1859-62   **Typeset**

12	A7	1c light blue, *bluish white*	15,000.	15,000.
a.		"1 Ce" omitted	—	22,500.
b.		"nt" omitted	—	—

No. 12a is unique.

13	A7	2c light blue, *bluish white*	6,250.	5,000.
a.		2c dark blue, *grayish white*	6,750.	5,000.
b.		Comma after "Cents"	—	6,750.
c.		No period after "Cents"	—	—
14	A7	2c black, *greenish blue* ('62)	8,000.	6,000.
a.		"2-Cents."	—	—

1859-63

15	A7	1c black, *grayish* ('63)	650.	2,750.
a.		Tête bêche pair	9,000.	
b.		"NTER"	—	—
c.		Period omitted after "Postage"	850.	
d.		1c black, *bluish gray*	850.	
16	A7	2c black, *grayish*	1,000.	850.
a.		"2" at top of rectangle	3,750.	3,750.
b.		Printed on both sides	—	21,000.
c.		"NTER"	3,250.	6,500.
d.		2c black, *grayish white*	1,000.	850.
e.		Period omitted after "Cents"	—	—
f.		Overlapping impressions	—	—
g.		"TAGE"	—	—

17	A7	2c dark blue, *bluish* ('63)	12,000.	8,750.
a.		"ISL"	—	—
18	A7	2c black, *blue gray* ('63)	3,250.	6,000.

1864-65

19	A7	1c black	625.	10,000.
20	A7	2c black	775.	1,500.
21	A8	5c blue, *blue* ('65)	900.	700.
a.		Tête bêche pair	10,500.	
b.		5c bluish black, *grayish white*	11,000.	3,750.

No. 21b unused is unique. No. 21b used is also unique but defective.

22	A9	5c blue, *blue* ('65)	575.	900.
a.		Tête bêche pair	18,000.	
b.		5c blue, *grayish white*	—	
c.		Overlapping impressions	—	

1864   **Laid Paper**

23	A7	1c black	300.	2,500.
a.		"HA" instead of "HAWAI-IAN"	3,500.	
b.		Tête bêche pair	6,000.	
c.		Tête bêche pair, Nos. 23, 23a	18,000.	
24	A7	2c black	350.	1,050.
a.		"NTER"	3,250.	
b.		"S" of "POSTAGE" omitted	1,500.	
c.		Tête bêche pair	7,000.	

A10

1865   **Wove Paper**

25	A10	1c dark blue	350.	—
a.		Double impression	—	
b.		With inverted impression of No. 21 on face	18,500.	
26	A10	2c dark blue	350.	

Nos. 12 to 26 were typeset and were printed in settings of ten, each stamp differing from the others.

King Kamehameha IV — A11

1861-63   **Litho.**

Horizontally Laid Paper

27	A11	2c pale rose	350.	350.
a.		2c carmine rose ('63)	3,000.	2,850.

Vertically Laid Paper

28	A11	2c pale rose	325.	325.
a.		2c carmine rose ('63)	400.	450.

RE-ISSUE

1869   **Engr.**   **Thin Wove Paper**

29	A11	2c red	45.00	—

No. 29 was not issued for postal purposes although canceled examples are known. It was sold only at the Honolulu post office, at first without overprint and later with overprint "CANCELLED." See No. 29S in the Scott U.S. Specialized Catalogue.

See Nos. 50-51 and note following No. 51.

Princess Victoria Kamamalu — A12

King Kamehameha IV — A13   King Kamehameha V — A14

King Kamehameha V — A15

Mataio Kekuanaoa — A16

1864-86   **Engr.**   **Perf. 12**

Wove Paper

30	A12	1c purple ('86)	11.00	8.00
		Never hinged	25.00	
a.		1c mauve ('71)	60.00	20.00
		Never hinged	95.00	
b.		1c violet ('78)	20.00	10.00
		Never hinged	45.00	
31	A13	2c rose vermilion	65.00	12.50
		Never hinged	150.00	
a.		2c vermilion ('86)	55.00	17.50
		Never hinged	130.00	
b.		Half used as 1c on cover with #32		7,500.
32	A14	5c blue ('66)	175.00	30.00
		Never hinged	375.00	
33	A15	6c yellow green ('71)	45.00	10.00
		Never hinged	100.00	
a.		6c bluish green ('78)	35.00	10.00
		Never hinged	85.00	
b.		As "a," horiz. pair, imperf.	2,250.	
34	A16	18c dull rose ('71)	100.00	45.00
		Never hinged	220.00	
		Nos. 30-34 (5)	396.00	105.50
		Set, never hinged	860.00	

No. 32 has traces of rectangular frame lines surrounding the design. Nos. 39 and 52C have no such frame lines.

For overprints see Nos. 53, 58-60, 65, 66C, 71.

King David Kalakaua A17   Prince William Pitt Leleiohoku A18

1875

35	A17	2c brown	9.00	3.00
		Never hinged	22.00	
36	A18	12c black	75.00	32.50
		Never hinged	165.00	

See Nos. 38, 43, 46. For overprints see Nos. 56, 62-63, 66, 69.

Princess Likelike A19   King David Kalakaua A20

Queen Kapiolani — A21

Statue of King Kamehameha I — A22   King William Lunalilo — A23

Queen Emma Kaleleonalani — A24

1882

37	A19	1c blue	11.00	6.00
		Never hinged	27.50	
38	A17	2c lilac rose	125.00	47.50
		Never hinged	275.00	
39	A14	5c ultramarine	15.00	3.00
		Never hinged	35.00	
a.		Vert. pair, imperf. horiz.	5,000.	6,000.
40	A20	10c black	50.00	25.00
		Never hinged	115.00	
41	A21	15c red brown	70.00	27.50
		Never hinged	150.00	
		Nos. 37-41 (5)	271.00	109.00
		Set, never hinged	602.50	

1883-86

42	A19	1c green	3.00	2.00
		Never hinged	7.00	
43	A17	2c rose ('86)	5.00	1.00
		Never hinged	11.00	
a.		2c dull red	65.00	22.50
		Never hinged	140.00	
44	A20	10c red brown ('84)	40.00	12.00
		Never hinged	90.00	
45	A20	10c vermilion	45.00	14.00
		Never hinged	100.00	
46	A18	12c red lilac	90.00	40.00
		Never hinged	225.00	
47	A22	25c dark violet	160.00	65.00
		Never hinged	350.00	
48	A23	50c red	200.00	95.00
		Never hinged	425.00	
49	A24	$1 rose red	325.00	275.00
		Never hinged	675.00	8,000.
		Maltese cross cancellation		150.00
		Nos. 42-49 (8)	868.00	504.00
		Set, never hinged	1,833.	

Other fiscal cancellations exist on No. 49.
Nos. 48-49 are valued used with postal cancels. Canceled-to-order cancels exist and are worth less.

REPRODUCTION and REPRINT

Yellowish Wove Paper

1886-89   **Engr.**   **Imperf.**

50	A11	2c orange vermilion	170.00
		Never hinged	275.00
51	A11	2c carmine ('89)	35.00
		Never hinged	50.00

In 1885, the Postmaster General wished to have on sale complete sets of Hawaii's portrait stamps, but was unable to find either the stone from which Nos. 27 and 28 were printed, or the plate from which No. 29 was printed. He therefore sent an example of No. 29 to the American Bank Note Company, with an order to engrave a new plate like it and print 10,000 stamps therefrom, of which 5000 were overprinted "SPECIMEN" in blue.

The original No. 29 was printed in sheets of fifteen (5x3), but the plate of these "Official Imitations" was made up of fifty stamps (10x5). Later, in 1887, the original die for No. 29 was discovered, and, after retouching, a new plate was made and 37,500 stamps were printed (No. 51). These, like the originals, were printed in sheets of fifteen. They were delivered during 1889 and 1890. In 1892, all remaining unsold in the Post Office were overprinted "Reprint".

No. 29 is red in color, and printed on very thin white wove paper. No. 50 is orange vermilion in color, on medium, white to buff paper. In No. 50 the vertical line on the left side of the portrait touches the horizontal line over the label "Elua Keneta", while in the other two varieties, Nos. 29 and 51, it does not touch the horizontal line by half a millimeter. In No. 51 there are three parallel lines on the left side of the King's nose, while in No. 29 and No. 50 there are no such lines. No. 51 is carmine in color and printed on thick, yellowish to buff, wove paper.

It is claimed that both Nos. 50 and 51 were available for postage, although not made to fill a postal requirement. They exist with favor cancellation. No. 51 also is known postally used. See Nos. 50S-51S in the Scott U.S. specialized catalogue.

Queen Liliuokalani — A25

1890-91   *Perf. 12*

52	A25	2c dull violet ('91)	15.00	1.50
		Never hinged	25.00	
a.		Vert. pair, imperf. horiz.	3,750.	
52C	A14	5c deep indigo	125.00	150.00
		Never hinged	280.00	

Stamps of 1864-91
Overprinted in Red

Three categories of double overprints:
I. Both overprints heavy.
II. One overprint heavy, one of moderate strength.
III. One overprint heavy, one of light or weak strength.

1893   **Overprinted in Red**

53	A12	1c violet	9.00	13.00
		Never hinged	20.00	
a.		"189" instead of "1893"	600.00	—
b.		No period after "GOVT"	275.00	275.00
f.		Double overprint (III)	600.00	
54	A19	1c blue	9.00	15.00
		Never hinged	21.00	
b.		No period after "GOVT"	140.00	150.00
e.		Double overprint (II)	1,500.	
f.		Double overprint (III)	400.00	
55	A19	1c green	2.00	3.00
		Never hinged	4.00	
d.		Double overprint (I)	650.00	650.00
f.		Double overprint (III)	250.00	250.00
g.		Pair, one without ovpt.	10,000.	
56	A17	2c brown	12.50	20.00
		Never hinged	27.50	
b.		No period after "GOVT"	325.00	—
57	A25	2c dull violet	2.00	1.50
		Never hinged	3.00	
a.		"18 3" instead of "1893"	900.00	900.00
d.		Double overprint (I)	1,300.	1,000.
f.		Double overprint (III)	190.00	190.00
g.		Inverted overprint	4,000.	4,750.
58	A14	5c deep indigo	15.00	30.00
		Never hinged	32.00	
b.		No period after "GOVT"	275.00	275.00
f.		Double overprint (III)	1,250.	675.00
59	A14	5c ultramarine	7.00	3.00
		Never hinged	15.00	
d.		Double overprint (I)	6,500.	
e.		Double overprint (II)	3,750.	3,750.
f.		Double overprint (III)	600.00	
g.		Inverted overprint	1,500.	1,500.
60	A15	6c green	17.50	25.00
		Never hinged	40.00	
e.		Double overprint (II)	1,100.	
61	A20	10c black	14.00	20.00
		Never hinged	30.00	
e.		Double overprint (II)	1,000.	900.00
f.		Double overprint (III)	225.00	
61B	A20	10c red brown	15,000.	29,000.
		Never hinged	25,000.	
62	A18	12c black	14.00	20.00
		Never hinged	30.00	
d.		Double overprint (I)	1,500.	
e.		Double overprint (II)	1,100.	
f.		Double overprint (III)	—	
63	A18	12c red lilac	175.00	250.00
		Never hinged	400.00	
64	A22	25c dark violet	35.00	45.00
		Never hinged	70.00	
b.		No period after "GOVT"	350.00	350.00
		Never hinged	600.00	
f.		Double overprint (III)	1,250.	

Nos. 53-61,62-64 (12)   312.00   445.50
Nos. 53-61, 62-64
never hinged   692.75

Virtually all known examples of No. 61B are cut in at the top.

Overprinted in Black

65	A13	2c vermilion	85.00	90.00
		Never hinged	200.00	
b.		No period after "GOVT"	300.00	300.00
66	A17	2c rose	2.50	2.50
		Never hinged	3.75	
b.		No period after "GOVT"	70.00	70.00
d.		Double overprint (I)	4,000.	

e.		Double overprint (II)	2,750.	
f.		Double overprint (III)	300.00	
66C	A15	6c green	15,000.	29,000.
67	A20	10c vermilion	22.50	30.00
		Never hinged	45.00	
f.		Double overprint (III)	1,250.	
68	A20	10c red brown	12.00	13.00
		Never hinged	24.00	
f.		Double overprint (III)	4,000.	
69	A18	12c red lilac	350.00	500.00
		Never hinged	575.00	
70	A21	15c red brown	27.50	35.00
		Never hinged	55.00	
e.		Double overprint (II)	2,000.	
71	A16	18c dull rose	40.00	40.00
		Never hinged	80.00	
a.		"18 3" instead of "1893"	525.00	525.00
b.		No period after "GOVT"	350.00	350.00
d.		Double overprint (I)	650.00	
f.		Double overprint (III)	275.00	—
g.		Pair, one without ovpt.	3,500.	
h.		As "b," double overprint (II)	1,750.	
72	A23	50c red	90.00	120.00
		Never hinged	180.00	
b.		No period after "GOVT"	500.00	500.00
		Never hinged	775.00	
f.		Double overprint (III)	1,000.	
73	A24	$1 rose red	160.00	190.00
		Never hinged	325.00	
b.		No period after "GOVT"	525.00	500.00

Nos. 65-66,67-73 (9)   789.50   1,021.
Nos. 65-66, 67-73 never
hinged   1,485.

Coat of Arms — A26

View of Honolulu — A27

Statue of Kamehameha I — A28

Stars and Palms — A29

S. S. "Arawa" — A30

Pres. Sanford Ballard Dole — A31

1894

74	A26	1c yellow	2.00	1.50
		Never hinged	4.00	
75	A27	2c brown	2.00	.60
		Never hinged	4.00	
76	A28	5c rose lake	5.00	2.00
		Never hinged	11.00	
77	A29	10c yellow green	8.00	5.00
		Never hinged	18.00	
78	A30	12c blue	17.50	20.00
		Never hinged	37.50	
79	A31	25c deep blue	22.50	17.50
		Never hinged	47.50	

Nos. 74-79 (6)   57.00   46.60
Set, never hinged   122.50

Numerous double transfers exist on Nos. 75 and 81.

"CENTS" Added — A32

1899

80	A26	1c dark green	2.00	1.50
		Never hinged	4.50	
81	A27	2c rose	1.50	1.00
		Never hinged	3.50	
a.		2c salmon	1.50	1.50
		Never hinged	3.50	
b.		Vert. pair, imperf. horiz.	4,250.	

82	A32	5c blue	8.00	4.00
		Never hinged	20.00	

Nos. 80-82 (3)   11.50   6.50
Set, never hinged   28.00

OFFICIAL STAMPS

Lorrin Andrews Thurston — O1

1896   **Engr.**   **Unwmk.**   *Perf. 12*

O1	O1	2c green	45.00	20.00
		Never hinged	90.00	
O2	O1	5c black brown	45.00	20.00
		Never hinged	90.00	
O3	O1	6c deep ultramarine	45.00	20.00
		Never hinged	90.00	
O4	O1	10c bright rose	45.00	20.00
		Never hinged	90.00	
O5	O1	12c orange	55.00	22.50
		Never hinged	110.00	
O6	O1	25c gray violet	65.00	22.50
		Never hinged	130.00	

Nos. O1-O6 (6)   300.00   125.00
Set, never hinged   600.00

Used values for Nos. O1-O6 are for stamps canceled-to-order "FOREIGN OFFICE/HONOLULU H.I." in double circle without date. Values of postally used stamps: Nos. O1-O2, O4, $50 each; No. O3, $125; No. O5, $160; No. O6, $200.

The stamps of Hawaii were replaced by those of the United States.

PHILIPPINES

ˌfi-lə-ˈpēnz

LOCATION — Group of 7,100 islands and islets in the Malay Archipelago, north of Borneo, in the North Pacific Ocean
GOVT. — US Admin., 1898-1946
AREA — 115,748 sq. mi.
POP. — 16,971,100 (est. 1941)
CAPITAL — Quezon City

The islands were ceded to the US by Spain in 1898. On Nov. 15, 1935, they were given their independence, subject to a transition period which ended July 4, 1946. On that date the Commonwealth became the "Republic of the Philippines."

100 Cents = 1 Dollar (1899)

100 CENTAVOS = 1 PESO (1906)

Wmk. 191PI — Double-lined PIPS

Wmk. 190PI — Single-lined PIPS

Wmk. 257 — Curved Wavy Lines

Issued under U.S. Administration

Regular Issues of the United States Overprinted in Black

1899-1901   **Unwmk.**   *Perf. 12*
On U.S. Stamp No. 260

212	A96	50c orange	300.	225.
		Never hinged	775.	

On U.S. Stamps Nos. 279, 279B, 279Bd, 279Bj, 279Bf, 279Bc, 268, 281, 282C, 283, 284, 275, 275a
Wmk. Double-lined USPS (191)

213	A87	1c yellow green	3.50	.60
		Never hinged	10.00	
a.		Inverted overprint	77,500.	
214	A88	2c red, type IV	1.75	.60
		Never hinged	4.25	
a.		2c orange red, type IV, ('01)	1.75	.60
		Never hinged	4.25	
b.		Bklt. pane of 6, red, type IV ('00)	200.00	300.00
		Never hinged	450.00	
c.		2c reddish carmine, type IV	2.50	1.00
		Never hinged	6.00	
d.		2c rose carmine, type IV	3.00	1.10
		Never hinged	7.25	
215	A89	3c purple	9.00	1.25
		Never hinged	21.50	
216	A91	5c blue	9.00	1.00
		Never hinged	21.50	
a.		Inverted overprint		6,500.

No. 216a is valued in the grade of fine.

217	A94	10c brown, type I	35.00	4.00
		Never hinged	80.00	
217A	A94	10c org brn, type II	110.00	27.50
		Never hinged	275.00	

No. 217A was overprinted on U.S. No. 283a, vertical watermark. The watermark on No. 217 is horizontal.

218	A95	15c olive green	40.00	8.00
		Never hinged	95.00	
219	A96	50c orange	125.00	37.50
		Never hinged	300.00	
a.		50c red orange	250.00	55.00
		Never hinged	600.00	

Nos. 213-219 (8)   333.25   80.45

Regular Issue
Same Overprint in Black On U.S. Stamps Nos. 280b, 282 and 272

1901, Aug. 30

220	A90	4c orange brown	35.00	5.00
		Never hinged	80.00	
221	A92	6c lake	40.00	7.00
		Never hinged	95.00	
222	A93	8c violet brown	40.00	7.50
		Never hinged	95.00	

Nos. 220-222 (3)   115.00   19.50

Same Overprint in Red On U.S. Stamps Nos. 276, 276A, 277a and 278

223	A97	$1 black, type I	300.00	200.00
		Never hinged	1,000.	
223A	A97	$1 black, type II	1,500.	750.00
		Never hinged	5,000.	
224	A98	$2 dark blue	350.00	325.00
		Never hinged	1,150.	
225	A99	$5 dark green	500.00	900.00
		Never hinged	1,600.	

Regular Issue
Same Overprint in Black On U.S. Stamps Nos. 300 to 310 and Shades

1903-04

226	A115	1c blue green	7.00	.40
		Never hinged	15.50	
227	A116	2c carmine	9.00	1.10
		Never hinged	20.00	
228	A117	3c bright violet	67.50	12.50
		Never hinged	150.00	
229	A118	4c brown	80.00	22.50
		Never hinged	175.00	
a.		4c orange brown	80.00	20.00
		Never hinged	175.00	
230	A119	5c blue	17.50	1.00
		Never hinged	40.00	
231	A120	6c brnsh lake	85.00	22.50
		Never hinged	190.00	
232	A121	8c violet black	50.00	15.00
		Never hinged	110.00	
233	A122	10c pale red brn	35.00	2.25
		Never hinged	80.00	
a.		10c red brown	35.00	3.00
		Never hinged	80.00	
b.		Pair, one without overprint		1,500.
234	A123	13c purple black	35.00	17.50
		Never hinged	80.00	
a.		13c brown violet	35.00	17.50
		Never hinged	80.00	
235	A124	15c olive green	60.00	15.00
		Never hinged	135.00	
236	A125	50c orange	125.00	35.00
		Never hinged	275.00	

Nos. 226-236 (11)   571.00   144.75
Set, never hinged   1,285.

Same Overprint in Red On U.S. Stamps Nos. 311, 312 and 313

237	A126	$1 black	300.00	200.00
		Never hinged	800.00	
238	A127	$2 dark blue	550.00	800.00
		Never hinged	1,500.	
239	A128	$5 dark green	800.00	2,750.
		Never hinged	2,000.	

Same Overprint in Black On U.S. Stamp Nos. 319 and 319c

240	A129	2c carmine	8.00	2.25
		Never hinged	17.50	
a.		Booklet pane of 6	1,500.	
b.		2c scarlet	8.00	2.75
		Never hinged	19.00	
c.		As "b," booklet pane of 6	—	

José Rizal — A40

Designs: 4c, McKinley. 6c, Ferdinand Magellan. 8c, Miguel Lopez de Legaspi. 10c, Gen. Henry W. Lawton. 12c, Lincoln. 16c, Adm. William T. Sampson. 20c, Washington. 26c, Francisco Carriedo. 30c, Franklin. 1p-10p, Arms of City of Manila.

Wmk. Double-lined PIPS (191PI)

1906, Sept. 8   **Perf. 12**

241	A40	2c deep green	.40	.25
		Never hinged	1.00	
a.		2c yellow green ('10)	.60	.25
		Never hinged	1.50	
b.		Booklet pane of 6	750.00	800.00
		Never hinged	1,500.	
242	A40	4c carmine	.50	.25
		Never hinged	1.25	
a.		4c carmine lake ('10)	1.00	.25
		Never hinged	2.50	
b.		Booklet pane of 6	650.00	700.00
		Never hinged	1,250.	
243	A40	6c violet	2.50	.25
		Never hinged	6.25	
244	A40	8c brown	4.50	.90
		Never hinged	11.00	
245	A40	10c blue	3.50	.30
		Never hinged	8.75	
a.		10c dark blue	3.50	.30
		Never hinged	8.75	
246	A40	12c brown lake	9.00	2.50
		Never hinged	22.50	
247	A40	16c violet black	6.00	.35
		Never hinged	15.00	
248	A40	20c org brn	7.00	.35
		Never hinged	17.50	
249	A40	26c vio brn	11.00	3.00
		Never hinged	27.50	
250	A40	30c olive green	6.50	1.75
		Never hinged	16.00	
251	A40	1p orange	55.00	17.50
		Never hinged	130.00	
252	A40	2p black	50.00	1.75
		Never hinged	130.00	
253	A40	4p dark blue	160.00	20.00
		Never hinged	375.00	
254	A40	10p dark green	225.00	80.00
		Never hinged	575.00	
		Nos. 241-254 (14)	540.90	129.15
		Set, never hinged	1,316.	

1909-13   **Change of Colors**

255	A40	12c red orange	11.00	3.00
		Never hinged	27.50	
256	A40	16c olive green	6.00	.75
		Never hinged	15.00	
257	A40	20c yellow	9.00	1.25
		Never hinged	22.50	
258	A40	26c blue green	3.50	1.25
		Never hinged	8.75	
259	A40	30c ultramarine	13.00	3.50
		Never hinged	32.50	
260	A40	1p pale violet	45.00	5.00
		Never hinged	110.00	
260A	A40	2p vio brn ('13)	100.00	12.00
		Never hinged	250.00	
		Nos. 255-260A (7)	187.50	26.75
		Set, never hinged	466.25	

Wmk. Single-lined PIPS (190PI)

1911

261	A40	2c green	.75	.25
		Never hinged	1.80	
a.		Booklet pane of 6	800.00	900.00
		Never hinged	1,400.	
262	A40	4c carmine lake	3.00	.25
		Never hinged	6.75	
a.		4c carmine	—	—
b.		Booklet pane of 6	600.00	700.00
		Never hinged	1,100.	
263	A40	6c deep violet	3.00	.25
		Never hinged	6.75	
264	A40	8c brown	9.50	.50
		Never hinged	21.50	
265	A40	10c blue	4.00	.25
		Never hinged	9.00	
266	A40	12c orange	4.00	.45
		Never hinged	9.00	
267	A40	16c olive green	4.50	.40
		Never hinged	10.00	
a.		16c pale olive green	4.50	.50
		Never hinged	10.00	
268	A40	20c yellow	3.50	.25
		Never hinged	7.75	
a.		20c orange	4.00	.30
		Never hinged	9.00	
269	A40	26c blue green	6.00	.30
		Never hinged	13.50	
270	A40	30c ultramarine	6.00	.50
		Never hinged	13.50	
271	A40	1p pale violet	27.50	.60
		Never hinged	62.50	
272	A40	2p violet brown	45.00	1.00
		Never hinged	100.00	
273	A40	4p deep blue	550.00	110.00
		Never hinged	1,100.	

274	A40	10p deep green	200.00	30.00
		Never hinged	400.00	
		Nos. 261-274 (14)	866.75	145.00
		Set, never hinged	1,862.	

1914

275	A40	30c gray	12.00	.50
		Never hinged	27.50	

1914   **Perf. 10**

276	A40	2c green	3.00	.25
		Never hinged	7.00	
a.		Booklet pane of 6	600.00	800.00
		Never hinged	1,250.	
277	A40	4c carmine	4.00	.30
		Never hinged	9.00	
a.		Booklet pane of 6	600.00	
		Never hinged	1,300.	
278	A40	6c light violet	45.00	9.50
		Never hinged	100.00	
a.		6c deep violet	50.00	6.25
		Never hinged	110.00	
279	A40	8c brown	55.00	10.50
		Never hinged	125.00	
280	A40	10c dark blue	30.00	.25
		Never hinged	67.50	
281	A40	16c olive green	100.00	5.00
		Never hinged	225.00	
282	A40	20c orange	40.00	1.00
		Never hinged	85.00	
283	A40	30c gray	60.00	4.50
		Never hinged	130.00	
284	A40	1p pale violet	150.00	3.75
		Never hinged	350.00	
		Nos. 276-284 (9)	487.00	35.05
		Set, never hinged	1,020.	

Wmk. Single-lined PIPS (190PI)

1918   **Perf. 11**

285	A40	2c green	21.00	4.25
		Never hinged	40.00	
a.		Booklet pane of 6	600.00	800.00
		Never hinged	1,100.	
286	A40	4c carmine	26.00	6.00
		Never hinged	55.00	
a.		Booklet pane of 6	1,350.	2,000.
287	A40	6c deep violet	40.00	6.00
		Never hinged	90.00	
287A	A40	8c light brown	220.00	25.00
		Never hinged	400.00	
288	A40	10c dark blue	60.00	3.00
		Never hinged	140.00	
289	A40	16c olive green	110.00	10.00
		Never hinged	250.00	
289A	A40	20c orange	175.00	12.00
		Never hinged	400.00	
289C	A40	30c gray	95.00	18.00
		Never hinged	215.00	
289D	A40	1p pale violet	100.00	25.00
		Never hinged	225.00	
		Nos. 285-289D (9)	847.00	109.25
		Set, never hinged	1,815.	

1917   **Unwmk.**   **Perf. 11**

290	A40	2c yellow green	.25	.25
		Never hinged	.55	
a.		2c dark green	.30	.25
		Never hinged	.65	
b.		Vert. pair, imperf. horiz.	2,750.	
c.		Horiz. pair, imperf. between	1,500.	—
d.		Vertical pair, imperf. btwn.	1,750.	1,000.
e.		Booklet pane of 6	27.50	30.00
		Never hinged	60.00	
291	A40	4c carmine	.30	.25
		Never hinged	.65	
a.		4c light rose	.30	.25
		Never hinged	.65	
b.		Booklet pane of 6	20.00	22.50
		Never hinged	35.00	
292	A40	6c deep violet	.35	.25
		Never hinged	.70	
a.		6c lilac	.40	.25
		Never hinged	.80	
b.		6c red violet	.40	.25
		Never hinged	.70	
c.		Booklet pane of 6	550.00	800.00
		Never hinged	900.00	
293	A40	8c yellow brown	.30	.25
		Never hinged	.50	
a.		8c orange brown	.30	.25
		Never hinged	.50	
294	A40	10c deep blue	.30	.25
		Never hinged	.65	
295	A40	12c red orange	.35	.25
		Never hinged	.75	
296	A40	16c light olive green	65.00	.25
		Never hinged	130.00	
a.		16c olive bister	65.00	.50
		Never hinged	130.00	
297	A40	20c orange yellow	.35	.25
		Never hinged	.75	
298	A40	26c green	.50	.45
		Never hinged	1.10	
a.		26c blue green	.60	.25
		Never hinged	1.35	
299	A40	30c gray	.55	.25
		Never hinged	1.35	
300	A40	1p pale violet	40.00	2.00
		Never hinged	90.00	
a.		1p red lilac	40.00	2.50
		Never hinged	90.00	
b.		1p pale rose lilac	40.00	1.10
		Never hinged	90.00	
301	A40	2p violet brown	35.00	1.00
		Never hinged	77.50	
302	A40	4p blue	32.50	.50
		Never hinged	72.50	
a.		4p dark blue	35.00	.55
		Never hinged	77.50	
		Nos. 290-302 (13)	175.75	6.20
		Set, never hinged	377.00	

1923-26

Design: 16c, Adm. George Dewey.

303	A40	16c olive bister	1.00	.25
		Never hinged	2.25	
		16c olive green	1.25	.25
		Never hinged	2.75	
304	A40	10p dp grn ('26)	50.00	20.00
		Never hinged	110.00	

Legislative Palace A42

1926, Dec. 20   **Perf. 12**

319	A42	2c green & black	.50	.25
		Never hinged	1.25	
a.		Horiz. pair, imperf. between	200.00	
b.		Vert. pair, imperf. between	375.00	
320	A42	4c car & blk	.55	.40
		Never hinged	1.20	
a.		Horiz. pair, imperf. between	275.00	
b.		Vert. pair, imperf. between	400.00	
321	A42	16c ol grn & blk	1.00	.65
		Never hinged	2.25	
a.		Horiz. pair, imperf. between	250.00	
b.		Vert. pair, imperf. between	425.00	
c.		Double impression of center	675.00	
322	A42	18c lt brn & blk	1.10	.50
		Never hinged	2.50	
a.		Double impression of center	850.00	
b.		Vertical pair, imperf. between	475.00	
323	A42	20c orange & black	2.00	1.00
		Never hinged	4.50	
a.		20c orange & brown	600.00	—
b.		As No. 323, imperf., pair	575.00	575.00
c.		As "a," imperf., pair	1,750.	
d.		Vert. pair, imperf. between	500.00	
324	A42	24c gray & black	1.00	.55
		Never hinged	2.25	
a.		Vert. pair, imperf. between	500.00	
325	A42	1p rose lil & blk	47.50	50.00
		Never hinged	70.00	
a.		Vert. pair, imperf. between	500.00	
		Nos. 319-325 (7)	53.65	53.35
		Set, never hinged	83.95	

Opening of the Legislative Palace. No. 322a is valued in the grade of fine. For overprints, see Nos. O1-O4.

Rizal Type of 1906 Coil Stamp

1928   **Perf. 11 Vertically**

326	A40	2c green	7.50	12.50
		Never hinged	19.00	

Types of 1906-1923

1925-31   **Imperf.**

340	A40	2c yel green ('31)	.50	.50
		Never hinged	.90	
a.		2c green ('25)	.80	.75
		Never hinged	1.80	
341	A40	4c car rose ('31)	.50	1.00
		Never hinged	1.00	
a.		4c carmine ('25)	1.20	1.00
		Never hinged	2.75	
342	A40	6c violet ('31)	3.00	3.75
		Never hinged	5.00	
a.		6c deep violet ('25)	12.00	8.00
		Never hinged	26.00	
343	A40	8c brown ('31)	2.00	5.00
		Never hinged	4.00	
a.		8c yellow brown ('25)	13.00	8.00
		Never hinged	26.00	
344	A40	10c blue ('31)	5.00	7.50
		Never hinged	12.00	
a.		10c deep blue ('25)	45.00	20.00
		Never hinged	100.00	
345	A40	12c dp orange ('31)	8.00	10.00
		Never hinged	15.00	
a.		12c red orange ('25)	60.00	35.00
		Never hinged	135.00	
346	A40	16c olive green ('31)	6.00	7.50
		Never hinged	11.00	
a.		16c bister green ('25)	42.50	18.00
		Never hinged	100.00	
347	A40	20c dp yel org ('31)	5.00	7.50
		Never hinged	11.00	
a.		20c yellow orange ('25)	45.00	20.00
		Never hinged	100.00	
348	A40	26c green ('31)	6.00	9.00
		Never hinged	11.00	
a.		26c blue green ('25)	45.00	25.00
		Never hinged	110.00	
349	A40	30c light gray ('31)	8.00	10.00
		Never hinged	16.00	
a.		30c gray ('25)	45.00	25.00
		Never hinged	110.00	
350	A40	1p light violet ('31)	10.00	15.00
		Never hinged	20.00	
a.		1p violet ('25)	200.00	100.00
		Never hinged	425.00	
351	A40	2p brn vio ('31)	30.00	45.00
		Never hinged	80.00	
a.		2p violet brown ('25)	400.00	400.00
		Never hinged	675.00	
352	A40	4p blue ('31)	80.00	90.00
		Never hinged	150.00	
a.		4p deep blue ('25)	2,200.	1,100.
		Never hinged	3,500.	

353	A40	10p green ('31)	175.00	225.00
		Never hinged	300.00	
a.		10p deep green ('25)	2,750.	2,950.
		Never hinged	4,250.	
		Nos. 340a-353 (14)	339.00	436.75
		Set, never hinged	636.90	
		Nos. 340a-353a (14)	5,860.	4,711.

Nos. 340a-353a were the original post office issue. These were reprinted twice in 1931 for sale to collectors (Nos. 340-353).

Mount Mayon, Luzon A43

Post Office, Manila A44

Pier No. 7, Manila Bay — A45

(See footnote) — A46

Rice Planting A47

Rice Terraces A48

Baguio Zigzag A49

1932, May 3   **Perf. 11**

354	A43	2c yellow green	.75	.30
		Never hinged	1.25	
355	A44	4c rose carmine	.75	.30
		Never hinged	1.25	
356	A45	12c orange	.90	.75
		Never hinged	1.30	
357	A46	18c red orange	45.00	15.00
		Never hinged	72.50	
358	A47	20c yellow	1.00	.75
		Never hinged	1.60	
359	A48	24c deep violet	1.60	1.00
		Never hinged	2.75	
360	A49	32c olive brown	1.60	1.00
		Never hinged	2.75	
		Nos. 354-360 (7)	51.60	19.10
		Set, never hinged	83.40	

The 18c vignette was intended to show Pagsanjan Falls in Laguna, central Luzon, and is so labeled. Through error the stamp pictures Vernal Falls in Yosemite National Park, California.

For overprints see #C29-C35, C47-C51, C63.

Nos. 302, 302a Surcharged in Orange or Red

1932

368	A40	1p on 4p blue (O)	6.00	1.00
		Never hinged	9.75	
a.		1p on 4p dark blue (O)	6.00	1.00
		Never hinged	9.25	
		P# block of 10, Impt.	140.00	
		Never hinged	175.00	
369	A40	2p on 4p dark blue (R)	9.00	1.50
		Never hinged	15.00	
		P# block of 10, Impt.	160.00	
		Never hinged	200.00	
a.		2p on 4p blue (R)	9.00	1.00
		Never hinged	15.00	

Far Eastern Championship
Issued in commemoration of the Tenth Far Eastern Championship Games.

Baseball Players A50

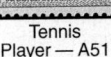

Tennis Player — A51   Basketball Players — A52

1934, Apr. 14   *Perf. 11½*

380	A50	2c yellow brown	1.50	.80
		Never hinged	2.25	
381	A51	6c ultramarine	.25	.25
		Never hinged	.30	
a.		Vertical pair, imperf. between	700.00	
		Never hinged	1,100.	
382	A52	16c violet brown	.50	.50
		Never hinged	.75	
a.		Vert. pair, imperf. horiz.	950.00	
		Never hinged	1,500.	
		Nos. 380-382 (3)	2.25	1.55
		Set, never hinged	3.30	

José Rizal — A53

Woman and Carabao A54

La Filipina — A55

Pearl Fishing A56

Fort Santiago A57

Salt Spring — A58

Magellan's Landing, 1521 — A59

"Juan de la Cruz" — A60

Rice Terraces A61

"Blood Compact," 1565 — A62

Barasoain Church, Malolos A63

Battle of Manila Bay, 1898 A64

Montalban Gorge A65

George Washington A66

1935, Feb. 15   *Perf. 11*

383	A53	2c rose	.25	.25
		Never hinged	.25	
384	A54	4c yellow green	.25	.25
		Never hinged	.25	
385	A55	6c dark brown	.25	.25
		Never hinged	.35	
386	A56	8c violet	.25	.25
		Never hinged	.35	
387	A57	10c rose carmine	.30	.25
		Never hinged	.45	
388	A58	12c black	.35	.25
		Never hinged	.50	
389	A59	16c dark blue	.35	.25
		Never hinged	.55	
390	A60	20c light olive green	.35	.25
		Never hinged	.45	
391	A61	26c indigo	.40	.40
		Never hinged	.60	
392	A62	30c orange red	.40	.40
		Never hinged	.60	
393	A63	1p red org & blk	2.00	1.25
		Never hinged	3.00	
394	A64	2p bis brn & blk	12.00	2.00
		Never hinged	16.00	
395	A65	4p blue & black	12.00	4.00
		Never hinged	16.00	
396	A66	5p green & black	25.00	5.00
		Never hinged	50.00	
		Nos. 383-396 (14)	54.15	15.05
		Set, never hinged	74.45	

For overprints & surcharges see Nos. 411-424, 433-446, 449, 463-466, 468, 472-474,

478-484, 485-494, C52-C53, O15-O36, O38, O40-O43, N2-N9, N28, NO2-NO6.

Issues of the Commonwealth
Issued to commemorate the inauguration of the Philippine Commonwealth, Nov. 15, 1935.

The Temples of Human Progress — A67

1935, Nov. 15

397	A67	2c carmine rose	.25	.25
		Never hinged	.35	
398	A67	6c deep violet	.25	.25
		Never hinged	.35	
399	A67	16c blue	.25	.25
		Never hinged	.40	
400	A67	36c yellow green	.40	.30
		Never hinged	.65	
401	A67	50c brown	.70	.55
		Never hinged	1.00	
		Nos. 397-401 (5)	1.85	1.60
		Set, never hinged	2.75	

Jose Rizal Issue
75th anniversary of the birth of Jose Rizal (1861-1896), national hero of the Filipinos.

Jose Rizal — A68

1936, June 19   *Perf. 12*

402	A68	2c yellow brown	.25	.25
		Never hinged	.25	
403	A68	6c slate blue	.25	.25
		Never hinged	.25	
a.		Imperf. vertically, pair	1,000.	
		Never hinged	1,500.	
404	A68	36c red brown	.50	.70
		Never hinged	.75	
		Nos. 402-404 (3)	1.00	1.20
		Set, never hinged	1.25	

Commonwealth Anniversary Issue
Issued in commemoration of the first anniversary of the Commonwealth.

President Manuel L. Quezon — A69

1936, Nov. 15   *Perf. 11*

408	A69	2c orange brown	.25	.25
		Never hinged	.30	
409	A69	6c yellow green	.25	.25
		Never hinged	.30	
410	A69	12c ultramarine	.25	.25
		Never hinged	.30	
		Nos. 408-410 (3)	.75	.75
		Set, never hinged	.90	

Stamps of 1935 Overprinted in Black

a

b

1936-37

411	A53(a)	2c rose	.25	.25
		Never hinged	.25	
a.		Bklt. pane of 6 ('37)	2.50	2.00
		Never hinged	4.00	
b.		Hyphen omitted	125.00	100.00
412	A54(b)	4c yel grn ('37)	.45	4.00
		Never hinged	.70	
		P# block of 6	35.00	
		Never hinged	45.00	
413	A55(a)	6c dark brown	.25	.25
		Never hinged	.25	
414	A56(b)	8c violet ('37)	.25	.25
		Never hinged	.35	
415	A57(b)	10c rose carmine	.25	.25
		Never hinged	.25	
a.		"COMMONWEALT"	20.00	—
		Never hinged	30.00	
416	A58(b)	12c black ('37)	.25	.25
		Never hinged	.30	
417	A59(b)	16c dark blue	.25	.25
		Never hinged	.40	
418	A60(a)	20c lt ol grn ('37)	.90	.40
		Never hinged	1.50	
419	A61(b)	26c indigo ('37)	.80	.35
		Never hinged	1.40	
420	A62(b)	30c orange red	.45	.25
		Never hinged	.75	
421	A63(b)	1p red org & blk	.90	.25
		Never hinged	1.50	
422	A64(b)	2p bis brn & blk ('37)	12.50	4.00
		Never hinged	21.00	
423	A65(b)	4p bl & blk ('37)	45.00	8.00
		Never hinged	72.50	
424	A66(b)	5p grn & blk ('37)	12.50	*25.00*
		Never hinged	21.00	
		Nos. 411-424 (14)	75.00	43.75
		Set, never hinged	122.15	

Eucharistic Congress Issue
Issued to commemorate the 33rd International Eucharistic Congress held at Manila, Feb. 3-7, 1937.

Map of Philippines — A70

1937, Feb. 3

425	A70	2c yellow green	.25	.25
		Never hinged	.25	
426	A70	6c light brown	.25	.25
		Never hinged	.25	
427	A70	12c sapphire	.25	.25
		Never hinged	.25	
428	A70	20c deep orange	.30	.25
		Never hinged	.50	
429	A70	36c deep violet	.55	.40
		Never hinged	.80	
430	A70	50c carmine	.70	.35
		Never hinged	1.10	
		Nos. 425-430 (6)	2.30	1.75
		Set, never hinged	3.15	

Arms of Manila — A71

1937, Aug. 27

431	A71	10p gray	5.00	2.00
		Never hinged	7.25	
		P# block of 6	67.50	
		Never hinged	85.00	
432	A71	20p henna brown	4.00	1.40
		Never hinged	6.50	

Stamps of 1935 Overprinted in Black

a

b

1938-40

433	A53(a)	2c rose ('39)	.25	.25
		Never hinged	.25	
		P# block of 6	8.00	
		Never hinged	10.00	
a.		Booklet pane of 6	3.50	3.50
		Never hinged	5.50	

b.	As "a," lower left-hand stamp overprinted "WEALTH COMMON-"		*2,000.*	
	Never hinged		*3,250.*	
c.	Hyphen omitted		100.00	50.00
434	A54(b)	4c yel grn ('40)	3.00	30.00
	Never hinged		4.75	
	P# block of 6		35.00	
	Never hinged		45.00	
435	A55(a)	6c dk brn ('39)	.25	.25
	Never hinged		.40	
a.	6c golden brown		.25	.25
	Never hinged		.40	
	P# block of 6		5.50	
	Never hinged		7.00	
436	A56(b)	8c violet ('39)	.25	1.75
	Never hinged		.25	
	P# block of 6		8.00	
	Never hinged		10.00	
a.	"COMMONWEALT" (LR 31)		90.00	
	Never hinged		140.00	
437	A57(b)	10c rose car ('39)	.25	.25
	Never hinged		.25	
	P# block of 6		8.00	
	Never hinged		10.00	
a.	"COMMONWEALT" (LR 31)		65.00	—
	Never hinged		100.00	
438	A58(b)	12c black ('40)	.25	1.00
	Never hinged		.25	
	P# block of 6		8.00	
	Never hinged		10.00	
439	A59(b)	16c dark blue ('39)	.25	.25
	Never hinged		.25	
	P# block of 6		16.00	
	Never hinged		20.00	
440	A60(a)	20c lt ol grn ('39)	.25	.25
	Never hinged		.25	
	P# block of 6		12.00	
	Never hinged		15.00	
441	A61(b)	26c indigo ('40)	1.00	2.50
	Never hinged		1.50	
	P# block of 6		16.00	
	Never hinged		20.00	
442	A62(b)	30c org red ('39)	3.00	.70
	Never hinged		5.00	
	P# block of 6		22.50	
	Never hinged		35.00	
443	A63(b)	1p red org & blk	.60	.25
	Never hinged		1.00	
444	A64(b)	2p bis brn & blk ('39)	10.00	1.00
	Never hinged		15.00	
	P# block of 4		87.50	
	Never hinged		110.00	
445	A65(b)	4p bl & blk ('40)	150.00	250.00
	Never hinged		325.00	
446	A66(b)	5p grn & blk ('40)	20.00	8.00
	Never hinged		35.00	
	P# block of 4		200.00	
	Never hinged		250.00	
	Nos. 433-446 (14)		*189.35*	*296.45*
	Set, never hinged		414.15	

Overprint "b" measures 18½x1¾mm.
No. 433b occurs in booklet pane, No. 433a, position 5; all examples are straight-edged, left and bottom.

First Foreign Trade Week Issue
Nos. 384, 298a and 432 Surcharged in Red, Violet or Black

a

b

c

1939, July 5

449	A54(a)	2c on 4c yel grn (R)	.25	.25
	Never hinged		.35	
450	A40(b)	6c on 26c blue grn (V)	.25	.50
	Never hinged		.35	
a.	6c on 26c green		3.00	1.00
	Never hinged		5.00	
451	A71(c)	50c on 20p henna brn (Bk)	1.25	1.00
	Never hinged		2.00	5.00
	Nos. 449-451 (3)		*1.75*	*1.75*
	Set, never hinged		2.70	

Commonwealth 4th Anniversary Issue (#452-460)

Triumphal Arch — A72

1939, Nov. 15

452	A72	2c yellow green	.25	.25
	Never hinged		.25	
453	A72	6c carmine	.25	.25
	Never hinged		.25	
454	A72	12c bright blue	.25	.25
	Never hinged		.25	
	Nos. 452-454 (3)		*.75*	*.75*
	Set, never hinged		.75	

For overprints see Nos. 469, 476.

Malacañan Palace A73

1939, Nov. 15

455	A73	2c green	.25	.25
	Never hinged		.25	
456	A73	6c orange	.25	.25
	Never hinged		.25	
457	A73	12c carmine	.25	.25
	Never hinged		.25	
	Nos. 455-457 (3)		*.75*	*.75*
	Set, never hinged		.75	

For overprint, see No. 470.

Pres. Quezon Taking Oath of Office — A74

1940, Feb. 8

458	A74	2c dark orange	.25	.25
	Never hinged		.25	
459	A74	6c dark green	.25	.25
	Never hinged		.25	
460	A74	12c purple	.25	.25
	Never hinged		.30	
	Nos. 458-460 (3)		*.75*	*.75*
	Set, never hinged		.80	

For overprints, see Nos. 471, 477.

José Rizal — A75

ROTARY PRESS PRINTING
1941, Apr. 14   **Perf. 11x10½**
Size: 19x22½mm

461	A75	2c apple green	.25	*.50*
	Never hinged		.25	

FLAT PLATE PRINTING
1941, Nov. 14   **Perf. 11**
Size: 18¾x22¼mm

462	A75	2c pale apple green	1.00	—
	Never hinged		1.25	
a.	Booklet pane of 6		6.00	
	Never hinged		7.50	

No. 461 was issued only in sheets. No. 462 was issued only in booklet panes on Nov. 14, 1941, just before the war, and only a few used stamps and covers exist. All examples have one or two straight edges. Mint booklets reappeared after the war. In August 1942, the booklet pane was reprinted in a darker shade (apple green). However, the apple green panes were available only to U.S. collectors during the war years, so no war-period used stamps from the Philippines exist. Value of apple green booklet pane, never hinged, $6.
For type A75 overprinted, see Nos. 464, O37, O39, N1 and NO1.

Philippine Stamps of 1935-41, Handstamped in Violet

1944   **Perf. 11, 11x10½**

463	A53	2c rose (On 411)	1,250.	650.00
a.	Booklet pane of 6		12,500.	
463B	A53	2c rose (On 433)	2,000.	1,750.
464	A75	2c apple grn (On 461)	12.50	10.00
a.	Pair, one without ovpt.		22.50	—
465	A54	4c yel grn (On 384)	47.50	*50.00*
	Never hinged		80.00	
466	A55	6c dk brn (On 385)	3,250.	2,000.
467	A69	6c yel grn (On 409)	300.00	150.00
	Never hinged		525.00	
468	A55	6c dk brn (On 413)	4,000.	825.00
469	A72	6c car (On 453)	350.00	125.00
470	A73	6c org (On 456)	1,750.	725.00
471	A74	6c dk grn (On 459)		
			350.00	225.00
472	A56	8c vio (On 436)	17.50	*30.00*
	Never hinged		30.00	
473	A57	10c car rose (On 415)	350.00	150.00
474	A57	10c car rose (On 437)	275.00	200.00
	Never hinged		475.00	
475	A69	12c ultra (On 410)	1,100.	400.00
476	A72	12c brt bl (On 454)	7,000.	2,500.
477	A74	12c pur (On 460)	500.00	275.00
478	A59	16c dk bl (On 389)	3,000.	—
479	A59	16c dk bl (On 417)	1,500.	1,000.
480	A59	16c dk bl (On 439)	500.00	200.00
481	A60	20c lt ol grn (On 440)	140.00	35.00
	Never hinged		230.00	
482	A62	30c org red (On 420)	450.00	1,500.
483	A62	30c org red (On 442)	800.00	375.00
484	A63	1p red org & blk (On 443)	6,250.	4,500.

Nos. 463-484 are valued in the grade of fine to very fine.
No. 463 comes only from the booklet pane. All examples have one or two straight edges.

Types of 1935-37 Overprinted

a

b

Nos. 431-432 Overprinted in Black — c

1945   **Perf. 11**

485	A53(a)	2c rose	.25	.25
	Never hinged		.25	
486	A54(b)	4c yellow green	.25	.25
	Never hinged		.25	
487	A55(a)	6c golden brown	.25	.25
	Never hinged		.25	
488	A56(b)	8c violet	.25	.25
	Never hinged		.25	
489	A57(b)	10c rose carmine	.25	.25
	Never hinged		.25	
490	A58(b)	12c black	.25	.25
	Never hinged		.25	
491	A59(b)	16c dark blue	.25	.25
	Never hinged		.30	
492	A60(a)	20c lt olive green	.30	.25
	Never hinged		.40	
493	A62(b)	30c orange red	.50	.35
	Never hinged		.75	
494	A63(b)	1p red org & blk	1.10	.25
	Never hinged		1.60	
495	A71(c)	10p gray	55.00	13.50
	Never hinged		90.00	

496	A71(c)	20p henna brown	50.00	15.00
	Never hinged		75.00	
	Nos. 485-496 (12)		*108.65*	*31.10*
	Set, never hinged		169.55	

José Rizal — A76

1946, May 28   **Perf. 11x10½**

497	A76	2c sepia	.25	.25
	Never hinged		.25	

For overprints see Nos. 503, O44.

> Catalogue values for unused stamps in this section, from this point to the end of the section, are for Never Hinged items.

Later issues, released by the Philippine Republic on July 4, 1946, and thereafter, are listed in Scott's Standard Postage Stamp Catalogue, Vol. 5A.

AIR POST STAMPS

Madrid-Manila Flight Issue
Issued to commemorate the flight of Spanish aviators Gallarza and Loriga from Madrid to Manila.

Regular Issue of 1917-26 Overprinted in Red or Violet

Designs: Nos. C7-C8, Adm. William T. Sampson. No. C9, Adm. George Dewey.

1926, May 13   **Unwmk.**   **Perf. 11**

C1	A40	2c green (R)	20.00	17.50
	Never hinged		45.00	
C2	A40	4c carmine (V)	30.00	20.00
	Never hinged		55.00	
a.	Inverted overprint		2,600.	
C3	A40	6c lilac (R)	75.00	75.00
	Never hinged		125.00	
C4	A40	8c org brn (V)	75.00	60.00
	Never hinged		125.00	
C5	A40	10c deep blue (R)	75.00	60.00
	Never hinged		140.00	
C6	A40	12c red org (V)	80.00	65.00
	Never hinged		150.00	
C7	A40	16c lt ol grn (V)	2,800.	3,250.
C8	A40	16c ol bister (R)	5,000.	5,000.
C9	A40	16c ol grn (V)	100.00	70.00
	Never hinged		160.00	
C10	A40	20c org ye (V)	100.00	80.00
	Never hinged		160.00	
C11	A40	26c blue grn (V)	100.00	80.00
	Never hinged		160.00	
C12	A40	30c gray (V)	100.00	80.00
	Never hinged		160.00	
C13	A40	2p vio brn (R)	500.00	600.00
	Never hinged		1,100.	
C14	A40	4p dk blue (R)	800.00	750.00
	Never hinged		1,300.	
C15	A40	10p dp grn (V)	1,000.	1,350.

Same Overprint on No. 269
Wmk. Single-lined PIPS (190)
Perf. 12

C16	A40	26c blue grn (V)	5,000.	

Same Overprint on No. 284
Perf. 10

C17	A40	1p pale violet (V)	200.00	225.00
	Never hinged		450.00	

London-Orient Flight Issue
Issued Nov. 9, 1928, to celebrate the arrival of a British squadron of hydroplanes.

Regular Issue of 1917-25 Overprinted in Red

1928, Nov. 9   **Perf. 11**

C18	A40	2c green	1.00	1.00
	Never hinged		2.00	

C19	A40	4c carmine	1.25	1.50
		Never hinged	2.00	
C20	A40	6c violet	5.00	3.00
		Never hinged	10.00	
C21	A40	8c orange brown	5.00	3.00
		Never hinged	10.00	
C22	A40	10c deep blue	5.00	3.00
		Never hinged	10.00	
C23	A40	12c red orange	8.00	4.00
		Never hinged	12.00	
C24	A40	16c ol grn (No. 303a)	8.00	4.00
		Never hinged	12.00	
C25	A40	20c orange yellow	8.00	4.00
		Never hinged	12.00	
C26	A40	26c blue green	20.00	8.00
		Never hinged	35.00	
C27	A40	30c gray	20.00	8.00
		Never hinged	35.00	

Same Overprint on No. 271
Wmk. Single-lined PIPS (190)
Perf. 12

C28	A40	1p pale violet	55.00	30.00
		Never hinged	90.00	
		Nos. C18-C28 (11)	136.25	69.50
		Set, never hinged	230.00	

Von Gronau Issue
Commemorating the visit of Capt. Wolfgang von Gronau's airplane on its round-the-world flight.

Nos. 354-360 Overprinted

1932, Sept. 27   Unwmk.   Perf. 11

C29	A43	2c yellow green	.90	.60
		Never hinged	1.40	
C30	A44	4c rose carmine	.90	.40
		Never hinged	1.40	
C31	A45	12c orange	1.25	.65
		Never hinged	2.00	
C32	A46	18c red orange	5.00	5.00
		Never hinged	8.00	
C33	A47	20c yellow	3.50	3.50
		Never hinged	5.75	
C34	A48	24c deep violet	3.50	4.00
		Never hinged	5.75	
C35	A49	32c olive brown	3.50	3.00
		Never hinged	5.75	
		Nos. C29-C35 (7)	18.55	17.15
		Set, never hinged	31.55	

Rein Issue
Commemorating the flight from Madrid to Manila of the Spanish aviator Fernando Rein y Loring.

Regular Issue of 1917-25 Overprinted

1933, Apr. 11

C36	A40	2c green	.75	.45
		Never hinged	1.10	
C37	A40	4c carmine	.90	.45
		Never hinged	1.40	
C38	A40	6c deep violet	1.10	.80
		Never hinged	1.75	
C39	A40	8c orange brown	3.75	2.00
		Never hinged	5.75	
		P# block of 10, Impt.	120.00	
		Never hinged	150.00	
C40	A40	10c dark blue	3.75	2.25
		Never hinged	5.75	
		P# block of 10, Impt.	120.00	
		Never hinged	150.00	
C41	A40	12c orange	3.75	2.00
		Never hinged	5.75	
		P# block of 10, Impt.	120.00	
		Never hinged	150.00	
C42	A40	16c olive green	3.50	2.00
		Never hinged	5.25	
		P# block of 6	160.00	
		Never hinged	200.00	
C43	A40	20c yellow	3.75	2.00
		Never hinged	5.75	
		P# block of 10, Impt.	160.00	
		Never hinged	200.00	
C44	A40	26c green	3.75	2.75
		Never hinged	5.75	
a.		26c blue green	4.00	2.00
		Never hinged	6.00	
C45	A40	30c gray	4.00	3.00
		Never hinged	6.00	
		Nos. C36-C45 (10)	29.00	17.70
		Set, never hinged	44.25	

No. 290a Overprinted

Printed by the Philippine Bureau.
1933, May 26

C46	A40	2c green	.65	.40
		Never hinged	1.00	
		P# block of 6	12.00	
		Never hinged	15.00	

Regular Issue of 1932 Overprinted

C47	A44	4c rose carmine	.30	.25
		Never hinged	.45	
		P# block of 6	16.00	
		Never hinged	20.00	
C48	A45	12c orange	.60	.25
		Never hinged	.90	
		P# block of 6	20.00	
		Never hinged	25.00	
C49	A47	20c yellow	.60	.25
		Never hinged	.90	
		P# block of 6	20.00	
		Never hinged	25.00	
C50	A48	24c deep violet	.65	.25
		Never hinged	1.00	
		P# block of 6	24.00	
		Never hinged	30.00	
C51	A49	32c olive brown	.85	.35
		Never hinged	1.40	
		Nos. C46-C51 (6)	3.65	1.75
		Set, never hinged	5.65	

Transpacific Issue
Issued to commemorate the China Clipper flight from Manila to San Francisco, Dec. 2-5, 1935.

Nos. 387, 392 Overprinted in Gold

1935, Dec. 2

C52	A57	10c rose carmine	.40	.25
		Never hinged	.60	
C53	A62	30c orange red	.60	.35
		Never hinged	.90	

Manila-Madrid Flight Issue
Issued to commemorate the Manila-Madrid flight by aviators Antonio Arnaiz and Juan Calvo.

Regular Issue of 1917-25 Surcharged in Various Colors

1936, Sept. 6

C54	A40	2c on 4c carmine (Bl)	.25	.25
		Never hinged	.25	
C55	A40	6c on 12c red org (V)	.25	.25
		Never hinged	.30	
C56	A40	16c on 26c blue grn (Bk)	.25	.25
		Never hinged	.40	
a.		16c on 26c green	2.00	.70
		Never hinged	3.00	
		Nos. C54-C56 (3)	.75	.75
		Set, never hinged	.95	

Air Mail Exhibition Issue
Issued to commemorate the first Air Mail Exhibition, held Feb. 17-19, 1939.

Regular Issue of 1917-37 Surcharged in Black or Red

1939, Feb. 17

C57	A40	8c on 26c blue grn (Bk)	2.00	2.00
		Never hinged	4.00	
a.		8c on 26c green (Bk)	10.00	4.00
		Never hinged	16.00	
C58	A71	1p on 10p gray (R)	8.00	4.00
		Never hinged	12.00	

Moro Vinta and Clipper
AP1

1941, June 30

C59	AP1	8c carmine	2.00	.60
		Never hinged	2.75	
C60	AP1	20c ultramarine	3.00	.50
		Never hinged	4.00	
C61	AP1	60c blue green	3.00	1.00
		Never hinged	4.00	
C62	AP1	1p sepia	.70	.50
		Never hinged	1.00	
		Nos. C59-C62 (4)	8.70	2.60
		Set, never hinged	11.75	

For overprint see No. NO7. For surcharges see Nos. N10-N11, N35-N36.

No. C47 Hstmpd. in Violet

1944, Dec. 3

C63	A44	4c rose carmine	3,750.	2,750.

SPECIAL DELIVERY STAMPS

United States No. E5 Overprinted in Red

Wmk. Double-lined USPS (191)
1901, Oct. 15   Perf. 12

E1	SD3	10c dark blue	100.	80.
		Never hinged	185.	
a.		Dots in curved frame above messenger (Pl. 882)	175.	160.

Special Delivery Messenger SD2

Wmk. Double-lined PIPS (191PI)
1906, Sept. 8

E2	SD2	20c deep ultra	45.00	8.00
		Never hinged	90.00	
b.		20c pale ultramarine	35.00	8.00
		Never hinged	70.00	

See Nos. E3-E6. For overprints see Nos. E7-E10, EO1.

SPECIAL PRINTING

U.S. No. E6 Overprinted in Red

Wmk. Double-lined USPS (191)
1907

E2A	SD4	10c ultramarine	3,250.	

Wmk. Single-lined PIPS (190PI)
1911, Apr.

E3	SD2	20c deep ultra	22.00	1.75
		Never hinged	42.00	

1916   Perf. 10

E4	SD2	20c deep ultra	175.00	150.00
		Never hinged	275.00	

1919   Unwmk.   Perf. 11

E5	SD2	20c ultramarine	.60	.25
		Never hinged	.90	
a.		20c pale blue	.75	.25
		Never hinged	1.00	
b.		20c dull violet	.60	.25
		Never hinged	.90	

Type of 1906 Issue
1925-31   Imperf.

E6	SD2	20c dull violet ('31)	27.50	75.00
		Never hinged	40.00	
a.		20c violet blue ('25)	50.00	
		Never hinged	80.00	

Type of 1919 Overprinted in Black

1939, Apr. 27   Perf. 11

E7	SD2	20c blue violet	.25	.25
		Never hinged	.40	

Nos. E5b and E7, Hstmpd. in Violet

1944

E8	SD2	20c dull violet (On E5b)	1,400.	550.00
		On cover		
		Block of 4	6,000.	
E9	SD2	20c blue violet (On E7)	550.00	250.00

Type SD2 Overprinted

1945, May 1

E10	SD2	20c blue violet	.70	.55
		Never hinged	1.10	
a.		"IC" close together	3.25	2.75
		Never hinged	4.75	

SPECIAL DELIVERY OFFICIAL STAMP

Type of 1906 Issue Overprinted

1931   Unwmk.   Perf. 11

EO1	SD2	20c dull violet	3.00	75.00
		Never hinged	4.50	
		P# block of 6	150.00	
		Never hinged	190.00	
a.		No period after "B"	50.00	250.00
		Never hinged	75.00	
b.		Double overprint	—	

It is strongly recommended that expert opinion be acquired for Nos. EO1 and EO1a used.

POSTAGE DUE STAMPS

U.S. Nos. J38-J44 Overprinted in Black

Wmk. Double-lined USPS (191)
1899, Aug. 16   Perf. 12

J1	D2	1c deep claret	7.50	2.50
		Never hinged	15.00	
J2	D2	2c deep claret	7.50	2.50
		Never hinged	15.00	
J3	D2	5c deep claret	15.00	2.50
		Never hinged	30.00	
J4	D2	10c deep claret	19.00	5.50
		Never hinged	37.50	
J5	D2	50c deep claret	250.00	100.00
		Never hinged	425.00	

No. J1 was used to pay regular postage Sept. 5-19, 1902.

1901, Aug. 31

J6	D2	3c deep claret	17.50	7.00
		Never hinged	35.00	
J7	D2	30c deep claret	250.00	110.00
		Never hinged	415.00	
		Nos. J1-J7 (7)	566.50	230.00
		Set, never hinged	882.50	

Post Office
Clerk — D3

1928, Aug. 21　Unwmk.　Perf. 11

J8	D3	4c brown red	.25	.25
		Never hinged	.25	
		P# block of 6	14.00	
		Never hinged	17.50	
J9	D3	6c brown red	.30	.75
		Never hinged	.45	
		P# block of 6	14.00	
		Never hinged	17.50	
J10	D3	8c brown red	.25	.75
		Never hinged	.35	
		P# block of 6	14.00	
		Never hinged	17.50	
J11	D3	10c brown red	.30	.75
		Never hinged	.45	
		P# block of 6	14.00	
		Never hinged	17.50	
J12	D3	12c brown red	.25	.75
		Never hinged	.35	
		P# block of 6	14.00	
		Never hinged	17.50	
J13	D3	16c brown red	.30	.75
		Never hinged	.45	
		P# block of 6	14.00	
		Never hinged	17.50	
J14	D3	20c brown red	.30	.75
		Never hinged	.45	
		P# block of 6	14.00	
		Never hinged	17.50	
		Nos. J8-J14 (7)	1.95	4.75
		Set, never hinged	2.75	

No. J8 Surcharged in
Blue

1937, July 29　Unwmk.　Perf. 11

J15	D3	3c on 4c brown red	.25	.25
		Never hinged	.35	

See note after No. NJ1.

Nos. J8 to J14
Handstamped in Violet

1944, Dec. 3

J16	D3	4c brown red	150.00	—
J17	D3	6c brown red	100.00	—
J18	D3	8c brown red	110.00	350.00
J19	D3	10c brown red	100.00	—
J20	D3	12c brown red	100.00	—
J21	D3	16c brown red	100.00	350.00
a.		Pair, one without ovpt.	—	
J22	D3	20c brown red	110.00	—
		Nos. J16-J22 (7)	770.00	

OFFICIAL STAMPS

Official Handstamped Overprints

"Officers purchasing stamps for government business may, if they so desire, surcharge them with the letters O.B. either in writing with black ink or by rubber stamps but in such a manner as not to obliterate the stamp that postmasters will be unable to determine whether the stamps have been previously used." C.M. Cotterman, Director of Posts, December 26, 1905.

Beginning January 1, 1906, all branches of the Insular Government used postage stamps to prepay postage instead of franking them as before. Some officials used manuscript, some utilized the typewriting machines but by far the larger number provided themselves with rubber stamps. The majority of these read "O.B." but other forms were: "OFFICIAL BUSINESS" or "OFFICIAL MAIL" in two lines, with variations on many of these.

These "O.B." overprints are known on U.S. 1899-1901 stamps; on 1903-06 stamps in red and blue; on 1906 stamps in red, blue, black, yellow and green.

"O.B." overprints were also made on the centavo and peso stamps of the Philippines, per order of May 25, 1907.

Beginning in 1926 the Bureau of Posts issued press-printed official stamps, but many government offices continued to handstamp

ordinary postage stamps "O.B." The press-printed "O.B." overprints are listed below.

During the Japanese occupation period 1942-45, the same system of handstamped official overprints prevailed, but the handstamp usually consisted of "K.P.", initials of the Tagalog words, "Kagamitang Pampamahalaan" (Official Business) and the two Japanese characters used in the printed overprint on Nos. NO1 to NO4.

Regular
Issue of
1926
Ovptd. in
Red

1926, Dec. 20　Unwmk.　Perf. 12

O1	A42	2c green & black	3.00	1.00
		Never hinged	4.50	
O2	A42	4c car & blk	3.00	1.25
		Never hinged	4.50	
a.		Vertical pair, imperf. between	550.00	
O3	A42	18c lt brn & blk	8.00	4.00
		Never hinged	12.00	
O4	A42	20c org & blk	7.75	1.75
		Never hinged	11.50	
		Nos. O1-O4 (4)	21.75	8.00
		Set, never hinged	32.50	

Opening of the Legislative Palace.

Regular Issue of 1917-
26 Overprinted by the
U.S. Bureau of
Engraving and Printing

1931　　　　　　　　　　Perf. 11

O5	A40	2c green	.40	.25
		Never hinged	.65	
		P# block of 6	20.00	
		Never hinged	25.00	
a.		No period after "B"	17.50	17.50
		Never hinged	27.50	
b.		No period after "O"	40.00	30.00
O6	A40	4c carmine	.45	.25
		Never hinged	.70	
		P# block of 6	20.00	
		Never hinged	25.00	
a.		No period after "B"	40.00	20.00
		Never hinged	60.00	
O7	A40	6c deep violet	.75	.25
		Never hinged	1.25	
		P# block of 10, Impt.	40.00	
		Never hinged	50.00	
O8	A40	8c yellow brown	.75	.25
		Never hinged	1.25	
		P# block of 6	32.00	
		Never hinged	40.00	
		P# block of 10, Impt.	40.00	
		Never hinged	50.00	
O9	A40	10c deep blue	1.20	.25
		Never hinged	1.90	
		P# block of 10, Impt.	32.00	
		Never hinged	40.00	
O10	A40	12c red orange	2.00	.25
		Never hinged	3.00	
		P# block of 6	65.00	
		Never hinged	80.00	
		P# block of 10, Impt.	80.00	
		Never hinged	95.00	
a.		No period after "B"	80.00	80.00
		Never hinged	120.00	
O11	A40	16c lt ol grn	1.00	.25
		Never hinged	1.50	
		P# block of 6	24.00	
		Never hinged	30.00	
a.		16c olive bister	2.00	.25
		Never hinged	3.00	
		P# block of 6	20.00	
		Never hinged	25.00	
O12	A40	20c orange yellow	1.25	.25
		Never hinged	1.90	
		P# block of 10, Impt.	75.00	
		Never hinged	95.00	
a.		No period after "B"	80.00	80.00
		Never hinged	120.00	
O13	A40	26c green	2.00	1.00
		Never hinged	3.25	
		P# block of 6	120.00	
		Never hinged	150.00	
a.		26c blue green	2.50	1.50
		Never hinged	4.00	
		P# block of 6	130.00	
		Never hinged	165.00	
O14	A40	30c gray	2.00	.25
		Never hinged	3.25	
		P# block of 10, Impt.	80.00	
		Never hinged	100.00	
		Nos. O5-O14 (10)	11.80	3.25
		Set, never hinged	18.65	

Many collectors prefer to collect the plate blocks of 6 of Nos. O5-O6, O8, O10-O11a and O14 as blocks of 10 so they fit aesthetically with the other plate blocks of 10 with imprints.

Overprinted on Nos.
383-392

1935

O15	A53	2c rose	.25	.25
		Never hinged	.30	
		P# block of 6	4.75	
		Never hinged	6.00	
a.		No period after "B"	15.00	10.00
		Never hinged	22.50	
b.		No period after "O"	—	
O16	A54	4c yellow green	.25	.25
		Never hinged	.30	
		P# block of 6	4.00	
		Never hinged	5.00	
a.		No period after "B"	15.00	40.00
		Never hinged	22.50	
O17	A55	6c dark brown	.25	.25
		Never hinged	.40	
		P# block of 6	8.00	
		Never hinged	10.00	
a.		No period after "B"	35.00	35.00
		Never hinged	52.50	
O18	A56	8c violet	.30	.25
		Never hinged	.45	
		P# block of 6	9.50	
		Never hinged	12.00	
O19	A57	10c rose carmine	.30	.25
		Never hinged	.45	
		P# block of 6	8.00	
		Never hinged	10.00	
O20	A58	12c black	.75	.25
		Never hinged	1.10	
		P# block of 6	8.00	
		Never hinged	10.00	
O21	A59	16c dark blue	.55	.25
		Never hinged	.85	
		P# block of 6	8.00	
		Never hinged	10.00	
O22	A60	20c light olive green	.60	.25
		Never hinged	.90	
		P# block of 6	12.00	
		Never hinged	15.00	
O23	A61	26c indigo	.90	.25
		Never hinged	1.50	
		P# block of 6	20.00	
		Never hinged	25.00	
O24	A62	30c orange red	.80	.25
		Never hinged	1.20	
		P# block of 6	20.00	
		Never hinged	25.00	
		Nos. O15-O24 (10)	4.95	2.50
		Set, never hinged	7.40	

Nos. 411 and 418 with
Additional Overprint in
Black

1937-38

O25	A53	2c rose	.25	.25
		Never hinged	.30	
a.		No period after "B"	25.00	25.00
		Never hinged	45.00	
b.		Period after "B" raised (UL 4)	150.00	
O26	A60	20c lt ol grn ('38)	.70	.50
		Never hinged	1.10	
		P# block of 6	20.00	
		Never hinged	25.00	

Regular Issue of 1935 Overprinted In Black

a

b

1938-40

O27	A53(a)	2c rose	.25	.25
		Never hinged	.30	
		P# block of 6	4.75	
		Never hinged	6.00	
a.		Hyphen omitted	10.00	10.00
		Never hinged	15.00	
b.		No period after "B"	20.00	30.00
		Never hinged	30.00	
O28	A54(b)	4c yellow green	.75	1.00
		Never hinged	1.10	
		P# block of 6	24.00	
		Never hinged	30.00	
O29	A55(a)	6c dark brown	.30	.25
		Never hinged	.45	
		P# block of 6	12.00	
		Never hinged	15.00	
O30	A56(b)	8c violet	.75	.85
		Never hinged	1.10	
		P# block of 6	9.50	
		Never hinged	12.00	
O31	A57(b)	10c rose carmine	.25	.25
		Never hinged	.30	
		P# block of 6	16.00	
		Never hinged	20.00	
a.		No period after "O"	50.00	40.00
		Never hinged	75.00	
O32	A58(b)	12c black	.30	.25
		Never hinged	.45	
		P# block of 6	12.00	
		Never hinged	15.00	

O33	A59(b)	16c dark blue	.30	.25
		Never hinged	.45	
		P# block of 6	16.00	
		Never hinged	20.00	
O34	A60(a)	20c lt ol grn ('40)	.55	.85
		Never hinged	.85	
		P# block of 6	16.00	
		Never hinged	20.00	
O35	A61(b)	26c indigo	1.50	2.00
		Never hinged	2.25	
		P# block of 6	12.00	
		Never hinged	15.00	
O36	A62(b)	30c orange red	.75	.85
		Never hinged	1.10	
		P# block of 6	16.00	
		Never hinged	20.00	
		Nos. O27-O36 (10)	5.70	6.80
		Set, never hinged	8.25	

No. 461 Overprinted in
Black — c

1941, Apr. 14　　　Perf. 11x10½

O37	A75(c)	2c apple green	.25	.40
		Never hinged	.30	

Official Stamps
Handstamped in Violet

1944　　　　Perf. 11, 11x10½

O38	A53	2c rose (On O27)	375.00	200.00
		Never hinged	750.00	
O39	A75	2c apple grn (On O37)	15.00	20.00
		Never hinged	20.00	
O40	A54	4c yel grn (On O16)	45.00	30.00
		Never hinged	80.00	
O40A	A55	6c dk brn (On O29)	8,000.	—
O41	A57	10c rose car (On O31)	500.00	—
a.		No period after "O"	4,000.	
O42	A60	20c lt ol grn (On O22)	8,000.	
O43	A60	20c lt ol grn (On O26)	1,750.	

No. 497 Overprinted Type "c" in Black

1946, June 19　　　Perf. 11x10½

O44	A76	2c sepia	.25	.25
		Never hinged	.25	
a.		Vertical pair, bottom stamp without ovpt.		

OCCUPATION STAMPS

Issued Under Japanese Occupation

No. 461 Overprinted in
Black

No. 438
Overprinted
in Black

No. 439
Overprinted
in Black

1942-43　Unwmk.　Perf. 11x10½, 11

N1	A75	2c apple green	.25	1.00
		Never hinged	.30	
a.		Pair, one without overprint		
N2	A58	12c black ('43)	.25	2.00
		Never hinged	.40	
		P# block of 6	12.00	
		Never hinged	15.00	

N3 A59 16c dark blue ... 5.00 3.75
  Never hinged ... 7.50
  P# block of 6 ... 37.50
  Never hinged ... 55.00
  Nos. N1-N3 (3) ... 5.50 6.75
  Set, never hinged ... 8.20

Nos. 435a, 435, 442, 443, and 423 Surcharged in Black

a

b

c

d

Type I

Type II

Two types of 50c surcharge
Type I: Center of "A" is a triangle.
Type II: Center of "A" is a pin hole.

1942-43   **Perf. 11**
N4 A55(a) 5(c) on 6c golden brown ... .25 .75
  Never hinged ... .35
  a. Top bar shorter and thinner ... .25 1.00
   Never hinged ... .35
   P# block of 6 ... 50.00
   Never hinged ... 60.00
  b. 5(c) on 6c dark brown ... .25 .85
   Never hinged ... .35
  c. As "b," top bar shorter and thinner ... .25 1.00
   Never hinged ... .35
  d. Double surcharge, on cover ... —
N5 A62(b) 16(c) on 30c org red ('43) ... .25 .60
  Never hinged ... .45
N6 A63(c) 50c on 1p red org & blk ('43) ... .75 1.25
  Never hinged ... 1.10
  P# block of 4, 2 P# ... 16.00
  Never hinged ... 20.00
  a. Double surcharge ... 300.00
  b. Type I surcharge ... 100.00 90.00
   Never hinged ... 125.00
   P# block of 4 ... 500.00
   Never hinged ... 600.00
N7 A65(d) 1p on 4p bl & blk ('43) ... 100.00 150.00
  Never hinged ... 155.00
  Nos. N4-N7 (4) ... 101.25 152.60
  Set, never hinged ... 156.90

On Nos. N4 and N4b, the top bar measures 1½x22½mm. On Nos. N4a and N4c, the top bar measures 1x21mm and the "5" is smaller and thinner.
The used value for No. N7 is for postal cancellation. Used stamps exist with first day cancellations. They are worth somewhat less.

No. 384 Surcharged in Black

1942, May 18
N8 A54 2(c) on 4c yellow green ... 4.00 5.00
  Never hinged ... 8.75

Issued to commemorate Japan's capture of Bataan and Corregidor. The American-Filipino forces finally surrendered May 7, 1942. No. N8 exists with "R" for "B" in BATAAN.

No. 384 Surcharged in Black

1942, Dec. 8
N9 A54 5(c) on 4c yellow green ... .50 1.00
  Never hinged ... .75

1st anniversary of the "Greater East Asia War."

Nos. C59 and C62 Surcharged in Black

1943, Jan. 23
N10 AP1 2(c) on 8c carmine ... .25 1.00
  Never hinged ... .35
  P# block of 6 ... 20.00
  Never hinged ... 25.00
N11 AP1 5c on 1p sepia ... .50 1.50
  Never hinged ... .75

1st anniv. of the Philippine Executive Commission.

Nipa Hut OS1

Rice Planting OS2

Mt. Mayon and Mt. Fuji — OS3

Moro Vinta — OS4

The "c" currency is indicated by four Japanese characters, "p" currency by two.

Engraved; Typographed (2c, 6c, 25c)

1943-44   **Wmk. 257**   **Perf. 13**
N12 OS1 1c dp orange ... .25 .40
  Never hinged ... .30
  Margin block of 6, inscription ... 2.40
  Never hinged ... 3.00
N13 OS2 2c brt green ... .25 .40
  Never hinged ... .30
  Margin block of 6, inscription ... 2.40
  Never hinged ... 3.00
N14 OS1 4c slate green ... .25 .40
  Never hinged ... .30
  Margin block of 6, inscription ... 2.40
  Never hinged ... 3.00
N15 OS3 5c orange brown ... .25 .40
  Never hinged ... .30
  Margin block of 6, inscription ... 2.40
  Never hinged ... 3.00

N16 OS2 6c red ... .25 .60
  Never hinged ... .30
  Margin block of 6, inscription ... 2.40
  Never hinged ... 3.00
N17 OS3 10c blue green ... .25 .40
  Never hinged ... .30
  Margin block of 6, inscription ... 2.40
  Never hinged ... 3.00
N18 OS4 12c steel blue ... 1.00 1.50
  Never hinged ... 1.50
  Margin block of 6, inscription ... 11.00
  Never hinged ... 14.00
N19 OS4 16c dk brown ... .25 .40
  Never hinged ... .30
  Margin block of 6, inscription ... 2.40
  Never hinged ... 3.00
N20 OS1 20c rose violet ... 1.25 1.75
  Never hinged ... 1.90
  Margin block of 6, inscription ... 15.00
  Never hinged ... 19.00
N21 OS3 21c violet ... .25 .40
  Never hinged ... .35
  Margin block of 6, inscription ... 2.40
  Never hinged ... 3.00
N22 OS2 25c pale brown ... .25 .40
  Never hinged ... .35
  Margin block of 6, inscription ... 2.40
  Never hinged ... 3.00
N23 OS3 1p dp carmine ... .75 1.25
  Never hinged ... 1.15
  Margin block of 6, inscription ... 9.50
  Never hinged ... 12.00
N24 OS4 2p dull violet ... 6.50 6.50
  Never hinged ... 10.00
N25 OS4 5p dark olive ... 16.00 18.00
  Never hinged ... 25.00
  Nos. N12-N25 (14) ... 27.75 32.80
  Set, never hinged ... 42.00

Issued: Nos. N13, N15, 4/1; Nos. N12, N14, N23, 6/7; Nos. N16-N19, 7/14; Nos. N20-N22, 8/16; No. N24, 9/16; No. N25, 4/1/44.
For surcharges see Nos. NB5-NB7.

OS5

1943, May 7   **Photo.**   **Unwmk.**
N26 OS5 2c carmine red ... .25 .75
  Never hinged ... .30
  Margin block of 6, inscription ... 4.00
  Never hinged ... 5.00
N27 OS5 5c bright green ... .25 1.00
  Never hinged ... .35
  Margin block of 6, inscription ... 6.50
  Never hinged ... 8.00

1st anniversary of the fall of Bataan and Corregidor.

No. 440 Surcharged in Black

1943, June 20   **Engr.**   **Perf. 11**
N28 A60 12(c) on 20c light olive green ... .25 .75
  Never hinged ... .35
  a. Double surcharge

350th anniversary of the printing press in the Philippines. "Limbagan" is Tagalog for "printing press."

Rizal Monument, Filipina and Philippine Flag — OS6

1943, Oct. 14   **Photo.**   **Perf. 12**
N29 OS6 5c light blue ... .25 .90
  Never hinged ... .30
  a. Imperf. ... .25 .90
N30 OS6 12c orange ... .25 .90
  Never hinged ... .30
  a. Imperf. ... .25 .90
N31 OS6 17c rose pink ... .25 .90
  Never hinged ... .30
  a. Imperf. ... .25 .90
  Nos. N29-N31 (3) ... .75 2.70
  Set, never hinged ... .90

"Independence of the Philippines." Japan granted "independence" Oct. 14, 1943, when the puppet republic was founded.

The imperforate stamps were issued without gum.

José Rizal — OS7

Rev. José Burgos — OS8

Apolinario Mabini — OS9

1944, Feb. 17   **Litho.**
N32 OS7 5c blue ... .25 1.00
  Never hinged ... .30
  a. Imperf. ... .25 2.00
   Never hinged ... .35
N33 OS8 12c carmine ... .25 1.00
  Never hinged ... .30
  a. Imperf. ... .25 2.00
   Never hinged ... .35
N34 OS9 17c deep orange ... .25 1.00
  Never hinged ... .30
  a. Imperf. ... .25 2.00
   Never hinged ... .35
  Nos. N32-N34 (3) ... .75 3.00
  Set, never hinged ... .90

See No. NB8.

Nos. C60 and C61 Surcharged in Black

1944, May 7   **Perf. 11**
N35 AP1 5(c) on 20c ultra ... .50 1.00
  Never hinged ... .75
  P# block of 6 ... 32.50
  Never hinged ... 40.00
N36 AP1 12(c) on 60c blue green ... 1.75 1.75
  Never hinged ... 2.50
  P# block of 6 ... 42.50
  Never hinged ... 52.50

2nd anniversary of the fall of Bataan and Corregidor.

OS10

1945, Jan. 12   **Litho.**   **Imperf. Without Gum**
N37 OS10 5c dull violet brown ... .25 .50
  Never hinged ... .30
N38 OS10 7c blue green ... .25 .50
  Never hinged ... .30
N39 OS10 20c chalky blue ... .25 .50
  Never hinged ... .30
  Nos. N37-N39 (3) ... .75 1.50
  Set, never hinged ... .90

Issued belatedly on Jan. 12, 1945, to commemorate the first anniversary of the puppet Philippine Republic, Oct. 14, 1944. "S" stands for "sentimos."

OCCUPATION SEMI-POSTAL STAMPS

Woman, Farming and Cannery — OSP1

Unwmk.
1942, Nov. 12   **Litho.**   **Perf. 12**
NB1 OSP1 2c + 1c pale violet ... .25 .60
  Never hinged ... .30

NB2 OSP1 5c + 1c brt grn   .25 *1.00*
    Never hinged   .30
NB3 OSP1 16c + 2c orange   25.00 *32.50*
    Never hinged   42.00
    Nos. NB1-NB3 (3)   25.50 *34.10*
    Set, never hinged   42.60

Issued to promote the campaign to produce and conserve food. The surtax aided the Red Cross.

Souvenir Sheet

OSP2

1943, Oct. 14 Without Gum *Imperf.*
NB4 OSP2 Sheet of 3   60.00 *17.50*

"Independence of the Philippines."
No. NB4 contains one each of Nos. N29a-N31a. Marginal inscription is from Rizal's "Last Farewell." Sold for 2.50p.
The value for No. NB4 used is for a sheet from a first day cover. Commercially used sheets are extremely scarce and worth much more.

Nos. N18, N20 and N21 Surcharged in Black

1943, Dec. 8   Wmk. 257   Perf. 13
NB5 OS4 12c + 21c steel blue   .25 *1.50*
    Never hinged   .30
    Margin block of 6, inscription   4.00
    Never hinged   5.00
NB6 OS1 20c + 36c rose violet   .25 *1.50*
    Never hinged   .30
    Margin block of 6, inscription   4.00
    Never hinged   5.00
NB7 OS3 21c + 40c violet   .25 *2.00*
    Never hinged   .30
    Margin block of 6, inscription   4.75
    Never hinged   6.00
    Nos. NB5-NB7 (3)   .75 *5.00*
    Set, never hinged   .90

The surtax was for the benefit of victims of a Luzon flood. "Baha" is Tagalog for "flood."

Souvenir Sheet

OSP3

Unwmk.
1944, Feb. 9   Litho.   Imperf.
Without Gum
NB8 OSP3 Sheet of 3   6.50 3.50

No. NB8 contains 1 each of Nos. N32a-N34a.
Sheet sold for 1p, surtax going to a fund for the care of heroes' monuments.
The value for No. NB8 used is for a stamp from a first day cover. Commercially used examples are worth much more.

OCCUPATION POSTAGE DUE STAMP

No. J15 Overprinted in Blue

1942, Oct. 14   Unwmk.   Perf. 11
NJ1 D3 3c on 4c brown red   25.00 *35.00*
    Never hinged   37.50

On examples of No. J15, two lines were drawn in India ink with a ruling pen across "United States of America" by employees of the Short Paid Section of the Manila Post Office to make a provisional 3c postage due stamp which was used from Sept. 1, 1942 (when the letter rate was raised from 2c to 5c) until Oct. 14 when No. NJ1 went on sale. Value on cover, $175.
Bottom plate blocks of 6 of No. NJ1 are much scarcer than the right side plate blocks. Value $325 hinged, $450 never hinged.

OCCUPATION OFFICIAL STAMPS

Nos. 461, 413, 435, 435a and 442 Ovptd. or Srchd. in Black with Bars and

1943-44   Unwmk.   Perf. 11x10½, 11
NO1 A75 2c apple green   .25 *.75*
    Never hinged   .30
  a. Double overprint   400.00
    Never hinged   600.00
NO2 A55 5c on 6c dk brn
    (On No. 413)
    ('44)   40.00 *45.00*
    Never hinged   55.00
NO3 A55 5c on 6c golden
    brn (On No.
    435a)   .25 *.90*
    Never hinged   .35
    P# block of 6   14.00
    Never hinged   17.50
  a. Narrower spacing between
    bars   .25 *.90*
    Never hinged   .35
  b. 5(c) on 6c dark brown (On
    No. 435)   .25 *.90*
    Never hinged   .35
  c. As "b," narrower spacing
    between bars   .25 *.90*
    Never hinged   .35
  d. Double overprint   —
NO4 A62 16(c) on 30c org
    red   .30 *1.25*
    Never hinged   .45
    P# block of 6   20.00
    Never hinged   25.00
  a. Wider spacing between
    bars   .30 *1.25*
    Never hinged   .45
    Nos. NO1-NO4 (4)   40.80 *47.90*
    Set, never hinged   56.10

On Nos. NO3 and NO3b the bar deleting "United States of America" is 9¾ to 10mm above the bar deleting "Common." On Nos. NO3a and NO3c, the spacing is 8 to 8½mm.
On No. NO4, the center bar is 19mm long, 3½mm below the top bar and 6mm above the Japanese characters. On No. NO4a, the center bar is 20½mm long, 9mm below the top bar and 1mm above the Japanese characters.
"K.P." stands for Kagamitang Pampamahalaan, "Official Business" in Tagalog.

Nos. 435 & 435a Surcharged in Black

1944, Aug. 28   Perf. 11
NO5 A55 (5c) on 6c gldn brn   .30 *.40*
    Never hinged   .45
    P# block of 6   20.00
    Never hinged   25.00
  a. 5(c) on 6c dark brown   .30 *.40*
    Never hinged   .45
    P# block of 6   20.00
    Never hinged   25.00

Nos. O34 and C62 Overprinted in Black

a

b

NO6 A60(a) 20c light olive
    green   .40 *.50*
    Never hinged   .60
    P# block of 6   12.00
    Never hinged   15.00
NO7 AP1(b) 1p sepia   .90 *1.00*
    Never hinged   1.45
    P# block of 6   20.00
    Never hinged   25.00
    Nos. NO5-NO7 (3)   1.60 *1.90*
    Set, never hinged   2.05

PUERTO RICO

ˌpwer-tə-ˈrē-ˌkō

(Porto Rico)

LOCATION — Large island in the West Indies, east of Hispaniola
GOVT. — Former Spanish possession
AREA — 3,435 sq. mi.
POP. — 953,243 (1899)
CAPITAL — San Juan

The island was ceded to the US by the Treaty of 1898.
Spanish issues of 1855-73 used in both Puerto Rico and Cuba are listed as Cuba Nos. 1-4, 9-14, 18-21, 32-34, 35A-37, 39-41, 43-45, 47-49, 51-53, 55-57.
Spanish issues of 1873-1898 for Puerto Rico only are listed in Vol. 4 of this Catalogue.

100 Cents = 1 Dollar (1898)

Issued under U.S. Administration
LOCAL ISSUES
Ponce Issue

A11

Handstamped
1898   Unwmk.   Imperf.
200 A11 5c violet

No. 200 is a violet handstamp and control mark used on envelopes. Some examples have no control mark. There are three types of circular markings known, and two control marks. Uses on 2¢ U.S. stamps on cover were strictly as a cancellation, not as local postage. Because genuine usage is extremely difficult to authenticate with certainty, certification by competent authorities is essential.

Coamo Issue

A12

Typeset, setting of 10
1898, Aug.
201 A12 5c black   700. *1,250.*

See the Scott U.S. Specialized Catalogue for more detailed listings.
The stamps bear the control mark "F. Santiago" in violet. About 500 were issued.
Dangerous forgeries exist.

Regular Issue

United States Nos. 279, 279Bf, 281, 272 and 282C Overprinted in Black at 36 degree angle

1899   Wmk. 191   Perf. 12
210 A87 1c yellow green   6.00 *1.40*
    Never hinged   13.00
  a. Overprint at 25 degree
    angle   8.00 *2.25*
    Never hinged   17.50
211 A88 2c redsh car,
    type IV   5.00 *1.25*
    Never hinged   11.00
  a. Overprint at 25 degree
    angle, *Mar. 15*   6.50 *2.25*
    Never hinged   27.50
212 A91 5c blue   12.50 *2.50*
    Never hinged   27.50
213 A93 8c violet brown   40.00 *17.50*
    Never hinged   90.00
  a. Overprint at 25 degree
    angle   45.00 *19.00*
    Never hinged   100.00
  c. "PORTO RIC"   150.00 *110.00*
214 A94 10c brown, type I 22.50 *6.00*
    Never hinged   50.00
    Nos. 210-214 (5)   86.00 *28.65*

Misspellings of the overprint on Nos. 210-214 (PORTO RICU, PORTU RICO, FORTO RICO) are actually broken letters.

United States Nos. 279 and 279B Overprinted Diagonally in Black

1900
215 A87 1c yellow green   7.50 *1.40*
    Never hinged   17.50
216 A88 2c red, type IV   5.50 *2.00*
    Never hinged   12.50
  b. Inverted overprint   *12,500.*

POSTAGE DUE STAMPS

United States Nos. J38, J39 and J42 Overprinted in Black at 36 degree angle

1899   Wmk. 191   Perf. 12
J1 D2 1c deep claret   22.50 *5.50*
    Never hinged   50.00
  a. Overprint at 25 degree an-
    gle   22.50 *7.50*
    Never hinged   50.00
J2 D2 2c deep claret   20.00 *6.00*
    Never hinged   45.00
  a. Overprint at 25 degree an-
    gle   20.00 *7.00*
    Never hinged   45.00
J3 D2 10c deep claret   180.00 *55.00*
    Never hinged   375.00
  a. Overprint at 25 degree an-
    gle   160.00 *75.00*
    Never hinged   330.00
    Nos. J1-J3 (3)   222.50 *66.50*

Stamps of Puerto Rico were replaced by those of the United States.

RYUKYU ISLANDS

rē-'yü-ˌkyü 'ī-ləndz

LOCATION — Chain of 63 islands between Japan and Formosa, separating the East China Sea from the Pacific Ocean.
GOVT. — Semi-autonomous under United States administration.
AREA — 848 sq. mi.
POP. — 945,465 (1970)
CAPITAL — Naha, Okinawa

The Ryukyus were part of Japan until American forces occupied them in 1945. The islands reverted to Japan May 15, 1972.

Before the general issue of 1948, a number of provisional stamps were used. These included a mimeographed-handstamped adhesive for Kume Island, and various current stamps of Japan handstamped with chops by the postmasters of Okinawa, Amami, Miyako and Yaeyama. Although authorized by American authorities, these provisionals were local in nature, so are omitted in the listings that follow. They are listed in the *Scott United States Specialized Catalogue.*

100 Sen = 1 Yen
100 Cents = 1 Dollar (1958)

Catalogue values for unused stamps in this country are for Never Hinged items.

Wmk. 257

Cycad — A1

Lily — A2

Sailing Ship — A3

Farmer — A4

1948-49 Typo. Wmk. 257 Perf. 13
Second Printing, July 18, 1949

1	A1	5s magenta	2.00	2.00
2	A2	10s yellow green	5.00	5.00
3	A1	20s yellow green	3.00	3.00
4	A3	30s vermilion	1.25	1.25
5	A2	40s magenta	1.25	1.25
6	A3	50s ultramarine	5.00	4.00
7	A4	1y ultramarine	5.00	5.00
		Nos. 1-7 (7)	22.50	21.50

First Printing, July 1, 1948

1a	A1	5s magenta	3.00	3.50
2a	A2	10s yellow green	2.00	2.00
3a	A1	20s yellow green	2.00	2.00
4a	A3	30s vermilion	4.00	3.50
5a	A2	40s magenta	50.00	50.00
6a	A3	50s ultramarine	4.00	4.00
7a	A4	1y ultramarine	400.00	325.00
		Nos. 1a-7a (7)	465.00	390.00

First printing: thick yellow gum, dull colors, rough perforations, grayish paper. Second printing: white gum, sharp colors, clean-cut and rough perforations, white paper. Third printing (Sept. 28, 1950): 5s to 50s denominations, white gum, clean-cut perforations, cream paper (same values as second printing).

Tile Rooftop and Shishi — A5

Designs: 50s, Tile rooftop and Shisa. 1y, Ryukyuan girl. 2y, Main hall of Shuri Castle. 3y, Female dragonhead statue. 4y, Two women. 5y, Sea shells.

Perf. 13x13¼
1950, Jan. 21 Photo. Unwmk.
Off-white Paper

8	A5	50s dark carmine rose	.25	.25
a.		White paper, third printing, Sept. 6, 1958	.50	.50
b.		"White Sky" variety (pos. 76)	3.50	3.50
9	A5	1y deep blue	3.25	3.00
10	A5	2y rose violet	9.00	6.00
11	A5	3y carmine rose	22.50	11.00
12	A5	4y greenish gray	11.00	11.00
13	A5	5y blue green	6.50	6.00
		Nos. 8-13 (6)	52.50	37.25

The original first two printings (No. 8) were printed on off-white paper with yellowish gum and a 5-character imprint in the sheet margin. The first printing is a deep carmine red or dark red, and the second printing a dark carmine rose. The first printing was issued Jan. 21, 1950; the second printing received in Naha Sept. 22, 1950; and the third printing (No. 8a) Sept. 6, 1958. Quantities: first printing: 300,000; second printing: 3,000,000; and third printing: 300,000. The first printing unused is much scarcer than the second printing because most of the first printing was used as postage.

No. 8a has colorless gum and an 8-character imprint in the sheet margin. The color is a deep red.

For No. 8b, a defect in position 76 of the plates used resulted in the sky above the roof being predominantly white in the second printing, whereas in the first printing the 'white sky' is not as pronounced. The master negative and plate were reworked for the third printing, so position 76 in this printing does not have the "white sky" variety.

For surcharges see Nos. 16-17.

Ryukyu University and Female Dragonhead Statue — A6

1951, Feb. 12 Perf. 13½x13¼
14	A6	3y red brown	45.00	25.00

Opening of Ryukyu University, Feb. 12.

Ryukyuan Pine Tree — A7

1951, Feb. 19 Perf. 13¼
15	A7	3y dark green	40.00	22.50

Reforestation Week, Feb. 18-24.

No. 8 surcharged in Black

Type I   Type II

Type III

There are three types of 10y surcharge:
Type I: narrow-spaced rules, "10" normal spacing, "Kai Tei" characters in 9-point type. First printing, Jan. 1, 1952.

Type II: wide-spaced rules, "10" normal spacing, "Kai Tei" characters in 9-point type. Second printing, June 5, 1952.
Type III: rules and "10" both wide-spaced, "Kai Tei" characters in 8-point type. Third printing, Dec. 8, 1952.

Both eight and nine point type were used in overprinting Nos. 16-17. In the varieties listed below, the first number indicates the size of the "Kai" character, and the second number is the size of the "Tei" character.

1952 Perf. 13½x13
16	A5	10y on 50s dark carmine rose (II)	8.00	8.00
c.		8/8 point Kai Tei	8.00	8.00
d.		9/8 point Kai Tei	80.00	80.00
f.		Surcharge transposed	900.00	—
g.		Legend of surcharge only (no obliteration bars)	1,200.	
h.		Wrong font for "0" (pos. 59)	150.00	150.00
i.		Wrong font for "Yen" symbol (pos. 69)	150.00	150.00
j.		Surcharge on "white sky" variety (No. 8b) (pos. 76)	150.00	150.00

On No. 16e, the entire obliteration-bars portion of the surcharge normally under the 10 Yen must be visible at the top of the stamp. Ten examples of No. 16e exist (pos. 91-100) with the full obliteration bars also in the bottom selvage.

Forgeries to defraud the Postal Agency of revenue are known, used only, at the Gusikawa Post Office. Two types. Value, $500 each.

16A	A5	10y on 50s dark carmine rose (I)	30.00	30.00
a.		8/8 point Kai Tei	30.00	30.00
b.		Bottom two bars inverted (pos. 17)	150.00	150.00
c.		Wrong font for "0" (pos. 73)	250.00	250.00
d.		Surcharge on "white sky" variety (No. 8b) (pos. 76)	250.00	250.00
e.		Wide spaced obliterating bars (pos. 72)	150.00	150.00
f.		Wide spaced bottom obliterating bars (pos. 86, 95)	80.00	80.00

16B	A5	10y on 50s dark carmine rose (III)	45.00	35.00
a.		Wrong font for "Yen" symbol (pos. 25, 35, 85)	200.00	200.00
b.		Wrong font for "Tei" (pos. 26)	350.00	350.00
c.		Asterisk missing (pos. 54)	—	—
d.		"Kai Tei" 1.25mm above asterisk (pos. 54)	350.00	350.00
e.		"Kai" omitted (pos. 71)	350.00	350.00
f.		Narrow spaced "10" (pos. 96)	350.00	350.00
g.		Surcharge on "white sky" variety (No. 8b)	350.00	350.00
h.		Extra wide spaced "10" (pos. 60)	200.00	200.00
i.		Asterisk within 2.0mm of "Kai Tei" (pos. 87)	200.00	200.00

The Kai Tei of the third printing measures the same as the 8-point type in the earlier printings but has differing characteristics. The Top curved line of the Kai is shorter and the lower curved line is also much shorter.

No. 10 surcharged 100y in black

17	A5	100y on 2y rose violet, Kai Tei characters in 9/9-point type, June 16, 1952	2,000.	1,400.
a.		8/8 point Kai Tei	2,000.	1,400.
b.		9/8 point Kai Tei	3,250.	3,250.
c.		Center "0" in wrong font, stamp with 9/9 Kai Tei (pos. 42)	4,000.	4,000.
d.		Center "0" in wrong font, stamp with 8/8 Kai Tei (pos. 67, 86)	3,500.	3,500.
e.		Center "0" in wrong font, stamp with 9/8 Kai Tei (pos. 53)	5,000.	5,000.
f.		Wrong font for last "0" (pos. 59)	5,000.	5,000.
g.		Wrong font for "yen" symbol (pos. 69)	5,000.	5,000.
h.		"Tei" in wrong font (pos. 9)	4,000.	4,000.

Varieties of shifted and damaged surcharge characters exist, most notably a damaged ("clipped") Kai (pos. 26, 85).

The "Tei" on No. 17h is the character used on Nos. 16 and 16A.

See note after 16B to differentiate between 8-point and 9-point characters.

Surcharge forgeries are known. Authentication by competant experts is recommended.

Dove, Bean Sprout and Map — A8

1952, Apr. 1 Perf. 13¼
18	A8	3y deep plum	80.00	40.00

Establishment of the Government of the Ryukyu Islands (GRI), April 1, 1952.

Madanbashi Bridge — A9

Designs: 2y, Main Hall, Shuri Castle. 3y, Shureimon Gate. 6y, Stone Gate, Sogen-ji Temple, Naha. 10y, Benzaiten-do Temple. 30y, Sonohyan Utaki (altar) at Shuri Castle. 50y, Tamaudun (royal mausoleum). Shuri. 100y, Stone Bridge, Hojo Pond, Enkaku Temple.

1952-53 Perf. 13x13¼
19	A9	1y red	.30	.30
20	A9	2y green	.40	.40
21	A9	3y aquamarine	.50	.50
22	A9	6y blue	2.00	2.00
23	A9	10y crimson rose	2.50	1.00
24	A9	30y olive green	9.00	7.50
a.		30y light olive green, 1958	50.00	
25	A9	50y rose violet	12.50	9.00
26	A9	100y claret	15.00	5.00
		Nos. 19-26 (8)	42.20	25.70

Issued: 1y, 2y and 3y, 11/20/52. Others, 1/20/53.

Reception at Shuri Castle — A10

Perry and American Fleet in Naha Port A11

1953, May 26 Perf. 13x13¼
27	A10	3y deep magenta	12.00	6.50
28	A11	6y dull blue	1.25	1.50

Centenary of the arrival of Commodore Matthew Calbraith Perry at Naha, Okinawa.

Chofu Ota and Pencil-shaped Matrix — A12

1953, Oct. 1 Perf. 13¼x13
29	A12	4y yellow brown	11.00	5.00

Third Newspaper Week, Oct. 1-7.

Shigo Toma and
Pen — A13

1954, Oct. 1
30 A13 4y blue   10.00   7.50
Fourth Newspaper Week, Oct. 1-7.

Ryukyu Pottery — A14

Designs: 4y, Dachibin (sake or water flask).
15y, Tsuikin lacquerware tray. 20y, Kajimayaa
pattern on Kijoka-bashofu textile.

1954-55   Photo.   Perf. 13x13¼
31 A14 4y brown   .90   .50
32 A14 15y vermilion   3.50   3.50
33 A14 20y yellow orange   2.25   2.25
        Nos. 31-33 (3)   6.65   6.25
For surcharges see Nos. C19, C21, C23.

Noguni Shrine and
Sweet Potato
Plant — A15

1955, Nov. 26   Perf. 13¼
34 A15 4y blue   10.00   7.00
350th anniv. of the introduction of the sweet
potato to the Ryukyu Islands.

Stylized
Trees — A16

1956, Feb. 18   Perf. 13
35 A16 4y bluish green   10.00   6.00
Arbor Week, Feb. 18-24.

Yanaji (Willow)
Dance — A17

8y, Munjuru (Straw Hat) Dance. 14y, Nido
Tichiuchi Dance.

1956, May 1   Perf. 13x13¼
36 A17 5y rose lilac   1.00   .60
37 A17 8y violet blue   2.00   2.00
38 A17 14y reddish brown   2.50   2.50
        Nos. 36-38 (3)   5.50   5.10
For surcharges see Nos. C20, C22.

Telephone — A18

1956, June 8
39 A18 4y violet blue   12.50   8.00
Establishment of dial telephone system.

Garland of Pine,
Bamboo and
Plum — A19

1956, Dec. 1   Perf. 13¼
40 A19 2y multicolored   1.60   1.60
New Year, 1957.

Map of Okinawa and
Pencil Rocket — A20

1957, Oct. 1   Photo.   Perf. 13
41 A20 4y deep violet
              blue   1.00   1.00
Seventh Newspaper Week, Oct. 1-7.

Phoenix — A21

1957, Dec. 1   Perf. 13x13¼
42 A21 2y multicolored   .25   .25
New Year, 1958.

Ryukyu Stamps — A22

1958, July 1   Perf. 13½
43 A22 4y multicolored   .80   .80
10th anniv. of 1st Ryukyu stamps.

Yen Symbol and Dollar
Sign — A23

Perf. 10.3, 10.8, 11.1 & Compound
1958, Sept. 16   Typo.
Without Gum
44 A23 ½c orange   .80   .80
a.   Imperf., pair   1,500.
b.   Horiz. pair, imperf. be-
         tween   225.00
c.   Vert. pair, imperf. between   575.00
d.   Vert. strip of 4, imperf. be-
         tween   800.00
45 A23 1c yellow green   1.25   1.25
a.   Horiz. pair, imperf. be-
         tween   200.00
b.   Vert. pair, imperf. between   150.00
c.   Vert. strip of 3, imperf. be-
         tween   650.00
d.   Vert. strip of 4, imperf. be-
         tween   800.00
e.   Block of 4, imperf. btwn.
         vert. & horiz.   10,000.
46 A23 2c dark blue   2.00   2.00
a.   Horiz. pair, imperf. be-
         tween   200.00
b.   Vert. pair, imperf. between   2,200.
c.   Horiz. strip of 3, imperf.
         between   450.00
d.   Horiz. strip of 4, imperf.
         between   700.00
47 A23 3c deep carmine   1.50   1.50
a.   Horiz. pair, imperf. be-
         tween   200.00
b.   Vert. pair, imperf. between   150.00

---

c.   Vert. strip of 3, imperf. be-
         tween   400.00
d.   Vert. strip of 4, imperf. be-
         tween   750.00
e.   Block of 4, imperf. btwn.
         vert. & horiz.   10,000.
48 A23 4c bright green   2.00   2.00
a.   Horiz. pair, imperf. be-
         tween   400.00
b.   Vert. pair, imperf. between   175.00
49 A23 5c orange   4.00   3.75
a.   Horiz. pair, imperf. be-
         tween   200.00
b.   Vert. pair, imperf. between   850.00
50 A23 10c aquamarine   5.25   4.75
a.   Horiz. pair, imperf. be-
         tween   200.00
b.   Vert. pair, imperf. between   150.00
c.   Vert. strip of 3, imperf. be-
         tween   750.00
51 A23 25c bright violet
              blue   7.50   6.00
a.   Gummed paper, perf. 10.3
         ('61)   15.00   15.00
b.   Horiz. pair, imperf. be-
         tween   2,200.
c.   Vert. pair, imperf. between   5,000.
d.   Vert. strip of 3, imperf. be-
         tween   900.00
52 A23 50c gray   15.00   10.00
a.   Gummed paper, perf. 10.3
         ('61)   15.00   15.00
b.   Horiz. pair, imperf. be-
         tween   1,750.
53 A23 $1 rose lilac   11.00   5.50
a.   Horiz. pair, imperf. be-
         tween   450.00
b.   Vert. pair, imperf. between   2,250.
        Nos. 44-53 (10)   50.30   37.55
Printed locally. Perforation, paper and
shade varieties exist. Nos. 51a and 52a are on
off-white paper and perf 10.3.

Gate of Courtesy — A24

1958, Oct. 15   Photo.   Perf. 13x13¼
54 A24 3c multicolored   1.25   1.25
Restoration of Shureimon, Gate of Courtesy, on road leading to Shuri City.
Imitations of this stamp were distributed in
1972 to discourage speculation in Ryukyuan
stamps. The imitations were printed without
gum and have a lengthy message in light blue
printed on the back. A second type exists, with
printed black perforations and three Japanese
characters on the back ("Mozo Hin" — imitation) in black. Value, sheet of 10 $15.

Lion
Dance — A25

1958, Dec. 10   Perf. 13¼x13
55 A25 1½c multicolored   .30   .30
New Year, 1959.

Trees and
Mountains — A26

1959, Apr. 30   Perf. 13¼
56 A26 3c blue, yellow green,
              green & red   .70   .60
"Make the Ryukyus Green" movement.

 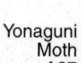

Yonaguni
Moth
A27

1959, July 23 Photo. Perf. 13x13¼
57 A27 3c multicolored   1.20   1.00
Meeting of the Japanese Biological Education Society in Okinawa.

Hibiscus — A28

Inscribed 琉球郵便

Designs: 3c, Fish (Moorish idol). 8c, Sea
shell (Phalium bandatum). 13c, Butterfly (Kal-
linia inachus eucerca), denomination at left,
butterfly going up. 17c, Jellyfish (Dactylometra
pacifera Goette).

1959, Aug. 10   Perf. 12¾x13
58 A28 ½c multicolored   .30   .25
59 A28 3c multicolored   .75   .40
60 A28 8c light ul-
              tramarine,
              black & ocher   10.00   5.50
61 A28 13c light blue, gray
              & orange   1.75   1.75
62 A28 17c violet blue, red
              & yellow   20.00   9.00
        Nos. 58-62 (5)   32.80   16.90
Four-character inscription measures
10x2mm on ½c; 12x3mm on 3c, 8c; 8½x2mm
on 13c, 17c. See Nos. 76-80.

Toy (Yakaji) — A29

1959, Dec. 1   Perf. 13x13¼
63 A29 1½c gold & multi   55   45
New Year, 1960.

University
Badge
A30

1960, May 22   Photo.
64 A30 3c multicolored   .95   .75
10th anniv. opening of Ryukyu University.

Straw Hat Folk
Dancer — A31

Designs: 2½c, Nufwabushi. 5c,
Hatumabushi. 10c, Hanafu.

1960, Nov. 1   Photo.   Perf. 13¼
Dark Gray Background
65 A31 1c yel, red & vio   2.00   .80
66 A31 2½c crim, blue & yel   3.00   1.00
67 A31 5c dk blue, yel & red   1.00   .50
68 A31 10c dk blue, yel & red   1.00   .70
        Nos. 65-68 (4)   7.00   3.00
See Nos. 81-87, 220.

Torch and Nago Bay A32

Runners at Starting Line A33

1960, Nov. 8   Litho.   Perf. 13x13¼
72   A32   3c lt blue, grn & red   5.00 3.00
73   A33   8c org & slate grn   1.00   .75

8th Kyushu Inter-Prefectural Athletic Meet, Nago, Northern Okinawa, Nov. 6-7.

Little Egret and Rising Sun A34

1960, Dec. 1   Photo.
74   A34   3c reddish brown   5.00 3.50

National census.

Okinawa Bull Fight — A35

1960, Dec. 10
75   A35   1½c bister, dark blue & red brown   1.50 1.50

New Year, 1961.

Type of 1959 With Japanese Inscription Redrawn

A28a

1960-61   Photo.
76   A28a   ½c multicolored   .60   .45
77   A28a   3c multicolored   1.00   .35
78   A28a   8c lt ultra, blk & ocher   1.25   .80
79   A28a 13c blue, brown & red   1.50   .90
80   A28a 17c vio blue, red & yel   12.50 6.00
        Nos. 76-80 (5)   16.85 8.50

Size of Japanese inscription on Nos. 78-80 is 10½x1½mm. On No.79 the denomination is at right, butterfly going down.
Issued: Nos. 78-80, 7/1/60; No. 77, 8/23/61; No. 76, 10/61.

Dancer Type of 1960 with "RYUKYUS" Added in English

Designs: 20c, Shudun. 25c, Haodori. 50c, Nubui Kuduchi. $1, Koteibushi.

1961-64   Perf. 13¼
81   A31   1c multicolored   .25   .25
82   A31   2½c multicolored   .25   .25
83   A31   5c multicolored   .25   .25
84   A31   10c multicolored   .45   .40
84A A31   20c multicolored   3.00 1.40
85   A31   25c multicolored   1.00   .90
86   A31   50c multicolored   2.50 1.40
87   A31 $1 multicolored   5.50   .25
        Nos. 81-87 (8)   13.20 5.10

Issued: Nos. 86-87, 9/1/61; No. 81, 12/5/61; No. 85, 2/1/62; Nos. 82-84, 6/20/62; No. 84A, 1/20/64.

Pine Tree — A36

1961, May 1   Litho.
88   A36   3c yel grn & red   1.75 1.25

"Make the Ryukyus Green" movement.

Naha, Steamer and Sailboat A37

1961, May 20   Photo.
89   A37   3c aquamarine   2.25 1.50

40th anniv. of Naha.

White Silver Temple — A38

Perf. 10¾, 10¾x10¼
1961, Oct. 1   Typo.   Unwmk.
90   A38   3c red brown   2.50 2.00
  a. Horiz. pair, imperf. between   1,000.
  b. Vert. pair, imperf. between   700.00

Merger of townships Takamine, Kanegushiku and Miwa with Itoman.

A 3-cent stamp to commemorate the merger of two cities, Shimoji-cho and Hirara-shi of Miyako Island, was scheduled to be issued on Oct. 30, 1961. However, the merger was called off and the stamp never issued. It features a white chaplet on Kiyako linen on a blue background.

Books and Bird — A39

1961, Nov. 12   Litho.   Perf. 13¼
91   A39   3c multicolored   1.10   .90

Book Week, 10th anniversary.

Rising Sun and Eagles — A40

1961, Dec. 10   Photo.
92   A40   1½c gold, ver & blk   2.00 2.00

New Year, 1962.

Symbolic Steps, Trees and Government Building — A41

Design: 3c, Government Building.

1962, Apr. 1   Perf. 13½
93   A41   1½c multicolored   .60   .60
94   A41   3c brt grn, red & gray   .80   .80

10th anniv. of the Government of the Ryukyu Islands (GRI).

Anopheles Hyrcanus Sinensis — A42

Design: 8c, Malaria eradication emblem and Shurei gate.

1962, Apr. 7   Perf. 13¼x13
95   A42   3c multicolored   .60   .60
96   A42   8c multicolored   .90   .75

World Health Organization drive to eradicate malaria.

Dolls and Toys — A43

1962, May 5   Perf. 13x13¼
97   A43   3c red, black, blue & buff   1.10 1.00

Children's Day, 1962.

Linden or Sea Hibiscus — A44

Flowers: 3c, Deigo tree (Erythrina variegata var. orientealis). 8c, Iju (Schima liukiuensis Nakal). 13c, Touch-me-not (Impatiens balsamina). 17c, Shell flower (Alpinia speciosa).

1962, June 1   Photo.   Perf. 13¼
98   A44   ½c multicolored   .35   .25
99   A44   3c multicolored   .30   .25
100   A44   8c multicolored   .55   .45
101   A44   13c multicolored   .75   .60
102   A44   17c multicolored   1.25   .80
        Nos. 98-102 (5)   3.20 2.35

See Nos. 107 and 114 for 1½c and 15c flower stamps. For surcharge see No. 190.

Akae (Earthenware) — A45

1962, July 5
103   A45   3c multicolored   3.50 2.50

Philatelic Week, July 5-12.

Japanese Fencing (Kendo) A46

1962, July 25   Perf. 13¼x13
104   A46   3c multicolored   3.50 2.50

All-Japan Kendo Meeting in Okinawa, July 24-25, 1962.

Rabbit Playing near Water, Bingata Cloth Design — A47

1962, Dec. 10   Perf. 13¼
105   A47   1½c gold & multi   1.00   .80

New Year, 1963.

Young Man and Woman, Stone Relief — A48

1963, Jan. 15   Photo.
106   A48   3c gold, black & blue   .90   .80

Adult Day.

Gooseneck Cactus (Epiphyllum strictum) — A49

1963, Apr. 5   Perf. 13x13¼
107   A49   1½c dark blue green, yellow & pink   .25   .25

Trees and Wooded Hills — A50

1963, Mar. 25   Perf. 13¼
108   A50   3c ultra, grn & red brn   1.00   .80

"Make the Ryukyus Green" movement.

Map of Okinawa — A51

1963, Apr. 30
109   A51   3c multicolored   1.25 1.00

Opening of the Round Road on Okinawa.

Hawks over Islands — A52

1963, May 10   Photo.
110   A52   3c multicolored   1.10   .95

Bird Day, May 10.

Shioya Bridge — A53

1963, June 5
111   A53   3c multicolored   1.10   .95

Opening of Shioya Bridge over Shioya Bay.

Tsuikin-wan Lacquerware Bowl — A54

1963, July 1   *Perf. 13¼*
112   A54   3c multicolored   2.75   2.50
    Philatelic Week.

Map of Far East and JCI Emblem A55

1963, Sept. 16   *Photo.*
113   A55   3c multicolored   .70   .70
   Meeting of the International Junior Chamber of Commerce (JCI), Naha, Okinawa, Sept. 16-19.

Hamaomoto (Crinum asiaticum var. japonica) — A56

1963, Oct. 15   *Perf. 13x13¼*
114   A56   15c multicolored   1.25   .80

Site of Nakagusuku Castle — A57

1963, Nov. 1   *Perf. 13¼*
115   A57   3c multicolored   .60   .60
   Protection of national cultural treasures.

Flame — A58

1963, Dec. 10
116   A58   3c red, dark blue & yellow   .65   .60
   15th anniv. of the Universal Declaration of Human Rights.

Dragon — A59

1963, Dec. 10   *Photo.*
117   A59   1½c multicolored   .55   .50
    New Year, 1964.

Carnation — A60

1964, May 10   *Perf. 13¼*
118   A60   3c blue, yel, blk & car   .40   .35
    Mothers Day.

Pineapples and Sugar Cane — A61

1964, June 1
119   A61   3c multicolored   .40   .35
    Agricultural census.

Minsah Obi (Sash Woven of Kapok) — A62

1964, July 1   *Perf. 13¼*
120   A62   3c deep blue, rose pink & ocher   .50   .50
   a.   3c deep blue, deep carmine & ocher   .65   .65
    Philatelic Week.

Girl Scout and Emblem A63

1964, Aug. 31   *Photo.*
121   A63   3c multicolored   .40   .35
    10th anniv. of Ryukyuan Girl Scouts.

Shuri Relay Station — A64   Parabolic Antenna and Map — A65

1964, Sept. 1   **Unwmk.**
Black Overprint
122   A64   3c deep green   .65   .65
   a.   Figure "1" inverted   30.00   30.00
   b.   Overprint inverted   1,500.
   c.   Overprint missing   3,500.
   d.   Overprint inverted and figure "1" inverted   5,000.
123   A65   8c ultramarine   1.25   1.25
   a.   Overprint missing   3,500.
   Opening of the Ryukyu Islands-Japan microwave system carrying telephone and telegraph messages. The overprints indicate the system was not actually opened until 1964.
   Many of the stamps with overprint errors listed above are damaged. The values listed here are for stamps in very fine condition.

Gate of Courtesy, Olympic Torch and Emblem — A66

1964, Sept. 7   *Photo.*   *Perf. 13¼*
124   A66   3c ultra, yel & red   .30   .25
   Relaying the Olympic torch on Okinawa en route to Tokyo.

"Naihanchi," Karate Stance — A67

"Makiwara," Strengthening Hands and Feet — A68

"Kumite," Simulated Combat — A69

1964-65   **Photo.**
125   A67   3c dull clar, yel & blk   .50   .45
126   A68   3c yel & multi   .40   .40
127   A69   3c gray, red & blk   .40   .40
    Nos. 125-127 (3)   1.30   1.25
   Karate, Ryukyuan self-defense sport. Issued: No. 125, 10/5/64; No. 126, 2/5/65; No. 127, 6/5/65.

Miyara Dunchí — A70

1964, Nov. 1
128   A70   3c multicolored   .30   .25
   Protection of national cultural treasures. Miyara Dunchi was built as a residence by Peichin Miyara Touen in 1819.

Snake and Iris (Bingata) — A71

1964, Dec. 10   *Photo.*
129   A71   1½c multicolored   .30   .25
    New Year, 1965.

Boy Scouts — A72

1965, Feb. 6   *Perf. 13¼*
130   A72   3c light blue & multi   .45   .40
    10th anniv. of Ryukyuan Boy Scouts.

Main Stadium, Onoyama A73

1965, July 1   *Perf. 13x13¼*
131   A73   3c multicolored   .25   .25
   Inauguration of the main stadium of the Onoyama athletic facilities.

Samisen of King Shoko — A74

1965, July 1   *Photo.*   *Perf. 13¼*
132   A74   3c buff & multi   .45   .40
    Philatelic Week.

Kin Power Plant — A75

1965, July 1
133   A75   3c green & multi   .25   .20
    Completion of Kin power plant.

ICY Emblem, Ryukyu Map — A76

1965, Aug. 24   *Photo.*
134   A76   3c multicolored   .25   .25
   20th anniv. of the UN and International Cooperation Year, 1964-65.

Naha City Hall — A77

1965, Sept. 18
135   A77   3c blue & multi   .35   .25
    Completion of Naha City Hall.

Chinese Box Turtle (Cyclemys flavomarginata) A78

Turtles: No. 137, Hawksbill turtle (Eretochelys imbricata bissa) (denomination at top, country name at bottom). No. 138, Asian terrapin (Geoemyda japonica) (denomination and country name at top).

1965-66　　**Photo.**　　*Perf. 13¼*
136 A78 3c golden brown & multi　.30　.30
137 A78 3c black, yel & brown　.30　.30
138 A78 3c gray & multicolored　.30　.30
　　Nos. 136-138 (3)　　.90　.90

　Issued: No. 136, 10/20/65; No. 137, 1/20/66; No. 138, 4/20/66.

Horse (Bingata) — A79

1965, Dec. 10　　**Photo.**
139 A79 1½c multicolored　.25　.25
　a.　Gold omitted　2,000.　2,000.
　　New Year, 1966.
　There are 92 unused and 2 used examples of No. 139a known.

Noguchi's Okinawa Woodpecker (Dendrocopus noguchii) — A80

Sika Deer (Cervus nippon var. keramae) — A81

Design: No. 142, Dugong (Dugong dugong).

1966　　　　**Photo.**
140 A80 3c blue green & multi　.25　.25
141 A81 3c bl, red, blk, brn & grn　.25　.25
142 A81 3c bl, yel grn, blk & red　.25　.25
　　Nos. 140-142 (3)　　.75　.75

　Nature Conservation. Issued No. 140, 2/15; No. 141, 3/15; No. 142, 4/20.

Ryukyu Bungalow Swallow (Hirundo tahitica) — A82

1966, May 10　　**Photo.**　　*Perf. 13¼*
143 A82 3c sky blue, black & brown　.25　.25
　　4th Bird Week, May 10-16.

Lilies and Ruins A83

1966, June 23　　　　*Perf. 13*
144 A83 3c multicolored　　.25　.25
　Memorial Day, end of the Battle of Okinawa, June 23, 1945.

University of the Ryukyus A84

1966, July 1
145 A84 3c multicolored　　.25　.25
　Transfer of the University of the Ryukyus from U.S. authority to the Ryukyu Government.

Chinkin Ukuhan Lacquerware, 18th Century — A85

1966, Aug. 1　　　　*Perf. 13¼*
146 A85 3c gray & multicolored　.25　.25
　　Philatelic Week.

Tile-Roofed House and UNESCO Emblem — A86

1966, Sept. 20　　**Photo.**
147 A86 3c multicolored　　.25　.25
　　20th anniv. of UNESCO.

Government Museum and Dragon Statue — A87

1966, Oct. 6
148 A87 3c multicolored　　.25　.25
　Completion of the GRI (Government of the Ryukyu Islands) Museum, Shuri.

Tomb of Nakasone-Toyomiya Genga, Ruler of Miyako — A88

1966, Nov. 1　　　　**Photo.**
149 A88 3c multicolored　　.25　.25
　Protection of national cultural treasures.

Ram in Iris Wreath (Bingata) — A89

1966, Dec. 10　　**Photo.**　　*Perf. 13¼*
150 A89 1½c dark blue & multi　.25　.25
　　New Year, 1967.

Clown Fish (Amphiprion frenatus) A90

　Fish: No. 152, Young boxfish (Ostracion cubicus) (white numeral at lower left). No. 153, Forceps fish (Forcipiger longirostris) (pale buff numeral at lower right). No. 154, Spotted trigerfish (Balistoides conspicillum) (orange numeral). No. 155, Saddleback butterflyfish (Chaetodon ephippium) (carmine numeral, lower left).

1966-67
151 A90 3c orange red & multi　.25　.25
152 A90 3c org yel & multi　.25　.25
153 A90 3c multicolored　.40　.25
154 A90 3c multicolored　.35　.25
155 A90 3c multicolored　.30　.25
　　Nos. 151-155 (5)　　1.55　1.25

　Issued No. 151, 12/20/66; No. 152, 1/10/67; No. 153, 4/10/67; No. 154, 5/25/67; No. 155, 6/10/67.

　A 3-cent stamp to commemorate Japanese-American-Ryukyuan Joint Arbor Day was scheduled for release on March 16, 1967. However, it was not released. The stamp in light blue and white features American and Japanese flags joined by a shield containing a tree.

Tsuboya Urn — A91

1967, Apr. 20
156 A91 3c yellow & multicolored　.25　.25
　　Philatelic Week.

Episcopal Miter (Mitra mitra) — A92

　Seashells: No. 158, Venus comb murex (Murex pecten). No. 159, Chiragra spider (Lambis chiragra). No. 160, Green turban (Turbo marmoratus). No. 161, Bubble conch (Euprotomus bulla).

1967-68　　**Photo.**　　*Perf. 13¼*
157 A92 3c light green & multi　.25　.25
158 A92 3c grnsh bl & multi　.25　.25
159 A92 3c emerald & multi　.25　.25
160 A92 3c light blue & multi　.30　.25
161 A92 3c bright blue & multi　.60　.50
　　Nos. 157-161 (5)　　1.65　1.50

　Issued: No. 157, 6/20/67; No. 159, 1/18/68; No. 160, 2/20/68; No. 161, 6/5/68; No. 158, 8/30/68.

Red-tiled Roofs and ITY Emblem A93

1967, Sept. 11　　**Photo.**
162 A93 3c multicolored　　.25　.25
　　International Tourist Year.

Mobile TB Clinic — A94

1967, Oct. 13　　**Photo.**
163 A94 3c lilac & multicolored　.25　.25
　15th anniv. of the Anti-Tuberculosis Society.

Hojo Bridge, Enkaku Temple, 1498 — A95

1967, Nov. 1
164 A95 3c blue green & multi　.25　.25
　Protection of national cultural treasures.

Monkey (Bingata) — A96

1967, Dec. 11　**Photo.**　*Perf. 13¼*
165 A96 1½c silver & multi　　.25　.25
　　New Year, 1968.

TV Tower and Map — A97

1967, Dec. 22
166 A97 3c multicolored　　.25　.25
　Opening of Miyako and Yaeyama television stations.

Dr. Kijin Nakachi and Helper — A98

1968, Mar. 15　　　　**Photo.**
167 A98 3c multicolored　　.30　.25
　120th anniv. of the first vaccination in the Ryukyu Islands, by Dr. Kijin Nakachi.

Pill Box (Inro) — A99

1968, Apr. 18
168 A99 3c gray & multicolored　.45　.45
　　Philatelic Week.

Young Man,
Library, Book
and Map of
Ryukyu
Islands
A100

1968, May 13
169 A100 3c multicolored   .30   .25

10th International Library Week.

Mailmen's
Uniforms
and Stamp
of 1948
A101

1968, July 1   Photo.   Perf. 13¼
170 A101 3c multicolored   .30   .25

First Ryukyuan postage stamps, 20th anniv.

Main Gate,
Enkaku
Temple
A102

1968, July 15   Photo. & Engr.
171 A102 3c multicolored   .30   .25

Restoration of the main gate Enkaku Temple, built 1492-1495, destroyed during World War II.

Old Man's
Dance — A103

1968, Sept. 15   Photo.
172 A103 3c gold & multicolored   .30   .25

Old People's Day.

Mictyris
Longicarpus
A104

Crabs: No. 174, Uca dubia stimpson. No. 175, Baptozius vinosus. No. 176, Cardisoma carnifex. No. 177, Ocypode ceratophthalma pallas.

1968-69   Photo.   Perf. 13¼
173 A104 3c blue, ocher & black   .30   .25
174 A104 3c lt bl grn & multi   .35   .30
175 A104 3c light green & multi   .35   .30
176 A104 3c light ultra & multi   .45   .40
177 A104 3c light ultra & multi   .45   .40
     Nos. 173-177 (5)   1.90 1.65

Issued: No. 173, 10/10/68; No. 174, 2/5/69; No. 175, 3/5/69; No. 176, 5/15/69; No. 177, 6/2/69.

Saraswati
Pavilion
(Benzaitan-do
Temple)
A105

1968, Nov. 1   Photo.
178 A105 3c multicolored   .30   .25

Restoration of the Sarawati Pavilion (in front of Enkaku Temple), destroyed during World War II.

Tennis
Player — A106

1968, Nov. 23   Photo.
179 A106 3c green & multi   .40   .35

35th All-Japan East-West Men's Soft-ball Tennis Tournament, Naha City, Nov. 23-24.

Cock and Iris
(Bingata) — A107

1968, Dec. 10
180 A107 1½c orange & multi   .25   .25

New Year, 1969.

Boxer — A108

1969, Jan. 3
181 A108 3c gray & multi   .40   .30

20th All-Japan Amateur Boxing Championships held at the University of the Ryukyus, Jan. 3-5.

Ink Slab
Screen — A109

1969, Apr. 17 Photo. Perf. 13¼x13
182 A109 3c salmon, indigo &
           red   .40   .35

Philatelic Week.

Box Antennas and
Map of Radio
Link — A110

1969, July 1   Photo.
183 A110 3c multicolored   .30   .25

Opening of the UHF (radio) circuit system between Okinawa and the outlying Miyako-Yaeyama Islands.

Gate of Courtesy
and
Emblems — A111

1969, Aug. 1   Photo.
184 A111 3c Prussian blue,
           gold & vermilion   .30   .25

22nd All-Japan Formative Education Study Conf., Naha, Aug. 1-3.

Tug of
War
Festival
A112

Hari Boat
Race
A113

Izaiho
Ceremony,
Kudaka
Island
A114

Mortar Drum Dance
(Ushideiku) — A115

Sea God
Dance
(Ungami)
A116

1969-70   Photo.   Perf. 13¼x13
185 A112 3c multicolored   .30   .25
186 A113 3c multicolored   .35   .30
187 A114 3c multicolored   .35   .30
188 A115 3c multicolored   .50   .45
189 A116 3c multicolored   .50   .45
     Nos. 185-189 (5)   2.00 1.75

Folklore. Issued, No. 185, 8/1/69; No. 186, 9/5/69; No. 187, 10/3/69; No. 188, 1/20/70; No. 189, 2/27/70.

No. 99 Surcharged

1969, Oct. 15   Photo.   Perf. 13¼
190 A44 ½c on 3c multicolored   1.00 1.00
     a.   "1/2c" only surcharge   950.00

No. 190a are right margin stamps from a pane with a leftward misregistration of the surcharging plate.

Nakamura-ke
Farm House,
Built 1713-51
A117

1969, Nov. 1 Photo. Perf. 13¼x13
191 A117 3c multicolored   .25   .25

Protection of national cultural treasures.

Statue of Kyuzo Toyama, Maps of
Hawaiian and Ryukyu Islands
A118

1969, Dec. 5   Photo.   Perf. 13¼
192 A118 3c light ultra &
           multi   .50   .50
     a.   Without overprint   3,000.
     b.   Wide-spaced bars   700.00 500.00

70th anniv. of Ryukyu-Hawaii emigration led by Kyuzo Toyama.
     The overprint "1969" at lower left and bars across "1970" at upper right was applied before No. 192 was issued.

Dog and Flowers
(Bingata) — A119

1969, Dec. 10   Perf. 13¼x13
193 A119 1½c pink & multi   .25   .25

New Year, 1970.

Sake Flask
Made from
Coconut
(Yashi-gwa)
A120

1970, Apr. 15   Photo.   Perf. 13¼
194 A120 3c multicolored   .25   .25

Philatelic Week, 1970.

"The Bell"
(Shushin
Kaneiri)
A121

Child and
Kidnapper
(Chu-nusudu)
A122

Robe of
Feathers
(Mekarushi)
A123

Vengeance of
Two Young
Sons
(Nidotichiuchi)
A124

The Virgin
and the
Dragon
(Kokonomaki)
A125

1970   Photo.   Perf. 13¼
195 A121 3c dull blue & multi   .60   .40
     a.   Souvenir sheet of 4   4.00 4.00
196 A122 3c light blue & multi   .60   .40
     a.   Souvenir sheet of 4   4.00 4.00
197 A123 3c bluish grn & multi   .60   .40
     a.   Souvenir sheet of 4   4.00 4.00
198 A124 3c dull bl grn & multi   .60   .40
     a.   Souvenir sheet of 4   4.00 4.00

199 A125 3c multicolored   .60   .40
 a.   Souvenir sheet of 4   4.00 4.00
      Nos. 195-199 (5)   3.00 2.00
      Nos. 195a-199a (5)   20.00 20.00
   Classic Opera. Issued No. 195, 4/28; No.
196, 5/29; No. 197, 6/30; No. 198, 7/30; No.
199, 8/25.

Underwater
Observatory
and Tropical
Fish — A126

1970, May 22
200 A126 3c blue green & multi   .30   .25
   Completion of the underwater observatory
of Busena-Misaki, Nago.

Noboru Jahana
(1865-1908),
Politician — A127

   Portraits: No. 202, Saion Gushichan
Bunjaku (1682-1761), statesman. No. 203,
Choho Giwan (1823-1876), regent and poet.

1970-71   **Engr.**
201 A127 3c rose claret   .50   .45
202 A127 3c dull blue green   .75   .65
203 A127 3c black   .50   .45
      Nos. 201-203 (3)   1.75 1.55
   Issued: No. 201, 9/25.70; No. 202,
12/22/70; No. 203, 1/22/71.

Map of Okinawa and
People — A128

1970, Oct. 1   **Photo.**
204 A128 3c red & multicolored   .25   .25
      Oct. 1, 1970 census.

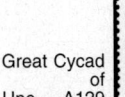

Great Cycad
of
Une — A129

1970, Nov. 2 **Photo.**   **Perf. 13¼**
205 A129 3c gold & multicolored   .25   .25
   Protection of national treasures.

Japanese
Flag, Diet and
Map of
Ryukyus
A130

1970, Nov. 15   **Photo.**
206 A130 3c ultra & multi   .80   .75
   Citizen's participation in national administration to Japanese law of Apr. 24, 1970.

Wild Boar and
Cherry Blossoms
(Bingata) — A131

1970, Dec. 10   **Perf. 13¼x13**
207 A131 1½c multicolored   .25   .25
   New Year, 1971.

Low Hand
Loom (Jibata)
A132

Farmer Wearing Palm Bark Raincoat
(Shurunnui) and Kuba Leaf Hat
(Kubagasa)
A133

Fisherman's
Wooden Box
(Yutui) and
Scoop (Umi-
fujo)
A134

   Designs: No. 209, Woman running a filature
(reel). No. 211, Woman hulling rice with cylindrical "Shiri-ushi."

1971   **Photo.**   **Perf. 13¼**
208 A132 3c light blue & multi   .30   .25
209 A132 3c pale grn & multi   .30   .25
210 A133 3c light blue & multi   .35   .30
211 A132 3c yellow & multi   .40   .35
212 A134 3c gray & multi   .35   .30
      Nos. 208-212 (5)   1.70 1.45
   Issued: No. 208, 2/16; No. 209, 3/16; No.
210, 4/30; No. 211, 5/20; No. 212, 6/15.

Water Carrier
(Taku) — A135

1971, Apr. 15   **Photo.**
213 A135 3c blue grn & multi   .35   .30
      Philatelic Week.

Old and
New
Naha,
and City
Emblem
A136

1971, May 20   **Perf. 13¼x13**
214 A136 3c ultra & multi   .25   .25
   50th anniv. of Naha as a municipality.

Ogocho (Caesalpinia
pulcherrima) — A137

   Design: 2c, Madder (Sandanka).

1971   **Photo.**   **Perf. 13¼**
215 A137 2c gray & multi   .25   .25
216 A137 3c gray & multi   .25   .25
   Issued No. 216, 5/10; No. 215, 9/30.

View from
Mabuni
Hill — A138

Mt. Arashi
from Haneji
Sea — A139

Yabuchi Island
from Yakena
Port — A140

1971-72
217 A138 3c green & multi   .25   .25
218 A139 3c blue & multi   .25   .25
219 A140 4c multicolored   .25   .25
      Nos. 217-219 (3)   .75   .75
   Government parks. Issued: No. 217,
7/30/71; No. 218, 8/30/71; No. 219, 1/20/72.

   For the 4-cent unissued "stamp" picturing Iriomote Park, originally planned
for issue in 1971 but never released,
see the note after No. RQ8 in the Scott
U.S. Specialized catalogue.

Dancer (Nu-fwa-
bushi)
A141

1971, Nov. 1 **Photo.**   **Perf. 13¼**
220 A141 4c Prussian blue &
            multicolored   .25   .25

Deva King
(Misshaku Kongo),
Torin-ji
Temple — A142

1971, Dec. 1
221 A142 4c dp blue & multi   .25   .25
   Protection of national cultural treasures.

Rat and
Chrysanthemums
A143

1971, Dec. 10   **Perf. 13¼x13**
222 A143 2c brown orange &
            multi   .25   .25
      New Year, 1972.

Student
Nurse — A144

1971, Dec. 24   **Perf. 13¼**
223 A144 4c lilac & multi   .25   .25
   Nurses' training, 25th anniversary.

Birds on   Sun over Islands
Seashore   A147
A145

Coral
Reef — A146

1972   **Photo.**
224 A145 5c brt blue & multi   .40   .35
225 A146 5c gray & multi   .40   .35
226 A147 5c ocher & multi   .40   .35
      Nos. 224-226 (3)   1.20 1.05
   Issued: No. 226, 3/21; No. 225, 3/30; No.
224, 4/14.

Dove, US and
Japanese
Flags — A148

1972, Apr. 17   **Photo.**
227 A148 5c bright blue & multi   .80   .80
   Ratification of Ryukya Islands Reversion
Agreement.

Antique Sake
Container
(Yushibin) — A149

1972, Apr. 20
228 A149 5c ultra & multi   .60   .60
   Philatelic Week.

   Ryukyu stamps were replaced by
those of Japan after May 15, 1972.

_____

AIR POST STAMPS

   Catalogue values for all unused
   stamps in this section are for
   Never Hinged items.

Dove and Map of
Ryukyus — AP1

Perf. 13x13¼

1950, Feb. 15   Photo.   Unwmk.

C1	AP1	8y bright blue	110.00	40.00
C2	AP1	12y green	17.50	17.50
C3	AP1	16y rose carmine	9.00	9.00
		Nos. C1-C3 (3)	136.50	66.50

Heavenly Maiden
AP2

1951-54   Perf. 13¼x13

C4	AP2	13y blue	2.00	2.00
C5	AP2	18y green	3.00	3.00
C6	AP2	30y cerise	4.50	1.50
C7	AP2	40y red violet	6.50	6.50
C8	AP2	50y yellow orange	7.50	7.50
		Nos. C4-C8 (5)	23.50	20.50

Issued: Nos. C4-C6, 10/1/51; Nos. C7-C8, 8/16/54.

Heavenly Maiden Playing Flute — AP3

1957, Aug. 1   Engr.   Perf. 13x13¼

C9	AP3	15y blue green	7.50	4.00
C10	AP3	20y rose carmine	9.00	7.00
C11	AP3	35y yellow green	10.00	8.00
a.		35y light yellow green, 1958	125.00	
C12	AP3	45y reddish brown	14.00	10.00
C13	AP3	60y gray	16.00	12.00
		Nos. C9-C13 (5)	56.50	41.00

On one printing of No. C10, position 49 shows an added spur on the right side of the second character from the left. Value unused, $175.

Same Surcharged in Brown Red or Light Ultramarine

1959, Dec. 20   Engr.

C14	AP3	9c on 15y blue green (BrR)	2.50	2.00
a.		Inverted surcharge	800.00	
b.		Pair, one without surcharge	—	
C15	AP3	14c on 20y rose carmine (L.U.)	3.00	3.25
C16	AP3	19c on 35y light yellow green (BrR)	7.00	6.00
C17	AP3	27c on 45y reddish brown (L.U.)	12.50	6.00
C18	AP3	35c on 60y gray (BrR)	11.00	9.00
		Nos. C14-C18 (5)	36.00	26.25

No. C15 is found with the variety described below No. C13. Value unused, $125.

Nos. 31-33, 36 and 38 Surcharged in Black, Brown, Red, Blue or Green

1960, Aug. 3   Photo.

C19	A14	9c on 4y brown	2.50	1.00
a.		Surcharge inverted and transposed	12,500.	12,500.
b.		Inverted surcharge (legend only)	10,000.	
c.		Surcharge transposed	800.00	
d.		Legend of surcharge only	3,500.	
e.		Vert. pair, one without surcharge	11,000.	

Nos. C19c and C19d are from a single sheet of 100 with surcharge shifted downward. Ten examples of No. C19c exist with "9c" also in bottom selvage. No. C19d is from the top row of the sheet.

No. C19e is unique, pos. 100, caused by paper foldover.

C20	A17	14c on 5y rose lilac (Br)	3.00	3.00
C21	A14	19c on 15y vermilion (R)	2.50	3.00

C22	A17	27c on 14y reddish brown (Bl)	7.00	2.50
C23	A14	35c on 20y yellow orange (G)	5.00	5.00
		Nos. C19-C23 (5)	20.00	14.50

Wind God — AP4

Designs: 9c, Heavenly Maiden (as on AP2). 14c, Heavenly Maiden (as on AP3). 27c, Wind God at right. 35c, Heavenly Maiden over treetops.

1961, Sept. 21   Perf. 13¼

C24	AP4	9c multicolored	.30	.25
C25	AP4	14c multicolored	.60	.75
C26	AP4	19c multicolored	.70	.85
C27	AP4	27c multicolored	3.00	.60
C28	AP4	35c multicolored	2.00	1.25
		Nos. C24-C28 (5)	6.60	3.70

Jet over Gate of Courtesy AP5   Jet Plane AP6

1963, Aug. 28   Perf. 13x13¼

C29	AP5	5½c multicolored	.25	.25
C30	AP6	7c multicolored	.30	.30

SPECIAL DELIVERY STAMP

Catalogue value for the unused stamp in this section is for a Never Hinged item.

Sea Horse and Map of Ryukyus — SD1

Perf. 13¼

1950, Feb. 15   Unwmk.   Photo.

E1	SD1	5y bright blue	25.00	17.50

UNITED NATIONS, OFFICES IN NEW YORK

yu-ˌnī-təd ˈnā-shənz

United Nations stamps are used on UN official mail sent from UN Headquarters in New York City, the UN European Office in Geneva, Switzerland, or from the Donaupark Vienna International Center or Atomic Energy Agency in Vienna, Austria to points throughout the world. They may be used on private correspondence sent through the UN post offices and are valid only at the individual UN post offices.

The UN stamps issued for use in Geneva and Vienna are listed in separate sections. Geneva issues were denominated in centimes and francs and Vienna issues in schillings (now cents and euros) and are valid only in Geneva or Vienna. The UN stamps issued for use in New York, denominated in cents and dollars, are valid only in New York.

Letters bearing Nos. 170-174 provide an exception as they were carried by the Canadian postal system.

See Switzerland Nos. 7O1-7O39 in Volume 6 of the Scott *Standard Postage Stamp Catalogue* for stamps issued by

---

the Swiss Government for official use of the UN European Office and other UN affiliated organizations. See France official stamp listings for stamps issued by the French Government for official use of UNESCO.

Catalogue values for all unused stamps in this section are for Never Hinged items. Values for used UN stamps are for postally used stamps with contemporaneous cancels. Used stamps soaked off of first day covers sell for less.

Stamps are inscribed in English, French, or Spanish or are multilingual.

Wmk. 309 — Wavy Lines

Peoples of the World — A1

UN Headquarters Building — A2   "Peace, Justice, Security" — A3

UN Flag — A4

UN Children's Fund — A5

World Unity — A6

Perf. 13x12½, 12½x13

1951		**Engr. and Photo.**	**Unwmk.**	
1	A1	1c magenta	.25	.25
2	A2	1½c blue green	.25	.25
3	A3	2c purple	.25	.25
4	A4	3c magenta & blue	.25	.25
5	A5	5c blue	.25	.25
6	A1	10c chocolate	.25	.25
7	A4	15c violet & blue	.25	.25
8	A6	20c dark brown	.30	.25
9	A4	25c olive gray & blue	.35	.25
10	A2	50c indigo	3.00	1.50
11	A3	$1 red	1.25	.90
		Nos. 1-11 (11)	6.65	4.65

Veteran's War Memorial Building, San Francisco A7

7th anniversary of the signing of the United Nations Charter.

1952, Oct. 24   Perf. 12

12	A7	5c blue	.50	.35

Globe and Encircled Flame A8

4th anniversary of the adoption of the Universal Declaration of Human Rights.

1952, Dec. 10   Perf. 13½x14

13	A8	3c deep green	.45	.35
14	A8	5c blue	.55	.40

Refugee Family — A9

Issued to publicize "Protection for Refugees."

1953, Apr. 24   Perf. 12½x13

15	A9	3c dark red brown & rose	.25	.25
16	A9	5c indigo & blue	.45	.40

Envelope, UN Emblem and Map A10

Issued to honor the UPU.

1953, June 12   Perf. 13

17	A10	3c black brown	.40	.40
18	A10	5c dark blue	1.25	1.00

Gearwheels and UN Emblem — A11

UN activities in the field of technical assistance.

1953, Oct. 24   Perf. 13x12½

19	A11	3c dark gray	.25	.25
20	A11	5c dark green	.40	.45

Hands Reaching Toward Flame — A12

Human Rights Day.

1953, Dec. 10   Perf. 12½x13

21	A12	3c bright blue	.30	.30
22	A12	5c rose red	1.00	1.00

Ear of
Wheat — A13

Issued to honor the FAO.

1954, Feb. 11   **Perf. 12½x13**
23   A13   3c dark green & yellow   .30   .25
24   A13   8c indigo & yellow   .75   .50

UN Emblem and
Anvil — A14

Issued to honor the ILO.

1954, May 10   **Perf. 12½x13**
25   A14   3c brown   .25   .25
26   A14   8c magenta   1.00   .85

UN
European
Office,
Geneva
A15

Issued on the occasion of UN Day.

1954, Oct. 25   **Perf. 14**
27   A15   3c dark blue violet   1.25   1.00
28   A15   8c red   .35   .30

Mother and
Child — A16

Human Rights Day.

1954, Dec. 10   **Perf. 14**
29   A16   3c red orange   4.50   2.50
30   A16   8c olive green   1.00   .35

Symbol of
Flight
A17

International Civil Aviation Organization.

1955, Feb. 9   **Perf. 13½x14**
31   A17   3c blue   1.00   .75
32   A17   8c rose carmine   .60   .50

UNESCO
Emblem
A18

Issued to honor the UN Educational, Scientific and Cultural Organization.

1955, May 11   **Perf. 13½x14**
33   A18   3c lilac rose   .35   .30
34   A18   8c light blue   .30   .30

UN Charter
A19

10th anniversary of the United Nations.

1955, Oct. 24   **Perf. 13½x14**
35   A19   3c deep plum   .90   .55
36   A19   4c dull green   .50   .35
37   A19   8c bluish black   .35   .25
     Nos. 35-37 (3)   1.75   1.15

Souvenir Sheet

1955, Oct. 24   **Wmk. 309**   **Imperf.**
38   A19   Sheet of 3   50.00   18.00
  a.   3c deep plum   7.00   3.00
  b.   4c dull green   7.00   3.00
  c.   8c bluish black   7.00   3.00
  d.   As No. 38, corrected plates
      (see footnote)   55.00   27.50

Two printings were made of the sheet: No. 38 (200,000) and No. 38d (50,000). No. 38 may be distinguished by the broken lines in the background shading on the 8c. It leaves a small white spot below the left leg of the "n" of "Unies." On No. 38d, the broken line was retouched, eliminating the white spot. The 4c was also retouched.

Nos. 38 and 38d used are valued with first day of issue cancels. Postally used examples are worth substantially more.

Hand Holding
Torch — A20

Issued in honor of Human Rights Day.

1955, Dec. 9   Unwmk.   **Perf. 14x13½**
39   A20   3c ultramarine   .30   .30
40   A20   8c green   .40   .30

Symbols of Telecommunication — A21

Honoring the International Telecommunication Union.

1956, Feb. 17   **Perf. 14**
41   A21   3c turquoise blue   .25   .25
42   A21   8c deep carmine   .30   .30

Globe &
Caduceus — A22

Issued in honor of the World Health Organization.

1956, Apr. 6   **Perf. 14**
43   A22   3c bright greenish blue   .25   .25
44   A22   8c golden brown   .25   .25

General
Assembly
A23

Issued to commemorate UN Day.

1956, Oct. 24   **Perf. 14**
45   A23   3c dark olive   .25   .25
46   A23   8c gray olive   .25   .25

Flame and
Globe
A24

Issued to publicize Human Rights Day.

1956, Dec. 10   **Perf. 14**
47   A24   3c plum   .25   .25
48   A24   8c dark blue   .25   .25

Weather
Balloon — A25

Issued to honor the World Meterological Organization.

1957, Jan. 28   **Perf. 14**
49   A25   3c violet blue   .25   .25
50   A25   8c dark carmine rose   .25   .25

Badge of UN
Emergency
Force — A26

Issued in honor of the UN Emergency Force.

1957, Apr. 8   **Perf. 14x12½**
51   A26   3c light blue   .25   .25
52   A26   8c rose carmine   .25   .25

Nos. 51-52 Re-engraved
1957, Apr.-May   **Perf. 14x12½**
53   A26   3c blue   .25   .25
54   A26   8c rose carmine   .35   .25

On Nos. 53-54 the background within and around the circles is shaded lightly, giving a halo effect. The lettering is more distinct with a line around each letter.

UN Emblem and
Globe — A27

Issued to honor the Security Council.

1957, Oct. 24   **Perf. 12½x13**
55   A27   3c orange brown   .25   .25
56   A27   8c dark blue green   .25   .25

Flaming Torch — A28

Issued in honor of Human Rights Day.

1957, Dec. 10   **Perf. 14**
57   A28   3c red brown   .25   .25
58   A28   8c black   .25   .25

Atom & UN
Emblem — A29

Issued in honor of the International Atomic Energy Agency.

1958, Feb. 10   **Perf. 12**
59   A29   3c olive   .25   .25
60   A29   8c blue   .25   .25

Central Hall,
Westminster — A30

Central Hall, Westminster, London, was the site of the first session of the United Nations General Assembly, 1946.

1958, Apr. 14   **Perf. 12**
61   A30   3c violet blue   .25   .25
62   A30   8c rose claret   .25   .25

UN Seal — A31

Engraved and printed by Bradbury, Wilkinson & Co., Ltd., England. Panes of 50. Designed by Herbert M. Sanborn.

1958, Oct. 24   *Perf. 13½x14*
63   A31   4c red orange   .25   .25

1958, June 2   *Perf. 13x14*
64   A31   8c bright blue   .25   .25
      Issue dates: 4c, Oct. 24; 8c, June 2.

Gearwheels — A32

Issued to honor the Economic and Social Council.

1958, Oct. 24   **Unwmk.**   *Perf. 12*
65   A32   4c dark blue green   .25   .25
66   A32   8c vermilion   .25   .25

Hands Upholding Globe — A33

Human Rights Day and to commemorate the 10th anniversary of the signing of the Universal Declaration of Human Rights.

1958, Dec. 10   **Unwmk.**   *Perf. 12*
67   A33   4c yellow green   .25   .25
68   A33   8c red brown   .25   .25

New York City Building, Flushing Meadows A34

Site of many General Assembly meetings, 1946-50.

1959, Mar. 30   **Unwmk.**   *Perf. 12*
69   A34   4c light lilac rose   .25   .25
70   A34   8c aquamarine   .25   .25

UN Emblems and Symbols of Agriculture, Industry and Trade — A35

Issued to honor the Economic Commission for Europe.

1959, May 18   **Unwmk.**   *Perf. 12*
71   A35   4c blue   .25   .25
72   A35   8c red orange   .25   .25

Figure Adapted from Rodin's "Age of Bronze" — A36

Issued to honor the Trusteeship Council.

1959, Oct. 23   **Unwmk.**   *Perf. 12*
73   A36   4c bright red   .25   .25
74   A36   8c dark olive green   .25   .25

World Refugee Year Emblem — A37

World Refugee Year, July 1, 1959-June 30, 1960.

1959, Dec. 10   **Unwmk.**   *Perf. 12*
75   A37   4c olive & red   .25   .25
76   A37   8c ol & brt greenish blue   .25   .25

Chaillot Palace, Paris — A38

Chaillot Palace in Paris was the site of General Assembly meetings in 1948 and 1951.

1960, Feb. 29   **Unwmk.**   *Perf. 14*
77   A38   4c rose lilac & blue   .25   .25
78   A38   8c dull green & brown   .25   .25

Map of Far East and Steel Beam A39

Honoring the Economic Commission for Asia and the Far East (ECAFE).

1960, Apr. 11   **Photo.**   **Unwmk.**
79   A39   4c dp clar, blue grn & dull yel   .25   .25
80   A39   8c ol grn, blue & rose   .25   .25

Tree, FAO and UN Emblems — A40

Fifth World Forestry Congress, Seattle, Washington, Aug. 29-Sept. 10.

          Perf. 13½
1960, Aug. 29   **Photo.**   **Unwmk.**
81   A40   4c dk blue, grn & org   .25   .25
82   A40   8c yel grn, blk & org   .25   .25

UN Headquarters and Preamble to UN Charter — A41

Issued to commemorate the 15th anniversary of the United Nations.

1960, Oct. 24   **Unwmk.**   *Perf. 11*
83   A41   4c blue   .25   .25
84   A41   8c gray   .25   .25
            Souvenir Sheet
              Imperf
85   Sheet of 2   1.25 1.25
   a.   A41 4c blue   .55   .55
   b.   A41 8c gray   .55   .55

Block and Tackle — A42

Honoring the International Bank for Reconstruction and Development.

          Perf. 13½x13
1960, Dec. 9   **Photo.**   **Unwmk.**
86   A42   4c multicolored   .25   .25
87   A42   8c multicolored   .25   .25

Scales of Justice — A43

Issued to honor the International Court of Justice.

          Perf. 13½x13
1961, Feb. 13   **Photo.**   **Unwmk.**
88   A43   4c yel, org brn & blk   .25   .25
89   A43   8c yel, grn & blk   .25   .25

Seal of International Monetary Fund — A44

Issued to honor the International Monetary Fund.

          Perf. 13x13½
1961, Apr. 17   **Photo.**   **Unwmk.**
90   A44   4c bright bluish green   .25   .25
91   A44   7c terra cotta & yellow   .25   .25

Abstract Group of Flags — A45

          Perf. 11½
1961, June 5   **Photo.**   **Unwmk.**
92   A45   30c multicolored   .45   .30
      See UN Offices in Geneva No. 10.

Cogwheel and Map of Latin America — A46

Issued to honor the Economic Commission for Latin America.

          Perf. 13½
1961, Sept. 18   **Photo.**   **Unwmk.**
93   A46   4c blue, red & citron   .25   .25
94   A46   11c grn, lilac & org ver   .25   .25

Africa House, Addis Ababa, and Map — A47

Issued to honor the Economic Commission for Africa.

          Perf. 11½
1961, Oct. 24   **Photo.**   **Unwmk.**
95   A47   4c ultramarine, orange, yellow & brown   .25   .25
96   A47   11c emerald, orange, yellow & brown   .25   .25

Mother Bird Feeding Young and UNICEF Seal — A48

15th anniversary of the United Nations Children's Fund.

          Perf. 11½
1961, Dec. 4   **Photo.**   **Unwmk.**
97   A48   3c brown, gold, orange & yellow   .25   .25
98   A48   4c brown, gold, blue & emerald   .25   .25
99   A48   13c deep green, gold, purple & pink   .25   .25
      Nos. 97-99 (3)   .75   .75

Family and Symbolic Buildings A49

UN program for housing and urban development,

          Perf. 14½x14
1962, Feb. 28   **Photo.**   **Unwmk.**
   Central design multicolored
100 A49   4c bright blue   .25   .25
   a.   Black omitted   200.00
   b.   Yellow omitted   —
   c.   Brown omitted   —
101 A49   7c orange brown   .25   .25
   a.   Red omitted   —
   b.   Black omitted   —
   c.   Gold omitted   —

"The World Against Malaria" — A50

Issued in honor of the WHO and to call attention to the international campaign to eradicate malaria from the world.

          Perf. 14x14½
1962, Mar. 30   **Photo.**   **Unwmk.**
   Word frame in gray
102 A50   4c orange, yellow, brown, green & black   .25   .25
103 A50   11c green, yellow, brown & indigo   .25   .25

"Peace" — A51

UN Flag — A52

Hands Combining "UN" and Globe — A53

UN Emblem over Globe A54

Photo.; Engr. (5c)
Perf. 14x14½

1962, May 25 Unwmk.
104 A51 1c vermilion, blue, black & gray .25 .25
105 A52 3c light green, Prussian blue, yellow & gray .25 .25

Perf. 12
106 A53 5c dark carmine rose .25 .25

Perf. 12½
107 A54 11c dark & light blue & gold .25 .25
Nos. 104-107 (4) 1.00 1.00
See #167 and UN Offices in Geneva #2, 6. Compare A51 with A76.

Flag at Half-mast and UN Headquarters — A55

Issued on the 1st anniversary of the death of Dag Hammarskjold, Secretary General of the United Nations 1953-61, in memory of those who died in the service of the United Nations.

Perf. 11½
1962, Sept. 17 Photo. Unwmk.
108 A55 5c black, light blue & blue .25 .25
109 A55 15c black, gray olive & blue .25 .25

World Map Showing Congo — A56

Issued to commemorate the United Nations Operation in the Congo.

Perf. 11½
1962, Oct. 24 Photo. Unwmk.
110 A56 4c olive, orange, black & yellow .25 .25
111 A56 11c blue green, orange, black & yellow .25 .25

Globe in Universe and Palm Frond — A57

Issued to honor the Committee on Peaceful Uses of Outer Space.

Perf. 14x13½
1962, Dec. 3 Engr. Unwmk.
112 A57 4c violet blue .25 .25
113 A57 11c rose claret .25 .25

Development Decade Emblem — A58

UN Development Decade and UN Conference on the Application of Science and Technology for the Benefit of the Less Developed Areas, Geneva, Feb. 4-20.

Perf. 11½
1963, Feb. 4 Photo. Unwmk.
114 A58 5c pale green, maroon, dark blue & Prussian blue .25 .25
115 A58 11c yellow, maroon, dark blue & Prussian blue .25 .25

Stalks of Wheat — A59

Issued for the "Freedom from Hunger" campaign of the Food and Agriculture Organization.

Perf. 11½
1963, Mar. 22 Photo. Unwmk.
116 A59 5c vermilion, green & yellow .25 .25
117 A59 11c vermilion, deep claret & yellow .25 .25

Bridge over Map of New Guinea — A60

1st anniversary of the United Nations Temporary Executive Authority (UNTEA) in West New Guinea (West Irian).

Perf. 11½
1963, Oct. 1 Photo. Unwmk.
118 A60 25c blue, green & gray .50 .40

General Assembly Building, New York — A61

Since October 1955 all sessions of the General Assembly have been held in the General Assembly Hall, UN Headquarters, NY.

Unwmk.
1963, Nov. 4 Photo. Perf. 13
119 A61 5c violet blue, blue, yellow green & red .25 .25
120 A61 11c green, yellow green, blue, yellow & red .25 .25

Flame — A62

15th anniversary of the signing of the Universal Declaration of Human Rights.

Unwmk.
1963, Dec. 10 Photo. Perf. 13
121 A62 5c green, gold, red & yellow .25 .25
122 A62 11c carmine, gold, blue & yellow .25 .25

Ships at Sea and IMCO Emblem — A63

Issued to honor the Intergovernmental Maritime Consultative Organization.

Perf. 11½
1964, Jan. 13 Photo. Unwmk.
123 A63 5c blue, olive, ocher & yellow .25 .25
124 A63 11c dark blue, dark green, emerald & yellow .25 .25

Map of the World — A64

UN Emblem — A65

Three Men United Before Globe — A66

Stylized Globe and Weather Vane — A67

1964-71 Photo. Unwmk. Perf. 14
125 A64 2c light & dark blue, orange & yellow green .25 .25
a. Perf. 13x13½ .25 .25

Perf. 11½
126 A65 7c dark blue, orange brown & black .25 .25
127 A66 10c blue green, olive green & black .25 .25
128 A67 50c multicolored .55 .45
Nos. 125-128 (4) 1.30 1.20
Issued: 2c, 7c, May 29; 50c, Mar. 6.
See UN Offices in Geneva Nos. 3, 12.

Arrows Showing Global Flow of Trade A68

Issued to commemorate the UN Conference on Trade and Development, Geneva, Mar. 23-June 15.

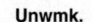

Unwmk.
1964, June 15 Photo. Perf. 13
129 A68 5c black, red & yellow .25 .25
130 A68 11c black, olive & yellow .25 .25

Poppy Capsule and Hands A69

Honoring international efforts and achievements in the control of narcotics.

Unwmk.
1964, Sept. 21 Engr. Perf. 12
131 A69 5c rose red & black .25 .25
132 A69 11c emerald & black .25 .25

Padlocked Atomic Blast — A70

Signing of the nuclear test ban treaty pledging an end to nuclear explosions in the atmosphere, outer space and under water.

Litho. and Engr.
Perf. 11x11½
1964, Oct. 23 Unwmk.
133 A70 5c dark red & dark brown .25 .25

"Education for Progress" — A71

Issued to publicize the UNESCO world campaign for universal literacy and for free compulsory primary education.

Perf. 12½
1964, Dec. 7 Photo. Unwmk.
134 A71 4c orange, red, bister, green & blue .25 .25
135 A71 5c bister, red, dark & light blue .25 .25
136 A71 11c green, light blue, black & rose .25 .25
Nos. 134-136 (3) .75 .75

Progress Chart, Key & Globe — A72

Issued to publicize the Special Fund program to speed economic growth and social advancement in low-income countries.

Perf. 13½x13
1965, Jan. 25 Photo. Unwmk.
137 A72 5c dull blue, dark blue, yellow & red .25 .25
138 A72 11c yellow green, dark blue, yellow & red .25 .25
a. Black omitted (UN emblem on key) —

Leaves & View of Cyprus — A73

Issued to honor the United Nations Peacekeeping Force on Cyprus.

Perf. 11½
1965, Mar. 4   Photo.   Unwmk.
139 A73 5c orange, olive &
          black   .25 .25
140 A73 11c yellow green, blue
          green & black   .25 .25

"From
Semaphore to
Satellite"
A74

Centenary of the International Telecommunication Union.

Perf. 11½
1965, May 17   Photo.   Unwmk.
141 A74 5c aquamarine, or-
          ange, blue & pur-
          ple   .25 .25
142 A74 11c light violet, red or-
          ange, bister &
          bright green   .25 .25

ICY
Emblem — A75

20th anniversary of the United Nations and International Cooperation Year.

Perf. 14x13½
1965, June 26   Engr.   Unwmk.
143 A75 5c dark blue   .25 .25
144 A75 15c lilac rose   .25 .25

Souvenir Sheet
145 A75 Sheet of two   .35 .35

"Peace" — A76

Opening Words,
UN
Charter — A77

UN
Headquarters,
Emblem — A78

UN
Emblem — A79

UN Emblem
A80

Perf. 13½x13
1965-66   Photo.   Unwmk.
146 A76 1c vermilion, blue,
          black & gray   .25 .25
Perf. 14
147 A77 15c olive bister, dull
          yellow, black &
          deep claret   .25 .25
Perf. 12
148 A78 20c dark blue, blue,
          red & yellow   .25 .25
  a.   Yellow omitted   —
Litho. and Embossed
Perf. 14
149 A79 25c light & dark blue   .30 .25
  a.   25c light & dark blue, new dk
        blue plate/cylinder (see foot-
        note)   .30 .25
  b.   As "a," tagged   10.00 10.00

Photo.
Perf. 11½
150 A80 $1 aquamarine &
          sapphire   1.60 1.60
     Nos. 146-150 (5)   2.65 2.60
Issued: 1c, No. 149, 9/20/65; No. 149a,
11/5/65; 15c, 20c, 10/25/65; $1, 3/25/66.
On No. 149, the dark blue "halo" of the U.N.
emblem is large, overlapping the "25c." On No.
149a, a new dark blue plate/cylinder was
used, making the "halo" of the U.N. emblem
smaller.
See UN Offices in Geneva Nos. 5, 9, 11.

Fields &
People — A81

Design: 11c, French inscription.
Issued to emphasize the importance of the
world's population growth and its problems
and to call attention to population trends and
development.

Unwmk.
1965, Nov. 29   Photo.   *Perf. 12*
151 A81 4c multicolored   .25 .25
152 A81 5c multicolored   .25 .25
153 A81 11c multicolored   .25 .25
     Nos. 151-153 (3)   .75 .75

Globe & Flags of UN
Members — A82

Design: 11c, French inscription.
Issued to honor the World Federation of
United Nations Associations.

Perf. 11½
1966, Jan. 31   Photo.   Unwmk.
154 A82 5c multicolored   .25 .25
155 A82 15c multicolored   .25 .25

WHO
Headquarters,
Geneva — A83

Design: 11c, French inscription.
Issued to commemorate the opening of the
World Health Organization Headquarters,
Geneva.

1966, May 26   Photo.   *Perf. 12½x12*
Granite Paper
156 A83 5c lt & dk blue, orange,
          green & bister   .25 .25
157 A83 11c orange, lt & dark
          blue, green & bis-
          ter   .25 .25

Coffee — A84

Design: 11c, Spanish inscription.
Issued to commemorate the International
Coffee Agreement of 1962.

1966, Sept. 19   Photo.   *Perf. 13½x13*
158 A84 5c orange, lt blue,
          green, red & dk
          brown   .25 .25
159 A84 11c lt blue, yellow,
          green, red & dk
          brown   .25 .25

UN Observer — A85

Issued to honor the Peace Keeping United
Nation Observers.
Printed by Courvoisier, S.A. Panes of 50.
Designed by Ole S. Hamann.

1966, Oct. 24   Photo.   *Perf. 11½*
Granite Paper
160 A85 15c steel blue, orange,
          black & green   .25 .25

Children of
Various
Races — A86

20th anniversary of the United Nations Children's Fund (UNICEF).

1966, Nov. 28   Litho.   *Perf. 13x13½*
161 A86 4c pink & multi   .25 .25
162 A86 5c pale green & multi   .25 .25
  a.   Yellow omitted   —
163 A86 11c light ultramarine &
          multi   .25 .25
  b.   Dark blue omitted   —
     Nos. 161-163 (3)   .75 .75

Hand Rolling
up Sleeve &
Chart Showing
Progress
A87

Design: 11c, French inscription.
United Nations Development Program.

1967, Jan. 23   Photo.   *Perf. 12½*
164 A87 5c green, yellow, pur-
          ple & orange   .25 .25
165 A87 11c blue, chocolate,
          light green & or-
          ange   .25 .25

Type of 1962 and

UN Headquarters, New York & World
Map — A88

1967   Photo.   *Perf. 11½*
166 A88 1½c ultramarine, black,
          orange & ocher   .25 .25
Size: 33x23mm
167 A53 5c red brown, brown &
          orange yellow   .25 .25
Issue dates: 1½c, Mar. 17; 5c, Jan. 23.
See UN Offices in Geneva No. 1.

Fireworks — A89

Design: 11c, French inscription.
Issued to honor all nations which gained
independence since 1945.

1967, Mar. 17   Photo.   *Perf. 14x14½*
168 A89 5c dark blue & multi   .25 .25
169 A89 11c brown lake & multi .25 .25

"Peace" — A90

UN Pavilion,
EXPO
'67 — A91

EXPO '67, International Exhibition, Montreal, Apr. 28-Oct. 27, 1967.

Engr. & Litho.
1967, Apr. 28   *Perf. 11*
170 A90 4c red & red brown   .25 .25
171 A90 5c blue & red brown   .25 .25
Litho.
172 A91 8c multicolored   .25 .25
Engr. and Litho.
173 A90 10c green & red brown   .25 .25
174 A90 15c dark brown & red
          brown   .25 .25
     Nos. 170-174 (5)   1.25 1.25
Nos. 170-174 were issued in Canadian
dollars.

Luggage
Tags and
UN
Emblem
A92

Issued to publicize International Tourist
Year, 1967.

1967, June 19   Litho.   *Perf. 14*
175 A92 5c reddish brown &
          multi   .25 .25
176 A92 15c ultramarine & multi .25 .25

Quotation
from Isaiah
2:4 — A93

Design: 13c, French inscription.
Issued to publicize the UN General Assembly's resolutions on general and complete disarmament and for suspension of nuclear and thermonuclear tests.

1967, Oct. 24   Photo.   *Perf. 14*
177 A93 6c ultramarine, yellow,
          gray & brown   .25 .25
178 A93 13c magenta, yellow,
          gray & brown   .25 .25

Art at UN Issue
Miniature Sheet

Memorial Window — A94

"The Kiss of Peace" — A95

1967, Nov. 17   Litho.   Rouletted 9
179 A94 6c Sheet of 6, #a.-f.   .40   .40

Perf. 13x13½
180 A95 6c multicolored   .25   .25

No. 179 contains six 6c stamps, each rouletted on 3 sides, imperf. on fourth side. Size: 124x80mm. On Nos. 179a-179c, "United Nations 6c" appears at top; on Nos. 179d-179f, at bottom. No. 179f includes name "Marc Chagall."

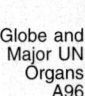

Globe and Major UN Organs A96

Design: 13c, French inscription.
Issued to honor the United Nations Secretariat.

1968, Jan. 16   Photo.   Perf. 11½
181 A96 6c multicolored   .25   .25
182 A96 13c multicolored   .25   .25

Art at UN Issue

Statue by Henrik Starcke — A97

1968, Mar. 1   Photo.   Perf. 11½
183 A97 6c blue & multi   .25   .25
184 A97 75c rose lake & multi   1.10   .90

The 6c is part of the "Art at the UN" series. The 75c belongs to the regular definitive series. The teakwood Starcke statue, which stands in the Trusteeship Council Chamber, represents mankind's search for freedom and happiness.
See UN Offices in Geneva No. 13.

Factories and Chart — A98

Design: 13c, French inscription ("ONUDI," etc.).
Issued to publicize the UN Industrial Development Organization.

1968, Apr. 18   Litho.   Perf. 12
185 A98 6c greenish blue, lt greenish blue, black & dull claret   .25   .25
186 A98 13c dull red brown, light red brown, black & ultra   .25   .25

UN Headquarters A99

1968, May 31   Litho.   Perf. 12x13½
187 A99 6c green, blue, black & gray   .25   .25

Radarscope and Globes — A100

Design: 20c, French inscription.
Issued to publicize World Weather Watch, a new weather system directed by the World Meteorological Organization.

1968, Sept. 19   Photo.   Perf. 13x13½
188 A100 6c green, black, ocher, red & blue   .25   .25
189 A100 20c lilac, black, ocher, red & blue   .30   .25

Human Rights Flame — A101

Design: 13c, French inscription.
Issued for International Human Rights Year, 1968.

Photo.; Foil Embossed
1968, Nov. 22   Perf. 12½
190 A101 6c bright blue, deep ultra & gold   .25   .25
191 A101 13c rose red, dark red & gold   .25   .25

Books and UN Emblem — A102

Design: 13c, French inscription in center, denomination panel at bottom.
United Nations Institute for Training and Research (UNITAR).

1969, Feb. 10   Litho.   Perf. 13½
192 A102 6c yellow green & multi   .25   .25
193 A102 13c bluish lilac & multi   .25   .25

UN Building, Santiago, Chile A103

Design: 15c, Spanish inscription.
The UN Building in Santiago, Chile, is the seat of the UN Economic Commission for Latin America and of the Latin American Institute for Economic and Social Planning.

1969, Mar. 14   Litho.   Perf. 14
194 A103 6c light blue, violet blue & light green   .25   .25
195 A103 15c pink, cream & red brown   .25   .25

"UN" and UN Emblem — A104

1969, Mar. 14   Photo.   Perf. 13½
196 A104 13c bright blue, black & gold   .25   .25
See UN Offices in Geneva No. 7.

UN Emblem and Scales of Justice — A105

Design: 13c, French inscription.
20th anniversary session of the UN International Law Commission.

Granite Paper
1969, Apr. 21   Photo.   Perf. 11½
197 A105 6c bright green, ultra & gold   .25   .25
198 A105 13c crimson, lilac & gold   .25   .25

Allegory of Labor, Emblems of UN and ILO A106

Design: 20c, French inscription.
Issued to publicize "Labor and Development" and to commemorate the 50th anniversary of the International Labor Organization.

1969, June 5   Photo.   Perf. 13
199 A106 6c blue, deep blue, yellow & gold   .25   .25
200 A106 20c orange vermilion, magenta, yellow & gold   .25   .25

Art at UN Issue

Ostrich, Tunisian Mosaic, 3rd Century — A107

Design: 13c, Pheasant; French inscription.

1969, Nov. 21   Photo.   Perf. 14
201 A107 6c blue & multi   .25   .25
202 A107 13c red & multi   .25   .25

Art at UN Issue

Peace Bell, Gift of Japanese A108

Design: 25c, French inscription.
The Peace Bell was a gift of the people of Japan in 1954, cast from donated coins and metals. It is housed in a Japanese cypress structure at UN Headquarters, New York.

1970, Mar. 13   Photo.   Perf. 13½x13
203 A108 6c violet blue & multi   .25   .25
204 A108 25c claret & multi   .30   .25

Mekong River, Power Lines and Map of Delta — A109

Design: 13c, French inscription.
Issued to publicize the Lower Mekong Basin Development project under UN auspices.

1970, Mar. 13   Perf. 14
205 A109 6c dark blue & multi   .25   .25
206 A109 13c deep plum & multi   .25   .25

"Fight Cancer" A110

Design: 13c, French inscription.
Issued to publicize the fight against cancer in connection with the 10th International Cancer Congress of the International Union Against Cancer, Houston, Texas, May 22-29.

1970, May 22   Litho.   Perf. 14
207 A110 6c blue & black   .25   .25
208 A110 13c olive & black   .25   .25

UN Emblem and Olive Branch A111

UN Emblem — A112

Design: 13c, French inscription.
25th anniv. of the UN. First day covers were postmarked at UN Headquarters, NY, and at San Francisco.

1970, June 26   Photo.   Perf. 11½
209 A111 6c red, gold, dark & light blue   .25   .25
210 A111 13c dark blue, gold, green & red   .25   .25

Perf. 12½
211 A112 25c dark blue, gold & light blue   .35   .25
Nos. 209-211 (3)   .85   .75

Souvenir Sheet
Imperf
212   Sheet of 3   .80   .80
a.   A111 6c red, gold & multicolored   .25   .25
b.   A111 13c violet blue, gold & multi   .25   .25
c.   A112 25c violet blue, gold & light blue   .30   .30

Scales, Olive Branch, Progress Symbol — A113

Design: 13c, French inscription.
Issued to publicize "Peace, Justice and Progress" in connection with the 25th anniversary of the United Nations.

1970, Nov. 20   Photo.   Perf. 13½
213 A113 6c gold & multi   .25   .25
214 A113 13c silver & multi   .25   .25

Sea Bed, Fish, Underwater Research — A114

Issued to publicize peaceful uses of the sea bed.

Photo. & Engr.
1971, Jan. 25   Perf. 13
215 A114 6c blue & multi   .25   .25
See UN Offices in Geneva No. 15.

Refugees,
Sculpture by
Kaare K.
Nygaard
A115

International support for refugees.

1971, Mar. 2   Litho.   Perf. 13x12½
216 A115   6c brown, ocher &
       black   .25   .25
217 A115   13c ultramarine, green-
       ish blue & black   .25   .25

See UN Offices in Geneva No. 16.

Wheat and
Globe — A116

Publicizing the UN World Food Program.

1971, Apr. 13   Photo.   Perf. 14
218 A116   13c red & multicolored   .25   .25

See UN Offices in Geneva No. 17.

UPU
Headquarters,
Bern — A117

Opening of new Universal Postal Union
Headquarters, Bern.

1971, May 28   Photo.   Perf. 11½
219 A117   20c brown orange &
       multi   .30   .25

See UN Offices in Geneva No. 18.

"Eliminate Racial
Discrimination"
A118

A119

International Year Against Racial
Discrimination.

1971, Sept. 21   Photo.   Perf. 13½
220 A118   8c yellow green &
       multi   .25   .25
221 A119   13c blue & multi   .25   .25

See UN Offices in Geneva Nos. 19-20.

UN Headquarters, New York — A120

UN
Emblem
and
Symbolic
Flags
A121

1971, Oct. 22   Photo.   Perf. 13½
222 A120   8c violet blue & multi   .25   .25
               Perf. 13
223 A121   60c ultra & multi   .80   .80

Maia by Pablo
Picasso — A122

To publicize the UN International School.

1971, Nov. 19   Photo.   Perf. 11½
224 A122   8c olive & multi   .25   .25
225 A122   21c ultra & multi   .25   .25

Letter
Changing
Hands
A123

1972, Jan. 5   Litho.   Perf. 14
226 A123   95c carmine & multi   1.30   1.10

"No More
Nuclear
Weapons"
A124

To promote non-proliferation of nuclear
weapons.

1972, Feb. 14   Photo.   Perf. 13½x14
227 A124   8c dull rose, black,
       blue & gray   .25   .25

See UN Offices in Geneva No. 23.

Proportions of Man
(c. 1509), by
Leonardo da
Vinci — A125

World Health Day, Apr. 7.

Litho. & Engr.
1972, Apr. 7   Perf. 13x13½
228 A125   15c black & multi   .25   .25

See UN Offices in Geneva No. 24.

"Human
Environment"
A126

UN Conf. on Human Environment, Stockholm, June 5-16, 1972.

Litho. & Embossed
1972, June 5   Perf. 12½x14
229 A126   8c red, buff, green &
       blue   .25   .25
230 A126   15c blue green, buff,
       green & blue   .25   .25

See UN Offices in Geneva Nos. 25-26.

"Europe" and UN
Emblem — A127

Economic Commission for Europe, 25th
anniversary.

1972, Sept. 11   Litho.   Perf. 13x13½
231 A127   21c yellow brown &
       multi   .30   .30

See UN Offices in Geneva No. 27.

Art at UN Issue

The Five
Continents, by José
Maria Sert — A128

1972, Nov. 17   Photo.   Perf. 12x12½
232 A128   8c gold, brown &
       golden brown   .25   .25
233 A128   15c gold, blue green &
       brown   .25   .25

See UN Offices in Geneva Nos. 28-29.

Olive Branch
and Broken
Sword
A129

Disarmament Decade, 1970-79.

1973, Mar. 9   Litho.   Perf. 13½x13
234 A129   8c blue & multi   .25   .25
235 A129   15c lilac rose & multi   .25   .25

See UN Offices in Geneva Nos. 30-31.

Poppy Capsule and
Skull — A130

Fight against drug abuse.

1973, Apr. 13   Photo.   Perf. 13½
236 A130   8c deep orange &
       multi   .25   .25
237 A130   15c pink & multi   .25   .25

See UN Offices in Geneva No. 32.

Honeycomb
A131

5th anniversary of the United Nations Volunteer Program.

1973, May 25   Photo.   Perf. 14
238 A131   8c olive bister & multi   .25   .25
239 A131   21c gray blue & multi   .30   .30

See UN Offices in Geneva No. 33.

Map of Africa
with Namibia
A132

To publicize Namibia (South-West Africa) for
which the UN General Assembly ended the
mandate of South Africa and established the
UN Council for Namibia to administer the territory until independence.

1973, Oct. 1   Photo.   Perf. 14
240 A132   8c emerald & multi   .25   .25
241 A132   15c bright rose & multi   .25   .25

See UN Offices in Geneva No. 34.

UN Emblem,
Human Rights
Flame
A133

25th anniversary of the adoption and proclamation of the Universal Declaration of Human
Rights.

1973, Nov. 16   Photo.   Perf. 13½
242 A133   8c deep carmine &
       multi   .25   .25
243 A133   21c blue green & multi   .25   .25

See UN Offices in Geneva Nos. 35-36.

ILO
Headquarters,
Geneva
A134

New Headquarters of International Labor
Organization.

1974, Jan. 11   Photo.   Perf. 14
244 A134   10c ultra & multi   .25   .25
245 A134   21c blue green & multi   .30   .25

See UN Offices in Geneva Nos. 37-38.

Post Horn
Encircling
Globe
A135

Centenary of Universal Postal Union.

1974, Mar. 22   Litho.   Perf. 12½
246 A135   10c gold & multi   .25   .25

See UN Offices in Geneva Nos. 39-40.

Art at UN Issue

Peace Mural,
by Candido
Portinari
A136

The mural, a gift of Brazil, is in the Delegates' Lobby, General Assembly Building.

1974, May 6   Photo.   Perf. 14
247 A136   10c gold & multi   .25   .25
248 A136   18c ultra & multi   .35   .30

See UN Offices in Geneva Nos. 41-42.

Dove & UN
Emblem
A137

UN
Headquarters
A138

Globe, UN
Emblem, Flags
A139

1974, June 10   Photo.   Perf. 14
249 A137 2c dark & light blue   .25 .25
250 A138 10c multicolored   .25 .25
251 A139 18c multicolored   .25 .25
     Nos. 249-251 (3)   .75 .75

Children of the
World — A140

World Population Year.

1974, Oct. 18   Photo.   Perf. 14
252 A140 10c light blue & multi   .25 .25
253 A140 18c lilac & multi   .35 .25

See UN Offices in Geneva Nos. 43-44.

Law of the
Sea — A141

Declaration of UN General Assembly that
the sea bed is common heritage of mankind,
reserved for peaceful purposes.

1974, Nov. 22   Photo.   Perf. 14
254 A141 10c green & multi   .25 .25
255 A141 26c orange red & multi   .35 .30

See UN Offices in Geneva No. 45.

Satellite and
Globe
A142

Peaceful uses (meteorology, industry, fishing, communications) of outer space.

1975, Mar. 14   Litho.   Perf. 13
256 A142 10c multicolored   .25 .25
257 A142 26c multicolored   .35 .30

See UN Offices in Geneva Nos. 46-47.

Equality
Between Men
and Women
A143

International Women's Year.

1975, May 9   Litho.   Perf. 15
258 A143 10c multicolored   .25 .25
259 A143 18c multicolored   .35 .30

See UN Offices in Geneva Nos. 48-49.

UN Flag and
"XXX" — A144

30th anniversary of the United Nations.

1975, June 26   Litho.   Perf. 13
260 A144 10c olive bister & multi   .25 .25
261 A144 26c purple & multi   .40 .35

Souvenir Sheet
Imperf
262   Sheet of 2   .60 .50
a.   A144 10c olive bister & mul-
     ticolored   .25 .25
b.   A144 26c purple & multicolored   .35 .25

See Offices in Geneva Nos. 50-52.

Hand Reaching up over Map of Africa
& Namibia — A145

"Namibia-United Nations direct responsibility." See note after No. 241.

1975, Sept. 22   Photo.   Perf. 13½
263 A145 10c multicolored   .25 .25
264 A145 18c multicolored   .30 .30

See UN Offices in Geneva Nos. 53-54.

Wild Rose Growing
from Barbed
Wire — A146

United Nations Peace-keeping Operations.

1975, Nov. 21   Engr.   Perf. 12½
265 A146 13c ultramarine   .25 .25
266 A146 26c rose carmine   .40 .40

See UN Offices in Geneva Nos. 55-56.

Symbolic Flags
Forming
Dove — A147

UN
Emblem — A149

People of
All Races
A148

UN Flag
A150

Dove and
Rainbow
A151

1976   Litho.   Perf. 13x13½, 13½x13
267 A147 3c multicolored   .25 .25
268 A148 4c multicolored   .25 .25

Photo.
Perf. 14
269 A149 9c multicolored   .25 .25

Litho.
Perf. 13x13½
270 A150 30c blue, emerald &
     black   .35 .35
271 A151 50c yellow green &
     multi   .65 .65
     Nos. 267-271 (5)   1.75 1.75

Issue dates: 3c, 4c, 30c, 50c, Jan. 6; 9c,
Nov. 19.
See UN Offices in Vienna No. 8.

Interlocking
Bands — A152

World Federation of United Nations
Associations.

1976, Mar. 12   Photo.   Perf. 14
272 A152 13c blue, green &
     black   .25 .25
273 A152 26c green & multi   .35 .30

See UN Offices in Geneva No. 57.

Cargo, Globe and
Graph — A153

UN Conference on Trade and Development
(UNCTAD), Nairobi, Kenya, May 1976.

1976, Apr. 23   Photo.   Perf. 11½
274 A153 13c deep magenta &
     multi   .25 .25
275 A153 31c dull blue & multi   .40 .30

See UN Offices in Geneva No. 58.

Houses Around
Globe — A154

Habitat, UN Conference on Human Settlements, Vancouver, Canada, May 31-June 11.

1976, May 28   Photo.   Perf. 14
276 A154 13c red brown & multi   .25 .25
277 A154 25c green & multi   .40 .30

See UN Offices in Geneva Nos. 59-60.

Magnifying
Glass, Sheet
of Stamps,
UN Emblem
A155

United Nations Postal Administration, 25th
anniversary.

1976, Oct. 8   Photo.   Perf. 11½
278 A155 13c blue & multi   .25 .25
279 A155 31c green & multi   1.40 1.40

See UN Offices in Geneva Nos. 61-62.

Grain — A156

World Food Council.

1976, Nov. 19   Litho.   Perf. 14½
280 A156 13c multicolored   .25 .25

See UN Offices in Geneva No. 63.

WIPO Headquarters, Geneva — A157

World Intellectual Property Organization
(WIPO).

1977, Mar. 11   Photo.   Perf. 14
281 A157 13c citron & multi   .25 .25
282 A157 31c bright green &
     multi   .45 .35

See UN Offices in Geneva No. 64.

Drops of Water
Falling into
Funnel — A158

UN Water Conference, Mar del Plata,
Argentina, Mar. 14-25.

1977, Apr. 22   Photo.   Perf. 13½x13
283 A158 13c yellow & multi   .25 .25
284 A158 25c salmon & multi   .40 .35

See UN Offices in Geneva Nos. 65-66.

Burning Fuse
Severed
A159

UN Security Council.

1977, May 27   Photo.   Perf. 14
285 A159 13c purple & multi   .25 .25
286 A159 31c dark blue & multi   .45 .30

See UN Offices in Geneva Nos. 67-68.

"Combat
Racism"
A160

Fight against racial discrimination.

1977, Sept. 19 Litho.   Perf. 13½x13
287 A160 13c black & yellow   .25   .25
288 A160 25c black & vermilion   .40   .30
See UN Offices in Geneva Nos. 60-70.

Atom, Grain, Fruit and Factory — A161

Peaceful uses of atomic energy.

1977, Nov. 18   Photo.   Perf. 14
289 A161 13c yellow bister & multi   .25   .25
290 A161 18c dull green & multi   .30   .25
See UN Offices in Geneva Nos. 71-72.

Opening Words of UN Charter A162

"Live Together in Peace" A163

People of the World — A164

1978, Jan. 27   Litho.   Perf. 14½
291 A162   1c gold, brown & red   .25   .25
292 A163 25c multicolored   .35   .30
293 A164 $1 multicolored   1.25   1.25
      Nos. 291-293 (3)   1.85   1.80
See UN Offices in Geneva No. 73.

Smallpox Virus — A165

Global eradication of smallpox.

1978, Mar. 31 Photo.   Perf. 12x11½
294 A165 13c rose & black   .25   .25
295 A165 31c blue & black   .40   .40
See UN Offices in Geneva Nos. 74-75.

Open Handcuff — A166

Liberation, justice and cooperation for Namibia.

1978, May 5   Photo.   Perf. 12
296 A166 13c multicolored   .25   .25
297 A166 18c multicolored   .30   .25
See UN Offices in Geneva No. 76.

Multicolored Bands and Clouds — A167

International Civil Aviation Organization for "Safety in the Air."

1978, June 12   Photo.   Perf. 14
298 A167 13c multicolored   .25   .25
299 A167 25c multicolored   .35   .30
See UN Offices in Geneva Nos. 77-78.

General Assembly A168

1978, Sept. 15 Photo.   Perf. 13½
300 A168 13c multicolored   .25   .25
301 A168 18c multicolored   .35   .30
See UN Offices in Geneva Nos. 79-80.

Hemispheres as Cogwheels A169

Technical Cooperation Among Developing Countries Conference, Buenos Aires, Argentina, Sept. 1978.

1978, Nov. 17   Photo.   Perf. 14
302 A169 13c multicolored   .25   .25
303 A169 31c multicolored   .50   .40
See UN Offices in Geneva No. 81.

Hand Holding Olive Branch — A170

Tree of Various Races — A171

Globe, Dove with Olive Branch — A172

Birds and Globe — A173

1979, Jan. 19   Photo.   Perf. 14
304 A170   5c multicolored   .25   .25
305 A171 14c multicolored   .25   .25
306 A172 15c multicolored   .25   .25
307 A173 20c multicolored   .30   .25
      Nos. 304-307 (4)   1.05   1.00

UNDRO Against Fire and Water A174

Office of the UN Disaster Relief Coordinator (UNDRO).

1979, Mar. 9   Photo.   Perf. 14
308 A174 15c multicolored   .25   .25
309 A174 20c multicolored   .35   .30
See UN Offices in Geneva Nos. 82-83.

Child and ICY Emblem A175

International Year of the Child.

1979, May 4   Photo.   Perf. 14
310 A175 15c multicolored   .25   .25
311 A175 31c multicolored   .35   .35
See UN Offices in Geneva Nos. 84-85.

Map of Namibia, Olive Branch — A176

For a free and independent Namibia.

1979, Oct. 5   Litho.   Perf. 13½
312 A176 15c multicolored   .25   .25
313 A176 31c multicolored   .30   .35
See UN Offices in Geneva No. 86.

Scales and Sword of Justice — A177

International Court of Justice, The Hague, Netherlands.

1979, Nov. 9   Litho.   Perf. 13x13½
314 A177 15c multicolored   .25   .25
315 A177 20c multicolored   .30   .35
See UN Offices in Geneva Nos. 87-88.

Graph of Economic Trends — A178

Key — A179

New International Economic Order.

1980, Jan. 11   Litho.   Perf. 15x14½
316 A178 15c multicolored   .25   .25
317 A179 31c multicolored   .45   .35
See UN Offices in Geneva No. 89; Vienna No. 7.

Women's Year Emblems A180

United Nations Decade for Women.

1980, Mar. 7   Litho.   Perf. 14½x15
318 A180 15c multicolored   .25   .25
319 A180 20c multicolored   .30   .25
See UN Offices in Geneva Nos. 90-91; Vienna Nos. 9-10.

UN Emblem and "UN" on Helmet A181

Arrows and UN Emblem A182

United Nations Peace-keeping Operations.

1980, May 16   Litho.   Perf. 14x13
320 A181 15c blue & black   .25   .25
321 A182 31c multicolored   .40   .40
See UN Offices in Geneva No. 92; Vienna No. 11.

"35" and Flags — A183

Globe and Laurel — A184

35th Anniversary of the United Nations.

1980, June 26   Litho.   Perf. 13x13½
322 A183 15c multicolored   .25   .25
323 A184 31c multicolored   .40   .35
           Souvenir Sheet
              Imperf
324   Sheet of 2   .65   .65
  a.   A183 15c multicolored   .25   .25
  b.   A184 31c multicolored   .40   .40
See UN Offices in Geneva Nos. 93-95; Vienna Nos. 12-14.

Flag of Turkey A185

1980, Sept. 26 Litho.   Perf. 12
           Granite Paper
325 A185 15c shown   .25   .25
326 A185 15c Luxembourg   .25   .25
327 A185 15c Fiji   .25   .25
328 A185 15c Viet Nam   .25   .25
  a.   Se-tenant block of 4, #325-328 1.00 1.00
329 A185 15c Guinea   .25   .25
330 A185 15c Surinam   .25   .25
331 A185 15c Bangladesh   .25   .25
332 A185 15c Mali   .25   .25
  a.   Se-tenant block of 4, #329-332 1.00 1.00
333 A185 15c Yugoslavia   .25   .25
334 A185 15c France   .25   .25
335 A185 15c Venezuela   .25   .25
336 A185 15c El Salvador   .25   .25
  a.   Se-tenant block of 4, #333-336 1.00 1.00
337 A185 15c Madagascar   .25   .25
338 A185 15c Cameroon   .25   .25
339 A185 15c Rwanda   .25   .25
340 A185 15c Hungary   .25   .25
  a.   Se-tenant block of 4, #337-340 1.00 1.00
      Nos. 325-340 (16)   4.00   4.00

Issued in 4 panes of 16. Each pane contains 4 blocks of 4 (Nos. 325-328, 329-332, 333-336, 337-340). A se-tenant block of 4 designs centers each pane.

See Nos. 350-365, 374-389, 399-414, 425-440, 450-465, 477-492, 499-514, 528-543, 554-569, 690-697, 719-726, 744-751, 795-802, 921-924, 1063-1066, 1083-1086.

Symbolic Flowers A186

Symbols of Progress
A187

1980, Nov. 21   Litho.   Perf. 13½x13
341 A186 15c multicolored .25 .25
342 A187 20c multicolored .40 .35

See UN Offices in Geneva, Nos. 96-97; Vienna Nos. 15-16.

Inalienable Rights of the Palestinian People
A188

1981, Jan. 30   Photo.   Perf. 12x11½
343 A188 15c multicolored .30 .25

See UN Offices in Geneva No. 98; Vienna No. 17.

Interlocking Puzzle Pieces — A189

Stylized Person — A190

International Year of the Disabled.

1981, Mar. 6   Photo.   Perf. 14
344 A189 20c multicolored .25 .25
345 A190 35c black & orange .40 .45

See UN Offices in Geneva Nos. 99-100; Vienna Nos. 18-19.

Art at UN Issue

Divislava and Sebastocrator Kaloyan, Bulgarian Mural, 1259, Boyana Church, Sofia — A191

1981, Apr. 15   Photo.   Perf. 11½
Granite Paper
346 A191 20c multicolored .25 .25
347 A191 31c multicolored .40 .45

See UN Offices in Geneva No. 101; Vienna No. 20.

Solar Energy
A192

Conference Emblem
A193

Conference on New and Renewable Sources of Energy, Nairobi, Aug. 10-21.

1981, May 29   Litho.   Perf. 13
348 A192 20c multicolored .25 .25
349 A193 40c multicolored .50 .50

See UN Offices in Geneva No. 102; Vienna No. 21.

Flag Type of 1980
1981, Sept. 25   Litho.
Granite Paper
350 A185 20c Djibouti .25 .25
351 A185 20c Sri Lanka .25 .25
352 A185 20c Bolivia .25 .25
353 A185 20c Equatorial Guinea .25 .25
  a.   Se-tenant block of 4, #350-353 1.00 1.00
354 A185 20c Malta .25 .25
355 A185 20c Czechoslovakia .25 .25
356 A185 20c Thailand .25 .25
357 A185 20c Trinidad & Tobago .25 .25
  a.   Se-tenant block of 4, #354-357 1.00 1.00
358 A185 20c Ukrainian SSR .25 .25
359 A185 20c Kuwait .25 .25
360 A185 20c Sudan .25 .25
361 A185 20c Egypt .25 .25
  a.   Se-tenant block of 4, #358-361 1.00 1.00
362 A185 20c US .25 .25
363 A185 20c Singapore .25 .25
364 A185 20c Panama .25 .25
365 A185 20c Costa Rica .25 .25
  a.   Se-tenant block of 4, #362-365 1.00 1.00
    Nos. 350-365 (16) 4.00 4.00

See note after No. 340.

Seedling and Tree Cross Section
A194

"10" and Symbols of Progress
A195

United Nations Volunteers Program, 10th anniv.

1981, Nov. 13   Litho.
366 A194 18c multicolored .25 .25
367 A195 28c multicolored .55 .55

See UN Offices in Geneva Nos. 103-104; Vienna Nos. 22-23.

Respect for Human Rights — A196

Independence of Colonial Countries and People — A197

Second Disarmament Decade — A198

1982, Jan. 22   Perf. 11½x12
368 A196 17c multicolored .25 .25
369 A197 28c multicolored .45 .40
370 A198 40c multicolored .75 .70
    Nos. 368-370 (3) 1.45 1.35

A199

A200

10th Anniversary of United Nations Environment Program.

1982, Mar. 19   Litho.   Perf. 13½x13
371 A199 20c multicolored .25 .25
372 A200 40c multicolored .65 .65

See UN Offices in Geneva Nos. 107-108; Vienna Nos. 25-26.

UN Emblem and Olive Branch in Outer Space
A201

Exploration and Peaceful Uses of Outer Space.

1982, June 11   Litho.   Perf. 13x13½
373 A201 20c multicolored .45 .45

See UN Offices in Geneva Nos. 109-110; Vienna No. 27.

Flag Type of 1980
1982, Sept. 24   Litho.   Perf. 12
Granite Paper
374 A185 20c Austria .25 .25
375 A185 20c Malaysia .25 .25
376 A185 20c Seychelles .25 .25
377 A185 20c Ireland .25 .25
  a.   Se-tenant block of 4, #374-377 1.50 1.50
378 A185 20c Mozambique .25 .25
379 A185 20c Albania .25 .25
380 A185 20c Dominica .25 .25
381 A185 20c Solomon Islnads .25 .25
  a.   Se-tenant block of 4, #378-381 1.50 1.50
382 A185 20c Philippines .25 .25
383 A185 20c Swaziland .25 .25
384 A185 20c Nicaragua .25 .25
385 A185 20c Burma .25 .25
  a.   Se-tenant block of 4, #382-385 1.50 1.50
386 A185 20c Cape Verde .25 .25
387 A185 20c Guyana .25 .25
388 A185 20c Belgium .25 .25
389 A185 20c Nigeria .25 .25
  a.   Se-tenant block of 4, #386-389 1.50 1.50
    Nos. 374-389 (16) 4.00 4.00

See note after No. 340.

Conservation and Protection of Nature — A202

1982, Nov. 19   Photo.   Perf. 14
390 A202 20c Leaf .30 .30
391 A202 28c Butterfly .55 .50

See UN Offices in Geneva Nos. 111-112; Vienna Nos. 28-29.

A203

World Communications Year — A204

World Communications Year.

1983, Jan. 28   Litho.   Perf. 13
392 A203 20c multicolored .25 .25
393 A204 40c multicolored .65 .65

See UN Offices in Geneva No. 113; Vienna No. 30.

A205

Safety at Sea — A206

Safety at Sea.

1983, Mar. 18   Litho.   Perf. 14½
394 A205 20c multicolored .25 .25
395 A206 37c multicolored .60 .55

See UN Offices in Geneva Nos. 114-115; Vienna Nos. 31-32.

World Food Program
A207

1983, Apr. 22   Engr.   Perf. 13½
396 A207 20c rose lake .35 .35

See UN Offices in Geneva No. 116; Vienna Nos. 33-34.

A208

Trade and Development
A209

UN Conference on Trade and Development.

1983, June 6   Litho.   Perf. 14
397 A208 20c multicolored .25 .35
398 A209 28c multicolored .70 .65

See UN Offices in Geneva Nos. 117-118; Vienna Nos. 35-36.

Flag Type of 1980
1983, Sept. 23   Photo.   Perf. 12
Granite Paper
399 A185 20c Great Britain .25 .25
400 A185 20c Barbados .25 .25
401 A185 20c Nepal .25 .25
402 A185 20c Israel .25 .25
  a.   Se-tenant block of 4, #399-402 1.50 1.50
403 A185 20c Malawi .25 .25
404 A185 20c Byelorussian SSR .25 .25
405 A185 20c Jamaica .25 .25
406 A185 20c Kenya .25 .25
  a.   Se-tenant block of 4, #403-406 1.50 1.80
407 A185 20c People's Republic
                of China .25 .25
408 A185 20c Peru .25 .25
409 A185 20c Bulgaria .25 .25
410 A185 20c Canada .25 .25
  a.   Se-tenant block of 4, #407-410 1.50 1.80
411 A185 20c Somalia .25 .25
412 A185 20c Senegal .25 .25
413 A185 20c Brazil .25 .25
414 A185 20c Sweden .25 .25
  a.   Se-tenant block of 4, #411-414 1.50 1.80
    Nos. 399-414 (16) 4.00 4.00

See note after No. 340.

A210

35th Anniv. of
the Universal
Declaration of
Human
Rights — A211

35th Anniversary of the Universal Declaration of Human Rights.

Photo. & Engr.
1983, Dec. 9　　　　　**Perf. 13½**
415 A210 20c multicolored　　　.30　.25
416 A211 40c multicolored　　　.70　.65
　　See UN Offices in Geneva Nos. 119-120;
Vienna Nos. 37-38.

Intl. Population
Conference
A212

1984, Feb. 3　　　**Litho.**　　**Perf. 14**
417 A212 20c multicolored　　　.25　.25
418 A212 40c multicolored　　　.65　.65
　　See UN Offices in Geneva No. 121; Vienna
No. 39.

Tractor
Plowing
A213

Rice
Paddy
A214

World Food Day, Oct. 16.

1984, Mar. 15　　**Litho.**　　**Perf. 14½**
419 A213 20c multicolored　　　.30　.30
420 A214 40c multicolored　　　.60　.60
　　See UN Offices in Geneva Nos. 122-123;
Vienna Nos. 40-41.

Grand
Canyon
A215

Ancient City
of
Polonnaruwa,
Sri Lanka
A216

World Heritage.

1984, Apr. 18　　**Litho.**　　**Perf. 14**
421 A215 20c multicolored　　　.25　.25
422 A216 50c multicolored　　　.75　.75
　　See Nos. 601-602, UN Offices in Geneva
Nos. 124-125, 211-212; Vienna Nos. 42-43,
125-126.

A217　　　　　　A218

Future for Refugees.

1984, May 29　　**Photo.**　　**Perf. 11½**
423 A217 20c multicolored　　　.30　.30
424 A218 50c multicolored　　　.90　.90
　　See UN Offices in Geneva Nos. 126-127;
Vienna Nos. 44-45.

Flag Type of 1980
1984, Sept. 21　　**Photo.**　　**Perf. 12**
Granite Paper
425 A185 20c Burundi　　　　　.25　.25
426 A185 20c Pakistan　　　　　.25　.25
427 A185 20c Benin　　　　　　.25　.25
428 A185 20c Italy　　　　　　.25　.25
　a.　　Se-tenant block of 4, #425-428　1.80　1.80
429 A185 20c Tanzania　　　　.25　.25
430 A185 20c United Arab Emir-
　　　　　　ates　　　　　　　.25　.25
431 A185 20c Ecuador　　　　　.25　.25
432 A185 20c Bahamas　　　　　.25　.25
　a.　　Se-tenant block of 4, #429-432　1.80　1.80
433 A185 20c Poland　　　　　　.25　.25
434 A185 20c Papua New Guin-
　　　　　　ea　　　　　　　.25　.25
435 A185 20c Uruguay　　　　　.25　.25
436 A185 20c Chile　　　　　　.25　.25
　a.　　Se-tenant block of 4, #433-436　1.80　1.80
437 A185 20c Paraguay　　　　　.25　.25
438 A185 20c Bhutan　　　　　　.25　.25
439 A185 20c Central African
　　　　　　Republic　　　　.25　.25
440 A185 20c Australia　　　　　.25　.25
　a.　　Se-tenant block of 4, #437-440　1.80　1.80
　　Nos. 425-440 (16)　　　　4.00　4.00
　　See note after No. 340.

Intl. Youth
Year — A219

1984, Nov. 15　　**Litho.**　　**Perf. 13½**
441 A219 20c multicolored　　　.35　.35
442 A219 35c multicolored　　　.85　.85
　　See UN Offices in Geneva No. 128; Vienna
Nos. 46-47.

ILO Turin
Center — A220

Printed by the Government Printing Bureau,
Japan. Panes of 50. Engraved by Mamoru
Iwakuni and Hiroshi Ozaki, Japan.

1985, Feb. 1　　**Engr.**　　**Perf. 13½**
443 A220 23c blue　　　　　　.45　.45
　　See UN Offices in Geneva Nos. 129-130;
Vienna No. 48.

UN
University
A221

50c, Farmer plowing, discussion group.

1985, Mar. 15　　**Photo.**　　**Perf. 11½**
444 A221 50c multi　　　　　.95　.95
　　See UN Offices in Geneva Nos. 131-132;
Vienna No. 49.

Peoples of
the World
A222

Painting UN
Emblem
A223

1985, May 10　　**Litho.**　　**Perf. 14**
445 A222 22c multicolored　　　.30　.30
446 A223 $3 multicolored　　　3.75　1.50
　　See UN Offices in Geneva Nos. 133-134;
Vienna Nos. 50-51.

The
Corner
A224

Alvaro
Raking
Hay
A225

UN 40th anniversary. Oil paintings (details)
by American artist Andrew Wyeth (b. 1917).

Perf. 12 x 11½
1985, June 26　　　　　**Photo.**
447 A224 22c multicolored　　　.35　.35
448 A225 45c multicolored　　　1.00　1.00

Souvenir Sheet
Imperf
449　　Sheet of 2　　　　1.10　1.30
　a.　A224 22c multicolored　　.40　.50
　b.　A225 45c multicolored　　.70　.80
　　See UN Offices in Geneva Nos. 135-137;
Vienna Nos. 52-54.

Flag Type of 1980
1985, Sept. 20　　**Photo.**　　**Perf. 12**
Granite Paper
450 A185 22c Grenada　　　　　.30　.30
451 A185 22c Federal Republic
　　　　　　of Germany　　　.30　.30
452 A185 22c Saudi Arabia　　　.30　.30
453 A185 22c Mexico　　　　　.30　.30
　a.　　Se-tenant block of 4, #450-453　2.75　3.00
454 A185 22c Uganda　　　　　.30　.30
455 A185 22c St. Thomas &
　　　　　　Prince　　　　　.30　.30
456 A185 22c USSR　　　　　.30　.30
457 A185 22c India　　　　　　.30　.30
　a.　　Se-tenant block of 4, #454-457　2.75　3.00
458 A185 22c Liberia　　　　　.30　.30
459 A185 22c Mauritius　　　　.30　.30
460 A185 22c Chad　　　　　　.30　.30
461 A185 22c Dominican Re-
　　　　　　public　　　　　.30　.30
　a.　　Se-tenant block of 4, #458-461　2.75　3.00
462 A185 22c Sultanate of
　　　　　　Oman　　　　　.30　.30
463 A185 22c Ghana　　　　　.30　.30
464 A185 22c Sierra Leone　　　.30　.30
465 A185 22c Finland　　　　　.30　.30
　a.　　Se-tenant block of 4, #462-465　2.75　3.00
　　Nos. 450-465 (16)　　　　4.80　4.80
　　See note after 340.

A226

UNICEF Child Survival Campaign.

Photo. & Engr.
1985, Nov. 22　　　　　**Perf. 13½**
466 A226 22c Asian Toddler　　.30　.30
467 A226 33c Breastfeeding　　.65　.65
　　See UN Offices in Geneva Nos. 138-139;
Vienna Nos. 55-56.

A227

Africa in Crisis, campaign against hunger.

1986, Jan. 31　　**Photo.**　　**Perf. 11½x12**
468 A227 22c multicolored　　　.40　.40
　　See UN Offices in Geneva No. 140; Vienna
No. 57.

Water
Resources
A228

1986, Mar. 14　　　　　**Photo.**　　**Perf. 13½**
469 A228 22c Dam　　　　　　.60　.60
470 A228 22c Irrigation　　　　.60　.60
471 A228 22c Hygiene　　　　　.60　.60
472 A228 22c Well　　　　　　.60　.60
　a.　　Block of 4, #469-472　　2.75　2.75
　　UN Development Program. No. 472a has
continuous design. See UN Offices in Geneva
Nos. 141-144; Vienna Nos. 58-61.

Human Rights
Stamp of
1954 — A229

Stamp collecting: 44c, Engraver.

1986, May 22　　**Engr.**　　**Perf. 12½**
473 A229 22c dk vio & brt blue　.25　.25
474 A229 44c brn & emer grn　　.75　.75
　　See UN Offices in Geneva Nos. 146-147;
Vienna Nos. 62-63.

Birds Nest in
Tree — A230

Peace in
Seven
Languages
A231

Photo. & Embossed
1986, June 20　　　　　**Perf. 13½**
475 A230 22c multicolored　　　.50　.50
476 A231 33c multicolored　　　1.25　1.25
　　International Peace Year.
　　See UN Offices in Geneva Nos. 148-149;
Vienna Nos. 64-65.

Flag Type of 1980

1986, Sept. 19   Photo.   Perf. 12
Granite Paper

477	A185 22c New Zealand	.30	.30
478	A185 22c Lao PDR	.30	.30
479	A185 22c Burkina Faso	.30	.30
480	A185 22c Gambia	.30	.30
a.	Se-tenant block of 4, #477-480	2.75	3.00
481	A185 22c Maldives	.30	.30
482	A185 22c Ethiopia	.30	.30
483	A185 22c Jordan	.30	.30
484	A185 22c Zambia	.30	.30
a.	Se-tenant block of 4, #481-484	2.75	3.00
485	A185 22c Iceland	.30	.30
486	A185 22c Antigua & Barbuda	.30	.30
487	A185 22c Angola	.30	.30
488	A185 22c Botswana	.30	.30
a.	Se-tenant block of 4, #485-488	2.75	3.00
489	A185 22c Romania	.30	.30
490	A185 22c Togo	.30	.30
491	A185 22c Mauritania	.30	.30
492	A185 22c Colombia	.30	.30
a.	Se-tenant block of 4, #489-492	2.75	3.00
	Nos. 477-492 (16)	4.80	4.80

See note after No. 340.

Souvenir Sheet

World Federation of UN Associations, 40th Anniv. — A232

22c, Mother Earth, by Edna Hibel, U.S. 33c, Watercolor by Salvador Dali (b. 1904), Spain. 39c, New Dawn, by Dong Kingman, U.S. 44c, Watercolor by Chaim Gross, U.S.

1986, Nov. 14   Litho.   Perf. 13x13½

493	A232 Sheet of 4	2.50	2.50
a.	22c multicolored	.30	.40
b.	33c multicolored	.40	.40
c.	39c multicolored	.60	.50
d.	44c multicolored	.90	.75

See UN Offices in Geneva No. 150; Vienna No. 66.

Trygve Halvdan Lie (1896-1968), 1st Secretary-General A233

Photo. & Engr.
1987, Jan. 30   Perf. 13½

494	A233 22c multicolored	.75	.75

See Offices in Geneva No. 151; Vienna No. 67.

Intl. Year of Shelter for the Homeless A234

22c, Surveying and blueprinting. 44c, Cutting lumber.

Perf. 13½x12½
1987, Mar. 13   Litho.

495	A234 22c multicolored	.35	.35
496	A234 44c multicolored	.90	.90

See Offices in Geneva Nos. 154-155; Vienna Nos. 68-69.

Fight Drug Abuse A235

22c, Construction. 33c, Education.

1987, June 12   Litho.   Perf. 14½x15

497	A235 22c multicolored	.45	.45
498	A235 33c multicolored	.90	.90

See Offices in Geneva Nos. 156-157; Vienna Nos. 70-71.

Flag Type of 1980

1987, Sept. 18   Photo.   Perf. 12
Granite Paper

499	A185 22c Comoros	.30	.35
500	A185 22c Yemen PDR	.30	.35
501	A185 22c Mongolia	.30	.35
502	A185 22c Vanuatu	.30	.35
a.	Se-tenant block of 4, #499-502	3.25	3.25
503	A185 22c Japan	.30	.35
504	A185 22c Gabon	.30	.35
505	A185 22c Zimbabwe	.30	.35
506	A185 22c Iraq	.30	.35
a.	Se-tenant block of 4, #503-506	3.25	3.25
507	A185 22c Argentina	.30	.35
508	A185 22c Congo	.30	.35
509	A185 22c Niger	.30	.35
510	A185 22c St. Lucia	.30	.35
a.	Se-tenant block of 4, #507-510	3.25	3.25
511	A185 22c Bahrain	.30	.35
512	A185 22c Haiti	.30	.35
513	A185 22c Afghanistan	.30	.35
514	A185 22c Greece	.30	.35
a.	Se-tenant block of 4, #511-514	3.25	3.25
	Nos. 499-514 (16)	4.80	5.60

See note after No. 340.

UN Day — A236

Multinational people in various occupations.

1987, Oct. 23   Litho.   Perf. 14½x15

515	A236 22c multicolored	.35	.35
516	A236 39c multicolored	.55	.55

See Offices in Geneva Nos. 158-159; Vienna Nos. 74-75.

Immunize Every Child — A237

22c, Measles. 44c, Tetanus.

1987, Nov. 20   Litho.   Perf. 15x14½

517	A237 22c multicolored	.75	.75
518	A237 44c multicolored	1.50	1.50

See Offices in Geneva Nos. 160-161; Vienna Nos. 76-77.

Intl. Fund for Agricultural Development (IFAD) — A238

22c, Fishing. 33c, Farming.

1988, Jan. 29   Litho.   Perf. 13½

519	A238 22c multicolored	.35	.35
520	A238 33c multicolored	.75	.75

See Offices in Geneva Nos. 162-163; Vienna Nos. 78-79.

A239

1988, Jan. 29   Photo.   Perf. 13½x14

521	A239 3c multicolored	.25	.25

Survival of the Forests A240

Tropical rain forest: 25c, Treetops. 44c, Ground vegetation and tree trunks. Printed se-tenant in a continuous design.

1988, Mar. 18   Litho.   Perf. 14x15

522	A240 25c multicolored	.75	.75
523	A240 44c multicolored	1.00	1.00
a.	Pair, #522-523	2.00	3.00

See Offices in Geneva Nos. 165-166; Vienna Nos. 80-81.

Intl. Volunteer Day — A241

25c, Edurahon. 50c, Vocational training, horiz.

Perf. 13x14, 14x13
1988, May 6   Litho.

524	A241 25c multicolored	.45	.45
525	A241 50c multicolored	.95	.95

See Offices in Geneva Nos. 167-168; Vienna Nos. 82-83.

Health in Sports — A242

25c, Cycling, vert. 35c, Marathon.

Perf. 13½x13, 13x13½
1988, June 17   Litho.

526	A242 25c multicolored	.45	.45
527	A242 38c multicolored	1.00	1.00

See Offices in Geneva Nos. 169-170; Vienna Nos. 84-85.

Flag Type of 1980

1988, Sept. 15   Photo.   Perf. 12
Granite Paper

528	A185 25c Spain	.45	.45
529	A185 25c St. Vincent & Grenadines	.45	.45
530	A185 25c Ivory Coast	.45	.45
531	A185 25c Lebanon	.45	.45
a.	Se-tenant block of 4, #528-531	3.00	3.00
532	A185 25c Yemen (Arab Republic)	.45	.45
533	A185 25c Cuba	.45	.45
534	A185 25c Denmark	.45	.45
535	A185 25c Libya	.45	.45
a.	Se-tenant block of 4, #532-535	3.00	3.00
536	A185 25c Qatar	.45	.45
537	A185 25c Zaire	.45	.45
538	A185 25c Norway	.45	.45
539	A185 25c German Democratic Republic	.45	.45
a.	Se-tenant block of 4, #536-539	3.00	3.00
540	A185 25c Iran	.45	.45
541	A185 25c Tunisia	.45	.45
542	A185 25c Samoa	.45	.45
543	A185 25c Belize	.45	.45
a.	Se-tenant block of 4, #540-543	3.00	3.00
	Nos. 528-543 (16)	7.20	7.20

See note after No. 340.

A243

Photo. & Engr.
1988, Dec. 9   Perf. 11x11½

544	A243 25c multicolored	.45	.45

Souvenir Sheet

545	A243 $1 multicolored	1.00	1.00

Universal Declaration of Human Rights, 40th anniv.
See Offices in Geneva Nos. 171-172; Vienna Nos. 86-87.

A244

1989, Jan. 27   Litho.   Perf. 13x14

546	A244 25c Energy and nature	.60	.60
547	A244 45c Agriculture	1.10	1.10

World Bank. See Offices in Geneva Nos. 173-174; Vienna Nos. 88-89.

UN Peace-Keeping Force, 1988 Nobel Peace Prize Winner — A245

UN Peace-Keeping Force, awarded 1988 Nobel Peace Prize.

1989, Mar. 17   Litho.   Perf. 14x13½

548	A245 25c multicolored	.45	.45

See Offices in Geneva No. 175; Vienna No. 90.

Aerial Photograph of New York Headquarters — A246

1989, Mar. 17   Litho.   Perf. 14½x14

549	A246 45c multicolored	.65	.65

World Weather Watch, 25th Anniv. (in 1988) — A247

Satellite photographs: 25c, Storm system off the U.S. east coast. 36c, Typhoon Abby in the north-west Pacific.

1989, Apr. 21   Litho.   Perf. 13x14

550	A247 25c multicolored	.50	.50
551	A247 36c multicolored	1.10	1.10

See Offices in Geneva Nos. 176-177; Vienna Nos. 91-92.

A248   A249

Photo. & Engr., Photo. (90c)
1989, Aug. 23   **Perf. 14**
552 A248 25c multicolored   1.25 1.25
553 A249 90c multicolored   2.50 2.50

See Offices in Geneva Nos. 178-179; Vienna Nos. 93-94.

Flag Type of 1980
1989, Sept. 22   Photo.   Perf. 12
Granite Paper
554 A185 25c Indonesia   .55 .55
555 A185 25c Lesotho   .55 .55
556 A185 25c Guatemala   .55 .55
557 A185 25c Netherlands   .55 .55
  a.   Se-tenant block of 4, #554-557   4.00 4.00
558 A185 25c South Africa   .55 .55
559 A185 25c Portugal   .55 .55
560 A185 25c Morocco   .55 .55
561 A185 25c Syrian Arab Re-
          public   .55 .55
  a.   Se-tenant block of 4, #558-561   4.00 4.00
562 A185 25c Honduras   .55 .55
563 A185 25c Kampuchea   .55 .55
564 A185 25c Guinea-Bissau   .55 .55
565 A185 25c Cyprus   .55 .55
  a.   Se-tenant block of 4, #562-565   4.00 4.00
566 A185 25c Algeria   .55 .55
567 A185 25c Brunei   .55 .55
568 A185 25c St. Kitts and Nev-
          is   .55 .55
569 A185 25c United Nations   .55 .55
  a.   Se-tenant block of 4, #566-569   4.00 4.00
      Nos. 554-569 (16)   8.80 8.80

See note after No. 340.

Declaration of Human Rights, 40th Anniv. (in 1988) — A250

Paintings: 25c, The Table of Universal Brotherhood, by Jose Clemente Orozco. 45c, Study for Composition II, by Vassily Kandinsky.

1989, Nov. 17   Litho.   Perf. 13½
570 A250 25c multicolored   .35 .35
571 A250 45c multicolored   .80 .80

Panes of 12+12 se-tenant labels containing Articles 1 (25c) or 2 (45c) inscribed in English, French or German.

See Nos. 582-583, 599-600, 616-617, 627-628; Offices in Geneva Nos. 180-181, 193-194, 209-210, 224-225, 234-235; Vienna Nos. 95-96, 108-109, 123-124, 139-140, 150-151.

Intl. Trade Center A251

1990, Feb. 2   Litho.   Perf. 14½x15
572 A251 25c multicolored   1.00 1.00

See Offices in Geneva No. 182; Vienna No. 97.

Fight AIDS Worldwide A252

40c, Shadow over crowd.

Perf. 13½x12½
1990, Mar. 16   **Litho.**
573 A252 25c multicolored   .35 .35
574 A252 40c multicolored   1.15 1.15

See Offices in Geneva Nos. 184-185, Vienna Nos. 99-100.

Medicinal Plants — A253

25c, Catharanthus roseus. 90c, Panax quinquefolium.

1990, May 4   Photo.   Perf. 11½
Granite Paper
575 A253 25c multi   .45 .45
576 A253 90c multi   1.40 1.40

See Offices in Geneva Nos. 186-187, Vienna Nos. 101-102.

United Nations, 45th Anniv. A254

45c, "45," emblem.

1990, June 26   Litho.   Perf. 14½x13
577 A254 25c multicolored   .50 .50
578 A254 45c multicolored   1.90 1.90
Souvenir Sheet
579   Sheet of 2, #577-578   3.50 3.50

See Offices in Geneva Nos. 188-190; Vienna Nos. 103-105.

Crime Prevention — A255

1990, Sept. 13   Photo.   Perf. 14
580 A255 25c Crimes of youth   .65 .65
581 A255 36c Organized crime   1.25 1.25

See Offices in Geneva Nos. 191-192; Vienna Nos. 106-107.

Human Rights Type of 1989
25c, Fragment from the sarcophagus of Plotinus, c. 270 A.D. 45c, Combined Chambers of the High Court of Appeal by Charles Paul Renouard.

1990, Nov. 16   Litho.   Perf. 13½
582 A250 25c black, gray & tan   .35 .35
583 A250 45c black & brown   .65 .65

See Offices in Geneva Nos. 193-194; Vienna Nos. 108-109.

Economic Commission for Europe A256

1991, Mar. 15   Litho.   Perf. 14
584 A256 30c Two storks   .85 .85
585 A256 30c Woodpecker, ibex   .85 .85
586 A256 30c Capercaille, plover   .85 .85
587 A256 30c Falcon, marmot   .85 .85
  a.   Block of 4, #584-587   3.75 3.75

See Offices in Geneva Nos. 195-198; Vienna Nos. 110-113.

Namibian Independence A257

1991, May 10   Litho.   Perf. 14
588 A257 30c Dunes, Namib De-
          sert   .50 .50
589 A257 50c Savanna   1.10 1.00

See Offices in Geneva Nos. 199-200; Vienna Nos. 114-115.

A258

The Golden Rule by Norman Rockwell — A259

UN Headquarters, New York — A260

1991   Litho.   Perf. 13½
590 A258 30c multi   .60 .60
Photo.
Perf. 12x11½
591 A259 50c multi   1.00 1.00
Engr.
592 A260 $2 dark blue   2.75 2.75

Rights of the Child — A261

1991, June 14   Litho.   Perf. 14½
593 A261 30c Children, globe   1.00 1.00
594 A261 70c House, rainbow   2.00 2.00

See Offices in Geneva Nos. 203-204; Vienna Nos. 117-118.

Banning of Chemical Weapons A262

90c, Hand holding back chemical drums.

1991, Sept. 11   Litho.   Perf. 13½
595 A262 30c multicolored   .75 .75
596 A262 90c multicolored   2.25 2.25

See Offices in Geneva Nos. 205-206; Vienna Nos. 119-120.

UN Postal Administration, 40th Anniv. — A263

1991, Oct. 24   Litho.   Perf. 14x15
597 A263 30c No. 1   .65 .65
598 A263 40c No. 3   .85 .85

See Offices in Geneva Nos. 207-208; Vienna Nos. 121-122.

Human Rights Type of 1989
30c, The Last of England, by Ford Madox Brown. 40c, The Emigration to the East, by Tito Salas.

1991, Nov. 20   Litho.   Perf. 13½
599 A250 30c multicolored   .35 .35
600 A250 50c multicolored   .80 1.00

See Offices in Geneva Nos. 209-210; Vienna Nos. 123-124.

World Heritage Type of 1984
30c, Uluru Natl. Park, Australia. 50c, The Great Wall of China.

1992, Jan. 24   Litho.   Perf. 13
Size: 35x28mm
601 A215 30c multicolored   .55 .55
602 A215 50c multicolored   .90 .90

See Offices in Geneva Nos. 211-212; Vienna Nos. 125-126.

Clean Oceans — A264

1992, Mar. 13   Litho.   Perf. 14
603 A264 29c Ocean surface   .45 .50
604 A264 29c Ocean bottom   .45 .50
  a.   Pair, #603-604   .90 1.10

See Offices in Geneva Nos. 214-215, Vienna Nos. 127-128.

Earth Summit — A265

No. 605, Globe at LR. No. 606, Globe at LL. No. 607, Globe at UR. No. 608, Globe at UL.

1992, May 22   Photo.   Perf. 11½
605 A265 29c multicolored   .65 .65
606 A265 29c multicolored   .65 .65
607 A265 29c multicolored   .65 .65
608 A265 29c multicolored   .65 .65
  a.   Block of 4, #605-608   4.00 3.50

See Offices in Geneva Nos. 216-219, Vienna Nos. 129-132.

Mission to Planet Earth — A266

No. 609, Satellites over city, sailboats, fishing boat. No. 610, Satellite over coast, passenger liner, dolphins, whale, volcano.

1992, Sept. 4   Photo.   Rouletted 8
Granite Paper
609 A266 29c multicolored   1.50 1.50
610 A266 29c multicolored   1.50 1.50
  a.   Pair, #609-610   3.00 3.00

See Offices in Geneva Nos. 220-221, Vienna Nos. 133-134.

Science and Technology for
Development — A267

50c, Animal, man drinking.

1992, Oct. 2   Litho.   Perf. 14
611 A267 29c multicolored   .40   .40
612 A267 50c multicolored   .70   .70

UN
University
Building,
Tokyo
A268

UN
Headquarters
A269

40c, UN University Building, Tokyo, diff.

Perf. 14, 13½x13 (29c)
1992, Oct. 2   Litho.
613 A268   4c multicolored   .25   .25
614 A269 29c multicolored   .50   .50
615 A268 40c multicolored   .65   .65
        Nos. 613-615 (3)   1.40 1.40

Human Rights Type of 1989
29c, Lady Writing a Letter with her Maid, by
Vermeer. 50c, The Meeting, by Ester Almqvist.

1992, Nov. 20   Litho.   Perf. 13½
616 A250 29c multicolored   .40   .40
617 A250 50c multicolored   .60   .60

   See Offices in Geneva Nos. 224-225;
Vienna Nos. 139-140.

Aging With
Dignity — A270

29c, Elderly couple, family. 52c, Old man,
physician, woman holding fruit basket.

1993, Feb. 5   Litho.   Perf. 13
618 A270 29c multicolored   .45   .45
619 A270 52c multicolored   1.00 1.00

   See Offices in Geneva Nos. 226-227;
Vienna Nos. 141-142.

Endangered
Species
A271

   No. 620, Hairy-nosed wombat. No. 621,
Whooping crane. No. 622, Giant clam. No.
623, Giant sable antelope.

1993, Mar. 2   Litho.   Perf. 13x12½
620 A271 29c multicolored   .45   .45
621 A271 29c multicolored   .45   .45
622 A271 29c multicolored   .45   .45
623 A271 29c multicolored   .45   .45
   a.   Block of 4, #620-623   2.00 2.00

   See Nos. 639-642, 657-660, 674-677, 700-
703, 730-733, 757-760, 773-776; Offices in
Geneva Nos. 228-231, 246-249, 264-267,
280-283, 298-301, 318-321, 336-339, 352-
355; Vienna Nos. 143-146, 162-165, 180-183,
196-199, 214-217, 235-238, 253-256, 269-
272.

Healthy
Environment
A272

29c, Personal. 50c, Family.

1993, May 7   Litho.   Perf. 15x14½
624 A272 29c Man   .50   .50
625 A272 50c Family   .90   .90

   See Offices in Geneva Nos. 232-233;
Vienna Nos. 147-148.

A273

1993, May 7   Litho.   Perf. 15x14
626 A273   5c multicolored   .25   .25

Human Rights Type of 1989
29c, Shucking Corn, by Thomas Hart Benton. 35c, The Library, by Jacob Lawrence.

1993, June 11   Litho.   Perf. 13½
627 A250 29c multicolored   .40   .40
628 A250 35c multicolored   .45   .45

   See Offices in Geneva Nos. 234-235;
Vienna Nos. 150-151.

Intl. Peace Day — A274

   Denomination at: #629, UL. #630, UR.
#631, LL. #632, LR.

Rouletted 12½
1993, Sept. 21   Litho. & Engr.
629 A274 29c blue & multi   1.00 1.00
630 A274 29c blue & multi   1.00 1.00
631 A274 29c blue & multi   1.00 1.00
632 A274 29c blue & multi   1.00 1.00
   a.   Block of 4, #629-632   6.00 6.00

   See Offices in Geneva Nos. 236-239;
Vienna Nos. 152-155.

Environment-Climate — A275

   No. 633, Chameleon. No. 634, Palm trees,
top of funnel cloud. No. 635, Bottom of funnel
cloud, deer, antelope. No. 636, Bird of
paradise.

1993, Oct. 29   Litho.   Perf. 14½
633 A275 29c multicolored   .90   .90
634 A275 29c multicolored   .90   .90
635 A275 29c multicolored   .90   .90
636 A275 29c multicolored   .90   .90
   a.   Strip of 4, #633-636   4.75 4.75

   See Offices in Geneva Nos. 240-243;
Vienna Nos. 156-159.

Intl. Year of the
Family — A276

   29c, Mother holding child, two children,
woman. 45c, People tending crops.

1994, Feb. 4   Litho.   Perf. 13.1
637 A276 29c green & multi   .70   .70
638 A276 45c blue & multi   .90   .90

   See Offices in Geneva Nos. 244-245;
Vienna Nos. 160-161.

Endangered Species Type of 1993
   No. 639, Chimpanzee. No. 640, St. Lucia
Amazon. No. 641, American crocodile. No.
642, Dama gazelle.

1994, Mar. 18   Litho.   Perf. 12.7
639 A271 29c multicolored   .45   .45
640 A271 29c multicolored   .45   .45
641 A271 29c multicolored   .45   .45
642 A271 29c multicolored   .45   .45
   a.   Block of 4, #639-642   2.00 2.00

   See Offices in Geneva Nos. 246-249;
Vienna Nos. 162-165.

Protection for
Refugees — A277

1994, Apr. 29   Litho.   Perf. 14.3x14.8
643 A277 50c multicolored   .90   .90

   See Offices in Geneva No. 250; Vienna No.
166.

Dove of
Peace — A278

Sleeping Child,
by Stanislaw
Wyspianski
A279

Mourning Owl,
by Vanessa Isitt
A280

1994, Apr. 29   Litho.   Perf. 12.9
644 A278 10c multicolored   .25   .25
645 A279 19c multicolored   .30   .30

Engr.
Perf. 13.1
646 A280 $1 red brown   1.50 1.50
        Nos. 644-646 (3)   2.05 2.05

Intl. Decade for
Natural
Disaster
Reduction
A281

   Earth seen from space, outline map of:
#647, North America. #648, Eurasia. #649,
South America, #650, Australia and South
Asia.

1994, May 27   Litho.   Perf. 13.9x14.2
647 A281 29c multicolored   1.75 1.75
648 A281 29c multicolored   1.75 1.75
649 A281 29c multicolored   1.75 1.75
650 A281 29c multicolored   1.75 1.75
   a.   Block of 4, #647-650   7.50 7.50

   See Offices in Geneva Nos. 251-254;
Vienna Nos. 170-173.

Population and Development — A282

   29c, Children playing. 52c, Family with
house, car, other possessions.

1994, Sept. 1   Litho.   Perf. 13.2x13.6
651 A282 29c multicolored   .40   .40
652 A282 52c multicolored   .80   .80

   See Offices in Geneva Nos. 258-259;
Vienna Nos. 174-175.

UNCTAD,
30th Anniv.
A283

1994, Oct. 28
653 A283 29c multicolored   .40   .40
654 A283 50c multi, diff.   .80   .80

   See Offices in Geneva Nos. 260-261;
Vienna Nos. 176-177.

UN, 50th
Anniv. — A284

Litho. & Engr.
1995, Jan. 1   Perf. 13.4
655 A284 32c multicolored   .90   .90

   See Offices in Geneva No. 262; Vienna No.
178.

Social Summit,
Copenhagen
A285

656 A285 50c multicolored   1.00 1.00

   See Offices in Geneva No. 263; Vienna No.
179.

Endangered Species Type of 1993
   No. 657, Giant armadillo. No. 658, American
bald eagle. No. 659, Fijian/Tongan banded
iguana. No. 660, Giant panda.

1995, Mar. 24   Litho.   Perf. 13x12½
657 A271 32c multicolored   .40   .40
658 A271 32c multicolored   .40   .40
659 A271 32c multicolored   .40   .40
660 A271 32c multicolored   .40   .40
   a.   Block of 4, 657-660   2.25 2.25

   See Offices in Geneva Nos. 264-267;
Vienna Nos. 180-183.

Intl. Youth
Year, 10th
Anniv.
A286

32c, Seated child. 55c, Children cycling.

1995, May 26   Litho.   Perf. 14.4x14.7
661 A286 32c multicolored   .55   .55
662 A286 55c multicolored   .95   .95

   See Offices in Geneva Nos. 268-269;
Vienna Nos. 184-185.

UN, 50th
Anniv. — A287

32c, Hand with pen signing UN Charter,
flags. 50c, Veterans' War Memorial, Opera
House, San Francisco.

Perf. 13.3x13.6

			Engr.	
1995, June 26				
663	A287	32c black	.55	.55
664	A287	50c maroon	1.00	1.00

Souvenir Sheet
Litho. & Engr.
Imperf

665		Sheet of 2, #663-664	3.00	3.00
a.	A287	32c black	1.25	1.25
b.	A287	50c maroon	1.50	1.50

No. 665 exists with gold China 1996 over-
print. Value $20.
See Offices in Geneva Nos. 270-272;
Vienna Nos. 186-188.

4th World
Conference
on Women,
Beijing
A288

32c, Mother and child. 40c, Seated woman,
cranes flying above.

1995, Sept. 5		Photo.	Perf. 12	
666	A288	32c multicolored	.50	.50

Size: 28x50mm

| 667 | A288 | 40c multicolored | .85 | .85 |

See Offices in Geneva Nos. 273-274;
Vienna Nos. 189-190.

UN Headquarters — A289

1995, Sept. 5		Litho.	Perf. 15	
668	A289	20c multicolored	.35	.35

Miniature Sheet

United Nations, 50th Anniv. — A290

1995, Oct. 24		Litho.	Perf. 14	
669	A290	Sheet of 12	5.00	5.00
a.-l.		32c any single	.40	.40
670		Souvenir booklet	5.50	
a.	A290	32c Booklet pane of 3, vert. strip of 3 from UL of sheet	1.35	1.35
b.	A290	32c Booklet pane of 3, vert. strip of 3 from UR of sheet	1.35	1.35
c.	A290	32c Booklet pane of 3, vert. strip of 3 from LL of sheet	1.35	1.35

| *d.* | A290 | 32c Booklet pane of 3, vert. strip of 3 from LR of sheet | 1.35 | 1.35 |

See Offices in Geneva Nos. 275-276;
Vienna Nos. 191-192.

WFUNA, 50th
Anniv. — A291

1996, Feb. 2		Litho.	Perf. 13x13½	
671	A291	32c multicolored	.50	.50

See Offices in Geneva No. 277; Vienna No.
193.

Mural, by
Fernand
Leger — A292

1996, Feb. 2		Litho.	Perf. 14½x15	
672	A292	32c multicolored	.45	.45
673	A292	60c multi, diff.	.95	.95

Endangered Species Type of 1993

No. 674, Masdevallia veitchiana. No. 675,
Saguaro cactus. No. 676, West Australian
pitcher plant. No. 677, Encephalartos
horridus.

1996, Mar. 14		Litho.	Perf. 12½	
674	A271	32c multicolored	.45	.45
675	A271	32c multicolored	.45	.45
676	A271	32c multicolored	.45	.45
677	A271	32c multicolored	.45	.45
a.		Block of 4, #674-677	2.25	2.25

See Offices in Geneva Nos. 280-283;
Vienna Nos. 196-199.

City Summit
(Habitat
II) — A293

No. 678, Deer. No. 679, Man, child, dog
sitting on hill, overlooking town. No. 680, People walking in park, city skyline. No. 681, Tropical park, Polynesian woman, boy. No. 682,
Polynesian village, orchids, bird.

1996, June 3		Litho.	Perf. 14x13½	
678	A293	32c multicolored	.80	.80
679	A293	32c multicolored	.80	.80
680	A293	32c multicolored	.80	.80
681	A293	32c multicolored	.80	.80
682	A293	32c multicolored	.80	.80
a.		Strip of 5, #678-682	7.00	7.00

See Offices in Geneva Nos. 284-288;
Vienna Nos. 200-204.

Sport and the
Environment
A294

32c, Men's basketball. 50c, Women's volleyball, horiz.

Perf. 14x14½, 14½x14

1996, July 19			Litho.	
683	A294	32c multicolored	.65	.65
684	A294	50c multicolored	1.40	1.40

Souvenir Sheet

685	A294	Sheet of 2, #683-684	2.50	2.50

See Offices in Geneva Nos. 289-291;
Vienna Nos. 205-207.
1996 Summer Olympic Games, Atlanta, GA.

Plea for
Peace — A295

32c, Doves. 60c, Stylized dove.

1996, Sept. 17		Litho.	Perf. 14½x15	
686	A295	32c multicolored	.50	.50
687	A295	60c multicolored	.90	.90

See Offices in Geneva Nos. 292-293;
Vienna Nos. 208-209.

UNICEF, 50th
Anniv.
A296

Fairy Tales: 32c, Yeh-Shen, China. 60c, The
Ugly Duckling, by Hans Christian Andersen.

1996, Nov. 20		Litho.	Perf. 14½x15	
688	A296	32c multicolored	.45	.45
689	A296	60c multicolored	1.10	1.10

See Offices in Geneva Nos. 294-295;
Vienna Nos. 210-211.

Flag Type of 1980

1997, Feb. 12		Photo.	Perf. 12	
		Granite Paper		
690	A185	32c Tadjikistan	.75	1.00
691	A185	32c Georgia	.75	1.00
692	A185	32c Armenia	.75	1.00
693	A185	32c Namibia	.75	1.00
a.		Block of 4, #690-693	10.00	13.00
694	A185	32c Liechtenstein	.75	1.00
695	A185	32c Republic of Ko- rea	.75	1.00
696	A185	32c Kazakhstan	.75	1.00
697	A185	32c Latvia	.75	1.00
a.		Block of 4, #694-697	10.00	13.00

See note after No. 610.

Cherry Blossoms,
UN Headquarters
A297

Peace
Rose — A298

1997, Feb. 12		Litho.	Perf. 14½	
698	A297	8c multicolored	.25	.25
699	A298	55c multicolored	.90	.90

Endangered Species Type of 1993

No. 700, African elephant. No. 701, Major
Mitchell's cockatoo. No. 702, Black-footed ferret. No. 703, Cougar.

1997, Mar. 13		Litho.	Perf. 12½	
700	A271	32c multicolored	.40	.40
701	A271	32c multicolored	.40	.40
702	A271	32c multicolored	.40	.40
703	A271	32c multicolored	.40	.40
a.		Block of 4, #700-703	2.25	2.25

See Offices in Geneva Nos. 298-301;
Vienna Nos. 214-217.

Earth Summit,
5th Anniv.
A299

No. 704, Sailboat. No. 705, Three sailboats.
No. 706, Two people watching sailboat, sun.
No. 707, Person, sailboat.
$1, Combined design similar to Nos. 704-
707.

1997, May 30		Photo.	Perf. 11.5	
		Granite Paper		
704	A299	32c multicolored	.90	.90
705	A299	32c multicolored	.90	.90
706	A299	32c multicolored	.90	.90
707	A299	32c multicolored	.90	.90
a.		Block of 4, #704-707	5.00	5.00

Souvenir Sheet

708	A299	$1 multicolored	3.25	3.25
a.		Ovptd. in sheet margin	17.50	17.50

See Offices in Geneva Nos. 302-306;
Vienna Nos. 218-222.

No. 708 contains one 60x43mm stamp.
Overprint in sheet margin of No. 708a reads
"PACIFIC 97 / World Philatelic Exhibition / San
Francisco, California / 29 May - 8 June 1997".

Transportation
A300

Ships: No. 709, Clipper ship. No. 710, Paddle steamer. No. 711, Ocean liner. No. 712,
Hovercraft. No. 713, Hydrofoil.

1997, Aug. 29		Litho.	Perf. 14x14½	
709	A300	32c multicolored	.65	.65
710	A300	32c multicolored	.65	.65
711	A300	32c multicolored	.65	.65
712	A300	32c multicolored	.65	.65
713	A300	32c multicolored	.65	.65
a.		Strip of 5, #709-713	1.00	1.00

See Offices in Geneva Nos. 307-311;
Vienna Nos. 223-227.

No. 713a has continuous design.

Philately — A301

32c, No. 473. 50c, No. 474.

1997, Oct. 14		Litho.	Perf. 13½x14	
714	A301	32c multicolored	.60	.60
715	A301	50c multicolored	1.50	1.50

See Offices in Geneva Nos. 312-313;
Vienna Nos. 228-229.

World Heritage
Convention, 25th
Anniv. — A302

Terracotta warriors of Xian: 32c, Single war-
rior. 60c, Massed warriors. No. 718a, like
#716. No. 718b, like #717. No. 718c, like
Geneva #314. No. 718d, like Geneva #315.
No. 718e, like Vienna #230. No. 718f, like
Vienna #231.

1997, Nov. 19   Litho.   Perf. 13½

716	A302	32c multicolored	.75 .75
717	A302	60c multicolored	1.25 1.25
718		Souvenir booklet	8.50
a.-f.	A302 8c any single		.35 .35
g.	Booklet pane of 4 #718a		1.40 1.40
h.	Booklet pane of 4 #718b		1.40 1.40
i.	Booklet pane of 4 #718c		1.40 1.40
j.	Booklet pane of 4 #718d		1.40 1.40
k.	Booklet pane of 4 #718e		1.40 1.40
l.	Booklet pane of 4 #718f		1.40 1.40

See Offices in Geneva Nos. 314-316; Vienna Nos. 230-232.

Flag Type of 1980

No. 719, Micronesia. No. 720, Slovakia. No. 721, Democratic People's Republic of Korea. No. 722, Azerbaijan. No. 723, Uzbekistan. No. 724, Monaco. No. 725, Czech Republic. No. 726, Estonia.

1998, Feb. 13   Photo.   Perf. 12
Granite Paper

719	A185	32c multicolored	.80 .80
720	A185	32c multicolored	.80 .80
721	A185	32c multicolored	.80 .80
722	A185	32c multicolored	.80 .80
a.	Block of 4, #719-722		12.50 12.50
723	A185	32c multicolored	.80 .80
724	A185	32c multicolored	.80 .80
725	A185	32c multicolored	.80 .80
726	A185	32c multicolored	.80 .80
a.	Block of 4, #723-726		12.50 12.50
	Nos. 719-726 (8)		6.40 6.40

A303

A304

A305

Perf. 14½x15, 15x14½

1998, Feb. 13   Litho.

727	A303	1c multicolored	.25 .25
728	A304	2c multicolored	.25 .25
729	A305	21c multicolored	.40 .40
	Nos. 727-729 (3)		.90 .90

Endangered Species Type of 1993

No. 730, Lesser galago. No. 731, Hawaiian goose. No. 732, Golden birdwing. No. 733, Sun bear.

1998, Mar. 13   Litho.   Perf. 12½

730	A271	32c multicolored	.45 .45
731	A271	32c multicolored	.45 .45
732	A271	32c multicolored	.45 .45
733	A271	32c multicolored	.45 .45
a.	Block of 4, #730-733		2.25 2.25

See Offices in Geneva Nos. 318-321; Vienna Nos. 235-238.

Intl. Year of the Ocean — A306

1998, May 20   Litho.   Perf. 13x13½

734	A306	Sheet of 12	12.50 12.50
a.-l.	32c any single		1.00 1.00

See Offices in Geneva No. 322; Vienna No. 239.

Rain Forests A307

1998, June 19   Litho.   Perf. 13x13½

735	A307	32c Jaguar	.50 .50

Souvenir Sheet

736	A307	$2 like #735	3.00 3.00

See Offices in Geneva Nos. 323-324; Vienna Nos. 240-241.

U.N. Peacekeeping Forces, 50th Anniv. — A308

33c, Commander with binoculars. 40c, Two soldiers on vehicle.

1998, Sept. 15   Photo.   Perf. 12

737	A308	33c multicolored	.50 .50
738	A308	40c multicolored	.75 .75

See Offices in Geneva Nos. 325-326; Vienna Nos. 242-243.

Universal Declaration of Human Rights, 50th Anniv. — A309

Stylized people: 32c, Carrying flag. 55c, Carrying pens.

Litho. & Photo.

1998, Oct. 27   Perf. 13

739	A309	32c multicolored	.45 .45
740	A309	55c multicolored	.90 .90

See Offices in Geneva Nos. 327-328; Vienna Nos. 244-245.

Schönnbrun Palace, Vienna — A310

33c, #743f, The Gloriette. 60c, #743b, Wall painting on fabric (detail), by Johann Wenzl Bergl, vert. No. 743a, Blue porcelain vase, vert. No. 743c, Porcelain stove, vert. No. 743d, Palace. No. 743e, Great Palm House (conservatory).

1998, Dec. 4   Litho.   Perf. 14

741	A310	33c multicolored	.55 .55
742	A310	60c multicolored	1.25 1.00

Souvenir Booklet

743		Booklet	19.50
a.-c.	A310 11c any single		.35 .35
d.-f.	A310 15c any single		1.40 1.40
g.	Booklet pane of 4 #743d		5.50 5.50
h.	Booklet pane of 3 #743a		1.00 1.00
i.	Booklet pane of 3 #743b		1.00 1.00
j.	Booklet pane of 3 #743c		1.00 1.00
k.	Booklet pane of 4 #743e		5.50 5.50
l.	Booklet pane of 4 #743f		5.50 5.50

See Offices in Geneva Nos. 329-331; Vienna Nos. 246-248.

Flag Type of 1980

1999, Feb. 5   Photo.   Perf. 12

744	A185	33c Lithuania	.75 .75
745	A185	33c San Marino	.75 .75
746	A185	33c Turkmenistan	.75 .75
747	A185	33c Marshall Islands	.75 .75
a.	Block of 4, #744-747		8.00 8.00
748	A185	33c Moldova	.75 .75
749	A185	33c Kyrgyzstan	.75 .75
750	A185	33c Bosnia & Herze-govina	.75 .75
751	A185	33c Eritrea	.75 .75
a.	Block of 4, #748-751		8.00 8.00
	Nos. 744-751 (8)		6.00 6.00

See note after No. 340.

Flags and Globe — A311   Roses — A312

1999, Feb. 5   Litho.   Perf. 14x13½

752	A311	33c multicolored	.50 .50

Photo.
Granite Paper
Perf. 11½x12

753	A312	$5 multicolored	7.50 7.50

World Heritage Sites, Australia A313

33c, #756f, Willandra Lakes region. 60c, #756b, Wet tropics of Queensland. No. 756a, Tasmanian wilderness. No. 756c, Great Barrier Reef. No. 756d, Uluru-Kata Tjuta Natl. Park. No. 756e, Kakadu Natl. Park.

1999, Mar. 19   Litho.   Perf. 13

754	A313	33c multicolored	.60 .60
755	A313	60c multicolored	1.25 1.25

Souvenir Booklet

756		Booklet	35.00
a.-c.	A313 5c any single		.70 .70
d.-f.	A313 15c any single		1.50 1.50
g.	Booklet pane of 4, #756a		2.80 2.80
h.	Booklet pane of 4, #756d		6.00 6.00
i.	Booklet pane of 4, #756b		2.80 2.80
j.	Booklet pane of 4, #756e		6.00 6.00
k.	Booklet pane of 4, #756c		2.80 2.80
l.	Booklet pane of 4, #756f		6.00 6.00

See Offices in Geneva Nos. 333-335; Vienna Nos. 250-252.

Endangered Species Type of 1993

No. 757, Tiger. No. 758, Secretary bird. No. 759, Green tree python. No. 760, Long-tailed chinchilla.

1999, Apr. 22   Litho.   Perf. 12½

757	A271	33c multicolored	.60 .60
758	A271	33c multicolored	.60 .60
759	A271	33c multicolored	.60 .60
760	A271	33c multicolored	.60 .60
a.	Block of 4, #757-760		3.00 3.00

See Offices in Geneva Nos. 336-339; Vienna Nos. 253-256.

UNISPACE III, Vienna — A314

No. 761, Probe on planet's surface. No. 762, Planetary rover. No. 763, Composite of #761-762.

1999, July 7   Photo.   Rouletted 8

761	A314	33c multicolored	.50 .50
762	A314	33c multicolored	.50 .50
a.	Pair, #761-762		1.75 1.75

Souvenir Sheet
Perf. 14½

763	A314	$2 multicolored	4.00 4.00
a.	Ovptd. in sheet margin		18.00 18.00

No. 763a was issued 7/7/00 and is overprinted in violet blue "WORLD STAMP EXPO 2000 / ANAHEIM, CALIFORNIA / U.S.A./ 7-16 JULY 2000."

See Offices in Geneva Nos. 340-342; Vienna Nos. 257-259.

UPU, 125th Anniv. — A315

Various people, 19th century methods of mail transportation, denomination at: No. 764, UL. No. 765, UR. No. 766, LL. No. 767, LR.

1999, Aug. 23   Photo.   Perf. 11¾

764	A315	33c multicolored	.45 .45
765	A315	33c multicolored	.45 .45
766	A315	33c multicolored	.45 .45
767	A315	33c multicolored	.45 .45
a.	Block of 4, #764-767		2.50 2.50

See Offices in Geneva Nos. 343-346; Vienna Nos. 260-263.

In Memoriam A316

Designs: 33c, $1, UN Headquarters. Size of $1 stamp: 34x63mm.

1999, Sept. 21   Litho.   Perf. 14½x14

768	A316	33c multicolored	.80 .80

Souvenir Sheet
Perf. 14

769	A316	$1 multicolored	2.00 2.00

Education, Keystone to the 21st Century — A317

Perf. 13½x13¾

1999, Nov. 18   Litho.

770	A317	33c Two readers	.50 .50
771	A317	60c Heart	1.00 1.00

See Offices in Geneva Nos. 349-350; Vienna Nos. 266-267.

International Year of Thanksgiving A318

2000, Jan. 1   Litho.   Perf. 13¼x13½

772	A318	33c multicolored	.75 .75

On No. 772 parts of the design were applied by a thermographic process producing a shiny, raised effect. See Offices in Geneva No. 351, Vienna No. 268.

Endangered Species Type of 1993

No. 773, Brown bear. No. 774, Black-bellied bustard. No. 775, Chinese crocodile lizard. No. 776, Pygmy chimpanzee.

2000, Apr. 6   Litho.   Perf. 12¾x12½

773	A271	33c multicolored	.50	.50
774	A271	33c multicolored	.50	.50
775	A271	33c multicolored	.50	.50
776	A271	33c multicolored	.50	.50
a.		Block of 4, #773-776	2.50	2.50

See Offices in Geneva Nos. 352-355; Vienna Nos. 269-272.

Our World 2000 A319

Winning artwork in Millennium painting competition: 33c, Crawling Toward the Millennium, by Sam Yeates, US. 60c, Crossing, by Masakazu Takahata, Japan, vert.

Perf. 13x13½, 13½x13

2000, May 30   Litho.

777	A319	33c multicolored	.60	.60
778	A319	60c multicolored	1.00	1.00

See Offices in Geneva No. 356-357, Vienna No. 273-274.

UN, 55th Anniv. — A320

33c, Workmen removing decorative discs in General Assembly Hall, 1956. 55c, UN Building in 1951.

2000, July 7   Litho.   Perf. 13¼x13

779	A320	33c multicolored	.55	.55
780	A320	55c multicolored	.95	.95

Souvenir Sheet

781	A320	Sheet of 2, #779-780	3.00	3.00

See Offices in Geneva No. 358-360, Vienna No. 275-277.

International Flag of Peace — A321

2000, Sept. 15   Litho.   Perf. 14½x14

782	A321	33c multicolored	.65	.65

The UN in the 21st Century — A322

No. 783: a, Farmers, animals in rice paddy. b, Vehicle chassis being lifted. c, People voting. d, Baby receiving inoculation. e, Woman, man at pump. f, Mason, construction workers.

2000, Sept. 15   Litho.   Perf. 14

783	A322	Sheet of 6	7.50	7.50
a.-f.		33c any single	1.25	1.25

See Offices in Geneva No. 361; Vienna No. 278.

World Heritage Sites, Spain — A323

Nos. 784, 786a, Alhambra, Generalife and Albayzin, Granada. Nos. 785, 786d, Amphitheater of Mérida. #786b, Walled Town of Cuenca. #786c, Aqueduct of Segovia. #786e, Toledo. #786f, Güell Park, Barcelona.

2000, Oct. 6   Litho.   Perf. 14¾x14½

784	A323	33c multicolored	.55	.55
785	A323	60c multicolored	1.10	1.10

Souvenir Booklet

786		Booklet	15.00	
a.-c.		A323 5c any single	.45	.45
d.-f.		A323 15c any single	.80	.80
g.		Booklet pane of 4, #786a	1.80	1.80
h.		Booklet pane of 4, #786d	3.20	3.20
i.		Booklet pane of 4, #786b	1.80	1.80
j.		Booklet pane of 4, #786e	3.20	3.20
k.		Booklet pane of 4, #786c	1.80	1.80
l.		Booklet pane of 4, #786f	3.20	3.20

See Offices in Geneva Nos. 362-364, Vienna Nos. 279-281.

Rocpoot for Refugees A324

2000, Nov. 9   Litho.   Perf. 13¼x12¾

787	A324	33c multicolored	.75	.75

Souvenir Sheet

788	A324	$1 multicolored	2.00	2.00

See Offices in Geneva Nos. 365-366, Vienna Nos. 282-283.

Endangered Species Type of 1993

No. 789, Common spotted cuscus. No. 790, Resplendent quetzal. No. 791, Gila monster. No. 792, Guereza.

2001, Feb. 1   Litho.   Perf. 12¾x12½

789	A271	34c multicolored	.60	.60
790	A271	34c multicolored	.60	.60
791	A271	34c multicolored	.60	.60
792	A271	34c multicolored	.60	.60
a.		Block of 4, #789-792	3.00	3.00

See Offices in Geneva Nos. 367-370; Vienna Nos. 284-287.

Intl. Volunteers Year — A325

Paintings by: 34c, Jose Zaragoza, Brazil. 80c, John Terry, Australia.

2001, Mar. 29   Litho.   Perf. 13¼

793	A325	34c multicolored	.65	.65
794	A325	80c multicolored	1.60	1.60

See Offices in Geneva Nos. 371-372; Vienna Nos. 288-289.

Flag Type of 1980

No. 795, Slovenia. No. 796, Palau. No. 797, Tonga. No. 798, Croatia. No. 799, Former Yugoslav Republic of Macedonia. No. 800, Kiribati. No. 801, Andorra. No. 802, Nauru.

2001, May 25   Photo.   Perf. 12

Granite Paper

795	A185	34c multicolored	1.25	1.25
796	A185	34c multicolored	1.25	1.25
797	A185	34c multicolored	1.25	1.25
798	A185	34c multicolored	1.25	1.25
a.		Block of 4, #795-798	15.00	15.00
799	A185	34c multicolored	1.25	1.25
800	A185	34c multicolored	1.25	1.25
801	A185	34c multicolored	1.25	1.25
802	A185	34c multicolored	1.25	1.25
a.		Block of 4, #799-802	15.00	15.00
		Nos. 795-802 (8)	10.00	10.00

Sunflower — A326

Rose — A327

2001, May 25   Litho.   Perf. 13¼x13¾

803	A326	7c multicolored	.25	.25
804	A327	34c multicolored	.60	.60

World Heritage Sites, Japan — A328

34c, #807a, Kyoto. 70c, #807d, Shirakawa-Go and Gokayama. #807b, Nara. #807c, Himeji-Jo. #807e, Itsukushima Shinto Shrine. #807f, Nikko.

2001, Aug. 1   Litho.   Perf. 12¾x13¼

805	A328	34c multicolored	.60	.60
806	A328	70c multicolored	1.25	1.25

Souvenir Booklet

807		Booklet	14.00	
a.-c.		A328 5c any single	.40	.40
d.-f.		A328 20c any single	.75	.75
g.		Booklet pane of 4, #807a	1.60	1.60
h.		Booklet pane of 4, #807a	3.00	3.00
i.		Booklet pane of 4, #807b	1.60	1.60
j.		Booklet pane of 4, #807c	3.00	3.00
k.		Booklet pane of 4, #807c	1.60	1.60
l.		Booklet pane of 4, #807f	3.00	3.00

See Offices in Geneva Nos. 373-375, Vienna Nos. 290-292.

Dag Hammarskjöld (1905-61), UN Secretary General — A329

2001, Sept. 18   Engr.   Perf. 11x11¼

808	A329	80c blue	1.50	1.50

See Offices in Geneva No. 376, Vienna No. 293.

A330

UN Postal Administration, 50th Anniv. — A331

2001, Oct. 18   Litho.   Perf. 13½

809	A330	34c Stamps, streamers	.55	.55
810	A330	80c Stamps, gifts	1.50	1.50

Souvenir Sheet

811	A331	Sheet of 2 #811a	8.00	8.00
a.		$1 blue & light blue, 38mm diameter	4.00	4.00

See Offices in Geneva Nos. 377-379, Vienna Nos. 294-296.

Climate Change — A332

No. 812, Canada geese, greenhouses, butterfly, thistle. No. 813, Canada geese, iceberg, penguins, tomato plant. No. 814, Palm tree, solar collector. No. 815, Hand planting ginkgo cutting.

2001, Nov. 16   Litho.   Perf. 13¼

812	A332	34c multicolored	1.00	1.00
813	A332	34c multicolored	1.00	1.00
814	A332	34c multicolored	1.00	1.00
815	A332	34c multicolored	1.00	1.00
a.		Horiz. strip, #812-815	4.50	4.50

See Offices in Geneva Nos. 380-383, Vienna Nos. 297-300.

Awarding of Nobel Peace Prize to Secretary General Kofi Annan and UN — A333

2001, Dec. 10   Litho.   Perf. 13¼

816	A333	34c multicolored	.70	.70

See Offices in Geneva Nos. 384, Vienna Nos. 301.

Children and Stamps
A334

2002, Mar. 1 Litho. Perf. 13¾
817 A334 80c multicolored 1.40 1.40

Endangered Species Type of 1993
No. 818, Hoffmann's two-toed sloth. No. 819, Bighorn sheep. No. 820, Cheetah. No. 821, San Esteban Island chuckwalla.

2002, Apr. 4 Litho. Perf. 12¾x12½
818 A271 34c multicolored .80 .80
819 A271 34c multicolored .80 .80
820 A271 34c multicolored .80 .80
821 A271 34c multicolored .80 .80
a. Block of 4, #818-821 3.25 3.25

See Offices in Geneva Nos. 386-389; Vienna 308-311.

Independence of East Timor — A335

34c, Wooden ritual mask. 57c, Decorative door panel.

2002, May 20 Litho. Perf. 14x14½
822 A335 34c multicolored .70 .70
823 A335 57c multicolored 1.20 1.20

See Offices in Geneva Nos. 390-391; Vienna Nos. 312-313.

Intl. Year of Mountains
A336

No. 824, Khan Tengri, Kyrgyzstan. No. 825, Mt. Kilimanjaro, Tanzania. No. 826, Mt. Foraker, US. No. 827, Paine Grande, Chile.

2002, May 24 Litho. Perf. 13x13¼
824 A336 34c multicolored .75 .75
825 A336 34c multicolored .75 .75
826 A336 80c multicolored 1.25 1.50
827 A336 80c multicolored 1.25 1.50
a. Vert. strip or block of four, #824-827 8.00 10.00

See Offices in Geneva Nos. 392-395; Vienna Nos. 314-317.

World Summit on Sustainable Development, Johannesburg — A337

No. 828, Sun, Earth, planets, stars. No. 829, Three women. No. 830, Sailboat. No. 831, Three faceless people.

2002, June 27 Litho. Perf. 14½x14
828 A337 37c multicolored .75 .75
829 A337 37c multicolored .75 .75
830 A337 60c multicolored 1.25 1.25
831 A337 60c multicolored 1.25 1.25
a. Vert. strip or block of four, #828-831 8.00 10.00

See Offices in Geneva Nos. 396-399; Vienna Nos. 318-321.

World Heritage Sites, Italy — A338

37c, #834d, Florence. 70c, #834a, Amalfi Coast. #834b, Aeolian Islands. #834c, Rome. #834e, Pisa. #834f, Pompeii.

Perf. 13½x13¼
2002, Aug. 30 Litho.
832 A338 37c multicolored .70 .70
833 A338 70c multicolored 1.40 1.40

Souvenir Booklet
834 Booklet 16.00
a.-c. A338 5c any single .40 .40
d.-f. A338 15c any single .90 .90
g. Booklet pane of 4, #834d 3.60 3.60
h. Booklet pane of 4, #834a 1.60 1.60
i. Booklet pane of 4, #834e 3.60 3.60
j. Booklet pane of 4, #834b 1.60 1.60
k. Booklet pane of 4, #834f 3.60 3.60
l. Booklet pane of 4, #834c 1.60 1.60

See Offices in Geneva Nos. 400-402, Vienna Nos. 322-324.
See Italy Nos. 2506-2507.

AIDS Awareness
A339

2002, Oct. 24 Litho. Perf. 13½
835 A339 70c multicolored 1.50 1.50

See No. B1, Offices in Geneva Nos. 403, B1, Vienna Nos. 325, B1.

Indigenous Art — A340

No. 836: a, Detail of Paracas textile, Peru. b, Sinu culture anthropo-zoomorphic pendant, Colombia. c, Hicholi Indian embroidery, Mexico. d, Rigpaktsa back ornament, Brazil. e, Wool crafts, Chile. f, Huari feathered woven hat, Bolivia.

2003, Jan. 31 Litho. Perf. 14¼
836 A340 Sheet of 6 8.50 8.50
a.-f. 37c Any single 1.40 1.40

See Offies in Geneva No. 405; Vienna No. 326.

Clasped Hands — A341

UN Emblem
A342

UN Headquarters
A343

2003, Mar. 28 Litho. Perf. 14¼
837 A343 23c multicolored .40 .40
Litho. with Foil Application
838 A342 37c gold & multicolored .60 .60
Litho. with Hologram
Perf. 13¼x12¾
839 A343 70c multicolored 1.40 1.40

Powered Flight, Cent. — A344

Perf. 13½x13¾
2003, Mar. 28 Litho.
840 23c multicolored 1.25 1.25
841 70c multicolored 2.75 2.75
a. A344 Tete beche pair, #840-841 5.00 5.00

Endangered Species Type of 1993
No. 842, Great hornbill. No. 843, Scarlet ibis. No. 844, Knob-billed goose. No. 845, White-faced whistling duck.

2003, Apr. 3 Litho. Perf. 12¾x12½
842 A271 37c multicolored .80 .80
843 A271 37c multicolored .80 .80
844 A271 37c multicolored .80 .80
845 A271 37c multicolored .80 .80
a. Block of 4, #842-845 3.25 3.25

See Offices in Geneva Nos. 407-410; Vienna Nos. 329-332.

Intl. Year of Freshwater
A345

Perf. 14¼x14½
2003, June 20 Litho.
846 A345 23c Wildlife, garbage 1.50 1.50
847 A345 37c Trees, canoe 2.00 2.00
a. Horiz. pair, #846-847 7.50 7.50

See Offices in Geneva, Nos. 411-412; Vienna Nos. 333-334.

Ralph Bunche (1903-71), Diplomat — A346

Litho. With Foil Application
2003, Aug. 7 Perf. 13½x14
848 A346 37c blue & multi .80 .80

See Offices in Geneva No. 413; Vienna No. 336.

In Memoriam of Victims of Aug. 19 Bombing of UN Complex in Baghdad, Iraq — A347

2003, Oct. 24 Litho. Perf. 13¼x13
849 A347 60c multicolored 1.25 1.25

See Offices in Geneva No. 414, Vienna No. 337.

World Heritage Sites, United States
A348

37c, #852a, Yosemite National Park. 60c, #852d, Hawaii Volcanoes National Park. #852b, Great Smoky Mountains National Park. #852c, Olympic National Park. #852e, Everglades National Park. #852f, Yellowstone National Park.

2003, Oct. 24 Litho. Perf. 14½x14¼
850 A348 37c multicolored .90 .90
851 A348 60c multicolored 1.50 1.50

Souvenir Booklet
852 Booklet 14.00
a.-c. A348 10c any single .35 .35
d.-f. A348 20c any single .70 .70
g. Booklet pane of 4 #852a 1.40 1.40
h. Booklet pane of 4 #852d 2.80 2.80
i. Booklet pane of 4 #852b 1.40 1.40
j. Booklet pane of 4 #852e 2.80 2.80
k. Booklet pane of 4 #852c 1.40 1.40
l. Booklet pane of 4 #852f 2.80 2.80

See Offices in Geneva Nos. 415-417, Vienna Nos. 338-340.

UN Security Council — A349

UN Emblem — A350

UN General Assembly — A351

Flags — A352

UN Headquarters — A353

2003, Nov. 26   Litho.   Perf. 13¼
853	A349 37c multi + label	12.50	12.50
854	A350 37c multi + label	12.50	12.50
855	A351 37c multi + label	12.50	12.50
856	A352 37c multi + label	12.50	12.50
857	A353 37c multi + label	12.50	12.50
a.	Vert. strip of 5, #853-857, + 5 labels	65.00	65.00

The full sheet sold for $14.95 with or without personalized labels. The personalization of labels was available only at UN Headquarters, and not through mail order.

One thousand full sheets with sheet margins inscribed "Hong Kong Stamp Expo" were sold only at that venue. Value $135. Also exists with sheet margins inscribed "Essen." Value $125.

A sheet containing two strips of five stamps similar to Nos. 853-857 but dated "2005" and ten labels sold for $4.95. These sheets were only available canceled. Value $100. An imperforate error of this sheet is known.

Endangered Species Type of 1993

No. 858, American black bear. No. 859, Musk deer. No. 860, Golden snub-nosed monkey. No. 861, Wild yak.

2004, Jan. 29   Litho.   Perf. 12¾x12½
858	A271 37c multicolored	.90	.90
859	A271 37c multicolored	.90	.90
860	A271 37c multicolored	.90	.90
861	A271 37c multicolored	.90	.90
a.	Block of 4, #858-861	4.00	4.00

See Offices in Geneva Nos. 418-421; Vienna Nos. 342-345.

Indigenous Art Type of 2003

No. 862: a, Viking wood carving depicting Saga of Sigurd Favnesbane, Norway. b, Stele, Italy. c, Detail of matador's suit, Spain. d, Amphora, Greece. e, Bronze figurine of bull, Czech Republic. f, Detail of lacquer box illustration depicting scene from "On the Seashore," by Alexander Pushkin, Russia.

2004, Mar. 4   Litho.   Perf. 13¼
862	A340 Sheet of 6	6.00	6.00
a.-f.	37c Any single	1.00	1.00

See Offices in Geneva No. 422; Vienna No. 346.

Road Safety A354

Road map art with: 37c, Automobile with road signs, city skyline. 70c, Automobile, hand, vert.

Perf. 13x13¼, 13¼x13
2004, Apr. 7   Litho.
863	A354 37c multicolored	.85	.85
864	A354 70c multicolored	1.40	1.40

See Offices in Geneva Nos. 423-424, Vienna Nos. 347-348.

Japanese Peace Bell, 50th Anniv. — A355

Litho. & Engr.
2004, June 3   Perf. 13¼x13
865	A355 80c multicolored	1.25	1.25

See Offices in Geneva No. 425; Vienna No. 349.

World Heritage Sites, Greece — A356

No. 866, Acropolis, Athens. Nos. 867, 868e, Delos. No. 868a, Delphi. No. 868b, Pythagoreion and Heraion of Samos. No. 868c, Olympia. No. 868d, Mycenae and Tiryns.

2004, Aug. 12   Litho.   Perf. 14x13¼
866	A356 37c multicolored	.70	.70
a.	Booklet pane of 4	3.00	
867	A356 60c multicolored	1.10	1.10

Souvenir Booklet
868	Booklet, #866a, 868f-868j	15.00	
a.-d.	A356 23c any single	.55	.55
e.	A356 37c multi	.90	.90
f.	Booklet pane of 4 #868a	2.20	2.20
g.	Booklet pane of 4 #868b	2.20	2.20
h.	Booklet pane of 4 #868c	2.20	2.20
i.	Booklet pane of 4 #868d	2.20	2.20
j.	Booklet pane of 4 #868e	3.60	3.60

See Offices in Geneva Nos. 426-428, Vienna Nos. 350-352. No. 868 sold for $7.20.

My Dream for Peace — A357

Winning designs of Lions Club International children's global peace poster contest by: 37c, Sittichok Pariyaket, Thailand. 80c, Bayan Fais Abu Bial, Israel.

2004, Sept. 21   Litho.   Perf. 14
869	A357 37c multicolored	.60	.60
870	A357 80c multicolored	1.40	1.40

See Offices in Geneva Nos. 429-430, Vienna Nos. 353-354.

A358

Human Rights — A359

2004, Oct. 14   Litho.   Perf. 11¼
871	A358 37c multicolored	.75	.75
872	A359 70c multicolored	1.40	1.40

See Offices in Geneva Nos. 431-432, Vienna Nos. 355-356.

Disarmament A360

2004, Oct. 15   Litho.   Perf. 13¾
873	A360 37c multicolored	.80	.80

United Nations, 60th Anniv. — A361

Litho. & Engr.
2005, Feb. 4   Perf. 11x11¼
874	A361 80c multicolored	1.50	1.50

Souvenir Sheet
Litho.
Imperf
875	A361 $1 multicolored	17.50	17.50

See Offices in Geneva Nos. 434-435; Vienna Nos. 357-358.

Endangered Species Type of 1993

Designs: No. 876, Blue orchid. No. 877, Swan orchid. No. 878, Christmas orchid. No. 879, Aerangis modesta.

2005, Mar. 3   Litho.   Perf. 12¾x12½
876	A271 37c multicolored	1.10	1.10
877	A271 37c multicolored	1.10	1.10
878	A271 37c multicolored	1.10	1.10
879	A271 37c multicolored	1.10	1.10
a.	Block of 4, #876-879	4.50	4.50

See Offices in Geneva Nos. 436-439; Vienna Nos. 360-363.

Non-Violence, Sculpture by Carl Fredrik Reuterswärd, New York — A362

Armillary Sphere, Sculpture by Paul Manship, Geneva — A363

Terra Cotta Warriors, Vienna — A364

Single Form, Sculpture by Barbara Hepworth, New York — A365

Sphere Within a Sphere, Sculpture by Arnaldo Pomodoro, New York — A366

2005, Mar. 3   Litho.   Perf. 13¼
880	A362 80c multi + label	50.00	50.00
881	A363 80c multi + label	50.00	50.00
882	A364 80c multi + label	50.00	50.00
883	A365 80c multi + label	50.00	50.00
884	A366 80c multi + label	50.00	50.00
a.	Vert. strip of 5, #880-884, + 5 labels	250.00	250.00
b.	Sheet of 10, both #884 37c (error)	3,250.	
c.	Vert. strip of 5, #884 37c (error)	1,450.	

The full sheet sold for $14.95 with or without personalized labels. The personalization of labels was available only at UN Headquarters, and not through mail order.

The full sheet exists with sheet margins and labels commemorating the Riccione 2005 Philatelic Exhibition. This sheet went on sale 8/20/05 and was also sold for $14.95. Value $175.

Nature's Wisdom — A367

37c, Ice climber, Norway. 80c, Egret, Japan.

2005, Apr. 21   Litho.   Perf. 13½x13¼
885	A367 37c multicolored	.65	.65
886	A367 80c multicolored	1.50	1.50

See Offices in Geneva Nos. 440-441, Vienna Nos. 364-365.

Intl. Year of Sport A368

2005, June 3   Litho.   Perf. 13x13¼
887	A368 37c Sailing	.65	.65
888	A368 70c Running	1.25	1.25

See Offices in Geneva Nos. 442-443; Vienna Nos. 366-367.

World Heritage Sites, Egypt — A369

Nos. 889, 891a, Memphis and its Necropolis. Nos. 890, 891d, Ancient Thebes. No. 891b, Philae. No. 891c, Abu Mena. No. 891e, Islamic Cairo. No. 891f, St. Catherine area.

2005, Aug. 4   Litho.   Perf. 14x13¼
889	A369 37c multicolored	.60	.60
890	A369 80c multicolored	1.40	1.40

Souvenir Booklet

891	Booklet, #891g-891I	15.00	
a.-c.	A369 23c any single	.50	.50
d.-f.	A369 37c any single	.75	.75
g.	Booklet pane of 4 #891a	2.00	2.00
h.	Booklet pane of 4 #891b	2.00	2.00
i.	Booklet pane of 4 #891c	2.00	2.00
j.	Booklet pane of 4 #891d	3.00	3.00
k.	Booklet pane of 4 #891e	3.00	3.00
l.	Booklet pane of 4 #891f	3.00	3.00

See Offices in Geneva Nos. 444-446, Vienna Nos. 368-370.

My Dream for Peace Type of 2004

Winning designs of Lions Club International children's global peace poster contest by: 37c, Vittoria Sansebastiano, Italy. 80c, Jordan Harris, US.

2005, Sept. 21   Litho.   Perf. 14

892	A357	37c multicolored	.60	.60
893	A357	80c multicolored	1.40	1.40

See Offices in Geneva Nos. 447-448, Vienna Nos. 371-372.

Food for Life A370

37c, Oats, children and adults. 80c, Wheat, mothers breastfeeding babies.

2005, Oct. 20   Litho.   Perf. 13¾

894	A370	37c multicolored	.60	.60
895	A370	80c multicolored	1.40	1.40

See Offices in Geneva Nos. 449-450; Vienna Nos. 373-374.

Stylized Flags in Heart and Hands A371

2006, Feb. 3   Litho.   Perf. 13x13¼

896	A371	25c multicolored	.75	.75

Indigenous Art Type of 2003

No. 897 — Musical instruments: a, Drum, Ivory Coast. b, Drum, Tunisia. c, Stringed instruments, Morocco. d, Drums, Sudan. e, Instruments, Cameroun. f, Harp, Congo.

2006, Feb. 3   Litho.   Perf. 13¼

897	A340	Sheet of 6	10.00	10.00
a.-f.		37c Any single	1.50	1.50

See Offices in Geneva No. 452; Vienna No. 375.

UN Symbols Type of 2003

2006, Mar. 6   Litho.   Perf. 13¼

898	A349	39c multi + label	5.00	5.00
899	A350	39c multi + label	5.00	5.00
900	A351	39c multi + label	5.00	5.00
901	A352	39c multi + label	5.00	5.00
902	A353	39c multi + label	5.00	5.00
a.		Vert. strip of 5, #898-902, + 5 labels	25.00	25.00

The full sheet sold for $14.95 with or without personalized labels. The personalization of labels was available only at UN Headquarters, and not through mail order.

Sculpture Type of 2005

2006, Mar. 6   Litho.   Perf. 13¼

903	A362	84c multi + label	12.00	12.00
a.		Perf. 14½x14 + label	16.00	16.00
904	A363	84c multi + label	12.00	12.00
a.		Perf. 14½x14 + label	16.00	16.00
905	A364	84c multi + label	12.00	12.00
a.		Perf. 14½x14 + label	16.00	16.00
906	A365	84c multi + label	12.00	12.00
a.		Perf. 14½x14 + label	16.00	16.00
907	A366	84c multi + label	12.00	12.00
a.		Perf. 14½x14 + label	16.00	16.00
b.		Vert. strip of 5, #903-907, + 5 labels	60.00	60.00
c.		Vert. strip of 5, #903a-907a, + 5 labels	80.00	80.00

The full sheet sold for $14.95 with or without personalized labels. The personalization of labels was available only at UN Headquarters, and not through mail order. Nos. 903a-907a issued 9/21/06. Nos. 903a-907a were from sheet for 2006 Berlin Stamp

Show. The year "2006" is slightly smaller on Nos. 903a-907a than on Nos. 903-907.

Full sheets with different margins were sold at the Washington 2006 World Philatelic Exhibition, where the labels could be personalized. These are worth slightly more than the generic No. 907b sheet.

Endangered Species Type of 1993

No. 908, Golden mantella. No. 909, Panther chameleon. No. 910, Peruvian rainbow boa. No. 911, Dyeing poison frog.

Perf. 12¾x12½

2006, Mar. 16   Litho.

908	A271	39c multicolored	.90	.90
909	A271	39c multicolored	.90	.90
910	A271	39c multicolored	.90	.90
911	A271	39c multicolored	.90	.90
a.		Block of 4, #908-911	4.00	4.00

See Offices in Geneva Nos. 453-456; Vienna Nos. 376-379.

Dove Between War and Peace — A372

2006, Apr. 10   Litho.   Perf. 13¼

912	A372	75c multi + label	5.50	5.00

The full sheet sold for $14.95 with or without personalized labels. The personalization of labels was available only at UN Headquarters, and not through mail order.

Intl. Day of Families A373

39c, Family harvesting grapes. 84c, Children playing with toy sailboats.

2006, May 27   Litho.   Perf. 14x13½

913	A373	39c multicolored	.70	.70
914	A373	84c multicolored	1.50	1.50

See Offices in Geneva Nos. 457-458; Vienna Nos. 380-381.

World Heritage Sites, France — A374

Eiffel Tower and: Nos. 915, 917a, Banks of the Seine. Nos. 916, 917d, Roman Aqueduct. No. 917b, Provins. No. 917c, Carcassonne. No. 917e, Mont Saint-Michel. No. 917f, Chateau de Chambord.

Litho. & Embossed with Foil Application

2006, June 17   Perf. 13½x13¼

915	A374	39c multicolored	.75	.75
916	A374	84c multicolored	1.75	1.75

Souvenir Booklet

917	Booklet, #917g-917I	16.00	
a.-c.	A374 24c any single	.50	.50
d.-f.	A374 39c any single	.80	.80
g.	Booklet pane of 4 #917a	2.00	2.00
h.	Booklet pane of 4 #917b	2.00	2.00
i.	Booklet pane of 4 #917c	2.00	2.00
j.	Booklet pane of 4 #917d	3.25	3.25
k.	Booklet pane of 4 #917e	3.25	3.25
l.	Booklet pane of 4 #917f	3.25	3.25

See Offices in Geneva Nos. 459-461, Vienna Nos. 382-384.

My Dream for Peace Type of 2004

Winning designs of Lions Club International children's global peace poster contest by: 39c, Cheuk Tat Li, Hong Kong. 84c, Kosshapan Paitoon, Thailand.

2006, Sept. 21   Litho.   Perf. 13½x13

918	A357	39c multicolored	.80	.80
919	A357	84c multicolored	1.75	1.75

See Offices in Geneva Nos. 462-463; Vienna Nos. 385-386.

Flags and Coins — A375

No. 920 — Flag of: a, People's Republic of China, 1 yuan coin. b, Australia, 1 dollar coin. c, Ghana, 50 cedi coin. d, Israel, 10 agorot coin. e, Russia, 1 ruble coin. f, Mexico, 10 peso coin. g, Japan, 10 yen coin. h, Cambodia, 200 riel coin.

2006, Oct. 5   Litho.   Perf. 13¼x13

920		Sheet of 8	8.00	8.00
a.-h.	A375	39c Any single	1.00	1.00

A column of rouletting in the middle of the sheet separates it into two parts. See Nos. 930, 953, 998, 1022, 1039, 1078, 1103; Offices in Geneva Nos. 464, 469, 484, 512, 532, 546, 576, 594; Vienna Nos. 387, 392, 421, 459, 483, 507, 539, 558.

Flag Type of 1980

2007, Feb. 2   Litho.   Perf. 14

921	A185	39c Tuvalu	1.10	1.10
922	A185	39c Switzerland	1.10	1.10
923	A185	39c Timor-Leste	1.10	1.10
924	A185	39c Montenegro	1.10	1.10
a.		Block of 4, #921-924	12.50	12.50
		Nos. 921-924 (4)	4.40	4.40

Endangered Species Type of 1993

No. 925, Drill. No. 926, Common squirrel monkey. No. 927, Ring-tailed lemur. No. 928, Collared mangabey.

Perf. 12¾x12½

2007, Mar. 15   Litho.

925	A271	39c multicolored	.85	.85
926	A271	39c multicolored	.85	.85
927	A271	39c multicolored	.85	.85
928	A271	39c multicolored	.85	.85
a.		Block of 4, #925-928	3.50	3.50

See Offices in Geneva Nos. 465-468; Vienna Nos. 388-391.

UN Emblem — A376

2007, Feb. 5   Litho.   Perf. 14½x14

929	A376	84c dk blue + label	17.50	17.50

The full sheet sold for $14.95. The sheet has two each of five different labels that could not be personalized. The sheet was distributed to members of the Japanese mission on Sept. 21, 2006, but it was not sold to the public until 2007. The sheet's availability to the public was not announced through press releases or on the UNPA website prior to the day of issue or afterward. It was sent to standing order customers in May 2007.
Compare with Type A377.

Flags and Coins Type of 2006

No. 930 — Flag of: a, Brazil, 50 centavo coin. b, Thailand, 1 baht coin. c, Viet Nam, 5,000 dong coin. d, Ecuador, 10 centavo coin. e, India, 5 rupee coin. f, South Africa, 5 cent coin. g, Barbados, 25 cent coin. h, Republic of Korea, 500 won coin.

2007, May 3   Litho.   Perf. 13¼x13

930		Sheet of 8	9.00	9.00
a.-h.	A375	39c Any single	1.10	1.10

A column of rouletting in the middle of the sheet separates it into two parts. See Offices in Geneva No. 469; Vienna No. 392.

UN Emblem — A377

2007, June 1   Litho.   Perf. 13¼

931	A377	84c blue + label	4.50	4.50

The full sheet sold for $14.95. The sheet has two each of five different labels that could not be personalized.
Compare with Type A376.

Peaceful Visions — A378

39c, "Nest." 84c, "Sisters Weave the Olive Branch."

2007, June 1   Litho.   Perf. 13x12½

932	A378	39c multicolored	.90	.90
933	A378	84c multicolored	1.80	1.80

See Offices in Geneva Nos. 470-471; Vienna Nos. 398-399.

UN Symbols Type of 2003

2007, May 14   Litho.   Perf. 13¼

934	A349	41c multi + label	3.25	3.25
935	A350	41c multi + label	3.25	3.25
936	A351	41c multi + label	3.25	3.25
937	A352	41c multi + label	3.25	3.25
938	A353	41c multi + label	3.25	3.25
a.		Vert. strip of 5, #934-938, + 5 labels	17.00	17.00

The full sheet sold for $14.95 with or without personalized labels. The personalization of labels was available only at UN Headquarters, and not through mail order.

UN Flag — A379

2007, May 14   Litho.   Perf. 13¼

939	A379	90c blue + label	6.00	6.00

The full sheet sold for $14.95. The sheet has two each of five different labels that could not be personalized.
A second printing of No. 939 has the "U" and "N" more closely spaced, and it has different labels and different pane borders. Value about the same.

Helmet of UN Peacekeeper A380

2007, Aug. 9   Litho.   Perf. 12½x13¼

940	A380	90c multicolored	1.90	1.90

World Heritage Sites, South
America — A381

No. 941, Galapagos Islands, Ecuador. Nos.
942, 943a, Rapa Nui, Chile. No. 943b, Cueva
de las Manos, Argentina. No. 943c, Machu
Picchu, Peru. No. 943d, Tiwanaku, Bolivia.
No. 943e, Iguaçu National Park, Brazil.

2007, Aug. 9   Litho.   Perf. 13¼x13
941 A381 41c multicolored   .85   .85
  a.   Booklet pane of 4   3.40
942 A381 90c multicolored   1.90 1.90

Souvenir Booklet
943   Booklet, #941a, 943f-
           943j   17.00
  a.-c. A381 26c Any single   .60   .60
  d.-e. A381 41c Either single   1.00 1.00
     f. Booklet pane of 4 #943a   2.40 2.40
     g. Booklet pane of 4 #943b   2.40 2.40
     h. Booklet pane of 4 #943c   2.40 2.40
     i. Booklet pane of 4 #943d   4.00 4.00
     j. Booklet pane of 4 #943e   4.00 4.00

See Offices in Geneva Nos. 472-474,
Vienna Nos. 400-402. No. 943 sold for $8.50.

Humanitarian
Mail — A382

2007, Sept. 6 Litho.   Perf. 12½x13¼
944 A382 90c multicolored   1.90 1.90

See Offices in Geneva No. 475, Vienna No.
403, Switzerland No. 9O21.

Space for
Humanity
A383

41c, Space Shuttle. 90c, Astronauts
spacewalking.
$1, International Space Station.

2007, Oct. 25 Litho.   Perf. 13½x14
945 A383 41c multicolored   .85   .85
946 A383 90c multicolored   1.90 1.90

Souvenir Sheet
947 A383 $1 multicolored   2.50 2.50
  a.   With World Space Week em-
           blem in margin   3.00 3.00

See Offices in Geneva Nos. 476-478,
Vienna Nos. 409-411.

Intl. Holocaust Remembrance
Day — A384

2008, Jan. 27   Litho.   Perf. 13
948 A384 41c multicolored   .85   .85

See Offices in Geneva No. 479, Vienna No.
412, Israel No. 1715.

Endangered Species Type of 1993

No. 949, South African fur seal. No. 950,
Orange cup coral. No. 951, Longsnout seahorse. No. 952, Gray whale.

2008, Mar. 6 Litho.   Perf. 12¾x12½
949 A271 41c multicolored   1.00 1.00
950 A271 41c multicolored   1.00 1.00
941 A271 41c multicolored   1.00 1.00
952 A271 41c multicolored   1.00 1.00
  a.   Block of 4, #949-952   4.50 4.50

See Offices in Geneva Nos. 480-483;
Vienna Nos. 417-420.

Flags and Coins Type of 2006

No. 953 — Flag of: a, United Kingdom, 2
pound coin. b, Singapore, 5 dollar coin. c,
Colombia, 500 peso coin. d, Sri Lanka, 10
rupee coin. e, Philippines, 1 peso coin. f, Indonesia, 500 rupiah coin. g, United Arab Emirates, 1 dirham coin. h, Libya, 50 dinar coin.

2008, May 8   Litho.   Perf. 13¼x13
953   Sheet of 8   7.00 7.00
  a.-h. A375 41c Any single   .85   .85

A column of rouletting in the middle of the
sheet separates it into two parts. See Offices
in Geneva No. 484; Vienna No. 421.

Sculpture and Flags — A385

UN Flag — A386

UN General Assembly — A387

Flags — A388

UN Headquarters — A389

2008, May 12   Litho.   Perf. 13¼
954 A385 42c multi + label   3.50 3.50
955 A386 42c multi + label   3.50 3.50
956 A387 42c multi + label   3.50 3.50
957 A388 42c multi + label   3.50 3.50
958 A389 42c multi + label   3.50 3.50
  a.   Vert. strip of 5, #954-958, + 5
           labels   17.50 17.50

The full sheet sold for $14.95 with or without
personalized labels. The personalization of
labels was available only at UN Headquarters,
and not through mail order.

UN Emblem — A390

2008, May 12   Litho.   Perf. 13¼
959 A390 94c blue + label   4.50 4.50

The full sheet sold for $14.95 with or without
labels that could be personalized. There are
five non-personalized labels. The personalization of labels was available only at UN Headquarters, and not through mail order.

Wheelchair
Accessibility
Symbol — A391

"UN" in
Braille — A392

Litho. & Embossed
2008, June 6   Perf. 14x13¼
960 A391 42c blue & yellow   .85   .85
961 A392 94c yellow & blue   1.90 1.90

Convention on the Rights of Persons with
Disabilities. See Offices in Geneva Nos. 485-
486, Vienna Nos. 427-428.

Sport for Peace — A393

42c, $1.25, Sprinter. 94c, Hurdler.

2008, Aug. 8   Litho.   Perf. 14½
962 A393 42c multicolored   .85   .85
963 A393 94c multicolored   1.90 1.90

Souvenir Sheet
Perf. 12¾x13¼
964 A393 $1.25 multicolored   6.00 6.00

2008 Summer Olympics, Beijing. See
Offices in Geneva Nos. 487-489, Vienna Nos.
429-431.

Sport for Peace — A394

2008, Aug. 8   Litho.   Perf. 13¼
965 A394 94c multi + label   3.75 3.75

2008 Summer Olympics, Beijing. The full
pane sold for $14.95 with or without personal-
ized labels. There are two non-personalized
labels. The personalization of labels was available only at UN Headquarters, and not
through mail order.
No. 965 is often collected as a single stamp
with the two different labels attached; value
thus $6.50.

"We Can End Poverty" — A395

Winning designs in children's art contest by:
42c, Grace Tsang, Hong Kong. 94c, Bryan
Jevoncia, Indonesia, vert.

Perf. 12¾x12½
2008, Sept. 18   Litho.
966 A395 42c multicolored   .85   .85
Perf. 12½x12¾
967 A395 94c multicolored   1.90 1.90

See Offices in Geneva Nos. 490-491,
Vienna Nos. 432-433.

Climate Change Types of Geneva
and Vienna and

A396

Climate Change — A397

No. 968 — Parched ground and snail shell
with quarter of Earth in: a, LR. b, LL. c, UR. d,
UL.
No. 969 — Coral reef with quarter of Earth
in. a, LR. b, LL. c, UR. d, UL.
No. 970: a, Like #969a. b, Like #969b. c,
Like #969c. d, Like #969d. e, Like Geneva
#493a. f, Like Geneva #493b. g, Like Geneva
#493c. h, Like Geneva #493d. i, Like Vienna
#434a. j, Like Vienna #434b. k, Like Vienna
#434c. l, Like Vienna #434d. m, Like Geneva
#492a. n, Like Geneva #492b. o, Like Geneva
#492c. p, Like Geneva #492d. q, Like Vienna
#435a. r, Like Vienna #435b. s, Like Vienna
#435c. t, Like Vienna #435d.
All stamps have blue panels inscribed "Cli-
mate Change."

2008, Oct. 23   Litho.   Perf. 13¼x13
968   Sheet of 4   4.75 4.75
  a.-d. A396 42c Any single   1.10 1.10
     e. Booklet pane of 4, #968a-
           968d   6.00 6.00
969   Sheet of 4   10.00 10.00
  a.-d. A397 94c Any single   2.50 2.50

Souvenir Booklet
970   Booklet, #968e,
           970u-970y   20.00
  a.-d. A397 27c Any single   .75   .75
  e.-h. G77 27c Any single   .75   .75
  i.-l. V72 27c Any single   .75   .75
  m.-p. G76 42c Any single   1.00 1.00
  q.-t. V73 42c Any single   1.00 1.00
     u. Booklet pane of 4, #970a-
           970d   3.00 3.00
     v. Booklet pane of 4, #970e-
           970h   3.00 3.00
     w. Booklet pane of 4, #970i-970l 3.00 3.00
     x. Booklet pane of 4, #970m-
           970p   4.00 4.00
     y. Booklet pane of 4, #970q-
           970t   4.00 4.00

No. 970 sold for $9. See Offices in Geneva
Nos. 492-494, Vienna Nos. 434-436.

A398

Designs: 1c, Cielo rosado. 9c, Rosa de sangre. 10c, Espíritu de mujer.

2009, Feb. 6   Litho.   Perf. 13¼

971	A398	1c multicolored	.30	.30
972	A398	9c multicolored	.30	.30
973	A398	10c multicolored	.30	.30
	Nos. 971-973 (3)		.90	.90

A399

Litho. With Foil Application

2009, Feb. 6   Perf. 14x13½

974	A399	94c purple & multi	2.00	2.00

See Offices in Geneva No. 495, Vienna No. 437.

Endangered Species Type of 1993

No. 975, Emperor dragonfly. No. 976, Southern wood ant. No. 977, Rosalia longicorn. No. 978, Apollo butterfly.

2009, Apr. 16   Litho.   Perf. 12¾x12½

975	A271	42c multicolored	1.25	1.25
976	A271	42c multicolored	1.25	1.25
977	A271	42c multicolored	1.25	1.25
978	A271	42c multicolored	1.25	1.25
a.		Block of 4, #975-978	5.50	5.50
b.		Pane of 16, imperf.	5,000.	

See Offices in Geneva Nos. 496-499; Vienna Nos. 438-441.

A400

Nos. 979, 981a, Town Hall and Roland on the Marketplace, Bremen. Nos. 980, 981d, Aachen Cathedral. No. 981b, Wartburg Castle. No. 981c, Palaces and Parks of Potsdam and Berlin. No. 981e, Luther Memorials in Eisleben and Wittenberg. No. 981f, Monastic Island of Reichenau.

2009, May 7   Litho.   Perf. 14x13½

979	A400	44c multicolored	.90	.90
980	A400	98c multicolored	2.00	2.00

Souvenir Booklet

981		Booklet, #981g-981l	20.00
a.-c.		A400 27c any single	.60	.60
d.-f.		A400 42c any single	1.00	1.00
g.		Booklet pane of 4 #981a	2.40	2.40
h.		Booklet pane of 4 #981b	2.40	2.40
i.		Booklet pane of 4 #981c	2.40	2.40
j.		Booklet pane of 4 #981d	4.00	4.00
k.		Booklet pane of 4 #981e	4.00	4.00
l.		Booklet pane of 4 #981f	4.00	4.00

See Offices in Geneva Nos. 500-502, Vienna Nos. 442-444.

UN Flag — A401

Let Us Beat Swords Into Plowshares,
Sculpture by Evgeny
Vuchetich — A402

Single Form, Sculpture by Barbara
Hepworth — A403

Window Cleaner — A404

UN Headquarters — A405

2009, June 5   Perf. 13¼

982	A401	44c multi + label	2.00	2.00
a.		Perf. 11¼x11 + label	10.00	10.00
b.		Perf. 14¼x14½ + label	1.80	1.80
983	A402	44c multi + label	2.00	2.00
a.		Perf. 11¼x11 + label	10.00	10.00
b.		Perf. 14¼x14½ + label	1.80	1.80
984	A403	44c multi + label	2.00	2.00
a.		Perf. 11¼x11 + label	10.00	10.00
b.		Perf. 14¼x14½ + label	1.80	1.80
985	A404	44c multi + label	2.00	2.00
a.		Perf. 11¼x11 + label	10.00	10.00
b.		Perf. 14¼x14½ + label	1.80	1.80
986	A405	44c multi + label	2.00	2.00
a.		Perf. 11¼x11 + label	10.00	10.00
b.		Perf. 14¼x14½ + label	1.80	1.80
c.		Vert. strip of 5, #982-986, + 5 labels	10.00	10.00
d.		Vert. strip of 5, #982a-986a, + 5 labels	50.00	50.00
e.		Vert. strip of 5, #982b-986b, + 5 labels	9.00	7.50

The full sheets sold for $14.95 with or without personalized labels. The personalization of labels was available only at UN Headquarters, and not through mail order. The sheet of No. 986d has "ver. 2" in the lower right selvage. The sheet of No. 986e has "Ver. 3" in the lower right selvage.

Flags and UN Headquarters — A406

Single Form, Sculpture by Barbara
Hepworth — A407

Sphere Within a Sphere, Sculpture by
Arnaldo Pomodoro — A409

UN Headquarters and Chrysler
Building — A410

2009, June 5

987	A406	98c multi + label	4.00	4.00
a.		Perf. 11¼x11 + label	9.00	9.00
b.		Perf. 14¼x14½ + label	3.50	3.50
988	A407	98c multi + label	4.00	4.00
a.		Perf. 11¼x11 + label	9.00	9.00
b.		Perf. 14¼x14½ + label	3.50	3.50
989	A408	98c multi + label	4.00	4.00
a.		Perf. 11¼x11 + label	9.00	9.00
b.		Perf. 14¼x14½ + label	3.50	3.50
990	A409	98c multi + label	4.00	4.00
a.		Perf. 11¼x11 + label	9.00	9.00
b.		Perf. 14¼x14½ + label	3.50	3.50
991	A410	98c multi + label	4.00	4.00
a.		Perf. 11¼x11 + label	9.00	9.00
b.		Perf. 14¼x14½ + label	3.50	3.50
c.		Vert. strip of 5, #987-991, + 5 labels	20.00	20.00
d.		Vert. strip of 5, #987a-991a, + 5 labels	45.00	45.00
e.		Vert. strip of 5, #987b-991b, + 5 labels	17.50	17.50

The full sheets sold for $14.95 with or without personalized labels. The personalization of labels was available only at UN Headquarters, and not through mail order. The sheet of No. 991d has "ver. 2" in the lower right selvage. The sheet of No. 991e has "VER. 3" in the lower right selvage.

Economic and Social Council — A411

Designs: 44c, Water and sanitation. 98c, Traditional medicines.

2009, Aug. 6   Perf. 12¾x12½

992	A411	44c multicolored	2.00	.90
993	A411	98c multicolored	5.00	2.00

See Offices in Geneva Nos. 503-504, Vienna Nos. 450-451.

UN Emblem — A412

2009, Sept. 22   Perf. 13¼

994	A412	98c multi + label	5.50	5.50
a.		Perf. 11¼x11 + label	5.00	5.00

The full sheets sold for $14.95 with or without personalized labels. There are five different non-personalized labels. The personalization of labels was available only at UN Headquarters, and not through mail order. The sheet of No. 994a has "ver. 2" in the lower right selvage.

Miniature Sheet

Millennium Development
Goals — A413

No. 995: a, Bowl of hot food. b, Pencil. c, Female symbol. d, Teddy bear. e, Pregnant woman, heart. f, Medicine bottle. g, Stylized tree. h, Conjoined people.

2009, Sept. 25

995	A413	Sheet of 8	10.00	10.00
a.-h.		44c Any single	1.20	1.20

See Offies in Geneva No. 505; Vienna No. 457.

Mohandas K.
Gandhi — A414

2009, Oct. 2

996	A414	$1 multicolored	2.25	2.25

Miniature Sheet

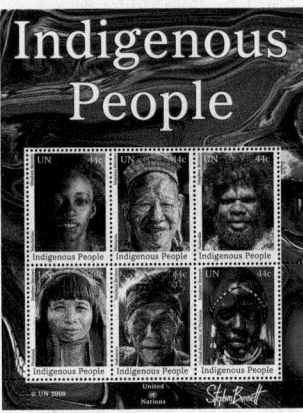

Indigenous People — A415

No. 997 — Portraits of person from: a, Seychelles. b, Malaysia. c, Australia. d, Thailand. e, Indonesia. f, Tanzania.

2009, Oct. 8   Perf. 12½

997	A415	Sheet of 6	7.00	7.00
a.-f.		44c Any single	1.15	1.15

See Offices in Geneva No. 511, Vienna No. 458.

Flags and Coins Type of 2006

No. 998 — Flag of: a, Bahamas, 10 cent coin. b, Jamaica, 20 dollar coin. c, Honduras, 50 centavo coin. d, Kuwait, 100 fils coin. e, Panama, 1 cuarto de Balboa coin. f, Guatemala, 50 centavo coin. g, St. Lucia, 1 cent coin. h, Yemen, 20 rial coin.

2010, Feb. 5   Litho.   Perf. 13¼x13

998		Sheet of 8	9.75	9.75
a.-h.		A375 44c Any single	1.20	1.20

A column of rouletting in the middle of the sheet separates it into two parts. See Offices in Geneva No. 512; Vienna No. 459.

Endangered Species Type of 1993

No. 999, Monkey puzzle tree. No. 1000, Quiver tree. No. 1001, Bristlecone pine tree. No. 1002, Scarlet ball cactus.

2010, Apr. 15 Litho. Perf. 12¾x12½

999	A271	44c multicolored	1.25 1.25
1000	A271	44c multicolored	1.25 1.25
1001	A271	44c multicolored	1.25 1.25
1002	A271	44c multicolored	1.25 1.25
a.		Block of 4, #999-1002	5.50 5.50

See Offices in Geneva Nos. 513-516; Vienna Nos. 465-468.

The stamp pictured above was printed in limited quantities and sold for far more than face value. The label attached to the stamp could not be personalized. Value for stamp and label, $3. A similar stamp dated "2011" with a different label attached exists.

One Planet, One Ocean Types of Geneva and Vienna and

A416

One Planet, One Ocean — A417

No. 1003: a, Turtle at top, eel at left, fish at LR. b, Fish at LL, turtle's flipper at bottom. c, Fish at left, yellow sponge at LR, Lobster at right. d, Lobster at left, turtle at right.

No. 1004: a, Octopus at left, fish at LR. b, Fish at left and right, turtle's head at bottom. c, Lobster at left, fish at LL and LR. d, Fish at LL and LR, turtle's body at UR.

No. 1005: a, Like #1003a. b, Like #1003b. c, Like #1003c. d, Like #1003d. e, Like Vienna #471a. f, Like Vienna #471b. g, Like Vienna #471c. h, Like Vienna #471d. i, Like Geneva #519a. j, Like Geneva #519b. k, Like Geneva #519c. l, Like Geneva #519d. m, Like #1004a. n, Like #1004b. o, Like #1004c. p, Like #1004d. q, Like Vienna #472a. r, Like Vienna #472b. s, Like Vienna #472c. t, Like Vienna #472d. u, Like Geneva #520a. v, Like Geneva #520b. w, Like Geneva #520c. x, Like Geneva #520d.

2010, May 6 Litho. Perf. 14x13¼

1003	A416	Sheet of 4	3.60 3.60
a.-d.		44c Any single	.90 .90
1004	A417	Sheet of 4	8.00 8.00
a.-d.		98c Any single	2.00 2.00

Souvenir Booklet
Perf. 13¼x13

1005		Booklet, #1005y-1005z, 1005aa-1005ad	18.00
a.-d.		A416 28c any single	.60 .60
e.-h.		V91 28c any single	.60 .60
i.-l.		G85 28c any single	.60 .60
m.-p.		A417 44c any single	.90 .90
q.-t.		V92 44c any single	.90 .90
u.-x.		G86 44c any single	.90 .90
y.		Booklet pane of 4 #1005a-1005d	2.40 2.40
z.		Booklet pane of 4 #1005e-1005h	2.40 2.40
aa.		Booklet pane of 4 #1005i-1005l	2.40 2.40
ab.		Booklet pane of 4 #1005m-1005p	3.60 3.60
ac.		Booklet pane of 4 #1005q-1005t	3.60 3.60
ad.		Booklet pane of 4 #1005u-1005x	3.60 3.60

Intl. Oceanographic Commission, 50th anniv. See Offices in Geneva Nos. 519-521, Vienna Nos. 471-473.

People of Different Cultures — A418

People of Different Cultures as New York Buildings A419

2010, June 4 Litho. Perf. 13

1006	A418	3c multicolored	.25 .25
1007	A419	4c multicolored	.25 .25

UN Headquarters and New York Skyline — A420

Shanghai Skyline — A421

2010, June 4 Litho. Perf. 13¼

1008	A420	98c multicolored	3.00 3.00
1009	A421	98c multicolored	3.00 3.00
a.		Horiz. pair, #1008-1009	6.00 6.00

Expo 2010, Shanghai. Nos. 1008-1009 were sold only in full panes for $14.95.

United Nations, 65th Anniv. — A422

Litho. With Foil Application
2010, June 28 Perf. 13¼

1010	A422	98c light blue & gold	2.25 2.25

Souvenir Sheet

1011		Sheet of 2 #1011a	5.00 5.00
a.		A422 98c dark blue & gold	2.50 2.50

See Offices in Geneva No. 522, Vienna No. 474.

A423

A424

A425

A426

United Nations Sea Transport — A427

2010, Sept. 2 Litho. Perf. 13¼x13

1012	A423	44c multicolored	.90 .90
1013	A424	44c multicolored	.90 .90
1014	A425	44c multicolored	.90 .90
1015	A426	44c multicolored	.90 .90
1016	A427	44c multicolored	.90 .90
a.		Horiz. strip of 5, #1012-1016	5.00 5.00

See Offices in Geneva Nos. 523-527, Vienna Nos. 475-479.

Intl. Year of Biodiversity A428

Drawings from Art Forms from Nature, by Ernst Heinrich: 15c, Hummingbird. $1.50, Liverwort.

2010, Oct. 18 Litho. Perf. 13

1017	A428	15c multicolored	.30 .30
1018	A428	$1.50 multicolored	3.00 3.00

See Offices in Geneva Nos. 517-518; Vienna Nos. 469-470.

Miniature Sheet

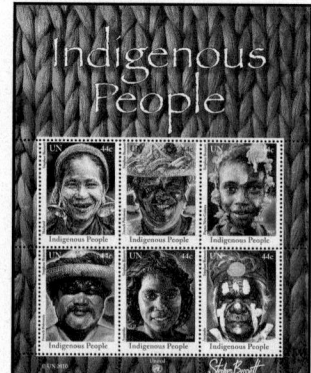

Indigenous People — A429

No. 1019 — Portraits of person from: a, Thailand. b, French Polynesia (woman, denomination in black). c, Papua New Guinea. d, French Polynesia (man, denomination in white). e, Australia (child). f, Australia (old man with headband).

2010, Oct. 21 Litho. Perf. 13

1019	A429	Sheet of 6	6.00 6.00
a.-f.		44c Any single	1.00 1.00

See Offices in Geneva No. 529; Vienna No. 480.

United Nations Headquarters, New York — A430

United Nations Headquarters: 11c, Aerial view. $5, Ground-level view.

2011, Feb. 4 Litho. Perf. 13

1020	A430	11c multicolored	.25 .25
1021	A430	$5 multicolored	9.00 9.00

See Offices in Geneva Nos. 530-531; Vienna Nos. 481-482.

Flags and Coins Type of 2006

No. 1022 — Flag of: a, Mauritius, 1 rupee coin. b, Guyana, 10 dollar coin. c, Timor, 5 cent coin. d, Iceland, 100 krónur coin. e, Chile, 1 peso coin. f, Norway, 20 kroner coin. g, Fiji, 50 cent coin. h, Comoro Islands, 100 franc coin.

2011, Mar. 3 Litho. Perf. 13¼x13

1022		Sheet of 8	8.75 8.75
a.-h.	A375	44c Any single	1.10 1.10

A column of rouletting in the middle of the sheet separates it into two parts. See Offices in Geneva No. 532; Vienna No. 483.

UN Emblem — A431

2011, Apr. 7 Litho. Perf. 14¾

1023	A431	98c blue + label	4.00 4.00

Printed in sheets of 10 + 10 different labels which are not personalizable. The full sheet sold for $14.95

Human Space Flight, 50th Anniv. — A432

No. 1024: Various parts of outer space scene.

No. 1025: a, Cosmonaut and rocket. b, Astronaut on ladder of Lunar Module.

2011, Apr. 12 Litho. Perf. 13x13¼

1024	A432	Sheet of 16	16.00 16.00
a.-p.		44c any single	1.00 1.00

Souvenir Sheet

1025	A432	Sheet of 2	15.00 15.00
a.		44c multi	4.50 4.50
b.		98c multi	11.50 11.50

See Offices in Geneva Nos. 533-534; Vienna Nos. 484-485. No. 1024 contains two 40x48mm stamps that were printed as part of a larger sheet of six stamps, Vienna No. 485c, which was broken up into its component two-stamp souvenir sheets, and also sold as one unit. Value $90, complete unit.

UNESCO World Heritage Sites in Nordic Countries — A433

Designs: 44c, Surtsey Volcanic Island, Iceland. 98c, Drottningholm Castle, Sweden.

2011, May 5   Litho.   Perf. 14x13½
1026 A433 44c multicolored   .90   .90
1027 A433 98c multicolored   2.00 2.00
   See Offices in Geneva Nos. 535-536; Vienna Nos. 496-497.

AIDS Ribbon — A434

2011, June 3   Litho.   Die Cut
Self-Adhesive
1028 A434 44c red & blue   1.75 1.75
   See Offices in Geneva No. 537; Vienna No. 498.

Economic and Social Council (ECOSOC) — A435

2011, July 1   Litho.   Perf. 14¼
1029 A435 44c multicolored   1.50 1.50
1030 A435 98c multicolored   3.50 3.50
   See Offices in Geneva Nos. 538-539; Vienna Nos. 499-500.

Endangered Species Type of 1993
   Designs: No. 1031, Bali starling. No. 1032, California condor. No. 1033, Japanese crane. No. 1034, Black-fronted piping-guan.

2011, Sept. 7   Perf. 12¾x12½
1031 A271 44c multicolored   1.10 1.10
1032 A271 44c multicolored   1.10 1.10
1033 A271 44c multicolored   1.10 1.10
1034 A271 44c multicolored   1.10 1.10
   a.   Block of 4, #1031-1034   5.00 5.00
   See Offices in Geneva Nos. 540-543; Vienna Nos. 501-504.

Intl. Year of Forests — A436

   Designs: 44c, Tree with wildlife, man with mask. 98c, Tree roots.

Litho. With Foil Application
2011, Oct. 13   Perf. 12½
1035 A436 44c multicolored   1.25 1.25
1036 A436 98c multicolored   2.50 2.50
   a.   A436 Vert. pair, #1035-1036 3.75 3.75
   See Offices in Geneva Nos. 544-545; Vienna Nos. 505-506.

UN Emblem — A437

2012, Jan. 23   Litho.   Perf. 14¾
1037 A437 $1.05 blue + label   2.75 2.75
      Sheet of 10 + 10 labels   27.50   —
   The full sheet sold for $14.95. The generic label exists as shown, and with dragon in yellow against red background. Labels could be personalized. The personalization of labels was available only at UN Headquarters, and not through mail order.

A438

   No. 1038: a, Desk in lobby. b, Sculpture of Jesus holding lamb. c, Stained-glass window. d, Meeting room. e, Guided tour. f, Flags in front of United Nations buildings. g, United Nations Peacekeepers helmet in showcase. h, Gift shop. i, View of curved floors above lobby. j, Street signs.

2012, Jan. 23   Litho.   Perf. 14¾
1038 A438 Sheet of 10   30.00 30.00
   a.-j. $1.05 Any single + label 3.00 3.00
   The full sheet sold for $14.95. The generic labels are shown. Labels could be personalized. The personalization of labels was available only at UN Headquarters, and not through mail order.

Flags and Coins Type of 2006
   No. 1039 — Flag of: a, Nepal, 1 rupee coin. b, Bahrain, 100 fils coin. c, Paraguay, 1000 guarani coin. d, Ethiopia, 25 cent coin. e, Peru, 1 sol coin. f, Solomon Islands, 20 cent coin. g, Dominican Republic, 1 peso coin. h, Canada, 1 dollar coin.

2012, Feb. 3   Litho.   Perf. 13¼x13
1039 Sheet of 8   7.25 7.25
   a.-h.   A375 45c Any single   .90   .90
   A column of rouletting in the middle of the sheet separates it into two parts. See Offices in Geneva No. 546; Vienna No. 507.

Autism Awareness A439

Autism Awareness A440

   Drawings by autistic people: No. 1040, An Abstract Garden II, by Trent Altman, U.S. No. 1041, Crazy Love, by Hannah Kandel, U.S.

2012, Apr. 2   Litho.   Perf. 14x13½
1040 A439 $1.05 multicolored   2.10 2.10
1041 A440 $1.05 multicolored   2.10 2.10
   a.   Pair, #1040-1041   4.20 4.20
   See Offices in Geneva Nos. 547-548; Vienna Nos. 508-509.

Endangered Species Type of 1993
   Designs: No. 1042, Giant panda. No. 1043, Short-horned chameleon. No. 1044, Oncilla. No. 1045, Cotton-headed tamarin.

2012, Apr. 19   Litho.   Perf. 12¾x12½
1042 A271 45c multicolored   1.10 1.10
1043 A271 45c multicolored   1.10 1.10
1044 A271 45c multicolored   1.10 1.10
1045 A271 45c multicolored   1.10 1.10
   a.   Block of 4, #1042-1045   5.00 5.00
   See Offices in Geneva Nos. 549-552; Vienna Nos. 511-514.

Tinker Bell — A441

Tinker Bell — A442

2012, June 1   Litho.   Perf. 14¾
1046 A441 $1.05 multi + label   3.00 3.00
1047 A442 $1.05 multi + label   3.00 3.00
   a.   Vert. pair, #1046-1047, + 2 labels   6.00 6.00
      Sheet of 10, 5 each #1046-1047, + 10 labels   30.00 30.00
   The full sheet sold for $14.95. The generic labels are shown. Labels could be personalized. The personalization of labels was available only at UN Headquarters, and not through mail order.

Rio + 20 Conference on Sustainable Development, Rio de Janeiro A443

2012, June 1   Litho.   Perf. 13x13¼
1048 A443 $1.05 multicolored   2.10 2.10
   See Offices in Geneva No. 553; Vienna No. 515.

Sport for Peace — A444

   2012 Paralympics events: 45c, Goalball. $1.05, Sitting volleyball.

Litho. With Foil Application
2012, Aug. 17   Perf. 14½
1049 A444 45c multicolored   .90   .90
1050 A444 $1.05 multicolored   2.10 2.10
   a.   Souvenir sheet of 1   3.50 3.50
   See Offices in Geneva Nos. 554-555; Vienna Nos. 516-517.

UNESCO World Heritage Sites in Africa — A445

   Designs: 45c, Kilamanjaro National Park, Tanzania. $1.05, Old Towns of Djenné, Mali.

2012, Sept. 5   Litho.   Perf. 13¼
1051 A445 45c multicolored   .90   .90
1052 A445 $1.05 multicolored   2.10 2.10
   See Offices in Geneva Nos. 556-557; Vienna Nos. 518-519.

Miniature Sheet

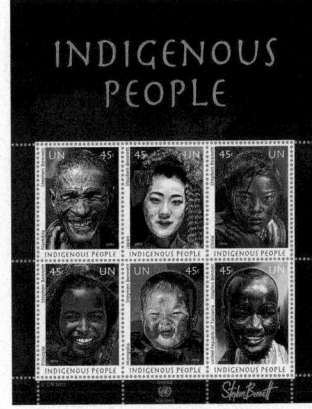

Indigenous People — A446

   No. 1053 — Portrait of person from: a, Namibia. b, Japan. c, China. d, Ethiopia. e, Mongolia. f, Tanzania.

2012, Oct. 11   Litho.   Perf. 13¼x13
1053 A446 Sheet of 6   5.50 5.50
   a.-f.   45c Any single   .90   .90
   See Offices in Geneva No. 558; Vienna No. 520.

UN Emblem — A447

2013, Jan. 28   Litho.   Perf. 14¾
1054 A447 $1.10 multi + label   4.00 4.00
      Sheet of 10 + 10 labels   40.00   —
   The full sheet sold for $14.95. The generic label exists as shown, and with snake against red background. Labels could be personalized. The personalization of labels was available only at UN Headquarters, and not through mail order.

A448

   No. 1055: a, Flags in front of Secretariat Building, brown panel at right. b, Aerial view of headquarters and East River, yellow orange panel at left. c, Secretariat Building and wall of General Assembly building, yellow orange panel at left. d, Headquarters and East River, brown panel at right. e, General Asembly and Secretariat Buildings, flags at right, brown panel at right. f, Sculpture and fountain at night, yellow orange panel at left. g, Secretariat Building and cherry blossoms, yellow orange panel at left. h, Secretariat Building, trees without leaves, flags at left, brown panel at right. i, Aerial view of headquarters at night, brown panel at right. j, Headquarters, yellow panel at left.

2013, Jan. 28   Litho.   Perf. 14¾
1055 A448 Sheet of 10   30.00 30.00
a.-j. $1.10 Any single + label   3.00   3.00

The full sheet sold for $14.95. The generic labels are shown. Labels could be personalized. The personalization of labels was available only at UN Headquarters, and not through mail order.

World Radio Day — A449

Designs: 46c, Radio antenna. $1.10, Audrey Hepburn at microphone.

2013, Feb. 13   Litho.   Perf. 13¼x13
1056 A449 46c multicolored   .95   .95
1057 A449 $1.10 multicolored   2.25 2.25

See Offices in Geneva Nos. 559-560; Vienna Nos. 521-522.

Circle of People A450

United Nations Headquarters A451

2013, Mar. 5   Litho.   Perf. 14x13½
1058 A450 $1.10 multicolored   2.25 2.25
Perf. 13½x14
1059 A451 $3 multicolored   6.00 6.00

See Offices in Geneva Nos. 561-562; Vienna Nos. 523-524.

World Heritage Sites, China — A452

Designs: Nos. 1060, 1062a, Mogao Caves. Nos. 1061, 1062d, Imperial Palace, Beijing. No. 1062b, Potala Palace, Lhasa. No. 1062c, Great Wall of China. No. 1062e, Mount Huangshan. No. 1062f, Mausoleum of the First Qing Emperor.

2013, Apr. 11   Litho.   Perf. 14x13½
1060 A452 46c multicolored   .95   .95
1061 A452 $1.10 multicolored   2.25 2.25
Souvenir Booklet
1062 Booklet, #1062g-1062l   20.00
a.-c. A452 33c any single   .70   .70
d.-f. A452 46c any single   .95   .95
g. Booklet pane of 4 #1062a   2.80   —
h. Booklet pane of 4 #1062b   2.80   —
i. Booklet pane of 4 #1062c   2.80   —

j. Booklet pane of 4 #1062d   3.80
k. Booklet pane of 4 #1062e   3.80
l. Booklet pane of 4 #1062f   3.80

See Offices in Geneva Nos. 563-565, Vienna Nos. 525-527.

Flag Type of 1980
Printed by Lowe Martin Group, Canada. Designed by Rorie Katz, US. Issued in panes of 16; each pane contains 4 blocks of 4. A setenant block of 4 designs centers each pane.

2013, May 2   Litho.   Perf. 13
1063 A185 $1.10 Myanmar   2.25 2.25
1064 A185 $1.10 Russian Federation 2.25 2.25
1065 A185 $1.10 South Sudan   2.25 2.25
1066 A185 $1.10 Cape Verde   2.25 2.25
a.   Block of 4, #1063-1066   12.00 12.00
      Nos. 1063-1066 (4)   9.00 9.00

World Oceans Day — A453

No. 1067 — Fish from One Fish, Two Fish, Red Fish, Blue Fish, by Dr. Seuss: a, Green fish, red fish, sign. b, Red fish facing right. c, Green fish facing left, sign. d, Yellow fish, sign. e, Blue fish. f, Red fish facing left, sign. g, Red fish facing right, water droplets, tail of yellow and red fish, sign. h, Yellow and red fish, green fish, side of blue fish. i, Head of blue fish, sign post. j, Sign and wave. k, Sign, red fish, side and tail of blue fish, wave. l, Side of blue fish, green fish, wave.

2013, May 31   Litho.   Perf. 13
1067 A453 Sheet of 12   11.50 11.50
a.-l.   46c any single   .95   .95

See Offices in Geneva No. 566, Vienna No. 528.

Nebulae — A454

Designs: No. 1068, V838 Mon. No. 1069, WR 25, Tr16-244. 46c, 30 Doradus.

2013, Aug. 9   Litho.   Perf. 13¼
1068 A454 $1.10 multicolored   2.25 2.25
1069 A454 $1.10 multicolored   2.25 2.25
a.   Pair, #1068-1069   4.50 4.50
Souvenir Sheet
1070 A454 46c multicolored   2.50 2.50

No. 1070 contains one 44x44mm stamp. See Offices in Geneva Nos. 567-569; Vienna Nos. 529-531.

World Humanitarian Day — A455

No. 1071 — "The World Needs More" in speech balloon in: a, Somali (Uduunku. . .). b,

Thai. c, Arabic (people in background). d, Portuguese (O Mundo. . .). e, Russian. f, Korean. g, Swahili (Mahitaji. . .). h, Chinese. i, Urdu (aerial view of village in background). j, English.

2013, Aug. 19   Litho.   Perf. 14¾
1071 A455 Sheet of 10   30.00 30.00
a.-j. $1.10 Any single + label 3.00 3.00

The full sheet sold for $14.95. The generic labels are shown. Labels could be personalized. The personalization of labels was available only at UN Headquarters, and not through mail order.

Works of Disabled Artists — A456

Designs: 46c, Self-portrait II by Chuck Close, U.S. $1.10, Tears and Laughter, by Josephine King, United Kingdom.

2013, Sept. 20   Litho.   Perf. 13¼x13
1072 A456 46c multicolored   .95   .95
1073 A456 $1.10 multicolored   2.25 2.25

See Offices in Geneva Nos. 570-571; Vienna Nos. 532-533.

Endangered Species Type of 1993
Designs: No. 1074, Asian tapir. No. 1075, Mongoose lemur. No. 1076, Flat-headed cat. No. 1077, Aye-aye.

2013, Oct. 10   Litho.   Perf. 12¾x12½
1074 A271 $1.10 multicolored   2.50 2.50
1075 A271 $1.10 multicolored   2.50 2.50
1076 A271 $1.10 multicolored   2.50 2.50
1077 A271 $1.10 multicolored   2.50 2.50
a.   Block of 4, #1074-1077   11.00 11.00

See Offices in Geneva Nos. 572-575; Vienna Nos. 534-537.

Flags and Coins Type of 2006
No. 1078 — Flag of: a, Montenegro, 20 cent coin. b, Grenada, 5 cent coin. c, United States, 25 cent coin. d, Gabon, 100 franc coin. e, Palau, 1 cent coin. f, Niger, 100 franc coin. g, Saint Kitts and Nevis, 5 cent coin. h, Venezuela, 1 bolivar coin.

2013, Nov. 6   Litho.   Perf. 13¼x13
1078 A375 Sheet of 8   7.75 7.75
a.-h.   A375 46c Any single   .95   .95

A column of rouletting in the middle of the sheet separates it into two parts. See Offices in Geneva No. 576; Vienna No. 539.

UN Emblem — A457

2014, Jan. 28   Litho.   Perf. 14¾
1079 A457 $1.15 multi + label   3.00 3.00

A458

No. 1080: a, The Golden Rule, mosaic by Norman Rockwell, dark green panel at right. b, Renovated Delegate's Lounge, yellow green panel at left. c, Renovated ECOSOC Chamber, red brown panel at left. d, Dag Hammarskjold Library, dark blue panel at right. e, Helmet of United Nations Peacekeeper and

United Nations Flag, dark blue panel at right. f, United Nations Headquarters, dark green panel at right. g, Renovated Security Council Chamber, yellow green panel at left. h, Flags of member nations, red brown panel at right. i, Mankind's Struggle for Lasting Peace, by José Vela-Zanetti, dark blue panel at right. j, Relational Painting No. 90, by Fritz Glarner, yellow green panel at left.

2014, Jan. 28   Litho.   Perf. 14¾
1080 A458 Sheet of 10   30.00 30.00
a.-j. $1.15 Any single + label 3.00 3.00

The full sheet sold for $14.95. The generic labels are shown. Labels could be personalized. The personalization of labels was available only at UN Headquarters, and not through mail order.

International Day of Happiness A459

Designs: 47c, Woman smiling, photograph by Mario Castello, "Happy." $1.15, People kissing on beach, photograph by Henryk T. Kaiser, "Feliz."

2014, Mar. 17   Litho.   Perf. 13¼x13
1081 A459 47c multicolored   .95   .95
1082 A459 $1.15 multicolored   2.40 2.40

See Offices in Geneva Nos. 577-578; Vienna Nos. 540-541.

Flag Type of 1980
Printed by Lowe Martin Group, Canada. Designed by Rorie Katz, U.S. Issued in panes of 16; each pane contains 4 blocks of 4. A setenant block of 4 designs centers each pane.

2014, Mar. 27   Litho.   Perf. 13x13¼
1083 A185 $1.15 Afghanistan   3.00 3.00
1084 A185 $1.15 Serbia   3.00 3.00
1085 A185 $1.15 Cambodia   3.00 3.00
1086 A185 $1.15 Democratic Republic of the Congo 3.00 3.00
a.   Block of 4, #1083-1086   15.00 15.00
      Nos. 1083-1086 (4)   12.00 12.00

Miniature Sheet

International Year of Jazz — A460

No. 1087: a, Trumpeter with cap and mute in trumpet. b, Silhouette of trumpeter in tan. c, Saxophone. d, Trumpet. e, Silhouette of trumpeter in lilac. f, Saxophonist wearing hat. g, Man with hat holding trombone. h, Green saxophone. i, Saxophonist without hat. j, Trombone. k, Trumpeter wearing hat. l, Microphone.

2014, Apr. 30   Litho.   Perf. 13x13¼
1087 A460 Sheet of 12   12.00 12.00
      First day cover   15.00
a.-l.   49c Any single   1.00 1.00

See Offices in Geneva No. 579; Vienna No. 542.

A461

A462

Printed by Lowe-Martin Group, Canada. Panes of 20. Designed by Sergio Baradat, U.S.

2014, June 6   Litho.   Perf. 13¼x13

| 1088 | A461 | 33c multicolored | .70 | .70 |
| 1089 | A462 | $2 multicolored | 4.00 | 4.00 |

See Offices in Geneva Nos. 580-581; Vienna Nos. 544-545.

Taj Mahal and Tourists — A463

Taj Mahal and Pink Sky — A464

Taj Mahal and Sun — A465

Taj Mahal and Reflecting Pool — A466

Taj Mahal and Camel — A467

Taj Mahal and Elephant — A468

2014, July 16   Engr.   Perf. 13¼x13

| 1090 | A463 | 49c multicolored | 1.00 | 1.00 |
| 1091 | A464 | $1.15 multicolored | 2.40 | 2.40 |

Souvenir Booklet

1092		Booklet, #1092g-1092l	20.50	
a.	A463	34c multi	.70	.70
b.	A465	34c multi	.70	.70
c.	A466	34c multi	.70	.70
d.	A464	49c multi	1.00	1.00
e.	A467	49c multi	1.00	1.00
f.	A468	49c multi	1.00	1.00
g.		Booklet pane of 4 #1092a	2.80	—
h.		Booklet pane of 4 #1092b	2.80	—
i.		Booklet pane of 4 #1092c	2.80	—
j.		Booklet pane of 4 #1092d	4.00	—
k.		Booklet pane of 4 #1092e	4.00	—
l.		Booklet pane of 4 #1092f	4.00	—

See Offices in Geneva Nos. 582-584; Vienna Nos. 546-548.

International Year of Family Farming — A469

2014, Aug. 21   Litho.   Perf. 13x13¼

| 1093 | A469 | 49c multicolored | 1.00 | 1.00 |
| 1094 | A469 | $1.15 multicolored | 2.40 | 2.40 |

See Offices in Geneva Nos. 585-586; Vienna Nos. 549-550.

Global Education First Initiative A470

Designs: $1.15, Teacher and students in forest. $1.50, Chemistry teacher and student.

2014, Sept. 18   Litho.   Perf. 13x13¼

| 1095 | A470 | $1.15 multicolored | 2.40 | 2.40 |

Souvenir Sheet
Perf. 12½

| 1096 | A470 | $1.50 multicolored | 6.00 | 5.00 |

No. 1096 contains one 32x32mm stamp. See Offices in Geneva Nos. 588-589; Vienna Nos. 551-552.

Endangered Species A471

Maps and: No. 1097, Denise's pygmy seahorses. No. 1098, Whale shark. No. 1099, Scalloped hammerhead shark. No. 1100, Asian arowana.

2014, Oct. 23   Litho.   Perf. 12¾x12½

1097	A471	$1.15 multicolored	2.40	2.40
1098	A471	$1.15 multicolored	2.40	2.40
1099	A471	$1.15 multicolored	2.40	2.40
1100	A471	$1.15 multicolored	2.40	2.40
a.		Block of 4, #1097-1100	9.75	9.75

See Offices in Geneva Nos. 590-593; Vienna Nos. 553-556.

A472

No. 1101: a, United Nations emblem in gray, bottom panel in blue. b, Aerial view of United Nations Headquarters, bottom panel in red, year date at left. c, View of United Nations Headquarters from across East River, bottom panel in red, year date at right. d, Interior balconies, bottom panel in blue. e, Crowd in lobby, bottom panel in blue. f, Sun reflecting off United Nations Building, street lights, bottom panel in red. g, United Nations emblem in brown, bottom panel in red. h, Woman and two men near General Assembly Building, bottom panel in blue. i, United Nations Building, trees without leaves, bottom panel in blue. j, General Assembly and United Nations Buildings, bottom panel in red.

2014, Oct. 23   Litho.   Perf. 14¾

| 1101 | A472 | Sheet of 10 | 32.50 | 32.50 |
| a.-j. | | $1.15 Any single + label | 3.00 | 3.00 |

The full sheet sold for $14.95. The generic labels are shown. Labels could be personalized. The personalization of labels was available only at UN Headquarters, and not through mail order.

UN Emblem — A473

2015, Jan. 23   Litho.   Perf. 14¾

| 1102 | A473 | $1.15 multi + label | 3.00 | 3.00 |
| | | Sheet of 10 + 10 labels | 30.00 | — |

The full sheet sold for $14.95. The generic label exists as shown, with ram on deep bister background. Labels could be personalized. The personalization of labels was available only at UN Headquarters, and not through mail order.

Flags and Coins Type of 2006

No. 1103 — Flag of: a, Kiribati, 10 cent coin. b, Tonga, 2 seniti coin. c, Costa Rica, 10 centimos coin. d, Bhutan, 25 chetrum coin. e, Zimbabwe, 5 dollar coin. f, Angola, 1 kwanza coin. g, Congo Democratic Republic, 1 franc coin. h, Liberia, 25 cent coin.

2015, Feb. 6   Litho.   Perf. 13¼x13

| 1103 | | Sheet of 8 | 8.00 | 8.00 |
| a.-h. | A375 | 49c Any single | 1.00 | 1.00 |

A column of rouletting in the middle of the sheet separates it into two parts. See Offices in Geneva No. 594; Vienna No. 558.

Miniature Sheets

A474

World Poetry Day — A475

No. 1104: a, Black pen, denomination in red brown. b, William Wordsworth quotation in white, denomination in red. c, Wordsworth quotation in red brown, denomination in white. d, Gold pen, denomination in white. e, Black pen, denomination in white. f, Wordsworth quotation in black, denomination in red brown.
No. 1105: a, Gold pen, denomination in white, tree top and rose in background. b, José Martí quotation, denomination in lilac, tree tops in background. c, Martí quotation, denomination in white, tree top and rose in background. d, Gold pen, denomination in lilac, tree trunks and tree top in background. e, Gold pen, denomination in lilac, tree trunks and rose in background. f, Martí quotation, denomination in lilac, tree trunks in background.

Perf. 14½x14¼

2015, Mar. 20   Litho.

1104	A474	Sheet of 6	6.00	6.00
a.-f.		49c Any single	1.00	1.00
1105	A475	Sheet of 6	14.50	14.50
a.-f.		$1.20 Any single	2.40	2.40

See Offices in Geneva Nos. 595-596; Vienna Nos. 559-560.

Endangered Species — A476

Designs: No. 1106, King bird-of-paradise. No. 1107, Blue bird-of-paradise. No. 1108, Princess Stephanie's bird-of-paradise. No. 1109, Carola's parotia.

2015, Apr. 16   Litho.   Perf. 12½x12¾

1106	A476	$1.20 multicolored	2.40	2.40
1107	A476	$1.20 multicolored	2.40	2.40
1108	A476	$1.20 multicolored	2.40	2.40
1109	A476	$1.20 multicolored	2.40	2.40
a.		Block of 4, #1106-1109	9.75	9.75
		Nos. 1106-1109 (4)	9.60	9.60

See Offices in Geneva Nos. 597-600; Vienna Nos. 561-564.

A477

A478

2015, May 7   Litho.   Perf. 13¼x13

| 1110 | A477 | 35c multicolored | .70 | .70 |
| 1111 | A478 | 40c multicolored | .80 | .80 |

See Offices in Vienna Nos. 565-566.

Miniature Sheet

A479

No. 1112: a, United Nations Headquarters and flags, panel at right. b, Flags, panel at left. c, Stairway and pillars, panel at left. d, Reflection of buildings in windows, panel at right. e, Circular meeting room, panel at right. f, United Nations Headquarters, panel at left. g, Trees and United Nations Building, panel at left. h, Let Us Beat Swords Into Plowshares statue, panel at right. i, General Assembly Building, flags and street, panel at right. j, Arrival sculpture, panel at left.

2015, May 7   **Litho.**   *Perf. 14¾*
1112	A479	Sheet of 10	30.00 30.00
a.-j.		$1.20 Any single + label	3.00 3.00

The full sheet sold for $14.95. The generic labels are shown. Labels could be personalized. The personalization of labels was available only at UN Headquarters, and not through mail order.

World Heritage Sites, Southeast Asia — A480

Designs: Nos. 1113, 1115a, Luang Prabang, Laos. Nos. 1114, 1115d, Borobodur Temple, Indonesia. No. 1115b, Angkor Wat, Cambodia. No. 1115c, Ayutthaya, Thailand. No. 1115e, Cordillera, Philippines. No. 1115f, Hué Monuments, Viet Nam.

2015, June 5   **Litho.**   *Perf. 14x13½*
1113	A480	49c multicolored	1.00 1.00
1114	A480	$1.20 multicolored	2.40 2.40

Souvenir Booklet
1115		Booklet, #1115g-1115l	20.50
a.-c.	A480	35c any single	.70 .70
d.-f.	A480	49c any single	1.00 1.00
g.		Booklet pane of 4 #1115a	2.80 —
h.		Booklet pane of 4 #1115b	2.80 —
i.		Booklet pane of 4 #1115c	2.80 —
j.		Booklet pane of 4 #1115d	4.00 —
k.		Booklet pane of 4 #1115e	4.00 —
l.		Booklet pane of 4 #1115f	4.00 —

See Offices in Geneva Nos. 601-603, Vienna Nos. 567-569.

End Violence Against Children — A481

Designs: 49c, Armed violence reduction. $1.20, Sexual violence against children.

        Perf. 14½x14¼
2015, Aug. 20   **Litho.**
1116	A481	49c multicolored	1.00 1.00
1117	A481	$1.20 multicolored	2.40 2.40

See Offices in Geneva Nos. 604-605; Vienna Nos. 570-571.

United Nations, 70th Anniv. — A482

Designed by Sergio Baradat, U.S.

2015, Sept. 25   **Litho.**   *Perf. 14¾*
1118	A482	$1.20 multi + label	3.00 3.00
		Sheet of 10 + 10 labels	30.00 —

The full sheet sold for $14.95. The generic label exists as shown, depicting Pope Francis. Labels could be personalized. The personalization of labels was available only at UN Headquarters, and not through mail order. On Sept. 27, No. 1118 was issued in a sheet of 10 + 10 labels depicting Chinese characters. See Vienna No. 577.

General Assembly Hall A483

Visitors Lobby A484

Security Council A485

Woodrow Wilson Reading Room of Dag Hammarskjöld Library — A486

General Assembly Hall — A487

Printed by Cartor Security Printing, France. Panes of 6. Designed by Rorie Katz, U.S.

2015, Oct. 25   **Litho.**   *Perf. 13¾*
1119	A483	49c multicolored	1.00 1.00
1120	A484	49c multicolored	1.00 1.00
a.		Pair, #1119-1120	2.00 2.00
1121	A485	$1.20 multicolored	2.40 2.40
1122	A486	$1.20 multicolored	2.40 2.40
a.		Pair, #1121-1122	4.80 4.80
		Nos. 1119-1122 (4)	6.80 6.80

Souvenir Sheet
Perf. 13½
1123	A487	$1.20 multicolored	4.00 4.00

United Nations, 70th anniv. See Offices in Geneva Nos. 607-611; Vienna Nos. 572-576.

United Nations Educational, Scientific and Cultural Organization (UNESCO), 70th Anniv. — A488

2015, Nov. 5   **Litho.**   *Perf. 14¾*
1124	A488	$1.20 multi + label	3.50 3.50
		Sheet of 10 + 10 labels	35.00 —

The full sheet sold for $14.95. Ten different generic labels, one of which is shown, are on the sheet. Labels could be personalized. The personalization of labels was available only at UN Headquarters, and not through mail order.

21st United Nations Climate Change Conference, Paris A489

2015, Nov. 24   **Litho.**   *Perf. 13¼*
1125	A489	$1.20 multicolored	2.40 2.40

Values are for stamps with surrounding selvage. See Offices in Geneva No. 612; Vienna No. 578.

UN Emblem — A490

2016, Jan. 8   **Litho.**   *Perf. 14¾*
1126	A490	$1.20 multicolored + label	3.00 3.00
		Sheet of 10 + 10 labels	30.00 —

The full sheet sold for $14.95. The generic label, with monkey on red background, is shown. A sheet of 10 No. 1126 + 10 labels depicting M. S. Subbulaskshmi was issued on Oct. 2, 2016. Labels could be personalized. The personalization of labels was available only at UN Headquarters, and not through mail order. See No. 1231.

Free and Equal — A491

Designs: 49c, Group of stylized people. $1.20, Woman with butterfly wings.

2016, Feb. 5   **Litho.**   *Perf. 13½x13¼*
1127	A491	49c multicolored	1.00 1.00
1128	A491	$1.20 multicolored	2.40 2.40

See Offices in Geneva Nos. 613-614; Vienna Nos. 579-580.

HeForShe Movement A492

Designs: 49c, Man, green background. $1.20, Woman, yellow background.

2016, Mar. 8   **Litho.**   *Perf. 12½x13*
1129	A492	49c multicolored	1.00 1.00
1130	A492	$1.20 multicolored	2.40 2.40

See Offices in Geneva Nos. 615-616; Vienna Nos. 581-582.

Miniature Sheet

Angry Birds — A493

No. 1131: a, Red, the Pigs, double-decker bus. b, Red with wing extended. c, Red and five Hatchlings. d, Red, New York City skyscrapers. e, Red, Eiffel Tower, recycling container. f, Hed in jungle. g, Earth, Hatchlings, Chuck, Red, Bomb, Stella and Matilda. h, Red turning faucet, Pigs in tub. i, Red drinking from squirt bottle, Lower Manhattan skyline. j, Red with shovel, Pyramids.

2016, Apr. 22   **Litho.**   *Perf. 14¾*
1131	A493	Sheet of 10	30.00 30.00
a.-j.		$1.15 Any single + label	3.00 3.00

The full sheet sold for $14.95. The generic labels are shown. Labels could be personalized. The personalization of labels was available only at UN Headquarters, and not through mail order.

Miniature Sheets

International Dance Day

A494

International Dance Day — A495

No. 1132 — Illustration of Chinese dancers by Marcos Chin: a, Woman with arm extended upward. b, Two women, denomination in magenta. c, Woman facing left with arm extended outward. d, Two women, denomination in white. e, Woman with closed eyes. f, Woman with closed eyes with two pale yellow lines touching flower.

No. 1133 — Illustration of Thai dancers by Chin: a, Back of dancer's head, hand of another dancer. b, Dancer wearing mask, leg and arm of other dancers. c, Dancer with costume with blue shoulders, dancer with arm extended. d, Dancer with arm extended, leg and arm of other dancers. e, Two dancers with green and yellow costumes. f, Dancer with green and yellow costume.

2016, Apr. 29	**Litho.**		**Perf. 13¼x13**	
1132	A494	Sheet of 6	5.75	5.75
a.-f.		47c Any single	.95	.95
1133	A495	Sheet of 6	14.50	14.50
a.-f.		$1.15 Any single	2.40	2.40
g.		As #1133, with "Thailand 2018 / World Stamp Exhibition / 28 Nov. - 3 Dec." overprinted in sheet margin	65.00	65.00

Issued: No. 1133g, 11/28/18. See Offices in Geneva Nos. 617-618; Vienna Nos. 583-584.

International Day of United Nations Peacekeepers A496

Designs: 47c, Peacekeeper saluting. $1.15, Man disabling landmine.

Litho. With Foil Application
2016, May 29			**Perf. 13¼x13**	
1134	A496	47c multicolored	.95	.95
1135	A496	$1.15 multicolored	2.40	2.40

See Offices in Geneva Nos. 619-620; Vienna Nos. 586-587.

Miniature Sheet

United Nations Postal Administration, 65th Anniv. — A497

No. 1136 — Old United Nations stamps: a, New York #1. b, New York #127. c, Vienna #86. d, New York #415. e, New York #301. f, New York #548. g, New York #474. h, Vienna #100. i, New York #476. j, Vienna #122.

2016, May 30	**Litho.**	**Perf. 14¾**		
1136	A497	Sheet of 10	30.00	30.00
a.-j.		$1.15 Any single + label	3.00	3.00

The full sheet sold for $14.95. The generic labels are shown. Labels could be personalized. The personalization of labels was available only at UN Headquarters, and not through mail order.

Sport for Peace — A498

Olympic rings and: No. 1137, Shot put, high jump. No. 1138, Runner, javelin. No. 1139, Dove facing left. No. 1140, Dove facing right.

2016, July 22	**Litho.**	**Perf. 14¼**		
1137	A498	47c multicolored	.95	.95
1138	A498	47c multicolored	.95	.95
a.		Pair, #1137-1138	1.90	1.90
1139	A498	$1.15 multicolored	2.40	2.40
1140	A498	$1.15 multicolored	2.40	2.40
a.		Pair, #1139-1140	4.80	4.80
		Nos. 1137-1140 (4)	6.70	6.70

See Offices in Geneva Nos. 621-624; Vienna Nos. 588-591.

Souvenir Sheet

United Nations Economic and Social Commission for Asia and the Pacific Building, Bangkok — A499

No. 1141: a, Left third of building. b, Center third of building. c, Right third of building.

2016, Aug. 10	**Litho.**	**Perf. 13¼x13**		
1141	A499	Sheet of 3	24.00	24.00
a.		$1.15 multi	5.00	5.00
b.		2fr multi	9.50	9.50
c.		€1.70 multi	8.50	8.50

32nd Asian International Stamp Exhibition. No. 1141 sold for $6.

World Heritage Sites, Czech Republic — A500

Designs: Nos. 1142, 1144a, Historic Center of Prague. Nos. 1143, 1144d, Holy Trinity Column, Olomouc. No. 1144b, Gardens and Castle at Kromeríz. No. 1144c, Historic Town Center of Kutná Hora. No. 1144e, Lednice-Valtice Cultural Landscape. No. 1144f, Historic Center of Cesky Krumlov.

2016, Sept. 8	**Litho.**	**Perf. 14¼**		
1142	A500	47c multicolored	.95	.95
1143	A500	$1.15 multicolored	2.40	2.40

Souvenir Booklet

1144		Booklet, #1144g-1144l	20.00	
a.-c.		A500 34c any single	.70	.70
d.-f.		A500 47c any single	.95	.95
g.		Booklet pane of 4 #1144a	2.80	—
h.		Booklet pane of 4 #1144b	2.80	—
i.		Booklet pane of 4 #1144c	2.80	—
j.		Booklet pane of 4 #1144d	3.80	—
k.		Booklet pane of 4 #1144e	3.80	—
l.		Booklet pane of 4 #1144f	3.80	—

See Offices in Geneva Nos. 625-627; Vienna Nos. 592-594, Czech Republic Nos. 3683-3684.

Miniature Sheet

World Wildlife Conference, Johannesburg — A501

No. 1145 — Part of map of Africa and: a, Addax. b, White rhinoceros. c, African lion. d, Disa uniflora.

2016, Sept. 24	**Litho.**	**Perf. 13x13½**		
1145	A501	Sheet of 4	9.75	9.75
a.-d.		$1.15 Any single	2.40	2.40

See Offices in Geneva No. 628; Vienna No. 596.

Miniature Sheet

World Post Day — A502

No. 1146 — Mail box from: a, Japan. b, Spain. c, Germany. d, Brazil. e, China. f, Denmark. g, India. h, Austria. i, England. j, United States.

2016, Oct. 6	**Litho.**	**Perf. 14¾**		
1146	A502	Sheet of 10	30.00	30.00
a.-j.		$1.15 Any single + label	3.00	3.00

The full sheet sold for $14.95. The generic labels are shown. Labels could be personalized. The personalization of labels was available only at UN Headquarters, and not through mail order.

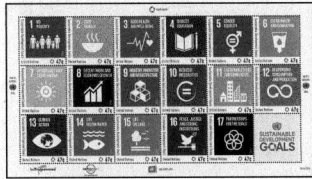

Sustainable Development Goals — A503

No. 1147 — Inscription: a, 1 No poverty. b, 2 Zero hunger. c, 3 Good health and well-being. d, 4 Quality education. e, 5 Gender equality. f, 6 Clean water and sanitation. g, 7 Affordable and clean energy. h, 8 Decent work and economic growth. i, 9 Industry, innovation and infrastructure. j, 10 Reduced inequalities. k, 11 Sustainable cities and communities. l, 12 Responsible consumption and production. m, 13 Climate action. n, 14 Life below water. o, 15 Life on land. p, 16 Peace, justice and strong institutions. q, 17 Partnerships for the goals.

2016, Oct. 24	**Litho.**	**Perf. 13¼**		
1147	A503	Sheet of 17 + label	17.00	17.00
a.-q.		47c Any single	1.00	1.00

See Offices in Geneva No. 629; Vienna No. 597.

Souvenir Sheet

Monkey King From Chinese Novel *Journey to the West* — A504

No. 1148 — Various depictions of Monkey King with inscriptions in: a, English. b, French. c, German.

Litho. With Foil Application
2016, Dec. 2			**Perf. 12**	
1148	A504	Sheet of 3	20.00	20.00
a.		$1.15 multi	4.00	4.00
b.		2fr multi	7.00	7.00
c.		€1.70 multi	6.75	6.75

33rd Asian International Stamp Exhibition, Nanning, People's Republic of China. No. 1148 sold for $6.

United Nations Emblem Type of 2014 Dated "2017" in Purple

2017, Jan. 13	**Litho.**	**Perf. 14¾**		
1149	A457	$1.15 multi + label	3.00	3.00

The full sheet sold for $14.95. The generic label exists as shown, with rooster on red background. Labels could be personalized. The personalization of labels was available only at UN Headquarters, and not through mail order.

Flag Type of 1980

Printed by Lowe Martin Company, Inc., Canada. Designed by Sergio Baradat, U.S. Issued in panes of 16; each pane contains 4 blocks of 4. A se-tenant block of 4 designs centers each pane.

2017, Feb. 3	**Litho.**	**Perf. 13x13¼**		
1150	A185	$1.15 Albania	2.40	2.40
1151	A185	$1.15 Benin	2.40	2.40
1152	A185	$1.15 Bulgaria	2.40	2.40
1153	A185	$1.15 Comoros	2.40	2.40
a.		Block of 4, #1150-1153	12.00	12.00
1154	A185	$1.15 Congo Republic	2.40	2.40
1155	A185	$1.15 Ethiopia	2.40	2.40
1156	A185	$1.15 Georgia	2.40	2.40
1157	A185	$1.15 Iraq	2.40	2.40
a.		Block of 4, #1154-1157	12.00	12.00
		Nos. 1150-1157 (8)	19.20	19.20

Miniature Sheet

A505

No. 1158: a, Three Smurfs. b, Smurf holding glass of water. c, Smurf holding fruit. d, Smurf with backpack with solar panels. e, Smurf lifting dumbbell. f, Smurf carrying mallet. g, Smurf holding book. h, Two Smurfs with ladder. i, Male and female Smurfs. j, Butterfly.

2017, Mar. 20	**Litho.**	**Perf. 14¾**		
1158	A505	Sheet of 10	30.00	30.00
a.-j.		$1.15 Any single + label	3.00	3.00

The full sheet sold for $14.95. The generic labels are shown. Labels could be personalized. The personalization of labels was available only at UN Headquarters, and not through mail order.

Miniature Sheets

A506

International Dance — A507

No. 1159 — Illustration of Polynesian dancers by Pascal Campion: a, Woman with arms raised, denomination at LR. b, Woman with arms raised, denomination at UL. c, Two women wearing head coverings, red necklace, denomination at UR. d, One woman wearing head covering and red necklace, denomination at UR. e, Woman with feathered headdress, green necklace, hair of another woman at right, denomination at UR. f, Woman wearing feathered headdress and green necklace, denomination at UR.

No. 1160 — Illustration of Native American tribal dancers by Campion: a, Dancer facing right, denomination in blue at UL. b, Dancer, denomination in orange at UL. c, Back of dancer, denomination in gray lilac at UR. d, Dancer looking downward, denomination in gray lilac at UL. e, Dancer with headband over eyebrows, denomination in orange red at UR, "International Dance" in white. f, Dancer, denomination in orange red at UR, "International Dance" in light blue.

2017, Mar. 23   Litho.   Perf. 13¼x13
1159	A506	Sheet of 6	6.00	6.00
a.-f.		49c Any single	1.00	1.00
1160	A507	Sheet of 6	14.50	14.50
a.-f.		$1.15 Any single	2.40	2.40

See Offices in Geneva Nos. 630-631; Vienna Nos. 599-600.

Souvenir Sheet

Australian Animals — A508

No. 1161: a, Koalas. b, Kangaroos. c, Emu.

Litho. With Foil Application
2017, Mar. 30   Perf. 13¼x13
1161	A508	Sheet of 3	12.00	12.00
a.		$1.15 multi	4.00	4.00
b.		2fr multi	4.00	4.00
c.		€1.70 multi	4.00	4.00

2017 FIAP International Stamp Exhibition, Melbourne, Australia. No. 1161 sold for $6.

Endangered Species A509

Designs: No. 1162, Masobe gecko. No. 1163, Thresher shark. No. 1164, Clarion angelfish. No. 1165, Blaine's fishhook cactus.

2017, May 11   Litho.   Perf. 12¾x12½
1162	A509	$1.15 multicolored	2.40	2.40
1163	A509	$1.15 multicolored	2.40	2.40
1164	A509	$1.15 multicolored	2.40	2.40
1165	A509	$1.15 multicolored	2.40	2.40
a.		Block of 4, #1162-1165	9.75	9.75
		Nos. 1162-1165 (4)	9.60	9.60

See Offices in Geneva Nos. 632-635; Vienna Nos. 601-604.

World Environment Day — A510

Designs: 49c, Hopewell Rocks, New Brunswick, Canada. $1.15, Polar bear, Baffin Island, Nunavut, Canada.

2017, June 5   Litho.   Perf. 13¼
1166	A510	49c multicolored	1.00	1.00
1167	A510	$1.15 multicolored	2.40	2.40

See Offices in Geneva Nos. 636-637; Vienna Nos. 605-606.

Miniature Sheet

International Day of Yoga — A511

No. 1168: a, Orange woman on stomach holding her legs. b, Dark blue man siting with legs raised. c, Blue woman with arms extended. d, Beige man sitting with legs crossed and arms raised. e, Purple man with arms extended leaning backward to touch toes. f, Light blue woman bent backward with feet and hands on ground. g, Blue violet woman bent backward to touch raised leg. h, Red woman on one knee. i, Pale blue woman with arms extended touching raised leg. j, Orange man bent over with hands on ground.

2017, June 21   Litho.   Perf. 14¾
1168	A511	Sheet of 10	30.00	30.00
a.-j.		$1.15 Any single + label	3.00	3.00

The full sheet sold for $14.95. The generic labels are shown. Labels could be personalized. The personalization of labels was available only at UN Headquarters, and not through mail order.

World Heritage Sites Along the Silk Roads — A512

Designs: Nos. 1169, 1171a, Longmen Grottoes, People's Republic of China. Nos. 1170, 1171d, Sulaiman-Too Sacred Mountain, Kyrgyzstan. No. 1171b, Historic Center of Bukhara, Uzbekistan. No. 1171c, Tabriz Historic Bazaar Complex, Iran. No. 1171e, Kunya-

---

Urgench, Turkmenistan. No. 1171f, Safranbolu, Turkey.

2017, Aug. 3   Litho.   Perf. 14¼
1169	A512	49c multicolored	1.00	1.00
1170	A512	$1.15 multicolored	2.40	2.40

Souvenir Booklet
1171		Booklet, #1115g-1115l	22.50	
a.-c.		A512 34c any single	.75	.75
d.-f.		A512 49c any single	1.10	1.10
g.		Booklet pane of 4 #1171a	3.00	—
h.		Booklet pane of 4 #1171b	3.00	—
i.		Booklet pane of 4 #1171c	3.00	—
j.		Booklet pane of 4 #1171d	4.50	—
k.		Booklet pane of 4 #1171e	4.50	—
l.		Booklet pane of 4 #1171f	4.50	—

Complete booklet sold for $11. See Offices in Geneva Nos. 638-640; Vienna Nos. 607-609.

Doves — A513

Moths — A514

Doves — A515

Printed by Johann Enschedé and Sons, the Netherlands. Panes of 20. Designed by Stranger and Stranger, U.S.

2017, Sept. 21   Litho.   Perf. 14x14¼
1172	A513	49c multicolored	1.00	1.00
1173	A514	$1.15 multicolored	2.40	2.40

Souvenir Sheet
Perf. 14¼x13¾
1174	A515	$1.15 multicolored	2.40	2.40

International Day of Peace. See Offices in Geneva Nos. 641-643; Vienna Nos. 611-613.

World Food Day — A516

Designs: 49c, Vegetables. $1.15, Bowls of food, jar of oil.

2017, Oct. 16   Litho.   Perf. 13¼x14
1175	A516	49c multicolored	1.00	1.00
1176	A516	$1.15 multicolored	2.40	2.40

See Offices in Geneva Nos. 644-645; Vienna Nos. 614-615.

Souvenir Sheet

Universal Declaration of Human Rights — A517

No. 1177 — Text of Universal Declaration of Human Rights in: a, English. b, French. c, German.

Litho. With Foil Application
2017, Oct. 27   Perf. 14x13¼
1177	A517	Sheet of 3	12.00	12.00
a.		$1.15 multi	4.00	4.00
b.		2fr multi	4.00	4.00
c.		€1.70 multi	4.00	4.00

United Nations Expo 2017, Bellefonte, Pennsylvania. No. 1177 sold for $6.

Souvenir Sheet

Landmarks in Paris — A518

No. 1178: a, Fame of Louis XVI, statue by Antoine Coysevox. b, Fontaines de la Concorde. c, Gargolye on Notre Dame Cathedral.

2017, Nov. 9   Litho.   Perf. 13¼x14
1178	A518	Sheet of 3	12.00	12.00
a.		$1.15 multi	4.00	4.00
b.		2fr multi	4.00	4.00
c.		€1.70 multi	4.00	4.00

Autumn Philatelic Show, Paris. No. 1178 sold for $6.

Flag Type of 1980

Printed by Lowe Martin Group, Canada. Designed by Rorie Katz, U.S. Issued in panes of 16; each pane contains 4 blocks of 4. A setenant block of 4 designs centers each pane.

2018, Jan. 12   Litho.   Perf. 13x13¼
1179	A185	$1.15 Lesotho	2.40	2.40
1180	A185	$1.15 Libya	2.40	2.40
1181	A185	$1.15 Mozambique	2.40	2.40
1182	A185	$1.15 Romania	2.40	2.40
a.		Block of 4, #1179-1182	12.00	12.00
1183	A185	$1.15 Rwanda	2.40	2.40
1184	A185	$1.15 Seychelles	2.40	2.40
1185	A185	$1.15 South Africa	2.40	2.40
1186	A185	$1.15 Ukraine	2.40	2.40
a.		Block of 4, #1183-1186	12.00	12.00
		Nos. 1179-1186 (8)	19.20	19.20

United Nations Emblem Type of 2014 Dated "2018" in Purple
2018, Feb. 2   Litho.   Perf. 14¾
1187	A457	$1.15 multi + label	3.00	3.00

The full sheet sold for $14.95. The generic label depicts a dog. Labels could be personalized. The personalization of labels was available only at UN Headquarters, and not through mail order.

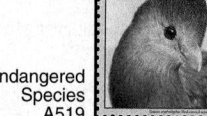

Endangered Species A519

Designs: No. 1188, Red-crested turaco. No. 1189, Andean hairy armadillo. No. 1190, Lurestan newt. No. 1191, Goldenseal.

2018, Mar. 2   Litho.   Perf. 12¾x12½
1188	A519	$1.15 multicolored	2.40	2.40
1189	A519	$1.15 multicolored	2.40	2.40
1190	A519	$1.15 multicolored	2.40	2.40

1191	A519 $1.15 multicolored	2.40	2.40
a.	Block of 4, #1188-1191	9.75	9.75
	Nos. 1188-1191 (4)	9.60	9.60

See Offices in Geneva Nos. 646-649; Vienna Nos. 616-619.

World Health Day A520

Designs: 50c, Heart, pill, bandage, letter from eye chart, syringe and stethoscope. $1.15, Head with gears, heart, clock, stylized people, circle with arrows.

2018, Apr. 6 Litho. Perf. 13x13¼

| 1192 | A520 50c multicolored | 1.00 | 1.00 |
| 1193 | A520 $1.15 multicolored | 2.40 | 2.40 |

See Offices in Geneva Nos. 650-651; Vienna Nos. 620-621.

Universal Declaration of Human Rights, 70th Anniv. — A521

2018, May 3 Litho. Perf. 13¼

| 1194 | A521 $2.50 multicolored | 5.00 | 5.00 |

United Nations Headquarters A522

2018, May 29 Litho. Perf. 13¼

| 1195 | A522 65c multicolored | 1.40 | 1.40 |

UNISPACE + 50 Conferences — A523

Designs: 50c, Milky Way Galaxy. No. 1197, International Space Station and Space Shuttle Endeavour.
No. 1198, Astronaut Scott Kelly during spacewalk.

2018, June 20 Litho. Perf. 14x14¼

| 1196 | A523 50c multicolored | 1.00 | 1.00 |
| 1197 | A523 $1.15 multicolored | 2.40 | 2.40 |

Souvenir Sheet
Perf. 13¾

| 1198 | A523 $1.15 multicolored | 2.40 | 2.40 |

No. 1198 contains one 45x45mm stamp. See Offices in Geneva Nos. 653-655; Vienna Nos. 623-625.

World Heritage Sites in the United Kingdom — A524

Designs: Nos. 1199, 1201a, Giant's Causeway. Nos. 1200, 1201d, Palace of Westminster. No. 1201b, Stonehenge. No. 1201c, Conwy Castle. No. 1201e, Edinburgh. No. 1201f, Maritime Greenwich.

2018, Aug. 15 Litho. Perf. 14¼

| 1199 | A524 50c multicolored | 1.00 | 1.00 |
| 1200 | A524 $1.15 multicolored | 2.40 | 2.40 |

Souvenir Booklet

1201	Booklet, #1115g-		
	1115l	22.50	
a.-c.	A524 35c any single	.75	.75
d.-f.	A524 50c any single	1.10	1.10
g.	Booklet pane of 4 #1201a	3.00	—
h.	Booklet pane of 4 #1201b	3.00	—
i.	Booklet pane of 4 #1201c	3.00	—
j.	Booklet pane of 4 #1201d	4.50	—
k.	Booklet pane of 4 #1201e	4.50	—
l.	Booklet pane of 4 #1201f	4.50	—

Complete booklet sold for $11. See Offices in Geneva Nos. 657-659; Vienna Nos. 626-628.

Miniature Sheet

Thomas the Tank Engine — A525

No. 1202: a, Thomas and four people. b, Reg lifting bicycle. c, Thomas, conductor holding potted plant. d, Ashima and Thomas. e, Thomas and Nia. f, Passenger car, children and tuba. g, Thomas and giraffe. h, Monkeys on Thomas. i, Water splashing on grimy Thomas. j, Nia, Thomas and ring of colors.

2018, Sept. 12 Litho. Perf. 14¾

| 1202 | A525 Sheet of 10 | 30.00 | 30.00 |
| a.-j. | $1.15 any single + label | 3.00 | 3.00 |

The full sheet sold for $14.95. The generic labels are shown. Labels could be personalized. The personalization of labels was available only at UN Headquarters, and not through mail order.

Souvenir Sheet

Characters From Cantonese Opera
Hua Mulan — A526

No. 1203: a, Baozhen. b, Guanyu. c, Mulan.

2018, Sept. 21 Litho. Perf. 13¼x13

1203	A526 Sheet of 3	13.00	13.00
a.	$1.15 multi	4.25	4.25
b.	2fr multi	4.25	4.25
c.	€1.80 multi	4.25	4.25

Macao 2018 Asian International Stamp Exhibition. The vignettes are laser cut. No. 1203 sold for $6.30.

Miniature Sheet

International Music Day — A527

No. 1204: a, Trombone. b, Flute and clarinet. c, Cornet. d, Tuba, bell at right. e, Tuba, bell at left, red in background. f, French horn, red in background. g, Trumpet, bell at UR. h, Baritone horn. i, Saxophone. j, French horn, blue in background. k, Trumpet, bell at LR. l, Tuba, bell at left, blue in background.

2018, Oct. 1 Litho. Perf. 14x13¼

| 1204 | A527 Sheet of 12 | 12.00 | 12.00 |
| a.-l. | 50c Any single | 1.00 | 1.00 |

See Offices in Geneva No. 660; Vienna No. 629.

Non-Violence, Sculpture by Carl Fredrik Reuterswärd A528

Printed by Johann Enschedé Stamps BV, the Netherlands. Panes of 50. Designed by Martin Mörck, Norway.

2018, Oct. 2 Litho. Perf. 13¼x14

| 1205 | A528 1c multicolored | .25 | .25 |

See Offices in Vienna Nos. 630-631.

Diwali Candles — A529

Diwali Candles — A530

2018, Oct. 19 Litho. Perf. 14¾

1206	A529 $1.15 multi + label	3.00	3.00
1207	A530 $1.15 multi + label	3.00	3.00
a.	Vert. pair, #1206-1207, + 2 labels	6.00	6.00
	Sheet of 10, 5 each #1206-1207, + 10 labels	30.00	30.00

The full sheet sold for $14.95. The generic labels are shown. Labels could be personalized. The personalization of labels was available only at UN Headquarters, and not through mail order.

Souvenir Sheet

Arena di Verona — A531

No. 1208: a, Left side of Arena. b, Central portion of Arena with four upper-tier arches. c, Right side of Arena.

2018, Nov. 23 Litho. Perf. 13¼x13

1208	A531 Sheet of 3	13.00	13.00
a.	$1.15 multi	4.25	4.25
b.	2fr multi	4.25	4.25
c.	€1.80 multi	4.25	4.25

Veronafil 2018 Stamp Exhibition, Verona, Italy. No. 1208 sold for $6.30.

United Nations Emblem Type of 2014 Dated "2019" in Purple

2019, Jan. 11 Litho. Perf. 14¾

| 1209 | A457 $1.15 multi + label | 3.00 | 3.00 |
| | Sheet of 10 + 10 labels | 30.00 | — |

The full sheet sold for $14.95. The generic label depicts a pig. Labels could be personalized. The personalization of labels was available only at UN Headquarters, and not through mail order.

Miniature Sheet

World Languages — A532

No. 1210 — Word bubbles with word for "Hello" in: a, Chinese and Portuguese (Olá). b, Swahili (Habari) and Persian. c, Italian (Ciao). d, Bengali. e, English. f, Thai and Czech or Slovak (Ahoj).

2019, Feb. 21 Litho. Perf. 13¼x13

| 1210 | A532 Sheet of 6 | 6.75 | 6.75 |
| a.-f. | 55c Any single | 1.10 | 1.10 |

See Offices in Geneva No. 661; Vienna No. 632.

Stop Sexual Exploitation and Abuse — A533

Printed by Lowe-Martin Group, Canada. Panes of 20. Designed by Chris Gash, U.S.

2019, Mar.15 Litho. Perf. 13¼x13

| 1211 | A533 85c multicolored | 1.75 | 1.75 |

Endangered Species A534

Designs: No. 1212, Hawksbill turtle. No. 1213, Queen conch. No. 1214, Mushroom coral. No. 1215, Humpback whale.

2019, Apr. 26 Litho. Perf. 12¾x12½

1212	A534	$1.15 multicolored	2.40	2.40
1213	A534	$1.15 multicolored	2.40	2.40
1214	A534	$1.15 multicolored	2.40	2.40
1215	A534	$1.15 multicolored	2.40	2.40
a.		Block of 4, #1212-1215	9.75	9.75

See Offices in Geneva Nos. 663-666; Vienna Nos. 634-637.

Souvenir Sheet

Diphaglossine Bee and Corydalis Flavula — A535

Litho. With Foil Application

2019, May 20   Perf. 13

1216	A535	$3 multicolored	7.50	7.50

World Bee Day. See Offices in Geneva No. 667; Vienna No. 638.

Kofi Annan (1938-2018), Seventh United Nations Secretary-General — A536

2019, May 31 Litho. Perf. 14x14¼

1217	A536	$1.30 gray blue & black	2.60	2.60

Souvenir Sheet

Pandas — A537

No. 1218: a, Qiqia. b, Qiqi and Diandian. c, Diandian.

2019, June 11 Litho. Perf. 13½x13

1218	A537	Sheet of 3	13.00	13.00
a.		$1.15 multi	4.25	4.25
b.		2fr multi	4.25	4.25
c.		€1.80 multi	4.25	4.25

China 2019 World Stamp Exhibition, Wuhan, People's Republic of China. On July 31, 2019, a sheet containing Nos. 1218a-1218c with a different sheet margin was issued for Singpex 2019 International Stamp Exhibition, with a printing quantity of 21,000 sheets. No. 1218 and the sheet issued in July each sold for $6.30.

A538

A539

A540

A541

International Labor Organization, Cent. — A542

2019, June 28 Litho. Perf. 13½x14

1219	A538	55c multicolored	1.10	1.10
1220	A539	55c multicolored	1.10	1.10
1221	A540	55c multicolored	1.10	1.10
1222	A541	55c multicolored	1.10	1.10
1223	A542	55c multicolored	1.10	1.10
a.		Horiz. strip of 5, #1219-1223	5.50	5.50
		Nos. 1219-1223 (5)	5.50	5.50

See Offices in Geneva Nos. 668-672, Vienna Nos. 639-643.

Climate Change — A543

Designs: 55c, Mountain. No. 1225, Fish. No. 1226, Polar bear.

2019, Sept. 23 Litho. Perf. 14¼

1224	A543	55c multicolored	1.10	1.10
1225	A543	$1.15 multicolored	2.40	2.40

Souvenir Sheet
Perf.

1226	A543	$1.15 multicolored	2.40	2.40

2019 United Nations Climate Change Conference, Madrid. No. 1226 contains one 47mm diameter stamp. See Offices in Geneva Nos. 673-675; Vienna Nos. 649-651.

Mohandas K. Gandhi (1869-1948), Indian Nationalist Leader — A544

Printed by Johann Enschedé Stamps BV, the Netherlands. Panes of 20. Designed by Rorie Katz, U.S.

2019, Oct. 2 Litho. Perf. 14¼

1227	A544	$2.75 gray blue & black	5.50	5.50

World Heritage Sites in Cuba — A545

Designs: Nos. 1228, 1230a, Morro Castle. Nos. 1229, 1230d, Vinales Valley. No. 1230b, Trinidad. No. 1230c, Camagüey. No. 1230e, Cienfuegos. No. 1230f, San Pedro de la Rosa Castle.

Litho. With Foil Application

2019, Oct. 24   Perf. 14¼

1228	A545	55c multicolored	1.10	1.10
1229	A545	$1.15 multicolored	2.40	2.40

Souvenir Booklet

1230		Booklet, #1115g-1115l	24.00	
a.-c.	A545	35c Any single	.75	.75
d.-f.	A545	55c Any single	1.25	1.25
g.		Booklet pane of 4 #1230a	3.00	—
h.		Booklet pane of 4 #1230b	3.00	—
i.		Booklet pane of 4 #1230c	3.00	—
j.		Booklet pane of 4 #1230d	5.00	—
k.		Booklet pane of 4 #1230e	5.00	—
l.		Booklet pane of 4 #1230f	5.00	—

Complete booklet sold for $12. See Offices in Geneva Nos. 677-679; Vienna Nos. 652-654.

United Nations Emblem Type of 2016 Dated "2020" in Purple

2020, Jan. 10 Litho. Perf. 14¾

1231	A490	$1.20 multicolored + label	3.00	3.00

The full sheet sold for $14.95. The generic label, with rat on red background, is shown. The personalization of labels was available only at UN Headquarters, and not through mail order.

Endangered Species A546

Designs: No. 1232, Great hammerhead shark. No. 1233, Egyptian vulture. No. 1234, Andean flamingo. No. 1235, Argali sheep.

Perf. 12¾x12½

2020, Feb. 17   Litho.

1232	A546	$1.20 multicolored	2.40	2.40
1233	A546	$1.20 multicolored	2.40	2.40
1234	A546	$1.20 multicolored	2.40	2.40
1235	A546	$1.20 multicolored	2.40	2.40
a.		Block of 4, #1232-1235	9.75	9.75

See Offices in Geneva Nos. 680-683; Vienna Nos. 655-658.

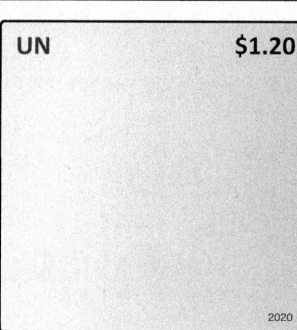

Blank Stamp On Which Stickers Can Be Applied — A547

Designs: No. 1212, Hawksbill turtle. No. 1213, Queen conch. No. 1214, Mushroom coral. No. 1215, Humpback whale.

2020, Mar. 19 Litho. Die Cut
Self-Adhesive

1236	A547	$1.20 multicolored with rounded corners	2.40	2.40
a.		With perpendicular corners and black frame line	2.40	2.40
b.		Booklet pane of 6 #1236a	14.50	

No. 1236 was issued as a souvenir sheet having two different sheet margins, each with different stickers. No. 1236a was issued in a booklet containing six panes of one stamp, with each pane having different margins and stickers. Each booklet pane contained one sticker depicting Hello Kitty, a color wheel with Hello Kitty at the center, one of six different Sustainable Development Goal emblems, along with a variety of other stickers. The two souvenir sheets had the same sheet margin and stickers found on two of the panes of No. 1236b. No. 1236b was sold folded, without any means of separation between the individual panes.

Miniature Sheet

Act Now Climate Action Campaign — A548

No. 1237: a, Man in shower. b, Hand on light switch. c, Bicyclist. d, Electric plug and socket. e, Knife, fork, vegetables. f, Hand, container and recycling arrow. g, Produce stand. h, Clothing on clothes hanger. i, Man placing bottle in recycling bin. j, Man carrying reusable shopping bag.

2020, Mar. 27 Litho. Perf. 14¾

1237	A548	Sheet of 10 + 10 labels	30.00	30.00
a.-j.		$1.20 Any single + label	3.00	3.00

The full sheet sold for $14.95. The generic labels are shown. Labels could be personalized. The personalization of labels was available only at UN Headquarters, and not through mail order.

Linblad Cove, Antarctica, Drawing by Zaria Forman — A549

Our Changing Seas IV, Glazed Stoneware and Porcelain Item by Courtney Mattison — A550

2020, Apr. 22   Litho.   Perf. 13¼
1238	A549	55c multicolored	1.10	1.10
1239	A550	$1.20 multicolored	2.40	2.40

Earth Day, 50th anniv. Because of the COVID-19 pandemic, Nos. 1238-1239 were not available for sale on day of issue stated on the first-day covers as they had not yet been printed and delivered. See Offices in Geneva Nos. 685-686; Vienna Nos. 660-661.

United Nations Peacekeeping Vehicles — A551

United Nations Peacekeepers — A552

Two Female United Nations Peacekeepers and Helicopter — A553

United Nations Peacekeeping Vehicles — A554

Helmet and Knapsacks of United Nations Peacekeepers — A555

2020, May 29   Litho.   Perf. 14¾
1240	A551	$1.20 multi + label	3.00	3.00
1241	A552	$1.20 multi + label	3.00	3.00
1242	A553	$1.20 multi + label	3.00	3.00
1243	A554	$1.20 multi + label	3.00	3.00
1244	A555	$1.20 multi + label	3.00	3.00
a.		Vert. strip of 5, #1240-1244, + 5 labels	15.00	15.00

International Day of United Nations Peacekeepers. The full sheet sold for $14.95. The generic labels are shown. Labels could be personalized. The personalization of labels was available only at UN Headquarters, and not through mail order.

Flag Type of 1980
2020, Aug. 20   Litho.   Perf. 14x13¼
1245	A185	$1.20 Bahrain	2.40	2.40
1246	A185	$1.20 Belarus	2.40	2.40
1247	A185	$1.20 Brazil	2.40	2.40
1248	A185	$1.20 Cyprus	2.40	2.40
a.		Block of 4, #1245-1248	9.60	9.60

1249	A185	$1.20 Dominica	2.40	2.40
1250	A185	$1.20 Mauritania	2.40	2.40
1251	A185	$1.20 Mongolia	2.40	2.40
1252	A185	$1.20 Paraguay	2.40	2.40
a.		Block of 4, #1249-1252	9.60	9.60
		Nos. 1245-1252 (8)	19.20	19.20

World Heritage Sites in Russia — A556

Designs: Nos. 1253, 1255a, Lake Baikal. Nos. 1254, 1255d, Kremlin and Red Square, Moscow. No. 1255b, Kazan Kremlin. No. 1255c, Novodevichy Convent. No. 1255e, Saint Petersburg. No. 1255f, Kizhi Pogost.

Perf. 14½x14¼
2020, Sept. 11   Litho.
1253	A556	55c multicolored	1.10	1.10
1254	A556	$1.20 multicolored	2.40	2.40

Souvenir Booklet
1255		Booklet, #1115g-1115l	24.00	
a.-c.		A556 35c any single	.75	.75
d.-f.		A556 55c any single	1.25	1.25
g.		Booklet pane of 4 #1255a	3.00	—
h.		Booklet pane of 4 #1255b	3.00	—
i.		Booklet pane of 4 #1255c	3.00	—
j.		Booklet pane of 4 #1255d	5.00	—
k.		Booklet pane of 4 #1255e	5.00	—
l.		Booklet pane of 4 #1255f	5.00	—

Complete booklet sold for $12. See Offices in Geneva Nos. 688-690; Vienna Nos. 663-665.

Souvenir Sheet

United Nations, 75th Anniv. — A557

No. 1256: a, Pink "U," yellow "N." b, Green "7," red "5."

2020, Oct. 24   Litho.   Perf. 13¼
1256	A557	Sheet of 2	4.80	4.80
a.-b.		$1.20 Either single	2.40	2.40

See Offices in Geneva No. 691; Vienna No. 667.

Souvenir Sheet

United Nations Building and Emblem — A558

Litho. With Foil Application
2020, Nov. 24   Die Cut Perf. 11½
Self-Adhesive
1257	A558	$7.75 multicolored	15.50	15.50

Crypto stamp. Unused value is for sheets with unscratched panels at right. See Offices in Geneva No. 692; Vienna No. 668.

Fish — A559

Grain Stalk — A560

Butterfly — A561

Elephants — A562

Tree — A563

2020, Dec. 5   Litho.   Perf. 14¾
1258	A559	$1.20 multi + label	3.00	3.00
1259	A560	$1.20 multi + label	3.00	3.00
1260	A561	$1.20 multi + label	3.00	3.00
1261	A562	$1.20 multi + label	3.00	3.00
1262	A563	$1.20 multi + label	3.00	3.00
a.		Vert. strip of 5, #1258-1262, + 5 labels	15.00	15.00
		Sheet of 10, 2 each #1258-1262, + 10 labels	30.00	30.00
		Nos. 1258-1262 (5)	15.00	15.00

World Soil Day. The full sheet sold for $14.95. The generic labels are shown. Labels could be personalized. The personalization of labels was available only at UN Headquarters, and not through mail order.

SEMI-POSTAL STAMPS

Souvenir Sheet

AIDS Awareness — SP1

2002, Oct. 24   Litho.   Perf. 14½
B1 SP1 37c + 6c multicolored   3.50 3.50
  See Offices in Geneva No. B1, Vienna No. B1.

Miniature Sheet

Campaign Against COVID-19 Pandemic — SP2

No. B2: a, Hand washing. b, Question mark in speech bubble. c, Social distancing. d, Smiling face. e, Cross in broken circle. f, Hands making heart shape.

2020, Aug. 11   Litho.   Perf. 13¼
B2 SP2 Sheet of 2   21.00 21.00
  a.   55c+50c multi   2.10   2.10
  b. $1.20+50c multi   3.50   3.50
  c.   1fr+50c multi   3.50   3.50
  d.   1.50fr+50c multi   4.50   4.50
  e.   85c+50c multi   3.50   3.50
  f.   €1+50c multi   3.75   3.75
  Surtax for World Health Organization COVID Solidarity Response Fund.

AIR POST STAMPS

Plane and Gull — AP1

Swallows and UN Emblem AP2

1951, Dec. 14   Unwmk.   Perf. 14
C1 AP1   6c henna brown   .25   .25
C2 AP1 10c brt blue grn   .30   .30
C3 AP2 15c deep ultra   .40   .40
  a.   15c Prussian blue   65.00
C4 AP2 25c gray black   .85   .85
  Nos. C1-C4 (4)   1.80 1.80

Airplane Wing and Globe — AP3

1957, May 27   Perf. 12½x14
C5 AP3 4c maroon   .25   .25

Type of 1957 and

UN Flag and Plane AP4

Perf. 12½x13½
1959, Feb. 9   Unwmk.
C6 AP3 5c rose red   .25   .25
Perf. 13½x14
C7 AP4 7c ultramarine   .25   .25

Outer Space — AP5

UN Emblem — AP6

Bird of Laurel Leaves — AP7

Perf. 11½
1963, June 17   Photo.   Unwmk.
C8 AP5   6c blk, blue & yel grn   .25   .25
C9 AP6   8c yel, ol grn & red   .25   .25
Perf. 12½x12
C10 AP7 13c ultra, aquamarine, gray & carmine   .25   .25

"Flight Across Globe" — AP8

Jet Plane and Envelope AP9

Perf. 11½x12, 12x11½
1964, May 1   Photo.   Unwmk.
C11 AP8 15c vio, buff, gray & pale grn   .30   .30
  a.   Gray omitted   225.00
C12 AP9 25c yel, org, gray, blue & red   .50   .50
  Nos. C8-C12 (5)   1.55 1.55
  See UN Offices in Geneva No. 8.

Jet Plane and UN Emblem AP10

1968, Apr. 18   Litho.   Perf. 13
C13 AP10 20c multicolored   .35   .35

Wings, Envelopes and UN Emblem AP11

1969, Apr. 21   Litho.   Perf. 13
C14 AP11 10c org ver, org, yel & blk   .25   .25

UN Emblem and Stylized Wing — AP12

Birds in Flight — AP13

Clouds AP14

"UN" and Plane — AP15

Litho. & Engr.
1972, May 1   Perf. 13x13½
C15 AP12 9c lt blue, dk red & vio blue   .25   .25
Photo.
Perf. 14x13½
C16 AP13 11c blue & multi   .25   .25
Perf. 13½x14
C17 AP14 17c yel, red & org   .25   .25
Perf. 13
C18 AP15 21c silver & multi   .25   .25
  Nos. C15-C18 (4)   1.00 1.00

Globe and Jet — AP16

Pathways Radiating from UN Emblem AP17

Bird in Flight, UN Headquarters AP18

Perf. 13, 12½x13 (18c)
1974, Sept. 16   Litho.
C19 AP16 13c multicolored   .25   .25
C20 AP17 18c gray olive & multi   .25   .25
C21 AP18 26c blue & multi   .35   .35
  Nos. C19-C21 (3)   .85   .85

Winged Airmail Letter — AP19

Symbolic Globe and Plane — AP20

1977, June 27   Photo.   Perf. 14
C22 AP19 25c greenish blue & multi   .35   .35
C23 AP20 31c magenta   .45   .45

OFFICES IN GENEVA, SWITZERLAND

For use only on mail posted at the Palais des Nations (UN European Office), Geneva. Inscribed in French unless otherwise stated.

100 Centimes = 1 Franc

Catalogue values for all unused stamps in this country are for Never Hinged items.

Types of United Nations Issues 1961-69 and

UN European Office, Geneva — G1

Designs: 5c, UN Headquarters, New York, and world map. 10c, UN flag. 20c, Three men united before globe. 50c, Opening words of UN Charter. 60c, UN emblem over globe. 70c, "un" and UN emblem. 75c, "Flight Across Globe." 80c, UN Headquarters and emblem. 90c, Abstract group of flags. 1fr, UN emblem. 2fr, Stylized globe and weather vane. 3fr, Statue by Henrik Starcke. 10fr, "Peace, Justice, Security."

The 20c, 80c and 90c are inscribed in French. The 75c and 10fr carry French inscription at top, English at bottom.

		1969-70	Photo.	Unwmk.
		Perf. 13 (5c, 70c, 90c); 12½x12 (10c);		
1	A88	5c purple & multi	.25	.30
a.		Green omitted	—	
2	A52	10c salmon & multi	.25	.30
		Perf. 11½ (20c-60c, 3fr)		
3	A66	20c black & multi	.25	.30
4	G1	30c dark blue & multi	.25	.30
5	A77	50c ultra & multi	.25	.30
6	A54	60c dark brown, salmon & gold	.25	.30
7	A104	70c red, black & gold	.30	.35
		Perf. 11½x12 (75c)		
8	AP8	75c carmine rose & multi	.35	.40
		Perf. 13½x14 (80c)		
9	A78	80c blue green, red & yellow	.35	.40
10	A45	90c blue & multi	.40	.45
		Litho. & Embossed		
		Perf. 14 (1fr)		
11	A79	1fr light & dark green	.40	.45
		Photo.		
		Perf. 12x11½ (2fr)		
12	A67	2fr blue & multi	.75	.85
13	A97	3fr olive & multi	1.00	1.10
		Engr.		
		Perf. 12 (10fr)		
14	A3	10fr dark blue	3.50	3.75
		Nos. 1-14 (14)	8.55	9.55

Sea Bed Type of UN

Photo. & Engr.

		1971, Jan. 25	*Perf. 13*	
15	A114	30c green & multi	.25	.30

Refugee Type of UN

		1971, Mar. 12	Litho.	*Perf. 13x12½*
16	A115	50c dp car, dp org & blk	.25	.30

World Food Program Type of UN

		1971, Apr. 13	Photo.	*Perf. 14*
17	A116	50c dark vio & multi	.25	.30

UPU Headquarters Type of UN

		1971, May 28	Photo.	*Perf. 11½*
18	A117	75c green & multi	.35	.40

Eliminate Racial Discrimination Types of UN

		1971, Sept. 21	Photo.	*Perf. 13½*
19	A118	30c blue & multi	.25	.30
20	A119	50c yellow grn & multi	.25	.30

Picasso Type of UN

		1971, Nov. 19	Photo.	*Perf. 11½*
21	A122	1.10fr multicolored	.75	.80

Palais des Nations, Geneva G2

		1972, Jan. 5	Photo.	*Perf. 11½*
22	G2	40c ol, blue, sal & dk grn	.25	.30

Nuclear Weapons Type of UN

		1972, Feb. 14	Photo.	*Perf. 13½x14*
23	A124	40c yel, grn, blk, rose & gray	.25	.30

World Health Day Type of UN

Litho. & Engr.

		1972, Apr. 7		*Perf. 13x13½*
24	A125	80c black & multi	.45	.50

Human Environment Type of UN

Lithographed & Embossed

		1972, June 5		*Perf. 12½x14*
25	A126	40c ol, lemon, grn & blue	.25	.30
26	A126	80c ultra, pink, grn & blue	.45	.50

Economic Commission for Europe Type of UN

		1972, Sept. 11	Litho.	*Perf. 13x13½*
27	A127	1.10fr red & multi	1.00	1.10

Art at UN (Sert) Type of UN

		1972, Nov. 17	Photo.	*Perf. 12x12½*
28	A128	40c gold, red & brn	.30	.35
29	A128	80c gold, brn & olive	.60	.65

Disarmament Decade Type of UN

		1973, Mar. 9	Litho.	*Perf. 13½x13*
30	A129	60c vio & multi	.40	.45
31	A129	1.10fr olive & multi	.85	.90

Drug Abuse Type of UN

		1973, Apr. 13	Photo.	*Perf. 13½*
32	A130	60c blue & multi	.45	.50

Volunteers Type of UN

		1973, May 25	Photo.	*Perf. 14*
33	A131	80c gray grn & multi	.35	.40

Namibia Type of UN

		1973, Oct. 1	Photo.	*Perf. 13½*
34	A132	60c red & multi	.35	.40

Human Rights Type of UN

		1973, Nov. 16	Photo.	*Perf. 13½*
35	A133	40c ultra & multi	.30	.35
36	A133	80c olive & multi	.50	.55

ILO Headquarters Type of UN

		1974, Jan. 11	Photo.	*Perf. 14*
37	A134	60c violet & multi	.45	.50
38	A134	80c brown & multi	.65	.70

Centenary of UPU Type of UN

		1974, Mar. 22	Litho.	*Perf. 12½*
39	A135	30c gold & multi	.25	.30
40	A135	60c gold & multi	.60	.65

Art at UN (Portinari) Type of UN

		1974, May 6	Photo.	*Perf. 14*
41	A136	60c dark red & multi	.40	.45
42	A136	1fr green & multi	.70	.75

World Population Year Type of UN

		1974, Oct. 18	Photo.	*Perf. 14*
43	A140	60c brt grn & multi	.50	.55
44	A140	80c brown & multi	.70	.75

Law of the Sea Type of UN

		1974, Nov. 22	Photo.	*Perf. 14*
45	A141	1.30fr blue & multi	1.00	1.10

Outer Space Type of UN

		1975, Mar. 14	Litho.	*Perf. 13*
46	A142	60c multicolored	.50	.55
47	A142	90c multicolored	.75	.80

International Women's Year Type of UN

		1975, May 9	Litho.	*Perf. 15*
48	A143	60c multicolored	.40	.45
49	A143	90c multicolored	.70	.75

30th Anniversary Type of UN

		1975, June 26	Litho.	*Perf. 13*
50	A144	60c green & multi	.40	.45
51	A144	90c violet & multi	.70	.75

Souvenir Sheet

Imperf

52		Sheet of 2	1.00	1.10
a.		A144 60c green & multicolored	.30	.35
b.		A144 90c violet & multicolored	.60	.65

Namibia Type of UN

		1975, Sept. 22	Photo.	*Perf. 13½*
53	A145	50c multicolored	.30	.35
54	A145	1.30fr multicolored	.85	.90

Peace-keeping Operations Type of UN

		1975, Nov. 21	Engr.	*Perf. 12½*
55	A146	60c greenish blue	.35	.40
56	A146	70c bright violet	.65	.65

WFUNA Type of UN

		1976, Mar. 12	Photo.	*Perf. 14*
57	A152	90c multicolored	.90	.95

UNCTAD Type of UN

		1976, Apr. 23	Photo.	*Perf. 11½*
58	A153	1.10fr sepia & multi	.90	.95

Habitat Type of UN

		1976, May 28	Photo.	*Perf. 14*
59	A154	40c dull blue & multi	.25	.30
60	A154	1.50fr violet & multi	.75	.80

UN Emblem, Post Horn and Rainbow G3

UN Postal Administration, 25th anniversary.

		1976, Oct. 8	Photo.	*Perf. 11½*
61	G3	80c tan & multi	.50	.55
62	A3	1.10fr lt grn & multi	1.60	1.75

World Food Council Type of UN

		1976, Nov. 19	Litho.	*Perf. 14½*
63	A156	70c multicolored	.50	.55

WIPO Type of UN

		1977, Mar. 11	Photo.	*Perf. 14*
64	A157	80c red & multi	.60	.65

Drop of Water and Globe — G4

UN Water Conference, Mar del Plata, Argentina, Mar. 14-25.

		1977, Apr. 22	Photo.	*Perf. 13½x13*
65	G4	80c ultra & multi	.50	.55
66	G4	1.10fr dark car & multi	.80	.85

Hands Protecting UN Emblem — G5

UN Security Council.

		1977, May 27	Photo.	*Perf. 11*
67	G5	80c blue & multi	.50	.55
68	G5	1.10fr emerald & multi	.80	.85

Colors of Five Races Spun into One Firm Rope — G6

Fight against racial discrimination.

		1977, Sept. 19	Litho.	*Perf. 13½x13*
69	G6	40c multicolored	.25	.30
70	G6	1.10fr multicolored	.65	.70

Atomic Energy Turning Partly into Olive Branch — G7

Peaceful uses of atomic energy.

		1977, Nov. 18	Photo.	*Perf. 14*
71	G7	80c dark car & multi	.55	.60
72	G7	1.10fr Prussian blue & multi	.75	.80

"Tree" of Doves — G8

		1978, Jan. 27	Litho.	*Perf. 14½*
73	G8	35c multicolored	.25	.30

Globes with Smallpox Distribution G9

Global eradication of smallpox.

		1978, Mar. 31	Photo.	*Perf. 12x11½*
74	G9	80c yel & multi	.60	.65
75	G9	1.10fr lt grn & multi	.90	.95

Namibia Type of UN

		1978, May 5	Photo.	*Perf. 12*
76	A166	80c multicolored	.85	.90

Jets and Flight Patterns — G10

International Civil Aviation Organization for "Safety in the Air."

		1978, June 12	Photo.	*Perf. 14*
77	G10	70c multicolored	.40	.45
78	G10	80c multicolored	.70	.75

General Assembly, Flags and Globe — G11

		1978, Sept. 15	Photo.	*Perf. 13½*
79	G11	70c multicolored	.45	.50
80	G11	1.10fr multicolored	.85	.90

Technical Cooperation Type of UN

		1978, Nov. 17	Photo.	*Perf. 14*
81	A169	80c multicolored	.70	.75

Seismograph
Recording
Earthquake
G12

Office of the UN Disaster Relief Coordinator
(UNDRO).

1979, Mar. 9	Photo.	Perf. 14	
82	G12	80c multicolored	.50 .55
83	G12	1.50fr multicolored	.80 .85

Children and
Rainbow
G13

International Year of the Child.

1979, May 4	Photo.	Perf. 14	
84	G13	80c multicolored	.35 .40
85	G13	1.10fr multicolored	.65 .70

Namibia Type of UN

1979, Oct. 5	Litho.	Perf. 13½	
86	A176	1.10fr multicolored	.60 .65

International Court
of Justice,
Scales — G14

International Court of Justice, The Hague,
Netherlands.

1979, Nov. 9	Litho.	Perf. 13x13½	
87	G14	80c multicolored	.40 .45
88	G14	1.10fr multicolored	.60 .65

New Economic Order Type of UN

1980, Jan. 11	Litho.	Perf. 15x14½	
89	A179	80c multicolored	.85 .90

Women's Year
Emblem
G15

United Nations Decade for Women.

1980, Mar. 7	Litho.	Perf. 14½x15	
90	G15	40c multicolored	.30 .35
91	G15	70c multicolored	.70 .75

**Peace-keeping Operations Type of
UN**

1980, May 16	Litho.	Perf. 14x13	
92	A181	1.10fr blue & green	.85 .90

Dove and
"35" — G16

35th Anniversary of the United Nations.

1980, June 26	Litho.	Perf. 13x13½	
93	G16	40c blue grn & blk	.35 .40
94	A183	70c multicolored	.65 .70

Souvenir Sheet
Imperf

95		Sheet of 2	1.10 1.20
a.		G16 40c blue green & black	.30 .35
b.		A183 70c multicolored	.80 .85

ECOSOC Type of UN and

Family
Climbing Line
Graph — G17

1980, Nov. 21	Litho.	Perf. 13½x13	
96	A186	40c multicolored	.30 .35
97	G17	70c multicolored	.60 .65

Palestinian Rights

1981, Jan. 30	Photo.	Perf. 12x11½	
98	A188	80c multicolored	.55 .60

International Year of the Disabled.

1981, Mar. 6	Photo.	Perf. 14	
99	A190	40c black & blue	.25 .30
100	V4	1.50fr black & red	1.00 1.10

Art Type of UN

1981, Apr. 15	Photo.	Perf. 11½	
	Granite Paper		
101	A191	80c multicolored	.80 .85

Energy Type of 1981

1981, May 29	Litho.	Perf. 13	
102	A192	1.10fr multicolored	.75 .80

Volunteers Program Type and

Volunteers
Program Type
and Symbols
of Science,
Agriculture
and Industry
G18

1981, Nov. 13		Litho.	
103	A194	40c multicolored	.45 .50
104	G18	70c multicolored	.90 .95

Fight Against
Apartheid
G19

Flower of Flags
G20

1982, Jan. 22		Perf. 11½x12	
105	G19	30c multicolored	.25 .30
106	G20	1fr multicolored	.80 .85

**Human Environment Type of UN
and**

Human
Environment — G21

10th Anniversary of United Nations Environment Program.

1982, Mar. 19	Litho.	Perf. 13½x13	
107	G21	40c multicolored	.30 .35
108	A199	1.20fr multicolored	1.10 1.40

Outer Space Type of UN and

Satellite
Applications
of Space
Technology
G22

Exploration and Peaceful Uses of Outer
Space.

1982, June 11	Litho.	Perf. 13x13½	
109	A201	80c multicolored	.60 .65
110	G22	1fr multicolored	.80 .85

Conservation & Protection of Nature

1982, Nov. 19	Photo.	Perf. 14	
111	A202	40c Bird	.45 .50
112	A202	1.50fr Reptile	1.10 1.20

World Communications Year

1983, Jan. 28	Litho.	Perf. 13	
113	A204	1.20fr multicolored	1.25 1.40

Safety at Sea Type of UN and

Life Preserver and
Radar — G23

1983, Mar. 18	Litho.	Perf. 14½	
114	A205	40c multicolored	.40 .45
115	G23	80c multicolored	.80 .85

World Food Program

1983, Apr. 22	Engr.	Perf. 13½	
116	A207	1.50fr blue	1.25 1.40

Trade Type of UN and

G24

1983, June 6	Litho.	Perf. 14	
117	A208	80c multicolored	.50 .55
118	G24	1.10fr multicolored	.90 .95

G25

35th Anniv. of
the Universal
Declaration of
Human
Rights — G26

Photo. & Engr.

1983, Dec. 9		Perf. 13½	
119	G25	40c multicolored	.45 .50
120	G26	1.20fr multicolored	.95 1.00

**International Conference on
Population Type**

1984, Feb. 3	Litho.	Perf. 14	
121	A212	1.20fr multicolored	.90 .95

Fishing
G27

Women
Farm
Workers,
Africa
G28

World Food Day, Oct. 16

1984, Mar. 15	Litho.	Perf. 14½	
122	G27	50c multicolored	.30 .35
123	G28	80c multicolored	.60 .65

Valletta,
Malta — G29

Los Glaciares
Natl. Park,
Argentina
G30

World Heritage

1984, Apr. 18	Litho.	Perf. 14	
124	G29	50c multicolored	.60 .65
125	G30	70c multicolored	.85 .90

G31　　　　　　G32

Future for Refugees

1984, May 29	Photo.	Perf. 11½	
126	G31	35c multicolored	.30 .35
127	G32	1.50fr multicolored	1.10 1.20

International Youth
Year — G33

1984, Nov. 15	Litho.	Perf. 13½	
128	G33	1.20fr multicolored	1.25 1.40

ILO Type of UN and

Turin
Center — G34

1985, Feb. 1	Engr.	Perf. 13½	
129	A220	80c dull red	.70 .75
130	G34	1.20fr U Thant Pavilion	1.10 1.20

UN University Type

50c, Pastoral scene, advanced
communications.

1985, Mar. 15	Photo.	Perf. 11½	
131	A221	50c multicolored	.60 .65
132	A221	80c like No. 131	1.00 1.10

Postman
G35

Doves — G36

1985, May 10   Litho.   Perf. 14
133 G35   20c multicolored   .25   .30
134 G36   1.20fr multicolored   1.25 1.40

40th Anniversary Type
Perf. 12 x 11½
1985, June 26   Photo.
135 A224   50c multicolored   .60   .65
136 A225   70c multicolored   .90   .95

Souvenir Sheet
Imperf
137   Sheet of 2   2.25 2.40
  a.   A224 50c multicolored   .85   .90
  b.   A225 70c multicolored   1.10 1.20

UNICEF Child Survival Campaign Type
Photo. & Engr.
1985, Nov. 22   Perf. 13½
138 A226   50c Three girls   .40   .45
139 A226   1.20fr Infant drinking   1.10 1.20

Africa in Crisis Type
1986, Jan. 31 Photo. Perf. 11½x12
140 A227   1.40fr Mother, hungry
                   children   1.25 1.40

UN Development Program Type
Forestry.
1986, Mar. 14   Photo.   Perf. 13½
141 A228   35c Erosion control   1.60 1.75
142 A228   35c Logging   1.60 1.75
143 A228   35c Lumber transport   1.60 1.75
144 A228   35c Nursery   1.60 1.75
  a.   Block of 4, #141-144   6.50 7.50

Doves and Sun — G37

1986, Mar. 14   Litho.   Perf. 15x14½
145 G37   5c multicolored   .25   .30

Stamp Collecting Type
Designs: 50c, UN Human Rights stamp.
80c, UN stamps.
1986, May 22   Engr.   Perf. 12½
146 A229   50c dark grn & hen brn   .60   .65
147 A229   80c dark grn & yel org   .90   .95

Flags and Globe as Dove — G38

Peace in French — G39

International Peace Year.
Photo. & Embossed
1986, June 20   Perf. 13½
148 G38   45c multicolored   .60   .65
149 G39   1.40fr multicolored   1.25 1.40

WFUNA Anniversary Type
Souvenir Sheet
Designs: 35c, Abstract by Benigno Gomez, Honduras. 45c, Abstract by Alexander Calder (1898-1976), US. 50c, Abstract by Joan Miro (b. 1893), Spain. 70c, Sextet with Dove, by Ole Hamann, Denmark.

1986, Nov. 14   Litho.   Perf. 13x13½
150   Sheet of 4   3.75 4.00
  a.   A232 35c multicolored   .50   .55
  b.   A232 45c multicolored   .70   .75
  c.   A232 50c multicolored   .90 1.00
  d.   A232 70c multicolored   1.25 1.40
No. 150 has inscribed margin picturing UN and WFUNA emblems.

Trygve Lie Type
Photo. & Engr.
1987, Jan. 30   Perf. 13½
151 A233   1.40fr multicolored   1.10 1.20

Sheaf of Colored Bands, by Georges Mathieu — G40

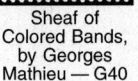

Armillary Sphere, Palais des Nations — G41

Photo., Photo. & Engr. (#153)
1987, Jan. 30   Perf. 11½x12, 13½
152 G40   90c multicolored   .65   .70
153 G41   1.40fr multicolored   1.25 1.40

Shelter for the Homeless Type
Designs: 50c, Cement-making and brick-making. 90c, Interior construction and decorating.
Perf. 13½x12½
1987, Mar. 13   Litho.
154 A234   50c multicolored   .50   .55
155 A234   90c multicolored   1.00 1.10

Fight Drug Abuse Type
Designs: 80c, Mother and child. 1.20fr, Workers in rice paddy.
1987, June 12 Litho. Perf. 14½x15
156 A235   80c multicolored   .50   .55
157 A235   1.20fr multicolored   1.00 1.10

UN Day Type
Designs: Multinational people in various occupations.
1987, Oct. 23 Litho. Perf. 14½x15
158 A236   35c multicolored   .55   .60
159 A236   50c multicolored   .80   .85

Immunize Every Child Type
Designs: 90c, Whooping cough. 1.70fr, Tuberculosis.
1987, Nov. 20 Litho. Perf. 15x14½
160 A237   90c multicolored   1.50 1.65
161 A237   1.70fr multicolored   2.75 3.00

IFAD Type
Designs: 35c, Flocks, dairy products. 1.40fr, Fruit.
1988, Jan. 29   Litho.   Perf. 13½
162 A238   35c multicolored   .35   .40
163 A238   1.40fr multicolored   1.40 1.50

For A Better World — G42

1988, Jan. 29   Photo.   Perf. 14
164 G42   50c multicolored   .80   .85

Survival of the Forests Type
Pine forest: 50c, Treetops, mountains. 1.10fr, Lake, tree trunks. Printed se-tenant in a continuous design.
1988, Mar. 18   Litho.   Perf. 14x15
165 A240   50c multicolored   1.25 1.40
166 A240   1.10fr multicolored   3.50 3.75
  a.   Pair, #165-166   5.50 6.00

Intl. Volunteer Day Type
Designs: 80c, Agriculture, vert. 90c, Veterinary medicine.
Perf. 13x14, 14x13
1988, May 6   Litho.
167 A241   80c multicolored   .80   .85
168 A241   90c multicolored   1.00 1.10

Health in Sports Type
Paintings by LeRoy Neiman, American sports artist: 50c, Soccer, vert. 1.40fr, Swimming.
Perf. 13½x13, 13x13½
1988, June 17   Litho.
169 A242   50c multicolored   .40   .45
170 A242   1.40fr multicolored   1.40 1.50

Universal Declaration of Human Rights 40th Anniv. Type
Photo. & Engr.
1988, Dec. 9   Perf. 12
171 A243   90c multicolored   .70   .75
Souvenir Sheet
172 A243   2fr multicolored   2.75 3.00

World Bank Type
80c, Telecommunications. 1.40fr, Industry.
1989, Jan. 27   Litho.   Perf. 13x14
173 A244   80c multicolored   1.00 1.10
174 A244   1.40fr multicolored   2.00 2.20

Peace-Keeping Force Type
1989, Mar. 17   Perf. 14x13½
175 A245   90c multicolored   1.25 1.40

World Weather Watch Type
Satellite photographs: 90c, Europe under the influence of Arctic air. 1.10fr, Surface temperatures of sea, ice and land surrounding the Kattegat between Denmark and Sweden.
1989, Apr. 21   Litho.   Perf. 13x14
176 A247   90c multicolored   1.25 1.40
177 A247   1.10fr multicolored   2.00 2.20

G43   G44

Photo., Photo. & Engr. (2fr)
1989, Aug. 23   Perf. 14
178 G43   50c multicolored   .75 1.10
179 G44   2fr multicolored   2.50 3.75
Offices in Vienna, 10th anniv.

Human Rights Type of 1989
Artwork: 35c, Young Mother Sewing, by Mary Cassatt. 80c, The Unknown Slave, sculpture by Albert Mangones.
1989, Nov. 17   Perf. 13½
180 A250   35c multicolored   .35   .40
181 A250   80c multicolored   1.00 1.10
Printed in panes of 12+12 se-tenant labels containing Articles 3 (35c) or 4 (80c) inscribed in English, French or German.
See Nos. 193-194, 209-210,34-235.

Intl. Trade Center Type
1990, Feb. 2   Litho.   Perf. 14½x15
182 A251   1.50fr multicolored   2.25 2.50

G45

1990, Feb. 2   Photo.   Perf. 14x13½
183 G45   5fr multicolored   4.75 5.25

G46

Fight AIDS Worldwide — G46a

Fight AIDS Type
Designs: 50c, "SIDA." 80c, Proportional drawing of man like the illustration by Leonardo da Vinci.
Perf. 13½x12½
1990, Mar. 16   Litho.
184 G46   50c multicolored   1.00 1.10
185 G46a   80c multicolored   1.75 1.90

Medicinal Plants Type
1990, May 4   Photo.   Perf. 11½
Granite Paper
186 A253   90c Plumeria rubra   1.00 1.10
187 A253   1.40fr Cinchona of-
                   ficinalis   2.00 2.20

UN 45th Anniv. Type
"45," emblem and: 90c, Symbols of clean environment, transportation and industry. 1.10fr, Dove in silhouette.
1990, June 26 Litho. Perf. 14½x13
188 A254   90c multicolored   1.10 1.20
189 A254   1.10fr multicolored   2.25 2.50
Souvenir Sheet
190   Sheet of 2, #188-189   6.00 6.50

Crime Prevention Type
1990, Sept. 13   Photo.   Perf. 14
191 A255   50c Official corruption   1.25 1.40
192 A255   2fr Environmental
                   crime   3.00 3.25

Human Rights Type of 1989
Artwork: 35c, The Prison Courtyard by Vincent Van Gogh. 90c, Katho's Son Redeems the Evil Doer From Execution by Albrecht Durer.
1990, Nov. 16   Litho.   Perf. 13½
193 A250   35c multicolored   .45   .50
194 A250   90c blk & brn   1.25 1.40

Economic Commission for Europe Type
1991, Mar. 15   Litho.   Perf. 14
195 A256   90c Owl, gull   1.40 1.60
196 A256   90c Bittern, otter   1.40 1.60
197 A256   90c Swan, lizard   1.40 1.60
198 A256   90c Great crested
                   grebe   1.40 1.60
  a.   Block of 4, #195-198   5.60 6.50

Namibian Independence Type
1991, May 10   Litho.   Perf. 14
199 A257   70c Mountains   1.00 1.10
200 A257   90c Baobab tree   2.00 2.20

Ballots Filling Ballot Box — G47   UN Emblem — G48

1991, May 10   Litho.   Perf. 15x14½
201 G47   80c multicolored   .75   .80
202 G48   1.50fr multicolored   2.00 2.20

G49

Rights of
the Child
G50

1991, June 14   Litho.   Perf. 14½
203 G49 80c Hands holding in-
              fant   1.00 1.10
204 G50 1.10fr Children, flowers   2.00 2.20

G51

Banning of
Chemical
Weapons
G52

1991, Sept. 11   Litho.   Perf. 13½
205 G51 80c multicolored   2.00 2.20
206 G52 1.40fr multicolored   3.00 3.25

UN Postal Administration, 40th Anniv. Type
1991, Oct. 24   Perf. 14x15
207 A263   50c UN NY No. 7   .80 .85
208 A263 1.60fr UN NY No. 10   2.20 2.40

Human Rights Type of 1989
Artwork: 50c, Early Morning in Rio...1925,
by Paul Klee. 90c, Marriage of Giovanni (?)
Arnolfini and Giovanna Cenami (?), by Jan
Van Eyck.

1991, Nov. 20   Litho.   Perf. 13½
209 A250 50c multicolored   .75 .80
210 A250 90c multicolored   1.25 1.40

Panes of 12+12 se-tenant labels containing
Articles 15 (50c) or 16 (90c) inscribed in
French, German or English.

World Heritage Type of 1984
Designs: 50c, Sagarmatha Natl. Park,
Nepal. 1.10fr, Stonehenge, United Kingdom.

1992, Jan. 24   Litho.   Perf. 13
Size: 35x28mm
211 G29   50c multicolored   .80 .85
212 G29 1.10fr multicolored   1.90 2.10

G53

1992, Jan. 24   Litho.   Perf. 15x14½
213 G53 3fr multicolored   3.00 3.25

Clean Oceans Type
1992, Mar. 13   Litho.   Perf. 14
214 A264 80c Ocean surface,
              diff.   .90 .95
215 A264 80c Ocean bottom, diff. .90 .95
  a.   Pair, #214-215   1.80 2.10

Earth Summit Type
Designs: No. 216, Rainbow. No. 217, Two
clouds shaped as faces. No. 218, Two sailboats. No. 219, Woman with parasol, boat,
flowers.

1992, May 22   Photo.   Perf. 11½
216 A265 75c multicolored   1.50 1.60
217 A265 75c multicolored   1.50 1.60
218 A265 75c multicolored   1.50 1.60
219 A265 75c multicolored   1.50 1.60
  a.   Block of 4, #216-219   6.00 6.50

Mission to Planet Earth Type
Designs: No. 220, Space station. No. 221,
Probes near Jupiter.

1992, Sept. 4   Photo.   Rouletted 8
Granite Paper
220 A266 1.10fr multicolored   2.40 2.60
221 A266 1.10fr multicolored   2.40 2.60
  a.   Pair, #220-221   5.00 5.25

Science and Technology Type of 1992
Designs: 90c, Doctor, nurse. 1.60fr, Graduate seated before computer.

1992, Oct. 2   Litho.   Perf. 14
222 A267 90c multicolored   1.25 1.40
223 A267 1.60fr multicolored   3.00 3.25

Human Rights Type of 1989
Artwork: 50c, The Oath of the Tennis Court,
by Jacques Louis David. 90c, Rocking Chair I,
by Henry Moore.

1992, Nov. 20   Litho.   Perf. 13½
224 A250 50c multicolored   .75 .80
225 A250 90c multicolored   1.25 1.40

Panes of 12+12 se-tenant labels containing
Articles 21 (50c) and 22 (90c) inscribed in
French, German or English.

Aging With Dignity Type
Designs: 50c, Older man coaching soccer.
1.60fr, Older man working at computer
terminal.

1993, Feb. 5   Litho.   Perf. 13
226 A270 50c multicolored   .50 .55
227 A270 1.60fr multicolored   1.50 1.65

Endangered Species Type
Designs: No. 228, Pongidae (gorilla). No.
229, Falco peregrinus (peregrine falcon). No.
230, Trichechus inunguis (Amazonian manatee). No. 231, Panthera uncia (snow leopard).

1993, Mar. 2   Litho.   Perf. 13x12½
228 A271 80c multicolored   1.10 1.20
229 A271 80c multicolored   1.10 1.20
230 A271 80c multicolored   1.10 1.20
231 A271 80c multicolored   1.10 1.20
  a.   Block of 4, #228-231   4.50 4.80

Healthy Environment Type
1993, May 7   Litho.   Perf. 15x14½
232 A272 60c Neighborhood   .75 .80
233 A272 1fr Urban skyscrapers   1.75 1.90

Human Rights Type of 1989
Artwork: 50c, Three Musicians, by Pablo
Picasso. 90c, Voice of Space, by Rene
Magritte.

1993, June 11   Litho.   Perf. 13½
234 A250 50c multicolored   .75 .80
235 A250 90c multicolored   1.75 1.90

Printed in panes of 12 + 12 se-tenant labels
containing Article 27 (50c) and 28 (90c)
inscribed in French, German or English.

Intl. Peace Day Type
Denomination at: No. 236, UL. No. 237, UR.
No. 238, LL. No. 239, LR.

Rouletted 12½
1993, Sept. 21   Litho. & Engr.
236 A274 60c purple & multi   2.00 2.20
237 A274 60c purple & multi   2.00 2.20
238 A274 60c purple & multi   2.00 2.20
239 A274 60c purple & multi   2.00 2.20
  a.   Block of 4, #236-239   8.00 9.00

Environment-Climate Type
1993, Oct. 29   Litho.   Perf. 14½
240 A275 1.10fr Polar bears   2.40 2.40
241 A275 1.10fr Whale sound-
              ing   2.40 2.40
242 A275 1.10fr Elephant seal   2.40 2.40
243 A275 1.10fr Penguins   2.40 2.40
  a.   Strip of 4, #240-243   9.75 10.75

Intl. Year of the Family Type of 1993
Designs: 80c, Parents teaching child to
walk. 1fr, Two women and child picking plants.

1994, Feb. 4   Litho.   Perf. 13.1
244 A276   80c rose vio & multi 1.00 1.10
245 A276   1fr brown & multi   1.40 1.50

Endangered Species Type of 1993
Designs: No. 246, Mexican prairie dog. No.
247, Jabiru. No. 248, Blue whale. No. 249,
Golden lion tamarin.

1994, Mar. 18   Litho.   Perf. 12.7
246 A271 80c multicolored   1.10 1.20
247 A271 80c multicolored   1.10 1.20
248 A271 80c multicolored   1.10 1.20
249 A271 80c multicolored   1.10 1.20
  a.   Block of 4, #246-249   4.50 5.00

Protection for Refugees Type of 1994
Design: 1.20fr, Hand lifting figure over
chasm.

1994, Apr. 29   Litho.   Perf. 14.3x14.8
250 A277 1.20fr multicolored   2.25 2.40

Intl. Decade for Natural Disaster Reduction Type of 1994
Earth seen from space, outline map of: No.
251, North America. No. 252, Eurasia. No.
253, South America. No. 254, Australia and
South Pacific region.

1994, May 27   Litho.   Perf. 13.9x14.2
251 A281 60c multicolored   1.75 1.90
252 A281 60c multicolored   1.75 1.90
253 A281 60c multicolored   1.75 1.90
254 A281 60c multicolored   1.75 1.90
  a.   Block of 4, #251-254   7.00 7.75

Palais des
Nations,
Geneva
G54

Creation of
the World, by
Oili
Maki — G55

1994, Sept. 1   Litho.   Perf. 14.3x14.6
255 G54 60c multicolored   .75 .80
256 G55 80c multicolored   1.00 1.10
257 G54 1.80fr multi, diff.   2.25 2.50
  Nos. 255-257 (3)   4.00 4.40

Population and Development Type of 1994
Designs: 60c, People shopping at open-air
market. 80c, People on vacation crossing
bridge.

1994, Sept. 1   Litho.   Perf. 13.2x13.6
258 A282 60c multicolored   1.00 1.10
259 A282 80c multicolored   1.25 1.40

UNCTAD Type of 1994
1994, Oct. 28
260 A283 80c multi, diff.   1.10 1.20
261 A283 1fr multi, diff.   1.50 1.65
  a.   Grayish green omitted   —

UN 50th Anniv. Type of 1995
Litho. & Engr.
1995, Jan. 1   Perf. 13.4
262 A284 80c multicolored   1.10 1.20

Social Summit Type of 1995
Photo. & Engr.
1995, Feb. 3   Perf. 13.6x13.9
263 A285 1fr multi, diff.   1.25 1.40

Endangered Species Type of 1993
Designs: No. 264, Crowned lemur, Lemur
coronatus. No. 265, Giant Scops owl, Otus
gurneyi. No. 266, Zetek's frog, Atelopus varius
zeteki. No. 267, Wood bison, Bison bison
athabascae.

1995, Mar. 24   Litho.   Perf. 13x12½
264 A271 80c multicolored   1.10 1.20
265 A271 80c multicolored   1.10 1.20
266 A271 80c multicolored   1.10 1.20
267 A271 80c multicolored   1.10 1.20
  a.   Block of 4, 264-267   4.50 5.00

Intl. Youth Year Type of 1995
Designs: 80c, Farmer on tractor, fields at
harvest time. 1fr, Couple standing by fields at
night.

1995, May 26   Litho.   Perf. 14.4x14.7
268 A286 80c multicolored   1.25 1.40
269 A286 1fr multicolored   2.00 2.20

UN, 50th Anniv. Type of 1995
Designs: 60c, Like No. 663. 1.80fr, Like No.
664.

Perf. 13.3x13.6
1995, June 26   Engr.
270 A287   60c maroon   .80 .85
271 A287 1.80fr green   3.00 3.25

Souvenir Sheet
Litho. & Engr.
Imperf
272   Sheet of 2, #270-271   4.25 4.50
  a.   A287 60c maroon   1.00 1.10
  b.   A287 1.80fr green   3.25 3.40

Conference on Women Type of 1995
Designs: 60c, Black woman, cranes flying
above. 1fr, Women, dove.

1995, Sept. 5   Photo.   Perf. 12
273 A288 60c multicolored   1.00 1.10
Size: 28x50mm
274 A288 1fr multicolored   2.00 2.20

UN People, 50th Anniv. Type of 1995
1995, Oct. 24   Litho.   Perf. 14
275   Sheet of 12   14.00 15.00
  a.-l. A290 30c each   1.20 1.20
276   Souvenir booklet   15.00
  a.   A290 30c Booklet pane of 3,
              vert. strip of 3 from UL of
              sheet   3.75 3.75
  b.   A290 30c Booklet pane of 3,
              vert. strip of 3 from UR of
              sheet   3.75 3.75
  c.   A290 30c Booklet pane of 3,
              vert. strip of 3 from LL of
              sheet   3.75 3.75
  d.   A290 30c Booklet pane of 3,
              vert. strip of 3 from LR of
              sheet   3.75 3.75

WFUNA, 50th Anniv. Type
Design: 80c, Fishing boat, fish in net.

1996, Feb. 2   Litho.   Perf. 13x13½
277 A291 80c multicolored   1.25 1.40

The Galloping Horse Treading on a
Flying Swallow, Chinese Bronzework,
Eastern Han Dynasty (25-220
A.D.) — G56

Palais des
Nations,
Geneva
G57

1996, Feb. 2   Litho.   Perf. 14½x15
278 G56 40c multicolored   .50 .55
279 G57 70c multicolored   .90 .95

Endangered Species Type of 1993
Designs: No. 280, Paphiopedilum delenatii.
No. 281, Pachypodium baronii. No. 282,
Sternbergia lutea. No. 283, Darlingtonia
californica.

1996, Mar. 14   Litho.   Perf. 12½
280 A271 80c multicolored   1.00 1.10
281 A271 80c multicolored   1.00 1.10
282 A271 80c multicolored   1.00 1.10
283 A271 80c multicolored   1.00 1.10
  a.   Block of 4, #280-283   4.00 4.50

City Summit Type of 1996
Designs: No. 284, Asian family. No. 285,
Oriental garden. No. 286, Fruit, vegetable vendor, mosque. No. 287, Boys playing ball. No.
288, Couple reading newspaper.

1996, June 3   Litho.   Perf. 14x13½
284 A293 70c multicolored   1.50 1.65
285 A293 70c multicolored   1.50 1.65
286 A293 70c multicolored   1.50 1.65
287 A293 70c multicolored   1.50 1.65
288 A293 70c multicolored   1.50 1.65
  a.   Strip of 5, #284-288   7.50 8.25

Sport and the Environment Type
Designs: 70c, Cycling, vert. 1.10fr,
Sprinters.

Perf. 14x14½, 14½x14
1996, July 19   Litho.
289 A294   70c multicolored   1.00 1.10
290 A294 1.10fr multicolored   1.50 1.65

Souvenir Sheet
291 A294   Sheet of 2,
      #289-290   3.00 3.25

Plea for Peace Type
Designs: 90c, Tree filled with birds, vert. 1.10fr, Bouquet of flowers in rocket tail vase, vert.

1996, Sept. 17   Litho.   *Perf. 15x14½*
292 A295   90c multicolored   1.25 1.40
293 A295 1.10fr multicolored   1.50 1.65

UNICEF Type
Fairy Tales: 70c, The Sun and the Moon, South America. 1.80fr, Ananse, Africa.

1996, Nov. 20   Litho.   *Perf. 14½x15*
294 A296   70c multicolored   .80 .85
295 A296 1.80fr multicolored   2.00 2.20

UN Flag — G58

Palais des Nations Under Construction, by Massimo Campigli G59

1997, Feb. 12   Litho.   *Perf. 14½*
296 G58   10c multicolored   .25 .30
297 G59 1.10fr multicolored   1.25 1.40

Endangered Species Type of 1993
Designs: No. 298, Ursus maritimus (polar bear). No. 299, Goura cristata (blue-crowned pigeon). No. 300, Amblyrhynchus cristatus (marine iguana). No. 301, Lama guanicoe (guanaco).

1997, Mar. 13   Litho.   *Perf. 12½*
298 A271   80c multicolored   .90 .95
299 A271   80c multicolored   .90 .95
300 A271   80c multicolored   .90 .95
301 A271   80c multicolored   .90 .95
  a.   Block of 4, #298-301   3.60 3.90

Earth Summit Anniv. Type
Designs: No. 302, Person flying over mountain. No. 303, Mountain, person's face. No. 304, Person standing on mountain, sailboats. No. 305, Person, mountain, trees.
1.10fr, Combined design similar to Nos. 302-305.

1997, May 30   Photo.   *Perf. 11½*
Granite Paper
302 A299   45c multicolored   1.00 1.10
303 A299   45c multicolored   1.00 1.10
304 A299   45c multicolored   1.00 1.10
305 A299   45c multicolored   1.00 1.10
  a.   Block of 4, #302-305   4.00 4.50

Souvenir Sheet
306 A299 1.10fr multicolored   4.00 4.25

Transportation Type of 1997
Air transportation: No. 307, Zeppelin, Fokker tri-motor. No. 308, Boeing 314 Clipper, Lockheed Constellation. No. 309, DeHavilland Comet. No. 310, Boeing 747, Illyushin jet. No. 311, Concorde.

1997, Aug. 29   Litho.   *Perf. 14x14½*
307 A300   70c multicolored   1.00 1.10
308 A300   70c multicolored   1.00 1.10
309 A300   70c multicolored   1.00 1.10
310 A300   70c multicolored   1.00 1.10
311 A300   70c multicolored   1.00 1.10
  a.   Strip of 5, #307-311   5.00 5.50

Philately Type
Designs: 70c, No. 146. 1.10fr, No. 147.

1997, Oct. 14   Litho.   *Perf. 13½x14*
312 A301   70c multicolored   .80 .85
313 A301 1.10fr multicolored   1.50 1.65

World Heritage Convention Type
Terracotta warriors of Xian: 45c, Single warrior. 70c, Massed warriors. No. 316a, like NY No. 716. No. 316b, like NY No. 717. No. 316c, like Geneva No. 314. No. 316d, like Geneva

---

No. 315. No. 316e, like Vienna No. 230. No. 316f, like Vienna No. 231.

1997, Nov. 19   Litho.   *Perf. 13½*
314 A302   45c multicolored   1.25 1.40
315 A302   70c multicolored   2.25 2.50
316   Souvenir booklet   12.00
  a.-f. A302 10c any single   .45 .50
  g.   Booklet pane of 4 #316a   2.00 2.00
  h.   Booklet pane of 4 #316b   2.00 2.00
  i.   Booklet pane of 4 #316c   2.00 2.00
  j.   Booklet pane of 4 #316d   2.00 2.00
  k.   Booklet pane of 4 #316e   2.00 2.00
  l.   Booklet pane of 4 #316f   2.00 2.00

Palais des Nations, Geneva G60

1998, Feb. 13   Litho.   *Perf. 14½x15*
317 G60   2fr multicolored   1.50 1.65

Endangered Species Type of 1993
Designs: No. 318, Macaca thibetana (short-tailed Tibetan macaque). No. 319, Phoenicopterus ruber (Caribbean flamingo). No. 320, Ornithoptera alexandrae (Queen Alexandra's birdwing). No. 321, Dama mesopotamica (Persian fallow deer).

1998, Mar. 13   Litho.   *Perf. 12½*
318 A271   80c multicolored   1.00 1.10
319 A271   80c multicolored   1.00 1.10
320 A271   80c multicolored   1.00 1.10
321 A271   80c multicolored   1.00 1.10
  a.   Block of 4, #318-321   4.00 4.50

Intl. Year of the Ocean — G61

1998, May 20   Litho.   *Perf. 13x13½*
322   G61   Pane of 12   11.00 12.00
  a.-l.   45c any single   .90 1.00

Rain Forests Type
1998, June 19   *Perf. 13x13½*
323 A307   70c Orangutans   .90 1.00

Souvenir Sheet
324 A307   3fr like #323   4.00 7.50

Peacekeeping Type
Designs: 70c, Soldier with two children. 90c, Two soldiers, children.

1998, Sept. 15   Photo.   *Perf. 12*
325 A308   70c multicolored   .85 .90
326 A308   90c multicolored   1.40 1.50

Declaration of Human Rights Type of 1998
Designs: 90c, Stylized birds. 1.80fr, Stylized birds flying from hand.

Litho. & Photo.
1998, Oct. 27   *Perf. 13*
327 A309   90c multicolored   .95 1.05
328 A309 1.80fr multicolored   2.00 2.20

Schönbrunn Palace Type
Designs: 70c, No. 331b, Great Palm House. 1.10fr, No. 331d, Blue porcelain vase, vert. No. 331a, Palace. No. 331c, The Gloriette (archway). No. 331e, Wall painting on fabric (detail), by Johann Wenzl Bergl, vert. No. 331f, Porcelain stove, vert.

1998, Dec. 4   Litho.   *Perf. 14*
329 A310   70c multicolored   .90 1.00
330 A310 1.10fr multicolored   1.20 1.30

Souvenir Booklet
331   Booklet   21.50
  a.-c. A310 10c any single   .55 .55
  d.-f. A310 30c any single   1.65 1.65
  g.   Booklet pane of 4 #331a   2.20 2.20
  h.   Booklet pane of 3 #331d   5.00 5.00
  i.   Booklet pane of 3 #331e   5.00 5.00
  k.   Booklet pane of 4 #331b   2.20 2.20
  l.   Booklet pane of 4 #331c   2.20 2.20

Palais Wilson, Geneva G62

1999, Feb. 5   Photo.   *Perf. 11½*
Granite Paper
332 G62 1.70fr brown red   1.75 1.90

World Heritage, Australia Type
Designs: 90c, No. 335e, Kakadu Natl. Park. 1.10fr, No. 335c, Great Barrier Reef. No. 335a, Tasmanian Wilderness. No. 335b, Wet tropics of Queensland. No. 335d, Uluru-Kata Tjuta Natl. Park. No. 335f, Willandra Lakes region.

1999, Mar. 19   Litho.   *Perf. 13*
333 A313   90c multicolored   1.25 1.40
334 A313 1.10fr multicolored   1.50 1.65

Souvenir Booklet
335   Booklet   16.50
  a.-c. A313 10c any single   .45 .50
  d.-f. A313 20c any single   .90 1.00
  g.   Booklet pane of 4, #335a   1.80 2.00
  h.   Booklet pane of 4, #335d   3.60 4.00
  i.   Booklet pane of 4, #335b   1.80 2.00
  j.   Booklet pane of 4, #335e   3.60 4.00
  k.   Booklet pane of 4, #335c   1.80 2.00
  l.   Booklet pane of 4, #335f   3.60 4.00

Endangered Species Type of 1993
Designs: No. 336, Equus hemionus (Asiatic wild ass). No. 337, Anodorhynchus hyacinthinus (hyacinth macaw). No. 338, Epicrates subflavus (Jamaican boa). No. 339, Dendrolagus bennettianus (Bennetts' tree kangaroo).

1999, Apr. 22   Litho.   *Perf. 12½*
336 A271   90c multicolored   1.00 1.10
337 A271   90c multicolored   1.00 1.10
338 A271   90c multicolored   1.00 1.10
339 A271   90c multicolored   1.00 1.10
  a.   Block of 4, #336-339   4.00 4.50

UNISPACE III Type
Designs: No. 340, Farm, satellite dish. No. 341, City, satellite in orbit. No. 342, Composite of Nos. 340-341.

1999, July 7   Photo.   *Rouletted 8*
340 A314   45c multicolored   .90 1.00
341 A314   45c multicolored   .90 1.00
  a.   Pair, #340-341   2.00 2.20

Souvenir Sheet
Perf. 14½
342 A314   2fr multicolored   4.50 5.00
  a.   Ovptd. in sheet margin   9.50 10.50

UPU Type
Various people, early 20th century methods of mail transportation, denomination at: No. 343, UL. No. 344, UR. No. 345, LL. No. 346, LR.

1999, Aug. 23   Photo.   *Perf. 11¾*
343 A315   70c multicolored   .90 1.00
344 A315   70c multicolored   .90 1.00
345 A315   70c multicolored   .90 1.00
346 A315   70c multicolored   .90 1.00
  a.   Block of 4, #343-346   3.60 4.00

In Memoriam Type
Designs: 1.10fr, 2fr, Armillary sphere, Palais de Nations. Size of 2fr stamp: 34x63mm.

1999, Sept. 21   Litho.   *Perf. 14½x14*
347 A316 1.10fr multicolored   1.25 1.40

Souvenir Sheet
Perf. 14
348 A316   2fr multicolored   3.00 3.25

Education Type
90c, Rainbow over globe. 1.80fr, Fish, tree, globe, book.

Perf. 13½x13¾
1999, Nov. 18   Litho.
349 A317   90c multi   .75 .80
350 A317 1.80fr multi   1.75 1.90

Intl. Year Of Thanksgiving Type
2000, Jan 1   Litho.   *Perf. 13¼x13½*
351 A318   90c multicolored   1.00 1.10
On No. 351 portions of the design were applied by a thermographic process producing a shiny, raised effect.

Endangered Species Type of 1993
Designs: No. 352, Hippopotamus amphibius (hippopotamus). No. 353, Coscoroba coscoroba (Coscoroba swan). No. 354, Varanus prasinus (emerald monitor). No. 355, Enhydra lutris (sea otter).

2000, Apr. 6   Litho.   *Perf. 12¾x12½*
352 A271   90c multicolored   1.25 1.40
353 A271   90c multicolored   1.25 1.40
354 A271   90c multicolored   1.25 1.40
355 A271   90c multicolored   1.25 1.40
  a.   Block of 4, #352-355   5.00 5.75

Our World 2000 Type
Winning artwork in Millennium painting competition: 90c, The Embrace, by Rita Adaimy, Lebanon. 1.10fr, Living Single, by Richard Kimanthi, Kenya, vert.

Perf. 13x13½, 13½x13
2000, May 30   Litho.
356 A319   90c multicolored   1.00 1.10
357 A319 1.10fr multicolored   1.25 1.40

55th Anniversary Type
Designs: 90c, Trygve Lie, Harry S Truman, workers at cornerstone dedication ceremony, 1949. 1.40fr, Window cleaner on Secretariat Building, General Assembly Hall under construction, 1951.

2000, July 7   Litho.   *Perf. 13¼x13*
358 A320   90c multicolored   1.00 1.10
359 A320 1.40fr multicolored   1.50 1.65

Souvenir Sheet
360 A320   Sheet of 2,
      #358-359   3.50 3.75

The UN in the 21st Century — G63

No. 361: a, Two people, terraced rice paddy. b, Man carrying bricks on head. c, UN Peacekeeper with binoculars. d, Dam, doves. e, Men with shovels. f, People working on irrigation system.

2000, Sept. 15   Litho.   *Perf. 14*
361   G63   Pane of 6   9.00 10.00
  a.-f.   50c any single   1.50 1.65

World Heritage, Spain Type
Designs: Nos. 362, 364b, Walled Town of Cuenca. Nos. 363, 364e, Toledo. No. 364a, Alhambra, Generalife and Albayzin, Granada. No. 364c, Aqueduct of Segovia. No. 364d, Amphitheater of Mérida. No. 364f, Güell Park, Barcelona.

2000, Oct. 6   Litho.   *Perf. 14¾x14½*
362 A323   1fr multicolored   1.40 1.50
363 A323 1.20fr multicolored   1.60 1.75

Souvenir Booklet
364   Booklet   11.00
  a.-c. A323 10c any single   .30 .35
  d.-f. A323 20c any single   .60 .65
  g.   Booklet pane of 4, #364a   1.20 1.40
  h.   Booklet pane of 4, #364d   2.40 2.60
  i.   Booklet pane of 4, #364b   1.20 1.40
  j.   Booklet pane of 4, #364e   2.40 2.60
  k.   Booklet pane of 4, #364c   1.20 1.40
  l.   Booklet pane of 4, #364f   2.40 2.60

Respect for Refugees Type
Designs: 80c, 1.80fr, Refugee with cane, four other refugees.

2000, Nov. 9   Litho.   *Perf. 13¼x12¾*
365   A324   80c multicolored   1.25 1.40
Souvenir Sheet
366   A324   1.80fr multicolored   2.50 2.75

Endangered Species Type of 1993
Designs: No. 367, Felis lynx canadensis (North American lynx). No. 368, Pavo muticus (green peafowl). No. 369, Geochelone elephantopus (Galapagos giant tortoise). No. 370, Lepilemur spp. (sportive lemur).

2001, Feb. 1   Litho.   *Perf. 12¾x12½*
367   A271   90c multicolored   1.25 1.40
368   A271   90c multicolored   1.25 1.40
369   A271   90c multicolored   1.25 1.40
370   A271   90c multicolored   1.25 1.40
a.   Block of 4, #367-370   5.00 5.75

Intl. Volunteers Year — G64

Paintings by: 90c, Ernest Pignon-Ernest, France. 1.30fr, Paul Siché, France.

2001, Mar. 29   Litho.   *Perf. 13¼*
371   G64   90c multicolored   1.10 1.20
372   G64   1.30fr multicolored   1.60 1.75

World Heritage, Japan Type
Designs: 1.10fr, No. 375b, Nara. 1.30fr, No. 375e, Itsukushima Shinto Shrine. No. 375a, Kyoto. No. 375c, Himeji-Jo. No. 375d, Shirakawa-Go and Gokayama. No. 375f, Nikko.

2001, Aug. 1   Litho.   *Perf. 12¾x13¼*
373   A328   1.10fr multicolored   1.30 1.40
374   A328   1.30fr multicolored   1.50 1.65
Souvenir Booklet
375   Booklet   15.00
a.-c.   A328 10c any single   .50   .55
d.-f.   A328 30c any single   .75   .80
g.   Booklet pane of 4, #375a   2.00 2.20
h.   Booklet pane of 4, #375d   3.00 3.20
i.   Booklet pane of 4, #375b   2.00 2.20
j.   Booklet pane of 4, #375e   3.00 3.20
k.   Booklet pane of 4, #375c   2.00 2.20
l.   Booklet pane of 4, #375f   3.00 3.20

Dag Hammarskjöld Type
2001, Sept. 18   Engr.   *Perf. 11x11¼*
376   A329   2fr car lake   2.50 2.75

UN Postal Administration, 50th Anniv. Types
2001, Oct. 18   Litho.   *Perf. 13½*
377   A330   90c Stamps, globe   1.00 1.10
378   A330   1.30fr Stamps, horns 1.75 1.90
Souvenir Sheet
379   A331   Sheet of 2   12.50 13.50
a.   1.30fr red & light blue, 38mm
       diameter   5.00 5.50
b.   1.80fr red & light blue, 38mm
       diameter   7.50 8.00

Climate Change Type
Designs: No. 380, Lizard, flowers, shoreline. No. 381, Windmills, construction workers. No. 382, Non-polluting factory. No. 383, Solar oven, city, village, picnickers.

2001, Nov. 16   Litho.   *Perf. 13¼*
380   A332   90c multicolored   1.10 1.20
381   A332   90c multicolored   1.10 1.20
382   A332   90c multicolored   1.10 1.20
383   A332   90c multicolored   1.10 1.20
a.   Horiz. strip, #380-383   4.50 5.00

Nobel Peace Prize Type
2001, Dec. 10   Litho.   *Perf. 13¼*
384   A333   90c multicolored   1.10 1.20

Palais des Nations G65

2002, Mar. 1   Litho.   *Perf. 13¾*
385   G65   1.30fr multicolored   1.40 1.50

Endangered Species Type of 1993
Designs: No. 386, Cacajao calvus (white uakari). No. 387, Mellivora capensis (honey badger). No. 388, Otocolobus manul (manul). No. 389, Varanus exantematicus (Bosc's monitor).

2002, Apr. 4   Litho.   *Perf. 12¾x12½*
386   A271   90c multicolored   1.50 1.65
387   A271   90c multicolored   1.50 1.65
388   A271   90c multicolored   1.50 1.65
389   A271   90c multicolored   1.50 1.65
a.   Block of 4, #386-389   6.00 6.75

Independence of East Timor Type
Designs: 90c, Wooden statue of male figure. 1.30fr, Carved wooden container.

2002, May 20   Litho.   *Perf. 14x14½*
390   A335   90c multicolored   1.25 1.40
391   A335   1.30fr multicolored   1.75 1.90

Intl. Year of Mountains Type
Designs: No. 392, Weisshorn, Switzerland. No. 393, Mt. Fuji, Japan. No. 394, Vinson Massif, Antarctica. No. 395, Mt. Kamet, India.

2002, May 24   Litho.   *Perf. 13x13¼*
392   A336   70c multicolored   1.00 1.10
393   A336   70c multicolored   1.00 1.10
394   A336   1.20fr multicolored   1.75 1.90
395   A336   1.20fr multicolored   1.75 1.90
a.   Vert. strip or block of four,
         #392-395   8.50 9.50

World Summit on Sustainable Development (Peter Max) Type
Designs: No. 396, Sun, birds, flowers, heart. No. 397, Three faceless people, diff. No. 398, Three women, diff. No. 399, Sailboat, mountain.

2002, June 27   Litho.   *Perf. 14½x14*
396   A337   90c multicolored   1.25 1.40
397   A337   90c multicolored   1.25 1.40
398   A337   1.80fr multicolored   2.50 2.75
399   A337   1.80fr multicolored   2.50 2.75
a.   Vert. strip or block of four,
         #396-399   10.00 11.00

World Heritage, Italy Type
Designs: 90c, No. 402e, Pisa. 1.30fr, No. 402b, Aeolian Islands. No. 402a, Amalfi Coast. No. 402c, Rome. No. 402d, Florence. No. 402f, Pompeii.

**   *Perf. 13½x13¼***
2002, Aug. 30   Litho.
400   A338   90c multicolored   1.25 1.40
401   A338   1.30fr multicolored   2.00 2.20
Souvenir Booklet
402   Booklet   29.00
a.-c.   A338 10c any single   .60   .80
d.-f.   A338 20c any single   1.75 2.00
g.   Booklet pane of 4, #402d   7.00 8.00
h.   Booklet pane of 4, #402e   2.40 2.75
i.   Booklet pane of 4, #402a   7.00 8.00
j.   Booklet pane of 4, #402b   2.40 2.75
k.   Booklet pane of 4, #402f   7.00 8.00
l.   Booklet pane of 4, #402c   2.40 2.75

AIDS Awareness Type
2002, Oct. 24   Litho.   *Perf. 13½*
403   A339   1.30fr multicolored   2.00 2.20

Entry of Switzerland into United Nations G66

2002, Oct. 24   Litho.   *Perf. 14½x14¾*
404   G66   3fr multicolored   3.50 3.75

Indigenous Art — G67

No. 405: a, Detail of Inca poncho, Peru. b, Bahia culture seated figure, Brazil. c, Blanket, Ecuador. d, Mayan stone sculpture, Belize. e, Embroidered fabric, Guatemala. f, Colima terra-cotta dog sculpture, Mexico.

2003, Jan. 31   Litho.   *Perf. 14¼*
405   G67   Pane of 6   7.50 8.50
a.-f.   90c Any single   1.25 1.35

New Inter-Parliamentary Union Headquarters, Geneva — G68

2003, Feb. 20   Litho.   *Perf. 14½x14*
406   G68   90c multicolored   1.75 1.75

Endangered Species Type of 1993
Designs: No. 407, Branta ruficollis (red-breasted goose). No. 408, Geronticus calvus (bald ibis). No. 409, Dendrocygna bicolor (fulvous whistling duck). No. 410, Ramphastos vitellinus (channel-billed toucan).

2003, Apr. 3   Litho.   *Perf. 12¾x12½*
407   A271   90c multicolored   1.25 1.25
408   A271   90c multicolored   1.25 1.25
409   A271   90c multicolored   1.25 1.25
410   A271   90c multicolored   1.25 1.25
a.   Block of 4, #407-410   5.00 5.00

International Year of Freshwater Type of 2003
**   *Perf. 14¼x14½***
2003, June 20   Litho.
411   A345   70c Waterfall   1.25 1.25
412   A345   1.30fr People, moun-
                tain   2.25 2.25
a.   Horiz. pair, #411-412   5.00 5.00

Ralph Bunche Type
Litho. With Foil Application
2003, Aug. 7   *Perf. 13½x14*
413   A346   1.80fr brn red & multi 2.75 2.75

In Memoriam Type of 2003
2003, Oct. 24   Litho.   *Perf. 13¼x13*
414   A347   85c multicolored   1.50 1.50

World Heritage Sites, United States Type
Designs: 90c, No. 417b, Great Smoky Mountains National Park. 1.30fr, No. 417f, Yellowstone National Park. No. 417a, Yosemite National Park. No. 417c, Olympic National Park. No. 417d, Hawaii Volcanoes National Park. No. 417e, Everglades National Park.

2003, Oct. 24   Litho.   *Perf. 14½x14¼*
415   A348   90c multicolored   1.50 1.50
416   A348   1.30fr multicolored   2.25 2.25
Souvenir Booklet
417   Booklet   12.00
a.-c.   A348 10c any single   .30   .30
d.-f.   A348 30c any single   .65   .65
g.   Booklet pane of 4 #417a   1.20 1.20
h.   Booklet pane of 4 #417d   2.60 2.60
i.   Booklet pane of 4 #417b   1.20 1.20
j.   Booklet pane of 4 #417e   2.60 2.60
k.   Booklet pane of 4 #417c   1.20 1.20
l.   Booklet pane of 4 #417f   2.60 2.60

Endangered Species Type of 1993
Designs: No. 418, Ursus thibetanus (Asiatic black bear). No. 419, Hippocamelus antisensis (Northern Andean deer). No. 420, Macaca silenus (Lion-tailed macaque). No. 421, Bos gaurus (Gaur).

2004, Jan. 29   Litho.   *Perf. 12¾x12½*
418   A271   1fr multicolored   1.60 1.60
419   A271   1fr multicolored   1.60 1.60
420   A271   1fr multicolored   1.60 1.60
421   A271   1fr multicolored   1.60 1.60
a.   Block of 4, #418-421   6.50 6.50

Indigenous Art Type of 2003
No. 422: a, Decoration for cows, Switzerland. b, Stone Age terra cotta sculpture of seated woman, Romania. c, Butter stamps, France. d, Detail of herald's tabard, United Kingdom. e, Woodcut print of medieval Cologne, Germany. f, Mesolithic era terra cotta sculpture of mother and child, Serbia and Montenegro.

2004, Mar. 4   Litho.   *Perf. 13¼*
422   G67   Sheet of 6   7.50 7.50
a.-f.   1fr Any single   1.25 1.25

Road Safety Type
Road map art with: 85c, Man on hand. 1fr, Person, seat belt, vert.

**   *Perf. 13x13¼, 13¼x13***
2004, Apr. 7   Litho.
423   A354   85c multicolored   1.40 1.40
424   A354   1fr multicolored   1.75 1.75
See France No. 3011.

Japanese Peace Bell, 50th Anniv. Type
Litho. & Engr.
2004, June 3   *Perf. 13¼x13*
425   A355   1.30fr multicolored   2.00 2.00

World Heritage Sites, Greece Type
Designs: 1fr, No. 428b, Delphi. 1.30fr, No. 428e, Pythagoreion and Heraion of Samos. No. 428a, Acropolis, Athens. No. 428c, Olympia. No. 428d, Delos. No. 428f, Mycenae and Tiryns.

2004, Aug. 12   Litho.   *Perf. 14x13¼*
426   A356   1fr multicolored   1.50 1.50
427   A356   1.30fr multicolored   2.00 2.00
Souvenir Booklet
428   Booklet   13.50
a.-c.   A356 20c any single   .30   .30
d.-f.   A356 50c any single   .80   .80
g.   Booklet pane of 4 #428a   1.25 1.25
h.   Booklet pane of 4 #428b   1.25 1.25
i.   Booklet pane of 4 #428c   1.25 1.25
j.   Booklet pane of 4 #428d   3.25 3.25
k.   Booklet pane of 4 #428e   3.25 3.25
l.   Booklet pane of 4 #428f   3.25 3.25

My Dream for Peace Type
Winning designs of Lions Club International children's global peace poster contest by: 85c, Anggun Sita Rustinya, Indonesia. 1.20fr, Amanda Nunez, Belize.

2004, Sept. 21   Litho.   *Perf. 14*
429   A357   85c multicolored   1.40 1.40
430   A357   1.20fr multicolored   2.00 2.00

G69

Human Rights — G70

2004, Oct. 14   Litho.   *Perf. 11¼*
431   G69   85c multicolored   1.25 1.25
432   G70   1.30fr multicolored   2.25 2.25

Sports G71

2004, Nov. 23   Litho.   *Perf. 13x13½*
433   G71   180c multicolored   3.25 3.25
See Switzerland No. 1196.

United Nations, 60th Anniv. Type of 2005
Litho. & Engr.
2005, Feb. 4   *Perf. 11x11¼*
434   A361   1.30fr multicolored   2.50 2.50
Souvenir Sheet
Litho.
**   *Imperf***
435   A361   3fr multicolored   7.50 7.50

Endangered Species Type of 1993

Designs: No. 436, Laelia milleri. No. 437, Psygmorchis pusilla. No. 438, Dendrobium cruentum. No. 439, Orchis purpurea.

2005, Mar. 3   Litho.   Perf. 12¾x12½
436	A271	1fr multicolored	2.00	2.00
437	A271	1fr multicolored	2.00	2.00
438	A271	1fr multicolored	2.00	2.00
439	A271	1fr multicolored	2.00	2.00
a.		Block of 4, #436-439	8.00	8.00

Nature's Wisdom — G72

Designs: 1fr, Children collecting water, India. 80c, Ruby brittle star, Bahamas.

2005, Apr. 21   Litho.   Perf. 13½x13¼
440	G72	1fr multicolored	1.75	1.75
441	G72	1.30fr multicolored	2.00	2.00

Intl. Year of Sport Type

2005, June 3   Litho.   Perf. 13x13¼
442	A368	1fr Wheelchair racing	1.75	1.75
443	A368	1.30fr Cycling	2.25	2.25

World Heritage Sites, Egypt Type

Designs: Nos. 444, 446b, Philae. Nos. 445, 446e, Islamic Cairo. No. 446a, Memphis and its Necropolis. No. 446c, Abu Mena. No. 446d, Ancient Thebes. No. 446f, St. Catherine area.

2005, Aug. 4   Litho.   Perf. 14x13¼
444	A369	1fr multicolored	2.00	2.00
445	A369	1.30fr multicolored	2.50	2.50

Souvenir Booklet
446		Booklet, #446g-446l	16.50	
a.-c.	A369	20c any single	.40	.40
d.-f.	A369	50c any single	.90	.90
g.		Booklet pane of 4 #446a	1.60	1.60
h.		Booklet pane of 4 #446b	1.60	1.60
i.		Booklet pane of 4 #446c	1.60	1.60
j.		Booklet pane of 4 #446d	3.75	3.75
k.		Booklet pane of 4 #446e	3.75	3.75
l.		Booklet pane of 4 #446f	3.75	3.75

My Dream for Peace Type

Winning designs of Lions Club International children's global peace contest by: 1fr, Marisa Harun, Indonesia. 1.30fr, Carlos Javier Parramón Teixidó, Spain.

2005, Sept. 21   Litho.   Perf. 14
447	A357	1fr multicolored	1.75	1.75
448	A357	1.30fr multicolored	2.00	2.00

Food for Life Type

Designs: 1fr, Rye, airplane dropping parcels, camel caravan. 1.30fr, Sorghum, people carrying grain sacks, trucks.

2005, Oct. 20   Litho.   Perf. 13¾
449	A370	1fr multicolored	1.90	1.90
450	A370	1.30fr multicolored	2.40	2.40

Armillary Sphere, Palais des Nations — G73

Litho. with Hologram
2006, Feb. 3   Perf. 13¼x13½
451	G73	1.30fr multicolored	2.25	2.25

Indigenous Art Type of 2003

No. 452 — Musical instruments: a, Bell, Benin. b, Drum, Swaziland. c, Sanza, Congo. d, Stringed instruments, Cape Verde. e, Caixixi, Ghana. f, Bells, Central Africa.

2006, Feb. 3   Litho.   Perf. 13¼
452	G67	Pane of 6	12.00	12.00
a.-f.		1.20fr Any single	2.00	2.00

Endangered Species Type of 1993

Designs: No. 453, Dyscophus antongilii. No. 454, Chamaeleo dilepsis. No. 455, Corallus caninus. No. 456, Phyllobates vittatus.

Perf. 12¾x12½
2006, Mar. 16   Litho.
453	A271	1fr multicolored	1.75	1.75
454	A271	1fr multicolored	1.75	1.75
455	A271	1fr multicolored	1.75	1.75
456	A271	1fr multicolored	1.75	1.75
a.		Block of 4, #453-456	7.00	7.00

Intl. Day of Families Type

Designs: 1fr, Family reading together. 1.30fr, Family on motorcycle.

2006, May 27   Litho.   Perf. 14x13½
457	A373	1fr multicolored	1.25	1.25
458	A373	1.30fr multicolored	1.75	1.75

World Heritage Sites, France Type

Eiffel Tower and: Nos. 459, 461b, Provins. Nos. 460, 461e, Mont Saint-Michel. No. 461a, Banks of the Seine. No. 461c, Carcasonne. No. 461d, Roman Aqueduct. No. 446f, Chateau de Chambord.

Litho. & Embossed with Foil Application
2006, June 17   Perf. 13½x13¼
459	A374	1fr multicolored	1.75	1.75
460	A374	1.30fr multicolored	2.25	2.25

Souvenir Booklet
461		Booklet, #461g-461l	15.00	
a.-c.	A374	20c any single	.35	.35
d.-f.	A374	50c any single	.85	.85
g.		Booklet pane of 4 #461a	1.40	1.40
h.		Booklet pane of 4 #461b	1.40	1.40
i.		Booklet pane of 4 #461c	1.40	1.40
j.		Booklet pane of 4 #461d	3.50	3.50
k.		Booklet pane of 4 #461e	3.50	3.50
l.		Booklet pane of 4 #461f	3.50	3.50

See France Nos. 3219-3220.

My Dream for Peace Type of 2004

Winning designs of Lions Club International children's global peace poster contest by: 85c, Ariam Boaglio, Italy. 1.20fr, Sierra Spicer, US.

2006, Sept. 21   Litho.   Perf. 13½x13
462	A357	85c multicolored	1.60	1.60
463	A357	1.20fr multicolored	2.25	2.25

Flags and Coins Type

No. 464 — Flag of: a, Uganda, 500 shilling coin. b, Luxembourg, 1 euro coin. c, Cape Verde, 20 escudo coin. d, Belgium, 1 euro coin. e, Italy, 1 euro coin. f, New Zealand, 1 dollar coin. g, Switzerland, 2 franc coin. h, Lebanon, 500 pound coin.

2006, Oct. 5   Litho.   Perf. 13¼x13
464		Pane of 8	15.00	15.00
a.-h.	A375	85c Any single	1.50	1.50

A column of rouletting in the middle of the pane separates it into two parts.

Endangered Species Type of 1993

Designs: No. 465, Theropithecus gelada. No. 466, Cercopithecus neglectus. No. 467, Varecia variegata. No. 468, Hylobates moloch.

Perf. 12¾x12½
2007, Mar. 15   Litho.
465	A271	1fr multicolored	1.75	1.75
466	A271	1fr multicolored	1.75	1.75
467	A271	1fr multicolored	1.75	1.75
468	A271	1fr multicolored	1.75	1.75
a.		Block of 4, #465-468	7.00	7.00

Flags and Coins Type of 2006

No. 469 — Flag of: a, Burkina Faso, 500 franc coin. b, France, 50 cent coin. c, Moldova, 50 bani coin. d, Papua New Guinea, 1 kina coin. e, Bolivia, 1 boliviano coin. f, Myanmar, 100 kyat coin. g, Mali, 500 franc coin. h, Tunisia, 5 dinar coin.

2007, May 3   Litho.   Perf. 13¼x13
469		Sheet of 8	12.50	12.50
a.-h.	A375	85c Any single	1.50	1.50

A column of rouletting in the middle of the sheet separates it into two parts.

Peaceful Visions Type of 2007

Designs: 1.20fr, "Harvest for All." 1.80fr, "This Dream Has Wings."

2007, June 1   Litho.   Perf. 13x12½
470	A378	1.20fr multicolored	2.25	2.25
471	A378	1.80fr multicolored	3.25	3.25

World Heritage Sites, South America Type

Designs: Nos. 472, 474a, Tiwanaku, Bolivia. Nos. 473, 474f, Machu Picchu, Peru. No.

474b, Iguaçu National Park, Brazil. No. 474c, Galapagos Islands, Ecuador. No. 474d, Rapa Nui, Chile. No. 474e, Cueva de las Manos, Argentina.

2007, Aug. 9   Litho.   Perf. 13¼x13
472	A381	1fr multicolored	1.90	1.90
473	A381	1.80fr multicolored	3.25	3.25

Souvenir Booklet
474		Booklet, #474g-474l	16.00	
a.-c.	A381	20c Any single	.40	.40
d.-f.	A381	50c Any single	.90	.90
g.		Booklet pane of 4 #474a	1.60	1.60
h.		Booklet pane of 4 #474b	1.60	1.60
i.		Booklet pane of 4 #474c	1.60	1.60
j.		Booklet pane of 4 #474d	3.60	3.60
k.		Booklet pane of 4 #474e	3.60	3.60
l.		Booklet pane of 4 #474f	3.60	3.60

Humanitarian Mail Type

2007, Sept. 6   Litho.   Perf. 12½x13¼
475	A382	1.80fr multicolored	3.00	3.00

Space for Humanity Type

Designs: 1fr, Astronaut spacewalking. 1.80fr, International Space Station, space probe, Jupiter. 3fr, Astronauts spacewalking.

2007, Oct. 25   Litho.   Perf. 13½x14
476	A383	1fr multicolored	1.90	1.90
477	A383	1.80fr multicolored	3.25	3.25

Souvenir Sheet
478	A383	3fr multicolored	7.50	7.50

Intl. Holocaust Remembrance Day Type

2008, Jan. 27   Litho.   Perf. 13
479	A384	85c multicolored	3.00	3.00

Endangered Species Type of 1993

Designs: No. 480, Odobenus rosmarus. No. 481, Platygyra daedalea. No. 482, Hippocampus bargibanti. No. 483, Delphinapterus leucas.

2008, Mar. 6   Litho.   Perf. 12¾x12½
480	A271	1fr multicolored	2.00	2.00
481	A271	1fr multicolored	2.00	2.00
482	A271	1fr multicolored	2.00	2.00
483	A271	1fr multicolored	2.00	2.00
a.		Block of 4, #480-483	8.00	8.00

Flags and Coins Type of 2006

No. 484 — Flag of: a, Madagascar, 1 ariary coin. b, Rwanda, 50 franc coin. c, Benin, 10 franc coin. d, Iran, 500 rial coin. e, Namibia, 5 dollar coin. f, Maldives, 1 rufiyaa coin. g, Albania, 10 lek coin. h, Turkey, 1 lira coin.

2008, May 8   Litho.   Perf. 13¼x13
484		Sheet of 8	15.00	15.00
a.-h.	A375	85c Any single	1.75	1.75

A column of rouletting in the middle of the sheet separates it into two parts.

Handshake
G74

Sign Language — G75

Litho. & Embossed
2008, June 6   Perf. 14x13¼
485	G74	1fr org & red	2.25	2.25
486	G75	1.80fr red & org	4.00	4.00

Convention on the Rights of Persons with Disabilities.

Sport for Peace Type of 2008

Designs: 1fr, 3fr, Gymnast. 1.80fr, Tennis player.

2008, Aug. 8   Litho.   Perf. 14½
487	A393	1fr multicolored	2.25	2.25

488	A393	1.80fr multicolored	4.00	4.00

Souvenir Sheet
Perf. 12¾x13¼
489	A393	3fr multicolored	9.00	9.00

2008 Summer Olympics, Beijing.

"We Can End Poverty" Type of 2008

Winning designs in children's art contest by: 1fr, Ranajoy Banerjee, India, vert. 1.80fr, Elizabeth Elaine Chun Nig Au, Hong Kong, vert.

Perf. 12½x12¾
2008, Sept. 18   Litho.
490	A395	1fr multicolored	2.25	2.25
491	A395	1.80fr multicolored	3.75	3.75

Climate Change Types of New York and Vienna and

G76

Climate Change — G77

No. 492 — Polar bear with quarter of Earth in: a, LR. b, LL. c, UR. d, UL.
No. 493 — Ship and sea ice with quarter of Earth in: a, LR. b, LL. c, UR. d, UL.
No. 494: a, Like New York #969a. b, Like New York #969b. c, Like New York #969c. d, Like New York #969d. e, Like Geneva #493a. f, Like Geneva #493b. g, Like Geneva #493c. h, Like Geneva #493d. i, Like Vienna #434a. j, Like Vienna #434b. k, Like Vienna #434c. l, Like Vienna #434d. m, Like New York #968a. n, Like New York #968b. o, Like New York #968c. p, Like New York #968d. q, Like Geneva #492a. r, Like Geneva #492b. s, Like Geneva #492c. t, Like Geneva #492d. u, Like Vienna #435a. v, Like Vienna #435b. w, Like Vienna #435c. x, Like Vienna #435d.

All stamps have red panels inscribed "Changement de climat."

2008, Oct. 23   Litho.   Perf. 13¼x13
492		Sheet of 4	10.50	10.50
a.-d.	G76	1.20fr Any single	2.60	2.60
493		Sheet of 4	15.50	15.50
a.-d.	G77	1.80fr Any single	3.75	3.75

Souvenir Booklet
494		Booklet, #494y-494ad	25.00	
a.-d.	A397	35c Any single	.75	.75
e.-h.	G77	35c Any single	.75	.75
i.-l.	V72	35c Any single	.75	.75
m.-p.	A396	50c Any single	1.00	1.00
q.-t.	G76	50c Any single	1.00	1.00
u.-x.	V73	50c Any single	1.00	1.00
y.		Booklet pane of 4, #494a-494d	3.00	3.00
z.		Booklet pane of 4, #494e-494h	3.00	3.00
aa.		Booklet pane of 4, #494i-494l	3.00	3.00
ab.		Booklet pane of 4, #494m-494p	4.25	4.25
ac.		Booklet pane of 4, #494q-494t	4.25	4.25
ad.		Booklet pane of 4, #494u-494x	4.25	4.25

U Thant Type of 2009
Litho. With Foil Application
2009, Feb. 6   Perf. 14x13½
495	A399	1.30fr red & multi	3.25	3.25

Endangered Species Type of 1993

No. 496, Maculinea arion. No. 497, Dolomedes plantarius. No. 498, Cerambyx cerdo. No. 499, Coenagrion mercurialia.

2009, Apr. 16   Litho.   Perf. 12¾x12½
496	A271	1fr multicolored	1.90	1.90
497	A271	1fr multicolored	1.90	1.90
498	A271	1fr multicolored	1.90	1.90
499	A271	1fr multicolored	1.90	1.90
a.		Block of 4, #496-499	7.75	7.75
b.		Pane of 16, imperf.	5,000.	

World Heritage Sites, Germany Type of 2009

Designs: Nos. 500, 502b, Wartburg Castle. Nos. 501, 502f, Monastic Island of Reichenau.

No. 502a, Town Hall and Roland on the Marketplace, Bremen. No. 502c, Palaces and Parks of Potsdam and Berlin. No. 502d, Aachen Cathedral. No. 502e, Luther Memorials in Eisleben and Wittenberg.

2009, May 7   Litho.   Perf. 14x13½

500	A400	1fr multicolored	2.25	2.25
501	A400	1.30fr multicolored	2.75	2.75

Souvenir Booklet

502		Booklet, #502g-502l	18.00
a.-c.	A400 30c any single		.55	.55
d.-f.	A400 50c any single		.90	.90
g.	Booklet pane of 4 #502a		2.25	2.25
h.	Booklet pane of 4 #502b		2.25	2.25
i.	Booklet pane of 4 #502c		2.25	2.25
j.	Booklet pane of 4 #502d		3.75	3.75
k.	Booklet pane of 4 #502e		3.75	3.75
l.	Booklet pane of 4 #502f		3.75	3.75

Economic and Social Council (ECOSOC) Type of 2009

Designs: 85c, Improving maternal health. 1.80fr, Access to essential medicines.

2009, Aug. 6   Perf. 12¾x12½

503	A411	85c multicolored	2.00	2.00
504	A411	1.80fr multicolored	4.00	4.00

Millennium Development Goals Type of 2009

Miniature Sheet

No. 505: a, Bowl of hot food. b, Pencil. c, Female symbol. d, Teddy bear. e, Pregnant woman, heart. f, Medicine bottle. g, Stylized tree. h, Conjoined people.

2009, Sept. 25   Perf. 13¼

505	A413	Sheet of 8	18.00	18.00
a.-h.		1.10fr Any single	2.25	2.25

Palais des Nations — G78

Palais des Nations — G79

Flags of United Nations and Switzerland — G80

Meeting Room — G81

Armillary Sphere — G82

2009, Oct. 2   Perf. 13¼

506	G78 1fr multi + label		6.00	6.00
a.	Perf. 11¼x11 + label		5.00	5.00
507	G79 1fr multi + label		6.00	6.00
a.	Perf. 11¼x11 + label		5.00	5.00
508	G80 1fr multi + label		6.00	6.00
a.	Perf. 11¼x11 + label		5.00	5.00
509	G81 1fr multi + label		6.00	6.00
a.	Perf. 11¼x11 + label		5.00	5.00

510	G82 1fr multi + label		6.00	6.00
a.	Perf. 11¼x11 + label		5.00	5.00
b.	Vert. strip of 5, #506-510, + 5 labels		30.00	30.00
c.	Vert. strip of 5, #506a-510a, + 5 labels		25.00	25.00

United Nations Postal Administration in Geneva, 40th anniv. The full sheets sold for €19.90 or $14.95. Labels could not be personalized. The sheet of No. 510c has "VER. 2" in the lower right selvage.

Miniature Sheet

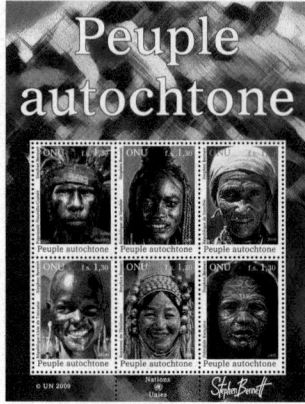

Indigenous People — G83

No. 511 — Portraits of person from: a, Papua New Guinea. b, Namibia (young woman). c, Namibia (old man). d, Tanzania. e, Thailand. f, French Polynesia.

2009, Oct. 8   Perf. 12½

511	G83	Sheet of 6	16.00	16.00
a.-f.		1.30fr Any single	2.60	2.60

Flags and Coins Type of 2006

No. 512 — Flag of: a, Equatorial Guinea, 100 franc coin. b, Laos, 20 kip coin. c, Seychelles, 5 rupee coin. d, Mauritania, 1 ougiya coin. e, Argentina, 1 peso coin. f, Morocco, 1 dirham coin. g, Sudan, 20 piaster coin. h, Brunei, 50 cent coin.

2010, Feb. 5   Litho.   Perf. 13¼x13

512		Sheet of 8	15.00	15.00
a.-h.	A375 85c Any single		1.75	1.75

A column of rouletting in the middle of the sheet separates it into two parts.

Endangered Species Type of 1993

No. 513, Fouquieria columnaris. No. 514, Aloe arborescens. No. 515, Galanthus krasnovii. No. 516, Dracaena draco.

2010, Apr. 15   Litho.   Perf. 12¾x12½

513	A271	1fr multicolored	2.25	2.25
514	A271	1fr multicolored	2.25	2.25
515	A271	1fr multicolored	2.25	2.25
516	A271	1fr multicolored	2.25	2.25
a.		Block of 4, #513-516	9.00	9.00

Intl. Year of Biodiversity G84

Drawings from Art Forms from Nature, by Ernst Heinrich: 1.60fr, Arachnid. 1.90fr, Starfish.

2010, Apr. 15   Litho.   Perf. 13

517	G84 1.60fr multicolored		3.75	3.75
518	G84 1.90fr multicolored		4.25	4.25

One Planet, One Ocean Types of New York and Vienna and

G85

G86

No. 519: a, Turtles at left and top, fish at bottom. b, Hammerhead shark. c, Fish at left and center, corals. d, Fish at left, coral.

No. 520: a, Dolphins. b, Shark, head of fish at right, small fish in background. c, Ray and fish. d, Fish at bottom, coral and sponges.

No. 521: a, Like New York #1003a. b, Like New York #1003b, c, Like New York #1003c, d, Like New York #1003d. e, Like Vienna #471a. f, Like Vienna #471b. g, Like Vienna #471c, h, Like Vienna #471d. i, Like #519a. j, Like #519b, k, Like #519c. l, Like #519d. m, Like New York #1004a. n, Like New York #1004b. o, Like New York #1004c, p, Like New York #1004d. q, Like Vienna #472a. r, Like Vienna #472b. s, Like Vienna #472c. t, Like Vienna #472d. u, Like #520a. v, Like #520b. w, Like #520c. x, Like #520d.

2010, May 6   Litho.   Perf. 14x13¼

519	G85	Sheet of 4	8.00	8.00
a.-d.		2fr Any single	2.00	2.00
520	G86	Sheet of 4	10.00	10.00
a.-d.		1fr Any single	2.50	2.50

Souvenir Booklet
Perf. 13¼x13

521		Booklet, #521y-521z, 521aa-521ad	22.00	
a.-d.	A416 30c any single		.70	.70
e.-h.	V91 30c any single		.70	.70
i.-l.	G85 30c any single		.70	.70
m.-p.	A417 50c any single		1.10	1.10
q.-t.	V92 50c any single		1.10	1.10
u.-x.	G86 50c any single		1.10	1.10
y.	Booklet pane of 4 #521a-521d		2.80	2.80
z.	Booklet pane of 4 #521e-521h		2.80	2.80
aa.	Booklet pane of 4 #521i-521l		2.80	2.80
ab.	Booklet pane of 4 #521m-521p		4.40	4.40
ac.	Booklet pane of 4 #521q-521t		4.40	4.40
ad.	Booklet pane of 4 #521u-521x		4.40	4.40

Intl. Oceanographic Commission, 50th anniv.

United Nations, 65th Anniv. Type of 2010

Litho. With Foil Application

2010, June 28   Perf. 13¼

522	A422 1.90fr red & gold		4.00	4.00
a.	Souvenir sheet of 2		8.00	8.00

G87

G88

G89

G90

United Nations Land Transport — G91

2010, Sept. 2   Litho.   Perf. 13¼x13

523	G87	1fr multicolored	1.80	1.80
524	G88	1fr multicolored	1.80	1.80
525	G89	1fr multicolored	1.80	1.80
526	G90	1fr multicolored	1.80	1.80
527	G91	1fr multicolored	1.80	1.80
a.		Horiz. strip of 5, #523-527	9.00	9.00

Miniature Sheet

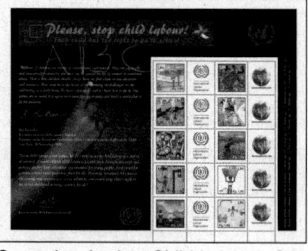

Campaign Against Child Labor — G92

No. 528: a, Child, buildings, road, burning can. b, Child with full basket on back, children playing in background. c, Child working, children on school bus. d, Child with mining helmet, three other children. e, Child near tubs, children working, child being beaten. f, Child with hoe. g, Marionette, traffic light. h, Child carrying basket on head. i, Children on rock field near hills. j, Child holding bags in road.

2010, Sept. 2   Litho.   Perf. 14¾

528	G92	Sheet of 10 + 10 labels	32.50	32.50
a.-j.		1.90fr Any single + label	3.25	3.25

No. 528 sold for $14.95, 15fr and €11.46, each of which was far lower than the level at which 19fr, the total face value of the stamps on the sheet, was worth on the day of issue. Labels could not be personalized.

Miniature Sheet

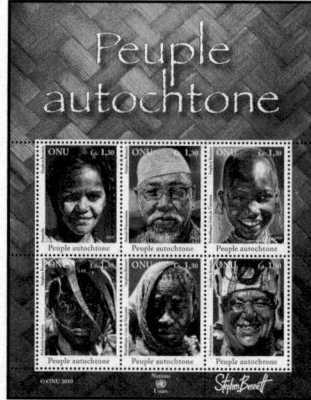

Indigenous People — G93

No. 529 — Portraits of person from: a, Australia. b, Brunei. c, Tanzania (girl with bald head). d, French Polynesia (man with headdress of leaves). e, Tanzania (man with headdress). f, French Polynesia (man with white headdress).

2010, Oct. 21   Litho.   Perf. 13

529	G93	Pane of 6	14.50	14.50
a.-f.		1.30fr Any single	2.40	2.40

United Nations
Headquarters,
Geneva — G94

United Nations Headquarters, Geneva: 10c,
Aerial view. 50c, Ground-level view.

2011, Feb. 4   Litho.   Perf. 13
530 G94 10c multicolored   .35   .35
531 G94 50c multicolored   1.25 1.25

Flags and Coins Type of 2006

No. 532 — Flag of: a, Mongolia, 500 tugrik
coin. b, Senegal, 500 franc coin. c, Egypt, 100
piaster coin. d, Congo, 100 franc coin. e, Nicaragua, 1 Córdoba coin. f, Central African
Republic, 100 franc coin. g, Algeria, 5 dinar
coin. h, Ukraine, 5 hryvnia coin.

2011, Mar. 3   Litho.   Perf. 13¼x13
532   Sheet of 8   15.00 15.00
a.-h.   A375 85c Any single   1.75 1.75

A column of rouletting in the middle of the
sheet separates it into two parts.

Human Space Flight, 50th
Anniv. — G95

No. 533: Various parts of outer space
scene.
No. 534, vert.: a, International Space Station. b, International Space Station, diff.

2011, Apr. 12   Litho.   Perf. 13x13¼
533   G95   Sheet of 16   18.00 18.00
a.-p.   50c any single   1.10 1.10

Souvenir Sheet
534   G95   Sheet of 2   15.00 15.00
a.   85c multi   6.50 6.50
b.   1fr multi   8.50 8.50

No. 534 contains two 40x48mm stamps that
were printed as part of a larger sheet of six
stamps, Vienna No. 485c, which was broken
up into its component two-stamp souvenir
sheets, and also sold as one unit. Value, $90,
complete unit.

**UNESCO World Heritage Sites in
Nordic Countries Type of 2011**

Designs: 85c, Kronborg Castle, Denmark.
1fr, Suomenlinna Fortress, Finland.

2011, May 5   Litho.   Perf. 14x13½
535 A433 85c multicolored   1.90 1.90
536 A433 1fr multicolored   2.25 2.25

AIDS Ribbon Type of 2011

2011, June 3   Litho.   Die Cut
Self-Adhesive
537 A434 1.30fr red & orange   5.00 5.00

ECOSOC Type of 2011

2011, July 1   Litho.   Perf. 14¼
538 A435 1fr multicolored   3.00 3.00
539 A435 1.30fr multicolored   4.00 4.00

Endangered Species Type of 1993

Designs: No. 540, Strigops habroptilus
(Kakapo). No. 541, Lophophorus impejanus
(Himalayan monal). No. 542, Ciconia nigra
(Black stork). No. 543, Pithecophaga jeffreyi
(Philippine eagle).

2011, Sept. 7   Litho.   Perf. 12¾x12½
540 A271 1fr multicolored   2.60 2.60
541 A271 1fr multicolored   2.60 2.60
542 A271 1fr multicolored   2.60 2.60
543 A271 1fr multicolored   2.60 2.60
a.   Block of 4, #540-543 10.40 10.40

Intl. Year of Forests Type of 2011

Designs: 85c, Birds and butterflies, tree
tops. 1.40fr, Fish and coral.

Litho. With Foil Application
2011, Oct. 13   Perf. 12½
544   85c multicolored   2.25 2.25
545   1.40fr multicolored   3.75 3.75
a.   A436 Vert. pair, #544-545 6.00 6.00

Flags and Coins Type of 2006

No. 546 — Flag of: a, Saudi Arabia, 100
halala coin. b, Georgia, 2 lari coin. c, Democratic People's Republic of Korea, 50 won
coin. d, Lesotho, 50 lisente coin. e, Serbia, 5
dinar coin. f, Djibouti, 20 franc coin. g, Belize,
1 dollar coin. h, Liechtenstein, 20 centime
coin.

2012, Feb. 3   Litho.   Perf. 13¼x13
546   Sheet of 8   16.50 16.50
a.-h.   A375 85c Any single   2.00 2.00

A column of rouletting in the middle of the
sheet separates it into two parts.

G96

Autism
Awareness
G97

Drawings by autistic people: No. 547, Victory, by J.A Tan, Canada. No. 548, Untitled
drawing, by Michael Augello, U.S.

2012, Apr. 2   Litho.   Perf. 14x13½
547 G96 1.40fr multicolored   3.50 3.50
548 G97 1.40fr multicolored   3.50 3.50
a.   Pair, #547-548   7.00 7.00

Endangered Species Type of 1993

Designs: No. 549, Panthera tigris altaica.
No. 550, Psitacella picta. No. 551, Iguana
iguana. No. 552, Propithecus tattersalli.

2012, Apr. 19   Litho.   Perf. 12¾x12½
549 A271 1fr multicolored   2.40 2.40
550 A271 1fr multicolored   2.40 2.40
551 A271 1fr multicolored   2.40 2.40
552 A271 1fr multicolored   2.40 2.40
a.   Block of 4, #549-552   9.75 9.75

Rio + 20 Type of 2012

2012, June 1   Litho.   Perf. 13x13¼
553 A443 1.40fr multicolored   4.00 4.00

Sport for Peace Type of 2012

2012 Paralympics events: 1fr, Track. 1.40fr,
Archery.

Litho. With Foil Application
2012, Aug. 17   Perf. 14½
554 A444   1fr multicolored   2.40 2.40
555 A444 1.40fr multicolored   3.50 3.50
a.   Souvenir sheet of 1   3.50 3.50

**UNESCO World Heritage Sites in
Africa Type of 2012**

Designs: 85c, Virunga National Park, Congo
Democratic Republic. 1fr, Amphitheater of El
Jem, Tunisia.

2012, Sept. 5   Litho.   Perf. 13¼
556 A445 85c multicolored   2.00 2.00
557 A445 1fr multicolored   2.40 2.40

Miniature Sheet

Indigenous People — G98

No. 558 — Portrait of person from: a, China.
b, Tibet, China. c, Mongolia. d, Mexico. e,
Papua New Guinea. f, Haiti.

2012, Oct. 11   Litho.   Perf. 13¼x13
558   G98   Sheet of 6   13.50 13.50
a.-f.   85c Any single   2.25 2.25

World Radio Day Type of 2013

Designs: 1.40fr, Reporter with microphone
and tape recorder. 1.90fr, Engineers in studio.

2013, Feb. 13   Litho.   Perf. 13¼x13
559 A448 1.40fr multicolored   3.50 3.50
560 A448 1.90fr multicolored   4.50 4.50

Person on
Leaf
G99

Dove and
People — G100

2013, Mar. 5   Litho.   Perf. 14x13½
561 G99   1fr multicolored   2.40 2.40
Perf. 13½x14
562 G100 1.40fr multicolored   3.50 3.50

**World Heritage Sites, China, Type of
2013**

Designs: Nos. 563, 565b, Potala Palace,
Lhasa. Nos. 564, 565e, Mount Huangshan.
No. 565a, Mogao Caves. No. 565c, Great Wall
of China. No. 565d, Imperial Palace, Beijing.
No. 565f, Mausoleum of the First Qing
Emperor.

2013, Apr. 11   Litho.   Perf. 14x13½
563 A452 1.40fr multicolored   3.50 3.50
564 A452 1.90fr multicolored   4.50 4.50

Souvenir Booklet
565   Booklet, #565g-565l 24.00
a.-c.   A452 30c any single   .75   .75
d.-f.   A452 50c any single   1.25 1.25
g.   Booklet pane of 4 #565a 3.00   —
h.   Booklet pane of 4 #565b 3.00   —
i.   Booklet pane of 4 #565c 3.00   —
j.   Booklet pane of 4 #565d 5.00   —
k.   Booklet pane of 4 #565e 5.00   —
l.   Booklet pane of 4 #565f 5.00   —

World Oceans Day — G101

No. 566 — Fish from One Fish, Two Fish,
Red Fish, Blue Fish, by Dr. Seuss: a, Three
red fish facing right. b, Green fish, tail of yellow
fish. c, Three red fish facing right, part of tail of
red fish. d, Two entire green fish facing left, tail
of bottom fish ends above "n" in "océan." e,
Red fish with eye open facing left. f, Tail of red
fish, yellow and red fish facing left. g, Red fish
facing right, water droplets. h, Yellow and red
fish facing right. i, Two green fish facing left,
tail of bottom fish ends to right of "océan." j,
Red fish and wave. k, Two green fish, red fish,
wave. l, Yellow fish in car, wave.

2013, May 31   Litho.   Perf. 13
566   G101 Sheet of 12   20.00 20.00
a.-l.   85c any single   1.60 1.60

Nebulae Type of 2013

Designs: No. 567, NGC 2346. No. 568, Sh
2-106.
1fr, Messier 16.

2013, Aug. 9   Litho.   Perf. 13¼
567 A454 1.40fr multicolored   3.50 3.50
568 A454 1.40fr multicolored   3.50 3.50
a.   Pair, #567-568   7.00 7.00

Souvenir Sheet
569 A454   1fr multicolored   2.40 2.40

No. 569 contains one 44x44mm stamp.

**Works of Disabled Artists Type of
2013**

Designs: 1.40fr, See the Girl with the Red
Dress On, by Sargy Mann, United Kingdom.
1.90fr, Performers in China Disabled People's
Performing Art Troupe, People's Republic of
China.

2013, Sept. 20   Litho.   Perf. 13¼x13
570 A456 1.40fr multicolored   3.50 3.50
571 A456 1.90fr multicolored   4.50 4.50

Endangered Species Type of 1993

Designs: No. 572, Smutsia temminckii. No.
573, Perodicticus potto. No. 574, Tarsius
syrichta. No. 575, Pteropus livingstonii.

2013, Oct. 10   Litho.   Perf. 12¾x12½
572 A271 1.40fr multicolored   3.25 3.25
573 A271 1.40fr multicolored   3.25 3.25
574 A271 1.40fr multicolored   3.25 3.25
575 A271 1.40fr multicolored   3.25 3.25
a.   Block of 4, #572-575 13.00 13.00

Flags and Coins Type of 2006

No. 576 — Flag of: a, Ivory Coast, 100 franc
coin. b, Marshall Islands, 10 cent coin. c,
Andorra, 20 cent coin. d, Guinea-Bissau, 100
franc coin. e, Kenya, 20 shilling coin. f, Antigua
and Barbuda, 5 cent coin. g, Tajikistan, 50
diram coin. h, Micronesia, 5 cent coin.

2013, Nov. 6   Litho.   Perf. 13¼x13
576   Sheet of 8   26.00 26.00
a.-h.   A375 1.40fr Any single   3.25 3.25

A column of rouletting in the middle of the
sheet separates it into two parts.

**International Day of Happiness Type
of 2014**

Designs: 1fr, A Sweet Dog's Muzzle, photograph by Jaymi Heimbuch, "Heureux." 1.40fr,
Two women making heart with hands, photograph by Glow Images, Chinese characters for
"Happy."

2014, Mar. 17   Litho.   Perf. 13¼x13
577 A459   1fr multicolored   2.50 2.50
578 A459 1.40fr multicolored   3.50 3.50

Miniature Sheet

International Year of Jazz — G102

No. 579: a, Woman behind microphone. b, Saxophone. c, Silhouette of pianist at grand piano. d, Cymbal and silhouette of man holding trumpet. e, Cymbal and clarinet. f, Clarinet and drum. g, Hi-hat. h, Silhouette of drummer and drum set. i, Trumpeter with hat. j, Microphone and cymbal stands. k, Clarinetist. l, Bass player.

2014, Apr. 30   Litho.   Perf. 13x13¼
579	G102	Sheet of 12	29.50	29.50
		First day cover		31.00
a.-l.		1fr Any single	2.40	2.40

G103

G104

2014, June 6   Litho.   Perf. 13¼x13
580	G103	2.20fr multicolored	5.50	5.50
581	G104	2.60fr multicolored	6.50	6.50

Taj Mahal Types of 2014

2014, July 16   Engr.   Perf. 13¼x13
582	A465	1.40fr multicolored	3.50	3.50
583	A467	1.90fr multicolored	4.75	4.75

Souvenir Booklet
584		Booklet, #584g-584l	24.00	
a.	A463	30c multi	.75	.75
b.	A465	30c multi	.75	.75
c.	A466	50c multi	1.25	1.25
d.	A464	50c multi	1.25	1.25
e.	A467	30c multi	.75	.75
f.	A468	50c multi	1.25	1.25
g.		Booklet pane of 4 #584a	3.00	—
h.		Booklet pane of 4 #584b	3.00	—
i.		Booklet pane of 4 #584c	3.00	—
j.		Booklet pane of 4 #584d	5.00	—
k.		Booklet pane of 4 #584e	5.00	—
l.		Booklet pane of 4 #584f	5.00	—

International Year of Family Farming — G105

2014, Aug. 21   Litho.   Perf. 13x13¼
585	G105	1.30fr multicolored	3.25	3.25
586	G105	1.60fr multicolored	4.00	4.00

G106

No. 587: a, Room with painted ceiling. b, Peacock with spread tail. c, Rows of flags, brown panel at bottom. d, Rows of flags near Palais des Nations, tan panel at top. e, Meeting hall with United nations emblem on rear wall. f, Armillary sphere and Palais des Nations. g, Meeting hall with movie screen on rear wall. h, Circular meeting hall. i, Farm animals on grass near buildings. j, Peacock with tail down.

2014, Sept. 12   Litho.   Perf. 14¾
587	G106	Sheet of 10	35.00	35.00
a.-j.		1.30fr Any single + label	3.50	3.50

The full sheet sold for 14.95fr. The generic labels are shown. Labels could be personalized.

Global Education First Initiative Type of 2014

Designs: No. 588, Students in art museum. No. 589, Student in library.

2014, Sept. 18   Litho.   Perf. 13x13¼
588	A470	1.90fr multicolored	4.75	4.75

Souvenir Sheet
Perf. 12½
589	A470	1.90fr multicolored	4.75	4.75

No. 589 contains one 32x32mm stamp.

Endangered Species Type of 2014

Maps and: No. 590, Arapaima gigas. No. 591, Cetorhinus maximus. No. 592, Pristis pristis. No. 593, Acipenser baerii.

2014, Oct. 23   Litho.   Perf. 12¾x12½
590	A471	1.40fr multicolored	3.50	3.50
591	A471	1.40fr multicolored	3.50	3.50
592	A471	1.40fr multicolored	3.50	3.50
593	A471	1.40fr multicolored	3.50	3.50
a.		Block of 4, #590-593	14.00	14.00

Flags and Coins Type of 2006

No. 594 — Flag of: a, Vanuatu, 10 vatu coin. b, Nauru, 1 dollar coin. c, Eritrea, 100 cent coin. d, El Salvador, 1 colon coin. e, Mozambique, 50 centavo coin. f, Burundi, 1 franc coin. g, Turkmenistan, 10 tenge coin. h, Guinea, 1 franc coin.

2015, Feb. 6   Litho.   Perf. 13¼x13
594		Sheet of 8	16.50	16.50
a.-h.	A375	90c Any single	2.00	2.00

A column of rouletting in the middle of the sheet separates it into two parts.

Miniature Sheets

G107

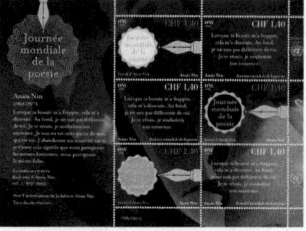

World Poetry Day — G108

No. 595: a, Pen and gray circle. b, Li Bai quotation in Chinese, denomination in light blue green. c, Li Bai quotation in Chinese, denomination in red. d, Pen and red circle. e, Pen and orange circle. f, Li Bai quotation in Chinese, denomination in white.

No. 596: a, Pen and light green circle. b, Anaïs Nin quotation, denomination and "Journée mondiale de poésie" in light blue. c, As "b," with "Journée mondiale de poésie" in white, dark blue area below and to left of date. d, Pen and black circle. e, Pen and lilac circle. f, As "c," with dark blue area below and to right of date.

Perf. 14½x14¼
2015, Mar. 20   Litho.
595	G107	Sheet of 6	14.00	14.00
a.-f.		1fr Any single	2.25	2.25
596	G108	Sheet of 6	19.50	19.50
a.-f.		1.40fr Any single	3.25	3.25

Endangered Species Type of 2015

Designs: No. 597, Diphyllodes respublica. No. 598, Ptiloris paradiseus. No. 599, Semioptera wallacii. No. 600, Paradisaea decora.

2015, Apr. 16   Litho.   Perf. 12½x12¾
597	A476	1.40fr multicolored	3.25	3.25
598	A476	1.40fr multicolored	3.25	3.25
599	A476	1.40fr multicolored	3.25	3.25
600	A476	1.40fr multicolored	3.25	3.25
a.		Block of 4, #597-600	13.00	13.00
		Nos. 597-600 (4)	13.00	13.00

World Heritage Sites, Southeast Asia, Type of 2015

Designs: Nos. 601, 603b, Angkor Wat, Cambodia. Nos. 602, 603e, Cordillera, Philippines. No. 603a, Luang Prabang, Laos. No. 603c, Ayutthaya, Thailand. No. 565d, Borobudur Temple, Indonesia. No. 603f, Hué Monuments, Viet Nam.

2015, June 5   Litho.   Perf. 14x13½
601	A480	1.40fr multicolored	3.25	3.25
602	A480	1.90fr multicolored	4.50	4.50

Souvenir Booklet
603		Booklet, #603g-603l	23.50	
a.-c.	A480	30c any single	.70	.70
d.-f.	A480	50c any single	1.25	1.25
g.		Booklet pane of 4 #603a	2.80	—
h.		Booklet pane of 4 #603b	2.80	—
i.		Booklet pane of 4 #603c	2.80	—
j.		Booklet pane of 4 #603d	5.00	—
k.		Booklet pane of 4 #603e	5.00	—
l.		Booklet pane of 4 #603f	5.00	—

End Violence Against Children Type of 2015

Designs: 1fr, Child marriage. 1.40fr, Child trafficking.

Perf. 14½x14¼
2015, Aug. 20   Litho.
604	A481	1fr multicolored	2.40	2.40
605	A481	1.40fr multicolored	3.25	3.25

Miniature Sheet

G109

No. 606: a, Balcony above auditorium seats. b, Flags. c, Spiral staircase. d, Stylized horned mammal. e, Painting of trees. f, Auditorium seats facing stage with dais. g, Side view of auditorium seats, painting on wall. h, United Nations emblem. i, Armillary Sphere. j, Palais des Nations and flowers.

2015, Sept. 3   Litho.   Perf. 14¾
606	G109	Sheet of 10 + 10 labels	35.00	35.00
a.-j.		1.40fr Any single + label	3.50	3.50

The full sheet sold for $18.39 or 14.95fr. The generic labels are shown. Labels could be personalized. The personalization of labels was available only at UN Headquarters, and not through mail order.

Visitors Lobby G110

ECOSOC Chamber G111

Façade of Secretariat — G112

Chairs in ECOSOC Chamber — G113

Visitors Lobby — G114

Printed by Cartor Security Printing, France. Panes of 6. Designed by Rorie Katz, U.S.

2015, Oct. 25   Litho.   Perf. 13¾
607	G110	1fr multicolored	2.40	2.40
608	G111	1fr multicolored	2.40	2.40
a.		Pair, #607-608	4.80	4.80
609	G112	1.90fr multicolored	4.50	4.50
610	G113	1.90fr multicolored	4.50	4.50
a.		Pair, #609-610	9.00	9.00
		Nos. 607-610 (4)	13.80	13.80

Souvenir Sheet
Perf. 13½
611	G114	1.40fr multicolored	4.50	4.50

United Nations, 70th anniv.

21st United
Nations
Climate
Change
Conference,
Paris
G115

2015, Nov. 24   Litho.   Perf. 13¼
612 G115 1.40fr multicolored   3.25 3.25

Values are for stamps with surrounding
selvage.

Free and Equal Type of 2016

Designs: 1fr, Lesbians. 1.50fr, Gay family.

2016, Feb. 5   Litho.   Perf. 13½x13¼
613 A491 1fr multicolored   2.25 2.25
614 A491 1.50fr multicolored   3.50 3.50

HeForShe Type of 2016

Designs: 1fr, Man, blue background. 2fr,
Woman, mauve background.

2016, Mar. 8   Litho.   Perf. 12½x13
615 A492 1fr multicolored   2.25 2.25
616 A492 2fr multicolored   4.50 4.50

Miniature Sheets

G116

International Dance Day — G117

No. 617 — Illustration of Swedish dancers
by Karin Römark: a, Two male dancers. b,
Male dancer on one knee with female dancer.
c, Male dancer with yellow cap and female
dancer. d, Male dancer with red cap and vest
with female dancer. e, Three dancers, with
woman with red skirt at LR. f, Three dancers,
with woman with blue skirt at LR.
No. 618 — Illustration of African dancers by
Rönmark: a, Four dancers with sticks. b, Three
dancers with sticks. c, Dancers without sticks.
d, Dancer with blue and white mask. e, Two
masked dancers with sticks. f, Masked dancer
with two sticks.

2016, Apr. 29   Litho.   Perf. 13¼x13
617 G116   Sheet of 6   13.50 13.50
a.-f.   1fr Any single   2.25 2.25
618 G117   Sheet of 6   20.00 20.00
a.-f.   1.50fr Any single   3.25 3.25

International Day of United Nations Peacekeepers Type of 2016

Designs: 1fr, Helmeted peacekeepers.
1.50fr, Peacekeeper with African women.

Litho. With Foil Application
2016, May 29   Perf. 13¼x13
619 A496 1fr multicolored   2.25 2.25
620 A496 1.50fr multicolored   3.50 3.50

Sport for Peace Type of 2016

Olympic rings and: No. 621, Rowers,
denomination at UR. No. 622, Rowers,
denomination at UL. No. 623, Rhythmic gymnast facing forward, eyes open. No. 624,
Rhythmic gymnast facing left, eyes closed.

2016, July 22   Litho.   Perf. 14¼
621 A498 1fr multicolored   2.25 2.25
622 A498 1fr multicolored   2.25 2.25
a.   Pair, #621-622   4.50 4.50
623 A498 2fr multicolored   4.50 4.50
624 A498 2fr multicolored   4.50 4.50
a.   Pair, #623-624   9.00 9.00
    Nos. 621-624 (4)   13.50 13.50

Souvenir sheets of three bearing
three stamps, one from each office are
listed under United Nations, Offices in
New York as Nos. 1141, 1161, 1177-
1178, 1203, and 1208.

World Heritage Sites, Czech Republic Type of 2016

Designs: Nos. 625, 627b, Gardens and
Castle at Kroměříž. Nos. 626, 627e, Lednice-
Valtice Cultural Landscape. No. 627a, Historic
Center of Prague. No. 627d, Holy Trinity Col-
umn, Olomouc. No. 627c, Historic Town
Center of Kutná Hora. No. 627f, Historic
Center of Cesky Krumlov.

2016, Sept. 8   Litho.   Perf. 14¼
625 A500 1fr multicolored   2.25 2.25
626 A500 1.50fr multicolored   3.50 3.50

Souvenir Booklet
627   Booklet, #627g-627l   22.00
a.-c.   A500 30c any single   .65   .65
d.-f.   A500 50c any single   1.10 1.10
g.   Booklet pane of 4 #627a   2.75
h.   Booklet pane of 4 #627b   2.75
i.   Booklet pane of 4 #627c   2.75
j.   Booklet pane of 4 #627d   4.50
k.   Booklet pane of 4 #627e   4.50
l.   Booklet pane of 4 #627f   4.50

Miniature Sheet

World Wildlife Conference,
Johannesburg — G118

No. 628 — Part of map of Africa and: a,
Grue royale (gray-crowned crane). b, Mantella
madagascariensis. c, Gorille des montagnes
(mountain gorilla). d, Avonia quinaria.

2016, Sept. 24   Litho.   Perf. 13x13½
628 G118   Sheet of 4   18.00 18.00
a.-d.   2fr Any single   4.50 4.50

Sustainable Development Goals Type of 2016

No. 629 — Inscription: a, 1 Pas de pauvreté.
b, 2 Faim "zéro." c, 3 Bonne santé et bien-être.
d, 4 Education de qualité. e, 5 Egalité entre les
sexes. f, 6 Eau propre et assainissement. g, 7
Energie propre et d'un coût abordable. h, 8
Travail décent et croissance économnique. i, 9
Industrie, innovation et infrastructure. j, 10 Iné-
galités réduites. k, 11 Villes et communautés
durables. l, 12 Consommation et production
responsables. m, 13 Mesures relatives à la
lutte contre les changements climatiques. n,
14 Vie aquatique. o, 15 Vie terrestre. p, 16
Paix, justice et institutions efficaces. q, 17
Partneriats pour la réalisation des objectifs.

2016, Oct. 24   Litho.   Perf. 13¼
629   Sheet of 17 + label   39.00 39.00
a.-q.   A503 1fr Any single   2.25 2.25

Miniature Sheets

G119

International Dance — G120

No. 630 — Illustration of Quadrille dancers
by Jean François Martin: a, Female dancer
wearing red mask facing right, striped pole. b,
Male dancer wearing brown mask, harlequin
costume, facing right. c, Masked male dancer
with red mask facing right. d, Female dancer
with brown mask facing left. e, Woman holding
black mask facing right. f, Man wearing tan
mask facing left.
No. 631 — Illustration of Japanese fan
dancers by Martin: a, Dancer holding fan and
other hand near her hair. b, Dancer with arm
upraised at UR. c, Head of dancer, hand of
dancer holding umbrella. d, Dancer, part of fan
at LR, e, Dancer's hand holding fan. f, Face of
dancer, no hands visible.

2017, Mar. 23   Litho.   Perf. 13¼x13
630 G119   Sheet of 6   13.00 13.00
a.-f.   1fr Any single   2.10 2.10
631 G120   Sheet of 6   19.50 19.50
a.-f.   1.50fr Any single   3.25 3.25

Endangered Species Type of 2017

Designs: No. 632, Rhampholeon spp. No.
633, Mobula spp. No. 634, Adansonia
grandidieri.   No. 635, Scaphiophryne
marmorata.

2017, May 11   Litho.   Perf. 12¾x12½
632 A509 1.50fr multicolored   3.25 3.25
633 A509 1.50fr multicolored   3.25 3.25
634 A509 1.50fr multicolored   3.25 3.25
635 A509 1.50fr multicolored   3.25 3.25
a.   Block of 4, #632-635   13.00 13.00
    Nos. 632-635 (4)   13.00 13.00

World Environment Day Type of 2017

Designs: 1fr, Snowy owl, Quebec, Canada.
2fr, Red maple and aspen trees, Canada.

2017, June 5   Litho.   Perf. 13¼
636 A510 1fr multicolored   2.25 2.25
637 A510 2fr multicolored   4.50 4.50

World Heritage Sites Along the Silk Roads Type of 2017

Designs: Nos. 638, 640b, Historic Center of
Bukhara, Uzbekistan. Nos. 639, 640e, Kunya-
Urgench, Turkmenistan. No. 640a, Longmen
Grottoes, People's Republic of China. No.
640c, Tabriz Historic Bazaar Complex, Iran.
No. 640d, Sulaiman-Too Sacred Mountain,
Kyrgyzstan. No. 640f, Safranbolu, Turkey.

2017, Aug. 3   Litho.   Perf. 14¼
638 A512   1fr multicolored   2.40 2.40
639 A512 1.50fr multicolored   3.50 3.50

Souvenir Booklet
640   Booklet, #1115g-   26.50
    1115l
a.-c.   A512 30c any single   .80   .80
d.-f.   A512 50c any single   1.40 1.40
g.   Booklet pane of 4 #640a   3.20   —
h.   Booklet pane of 4 #640b   3.20   —
i.   Booklet pane of 4 #640c   3.20   —
j.   Booklet pane of 4 #640d   5.60   —
k.   Booklet pane of 4 #640e   5.60   —
l.   Booklet pane of 4 #640f   5.60   —

Hare, Fox and
Dove — G121

Heads and
Flowers
G122

Heads and Flowers — G123

Designs: 1fr, Snowy owl, Quebec, Canada.
2fr, Red maple and aspen trees, Canada.

2017, Sept. 21   Litho.   Perf. 14¼x14
641 G121 1fr multicolored   2.40 2.40
642 G122 2fr multicolored   4.75 4.75

Souvenir Sheet
Perf. 14¼x13¾
643 G123 2fr multicolored   4.75 4.75
International Day of Peace.

World Food Day Type of 2017

Designs: 1fr, Milk, yogurt and cheeses.
1.50fr, Fruits.

2017, Oct. 16   Litho.   Perf. 13¼x14
644 A516   1fr multicolored   2.40 2.40
645 A516 1.50fr multicolored   3.50 3.50

Endangered Species Type of 2018

Designs: No. 646, Saiga tatarica. No. 647,
Uncarina grandidieri. No. 648, Polymita picta.
No. 649, Carcharhinus falciformis.

2018, Mar. 2   Litho.   Perf. 12¾x12½
646 A519 1.50fr multicolored   3.50 3.50
647 A519 1.50fr multicolored   3.50 3.50
648 A519 1.50fr multicolored   3.50 3.50
649 A519 1.50fr multicolored   3.50 3.50
a.   Block of 4, #646-649   14.00 14.00
    Nos. 646-649 (4)   14.00 14.00

World Health Day Type of 2018

Designs: 1fr, Microbes and microscope. 2fr,
Child, apple, pencil, triangle, numbers, glass
of milk.

2018, Apr. 6   Litho.   Perf. 13x13¼
650 A520 1fr multicolored   2.25 2.25
651 A520 2fr multicolored   4.50 4.50

Miniature Sheet

G124

No. 652: a, Cathedral of St. Lawrence belltower and buildings on hillside. b, Bank with curved glass facade. c, Table and chairs along footpath in city. d, Villa Saroli (yellow building). e, People near door of Santa Maria degli Angioli Church. f, Lugano Arts and Cultural Center (building with four large windows). g, Storefronts along hill on Via Cattedrale. h, Gates of Villa Ciani. i, Arches along Via della Posta. j, William Tell Monument.

2018, May 17   Litho.   Perf. 14¾
652   G124   Sheet of 10 + 10
             labels   38.50 38.50
a.-j.   1.50fr Any single + label   3.75   3.75

The full sheet sold for $19.06 or 16.95fr. The generic labels are shown. Labels could be personalized. The personalization of labels was available only at UN Headquarters, and not through mail order.

UNISPACE + 50 Conferences Type of 2018

Designs: 1fr, View of Earth from space. 1.50fr, Launch of Tiangong 1. 2fr, Widefield Infrared Survey Explorer photograph of Comet 65P/Gunn.

2018, June 20   Litho.   Perf. 14x14¼
653   A523   1fr multicolored   2.25 2.25
654   A523   1.50fr multicolored   3.50 3.50

Souvenir Sheet
Perf. 13¾
655   A523   2fr multicolored   4.50 4.50

No. 655 contains one 45x45mm stamp.

Nelson Mandela (1918-2013), President of South Africa — G125

Printed by Lowe-Martin Group, Canada. Panes of 20. Designed by Martin Morck, Norway.

2018, July 18   Litho.   Perf. 13¼
656   G125   2fr buff & black   4.50 4.50

World Heritage Sites in the United Kingdom Type of 2016

Designs: Nos. 657, 659b, Stonehenge. Nos. 658, 659e, Edinburgh. No. 659a, Giant's Causeway. No. 659c, Conwy Castle. No. 659d, Palace of Westminster. No. 659f, Maritime Greenwich.

2018, Aug. 15   Litho.   Perf. 14¼
657   A524   1fr multicolored   2.25 2.25
658   A524   1.50fr multicolored   3.50 3.50

Souvenir Booklet
659   Booklet, #1115g-
           1115l   23.50
a.-c.   A524 30c any single   .75   .75
d.-f.   A524 50c any single   1.10 1.10
g.   Booklet pane of 4 #659a   3.00   —
h.   Booklet pane of 4 #659b   3.00   —
i.   Booklet pane of 4 #659c   3.00   —
j.   Booklet pane of 4 #659d   4.75   —
k.   Booklet pane of 4 #659e   4.75   —
l.   Booklet pane of 4 #659f   4.75   —

Miniature Sheet

International Music Day — G126

No. 660: a, Electric guitars with carved necks. b, Veena. c, Cello. d, Erhu. e, Ektara. f, Domra. g, Viola da gamba. h, Bazouki. i, Stringed instrument with bow. j, Violin with chin rest. k, Sitars. l, Zither.

2018, Oct. 1   Litho.   Perf. 14x13¼
660   G126   Sheet of 12   27.00 27.00
a.-l.   1fr Any single   2.25 2.25

Miniature Sheet

World Languages — G127

No. 661 — Word bubbles with word for "Hello" in: a, French (Bonjour). b, Russian ("Langues du Monde" in lilac). c, Hebrew and Polish (Czesc), d, Hindi ("Langues du Monde" in white). e, Danish or Swedish (Hej). f, Japanese ("Langues du Monde" in dark gray).

2019, Feb. 21   Litho.   Perf. 13¼x13
661   G127   Sheet of 6   13.50 13.50
a.-f.   1fr Any single   2.25 2.25

Gender Equality — G128

Printed by Lowe-Martin Group, Canada. Panes of 20. Designed by Chris Gash, U.S.

2019, Mar.15   Litho.   Perf. 13¼x13
662   G128   1.50fr multicolored   3.50 3.50

Endangered Species Type of 2019

Designs: No. 663, Hippocampus kuda. No. 664, Dugong dugon. No. 665, Stylophora pistillata. No. 666, Lamna nasus.

2019, Apr. 26   Litho.   Perf. 12¾x12½
663   A534   1.50fr multicolored   3.25 3.25
664   A534   1.50fr multicolored   3.25 3.25
665   A534   1.50fr multicolored   3.25 3.25
666   A534   1.50fr multicolored   3.25 3.25
a.   Block of 4, #663-666   13.50 13.50
         Nos. 663-666 (4)   13.00 13.00

Souvenir Sheet

Bumblebee and Lobelia Cardinalis — G129

Litho. With Foil Application
2019, May 20   Perf. 13
667   G129   2.60fr multicolored   6.00 6.00
World Bee Day.

G130

G131

G132

G133

International Labor Organization, Cent. — G134

2019, June 28   Litho.   Perf. 13½x14
668   G130   1fr multicolored   2.25 2.25
669   G131   1fr multicolored   2.25 2.25
670   G132   1fr multicolored   2.25 2.25
671   G133   1fr multicolored   2.25 2.25
672   G134   1fr multicolored   2.25 2.25
a.   Horiz. strip of 5, #668-672 11.25 11.25
        Nos. 668-672 (5)   11.25 11.25

Climate Change Type of 2019

Designs: 1fr, Fruit tree and burnt forest. 1.50fr, Field of flowers and traffic jam. 2fr, Clouds.

2019, Sept. 23   Litho.   Perf. 14¼
673   A543   1fr multicolored   2.25 2.25
674   A543   1.50fr multicolored   3.50 3.50

Souvenir Sheet
Perf.
675   A543   2fr multicolored   4.50 4.50

2019 United Nations Climate Change Conference, Madrid. No. 675 contains one 47mm diameter stamp.

Miniature Sheet

United Nations Postal Administration in Geneva, 50th Anniv. — G135

No. 676: a, Palais des Nations and Armillary Sphere, green panels. b, Palais des Nations and flags, gray panels. c, Assembly Hall, Palais des Nations, violet blue panels. d, Meeting room of Human Rights Council, light blue panels. e, Armillary Sphere in reflecting pond and Lake Geneva, violet black panels. f, Palais des Nations and flags, red panels. g, Palais des Nations and flags, orange yellow panels. h, Palais des Nations and United Nations flag, dark green panels. i, Peacock, blue green panels. j, Council Chamber, blue gray panels.

2019, Oct. 18   Litho.   Perf. 14¾
676   G135   Sheet of 10 + 10
             labels   38.00 38.00
a.-j.   1.50fr Any single + label   3.75 3.75

The full sheet sold for $18.80 or 16.95fr. The generic labels are shown. Labels could be personalized. The personalization of labels was available only at UN Headquarters, and not through mail order.

World Heritage Sites in Cuba Type of 2019

Designs: Nos. 677, 679b, Trinidad. Nos. 678, 679e, Cienfuegos. No. 679a, Morro Castle. No. 679c, Camagüey. No. 679d, Vinales Valley. No. 679f, San Pedro de la Rosa Castle.

Litho. With Foil Application
2019, Oct. 24   Perf. 14¼
677   A545   1fr multicolored   2.25 2.25
678   A545   1.50fr multicolored   3.50 3.50

Souvenir Booklet
679   Booklet, #1115g-
           1115l   24.50
a.-c.   A545 30c Any single   .75   .75
d.-f.   A545 50c Any single   1.25 1.25
g.   Booklet pane of 4 #679a   3.00   —
h.   Booklet pane of 4 #679b   3.00   —
i.   Booklet pane of 4 #679c   3.00   —
j.   Booklet pane of 4 #679d   5.00   —
k.   Booklet pane of 4 #679e   5.00   —
l.   Booklet pane of 4 #679f   5.00   —

Complete booklet sold for $12.20.

Endangered Species Type of 2020

Designs: No. 680, Leucogeranus leucogeranus. No. 681, Addax nasomaculatus. No. 682, Falco cherrug. No. 683, Monodon monoceros.

Perf. 12¾x12½
2020, Feb. 17   Litho.
680   A546   1.50fr multicolored   3.50 3.50
681   A546   1.50fr multicolored   3.50 3.50
682   A546   1.50fr multicolored   3.50 3.50
683   A546   1.50fr multicolored   3.50 3.50
a.   Block of 4, #680-683   14.00 14.00
         Nos. 680-683 (4)   14.00 14.00

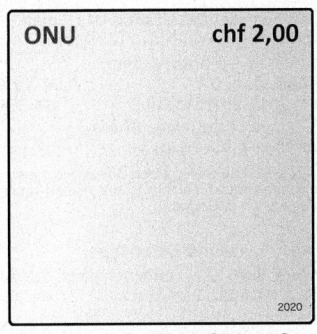

Blank Stamp On Which Stickers Can Be Applied — G136

Designs: No. 1212, Hawksbill turtle. No. 1213, Queen conch. No. 1214, Mushroom coral. No. 1215, Humpback whale.

2020, Mar. 19   Litho.   Die Cut
Self-Adhesive

684	G136	2fr multicolored with rounded corners	4.75	4.75
a.		With perpendicular corners and black frame line	4.75	4.75
b.		Booklet pane of 6 #1236a	28.50	

No. 684 was issued as a souvenir sheet having two different sheet margins, each with different stickers. No. 684a was issued in a booklet containing six panes of one stamp, with each pane having different margins and stickers. Each booklet pane contained one sticker depicting Hello Kitty, a color wheel with Hello Kitty at the center, one of six different Sustainable Development Goal emblems, along with a variety of other stickers. The two souvenir sheets had the same sheet margin and stickers found on two of the panes of No. 684b. No. 684b was sold folded, without any means of separation between the individual panes.

Terre, Artwork by Mathilde Roussel — G137

Mermaids Hate Plastic, Photograph by Benjamin Von Wong — G138

2020, Apr. 22   Litho.   Perf. 13¼

685	G137	1fr multicolored	2.25	2.25
686	G138	2fr multicolored	4.50	4.50

Earth Day, 50th anniv. Because of the COVID-19 pandemic, Nos. 685-686 were not available for sale on day of issue stated on the first-day covers as they had not yet been printed and delivered.

Eradication of Smallpox, 40th Anniv. G139

Printed by Cartor Security Printing, France. Panes of 20. Designed by Sergio Baradat, U.S., and World Health Organization.

2020, May 8   Litho.   Perf. 13x13¼

687	G139	1.70fr multicolored	4.00	4.00

World Heritage Sites in Russia Type of 2020

Designs: Nos. 688, 690b, Kazan Kremlin. Nos. 689, 690e, Saint Petersburg. No. 690a, Lake Baikal. No. 690c, Novodevichy Convent.

No. 690d, Kremlin and Red Square, Moscow. No. 690f, Kizhi Pogost.

Perf. 14½x14¼

2020, Sept. 11   Litho.

688	A556	1fr multicolored	2.40	2.40
689	A556	1.50fr multicolored	3.75	3.75

Souvenir Booklet

690		Booklet, #1115g-1115l	28.00	
a.-c.		A556 30c any single	.85	.85
d.-f.		A556 50c any single	1.40	1.40
g.		Booklet pane of 4 #690a	3.50	—
h.		Booklet pane of 4 #690b	3.50	—
i.		Booklet pane of 4 #690c	3.50	—
j.		Booklet pane of 4 #690d	5.75	—
k.		Booklet pane of 4 #690e	5.75	—
l.		Booklet pane of 4 #690f	5.75	—

Complete booklet sold for $13.21 or 11fr.

Souvenir Sheet

United Nations, 75th Anniv. — G140

No. 691: a, Green "U," pink "N." b, Blue "7," yellow "5."

2020, Oct. 24   Litho.   Perf. 13¼

691	G140	Sheet of 2	10.00	10.00
a.-b.		2fr Either single	5.00	5.00

Souvenir Sheet

Palais des Nations and Emblem — G141

Litho. With Foil Application
2020, Nov. 24   Die Cut Perf. 11½
Self-Adhesive

692	G141	8fr multicolored	19.50	19.50

Crypto stamp. Unused value is for sheets with unscratched panels at right.

SEMI-POSTAL STAMPS

AIDS Awareness Semi-postal Type
Souvenir Sheet

2002, Oct. 24   Litho.   Perf. 14½

B1	SP1	90c + 30c multicolored	4.00	4.00

OFFICES IN VIENNA, AUSTRIA

For use only on mail posted at the Vienna International Center for the UN and the International Atomic Energy Agency.

100 Groschen = 1 Schilling
100 Cents = 1 Euro (2002)

> Catalogue values for all unused stamps in this country are for Never Hinged items.

Type of Geneva, 1978, UN Types of 1961-72 and

Donaupark, Vienna — V1

Aerial View — V2

1979, Aug. 24   Photo.   Perf. 11½
Granite Paper

1	G8	50g multicolored	.25	.30
2	A52	1s multicolored	.25	.30
3	V1	4s multicolored	.25	.30
4	AP13	5s multicolored	.30	.35
5	V2	6s multicolored	.35	.35
6	A45	10s multicolored	.60	.70
		Nos. 1-6 (6)	2.00	2.30

No. 6 has no frame.

New Economic Order Type of UN
1980, Jan. 11   Litho.   Perf. 15x14½

7	A178	4s multicolored	.60	.70

Dove Type of UN
1980, Jan. 11   Litho.   Perf. 14x13½

8	A147	2.50s multicolored	.25	.30

Women's Year Emblem on World Map — V3

United Nations Decade for Women
1980, Mar. 7   Litho.   Perf. 14½x15

9	V3	4s light green & dark green	.40	.45
10	V3	6s bister brown	.75	.85

Peace-keeping Operations Type of UN
1980, May 16   Litho.   Perf. 14x13

11	A182	6s multicolored	.40	.45

35th Anniversary Types of Geneva and UN
1980, June 26   Litho.   Perf. 13x13½

12	G16	4s carmine rose & black	.35	.40
13	A184	6s multicolored	.60	.65

Souvenir Sheet
Imperf

14		Sheet of 2	.90	1.00
a.		G16 4s carmine rose & black	.25	.30
b.		A184 6s multicolored	.65	.30

ECOSOC Types of UN and Geneva
1980, Nov. 21   Litho.   Perf. 13½x13

15	A187	4s multicolored	.30	.35
16	G17	6s multicolored	.60	.30

Palestinian Rights Type of UN
1981, Jan. 30   Photo.   Perf. 12x11½

17	A188	4s multicolored	.45	.50

Disabled Type of UN and

Interlocking Stitches — V4

1981, Mar. 6   Photo.   Perf. 14

18	A189	4s multicolored	.40	.45
19	V4	6s black & orange	.60	.70

Art Type of UN
1981, Apr. 15   Photo.   Perf. 11½
Granite Paper

20	A191	6s multicolored	.75	.85

Energy Type of UN
1981, May 29   Litho.   Perf. 13

21	A193	7.50s multicolored	.70	.80

Volunteers Program Types
1981, Nov. 13   Litho.

22	A195	5s multicolored	.40	.45
23	G18	7s multicolored	.90	1.00

"For a Better World" — V5

1982, Jan. 22   Perf. 11½x12

24	V5	3s multicolored	.35	.40

Human Environment Types of UN and Geneva
1982, Mar. 19   Litho.   Perf. 13½x13

25	A200	5s multicolored	.40	.45
26	G21	7s multicolored	.80	.90

Outer Space Type of Geneva
1982, June 11   Litho.   Perf. 13x13½

27	G22	5s multicolored	.60	.70

Conservation & Protection of Nature Type
1982, Nov. 16   Photo.   Perf. 14

28	A202	5s Fish	.50	.60
29	A202	7s Animal	.70	.80

World Communications Year Type
1983, Jan. 28   Litho.   Perf. 13

30	A203	4s multicolored	.40	.45

Safety at Sea Types of Geneva and UN
1983, Mar. 18   Litho.   Perf. 14½

31	G23	4s multicolored	.40	.45
32	A206	6s multicolored	.65	.75

World Food Program Type
1983, Apr. 22   Engr.   Perf. 13½

33	A207	5s green	.45	.50
34	A207	7s brown	.70	.80

UN Conference on Trade and Development Types of Geneva and UN
1983, June 6   Litho.   Perf. 14

35	G24	4s multicolored	.30	.35
36	A209	8.50s multicolored	.75	.85

V6

35th Anniv. of the Universal Declaration of Human Rights — V7

Photo. & Engr.

			Perf. 13½	
1983, Dec. 9				
37	V6	5s multicolored	.40	.45
38	V7	7s multicolored	.65	.75

International Conference on Population Type

			Perf. 14	
1984, Feb. 3		**Litho.**		
39	A212	7s multicolored	.65	.75

Field Irrigation V8

Harvesting Machine V9

World Food Day, Oct. 16

			Perf. 14½	
1984, Mar. 15				
40	V8	4.50s multicolored	.40	.45
41	V9	6s multicolored	.65	.75

Serengeti Park, Tanzania V10

Ancient City of Shiban, People's Democratic Rep. of Yemen — V11

World Heritage

			Perf. 14	
1984, Mar. 15		**Litho.**		
42	V10	3.50s multicolored	.25	.30
43	V11	15s multicolored	1.25	1.40

V12   V13

Future for Refugees

			Perf. 11½	
1984, May 29		**Photo.**		
44	V12	4.50s multicolored	.45	.50
45	V13	8.50s multicolored	1.25	1.40

International Youth Year — V14

			Perf. 13½	
1984, Nov. 15		**Litho.**		
46	V14	3.50s multicolored	.45	.50
47	V14	6.50s multicolored	.70	.80

ILO Type of Geneva

			Perf. 13½	
1985, Feb. 1		**Engr.**		
48	G34	7.50s U Thant Pavilion	.75	.85

UN University Type

			Perf. 11½	
1985, Mar. 15		**Photo.**		
49	A221	8.50s Rural scene, lab researcher	.75	.85

Ship of Peace — V15   Sharing Umbrella — V16

			Perf. 14	
1985, May 10		**Litho.**		
50	V15	4.50s multicolored	.30	.35
51	V16	15s multicolored	2.00	2.25

40th Anniversary Type

Perf. 12 x 11½

1985, June 26			**Photo.**	
52	A224	6.50s multicolored	.90	1.00
53	A225	8.50s multicolored	1.40	1.60

Souvenir Sheet
Imperf

54		Sheet of 2	2.50	2.75
a.		A224 6.50s multi	1.00	1.10
b.		A225 8.50s multi	1.40	1.50

UNICEF Child Survival Campaign Type

4s, Spoonfeeding children. 6s, Mother hugging infant.

Photo. & Engr.

			Perf. 13½	
1985, Nov. 22				
55	A226	4s multicolored	.75	.85
56	A226	6s multicolored	1.40	1.60

Africa in Crisis Type

			Perf. 11½x12	
1986, Jan. 31		**Photo.**		
57	A227	8s multicolored	.80	.90

UN Development Program Type

Agriculture: No. 58, Developing crop strains. No. 59, Animal husbandry. No. 60, Technical instruction. No. 61, Nutrition education.

			Perf. 13½	
1986, Mar. 14		**Photo.**		
58	A228	4.50s multicolored	1.40	1.60
59	A228	4.50s multicolored	1.40	1.60
60	A228	4.50s multicolored	1.40	1.60
61	A228	4.50s multicolored	1.40	1.60
a.		Block of 4, #58-61	6.25	7.00

No. 61a has a continuous design.

Stamp Collecting Type

Designs: 3.50s, UN stamps. 6.50s, Engraver.

			Perf. 12½	
1986, May 22		**Engr.**		
62	A229	3.50s dk ultra & dk brown	.40	.45
63	A229	6.50s int blue & brt rose	.90	1.00

Olive Branch, Rainbow, Earth — V17

Photogravure & Embossed

			Perf. 13½	
1986, June 20				
64	V17	5s shown	.75	.85
65	V17	6s Doves, UN emblem	1.00	1.10

WFUNA Anniversary Type
Souvenir Sheet

Designs: 4s, White stallion by Elisabeth von Janota-Bzowski, Germany. 5s, Surrealistic landscape by Ernst Fuchs, Austria. 6s, Geometric abstract by Victor Vasarely (b. 1908), France. 7s, Mythological abstract by Wolfgang Hutter (b. 1928), Austria.

			Perf. 13x13½	
1986, Nov. 14		**Litho.**		
66		Sheet of 4	4.00	4.25
a.		A232 4s multicolored	.75	.80
b.		A232 5s multicolored	.85	.90
c.		A232 6s multicolored	1.00	1.10
d.		A232 7s multicolored	1.25	1.40

No. 66 has inscribed margin picturing UN and WFUNA emblems.

Trygve Lie Type
Photogravure & Engraved

			Perf. 13½	
1987, Jan. 30				
67	A233	8s multicolored	.70	.80

Shelter for the Homeless Type

Designs: 4s, Family and homes. 9.50s, Family entering home.

			Perf. 13½x12½	
1987, Mar. 13			**Litho.**	
68	A234	4s multicolored	.50	.55
69	A234	9.50s multicolored	1.10	1.25

Fight Drug Abuse Type

Designs: 5s, Soccer players. 8s, Family.

			Perf. 14½x15	
1987, June 12		**Litho.**		
70	A235	5s multicolored	.40	.45
71	A235	8s multicolored	.90	1.00

Donaupark, Vienna — V18

Peace Embracing the Earth — V19

			Perf. 14½x15	
1987, June 12		**Litho.**		
72	V18	2s multicolored	.30	.35
73	V19	17s multicolored	1.60	1.75

UN Day Type

Designs: Multinational people in various occupations.

			Perf. 14½x15	
1987, Oct. 23		**Litho.**		
74	A236	5s multicolored	.75	.85
75	A236	9s multicolored	.90	1.00

Immunize Every Child Type

Designs: 4s, Poliomyelitis. 9.50s, Diphtheria.

			Perf. 15x14½	
1987, Nov. 20		**Litho.**		
76	A237	4s multicolored	.75	.85
77	A237	9.50s multicolored	2.00	2.25

IFAD Type

Designs: 4s, Grains. 6s, Vegetables.

			Perf. 13½	
1988, Jan. 29		**Litho.**		
78	A238	4s multicolored	.40	.45
79	A238	6s multicolored	.90	1.00

Survival of the Forests Type

Deciduous forest in fall: 4s, Treetops, hills and dales. 5s, Tree trunks. Printed se-tenant in a continuous design.

			Perf. 14x15	
1988, Mar. 18		**Litho.**		
80	A240	4s multicolored	2.25	2.40
81	A240	5s multicolored	3.00	3.25
a.		Pair, #80-81	5.25	5.75

Intl. Volunteer Day Type

Designs: 6s, Medical care, vert. 7.50s, Construction.

Perf. 13x14, 14x13

1988, May 6			**Litho.**	
82	A241	6s multicolored	.75	.85
83	A241	7.50s multicolored	1.00	1.10

Health in Sports Type

Paintings by LeRoy Neiman, American Sports artist: 6s, Skiing, vert. 8s, Tennis.

Perf. 13½x13, 13x13½

1988, June 17			**Litho.**	
84	A242	6s multicolored	.90	1.00
85	A242	8s multicolored	1.40	1.60

Universal Declaration of Human Rights 40th Anniv. Type
Photo. & Engr.

			Perf. 11½	
1988, Dec. 9				
86	A243	5s multicolored	.50	.55

Souvenir Sheet

87	A243	11s multicolored	1.25	1.40

No. 87 has multicolored decorative margin inscribed with preamble to the human rights declaration in German.

World Bank Type

			Perf. 13x14	
1989, Jan. 27		**Litho.**		
88	A244	5.50s Transportation	1.10	1.25
89	A244	8s Health care, education	1.75	1.90

Peace-Keeping Force Type

			Perf. 14x13½	
1989, Mar. 17		**Litho.**		
90	A245	6s multicolored	.85	.95

World Weather Watch Type

Satellite photograph and radar image: 4s, Helical cloud formation over Italy, the eastern Alps, and parts of Yugoslavia. 9.50s, Rainfall in Tokyo, Japan.

			Perf. 13x14	
1989, Apr. 21		**Litho.**		
91	A247	4s multicolored	1.00	1.10
92	A247	9.50s multicolored	2.10	2.25

V20   V21

Photo. & Engr., Photo. (7.50s)

			Perf. 14	
1989, Aug. 23				
93	V20	5s multicolored	1.25	1.50
94	V21	7.50s multicolored	1.25	1.50

Human Rights Type of 1989

Paintings: 4s, The Prisoners, by Kathe Kollwitz. 6s, Justice, by Raphael.

			Perf. 13½	
1989, Nov. 17		**Litho.**		
95	A250	4s multicolored	.50	.55
96	A250	6s multicolored	.75	.85

See Nos. 108-109, 123-124, 150-151.

Intl. Trade Center Type

			Perf. 14½x15	
1990, Feb. 2		**Litho.**		
97	A251	12s multicolored	1.25	1.40

Painting by Kurt Regschek V22

			Perf. 13x13½	
1990, Feb. 2		**Litho.**		
98	V22	1.50s multicolored	.30	.35

Designs: 5s, "SIDA." 11s, Stylized figures, ink blot.

V23

Perf. 13½x12½

1990, Mar. 16			**Litho.**	
99	V23	5s multicolored	1.00	1.10
100	V23	11s multicolored	2.25	2.40

Medicinal Plants Type

			Perf. 11½	
1990, May 4		**Photo.**		
		Granite Paper		
101	A253	4.50s Bixa orellana	1.25	1.40
102	A253	9.50s Momordica charantia	2.50	2.75

UN 45th Anniv. Type
Designs: 7s, 9s, "45" and emblem.

1990, June 26 Litho. Perf. 14½x13
103 A254 7s multicolored 1.40 1.60
104 A254 9s multicolored, diff. 2.40 2.75

Souvenir Sheet
105 Sheet of 2, #103-104 5.00 5.50

Crime Prevention Type
1990, Sept. 13 Photo. Perf. 14
106 A255 6s Domestic violence 1.00 1.10
107 A255 8s Crimes against cultural heritage 2.25 2.50

Human Rights Type of 1989
Paintings: 4.50s, Before the Judge, by Sandor Bihari. 7s, Young Man Greeted by a Woman Writing a Poem, by Suzuki Harunobu.

1990, Nov. 16 Litho. Perf. 13½
108 A250 4.50s multicolored .30 .35
109 A250 7s multicolored .90 1.00

Economic Commission for Europe Type
1991, Mar. 15 Litho. Perf. 14
110 A256 5s Weasel, hoopoe 1.40 1.60
111 A256 5s Warbler, swans 1.40 1.60
112 A256 5s Badgers, squirrel 1.40 1.60
113 A256 5s Fish 1.40 1.60
a. Block of 4, #110-113 5.60 6.50

Namibian Independence Type
1991, May 10 Litho. Perf. 14
114 A257 6s Mountains, clouds 1.00 1.25
115 A257 9.50s Dune, Namib Desert 2.25 2.50

V24

1991, May 10 Litho. Perf. 15x14½
116 V24 20s multicolored 1.75 2.00

V25

Rights of the Child V26

1991, June 14 Litho. Perf. 14½
117 V25 7s Stick drawings 1.00 1.25
118 V26 9s Child, clock, fruit 1.50 1.75

V27

Banning of Chemical Weapons V28

1991, Sept. 11 Litho. Perf. 13½
119 V27 5s multicolored .75 .90
120 V28 10s multicolored 1.75 2.00

UN Postal Administration, 40th Anniv. Type
1991, Oct. 24 Litho. Perf. 14x15
121 A263 5s UN NY No. 8 .75 .90
122 A263 8s UN NY No. 5 1.50 1.75

Human Rights Type of 1989
Artwork: 4.50s, Pre-columbian Mexican pottery. 7s, Windows, by Robert Delaunay.

1991, Nov. 20 Litho. Perf. 13½
123 A250 4.50s black & brown .50 .55
124 A250 7s multicolored .80 .90

World Heritage Type of 1984
Designs: 5s, Iguacu Natl. Park, Brazil. 9s, Abu Simbel, Egypt.

1992, Jan. 24 Litho. Perf. 13 Size: 35x28mm
125 V10 5s multicolored .75 .90
126 V10 9s multicolored 1.60 1.80

Clean Oceans Type
1992, Mar. 13 Litho. Perf. 14
127 A264 7s Ocean surface, diff. 1.00 1.10
128 A264 7s Ocean bottom, diff. 1.00 1.10
a. Pair, #127-128 2.25 2.50

Earth Summit Type
1992, May 22 Photo. Perf. 11½
129 A265 5.50s Man in space 1.30 1.50
130 A265 5.50s Sun 1.30 1.50
131 A265 5.50s Man fishing 1.30 1.50
132 A265 5.50s Sailboat 1.30 1.50
a. Block of 4, #129-132 5.50 6.00

Mission to Planet Earth Type
Designs: No. 133, Satellite, person's mouth. No. 134, Satellite, person's ear.

1992, Sept. 4 Photo. Rouletted 8 Granite Paper
133 A266 10s multicolored 3.00 3.25
134 A266 10s multicolored 3.00 3.25
a. Pair, #133-134 6.00 6.50

Science and Technology Type of 1992
Designs: 5.50s, Woman emerging from computer screen. 7s, Green thumb growing flowers.

1992, Oct. 2 Litho. Perf. 14
135 A267 5.50s multicolored .75 .85
136 A267 7s multicolored 1.40 1.60

V29

Intl. Center, Vienna — V30

1992, Oct. 2 Litho. Perf. 13x13½
137 V29 5.50s multicolored .90 1.00
Perf. 13½x13
138 V30 7s multicolored 1.25 1.40

Human Rights Type of 1989
Artwork: 6s, Les Constructeurs, by Fernand Leger. 10s, Sunday Afternoon on the Island of Le Grande Jatte, by Georges Seurat.

1992, Nov. 20 Litho. Perf. 13½
139 A250 6s multicolored .75 .85
140 A250 10s multicolored 1.25 1.40

Aging With Dignity Type
Designs: 5.50s, Elderly couple, family working in garden. 7s, Older woman teaching.

1993, Feb. 5 Litho. Perf. 13
141 A270 5.50s multicolored .75 .85
142 A270 7s multicolored 1.40 1.60

Endangered Species Type
Designs: No. 143, Equus grevyi (Grevy's zebra). No. 144, Spheniscus humboldti (Humboldt's penguins). No. 145, Varanus griseus

(desert monitor). No. 146, Canis lupus (gray wolf).

1993, Mar. 2 Litho. Perf. 13x12½
143 A271 7s multicolored .90 1.00
144 A271 7s multicolored .90 1.00
145 A271 7s multicolored .90 1.00
146 A271 7s multicolored .90 1.00
a. Block of 4, #143-146 3.60 4.00

Healthy Environment Type
1993, May 7 Litho. Perf. 15x14½
147 A272 6s Wave in ocean 1.25 1.40
148 A272 10s Globe 2.00 2.25

V31

1993, May 7 Photo. Perf. 11½ Granite Paper
149 V31 13s multicolored 2.00 2.25

Human Rights Type of 1989
Artwork: 5s, Lower Austrian Peasants' Wedding, by Ferdinand G. Waldmuller. 6s, Outback, by Sally Morgan.

1993, June 11 Litho. Perf. 13½
150 A250 5s multicolored .80 .90
151 A250 6s multicolored 1.00 1.10

Intl. Peace Day Type
Denomination at: No. 152, UL. No. 153, UR. No. 154, LL. No. 155, LR.

Rouletted 12½
1993, Sept. 21 Litho. & Engr.
152 A274 5.50s green & multi 1.80 2.00
153 A274 5.50s green & multi 1.80 2.00
154 A274 5.50s green & multi 1.80 2.00
155 A274 5.50s green & multi 1.80 2.00
a. Block of 4, #152-155 7.25 8.25

Environment-Climate Type
Designs: No. 156, Monkeys. No. 157, Bluebird, industrial pollution, volcano. No. 158, Volcano, nuclear power plant, tree stumps. No. 159, Cactus, tree stumps, owl.

1993, Oct. 29 Litho. Perf. 14½
156 A275 7s multicolored 2.50 2.75
157 A275 7s multicolored 2.50 2.75
158 A275 7s multicolored 2.50 2.75
159 A275 7s multicolored 2.50 2.75
a. Strip of 4, #156-159 10.00 11.00

Intl. Year of the Family Type of 1993
Designs: 5.50s, Adults, children holding hands. 8s, Two adults, child planting crops.

1994, Feb. 4 Litho. Perf. 13.1
160 A276 5.50s blue green & multi 1.00 1.10
161 A276 8s red & multi 1.25 1.40

Endangered Species Type of 1993
Designs: No. 162, Ocelot. No. 163, White-breasted silver-eye. No. 164, Mediterranean monk seal. No. 165, Asian elephant.

1994, Mar. 18 Litho. Perf. 12.7
162 A271 7s multicolored 1.00 1.10
163 A271 7s multicolored 1.00 1.10
164 A271 7s multicolored 1.00 1.10
165 A271 7s multicolored 1.00 1.10
a. Block of 4, #162-165 4.00 4.40

Protection for Refugees Type
Design: 12s, Protective hands surround group of refugees.

1994, Apr. 29 Litho. Perf. 14.3x14.8
166 A277 12s multicolored 1.50 1.75

V32

V33

V34

1994, Apr. 29 Litho. Perf. 12.9
167 V32 50g multicolored .25 .30
168 V33 4s multicolored .40 .45
169 V34 30s multicolored 4.00 4.50
Nos. 167-169 (3) 4.65 5.25

Intl. Decade for Natural Disaster Reduction Type
Earth seen from space, outline map of: No. 170, North America. No. 171, Eurasia. No. 172, South America. No. 173, Australia and South Asia.

1994, May 27 Litho. Perf. 13.9x14.2
170 A281 6s multicolored 1.75 1.90
171 A281 6s multicolored 1.75 1.90
172 A281 6s multicolored 1.75 1.90
173 A281 6s multicolored 1.75 1.90
a. Block of 4, #170-173 7.00 7.75

Population and Development Type
Designs: 5.50s, Women teaching, running machine tool, coming home to family. 7s, Family on tropical island.

1994, Sept. 1 Litho. Perf. 13.2x13.6
174 A282 5.50s multicolored .90 1.00
175 A282 7s multicolored 1.50 1.75

UNCTAD Type
1994, Oct. 28
176 A283 6s multi, diff. .90 1.00
177 A283 7s multi, diff. 1.50 1.75

UN 50th Anniv. Type
Litho. & Engr.
1995, Jan. 1 Perf. 13.4
178 A284 7s multicolored 1.25 1.40

Social Summit Type
Photo. & Engr.
1995, Feb. 3 Perf. 13.6x13.9
179 A285 14s multi, diff. 2.00 2.25

Endangered Species Type of 1993
Designs: No. 180, Black rhinoceros, Diceros bicornis. No. 181, Golden conure, Aratinga guarouba. No. 182, Douc langur, Pygathrix nemaeus. No. 183, Arabian oryx, Oryx leucoryx.

1995, Mar. 24 Litho. Perf. 13x12½
180 A271 7s multicolored 1.00 1.10
181 A271 7s multicolored 1.00 1.10
182 A271 7s multicolored 1.00 1.10
183 A271 7s multicolored 1.00 1.10
a. Block of 4, 180-183 4.00 4.50

Intl. Youth Year Type
Designs: 6s, Village in winter. 7s, Teepees.

1995, May 26 Litho. Perf. 14.4x14.7
184 A286 6s multicolored .80 .90
185 A286 7s multicolored 1.00 1.10

UN, 50th Anniv. Type
Designs: 7s, Like No. 663. 10s, Like No. 664.

Perf. 13.3x13.6
1995, June 26 Engr.
186 A287 7s green 1.20 1.30
187 A287 10s black 1.75 1.90

Souvenir Sheet
Litho. & Engr.
Imperf
188 Sheet of 2, #186-187 2.75 3.10
a. A287 7s green 1.10 1.25
b. A287 10s black 1.60 1.80

Conference on Women Type
Designs: 5.50s, Women amid tropical plants. 6s, Woman reading, swans on lake.

1995, Sept. 5 Photo. Perf. 12
189 A288 5.50s multicolored .80 .90
Size: 28x50mm
190 A288 6s multicolored 1.20 1.30

UN People, 50th Anniv. Type

1995, Oct. 24　Litho.　*Perf. 14*
191	Sheet of 12	9.00	10.00
a.-l.	A290 3s any single	.75	.85
192	Souvenir booklet	9.00	
a.	A290 3s Booklet pane of 3, vert. strip of 3 from UL of sheet	2.25	2.75
b.	A290 3s Booklet pane of 3, vert. strip of 3 from UR of sheet	2.25	2.75
c.	A290 3s Booklet pane of 3, vert. strip of 3 from LL of sheet	2.25	2.75
d.	A290 3s Booklet pane of 3, vert. strip of 3 from LR of sheet	2.25	2.75

WFUNA, 50th Anniv. Type

Design: 7s, Harlequin holding dove.

1996, Feb. 2　Litho.　*Perf. 13x13½*
193	A291 7s multicolored	1.00	1.10

UN Flag — V35

Abstract, by Karl Korab — V36

1996, Feb. 2　Litho.　*Perf. 15x14½*
194	V35　1s multicolored	.25	.30
195	V36 10s multicolored	1.60	1.75

Endangered Species Type of 1993

Designs: No. 196, Cypripedium calceolus. No. 197, Aztekium ritteri. No. 198, Euphorbia cremersii. No. 199, Dracula bella.

1996, Mar. 14　Litho.　*Perf. 12½*
196	A271 7s multicolored	.75	.85
197	A271 7s multicolored	.75	.85
198	A271 7s multicolored	.75	.85
199	A271 7s multicolored	.75	.85
a.	Block of 4, #196-199	3.00	3.40

City Summit Type

Designs: No. 200, Arab family selling fruits, vegetables. No. 201, Women beside stream, camels. No. 202, Woman carrying bundle on head, city skyline. No. 203, Woman threshing grain, yoke of oxen in field. No. 204, Native village, elephant.

1996, June 3　Litho.　*Perf. 14x13½*
200	A293 6s multicolored	1.50	1.75
201	A293 6s multicolored	1.50	1.75
202	A293 6s multicolored	1.50	1.75
203	A293 6s multicolored	1.50	1.75
204	A293 6s multicolored	1.50	1.75
a.	Strip of 5, #200-204	7.50	9.00

Sport and the Environment Type

6s, Men's parallel bars (gymnastics), vert. 7s, Hurdles.

Perf. 14x14½, 14½x14
1996, July 19　　　　Litho.
205	A294 6s multicolored	.80	.90
206	A294 7s multicolored	.90	1.00

Souvenir Sheet
207	A294	Sheet of 2, #205-206	1.75	1.90

Plea for Peace Type

Designs: 7s, Dove and butterflies. 10s, Stylized dove, diff.

1996, Sept. 17　Litho.　*Perf. 14½x15*
208	A295 7s multicolored	.80	.90
209	A295 10s multicolored	1.20	1.40

UNICEF Type

Fairy Tales: 5.50s, Hansel and Gretel, by the Brothers Grimm. 8s, How Maui Stole Fire from the Gods, South Pacific.

1996, Nov. 20　Litho.　*Perf. 14½x15*
210	A296 5.50s multicolored	.90	1.00
211	A296　8s multicolored	1.40	1.60

V37

Phoenixes Flying Down (Detail), by Sagenji Yoshida — V38

1997, Feb. 12　Litho.　*Perf. 14½*
212	V37　5s multicolored	.80	.90
213	V38　6s multicolored	.90	1.00

Endangered Species Type of 1993

Designs: No. 214, Macaca sylvanus (Barbary macaque). No. 215, Anthropoides paradisea (blue crane). No. 216, Equus przewalskii (Przewalski horse). No. 217, Myrmecophaga tridactyla (giant anteater).

1997, Mar. 13　Litho.　*Perf. 12½*
214	A271 7s multicolored	.75	.85
215	A271 7s multicolored	.75	.85
216	A271 7s multicolored	.75	.85
217	A271 7s multicolored	.75	.85
a.	Block of 4, #214-217	3.00	3.40

Earth Summit Anniv. Type

Designs: No. 218, Person running. No. 219, Hills, stream, trees. No. 220, Tree with orange leaves. No. 221, Tree with pink leaves. 11s, Combined design similar to Nos. 218-221.

1997, May 30　Photo.　*Perf. 11.5*
Granite Paper
218	A299 3.50s multicolored	1.50	1.75
219	A299 3.50s multicolored	1.50	1.75
220	A299 3.50s multicolored	1.50	1.75
221	A299 3.50s multicolored	1.50	1.75
a.	Block of 4, #218-221	6.00	7.00

Souvenir Sheet
222	A299	11s multicolored	2.40	2.60

Transportation Type

Ground transportation: No. 223, 1829 Rocket, 1901 Darraque. No. 224, Steam engine from Vladikawska Railway, trolley. No. 225, Double-decker bus. No. 226, 1950s diesel locomotive, semi-trailer. No. 227, High-speed train, electric car.

1997, Aug. 29　Litho.　*Perf. 14x14½*
223	A300 7s multicolored	1.25	1.40
224	A300 7s multicolored	1.25	1.40
225	A300 7s multicolored	1.25	1.40
226	A300 7s multicolored	1.25	1.40
227	A300 7s multicolored	1.25	1.40
a.	Strip of 5, #223-227	6.25	7.00

No. 227a has continuous design.

Philately Type

Designs: 6.50s, No. 62. 7s, No. 63.

1997, Oct. 14　Litho.　*Perf. 13½x14*
228	A301 6.50s multicolored	.80	.90
229	A301　7s multicolored	.90	1.00

World Heritage Convention Type

Terracotta warriors of Xian: 3s, Single warrior. 6s, Massed warriors. No. 232a, like No. 716. No. 232b, like No. 717. No. 232c, like Geneva No. 314. No. 232d, like Geneva No. 315. No. 232e, like Vienna No. 230. No. 232f, like Vienna No. 231.

1997, Nov. 19　Litho.　*Perf. 13½*
230	A302 3s multicolored	1.00	1.10
231	A302 6s multicolored	2.00	2.25
232	Souvenir booklet	12.00	
a.-f.	A302 1s any single	.50	.55
g.	Booklet pane of 4 #232a	2.00	2.25
h.	Booklet pane of 4 #232b	2.00	2.25
i.	Booklet pane of 4 #232c	2.00	2.25
j.	Booklet pane of 4 #232d	2.00	2.25
k.	Booklet pane of 4 #232e	2.00	2.25
l.	Booklet pane of 4 #232f	2.00	2.25

Japanese Peace Bell, Vienna — V39

Vienna Subway, Vienna Intl. Center — V40

1998, Feb. 13　Litho.　*Perf. 15x14½*
233	V39 6.50s multicolored	.80	.90
234	V40　9s multicolored	1.00	1.10

Endangered Species Type of 1993

Designs: No. 235, Chelonia mydas (green turtle). No. 236, Speotyto cunicularia (burrowing owl). No. 237, Trogonoptera brookiana (Rajah Brooke's birdwing). No. 238, Ailurus fulgens (lesser panda).

1998, Mar. 13　Litho.　*Perf. 12½*
235	A271 7s multicolored	.75	.85
236	A271 7s multicolored	.75	.85
237	A271 7s multicolored	.75	.85
238	A271 7s multicolored	.75	.85
a.	Block of 4, #235-238	3.00	3.40

Intl. Year of the Ocean — V41

1998, May 20　Litho.　*Perf. 13x13½*
239	V41　Sheet of 12	9.50	10.75
a.-l.	3.50s any single	.80	.90

Rain Forests Type

1998, June 19　　　　*Perf. 13x13½*
240	A307 6.50s Ocelot	.90	1.00

Souvenir Sheet
241	A307	22s like #240	3.00	3.25

Peacekeeping Type of 1998

Designs: 4s, Soldier passing out relief supplies. 7.50s, UN supervised voting.

1998, Sept. 15　Photo.　*Perf. 12*
242	A308　4s multicolored	.50	.60
243	A308 7.50s multicolored	1.00	1.10

Declaration of Human Rights Type

Designs: 4.50s, Stylized person. 7s, Gears.

Litho. & Photo.
1998, Oct. 27　　　　*Perf. 13*
244	A309 4.50s multicolored	.80	.90
245	A309　7s multicolored	1.25	1.40

Schönbrunn Palace Type

Designs: 3.50s, No. 248d, Palace. 7s, No. 248c, Porcelain stove, vert. No. 248a, Blue porcelain vase, vert. No. 248b, Wall painting on fabric (detail), by Johann Wenzl Bergl, vert. No. 248e, Great Palm House (conservatory). No. 248f, The Gloriette (archway).

1998, Dec. 4　Litho.　*Perf. 14*
246	A310 3.50s multicolored	.60	.70
247	A310　7s multicolored	1.10	1.25

Souvenir Booklet
248	Booklet	20.00	
a.-c.	A310 1s any single	.60	.70
d.-f.	A310 2s any single	1.20	1.30
g.	Booklet pane of 4 #248d	4.80	5.25
h.	Booklet pane of 3 #248a	1.80	2.00
i.	Booklet pane of 3 #248b	1.80	2.00
j.	Booklet pane of 3 #248c	1.80	2.00
k.	Booklet pane of 4 #248e	4.80	5.25
l.	Booklet pane of 4 #248f	4.80	5.25

Volcanic Landscape — V42

1999, Feb. 5　Litho.　*Perf. 13x13½*
249	V42 8s multicolored	1.25	1.40

World Heritage, Australia Type

Designs: 4.50s, No. 252d, Uluru-Kata Tjuta Natl. Park. 6.50s, No. 252a, Tasmanian Wilderness. No. 252b, Wet tropics of Queensland. No. 252c, Great Barrier Reef. No. 252e, Kakadu Natl. Park. No. 252f, Willandra Lakes region.

1999, Mar. 19　Litho.　*Perf. 13*
250	A313 4.50s multicolored	.75	.85
251	A313 6.50s multicolored	1.10	1.25

Souvenir Booklet
252	Booklet	12.00	
a.-c.	A313 1s any single	.35	.40
d.-f.	A313 2s any single	.65	.70
g.	Booklet pane of 4, #252a	1.40	1.60
h.	Booklet pane of 4, #252d	2.60	2.80
i.	Booklet pane of 4, #252b	1.40	1.60
j.	Booklet pane of 4, #252e	2.60	2.80
k.	Booklet pane of 4, #252c	1.40	1.60
l.	Booklet pane of 4, #252f	2.60	2.80

Endangered Species Type of 1993

Designs: No. 253, Pongo pygmaeus (orangutan). No. 254, Pelecanus crispus (Dalmatian pelican). No. 255, Eunectes notaeus (yellow anaconda). No. 256, Caracal.

1999, Apr. 22　Litho.　*Perf. 12½*
253	A271 7s multicolored	.75	.85
254	A271 7s multicolored	.75	.85
255	A271 7s multicolored	.75	.85
256	A271 7s multicolored	.75	.85
a.	Block of 4, #253-256	3.00	3.40

UNISPACE III Type

Designs: No. 257, Satellite over ships. No. 258, Satellite up close. No. 259, Composite of Nos. 257-258.

1999, July 7　Photo.　*Rouletted 8*
257	A314 3.50s multicolored	.75	.85
258	A314 3.50s multicolored	.75	.85
a.	Pair, #257-258	1.60	1.70

Souvenir Sheet
Perf. 14½
259	A314	13s multicolored	4.50	5.00

UPU Type

Various people, late 20th century methods of mail transportation, denomination at: No. 260, UL. No. 261, UR. No. 262, LL. No. 263, LR.

1999, Aug. 23　Photo.　*Perf. 11¾*
260	A315 6.50s multicolored	1.00	1.10
261	A315 6.50s multicolored	1.00	1.10
262	A315 6.50s multicolored	1.00	1.10
263	A315 6.50s multicolored	1.00	1.10
a.	Block of 4, #260-263	4.00	4.50

In Memoriam Type

Designs: 6.50s, 14s, Donaupark. Size of 14s stamp: 34x63mm.

1999, Sept. 21　Litho.　*Perf. 14½x14*
264	A316 6.50s multicolored	.90	1.00

Souvenir Sheet
Perf. 14
265	A316	14s multicolored	3.00	3.25

Education Type
Perf. 13½x13¾
1999, Nov. 18　　　　Litho.
266	A317　7s Boy, girl, book	.75	.85
267	A317 13s Group reading	1.75	1.90

Intl. Year of Thanksgiving Type

2000, Jan. 1　Litho.　*Perf. 13¼x13½*
268	A318 7s multicolored	.80	.90

On No. 268 parts of the design were applied by a thermographic process producing a shiny, raised effect.

Endangered Species Type of 1993

Designs: No. 269, Panthera pardus (leopard). No. 270, Platalea leucorodia (white spoonbill). No. 271, Hippocamelus bisulcus (huemal). No. 272, Orcinus orca (killer whale).

2000, Apr. 6 Litho. Perf. 12¾x12½
269 A271 7s multicolored 1.10 1.25
270 A271 7s multicolored 1.10 1.25
271 A271 7s multicolored 1.10 1.25
272 A271 7s multicolored 1.10 1.25
a.   Block of 4, #269-272 4.50 5.00

Our World 2000 Type

Winning artwork in Millennium painting competition: 7s, Tomorrow's Dream, by Voltaire Perez, Philippines. 8s, Remembrance, by Dimitris Nalbandis, Greece, vert.

Perf. 13x13½, 13½x13
2000, May 30 Litho.
273 A319 7s multicolored .60 .70
274 A319 8s multicolored .75 .85

55th Anniversary Type

Designs: 7s, Secretariat Building, unfinished dome of General Assembly Hall, 1951. 9s, Trygve Lie and Headquraters Advisory Committee at topping-out ceremony, 1949.

2000, July 7 Litho. Perf. 13¼x13
275 A320 7s multicolored .90 1.00
276 A320 9s multicolored 1.25 1.40
Souvenir Sheet
277 A320 Sheet of 2, #275-276 2.75 3.25

The UN in the 21st Century — V43

No. 278: a, Farm machinery. b, UN Peacekeepers and children. c, Oriental farm workers. d, Peacekeepers searching for mines. e, Medical research. f, Handicapped people.

2000, Sept. 15 Litho. Perf. 14
278 V43 Sheet of 6 7.50 8.50
a.-f. 3.50s any single 1.25 1.40

World Heritage, Spain Type

Designs: Nos. 279, 281c, Aqueduct of Segovia. Nos. 280, 281f, Güell Park, Barcelona. No. 281a, Alhambra, Generalife and Albayzin, Granada. No. 281b, Walled Town of Cuenca. No. 281d, Amphitheater of Mérida. No. 281e, Toledo.

2000, Oct. 6 Litho. Perf. 14¾x14½
279 A323 4.50s multicolored .80 .90
280 A323 6.50s multicolored 1.20 1.40
Souvenir Booklet
281 Booklet 9.00
a.-c. A323 1s any single .25 .30
d.-f. A323 2s any single .50 .55
g. Booklet pane of 4, #281a 1.00 1.10
h. Booklet pane of 4, #281d 2.00 2.25
i. Booklet pane of 4, #281e 1.00 1.10
j. Booklet pane of 4, #281e 2.00 2.25
k. Booklet pane of 4, #281c 1.00 1.10
l. Booklet pane of 4, #281f 2.00 2.25

Respect for Refugees Type

Designs: 7s, 25s, Refugee with hat, three other refugees.

2000, Nov. 9 Litho. Perf. 13¼x12¾
282 A324 7s multicolored 1.10 1.25
Souvenir Sheet
283 A324 25s multicolored 3.75 4.25

Endangered Species Type of 1993

Designs: No. 284, Tremarctos ornatus (spectacled bear). No. 285, Anas laysanensis (Laysan duck). No. 286, Proteles cristatus (aardwolf). No. 287, Trachypithecus cristatus (silvered leaf monkey).

2001, Feb. 1 Litho. Perf. 12¾x12½
284 A271 7s multicolored 1.10 1.25
285 A271 7s multicolored 1.10 1.25
286 A271 7s multicolored 1.10 1.25
287 A271 7s multicolored 1.10 1.25
a.   Block of 4, #284-287 4.50 5.00

Intl. Volunteers Year — V44

Paintings by: 10s, Nguyen Thanh Chuong, Viet Nam. 12s, Ikko Tanaka, Japan.

2001, Mar. 29 Litho. Perf. 13¼
288 V44 10s multicolored 1.40 1.60
289 V44 12s multicolored 1.75 1.90

World Heritage, Japan Type

Designs: 7s, No. 290c, Himeji-Jo. 15s, No. 291f, Nikko. No. 292a, Kyoto. No. 292b, Nara. No. 292d, Shirakawa-Go and Gokayama. No. 292e, Itsukushima Shinto Shrine.

2001, Aug. 1 Litho. Perf. 12¾x13¼
290 A328 7s multicolored 1.00 1.10
291 A328 15s multicolored 2.10 2.25
Souvenir Booklet
292 Booklet 11.50
a.-c. A328 1s any single .30 .35
d.-f. A328 2s any single .60 .70
g. Booklet pane of 4, #292a 1.20 1.40
h. Booklet pane of 4, #292b 2.40 2.75
i. Booklet pane of 4, #292b 1.20 1.40
j. Booklet pane of 4, #292e 2.40 2.75
k. Booklet pane of 4, #292c 1.20 1.40
l. Booklet pane of 4, #292f 2.40 2.75

Dag Hammarskjöld Type
2001, Sept. 18 Engr. Perf. 11x11¼
293 A329 7s green 1.00 1.10

UN Postal Administration, 50th Anniv. Types
2001, Oct. 18 Litho. Perf. 13½
294 A330 7s Stamps, balloons 1.00 1.10
295 A330 8s Stamps, cake 1.10 1.25
Souvenir Sheet
296 A331 Sheet of 2 7.50 8.00
a.   7s green & light blue, 38mm diameter 2.50 2.75
b.   21s green & light blue, 38mm diameter 5.00 5.50

Climate Change Type

Designs: No. 297, Solar panels, automobile at pump. No. 298, Blimp, bicyclists, horse and rider. No. 299, Balloon, sailboat, lighthouse, train. No. 300, Bird, train, traffic signs.

2001, Nov. 16 Litho. Perf. 13¼
297 A332 7s multicolored 1.00 1.10
298 A332 7s multicolored 1.00 1.10
299 A332 7s multicolored 1.00 1.10
300 A332 7s multicolored 1.00 1.10
a.   Horiz. strip, #297-300 5.00 5.50

Nobel Peace Prize Type
2001, Dec. 10 Litho. Perf. 13¼
301 A333 7s multicolored 1.00 .55

100 Cents = 1 Euro (€)

Austrian Tourist Attractions V45

Designs: 7c, Semmering Railway. 51c, Pferdschwemme, Salzburg. 58c, Aggstein an der Donau Ruins. 73c, Hallstatt. 87c, Melk Abbey. €2.03, Kapitelschwemme, Salzburg.

2002, Mar. 1 Litho. Perf. 14½x14
302 V45 7c multicolored .25 .30
303 V45 51c multicolored .90 1.25
304 V45 58c multicolored 1.00 1.10
305 V45 73c multicolored 1.25 1.40
306 V45 87c multicolored 1.75 2.00
307 V45 €2.03 multicolored 3.50 3.75
Nos. 302-307 (6) 8.65 9.80

Endangered Species Type of 1993

Designs: No. 308, Hylobates syndactylus (siamang). No. 309, Spheniscus demersus (jackass penguin). No. 310, Prionodon linsang (banded linsang). No. 311, Bufo retiformis (Sonoran green toad).

2002, Apr. 4 Litho. Perf. 12¾x12½
308 A271 51c multicolored 1.25 1.25
309 A271 51c multicolored 1.25 1.25
310 A271 51c multicolored 1.25 1.25
311 A271 51c multicolored 1.25 1.25
a.   Block of 4, #308-311 5.00 5.00

Independence of East Timor Type

Designs: 51c, Deer horn container with carved wooden stopper. €1.09, Carved wooden tai weaving loom.

2002, May 20 Litho. Perf. 14x14½
312 A335 51c multicolored 1.00 1.00
313 A335 €1.09 multicolored 2.25 2.25

Intl. Year of Mountains Type

Designs: No. 314, Mt. Cook, New Zealand. No. 315, Mt. Robson, Canada. No. 316, Mt. Rakaposhi, Pakistan. No. 317, Mt. Everest (Sagarmatha), Nepal.

2002, May 24 Litho. Perf. 13x13¼
314 A336 22c multicolored .40 .40
315 A336 22c multicolored .40 .40
316 A336 51c multicolored 1.00 1.00
317 A336 51c multicolored 1.00 1.00
a.   Vert. strip or block of four, #314-317 12.50 12.50

World Summit on Sustainable Development (Peter Max) Type

Designs: No. 318, Rainbow. No. 319, Three women, diff. No. 320, Three faceless people. No. 321, Birds, wave.

2002, June 27 Litho. Perf. 14½x14
318 A337 51c multicolored 1.00 1.00
319 A337 51c multicolored 1.00 1.00
320 A337 58c multicolored 1.25 1.25
321 A337 58c multicolored 1.25 1.25
a.   Vert. strip or block of four, #318-321 10.00 8.50

World Heritage, Italy Type

Designs: 51c, No. 324f, Pompeii. 58c, No. 324c, Rome. No. 324a, Amalfi Coast. No. 324b, Aeolian Islands. No. 324d, Florence. No. 324e, Pisa.

Perf. 13½x13¼
2002, Aug. 30 Litho.
322 A338 51c multicolored 1.10 1.10
323 A338 58c multicolored 1.25 1.25
Souvenir Booklet
324 Booklet 15.00
a.-c. A338 7c any single .40 .40
d.-f. A338 15c any single .85 .85
g. Booklet pane of 4, #324d 3.40 3.40
h. Booklet pane of 4, #324a 1.60 1.60
i. Booklet pane of 4, #324b 3.40 3.40
j. Booklet pane of 4, #324b 1.60 1.60
k. Booklet pane of 4, #324f 3.40 3.40
l. Booklet pane of 4, #324c 1.60 1.60

AIDS Awareness Type
2002, Oct. 24 Litho. Perf. 13½
325 A339 €1.53 multicolored 2.50 2.75

Indigenous Art — V46

No. 326: a, Mola, Panama. b, Mochican llama-shaped spouted vessel, Peru. c, Tarabuco woven cloth, Bolivia. d, Masks, Cuba. e, Aztec priest's feather headdress, Mexico. f, Bird-shaped staff head, Colombia.

2003, Jan. 31 Litho. Perf. 14¼
326 V46 Sheet of 6 7.50 7.50
a.-f. 51c Any single 1.25 1.25

Austrian Tourist Attractions Type of 2002

Designs: 25c, Kunsthistorisches Museum, Vienna. €1, Belvedere Palace, Vienna.

2003, Mar. 28 Litho. Perf. 14½x14
327 V45 25c multicolored .55 .55
328 V45 €1 multicolored 2.25 2.25

Endangered Species Type of 1993

Designs: No. 329, Anas formosa (Baikal teal). No. 330, Bostrychia hagedash (Hadada ibis). No. 331, Ramphastos toco (toco toucan).

No. 332, Alopochen aegyptiacus (Egyptian goose).

2003, Apr. 3 Litho. Perf. 12¾x12½
329 A271 51c multicolored 1.25 1.25
330 A271 51c multicolored 1.25 1.25
331 A271 51c multicolored 1.25 1.25
332 A271 51c multicolored 1.25 1.25
a.   Block of 4, #329-332 5.00 5.00

International Year of Freshwater Type of 2003
Perf. 14¼x14½
2003, June 20 Litho.
333 A345 55c Bridge, bird 3.00 3.00
334 A345 75c Horse, empty river 5.00 5.00
a.   Horiz. pair, #333-334 8.00 8.00

Austrian Tourist Attractions Type of 2002

Design: 4c, Schloss Eggenberg, Graz.

2003, Aug. 7 Litho. Perf. 14x13¼
335 V45 4c multicolored .45 .45

Ralph Bunche Type
Litho. With Foil Application
2003, Aug. 7 Perf. 13½x14
336 A346 €2.10 olive green & multicolored 3.50 3.50

In Memoriam Type of 2003
2003, Oct. 24 Litho. Perf. 13¼x13
337 A347 €2.10 multicolored 5.00 5.00

World Heritage Sites, United States Type

Designs: 55c, No. 340c, Olympic National Park. 75c, No. 340e, Everglades National Park. No. 340a, Yosemite National Park. No. 340b, Great Smoky Mountains National Park. No. 340d, Hawaii Volcanoes National Park. No. 340f, Yellowstone National Park.

2003, Oct. 24 Litho. Perf. 14½x14¼
338 A348 55c multicolored 1.50 .75
339 A348 75c multicolored 2.00 1.00
Souvenir Booklet
340 Booklet 14.50
a.-c. A348 15c any single .55 .55
d.-f. A348 20c any single .65 .65
g. Booklet pane of 4 #340a 2.10 2.10
h. Booklet pane of 4 #340d 2.60 2.60
i. Booklet pane of 4 #340b 2.10 2.10
j. Booklet pane of 4 #340e 2.60 2.60
k. Booklet pane of 4 #340c 2.10 2.10
l. Booklet pane of 4 #340f 2.60 2.60

Austrian Tourist Attractions Type of 2002

Design: 55c, Schloss Schönbrunn, Vienna.

2004, Jan. 29 Litho. Perf. 13x13¼
341 V45 55c multicolored 1.50 1.50

Endangered Species Type of 1993

Designs: No. 342, Melursus ursinus (Sloth bear). No. 343, Cervus eldi (Eld's deer). No. 344, Cercocebus torquatus (Cherry-crowned mangabey). No. 345, Bubalus arnee (Wild water buffalo).

2004, Jan. 29 Litho. Perf. 12¾x12½
342 A271 55c multicolored 1.50 1.50
343 A271 55c multicolored 1.50 1.50
344 A271 55c multicolored 1.50 1.50
345 A271 55c multicolored 1.50 1.50
a.   Block of 4, #342-345 6.00 6.00

Indigenous Art Type of 2003

No. 346: a, Illuminated illustration from the Book of Kells, Ireland. b, Easter eggs, Ukraine. c, Venus of Willendorf, Paleolithic age limestone statue, Austria. d, Flatatunga panel, Iceland. e, Neolithic era idol, Hungary. f, Illuminated illustration from medical treatise, Portugal.

2004, Mar. 4 Litho. Perf. 13¼
346 V46 Sheet of 6 12.00 12.00
a.-f. 55c Any single 2.00 2.00

Road Safety Type

Road map art with: 55c, Automobile, alcohol bottles. 75c, Road, clouds in traffic light colors, vert.

Perf. 13x13¼, 13¼x13
2004, Apr. 7 Litho.
347 A354 55c multicolored 1.25 1.25
348 A354 75c multicolored 1.75 1.75

Japanese Peace Bell, 50th Anniv. Type
Litho. & Engr.
2004, June 3 Perf. 13¼x13
349 A355 €2.10 multicolored 4.50 4.50

World Heritage Sites, Greece Type

Designs: 55c, No. 352f, Mycenae and Tiryns. 75c, No. 352e, Olympia. No. 352a, Acropolis, Athens. No. 352b, Delos. No. 352c, Delphi. No. 352d, Pythagoreion and Heraion of Samos.

2004, Aug. 12   Litho.   Perf. 14x13¼
350	A356	55c multicolored	1.75	1.75
351	A356	75c multicolored	2.25	2.25

Souvenir Booklet
352		Booklet	16.00	
a.-d.	A356	25c any single	.60	.60
e.-f.	A356	30c either single	.70	.70
g.		Booklet pane of 4 #352a	2.40	2.40
h.		Booklet pane of 4 #352b	2.40	2.40
i.		Booklet pane of 4 #352c	2.40	2.40
j.		Booklet pane of 4 #352d	2.40	2.40
k.		Booklet pane of 4 #352e	2.80	2.80
l.		Booklet pane of 4 #352f	2.80	2.80

My Dream for Peace Type

Winning designs of Lions Club International children's global peace poster contest by: 55c, Henry Ulfe Renteria, Peru. €1, Michelle Fortaliza, Philippines.

2004, Sept. 21   Litho.   Perf. 14
353	A357	55c multicolored	1.40	1.40
354	A357	€1 multicolored	2.50	2.50

Human Rights — V48

2004, Oct. 14   Litho.   Perf. 11¼
355	V47	55c multicolored	1.00	1.00
356	V48	€1.25 multicolored	3.00	3.00

United Nations, 60th Anniv. Type of 2005

Litho. & Engr.
2005, Feb. 4   Perf. 11x11¼
357	A361	55c multicolored	2.50	2.50

Souvenir Sheet
Litho.
Imperf
358	A361	€2.10 multicolored	6.50	6.50

International Center, Vienna — V49

Litho. with Hologram
2005, Feb. 4   Perf. 13½x13¼
359	V49	75c multicolored	2.25	2.25

Endangered Species Type of 1993

Designs: No. 360, Ansellia africana. No. 361, Phragmipedium kovachii. No. 362, Cymbidium ensifolium. No. 363, Renanthera imschootiana.

2005, Mar. 3   Litho.   Perf. 12¾x12½
360	A271	55c multicolored	1.40	1.40
361	A271	55c multicolored	1.40	1.40
362	A271	55c multicolored	1.40	1.40
363	A271	55c multicolored	1.40	1.40
a.		Block of 4, #360-363	6.00	6.00

Nature's Wisdom — V50

Designs: 55c, Desert landscape, China. 80c, Cheetah family, Africa.

2005, Apr. 21   Litho.   Perf. 13½x13¼
364	V50	55c multicolored	1.60	1.60
365	V50	75c multicolored	2.25	2.25

Intl. Year of Sport Type

2005, June 3   Litho.   Perf. 13x13¼
366	A368	55c Equestrian	1.60	1.60
367	A368	€1.10 Soccer	3.25	3.25

World Heritage Sites, Egypt Type

Designs: Nos. 368, 370c, Abu Mena. Nos. 369, 370f, St. Catherine area. No. 370a, Memphis and its Necropolis. No. 370b, Philae. No. 370d, Ancient Thebes. No. 370e, Islamic Cairo.

2005, Aug. 4   Litho.   Perf. 14x13¼
368	A369	55c multicolored	1.60	1.60
369	A369	75c multicolored	2.25	2.25

Souvenir Booklet
370		Booklet, #370g-370l	19.50	
a.-c.	A369	25c any single	.75	.75
d.-f.	A369	30c any single	.85	.85
g.		Booklet pane of 4 #370a	3.00	3.00
h.		Booklet pane of 4 #370b	3.00	3.00
i.		Booklet pane of 4 #370c	3.00	3.00
j.		Booklet pane of 4 #370d	3.50	3.50
k.		Booklet pane of 4 #370e	3.50	3.50
l.		Booklet pane of 4 #370f	3.50	3.50

No. 370 sold for €6.80.

My Dream for Peace Type

Winning designs of Lions Club International children's global peace poster contest by: 55c, Lee Min Gi, Republic of Korea. €1, Natalie Chan, US.

2004, Sept. 21   Litho.   Perf. 14
371	A357	55c multicolored	1.60	1.60
372	A357	€1 multicolored	2.75	2.75

Food for Life Type

Designs: 55c, Corn, people with food bowls, teacher and students. €1.25, Rice, helicopter dropping food, elephant caravan.

2005, Oct. 20   Litho.   Perf. 13¾
373	A370	55c multicolored	1.60	1.60
374	A370	€1.25 multicolored	3.50	3.50

Indigenous Art Type of 2003

No. 375 — Musical instruments: a, Drum, Guinea. b, Whistle, Congo. c, Horn, Botswana. d, Drums, Burundi. e, Harp, Gabon. f, Bell, Nigeria.

2006, Feb. 3   Litho.   Perf. 13¼
375	V46	Sheet of 6	12.00	12.00
a.-f.		55c Any single	2.00	2.00

Endangered Species Type of 1993

Designs: No. 376, Dendrobates pumilio. No. 377, Furcifer lateralis. No. 378, Corallus hortulanus. No. 379, Dendrobates leucomelas.

Perf. 12¾x12½
2006, Mar. 16   Litho.
376	A271	55c multicolored	1.50	1.50
377	A271	55c multicolored	1.50	1.50
378	A271	55c multicolored	1.50	1.50
379	A271	55c multicolored	1.50	1.50
a.		Block of 4, #376-379	6.00	6.00

Intl. Day of Families Type

Designs: 55c, Family at water pump. €1.25, Family preparing food.

2006, May 27   Litho.   Perf. 14x13½
380	A373	55c multicolored	1.25	1.25
381	A373	€1.25 multicolored	2.50	2.50

World Heritage Sites, France Type

Eiffel Tower and: Nos. 382, 384c, Carcasonne. Nos. 383, 384f, Chateau de Chambord. No. 384a, Banks of the Seine. No.

384b, Provins. No. 384d, Roman Aqueduct. No. 384e, Mont Saint-Michel.

Litho. & Embossed with Foil Application

2006, June 17   Perf. 13½x13¼
382	A374	55c multicolored	1.50	1.50
383	A374	75c multicolored	2.00	2.00

Souvenir Booklet
384		Booklet, #384g-384l	18.00	
a.-c.	A374	25c any single	.65	.65
d.-f.	A374	30c any single	.80	.80
g.		Booklet pane of 4 #384a	2.60	2.60
h.		Booklet pane of 4 #384b	2.60	2.60
i.		Booklet pane of 4 #384c	2.60	2.60
j.		Booklet pane of 4 #384d	3.25	3.25
k.		Booklet pane of 4 #384e	3.25	3.25
l.		Booklet pane of 4 #384f	3.25	3.25

No. 384 sold for €6.80.

My Dream for Peace Type of 2004

Winning designs of Lions Club International children's global peace poster contest by: 55c, Klara Thein, Germany. €1, Laurensia Levina, Indonesia.

2006, Sept. 21   Litho.   Perf. 13½x13
385	A357	55c multicolored	1.60	1.60
386	A357	€1 multicolored	3.00	3.00

Flags and Coins Type

No. 387 — Flag of: a, Gambia, 1 dalasi coin. b, Pakistan, 1 rupee coin. c, Afghanistan, 2 afghani coin. d, Austria, 1 euro coin. e, Germany, 50 cent coin. f, Haiti, 50 centimes coin. g, Denmark, 20 krone coin. h, Netherlands, 1 euro coin.

2006, Oct. 5   Litho.   Perf. 13¼x13
387		Sheet of 8	14.00	14.00
a.-h.	A375	55c Any single	1.75	1.75

A column of rouletting in the middle of the sheet separates it into two parts.

Endangered Species Type of 1993

Designs: No. 388, Chlorocebus aethiops. No. 389, Nasalis larvatus. No. 390, Papio hamadryas. No. 391, Erythrocebus patas.

Perf. 12¾x12½
2007, Mar. 15   Litho.
388	A271	55c multicolored	1.60	1.60
389	A271	55c multicolored	1.60	1.60
390	A271	55c multicolored	1.60	1.60
391	A271	55c multicolored	1.60	1.60
a.		Block of 4, #388-391	6.40	6.40

Flags and Coins Type of 2006

No. 392 — Flag of: a, Trinidad and Tobago, 50 cent coin. b, Sierra Leone, 10 cent coin. c, Hungary, 100 forint coin. d, San Marino, 2 euro coin. e, Croatia, 1 kuna coin. f, Spain, 1 euro coin. g, Kazakhstan, 100 tenge coin. h, Ireland, 5 cent coin.

2007, May 3   Litho.   Perf. 13¼x13
392		Sheet of 8	13.00	13.00
a.-h.	A375	55c Any single	1.60	1.60

A column of rouletting in the middle of the sheet separates it into two parts.

Five 55c stamps depicting views of the Vienna International Center and the United Nations flag were released May 3, 2007. The editors have reason to believe that these stamps were not sold at the UN Post Office in Vienna. Value, strip of 5 with labels $45, sheet of 10 $90.

Peaceful Visions Type of 2007

Designs: 55c, "The Sowers." €1.25, "We All Thrive Under the Same Sky."

2007, June 1   Litho.   Perf. 13x12½
398	A378	55c multicolored	1.60	1.60
399	A378	€1.25 multicolored	3.75	3.75

World Heritage Sites, South America Type

Designs: Nos. 400, 402e, Iguaçu National Park, Brazil. Nos. 401, 402b, Cueva de las Manos, Argentina. No. 402a, Rapa Nui, Chile. No. 402c, Machu Picchu, Peru. No. 402d, Tiwanaku, Bolivia. No. 474f, Galapagos Islands, Ecuador.

2007, Aug. 9   Litho.   Perf. 13¼x13
400	A381	55c multicolored	2.00	2.00
401	A381	75c multicolored	2.75	2.75

Souvenir Booklet
402		Booklet, #402g-402l	20.00	
a.-c.	A381	25c Any single	.75	.75
d.-f.	A381	30c Any single	.90	.90
g.		Booklet pane of 4 #402a	3.00	3.00
h.		Booklet pane of 4 #402b	3.00	3.00
i.		Booklet pane of 4 #402c	3.00	3.00

j.		Booklet pane of 4 #402d	3.60	3.60
k.		Booklet pane of 4 #402e	3.60	3.60
l.		Booklet pane of 4 #402f	3.60	3.60

Humanitarian Mail Type

2007, Sept. 6   Litho.   Perf. 12½x13¼
403	A382	75c multicolored	2.25	2.25

Five 65c stamps depicting the International Space Station, astronauts and planets were released Oct. 1, 2007. The editors have reason to believe that these stamps were not sold at the UN Post Office in Vienna. Value, strip of 5 with labels $35, sheet of 10 $65.

Space for Humanity Type

Designs: 65c, Space stations. €1.15, Space Station.
€2.10, Space probe, Jupiter.

2007, Oct. 25   Litho.   Perf. 13½x14
409	A383	65c multicolored	2.00	2.00
410	A383	€1.15 multicolored	3.50	3.50

Souvenir Sheet
411	A383	€2.10 multicolored	8.00	8.00

Intl. Holocaust Remembrance Day Type

2008, Jan. 27   Litho.   Perf. 13
412	A384	65c multicolored	3.00	3.00

Johann Strauss Memorial, Vienna — V61

Pallas Athene Fountain, Vienna V62

Pegasus Fountain, Salzburg V63

Statue, Belvedere Palace Gardens, Vienna V64

2008, Jan. 28   Litho.   Perf. 13½x14
413	V61	10c black	.35	.35

Perf. 14x13½
414	V62	15c black	.50	.50
415	V63	65c black	2.25	2.25
416	V64	€1.40 black	4.75	4.75
		Nos. 413-416 (4)	7.85	7.85

Endangered Species Type of 1993

Designs: No. 4170, Mirounga angustirostris. No. 418, Millepora alcicornis. No. 419, Hippocampus histrix. No. 420, Physeter catodon.

2008, Mar. 6   Litho.   Perf. 12¾x12½
417	A271	65c multicolored	2.50	2.50
418	A271	65c multicolored	2.50	2.50
419	A271	65c multicolored	2.50	2.50
420	A271	65c multicolored	2.50	2.50
a.		Block of 4, #417-420	10.00	10.00

Flags and Coins Type of 2006

No. 421 — Flag of: a, Poland, 5 zloty coin. b, Latvia, 1 lat coin. c, Portugal, 1 euro coin. d, Armenia, 500 dram coin. e, Sweden, 1 krona coin. f, Cyprus, 1 euro coin. g, Slovakia, 1 koruna coin. h, Qatar, 50 dirham coin.

2008, May 8   Litho.   Perf. 13¼x13

421	Sheet of 8	18.00	18.00
a.-h.	A375 65c Any single	2.25	2.25

A column of rouletting in the middle of the sheet separates it into two parts.

Five 65c stamps depicting the Vienna International Center and its artwork were released May 12, 2008. The editors have reason to believe that these stamps were not sold at the UN Post Office in Vienna. Value, strip of 5 with labels $30, sheet of 10 $60.

Graduate — V70

Stylized Person, Heart, Brain, Hands — V71

Litho. & Embossed

2008, June 6   Perf. 14x13¼

427	V70	55c green & violet	2.00 2.00
428	V71	€1.40 violet & green	5.00 5.00

Convention on the Rights of Persons with Disabilities.

Sport for Peace Type of 2008

Designs: 65c, Man on rings. €1.30, €2.10, Swimmer.

2008, Aug. 8   Litho.   Perf. 14½

429	A393	65c multicolored	2.25 2.25
430	A393	€1.30 multicolored	4.50 4.50

Souvenir Sheet   Perf. 12¾x13¼

431	A393	€2.10 multicolored	9.00 9.00
a.		Overprinted in sheet margin	10.00 10.00

2008 Summer Olympics, Beijing. No. 431a is overprinted in black "Peking 2008" and medals with UN emblem.

"We Can End Poverty" Type of 2008

Winning designs in children's art contest: 65c, By Mariam Marukian, Armenia. 75c, By Rufaro Duri, Zimbabwe, vert.

Perf. 12¾x12½

432	A395	65c multicolored	2.25 2.25

Perf. 12½x12¾   Litho.

433	A395	75c multicolored	2.60 2.60

Five €1.40 stamps depicting views of the Vienna International Center and its artwork were released Sept. 18, 2008. The editors have reason to believe that these stamps were not sold at the UN Post Office in Vienna. Value, strip of 5 with labels $40, sheet of 10 $80.

Climate Change Types of New York and Geneva and

V72

Climate Change — V73

No. 434 — Smokestacks with quarter of Earth in: a, LR. b, LL. c, UR. d, UL.

No. 435 — Cut trees with quarter of Earth in: a, LR. b, LL. c, UR. d, UL.

No. 436: a, Like New York #969a. b, Like New York #969b. c, Like New York #969c. d, Like New York #969d. e, Like Geneva #493a. f, Like Geneva #493b. g, Like Geneva #493c. h, Like Geneva #493d. i, Like Vienna #434a. j, Like Vienna #434b. k, Like Vienna #434c. l, Like Vienna #434d. m, Like New York #968a. n, Like New York #968b. o, Like New York #968c. p, Like New York #968d. q, Like Geneva #492a. r, Like Geneva #492b. s, Like Geneva #492c. t, Like Geneva #492d. u, Like Vienna #435a. v, Like Vienna #435b. w, Like Vienna #435c. x, Like Vienna #435d.

All stamps have green panels inscribed "Klimawandel."

2008, Oct. 23   Litho.   Perf. 13¼x13

434		Sheet of 4	9.00 9.00
a.-d.	V72	65c Any single	2.25 2.25
435		Sheet of 4	16.00 16.00
a.-d.	V73	€1.15 Any single	4.00 4.00

Souvenir Booklet

436		Booklet, #436y-436ad	27.00
a.-d.		A397 30c Any single	1.00 1.00
e.-h.		G77 30c Any single	1.00 1.00
i.-l.		V72 30c Any single	1.00 1.00
m.-p.		A396 35c Any single	1.10 1.10
q.-t.		G76 35c Any single	1.10 1.10
u.-x.		V73 35c Any single	1.10 1.10
y.		Booklet pane of 4, #436a-436d	4.25 4.25
z.		Booklet pane of 4, #436e-436h	4.25 4.25
aa.		Booklet pane of 4, #436i-436l	4.25 4.25
ab.		Booklet pane of 4, #436m-436p	4.75 4.75
ac.		Booklet pane of 4, #436q-436t	4.75 4.75
ad.		Booklet pane of 4, #436u-436x	4.75 4.75

U Thant Type of 2009

Litho. With Foil Application

2009, Feb. 6   Perf. 14x13½

437	A399	€1.15 green & multi	4.50 4.50

Endangered Species Type of 1993

Designs: No. 438, Trogonoptera brookiana. No. 439, Pandinus imperator. No. 440, Carabus intricatus. No. 441, Brachypelma smithi.

2009, Apr. 16   Litho.   Perf. 12¾x12½

438	A271	65c multicolored	2.00 2.00
439	A271	65c multicolored	2.00 2.00
440	A271	65c multicolored	2.00 2.00
441	A271	65c multicolored	2.00 2.00
a.		Block of 4, #438-441	8.00 8.00

World Heritage Sites, Germany Type of 2009

Designs: Nos. 442, 444c, Palaces and Parks of Potsdam and Berlin. Nos. 443, 444e, Luther Memorials in Eisleben and Wittenberg. No. 444a, Town Hall and Roland on the Marketplace, Bremen. No. 444b, Wartburg Castle. No. 444d, Aachen Cathedral. No. 444f, Monastic Island of Reichenau.

2009, May 7   Litho.   Perf. 14x13½

442	A400	65c multicolored	1.90 1.90
443	A400	€1.40 multicolored	4.00 4.00

Souvenir Booklet

444		Booklet, #444g-444l	20.00
a.-c.		A400 30c any single	.75 .75
d.-f.		A400 35c any single	.90 .90
g.		Booklet pane of 4 #444a	3.00 3.00
h.		Booklet pane of 4 #444b	3.00 3.00
i.		Booklet pane of 4 #444c	3.00 3.00
j.		Booklet pane of 4 #444d	3.60 3.60
k.		Booklet pane of 4 #444e	3.60 3.60
l.		Booklet pane of 4 #444f	3.60 3.60

Memorial Plaza, Vienna International Center — V74

The First Swallows, Sculpture by Juozas Mikenas — V75

Conference Building, Vienna International Center — V76

Butterfly Tree, by Rudolf Hausner — V77

Flags in Memorial Plaza — V78

2009, May 7   Perf. 13¼

445	V74	65c multi + label	5.00 5.00
a.		Perf. 11¼x11	10.00 10.00
446	V75	65c multi + label	5.00 5.00
a.		Perf. 11¼x11	10.00 10.00
447	V76	65c multi + label	5.00 5.00
a.		Perf. 11¼x11	10.00 10.00
448	V77	65c multi + label	5.00 5.00
a.		Perf. 11¼x11	10.00 10.00
449	V78	65c multi + label	5.00 5.00
a.		Perf. 11¼x11	10.00 10.00
b.		Vert. strip of 5, #445-449, + 5 labels	25.00 25.00
c.		Vert. strip of 5, #445a-449a, + 5 labels	50.00 50.00

The sheet of No. 449c has "ver. 2" in the lower right selvage.

Economic and Social Council (ECOSOC) Type of 2009

Designs: 55c, Combat HIV/AIDS, malaria and other diseases. 65c, Reduce child mortality.

2009, Aug. 6   Litho.   Perf. 12¾x12½

450	A411	55c multicolored	2.25 2.25
451	A411	65c multicolored	3.50 3.50

V79

V80

V81

V82

Vienna International Center, 30th Anniv. — V83

2009, Aug. 24   Perf. 13¼

452	V79	€1.40 multi + label	6.00 6.00
a.		Perf. 11¼x11	20.00 20.00
453	V80	€1.40 multi + label	6.00 6.00
a.		Perf. 11¼x11	20.00 20.00
454	V81	€1.40 multi + label	6.00 6.00
a.		Perf. 11¼x11	20.00 20.00
455	V82	€1.40 multi + label	6.00 6.00
a.		Perf. 11¼x11	20.00 20.00
456	V83	€1.40 multi + label	6.00 6.00
a.		Perf. 11¼x11	20.00 20.00
b.		Vert. strip of 5, #452-456, + 5 labels	30.00 30.00
c.		Vert. strip of 5, #452a-456a, + 5 labels	100.00 100.00

The sheet of No. 456c has "ver. 2" in the lower right selvage.

Millennium Development Goals Type of 2009

Miniature Sheet

No. 457: a, Bowl of hot food. b, Pencil. c, Female symbol. d, Teddy bear. e, Pregnant woman, heart. f, Medicine bottle. g, Stylized tree. h, Conjoined people.

2009, Sept. 25

457	A413	Sheet of 8	16.00 16.00
a.-h.		65c Any single	2.00 2.00

Miniature Sheet

Indigenous People — V84

No. 458 — Portraits of person from: a, Tanzania. b, Australia. c, Namibia (small child). d, Indonesia. e, Namibia (young girl). f, Untied Arab Emirates.

2009, Oct. 8   Perf. 12½

458	V84	Sheet of 6	12.00 12.00
a.-f.		65c Any single	2.00 2.00

Flags and Coins Type of 2006

No. 459 — Flag of: a, Romania, 1 ban coin. b, Slovenia, 5 cent coin. c, Azerbaijan, 10 giapik coin. d, Bangladesh, 5 taka coin. e, Belarus, 1 ruble coin. f, Malta, 1 euro coin. g, Swaziland, 1 lilangeni coin. h, Jordan, 10 piaster coin.

2010, Feb. 5   Litho.   Perf. 13¼x13

459		Sheet of 8	16.00	16.00
a.-h.	A375 65c Any single		2.00	2.00

A column of rouletting in the middle of the sheet separates it into two parts.

People Pulling Rope — V85

Person With Hands Over Eyes — V86

Woman Touching Her Shoulder — V87

Man With Wheelbarrow — V88

Blue Heart — V89

Designed by Rorie Katz, US.

2010, Feb. 5   Litho.   Perf. 11¼x11

460	V85	65c multi + label	4.50	4.50
461	V86	65c multi + label	4.50	4.50
462	V87	65c multi + label	4.50	4.50
463	V88	65c multi + label	4.50	4.50
464	V89	65c multi + label	4.50	4.50
a.		Vert. strip of 5, #460-464, + 5 labels	22.50	22.50

The full sheet sold for $14.95 or €19.90. The labels could not be personalized.

Endangered Species Type of 1993

Designs: No. 465, Mammillaria zeilmanniana. No. 466, Hoodia gordonii. No. 467, Welwitschia mirabilis. No. 468, Euphorbia milii.

2010, Apr. 15   Litho.   Perf. 12¾x12½

465	A271	65c multicolored	2.25	2.25
466	A271	65c multicolored	2.25	2.25
467	A271	65c multicolored	2.25	2.25
468	A271	65c multicolored	2.25	2.25
a.		Block of 4, #465-468	9.00	9.00

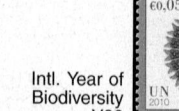

Intl. Year of Biodiversity V90

Drawings from Art Forms from Nature, by Ernst Heinrich: 5c, Colonial algae. 20c, Boxfish.

2010, Apr. 15   Litho.   Perf. 13

469	V90	5c multicolored	.25	.25
470	V90	20c multicolored	.70	.70

One Planet, One Ocean Types of New York and Geneva and

V91

V92

No. 471: a, Dolphin at left, fish at right. b, Fish at top, shark in center. c, Dolphin at left, fish at right and bottom. d, Fish at left, top and right.

No. 472: a, Dolphins. b, Shark and fish at center, ray at bottom. c, Fish at left, turtle at bottom. d, Fish and coral.

No. 473: a, Like New York #1003a. b, Like New York #1003b. c, Like New York #1003c. d, Like New York #1003d. e, Like #471a. f, Like #471b. g, Like #471c. h, Like #471d. i, Like Geneva #519a. j, Like Geneva #519b. k, Like Geneva #519c. l, Like Geneva #519d. m, Like New York #1004a. n, Like New York #1004b. o, Like New York #1004c. p, Like New York #1004d. q, Like #472a. r, Like #472b. s, Like #472c. t, Like #472d. u, Like Geneva #520a. v, Like Geneva #520b. w, Like Geneva #520c. x, Like Geneva #520d.

2010, May 6   Litho.   Perf. 14x13¼

471	V91	Sheet of 4	7.75	7.75
a.-d.		55c Any single	1.90	1.90
472	V92	Sheet of 4	9.00	9.00
a.-d.		65c Any single	2.25	2.25

Souvenir Booklet
Perf. 13¼x13

473		Booklet, #473y-473z, 473aa-473ad	27.00	
a.-d.	A416 30c any single		1.00	1.00
e.-h.	V91 30c any single		1.00	1.00
i.-l.	G85 30c any single		1.00	1.00
m.-p.	A417 35c any single		1.25	1.25
q.-t.	V92 35c any single		1.25	1.25
u.-x.	G86 35c any single		1.25	1.25
y.	Booklet pane of 4 #473a-473d		4.00	4.00
z.	Booklet pane of 4 #473e-473h		4.00	4.00
aa.	Booklet pane of 4 #473i-473l		4.00	4.00
ab.	Booklet pane of 4 #473m-473p		5.00	5.00
ac.	Booklet pane of 4 #473q-473t		5.00	5.00
ad.	Booklet pane of 4 #473u-473x		5.00	5.00

Intl. Oceanographic Commission, 50th anniv.

United Nations, 65th Anniv. Type of 2010

Litho. With Foil Application

2010, June 28   Perf. 13¼

474	A422	75c green & gold	3.00	3.00
a.		Souvenir sheet of 2	6.00	6.00

V93

V94

V95

UN TRANSPORT   V96

UN TRANSPORT   V97

2010, Sept. 2   Litho.   Perf. 13¼x13

475	V93	65c multicolored	1.90	1.90
476	V94	65c multicolored	1.90	1.90
477	V95	65c multicolored	1.90	1.90
478	V96	65c multicolored	1.90	1.90
479	V97	65c multicolored	1.90	1.90
a.		Horiz. strip of 5, #475-479	9.50	9.50

Miniature Sheet

Indigenous People — V98

No. 480 — Portraits of person from: a, French Polynesia (denomination in white). b, Tanzania (child with cloth head covering). c, Malaysia. d, French Polynesia (denomination in white and green). e, Namibia. f, Tanzania (man with band around forehead).

2010, Oct. 21   Litho.   Perf. 13

480	V98	Pane of 6	11.50	11.50
a.-f.		65c Any single	1.90	1.90

United Nations Headquarters, Vienna — V99

United Nations Headquarters, Geneva: €1.25, Aerial view. €2.85, Ground-level view.

2011, Feb. 4   Litho.   Perf. 13

481	V99	€1.25 multicolored	3.75	3.75
482	V99	€2.85 multicolored	8.25	8.25

Flags and Coins Type of 2006

No. 483 — Flag of: a, Lithuania, 2 lita coin. b, Greece, 1 euro coin. c, Kyrgyzstan, 50 tyiyn coin. d, Oman, 100 baisa coin. e, Estonia, 2 euro coin. f, Czech Republic, 5 koruna coin. g,

Uzbekistan, 100 som coin. h, Monaco, 1 euro coin.

2011, Mar. 3   Litho.   Perf. 13¼x13

483		Sheet of 8	15.00	15.00
a.-h.	A375 65c Any single		1.75	1.75

A column of rouletting in the middle of the sheet separates it into two parts.

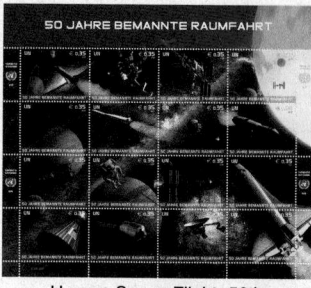

Human Space Flight, 50th Anniv. — V100

No. 484: Various parts of outer space scene.

No. 485, vert.: a, Space Shuttle. b, Space Station.

2011, Apr. 12   Litho.   Perf. 13x13¼

484	V100	Sheet of 16	16.50	16.50
a.-p.		35c any single	1.00	1.00

Souvenir Sheet

485	V100	Sheet of 2	12.00	12.00
a.		55c multi	5.50	5.50
b.		65c multi	6.50	6.50
c.		Souvenir sheet of 6, New York #1025a-1025b, Geneva #534a-b, Vienna #485a-485b	42.50	42.50

No. 485 contains two 40x48mm stamps that were printed as part of a larger sheet of six stamps, No. 485c, which was broken up into its component two-stamp souvenir sheets, and also sold as one unit. Value $90, complete unit.

Vienna International Center and Flagpoles — V101

Fish-eye View of Vienna International Center and Flagpole — V102

Vienna International Center and Train — V103

Aerial View of Vienna International Center — V104

Vienna International Center and Water — V105

Detail From La Pioggia, Stadt Unter de Regen, by Friedensreich Hundertwasser — V106

Hand in Hand, by Hans Dietrich — V107

The Scholars Pavilion — V108

Detail From Grupo Expectante, by Alfredo Sosabravo — V109

Yes to Life, No to Drugs, by Sami Burhan — V110

2011, May 1   Litho.   *Perf. 14¾*
486	V101	62c multi + label	2.50	2.50
487	V102	62c multi + label	2.50	2.50
488	V103	62c multi + label	2.50	2.50
489	V104	62c multi + label	2.50	2.50
490	V105	62c multi + label	2.50	2.50
a.		Vert. strip of 5, #486-490, + 5 labels	15.00	15.00
491	V106	70c multi + label	3.00	3.00
492	V107	70c multi + label	3.00	3.00
493	V108	70c multi + label	3.00	3.00
494	V109	70c multi + label	3.00	3.00
495	V110	70c multi + label	3.00	3.00
a.		Vert. strip of 5, #491-495, + 5 labels	17.50	17.50
		Nos. 486-495 (10)	25.50	25.50

The full sheet of Nos. 486-490 sold for $21.45 or €12.40. The full sheet of Nos. 491-495 sold for $14.26 or €9.90. The labels could be personalized.

UNESCO World Heritage Sites in Nordic Countries Type of 2011

Designs: 62c, Urnes Stave Church, Norway. 1fr, Struve Geodetic Arc, Norway, Finland and Sweden.

2011, May 5   Litho.   *Perf. 14x13½*
| 496 | A433 | 62c multicolored | 1.90 | 1.90 |
| 497 | A433 | 70c multicolored | 2.10 | 2.10 |

AIDS Ribbon Type of 2011
2011, June 3   Litho.   *Die Cut*
Self-Adhesive
| 498 | A434 | 70c red & green | 2.40 | 2.40 |

ECOSOC Type of 2011
2011, July 1   Litho.   *Perf. 14¼*
| 499 | A435 | 62c multicolored | 3.00 | 3.00 |
| 500 | A435 | 70c multicolored | 4.00 | 4.00 |

Endangered Species Type of 1993

Designs: No. 501, Cyanoramphus novaeze-landiae (Red-fronted parakeet). No. 502, Haliaeetus albicilla (White-tailed eagle). No. 503, Probosciger aterrimus (Black palm cockatoo). No. 504, Caloenas nicobarica (Nicobar pigeon).

2011, Sept. 7   Litho.   *Perf. 12¾x12½*
501	A271	70c multicolored	2.50	2.50
502	A271	70c multicolored	2.50	2.50
503	A271	70c multicolored	2.50	2.50
504	A271	70c multicolored	2.50	2.50
a.		Block of 4, #501-504	10.00	10.00

Intl. Year of Forests Type of 2011

Designs: 62c, Tree top, crosses, circles and ovals. 70c, Stylized people and trees.

Litho. With Foil Application
2011, Oct. 13   *Perf. 12½*
505		62c multicolored	2.00	2.00
506		70c multicolored	2.25	2.25
a.	A436	Vert. pair, #505-506	4.25	4.25

Flags and Coins Type of 2006

No. 507 — Flag of: a, Cameroun, 100 franc coin. b, Samoa, 2 tala coin. c, Surinam, 5 cent coin. d, Macedonia, 50 denar coin. e, Bulgaria, 50 stotinka coin. f, Tanzania, 100 shilling coin. g, Finland, 1 euro coin. h, Cuba, 1 peso coin.

2012, Feb. 3   Litho.   *Perf. 13¼x13*
| 507 | | Sheet of 8 | 16.50 | 16.50 |
| a.-h. | A375 | 70c Any single | 2.00 | 2.00 |

A column of rouletting in the middle of the sheet separates it into two parts.

Autism Awareness V112

V111

Drawings by autistic people: No. 508, The Path, by Ryan Smoluk, Canada. No. 509, Untitled drawing, by Colm Isherwood, Ireland.

2012, Apr. 2   Litho.   *Perf. 14x13½*
508	V111	70c multicolored	2.25	2.25
509	V112	70c multicolored	2.25	2.25
a.		Pair, #508-509	4.50	4.50

UN Emblem — V113

2012, Apr. 12   Litho.   *Perf. 14½*
| 510 | V113 | 70c pur, blk + label | 3.50 | 3.50 |
| | | Sheet of 10 + 10 labels | 35.00 | 35.00 |

The full sheet sold for $14.52 or €9.90. The labels could be personalized.

Endangered Species Type of 1993

Designs: No. 511, Panthera uncia. No. 512, Polyplectron schleiermacheri. No. 513, Tyto novaehollandiae. No. 514, Ambystoma mexicanum.

2012, Apr. 19   Litho.   *Perf. 12¾x12½*
511	A271	70c multicolored	2.25	2.25
512	A271	70c multicolored	2.25	2.25
513	A271	70c multicolored	2.25	2.25
514	A271	70c multicolored	2.25	2.25
a.		Block of 4, #511-514	9.00	9.00

Rio + 20 Type of 2012
2012, June 1   Litho.   *Perf. 13x13¼*
| 515 | A443 | 70c multicolored | 2.10 | 2.10 |

Sport for Peace Type of 2012
Litho. With Foil Application
2012, Aug. 17   *Perf. 14½*
516	A444	62c multicolored	1.90	1.90
517	A444	70c multicolored	2.10	2.10
a.		Souvenir sheet of 1	2.10	2.10

UNESCO World Heritage Sites in Africa Type of 2012

Designs: 62c, Kenya Lake System, Kenya. 70c, Medina of Marrakesh, Morocco.

2012, Sept. 5   Litho.   *Perf. 13¼*
| 518 | A445 | 62c multicolored | 1.75 | 1.75 |
| 519 | A445 | 70c multicolored | 2.00 | 2.00 |

Miniature Sheet

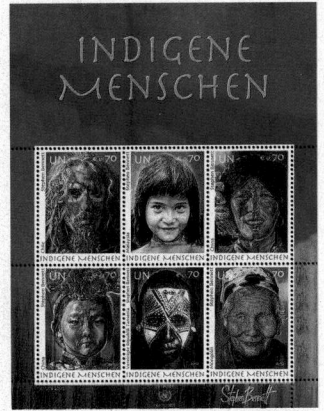

Indigenous People — V114

No. 520 — Portrait of person from: a, Chile. b, Malaysia. c, China (woman with black hair). d, China (woman with flower in hair). e, Tanzania. f, Mongolia.

2012, Oct. 11   Litho.   *Perf. 13¼x13*
| 520 | V114 | Sheet of 6 | 11.50 | 11.50 |
| a.-f. | | 70c Any single | 1.90 | 1.90 |

World Radio Day Type of 2013

Designs: 70c, Microphone and scripts. €1.70, Boy with radio.

2013, Feb. 13   Litho.   *Perf. 13¼x13*
| 521 | A448 | 70c multicolored | 2.00 | 2.00 |
| 522 | A448 | €1.70 multicolored | 5.00 | 5.00 |

People in Handprint V115

People in Heart — V116

2013, Mar. 5   Litho.   *Perf. 14x13½*
| 523 | V115 | 62c multicolored | 1.90 | 1.90 |

Perf. 13½x14
| 524 | V116 | €2.20 multicolored | 6.50 | 6.50 |

World Heritage Sites, China, Type of 2013

Designs: Nos. 525, 527c, Great Wall of China. Nos. 526, 527f, Mausoleum of the First Qing Emperor. No. 527a, Mogao Caves. No. 527b, Potala Palace, Lhasa. No. 527d, Imperial Palace, Beijing. No. 527e, Mount Huangshan.

2013, Apr. 11   Litho.   *Perf. 14x13½*
| 525 | A452 | 70c multicolored | 2.00 | 2.00 |
| 526 | A452 | €1.70 multicolored | 5.00 | 5.00 |

Souvenir Booklet
527		Booklet, #527g-527l	25.00	
a.-c.	A452	30c any single	.85	.85
d.-f.	A452	40c any single	1.10	1.10
g.		Booklet pane of 4 #527a	3.50	—
h.		Booklet pane of 4 #527b	3.50	—
i.		Booklet pane of 4 #527c	3.50	—
j.		Booklet pane of 4 #527d	4.75	—
k.		Booklet pane of 4 #527e	4.75	—
l.		Booklet pane of 4 #527f	4.75	—

World Oceans Day — V117

No. 528 — Fish from *One Fish, Two Fish, Red Fish, Blue Fish,* by Dr. Seuss: a, Green fish facing left, wave. b, Red fish facing right. c, Three green fish on plate. d, Red fish, back half of red fish, wave. e, Red fish facing left, front half of red fish, wave. f, Two red fish facing left. g, Two green fish facing right, wave. h, Red fish facing right, head of blue fish wearing hat. i, Yellow fish with green star, wave. j, Yellow fish, back of blue fish, wave. k, Two red fish, body of blue fish. l, Tail of yellow fish, two green fish facing left, wave.

2013, May 31   Litho.   *Perf. 13*
| 528 | V117 | Sheet of 12 | 24.00 | 24.00 |
| a.-l. | | 70c any single | | |

Nebulae Type of 2013

Designs: No. 567, NGC 2346. No. 568, Sh 2-106. 1fr, Messier 16.

2013, Aug. 9   Litho.   *Perf. 13¼*
529	A454	€1.70 multicolored	5.00	5.00
530	A454	€1.70 multicolored	5.00	5.00
a.		Pair, #529-530	10.00	10.00

Souvenir Sheet
| 531 | A454 | 62c multicolored | 1.90 | 1.90 |

No. 531 contains one 44x44mm stamp.

Works of Disabled Artists Type of 2013

Designs: 70c, Electro Man, by Pete Eckert, U.S. €1.70, Dive Bomb, by Matt Sesow, U.S.

2013, Sept. 20   Litho.   *Perf. 13¼x13*
| 532 | A456 | 70c multicolored | 2.00 | 2.00 |
| 533 | A456 | €1.70 multicolored | 5.00 | 5.00 |

Endangered Species Type of 1993

Designs: No. 534, Hemigalus derbyanus. No. 535, Bubo ascalaphus. No. 536, Nycticebus coucang. No. 537, Zaglossus spp.

2013, Oct. 10   Litho.   *Perf. 12¾x12½*
534	A271	70c multicolored	2.00	2.00
535	A271	70c multicolored	2.00	2.00
536	A271	70c multicolored	2.00	2.00
537	A271	70c multicolored	2.00	2.00
a.		Block of 4, #534-537	8.00	8.00

UN Emblem — V118

2013, Oct. 24   Litho.   Perf. 14½
538   V118   70c gray blue & blue
     + label   4.00   4.00

The full sheet sold for $14.20 or €9.90. The labels could be personalized.

Flags and Coins Type of 2006

No. 539 — Flag of: a, Malaysia, 50 sen coin. b, Nigeria, 1 naira coin. c, Zambia, 20 ngwee coin. d, Togo, 100 franc coin. e, Dominica, 5 cent coin. f, Chad, 100 franc coin. g, St. Vincent and the Grenadines, 5 cent coin. h, Syria, 25 pound coin.

2013, Nov. 6   Litho.   Perf. 13¼x13
539   Sheet of 8   16.00   16.00
a.-h.   A375 70c Any single   2.00   2.00

A column of rouletting in the middle of the sheet separates it into two parts.

International Day of Happiness Type of 2014

Designs: 90c, Happy Asian Boy at the Park, photograph by Alan Levenson, Russian word for "Happy." €1.70, Barbary Macacque with Baby, photograph by Gerhard Schulz, Arabic word for "Happy."

2014, Mar. 17   Litho.   Perf. 13¼x13
540   A459   90c multicolored   2.75   2.75
541   A459   €1.70 multicolored   5.25   5.25

Miniature Sheet

International Year of Jazz — V119

No. 542: a, Silhouette of saxophonist in blue. b, Woman singing. c, Silhouette of man in red, neon lights. d, Bass player. e, Trombone in gold. f, Silhouette of saxophonist in black, silhouette of man holding trombone. g, "Cocktails" neon sign . h, Silhouette of bass player in orange. i, Stack of record albums. j, Cymbal. k, Trombone in silver. l, Silhouette of clarinetist in black.

2014, Apr. 30   Litho.   Perf. 13x13¼
542   V119   Sheet of 12   24.00   24.00
a.-l.   70c Any single   2.00   2.00

Vienna International Center, 35th Anniv. — V120

No. 543: a, Vienna International Center under construction (towers and shadows), red panel. b, Vienna International Center, street light at left, green panel. c, Vienna International Center, curved building at left, green panel. d, Vienna International Center under construction (arch in foreground, cranes at right), red panel. e, Vienna International Center under construction (cranes at left, center and right), red panel. f, Doorway to Vienna International Center, green panel. g, View of curved buildings of Vienna International Center looking up from ground, green panel. h, Vienna International Center under construction (two cranes on central tower), red panel. i, Completed Vienna International Center, red panel. j, Flags in front of Vienna International Center.

2014, May 8   Litho.   Perf. 14¾
543   V120   Sheet of 10 + 10
     labels   30.00   30.00
a.-j.   70c Any single + label   3.00   3.00

The full sheet sold for $14.80 or €9.90. The generic labels are shown. Labels could be personalized.

V121

V122

Printed by Lowe-Martin Group, Canada. Panes of 20. Designed by Sergio Baradat, U.S.

2014, June 6   Litho.   Perf. 13¼x13
544   V121   70c multicolored   2.10   2.10
545   V122   €1.70 multicolored   5.25   5.25

Taj Mahal Types of 2014

2014, July 16   Engr.   Perf. 13¼x13
546   A466   90c multicolored   2.75   2.75
547   A468   €1.70 multicolored   5.25   5.25

Souvenir Booklet

548   Booklet, #548g-548l   25.00
a.   A463 30c multi   .85   .85
b.   A465 30c multi   .85   .85
c.   A466 30c multi   .85   .85
d.   A464 40c multi   1.20   1.20
e.   A467 40c multi   1.20   1.20
f.   A468 40c multi   1.20   1.20
g.   Booklet pane of 4 #548a   3.40   —
h.   Booklet pane of 4 #548b   3.40   —
i.   Booklet pane of 4 #548c   3.40   —
j.   Booklet pane of 4 #548d   4.80   —
k.   Booklet pane of 4 #548e   4.80   —
l.   Booklet pane of 4 #548f   4.80   —

International Year of Family Farming — V123

2014, Aug. 21   Litho.   Perf. 13x13¼
549   V123   62c multi   1.90   1.90
550   V123   €1.70 multi   5.25   5.25

Global Education First Initiative Type of 2014

Designs: €1.70, Children boarding school bus. €2, Tree growing from book held by students.

2014, Sept. 18   Litho.   Perf. 13x13¼
551   A470   €1.70 multicolored   5.25   5.25

Souvenir Sheet
Perf. 12½
552   A470   €2 multicolored   6.00   6.00

No. 552 contains one 32x32mm stamp.

Endangered Species Type of 2014

Maps and: No. 553, Cheilinus undulatus. No. 554, Carcharodon carcharias. No. 555, Manta birostris. No. 556, Polyodon spathula.

2014, Oct. 23   Litho.   Perf. 12¾x12½
553   A471   70c multicolored   2.10   2.10
554   A471   70c multicolored   2.10   2.10
555   A471   70c multicolored   2.10   2.10
556   A471   70c multicolored   2.10   2.10
a.   Block of 4, #553-556   8.50   8.50

Miniature Sheet

V124

No. 557: a, Flag on pole as seen from base of pole. b, Vienna International Center, structure in shadow at bottom. c, Persian Scholars Pavilion. d, Vienna International Center and fountain. e, Sailboat and Vienna International Center. f, Rowboat on water near Vienna International Center. g, Vienna International Center, flags and sculpture. h, Entrance to Vienna International Center. i, Woman Free sculpture near Vienna International Center. j, Aerial view of Vienna International Center.

2015, Jan. 23   Litho.   Perf. 14¾
557   V124   Sheet of 10   30.00   30.00
a.-j.   80c Any single + label   3.00   3.00

The full sheet sold for $15 or €10.90. The generic labels are shown. Labels could be personalized.

Flags and Coins Type of 2006

No. 558 — Flag of: a, Tuvalu, 10 cent coin. b, Malawi, 1 kwacha coin. c, Iraq, 50 dinar coin. d, St. Thomas and Prince Islands, 250 dobra coin. e, Botswana, 10 thebe coin. f, Uruguay, 5 peso coin. g, Bosnia and Herzegovina, 20 pfennig coin. h, Somalia, 25 shilling coin.

2015, Feb. 6   Litho.   Perf. 13¼x13
558   Sheet of 8   18.00   18.00
a.-h.   A375 80c Any single   2.25   2.25

A column of rouletting in the middle of the sheet separates it into two parts.

Miniature Sheets

V125

World Poetry Day — V126

No. 559: a, Aleksey Tolstoy quotation in Russian in red brown, date in red, "Welttag der Poesie" in red. b, Pen and circle, date in black, "Frühling" in purple. c, Pen and circle, date and "Frühling" in white, clouds above land in background. d, Tolstoy quotation in Russian in white, date in white, "Welttag der Poesie" in red. e, Tolstoy quotation in white, date and "Welttag der Poesie" in white. f, As "c," brown background.
No. 560: a, Rumi quotation in Arabic in light blue. b, Pen and red brown circle, denomination in red, purple jellyfish in background. c, Pen and red brown circle, denomination in white. d, Rumi quotation in orange, purple jellyfish tentacles in background. e, Rumi quotation in orange, red jellyfish tentacles in background. f, Pen and red brown circle, red denomination, red and purple jellyfish tentacles in background.

Perf. 14½x14¼
2015, Mar. 20   Litho.
559   V125   Sheet of 6   11.50   11.50
a.-f.   68c Any single   1.90   1.90
560   V126   Sheet of 6   13.50   13.50
a.-f.   80c Any single   2.25   2.25

Endangered Species Type of 2015

Designs: No. 561, Pteridophora alberti. No. 562, Astrapia splendidissima. No. 563, Paradisaea apoda. No. 564, Lophorina superba.

2015, Apr. 16   Litho.   Perf. 12½x12¾
561   A476   80c multicolored   2.00   2.00
562   A476   80c multicolored   2.00   2.00
563   A476   80c multicolored   2.00   2.00
564   A476   80c multicolored   2.00   2.00
a.   Block of 4, #561-564   8.00   8.00
    Nos. 561-564 (4)   8.00   8.00

V127

V128

2015, May 7   Litho.   Perf. 13¼x13
565   V127   68c multicolored   1.75   1.75
566   V128   80c multicolored   2.00   2.00

World Heritage Sites, Southeast Asia Type of 2015

Designs: Nos. 567, 569c, Ayutthaya, Thailand. Nos. 568, 569f, Hué Monuments, Viet Nam. No. 569a, Luang Prabang, Laos. No. 569b, Angkor Wat, Cambodia. No. 569d, Borobudur Temple, Indonesia. No. 569e, Cordillera, Philippines.

2015, June 5   Litho.   Perf. 14x13½
567   A480   80c multicolored   2.00   2.00
568   A480   €1.70 multicolored   4.25   4.25

Souvenir Booklet

569   Booklet, #569g-569l   21.00
a.-c.   A480 80c any single   .75   .75
d.-f.   A480 40c any single   1.00   1.00
g.   Booklet pane of 4 #569a   3.00   —
h.   Booklet pane of 4 #569b   3.00   —
i.   Booklet pane of 4 #569c   3.00   —
j.   Booklet pane of 4 #569d   4.00   —
k.   Booklet pane of 4 #569e   4.00   —
l.   Booklet pane of 4 #569f   4.00   —

End Violence Against Children Type of 2015

Designs: 68c, Gender-based violence. 80c, Child labor.

Perf. 14½x14¼
2015, Aug. 20   Litho.
570   A481   68c multicolored   1.75   1.75
571   A481   80c multicolored   2.00   2.00

ECOSOC Chamber V129

Trusteeship Council — V130

Visitors Lobby V131

General Assembly Hall V132

Trusteeship Council — V133

Printed by Cartor Security Printing, France. Panes of 6. Designed by Rorie Katz, U.S.

2015, Oct. 25		Litho.	Perf. 13¾	
572	V129	80c multicolored	2.00	2.00
573	V130	80c multicolored	2.00	2.00
a.		Pair, #572-573	4.00	4.00
574	V131	€1.70 multicolored	4.25	4.25
575	V132	€1.70 multicolored	4.25	4.25
a.		Pair, #574-575	8.50	8.50
		Nos. 572-575 (4)	12.50	12.50

Souvenir Sheet
Perf. 13½

576	V133	€1.70 multicolored	4.25	4.25

United Nations, 70th anniv.

United Nations, 70th Anniv. Type of 2015

Designed by Sergio Baradat, U.S.

2015, Nov. 5		Litho.	Perf. 14¾	
577	A482	80c multi + label	4.00	4.00
		Sheet of 10 + 10 labels	40.00	

The full sheet sold for $13.45 or €10.90. The sheet contains ten different generic labels. Labels could be personalized. The personalization of labels was available only at UN Headquarters, and not through mail order.

21st United Nations Climate Change Conference, Paris V134

2015, Nov. 24		Litho.	Perf. 13¼	
578	V134	80c multicolored	3.00	3.00

Values are for stamps with surrounding selvage.

Free and Equal Type of 2016

Designs: 68c, Person coming out of closet. 80c, Gay men.

2016, Feb. 5		Litho.	Perf. 13½x13¼	
579	A491	68c multicolored	1.75	1.75
580	A491	80c multicolored	2.00	2.00

HeForShe Type of 2016

Designs: 1fr, Man, red background. 2fr, Woman, orange brown background.

2016, Mar. 8		Litho.	Perf. 12½x13	
581	A492	68c multicolored	1.75	1.75
582	A492	80c multicolored	2.00	2.00

Miniature Sheets

V135

International Dance Day — V136

No. 583 — Illustration of Spanish dancers by Allison Seiffer: a, Female dancer with fan. b, Male dancer with crossed arms. c, Red dress of dancer. d, Female dancer with male guitarist. e, Feet of dancer in ochre and green dress. f, Feet of male and female dancers, rose on floor.

No. 584 — Illustration of Middle Eastern dancers by Seiffer: a, Head of female dancer, "Welttanztag" in red, denomination in yellow. b, Head of female dancer, "Welttanztag" and denomination in red. c, Torso of dancer. d, Dancer, "Welttanztag" in black, denomination in yellow. e, Feet of dancer, "Welttanztag" in black. f, Feet of dancer and drum, "Welttanztag" in yellow.

2016, Apr. 29		Litho.	Perf. 13¼x13	
583	V135	Sheet of 6	10.00	10.00
a.-f.		68c Any single	1.60	1.60
584	V136	Sheet of 6	12.00	12.00
a.-f.		80c Any single	2.00	2.00

United Nations Industrial Development Organization, 50th Anniv. — V137

2016, May 12		Litho.	Perf. 14¾	
585	V137	80c multi + label	2.60	2.60
		Sheet of 10 + 10 labels	26.50	

The full sheet sold for $13.12 and €10.90. One of the ten different generic labels is shown. Labels could be personalized. The personalization of labels was available only at UN Headquarters, and not through mail order.

International Day of United Nations Peacekeepers Type of 2016

Designs: 68c, Peacekeepers and African children. 80c, Peacekeepers in tank, Africans.

Litho. With Foil Application
2016, May 29			Perf. 13¼x13	
586	A496	68c multicolored	1.75	1.75
587	A496	80c multicolored	2.00	2.00

Sport for Peace Type of 2016

Olympic rings and: No. 588, Weight lifting, denomination at LR. No. 589, Weight lifting, denomination at LL. No. 590, Fencing, denomination at UR. No. 591, Fencing, denomination at UL.

2016, July 22		Litho.	Perf. 14¼	
588	A498	68c multicolored	1.75	1.75
589	A498	68c multicolored	1.75	1.75
a.		Pair, #588-589	3.50	3.50
590	A498	€1.70 multicolored	4.25	4.25
591	A498	€1.70 multicolored	4.25	4.25
a.		Pair, #590-591	8.50	8.50
		Nos. 588-591 (4)	12.00	12.00

Souvenir sheets of three bearing three stamps, one from each office are listed under United Nations, Offices in New York as Nos. 1141, 1161, 1177-1178, 1203, and 1208.

World Heritage Sites, Czech Republic Type of 2016

Designs: Nos. 592, 594c, Historic Town Center of Kutná Hora. Nos. 593, 594f, Historic Center of Cesky Krumlov. No. 594a, Historic Center of Prague. No. 594b, Gardens and Castle at Kromeriz. No. 594d, Holy Trinity Column, Olomouc. Nos. 594e, Lednice-Valtice Cultural Landscape.

2016, Sept. 8		Litho.	Perf. 14¼	
592	A500	68c multicolored	1.75	1.75
593	A500	€1.70 multicolored	4.25	4.25

Souvenir Booklet

594		Booklet, #594g-594l	20.50	
a.-c.		A500 30c any single	.65	.65
d.-f.		A500 40c any single	1.00	1.00
g.		Booklet pane of 4 #594a	2.75	—
h.		Booklet pane of 4 #594b	2.75	—
i.		Booklet pane of 4 #594c	2.75	—
j.		Booklet pane of 4 #594d	4.00	—
k.		Booklet pane of 4 #594e	4.00	—
l.		Booklet pane of 4 #594f	4.00	—

Comprehensive Nuclear Test-Ban Treaty Organization, 20th Anniv. — V138

2016, Sept. 23		Litho.	Perf. 14¾	
595	V138	80c multi + label	4.00	4.00

The full sheet sold for $13.27 and €10.90. One of the ten different generic labels is shown. Labels could be personalized. The personalization of labels was available only at UN Headquarters, and not through mail order.

Miniature Sheet

World Wildlife Conference, Johannesburg — V139

No. 596 — Part of map of Africa and: a, Nilkrokodil (Nile crocodile). b, Kapgeier (Cape vulture). c, Steppenschuppentier (Cape pangolin). d, Mystacidium capense.

2016, Sept. 24		Litho.	Perf. 13x13½	
596	V139	Sheet of 4	17.00	17.00
a.-d.		€1.70 Any single	4.25	4.25

Sustainable Development Goals Type of 2016

No. 597 — Inscription: a, 1 Keine armut. b, 2 Kein hunger. c, 3 Gesundheit und wohlergehen. d, 4 Hochwertige bildung. e, 5 Geschlechter-gleichheit. f, 6 Sauberes wasser und sanitär-einrichtungen. g, 7 Bezahlbare und saubere energie. h, 8 Menschenwürdige arbeit und wirtschafts-wachstum. i, 9 Industrie, innovation und infrastruktur. j, 10 Weniger ungleichheiten. k, 11 Nachhaltige städte und gemeinden. l, 12 Nachhaltige/r konsum und produktion. m, 13 Massnahmen zum klimaschutz. n, 14 Leben unter wasser. o, 15 Leben an land. p, 16 Frieden, gerechtigkeit und starke institutionen. q, 17 Partnerschaften zur erreichung der ziele.

2016, Oct. 24		Litho.	Perf. 13¼	
597		Sheet of 17 + label	28.50	28.50
a.-q.	A503	68c Any single	1.60	1.60

Miniature Sheet

V140

No. 598: a, Insect. b, Smurf wearing diving helmet. c, Smurf holding archery bow. d, Flower with eyes. e, Smurf in park. f, Smurf with police hat, whistle and baton. g, Smurf holding pitchfork. h, Two Smurfs wearing red caps. i, Smurf holding garbage can. j, Ladybug.

2017, Mar. 20		Litho.	Perf. 14¾	
598	V140	Sheet of 10 + 10 labels	30.00	30.00
a.-j.		80c Any single + label	3.00	3.00

The full sheet sold for $14.95. The generic labels are shown. Labels could be personalized.

Miniature Sheets

V141

International Dance — V142

No. 599 — Illustration of Samba dancers by Victo Ngai: a, Lion's head. b, Black and tan female dancers. c, Dancers holding drums. d, Black female dancer. e, White female dancer. f, Brown female dancer.

No. 600 — Illustration of Ballet dancers by Ngai: a, Blue dancer with hand bent downward. b, Blue dancer with arm raised above head. c, Blue dancer with arms extended to side. d, Dancer with black dress. e, Head of dancer, tip of dress at bottom. f, Head of dancer facing right.

2017, Mar. 23   Litho.   *Perf. 13¼x13*
599	V141	Sheet of 6	9.75 9.75
a.-f.		68c Any single	1.60 1.60
g.		As #599, with Brasilia 2017 World Stamp Exhibition emblem overprinted in sheet margin	10.50 10.50
600	V142	Sheet of 6	11.50 11.50
a.-f.		80c Any single	1.90 1.90

Endangered Species Type of 2017

Designs: No. 601, Capra caucasica. No. 602, Nautilidae spp. No. 603, Siphonochilus aethiopicus. No. 604, Lygodactylus williamsi.

2017, May 11   Litho.   *Perf. 12¾x12½*
601	A509	80c multicolored	1.90 1.90
602	A509	80c multicolored	1.90 1.90
603	A509	80c multicolored	1.90 1.90
604	A509	80c multicolored	1.90 1.90
a.		Block of 4, #601-604	7.75 7.75
		Nos. 601-604 (4)	7.60 7.60

World Environment Day Type of 2017

Designs: 68c, Supreme Court, Ottawa, Ontario, Canada. €1.70, Moraine Lake, Canada.

2017, June 5   Litho.   *Perf. 13¼*
605	A510	68c multicolored	1.60 1.60
606	A510	€1.70 multicolored	4.00 4.00

World Heritage Sites Along the Silk Roads Type of 2017

Designs: Nos. 607, 609c, Tabriz Historic Bazaar Complex, Iran. Nos. 608, 609f, Safranbolu, Turkey. No. 609a, Longmen Grottoes, People's Republic of China. No. 609b, Historic Center of Bukhara, Uzbekistan. No. 609d, Sulaiman-Too Sacred Mountain, Kyrgyzstan. No. 609e, Kunya-Urgench, Turkmenistan.

2017, Aug. 3   Litho.   *Perf. 14¼*
607	A512	80c multicolored	2.00 2.00
608	A512	€1.70 multicolored	4.25 4.25

Souvenir Booklet
609		Booklet, #609g-609l	23.50
a.-c.		A512 30c any single	.85 .85
d.-f.		A512 40c any single	1.10 1.10
g.		Booklet pane of 4 #609a	3.40 —
h.		Booklet pane of 4 #609d	3.40 —
i.		Booklet pane of 4 #609c	3.40 —
j.		Booklet pane of 4 #609d	4.40 —
k.		Booklet pane of 4 #609e	4.40 —
l.		Booklet pane of 4 #609f	4.40 —

Miniature Sheet

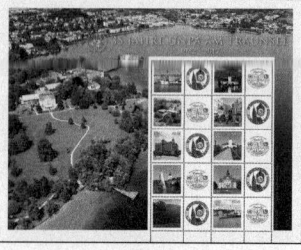

V143

No. 610: a, Traunsee with ships and lakeshore buildings. b, Ort Castle and bridge at dusk. c, Aerial view of Cumberland Castle. d, Street in Gmunden, Austria. e, Gmunden City Hall. f, Ort Castle and bridge. g, Sailboat near Ort Castle. h, Villa Toscana. i, Aerial view of Traunsee. j, Ships on Traunsee.

2017, Aug. 24   Litho.   *Perf. 14¾*
610	V143	Sheet of 10 + 10 labels	27.50 27.50
a.-j.		68c Any single + label	2.75 2.75

United Nations Postal Administration on the Traunsee, 35th anniv. The full sheet sold for $13.64. The generic labels are shown. Labels could be personalized.

Hands and Flower — V144

Handshake and Flowers — V145

Handshake and Flowers — V146

Printed by Johann Enschedé and Sons, the Netherlands. Panes of 20. Designed by Stranger and Stranger, U.S.

2017, Sept. 21   Litho.   *Perf. 14x14¼*
611	V144	68c multicolored	1.75 1.75
612	V145	€1.70 multicolored	4.25 4.25

Souvenir Sheet
Perf. 14¼x13¾
613	V146	€1.70 multicolored	4.25 4.25

International Day of Peace.

World Food Day Type of 2017

Designs: 68c, Breads and grains. 80c, Steak, fish, chicken drumstick, shrimp, egg, beans, lemon slice.

2017, Oct. 16   Litho.   *Perf. 13¼x14*
614	A516	68c multicolored	1.75 1.75
615	A516	80c multicolored	2.00 2.00

Endangered Species Type of 2018

Designs: No. 616, Hoodia pilifera. No. 617, Mantella madagascariensis. No. 618, Panshua sylhetensis. No. 619, Hippocampus zebra.

2018, Mar. 2   Litho.   *Perf. 12¾x12½*
616	A519	80c multicolored	2.00 2.00
617	A519	80c multicolored	2.00 2.00
618	A519	80c multicolored	2.00 2.00
619	A519	80c multicolored	2.00 2.00
a.		Block of 4, #616-619	8.00 8.00
		Nos. 616-619 (4)	8.00 8.00

World Health Day Type of 2018

Designs: 68c, Medical worker, people, globe, caduceus. €1.70, Coins entering piggy bank with white cross.

2018, Apr. 6   Litho.   *Perf. 13x13¼*
620	A520	68c multicolored	1.90 1.90
621	A520	€1.70 multicolored	4.50 4.50

United Nations Emblem — V147

2018   Litho.   *Perf. 14¾*
622	V147	80c multi + label	2.75 2.75
a.		Less distinct year date and frame, lighter blue emblem	2.75 2.75

Issued: No. 622, 5/26; No. 622a, 7/30. The full sheet sold for $14.32 and €10.90. One of the ten different generic labels is shown. Labels could be personalized. The personalization of labels was available only at UN Headquarters, and not through mail order.

UNISPACE + 50 Conferences Type of 2018

Designs: 68c, Great Red Spot of Jupiter. 80c, Aurora Australis from International Space Station.

€1.70, View of river delta from Copernicus Sentinel satellite.

2018, June 20   Litho.   *Perf. 14x14¼*
623	A523	68c multicolored	1.90 1.90
624	A523	80c multicolored	2.25 2.25

Souvenir Sheet
Perf. 13¾
625	A523	€1.70 multicolored	4.50 4.50

No. 625 contains one 45x45mm stamp.

World Heritage Sites In the United Kingdom Type of 2018

Designs: Nos. 626, 628c, Conwy Castle. Nos. 627, 628f, Maritime Greenwich. No. 628a, Giant's Causeway. No. 628b, Stonehenge. No. 628d, Palace of Westminster. No. 628e, Edinburgh.

2018, Aug. 15   Litho.   *Perf. 14¼*
626	A524	90c multicolored	2.40 2.40
627	A524	€1.80 multicolored	4.75 4.75

Souvenir Booklet
628		Booklet, #609g-609l	25.50
a.-c.		A524 35c any single	1.00 1.00
d.-f.		A524 40c any single	1.10 1.10
g.		Booklet pane of 4 #628a	4.00 —
h.		Booklet pane of 4 #628b	4.00 —
i.		Booklet pane of 4 #628c	4.00 —
j.		Booklet pane of 4 #628d	4.00 —
k.		Booklet pane of 4 #628e	4.50 —
l.		Booklet pane of 4 #628f	4.50 —

Miniature Sheet

International Music Day — V148

No. 629: a, Kalimba with three holes. b, Snare drum. c, Shekere. d, Castanets. e, Gong. f, Hourglass drum. g, Castanet with handles and tambourine stick. h, Cymbals. i, Djembe drum. j, Kalimba with one hole. k, Button accordion. l, Maracas and decorated stick.

2018, Oct. 1   Litho.   *Perf. 14x13¼*
629	V148	Sheet of 12	24.50 24.50
a.-l.		80c Any single	2.00 2.00

V149

Non-Violence, Sculpture by Carl Fredrik Reuterswärd — V150

Printed by Johann Enschedé Stamps BV, the Netherlands. Panes of 20. Designed by Martin Mörck, Norway.

2018, Oct. 2   Litho.   *Perf. 14x14¼*
630	V149	90c multicolored	2.40 2.40
631	V150	€2.30 multicolored	6.00 6.00

Miniature Sheet

World Languages — V151

No. 632 — Word bubbles with word for "Hello" in: a, Serbian or Croatian ("Sprachen der Welt" and denomination in red). b, Arabic ("Sprachen der Welt" and denomination in white). c, Korean ("Sprachen der Welt" in white, denomination in black), d, Dutch or German or Norwegian (Hallo). e, Greek and Turkish (Merhaba). f, Spanish (Hola).

2019, Feb. 21   Litho.   *Perf. 13¼x13*
632	V151	Sheet of 6	12.50 12.50
a.-f.		80c Any single	2.00 2.00

Migration — V152

Printed by Lowe-Martin Group, Canada. Panes of 20. Designed by Chris Gash, U.S.

2019, Mar.15   Litho.   *Perf. 13¼x13*
633	V152	€1.80 multicolored	4.75 4.75

Endangered Species Type of 2019

Designs: No. 634, Anguilla anguilla. No. 635, Dermochelys coriacea. No. 636, Acropora spp. No. 637, Huso huso.

2019, Apr. 26   Litho.   *Perf. 12¾x12½*
634	A534	90c multicolored	2.25 2.25
635	A534	90c multicolored	2.25 2.25
636	A534	90c multicolored	2.25 2.25
637	A534	90c multicolored	2.25 2.25
a.		Block of 4, #634-637	9.25 9.25
		Nos. 634-637 (4)	9.00 9.00

Souvenir Sheet

Long-horned Bee and Scutellaria Lateriflora — V153

Litho. With Foil Application
2019, May 20   *Perf. 13*
638	V153	€2.70 multicolored	7.00 7.00

World Bee Day.

V154

V155

V156

V157

International
Labor
Organization,
Cent. — V158

2019, June 28   Litho.   Perf. 13½x14

639	V154	80c multicolored	2.00	2.00
640	V155	80c multicolored	2.00	2.00
641	V156	80c multicolored	2.00	2.00
642	V157	80c multicolored	2.00	2.00
643	V158	80c multicolored	2.00	2.00
a.		Horiz. strip of 5, #639-643	10.00	10.00
		Nos. 639-643 (5)	10.00	10.00

V159

V160

V161

V162

United Nations
Postal
Administration in
Vienna, 40th
Anniv. — V163

2019, Aug. 23   Litho.   Perf. 14¾

644	V159	90c multi + label	3.00	3.00
645	V160	90c multi + label	3.00	3.00
646	V161	90c multi + label	3.00	3.00
647	V162	90c multi + label	3.00	3.00
648	V163	90c multi + label	3.00	3.00
a.		Vert. strip of 5, #644-648, + 5 labels	15.00	15.00
		Nos. 644-648 (5)	15.00	15.00

The full sheets sold for $14.94 or €15.33. The generic labels are shown. Labels could be personalized. The personalization of labels was available only at UN Headquarters, and not through mail order.

Climate Change Type of 2019

Designs: 80c, Canyon and mining operation. 90c, Clouds and smokestack. €1.80, Fish and corals.

2019, Sept. 23   Litho.   Perf. 14¼

649	A543	80c multicolored	2.00	2.00
650	A543	90c multicolored	2.25	2.25

Souvenir Sheet

Perf.

651	A543	€1.80 multicolored	4.50	4.50

2019 United Nations Climate Change Conference, Madrid. No. 651 contains one 47mm diameter stamp.

World Heritage Sites in Cuba Type of 2019

Designs: Nos. 652, 654c, Camagüey. Nos. 653, 654f, San Pedro de la Rosa Castle. No. 654a, Morro Castle. No. 664b, Trinidad. No. 654d, Vinales Valley. No. 654e, Cienfuegos.

Litho. With Foil Application

2019, Oct. 24   Perf. 14¼

652	A545	90c multicolored	2.25	2.25
653	A545	€1.80 multicolored	4.50	4.50

Souvenir Booklet

654		Booklet, #1115g-1115l	25.00	
a.-c.		A545 35c any single	.95	.95
d.-f.		A545 40c any single	1.10	1.10
g.		Booklet pane of 4 #654a	3.80	—
h.		Booklet pane of 4 #654b	3.80	—
i.		Booklet pane of 4 #654c	3.80	—
j.		Booklet pane of 4 #654d	4.40	—
k.		Booklet pane of 4 #654e	4.40	—
l.		Booklet pane of 4 #654f	4.40	—

Complete booklet sold for $12.27.

Endangered Species Type of 2020

Designs: No. 655, Panthera leo. No. 656, Pelecanus crispus. No. 657, Phocoena phocoena. No. 658, Equus africanus.

Perf. 12¾x12½

2020, Feb. 17   Litho.

655	A546	90c multicolored	2.25	2.25
656	A546	90c multicolored	2.25	2.25
657	A546	90c multicolored	2.25	2.25
658	A546	90c multicolored	2.25	2.25
a.		Block of 4, #655-658	9.00	9.00
		Nos. 655-658 (4)	9.00	9.00

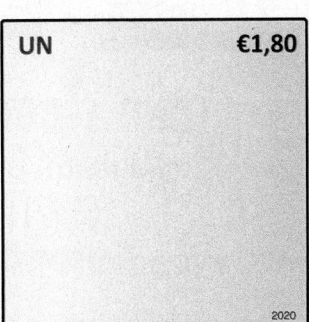

Blank Stamp On Which Stickers Can
Be Applied — V164

Designs: No. 1212, Hawksbill turtle. No. 1213, Queen conch. No. 1214, Mushroom coral. No. 1215, Humpback whale.

2020, Mar. 19   Litho.   Die Cut

Self-Adhesive

659	V164	€1.80 multicolored with rounded corners	4.50	4.50
a.		With perpendicular corners and black frame line	4.50	4.50
b.		Booklet pane of 6 #1236a	27.00	

No. 659 was issued as a souvenir sheet having two different sheet margins, each with different stickers. No. 659a was issued in a booklet containing six panes of one stamp, with each pane having different margins and stickers. Each booklet pane contained one sticker depicting Hello Kitty, a color wheel with Hello Kitty at the center, one of six different Sustainable Development Goal emblems, along with a variety of other stickers. The two souvenir sheets had the same sheet margin and stickers found on two of the panes of No. 659b. No. 659b was sold folded, without any means of separation between the individual panes.

Lepidopterist,
Artwork by Paul
Villinski — V165

Ruth, Costume by
Nicole
Dextras — V166

2020, Apr. 22   Litho.   Perf. 13¼

660	V165	85c multicolored	2.10	2.10
661	V166	€1.35 multicolored	3.50	3.50

Earth Day, 50th anniv. Because of the COVID-19 pandemic, Nos. 660-661 were not available for sale on day of issue stated on the first-day covers as they had not yet been printed and delivered.

Florence Nightingale (1820-1910),
Nurse — V167

2020, May 12   Litho.   Perf. 14

662	V167	€1.35 multicolored	3.50	3.50

International Year of the Nurse and the Midwife.

World Heritage Sites in Russia Type of 2020

Designs: Nos. 663, 665c, Novodevichy Convent. Nos. 664, 665f, Kizhi Pogost. No. 665a, Lake Baikal. No. 665b, Kazan Kremlin. No. 665d, Kremlin and Red Square, Moscow. No. 665e, Saint Petersburg.

Perf. 14½x14¼

2020, Sept. 11   Litho.

663	A556	€1 multicolored	2.60	2.60
664	A556	€1.80 multicolored	4.75	4.75

Souvenir Booklet

665		Booklet, #1115g-1115l	27.00	
a.-c.		A556 35c any single	1.00	1.00
d.-f.		A556 40c any single	1.25	1.25
g.		Booklet pane of 4 #665a	4.00	—
h.		Booklet pane of 4 #665b	4.00	—
i.		Booklet pane of 4 #665c	4.00	—
j.		Booklet pane of 4 #665d	5.00	—
k.		Booklet pane of 4 #665e	5.00	—
l.		Booklet pane of 4 #665f	5.00	—

Complete booklet sold for $12.94 or €10.

United Nations Emblem — V168

2020, Oct. 2   Litho.   Perf. 14¾

666	V168	€1 multi + label	3.25	3.25
		Sheet of 10 + 10 labels	33.50	—

The full sheet sold for $16.70 or €12.90. One of the ten different generic labels is shown. Labels could be personalized. The personalization of labels was available only at UN Headquarters, and not through mail order.

Souvenir Sheet

United Nations, 75th Anniv. — V169

No. 667: a, Red "U," blue "N." b, Pink "7," green "5."

2020, Oct. 24   Litho.   Perf. 13¼

667	V169	Sheet of 2	9.50	9.50
a.-b.		€1.80 Either single	4.75	4.75

Souvenir Sheet

Vienna International Center and
Emblem — V170

Litho. With Foil Application

2020, Nov. 24   Die Cut Perf. 11½

Self-Adhesive

668	V170	€7 multicolored	18.50	18.50

Crypto stamp. Unused value is for sheets with unscratched panels at right.

SEMI-POSTAL STAMPS

AIDS Awareness Semi-postal Type

Souvenir Sheet

2002, Oct. 24   Litho.   Perf. 14½

B1	SP1	51c + 25c multicolored	3.50	3.50

U.N. TEMPORARY EXECUTIVE AUTHORITY, WEST NEW GUINEA

Temporary Executive Authority

LOCATION — Western half of New Guinea, southwest Pacific Ocean
GOVT. — Province of Indonesia
AREA — In 1958, the size was 151,789 sq. mi.
POP. — estimated at 730,000 in 1958
CAPITAL — Hollandia

The former Netherlands New Guinea became a territory under the administration of the United Nations Temporary Executive Authority on Oct. 1, 1962.

The territory came under Indonesian administration on May 1, 1963. For stamps issued by Indonesia see West Irian in Volume 3.

100 Cents = 1 Gulden
100 Cents = 1 Gulden

> Catalogue values for all unused stamps in this country are for Never Hinged items.

First Printing (Hollandia)

Netherlands New Guinea Stamps of 1950-60 Overprinted

Overprint size: 17x3½mm. Top of "N" is slightly lower than the "U," and the base of the "T" is straight, or nearly so.

Photo.; Litho. (#4, 6, 8)
Perf. 12½x12, 12½x13½

1962, Oct. 1			Unwmk.	
1	A4	1c vermilion & yellow	.25	.25
2	A1	2c deep orange	.25	.25
3	A4	5c chocolate & yellow	.25	.25
4	A5	7c org red, bl & brn vio	.25	.35
5	A4	10c aqua & red brown	.25	.35
6	A5	12c green, bl & brn vio	.25	.35
7	A4	15c deep yel & red brn	.45	.45
8	A5	17c brown violet & blue	.55	.70
9	A4	20c lt bl grn & red brn	.60	.75
10	A6	25c red	.40	.55
11	A6	30c deep blue	.75	.75
12	A6	40c deep orange	.75	.75
13	A6	45c dark olive	1.25	1.50
14	A6	55c slate blue	29.00	2.25
15	A6	80c dull gray violet	6.00	6.00
16	A6	85c dark violet brown	3.00	3.00
17	A6	1g plum	9.25	3.00

Engr.

18	A3	2g reddish brown	12.50	30.00
19	A3	5g green	9.00	8.00
		Nos. 1-19 (19)	75.00	59.50

Overprinted locally and sold in West New Guinea. Stamps of the second printing were used to complete sets sold to collectors.

Second Printing (Haarlen, Netherlands)

Overprint size: 17x3½mm. Top of the "N" is slightly higher than the "U," and the base of the "T" is concave.

Photo.; Litho. (#4a, 6a, 8a)
Perf. 12½x12, 12½x13½

1962			Unwmk.	
1a	A4	1c vermilion & yellow	.25	.25
2a	A1	2c deep orange	.25	.25
3a	A4	5c chocolate & yellow	.25	.25
4a	A5	7c org red, bl & brn vio	.25	.25
5a	A4	10c aqua & red brown	.25	.25
6a	A5	12c green, bl & brn vio	.25	.25
7a	A4	15c deep yel & red brn	.50	.25
8a	A5	17c brown violet & blue	.60	.40
9a	A4	20c lt blue grn & red brn	.60	.40
10a	A6	25c red	.35	.35
11a	A6	30c deep blue	.90	.40
12a	A6	40c deep orange	.90	.40
13a	A6	45c dark olive	1.75	.75
14a	A6	55c slate blue	5.00	1.00
15a	A6	80c dull gray violet	7.00	9.00
16a	A6	85c dark violet brown	3.75	4.75
17a	A6	1g plum	4.25	2.00

Engr.

18a	A3	2g reddish brown	16.00	27.50
19a	A3	5g green	8.00	6.50
		Nos. 1a-19a (19)	51.10	55.20

Third Printing

Overprint 14mm long.

Photo.; Litho. (#4b, 6b, 8b)
Perf. 12½x12

1963, Mar.		Photo.	Unwmk.	
1b	A4	1c vermilion & yellow	5.00	3.00
3b	A4	5c chocolate & yellow	6.00	4.00
4b	A5	7c org red, bl & brn vio	20.00	20.00
5b	A4	10c aqua & red brown	6.00	4.00
6b	A5	12c green, bl & brn vio	35.00	35.00
7b	A4	15c deep yel & red brn	130.00	130.00
8b	A5	17c brown violet & blue	15.00	12.00
9b	A4	20c lt blue grn & red brn	7.50	5.00
		Nos. 1b-9b (8)	224.50	213.00

The third printing was applied in West New Guinea and it is doubtful whether it was regularly issued. Used values are for canceled to order stamps.

Fourth Printing

Overprint 19mm long.

Photogravure

1963, Mar.		Unwmk.	*Perf. 12½x12*	
1c	A4	1c vermilion & yellow	50.00	50.00
5c	A4	10c aqua & red brown	150.00	150.00

The fourth printing was applied in West New Guinea and it is doubtful whether it was regularly issued. Used values are for canceled to order stamps.

U.N. TRANSITIONAL AUTHORITY IN EAST TIMOR

A30

2000, Apr. 29		Litho.	*Perf. 12x11¾*	
350	A30	Dom. red & multi	35.00	102.50
351	A30	Int. blue & multi	47.50	112.50

No. 350 sold for 10c and No. 351 sold for 50c on day of issue.

U.N. INTERIM ADMINISTRATION, KOSOVO

These stamps were issued by the United Nations Interim Administration Mission in Kosovo and the Post & Telecommunications of Kosovo. Service was local for the first two months, with international use to start in mid-May.

100 pfennigs = 1 mark
100 cents = €1 (2002)

Catalogue values for all unused stamps in this country are for Never Hinged items.

Peace in Kosovo — A1

Designs: 20pf, Mosaic depicting Orpheus, c. 5th-6th cent., Podujeve. 30pf, Dardinian idol, Museum of Kosovo. 50pf, Silver coin of Damastion from 4th cent. B.C. 1m, Statue of Mother Teresa, Prizren. 2m, Map of Kosovo.

Perf. 13½x13, 13½x13¼ (30pf)

		2000, Mar. 14	Litho.	Unwmk.	
1	A1	20pf multicolored		.65	.65
2	A1	30pf multicolored		1.25	1.25
3	A1	50pf multicolored		1.60	1.60
4	A1	1m multicolored		2.00	1.80
5	A1	2m multicolored		3.75	3.50
		Nos. 1-5 (5)		9.25	8.80

Nos. 1-5 were demonetized July 1, 2002.

Beginning with No. 6, Kosovan stamps were not available to collectors through the United Nations Postal Administration.

Peace in Kosovo — A2

Designs: 20pf, Bird. 30pf, Street musician. 50pf, Butterfly and pear. 1m, Children and stars. 2m, Globe and handprints.

		2001, Nov. 12	Litho.	Perf. 14	
6	A2	20pf multicolored		1.00	1.00
7	A2	30pf multicolored		1.25	1.25
8	A2	50pf multicolored		2.00	2.00
9	A2	1m multicolored		4.00	4.00
10	A2	2m multicolored		7.50	7.50
		Nos. 6-10 (5)		15.75	15.75

Peace in Kosovo Type of 2001 With Denominations in Euros Only

		2002, May 2	Litho.	Perf. 14	
11	A2	10c Like #6		.75	.75
12	A2	15c Like #7		1.00	1.00
13	A2	26c Like #8		1.50	1.50
14	A2	51c Like #9		4.50	4.50
15	A2	€1.02 Like #10		8.00	8.00
		Nos. 11-15 (5)		15.75	15.75

Christmas — A3

Designs: 50c, Candles and garland. €1, Stylized men.

		2003, Dec. 20	Litho.	Perf. 14	
16	A3	50c multicolored		7.50	7.50
17	A3	€1 multicolored		14.50	14.50

Return of Refugees — A4

Five Years of Peace — A5

		2004, June 29	Litho.	Perf. 13¼x13	
18	A4	€1 multicolored		7.00	7.00
19	A5	€2 multicolored		16.00	16.00

Musical Instruments — A6

		2004, Aug. 31	Litho.	Perf. 13¼x13	
20	A6	20c Flute		5.00	5.00
21	A6	30c Ocarina		10.00	10.00

Aprons A7

Vests — A8

Designs: 20c, Apron from Prizren. 30c, Apron from Rugova. 50c, Three vests. €1, Two vests.

		2004, Oct. 28	Litho.	Perf. 13x13¼	
22	A7	20c multicolored		5.50	5.50
23	A7	30c multicolored		8.50	8.50
24	A8	50c multicolored		12.00	12.00
25	A8	€1 multicolored		26.00	26.00
		Nos. 22-25 (4)		52.00	52.00

Mirusha Waterfall A9

		2004, Nov. 26	Litho.	Perf. 13x13¼	
26	A9	€2 multicolored		7.50	7.50

House A10

		2004, Dec. 14	Litho.	Perf. 13x13¼	
27	A10	50c multicolored		4.50	4.50

Flowers — A11

		2005, June 29	Litho.	Perf. 13½	
28	A11	15c Peony		2.25	2.25
29	A11	20c Poppies		3.25	3.25
30	A11	30c Gentian		5.00	5.00
		Nos. 28-30 (3)		10.50	10.50

A12

Handicrafts A13

		2005, July 20	Perf. 13¼x13		
31	A12	20c shown		2.50	2.50
32	A12	30c Cradle		3.00	3.00
33	A13	50c shown		3.25	3.25
34	A12	€1 Necklace		4.25	4.25
		Nos. 31-34 (4)		13.00	13.00

Village A14

Town A15

City — A16

		2005, Sept. 15		Perf. 13x13½	
35	A14	20c multicolored		2.00	2.00
36	A15	50c multicolored		3.00	3.00
37	A16	€1 multicolored		6.00	6.00
		Nos. 35-37 (3)		11.00	11.00

Archaeological Artifacts — A17

		2005, Nov. 2		Perf. 13½x13	
38	A17	20c shown		1.25	1.25
39	A17	30c Statue		1.75	1.75
40	A17	50c Sculpture		2.50	2.50
41	A17	€1 Helmet		7.50	7.50
		Nos. 38-41 (4)		13.00	13.00

Minerals A18

		2005, Dec. 10		Perf. 13x13½	
42	A18	€2 multicolored		10.00	10.00

A19   Europa — A20

		2006, July 20		Perf. 13¼x13	
43	A19	50c multicolored		2.25	2.25
44	A20	€1 multicolored		4.25	4.25

Exists Imperf. Value set of two, $75.

Fauna A21

		2006, May 23	Litho.	Perf. 13	
45	A21	15c Wolf		1.00	1.00
46	A21	20c Cow		1.25	1.25
47	A21	30c Pigeon		1.40	1.40
48	A21	50c Swan		1.60	1.60
49	A21	€1 Dog		2.75	2.75
a.		Souvenir sheet, #45-49, + label		8.75	8.75
		Nos. 45-49 (5)		8.00	8.00

Nos. 45-49 are inscribed CPU. Stamps with "Leoprint" imprint are from No. 63a.
No. 49a exists in two shades of green selvage.

Children A22

Designs: 20c, Children in cradle. 30c, Children reading. 50c, Girls dancing. €1, Child in water.

		2006, June 30	Litho.	Perf. 13	
50	A22	20c multicolored		1.00	1.00
51	A22	30c multicolored		1.25	1.25
52	A22	50c multicolored		1.75	1.75
53	A22	€1 multicolored		3.50	3.50
a.		Souvenir sheet, #50-53		7.75	7.75
		Nos. 50-53 (4)		7.50	7.50

Nos. 50-53 were printed by CPU & Moare. No. 53a was printed by two printers: 7,500 inscribed "CPU&Moare," and 5,000 inscribed "Leoprint."
Nos. 50-53 from CPO & Moare exists imperforate. Value, set, $75.

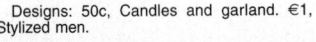

No. 53a by CPU & Moare exists imperforate. Value $75.

A23

A24

A25

Tourist Attractions — A26

2006, Sept. 1   Litho.   Perf. 13

54	A23	20c multicolored	1.00	1.00
55	A24	30c multicolored	1.25	1.25
56	A25	50c multicolored	1.75	1.75
57	A26	€1 multicolored	3.25	3.25
a.		Souvenir sheet, #54-57	9.50	9.50
		Nos. 54-57 (4)	7.25	7.25

Nos. 54-57 were printed by CPU & Moare. No. 57a was printed by two printers: 7,500 inscribed "CPU&Moare," and 5,000 inscribed "Leoprint."

Intl. Peace Day — A27

2006, Sept. 21   Litho.   Perf. 13

58	A27	€2 multicolored	7.00	7.00

Ancient Coins — A28

Various coins.

2006, Nov. 1   Litho.   Perf. 13

59	A28	20c multicolored	1.00	1.00
60	A28	30c multicolored	1.50	1.50
61	A28	50c multicolored	1.75	1.75
62	A28	€1 multicolored	3.25	3.25
a.		Souvenir sheet, #59-62	9.50	9.50
		Nos. 59-62 (4)	7.50	7.50

Nos. 59-62 are inscribed CPU. Stamps with "Leoprint" imprint are from No. 63a.
No. 62a exists imperforate. Value, $75.

Sculpture — A29

2006, Dec. 1   Litho.   Perf. 13

63	A29	€2 multicolored	8.00	8.00
a.		Miniature sheet, #45-57, 59-63, + 2 labels	80.00	80.00

Convention on the Rights of Persons With Disabilities — A30

Emblems of handicaps and: 20c, Children and butterfly. 50c, Handicapped women. 70c, Map of Kosovo. €1, Stylized flower.

2007, Apr. 23   Litho.   Perf. 14x14¼

64	A30	20c multicolored	1.25	1.25
65	A30	50c multicolored	2.50	2.50
66	A30	70c multicolored	3.00	3.00
67	A30	€1 multicolored	3.75	3.75
a.		Souvenir sheet, #64-67	12.50	12.50
		Nos. 64-67 (4)	10.50	10.50

Color shades vary widely. Printer's waste of this issue exists in the marketplace, including partial prints, missing design elements, and missing colors.
Two varieties of No. 67a, exist differing in text surrounding the stamps. It has not been established if both varieties were officially issued.

Scouting, Cent. — A31

Europa — A32

2007, May 12   Litho.   Perf. 13¼

68	A31	70c multicolored	4.25	4.25
69	A32	€1 multicolored	6.25	6.25
a.		Souvenir sheet, #68-69	90.00	90.00

A33

A34

A35

International Children's Day — A36

2007, June 1   Litho.   Perf. 13¼

70	A33	20c multicolored	1.25	1.25
71	A34	30c multicolored	1.50	1.50
72	A35	70c multicolored	2.50	2.50
73	A36	€1 multicolored	4.00	4.00
		Nos. 70-73 (4)	9.25	9.25

Nos. 70-73 exist imperf. Value, set $45

Native Costumes — A37

Designs: 20c, Serbian woman. 30c, Prizren Region woman. 50c, Sword dancer. 70c, Drenica Region woman. €1, Shepherd, Rugova.

2007, July 6   Litho.   Perf. 13½x13¼

74	A37	20c multicolored	1.25	1.25
75	A37	30c multicolored	1.75	1.75
76	A37	50c multicolored	2.00	2.00
77	A37	70c multicolored	2.50	2.50
78	A37	€1 multicolored	3.25	3.25
a.		Souvenir sheet, #74-78, + label	12.50	12.50
		Nos. 74-78 (5)	10.75	10.75

Masks — A38

Various masks.

Perf. 13½x13¼

2007, Sept. 11   Litho.

79	A38	15c multicolored	.75	.75
80	A38	30c multicolored	1.00	1.00
81	A38	50c multicolored	2.00	2.00
82	A38	€1 multicolored	3.00	3.00
		Nos. 79-82 (4)	6.75	6.75

Sports — A39

Designs: 20c, Soccer ball, basketball, two people standing, person in wheelchair. 50c, Wrestlers. €1, Symbols of 24 sports.

2007, Oct. 2   Litho.   Perf. 13¼x13½

83	A39	20c multicolored	1.00	1.00
84	A39	50c multicolored	2.25	2.25
85	A39	€1 multicolored	4.00	4.00
		Nos. 83-85 (3)	7.25	7.25

Nos. 83-85 exist imperf. Value, set $65.

Architecture A40

Designs: 30c, Stone bridge, Vushtrri. 50c, Hamam, Prizren. 70c, Tower. €1, Tower, diff.

2007, Nov. 6   Litho.   Perf. 13¼

86	A40	30c multicolored	1.50	1.50
87	A40	50c multicolored	2.00	2.00
88	A40	70c multicolored	2.50	2.50
89	A40	€1 multicolored	3.50	3.50
		Nos. 86-89 (4)	9.50	9.50

Nos. 86-89 exist imperf. Value, set $85.

Locomotives A41

Designs: €1, Diesel locomotive. €2, Steam locomotive

2007, Dec. 7   Litho.   Perf. 13¼

90	A41	€1 multicolored	4.00	4.00
91	A41	€2 multicolored	8.00	8.00

Nos. 90-91 exist imperf. Value, set $125.

Skanderbeg (1405-68), Albanian National Hero — A42

2008, Jan. 17   Litho.   Perf. 13¼

92	A42	€2 multicolored	7.50	7.50

No. 92 exists imperf. Value, $35.
Kosovo declared its independence from Serbia on Feb. 17, 2008, ending the United Nations Interim Administration. Stamps issued after Feb. 17, 2008, by the Republic of Kosovo will be listed under Kosovo in the *Scott Standard Postage Stamp Catalogue.*

ABU DHABI

,ä-bü-'thä-bē

LOCATION — Arabia, on Persian Gulf
GOVT. — Sheikdom under British
protection
POP. — 25,000 (estimated)
CAPITAL — Abu Dhabi

Abu Dhabi is one of six Persian Gulf sheikdoms to join the United Arab Emirates, which proclaimed its independence Dec. 2, 1971. See United Arab Emirates.

100 Naye Paise = 1 Rupee
1000 Fils = 1 Dinar (1966)

Catalogue values for all unused stamps in this country are for Never Hinged items.

Sheik Shakbut bin
Sultan — A1

Palace — A2

Designs: 40np, 50np, 75np, Gazelle. 5r, 10r, Oil rig and camels.

Perf. 14½
1964, Mar. 30   Photo.   Unwmk.

1	A1	5np brt yellow green	4.00	3.75
2	A1	15np brown	3.00	2.00
3	A1	20np brt ultra	3.25	1.75
a.		Perf 13x13½	575.00	
4	A1	30np red orange	3.25	1.25
5	A1	40np brt violet	6.00	1.00
6	A1	50np brown olive	6.50	2.25
7	A1	75np gray	9.00	6.75

Engr.   Perf. 13x13½

8	A2	1r light green	5.00	2.50
9	A2	2r black	9.00	5.00
10	A2	5r carmine rose	20.00	13.00
11	A2	10r dark blue	26.00	15.00
		Nos. 1-11 (11)	95.00	54.25

For surcharges see Nos. 15-25.

Falcon Perched on
Wrist — A3

40np, Falcon facing left. 2r, Falcon facing right.

1965, Mar. 30   Photo.   Perf. 14½

12	A3	20np chlky blue & brn	13.50	2.75
13	A3	40np ultra & brown	17.00	3.50
14	A3	2r brt blue grn & gray brn	29.00	16.00
		Nos. 12-14 (3)	59.50	22.25

Nos. 1-11 Surcharged

a   b

c

1966, Oct. 1   Photo.   Perf. 14½

15	A1 (a)	5f on 5np	10.00	5.00
16	A1 (a)	15f on 15np	12.00	9.00
17	A1 (a)	20f on 20np, perf 13x13½	14.00	7.00
a.		Perf 14½ (#3)	250.00	250.00
b.		As "a," inverted surcharge	600.00	850.00
		(#3a)		
18	A1 (a)	30f on 30np	14.00	16.50
a.		Double surcharge	400.00	
b.		Arabic surcharge "20f" instead of "30f"	9,000.	
19	A1 (b)	40f on 40np	13.00	1.50
20	A1 (b)	50f on 50np	35.00	32.50
21	A1 (b)	75f on 75np	35.00	32.50
a.		Double surcharge	400.00	

Engr.   Perf. 13x13½

22	A2 (c)	100f on 1r	17.00	4.00
23	A2 (c)	200f on 2r	17.50	13.00
24	A2 (c)	500f on 5r	42.50	47.50
25	A2 (c)	1d on 10r	62.50	72.50
		Nos. 15-25 (11)	272.50	241.00

Overprint on No. 25 has "1 Dinar" on 1 line and 3 bars through old denomination.

Sheik Zaid bin
Sultan al
Nahayan — A4

Dorcas Gazelle — A5

Designs: 5f, 15f, 20f, 35f, Crossed flags of Abu Dhabi. 200f, Falcon. 500f, 1d, Palace.

Engr.; Flags Litho.
1967, Apr. 1   Perf. 13x13½

26	A4	5f dull grn & red	.35	.25
27	A4	15f dk brown & red	.50	.25
28	A4	20f dk blue & red	.85	.25
29	A4	35f purple & red	1.00	.30

Engr.

30	A4	40f green	1.25	.30
31	A4	50f brown	1.50	.40
32	A4	60f blue	1.75	.45
33	A4	100f car rose	2.75	.65

Litho.

34	A5	125f green & brn ol	6.00	2.00
35	A5	200f sky blue & brn	26.00	9.50
36	A5	500f org & brt pur	19.00	8.00
37	A5	1d green & vio bl	47.50	17.50
		Nos. 26-37 (12)	108.45	39.85

For surcharge, see No. 55A.

Sheik Zaid bin
Sultan al
Nahayan — A6

1967, Aug. 6   Photo.   Perf. 14½x14

38	A6	40f Prussian green	4.00	2.50
39	A6	50f brown	5.00	2.00
40	A6	60f blue	17.50	4.00
41	A6	100f carmine rose	26.00	10.00
		Nos. 38-41 (4)	52.50	18.50

Human
Rights
Flame
and
Sheik
Zaid —
A6a

Perf. 14½x14
1968, Apr. 1   Photo.   Unwmk.
Emblem in Red and Green

42	A6a	35f peacock bl & gold	2.25	.90
43	A6a	60f dk blue & gold	3.50	1.25
44	A6a	150f dk brown & gold	9.00	3.00
		Nos. 42-44 (3)	14.75	5.15

International Human Rights Year.

Sheik
Zaid
and
Coat
of
Arms
A7

Perf. 14x14½
1968, Aug. 6   Photo.   Unwmk.

45	A7	5f multicolored	4.00	.60
46	A7	10f multicolored	4.00	.85
47	A7	100f multicolored	11.00	3.25
48	A7	125f multicolored	16.00	4.75
		Nos. 45-48 (4)	35.00	9.45

Accession of Sheik Zaid, 2nd anniversary.

Abu Dhabi Airport — A8

5f, Buildings under construction and earthmoving equipment. 35f, New bridge and falcon. Each stamp shows different portrait of Sheik Zaid.

Perf. 12, 12½x13 (10f)
1969, Mar. 28   Litho.
Size: 5f, 35f, 59x34mm

49	A8	5f multicolored	3.00	.55
50	A8	10f multicolored	7.50	1.00
51	A8	35f multicolored	32.50	8.00
		Nos. 49-51 (3)	43.00	9.55

Issued to publicize progress made in Abu Dhabi during preceding 2 years.

Sheik
Zaid and
Abu
Dhabi
Petroleum
Co. — A9

Designs: 60f, Abu Dhabi Marine Areas drilling platform and helicopter. 125f, Zakum Field separator at night. 200f, Tank farm.

1969, Aug. 6   Litho.   Perf. 14x13½

52	A9	35f olive grn & multi	2.00	.85
53	A9	60f yel brown & multi	9.50	2.25
54	A9	125f multicolored	11.00	4.00
55	A9	200f red brown & multi	15.00	7.00
		Nos. 52-55 (4)	37.50	14.10

Accession of Sheik Zaid, 3rd anniversary.

No. 27 Surcharged "25" in Arabic
1969, Dec. 13

55A	A4	25f on 15f dk brown & red	250.00	160.00

Because of local demand for 25f stamps for mailing Christmas greeting cards abroad, the Director of Posts ordered that 20,000 examples of No. 27 be surcharged "25" in Arabic for emergency use. This surcharge was applied locally, using a hand numbering machine. All stamps were sold at post office counters

between Dec. 13 and Dec. 24, and the majority were used on mail during this period. Stamps remained valid and exist on covers into 1970. Double overprints exist.

Sheik Zaid — A10

Sheik
Zaid
and
Stallion
A11

5f, 25f, 60f, 90f, Oval frame around portrait. 150f, Gazelle and Sheik. 500f, Fort Jahili and Sheik. 1d, Grand Mosque and Sheik.

1970-71   Litho.   Perf. 14

56	A10	5f lt green & multi	1.00	.25
57	A10	10f bister & multi	1.25	.25
58	A10	25f lilac & multi	2.00	.25
59	A10	35f violet & multi	2.25	.25
60	A10	50f sepia & multi	3.25	.40
61	A10	60f violet & multi	3.75	.50
62	A10	70f rose red & multi	6.00	.65
63	A10	90f car rose & multi	8.25	1.00
64	A11	125f multi ('71)	12.00	2.00
65	A11	150f multi ('71)	15.00	2.50
66	A11	500f multi ('71)	50.00	11.00
67	A11	1d multi ('71)	85.00	22.50
		Nos. 56-67 (12)	189.75	41.55

For surcharge see No. 80.

Sheik Zaid and Mt. Fuji — A12

1970, Aug.   Litho.   Perf. 13½x13

68	A12	25f multicolored	5.00	1.25
69	A12	35f multicolored	7.00	2.00
70	A12	60f multicolored	12.50	4.00
		Nos. 68-70 (3)	24.50	7.25

Issued to publicize EXPO '70 International Exhibition, Osaka, Japan, Mar. 15-Sept. 13.

Abu
Dhabi
Airport
A13

Designs: 60f, Airport entrance. 150f, Aerial view of Abu Dhabi Town, vert.

Perf. 14x13½, 13½x14
1970, Sept. 22   Litho.

71	A13	25f multicolored	5.25	.85
72	A13	60f multicolored	10.00	2.00
73	A13	150f multicolored	22.50	5.25
		Nos. 71-73 (3)	37.75	8.10

Accession of Sheik Zaid, 4th anniversary.

Gamal Abdel
Nasser — A14

1971, May 3　Litho.　Perf. 14
74　A14　25f deep rose & blk　8.00　3.50
75　A14　35f rose violet & blk　11.00　5.25

In memory of Gamal Abdel Nasser (1918-1970), President of UAR.

Scout Cars A15

Designs: 60f, Patrol boat. 125f, Armored car in desert. 150f, Meteor jet fighters.

1971, Aug. 6　Litho.　Perf. 13
76　A15　35f multicolored　7.00　1.50
77　A15　60f multicolored　9.50　2.25
78　A15　125f multicolored　20.00　3.75
79　A15　150f multicolored　25.00　7.50
　Nos. 76-79 (4)　61.50　15.00

Accession of Sheik Zaid, 5th anniversary.

No. 60 Surcharged in Green
5 Fils

1971, Dec. 8　Perf. 14
80　A10　5f on 50f multi　130.00　100.00

Dome of the Rock, Jerusalem — A16

Different views of Dome of the Rock.

1972, June 3　Perf. 13
81　A16　35f lt violet & multi　30.00　5.75
82　A16　60f lt violet & multi　55.00　9.50
83　A16　125f lilac & multi　100.00　20.00
　Nos. 81-83 (3)　185.00　35.25

Nos. 80-83 were issued after Abu Dhabi joined the United Arab Emirates Dec. 2, 1971. Stamps of UAE replaced those of Abu Dhabi. UAE Nos. 1-12 were used only in Abu Dhabi except the 10f and 25f which were issued later in Dubai and Sharjah.

ADEN

'ä-dən

LOCATION — Southern Arabia
GOVT. — British colony and protectorate
AREA — 112,075 sq. mi.
POP. — 220,000 (est. 1964)
CAPITAL — Aden

Aden used India stamps before 1937. In January, 1963, the colony of Aden (the port) and the sheikdoms and emirates of the Western Aden Protectorate formed the Federation of South Arabia. This did not include the Eastern Aden Protectorate with Kathiri and Qu'aiti States. Stamps of Aden, except those of Kathiri and Qu'aiti States, were replaced Apr. 1, 1965, by those of the Federation of South Arabia. See South

Arabia and People's Democratic Republic of Yemen, Vol. 6.

12 Pies = 1 Anna
16 Annas = 1 Rupee
100 Cents = 1 Shilling (1951)

Catalogue values for unused stamps in this country are for Never Hinged items.

ISSUES UNDER BRITISH ADMINISTRATION

Dhow — A1

Perf. 13x11½
1937, Apr. 1　Engr.　Wmk. 4
1　A1　½a lt green　4.50　3.00
2　A1　9p dark green　4.25　3.75
3　A1　1a black brown　4.00　2.25
4　A1　2a red　5.00　3.25
5　A1　2½a blue　7.25　2.50
6　A1　3a carmine rose　11.00　8.75
7　A1　3½a gray blue　9.50　6.00
8　A1　8a rose lilac　27.50　11.50
9　A1　1r brown　62.50　12.50
10　A1　2r orange yellow　125.00　40.00
11　A1　5r rose violet　300.00　100.00
12　A1　10r olive green　600.00　400.00
　Nos. 1-12 (12)　1,161.　593.50
　Set, hinged　775.00

Common Design Types pictured following the introduction.

Coronation Issue
Common Design Type
1937, May 12　Perf. 13½x14
13　CD302　1a black brown　.75　1.25
14　CD302　2½a blue　.85　1.40
15　CD302　3½a gray blue　1.10　3.00
　Nos. 13-15 (3)　2.70　5.65
　Set, hinged　1.75

Aidrus Mosque — A2

¾a, 5r, Camel Corpsman. 1a, 2r, Aden Harbor. 1½a, 1r, Adenese dhow. 2½a, 8a, Mukalla. 3a, 14a, 10r, Capture of Aden, 1839.

1939-48　Engr.　Wmk. 4　Perf. 12½
16　A2　½a green (7/42)　1.75　.50
17　A2　¾a red brn　2.50　1.10
18　A2　1a brt lt blue　1.40　.40
19　A2　1½a red　2.50　.60
20　A2　2a dark brown　1.60　.25
21　A2　2½a brt ultra　1.60　.30
22　A2　3a rose car & dk brn　1.60　.25
23　A2　8a orange　2.00　.40
23A　A2　14a lt bl & brn blk ('45)　3.75　.90
24　A2　1r bright green　4.50　2.25
25　A2　2r dp mag & bl blk ('44)　10.00　3.00
26　A2　5r dp ol & lake brn (1/44)　30.00　20.00
27a　A2　10r dk pur & lake brn　40.00　35.00
　Nos. 16-27a (13)　103.20　64.95
　Set, hinged　42.50

For shades, see the Scott Classic Specialized Catalogue.

Peace Issue
Common Design Type
Perf. 13½x14
1946, Oct. 15　Engr.　Wmk. 4
28　CD303　1½a carmine　.25　1.50
29　CD303　2½a deep blue　.70　1.00

Return to peace at end of World War II.

Silver Wedding Issue
Common Design Types
1949, Jan. 17　Photo.　Perf. 14x14½
30　CD304　1½a scarlet　.40　1.50
Engraved; Name Typographed
Perf. 11½x11
31　CD305　10r purple　40.00　55.00

25th anniv. of the marriage of King George VI and Queen Elizabeth.

UPU Issue
Common Design Types

Srchd. in Annas and Rupees

Engr.; Name typo. on Nos. 33-34
1949, Oct. 10　Perf. 13½, 11x11½
32　CD306　2½a on 20c dp ultra　.55　1.60
33　CD307　3a on 30c dp car　1.90　1.60
34　CD308　8a on 50c org　1.90　1.75
35　CD309　1r on 1sh blue　1.50　3.50
　Nos. 32-35 (4)　5.85　8.45

75th anniv. of the formation of the UPU.

Nos. 18 and 20-27 Surcharged in Black or Carmine

1951, Oct. 1　Wmk. 4　Perf. 12½
36　A2　5c on 1a #18a　.30　.40
37　A2　10c on 2a #20a　.25　.45
38　A2　15c on 2½a　.50　1.25
　a.　Double surcharge　1,600.
　　Hinged　1,000.
39　A2　20c on 3a　.50　.50
40　A2　30c on 8a #23b (C)　.85　.60
41　A2　50c on 8a #23b　1.50　.35
42　A2　70c on 14a (#23A)　2.25　1.40
43　A2　1sh on 1r #24a　3.00　.30
44　A2　2sh on 2r #25　13.00　3.50
45　A2　5sh on 5r #26　25.00　15.00
46　A2　10sh on 10r #27　35.00　15.00
　Nos. 36-46 (11)　82.15　38.75
　Set, hinged　42.50

Surcharge on No. 40 includes 2 bars.

Coronation Issue
Common Design Type
1953, June 2　Engr.　Perf. 13½x13
47　CD312　15c dk grn & blk　1.25　1.25

Minaret — A10　　　Camel Transport — A11

15c, Crater. 25c, Mosque. 35c, Dhow. 50c, Map. 70c, Salt works. 1sh, Colony Badge. 2sh, Aden Protectorate levy. 5sh, Crater Pass. 10sh, Tribesman. 20sh, Aden in 1572.

Perf. 12, 12x13½ ('56)
1953-59　Engr.　Wmk. 4
Size: 29x23, 23x29mm
48　A10　5c grn, perf 12x13½ ('56)　.25　.25
　a.　Perf. 12 ('55)　2.25　3.00
　b.　5c bluish grn, perf 12x13½ ('56)　.25　1.00
49　A11　10c orange　.35　.25
　a.　10c vermilion ('55)　　.30
50　A11　15c blue green　1.00　.55
　a.　15c grayish grn ('59)　7.00　6.00
51　A11　25c carmine　.75　.50
　a.　25c deep rose red ('56)　5.00　1.50
52　A10　35c ultra, perf. 12　2.00　1.00
　a.　35c dp bl, perf 12x13½ ('58)　5.00　5.00
　b.　35c vio bl, perf 12x13½ ('59)　12.50　4.00

53　A10　50c blue, perf 12　.35　.25
　a.　As "b," perf 12x13½ ('56)　1.00　.25
　b.　50c deep bl, perf 12 ('55)　3.00　2.00
54　A10　70c gray, perf 12　.50　.25
　a.　As "b," perf 12x13½ ('56)　1.75　.25
　b.　70c grayish blk, perf 12 ('54)　1.40　.90
55　A11　1sh pur & sepia　.50　.25
55A　A11　1sh vio & blk ('55)　1.40　.25
56　A10　1sh25c blk & lt blue ('56)　11.00　.45
57　A10　2sh car rose & sep　1.25　.50
57A　A10　2sh car & blk ('56)　11.50　.45
58　A10　5sh blue & sepia　2.00　1.00
58A　A10　5sh dk blue & blk ('56)　12.00　1.25
59　A10　10sh olive & sepia　2.00　7.50
60　A10　10sh ol gray & blk ('54)　12.50　1.50

Size: 36½x27mm
Perf. 13½x13
61　A11　20sh rose vio & dk brn　15.00　20.00
61A　A11　20sh lt vio & blk ('57)　45.00　18.00
　Nos. 48-61A (18)　119.35　54.20
　Set, hinged　70.00

No. 60 has heavier shading on tribesman's lower garment than No. 59.
See Nos. 66-75. For overprints see Nos. 63-64.

Type of 1953
Inscribed: "Royal Visit 1954"
1954, Apr. 27　Perf. 12
62　A11　1sh purple & sepia　.65　4.00

Nos. 50 & 56 Overprinted in Red

No. 63

No. 64

1959, Jan. 26　Perf. 12, 12x13½
63　A11　15c dark blue green　.55　2.00
64　A10　1sh25c blk & light blue　1.00　1.50

Introduction of a revised constitution.

Freedom from Hunger Issue
Common Design Type
1963, June 4　Photo.　Wmk. 314
65　CD314　1sh25c green　1.50　1.75

Types of 1953-57
Perf. 12x13½, 12 (#67-69, 73)
1964-65　Engr.　Wmk. 314
66　A10　5c green ('65)　4.25　9.50
67　A11　10c orange　2.00　1.00
68　A11　15c Prus green　.90　5.25
69　A11　25c carmine　3.00　.40
70　A10　35c dk blue　7.25　9.00
71　A10　50c dull blue　1.25　1.10
72　A10　70c gray　2.75　4.00
73　A11　1sh vio & black　10.00　15.00
74　A10　1sh25c blk & lt blue　16.00　2.00
75　A10　2sh car & blk ('65)　6.75　30.00
　Nos. 66-75 (10)　55.15　77.25

KATHIRI STATE OF SEIYUN

LOCATION — In Eastern Aden Protectorate
GOVT. — Sultanate
CAPITAL — Seiyun

The stamps of the Kathiri State of Seiyun were valid for use throughout Aden. Used stamps generally bear Aden GPO or Aden Camp cancels. Examples with cancels from offices in the Eastern Protectorate command a premium.

Sultan Ja'far bin Mansur al Kathiri — A1

Seiyun — A2

Minaret at Tarim — A3

Designs: 2½a, Mosque at Seiyun. 3a, Palace at Tarim. 8a, Mosque at Seiyun, horiz. 1r, South Gate, Tarim. 2r, Kathiri House. 5r, Mosque at Tarim.

1942 Engr. Wmk. 4 Perf. 13¾x14

1	A1	½a dark green	.25	1.40
2	A1	¾a copper brown	.50	3.00
3	A1	1a deep blue	.60	1.50

Perf. 13x11½, 11½x13

4	A2	1½a dark car rose	.65	1.75
5	A2	2a sepia brown	.40	1.75
6	A3	2½a deep blue	1.00	2.00
7	A2	3a dk car rose & dull brn	1.60	3.00
8	A2	8a orange red	3.00	1.25
9	A3	1r green	6.50	3.50
10	A2	2r rose vio & dk blue	13.50	18.00
11	A3	5r gray green & fawn	32.50	24.00
		Nos. 1-11 (11)	60.50	61.15
		Set, hinged	28.00	

For surcharges see Nos. 20-27.

Nos. 4, 6 Ovptd. in Black or Red

a

b

Perf. 13x11½, 11½x13

1946, Oct. 15 Wmk. 4

12	A2 (a)	1½a dark car rose	.25	.65
13	A3 (b)	2½a deep blue (R)	.25	.25
a.		Inverted overprint	1,300.	
		Hinged	775.00	
b.		Double overprint	1,800.	
		Hinged	1,050.	

Victory of the Allied Nations in WWII.
All examples of No. 13b have the 2nd overprint almost directly over the 1st.

Silver Wedding Issue
Common Design Types
1949, Jan. 17 Photo. Perf. 14x14½

14	CD304	1½a scarlet	.35	2.00

Engraved; Name Typo.
Perf. 11½x11

15	CD305	5r green	17.50	14.00

25th anniv. of the marriage of King George VI and Queen Elizabeth.

UPU Issue
Common Design Types

Srchd. in Annas and Rupees

Engr.; Name Typo. on Nos. 17-18
1949, Oct. 10 Perf. 13½, 11x11½

16	CD306	2½a on 20c dp ultra	.25	4.00
17	CD307	3a on 30c dp car	1.50	4.00
18	CD308	8a on 50c orange	.40	4.00
19	CD309	1r on 1sh blue	.60	4.00
		Nos. 16-19 (4)	2.75	16.00

75th anniv. of the formation of the UPU.

Nos. 3 and 5-11 Srchd. in Carmine or Black

Perf. 14, 13x11½, 11½x13
1951, Oct. 1 Engr. Wmk. 4

20	A1	5c on 1a (C)	.25	2.00
21	A3	10c on 2a #5a	.35	1.75
22	A3	15c on 2½a	.30	2.25
23	A2	20c on 3a #7	.35	2.50
24	A2	50c on 8a	.80	1.60
25	A3	1sh on 1r	2.50	3.75
26	A2	2sh on 2r #10	11.50	30.00
27	A3	5sh on 5r	34.00	47.50
		Nos. 20-27 (8)	50.05	91.35

Coronation Issue
Common Design Type
1953, June 2 Perf. 13½x13

28	CD312	15c dk green & blk	.75	1.50

Sultan Hussein A10

Seiyun Scene A11

25c, Minaret at Tarim, vert. 35c, Mosque at Seiyun, vert. 50c, Palace at Tarim. 1sh, Mosque at Seiyun. 2sh, South Gate, Tarim, vert.. 5sh, Kathiri house. 10sh, Mosque entrance, Tarim, vert.

1954, Jan. 15 Engr. Perf. 12½

29	A10	5c dark brown	.25	.25
30	A10	10c deep blue	.25	.25

Perf. 13x11½, 11½x13

31	A11	15c dk blue green	.25	.25
32	A11	25c dk car rose	.25	.25
33	A11	35c deep blue	.25	.25
34	A11	50c dk car rose & dk brn	.25	.25
35	A11	1sh deep orange	.25	.25
36	A11	2sh gray green	4.00	2.00
37	A11	5sh vio & dk blue	9.25	8.00
38	A11	10sh vio & yel brn	10.00	8.50
		Nos. 29-38 (10)	25.00	20.25

Perf. 11½x13, 13x11½
1964, July 1 Wmk. 314

Designs: 70c, Qarn Adh Dhabi. 1sh25c, Seiyun, horiz. 1sh50c, View of Gheil Omer, horiz.

39	A11	70c black	2.75	2.00
40	A11	1sh25c bright green	2.75	7.50
41	A11	1sh50c purple	2.75	8.00
		Nos. 39-41 (3)	8.25	17.50

QUAITI STATE OF SHIHR AND MUKALLA

LOCATION — In Eastern Aden Protectorate
GOVT. — Sultanate
CAPITAL — Mukalla

The stamps of the Quaiti State of Shihr and Mukalla were valid for use throughout Aden. Used stamps generally bear Aden GPO or Aden Camp cancels. Examples with cancels from offices in the Eastern Protectorate command a premium.

Sultan Sir Saleh bin Ghalib al Qu'aiti — A1

Mukalla Harbor — A2

Buildings at Shibam — A3

Designs: 2a, Gateway of Shihr. 3a, Outpost of Mukalla. 8a, View of 'Einat. 1r, Governor's Castle, Du'an. 2r, Mosque in Hureidha. 5r, Meshhed.

1942 Engr. Wmk. 4 Perf. 13¾x14

1	A1	½a dark green	1.40	.35
2	A1	¾a copper brown	2.00	.25
3	A1	1a deep blue	.80	.80

Perf. 13x11½, 11½x13

4	A2	1½a dk car rose	1.60	.35
5	A2	2a black brown	1.75	1.25
6	A3	2½a deep blue	.40	.25
7	A2	3a dk car rose & dl brn	1.00	.75
8	A2	8a orange red	1.10	.35
9	A2	1r green	6.00	3.50
a.		Missing "A" in "CA" of watermark	1,300.	1,200.
10	A3	2r rose vio & dk blue	16.00	12.00
11	A3	5r gray grn & fawn	32.50	16.00
		Nos. 1-11 (11)	64.55	35.85

For surcharges see Nos. 20-27.

Nos. 4, 6 Ovptd. in Black or Carmine like Kathiri Nos. 12-13
1946, Oct. 15 Perf. 11½x13, 13x11½

12	A2 (b)	1½a dk car rose	.25	1.00
13	A3 (a)	2½a deep blue (C)	.25	.25

Victory of the Allied Nations in WWII.

Silver Wedding Issue
Common Design Types
1949, Jan. 17 Photo. Perf. 14x14½

14	CD304	1½a scarlet	.55	2.50

Engraved; Name Typo.
Perf. 11½x11

15	CD305	5r green	18.00	10.00

25th anniv. of the marriage of King George VI and Queen Elizabeth.

UPU Issue
Surcharged in Annas and Rupees
Common Design Types

No. 16

No. 17

Engr.; Name Typo. on Nos. 17 and 18
1949, Oct. 10 Perf. 13½, 11x11½

16	CD306	2½a on 20c dp ultra	.25	2.00
17	CD307	3a on 30c dp car	1.50	2.00
18	CD308	8a on 50c org	.35	2.00
19	CD309	1r on 1sh blue	.50	2.00
a.		Surcharge omitted	4,250.	
		Hinged	2,750.	
		Nos. 16-19 (4)	2.60	8.00

Nos. 3, 5-11 & Types Surcharged in Carmine or Black

Nos. 20-21

Nos. 22-24

Nos. 25-27

Perf. 14, 13x11½, 11½x13
1951, Oct. 1 Engr. Wmk. 4

20	A1	5c on 1a (C)	.25	.25
21	A2	10c on 2a	.25	.25
22	A3	15c on 2½a	.25	.25
23	A2	20c on 3a #7	.30	.75
24	A3	50c on 8a org red	.45	2.50
25	A2	1sh on 1r	2.00	.55
26	A3	2sh on 2r	8.00	24.00
27	A3	5sh on 5r	17.00	34.00
		Nos. 20-27 (8)	28.50	62.55

Coronation Issue
Common Design Type
1953, June 2 Engr. Perf. 13½x13

28	CD312	15c dk blue & black	1.10	.60

Qu'aiti State in Hadhramaut

Metal Work — A10

Fisheries A11

Designs: 10c, Mat making. 15c, Weaving. 25c, Pottery. 35c, Building. 50c, Date cultivation. 90c, Agriculture. 1sh25c, 10sh, Lime burning. 2sh, Dhow building. 5sh, Agriculture.

Perf. 11½x13, 13½x14
1955, Sept. 1 Engr. Wmk. 4

29	A10	5c greenish blue	.75	.25
30	A10	10c black	1.00	.25
31	A10	15c dk green	.75	.25
32	A10	25c carmine	.40	.25
33	A10	35c ultra	.75	.25
34	A10	50c red orange	.75	.25
35	A10	90c brown	.55	.25
36	A11	1sh purple & blk	.75	.25
37	A11	1sh25c red org & blk	.60	.55
38	A11	2sh dk blue & blk	3.00	.60
39	A11	5sh green & blk	4.00	2.25
40	A11	10sh car & black	13.50	7.50
		Nos. 29-40 (12)	26.80	12.90

Types of 1955 with Portrait of Sultan Awadh Bin Saleh El-Qu'aiti
Design: 70c, Agriculture. Others as before.
1963, Oct. 20 Wmk. 314

41	A10	5c greenish blue	.25	1.40
42	A10	10c black	.25	1.15
43	A10	15c dark green	.25	1.40
44	A10	25c carmine	.25	.60
45	A10	35c ultra	.25	1.50
46	A10	50c red orange	.25	.75
47	A10	70c brown	.25	.60
48	A11	1sh purple & blk	.30	.30
49	A11	1sh25c red org & blk	.50	5.00
50	A11	2sh dk blue & blk	2.75	2.25
51	A11	5sh green & blk	12.50	25.00
52	A11	10sh car & black	27.00	26.00
		Nos. 41-52 (12)	44.80	65.95

AFARS & ISSAS
French Territory of the

'ä-färz and ē-'säz

LOCATION — East Africa
GOVT. — French Overseas Territory
AREA — 8,880 sq. mi.
POP. — 150,000 (est. 1974)
CAPITAL — Djibouti (Jibuti)

The French overseas territory of Somali Coast was renamed the French Territory of the Afars and Issas in 1967. It became the Djibouti Republic on June 27, 1977.

100 Centimes = 1 Franc

> Catalogue values for all unused stamps in this country are for Never Hinged items.

Imperforates
Most stamps of Afars and Issas exist imperforate in issued and trial colors, and also in small presentation sheets in issued colors.

Grayheaded Kingfisher — A48

Xerus Rutilus — A48a

10fr, Halcyon leucocephala. 15fr, Haematopus ostralegus. 50fr, Tringa nebularia. 55fr, Coracias abyssinicus.

1967		Unwmk.	Engr.	Perf. 13	
310	A48	10fr multicolored		4.00	3.00
311	A48	15fr multicolored		5.25	4.00
312	A48	50fr multicolored		12.50	8.00
313	A48	55fr multicolored		17.50	11.00
314	A48a	60fr multicolored		24.00	17.50
	Nos. 310-314 (5)			63.25	43.50
	Nos. 310-314,C50 (6)			80.75	55.50

Issued: 10fr, 55fr, Aug. 21; 15fr, 50fr, 60fr, Sept. 25. See No. C50.

Soccer A49

1967, Dec. 18		Engr.	Perf. 13	
315	A49	25fr shown	3.50	2.75
316	A49	30fr Basketball	4.00	2.75

Common Design Types
Pictured in section at front of book.

WHO Anniversary Issue
Common Design Type

1968, May 4		Engr.	Perf. 13	
317	CD126	15fr multicolored	3.00	3.00
	20th anniv. of WHO.			

Damerdjog Fortress A50

Administration Buildings: 25fr, Ali Adde. 30fr, Dorra. 40fr, Assamo.

1968, May 17		Engr.	Perf. 13	
318	A50	20fr slate, brn & emer	1.25	1.00
319	A50	25fr brt grn, bl & brn	1.50	1.25
320	A50	30fr brn ol, brn org & sl	2.00	1.40
321	A50	40fr brn ol, sl & brt grn	3.25	2.75
	Nos. 318-321 (4)		8.00	6.40

Human Rights Year Issue
Common Design Type

1968, Aug. 10		Engr.	Perf. 13	
322	CD127	10fr purple, ver & org	2.25	1.75
323	CD127	70fr green, pur & org	4.50	2.25

International Human Rights Year.

Radio-television Station, Djibouti — A52

High Commission Palace, Djibouti — A53

Designs: 2fr, Justice Building. 5fr, Chamber of Deputies. 8fr, Great Mosque. 15fr, Monument of Free French Forces, vert. 40fr, Djibouti Post Office. 70fr, Residence of Gov. Léonce Lagarde at Obock. No. 332, Djibouti Harbormaster's Building. No. 333, Control tower, Djibouti Airport.

1968-70		Engr.	Perf. 13	
324	A52	1fr multicolored	.50	.50
325	A52	2fr multicolored	.80	.75
326	A52	5fr multicolored	1.00	1.00
327	A52	8fr multicolored	1.25	1.25
328	A52	15fr multicolored	4.50	3.75
329	A52	40fr multicolored	3.75	2.75
330	A53	60fr multicolored	3.50	2.40
331	A52	70fr multicolored	4.25	3.00
332	A52	85fr multicolored	6.25	3.75
333	A52	85fr multicolored	6.50	4.25
	Nos. 324-333 (10)		32.30	23.40

Issued: No. 330, 1968; Nos. 324-328, 331-332, 1969; Nos. 329, 333, 1970. See Nos. C54-C55.

Locust A54

Designs: 50fr, Pest control by helicopter. 55fr, Pest control by plane.

1969, Oct. 6		Engr.	Perf. 13	
334	A54	15fr brn, grn & slate	4.75	2.25
335	A54	50fr dk grn, bl & ol brn	3.00	2.25
336	A54	55fr red brn, bl & brn	3.50	2.25
	Nos. 334-336 (3)		11.25	6.75

Campaign against locusts.

ILO Issue
Common Design Type

1969, Nov. 24		Engr.	Perf. 13	
337	CD131	30fr org, gray & lil	2.75	2.00

Afar Dagger in Ornamental Scabbard A56

1970, Apr. 3		Engr.	Perf. 13	
338	A56	10fr multicolored	1.40	.75
339	A56	15fr multicolored	1.75	.75
340	A56	20fr multicolored	2.00	1.00
341	A56	25fr multicolored	2.25	1.25
	Nos. 338-341 (4)		7.40	3.75

See No. 364.

UPU Headquarters Issue
Common Design Type

1970, May 20		Engr.	Perf. 13	
342	CD133	25fr brn, brt grn & choc	2.50	1.40

Trapshooting — A57

Motorboats A58

Designs: 50fr, Steeplechase. 55fr, Sailboat, vert. 60fr, Equestrians.

1970		Engr.	Perf. 13	
343	A57	30fr dp brn, yel grn & brt bl	2.75	1.75
344	A58	48fr blue & multi	5.00	2.50
345	A58	50fr cop red, bl & pur	5.00	2.50
346	A58	55fr red brn, bl & ol	5.25	2.50
347	A58	60fr ol, blk & red brn	5.50	3.50
	Nos. 343-347 (5)		23.50	12.75

Issued: 30fr, 6/5; 48fr, 10/9; 50fr, 60fr, 11/6.

Automatic Ferry, Tadjourah A59

1970, Nov. 25				
348	A59	48fr blue, brn & grn	3.75	2.50

Volcanic Geode A60

Diabase and Chrysolite A61

10fr, Doleritic basalt. 15fr, Olivine basalt.

1971		Photo.	Perf. 13	
349	A61	10fr black & multi	3.00	1.25
350	A61	15fr black & multi	3.50	1.75
351	A60	25fr black, crim & brn	7.00	3.25
352	A61	40fr black & multi	9.00	5.00
	Nos. 349-352 (4)		22.50	11.25

Issued: 10fr, 11/22; 15fr, 10/8; 25fr, 4/26; 40fr, 1/25.

A62

4fr, Manta birostris. 5fr, Coryphaena hippurus. 9fr, Pristis pectinatus.

1971, July 1		Photo.	Perf. 12x12½	
353	A62	4fr mulitcolored	2.25	1.25
354	A62	5fr multicolored	2.75	1.40
355	A62	9fr multicolored	4.75	2.25
	Nos. 353-355 (3)		9.75	4.90

See No. C60.

De Gaulle Issue
Common Design Type

Designs: 60fr, Gen. Charles de Gaulle, 1940. 85fr, Pres. de Gaulle, 1970.

1971, Nov. 9		Engr.	Perf. 13	
356	CD134	60fr ultra & blk	6.00	3.50
357	CD134	85fr dk vio bl & blk	6.50	4.00

A63

Shells: 4fr, Strawberry Top. 9fr, Cypraea pantherina. 20fr, Bull-mouth helmet. 50fr, Ethiopian volute.

1972, Mar. 8		Photo.	Perf. 12½x13	
358	A63	4fr olive & multi	1.75	1.25
359	A63	9fr dk blue & multi	2.25	1.50
360	A63	20fr dp green & multi	4.25	2.25
361	A63	50fr dp claret & multi	7.00	3.00
	Nos. 358-361 (4)		15.25	8.00

Shepherd — A64

Design: 10fr, Dromedary breeding.

1973, Apr. 11		Photo.	Perf. 13	
362	A64	9fr blue & multi	1.50	.80
363	A64	10fr blue & multi	1.75	.85

Afar Dagger — A65

1974, Jan. 29		Engr.	Perf. 13	
364	A65	30fr slate grn & dk brn	1.50	.85

For surcharge see No. 379.

Flamingos, Lake Abbe — A66

Flamingos and different views of Lake Abbe.

1974, Feb. 22   Photo.   Perf. 13
370 A66 5fr multicolored   1.75 1.00
371 A66 15fr multicolored   1.50 1.25
372 A66 50fr multicolored   3.00 2.00
       Nos. 370-372 (3)   6.25 4.25

Soccer Ball — A67

1974, May 24   Engr.   Perf. 13
373 A67 25fr black & emerald   3.00 1.75
World Cup Soccer Championship, Munich,
June 13-July 7.

Letters Around
UPU
Emblem — A68

1974, Oct. 9   Engr.   Perf. 13
374 A68 20fr multicolored   1.25 .80
375 A68 100fr multicolored   2.75 2.25
   Centenary of Universal Postal Union.

Oleo
Chrysophylla
A69

Designs: 15fr, Ficus species. 20fr, Solanum
adoense.

1974, Nov. 22   Photo.
376 A69 10fr shown   1.75 1.00
377 A69 15fr multicolored   2.00 1.10
378 A69 20fr multicolored   3.00 1.50
       Nos. 376-378 (3)   6.75 3.60
   Day Primary Forest.

No. 364 Surcharged
in Red

1975, Jan. 1   Engr.   Perf. 13
379 A65 40fr on 30fr multi   2.00 1.25

Treasury — A70

Design: 25fr, Government buildings.

1975, Jan. 7   Engr.   Perf. 13
380 A70 8fr blue, gray & red   .65 .50
381 A70 25fr red, blue & indigo   1.50 .45

Darioconus Textile — A71

Sea Shells: No. 383, Murex palmarosa. 10fr,
Conus sumatrensis. 15fr, Cypraea pulchra.
No. 386, 45fr, Murex scolopax. No. 387,
Cypraea exhusta. 40fr, Ranella spinosa. 55fr,
Cypraea erythraensis. 60fr, Conus taeniatus.

1975-76   Engr.   Perf. 13
382 A71 5fr blue grn & brn   1.25 .85
383 A71 5fr blue & multi ('76)   1.25 1.00
384 A71 10fr lilac, blk & brn   2.50 .90
385 A71 15fr blue, ind & brn   3.25 1.40
386 A71 20fr purple & lt brn   5.00 3.00
387 A71 20fr brt grn & multi
            ('76)   2.75 1.25
388 A71 40fr green & brown   4.50 1.25
389 A71 45fr green, bl & bister   4.75 1.40
390 A71 55fr turq & multi ('76)   3.50 2.00
391 A71 60fr buff & sepia ('76)   6.50 2.75
       Nos. 382-391 (10)   35.25 15.80

Hypolimnas
Misippus
A72

Butterflies: 40fr, Papilio nireus. 50fr, Acraea
anemosa. 65fr, Holocerina smilax menieri.
70fr, Papilio demodocus. No. 397, Papilio dar-
danus. No. 398, Balachowsky gonimbrasca.
150fr, Vanessa cardui.

1975-76   Photo.   Perf. 13
392 A72 25fr emerald & multi   3.75 1.60
393 A72 40fr yellow & multi   4.75 2.00
394 A72 50fr ultra & multi
            ('76)   5.50 1.75
395 A72 65fr ol & multi ('76)   5.50 2.50
396 A72 70fr violet & multi   6.75 3.00
397 A72 100fr blue & multi   8.50 3.75
398 A72 100fr Prus bl & multi
            ('76)   7.00 3.50
399 A72 150fr grn & multi ('76)   8.50 3.75
       Nos. 392-399 (8)   50.25 21.85

A73

Animals: No. 400, Hyaena hyaena. No. 401,
Cercopithecus aethiops. No. 402, Equus
asinus somalicus. No. 403, Dorcatragus
megalotis. No. 404, Ichneumia albicauda. No.
405, Hystrix galeata. No. 406, Ictonyx striatus.
No. 407, Orycteropus afer.

Perf. 13x12½, 12½x13
1975-76   Photo.
400 A73 10fr multicolored   1.25 1.00
401 A73 15fr multicolored   1.40 1.00
402 A73 15fr multicolored   1.60 1.25
403 A73 30fr multicolored   3.00 1.50
404 A73 50fr multicolored   2.75 1.75
405 A73 60fr multicolored   4.00 2.25
406 A73 70fr multicolored   5.50 2.75
407 A73 200fr multicolored   7.50 5.50
       Nos. 400-407 (8)   27.00 17.00
       Nos. 401-402, 405 are vert.
   Issued: 50fr, 60fr, 70fr, 2/21; No. 401, 200fr,
10/24; 10fr, No. 402, 30fr, 2/4/76.

Birds — A74

No. 413, Vidua macroura. No. 414, Psit-
tacula krameri. No. 415, Cinnyris venustus.
No. 416, Ardea goliath. No. 417, Scopus
umbretta. No. 418, Oena capensis. No. 419,
Platalea alba.

1975-76   Photo.   Perf. 12½x13
413 A74 20fr multicolored   1.75 1.40
414 A74 25fr multicolored   2.50 .75
415 A74 50fr multicolored   3.25 1.80
416 A74 60fr multicolored   5.75 2.50
417 A74 100fr multicolored   9.25 3.00
418 A74 100fr multicolored   5.00 1.75
419 A74 300fr multicolored   12.00 4.50
       Nos. 413-419 (7)   39.50 15.70
   Issued: 300fr, 6/15/76; 25fr, No. 418,
10/13/76; others 11/21 and 12/19/75.

Palms — A75

1975, Dec. 19   Engr.   Perf. 13
421 A75 20fr multicolored   1.10 1.00

Satellite and Alexander Graham
Bell — A76

1976, Mar. 10   Engr.   Perf. 13
422 A76 200fr dp bl, org & sl grn 3.25 3.00
   Centenary of the first telephone call by Alexander Graham Bell, Mar. 10, 1876.

Basketball
A77

1976, July 7   Litho.   Perf. 12½
423 A77 10fr shown   .75 .40
424 A77 15fr Bicycling   1.00 .50
425 A77 40fr Soccer   1.75 1.00
426 A77 60fr Running   2.50 1.50
       Nos. 423-426 (4)   6.00 3.40
   21st Olympic Games, Montreal, Canada,
July 17-Aug. 1.

Pterois Radiata — A78

1976, Aug. 10   Photo.   Perf. 13x13½
428 A78 45fr blue & multi   3.75 1.50

Psammophis Elegans — A79

Design: 70fr, Naja nigricollis, vert.

Perf. 13x13½, 13½x13
1976, Sept. 27   Photo.
430 A79 70fr ocher & multi   3.50 2.25
431 A79 80fr emerald & multi   6.00 2.75

Motorcyclist
A80

1977, Jan. 27   Litho.   Perf. 12x12½
432 A80 200fr multicolored   6.00 3.00
   Moto-Cross motorcycle race.

Conus Betulinus — A81

Sea Shells: 5fr, Cyprea tigris. 70fr, Conus
striatus. 85fr, Cyprea mauritiana.

1977   Engr.   Perf. 13
433 A81 5fr multicolored   2.50 1.00
434 A81 30fr multicolored   2.75 1.00
435 A81 70fr multicolored   7.00 2.50
436 A81 85fr multicolored   6.00 3.75
       Nos. 433-436 (4)   18.25 8.25

Gaterin
Gaterinus
A82

1977, Apr. 15   Photo.   Perf. 13x12½
437 A82 15fr shown   1.50 1.00
438 A82 65fr Barracudas   3.00 1.50

AIR POST STAMPS

AP16

200fr, Aquila rapax belisarius.

Unwmk.

1967, Aug. 21		**Engr.**		**Perf. 13**	
C50	AP16	200fr multicolored		17.50	12.00

AP17

48fr, Parachutists. 85fr, Water skier & skin diver.

1968		**Engr.**		**Perf. 13**	
C51	AP17	48fr multicolored		5.50	2.50
C52	AP17	85fr multicolored		7.00	4.50

Issue dates: 48fr, Jan. 5; 85fr, Mar. 15.

Aerial Map of the Territory — AP18

1968, Nov. 15		**Engr.**	**Perf. 13**	
C53	AP18	500fr bl, dk brn & ocher	23.00	13.00

Buildings Type of Regular Issue

100fr, Cathedral. 200fr, Sayed Hassan Mosque.

1969		**Engr.**		**Perf. 13**	
C54	A53	100fr multi, vert.		5.50	2.50
C55	A53	200fr multi, vert.		8.50	5.50

Issue dates: 100fr, Apr. 4; 200fr, May 8.

Concorde Issue
Common Design Type

1969, Apr. 17				
C56	CD129	100fr org red & ol	26.00	16.00

Arta Ionospheric Station — AP19

1970, May 8		**Engr.**	**Perf. 13**	
C57	AP19	70fr multicolored	4.00	3.25

Japanese Sword Guard, Fish Design — AP20

200fr, Japanese sword guard, horse design.

Gold embossed

1970, Oct. 26				**Perf. 12½**	
C58	AP20	100fr multicolored		9.50	7.50
C59	AP20	200fr multicolored		12.50	9.00

EXPO '70 International Exposition, Osaka, Japan, Mar. 15-Sept. 13.

Scarus vetula — AP21

1971, July 1		**Photo.**		**Perf. 12½**	
C60	AP21	30fr black & multi		6.00	3.75

Djibouti Harbor — AP22

1972, Feb. 3				
C61	AP22	100fr blue & multi	4.50	3.00

New Djibouti harbor.

AP23

30fr, Pterocles lichtensteini. 49fr, Uppupa epops. 66fr, Capella media. 500fr, Francolinus ochropectus.

1972		**Photo.**	**Perf. 12½x13**	
C62	AP23	30fr multi	3.75	2.75
C63	AP23	49fr multi	6.25	3.75
C64	AP23	66fr multi	8.50	5.00
C65	AP23	500fr multi	30.00	17.50
		Nos. C62-C65 (4)	48.50	29.00

Issue dates: No. C65, Nov. 3; others Apr. 21.

AP24

Olympic Rings and: 5fr, Running. 10fr, Basketball. 55fr, Swimming, horiz. 60fr, Olympic torch and Greek frieze, horiz.

1972, June 8		**Engr.**		**Perf. 13**	
C66	AP24	5fr multicolored		.90	.90
C67	AP24	10fr multicolored		1.00	.95
C68	AP24	55fr multicolored		2.25	1.75
C69	AP24	60fr multicolored		3.25	2.00
		Nos. C66-C69 (4)		7.40	5.60

20th Olympic Games, Munich, 8/26-9/11.

Louis Pasteur — AP25

100fr, Albert Calmette and C. Guérin.

1972, Oct. 5		**Engr.**		**Perf. 13**	
C70	AP25	20fr multicolored		2.75	1.10
C71	AP25	100fr multicolored		5.50	4.00

Pasteur, Calmette, Guerin, chemists and bacteriologists, benefactors of mankind.

Map and Views of Territory — AP26

200fr, Woman and Mosque of Djibouti, vert.

1973, Jan. 15		**Photo.**		**Perf. 13**	
C72	AP26	30fr brown & multi		6.00	4.25
C73	AP26	200fr multicolored		11.00	8.50

Visit of Pres. Georges Pompidou of France, Jan. 15-17.

AP27

30fr, Oryx beisa. 50fr, Madoqua saltiana. 66fr, Felis caracal.

1973, Feb. 26		**Photo.**	**Perf. 13x12½**		
C74	AP27	30fr multicolored		3.00	1.50
C75	AP27	50fr multicolored		4.25	2.75
C76	AP27	66fr multicolored		6.25	3.25
		Nos. C74-C76 (3)		13.50	7.50

See Nos. C94-C96.

Celts — AP28

Various pre-historic flint tools. 40fr, 60fr, horiz.

1973				**Perf. 13**	
C77	AP28	20fr yel grn, blk & brn		4.50	2.50
C78	AP28	40fr yellow & multi		4.75	3.00
C79	AP28	49fr lilac & multi		8.75	3.75
C80	AP28	60fr blue & multi		6.25	5.00
		Nos. C77-C80 (4)		24.25	14.25

Issued: 20fr, 49fr, 3/16; 40fr, 60fr, 9/7.

AP29

40fr, Octopus macropus. 60fr, Halicore dugong.

1973, Mar. 16					
C81	AP29	40fr multicolored		3.75	2.25
C82	AP29	60fr multicolored		7.50	3.75

AP30

Copernicus: 8fr, Nicolaus Copernicus, Polish astronomer. 9fr, Wilhelm C. Roentgen, physicist, X-ray discoverer. No. C85, Edward Jenner, physician, discoverer of vaccination. No. C86, Marie Curie, discoverer of radium and polonium. 49fr, Robert Koch, physician and bacteriologist. 50fr, Clement Ader (1841-1925), French aviation pioneer. 55fr, Guglielmo Marconi, Italian electrical engineer, inventor. 85fr, Moliere, French playwright. 100fr, Henri Farman (1874-1937), French aviation pioneer. 150fr, Andre-Marie Ampere (1775-1836), French physicist. 250fr, Michelangelo Buonarroti (1475-1564), Italian sculptor, painter and architect.

1973-75		**Engr.**		**Perf. 13**	
C83	AP30	8fr multicolored		1.00	1.00
C84	AP30	9fr multicolored		2.00	1.00
C85	AP30	10fr multicolored		2.25	1.00
C86	AP30	10fr multicolored		1.50	1.00
C87	AP30	49fr multicolored		4.00	2.50
C88	AP30	50fr multicolored		3.50	2.50
C89	AP30	55fr multicolored		2.25	2.00
C90	AP30	85fr multicolored		5.75	2.75
C91	AP30	100fr multicolored		3.75	3.00
C92	AP30	150fr multicolored		6.00	3.50
C93	AP30	250fr multicolored		9.00	6.00
		Nos. C83-C93 (11)		41.00	26.25

Issued: 8fr, 85fr, 5/9/73; 9fr, No. C85, 49fr, 10/12/73; 100fr, 1/29/74; 55fr, 3/22/74; No. C86, 8/23/74; 150fr, 7/24/75; 250fr, 6/26/75; 50fr, 9/25/75.

AP31

20fr, Papio anubis. 50fr, Genetta tigrina, horiz. 66fr, Lapus habessinicus.

Perf. 12½x13, 13x12½

1973, Dec. 12				**Photo.**	
C94	AP31	20fr multicolored		2.25	1.40
C95	AP31	50fr multicolored		3.75	2.00
C96	AP31	66fr multicolored		5.00	2.75
		Nos. C94-C96 (3)		11.00	6.15

Spearfishing — AP32

1974, Apr. 14 **Engr.** **Perf. 13**
C97 AP32 200fr multicolored 8.00 7.00

No. C97 was prepared for release in Nov. 1972, for the 3rd Underwater Spearfishing Contest in the Red Sea. Dates were obliterated with a rectangle, and the stamp was not issued without this obliteration. Value without rectangle, $400.

Rock Carvings, Balho — AP33

1974, Apr. 26
C98 AP33 200fr carmine & slate 9.00 7.00

Lake Assal — AP34

Designs (Lake Assal): 50fr, Rock formations on shore. 85fr, Crystallized wood.

1974, Oct. 25 **Photo.** **Perf. 13**
C99 AP34 49fr multicolored 2.25 1.75
C100 AP34 50fr multicolored 2.50 2.00
C101 AP34 85fr multicolored 5.00 3.75
   Nos. C99-C101 (3) 9.75 7.50

Columba
Guinea — AP35

1975, May 23 **Photo.** **Perf. 13**
C102 AP35 500fr multicolored 22.50 11.00

Djibouti Airport — AP36

1977, Mar. 1 **Litho.** **Perf. 12**
C103 AP36 500fr multicolored 12.50 9.00

Opening of new Djibouti Airport.

Thomas A. Edison and
Phonograph — AP37

Design: 75fr, Alexander Volta, electric train, lines and light bulb.

1977, May 5 **Engr.** **Perf. 13**
C104 AP37 55fr multicolored 4.00 2.75
C105 AP37 75fr multicolored 6.25 4.75

Famous inventors: Thomas Alva Edison and Alexander Volta (1745-1827).

POSTAGE DUE STAMPS

Nomad's Milk
Jug — D3

Perf. 14x13
1969, Dec. 15 **Engr.** **Unwmk.**
J49 D3 1fr red brn, red lil & sl .50 .65
J50 D3 2fr red brn, emer & sl .60 .80
J51 D3 5fr red brn, bl & slate 1.00 1.20
J52 D3 10fr red brn, brn & slate 1.75 2.00
   Nos. J49-J52 (4) 3.85 4.65

AFGHANISTAN

af-'ga-nə-,stan

LOCATION — Central Asia, bounded by Iran, Turkmenistan, Uzbekistan, Tajikistan, Pakistan, and China
GOVT. — Republic
AREA — 251,773 sq. mi.
POP. — 23,500,000 (1995 est.)
CAPITAL — Kabul

Afghanistan changed from a constitutional monarchy to a republic in July 1973.

12 Shahi = 6 Sanar = 3 Abasi =
2 Krans = 1 Rupee Kabuli
60 Paisas = 1 Rupee (1921)
100 Pouls = 1 Rupee Afghani (1927)

Catalogue values for unused stamps in this country are for Never Hinged items, beginning with Scott 364 in the regular postage section, Scott B1 in the semipostal section, Scott C7 in the airpost section, Scott O8 in officials section, and Scott RA6 in the postal tax section.

CHARACTERS OF VALUE.

From 1871 to 1892 and 1898, the Moslem year date appears on the stamp. Numerals as follows:

١	٢	٣	٤	٥
1	2	3	4	5
٦	٧	٨	٩	٠
6	7	8	9	0

Until 1891, cancellation consisted of cutting or tearing a piece from the stamps. Such examples should not be considered as damaged.

Values are for cut square examples of good color. Cut to shape or faded examples sell for much less, particularly Nos. 1-10.

Nos. 1-108 are on laid paper of varying thickness except where wove is noted.

Until 1907, all stamps were issued ungummed.

The tiger's head on types A1 to A11 symbolizes the name of the contemporary amir, Sher (Tiger, or Lion) Ali.

Kingdom of Kabul

A1

Tiger's Head, Type I — A2

Tiger's Head, Type II — A2a

Both circles dotted. Thick outer circle usually measures 27.5mm-28mm in diameter.
Type I: has well-defined inner and outer circles with evenly spaced dots.
Type II: Has less well-defined thin inner and outer circles, and the dots are randomly spaced.

1871 **Unwmk.** **Litho.** **Imperf.**
Dated "1288"
1 A1 1sh black (30mm
     diameter) 1,350. 60.00
2 A2 1sh black 925.00 50.00
2A A2a 1sh black 525.00 35.00
3 A2 1sa black 650.00 32.50
3A A2a 1sa black 210.00 55.00
4 A2a 1ab black 150.00 60.00
   Nos. 1-4A (6) 3,810. 292.50

Nos. 1-4 are usually identified by plating. No. 1 was printed in a sheet of 15 (referred to as plate A). Nos. 2 and 3 were printing in sheets of 15 (10 of No. 2 and 5 of No. 3), referred to as plate B. Nos. 2A and 3A-4A were printed in sheets of 15 (5 of each denomination), referred to as plate C.

Similar designs without the tiger's head in the center are revenues.

A3

Outer circle dotted; inner circle plain.

Dated "1288"
5 A3 1sh black 525.00 35.00
6 A3 1sa black 300.00 50.00
7 A3 1ab black 200.00 32.50
   Nos. 5-7 (3) 1,025. 117.50

Nos. 5-7 were printed in sheets of 15 (5 of each denomination), referred to as plate D.

A4

Toned Wove Paper
1872 **Dated "1289"**
8 A4 6sh violet 1,500. 900.
9 A4 1rup violet 1,750. 1,350.

Two varieties of each. Date varies in location. Printed in sheets of 4 (2x2) containing two of each denomination.

Most used examples are smeared with a greasy ink cancel.

A4a

White Laid Paper

1873 — Dated "1290"

10	A4a	1sh black	25.00	12.00
	a.	Corner ornament missing	750.00	750.00
	b.	Corner ornament retouched	75.00	45.00

15 varieties. Nos. 10a, 10b are the sixth stamp on the sheet.

A5

1873

11	A5	1sh black	22.50	11.00

Sixty varieties of each. No. 11 in violet is believed to be a proof.

1874 — Dated "1291"

12	A5	1ab black	90.00	55.00
13	A5	½rup black	37.50	20.00
14	A5	1rup black	40.00	24.00
		Nos. 12-14 (3)	167.50	99.00

Five varieties of each.
Nos. 12-14 were printed on the same sheet. Se-tenant varieties exist.

A6

1875 — Dated "1292"

15	A6	1sa black	*400.00*	*375.00*
	a.	Wide outer circle	*1,250.*	*750.00*
16	A6	1ab black	425.00	400.00
17	A6	1sa brown violet	75.00	30.00
	a.	Wide outer circle	300.00	190.00
18	A6	1ab brown violet	80.00	60.00

Ten varieties of the sanar, five of the abasi. Nos. 15-16 and 17-18 were printed in the same sheets. Se-tenant pairs exist.

A7

1876 — Dated "1293"

19	A7	1sh black	350.00	200.00
20	A7	1sa black	400.00	225.00
21	A7	1ab black	750.00	425.00
22	A7	½rup black	450.00	*275.00*
23	A7	1rup black	875.00	275.00
24	A7	1sh violet	*450.00*	275.00
25	A7	1sa violet	425.00	300.00
26	A7	1ab violet	525.00	275.00
27	A7	½rup violet	225.00	*60.00*
28	A7	1rup violet	225.00	*75.00*

12 varieties of the shahi and 3 each of the other values.

A8

1876 — Dated "1293"

29	A8	1sh gray	16.00	10.00
29A	A8a	1sh gray	65.00	30.00
30	A8	1sa gray	20.00	8.00
31	A8	1ab gray	42.50	20.00
32	A8	½rup gray	50.00	25.00
33	A8	1rup gray	50.00	17.50
34	A8	1sh olive blk	140.00	80.00
35	A8	1sa olive blk	190.00	100.00
36	A8	1ab olive blk	400.00	250.00
37	A8	½rup olive blk	275.00	275.00
38	A8	1rup olive blk	375.00	400.00
39	A8	1sh green	30.00	8.00
40	A8	1sa green	40.00	25.00
41	A8	1ab green	85.00	60.00
42	A8	½rup green	125.00	80.00
43	A8	1rup green	110.00	125.00
44	A8	1sh ocher	32.50	15.00
45	A8	1sa ocher	40.00	24.00
46	A8	1ab ocher	80.00	50.00
47	A8	½rup ocher	100.00	65.00
48	A8	1rup ocher	140.00	125.00
49	A8	1sh violet	37.50	15.00
50	A8	1sa violet	37.50	15.00
51	A8	1ab violet	50.00	15.00
52	A8	½rup violet	70.00	27.50
53	A8	1rup violet	100.00	40.00

24 varieties of the shahi, 4 of which show denomination written:

A8a

12 varieties of the sanar, 6 of the abasi and 3 each of the ½ rupee and rupee.

A9

1877 — Dated "1294"

54	A8a	1sh gray	10.00	*15.00*
55	A9	1sa gray	10.00	9.00
56	A9	1ab gray	11.00	9.00
57	A9	½rup gray	14.50	*20.00*
58	A9	1rup gray	16.00	20.00
59	A9	1sh black	14.50	*20.00*
60	A9	1sa black	25.00	10.00
61	A9	1ab black	42.50	15.00
62	A9	½rup black	45.00	30.00
63	A9	1rup black	45.00	30.00
64	A9	1sh green	32.50	32.50
65	A9	1sa green	15.00	12.00
66	A9	1ab green	17.50	16.00
67	A9	½rup green	30.00	30.00
68	A9	1rup green	27.50	*32.50*
69	A9	1sh ocher	12.50	5.25
70	A9	1sa ocher	12.50	7.25
71	A9	1ab ocher	32.50	24.50
72	A9	½rup ocher	40.00	35.00
73	A9	1rup ocher	50.00	35.00
74	A9	1sh violet	15.00	8.00
75	A9	1sa violet	12.50	5.00
76	A9	1ab violet	19.00	12.00
77	A9	½rup violet	27.50	30.00
78	A9	1rup violet	27.50	30.00

25 varieties of the shahi, 8 of the sanar, 3 of the abasi and 2 each of the ½ rupee and rupee.

Some examples of Nos. 54-78 show a "94" date. These are valued less.

Nos. 64-68 in sage green on wove paper are proofs.

A10   A11

1878 — Dated "95"

79	A10	1sh gray	5.00	10.00
80	A10	1sa gray	8.00	10.00
81	A10	1ab gray	12.50	10.00
82	A10	½rup gray	15.00	15.00
83	A10	1rup gray	15.00	15.00
84	A10	1sh black	10.00	
85	A10	1sa black	10.00	
86	A10	1ab black	37.50	
87	A10	½rup black	35.00	
88	A10	1rup black	35.00	
89	A10	1sh green	32.50	*55.00*
90	A10	1sa green	10.00	9.00
91	A10	1ab green	35.00	30.00
92	A10	½rup green	32.50	30.00
93	A10	1rup green	60.00	40.00
94	A10	1sh ocher	27.50	10.00
95	A10	1sa ocher	12.00	*15.00*
96	A10	1ab ocher	45.00	35.00
97	A10	½rup ocher	65.00	45.00
98	A10	1rup ocher	27.50	30.00
99	A10	1sh violet	10.00	*15.00*
100	A10	1sa violet	30.00	25.00
101	A10	1ab violet	17.50	15.00
102	A10	½rup violet	55.00	35.00
103	A10	1rup violet	45.00	30.00
104	A11	1sh gray	7.00	7.00
105	A11	1sh black	*100.00*	50.00
106	A11	1sh green	10.00	5.00
107	A11	1sh ocher	10.00	9.00
108	A11	1sh violet	8.00	8.00

40 varieties of the shahi, 30 of the sanar, 6 of the abasi and 2 each of the ½ rupee and 1 rupee.

The 1876, 1877 and 1878 issues were printed in separate colors for each main post office on the Peshawar-Kabul-Khulm (Tashkurghan) postal route. Some specialists consider the black printings to be proofs, trial colors or reprints from the original plates.

There are many shades of these colors.

1ab, Type I
(26mm) — A12

1ab, Type II
(28mm) — A13

A14

A15

Dated "1298", numerals
scattered through design

Handstamped, in watercolor

1881-90

Thin White Laid Batonne Paper

109	A12	1ab violet	5.00	3.00
109A	A13	1ab violet	8.00	3.00
110	A12	1ab black brn	8.00	3.00
	a.	Ordinary thin wove paper	—	20.00
111	A12	1ab rose	12.00	3.00
	b.	Se-tenant with No. 111A	16.00	
111A	A13	1ab rose	9.00	3.00
112	A14	2ab violet	10.00	3.00
113	A14	2ab black brn	12.00	6.00
114	A14	2ab rose	20.00	10.00
115	A15	1rup violet	12.00	12.00
116	A15	1rup black brn	14.00	10.00
117	A15	1rup rose	12.50	7.50

Thin White Wove Batonne Paper

118	A12	1ab violet	15.00	5.00
119	A12	1ab vermilion	30.00	10.00
120	A12	1ab rose	30.00	25.00
121	A14	2ab violet	30.00	25.00
122	A14	2ab vermilion	30.00	16.00
122A	A14	2ab black brn		
123	A15	1rup violet	15.00	8.00
124	A15	1rup vermilion	14.00	7.50
125	A15	1rup black brn	12.50	7.50

Thin White Laid Batonne Paper

126	A12	1ab brown org	20.00	8.00
126A	A13	1ab brn org (II)	22.50	9.00
127	A12	1ab carmine lake	20.00	8.00
	a.	Laid paper	22.50	10.00
128	A14	2ab brown org	20.00	8.00
129	A14	2ab carmine lake	20.00	8.00
130	A15	1rup brown org	35.00	15.00
131	A15	1rup car lake	37.50	15.00

Yellowish Laid Batonne Paper

132	A12	1ab purple	10.00	10.00
133	A12	1ab red	12.50	10.00

1884 — Colored Wove Paper

133A	A13	1ab purple, yel (II)	17.50	17.50
134	A12	1ab purple, grn	20.00	
135	A12	1ab purple, blue	32.50	21.00
136	A12	1ab red, grn	37.50	
137	A12	1ab red, yel	30.00	
139	A12	1ab red, rose	50.00	
140	A14	2ab red, yel	30.00	
142	A14	2ab red, rose	30.00	
143	A15	1rup red, yel	55.00	20.00
145	A15	1rup red, rose	65.00	25.00

Thin Colored Ribbed Paper

146	A14	2ab red, yellow	40.00	
147	A15	1rup red, yellow	80.00	
148	A12	1ab lake, lilac	40.00	
149	A14	2ab lake, lilac	40.00	
150	A15	1rup lake, lilac	40.00	
151	A12	1ab lake, green	40.00	
152	A14	2ab lake, green	40.00	
153	A15	1rup lake, green	40.00	

1886-88 — Colored Wove Paper

155	A12	1ab black, magenta	60.00	
156	A12	1ab claret brn, org	50.00	
156A	A12	1ab red, org	40.00	
156B	A14	2ab red, org	40.00	
156C	A15	1rup red, org	40.00	

Laid Batonné Paper

157	A12	1ab black, lavender	40.00	
158	A12	1ab cl brn, grn	40.00	
159	A12	1ab black, pink	60.00	
160	A14	2ab black, pink	100.00	
161	A15	1rup black, pink	70.00	

Laid Paper

162	A12	1ab black, pink	80.00	
163	A14	2ab black, pink	80.00	
164	A15	1rup black, pink	80.00	
165	A12	1ab brown, yel	80.00	
166	A14	2ab brown, yel	80.00	
167	A15	1rup brown, yel	80.00	
168	A12	1ab blue, grn	80.00	
169	A14	2ab blue, grn	80.00	
170	A15	1rup blue, grn	80.00	

1891 — Colored Wove Paper

175	A12	1ab green, rose	100.00	
176	A15	1rup pur, grn batonne	100.00	

Nos. 109-176 fall into three categories:

1. Those regularly issued and in normal postal use from 1881 on, handstamped on thin white laid or wove paper in strip sheets containing 12 or more impressions of the same denomination arranged in two irregular rows, with the impressions often touching or overlapping.

2. The 1884 postal issues provisionally printed on smooth or ribbed colored wove paper as needed to supplement low stocks of the normal white paper stamps.

3. The "special" printings made in a range of colors on several types of laid or wove colored papers, most of which were never used for normal printings. These were produced periodically from 1886 to 1891 to meet philatelic demands. Although nominally valid for postage, most of the special printings were exported directly to fill dealers' orders, and few were ever postally used. Many of the sheets contained all three denominations with impressions separated by ruled lines. Sometimes different colors were used, so se-tenant multiples of denomination or color exist. Many combinations of stamp and paper colors exist besides those listed.

Various shades of each color exist.

Type A12 is known dated "1297."

Counterfeits, lithographed or typographed, are plentiful.

Kingdom of Afghanistan

A16

A17

A18

Dated "1309"

1891   Pelure Paper   Litho.
177	A16	1ab slate blue	2.00	2.00
a.		Tete beche pair	19.00	
178	A17	2ab slate blue	12.00	12.00
179	A18	1rup slate blue	27.50	—
		Nos. 177-179 (3)	41.50	14.00

Revenue stamps of similar design exist in various colors.

Nos. 177-179 were printed in panes on the same sheet, so se-tenant gutter pairs exist. Examples in black or red are proofs.

A Mosque Gate and Crossed Cannons (National Seal)
A19

Dated "1310" in Upper Right Corner

1892   Flimsy Wove Paper
180	A19	1ab black, *green*	3.50	3.00
181	A19	1ab black, *orange*	4.50	4.50
182	A19	1ab black, *yellow*	3.50	3.00
183	A19	1ab black, *pink*	4.00	3.25
184	A19	1ab black, *lil rose*	4.00	4.00
185	A19	1ab black, *blue*	6.00	5.50
186	A19	1ab black, *salmon*	4.50	3.75
187	A19	1ab black, *magenta*	4.00	4.00
188	A19	1ab black, *violet*	4.00	4.00
188A	A19	1ab black, *scarlet*	4.00	3.00

Many shades exist.

A20

A21

Undated

1894   Flimsy Wove Paper
| 189 | A20 | 2ab black, *green* | 12.00 | 8.00 |
| 190 | A21 | 1rup black, *green* | 14.50 | 13.00 |

24 varieties of the 2 abasi and 12 varieties of the rupee.

Nos. 189-190 and F3 were printed se-tenant in the same sheet. Pairs exist.

A21a

Dated "1316"

1898   Flimsy Wove Paper
191	A21a	2ab black, *pink*	3.00	
192	A21a	2ab black, *magenta*	3.00	
193	A21a	2ab black, *yellow*	1.40	
193A	A21a	2ab black, *salmon*	3.50	
194	A21a	2ab black, *green*	1.75	
195	A21a	2ab black, *purple*	2.40	
195A	A21a	2ab black, *blue*	22.50	
		Nos. 191-195A (7)	37.55	

Nos. 191-195A were not regularly issued. Genuinely used examples are scarce. No.

195A was found in remainder stocks and probably was never released.

A22   A23

A24

1907   Engr.   Imperf.
Medium Wove Paper
196	A22	1ab blue green	50.00	30.00
a.		1ab emerald	—	30.00
b.		Double impression	500.00	
c.		Printed on both sides		450.00
197	A22	1ab brt blue	30.00	25.00
198	A23	2ab deep blue	30.00	25.00
a.		Double impression	550.00	
199	A24	1rup green	100.00	50.00
a.		1rup blue green		100.00

Zigzag Roulette 10
200	A22	1ab green	2,750.	450.00
a.		Double impression		1,500.
b.		Printed on both sides		1,750.
c.		Double impression and printed on both sides		2,500.
d.		1ab blue green	2,750.	450.00
201	A23	2ab blue	2,500.	—

1908   Serrate Roulette 13
201A	A22	1ab green		
b.		1ab emerald green		
201B	A23	2ab blue	3,500.	

Nos. 201A and 201Ab are only known used on cover.

No. 201B is known only unused.

Perf. 12 on 2, 3 or 4 Sides
202	A22	1ab green		65.00
203	A23	2ab deep blue	35.00	20.00
a.		Horiz. pair, imperf between	450.00	
204	A24	1rup blue green	125.00	65.00
c.		Pair, imperf. between	400.00	
		Nos. 202-204 (3)	160.00	150.00

Twelve varieties of the 1 abasi, 6 of the 2 abasi, 4 of the 1 rupee.

Nos. 196-204 were issued in small sheets containing 3 or 4 panes. Gutter pairs, normal and tete beche, exist.

Two plates were used for the 1 abasi: plate I, inner vert. lines extend into lower left panel; plate II, inner vert. lines do not extend into lower left panel.

A25   A26

A27

1909-19   Typo.   Perf. 12
205	A25	1ab ultra	5.00	2.00
a.		Imperf., pair	48.00	
206	A25	1ab red ('16)	1.60	1.25
a.		Imperf.	30.00	
207	A25	1ab rose ('18)	1.60	1.00
208	A26	2ab green	2.75	2.25
a.		Imperf., pair	48.00	
b.		Horiz. pair, imperf. btwn.		
208C	A26	2ab yellow ('16)	3.25	2.75
209	A26	2ab bis ('18-'19)	3.25	3.25
210	A27	1rup lilac brn	7.50	6.50
a.		1rup red brown	7.50	7.50
211	A27	1rup ol bis ('19)	10.00	8.00
		Nos. 205-211 (8)	34.95	27.00

A28

1913
| 212 | A28 | 2pa drab brown | 20.00 | 12.00 |
| a. | | 2pa red brown | 20.00 | 12.00 |

No. 212 is inscribed "Tiket waraq dak" (Postal card stamps). It was usable only on postcards and not accepted for postage on letters.
Nos. 196-212 sometimes show letters of a papermaker's watermark, "Howard & Jones, London."

Royal Star — A29

1920, Aug. 24   Perf. 12
Size: 39x46mm
214	A29	10pa rose	200.00	110.00
215	A29	20pa red brown	300.00	190.00
216	A29	30pa green	400.00	325.00
		Nos. 214-216 (3)	900.00	625.00

Independence Day. Issued to commemorate the first and second anniversaries of the signing of the armistice (Aug. 24, 1919) that ended the war of independence (Third Afghan War).

Issued in sheets of two settings: wide gutter, with 19mm between stamps, narrow gutter, with 12mm to 13mm between stamps.

No. 214 exists in two sizes: 38.5mmx46mm, position 1 in the wide gutter sheet; 38.5mmx46mm, position 2, in the wide gutter and position 1 in the narrow gutter sheet.

1921, Mar.   Size: 22½x28¼mm
217	A29	10pa rose	2.50	1.25
a.		Perf. 11 ('27)	22.50	13.00
218	A29	20pa red brown	4.50	2.50
219	A29	30pa yel green	6.50	3.00
a.		Tete beche pair	55.00	32.50
b.		30pa green	6.50	3.50
c.		As "b," Tete beche pair	55.00	32.50
		Nos. 217-219 (3)	13.50	6.75

3rd Independence Day.
Two types of the 10pa, three of the 20pa.

Hstmpd. in black on Nos. 217-219

1923, Feb. 26
219D	A29a	10pa rose	—	125.00
219E	A29a	20pa red brown	—	125.00
219F	A29a	30pa yel green	400.00	

5th Independence Day.
Two types of handstamp exist.
Forgeries exist.
See No. Q13B-Q13E.

These handstamps were used by the Kabul post office on incoming foreign mail from 1921 until Afghanistan joined the Universal Postal Union April 1, 1928. Afghan stamps were applied to foreign mail arriving in the country and were canceled with these postage-due handstamps to indicate that postage was to be collected from the addressee. The handstamps were applied primarily to Nos. 217-219, 227-235, 236, and 237-246. Values are the same as for stamps with postal cancellations. A third type of handstamp exists with no distinctive outer border.

A30

1924, Feb. 26   Perf. 12
| 220 | A30 | 10pa chocolate | 45.00 | 30.00 |
| a. | | Tete beche pair | 150.00 | 100.00 |

6th Independence Day.
Printed in sheets of four consisting of two tete beche pairs, and in sheets of two. Two types exist.

Some authorities believe that Nos. Q15-Q16 were issued as regular postage stamps.

Crest of King Amanullah
A32

Size: 29x37mm
1925, Feb. 26   Perf. 12
| 222 | A32 | 10pa light brown | 75.00 | 35.00 |

7th Independence Day.
Printed in sheets of 8 (two panes of 4).

Wove Paper
1926, Feb. 28   Size: 26x33mm
224	A32	10pa dark blue	8.00	8.00
a.		Imperf., pair	32.50	
b.		Horiz. pair, imperf. btwn.	75.00	
c.		Vert. pair, imperf. btwn.		
d.		Laid paper	40.00	13.00

7th anniv. of Independence. Printed in sheets of 4, and in sheets of 8 (two panes of 4). Tete beche gutter pairs exist.

Tughra and Crest of Amanullah A33

1927, Feb.
225 A33 10pa magenta 14.00 12.00
a. Vertical pair, imperf. between 75.00

Dotted Background
226 A33 10pa magenta 20.00 13.00
a. Horiz. pair, imperf. between 75.00

The surface of No. 226 is covered by a net of fine dots.

8th anniv. of Independence. Printed in sheets of 8 (two panes of 4).

Tete-beche gutter pairs exist. Value, pair $85.

National Seal — A34   A35

A36

1927, Oct.   *Imperf.*
227 A34 15p pink 1.40 1.40
228 A35 30p Prus green 2.75 1.25
229 A36 60p light blue 3.75 3.25
Nos. 227-229 (3) 7.90 5.90

1927, Nov.   *Perf. 11, 11¾*
230 A34 15p pink 1.75 1.40
231 A35 30p Prus green 3.25 1.40
232 A36 60p bright blue 3.50 2.00
a. Tete beche pair 17.50 17.50
Nos. 230-232 (3) 8.50 4.80

A37

A38   A39

A40

1928, Feb.   *Perf. 11, 11¾*
233 A37 10p gray green 1.25 .40
a. Tete beche pair 14.00 6.50
b. Vert. pair, imperf. horiz. 11.00 11.00
c. Vertical pair, imperf. between
234 A38 25p car rose 1.50 .40
235 A39 40p ultra 2.00 .75
a. Tete beche pair 15.00 16.00
236 A40 50p red 2.50 1.00
Nos. 233-236 (4) 7.25 2.55

Nos. 230-232 are usually imperforate on one or two sides. The sheets of these stamps

are often imperforate at the outer margin. No. 233 was printed in sheets of nine and sheets of 20.

Tughra and Crest of Amanullah — A41

1928, Feb. 27
236D A41 15p pink 5.00 5.00
a. Tete beche pair 12.00 10.00
b. Horiz. pair, imperf. vert. 22.50 19.00
c. As "a," imperf. vert., block of 4 75.00

9th anniv. of Independence. This stamp is always imperforate on one or two sides.

A 15p blue of somewhat similar design was prepared for the 10th anniv., but was not issued due to Amanullah's dethronement. Value, $15.

Types of 1927 in New Colors

A42

1929-30
236E A34 15p ultra 1.75 1.40
236F A42 30p dp green ('30) 1.75 1.25
236G A36 60p black ('29) 4.00 1.25
Nos. 236E-236G (3) 7.50 4.90

No. 236F has been redrawn. A narrow border of pearls has been added and "30," in European and Arabic numerals, inserted in the upper spandrels.

A43

1928-30   *Perf. 11, 12*
237 A43 2p dull blue 7.75 4.50
a. Vertical pair, imperf. between 20.00
238 A43 2p lt rose ('30) .65 .55
240 A37 10p choc ('30) 3.00 1.25
a. 10p brown purple ('29) 8.50 8.50
242 A38 25p Prus green ('29) 4.00 2.25
244 A39 40p rose ('29) 3.50 1.25
a. Tete beche pair 14.50
b. Vert. pair, imperf. horiz. 11.00
246 A40 50p dk blue ('29) 5.00 1.50
Nos. 237-246 (6) 23.90 10.30

The sheets of these stamps are often imperforate at the outer margins.
Nos. 237-238 are newspaper stamps.

This handstamp was used for 10 months by the Revolutionary Gov't in Kabul as a control mark on outgoing mail. It occasionally fell on the stamps but there is no evidence that it was officially used as an overprint. Unused examples were privately made. Forgeries exist.

Independence Monument A46

Laid Paper Without Gum Wmk. Large Seal in the Sheet
1931, Aug.   Litho.   *Perf. 12*
262 A46 20p red 2.50 1.25

13th Independence Day.

National Assembly Chamber A47

A48

National Assembly Building A49

A50

National Assembly Chamber A51

National Assembly Building A52

Wove Paper
1932   Unwmk.   Typo.   *Perf. 12*
263 A47 40p olive 1.15 .40
264 A48 60p violet 1.50 .80
265 A49 80p dark red 2.00 1.25
266 A50 1af black 16.00 7.50
267 A51 2af ultra 7.00 4.00
268 A52 3af gray green 7.50 3.50
Nos. 263-268 (6) 35.15 17.45

Formation of the Natl. Council. Imperforate or perforated examples on ungummed chalky paper are proofs. Covers of No. 263 imperf proofs are known used in May 1999.
See Nos. 304-305.

Mosque at Balkh — A53

Kabul Fortress A54

Parliament House, Darul Funun — A55

Parliament House, Darul Funun — A56

Arch of Qalai Bist — A57

Memorial Pillar of Knowledge and Ignorance A58

Independence Monument A59

Minaret at Herat — A60

Arch of Paghman A61

Ruins at Balkh — A62

Minarets of
Herat — A63

Great Buddha at
Bamian — A64

1932   **Typo.**   **Perf. 12**
269	A53 10p brown	.80	.25
270	A54 15p dk brown	.60	.30
271	A55 20p red	.95	.25
272	A56 25p dk green	1.35	.25
273	A57 30p red	1.35	.25
274	A58 40p orange	1.75	.50
275	A59 50p blue	2.40	1.40
a.	Tete beche pair	12.00	
276	A60 60p blue	2.25	.90
277	A61 80p violet	4.00	2.00
278	A62 1af dark blue	7.00	.80
279	A63 2af dk red violet	7.75	3.00
280	A64 3af claret	9.50	4.00
	Nos. 269-280 (12)	39.70	13.90

Counterfeits of types A53-A65 exist.
See Nos. 290-295, 298-299, 302-303.

Entwined 2's — A65

Type I   Type II

Two types:
Type I — Numerals shaded. Size about
21x29mm.
Type II — Numerals unshaded. Size about
21¾x30mm.

1931-38   **Perf. 12, 11x12**
281	A65 2p red brn (I)	.40	.50
282	A65 2p olive blk (I) ('34)	.30	.80
283	A65 2p grnsh gray (I) ('34)	.40	.75
283A	A65 2p black (I) ('36)	.25	.75
284	A65 2p salmon (II) ('38)	.50	.75
284A	A65 2p rose (I) ('38)	.50	.90
b.	Imperf., pair	10.00	

Imperf
285	A65 2p black (II) ('37)	.75	.75
286	A65 2p salmon (II) ('38)	.75	.75
	Nos. 281-286 (8)	3.85	5.95

The newspaper rate was 2 pouls.

Independence
Monument — A66

1932, Aug.   **Perf. 12**
287	A66 1af carmine	5.50	15.00

14th Independence Day.

A67

1929 Liberation Monument, Kabul.

1932, Oct.   **Typo.**
288	A67 80p red brown	2.00	*7.50*

Arch of Paghman — A68

1933, Aug.
289	A68 50p light ultra	3.00	*7.50*

15th Independence Day.
No. 289 exists imperf. Value, $5.

Types of 1932 and

Royal
Palace,
Kabul
A69

Darrah- Shikari
Pass, Hindu
Kush — A70

1934-38   **Typo.**   **Perf. 12**
290	A53 10p deep violet	.30	.25
291	A54 15p turq green	.50	.25
292	A55 20p magenta	.50	.25
293	A56 25p deep rose	.60	.25
294	A57 30p orange	.65	.30
295	A58 40p blue black	.75	.30
296	A69 45p dark blue	2.75	1.50
297	A69 45p red ('38)	.50	.25
298	A59 50p orange	.80	.25
299	A60 60p purple	1.00	.45
300	A70 75p red	4.00	2.00
301	A70 75p dk blue ('38)	1.00	.65
302	A61 80p brown vio	1.60	.80
303	A62 1af red violet	3.25	1.60
304	A51 2af gray black	5.25	2.40
305	A52 3af ultra	6.00	3.00
	Nos. 290-305 (16)	29.45	14.50

Nos. 290, 292, 300, 304, 305 exist imperf.

Independence Monument — A71

1934, Aug.   **Litho.**   **Without Gum**
306	A71 50p pale green	3.25	2.75
a.	Tete beche pair	11.50	11.50

16th year of Independence. Each sheet of
40 (4x10) included 4 tete beche pairs as lower
half of sheet was inverted.

Independence
Monument — A74

1935, Aug. 15   **Laid Paper**
309	A74 50p dark blue	3.50	2.40

17th year of Independence.

Fireworks
Display
A75

Wove Paper

1936, Aug. 15   **Perf. 12**
310	A75 50p red violet	3.25	2.50

18th year of Independence.

Independence Monument and Nadir
Shah — A76

1937
311	A76 50p vio & bis brn	2.75	2.10
a.	Imperf., pair	9.50	9.50

19th year of Independence.

Mohammed
Nadir
Shah — A77

1938   **Without Gum**   **Perf. 11x12**
315	A77 50p brt blue & sepia	2.75	2.40
a.	Imperf. pair	24.00	19.00

20th year of Independence.

Mohammed Nadir
Shah — A78

1939   **Perf. 11, 12x11**
317	A78 50p deep salmon	2.40	1.50

21st year of Independence.

National
Arms
A79

Parliament House, Darul Funun — A80

Royal
Palace,
Kabul
A81

Independence
Monument — A82

Independence Monument and Nadir
Shah — A83

Mohammed Zahir Shah — A84

Mohammed
Zahir Shah
A85

Perf. 11, 11x12, 12x11, 12
1939-61   **Typo.**
318	A79 2p intense blk	.30	*.70*
318A	A79 2p brt pink ('61)	.30	*.70*

Size: 36.5x24mm
319	A80 10p brt purple	.30	.25

Size: 31.5x21mm
320	A80 15p brt green	.35	.25

Size: 34x22.5mm
321	A80 20p red lilac	.50	.25
322	A81 25p rose red	.60	.30
322A	A81 25p green ('41)	.35	.25
323	A81 30p orange	.50	.25
a.	Vert. pair, imperf between		—
324	A81 40p dk gray	1.00	.50
325	A82 45p brt carmine	1.00	.40
326	A82 50p dp orange	.80	.25
327	A82 60p violet	1.00	.25
328	A83 75p ultra	3.00	.80
328A	A83 75p red vio ('41)	2.25	1.60
328C	A83 75p brt red ('44)	4.00	3.00
328D	A83 75p chnt brn ('49)	4.00	3.00
329	A83 80p chocolate	2.00	1.00
a.	80p dull red violet (error)		
330	A84 1af brt red violet	2.25	.80
330A	A85 1af brt red vio ('44)	2.25	.90
331	A85 2af copper red	3.00	.80
a.	2af deep rose red	4.25	1.75
332	A84 3af deep blue	5.00	2.40
	Nos. 318-332 (21)	34.75	18.65

Many shades exist in this issue.
On No. 332, the King faces slightly left.
No. 318A issued with and without gum.
See Nos. 795A-795B. For similar design
see No. 907A.

Mohammed Nadir
Shah — A86

1940, Aug. 23 **Perf. 11**
333 A86 50p gray green 2.00 1.50

22nd year of Independence.

Independence
Monument — A87

Arch of
Paghman — A88

1941, Aug. 23 **Perf. 12**
334 A87 15p gray green 25.00 5.00
335 A88 50p red brown 2.50 2.10

23rd year of Independence.

Sugar
Factory,
Baghlan
A89

1942, Apr. **Perf. 12**
336 A89 1.25af blue (shades) 2.00 1.50
a. 1.25af ultra 2.50 1.75

In 1949, a 1.50af brown, type A89, was sold
for 3af by the Philatelic Office, Kabul. It was
not valid for postage. Value $6.

Independence
Monument — A90

Mohammed
Nadir Shah
and Arch of
Paghman
A91

1942, Aug. 23 **Perf. 12**
337 A90 35p bright green 3.75 3.50
338 A91 125p chalky blue 3.00 2.00

24th year of Independence.

Independence Monument and Nadir
Shah — A92

Mohammed Nadir
Shah — A93

Perf. 11x12, 12x11
1943, Aug. 25 **Typo.** **Unwmk.**
339 A92 35p carmine 17.50 15.00
340 A93 1.25af dark blue 3.50 2.50

25th year of Independence.

Tomb of Gohar
Shad, Herat — A94

Ruins of
Qalai
Bist — A95

1944, May 1 **Perf. 12, 11x12**
341 A94 35p orange 1.50 .80
342 A95 70p violet 2.00 .80
a. 70p rose lilac 2.00 .80

A96

A97

1944, Aug. **Perf. 12**
343 A96 35p crimson 1.25 .65
344 A97 1.25af ultra 2.25 1.75

26th year of Independence.

> Catalogue values for unused
> stamps in this section, from this
> point to the end of the section, are
> for Never Hinged items.

A98

A99

1945, July
345 A98 35p deep red lilac 2.50 .80
346 A99 1.25af blue 4.00 2.00

27th year of Independence.

Mohammed Zahir Shah — A100

Independence
Monument
A101

Mohammed Nadir
Shah
A102

1946, July
347 A100 15p emerald 1.25 .70
348 A101 20p dp red lilac 2.00 .85
349 A102 125p blue 3.75 2.00
 Nos. 347-349 (3) 7.00 3.55

28th year of Independence.

Zahir Shah
and Ruins of
Qalai
Bist — A103

A104

A105

1947, Aug.
350 A103 15p yellow green .80 .55
351 A104 35p plum 1.00 .65
352 A105 125p deep blue 2.75 1.60
 Nos. 350-352 (3) 4.55 2.80

29th year of Independence.

Begging
Child
A106

A107

1948, May Unwmk. Typo. **Perf. 12**
353 A106 35p yel green 4.75 4.00
354 A107 125p gray blue 4.75 4.00

Children's Day, May 29, 1948, and valid only
on that day. Proceeds were used for Child
Welfare.

A108

A109

A110

1948, Aug.
355 A108 15p green .65 .30
356 A109 20p magenta .80 .30
357 A110 125p dark blue 1.60 .80
 Nos. 355-357 (3) 3.05 1.40

30th year of Independence.

United Nations Emblem — A111

1948, Oct. 24
358 A111 125p dk violet blue 9.50 8.00
 UN, 3rd anniv. Valid one day only. Sheets of
9.

Maiwand Victory
Column,
Kandahar — A112

Zahir Shah
and Ruins
of Qalai
Bist
A113

Independence Monument and Nadir
Shah — A114

1949, Aug. 24   Typo.   Perf. 12
359 A112   25p green   1.25 .50
360 A113   35p magenta   1.50 .65
361 A114   1.25af blue   2.50 1.25
   Nos. 359-361 (3)   5.25 2.40
   31st year of Independence.

Nadir
Shah — A117

1950, Aug.
364 A117   35p red brown   .75 .30
365 A117   125p blue   2.00 .50
   32nd year of Independence.

Medical
School
and
Nadir
Shah
A119

Size: 38x25mm

1950, Dec. 22   Typo.   Perf. 12
367 A119   35p emerald   1.25 .65

Size: 46x30mm
368 A119   1.25af deep blue   4.00 2.00
  a.   1.25af black (error)   7.00 2.50

19th anniv. of the founding of Afghanistan's
Faculty of Medicine. On sale and valid for use
on Dec. 22-28, 1950.
See Nos. RA9-RA10.

Minaret, Herat
A120

Zahir Shah
A121

Mosque of
Khodja Abu
Parsar,
Balkh — A122

A123

A124

20p, Buddha at Bamian. 40p, Ruined arch.
45p, Maiwand Victory monument. 50p, View of
Kandahar. 60p, Ancient tower. 70p, Afghanistan flag. 80p, 1af, Profile of Zahir Shah in
uniform.

**Imprint: "Waterlow & Sons Limited,
London"**

**Photogravure, Engraved, Engraved
and Lithographed**
Perf. 12, 12½, 13x12½, 13½
1951, Mar. 21   Unwmk.
369 A120   10p yellow & brn   .30 .25
370 A120   15p blue & brn   .55 .25
371 A120   20p black   8.00 7.00
372 A121   25p green   .50 .25
373 A122   30p cerise   .65 .25
374 A121   35p violet   .70 .25
375 A122   40p chestnut brn   .70 .25
376 A122   45p deep blue   .70 .25
377 A122   50p olive black   2.00 .25
378 A120   60p black   1.60 .30
379 A122   70p dk grn, blk,
                   red & grn   .90 .25
380 A123   75p cerise   1.25 .50
381 A123   80p carmine & blk 2.10 .90
382 A123   1af dp grn & vio   1.60 .65
383 A124   1.25af rose lil & blk 1.90 1.00
384 A124   2af ultra   2.75 .80
385 A124   3af ultra & blk   6.00 1.25
   Nos. 369-385 (17)   32.20 14.65

Nos. 372, 374 and 381 to 385 are engraved,
No. 379 is engraved and lithographed.
Imperfs. exist of the photogravure stamps.
See Nos. 445-451, 453, 552A-552D. For
surcharges see Nos. B1-B2.

Arch of
Paghman
A125

Nadir Shah
and
Independence
Monument
A126

Overprint in
Violet

Perf. 13½x13, 13
1951, Aug. 25   Engr.
386 A125   35p dk green & blk 1.10 .65
387 A126   1.25af deep blue   3.00 1.40

Overprint reads "Sol 33 Istiqlal" or "33rd
Year of Independence." Overprint measures
about 11mm wide.
See Nos. 398-399B, 441-442.

Proposed Flag of
Pashtunistan — A127

Design: 125p, Flag and Pashtunistan
warrior.

1951, Sept. 2   Litho.   Perf. 11½
388 A127   35p dull chocolate 1.50 .75
389 A127   125p blue   3.00 2.00

Issued to publicize "Free Pashtunistan" Day.
Exist Imperf.

Imperforates
From 1951 to 1958, quantities of
nearly all locally-printed stamps were
left imperforate and sold by the government at double face. From 1959 until
March, 1964, many of the imperforates
were sold for more than face value.

Avicenna — A128

1951, Nov. 4   Typo.   Perf. 11½
390 A128   35p deep claret   7.50 1.50
391 A128   125p blue   3.00 4.00

20th anniv. of the founding of the national
Graduate School of Medicine.
   Exist imperf. Value $27.50.

A129

Dove and UN
Symbols
A130

1951, Oct. 24
392 A129   35p magenta   .90 .40
393 A130   125p blue   2.25 1.75
   7th anniv. of the UN. Exist imperf.

Amir Sher Ali
Khan and
Tiger Head
Stamp
A131

Nos. 395, 397, Zahir Shah and stamp.

1951, Dec. 23   Litho.
394 A131   35p chocolate   .85 .40
395 A131   35p rose lilac   .85 .40
396 A131   125p ultra   1.25 .80
  a.   Cliche of 35p in plate of
          125p   110.00 200.00
397 A131   125p aqua   1.25 .80
   Nos. 394-397 (4)   4.20 2.40

76th anniv. of the UPU. Exist imperf. Values, set: unused $9; used $17.50.

Stamps of 1951 Without Overprint
Perf. 13½x13, 13
1952, Aug. 24   Engr.
398 A125   35p dk green & blk 1.50 .55
399 A126   1.25af deep blue   3.25 1.25

For overprints see Nos. 399A-399B, 441-
442.

Same
Overprinted in
Violet

399A A125   35p dk grn & blk   4.00 2.25
399B A126   1.25af deep blue   4.00 2.25

Nos. 398-399B issued for 34th Independence Day.

Globe — A132

Perf. 11½
1952, Oct. 25   Unwmk.   Litho.
400 A132   35p rose   .80 .65
401 A132   125p aqua   1.60 1.10

Issued to honor the United Nations. Exist
Imperf. Values, set: unused $6; used $7.25.

Symbol of
Medicine
A134

1952, Nov.   Perf. 11½
403 A134   35p chocolate   .70 .50
404 A134   125p violet blue 2.00 1.40

21st anniv. of the natl. Graduate School of
Medicine.
No. 404 is inscribed in French with white
letters on a colored background.
   Exist Imperf. Values, set: unused $3.50;
used $4.50.

Tribal Warrior,
Natl.
Flag — A135

1952, Sept. 1   Perf. 11
405 A135   35p red   .80 .80
406 A135   125p dark blue   1.25 1.25

No. 406 is inscribed in French "Pashtunistan
Day, 1952."
   Exist imperf. Values, set, unused or used,
$2.75.

Flags of
Afghanistan &
Pashtunistan
A139

Badge of
Pashtunistan
A140

Perf. 10½x11, 11
1953, Sept. 1   Unwmk.
411 A139   35p vermilion   .80 .80
412 A140   125p blue   1.25 1.25

Issued to publicize "Free Pashtunistan" Day.
   Exist imperf. Values, set: unused, $3.50;
used, $4.

Nadir Shah
and Flag
Bearer
A141

A142

1953, Aug. 24   Perf. 11
413 A141   35p green   .40 .25
414 A142   125p violet   .80 .55
   35th anniv. of Independence.

Exist imperf. Values, set: unused, $3.50; used, $4.

United Nations Emblem — A143

1953, Oct. 24
415 A143 35p lilac   1.00 .80
416 A143 125p violet blue   2.00 1.50

United Nations Day, 1953.
Exist imperf. Values, set, unused or used, $9.

A144

Nadir Shah — A145

1953, Nov. 29
417 A144 35p orange   1.50 1.50
418 A145 125p chalky blue   3.00 3.00

22nd anniv. of the founding of the Natl. Graduate School of Medicine.
Exist imperf. Values: set: unused $9; used, $12.50.

35p. Original — Right character in second line of Persian inscription

Redrawn — Persian character

Original

Redrawn

1953
419 A144 35p deep orange   9.50 9.50
420 A145 125p chalky blue   9.50 9.50

Exist imperf.

Nadir Shah and Symbols of Independence — A146

1954, Aug.   Typo.   Perf. 11
421 A146 35p carmine rose   .70 .40
422 A146 125p violet blue   2.00 .80

36th year of Independence.
Exist imperf. Values, set: unused, $6; used, $7.

Raising Flag of Pashtunistan A147

1954, Sept.   Perf. 11½
423 A147 35p chocolate   .70 .40
424 A147 125p blue   2.00 .80

Issued to publicize "Free Pashtunistan" Day.
Exist imperf. Values: set: unused, $4.75; used, $6.50.

UN Flag and Map — A148

1954, Oct. 24   Perf. 11
425 A148 35p carmine rose   1.25 1.25
426 A148 125p dk violet blue   3.25 2.25

9th anniv. of the United Nations.
Exist imperf. Values, set: unused $9; used, $10.

UN Symbols A149

Design: 125p, UN emblem & flags.

1955, June 26   Litho.   Perf. 11
    Size: 26½x36mm
427 A149 35p dark green   1.10 .55
    Size: 28½x36mm
428 A149 125p aqua   2.00 1.00

10th anniv. of the UN charter.
Exist imperf. Values, set: unused $12; used, $12.50.

Nadir Shah (center) and Brothers A150

1929 Civil War Scene and Zahir Shah — A151

1955, Aug.   Unwmk.   Perf. 11
429 A150 35p brt pink   .65 .40
430 A150 35p violet blue   .65 .40
431 A151 125p rose lilac   1.40 .90
432 A151 125p light violet   1.40 .90
    Nos. 429-432 (4)   4.10 2.60

37th anniv. of Independence.
Exist imperf. Values, set: unused, $12; used, $13.50.

Tribal Elders' Council and Pashtun Flag — A152

1955, Sept. 5
433 A152 35p orange brown   .60 .25
434 A152 125p yellow green   2.00 .55

Issued for "Free Pashtunistan" Day.
Exist imperf. Values, set: unused, $7; used, $9.

UN Flag — A153

1955, Oct. 24   Unwmk.   Perf. 11
435 A153 35p orange brown   1.10 .60
436 A153 125p brt ultra   2.00 1.10

10th anniv. of the United Nations.
Exist imperf. Value for set: unused, $15; used, $17.50.

A154

1956, Aug.   Litho.
437 A154 35p lt green   .55 .90
438 A154 140p lt violet blue   2.25 .90

38th year of Independence.
Exist imperf. Value for set: unused, $3; used, $4.

Jesh'n Exhibition Hall A155

1956, Aug. 25
439 A155 50p chocolate   .90 .40
440 A155 50p lt violet blue   .90 .40

International Exposition at Kabul.
Of the 50p face value, only 35p paid postage. The remaining 15p went to the Exposition.
Exist imperf. Value for set: unused, $7; used, $8.

Nos. 398-399 Handstamped in Violet

a

b

1957, Aug.   Engr.   Perf. 13½x13, 13
441 A125 (a) 35p dk green & blk   .65 .30
442 A126 (b) 1.25af deep blue   1.00 .70

Arabic overprint measures 19mm.
39th year of independence.

Pashtunistan Flag — A156

1957, Sept. 1   Litho.   Perf. 11
443 A156 50p pale lilac rose   1.00 .55
444 A156 155p light violet   1.50 1.00

Issued for "Free Pashtunistan" Day. French inscription on No. 444. 15p of each stamp went to the Pashtunistan Fund.
Exist imperf. Values, set: unused, $4; used, $4.50.

Types of 1951 and

Game of Buzkashi A157

Perf. 12, 12½, 12½x13, 13, 13x12, 13x12½, 13½x14
    Photo., Engr., Engr.& Litho.
1957, Nov. 23   Unwmk.
Imprint: "Waterlow & Sons Limited, London"
445 A122 30p brown   .40 .25
446 A122 40p rose red   .55 .25
447 A122 50p yellow   .65 .25
448 A120 60p ultra   .80 .25
449 A123 75p brt violet   1.00 .25
450 A123 80p violet & brn   1.10 .25
451 A123 1af carmine & ultra   1.75 .25
452 A157 140p olive & dp claret   2.75 .65
453 A124 3af orange & blk   2.75 .90
    Nos. 445-453 (9)   11.75 3.30

No. 452 lacks imprint.

Nadir Shah and Flag-bearer A158

1958, Aug. 25   Perf. 13½x14
454 A158 35p dp yellow green   .50 .25
455 A158 140p brown   1.25 1.00

40th year of Independence.

Exposition Buildings A159

1958, Aug. 23   Litho.   Perf. 11
456 A159 35p brt blue green   .50 .25
457 A159 140p vermilion   1.25 1.00

International Exposition at Kabul.
Exist imperf. Value set, unused or used, $4.

AFGHANISTAN

Pres. Celal Bayar
of Turkey — A160

1958, Sept. 13   **Unwmk.**
458 A160 50p lt blue   .30 .25
459 A160 100p brown   .65 .30

Visit of President Celal Bayar of Turkey.
Exists Imperf. Values, set: unused, $2.25; used, $3.25.

Flags of UN and
Afghanistan
A161

1958, Oct. 24   **Photo.**   **Perf. 14x13½**
Flags in Original Colors
460 A161 50p dark gray   .65 .65
461 A161 100p green   1.40 1.10

United Nations Day, Oct. 24.
Exist imperf. Value set, unused or used, $4.

Atomic Energy Encircling the
Hemispheres — A162

1958, Oct. 20   **Perf. 13½x14**
462 A162 50p blue   .55 .50
463 A162 100p dp red lilac   .90 .65

Issued to promote Atoms for Peace.
Exist imperf. Value set, unused or used, $3.

UNESCO
Building,
Paris
A163

1958, Nov. 3
464 A163 50p dp yellow grn   .70 .60
465 A163 100p brown olive   .70 .70

UNESCO Headquarters in Paris opening, Nov. 3.
Exist imperf. Value set, unused or used, $5.

Globe and
Torch
A164

Perf. 13½x14
1958, Dec. 10   **Unwmk.**
466 A164 50p lilac rose   .40 .40
467 A164 100p maroon   .90 1.00

10th anniv. of the signing of the Universal Declaration of Human Rights.
Exist imperf. Value set, unused or used, $3.50.

Nadir Shah
and Flags
A165

1959, Aug.   **Litho.**   **Perf. 11 Rough**
468 A165 35p light vermilion   .55 .50
469 A165 165p light violet   1.50 .65

41st year of Independence.
Exist imperf. Value set, unused or used, $2.50.

Uprooted Oak
Emblem — A166

1960, Apr. 7   **Perf. 11**
470 A166 50p deep orange   .25 .25
471 A166 165p blue   .35 .25

World Refugee Year, 7/1/59-6/30/60.
Two imperf. souvenir sheets exist. Both contain a 50p and a 165p, type A166, with marginal inscriptions and WRY emblem in maroon. On one sheet the stamps are in the colors of Nos. 470-471 (size 108x81mm). Value $4.50. On the other, the 50p is blue and the 165p is deep orange (size 107x80mm).Value $6.
For surcharges see Nos. B35-B36.
Exist imperf. Value set, unused or used, $3.50.

Buzkashi
A167

1960, May 4   **Perf. 11, Imperf.**
472 A167 25p rose red   .55 .25
473 A167 50p bluish green   1.40 .55
   a.   Cliche of 25p in plate of 50p   27.50 27.50

Exist imperf. Value set, unused or used, $2.50.
See Nos. 549-550A.

Independence
Monument
A168

1960, Aug.   **Perf. 11, 12**
474 A168 50p light blue   .40 .25
475 A168 175p bright pink   1.00 .40

42nd Independence Day.
Exist imperf. Value set, unused or used, $1.75.

Globe and
Flags
A169

1960, Oct. 24   **Litho.**   **Perf. 11, 12**
476 A169 50p rose lilac   .25 .25
477 A169 175p ultra   1.00 .65

UN Day.
Exist imperf. Value set, unused or used, $2.25.
An imperf. souvenir sheet contains one each of Nos. 476-477 with marginal inscriptions ("La Journée des Nations Unies 1960" in

French and Persian) and UN emblem in light blue. Size: 127x85½mm. Value $5.50.
This sheet was surcharged "+20ps" in 1962. Value $5.50.

Teacher
Pointing to
Globe
A170

1960, Oct. 23   **Perf. 11**
478 A170 50p brt pink   .40 .30
479 A170 100p brt green   1.00 .50

Issued to publicize Teacher's Day.
Exist imperf. Value set, unused or used, $2.50.

Mohammed Zahir Shah — A171

1960, Oct. 15
480 A171 50p red brown   .65 .25
481 A171 150p dk car rose   1.60 .55

Honoring the King on his 46th birthday.
Exist imperf. Value set, unused or used, $2.50.

Buzkashi
A172

1960, Nov. 9   **Perf. 11**
482 A172 175p lt red brown   2.40 .50

Exists imperf. Value, unused or used, $3.
See Nos. 551-552.

No. 482
Overprinted
in Bright
Green

1960, Dec. 24
483 A172 175p red brown   2.00 2.00
   a.   Souv. sheet of 1, imperf.   6.00 8.00

17th Olympic Games, Rome, 8/25-9/11.
Exists imperf.
Value, unused or used, $4.

Mir Wais — A173

1961, Jan. 5   **Unwmk.**   **Perf. 10½**
484 A173 50p brt rose lilac   .65 .40
485 A173 175p ultra   1.10 .40
   a.   Souv. sheet, #484-485, imperf.   3.25 3.25

Mir Wais (1665-1708), national leader.
Exist imperf. Value set, unused or used, $2.25.

No Postal Need
existed for the 1p-15p denominations issued with sets of 1961-63 (between Nos. 486 and 649, B37 and B65).
The lowest denomination actually used for non-philatelic postage in that period was 25p (except for the 2p newspaper rate for which separate stamps were provided).

Horse,
Sheep and
Camel
A174

Designs: No. 487, 175p, Rock partridge. 10p, 100p, Afghan hound. 15p, 150p, Grain & grasshopper, vert.

1961, Mar. 29   **Photo.**   **Perf. 13½x14**
486 A174 2p maroon & buff   .25 .25
487 A174 2p ultra & org   .25 .25
488 A174 5p brown & yel   .25 .25
489 A174 10p black & salmon   .25 .25
490 A174 15p blue grn & yel   .25 .25
491 A174 25p black & pink   .25 .25
492 A174 50p black & citron   .30 .30
493 A174 100p black & pink   .45 .40
494 A174 150p green & yel   .65 .65
495 A174 175p ultra & pink   .80 .65
   Nos. 486-495 (10)   3.70 3.50

Two souvenir sheets, perf. and imperf., contain 2 stamps, 1 each of No. 492-493. Value $3 each.

Afghan
Fencing
A175

Designs: No. 497, 5p, 25p, 50p, Wrestlers. 10p, 100p, Man with Indian clubs. 15p, 150p, Afghan fencing. 175p, Children skating.

1961, July 6   **Perf. 13½x14**
496 A175 2p green & rose lil   .25 .25
497 A175 2p brown & citron   .25 .25
498 A175 5p gray & rose   .25 .25
499 A175 10p blue & bister   .25 .25
500 A175 15p sl bl & dl lil   .25 .25
501 A175 25p black & dl bl   .25 .25
502 A175 50p sl grn & bis brn   .25 .25
503 A175 100p brown & bl grn   .55 .55
504 A175 150p brown & org yel   .90 .90
505 A175 175p black & blue   .95 .95
   Nos. 496-505 (10)   4.15 4.15

Issued for Children's Day.
A souvenir sheet exists, perf. and imperf., containing one each of Nos. 502-503. Values: perf $3.75; imperf $5.
For surcharges see Nos. B37-B41.

Bande Amir
Lakes
A176

1961, Aug. 7   **Photo.**   **Perf. 13½x14**
506 A176 3af brt blue   .50 .25
507 A176 10af rose claret   1.25 1.25

Nadir
Shah — A177

1961, Aug. 23　　　　　　　**Perf. 14x13½**
508 A177 50p rose red & blk　　　.55　.50
509 A177 175p brt grn & org brn　.90　.70

43rd Independence Day.
Exist imperf. Value set, unused or used, $2.50.
Two souvenir sheets, perf. and imperf., contain one each of Nos. 508-509. Value, each $2.50.

Girl Scout — A178

Perf. 14x13½
1961, July 23　　　　　　　　**Unwmk.**
510 A178 50p dp car & dk gray　.40　.25
511 A178 175p dp grn & rose
　　　　　　brn　　　　　　　1.25　.50

Issued for Women's Day.
Exist imperf. Value set, unused or used, $4.50.
Two souvenir sheets exist, perf. and imperf., containing one each of Nos. 510-511. Value $5 each.

Exhibition
Hall, Kabul
A179

1961, Aug. 23　　　　　　　**Perf. 13½x14**
512 A179 50p yel brn & yel grn　.25　.25
513 A179 175p blue & brn　　　.70　.50

International Exhibition at Kabul.

Pathan with
Pashtunistan
Flag — A180

1961, Aug. 31　Photo.　Perf. 14x13½
514 A180 50p blk, lil & red　　.30　.25
515 A180 175p brn, grnsh bl &
　　　　　　red　　　　　　　.65　.55

Issued for "Free Pashtunistan Day."
Exist imperf. Value set, unused or used, $1.60.
Souvenir sheets exist perf. and imperf., containing one each of Nos. 514-515. Value $2.25 each.

Assembly
Building.
A181

1961, Sept. 10　　　　　　　**Perf. 12**
516 A181 50p dk gray & brt grn　.25　.25
517 A181 175p ultra & brn　　　.65　.50

Anniv. of the founding of the Natl. Assembly.
Exist imperf. Value set, unused or used, $1.25.
Souvenir sheets exist, perf. and imperf., containing one each of Nos. 516-517. Value $1.50 each.

Exterminating Anopheles
Mosquito — A182

1961, Oct. 5　　　　　　　**Perf. 13½x14**
518 A182 50p blk & brn lil　　.60　.30
519 A182 175p maroon & brt grn　1.25　.90

Anti-Malaria campaign.
Exist imperf. Value set, unused or used, $4.
Souvenir sheets exist, perf. and imperf., containing one each of Nos. 518-519. Value $4.50 each.

Zahir
Shah — A183

1961, Oct. 15　　　　　　　**Perf. 13½**
520 A183 50p rose lilac &
　　　　　　grnish blue　　　.30　.25
521 A183 175p emerald & red
　　　　　　brn　　　　　　　.90　.50

Issued to honor King Mohammed Zahir Shah on his 47th birthday.
See Nos. 609-612.

Pomegranates — A184

Fruit: No. 523, 5p, 25p, 50p, Grapes. 10p, 150p, Apples. 15p, 175p, Pomegranates. 100p, Melons.

1961, Oct. 16　　　　　　　**Perf. 13½x14**
Fruit in Natural Colors

522 A184 2p black　　　.25　.25
523 A184 2p green　　　.25　.25
524 A184 5p lilac rose　.25　.25
525 A184 10p lilac　　　.25　.25
526 A184 15p dk blue　　.25　.25
527 A184 25p dull red　.25　.25
528 A184 50p purple　　.25　.25
529 A184 100p brt blue　.55　.55
530 A184 150p brown　　.90　.90
531 A184 175p olive gray　.95　.95
　　Nos. 522-531 (10)　4.15　4.15

For Afghan Red Crescent Society.
Souvenir sheets exist, perf. and imperf., containing one each of Nos. 528-529. Value $2.25 each.
For surcharges see Nos. B42-B46.

UN Headquarters, NY — A185

1961, Oct. 24　　　　　　　**Perf. 13½x14**
**Vertical Borders in Emerald, Red
and Black**

532 A185 1p rose lilac　.25　.25
533 A185 2p slate　　　.25　.25
534 A185 3p brown　　.25　.25
535 A185 4p ultra　　　.25　.25
536 A185 50p rose red　.25　.25
537 A185 75p gray　　.25　.25
538 A185 175p brt green　.55　.55
　　Nos. 532-538 (7)　2.05　2.05

16th anniv. of the UN.
Nos. 536-538 exist imperf. Values, unused or used: 50p, 40c; 75p, 65c; 175p, $1.40.

Souvenir sheets exist, perf. and imperf., containing one each of Nos. 536-538. Value $3 each.

Children Giving
Flowers to
Teacher — A186

Designs: No. 540, 5p, 25p, 50p, Tulips. 10p, 100p, Narcissus. 15p, 150p, Children giving flowers to teacher. 175p, Teacher with children in front of school.

1961, Oct. 26　Photo.　Perf. 12
539 A186 2p multicolored　.25　.25
540 A186 2p multicolored　.25　.25
541 A186 5p multicolored　.25　.25
542 A186 10p multicolored　.25　.25
543 A186 15p multicolored　.25　.25
544 A186 25p multicolored　.25　.25
545 A186 50p multicolored　.25　.25
546 A186 100p multicolored　.50　.50
547 A186 150p multicolored　.80　.80
548 A186 175p multicolored　.90　.90
　　Nos. 539-548 (10)　3.95　3.95

Issued for Teacher's Day.
Souvenir sheets exist, perf. and imperf. containing one each of Nos. 545-546. Value, 2 sheets, $4.50.
For surcharges see Nos. B47-B51.

Buzkashi Types of 1960

1961-72　Litho.　Perf. 10½, 11
549　A167 25p violet　　　　1.40　.25
　b.　25p brt vio, typo. ('72)
549A A167 25p citron ('63)　2.50　.25
550　A167 50p blue　　　　2.00　.25
550A A167 50p yel org ('69)　.50　.30
551　A172 100p citron　　　.80　.25
551A A172 150p orange ('64)　.65　.30
552　A172 2af lt green　　1.50　1.00
　　Nos. 549-552 (7)　9.35　2.60

Zahir Shah Types of 1951
Imprint: "Thomas De La Rue & Co. Ltd."

Photo., Engr., Engr. & Litho.
1962　　　　　　**Perf. 13x12, 13**
552A A123 75p brt purple　2.75　.25
552B A123 1af car & ultra　3.50　.30
552C A124 2af blue　　　7.25　.80
552D A124 3af orange & blk　10.00　1.00
　　Nos. 552A-552D (4)　23.50　2.35

People Raising
UNESCO
Symbol — A187

1962, July 2　Photo.　Perf. 14x13½
553 A187 2p rose lil & brn　.25　.25
554 A187 2p ol bis & brn　.25　.25
555 A187 5p dp org & dk grn　.25　.25
556 A187 10p gray & mag　.25　.25
557 A187 15p blue & brn　.25　.25
558 A187 25p org yel & pur　.25　.25
559 A187 50p lt grn & pur　.25　.25
560 A187 75p brt cit & brn　.25　.25
561 A187 100p dp org & brn　.30　.30
　　Nos. 553-561 (9)　2.30　2.30

15th anniv. of UNESCO. Souvenir sheets exist, perf. and imperf. One contains Nos. 558-559; the other contains Nos. 560-561. Value, $3.25 each perforated, $2.40 each imperf.
For surcharges see Nos. B52-B60.

Ahmad
Shah — A188

1962, Feb. 24　Photo.　Perf. 13½
562 A188 50p red brn & gray　.25　.25
563 A188 75p green & salmon　.30　.25
564 A188 100p claret & bister　.40　.30
　　Nos. 562-564 (3)　.95　.80

Ahmad Shah (1724-73), founded the Afghan kingdom in 1747 and ruled until 1773.

Afghan
Hound — A189

Designs: 5p, 75p, Afghan cock. 10p, 100p, Kondjid plant. 15p, 125p, Astrakhan skins.

1962, Apr. 21　　　　　　　**Perf. 14x13½**
565 A189 2p rose & brn　　.25　.25
566 A189 2p lt green & brn　.25　.25
567 A189 5p dp rose & claret　.25　.25
568 A189 10p lt grn & sl grn　.25　.25
569 A189 15p blue grn & blk　.25　.25
570 A189 25p blue & brn　　.25　.25
571 A189 50p gray & brn　　.30　.25
572 A189 75p rose lil & lil　.50　.30
573 A189 100p gray & dl grn　.55　.40
574 A189 125p rose brn & blk　.65　.50
　　Nos. 565-574 (10)　3.50　2.95

Agriculture Day.
Perf. and imperf. souvenir sheets exist. Set of 4 sheets, value $11.00.
Exist imperf. Value, set $5.50.

Athletes with
Flag and Nadir
Shah — A190

1962, Aug. 23　　　　　　　**Perf. 12**
575 A190 25p multicolored　.25　.25
576 A190 50p multicolored　.25　.25
577 A190 150p multicolored　.40　.30
　　Nos. 575-577 (3)　.90　.80

44th Independence Day.

Woman in National
Costume — A191

1962, Aug. 30　　　　　　　**Perf. 11½x12**
578 A191 25p lilac & brn　.25　.25
579 A191 50p green & brn　.25　.25
　　Nos. 578-579,C15-C16 (4)　1.90　1.90

Issued for Women's Day. A souvenir sheet exists containing one each of Nos. 578-579, C15-C16. Value $4.50.

Man and Woman
with Flag — A192

1962, Aug. 31   *Photo.*

580	A192	25p black, pale bl & red	.25	.25
581	A192	50p black, grn & red	.25	.25
582	A192	150p black, pink & red	.55	.40
		Nos. 580-582 (3)	1.05	.90

Issued for "Free Pashtunistan Day."

Malaria
Eradication
Emblem and
Swamp — A193

1962, Sept. 5   *Perf. 14x13½*

583	A193	2p dk grn & ol gray	.25	.25
584	A193	2p dk green & sal	.25	.25
585	A193	5p red brn & ol	.25	.25
586	A193	10p red brn & brt grn	.25	.25
587	A193	15p red brn & gray	.25	.25
588	A193	25p brt bl & bluish grn	.25	.25
589	A193	50p brt bl & rose lil	.25	.25
590	A193	75p black & blue	.25	.25
591	A193	100p black & brt pink	.30	.25
592	A193	150p black & bis brn	.50	.40
593	A193	175p black & orange	.55	.50
		Nos. 583-593 (11)	3.35	3.15

WHO drive to eradicate malaria.
Perf. and imperf. souvenir sheets exist. Set of 4 sheets, value $14.
Exist imperf. Value, set $10.
For surcharges see Nos. B61-B71.

National Assembly Building — A194

Perf. 10½, 11 (100p)

1962, Sept. 10   *Unwmk.*   *Litho.*

594	A194	25p lt green	.25	.25
595	A194	50p blue	.45	.45
596	A194	75p rose	.60	.60
597	A194	100p violet	.75	.75
598	A194	125p ultra	1.00	1.00
		Nos. 594-598 (5)	3.05	3.05

Establishment of the National Assembly.

Horse
Racing — A195

Designs: 2p, Horse racing. 3p, Wrestling. 4p, Weight lifting. 5p, Soccer.

1962, Sept. 22   *Photo.*   *Perf. 12*
Black Inscriptions

599	A195	1p lt ol & red brn	.25	.25
600	A195	2p lt grn & red brn	.25	.25
601	A195	3p yellow & dk pur	.25	.25
602	A195	4p pale bl & grn	.25	.25
603	A195	5p bluish grn & dk brn	.25	.25
		Nos. 599-603,C17-C22 (11)	4.85	4.85

4th Asian Games, Djakarta, Indonesia.
Exist imperf. Value, set of 11, unused or used, $17.50.
Two souvenir sheets exist. A perforated one contains a 125p blue, dark blue and brown

stamp in horse racing design. An imperf. one contains a 2af buff, purple and black stamp in soccer design. Value, $3.50 each.

Runners
A196

1p, 2p, Diver, vert. 4p, Peaches. 5p, Iris, vert.

Perf. 11½x12, 12x11½

1962, Oct. 2   *Unwmk.*

604	A196	1p rose lil & brn	.25	.25
605	A196	2p blue & brn	.25	.25
606	A196	3p brt blue & lil	.25	.25
607	A196	4p ol gray & multi	.25	.25
608	A196	5p gray & multi	.25	.25
		Nos. 604-608,C23-C25 (8)	4.45	4.45

Issued for Children's Day.
Exist imperf. Value, set of 8, unused or used, $27.50.

Zahir Shah Type of 1961, Dated "1962"

1962, Oct. 15   *Perf. 13½*
Various Frames

609	A183	25p lilac rose & brn	.25	.25
610	A183	50p orange brn & grn	.30	.25
611	A183	75p blue & lake	.50	.25
612	A183	100p green & red brn	.55	.25
		Nos. 609-612 (4)	1.60	1.00

Issued to honor King Mohammed Zahir Shah on his 48th birthday.

Grapes
A197

1962, Oct. 16   *Perf. 12*

613	A197	1p shown	.25	.25
614	A197	2p Grapes	.25	.25
615	A197	3p Pears	.25	.25
616	A197	4p Wistaria	.25	.25
617	A197	5p Blossoms	.25	.25
		Nos. 613-617,C26-C28 (8)	2.45	2.45

For the Afghan Red Crescent Society.
Exist imperf. Value, set of 8, unused or used, $20.

UN Headquarters, NY and Flags of
UN and Afghanistan — A198

1962, Oct. 24   *Unwmk.*

618	A198	1p multicolored	.25	.25
619	A198	2p multicolored	.25	.25
620	A198	3p multicolored	.25	.25
621	A198	4p multicolored	.25	.25
622	A198	5p multicolored	.25	.25
		Nos. 618-622,C29-C31 (8)	2.60	2.60

UN Day.
Exist imperf. Value, set of 8, unused or used, $9.50.
Souvenir sheets exist. One contains a single 4af ultramarine stamp, perforated; the other, a 4af ocher stamp, imperf. Value, 2 sheets, $9.25.

Boy
Scout — A199

1962, Oct. 18   *Photo.*   *Perf. 12*

623	A199	1p yel, dk grn & sal	.25	.25
624	A199	2p dl yel, slate & sal	.25	.25
625	A199	3p rose, blk & sal	.25	.25
626	A199	4p multicolored	.25	.25
		Nos. 623-626,C32-C35 (8)	3.65	3.65

Issued to honor the Boy Scouts.
Exist imperf. Value, set of 8, unused or used, $27.50.

Pole
Vault — A200

2p, Pole Vault. 3p, High jump. 4p, 5p, Different blossoms.

1962, Oct. 25   *Unwmk.*   *Perf. 12*

627	A200	1p lilac & dk grn	.25	.25
628	A200	2p yellow grn & brn	.25	.25
629	A200	3p bister & vio	.25	.25
630	A200	4p sal pink, grn & ultra	.25	.25
631	A200	5p yellow, grn & bl	.25	.25
		Nos. 627-631,C36-C37 (7)	2.75	2.75

Issued for Teacher's Day.
Exist imperf. Value, set of 7, unused or used, $12.

Rockets
A201

1962, Nov. 29

632	A201	50p pale lil & dk bl	.50	.50
633	A201	100p lt blue & red brn	1.25	1.25

UN World Meteorological Day.
Exist imperf. Value, set, unused or used, $25.
A souvenir sheet contains one 5af pink and green stamp. Value $6.

Ansari
Mausoleum,
Herat — A202

Perf. 13½

1963, Jan. 3   *Unwmk.*   *Photo.*

634	A202	50p purple & green	.25	.25
635	A202	75p gray & magenta	.25	.25
636	A202	100p orange brn & brn	.35	.35
		Nos. 634-636 (3)	.85	.85

Khwaja Abdullah Ansari, Sufi, religious leader and poet, on the 900th anniv. of his death.

Sheep
A203

Silkworm,
Cocoons,
Moth and
Mulberry
Branch
A204

1963, Mar. 1   *Perf. 12*

637	A203	1p grnsh blue & blk	.25	.25
638	A203	2p yellow grn & blk	.25	.25
639	A203	3p lilac rose & blk	.25	.25
640	A204	4p gray, grn & brn	.25	.25
641	A204	5p red lil, grn & brn	.25	.25
		Nos. 637-641,C42-C44 (8)	3.10	3.10

Issued for the Day of Agriculture.
Exist imperf. Value, set of 8, unused or used, $12.

Rice — A205

Designs: 3p, Corn. 300p, Wheat emblem.

1963, Mar. 27   *Unwmk.*   *Perf. 14*

642	A205	2p gray, claret & grn	.25	.25
643	A205	3p green, yel & ocher	.25	.25
644	A205	300p dk blue & yel	.60	.60
		Nos. 642-644,C45 (4)	2.20	2.20

FAO "Freedom from Hunger" campaign.

Meteorological Measuring
Instrument — A206

Designs: 3p, 10p, Weather station. 4p, 5p, Rockets in space.

1963, May 23   *Photo.*   *Perf. 13½x14*

645	A206	1p dp magenta & brn	.25	.25
646	A206	2p brt blue & brn	.25	.25
647	A206	3p red & brown	.25	.25
648	A206	4p orange & lilac	.25	.25
649	A206	5p green & dl vio	.25	.25

Imperf

650	A206	10p red brn & grn	.45	.40
		Nos. 645-650,C46-C50 (11)	11.15	10.50

3rd UN World Meteorological Day, Mar. 23.

Independence
Monument
A207

1963, Aug. 23   *Litho.*   *Perf. 10½*

651	A207	25p lt green	.25	.25
652	A207	50p orange	.35	.25
653	A207	150p rose carmine	.50	.30
		Nos. 651-653 (3)	1.10	.80

45th Independence Day.

Pathans
in Forest
A208

1963, Aug. 31   *Unwmk.*   *Perf. 10½*

654	A208	25p pale violet	.25	.25
655	A208	50p sky blue	.25	.25
655A	A208	150p dull red brn	.60	.40
		Nos. 654-655A (3)	1.10	.90

Issued for "Free Pashtunistan Day."

4th Asian
Games,
Djakarta —
A208a

2p, 250p, 300p, Wrestling. 3p, 10p, Tennis.
4p, 500p, Javelin. 5p, 9af, Shot put.

1963, Sept. 3　　Litho.　　Perf. 12
656	A208a	2p rose vio & brn	.25	.25
656A	A208a	3p olive grn &		
		brn	.25	.25
656B	A208a	4p blue & brn	.25	.25
656C	A208a	5p yel grn & brn	.25	.25
656D	A208a	10p lt bl grn & brn	.25	.25
656E	A208a	300p yellow & vio	.45	.45
656F	A208a	500p lt yel bis & brn	.85	.85
656G	A208a	9af pale grn & vio	1.40	1.40
	Nos. 656-656G (8)		3.95	3.95

Souvenir Sheets
656H	A208a	250p lilac & vio	2.00	2.00
656I	A208a	300p blue & blk	2.00	2.00

Nos. 656E-656F are airmail. Nos. 656-656I
exist imperf. Values, unused or used: set, $12;
souvenir sheets, each $11.

National Assembly Building — A209

1963, Sept. 10　　　　　Perf. 11
657	A209	25p gray	.25	.25
658	A209	50p dull red	.25	.25
659	A209	75p brown	.25	.25
660	A209	100p olive	.25	.25
661	A209	125p lilac	.40	.25
	Nos. 657-661 (5)		1.40	1.25

Issued to honor the National Assembly.

Balkh Gate
A210

1963, Oct. 8
662	A210	3af choc (screened		
		margins)	1.00	.30
a.		White margins	2.50	.55

In the original printing a halftone screen
extended across the plate, covering the space
between the stamps. A retouch removed the
screen between the stamps (No. 662a).

Intl. Red
Cross,
Cent. —
A210a

4p, 5p, 200p, 3af, Nurse holding patient,
vert. 10p, 4af, 6af, Crown Prince Ahmed Shah.

1963, Oct. 9　　　　　Perf. 13½
662B	A210a	2p olive, blk &		
		red	.25	.25
662C	A210a	3p blue, blk &		
		red	.25	.25
662D	A210a	4p lt brn, blk &		
		red	.25	.25
662E	A210a	5p lt vio, blk &		
		red	.25	.25
662F	A210a	10p gray grn, red		
		& blk	.25	.25
662G	A210a	100p dull bl grn,		
		red & blk	.25	.25
662H	A210a	200p lt brn, blk &		
		red	.25	.25
662I	A210a	4af brt bl grn, red		
		& blk	.25	.25
m.		Souvenir sheet of 1	1.75	1.60

662J	A210a	6af lt brn, red &		
		blk	.25	.25
	Nos. 662B-662J (9)		2.25	2.25

Souvenir Sheet
662K	A210a	3af dl blue, blk &	
		red	1.75

Nos. 662G-662K are airmail. Nos.
662B-662K exist imperf. Values,
unused or used: set, $12; souvenir sheets,
each $11.

Zahir
Shah — A211

1963, Oct. 15　　　　Perf. 10½
663	A211	25p green	.25	.25
663A	A211	50p gray	.25	.25
663B	A211	75p carmine rose	.30	.25
663C	A211	100p dull redsh brn	.50	.25
	Nos. 663-663C (4)		1.30	1.00

King Mohammed Zahir Shah, 49th birthday.

Kemal
Ataturk — A212

1963, Oct. 10　　　　Perf. 10½
664	A212	1af blue	.25	.25
665	A212	3af rose lilac	.65	.50

25th anniv. of the death of Kemal Ataturk,
president of Turkey.

Protection
of Nubian
Monuments
A213

Designs: 5af, 7.50af, 10af, Ruins, vert.

Perf. 12, Imperf. (150p, 250p, 10af)
1963, Nov. 16　　　　　Photo.
666	A213	100p lil rose & blk	.25	.25
666A	A213	150p rose lil & blk	.25	.30
666B	A213	200p brown & blk	.40	.40
666C	A213	250p ultra & blk	.50	.50
666D	A213	500p green & blk	1.00	1.00
666E	A213	5af greenish blue		
		& gray bl	1.00	1.00
666F	A213	7.50af red brn & gray		
		bl	1.75	1.75
666G	A213	10af ver & gray bl	1.90	1.90
	Nos. 666-666G (8)		7.05	7.10

Nos. 666E-666G are airmail. No. 666D
exists imperf. Value, unused or used, 95¢.

Women's Day —
A213a

1964, Jan. 5　　　　Perf. 14x13½
667	A213a	2p multicolored	.25	.25
667A	A213a	3p multicolored	.25	.25
667B	A213a	4p multicolored	.25	.25
667C	A213a	5p multicolored	.25	.25
667D	A213a	10p multicolored	.25	.25
	Nos. 667-667D (5)		1.25	1.25

Exist imperf. Value set, unused or used,
$2.40.

A213b

Boy and Girl
Scouts — A213c

Nos. 668F-668G, 668K-668M, Girl with flag.

1964, Jan. 5　Perf. 13½x14, 14x13½
668	A213b	2p multi	.25	.25
668A	A213b	3p multi	.25	.25
668B	A213b	4p multi	.25	.25
668C	A213b	5p multi	.25	.25
668D	A213b	10p multi	.25	.25
668E	A213c	2af multi	.25	.25
668F	A213c	2af multi	.25	.25
668G	A213c	2.50af multi	.25	.25
668H	A213c	3af multi	.30	.30
668I	A213c	4af multi	.40	.40
668J	A213c	5af multi	.50	.50
668K	A213c	12af multi	1.25	1.25
	Nos. 668-668K (12)		4.45	4.45

Souvenir Sheets
668L	A213c	5af multi	1.25	1.25
668M	A213c	6af multi	1.25	2.00
668N	A213c	6af multi	2.50	2.50
668O	A213c	10af multi	2.50	2.50

Nos. 668E-668O are airmail.
Nos. 668-668K, 668N-668O exist imperf.
Values, unused or used: set, $15; souvenir
sheets, each $7.

Children — A213d

2p, Playing ball. 4p, Swinging, jumping rope,
vert. 5p, Skiing, vert.

1964, Jan. 22　　　　　Perf. 12
669	A213d	2p multi	.25	.25
669A	A213d	3p like #669	.25	.25
669B	A213d	4p multi	.25	.25
669C	A213d	5p multi	.25	.25
669D	A213d	10p like #669	.25	.25
669E	A213d	200p like #669C	.75	.75
669F	A213d	300p like #669B	1.10	1.10
	Nos. 669-669F (7)		3.10	3.10

Nos. 669E-669F are airmail.
Nos. 669-669F exist imperf. Value set,
unused or used, $27.50.

Red Crescent Society — A213e

Designs: 100p, 200p, Pierre and Marie
Curie, physicists. 2.50af, 7.50af Nurse examining child. 3.50af, 5af, Nurse and patients.

Perf. 14, Imperf. (#670A, 670C-670D)
1964, Feb. 8
670	A213e	100p multi	.50	.50
670A	A213e	100p multi	.50	.50
670B	A213e	200p multi	.80	.80
670C	A213e	2.50af multi	1.25	1.25
670D	A213e	3.50af multi	1.90	1.90
670E	A213e	5af multi	2.10	2.10
670F	A213e	7.50af multi	3.00	3.00
	Nos. 670-670F (7)		10.05	10.05

Nos. 670A and 670E-F are airmail.

Teachers' Day
— A213f

Flowers: 2p, 3p, 3af, 4af, Tulips. 4p, 5p,
3.50af, 6af, Flax. 10p, 1.50af, 2af, Iris.

Perf. 12, Imperf. (1.50af, 2af)
1964, Mar. 3
671	A213f	2p multicolored	.25	.25
671A	A213f	3p multicolored	.25	.25
671B	A213f	4p multicolored	.25	.25
671C	A213f	5p multicolored	.25	.25
671D	A213f	10p multicolored	.25	.25
671E	A213f	1.50af multicolored	2.25	2.25
671F	A213f	2af multicolored	3.00	3.00
671G	A213f	3af multicolored	.90	.90
671H	A213f	3.50af multicolored	1.10	1.10
	Nos. 671-671H (9)		8.50	8.50

Souvenir Sheets
671I	A213f	4af multi	2.40	2.40
671J	A213f	6af multi, imperf	5.00	5.00

Nos. 671E-671J are airmail. Nos. 671-671D
exist imperf. Value, each 20¢.

A213g

UN Day: 5p, 10p, 2af, 3af, 4af, Doctor and
nurse, vert.

1964, Mar. 9　　　　　Perf. 14
672	A213g	2p multicolored	.25	.25
672A	A213g	3p multicolored	.25	.25
672B	A213g	4p multicolored	.25	.25
672C	A213g	5p multicolored	.25	.25
672D	A213g	10p multicolored	.25	.25
672E	A213g	100p multicolored	.65	.65
672F	A213g	2af multicolored	1.20	1.20
672G	A213g	3af multicolored	1.75	1.75
	Nos. 672-672G (8)		4.85	4.85

Souvenir Sheets
672H	A213g	4af multi, imperf.	14.50	14.50
672I	A213g	5af multi	3.25	3.25

Nos. 672E-672G are airmail.
Nos. 672-672G exist imperf. Value set,
unused or used, $20.
For surcharges see Nos. B71A-B71J.

UNICEF
— A213h

Design: 5af, 7.50af, 10af, Children eating.

Perf. 14x13½, Imperf. (150p, 250p,
10af)
1964, Mar. 15
673	A213h	100p multi	.30	.30
673A	A213h	150p multi	1.75	1.75
673B	A213h	200p multi	.65	.65
673C	A213h	250p multi	3.00	3.00
673D	A213h	5af multi	1.50	1.50
673E	A213h	7.50af multi	2.40	2.40
673F	A213h	10af multi	12.50	12.50
	Nos. 673-673F (7)		22.10	22.10

Nos. 673D-673F are airmail.

Eradication of Malaria — A213i

4p, 5p, 5af, 10af Spraying mosquitoes.

1964, Mar. 15 — **Perf. 13½**
674 A213i 2p lt red brn & yel grn .25 .25
674A A213i 3p olive grn & buff .25 .25
674B A213i 4p dk vio & bl grn .25 .25
674C A213i 5p brn & grn .25 .25
674D A213i 2af Prus bl & ver .65 .30
  h. Souvenir sheet of 1 4.75 4.75
674E A213i 5af dk grn & lt red brn, imperf. 5.25 5.25
  i. Souv. sheet of 1, imperf. 14.50 14.50
674F A213i 10af red brn & grnsh bl 2.75 1.75
  Nos. 674-674F (7) 9.65 8.30

Stamp Like No. 674B Surcharged in Black

674G A213i 10p on 4p Prus bl & rose .90 .25

No. 674G not issued without surcharge. Nos. 674D-674F are airmail. Nos. 674-674C, 674G exist imperf. Values, each $2.75.

"Tiger's Head" of 1878 — A214

1964, Mar. 22 — **Photo.** — **Perf. 12**
675 A214 1.25af gold, grn & blk .25 .25
676 A214 5af gold, rose car & blk .55 .35

Issued to honor philately.

Unisphere and Flags A215

1964, May 3 — **Perf. 13½x14**
677 A215 6af crimson, gray & grn .25 .25
New York World's Fair, 1964-65.

Hand Holding Torch — A216

1964, May 12 Photo. Perf. 14x13½
678 A216 3.75af multicolored .25 .25

1st UN Seminar on Human Rights in Kabul, May 1964. The denomination in Persian at right erroneously reads "3.25" but the stamp was sold and used as 3.75af.

Kandahar Airport A217

1964, Apr. Litho. Perf. 10½, 11
679 A217 7.75af dk red brown .65 .40
680 A217 9.25af lt blue .90 .80
681 A217 10.50af lt green 1.10 .95
682 A217 13.75af carmine rose 1.40 1.00
  Nos. 679-682 (4) 4.05 3.15
Inauguration of Kandahar Airport.

Snow Leopard A218

50p, Ibex, vert. 75p, Head of argali. 5af, Yak.

1964, June 25 Photo. Perf. 12
683 A218 25p yellow & blue 1.75 .25
684 A218 50p dl red & grn 2.00 .25
685 A218 75p Prus bl & lil 2.40 .25
686 A218 5af brt grn & dk brn 2.50 .90
  Nos. 683-686 (4) 8.65 1.65

View of Herat A219

Flag and Map of Afghanistan A220

Tourist publicity: 75p, Tomb of Queen Gowhar Shad, vert.

1964, July 12 Perf. 13½x14, 14x13½
687 A219 25p sepia & bl .25 .25
688 A219 75p dp blue & buff .30 .25
689 A220 3af red, blk & grn .55 .25
  Nos. 687-689 (3) 1.10 .75

Wrestling A221

25p, Hurdling, vert. 1af, Diving, vert. 5af, Soccer.

1964, July 26 Perf. 12
690 A221 25p ol bis, blk & car .25 .25
691 A221 1af bl grn, blk & car .25 .25
692 A221 3.75af yel grn, blk & car .40 .25
693 A221 5af brn, blk & car .50 .30
  a. Souv. sheet, #690-693, imperf. 1.25 1.25
  Nos. 690-693 (4) 1.40 1.05

18th Olympic Games, Tokyo, Oct. 10-25, 1964. No. 693a sold for 15af. The additional 5af went to the Afghanistan Olympic Committee.

Flag and Outline of Nadir Shah's Tomb — A222

1964, Aug. 24 Photo.
695 A222 25p multicolored .25 .25
696 A222 75p multicolored .30 .25

Independence Day. The stamps are printed with an erroneous inscription in upper left corner: "33rd year of independence." This was locally obliterated on all stamps with a typographed gold bar. Value for set with gold bar omitted, $10.

Pashtunistan Flag — A223

1964, Sept. 1 Unwmk.
697 A223 100p gold, blk, red, bl & grn .55 .25
Issued for "Free Pashtunistan Day."

Zahir Shah — A225

1964, Oct. 17 Perf. 14x13½
699 A225 1.25af gold & yel grn .25 .25
700 A225 3.75af gold & rose .40 .40
701 A225 50af gold & gray 3.50 2.25
  Nos. 699-701 (3) 4.15 2.90
King Mohammed Zahir Shah, 50th birthday.

Coat of Arms of Afghanistan and UN Emblem A226

1964, Oct. 24 Perf. 13½x14
702 A226 5af gold, blk & dl bl .25 .25
Issued for United Nations Day.

Emblem of Afghanistan Women's Association A227

1964, Nov. 9 Photo. Unwmk.
703 A227 25p pink, dk bl & emer .55 .30
704 A227 75p aqua, dk bl & emer .85 .40
705 A227 1af sil, dk bl & emer 1.10 .50
  Nos. 703-705 (3) 2.50 1.20
Issued for Women's Day.

Poet Mowlana Nooruddin Abdul Rahman Jami (1414-1492) A228

Perf. 11 Rough
1964, Nov. 23 Litho.
706 A228 1.50af blk, emer & yel .95 .95
No. 706 also exists clean-cut perf 10½.

Woodpecker A229

Birds: 3.75af, Black-throated jay, vert. 5af, Impeyan pheasant, vert.

Perf. 13½x14, 14x13½
1965, Apr. 20 Photo. Unwmk.
707 A229 1.25af multi 2.25 .40
708 A229 3.75af multi 4.90 .85
709 A229 5af multi 5.50 1.75
  Nos. 707-709 (3) 12.65 3.00

ITU Emblem, Old and New Communication Equipment — A230

1965, May 17 Perf. 13½x14
710 A230 5af lt bl, blk & red .50 .35
Cent. of the ITU.

"Red City," Bamian — A231

Designs: 3.75af, Ruins of ancient Bamian city. 5af, Bande Amir, mountain lakes.

1965, May 30 Perf. 13x13½
711 A231 1.25af pink & multi .40 .25
712 A231 3.75af lt blue & multi .65 .25
713 A231 5af yellow & multi .95 .25
  Nos. 711-713 (3) 2.00 .75
Issued for tourist publicity.

ICY Emblem A232

1965, June 25 Perf. 13½x13
714 A232 5af multicolored .50 .30
International Cooperation Year, 1965.

ARIANA Air Lines Emblem and DC-3 A233

5af, Airplane at right. 10af, Airplane on top.

Perf. 13½x14
1965, July 15 Photo. Unwmk.
715 A233 1.25af brt bl, gray & blk .30 .25
716 A233 5af red lil, blk & bl .90 .25
717 A233 10af bis, blk, bl gray & grn 1.50 .55
  a. Souv. sheet, #715-717, imperf 3.00 3.00
  Nos. 715-717 (3) 2.70 1.05
10th anniv. of Afghan Air Lines, ARIANA.

Nadir Shah — A234

1965, Aug. 23 Perf. 14x13½
718 A234 1af dl grn, blk & red brn .40 .25
For the 47th Independence Day.

Flag of Pashtunistan — A235

Perf. 13½x14
1965, Aug. 31   Photo.   Unwmk.
719 A235 1af multicolored   .40   .25
Issued for "Free Pashtunistan Day."

Zahir Shah Signing
Constitution — A236

1965, Sept. 11   Perf. 13x13½
720 A236 1.50af brt grn & blk   .40   .25
Promulgation of the new Constitution.

Zahir Shah and Oak
Leaves — A237

1965, Oct. 14   Perf. 14x13½
721 A237 1.25af blk, ultra & salmon   .25 .25
722 A237 6af blk, lt bl & rose lil   .40 .35
King Mohammed Zahir Shah, 51st birthday.

Flags of UN and
Afghanistan
A238

1965, Oct. 24   Perf. 13½x14
723 A238 5af multicolored   .25   .25
Issued for United Nations Day.

Dappled
Ground
Gecko
A239

Designs: 4af, Caucasian agamid (lizard).
8af, Horsfield's tortoise.

Perf. 13½x14
1966, May 10   Photo.   Unwmk.
724 A239 3af tan & multi   .90   .25
725 A239 4af brt grn & multi   1.10   .30
726 A239 8af violet & multi   1.75   .65
   Nos. 724-726 (3)   3.75 1.20

Soccer Player and
Globe — A240

1966, July 31   Litho.   Perf. 14x13½
727 A240 2af rose red & blk   .60   .25
728 A240 6af violet bl & blk   1.00   .30
729 A240 12af bister brn & blk   1.60   .60
   Nos. 727-729 (3)   3.20 1.15
World Cup Soccer Championship, Wembley, England, July 11-30.

Cotton
Flower and
Boll — A241

5af, Silkworm. 7af, Farmer plowing with oxen.

1966, July 31   Perf. 13½x14
730 A241 1af multicolored   .85   .25
731 A241 5af multicolored   1.60   .30
732 A241 7af multicolored   2.50   .50
   Nos. 730-732 (3)   4.95 1.05
Issued for the Day of Agriculture.

Independence Monument — A242

1966, Aug. 23   Photo.   Perf. 13½x14
733 A242 1af multicolored   .30   .25
734 A242 3af multicolored   .85   .30
Issued to commemorate Independence Day.

Flag of Pashtunistan — A243

Perf. 11 Rough
1966, Aug. 31   Litho.
735 A243 1af bright blue   .50   .25
"Free Pashtunistan Day."

Bagh-i-Bala
Park Casino
A244

Tourist publicity: 2af, Map of Afghanistan. 8af, Tomb of Abd-er-Rahman. The casino on 4af is the former summer palace of Abd-er-Rahman near Kabul.

1966, Oct. 3   Photo.   Perf. 13½x14
736 A244 2af red & multi   .40   .25
737 A244 4af multicolored   .80   .35
738 A244 8af multicolored   1.20   .80
   a.   Souvenir sheet of 3, #736-738,
        imperf.   3.50 3.50
   Nos. 736-738 (3)   2.40 1.40

Zahir
Shah — A245

1966, Oct. 14   Perf. 14x13½
739 A245 1af dk slate grn   .25   .25
740 A245 5af red brown   .55   .30
King Mohammed Zahir Shah, 52nd birthday. See Nos. 760-761.

UNESCO
Emblem — A246

1967, Mar. 6   Litho.   Perf. 12
741 A246 2af multicolored   .30   .25
742 A246 6af multicolored   .40   .25
743 A246 9af multicolored   .90   .25
   Nos. 741-743 (3)   1.60   .75
20th anniv. of UNESCO.

Zahir Shah
and UN
Emblem
A247

1967   Photo.
744 A247 5af multicolored   .40   .25
745 A247 10af multicolored   .80   .30
UN Intl. Org. for Refugees, 20th anniv.

New Power
Station
A248

5af, Carpet, vert. 8af, Cement factory.

1967, Jan. 7   Photo.   Perf. 13½x14
746 A248 2af red lil & ol grn   .30   .25
747 A248 5af multicolored   .30   .25
748 A248 8af blk, dk bl & tan   .60   .30
   Nos. 746-748 (3)   1.20   .80
Issued to publicize industrial development.

International
Tourist Year
Emblem
A249

Designs: 6af, International Tourist Year emblem and map of Afghanistan.

1967, May 11   Photo.   Perf. 12
749 A249 2af yel, blk & lt bl   .40   .25
750 A249 6af bis brn, blk & lt bl .65   .25
   a.   Souv. sheet of #749-750, imperf 2.00 1.25
Intl. Tourist Year, 1967. No. 750a sold for 10af.

Power Dam,
Dorunta
A250

6af, Sirobi Dam, vert. 8af, Reservoir at Jalalabad.

1967, July 2   Photo.   Perf. 12
751 A250 1af dk green & lil   .40   .25
752 A250 6af red brn & grnsh bl   .80   .25
753 A250 8af plum & dk bl   1.20   .40
   Nos. 751-753 (3)   2.40   .90
Progress in agriculture through electricity.

Macaque — A251

Designs: 6af, Striped hyena, horiz. 12af, Persian gazelles, horiz.

1967, July 28   Photo.   Perf. 12
754 A251 2af dull yel & indigo   .75   .25
755 A251 6af lt green & sepia   1.50   .30
756 A251 12af lt bl & red brn   2.25   .80
   Nos. 754-756 (3)   4.50 1.35

Pashtun
Dancers
A252

1967, Sept. 1   Photo.   Perf. 12
757 A252 2af magenta & violet   .70   .25
Issued for "Free Pashtunistan Day."

Retreat of
British at
Maiwand
A253

1967, Aug. 24
758 A253 1af dk brn & org ver   .40   .25
759 A253 2af dk brn & brt pink   .80   .25
Issued to commemorate Independence Day.

King Type of 1966
1967, Oct. 15   Photo.   Perf. 14x13½
760 A245 2af brown red   .25   .25
761 A245 8af dark blue   .65   .30
Issued to honor King Mohammed Zahir Shah on his 53rd birthday.

Fireworks and UN
Emblem — A254

1967, Oct. 24   Litho.   Perf. 12
762 A254 10af violet bl & multi   .70   .40
Issued for United Nations Day.

Greco-Roman
Wrestlers
A255

Design: 6af, Free style wrestlers.

1967, Nov. 20   Photo.
763 A255 4af ol grn & rose lil   .40   .25
764 A255 6af dp carmine & brn   .85   .25
   a.   Souv. sheet of #763-764, imperf 1.75 1.75
1968 Olympic Games.

Said Jamalluddin
Afghan — A256

1967, Nov. 27
765 A256 1af magenta .25 .25
766 A256 5af brown .40 .25
Said Jamalluddin Afghan, politician (1839-97).

Bronze Vase, 11th-12th
Centuries — A257

Design: 7af, Bronze vase, Ghasnavide era, 11th-12th centuries.

1967, Dec. 23   Photo.   Perf. 12
767 A257 3af lt green & brn .55 .25
768 A257 7af yel & slate grn 1.00 1.00
  a. Souv. sheet, #767-768, imperf 2.75 2.75

WHO Emblem
A258

1968, Apr. 7   Photo.   Perf. 12
769 A258 2af citron & brt bl .25 .25
770 A258 7af rose & brt bl .40 .30
20th anniv. of the WHO.

Karakul
A259

1968, May 20   Photo.   Perf. 12
771 A259 1af yellow & blk .25 .25
772 A259 6af lt blue & blk .85 .30
773 A259 12af ultra & dk brn 1.25 .50
  Nos. 771-773 (3) 2.35 1.05
Issued for the Day of Agriculture.

Map of
Afghanistan
A260

Victory Tower,
Ghazni — A261

Design: 16af, Mausoleum, Ghazni.

1968, June 3   Perf. 13½x14, 12
774 A260 2af red, blk, lt bl &
       grn .35 .25
775 A261 3af yel, dk brn & lt bl .45 .25
776 A261 16af pink & multi 1.50 .50
  Nos. 774-776 (3) 2.30 1.00
Issued for tourist publicity.

Cinereous
Vulture — A262

6af, Eagle owl. 7af, Greater flamingoes.

1968, July 3   Perf. 12
777 A262 1af sky blue & multi 1.75 .65
778 A262 6af yellow & multi 4.00 2.00
779 A262 7af multicolored 6.00 2.25
  Nos. 777-779 (3) 11.75 4.90

Game of
"Pegsticking"
A263

2af, Olympic flame & rings, vert. 12af, Buzkashi.

1968, July 20   Photo.   Perf. 12
780 A263 2af multicolored .35 .25
781 A263 8af orange & multi .50 .35
782 A263 12af multicolored 1.00 .60
  Nos. 780-782 (3) 1.85 1.20
19th Olympic Games, Mexico City, 10/12-27.

Flower-decked
Armored
Car — A264

1968, Aug. 23
783 A264 6af multicolored .60 .25
Issued to commemorate Independence Day.

Flag of
Pashtunistan
A265

1968 Aug. 31   Photo.   Perf. 12
784 A265 3af multicolored .35 .25
Issued for "Free Pashtunistan Day."

Zahir Shah — A266

1968, Oct. 14   Photo.   Perf. 12
785 A266 2af ultra .25 .25
786 A266 8af brown .55 .30
King Mohammed Zahir Shah, 54th birthday.

Human Rights
Flame — A267

1968, Oct. 24
787 A267 1af multicolored .25 .25
788 A267 2af violet, bis & blk .25 .25
789 A267 6af vio blk, bis & vio .60 .25
  Nos. 787-789 (3) 1.10 .75

Souvenir Sheet
Imperf
790 A267 10af plum, bis & red
       org 1.75 1.75
International Human Rights Year.

Maolana Djalalodine
Balkhi — A268

1968, Nov. 26   Photo.   Perf. 12
791 A268 4af dk green & mag .35 .25
Balkhi (1207-73), historian.

Kushan
Mural — A269

Design: 3af, Jug shaped like female torso.

1969, Jan. 2   Perf. 12
792 A269 1af dk grn, mar & yel .55 .25
793 A269 3af violet, gray & mar 1.20 .25
  a. Souv. sheet, #792-793, imperf 2.40 1.75
Archaeological finds at Bagram, 1st cent. B.C. to 2nd cent. A.D.

ILO
Emblem
A270

1969, Mar. 23   Photo.   Perf. 12
794 A270 5af lt yel, lemon & blk .30 .25
795 A270 8af lt bl, grnsh bl & blk .55 .30
50th anniv. of the ILO.

Arms Type of 1939
Rough Perf. 11
1969, May (?)   Typo.
795A A79 100p dark green .40 .25
795B A79 150p deep brown .55 .25
  Nos. 795A-795B were normally used as newspaper stamps.

Badakhshan
Scene
A271

Tourist Publicity: 2af, Map of Afghanistan. 7af, Three men on mules ascending the Pamir Mountains.

1969, July 6   Photo.   Perf. 13½x14
796 A271 2af ocher & multi .70 .25
797 A271 4af multicolored .90 .30
798 A271 7af multicolored 1.40 .65
  a. Souv. sheet, #796-798, imperf 3.00 2.40
  Nos. 796-798 (3) 3.00 1.20
No. 798a sold for 15af.

Bust, from Hadda
Treasure, 3rd-5th
Centuries — A272

Designs: 5af, Vase and jug. 10af, Statue of crowned woman. 5af and 10af from Bagram treasure, 1st-2nd centuries.

1969, Aug. 3   Photo.   Perf. 14x13½
799 A272 1af olive grn & gold .40 .25
800 A272 5af purple & gold .70 .25
801 A272 10af dp blue & gold 1.10 .30
  Nos. 799-801 (3) 2.20 .80

Zahir Shah and
Queen
Humeira — A273

1969, Aug. 23   Perf. 12
802 A273 5af gold, dk bl & red
       brn .45 .25
803 A273 10af gold, dp lil & bl
       grn .80 .40
Issued to commemorate Independence Day.

Map of
Pashtunistan
and Rising
Sun — A274

1969, Aug. 31   Typo.   Perf. 10½
804 A274 2af lt blue & red .40 .25
Issued for "Free Pashtunistan Day."

Zahir
Shah — A275

1969, Oct. 14   Photo.   Perf. 12
Portrait in Natural Colors
805 A275 2af dk brown & gold .25 .25
806 A275 6af brown & gold .55 .25
King Mohammed Zahir Shah, 55th birthday.

UN Emblem and Flag of
Afghanistan — A276

1969, Oct. 24   Litho.   Perf. 13½
807 A276 5af blue & multi .30 .25
Issued for United Nations Day.

ITU
Emblem — A277

1969, Nov. 12
808 A277 6af ultra & multi .30 .25
809 A277 12af rose & multi .70 .40
Issued for World Telecommunications Day.

Crested Porcupine A278

1af, Long-tailed porcupine. 8af, Red deer.

1969, Dec. 7   Photo.   Perf. 12
810 A278 1af yellow & multi .50 .30
811 A278 3af blue & multi 1.10 .50
812 A278 8af pink & multi 2.00 1.00
    Nos. 810-812 (3) 3.60 1.80

Man's First Footprints on Moon, and Earth — A279

1969, Dec. 28   Perf. 13½x14
813 A279 1af yel grn & multi .25 .25
814 A279 3af yellow & multi .30 .25
815 A279 6af blue & multi .45 .25
816 A279 10af rose & multi .60 .40
    Nos. 813-816 (4) 1.60 1.15

Moon landing. See note after Algeria No. 427.

Anti-cancer Symbol — A280

1970, Apr. 7   Photo.   Perf. 14
817 A280 2af dk grn & rose car .25 .25
818 A280 6af dk bl & rose claret .50 .25
Issued to publicize the fight against cancer.

Mirza Abdul Quader Bedel — A281

1970, May 6   Perf. 14x13½
819 A281 5af multicolored .40 .25

Mirza Abdul Quader Bedel (1643-1720), poet.

Education Year Emblem — A282

1970, June 7   Photo.   Perf. 12
820 A282 1af black .25 .25
821 A282 6af deep rose .30 .25
822 A282 12af green .75 .40
    Nos. 820-822 (3) 1.30 .90
International Education Year 1970.

Mother and Child — A283

1970, June 15   Perf. 13½
823 A283 6af yellow & multi .30 .25
Issued for Mother's Day.

UN Emblem, Scales of Justice, Spacecraft A284

1970, June 26
824 A284 4af yel, dk bl & dp bl .25 .25
825 A284 6af pink, dk bl & brt bl .35 .25
25th anniversary of United Nations.

Mosque of the Amir of the two Swords, Kabul A285

2af, Map of Afghanistan. 7af, Arch of Paghman.

1970, July 6   Perf. 12
    Size: 30½x30½mm
826 A285 2af lt bl, blk & citron .30 .25
    Size: 36x26mm
827 A285 3af pink & multi .50 .25
828 A285 7af yellow & multi .95 .25
    Nos. 826-828 (3) 1.75 .75
Issued for tourist publicity.

Zahir Shah Reviewing Troops — A286

1970, Aug. 23   Photo.   Perf. 13½
829 A286 8af multicolored .40 .25
Issued to commemorate Independence Day.

Pathans — A287

1970, Aug. 31   Typo.   Perf. 10½
830 A287 2af ultra & red .40 .25
Issued for "Free Pashtunistan Day."

Quail — A288

4af, Golden eagle. 6af, Ringnecked pheasant.

1970, Sept.   Photo.   Perf. 12
831 A288 2af multicolored 2.10 .65
832 A288 4af multicolored 4.00 .95
833 A288 6af multicolored 5.25 1.60
    Nos. 831-833 (3) 11.35 3.20

Zahir Shah — A289

1970, Oct. 14   Photo.   Perf. 14x13½
834 A289 3af green & vio .25 .25
835 A289 7af dk bl & vio brn .70 .30
King Mohammed Zahir Shah, 56th birthday.

Red Crescents A290

1970, Oct. 16   Typo.   Perf. 10½
836 A290 2af black, gold & red .30 .25
Issued for the Red Crescent Society.

UN Emblem and Charter A291

1970, Oct. 24   Photo.   Perf. 14
837 A291 1af gold & multi .25 .25
838 A291 5af gold & multi .30 .25
United Nations Day.

Tiger Heads of 1871 — A292

1970, Nov. 10   Perf. 12
839 A292 1af sal, lt grnsh bl & blk .30 .25
840 A292 4af lt ultra, yel & blk .55 .25
841 A292 12af lilac, lt bl & blk .95 .40
    Nos. 839-841 (3) 1.80 .90
Cent. of the 1st Afghan postage stamps. The postal service was established in 1870, but the 1st stamps were issued in May, 1871.

Globe and Waves A293

1971, May 17   Photo.   Perf. 13½
842 A293 12af green, blk & bl .70 .40
3rd World Telecommunications Day.

Callimorpha Principalis A294

Designs: 3af, Epizygaenella species. 5af, Parnassius autocrator.

1971, May 30   Perf. 13½x14
843 A294 1af vermilion & multi 1.25 .55
844 A294 3af yellow & multi 2.50 1.10
845 A294 5af ultra & multi 3.50 1.75
    Nos. 843-845 (3) 7.25 3.40

"UNESCO" and Half of Ancient Kushan Statue — A295

1971, June 26   Photo.   Perf. 13½
846 A295 6af ocher & vio .50 .25
847 A295 10af lt blue & mar .80 .35
UNESCO-sponsored Intl. Kushani Seminar.

Tughra and Independence Monument — A296

1971, Aug. 23
848 A296 7af rose red & multi .55 .25
849 A296 9af red orange & multi .90 .35
Independence Day.

Pashtunistan Square, Kabul — A297

1971, Aug. 31   Typo.   Perf. 10½
850 A297 5af deep rose lilac .50 .25
"Free Pashtunistan Day."

Zahir Shah — A298

1971, Oct. 14   Photo.   Perf. 12½x12
851 A298 9af lt green & multi   .55   .30
852 A298 17af yellow & multi   1.10   .65

King Mohammed Zahir Shah, 57th birthday.

A299

Design: Map of Afghanistan, red crescent, various activities.

1971, Oct. 16   Perf. 14x13½
853 A299 8af lt bl, red, grn & blk   .50   .30

For Afghan Red Crescent Society.

Equality Year Emblem A300

1971, Oct. 24   Perf. 12
854 A300 24af brt blue   1.50   .80

International Year Against Racial Discrimination and United Nations Day.

"Your Heart is your Health" — A301

1972, Apr. 7   Photo.   Perf. 14
855 A301 9af pale yel & multi   .90   .30
856 A301 12af gray & multi   1.75   .40

World Health Day.

Tulip — A302

Designs: 10af, Rock partridge, horiz. 12af, Lynx, horiz. 18af, Allium stipitatum (flower).

1972, June 5   Photo.   Perf. 14
857 A302 7af green & multi   1.25   .70
858 A302 10af blue & multi   7.50 1.60
859 A302 12af lt green & multi   2.40 1.25
860 A302 18af blue grn & multi   2.40 1.40
     Nos. 857-860 (4)   13.55 4.95

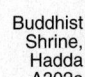

Buddhist Shrine, Hadda A302a

Designs: 7af, Greco-Bactrian animal seal, 250 B.C. 9af, Greco-Oriental temple, Ai-Khanoum, 3rd-2nd centuries B.C.

1972, July 16   Photo.   Perf. 12
861 A302a 3af brown & dl bl   .65   .25
862 A302a 7af rose claret & dl
            grn   .95   .30
863 A302a 9af green & lilac   1.40   .40
     Nos. 861-863 (3)   3.00   .95

Tourist publicity.

King and Queen Reviewing Parade — A303

1972, Aug. 23   Photo.   Perf. 13½
864 A303 25af gold & multi   4.50 1.25

Independence Day.
Used as a provisional in 1978 with king and queen portion removed.

Wrestling A304

10af, 19af, 21af, Wrestling, different hold.

1972, Aug. 26
865 A304 4af ol bis & multi   .25   .25
866 A304 8af lt blue & multi   .45   .25
867 A304 10af yel grn & multi   .60   .30
868 A304 19af multicolored   1.20   .45
869 A304 21af lilac & multi   1.25   .50
     a. Souv. sheet, #865-869, imperf 3.25 3.25
     Nos. 865-869 (5)   3.75 1.75

20th Olympic Games, Munich, Aug. 26-Sept. 11. No. 869a sold for 60af.

Pathan and View of Tribal Territory — A305

1972, Aug. 31   Perf. 12½x12
870 A305 5af ultra & multi   .50   .25

Pashtunistan day.

Zahir Shah — A306

1972, Oct. 14   Photo.   Perf. 14x13½
871 A306 7af gold, blk & Prus bl   .65   .25
872 A306 14af gold, blk & lt brn   1.00   .40

58th birthday of King Mohammed Zahir Shah.

City Destroyed by Earthquake, Refugees — A307

1972, Oct. 16   Perf. 13½
873 A307 7af lt bl, red & blk   .60   .25

For Afghan Red Crescent Society.

UN Emblem A308

1972, Oct. 24
874 A308 12af lt ultra & blk   .60   .30

UN Economic Commission for Asia and the Far East (ECAFE), 25th anniv.

Ceramics A309

Designs: 9af, Leather coat, vert. 12af, Metal ware, vert. 16af, Inlaid artifacts.

1972, Dec. 10   Photo.   Perf. 12
875 A309 7af gold & multi   .40   .25
876 A309 9af gold & multi   .65   .30
877 A309 12af gold & multi   .70   .35
878 A309 16af gold & multi   1.00   .45
     a. Souv. sheet, #875-878, imperf 3.50 3.50
     Nos. 875-878 (4)   2.75 1.35

Handicraft industries. No. 878a sold for 45af.

WMO and National Emblems — A310

1973, Apr. 3   Photo.   Perf. 14
879 A310 7af lt lil & dk grn   .55   .25
880 A310 14af lt bl & dp claret   1.40   .40

Cent. of intl. meteorological cooperation.

Abu Rayhan al-Biruni — A311

1973, June 16   Photo.   Perf. 13½
881 A311 10af multicolored   .50   .40

Millennium of birth (973-1048), philosopher and mathematician.

Family — A312

1973, June 30   Photo.   Perf. 13½
882 A312 9af orange & red lil   .65   .25

Intl. Family Planning Fed., 21st anniv.

Republic

Impeyan Pheasant A313

Birds: 9af, Great crested grebe. 12af, Himalayan snow cock.

1973, July 29   Photo.   Perf. 12x12½
883 A313 8af yellow & multi   2.75 1.75
884 A313 9af blue & multi   3.25 2.25
885 A313 12af multicolored   4.00 3.00
     Nos. 883-885 (3)   10.00 7.00

Stylized Buzkashi Horseman A314

1973, Aug.   Perf. 13½
886 A314 8af black   .55   .30

Tourist publicity.

Fireworks A315

1973, Aug. 23   Photo.   Perf. 12
887 A315 12af multicolored   .60   .30

55th Independence Day.

Lake Abassine, Pashtunistan Flag — A316

1973, Aug. 31   Perf. 14x13½
888 A316 9af multicolored   .55   .25

Pashtunistan Day.

Red Crescent
A317

1973, Oct. 16   **Perf. 13½**
889 A317 10af red, blk & gold   .90   .25
Red Crescent Society.

Kemal
Ataturk
A318

1973, Oct. 28   **Litho.**   **Perf. 10½**
890 A318 1af blue   .25   .25
891 A318 7af reddish brown   1.10   .25
50th anniversary of the Turkish Republic.

Human
Rights
Flame,
Arms of
Afghanistan
A319

1973, Dec. 10   **Photo.**   **Perf. 12**
892 A319 12af sil, blk & lt bl   .45   .35
25th anniversary of the Universal Declaration of Human Rights.

Asiatic
Black
Bears
A320

1974, Mar. 26   **Litho.**   **Perf. 12**
893 A320   5af shown   .65   .25
894 A320   7af Afghan hound   1.00   .40
895 A320 10af Persian goat   1.40   .50
896 A320 12af Leopard   1.75   .55
   a.   Souv. sheet, #893-896, imperf   10.00   10.00
    Nos. 893-896 (4)   4.80   1.70

Worker and
Farmer
A321

1974, May 1   **Photo.**   **Perf. 13½x12½**
897 A321 9af rose red & multi   .60   .30
International Labor Day, May 1.

Independence Monument and
Arch — A322

1974, May 27   **Photo.**   **Perf. 12**
898 A322   4af blue & multi   .40   .25
899 A322 11af gold & multi   .55   .25
56th Independence Day.

Arms of Afghanistan and Symbol of
Cooperation — A323

Pres. Mohammad
Daoud
Khan — A324

5af, Flag of Republic of Afghanistan. 15af, Soldiers, coat of arms of the Republic.

Sizes: 4af, 15af, 36x22mm; 5af, 7af, 36x26, 26x36mm

1974, July 25   **Perf. 13½x12½, 14**
900 A323   4af multicolored   .40   .25
901 A323   5af multicolored   .55   .25
902 A324   7af green, brn & blk   .65   .25
   a.   Souv. sheet, #901-902, imperf   1.75   1.75
903 A323 15af multicolored   1.25   .30
   a.   Souv. sheet, #900, 903, imperf   2.00   2.00
    Nos. 900-903 (4)   2.85   1.05
1st anniv. of the Republic of Afghanistan.

Lesser
Spotted
Eagle
A325

Birds: 6af, White-fronted goose, ruddy shelduck and gray-lag goose. 11af, European coots and European crane.

1974, Aug. 6   **Photo.**   **Perf. 13½x13**
904 A325   1af car rose & multi   2.00   .50
905 A325   6af blue & multi   4.50   .80
906 A325 11af yellow & multi   7.00   1.40
   a.   Strip of 3, #904-906   14.00   14.00

Flags of Pashtunistan and
Afghanistan — A326

1974, Aug. 31   **Photo.**   **Perf. 14**
907 A326 5af multicolored   .30   .25
Pashtunistan Day.

Coat of Arms — A326a

1974, Aug.   **Typo.**   **Rough Perf. 11**
907A A326a 100p green   4.00   .80

Coat of
Arms
A327

1974, Oct. 9
908 A327 7af gold, grn & blk   .30   .25
Centenary of Universal Postal Union.

"un" and
UN
Emblem
A328

1974, Oct. 24   **Photo.**   **Perf. 14**
909 A328 5af lt ultra & dk bl   .40   .25
United Nations Day.

Minaret of
Jam — A329

Buddha,
Hadda — A330

14af, Lady riding griffin, 2nd century, Bagram.

1975, May 5   **Photo.**   **Perf. 13½**
910 A329   7af multicolored   .40   .25
911 A330 14af multicolored   .75   .40
912 A330 15af multicolored   .95   .40
   a.   Souv. sheet, #910-912, imperf.   3.50   3.50
    Nos. 910-912 (3)   2.10   1.05
South Asia Tourism Year 1975.

New Flag
of
Afghanistan
A331

1975, May 27   **Photo.**   **Perf. 12**
913 A331 16af multicolored   .80   .25
57th Independence Day.

Celebrating Crowd — A332

1975, July 17   **Photo.**   **Perf. 13½**
914 A332   9af blue & multi   .50   .25
915 A332 12af carmine & multi   .65   .30
Second anniversary of the Republic.

Women's Year
Emblems
A333

1975, Aug. 24   **Photo.**   **Perf. 12**
916 A333 9af car, lt bl & blk   .50   .25
International Women's Year 1975.

Pashtunistan Flag,
Sun Rising Over
Mountains — A334

1975, Aug. 31   **Perf. 13½**
917 A334 10af multicolored   .40   .25
Pashtunistan Day.

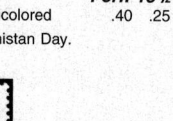

Mohammed
Akbar
Khan — A335

1976, Feb. 4   **Photo.**   **Perf. 14**
918 A335 15af lt brown & multi   .55   .40
Mohammed Akbar Khan (1816-1846), warrior son of Amir Dost Mohammed Khan.

A336

Pres. Mohammad
Daoud
Khan — A337

1974-78   **Photo.**   **Perf. 14**
919 A336   10af multi   .65   .25
920 A336   16af multi ('78)   2.40   .90
921 A336   19af multi   .90   .50
922 A336   21af multi   1.40   .55
923 A336   22af multi ('78)   3.50   1.90
924 A336   30af multi ('78)   4.75   2.75
925 A337   50af multi ('75)   2.75   1.40
926 A337 100af multi ('75)   5.50   2.40
    Nos. 919-926 (8)   21.85   10.65

Arms of Republic, Independence
Monument — A338

1976, June 1   Photo.   Perf. 14
927 A338 22af blue & multi   .70   .50
58th Independence Day.

Flag
Raising — A339

1976, July 17   Photo.   Perf. 14
928 A339 30af multicolored   .80   .55
Republic Day.

Mountain Peaks
and Flag of
Pashtunistan
A340

1976, Aug. 31   Photo.   Perf. 14
929 A340 16af multicolored   .65   .50
Pashtunistan Day.

Coat of
Arms
A340a

1976, Sept.   Litho.   Perf. 11 Rough
930 A340a 25p salmon   25.00   —
931 A340a 50p lt green   .55 .25
932 A340a 1af ultra   .55 .25
   Nos. 930-932 (3)   26.10 .50

Flag and
Views on
Open Book
A341

1977, May 27   Photo.   Perf. 14
937 A341 20af green & multi   .70   .60
59th Independence Day.

Pres. Daoud and National
Assembly — A342

President
Taking
Oath of
Office
A343

Designs: 10af, Inaugural address. 18af, Promulgation of Constitution.

1977, June 22
938 A342 7af multicolored   .80   .55
939 A343 8af multicolored   .90   .70
940 A343 10af multicolored   1.10   .90
941 A343 18af multicolored   1.90 1.50
  a. Souvenir sheet of 4   3.50 3.50
     Nos. 938-941 (4)   4.70 3.65

Election of 1st Pres. and promulgation of Constitution. No. 941a contains 4 imperf. stamps similar to Nos. 938-941.

Jamalluddin
Medal
A344

1977, July 6   Photo.   Perf. 14
942 A344 12af blue, blk & gold   .40   .30
Sajo Jamalluddin Afghani, reformer, 80th death anniversary.

Afghanistan Flag
over
Crowd — A345

1977, July 17
943 A345 22af multicolored   .70   .55

Dancers, Fountain, Pashtunistan
Flag — A346

1977, Aug. 31
944 A346 30af multicolored   1.10   .90
Pashtunistan Day.

Arms and
Carrier
Pigeon —
A346a

1977, Oct. 30   Litho.   Perf. 11
944A A346a 1af black & blue   5.00 2.50

Members of Parliament Congratulating
Pres. Daoud — A347

1978, Feb. 5   Litho.   Perf. 14
945 A347 20af multicolored   2.00 1.10
Election of first president, first anniversary.

Map of Afghanistan, UPU
Emblem — A348

1978, Apr. 1   Photo.   Perf. 14
946 A348 10af green, blk & gold   .40   .25
Afghanistan's UPU membership, 50th anniv.

Wall
Telephone
and
Satellite
Station
A349

1978, Apr. 12
947 A349 8af multicolored   .40   .25
Afghanistan's ITU membership, 50th anniv.

Democratic Republic

Arrows
Pointing to
Crescent,
Cross and
Lion — A350

1978, July 6   Litho.   Perf. 11 Rough
948 A350 3af black   1.25   .65
50th anniv. of Afghani Red Crescent Soc.

Khalq Party Emblem — A350a

1978, Aug.   Litho.   Perf. 11
948A A350a 1af rose red & gold   1.50   .65
948B A350a 4af rose red & gold   2.10   .90

Qalai Bist
Arch
A351

Hazara
Women —
A351a

16af, Bamian Buddha.

1978, Aug. 19   Perf. 14
949 A351 16af multicolored   1.25   .50
949A A351 22af shown   1.50   .65
949B A351a 30af shown   2.10 1.10
   Nos. 949-949B (3)   4.85 2.25

Men with
Pashtunistan
Flag — A352

1978, Aug. 31   Perf. 11 Rough
950 A352 7af ultra & red   .50   .25
Pashtunistan Day.

Coat of Arms
and Emblems
A353

1978, Sept. 8   Perf. 11
951 A353 20af rose red   .90   .40
World Literacy Day.

A354

Perf. 11½ Rough
1978, Oct. 25   Litho.
952 A354 18af light green   .95   .40
Hero of Afghanistan.

Khalq Party
Flag
A355

1978, Oct. 19   Photo.   Perf. 11½
953 A355 8af black, red & gold   .65   .25
954 A355 9af black, red & gold   .95   .25
"The mail serving the people."

Nour Mohammad Taraki — A356

1979, Jan. 1 Litho. *Perf. 12*
955 A356 12af multicolored .70 .25
Nour Mohammad Taraki, founder of People's Democratic Party of Afghanistan, installation as president.

Woman Breaking Chain — A357

1979, Mar. 8 Litho. *Perf. 11*
956 A357 14af red & ultra 1.25 .50
Women's Day. Inscribed "POSSTES."

Map of Afghanistan, Census Emblem — A358

1979, Mar. 25 Litho. *Perf. 12*
957 A358 3af multicolored .90 .70
First comprehensive population census.

Farmers A359

1979, Mar. 21
958 A359 1af multicolored .65 .30
Agricultural advances.

Pres. Taraki Reading First Issue of Khalq — A360

1979, Apr. 11 *Perf. 12½x12*
959 A360 2af multicolored .65 .25
Khalq, newspaper of People's Democratic Republic of Afghanistan.

Pres. Noor Mohammad Taraki A361

Plaza with Tank Monument and Fountain — A362

House where Revolution Started — A363

Designs: 50p, Taraki, tank. 12af, House where 1st Khalq Party Congress was held.

Perf. 12, 12½x12 (A362)
1979, Apr. 27 Litho.
959A A363 50p multicolored .65 .25
960 A361 4af multicolored .40 .25
961 A362 5af multicolored .55 .25
962 A363 6af multicolored .70 .25
963 A363 12af multicolored .80 .25
Nos. 959A-963 (5) 3.10 1.25
1st anniversary of revolution.

Carpenter and Blacksmith A364

1979, May 1 *Perf. 12*
964 A364 10af multicolored 1.10 .25
Int'l Labor Day.

Children, Flag and Map of Afghanistan — A366

1979, June 1 Litho. *Perf. 12½x12*
966 A366 16af multicolored 2.00 .90
International Year of the Child.

Doves Circling Asia in Globe A366a

1979 Litho. *Perf. 11x10½*
966A A366a 2af red & blue 1.25 .25

Armed Afghans, Kabul Memorial and Arch — A367

1979, Aug. 19 Litho. *Perf. 12*
967 A367 30af multicolored 1.50 .90
60th independence day.

Pashtunistan Citizens, Flag — A368

1979, Aug. 31
968 A368 9af multicolored .70 .25
Pashtunistan Day.

UPU Day A369

1979, Oct. 9 Litho. *Perf. 12*
969 A369 15af multicolored .65 .25

Tombstone — A369a

1979, Oct. 25 Litho. *Perf. 12½x12*
969A A369a 22af multicolored 2.40 1.25

International Women's Day — A370

1980, Mar. 8 Litho. *Perf. 12*
970 A370 8af multicolored 1.50 .50

Farmers' Day — A371

1980, Mar. 21 Litho. *Perf. 11½x12*
971 A371 2af multicolored 2.25 .70

Non-smoker and Smoker A372

1980, Apr. 7 *Perf. 11½*
972 A372 5af multicolored 1.75 .70
Anti-smoking campaign; World Health Day.

Lenin, 110th Birth Anniversary A373

1980, Apr. 22 *Perf. 12x12½*
973 A373 12af multicolored 2.50 .85

People and Fist on Map of Afghanistan — A374

1980, Apr. 27 Litho. *Perf. 12½x12*
974 A374 1af multicolored .70 .25
Saur Revolution, 2nd anniversary.

International Workers' Solidarity Day — A375

1980, May 1
975 A375 9af multicolored .50 .25

Wrestling, Moscow '80 Emblem A376

1980, July 19 *Perf. 12x12½, 12½x12*
976 A376 3af Soccer, vert. .60 .25
977 A376 6af shown .70 .25
978 A376 9af Buzkashi .80 .25
979 A376 10af Pegsticking .95 .25
Nos. 976-979 (4) 3.05 1.00
22nd Summer Olympic Games, Moscow, July 19-Aug. 3.

61st Anniversary of Independence — A377

1980, Aug. 19 Litho. Perf. 12½x12
980 A377 3af multicolored .85 .25

Pashtunistan Day — A378

1980, Aug. 30
981 A378 25af multicolored 1.00 .45

Intl. UPU Day A379

1980, Oct. 9 Litho. Perf. 12½x12
982 A379 20af multicolored 1.00 .45

The resistance group headed by Amin Wardak released some stamps in 1980. Some of these are inscribed "WARDAK AFGHANISTAN," others "Solidarite Internationale Avec la Resistance Afghane." The status of these labels is questionable.

International Women's Day — A381

1981, Mar. 9 Litho. Perf. 12½x12
984 A381 15af multicolored 1.25 .35

Farmers' Day — A382

1981, Mar. 20 Litho. Perf. 12½x12
985 A382 1af multicolored 1.00 .25

Bighorn Mountain Sheep (Protected Species) A383

1981, Apr. 4 Perf. 12x12½
986 A383 12af multicolored 2.40 .70

Saur Revolution, 3rd Anniversary A384

1981, Apr. 27 Perf. 11
987 A384 50p brown .70 .25

Intl. Workers' Solidarity Day — A385

1981, May 1 Perf. 12½x12
988 A385 10af multicolored .95 .35

13th World Telecommunications Day — A387

1981, May 17 Litho. Perf. 12½x12
990 A387 9af multicolored .70 .25

Intl. Children's Day — A388

1981, June 1 Perf. 12x12½
991 A388 15af multicolored .95 .45

People's Independence Monument 62nd Anniv. of Independence — A389

1981, Aug. 19
992 A389 4af multicolored 1.10 .30

Pashtunistan Day — A390

1981, Aug. 31 Litho. Perf. 12
992A A390 2af multicolored .70 .25

Intl. Tourism Day — A391

1981, Sept. 27 Perf. 12½x12
993 A391 5af multicolored .70 .25

World Food Day — A392

1981, Oct. 16
995 A392 7af multicolored .85 .25

Asia-Africa Solidarity Meeting — A393

1981, Nov. 18 Litho. Perf. 11
996 A393 8af blue .80 .25

Struggle Against Apartheid — A394

1981, Dec. 1 Perf. 12½x12
997 A394 4af multicolored 1.00 .25

1300th Anniv. of Bulgaria A395

1981, Dec. 9 Perf. 12x12½
998 A395 20af multicolored 1.75 .50

Buzkashi Game — A395a

1980 Photo. Perf. 14
998A A395a 50af multicolored 2.25 1.25
998B A395a 100af multicolored 4.50 1.75

Intl. Women's Day A396

1982, Mar. 8 Litho. Perf. 12
999 A396 6af multicolored .60 .25

Farmers' Day — A397

1982, Mar. 21
1000 A397 4af multicolored .70 .25

Judas Trees — A398

Designs: Various local plants.

1982, Apr. 9 Litho. Perf. 12
1001 A398 3af shown .40 .25
1002 A398 4af Rose of Sharon .70 .25
1003 A398 16af Rhubarb plant 1.60 .35
Nos. 1001-1003 (3) 2.70 .85

Saur Revolution, 4th Anniv. — A399

1982, Apr. 27
1004 A399 1af multicolored 1.50 .25

George Dimitrov (1882-1947), First Prime Minister of Bulgaria — A400

1982, Apr. 30
1005 A400 30af multicolored 2.40 .85

Intl. Workers' Solidarity Day A401

1982, May 1
1006 A401 10af multicolored　　　.85　.25

Storks — A402　　　Nightingales — A402a

1982, May 31
1007 A402　6af multicolored　　1.75　.50
1008 A402a 11af multicolored　　2.75　.60

Hedgehogs A403

1982, July 6　Litho.　Perf. 12
1009 A403　3af shown　　　　.75　.25
1010 A403 14af Cobra　　　　1.75　.25
See Nos. 1020-1022.

63rd Anniv. of Independence — A404

1982, Aug. 19
1011 A404 20af multicolored　　1.25　.50

Pashtunistan Day — A405

1982, Aug. 31
1012 A405 32af multicolored　　2.50　.75

World Tourism Day A406

1982, Sept. 27　Litho.　Perf. 12
1013 A406　9af multicolored　　.85　.35

UPU Day A407

1982, Oct. 9
1014 A407　4af multicolored　　.95　.25

World Food Day A408

1982, Oct. 16
1015 A408　9af multicolored　　1.50　.35

37th Anniv. of UN — A409

1982, Oct. 24
1016 A409 15af multicolored　　1.00　.45

ITU Plenipotentiaries Conference, Nairobi, Sept. — A410

1982, Oct. 26
1017 A410　8af multicolored　　.80　.25

TB Bacillus Centenary — A411

1982, Nov. 24　Litho.　Perf. 12
1018 A411　7af multicolored　　.50　.25

Human Rights Declaration, 34th Anniv. — A412

1982, Dec. 10
1019 A412　5af multicolored　　.45　.25

Animal Type of 1982
1982, Dec. 16
1020 A403　2af Lions　　　　.50　.25
1021 A403　7af Donkeys　　　1.00　.35
1022 A403 12af Marmots, vert.　2.25　.50
　　Nos. 1020-1022 (3)　　　3.75 1.10

Intl. Women's Day — A413

1983, Mar. 8
1023 A413　3af multicolored　　.25　.25

Mir Alicher Nawai Research Decade — A414

1983, Mar. 19
1024 A414 22af multicolored　　.95　.35

Farmers' Day A415

1983, Mar. 21　Litho.　Perf. 12
1025 A415 10af multicolored　　.75　.25

5th Anniv. of Saur Revolution A416

1983, Apr. 27　Litho.　Perf. 12
1026 A416 15af multicolored　　.70　.35

Intl. Workers' Solidarity Day — A417

1983, May 1
1027 A417　2af multicolored　　.70　.25

World Communications Year — A418

4af, Modes of communication. 11af, Building.

1983, May 17
1028 A418　4af multicolored　　.45　.25
1029 A418 11af multicolored　　.75　.25

Intl. Children's Day — A419

1983, June 1　Litho.　Perf. 12
1030 A419 25af multicolored　　.80　.35

2nd Anniv. of National Front — A420

1983, June 15
1031 A420　1af multicolored　　.35　.25

Local Butterflies A421

Various butterflies. 9af, 13af vert.

1983, July 6
1032 A421　9af multicolored　　1.10　.80
1033 A421 13af multicolored　　2.50 1.40
1034 A421 21af multicolored　　3.25 1.75
　　Nos. 1032-1034 (3)　　　6.85 3.95

Struggle Against Apartheid — A422

1983, Aug. 1　Litho.　Perf. 12
1035 A422 10af multicolored　　.55　.25

64th Anniv of Independence — A423

1983, Aug. 19
1036 A423　6af multicolored　　.45　.25

Parliament House — A423a

100af, Afghan Woman, Camel.

1983, Sept.　Litho.　Perf. 12
1036A A423a 50af shown　　　1.75　.35
1036B A423a 100af multi　　　4.25　.45

A424

World Tourism Day — A425

1983, Sept. 27   **Litho.**   **Perf. 12**
1037 A424 5af shown .45 .25
1038 A425 7af shown .60 .25
1039 A424 12af Golden statues .95 .25
1040 A425 16af Stone carving 1.25 .25
    Nos. 1037-1040 (4) 3.25 1.00

World Communications Year — A426

14af, Dish antenna, dove. 15af, Building, flag.

1983, Oct. 9   **Litho.**   **Perf. 12**
1041 A426 14af multicolored .90 .25
1042 A426 15af multicolored .90 .25

World Food Day — A427

1983, Oct. 16   **Litho.**   **Perf. 12**
1043 A427 14af multicolored .90 .25

Sports
A428

1983, Nov. 1   **Litho.**   **Perf. 12**
1044 A428 1af Soccer .25 .25
1045 A428 18af Boxing 1.00 .35
1046 A428 21af Wrestling 1.25 .35
    Nos. 1044-1046 (3) 2.50 .95

Pashtunistan Day
— A428a

3af, Pathans Waving Flag.

1983, Nov.   **Litho.**   **Perf. 12**
1046A A428a 3af multicolored .45 .25

Handicrafts
A429

2af, Jewelry. 8af, Stone ashtrays, dishes. 19af, Furniture. 30af, Leather goods.

1983, Nov. 22
1047 A429 2af multicolored .25 .25
1048 A429 8af multicolored .35 .25
1049 A429 19af multicolored .60 .25
1050 A429 30af multicolored 1.50 .40
    Nos. 1047-1050 (4) 2.70 1.15

UN
Declaration
of Human
Rights,
35th Anniv.
A430

1983, Dec. 10   **Litho.**   **Perf. 12**
1051 A430 20af multicolored .95 .25

Kabul Polytechnical Institute, 20th
Anniv. — A431

1983, Dec. 28   **Perf. 12½x12**
1052 A431 30af multicolored 1.25 .35

1984
Winter
Olympics
A432

1984, Jan.   **Perf. 12**
1053 A432 5af Figure skating .25 .25
1054 A432 9af Skiing .35 .25
1055 A432 11af Speed skating .50 .25
1056 A432 15af Hockey .60 .25
1057 A432 18af Biathlon .70 .25
1058 A432 20af Ski jumping .85 .25
1059 A432 22af Bobsledding 1.00 .25
    Nos. 1053-1059 (7) 4.25 1.75

Intl. Women's
Day — A433

1984, Mar. 8
1060 A433 4af multicolored .50 .25

Farmers'
Day
A434

Various agricultural scenes.

1984, Mar. 21   **Litho.**   **Perf. 12**
1061 A434 2af multicolored .25 .25
1062 A434 4af multicolored .25 .25
1063 A434 7af multicolored .25 .25
1064 A434 9af multicolored .25 .25
1065 A434 15af multicolored .45 .25
1066 A434 18af multicolored .50 .25
1067 A434 20af multicolored .70 .25
    Nos. 1061-1067 (7) 2.65 1.75

World
Aviation
Day
A435

1984, Apr. 12
1068 A435 5af Luna 1 .35 .25
1069 A435 8af Luna 2 .45 .25
1070 A435 11af Luna 3 .55 .25
1071 A435 17af Apollo 11 .70 .25
1072 A435 22af Soyuz 6 .90 .35
1073 A435 28af Soyuz 7 .90 .35
1074 A435 34af Soyuz 6, 7, 8 1.10 .45
    Nos. 1068-1074 (7) 4.95 2.15

Souvenir Sheet
Perf. 12x12½
1075 A435 25af S. Koroliov 1.50 .90
   No. 1075 contains one 30x41mm stamp.

Saur
Revolution,
6th Anniv.
A436

1984, Apr. 27   **Perf. 12**
1076 A436 3af multicolored .45 .25

65th Anniv. of Independence — A437

1984, Aug. 19   **Litho.**   **Perf. 12**
1077 A437 6af multicolored .65 .25

Pashto's
and
Balutchi's
Day
A438

3af, Symbolic sun, tribal terr.

1984, Aug. 31
1078 A438 3af multicolored .45 .25

Wildlife
A439

1af, Cape hunting dog, vert. 2af, Argali sheep, vert. 6af, Przewalski's horse. 8af, Wild boar, vert. 17af, Snow leopard. 19af, Tiger. 22af, Indian elephant, vert.

Perf. 12½x12, 12x12½
1984, May 5   **Litho.**
1079 A439 1af multicolored .25 .25
1080 A439 2af multicolored .25 .25
1081 A439 6af multicolored .60 .25
1082 A439 8af multicolored .90 .25
1083 A439 17af multicolored 1.75 .25
1084 A439 19af multicolored 3.00 .25
1085 A439 22af multicolored 3.25 .35
    Nos. 1079-1085 (7) 10.00 1.85

19th UPU
Congress,
Hamburg
A440

25af, German postman, 17th cent. 35af, Postrider, 16th cent. 40af, Carrier pigeon, letter.
50af, Hamburg No. 3 in black.

1984, June 18   **Perf. 12x12½**
1086 A440 25af multicolored .95 .30
1087 A440 35af multicolored 1.50 .45
1088 A440 40af multicolored 1.90 .55
    Nos. 1086-1088 (3) 4.35 1.30

Souvenir Sheet
1089 A440 50af multicolored 2.75 1.75
   No. 1089 contains one 30x40mm stamp.

Natl.
Aviation,
40th Anniv.
A441

Soviet civil aircraft.

1984, June 29
1090 A441 1af Antonov AN-2 .25 .25
1091 A441 4af Ilyushin IL-12 .25 .25
1092 A441 9af Tupolev TU-104 .60 .25
1093 A441 10af Ilyushin IL-18 .90 .25
1094 A441 13af Tupolev TU-134 1.10 .25
1095 A441 17af Ilyushin IL-62 1.50 .30
1096 A441 21af Ilyushin IL-28 1.75 .40
    Nos. 1090-1096 (7) 6.35 1.95

Ettore Bugatti (1881-1947), Type 43,
Italy — A442

Classic automobiles and their designers: 5af, Henry Ford, 1903 Model A, US. 8af, Rene Panhard (1841-1908), 1899 Landau, France. 11af, Gottlieb Daimler (1834-1900), 1935 Daimler-Benz, Germany. 12af, Carl Benz (1844-1929), 1893 Victoris, Germany. 15af, Armand Peugeot (1848-1915), 1892 Vis-a-Vis, France. 22af, Louis Chevrolet (1879-1941), 1925 Sedan, US.

1984, June 30
1097 A442 2af multicolored .25 .25
1098 A442 5af multicolored .35 .25
1099 A442 8af multicolored .60 .25
1100 A442 11af multicolored .75 .25
1101 A442 12af multicolored 1.00 .25
1102 A442 15af multicolored 1.10 .25
1103 A442 22af multicolored 1.50 .35
    Nos. 1097-1103 (7) 5.55 1.85

Qalai Bist
Arch
A443

World Tourism Day: 2af, Ornamental buckled harness. 5af, Victory Monument and Memorial Arch, Kabul. 9af, Standing sculpture of Afghani ruler and attendants. 15af, Buffalo riders in snow. 19af, Camel driver, tent, camel in caparison. 21af, Horsemen playing buzkashi.

1984, Sept. 27
1104 A443 1af multicolored .25 .25
1105 A443 2af multicolored .25 .25
1106 A443 5af multicolored .25 .25
1107 A443 9af multicolored .25 .25
1108 A443 15af multicolored .45 .25
1109 A443 19af multicolored .90 .25
1110 A443 21af multicolored 1.00 .25
    Nos. 1104-1110 (7) 3.35 1.75

UN World Food
Day — A444

Fruit-bearing trees.

1984, Oct. 16
1111 A444 2af multicolored .25 .25
1112 A444 4af multicolored .25 .25
1113 A444 6af multicolored .35 .25
1114 A444 9af multicolored .50 .25
1115 A444 13af multicolored .60 .25
1116 A444 15af multicolored .75 .25
1117 A444 26af multicolored 1.25 .25
    Nos. 1111-1117 (7) 3.95 1.75

People's
Democratic
Party, 20th
Anniv.
A445

1985, Jan. 1
1118 A445 25af multicolored   1.25   .45

Farmer's
Day
A446

1af, Oxen. 3af, Mare, foal. 7af, Brown horse. 8af, White horse, vert. 15af, Sheep, sheep-skins. 16af, Shepherd, cattle, sheep. 25af, Family, camels.

1985, Mar. 2
1119	A446	1af multicolored	.35	.25
1120	A446	3af multicolored	.35	.25
1121	A446	7af multicolored	.35	.25
1122	A446	8af multicolored	.60	.25
1123	A446	15af multicolored	.95	.25
1124	A446	16af multicolored	1.10	.35
1125	A446	25af multicolored	1.60	.45
		Nos. 1119-1125 (7)	5.30	2.05

Geologist's
Day — A447

1985, Apr. 5
1126 A447 4af multicolored   .35   .25

Lenin and
Peasant
Petitioners
A448

Lenin and: 10af, Lenin and Peasant Petitioners. 15af, Revolutionaries, 1917, Leningrad. 25af, Lenin leading Revolutionary Guards, 1917. 50af, Portrait.

1985, Apr. 21   *Perf. 12x12½*
1127	A448	10af multicolored	.70	.25
1128	A448	15af multicolored	.85	.25
1129	A448	25af multicolored	1.50	.40
		Nos. 1127-1129 (3)	3.05	.90

Souvenir Sheet
1130 A448 50af multicolored   2.50 1.50

Saur Revolution,
7th Anniv. — A449

1985, Apr. 27
1131 A449 21af multicolored   1.00   .30

Berlin-Treptow Soviet War Memorial,
Red Army at Siege of Berlin,
1945 — A450

9af, Victorious Motherland monument, fireworks over Kremlin. 10af, Caecilienhof, site of Potsdam Treaty signing, Great Britain, USSR & US flags.

1985, May 9   *Perf. 12½x12*
1132	A450	6af multicolored	.60	.25
1133	A450	9af multicolored	.85	.25
1134	A450	10af multicolored	1.10	.25
		Nos. 1132-1134 (3)	2.55	.75

End of World War II, defeat of Nazi Germany, 40th anniv.

INTELSAT,
20th Anniv.
A451

Designs: 6af, INTELSAT I satellite orbiting Earth. 9af, INTELSAT VI. 10af, Delta D rocket launch, Cape Canaveral, vert.

Perf. 12x12½, 12½x12
1985, Apr. 6   *Litho.*
1135	A451	6af multicolored	.50	.25
1136	A451	9af multicolored	.70	.25
1137	A451	10af multicolored	.95	.25
		Nos. 1135-1137 (3)	2.15	.75

12th World Youth
Festival,
Moscow — A452

7af, Olympic stadium, Moscow. 12af, Festival emblem. 13af, Kremlin. 18af, Folk doll, emblem.

1985, May 5
1138	A452	7af multicolored	.25	.25
1139	A452	12af multicolored	.45	.25
1140	A452	13af multicolored	.55	.35
1141	A452	18af multicolored	.70	.60
		Nos. 1138-1141 (4)	1.95	1.45

Intl. Child
Survival
Campaign
A453

1985, June 1
1142	A453	1af Weighing child	.25	.25
1143	A453	2af Immunization	.25	.25
1144	A453	4af Breastfeeding	.35	.25
1145	A453	5af Mother, child	.40	.25
		Nos. 1142-1145 (4)	1.25	1.00

Flowers
A454

2af, Oenothera affinis. 4af, Erythrina cristagalli. 8af, Tillandsia aeranthos. 13af, Vinca major. 18af, Mirabilis jalapa. 25af, Cypella herbertii. 30af, Clytostoma callistegioides. 75af, Sesbania punicea, horiz.

1985, July 5
1146	A454	2af multicolored	.25	.25
1147	A454	4af multicolored	.25	.25
1148	A454	8af multicolored	.45	.25
1149	A454	13af multicolored	.75	.25
1150	A454	18af multicolored	1.00	.30
1151	A454	25af multicolored	1.40	.30
1152	A454	30af multicolored	1.75	.30
		Nos. 1146-1152 (7)	5.85	1.90

Souvenir Sheet
Perf. 12½x11½
1153 A454 75af multicolored   4.50   .75

ARGENTINA '85.

Independence, 66th Anniv. — A455

1985, Aug. 19   *Perf. 12x12½*
1154 A455 33af Mosque   1.50   .45

Pashto's
and
Balutchi's
Day
A456

1985, Aug. 30
1155 A456 25af multicolored   1.50   .25

UN Decade
for Women
A457

1985, Sept. 22
1156 A457 10af Emblems   *2.50*   .25

World
Tourism
Day, 10th
Anniv. —
A457a

1af, Guldara Stupa. 2af, Mirwais Tomb, vert. 10af, Statue of Bamyan, vert. 13af, No Gumbad Mosque, vert. 14af, Pule Kheshti Mosque. 15af, Bost Citadel. 20af, Ghazni Minaret, vert.

1985, Sept. 27   *Litho.*   *Perf. 12*
1156A	A457a	1af multi	.25	.25
1156B	A457a	2af multi	.25	.25
1156C	A457a	10af multi	.60	.25
1156D	A457a	13af multi	.85	.25
1156E	A457a	14af multi	.95	.25
1156F	A457a	15af multi	1.00	.25
1156G	A457a	20af multi	1.40	.25
		Nos. 1156A-1156G (7)	5.30	1.75

Sports —
A457b

Perf. 12x12½, 12½x12
1985, Oct. 3   *Litho.*
1156H	A457b	1af Boxing	.25	.25
1156I	A457b	2af Volleyball	.25	.25
1156J	A457b	3af Soccer, vert.	.50	.25
1156K	A457b	12af Buzkashi	.75	.25
1156L	A457b	14af Weight lifting	.95	.25
1156M	A457b	18af Wrestling	1.00	.25
1156N	A457b	25af Peg sticking	1.25	.35
		Nos. 1156H-1156N (7)	4.95	1.85

World Food
Day —
A457c

1985, Oct. 16
1156O A457c 25af multicolored   .95   .30

UN 40th
Anniv. — A458

1985, Oct. 24   *Perf. 12½x12*
1157 A458 22af multicolored   1.10   .30

A459

A459a

A459b

A459c

Birds — A459d

2af, Jay. 4af, Plover, hummingbird. 8af, Pheasant. 13af, Hoopoe. 18af, Falcon. 25af, Partridge. 30af, Pelicans, horiz. 75af, Parakeets.

1985, Oct. 25 *Perf. 12½x12, 12x12½*
1158	A459	2af multicolored	.25	.25
1159	A459a	4af multicolored	.85	.45
1160	A459b	8af multicolored	.90	.45
1161	A459	13af multicolored	1.40	.75
1162	A459	18af multicolored	1.60	.85
1163	A459b	25af multicolored	2.40	1.25
1164	A459c	30af multicolored	3.00	1.50

Nos. 1158-1164 (7) 10.40 5.50

Souvenir Sheet
Perf. 12x12½
1165 A459d 75af multicolored 5.00 .75

Mushrooms A460

3af, Tricholomopsis rutilans. 4af, Boletus miniatoporus. 7af, Amanita rubescens. 11af, Boletus scaber. 12af, Coprinus atramentarius. 18af, Hypholoma. 20af, Boletus aurantiacus.

1985, June 10 *Litho. Perf. 12½x12*
1165A	A460	3af multicolored	.25	.25
1166	A460	4af multicolored	.40	.25
1167	A460	7af multicolored	.55	.30
1168	A460	11af multicolored	.80	.50
1169	A460	12af multicolored	1.00	.50
1170	A460	18af multicolored	1.40	.65
1171	A460	20af multicolored	1.60	.70

Nos. 1165A-1171 (7) 6.00 3.15

World Wildlife Fund — A461

1985, Nov. 25
1172	A461 2af Leopard, cubs	.40	.25
1173	A461 9af Adult's head	1.25	.40
1174	A461 11af Adult	2.40	.75
1175	A461 15af Cub	3.75	1.10

Nos. 1172-1175 (4) 7.80 2.50

Motorcycle, Cent. — A462

Designs: Different makes and landmarks.

1985, Dec. 16
1176	A462	2af multicolored	.25	.25
1177	A462	4af multicolored	.30	.25
1178	A462	8af multicolored	.50	.25
1179	A462	13af multicolored	.80	.25
1180	A462	18af multicolored	.90	.25
1181	A462	25af multicolored	1.25	.25
1182	A462	30af multicolored	1.25	.25

Nos. 1176-1182 (7) 5.25 1.75

Souvenir Sheet
Perf. 11½x12½
1183 A462 75af multicolored 5.00 .75

People's Democratic Party, 21st Anniv. — A463

1986, Jan. 1 *Perf. 12½x12*
1184 A463 2af multicolored .35 .25

27th Soviet Communist Party Congress — A464

1986, Mar. 31
1185 A464 25af Lenin .75 .40

First Man in Space, 25th Anniv. — A465

Designs: 3af, Spacecraft. 7af, Soviet space achievement medal, vert. 9af, Rocket lift-off, vert. 11af, Yuri Gagarin, military decorations, vert. 13af, Gagarin, cosmonaut. 15af, Gagarin, politician. 17af, Gagarin wearing flight suit, vert.

Perf. 12½x12, 12x12½
1986, Apr. 12 Litho.
1186	A465	3af multicolored	.25	.25
1187	A465	7af multicolored	.25	.25
1188	A465	9af multicolored	.35	.25
1189	A465	11af multicolored	.45	.25
1190	A465	13af multicolored	.50	.25
1191	A465	15af multicolored	.50	.25
1192	A465	17af multicolored	.75	.25

Nos. 1186-1192 (7) 3.05 1.75

Loya Jirgah (Grand Assembly) of the People's Democratic Republic, 1st Anniv. A465a

1986, Apr. 23 *Litho. Perf. 12x12½*
1192A A465a 3af multicolored .25 .25

Intl. Day of Labor Solidarity — A465b

1986, May 1 *Perf. 12½x12*
1192B A465b 5af multicolored .35 .25

Intl. Red Crescent Day A465c

1986, May 8 *Perf. 12x12½*
1192C A465c 7af multicolored .45 .25

Intl. Children's Day A466

1af, Mother, children, vert. 3af, Mother, child, vert. 9af, Children, map.

1986, June 1 *Perf. 12*
1193	A466	1af multicolored	.25	.25
1194	A466	3af multicolored	.25	.25
1195	A466	9af multicolored	.40	.25

Nos. 1193-1195 (3) .90 .75

World Youth Day A466a

1986, July 31 *Perf. 12x12½*
1195A A466a 15af multicolored .70 .45

Pashtos' and Baluchis' Day A467

1986, Aug. 31 *Perf. 12x12½*
1196 A467 4af multicolored .25 .25

Intl. Peace Year — A468

1986, Sept. 30 Photo. Perf. 12½x12
1197 A468 12af black & Prus blue .60 .25

A469

1986 World Cup Soccer Championships, Mexico — A470

Various soccer plays.

1986, Apr. 15 Litho. *Perf. 12*
1198	A469	3af multi, vert.	.25	.25
1199	A469	4af multicolored	.35	.25
1200	A469	7af multicolored	.40	.25
1201	A469	11af multi, vert.	.70	.25
1202	A469	12af multicolored	.85	.25
1203	A469	18af multi, vert.	1.25	.25
1204	A469	20af multi, vert.	1.50	.25

Nos. 1198-1204 (7) 5.30 1.75

Souvenir Sheet
Perf. 12½x12
1205 A470 75af multicolored 4.75 3.00

A471

1986, Apr. 21 *Perf. 12½x12*
1206 A471 16af Lenin .75 .45

A472

1986, Apr. 27 Litho. *Perf. 12½x12*
1207 A472 8af multicolored .60 .25

Saur revolution, 8th anniv.

Natl. Independence, 67th Anniv. — A473

1986, Aug. 19 Litho. *Perf. 12½x12*
1208 A473 10af multicolored .50 .25

Literacy Day A474

1986, Sept. 18 *Perf. 12x12½*
1209 A474 2af multicolored .25 .25

Dogs — A475

5af, St. Bernard. 7af, Collie. 8af, Pointer. 9af, Golden retriever. 11af, German shepherd. 15af, Bulldog. 20af, Afghan hound.

1986, May 19   Litho.   Perf. 12x12½
1210	A475	5af multicolored	.25 .25
1211	A475	7af multicolored	.40 .25
1212	A475	8af multicolored	.50 .25
1213	A475	9af multicolored	.60 .25
1214	A475	11af multicolored	.70 .25
1215	A475	15af multicolored	.95 .25
1216	A475	20af multicolored	1.25 .30
		Nos. 1210-1216 (7)	4.65 1.80

Lizards — A476

1986, July 7   Perf. 12x12½, 12½x12
1217	A476	3af Cobra	.25 .25
1218	A476	4af shown	.25 .25
1219	A476	5af Praying mantis	.35 .25
1220	A476	8af Beetle	.50 .25
1221	A476	9af Tarantula	.60 .30
1222	A476	10af Python	.70 .35
1223	A476	11af Scorpions	.85 .35
		Nos. 1217-1223 (7)	3.50 2.00

Nos. 1217, 1219, 1221-1223 horiz.

STOCKHOLMIA '86 — A477

Ships.

1986, Aug. 28   Perf. 12½x12
1224	A477	4af multicolored	.40 .25
1225	A477	5af multicolored	.60 .25
1226	A477	6af multicolored	.70 .25
1227	A477	7af multicolored	.85 .25
1228	A477	8af multicolored	1.00 .25
1229	A477	9af multicolored	1.10 .25
1230	A477	11af multicolored	1.40 .25
		Nos. 1224-1230 (7)	6.05 1.75

Souvenir Sheet
1231	A477	50af Galley	4.25 2.00

A479

1986, Sept. 14   Perf. 12
1232	A479	3af lt blue, blk & olive gray	.40 .25

Reunion of Afghan tribes under the Supreme Girgah.

A480

1986, Oct. 25   Perf. 12½x12
1233	A480	3af black & brt ver	.40 .25

Natl. youth solidarity.

Locomotives — A481

1986, June 21   Perf. 12½x12
1234	A481	4af multicolored	.25 .25
1235	A481	5af multicolored	.35 .25
1236	A481	6af multicolored	.45 .25
1237	A481	7af multicolored	.50 .25
1238	A481	8af multicolored	.65 .25
1239	A481	9af multicolored	.85 .25
1240	A481	11af multicolored	1.25 .25
		Nos. 1234-1240 (7)	4.30 1.75

Fish
A482

Various fish.

1986, May 25
1241	A482	5af multicolored	.25 .25
1242	A482	7af multicolored	.40 .25
1243	A482	8af multicolored	.50 .25
1244	A482	9af multicolored	.60 .25
1245	A482	11af multicolored	.85 .25
1246	A482	15af multicolored	1.10 .35
1247	A482	20af multicolored	1.50 .35
		Nos. 1241-1247 (7)	5.20 1.95

Saur Revolution, 9th Anniv. A483

1987, Apr. 27   Perf. 12
1248	A483	3af multicolored	.25 .25

Natl. Reconciliation — A484

1987, May 27   Perf. 12x12½
1249	A484	3af multicolored	.25 .25

A485

A486

UN Child Survival Campaign — A487

1987, June 1   Perf. 12
1250	A485	1af multicolored	.25 .25
1251	A486	5af multicolored	.25 .25
1252	A487	9af multicolored	.35 .25
		Nos. 1250-1252 (3)	.85 .75

Conference of Clergymen and Ulema, 1st Anniv. A488

1987, June 30
1253	A488	5af multicolored	.35 .25

Butterflies — A489

1987, July 3
1254	A489	7af multicolored	.60 .35
1255	A489	9af multi, diff.	.75 .35
1256	A489	10af multi, diff.	1.00 .50
1257	A489	12af multi, diff.	1.50 .50
1258	A489	15af multi, diff.	1.60 .70
1259	A489	22af multi, diff.	2.25 .95
1260	A489	25af multi, diff.	2.50 .95
		Nos. 1254-1260 (7)	10.20 4.30

10af, 15af and 22af horiz.

A490

1987, Aug. 11
1261	A490	1af multicolored	.25 .25

1st election of local representatives for State Power and Administration.

Natl. Independence, 68th Anniv. — A490a

1987, Aug. 19
1261A	A490a	3af multicolored	.25 .25

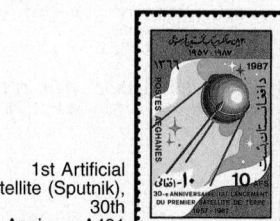

1st Artificial Satellite (Sputnik), 30th Anniv. — A491

1987, Oct. 4   Litho.   Perf. 12½x12
1262	A491	10af Sputnik	.40 .25
1263	A491	15af Rocket launch	.60 .25
1264	A491	25af Soyuz	.85 .25
		Nos. 1262-1264 (3)	1.85 .75

World Post Day A492

1987, Oct. 9   Perf. 12x12½
1265	A492	22af multicolored	1.10 .60

Intl. Communications and Transport Day — A493

1987, Oct. 24   Perf. 12½x12
1266	A493	42af multicolored	4.75 1.00

October Revolution in Russia, 70th Anniv. — A494

1987, Nov. 7
1267	A494	25af Lenin	1.25 .70

Mice — A495

Various mice. Nos. 1269-1272 horiz.

1987, Dec. 6   Perf. 12½x12, 12x12½
1268	A495	2af multicolored	.40 .25
1269	A495	4af multi, diff.	.50 .25
1270	A495	8af multi, diff.	.60 .25
1271	A495	16af multi, diff.	1.00 .25
1272	A495	20af multi, diff.	1.25 .25
		Nos. 1268-1272 (5)	3.75 1.25

Medicinal Plants — A496

1987, Nov. 11   Litho.   Perf. 12
1273	A496	3af Castor bean	.25 .25
1274	A496	6af Licorice	.45 .25
1275	A496	9af Chamomile	.75 .25
1276	A496	14af Datura	1.00 .25
1277	A496	18af Dandelion	1.25 .30
		Nos. 1273-1277 (5)	3.70 1.30

Pashto's and Baluchis' Day — A497

1987, Aug. 30
1278 A497 4af multicolored .25 .25

Dinosaurs A498

3af, Mesosaurus. 5af, Styracosaurus. 10af, Uinatherium. 15af, Protoceratops. 20af, Stegosaurus. 25af, Ceratosaurus. 30af, Dinornis maximus.

Perf. 12½x12, 12x12½
1988, June 6 Litho.
1279 A498 3af multicolored .25 .25
1280 A498 5af multicolored .25 .25
1281 A498 10af multicolored .50 .25
1282 A498 15af multicolored .75 .25
1283 A498 20af multicolored 1.00 .30
1284 A498 25af multicolored 1.40 .35
1285 A498 30af multicolored 1.90 .60
Nos. 1279-1285 (7) 6.05 2.25
Nos. 1280-1283 horiz.

Pashtos' and Baluchis' Day — A499

1988, Aug. 30 *Perf. 12½x12*
1286 A499 23af multicolored .95 .60

Afghan-Soviet Joint Space Flight — A500

1988, Aug. 30
1287 A500 32af multicolored 1.25 .50

Valentina Tereshkova, 1st Woman in Space, 25th Anniv. — A501

10af, Portrait, rocket, horiz. 15af, Lift-off, dove. 25af, Spacecraft, Earth, horiz.

1988, Oct. 16 *Perf. 12x12½, 12½x12*
1288 A501 10af multicolored .85 .35
1289 A501 15af multicolored .85 .30
1290 A501 25af multicolored 1.00 .45
Nos. 1288-1290 (3) 2.70 1.10

Traditional Crafts — A502

Perf. 12x12½, 12½x12
1988, Nov. 9 Litho.
1291 A502 2af Pitcher, bowls .25 .25
1292 A502 4af Vases .25 .25
1293 A502 5af Dress .25 .25
1294 A502 9af Mats, napkins .35 .25
1295 A502 15af Pocketbooks .60 .25
1296 A502 23af Jewelry .95 .25
1297 A502 50af Furniture 1.90 .25
Nos. 1291-1297 (7) 4.55 1.75
Nos. 1291-1292, 1294-1297 horiz.

Precious and Semiprecious Gems — A503

1988, Dec. 5 *Perf. 12½x12*
1298 A503 13af Emeralds 1.00 .25
1299 A503 37af Lapiz lazuli 2.25 .60
1300 A503 40af Rubies 2.50 .75
Nos. 1298-1300 (3) 5.75 1.60

1988 Winter Olympics, Calgary — A504

2af, Women's figure skating. 5af, Skiing. 9af, Bobsledding. 22af, Biathlon. 37af, Speed skating.
75af, Ice hockey.

1988, Dec. 25
1301 A504 2af multicolored .25 .25
1301A A504 5af multicolored .25 .25
1301B A504 9af multicolored .50 .25
1301C A504 22af multicolored 1.00 .35
1301D A504 37af multicolored 2.25 .65
Size: 80x60mm
1302 A504 75af multicolored 4.50 3.50
Nos. 1301-1302 (6) 8.75 5.25

A510

A511

A512

A513

A513a

Flowers — A514

Various flowering plants.

Perf. 12x12½, 12½x12
1988, Jan. 27 Litho.
1303 A510 3af multicolored .25 .25
1304 A511 5af multicolored .35 .25
1305 A512 7af multi, vert. .50 .25
1306 A512 9af multicolored .70 .25
1307 A513 12af multicolored 1.25 .35
1308 A513a 15af multicolored 1.60 .35
1309 A514 24af multicolored 2.25 .35
Nos. 1303-1309 (7) 6.90 2.05

Traditional Musical Instruments A515

String and percussion instruments.

1988, Jan. 15 Litho. *Perf. 12*
1310 A515 1af shown .25 .25
1311 A515 3af drums .25 .25
1312 A515 5af multi, diff. .30 .25
1313 A515 15af multi, diff. .70 .25
1314 A515 18af multi, diff. 1.00 .30
1315 A515 25af multi, diff. 1.40 .30
1316 A515 33af multi, diff. 1.90 .30
Nos. 1310-1316 (7) 5.80 1.90

Admission of Afghanistan to the ITU and UPU, 60th Anniv. — A516

1988, Apr. 13 Litho. *Perf. 12*
1317 A516 20af multicolored .85 .50

Saur Revolution, 10th Anniv. A517

1988, Apr. 23
1318 A517 10af multicolored .50 .35

Fruit A518

2af, Baskets, compote. 4af, Four baskets. 7af, Basket. 8af, Grapes, vert. 16af, Market. 22af, Market, diff. 25af, Vendor, vert.

1988, July 18 Litho. *Perf. 12*
1319 A518 2af multicolored .25 .25
1320 A518 4af multicolored .35 .25
1321 A518 7af multicolored .45 .25
1322 A518 8af multicolored .50 .25
1323 A518 16af multicolored .85 .35
1324 A518 22af multicolored 1.25 .35
1325 A518 25af multicolored 1.90 .35
Nos. 1319-1325 (7) 5.55 2.05

Jawaharlal Nehru (1889-1964), 1st Prime Minister of Independent India — A519

1988, Nov. 14
1326 A519 40af multicolored 2.25 .85

Natl. Independence, 69th Anniv. — A520

1988, Aug. 1
1327 A520 24af multicolored 1.25 .70

Intl. Red Cross and Red Crescent Organizations, 125th Annivs. — A521

1988, Sept. 26
1328 A521 10af multicolored .85 .50

Natl. Reconciliation Institute, 2nd Anniv. — A522

1989, Jan. 4
1329	A522	4af multicolored	.25	.25

Chess A523

Boards, early matches and hand-made chessmen.

1989, Feb. 2   Litho.   Perf. 12x12½
1330	A523	2af Bishop	.25	.25
1331	A523	3af Queen	.35	.25
1332	A523	4af King (bust)	.45	.25
1333	A523	7af King, diff.	.70	.25
1334	A523	16af Knight	1.10	.25
1335	A523	24af Pawn	1.60	.35
1336	A523	45af Bishop, diff.	2.75	.45
	Nos. 1330-1336 (7)		7.20	2.05

Paintings by Picasso — A524

Designs: 4af, *The Old Jew.* 6af, *The Two Mountebanks.* 8af, *Portrait of Ambrouse Vollar.* 22af, *Woman of Majorca.* 35af, *Acrobat on the Ball.* 75af, *Usine a Horta de Ebro.*

1989, Feb. 13   Litho.   Perf. 12½x12
1341	A524	4af multicolored	.35	.25
1342	A524	6af multicolored	.45	.25
1343	A524	8af multicolored	.55	.25
1344	A524	22af multicolored	1.25	.25
1345	A524	35af multicolored	2.50	.25

Size: 71x90mm
Imperf
1346	A524	75af multicolored	4.75	1.25
	Nos. 1341-1346 (6)		9.85	2.50

Fauna — A525

3af, *Allactaga euphratica.* 4af, *Equus hemionus.* 14af, *Felis lynx.* 35af, *Gypaetus barbatus.* 44af, *Capra falconeri.* 100af, *Naja oxiana.*

1989, Feb. 20   Litho.   Perf. 12½x12
1347	A525	3af multicolored	.35	.25
1348	A525	4af multicolored	.35	.25
1349	A525	14af multicolored	1.00	.35
1350	A525	35af multicolored	3.75	1.60
1351	A525	44af multicolored	2.50	1.25

Size: 71x91mm
Imperf
1352	A525	100af multicolored	7.75	3.00
	Nos. 1347-1352 (6)		15.70	6.70

Intl. Women's Day — A526

1989, Mar. 8   Perf. 12½x12
1353	A526	8af multicolored	.45	.25

Restoration and Development of San'a, Yemen — A527

1988, Dec. 27   Litho.   Perf. 12
1354	A527	32af multicolored	1.60	1.10

Agriculture Day A528

1af, Cattle. 2af, Old and new plows. 3af, Field workers.

1989, Mar. 21
1355	A528	1af multicolored	.25	.25
1356	A528	2af multicolored	.25	.25
1357	A528	3af multicolored	.25	.25
	Nos. 1355-1357 (3)		.75	.75

World Meteorology Day — A529

32af, Emblems. 40af, Weather station, balloon, vert.

1989, Mar. 23
1358	A529	27af shown	1.25	.25
1359	A529	32af multicolored	1.75	.25
1360	A529	40af multicolored	2.25	.25
	Nos. 1358-1360 (3)		5.25	.75

Saur Revolution, 11th Anniv. A530

1989, Apr. 27
1361	A530	20af multicolored	1.10	.25

Classic Automobiles — A531

5af, 1910 Duchs, Germany. 10af, 1911 Ford, US. 20af, 1911 Renault, France. 25af, 1911 Russo-Balte, Russia. 30af, 1926 Fiat, Italy.

1989, Dec. 30   Litho.   Perf. 12½x12
1362	A531	5af multi	.45	.25
1363	A531	10af multi	.75	.25
1364	A531	20af multi	1.40	.25
1365	A531	25af multi	1.60	.35
1366	A531	30af multi	1.90	.35
	Nos. 1362-1366 (5)		6.10	1.45

Asia-Pacific Telecommunity, 10th Anniv. — A532

27af, Emblem, satellite dish.

1989, Aug. 3   Perf. 12
1367	A532	3af shown	.25	.25
1368	A532	27af multicolored	1.10	.25

Teacher's Day A533

1989, May 30   Litho.   Perf. 12
1369	A533	42af multicolored	2.25	.35

French Revolution, Bicent. — A534

1989, July   Litho.   Perf. 12
1370	A534	25af multicolored	1.60	.95

Natl. Independence, 70th Anniv. — A535

1989, Aug. 18   Litho.   Perf. 12
1371	A535	25af multicolored	1.25	.35

A536

1989, Aug. 30
1372	A536	3af multicolored	.25	.25

Pashtos' and Baluchis' Day.

Birds — A537

3af, Platalea leucorodia. 5af, Porphyrio porhyrio. 10af, Botaurus stellaris, horiz. 15af, Pelecanus onocrotalus. 20af, Netta rufina. 25af, Cygnus olor. 30af, Phalacrocorax carbo, horiz.

1989, Dec. 5   Litho.   Perf. 12
1373	A537	3af multicolored	.25	.25
1374	A537	5af multicolored	.50	.25
1375	A537	10af multicolored	.95	.45
1376	A537	15af multicolored	1.25	.55
1377	A537	20af multicolored	1.60	.60
1378	A537	25af multicolored	2.25	.70
1379	A537	30af multicolored	2.50	.95
	Nos. 1373-1379 (7)		9.30	3.75

Tourism — A538

1af, Mosque. 2af, Minaret. 3af, Buzkashi, horiz. 4af, Jet over Hendo Kush, horiz.

1989, Dec.
1380	A538	1af multicolored	1.60	*3.25*
1381	A538	2af multicolored	3.25	*6.50*
1382	A538	3af multicolored	4.75	*9.50*
1383	A538	4af multicolored	6.50	*13.00*
	Nos. 1380-1383 (4)		16.10	*32.25*

Mavlavi Allahdad Balkhi, President of Post of the Afghanistan Postal Administration, has declared that "the stamps which have been printed after year 1989 are false stamps."

The following stamps have been condemned as unauthorized by the Afghan Ministry of Communications:

Dated 1996: *Mushrooms,* 6 stamps + souvenir sheet. *Bears,* 5 stamps + souvenir sheet. *1998 Word Soccer Cup Championships,* 6 stamps + souvenir sheet. *Silkworms,* 6 stamps + souvenir sheet. *Domestic Cats,* 6 stamps + souvenir sheet. *Horses,* 5 stamps + souvenir sheet. *Islamic Revolution,* 6 stamps. *Independence Anniv./Honoring Prophet Mohammed,* 2 stamps.

Dated 1997: *Tulips,* 6 stamps + souvenir sheet. *Llamas & Camels,* 6 stamps + souvenir sheet. *Domestic Cats,* 6 stamps + souvenir sheet. *Wildflowers,* 6 stamps + souvenir sheet. *Early Sailing Ships* (triangles), 6 stamps + souvenir sheet. *1998 Word Soccer Cup Championships,* 6 stamps + souvenir sheet. *Mushrooms,* 6 stamps + souvenir sheet.

Dated 1998: *Mushrooms,* 6 stamps + souvenir sheet. *Butterflies,* 6 stamps + souvenir sheet. *Princess Diana,* 9 stamps in a miniature sheet. *WWF (Wild Sheep),* strip of 4 stamps. *Wildlife,* 12 stamps. *Dogs,* 6 stamps + souvenir sheet. *Locomotives,* 6 stamps + souvenir sheet. *Prehistoric Animals,* 6 stamps + souvenir sheet. *Antique Cars,* 6 stamps + souvenir sheet. *Fish,* 6 stamps + souvenir sheet. *Birds,* 6 stamps + souvenir sheet.

Dated 1999: *Chess,* 6 stamps + souvenir sheet. *Mushrooms,* 6 stamps + souvenir sheet. *Locomotives,* 6 stamps + souvenir sheet. *Dogs,* 6 stamps + souvenir sheet. *Minerals,* 6 stamps + souvenir sheet. *Snails,* 6 stamps + souvenir sheet. *Vintage Race Cars,* 6 stamps + souvenir sheet. *China '99,* 12 stamps in a miniature sheet. *Cacti,* 6 stamps + souvenir sheet. *Horses,* 6 stamps + souvenir sheet. *Ferrari Automobiles,* 6 stamps + souvenir sheet. *Orchids,* 6 stamps + souvenir sheet. *Parrots,* 6 stamps + souvenir sheet. *Sailing Ships,* 6 stamps + souvenir sheet.

Dated 2000: *Cats,* 6 stamps + souvenir sheet. *WIPA 2000 (Birds),* 6 stamps + souvenir sheet.

Dated 2001: *Mushrooms,* 6 stamps + souvenir sheet. *Locomotives,* 6 stamps + souvenir sheet.

In addition to these sets, a number of bogus illegal issues have appeared. These issues include:

Beetles: miniature sheet of 9 different stamps.

Birds: 2 miniature sheets of 9 different stamps each.

Boats: 3 miniature sheets of 9 different stamps each.

Cars (Vintage): 3 miniature sheets of 9 different stamps each.

Cats: 3 miniature sheets of 9 different stamps each.

Chess: 3 miniature sheets of 9 different stamps each.

Dinosaurs: 3 miniature sheets of 9 different stamps each.

Dogs: 3 miniature sheets of 9 different stamps each.

Eagles & Owls: miniature sheet of 9 different stamps.

Eagles: miniature sheet of 9 different stamps.

Elvis Presley: 3 miniature sheets of 9 different stamps each.

Fauna of Afghanistan: miniature sheet of 9 different stamps.

Fish: miniature sheet of 9 different stamps.

Great People of the 20th Century: miniature sheet of 9 different stamps.

Horses: 2 miniature sheets of 9 different stamps each.

Korea/Japan World Soccer Cup: 2 souvenir sheets.

Locomotives: 2 souvenir sheets inscribed "Trains."

Locomotives: miniature sheet of 9 different stamps, inscribed "English Trains."

Marilyn Monroe: 3 miniature sheets of 9 different stamps each.

Marilyn Monroe: Block of 4 different stamps.

Mother Teresa & Pope John Paul II: 3 miniature sheets of 6 different stamps each + 3 souvenir sheets.

Osama Ben Laden Wanted Poster: 1 stamp in miniature sheet of 9.

Owls: 3 miniature sheets of 9 different stamps each + 2 souvenir sheets.

Paintings (Classic Posters): miniature sheet of 9 different stamps.

Paintings (Impressionists): 3 miniature sheets of 6 different stamps each + 3 souvenir sheets.

Plants: miniature sheet of 9 different stamps + souvenir sheet depicting orchid.

Princess Diana: miniature sheet of 9 different stamps.

Sports: 4 miniature sheets of 9 different stamps each, inscribed "Formula 2000."

Transitional Islamic State

Ahmed Shah Masood (1953?-2001), Military Leader — A539

2002   **Litho.**   **Perf. 13½x13**
1384 A539 14,000af multi   7.50 10.00

National Understanding — A540

2002, July 18 Litho.   Perf. 13x13½
1385 A540 11,000af multi   6.50 6.50

Destruction of Bamyan Buddha Statue by Taliban Government A541

2002, July 18   **Perf. 13½x13**
1386 A541 25,000af multi   7.50 10.00

On Oct. 8, 2002, a new currency was introduced. Old stamps not formerly authorized were issued and sold at face value without the zeros. The same was done with Nos. 1384-1386. Because there was no obliteration they can only be recognized with dated cancels.

Fourth Anniversary of the Islamic Revolution — A541a

2002   **Litho.**   **Perf. 12¾**
1386A A541a 800af multi   .75

No. 1386A was originally "issued" Dec. 20, 1996 but was not authorized for postal use until 2002. It was sold and valid for 8af.

Farmers' Day — A541b

2002   **Litho.**   **Perf. 12¾**
1386B A541b 1,500af multi   1.50

No. 1386B was originally "issued" Dec. 20, 1996 but was not authorized for postal use until 2002. It was sold and valid for 15af.

Mohammed's Birthday — A541c

2002   **Litho.**   **Perf. 12½x12¾**
1386C A541c 1,500af multi   1.50

No. 1386C was originally "issued" Dec. 26, 1996 but was not authorized for postal use until 2002. It was sold and valid for 15af.

77th Independence Day — A541d

2002   **Litho.**   **Perf. 12½x12¾**
1386D A541d 1,500af multi   .75

No. 1386D was originally "issued" Dec. 28, 1996 but was not authorized for postal use until 2002. It was sold and valid for 7af.

Universal Declaration of Human Rights, 55th Anniv. — A542

2002, Dec. 10 Litho.   Perf. 13x12¾
1387 A542 4af multi   3.50 3.50

Farmer's Day A543

Designs: 3af, Tractor. 6af, Oxen pulling plow.

2003, Mar. 21 Litho.   Perf. 12¾x13
1388 A543 3af shown   5.00 —
1389 A453 6af multi   10.00 —

Miniature Sheet

Orchids — A544

No. 1390: a, 9af, Calanthe veitchii. b, 13af, Eulanthe sanderiana. c, 17af, Ordontioda vuylstekeae. d, 20af, Dendrobium infundibulum. e, 30af, Miltonsiopsis roezlii. f, 40af, Cattleya labiata. g, 100af, Vanda coerulea.

2003, Apr. 17 Litho.   Perf. 13x12¾
1390 A544   Sheet of 7, #a-g,
          + 2 labels   22.50 22.50

No. 1390 exists in vertical (pictured) and horizontal formats. Value is the same.

Birthday of Mohammed — A545

2003, May 14 Litho.   Perf. 12¾x13
1391 A545 10af multi   6.00 6.00

World Tuberculosis Day — A546

Designs: 1af, Boy and girl holding sign. 4af, Caricatures of doctors and patients, horiz. 9af, Caricatures of patients, horiz.

Perf. 13x12¾, 12¾x13
2003, May 18   **Litho.**
1392-1394 A546   Set of 3   6.00 6.00

Loya Jurga A547

2003, June 16 Litho.   Perf. 12¾x13
1395 A547 20af multi   4.00 4.00

Day Against Narcotics — A548

Designs: 1af, Map of Afghanistan, poppy. 2af, Poppy capsule, skulls, vert. 5af, Farmer and tractor in poppy field.
10af, Poppy capsule, skulls.

Perf. 12¾x13, 13x12¾
2003, June 25   **Litho.**
1396-1398 A548   Set of 3   3.50 3.50
Souvenir Sheet
1398A A548 10af multi   2.75 2.75

Dogs — A549

Designs: 10af, Rottweiler. 20af, Cocker spaniel. 30af, Doberman pinscher. 40af, Afghan hound. 50af, Giant schnauzer. 60af, Boxer.
150af, Afghan hound, diff.

2003, July 4 Litho.   Perf. 13x12¾
1399-1404 A549   Set of 6   20.00 —
Souvenir Sheet
1405 A549 150af multi   14.50 —

Lighthouses A550

Designs: 10af, Bird Island, South Africa. 20af, Cordouan, France. 30af, Mahota Pagoda, China. 50af, Bay Canh, Viet Nam. 60af, Cap Roman Rock, South Africa. 100af, Mikomoto Shima, Japan.
150af, Bell Rock, Great Britain.

2003, Aug. 5
1406-1411 A550   Set of 6   22.50 —
Souvenir Sheet
1412 A550 150af multi   14.50 —

Independence, 84th Anniv. — A551

2003, Aug. 19   Litho.   Perf. 12¾x13
1413   A551   15af multi   3.50 3.50

Intl.
Literacy
Day
A552

2003, Sept. 8   Litho.   Perf. 12¾x13
1414   A552   2af multi   1.00 1.00

Miniature Sheet

Heritage of Afghanistan — A553

No. 1415: a, 20af, Fragments of rock drawing depicting a woman, Bamiyan. b, 40af,
Head of Buddha, Gandhara. c, 60af, Statue
from Takht-i-Bahi Monastery, Gandhara. d,
100af, Hand of Buddha, Bamiyan.

2003, Oct. 10   Litho.   Perf. 13x12¾
1415   A553   Sheet of 4, #a-d   22.50   —

Revelation of the Koran to
Mohammed — A554

2003, Nov. 23   Litho.   Perf. 12¾x13
1416   A554   9af multi   6.50 6.50

A555

Afghanistan Tourism Day—A555a

Designs: 8af, 25af, Fort. 12af, Bust, jar, historical artifacts.

2003, Dec. 16   Litho.   Perf. 12¾x13
1417   A555   4af shown   .75 .75
1418   A555a   8af ol grn & multi   1.00 1.00
1418A   A555   12af multi   1.25 1.25
      Nos. 1417-1418A (3)   3.00 3.00
Souvenir Sheet
1418B   A555a   25af lil & multi   3.00 3.00

Animals
A556

Designs: 6af, Leopard. 11af, Jackal. 15af,
Wild goat.
40af, Leopard facing left.

2003   Litho.   Perf. 12¾
1419-1421   A556   Set of 3   5.00 5.00
Souvenir Sheet
1422   A556   40af multi   8.25 8.25

World
Post Day
A557

2003, Oct. 9   Litho.   Perf. 12¾x13
1423   A557   8af multi   2.50 2.50

Int'l. Women's Day — A558

2004   Litho.   Perf. 12¾x13
1424   A558   6af multi   1.50 1.50

World Tuberculosis Day — A559

Designs: 1af, Woman, hands holding
medicine and bloody tissue. 4af, Woman
wearing mask, child. 9af, Eight men. 12af,
Man, map of Afghanistan, vert. 15af, Doctor
touching patient, people in white in background, vert.

Perf. 12¾x13, 13x12¾
2004, Mar. 23   Litho.
1425   A559   1af multi   .35   .35
1426   A559   4af multi   .75   .75
1427   A559   9af multi   1.50 1.50
1428   A559   12af multi   2.00 2.00
1429   A559   15af multi   2.50 2.50
      Nos. 1425-1429 (5)   7.10 7.10

Pres. Hamid
Karzai — A560

Karzai and Map
of Afghanistan
A561

2004, Oct. 7   Perf. 13x12¾
1430   A560   12af multi   3.00 3.00
1431   A561   12af multi   5.00 5.00

Oath of Pres. Karzai.

First Direct Presidential
Election — A562

Denominations: 15af, 25af.

2004, Oct. 9   Litho.   Perf. 12¾x13
1432-1433   A562   Set of 2   7.00 7.00
   Two types of Arabic inscriptions exist on
each stamp. Values the same.

Afghanistan postal officials declared
a set of eight stamps depicting soccer
players and a set of eight stamps
depicting FIFA Presidents as "not
authorized."
   The editors are seeking more information about the status of a set of four
Worldwide Fund for Nature stamps
depicting the Himalayan musk deer.

Souvenir Sheet

Inauguration of Pres. Karzai — A563

2004, Dec. 7   Litho.   Perf. 13½
1434   A563   100af multi   18.00 18.00

Diplomatic Relations Between
Afghanistan and People's Republic of
China, 50th Anniv. — A564

2005, Jan. 20   Litho.   Perf. 12
1435   A564   25af multi   3.00 3.00
Souvenir Sheet
Printed On Cloth
Without Gum
Perf. 13¼x13
1436   A564   150af multi   24.00 24.00
No. 1436 contains one 60x40mm stamp.

Mine
Clearance
Campaign
A565

Designs: 1af, Mine danger warning sign.
2af, Mine clearer with dog, vert. 3af. Mine
clearer with metal detector, vert.

2006, Apr. 4   Perf. 13¼x13, 13x13¼
1437-1439   A565   Set of 3   2.00 2.00

Independence,
87th
Anniv. — A566

2006, Aug. 19   Perf. 13x13¼
1440   A566   45af multi   8.00 8.00

World Literacy
Day — A567

2006, Sept. 8
1441   A567   12af multi   2.00 2.00

World Post
Day
A568

Color of "2006": No. 1442, 15af, Light green.
No. 1443, 15af, Black.

2006, Sept. 9   Perf. 13¼x13
1442-1443   A568   Set of 2   4.50 4.50
   The length of the Arabic inscription on the
top of the stamp is longer on No. 1442 than on
No. 1443.

World
Tourism
Day
A569

Designs: 15af, Lamp, pitchers, bowl, building. 30af, Pitchers, cup, mountain.

2006, Sept. 27   Litho.   Perf. 13¼x13
1444   A569   15af multi   2.50 2.50
1445   A569   30af multi   4.50 4.50

Campaign for
Elimination of
Violence Against
Women — A570

Designs: 12af, Woman behind barbed wire,
chain, hands unlocking lock. 14af, Woman,
roots. 19af, Eyes of woman, needle and
thread closing eye hole of burqa, horiz.

Perf. 13x13¼, 13¼x13
2006, Nov. 25   **Litho.**
1446-1448 A570 Set of 3   6.75 6.75

Mevlana Jalal ad-Din ar-Rumi (1207-73), Islamic Philosopher A571

Designs: 65af, Birthplace at Balkh. 85af, Mevlana and whirling dervishes, vert. 150af, Mevlana, whirling dervishes, birthplace at Balkh, horiz.

Perf. 13¼x13, 13x13¼
2006, Nov. 26
1449-1450 A571 Set of 2   15.00 —
Size: 106x78mm
Imperf
1451 A571 150af multi   30.00 30.00

No. 1451 contains two perforated labels lacking country name or value. See Iran No. 2911, Syria No. 1574, Turkey No. 2971.

Successful Completion of Bonn Process A572

2007, Apr. 19   **Perf. 13¼x13**
1452 A572 25af multi   4.00 4.00

Dated 2006.

Mevlana Jalal ad-Din ar-Rumi (1207-73), Islamic Philosopher A573

2007, May 24
1453 A573 40af multi   6.00 6.00

Milli Attan Dance A574

2007, Aug. 19
1454 A574 38af multi   6.00 6.00

Natl. Day of Fine Arts — A575

Singers: 20af, Ustad Awal Mir. 22af, Mirmun Parwin.

2007, Sept. 25   **Perf. 13x13¼**
1455-1456 A575 Set of 2   7.50 7.50

Third Meeting of Economic Cooperation Organization Postal Authorities, Tehran — A576

2007, Dec. 22   **Perf. 13¼x13**
1457 A576 8af multi   2.00 2.00

National Unity — A577

Emperors: 25af, Ahmad Shah Baba (c. 1723-73). 30af, Mirwais Nika. 34af, Sultan Mahmood Ghaznawi (979-1030).

2007, Dec. 22   **Perf. 13x13¼**
1458-1460 A577 Set of 3   12.00 12.00

Red Crescent Society — A578

2009, Jan. 21 **Litho.** **Perf. 13x13¼**
1461 A578 17af multi   2.40 2.40

Rudaki (c. 859-c.940), Poet — A579

2009, Jan. 21
1462 A579 55af multi   6.50 6.50

World Enviornmental Protection Day — A580

2010, Jan. 1 **Litho.** **Perf. 13½x12¾**
1463 A580 5af multi   1.25 1.25

World Literacy Day A581

2011, Jan. 1 **Litho.**   **Perf. 14**
1464 A581 22af multi   4.00 4.00

Khwaja Abdullah Ansari (1006-88), Religious Commentator A582

2012, Jan. 1 **Litho.**   **Perf. 14**
1465 A582 50af multi

Dated 2009. See Iran No. 3016, Tajikistan No. 366.

Emblem and Flags of Members of South Asian Association for Regional Cooperation A583

2012, Feb. 1 **Litho.** **Perf. 13½x12¾**
1466 A583 40af multi   6.50 6.50

World Peace Day — A584

2012, Feb. 1 **Litho.** **Perf. 13½x12¾**
1467 A584 50af multi   6.50 6.50

Dated 2011.

SEMI-POSTAL STAMPS

Catalogue values for unused stamps in this section are for Never Hinged items.

No. 373 Surcharged in Violet

1952, July 12 **Unwmk.** **Perf. 12½**
B1 A122 40p + 30p cerise   5.25 3.00
B2 A122 125p + 30p cerise   7.75 3.50

1000th anniv. of the birth of Avicenna.

Children at Play — SP1

1955, July 3 **Typo.**   **Perf. 11**
B3 SP1 35p + 15p dk green   1.25 .70
B4 SP1 125p + 25p purple   2.50 1.25

The surtax was for child welfare.
Exist imperf. Values, set: unused $6.50; used $7.

Amir Sher Ali Khan, Tiger Head Stamp and Zahir Shah — SP2

1955, July 2   **Litho.**
B5 SP2 35p + 15p carmine   1.00 .55
B6 SP2 125p + 25p pale vio bl 1.90 1.00

85th anniv. of the Afghan post.
Exist imperf. Values, set: unused $5; used $6.

Children at Play — SP3

1956, June 20   **Typo.**
B7 SP3 35p + 15p brt vio bl   .90 .40
B8 SP3 140p + 15p dk org brn 2.25 .85

Issued for Children's Day. The surtax was for child welfare. No. B8 inscribed in French.
Exist imperf. Values, set: unused $8; used $8.75.

Pashtunistan Monument, Kabul — SP4

1956, Sept. 1   **Litho.**
B9 SP4 35p + 15p dp violet   .40 .25
B10 SP4 140p + 15p dk brown   1.10 .75

"Free Pashtunistan" Day. The surtax aided the "Free Pashtunistan" movement.
No. B9 measures 30½x19½mm; No. B10, 29x19mm. On sale and valid for use only on Sept. 1-2.
Exist imperf. Values, set: unused $6; used $7.50.

Globe and Sun — SP5

1956, Oct. 24   **Perf. 11**
B11 SP5 35p + 15p ultra   1.00 .90
B12 SP5 140p + 15p red brown 1.90 1.60

Afghanistan's UN admission, 10th anniv.
Exist imperf. Values, set: unused $14; used $17.50.

Children on Seesaw SP6

1957, June 20   **Unwmk.**
B13 SP6 35p + 15p brt rose   .85 .55
B14 SP6 140p + 15p ultra   1.60 1.40

Children's Day. Surtax for child welfare.
Exist imperf. Values, set: unused $3.25; used $4.

UN Headquarters and Emblems SP7

1957, Oct. 24   Perf. 11 Rough
B15 SP7 35p + 15p red brown   .60   .40
B16 SP7 140p + 15p lt ultra   1.10 1.10
United Nations Day.
Exist imperf. Values, set: unused $6; used $7.50.

Swimming Pool
and Children
SP8

1958, June 22   Perf. 11
B17 SP8 35p + 15p rose   .65   .40
B18 SP8 140p + 15p dl red brn   .80   .65
Children's Day. Surtax for child welfare.
Exist imperf. Values, set: unused $5; used $6.

Pashtunistan
Flag — SP9

1958, Aug. 31
B19 SP9 35p + 15p lt blue   .40   .25
B20 SP9 140p + 15p red brown   1.00 .65
Issued for "Free Pashtunistan Day."
Exist imperf. Values, set: unused $4; used $5.

Children
Playing Tug
of
War — SP10

1959, June 23   Litho.   Perf. 11
B21 SP10 35p + 15p brown vio   .60   .35
B22 SP10 165p + 15p brt pink   1.25 .50
Children's Day. Surtax for child welfare.
Exist imperf. Value set, unused or used, $5.

Pathans in
Tribal Dance
SP11

Perf. 11 Rough
1959, Sept.   Unwmk.
B23 SP11 35p + 15p green   .60   .35
B24 SP11 165p + 15p orange   1.25 .75
Issued for "Free Pashtunistan Day."
Exist imperf. Value set, unused or used, $2.50.

Afghan
Cavalryman with
UN Flag — SP12

1959, Oct. 24   Perf. 11 Rough
B25 SP12 35p + 15p orange   .35   .25
B26 SP12 165p + 15p lt bl grn   .75   .45
Issued for United Nations Day.
Exist imperf. Value set, unused or used, $2.50.

Children
SP13

1960, Oct. 23   Litho.
B27 SP13 75p + 25p lt ultra   .90   .35
B28 SP13 175p + 25p lt green   1.75 .50
Children's Day. Surtax for child welfare.
Exist imperf. Value set, unused or used, $2.75.

Man with
Spray Gun
SP14

1960, Sept. 6   Perf. 11 Rough
B29 SP14 50p + 50p orange   1.40 1.25
B30 SP14 175p + 50p red brown   3.50 2.75
11th anniversary of the WHO malaria control program in Afghanistan.
Exist imperf. Value set, unused or used, $7.50.

SP15

1960, Sept. 1   Unwmk.
B31 SP15 50p + 50p rose   .60   .30
B32 SP15 175p + 50p dk blue   1.40 1.10
Issued for "Free Pashtunistan Day."
Exist imperf. Value set, unused or used, $3.25.

Ambulance — SP16

1960, Oct. 16   Perf. 11
Crescent in Red
B33 SP16 50p + 50p violet   .65   .50
B34 SP16 175p + 50p blue   1.75 1.00
Issued for the Red Crescent Society.
Exist imperf. Value set, unused or used, $3.25.

Nos. 470-471
Surcharged in Blue
or Orange

1960, Dec. 31   Litho.   Perf. 11
B35 A166 50p + 25p dp org (Bl)   1.75 1.75
B36 A166 165p + 25p blue (O)   1.75 1.75
Exist imperf. Value set, unused or used, $11.
The souvenir sheets described after No. 471 were surcharged in carmine "+25 Ps" on each stamp. Values: normal colors, unused $6, used $6.50; reversed colors, unused $7.50, used $9.50.
See general note after No. 485.

Nos. 496-
500
Surcharged

Perf. 13½x14
1961, July 6   Unwmk.   Photo.
B37 A175 2p + 25p green &
          rose lil   .50   .50
B38 A175 2p + 25p brown & cit   .50   .50
B39 A175 5p + 25p gray & rose   .50   .50
B40 A175 10p + 25p blue & bis   .50   .50
B41 A175 15p + 25p sl bl & dl lil .50 .50
    Nos. B37-B41 (5)   2.50 2.50
UNICEF. The same surcharge was applied to an imperf. souvenir sheet like that noted after No. 505. Value $5.

Nos. 522-526 Surcharged "+25PS" and Crescent in Red
1961, Oct. 16   Perf. 13½x14
B42 A184 2p + 25p black   .50   .50
B43 A184 2p + 25p green   .50   .50
B44 A184 5p + 25p lilac rose   .50   .50
B45 A184 10p + 25p lilac   .50   .50
B46 A184 15p + 25p dk blue   .50   .50
    Nos. B42-B46 (5)   2.50 2.50
Issued for the Red Crescent Society.

Nos. 539-543 Surcharged in Red: "UNESCO + 25PS"
1962   Perf. 12
B47 A186 2p + 25p multi   .40   .40
B48 A186 2p + 25p multi   .40   .40
B49 A186 5p + 25p multi   .40   .40
B50 A186 10p + 25p multi   .40   .40
B51 A186 15p + 25p multi   .40   .40
    Nos. B47-B51 (5)   2.00 2.00
UNESCO. The same surcharge was applied to the souvenir sheets mentioned after No. 548. Value, 2 sheets, $10.

Nos. 553-561 Surcharged: "Dag Hammarskjöld +20PS"
1962, Sept. 17   Perf. 14x13½
B52 A187 2p + 20p   .25   .25
B53 A187 2p + 20p   .25   .25
B54 A187 5p + 20p   .25   .25
B55 A187 10p + 20p   .25   .25
B56 A187 15p + 20p   .25   .25
B57 A187 25p + 20p   .25   .25
B58 A187 50p + 20p   .30   .30
B59 A187 75p + 20p   .50   .50
B60 A187 100p + 20p   .80   .80
    Nos. B52-B60 (9)   3.10 3.10
In memory of Dag Hammarskjold, Sec. Gen. of the UN, 1953-61. Perf. and imperf. souvenir sheets exist. Value, 2 sheets, $6.50.

Nos. 583-593 Surcharged "+15PS"
1963, Mar. 15   Perf. 14x13½
B61 A193 2p + 15p   1.00 1.00
B62 A193 3p + 15p   1.00 1.00
B63 A193 5p + 15p   1.00 1.00
B64 A193 10p + 15p   1.00 1.00
B65 A193 15p + 15p   1.00 1.00
B66 A193 25p + 15p   1.00 1.00
B67 A193 50p + 15p   1.00 1.00
B68 A193 75p + 15p   1.00 1.00
B69 A193 100p + 15p   1.00 1.00
B70 A193 150p + 15p   1.00 1.00
B71 A193 175p + 15p   1.00 1.00
    Nos. B61-B71 (11)   11.00 11.00
WHO drive to eradicate malaria.

Nos. 672-672G, 672I Surcharged in Various Positions

1964, Mar. 9
B71A A213g 2p + 50p   .25   .25
B71B A213g 3p + 50p   .25   .25
B71C A213g 4p + 50p   .25   .25
B71D A213g 5p + 50p   .25   .25
B71E A213g 10p + 50p   .25   .25
B71F A213g 100p + 50p   .70   .70

B71G A213g 2af + 50p   1.50 1.50
B71H A213g 3af + 50p   2.10 2.10
    Nos. B71A-B71H (8)   5.55 5.55
Souvenir Sheet
B71J A213g 5af + 50p   4.50 4.50
Nos. B71E-B71G are airmail semi-postals.

Blood Transfusion
Kit — SP17

1964, Oct. 18   Litho.   Perf. 10½
B72 SP17 1af + 50p black & rose .40   .30
Issued for the Red Crescent Society and Red Crescent Week, Oct. 18-24.

First Aid
Station
SP18

1965, Oct. 16   Photo.   Perf. 13½x14
B73 SP18 1.50af + 50p multi   .35   .25
Issued for the Red Crescent Society.

Children
Playing
SP19

1966, Nov. 28   Photo.   Perf. 13½x14
B74 SP19 1af + 1af yel grn & cl .30   .25
B75 SP19 3af + 2af yel & brn   .65   .30
B76 SP19 7af + 3af rose lil & grn .95 .50
    Nos. B74-B76 (3)   1.90 1.00
Children's Day.

Nadir Shah
Presenting
Society
Charter
SP20

1967, Feb. 15   Photo.   Perf. 13x14
B77 SP20 2af + 1af red & dk grn .35   .25
B78 SP20 5af + 1af lil rose & brn .75 .35
Issued for the Red Crescent Society.

Vaccination
SP21

1967, June 6   Photo.   Perf. 12
B79 SP21 2af + 1af yellow & blk .25   .25
B80 SP21 5af + 2af pink & brn   .65   .35
The surtax was for anti-tuberculosis work.

Red
Crescent — SP22

1967, Oct. 18   Photo.   *Perf. 12*
Crescent in Red

B81 SP22 3af + 1af gray ol & blk   .25   .25
B82 SP22 5af + 1af dl bl & blk   .40   .25
Issued for the Red Crescent Society.

Queen
Humeira — SP23

1968, June 14   Photo.   *Perf. 12*

B83 SP23 2af + 2af red brown   .35   .25
B84 SP23 7af + 2af dull green .90   .60
Issued for Mother's Day.

Red
Crescent — SP24

1968, Oct. 16   Photo.   *Perf. 12*

B85 SP24 4af + 1af yel, blk & red   .60   .25
Issued for the Red Crescent Society.

Red Cross,
Crescent, Lion
and Sun
Emblems — SP25

1969, May 5   Litho.   *Perf. 14x13½*

B86 SP25 3af + 1af multicolored   .65   .35
B87 SP25 5af + 1af multicolored   .80   .35
League of Red Cross Societies, 50th anniv.

Mother and
Child — SP26

1969, June 14   Photo.   *Perf. 12*

B88 SP26 1af + 1af yel org & brn   .30   .25
B89 SP26 4af + 1af rose lil & pur   .50   .35
  a.   Souvenir sheet of 2   2.50 2.50

Mother's Day. No. B89a contains 2 imperf.
stamps similar to Nos. B88-B89. Sold for 10af.

Red
Crescent — SP27

1969, Oct. 16   Photo.   *Perf. 12*

B90 SP27 6af + 1af multi   .80   .30
Issued for the Red Crescent Society.

UN and FAO Emblems,
Farmer — SP28

1973, May 24   Photo.   *Perf. 13½*

B91 SP28 14af + 7af grnsh bl &
                            lil   1.40   .90
World Food Program, 10th anniversary.

Dome of the
Rock, Jerusalem
SP29

1977, Sept. 11   Photo.   *Perf. 14*

B92 SP29 12af + 3af multi   2.10   .60
Surtax for Palestinian families and soldiers.

15 Cent. (lunar) of Islamic Pilgrimage
(Hegira) — SP30

1981, Jan. 17   Litho.   *Perf. 12½x12*

B93 SP30 13af + 2af multi   1.75   .30

Red
Crescent Aid
Programs
SP31

1981, May 8   *Perf. 12x12½*

B94 SP31 1af + 4af multi   .65   .80

Intl. Year of
the Disabled
SP32

1981, Oct. 12   *Perf. 12x12½*

B95 SP32 6af + 1af multi   .90   .50

AIR POST STAMPS

Plane over
Kabul
AP1

Perf. 12, 12x11, 11
1939, Oct. 1   Typo.   Unwmk.

C1   AP1 5af orange   5.00   4.00
  a.   Imperf., pair ('47)   29.00 29.00
  b.   Horiz. pair, imperf. vert. 32.50 32.50
C2   AP1 10af blue   5.00   4.00
  a.   10af lt bl   8.00   6.00
  b.   Imperf., pair ('47)   29.00
  c.   Horiz. pair, imperf. vert. 32.50

C3   AP1 20af emerald   10.00   6.00
  a.   Imperf., pair ('47)   29.00
  b.   Horiz. pair, imperf. vert. 32.50
  c.   Vert. pair, imperf. horiz. 35.00
       Nos. C1-C3 (3)   20.00 14.00

These stamps come with clean-cut or rough
perforations.
Exist imperf. Value, set $30.
Counterfeits exist.

> **Catalogue values for unused stamps in this section, from this point to the end of the section, are for Never Hinged items.**

1948, June 14   *Perf. 12x11½*

C4   AP1 5af emerald   20.00 20.00
C5   AP1 10af red orange   20.00 20.00
C6   AP1 20af blue   20.00 20.00
       Nos. C4-C6 (3)   60.00 60.00
Imperforates exist.
Forgeries exist.

Plane over
Palace
Grounds,
Kabul
AP2

Imprint: "Waterlow & Sons, Limited, London"

1951-54   Engr.   *Perf. 13½*

C7   AP2 5af henna brn   3.00   .60
C8   AP2 5af dp grn ('54)   1.60   .40
C9   AP2 10af gray   6.50   1.60
C10 AP2 20af dark blue   9.00   2.50

1957

C11 AP2 5af ultra   1.75   .50
C12 AP2 10af dark vio   2.50   .90
       Nos. C7-C12 (6)   24.35   6.50
See No. C38.

Ariana
Plane over
Hindu
Kush
AP3

Perf. 11, Imperf.
1960-63   Litho.   Unwmk.

C13 AP3 75p light vio   .55   .25
C14 AP3 125p blue   .75   .35

Perf. 10½, 11

C14A AP3 5af citron ('63)   1.25   .80
        Nos. C13-C14A (3)   2.55 1.40

Imperf examples of Nos. C13-C14 are valued at approx. 50 percent more than the values shown.

Girl Scout — AP4

1962, Aug. 30   Photo.   *Perf. 11½x12*

C15 AP4 100p ocher & brn   .50   .50
C16 AP4 175p brt yel grn & brn   .90   .90

Women's Day. See Nos. 578-579 and note
on souvenir sheet.

Sports Type of Regular Issue, 1962

25p, 50p, Horse racing. 75p, 100p, Wrestling. 150p, Weight lifting. 175p, Soccer.

1962, Sept. 25   Unwmk.   *Perf. 12*
Black Inscriptions

C17 A195 25p rose & red brn   .25   .25
C18 A195 50p gray & red brn   .30   .30
C19 A195 75p pale vio & dk grn   .50   .50
C20 A195 100p gray ol & dk pur   .65   .65
C21 A195 150p rose lil & grn   .90   .90
C22 A195 175p sal & brn   1.00   1.00
        Nos. C17-C22 (6)   3.60   3.60

Children's Day Type of Regular Issue
Perf. 11½x12, 12x11½
1962, Oct. 14   Unwmk.

C23 A196 75p Runners   .60   .60
C24 A196 150p Peaches   1.10   1.10
C25 A196 200p Iris, vert.   1.50   1.50
        Nos. C23-C25 (3)   3.20   3.20
A souvenir sheet contains one each of Nos.
C23-C25. Value $4.00.

Red Crescent Type of Regular Issue
1962, Oct. 16   *Perf. 12*
Fruit and Flowers in Natural Colors;
Carmine Crescent

C26 A197 25p Grapes   .25   .25
C27 A197 50p Pears   .30   .30
C28 A197 100p Wistaria   .65   .65
        Nos. C26-C28 (3)   1.20   1.20

Two souvenir sheets exist. One contains a
150p gray brown stamp in blossom design, the
other a 200p gray stamp in wistaria design,
imperf. Value, each $5.00.

UN Type of Regular Issue
1962, Oct. 24   Photo.
Flags in Original Colors, Black
Inscriptions

C29 A198 75p blue   .30   .30
C30 A198 100p lt brn   .45   .45
C31 A198 125p brt grn   .60   .60
        Nos. C29-C31 (3)   1.35   1.35

Boy Scout Type of Regular Issue
1962, Oct. 25   Unwmk.   *Perf. 12*

C32 A199 25p gray, blk, dl grn
                            & sal   .30   .30
C33 A199 50p grn, brn & sal   .55   .55
C34 A199 75p bl grn, red brn &
                            sal   .80   .80
C35 A199 100p bl, slate & sal   1.00   1.00
        Nos. C32-C35 (4)   2.65   2.65

Teacher's Day Type of Regular Issue
1962, Oct. 25

C36 A200 100p Pole vault   .60   .60
C37 A200 150p High jump   .90   .90

A souvenir sheet contains one 250p pink
and slate green stamp in design of 150p. Values: perf $2.50; imperf $21.

Type of 1951-54
Imprint: "Thomas De La Rue & Co. Ltd."
1962   Engr.   *Perf. 13½*

C38 AP2 5af ultra   12.00   .90

Agriculture Types of Regular Issue
Unwmk.
1963, Mar. 1   Photo.   *Perf. 12*

C42 A204 100p dk car, grn & brn   .35   .35
C43 A203 150p ocher & blk   .60   .60
C44 A204 200p ultra, grn & brn   .90   .90
        Nos. C42-C44 (3)   1.85   1.85

Hands
Holding
Wheat
Emblem
AP5

1963, Mar. 27   Photo.   *Perf. 14*

C45 AP5 500p lil, lt brn & brn   1.10   1.10
FAO "Freedom from Hunger" campaign.
Two souvenir sheets exist. One contains a
1000p blue green, light brown and brown, type
AP5, imperf. The other contains a 200p brown
and green and 300p ultramarine, yellow and
ocher in rice and corn designs, type A205.
Values $5.50 and $4.

Meteorological Day Type of Regular Issue

Designs: 100p, 500p, Meteorological measuring instrument. 200p, 400p, Weather station. 300p, Rockets in space.

1963, May 23   *Imperf.*

C46 A206 100p brn & bl   3.00   3.00

Perf. 13½x14

C47 A206 200p brt grn & lil   .90   .90
C48 A206 300p dk bl & rose   1.40   1.20
C49 A206 400p bl & dl red brn   1.90   1.75

C50 A206 500p car rose &
                   gray grn   2.25   2.00
      Nos. C47-C50 (4)   6.45   5.85
  Nos. C47 and C50 printed se-tenant.
  Nos. C47 and C50 exist imperf. Values,
unused or used: 200p, $6; 500p, $16.
  Two souvenir sheets exist. One contains a
125p red and brown stamp in rocket design.
The other contains a 100p blue and dull red
brown in "rockets in space" design. Values
$4.50 and $11.

Kabul International Airport — AP8

Perf. 12x11½

1964, Apr.   Unwmk.   Photo.
C57 AP8 10af red lil & grn   .75   .25
C58 AP8 20af dk grn & red lil   .90   .35
  a.   Perf. 12 ('68)   5.00   3.00
C59 AP8 50af dk bl & grnsh bl   2.50   1.00
  a.   Perf. 12 ('68)   8.00   5.00
      Nos. C57-C59 (3)   4.15   1.60

  Inauguration of Kabul Airport Terminal.
Nos. C58a-C59a are 36mm wide. Nos.
C58-C59 are 35½mm wide.

Zahir Shah and Kabul Airport — AP9

100af, Zahir Shah and Ariana Plane.

1971   Photo.   Perf. 12½x13½
C60 AP9 50af multi   4.00   4.00
C61 AP9 100af blk, red & grn   5.00   3.00

  Remainders of No. C60 were used, summer
in 1978, with king's portrait torn or cut off.

REGISTRATION STAMPS

R1

**Dated "1309"
Pelure Paper**

1891   Unwmk.   Litho.   *Imperf.*
F1 R1 1r slate blue   2.40
  a.   Tete beche pair   13.50

  Genuinely used examples of No. F1 are
rare. Counterfeit cancellations exist.

R2

Dated "1311"

1893   Thin Wove Paper
F2 R2 1r black, *green*   2.00

  Genuinely used examples of No. F2 are
rare. Counterfeit cancellations exist.

R3

1894   Undated
F3 R3 2ab black, *green*   9.50   11.00

  12 varieties. See note below Nos. 189-190.

R4

1898-1900   Undated
F4   R4 2ab black, *deep rose*   4.50   4.50
F5   R4 2ab black, *lilac rose* 6.50   5.00
F6   R4 2ab black, *magenta*   8.00   5.00
F7   R4 2ab black, *salmon*   4.50   4.50
F8   R4 2ab black, *orange*   4.50   4.50
F9   R4 2ab black, *yellow*   4.50   3.50
F10 R4 2ab black, *green*   4.50   3.50
      Nos. F4-F10 (7)   37.00 30.50

  Many shades of paper.
  Nos. F4-F10 come in two sizes, measured
between outer frame lines: 52x36mm, 1st
printing; 46x33mm, 2nd printing. The outer
frame line (not pictured) is 3-6mm from inner
frame line.
  Used on P.O. receipts.

OFFICIAL STAMPS

Coat of
Arms
O1

**1909   Unwmk.   Typo.   Perf. 12
Wove Paper**

O1 O1 red   1.25   1.25
  a.   Carmine ('19?)   2.50   6.50

  Later printings of No. O1 in scarlet, vermilion, claret, etc., on various types of paper,
were issued until 1927.

Coat of Arms — O2

1939-68?   Typo.   Perf. 11, 12
O3 O2 15p emerald   1.10   .80
O4 O2 30p ocher ('40)   1.50   1.50
O5 O2 45p dark carmine   1.25   1.25
O6 O2 50p brt car ('68)   .70   .70
  a.   50p carmine rose ('55)   1.25   .70
O7 O2 1af brt red violet   2.00   1.75
      Nos. O3-O7 (5)   6.55   6.00

  Size of 50p, 24x31mm, others 22½x28mm.

┌─────────────────────────────────┐
│ **Catalogue values for unused** │
│ **stamps in this section, from this** │
│ **point to the end of the section, are** │
│ **for Never Hinged items.** │
└─────────────────────────────────┘

1964-65   Litho.   Perf. 11
O8 O2 50p rose   .90   .90
  a.   50p salmon ('65)   2.00   2.00

Stamps of this type are revenues.

PARCEL POST STAMPS

Coat of
Arms — PP1

PP2

PP3

PP4

1909   Unwmk.   Typo.   Perf. 12
Q1 PP1 3sh bister   1.25   2.25
  a.   Imperf., pair   —
Q2 PP2 1kr olive gray   3.50   3.50
  a.   Imperf., pair   —
Q3 PP3 1r orange   3.25   3.25
Q4 PP3 1r olive green   24.00   4.50
Q5 PP4 2r red   4.00   4.00
      Nos. Q1-Q5 (5)   36.00 17.50

Type I

Type II

  A 1909 undenominated dull olive
green Official parcel post stamp exists
with two types. Type I has thinner and
more rays below the crest; Type II has

---

fewer and wider rays. Values: $450
each. A pair, imperf between, exists.
Value, $1,500. A complete sheet of two
is known perforated on all sides.

1916-18
Q6 PP1 3sh green   1.75   3.50
Q7 PP2 1kr pale red   3.00   1.50
  a.   1kr rose red ('18)   4.00   4.00
Q8 PP3 1r brown org   3.50   1.75
  a.   1r deep brown ('18)   12.00   3.00
Q9 PP4 2r blue   6.25   6.50
      Nos. Q6-Q9 (4)   14.50 13.25

  Nos. Q1-Q9 sometimes show letters of the
papermaker's watermark "HOWARD &
JONES LONDON."
  Ungummed stamps are remainders. They
sell for one-third the price of mint stamps.

Old Habibia College, Near
Kabul — PP5

1921   Wove Paper
Q10 PP5 10pa chocolate   5.00   5.75
  a.   Tete beche pair   22.50 22.50
Q11 PP5 15pa light brn   7.00   7.50
  a.   Tete beche pair   27.50 27.50
Q12 PP5 30pa red violet   12.50   7.50
  a.   Tete beche pair   40.00 40.00
  b.   Laid paper   15.00 15.00
Q13 PP5 1r brt blue   14.00 14.00
  a.   Tete beche pair   65.00 65.00
      Nos. Q10-Q13 (4)   38.50 34.75

  Stamps of this issue are usually perforated
on one or two sides only.
  The laid paper of No. Q12b has a
papermaker's watermark in the sheet.

**Handstamped in black on Nos. Q10-
Q13**

PP5a

1923, Feb. 26
Q13B PP5a 10pa chocolate   —   —
Q13C PP5a 15pa light brn   —   —
Q13D PP5a 30pa red violet   —   —
Q13E PP5a 1r brt blue   —   —

  5th Independence Day.
  Two types of handstamp exist.
  Forgeries exist.
  The existence of No. Q13E has been ques-
tioned. The editors are seeking information on
this stamp.

PP6

1924-26   **Wove Paper**
Q15 PP6 5kr ultra ('26)   400.00 400.00
Q16 PP6 5r lilac   20.00 25.00

A 15r rose exists, but is not known to have been placed in use. Value, unused $400.

PP7

PP8

1928-29   *Perf. 11, 11 Horizontally*
Q17 PP7 2r yellow orange   8.00 7.00
Q18 PP7 2r green ('29)   7.50 7.50
Q19 PP8 3r deep green   10.50 10.50
Q20 PP8 3r brown ('29)   9.50 10.50
   Nos. Q17-Q20 (4)   35.50 35.50

A 3r violet imperforate stamp in design No. PP8 exists and is likely a proof. Value, *$250.*

POSTAL TAX STAMPS

Aliabad Hospital near Kabul PT1

Pierre and Marie Curie PT2

    Perf. 12x11½, 12
1938, Dec. 22   **Typo.**   **Unwmk.**
RA1 PT1 10p peacock grn   3.25 *5.00*
RA2 PT2 15p dull blue   3.25 *5.00*

Obligatory on all mail Dec. 22-28, 1938. The money was used for the Aliabad Hospital. See note with CD80.

> Catalogue values for unused stamps in this section, from this point to the end of the section, are for Never Hinged items.

PT3

Begging Child — PT4

1949, May 28   **Typo.**   *Perf. 12*
RA3 PT3 35p red orange   3.25 2.10
RA4 PT4 125p ultra   4.00 2.10

United Nations Children's Day, May 28. Obligatory on all foreign mail on that date. Proceeds were used for child welfare.

Paghman Arch and UN Emblem PT5

1949, Oct. 24
RA5 PT5 125p dk blue green   15.00 9.00

4th anniv. of the UN. Valid one day only. Issued in sheets of 9 (3x3).

Zahir Shah and Map of Afghanistan — PT6

1950, Mar. 30   **Typo.**
RA6 PT6 125p blue green   4.50 1.50

Return of Zahir Shah from a trip to Europe for his health. Valid for two weeks. The tax was used for public health purposes.

Hazara Youth — PT7

1950, May 28   **Typo.**   *Perf. 11½*
RA7 PT7 125p dk blue green   4.50 2.50

Tax for Child Welfare. Obligatory and valid only on May 28, 1950, on foreign mail.

Ruins of Qalai Bist and Globe — PT8

1950, Oct. 24
RA8 PT8 1.25af ultramarine   9.00 5.25

5th anniv. of the UN. Proceeds went to Afghanistan's UN Projects Committee.

Zahir Shah and Medical Center PT9

1950, Dec. 22   **Typo.**   *Perf. 11½*
     Size: 38x25mm
RA9 PT9   35p carmine   1.25 .60
     Size: 46x30mm
RA10 PT9 1.25af black   7.50 2.50

The tax was for the national Graduate School of Medicine.

Koochi Girl with Lamb PT10

Kohistani Boy and Sheep — PT11

1951, May 28
RA11 PT10   35p emerald   1.50 .90
RA12 PT11 1.25af ultramarine   1.50 .90

The tax was for Child Welfare.

Distributing Gifts to Children — PT12

Qandahari Boys Dancing the "Attan" PT13

1952, May 28   **Litho.**
RA13 PT12 35p chocolate   .80 .65
RA14 PT13 125p violet   1.60 .95

The tax was for Child Welfare. Exist imperf. Values, set: unused $6; used $9.50.

Soldier Receiving First Aid — PT14

1952, Oct. 19
RA15 PT14 10p light green   .80 .65

Exist imperf. Value: unused $2.50; used $4.

Stretcher-bearers and Wounded — PT15

Soldier Assisting Wounded — PT16

1953, Oct.
RA16 PT15 10p yel grn & org red   .80 .80
RA17 PT16 10p vio brn & org red   .80 .80

Exist imperf. Values, set: unused $4; used $5.

Prince Mohammed Nadir — PT17

1953, May 28
RA18 PT17 35p orange yellow   .50 .25
RA19 PT17 125p chalky blue   .90 .55

No. RA19 is inscribed in French "Children's Day." The tax was for child welfare.
Exist imperf. Values, set: unused $4; used $5.

Map and
Young
Musicians
PT18

1954, May 28   Unwmk.   Perf. 11
RA20 PT18 35p purple   .65 .40
RA21 PT18 125p ultra   1.90 1.25
No. RA21 is inscribed in French. The tax
was for child welfare.
Exist imperf. Values, set: unused $4.50;
used $6.50.

PT19

1954, Oct. 17   Perf. 11½
RA22 PT19 20p blue & red   .75 .35
Exists imperf. Values: unused $2; used
$2.50.

Red Crescent
PT20

1955, Oct. 18   Perf. 11
RA23 PT20 20p dull grn & car   .70 .35
Exists imperf. Values: unused $1.50; used
$2.

Zahir Shah and
Red Crescent
PT21

1956, Oct. 18
RA24 PT21 20p lt grn & rose car   .40 .25
Exists imperf. Value, unused or used, $1.25.

Red Crescent Headquarters,
Kabul — PT22

1957, Oct. 17
RA25 PT22 20p lt ultra & car   .90 .60
Exists imperf. Values: unused $2; used
$2.50.

Map and
Crescent
PT23

1958, Oct.   Unwmk.   Perf. 11
RA26 PT23 25p yel grn & red   .40 .30
Exists imperf. Values: unused 50¢; used 80¢.

PT24

1959, Oct. 17   Litho.   Perf. 11
RA27 PT24 25p lt violet & red   .40 .25
The tax on Nos. RA15-RA17, RA22-RA27
was for the Red Crescent Society. Use of
these stamps was required for one week.
Exists imperf. Values: unused 50¢; used
80¢.

AGÜERA, LA

ä-gwä'rä

LOCATION — An administrative district in southern Rio de Oro on the northwest coast of Africa.
GOVT. — Spanish possession
AREA — Because of indefinite political boundaries, figures for area and population are not available.

100 Centimos = 1 Peseta

Type of 1920 Issue of
Rio de Oro Overprinted

1920, June   Typo.   Unwmk.   Perf. 13

1	A8	1c blue green	2.75	3.25
2	A8	2c olive brown	2.75	3.25
3	A8	5c deep green	2.75	3.25
4	A8	10c light red	2.75	3.25
5	A8	15c yellow	2.75	3.25
6	A8	20c lilac	2.75	3.25
7	A8	25c deep blue	2.75	3.25
8	A8	30c dark brown	2.75	3.25
9	A8	40c pink	2.75	3.25
10	A8	50c bright blue	9.00	10.00
11	A8	1p red brown	15.00	20.00
12	A8	4p dark violet	42.50	50.00
13	A8	10p orange	90.00	115.00
		Nos. 1-13 (13)	181.25	224.25
		Set, never hinged	400.00	

Very fine examples of Nos. 1-13 will be somewhat off center. Well-centered examples are uncommon and will sell for more.

King Alfonso XIII — A2

1922, June

14	A2	1c turquoise bl (I)	1.00	1.50
15	A2	2c dark green	1.50	1.50
16	A2	5c blue green	1.50	1.50
17	A2	10c red	1.50	1.50
18	A2	15c red brown	1.50	1.50
19	A2	20c yellow	1.50	1.50
20	A2	25c deep blue	1.50	1.50
21	A2	30c dark brown	1.50	1.50
22	A2	40c rose red	1.75	2.00
23	A2	50c red violet	6.25	5.75
24	A2	1p rose	14.50	15.00
25	A2	4p violet	37.50	40.00
26	A2	10p orange	55.00	60.00
		Nos. 14-26 (13)	126.50	134.75
		Set, never hinged	200.00	

Nos. 1-26 with A.000.000 on reverse are specimens. For detailed listings, see the Scott Classic Specialized catalog.
For later issues, see Spanish Sahara.

AITUTAKI

į̇t-ə-'täk-ē

LOCATION — One of the larger Cook Islands, in the South Pacific Ocean northeast of New Zealand
GOVT. — A dependency of New Zealand
AREA — 7 sq. mi.
POP. — 2,335 (1981)

The Cook Islands were attached to New Zealand in 1901. Stamps of Cook Islands were used in 1892-1903 and 1932-72.

Aitutaki acquired its own postal service in August 1972, though remaining part of Cook Islands.

12 Pence = 1 Shilling
100 Cents = 1 Dollar (1972)

> **Catalogue values for unused stamps in this country are for Never Hinged items, beginning with Scott 37.**

Watermark

Wmk. 61- Single-lined NZ and Star Close Together

Stamps of New Zealand Surcharged in Red or Blue

a   b

1903   Engr.   Wmk. 61   Perf. 14

1	A18(a)	½p green (R)	5.00	7.00
2	A35(b)	1p rose (Bl)	5.25	6.25

c

d   e

f

Perf. 11

3	A22(c)	2½p blue (R)	19.50	15.00
4	A23(d)	3p yel brn (Bl)	19.00	16.50
5	A26(e)	6p red (Bl)	32.50	27.50
6	A29(f)	1sh scar (Bl)	60.00	95.00
a.		1sh orange red (Bl)	72.50	105.00

1911, Sept.   Typo.   Perf. 14x15

7	A41(a)	½p yel grn (R)	1.00	8.75

Engr.
Perf. 14

9	A22(c)	2½p dp blue (R)	8.50	19.00

g   h

1913-16   Typo.

10	A42(b)	1p rose (Bl)	3.25	13.50

Engr.

12	A41(g)	6p car rose (Bl) ('16)	52.50	145.00
13	A41(h)	1sh ver (Bl) ('14)	62.50	150.00

1916-17   Perf. 14x13½, 14x14½

17	A45(g)	6p car rose (Bl)	9.00	29.00
18	A45(h)	1sh ver (Bl) ('17)	14.00	95.00
		Nos. 1-18 (13)	292.00	627.50

New Zealand Stamps of 1909-19 Overprinted in Red or Dark Blue

1917-20   Typo.   Perf. 14x15

19	A43	½p yellow grn ('20)	1.00	6.25
20	A42	1p car (Bl) ('20)	5.00	35.00
21	A47	1½p gray black	4.50	32.50
22	A47	1½p brown org ('19)	.90	7.50
23	A43	3p choc (Bl) ('19)	3.75	22.00

Perf. 14x13½, 14x14½
Engr.

24	A44	2½p dull blue ('18)	1.90	16.00
25	A45	3p vio brn (Bl) ('18)	1.75	32.50
26	A45	6p car rose (Bl)	5.00	22.50
27	A45	1sh vermilion (Bl)	13.00	35.00
		Nos. 19-27 (9)	36.80	209.25

Landing of Capt. Cook   A15   Avarua Waterfront   A16

Capt. James Cook — A17   Palm — A18

Houses at Arorangi — A19

Avarua Harbor — A20

1920   Engr.   Unwmk.   Perf. 14

28	A15	½p green & black	3.75	26.00
29	A16	1p car & blk	3.75	18.00
30	A17	1½p brown & blk	6.25	13.00
31	A18	3p dp blue & blk	2.75	15.00
32	A19	6p slate & red brn	6.25	15.00
33	A20	1sh claret & blk	10.00	22.50
		Nos. 28-33 (6)	32.75	109.50

Inverted centers, double frames, etc. are from printers waste.

Rarotongan Chief (Te Po) — A21

1924-27   Wmk. 61   Perf. 14

34	A15	½p green & blk ('27)	2.10	25.00
35	A16	1p carmine & blk	6.25	12.50
36	A21	2½p blue & blk ('27)	8.00	80.00
		Nos. 34-36 (3)	16.35	117.50

> **Catalogue values for unused stamps in this section, from this point to the end of the section, are for Never Hinged items.**

Cook Islands Nos. 199-200, 202, 205-206, 210, 212-213, 215-217 Ovptd.

1972   Photo.   Unwmk.   Perf. 14x13½

37	A34	½c gold & multi	.40	.90
38	A34	1c gold & multi	.85	1.25
39	A34	2½c gold & multi	2.50	7.50
40	A34	4c gold & multi	.85	1.00
41	A34	5c gold & multi	3.00	8.50
42	A34	10c gold & multi	3.00	6.25
43	A34	20c gold & multi	3.75	1.10
44	A34	25c gold & multi	.90	1.25
45	A34	50c gold & multi	2.75	3.25
46	A35	$1 gold & multi	4.50	6.00
47	A35	$2 gold & multi	1.00	1.10
		Nos. 37-47 (11)	23.50	38.10

Overprint horizontal on Nos. 46-47. On $2, overprint is in capitals of different font; size: 21x3mm.
Issued: Nos. 37-46, Aug. 9; No. 47, Nov. 24.

Same Overprint Horizontal in Silver On Cook Islands Nos. 330-332

1972, Oct. 27   Perf. 13½

48	A53	1c gold & multi	.25	.25
49	A53	5c gold & multi	.25	.25
50	A53	10c gold & multi	.30	.30
		Nos. 48-50 (3)	.80	.80

Fluorescence

Starting in 1972, stamps carry a "fluorescent security underprinting" in a multiple pattern of New Zealand's coat of arms with "Aitutaki" above, "Cook Islands" below and two stars at each side.

Silver Wedding Type of Cook Islands

1972, Nov. 20   Photo.   Perf. 13½
Size: 29x40mm

51	A54	5c silver & multi	3.25	2.50

Size: 66x40mm

52	A54	15c silver & multi	1.25	1.25

25th anniversary of the marriage of Queen Elizabeth II and Prince Philip. Nos. 51-52 printed in sheets of 5 stamps and one label.

Flower Issue of Cook Islands Overprinted

1972, Dec. 11   Photo.   Perf. 14x13½

53	A34	½c on #199	.25	.25
54	A34	1c on #200	.25	.25
55	A34	2½c on #202	.25	.25
56	A34	4c on #205	.30	.25
57	A34	5c on #206	.30	.25
58	A34	10c on #210	.40	.35
59	A34	20c on #212	1.25	.45
60	A34	25c on #213	.55	.60
61	A34	50c on #215	.85	.90
62	A35	$1 on #216	1.25	1.75
		Nos. 53-62 (10)	5.65	5.30

See Nos. 73-76.

The Passion of
Christ, by Mathias
Grunewald — A22

Paintings: No. 63b, St. Veronica, by Rogier van der Weyden. No. 63c, Crucifixion, by Raphael. No. 63d, Resurrection, by della Francesca. No. 64a, Last Supper, by Master of Amiens. No. 64b, Condemnation of Christ, by Hans Holbein, the Elder. No. 64c, Crucifixion, by Rubens. No. 64d, Resurrection, by El Greco. No. 65a, Passion of Christ, by El Greco. No. 65b, St. Veronica, by Jakob Cornelisz. No. 65c, Crucifixion, by Rubens. No. 65d, Resurrection, by Dierik Bouts.

Perf. 13½

1973, Apr. 6	**Photo.**		**Unwmk.**
63	Block of 4	1.00	.40
a.-d.	A22 1c any single	.25	.25
64	Block of 4	1.25	1.00
a.-d.	A22 5c any single	.30	.25
65	Block of 4	1.40	1.75
a.-d.	A22 10c any single	.35	.25
	Nos. 63-65 (3)	3.65	3.15

Easter. Printed in blocks of 4 in sheets of 40. Design descriptions in top and bottom margins.

Coin Type of Cook Islands

Queen Elizabeth II Coins: 1c, Taro leaf. 2c, Pineapples. 5c, Hibiscus. 10c, Oranges. 20c, Fairy terns. 50c, Bonito. $1, Tangaroa, Polynesian god of creation, vert.

1973, May 14	**Perf. 13x13½**		
	Size: 37x24mm		
66	A55 1c dp car & multi	.25	.25
67	A55 2c blue & multi	.25	.25
68	A55 5c green & multi	.25	.25
	Size: 46x30mm		
69	A55 10c vio blue & multi	.25	.25
70	A55 20c green & multi	.30	.30
71	A55 50c dp car & multi	.60	.40
	Size: 32x54½mm		
72	A55 $1 blue, blk & sil	.80	.50
	Nos. 66-72 (7)	2.70	2.20

Cook Islands coinage commemorating silver wedding anniv. of Queen Elizabeth II.
Printed in sheets of 20 stamps and label showing Westminster Abbey.

Cook Islands Nos. 208, 210, 212 and 215 Overprinted Like Nos. 53-62 and: "TENTH ANNIVERSARY/ CESSATION/ OF/ NUCLEAR TESTING/ TREATY"

1973, July	**Photo.**	**Perf. 14x13½**	
73	A34 8c gold & multi	.25	.25
74	A34 10c gold & multi	.25	.25
75	A34 20c gold & multi	.35	.35
76	A34 50c gold & multi	.75	.75
	Nos. 73-76 (4)	1.60	1.60

Nuclear Test Ban Treaty, 10th anniv., protest against French nuclear testing on Mururoa Atoll.

Princess
Anne,
Hibiscus
A23

Design: 30c, Mark Phillips and hibiscus.

1973, Nov. 14	**Photo.**	**Perf. 13½x14**	
77	A23 25c gold & multi	.25	.25
78	A23 30c gold & multi	.30	.30
a.	Souvenir sheet of 2, #77-78	.65	.65

Wedding of Princess Anne and Capt. Mark Phillips.

Virgin and Child, by Il Perugino — A24

Paintings of the Virgin and Child by various masters — No. 79: a, Van Dyck. b, Bartolommeo Montagna. c, Carlo Crivelli. d, Il Perugino. No. 80: a, Cima da Conegliano. b, Memling. c, Veronese. d, Veronese. No. 81: a, Raphael. b, Lorenzo Lotto. c, Del Colle. d, Memling.

1973, Dec.	**Photo.**	**Perf. 13**	
79	A24 1c Block of 4, #a.-d.	.50	.50
80	A24 5c Block of 4, #a.-d.	1.00	1.00
81	A24 10c Block of 4, #a.-d.	1.25	1.25
	Nos. 79-81 (3)	2.75	2.75

Christmas. Printed in blocks of 4 in sheets of 48. Design descriptions in margins.

Murex
Ramosus
A25

Terebra Maculata — A26

Pacific Shells: 1c, Nautilus macromphalus. 2c, Harpa major. 3c, Phalium strigatum. 4c, Cypraea talpa. 5c, Mitra stictica. 8c, Charonia tritonis. 10c, Murex triremis. 20c, Oliva sericea. 25c, Tritonalia rubeta. 60c, Strombus latissimus. $1, Biplex perca. $5, Cypraea hesitata.

1974-75	**Photo.**	**Perf. 13**	
82	A25 ½c silver & multi	.95	.95
83	A25 1c silver & multi	.95	.95
84	A25 2c silver & multi	.95	.95
85	A25 3c silver & multi	.95	.95
86	A25 4c silver & multi	.95	.95
87	A25 5c silver & multi	.95	.95
88	A25 8c silver & multi	.95	.95
89	A25 10c silver & multi	.95	.85
90	A25 20c silver & multi	1.25	.85
91	A25 25c silver & multi	1.25	.85
92	A25 60c silver & multi	3.75	1.10
93	A25 $1 silver & multi	2.50	1.25
	Perf. 14		
94	A26 $2 silver & multi	6.00	6.00
95	A26 $5 silver & multi	27.50	9.50
	Nos. 82-95 (14)	49.85	27.05

Issued: Nos. 82-93, 1/31/74; $2, 1/20/75; $5, 2/28/75.

For overprints see Nos. O1-O16.

William
Bligh and
"Bounty"
A27

No. 96, shown. No. 97, "Bounty" at sea. No. 98, Bligh and "Bounty" off Aitutaki. No. 99, Chart of Aitutaki, 1856. No. 100, James Cook and "Resolution". No. 101, Maps of Aitutaki and Pacific Ocean.

Size: 38x22mm

1974, Apr. 11	**Photo.**	**Perf. 13**	
96	A27 1c multicolored	.45	.45
97	A27 1c multicolored	.45	.45
a.	Pair, #96-97	1.00	1.00
98	A27 5c multicolored	1.00	1.00
99	A27 5c multicolored	1.00	1.00
a.	Pair, #98-99	2.25	2.25
100	A27 8c multicolored	1.25	1.25
101	A27 8c multicolored	1.25	1.25
a.	Pair, #100-101	2.75	2.75
	Nos. 96-101,C1-C6 (12)	10.60	10.10

Capt. William Bligh (1754-1817), European discoverer of Aitutaki, Apr. 11, 1789.

Aitutaki
Nos. 1 &
2 Map
and UPU
Emblem
A28

Design: 50c, Aitutaki Nos. 4 and 28, map of Aitutaki and UPU emblem.

1974, July 15	**Photo.**	**Perf. 13½**	
102	A28 25c blue & multi	.75	.75
103	A28 50c blue & multi	1.00	1.00
a.	Souvenir sheet of 2, #102-103	2.00	2.00

UPU, cent. Printed in sheets of 5 plus label showing UPU emblem.

A29

Designs: Paintings of the Virgin and Child by: 1c, Van der Goes. 5c, Giovanni Bellini. 8c, Gerard David. 10c, Antonello da Messina. 25c, Joos van Cleve. 30c, Maitre de St. Catherine.

1974, Oct. 11	**Photo.**	**Perf. 13½**	
104	A29 1c multicolored	.25	.25
105	A29 5c multicolored	.25	.25
106	A29 8c multicolored	.25	.25
107	A29 10c multicolored	.05	.05
108	A29 25c multicolored	.35	.35
109	A29 30c multicolored	.75	.75
a.	Souvenir sheet of 6, #104-109	2.00	2.00
	Nos. 104-109 (6)	2.10	2.10

Christmas. Nos. 104-109 printed in sheets of 15 stamps and corner label. See Nos. B1-B6.

A30

Designs: Churchill portraits — 10c, Dublin, Age 5. 25c, As young man. 30c, Inspecting troops, WWII. 50c, Painting. $1, Giving V sign.

1974, Nov. 29	**Photo.**	**Perf. 14**	
110	A30 10c multicolored	.25	.25
111	A30 25c multicolored	.25	.25
112	A30 30c multicolored	.30	.25
113	A30 50c multicolored	.50	.50
114	A30 $1 multicolored	.85	.85
a.	Souvenir sheet of 5, #110-114 + label, perf. 13½	4.50	4.50
	Nos. 110-114 (5)	2.15	2.10

Sir Winston Churchill (1874-1965). Nos. 110-114 printed in sheets of 5 stamps and corner label.

Emblem
US &
USSR
Flags
A31

50c, Icarus and Apollo Soyuz spacecraft.

1975, July 24	**Photo.**	**Perf. 13x14½**	
115	A31 25c multicolored	.30	.30
116	A31 50c multicolored	.65	.65
a.	Souvenir sheet of 2	1.40	1.40

Apollo Soyuz space test project (Russo-American cooperation), launching July 15; link-up July 17. Nos. 115 and 116 each printed in sheets of 5 stamps and one label showing area of Apollo splash-downs. No. 116a contains one each of Nos. 115-116 with gold and black border and inscription.

Madonna and Child, by Pietro
Lorenzetti — A32

Paintings: 7c, Adoration of the Kings, by Rogier van der Weyden. 15c, Madonna and Child, by Bartolommeo Montagna. 20c, Adoration of the Shepherds.

1975, Nov. 24	**Photo.**	**Perf. 14x13½**	
117	A32 Strip of 3	.35	.35
a.	6c St. Francis	.25	.25
b.	6c Madonna and Child	.25	.25
c.	6c St. John the Evangelist	.25	.25
118	A32 Strip of 3	.40	.40
a.	7c One King	.25	.25
b.	7c Madonna and Child	.25	.25
c.	7c Two Kings	.25	.25
119	A32 Strip of 3	.75	.75
a.	15c St. Joseph	.25	.25
b.	15c Madonna and Child	.25	.25
c.	15c St. John the Baptist	.25	.25
120	A32 Strip of 3	1.10	1.10
a.	20c One Shepherd	.25	.25
b.	20c Madonna and Child	.25	.25
c.	20c Two Shepherds	.25	.25
d.	Souv. sheet of 12, #117-120, perf. 13½	2.75	2.75
	Nos. 117-120 (4)	2.60	2.60

Christmas. Nos. 117-120 printed in sheets of 30 (10 strips of 3).
For surcharges see Nos. B7-B10.

Descent from the
Cross,
detail — A33

Designs (Painting, Flemish School, 16th Century): 30c, Virgin Mary, disciple and body of Jesus. 35c, Mary Magdalene and disciple.

1976, Apr. 5	**Photo.**	**Perf. 13½**	
121	A33 15c gold & multi	.25	.25
122	A33 30c gold & multi	.30	.30
123	A33 35c gold & multi	.45	.45
a.	Souvenir sheet of 3	1.25	1.25
	Nos. 121-123 (3)	1.00	1.00

Easter. No. 123a contains 3 stamps similar to Nos. 121-123, perf. 13, in continuous design without gold frames and white margins.

Declaration of Independence — A34

Paintings by John Trumbull: 35c, Surrender of Cornwallis at Yorktown. 50c, Washington's Farewell Address. a, "1976 BICENTENARY." b, "UNITED STATES." c, "INDEPENDENCE 1776."

1976, June 1   Photo.   Perf. 13½

124	A34	Strip of 3	1.25 1.25
a.-c.		30c any single	.30 .30
125	A34	Strip of 3	1.50 1.50
a.-c.		35c any single	.40 .40
126	A34	Strip of 3	2.00 2.00
a.-c.		50c any single	.55 .55
d.		Souvenir sheet of 9 (3x3)	5.00 5.00
		Nos. 124-126 (3)	4.75 4.75

American Bicentennial. Nos. 124-126 printed in sheets of 5 strips of 3 and 3-part corner label showing portrait of John Trumbull, commemorative inscription and portraits of Washington (30c), John Adams (35c) and Jefferson (50c). No. 126d contains 3 strips similar to Nos. 124-126.

Bicycling A35

Montreal Olympic Games Emblem and: 35c, Sailing. 60c, Field hockey. 70c, Running.

1976, July 15   Photo.   Perf. 13x14

127	A35	15c multicolored	.30 .30
128	A35	35c multicolored	.50 .45
129	A35	60c multicolored	.75 .70
130	A35	70c multicolored	1.00 .90
a.		Souvenir sheet of 4	3.00 3.00
		Nos. 127-130 (4)	2.55 2.55

21st Olympic Games, Montreal, Canada, July 17-Aug. 1. Nos. 127-130 printed in sheets of 5 stamps and label showing coat of Arms and Montreal Olympic Games emblem. No. 130a contains 4 stamps similar to Nos. 127-130 with gold margin around each stamp.

Nos. 127-130a Overprinted

1976, July 30

131	A35	15c multicolored	.25 .25
132	A35	35c multicolored	.40 .40
133	A35	60c multicolored	.80 .80
134	A35	70c multicolored	.80 .80
a.		Souvenir sheet of 4	2.50 2.50
		Nos. 131-134 (4)	2.25 2.25

Visit of Queen Elizabeth II to Montreal and official opening of the Games. Each stamp of No. 134a has diagonal overprint. Sheet margin has additional overprint: "ROYAL VISIT OF H.M. QUEEN ELIZABETH II/OFFICIALLY OPENED 17 JULY 1976."

Annunciation — A36

Designs: Nos. 137-138, Angel appearing to the shepherds. Nos. 139-140, Nativity. Nos. 141-142, Three Kings.

1976, Oct. 18   Perf. 13½x13

135		6c dk green & gold	.25 .25
136		6c dk green & gold	.25 .25
a.		A36 Pair, #135-136	.25 .25
137		7c dk brown & gold	.25 .25
138		7c dk brown & gold	.25 .25
a.		A36 Pair, #137-138	.25 .25
139		15c dk blue & gold	.25 .25
140		15c dk blue & gold	.25 .25
a.		A36 Pair, #139-140	.30 .30

141		20c purple & gold	.25 .25
142		20c purple & gold	.25 .25
a.		A36 Pair, #141-142	.40 .40
b.		Souvenir sheet of 8	1.50 1.50
		Nos. 135-142 (8)	2.00 2.00

Christmas. No. 142b contains 8 stamps similar to Nos. 135-142 with white margin around each pair of stamps.
For overprints see Nos. B11-B18.

A. G. Bell and 1876 Telephone — A38

Design: 70c, Satellite and radar.

1977, Mar. 3   Photo.   Perf. 13½x13

143	A38	25c rose & multi	.25 .25
144	A38	70c violet & multi	.40 .40
a.		Souvenir sheet of 2	1.50 1.50

Centenary of first telephone call by Alexander Graham Bell, Mar. 10, 1876. No. 144a contains a 25c in colors of 70c and 70c in colors of 25c.

Calvary (detail), by Rubens A39

Paintings by Rubens: 20c, Lamentation. 35c, Descent from the Cross.

1977, Mar. 31   Photo.   Perf. 13½x14

145	A39	15c gold & multi	.50 .50
146	A39	20c gold & multi	.65 .65
147	A39	35c gold & multi	.85 .85
a.		Souv. sheet, #145-147, perf. 13	2.25 2.25
		Nos. 145-147 (3)	2.00 2.00

Easter, and 400th birth anniv. of Peter Paul Rubens (1577-1640), Flemish painter.

Capt. Bligh, "Bounty" and George III — A40

Designs: 35c, Rev. John Williams, George IV, First Christian Church. 50c, British flag, map of Aitutaki, Queen Victoria. $1, Elizabeth II and family on balcony after coronation.

1977, Apr. 21   Perf. 13½

148	A40	25c gold & multi	.25 .25
149	A40	35c gold & multi	.30 .30
150	A40	50c gold & multi	.50 .50
151	A40	$1 gold & multi	1.25 1.25
a.		Souvenir sheet of 4, #148-151	2.25 2.25
		Nos. 148-151 (4)	2.30 2.30

Reign of Queen Elizabeth II, 25th anniv. For overprint & surcharge see Nos. O11, O15.

Annunciation — A41

Designs: No. 154, Virgin, Child and ox. No. 155, Joseph and donkey (Nativity). No. 156, Three Kings. No. 157, Virgin and Child. No. 158, Joseph. No. 159, Virgin, Child and donkey (Flight into Egypt).

1977, Oct. 14   Photo.   Perf. 13½x14

152		6c multicolored	.25 .25
153		6c multicolored	.25 .25
a.		A41 Pair, #152-153	.25 .25
154		7c multicolored	.25 .25
155		7c multicolored	.25 .25
a.		A41 Pair, #154-155	.25 .25
156		15c multicolored	.25 .25
157		15c multicolored	.25 .25
a.		A41 Pair, #156-157	.30 .30
158		20c multicolored	.25 .25
159		20c multicolored	.25 .25
a.		A41 Pair, #158-159	.40 .40
b.		Souvenir sheet of 8, #152-159	1.75 1.75
		Nos. 152-159 (8)	2.00 2.00

Christmas.
For surcharges see Nos. B19-B26a.

Hawaiian Wood Figurine — A43

Designs: 50c, Talbot hunting dog, figurehead of "Resolution", horiz. $1, Temple figure.

1978, Jan. 19   Litho.   Perf. 13½

160	A43	35c multicolored	.45 .45
161	A43	50c multicolored	.70 .70
162	A43	$1 multicolored	1.00 1.00
a.		Souvenir sheet of 3, #160-162	2.75 2.75
		Nos. 160-162 (3)	2.15 2.15

Bicentenary of Capt. Cook's arrival in Hawaii. Nos. 160-162 issued in sheets of 6.

Jesus Carrying Cross, by Simone di Martini A44

Paintings: 20c, Avignon Pietà, 15th Century. 35c, Christ at Emmaus, by Rembrandt.

1978, Mar. 17   Photo.   Perf. 13½x14

163	A44	15c gold & multi	.25 .25
164	A44	20c gold & multi	.25 .25
165	A44	35c gold & multi	.30 .30
a.		Souvenir sheet of 3	1.00 1.00
		Nos. 163-165 (3)	.80 .80

Easter. No. 165a contains one each of Nos. 163-165, perf. 13½, and label showing Louvre, Paris. See Nos. B27-B29.

Souvenir Sheet

25th Anniv. of Coronation of Queen Elizabeth II. — A45

1978, June 15   Photo.   Perf. 13½x13

166	A45	Sheet of 6	2.50 2.50
a.		$1 Yale of Beaufort	.35 .35
b.		$1 Elizabeth II	.35 .35
c.		$1 Ancestral statue	.35 .35
d.		Souvenir sheet of 6	2.25 2.25

No. 166d contains 2 strips of Nos. 166a-166c separated by horizontal slate green gutter showing Royal family on balcony, silver marginal inscription.

Virgin and Child, by Dürer — A46

Designs: Various paintings of the Virgin and Child by Albrecht Dürer.

1978, Dec. 4   Photo.   Perf. 14½x13

167	A46	15c multicolored	.35 .35
168	A46	17c multicolored	.40 .40
169	A46	30c multicolored	.55 .55
170	A46	35c multicolored	.65 .65
		Nos. 167-170 (4)	1.95 1.95

Christmas; 450th death anniv. of Albrecht Dürer (1471-1528), German painter. Nos. 167-170 issued in sheets of 5 stamps and corner label. See No. B30.

Capt. Cook, by Nathaniel Dance — A47

Design: 75c, "Resolution" and "Adventure," by William Hodges.

1979, July 20   Photo.   Perf. 14x13½

171	A47	50c multicolored	1.50 1.00
172	A47	75c multicolored	2.00 1.50
a.		Souvenir sheet of 2, #171-172	2.75 2.75

Capt. James Cook (1728-1779), explorer, death bicentenary.

Boy Holding Hibiscus, IYC Emblem — A48

IYC Emblem and: 35c, Boy playing guitar. 65c, Boys in outrigger canoe.

1979, Oct. 1   Photo.   Perf. 14x13½

173	A48	30c multicolored	.25 .25
174	A48	35c multicolored	.35 .35
175	A48	65c multicolored	.45 .45
		Nos. 173-175 (3)	1.05 1.05

See No. B31.

Aitutaki No. 102, Hill, Penny Black A49

Designs: Nos. 176, 178-179, 181, paintings of letter writers, Flemish School, 17th century.

1979, Nov. 14   Photo.   Perf. 13

176	A49	50c Gabriel Metsu	.50 .50
177	A49	50c shown	.50 .50
178	A49	50c Jan Vermeer	.50 .50
a.		Strip of 3, #176-178	1.50 1.50
179	A49	65c Gerard Terborch	.60 .60
180	A49	65c No. 103 (like No. 177)	.60 .60
181	A49	65c Jan Vermeer	.60 .60
a.		Strip of 3, #179-181	2.00 2.00
		Nos. 176-181 (6)	3.30 3.30

Souvenir Sheet

182		Sheet of 6	2.75 2.75
a.		A49 30c like No. 176	.40 .40
b.		A49 30c like No. 177	.40 .40
c.		A49 30c like No. 178	.40 .40

d.	A49 30c like No. 179	.40	.40
e.	A49 30c like No. 180	.40	.40
f.	A49 30c like No. 181	.40	.40

Sir Rowland Hill (1795-1879), originator of penny postage. Nos. 176-178 and 179-181 printed in sheets of 9.

Descent from the Cross, Detail — A50

Easter: 30c, 35c, Descent from the Cross, by Quentin Metsys (details).

1980, Apr. 3　Photo.　Perf. 13x13½

183	A50 20c multicolored	.50	.40
184	A50 30c multicolored	.60	.50
185	A50 35c multicolored	.70	.60
	Nos. 183-185 (3)	*1.80*	*1.50*

See No. B32.

Albert Einstein — A51

No. 187, Formula, atom structure. No. 188, Portrait, diff. No. 189, Atomic blast. No. 190, Portrait, diff. No. 191, Atomic blast, trees.

1980, July 21　Photo.　Perf. 14

186	A51 12c shown	.65	.65
187	A51 12c multicolored	.65	.65
a.	Pair, #186-187	1.50	1.50
188	A51 15c multicolored	.70	.70
189	A51 15c multicolored	.70	.70
a.	Pair, #188-189	1.60	1.60
190	A51 20c multicolored	.80	.80
191	A51 20c multicolored	.80	.80
a.	Pair, #190-191	2.00	2.00
b.	Souv. sheet of 6, #186-191, perf. 13	5.00	5.00
	Nos. 186-191 (6)	*4.30*	*4.30*

Albert Einstein (1879-1955), theoretical physicist.

A52

No. 192, Ancestral Figure, Aitutaki. No. 193, God image staff, Rarotonga. No. 194, Trade adze, Mangaia. No. 195, Tangaroa carving, Rarotonga. No. 196, Wooden image, Aitutaki. No. 197, Hand club, Rarotonga. No. 198, Carved mace, Mangaia. No. 199, Fisherman's god, Rarotonga. No. 200, Ti'i image, Aitutaki. No. 201, Fisherman's god, diff. No. 202, Carved mace, Cook Islands. No. 203, Tangaroa, diff. No. 204, Chief's headdress, Aitutaki. No. 205, Carved mace, diff. No. 206, God image staff, diff.

1980, Sept. 26　Photo.　Perf. 14

192	A52 6c multicolored	.25	.25
193	A52 6c multicolored	.25	.25
194	A52 6c multicolored	.25	.25
195	A52 6c multicolored	.25	.25
a.	Block of 4, #192-195	.60	.60
196	A52 12c multicolored	.25	.25
197	A52 12c multicolored	.25	.25
198	A52 12c multicolored	.25	.25
199	A52 12c multicolored	.25	.25
a.	Block of 4, #196-199	.85	.85
200	A52 15c multicolored	.25	.25
201	A52 15c multicolored	.25	.25
202	A52 15c multicolored	.25	.25
203	A52 15c multicolored	.25	.25
a.	Block of 4, #200-203	1.00	1.00

204	A52 20c multicolored	.40	.40
205	A52 20c multicolored	.40	.40
206	A52 20c multicolored	.40	.40
207	A52 20c like #195	.40	.40
a.	Block of 4, #204-207	1.50	1.50
b.	Souvenir sheet of 16, #192-207	4.00	4.00

Third South Pacific Arts Festival, Port Moresby, Papua New Guinea.

A53

Virgin and Child, Sculptures.

1980, Nov. 21　Photo.　Perf. 13x13½

208	A53 15c 13th cent.	.25	.25
209	A53 20c 14th cent.	.25	.25
210	A53 25c 15th cent.	.30	.30
211	A53 15c 15th cent., diff.	.40	.40
	Nos. 208-211 (4)	*1.20*	*1.20*

Christmas. See No. B33.

Mourning Virgin, by Pedro Roldan — A54

Easter (Roldan Sculptures): 40c, Christ. 50c, Mourning St. John.

1981, Mar. 31　Photo.　Perf. 14

212	A54 30c green & gold	.35	.35
213	A54 40c brt purple & gold	.40	.40
214	A54 50c dk blue & gold	.45	.45
	Nos. 212-214 (3)	*1.20*	*1.20*

See No. B34.

Sturnus Vulgaris — A55

No. 216, Poephila gouldiae. No. 217, Petroica multicolor. No. 218, Pachycephala pectoralis. No. 219, Falco peregrinus. No. 220, Rhipidura rufifrons. No. 221, Tyto alba. No. 222, Padda oryzivora. No. 223, Artamus leucorhynchus. No. 224, Vini peruviana. No. 225, Columba livia. No. 226, Porphyrio porphyria. No. 227, Geopelia striata. No. 228, Lonchura castaneothorax. No. 229, Acridotheres tristis. No. 230, Egretta sacra. No. 231, Diomeda melanophris. No. 232, Numenius phaeopus. No. 233, Gygis alba. No. 234, Pluvialis dominica. No. 235, Sula leucogaster. No. 236, Anas superciliosa. No. 237, Anas acuta. No. 238, Fregata minor. No. 239, Stercorarius pomarinus. No. 240, Conopoderas caffra. No. 241, Lalage maculosa. No. 242, Gallirallus philippensis. No. 243, Vini stepheni. No. 244, Diomedea epomophora. No. 245, Ptilinopus victor. No. 246, Erythrura cyaneovirens. $2, Myiagra azureocapilla. $4, Amandava amandava. $5, Halcyon recurvirostris.

1981-82　　Perf. 14x13½, 13½x14

215	A55 1c shown	.40	.25
216	A55 1c multicolored	.40	.25
a.	Pair, #215-216	1.00	.30
217	A55 2c multicolored	.45	.25
218	A55 2c multicolored	.45	.25
a.	Pair, #217-218	1.10	.30
219	A55 3c multicolored	.55	.25
220	A55 3c multicolored	.55	.25
a.	Pair, #219-220	1.25	.30
221	A55 4c multicolored	.65	.25
222	A55 4c multicolored	.65	.25
a.	Pair, #221-222	1.50	.35

223	A55 5c multicolored	.70	.25
224	A55 5c multicolored	.70	.25
a.	Pair, #223-224	1.60	.40
225	A55 6c multicolored	.75	.25
226	A55 6c multicolored	.75	.25
a.	Pair, #225-226	1.75	.40
227	A55 10c multicolored	.85	.25
228	A55 10c multicolored	.85	.25
a.	Pair, #227-228	2.00	.75
229	A55 12c multicolored	.90	.30
230	A55 12c multicolored	.90	.30
a.	Pair, #229-230	2.10	.85
231	A55 15c multicolored	1.00	.40
232	A55 15c multicolored	1.00	.40
a.	Pair, #231-232	2.75	1.25
233	A55 20c multicolored	1.25	.50
234	A55 20c multicolored	1.25	.50
a.	Pair, #233-234	3.25	1.50
235	A55 25c multicolored	1.40	.60
236	A55 25c multicolored	1.40	.60
a.	Pair, #235-236	3.75	1.60
237	A55 30c multicolored	1.50	.65
238	A55 30c multicolored	1.50	.65
a.	Pair, #237-238	4.00	2.00
239	A55 35c multicolored	1.60	.75
240	A55 35c multicolored	1.60	.75
a.	Pair, #239-240	4.25	3.00
241	A55 40c multicolored	1.75	.90
242	A55 40c multicolored	1.75	.90
a.	Pair, #241-242	4.50	3.25
243	A55 50c multicolored	2.00	1.00
244	A55 50c multicolored	2.00	1.00
a.	Pair, #243-244	5.00	3.50
245	A55 70c multicolored	4.25	2.00
246	A55 70c multicolored	4.25	2.00
e.	Pair, #245-246	11.00	7.50

Size: 35x47mm

Photo.　Perf. 13½

246A	A55 $1 multicolored	5.00	3.75
246B	A55 $2 multicolored	5.50	7.50
246C	A55 $4 multicolored	9.00	13.50
246D	A55 $5 multicolored	11.00	17.50
	Nos. 215-246D (36)	*70.50*	*59.95*

Issued: Nos. 215-230, 4/6; Nos. 231-238, 5/8; Nos. 239-246, 1/14/82; Nos. 246A-246B, 2/15/82.
Nos. 231-246 horiz.
For surcharges and overprint see Nos. 293-306, 452-454, O40-O41.

Prince Charles and Lady Diana — A56

Perf. 13x13½, 13½x13

1981, June 10　　　　Photo.

247	A56 60c Charles, vert.	.40	.40
248	A56 80c Lady Diana, vert.	.50	.50
	Complete booklet, one sheet of 4 each #247-248	6.00	
249	A56 $1.40 Shown	.60	.60
	Nos. 247-249 (3)	*1.50*	*1.50*

Royal Wedding. Issued in sheets of 4.
For overprints and surcharges see Nos. 265-267, 307, 309, 355, 405-407, B35-B37.

1982 World Cup Soccer — A57

Designs: Various soccer players.

1981, Nov. 30　Photo.　Perf. 14

250	A57 12c Pair, #250a-250b	1.10	1.00
251	A57 15c Pair, #251a-251b	1.25	1.10
252	A57 20c Pair, #252a-252b	1.50	1.25
253	A57 25c Pair, #253a-253b	1.75	1.40
	Nos. 250-253 (4)	*5.60*	*4.75*

See No. B38.

Christmas A58

Rembrandt Etchings: 15c, Holy Family, 1632, vert. 30c, Virgin with Child, 1634, vert. 40c, Adoration of the Shepherds, 1654. 50c, Holy Family with Cat, 1644.

1981, Dec. 10　　　　　Perf. 14

254	A58 15c gold & dk brown	.50	.50
255	A58 30c gold & dk brown	.65	.60
256	A58 40c gold & dk brown	.75	.75
257	A58 50c gold & dk brown	1.00	1.00
	Nos. 254-257 (4)	*2.90*	*2.85*

Souvenir Sheets

258	A58 80c + 5c like #254	.80	.75
259	A58 80c + 5c like #255	.80	.75
260	A58 80c + 5c like #256	.80	.75
261	A58 80c + 5c like #257	.80	.75

Nos. 258-261 have multicolored margins showing entire etching. Surtax on Nos. 258-261 was for local charities.

21st Birthday of Princess Diana — A59

1982, June 24　Photo.　Perf. 14

262	A59 70c shown	1.75	.75
263	A59 $1 Wedding portrait	1.75	.90
264	A59 $2 Diana, diff.	2.75	1.50
a.	Souvenir sheet of 3, #262-264	6.00	6.00
	Nos. 262-264 (3)	*6.25*	*3.15*

See Nos. 268-270a. For surcharges see Nos. 308, 310.

Nos. 247-249 Overprinted

a　　　　　　b

1982, July 13　Perf. 13x13½, 13½x13

265	A56 60c Pair, #a.-b.	1.50	1.25
266	A56 80c Pair, #a.-b.	2.25	2.00
267	A56 $1.40 Pair, diff.	3.75	3.25
	Nos. 265-267 (3)	*7.50*	*6.50*

Nos. 265-267 were overprinted with alternating inscriptions within the sheet.

Nos. 262-264a
Inscribed: "Royal Birth 21 June 1982 Prince William Of Wales"

1982, Aug. 5　　　　　Perf. 14

268	A59 70c multicolored	.70	.70
269	A59 $1 multicolored	1.50	1.50
270	A59 $2 multicolored	2.00	2.00
a.	Souvenir sheet of 3	5.00	5.00
	Nos. 268-270 (3)	*4.20*	*4.20*

Christmas — A60

Madonna and Child Sculptures, 12th-15th Cent.

1982, Dec. 10　Photo.　Perf. 13

271	A60 18c multicolored	.65	.65
272	A60 36c multicolored	.75	.75
273	A60 48c multicolored	.90	.90
274	A60 60c multicolored	1.25	1.25
	Nos. 271-274 (4)	*3.55*	*3.55*

Souvenir Sheet

275		Sheet of 4	4.50	4.50
a.	A60	18c + 2c like 18c	.70	.70
b.	A60	36c + 2c like 36c	.80	.80
c.	A60	48c + 2c like 48c	1.00	1.00
d.	A60	60c + 2c like 60c	1.25	1.25

Surtax was for children's charities.

Commonwealth Day — A61

1983, Mar. 14   Photo.   Perf. 13x13½

276	A61	48c Bananas	.95	.95
277	A61	48c Ti'i statuette	.95	.95
278	A61	48c Boys canoeing	.95	.95
279	A61	48c Capt. Bligh, Bounty	.95	.95
a.		Block of 4, #276-279	4.75	4.75

Scouting
Year
A62

1983, Apr. 18   Photo.   Perf. 14

280	A62	36c Campfire	.50	.50
281	A62	48c Salute	.60	.60
282	A62	60c Hiking	.70	.70
		Nos. 280-282 (3)	1.80	1.80

Souvenir Sheet
Perf. 13½

283		Sheet of 3	2.50	2.50
a.	A62	36c + 3c like #280	.60	.60
b.	A62	48c + 3c like #281	.70	.70
c.	A62	60c + 3c like #282	.90	.90

Surtax was for benefit of Scouting.

Nos. 280-283 Overprinted

1983, July 11   Photo.   Perf. 14

284	A62	36c multicolored	.85	.85
285	A62	48c multicolored	1.00	1.00
286	A62	60c multicolored	1.25	1.25
		Nos. 284-286 (3)	3.10	3.10

Souvenir Sheet

287		Sheet of 3	3.00	3.00
a.	A62	36c + 3c like #284	.65	.65
b.	A62	48c + 3c like #285	.80	.80
c.	A62	60c + 3c like #286	1.00	1.00

A63

Manned Flight Bicentenary: Modern sport balloons.

1983, July 22   Photo.   Perf. 14x13

288	A63	18c multicolored	.60	.60
289	A63	36c multicolored	.75	.75
290	A63	48c multicolored	1.00	1.00
291	A63	60c multicolored	1.25	1.25
		Nos. 288-291 (4)	3.60	3.60

Souvenir Sheet

292	A63	$2.50 multicolored	3.25	3.25

Nos. 233-
246, 246D,
248-249
Surcharged
in Black

Nos. 263-264
Surcharged in Black
and Gold

1983, Sept. 22

293	A55	18c on 20c, #233	2.75	1.00
294	A55	18c on 20c, #234	2.75	1.00
a.		Pair, #293-294	6.00	2.25
295	A55	36c on 25c, #235	3.25	1.25
296	A55	36c on 25c, #236	3.25	1.25
a.		Pair, #295-296	7.25	3.00
297	A55	36c on 30c, #237	3.25	1.25
298	A55	36c on 30c, #238	3.25	1.25
a.		Pair, #297-298	7.25	3.00
299	A55	36c on 35c, #239	3.50	1.40
300	A55	36c on 35c, #240	3.50	1.40
a.		Pair, #299-300	7.50	3.25
301	A55	48c on 40c, #241	4.50	1.40
302	A55	48c on 40c, #242	4.50	1.40
a.		Pair, #301-302	10.00	3.25
303	A55	48c on 50c, #243	4.50	1.40
304	A55	48c on 50c, #244	4.50	1.40
a.		Pair, #303-304	10.00	3.25
305	A55	72c on 70c, #245	7.50	2.50
306	A55	72c on 70c, #246	7.50	2.50
a.		Pair, #305-306	16.50	7.50
307	A56	96c on 80c, #248	3.00	2.25
308	A59	96c on $1, #263	2.75	1.00
309	A56	$1.20 on $1.40,		
		#249	3.00	2.25
310	A59	$1.20 on $2, #264	2.75	2.00

Size: 35x47mm

311	A55	$5.60 on $5, #246D	20.00	10.00
		Nos. 293-311 (19)	90.00	38.90

Nos. 307-308, 310-311 vert.

A64

60, Global coverage. 96c, Communications satellite.

1983, Sept. 29   Photo.   Perf. 14

312	A64	48c shown	.80	.55
313	A64	60c multicolored	1.25	.70
314	A64	96c multicolored	1.50	1.25
a.		Souvenir sheet of 3, #312-314	3.25	3.25
		Nos. 312-314 (3)	3.55	2.50

World Communications Year.

Raphael Paintings — 36c, Madonna of the Chair. 48c, Alba Madonna. 60c, Connestabile Madonna.

Christmas
A65

1983, Nov. 21   Photo.   Perf. 13½x14

315	A65	36c multicolored	.75	.40
316	A65	48c multicolored	1.00	.80
317	A65	60c multicolored	1.50	1.00
		Nos. 315-317 (3)	3.25	2.20

Souvenir Sheet

318		Sheet of 3	3.50	3.50
a.	A65	36c + 3c like #315	1.00	1.00
b.	A65	48c + 3c like #316	1.10	1.10
c.	A65	60c + 3c like #317	1.25	1.25

1983, Dec. 15   Imperf.
Size: 46x46mm

319	A65	85c + 5c like #315	1.50	1.50
320	A65	85c + 5c like #316	1.50	1.50
321	A65	85c + 5c like #317	1.50	1.50
		Nos. 319-321 (3)	4.50	4.50

Surtax was for children's charities.

Local
Birds — A66

1984   Photo.   Perf. 14

322	A66	2c as No. 216	1.75	.90
323	A66	3c as No. 215	1.75	.90
324	A66	5c as No. 217	1.75	1.00
325	A66	10c as No. 218	2.50	1.00
326	A66	12c as No. 220	2.50	1.00
327	A66	18c as No. 219	2.50	1.25
328	A66	24c as No. 221	2.50	1.25
329	A66	30c as No. 222	2.50	1.25
330	A66	36c as No. 223	2.50	1.25
331	A66	48c as No. 224	2.50	1.25
332	A66	50c as No. 225	2.75	1.75
333	A66	60c as No. 226	2.75	1.75
334	A66	72c as No. 227	3.25	1.75
335	A66	96c as No. 228	3.25	1.75
336	A66	$1.20 as No. 229	3.25	2.50
337	A66	$2.10 as No. 230	3.75	3.50
338	A66	$3 as No. 246A	5.25	4.50
339	A66	$4.20 as No. 246B	4.00	5.75
340	A66	$5.60 as No. 246C	5.25	7.00
341	A66	$9.60 as No. 246D	8.00	10.00
		Nos. 322-341 (20)	64.25	51.30

For overprints and surcharges see Nos. O17-O39.

1984 Summer
Olympics — A67

1984, July 24   Photo.   Perf. 13x13½

342	A67	36c Javelin	.50	.50
343	A67	48c Shot put	.60	.60
344	A67	60c Hurdles	.70	.70
345	A67	$2 Handball	2.00	2.00
		Nos. 342-345 (4)	3.80	3.80

Souvenir Sheet

346		Sheet of 4	3.50	3.50
a.	A67	36c + 5c like #342	.40	.40
b.	A67	48c + 5c like #343	.55	.55
c.	A67	60c + 5c like #344	.65	.65
d.	A67	$2 + 5c like #345	1.50	1.50

Surtax was for benefit of local sports.

Nos. 342-345
Overprinted in
Gold and Black

1984, Aug. 21   Photo.   Perf. 13x13½

347	A67	36c multicolored	.40	.40
348	A67	48c multicolored	.50	.50
349	A67	60c multicolored	.60	.60
350	A67	$2 multicolored	1.75	1.75
		Nos. 347-350 (4)	3.25	3.25

Ausipex
'84 — A68

60c, William Bligh, map. 96c, Bounty, map. $1.40, Stamps, map.

1984, Sept. 14   Photo.   Perf. 14

351	A68	60c multicolored	3.75	3.75
352	A68	96c multicolored	3.75	3.75
353	A68	$1.40 multicolored	3.75	3.75
		Nos. 351-353 (3)	11.25	11.25

Souvenir Sheet

354		Sheet of 3	8.00	8.00
a.	A68	60c + 5c like #351	1.75	1.75
b.	A68	96c + 5c like #352	2.25	2.25
c.	A68	$1.40 + 5c like #353	3.50	3.50

For overprint see No. 399.

No. 247 Surcharged

1984, Oct. 10   Photo.   Perf. 13x13½

355	A56	$3 on 60c multi	2.75	3.00

Issued in sheets of 4.

A69

1984, Nov. 16   Photo.   Perf. 13

356	A69	36c Annunciation	.45	.45
357	A69	48c Nativity	.55	.55
358	A69	60c Epiphany	.65	.65
359	A69	96c Flight into Egypt	.85	.85
		Nos. 356-359 (4)	2.50	2.50

Souvenir Sheets
Size: 45x53mm
Imperf

360	A69	90c + 7c like #356	1.10	1.10
361	A69	90c + 7c like #357	1.10	1.10
362	A69	90c + 7c like #358	1.10	1.10
363	A69	90c + 7c like #359	1.10	1.10

Christmas.

A70

1984, Dec. 10   Photo.   Perf. 13½x14

364	A70	48c Diana, Henry	2.25	2.25
365	A70	60c William, Henry	2.25	2.25
366	A70	$2.10 Family	3.00	3.00
		Nos. 364-366 (3)	7.50	7.50

Souvenir Sheet

367		Sheet of 3	6.00	6.00
a.	A70	96c + 7c like #364	2.00	2.00
b.	A70	96c + 7c like #365	2.00	2.00
c.	A70	96c + 7c like #366	2.00	2.00

Christmas, Birth of Prince Henry, Sept. 15. Surtax was for benefit of local children's charities.

Audubon Birth
Bicentenary
A71

Illustrations of bird species by John J. Audubon — 55c, Gray kingbird. 65c, Bohemian waxwing. 75c, Summer tanager. 95c, Cardinal. $1.15, White-winged crossbill.

1985, Mar. 22		Litho.	Perf. 13	
368	A71	55c multicolored	1.10	1.10
369	A71	65c multicolored	1.25	1.25
370	A71	75c multicolored	1.50	1.50
371	A71	95c multicolored	1.75	1.75
372	A71	$1.15 multicolored	2.25	2.25
		Nos. 368-372 (5)	7.85	7.85

Queen
Mother,
85th
Birthday
A72

Photographs: 55c, Lady Elizabeth Bowes-Lyon, age 7. 65c, Engaged to the Duke of York, 75c, Duchess of York with daughter, Elizabeth. $1.30, Holding the infant Prince Charles. $3, Portrait taken on 63rd birthday.

1985-86			Perf. 13½x13	
373	A72	55c multicolored	.55	.55
374	A72	65c multicolored	.65	.65
375	A72	75c multicolored	.75	.75
376	A72	$1.30 multicolored	1.25	1.25
a.		Souvenir sheet of 4, #373-376	8.25	8.25
		Nos. 373-376 (4)	3.20	3.20

Souvenir Sheet

377	A72	$3 multicolored	3.50	3.50

Nos. 373-376 printed in sheets of 4.
Issued: No. 376a, 8/4/86; others, 6/14/85.
For overprint see No. 446.

Intl. Youth
Year
A73

Designs: 75c, The Calmady Children, by Thomas Lawrence (1769-1830). 90c, Madame Charpentier's Children, by Renoir (1841-1919). $1.40, Young Girls at Piano, by Renoir.

1985, Sept. 16		Photo.	Perf. 13	
378	A73	75c multicolored	2.50	2.50
379	A73	90c multicolored	2.50	2.50
380	A73	$1.40 multicolored	3.00	3.00
		Nos. 378-380 (3)	8.00	8.00

Souvenir Sheet

381		Sheet of 3	6.50	6.50
a.	A73	75c + 10c like #378	1.50	1.50
b.	A73	90c + 10c like #379	1.75	1.75
c.	A73	$1.40 + 10c like #380	2.50	2.50

Surcharged for children's activities.

Adoration of the Magi, by Giotto di
Bondone (1276-1337) — A74

Nos. 382, 384, Giotto probe. Nos. 383, 385, Planet A probe.

1985, Nov. 15		Photo.	Perf. 13½x13	
382	A74	95c multicolored	1.50	1.50
383	A74	95c multicolored	1.50	1.50
a.		Pair, #382-383	3.50	3.50

384	A74	$1.15 multicolored	1.50	1.50
385	A74	$1.15 multicolored	1.50	1.50
a.		Pair, #384-385	3.50	3.50
		Nos. 382-385 (4)	6.00	6.00

Souvenir Sheet
Imperf

386	A74	$6.40 multicolored	13.50	13.50

Christmas, return of Halley's Comet, 1985-86.

Halley's
Comet
A75

Designs: 90c, Halley's Comet, A.D. 684, wood engraving, Nuremberg Chronicles. $1.25, Sighting of 1066, Bayeux Tapestry, detail, c. 1092, France. $1.75, The Comet Inflicting Untold Disasters, 1456, Lucerne Chronicles, by Diebolt Schilling. $4.20, Melancolia I, engraving by Durer.

1986, Feb. 25		Photo.	Perf. 13½x13	
387	A75	90c multicolored	1.25	1.25
388	A75	$1.25 multicolored	1.50	1.50
389	A75	$1.75 multicolored	2.25	2.25
		Nos. 387-389 (3)	5.00	5.00

Souvenir Sheets

390		Sheet of 3 + label	6.50	6.50
a.	A75	95c, like #387	2.00	2.00
b.	A75	95c, like #388	2.00	2.00
c.	A75	95c, like #389	2.00	2.00

Imperf

391	A75	$4.20 multicolored	5.75	5.75

Elizabeth II, 60th
Birthday — A76

1986, Apr. 21			Perf. 14	
392	A76	95c Coronation portrait	1.10	1.10

Souvenir Sheet
Perf. 13½

393	A76	$4.20 Portrait, diff.	5.25	5.25

No. 392 printed in sheets of 5 with label picturing U.K. flag and Queen's flag for New Zealand.

Statue of
Liberty,
Cent.
A77

1986, June 27		Photo.	Perf. 14	
394	A77	$1 Liberty head	1.50	1.50
395	A77	$2.75 Statue	3.00	3.00

Souvenir Sheet
Perf. 13½

396		Sheet of 2	3.25	3.25
a.	A77	$1.25 like $1	1.50	1.50
b.	A77	$1.25 like $2.75	1.50	1.50

For surcharges see Nos B45, B49.

Wedding of
Prince Andrew
and Sarah
Ferguson — A78

1986, July 23			Perf. 14	
397	A78	$2 multicolored	2.60	2.60

Souvenir Sheet
Perf. 13½

398	A78	$5 multicolored	6.00	6.00

No. 397 printed in sheets of 5 plus label picturing Westminster Abbey.
For surcharge see No. B48.

No. 354 Overprinted

STAMPEX '86

1986, Aug. 4		Photo.	Perf. 14	
399		Sheet of 3	13.00	13.00
a.	A68	60c + 5c like #351	3.00	3.00
b.	A68	96c + 5c like #352	3.50	3.50
c.	A68	$1.40 + 5c like #353	6.00	6.00

STAMPEX '86, Adelaide, Aug. 4-10.

Christmas
A79

Paintings by Albrecht Durer: 75c, No. 404a, St. Anne with Virgin and Child. $1.35, No. 404b, Virgin and Child. $1.95, No. 404c, Adoration of the Magi. $2.75, No. 404d, Rosary Festivity.

1986, Nov. 21		Litho.	Perf. 13½	
400	A79	75c multicolored	1.25	1.25
401	A79	$1.35 multicolored	2.00	2.00
402	A79	$1.95 multicolored	3.00	3.00
403	A79	$2.75 multicolored	4.25	4.25
		Nos. 400-403 (4)	10.50	10.50

Souvenir Sheet

404		Sheet of 4	14.00	14.00
a.-d.	A79	$1.65 any single	3.25	3.25

For surcharges see Nos. B39-B44, B46-B47, B50-B54.

Nos. 247-249
Srchd. in Gold
and Black

1987, Nov. 20		Photo.	Perf. 13x12½	
405	A56	$2.50 on 60c No. 247	2.40	2.40
406	A56	$2.50 on 80c No. 248	2.40	2.40
407	A56	$2.50 on $1.40 No. 249	2.40	2.40
		Nos. 405-407 (3)	7.20	7.20

Issued in sheets of 4 with margin inscriptions overprinted with gold bar and "40th Anniversary of the Royal Wedding / 1947-1987" in black; "OVERPRINTED BY NEW ZEALAND GOVERNMENT PRINTER, / WELLINGTON, NOVEMBER 1987" at left.

A80

The Virgin with Garland, by
Rubens — A81

Painting details.

1987, Dec. 10		Photo.	Perf. 13x13½	
408	A80	70c UL	2.00	2.00
409	A80	85c UR	2.10	2.10
410	A80	$1.50 LL	2.25	2.25
411	A80	$1.85 LR	3.00	3.00
		Nos. 408-411 (4)	9.35	9.35

Souvenir Sheets

412		Sheet of 4	13.00	13.00
a.	A80	95c like No. 408	3.00	3.00
b.	A80	95c like No. 409	3.00	3.00
c.	A80	95c like No. 410	3.00	3.00
d.	A80	95c like No. 411	3.00	3.00

Perf. 13

413	A81	$6 multicolored	14.00	14.00

Christmas.

1988 Summer Olympics, Seoul — A82

Flags of Korea, Aitutaki, ancient and modern events, and Seoul Games emblem or $50 silver coin issued to commemorate the participation of Aitutaki athletes in the Olympics for the 1st time: 70c, No. 418a, Obverse of silver coin, chariot race, running. 85c, Emblem, running, soccer. 95c, Emblem, boxing, handball. $1.40, No. 418b, Reverse of coin, spearmen, women's tennis.

1988, Aug. 22		Photo.	Perf. 14½x15	
414	A82	70c multicolored	2.00	2.00
415	A82	85c multicolored	2.25	2.25
416	A82	95c multicolored	2.50	2.50
417	A82	$1.40 multicolored	3.00	3.00
		Nos. 414-417 (4)	9.75	9.75

Souvenir Sheet

418		Sheet of 2	7.50	7.50
a.-b.	A82	$2 any single	3.25	3.25

**Nos. 414-417 Ovptd. with Names of
1988 Olympic Gold Medalists**

FLORENCE GRIFFTH JOYNER
UNITED STATES
100 M AND 200 M

a

GELINDO BORDIN
ITALY
MARATHON

85c

b

HITOSHI SAITO
JAPAN
JUDO

95c

c

STEFFI GRAF
WEST GERMANY
WOMEN'S TENNIS

1.40

d

1988, Oct. 10   Litho.   Perf. 14½x15

419	A82 (a)	70c on No. 414	1.75 1.75
420	A82 (b)	85c on No. 415	1.75 1.75
421	A82 (c)	95c on No. 416	2.75 2.75
422	A82 (d)	$1.40 on No. 417	2.75 2.75
		Nos. 419-422 (4)	9.00 9.00

Griffith is spelled incorrectly on No. 419.

Christmas
A83

Paintings by Rembrandt: 55c, Adoration of the Shepherds (detail), National Gallery, London. 70c, Holy Family, Alte Pinakothek, Munich. 85c, Presentation in the Temple, Kunsthalle, Hamburg. 95c, The Holy Family, Louvre, Paris. $1.15, Presentation in the Temple, diff., Mauritshuis, The Hague. $4.50, Adoration of the Shepherds (entire painting).

1988, Nov. 2   Photo.   Perf. 13½

423	A83	55c multicolored	1.75 1.75
424	A83	70c multicolored	1.90 1.90
425	A83	85c multicolored	2.00 2.00
426	A83	95c multicolored	2.25 2.25
427	A83	$1.15 multicolored	2.50 2.50
		Nos. 423-427 (5)	10.40 10.40

Souvenir Sheet
Perf. 14

428	A83	$4.50 multicolored	8.00 8.00

No. 428 contains one 52x34mm stamp.

A84

BICENTENARY of the DISCOVERY of AITUTAKI

26 APRIL 1789 - MUTINY ON THE BOUNTY - BLIGH SET ADRIFT IN LAUNCH

Mutiny on the *Bounty*, 200th
Anniv. — A85

55c, Ship, Capt. Bligh. 65c, Breadfruit. 75c, Bligh, chart. 95c, Bounty off Aitutaki. $1.65, Christian, Bligh. $4.20, Castaways.

1989, July 3   Photo.   Perf. 13½

429	A84	55c multicolored	2.00 2.00
430	A84	65c multicolored	2.25 2.25
431	A84	75c multicolored	2.50 2.50
432	A84	95c multicolored	2.75 2.75
433	A84	$1.65 multicolored	3.75 3.75
		Nos. 429-433 (5)	13.25 13.25

Souvenir Sheet

434	A85	$4.20 multicolored	11.00 11.00

Discovery of Aitutaki by William Bligh, bicent.

1st Moon Landing, 20th Anniv. — A86

Apollo 11 mission emblem, American flag, eagle, "The Eagle has landed": 75c, Astronaut standing on the lunar surface. $1.15, Conducting an experiment in front of the lunar module. $1.80, Carrying equipment. $6.40, Raising the flag.

1989, July 28   Photo.   Perf. 13½x13

435	A86	75c multicolored	2.50 2.50
436	A86	$1.15 multicolored	3.25 3.25
437	A86	$1.80 multicolored	3.75 3.75
		Nos. 435-437 (3)	9.50 9.50

Souvenir Sheet
Perf. 13½

438	A86	$6.40 multicolored	9.50 9.50

No. 438 contains one 42x31mm stamp.

Christmas — A87

Details from *Virgin in Glory*, by Titian: 70c, Virgin. 85c, Christ child. 95c, Angel. $1.25, Cherubs. $6, Entire painting.

1989, Nov. 20   Photo.   Perf. 13½x13

439	A87	70c multicolored	2.10 2.10
440	A87	85c multicolored	2.25 2.25
441	A87	95c multicolored	2.40 2.40
442	A87	$1.25 multicolored	3.50 3.50
		Nos. 439-442 (4)	10.25 10.25

Souvenir Sheet
Perf. 13½

443	A87	$6 multicolored	11.00 11.00

No. 443 contains one 45x60mm stamp.

World Environmental Protection — A88

Designs: a, Human comet, World Philatelic Programs emblem. b, Comet tail and "Protect The Endangered Earth!" $3, Human comet, emblem and inscription.

1990, Feb. 16   Photo.   Perf. 13½x13

444	A88	Pair	5.75 5.75
a.-b.		$1.75 any single	2.50 2.50

Souvenir Sheet

445	A88	$3 multicolored	7.00 7.00

No. 376a Overprinted

Designs: 55c, Lady Elizabeth Bowes-Lyon, 1907. 65c, Lady Elizabeth engaged to Duke of York. 75c, As Duchess of York with daughter Elizabeth. $1.30, As Queen Mother with grandson.

1990, July 16   Litho.   Perf. 13½x13

446		Sheet of 4	13.00 13.00
a.	A72	55c multicolored	2.75 2.75
b.	A72	65c multicolored	3.00 3.00
c.	A72	75c multicolored	3.25 3.25
d.	A72	$1.30 multicolored	3.50 3.50

Christmas — A89

Paintings: 70c, Madonna of the Basket by Correggio. 85c, Virgin and Child by Morando. 95c, Adoration of the Child by Tiepolo. $1.75, Mystic Marriage of St. Catherine by Memling. $6, Donne Triptych by Memling.

1990, Nov. 28   Litho.   Perf. 14

447	A89	70c multicolored	1.50 1.50
448	A89	85c multicolored	1.60 1.60
449	A89	95c multicolored	1.75 1.75
450	A89	$1.75 multicolored	2.50 2.50
		Nos. 447-450 (4)	7.35 7.35

Souvenir Sheet

451	A89	$6 multicolored	13.00 13.00

Nos. 246A-
246B
Overprinted

1990, Dec. 5   Photo.   Perf. 13½

452	A55	$1 multicolored	4.75 4.75
453	A55	$2 multicolored	5.75 5.75

Birdpex '90, 20 Intl. Ornithological Congress, New Zealand.

No. 246D
Overprinted

COMMEMORATING
65th BIRTHDAY
OF H.M. QUEEN
ELIZABETH II

1991, Apr. 22   Photo.   Perf. 13

454	A55	$5 multicolored	11.00 11.00

Christmas — A90

Paintings: 80c, The Holy Family, by Mengs. 90c, Virgin and Child, by Fra Filippo Lippi. $1.05, Virgin and Child, by Durer. $1.75, Adoration of the Shepherds, by De La Tour. $6, The Holy Family, by Michelangelo.

1991, Nov. 13   Litho.   Perf. 14

455	A90	80c multicolored	1.75 1.75
456	A90	90c multicolored	1.90 1.90
457	A90	$1.05 multicolored	2.00 2.00
458	A90	$1.75 multicolored	2.50 2.50
		Nos. 455-458 (4)	8.15 8.15

Souvenir Sheet

459	A90	$6 multicolored	13.00 13.00

1992 Summer Olympics,
Barcelona — A91

1992, July 29   Litho.   Perf. 14

460	A91	95c Hurdles	2.00 2.00
461	A91	$1.25 Weight lifting	2.25 2.25
462	A91	$1.50 Judo	2.75 2.75
463	A91	$1.95 Soccer	3.25 3.25
		Nos. 460-463 (4)	10.25 10.25

6th Festival of Pacific Arts,
Rarotonga — A92

Canoes: 30c, Vaka Motu. 50c, Hamatafua. 95c, Alia Kalia Ndrua. $1.75, Hokule'a Hawaiian. $1.95, Tuamotu Pahi.

1992, Oct. 16   Litho.   Perf. 14x15

464	A92	30c multicolored	.85 .85
465	A92	50c multicolored	1.00 1.00
466	A92	95c multicolored	2.00 2.00
467	A92	$1.75 multicolored	3.00 3.00
468	A92	$1.95 multicolored	3.50 3.50
		Nos. 464-468 (5)	10.35 10.35

For overprints see Nos. 524-528.

Nos. 464-468 Overprinted

ROYAL VISIT

1992, Oct. 16

469	A92	30c on #464	1.00 1.00
470	A92	50c on #465	1.75 1.75
471	A92	95c on #466	2.75 2.75
472	A92	$1.75 on #467	3.75 3.75
473	A92	$1.95 on #468	4.50 4.50
		Nos. 469-473 (5)	13.75 13.75

Christmas
A93

Designs: Different details from Virgin's Nativity, by Guido Reni.

1992, Nov. 19   Litho.   Perf. 13½
474 A93   80c multicolored   1.90   1.90
475 A93   90c multicolored   2.00   2.00
476 A93 $1.05 multicolored   2.10   2.10
477 A93 $1.75 multicolored   2.50   2.50
   Nos. 474-477 (4)   8.50   8.50
Souvenir Sheet
478 A93 $6 like #476   8.00   8.00

No. 478 contains one 39x50mm stamp.

Discovery of America, 500th
Anniv. — A94

Designs: $1.25, Columbus being blessed as he departs from Spain. $1.75, Map of Columbus' four voyages. $1.95, Columbus landing in New World.

1992, Dec. 11   Perf. 14x15
479 A94 $1.25 multicolored   2.75   2.75
480 A94 $1.75 multicolored   3.50   3.50
481 A94 $1.95 multicolored   3.75   3.75
   Nos. 479-481 (3)   10.00   10.00

Coronation of Queen Elizabeth II, 40th
Anniv. — A95

Designs: a, Victoria, Edward VII. b, George V, George VI. c, Elizabeth II.

1993, June 4   Litho.   Perf. 14
482 A97 $1.75 Strip of 3, #a.-
   c.   10.00   10.00

Christmas — A96

Religious sculpture: 80c, Madonna and Child, by Nino Pisano. 90c, Virgin on Rosebush, by Luca Della Robbia. $1.15, Virgin with Child and St. John, by Juan Francisco Rustici. $1.95, Virgin with Child, by Michelangelo. $3, Madonna and Child, by Jacopo Della Quercia.

1993, Oct. 29   Litho.   Perf. 14
483 A96   80c multicolored   1.00   1.00
484 A96   90c multicolored   1.25   1.25
485 A96 $1.15 multicolored   1.75   1.75
486 A96 $1.95 multicolored   2.50   2.50
Size: 32x47mm
Perf. 13½
487 A96 $3 multicolored   3.50   3.50
   Nos. 483-487 (5)   10.00   10.00

1994 Winter Olympics,
Lillehammer — A97

Designs: a, Ice hockey. b, Ski jumping. c, Cross-country skiing.

1994, Feb. 11   Litho.   Perf. 14
488 A97 $1.15 Strip of 3, #a.-
   c.   12.00   12.00

Flowers — A98

Hibiscus
A98a

1994-97   Litho.   Perf. 13½
489 A98   5c Prostrate morning glory   .50   .50
490 A98   10c White frangipani   .60   .60
491 A98   15c Red hibiscus   .75   .75
492 A98   20c Yellow alla-
   manda   .85   .85
493 A98   25c Royal poinciana   .85   .85
494 A98   30c White gardenia   .85   .85
495 A98   50c Pink frangipani   1.00   1.00
496 A98   80c Morning glory   1.25   1.25
497 A98   85c Yellow mallow   1.50   1.50
498 A98   90c Red coral tree   1.50   1.50
499 A98 $1 Cup of gold   1.60   1.60
500 A98 $2 Red cordia   2.00   2.00
501 A98a $3 multicolored   4.25   4.25
502 A98a $5 multicolored   5.00   5.00
503 A98a $8 multicolored   8.00   8.00
   Nos. 489-503 (15)   30.50   30.50

Issued: 5c-90c, 2/17; $1, $2, 4/29; $3, $5, 11/18; $8, 11/21/97.

First
Manned
Moon
Landing,
25th
Anniv.
A99

Designs: No. 506, Astronauts Collins, Armstrong, Aldrin. No. 507, Splash down in South Pacific.

1994, July 20   Litho.   Perf. 14
506 A99 $2 multicolored   6.50   6.50
507 A99 $2 multicolored   6.50   6.50

Christmas — A100

Paintings: No. 508a, The Madonna of the Basket, by Corregio. b, Virgin & Child with Saints, by Hans Memling. c, The Virgin & Child with Flowers, by Dolci. d, Virgin & Child with Angels, by Bergognone.
   No. 509a, The Adoration of the Kings, by Dosso. b, The Virgin & Child, by Bellini. c, The Virgin & Child, by Schiavone. d, Adoration of the Kings, by Dolci.

1994, Nov. 30   Litho.   Perf. 14
508 A100   85c Block of 4, #a.-d.   4.75   4.75
509 A100   90c Block of 4, #a.-d.   5.50   5.50

End of World War II, 50th
Anniv. — A101

Designs: a, Battle of Britain, 1940. b, Battle of Midway, June 1942.

1995, Sept. 4   Litho.   Perf. 13½x13
510 A101 $4 Pair, #a.-b.   20.00   20.00

No. 510 issued in sheets of 4 stamps.

Queen
Mother, 95th
Birthday
A102

1995, Sept. 14   Litho.   Perf. 13x13½
511 A102 $4 multicolored   9.50   9.50

UN, 50th Anniv. — A103

1995, Oct. 18   Litho.   Perf. 13½
512 A103 $4.25 multicolored   7.50   7.50

Year of the
Sea Turtle
A104

1995, Dec. 1   Litho.   Perf. 14x13½
513 A104   95c Green   2.25   2.25
514 A104 $1.15 Leatherback   2.75   2.75
515 A104 $1.50 Olive Ridley   3.00   3.00
516 A104 $1.75 Loggerhead   3.25   3.25
   Nos. 513-516 (4)   11.25   11.25

Queen
Elizabeth
II, 70th
Birthday
A105

1996, June 24   Litho.   Perf. 14
517 A105 $4.50 multicolored   8.25   8.25

No. 517 was issued in sheets of 4.

Modern
Olympic
Games,
Cent.
A106

Designs: No. 518, Pierre de Coubertin, Olympic torch, parading athletes, 1896. No. 519, Modern sprinters, US flag, Atlanta, 1996.

1996, July 11   Litho.   Perf. 14
518 A106 $2 multicolored   4.50   4.50
519 A106 $2 multicolored   4.50   4.50
   a.   Pair, #518-519   10.00   10.00

Queen Elizabeth II and Prince Philip,
50th Wedding Anniv.
A107

Designs: $2.50, Queen Elizabeth II, Prince Philip, Queen Mother, and King George VI. $6, like No. 520, close-up.

1997, Nov. 20   Litho.   Perf. 14
520 A107 $2.50 multicolored   3.75   3.75
Souvenir Sheet
521 A107 $6 multicolored   8.00   8.00

No. 520 was issued in sheets of 4.

Diana, Princess of
Wales (1961-
97) — A108

1998, Apr. 15   Litho.   Perf. 14
522 A108 $1 multicolored   1.00   1.00
Souvenir Sheet
523 A108 $4 like #522   5.00   5.00

No. 522 was issued in sheets of 5 + label. No. 523 is a continuous design. For surcharge see No. B55.

Nos. 464-468 Overprinted

1999, Dec. 31   Litho.   Perf. 14x15
524	A92	30c on #464	.55	.55
525	A92	50c on #465	.70	.70
526	A92	95c on #466	1.00	1.00
527	A92	$1.75 on #467	1.50	1.50
528	A92	$1.95 on #468	1.75	1.75
		Nos. 524-528 (5)	5.50	5.50

Queen Mother, 100th Birthday — A109

No. 529: a, Wearing crown, blue-toned photograph. b, Wearing crown, color photograph. c, Wearing hat. d, With King George VI.

2000, Oct. 20   Litho.   Perf. 14
529	A109	$3 Sheet of 4, #a-d	11.00	11.00

Souvenir Sheet
530	A109	$7.50 With flowers	7.00	7.00

2000 Summer Olympics, Sydney — A110

No. 531: a, Ancient wrestling. b, Wrestling. c, Ancient boxer. d, Boxing.

2000, Dec. 14   Litho.   Perf. 14
531	A110	$2 Sheet of 4, #a-d	7.25	7.25

Souvenir Sheet
532	A110	$2.75 Torch relay	3.00	3.00

Worldwide Fund for Nature (WWF) A111

Various views of two blue lorikeets: 80c, 90c, $1.15, $1.95.

2002, Sept. 3   Litho.   Perf. 14
533-536	A111	Set of 4	5.75	5.75

Nos. 533-536 were each issued in sheets of four with a label featuring an enlarged design of the stamp. Value, set of four sheets $24.

United We Stand — A112

2003, Sept. 30   Litho.   Perf. 14
537	A112	$1.15 multi	1.50	1.50

Printed in sheets of 4.

Pope John Paul II (1920-2005) A113

2005, Nov. 11   Litho.   Perf. 14
538	A113	$1.95 multi	3.75	3.75

Printed in sheets of 5 + label.

Worldwide Fund for Nature (WWF) — A114

Blue moon butterfly: 80c, Caterpillar and chrysalis. 90c, Female. $1.15, Male. $1.95, Male, diff.

2008, Nov. 18   Litho.   Perf. 13½
539-542	A114	Set of 4	6.00	6.00

Nos. 539-542 were each issued in sheets of four with a label featuring an enlarged design of the stamp. Value, set of four sheets $25.

Worldwide Fund for Nature (WWF) — A115

Designs: 80c, Tomato grouper. 90c, Peacock grouper. $1.10, Pair of Tomato groupers. $1.20, Head of Peacock grouper.

2010, Dec. 9   Perf. 14
543-546	A115	Set of 4	5.00	5.00

Tourism A116

Designs: 10c, Airplane, island. 20c, Bent palm tree, sun on horizon. 30c, Beach. 40c, Ship, islands. 50c, Road in forest. 60c, Islands and beach (at right) under dark skies. 70c, People fishing. 80c, Bent palm tree. 90c, Huts. $1, Islands and beach (at left). $1.10, Fence near beach. $1.20, Sun at horizon. $1.50, Moon above island. $2, Mountain on island. $3, Building and courtyard.

2010, Dec. 10
547	A116	10c multi	.30	.30
548	A116	20c multi	.35	.35
549	A116	30c multi	.40	.40
550	A116	40c multi	.90	.90
551	A116	50c multi	.70	.70
552	A116	60c multi	.85	.85
553	A116	70c multi	1.00	1.00
554	A116	80c multi	1.10	1.10
555	A116	90c multi	1.15	1.15
556	A116	$1 multi	1.25	1.25
557	A116	$1.10 multi	1.40	1.40
558	A116	$1.20 multi	1.50	1.50
559	A116	$1.50 multi	1.75	1.75
560	A116	$2 multi	2.25	2.25
561	A116	$3 multi	3.75	3.75
a.		Sheet of 15, #547-561	19.50	19.50
		Nos. 547-561 (15)	18.65	18.65

A117

Engagement of Prince William and Catherine Middleton — A118

Designs: Nos. 562, 565a, 567, 50c, Middleton. Nos. 563, 565b, 568, $5, Prince playing polo.
No. 564: a, Prince in military uniform. b, Prince playing polo. c, Middleton, fence. d, Prince, man and woman in background. e, Middleton, woman in background. f, Couple, Prince at left. g, Middleton with black hat. h, Prince. i, Couple, Middleton at left. j, Hands of couple, engagement ring.
$8.10, Couple, Prince in uniform at left.

2011, Jan. 14   Perf. 14
562	A117	50c multi	.75	.75
563	A117	$5 multi	7.00	7.00

Miniature Sheets
564	A118	$1 Sheet of 10, #a-j	12.50	12.50

Perf. 13¾x13½
565	A117	Sheet of 2, #a-b + label	8.00	8.00

Souvenir Sheets
Perf. 14¼
566	A117	$8.10 multi	11.00	11.00
567	A117	$11 multi	16.00	16.00
568	A117	$11 multi	16.00	16.00
		Nos. 566-568 (3)	43.00	43.00

No. 565 contains two 28x44mm stamps. Nos. 566-568 each contain one 38x50mm stamp.

Peonies A119

2011, Apr. 8   Litho.   Perf. 13¼
569	A119	90c multi	1.25	1.25

Souvenir Sheet
Perf. 14¾x14
570	A119	$6.60 Peonies in vase, horiz.	10.50	10.50

No. 569 was printed in sheets of 6. No. 570 contains one 48x42mm stamp.

Souvenir Sheet

Wedding of Prince William and Catherine Middleton — A120

No. 571 — Bride and groom: a, $1.10, Walking down aisle. b, $1.20, Kneeling.

2011, July 15   Perf. 15x14¼
571	A120	Sheet of 2, #a-b	4.00	4.00

Aitutaki Marine Research Center — A121

Designs: 10c, Suspended cages underwater. 20c, Station manager Richard Story. 80c, Tridacna maxima. 90c, Tridacna maxima, diff. $1.10, Tridacna derasa. $1.20, Tridacna derasa, diff.
No. 578, vert.: a, $2, Researcher underwater. b, $3, Researcher lifting cage on boat.

2011, July 25   Perf. 14¼x14
572-577	A121	Set of 6	7.25	7.25

Souvenir Sheet
Perf. 13¾
578	A121	Sheet of 2, #a-b	8.50	8.50

Nos. 572-577 each were printed in sheets of 4. No. 578 contains two 30x38mm stamps.

Christmas A122

No. 579 — Items from Christmas song "The Twelve Days of Christmas": a, Nine ladies dancing. b, Ten lords a leaping. c, Eleven pipers piping. d, Twelve drummers drumming.

2011, Dec. 24   Litho.   Perf. 13¼
579		Horiz. strip of 4	8.25	8.25
a.	A122	90c multi	1.50	1.50
b.	A122	$1 multi	1.60	1.60
c.	A122	$1.20 multi	1.90	1.90
d.	A122	$2 multi	3.25	3.25
e.		Souvenir sheet of 4, #579a-579d	8.25	8.25

No. 579 was printed in sheets containing three strips.

Beatification of Pope John Paul II — A123

No. 580: a, $1.10, Pope Benedict XVI. b, $5.10, Pope John Paul II.

2012, Jan. 10　　　**Perf. 13¾**
580 A123　Horiz. pair, #a-b　10.50 10.50

No. 580 was printed in sheets containing two pairs.

Cetaceans — A124

Designs: Nos. 581, 593a, 20c, Humpback whale. Nos. 582, 593b, 30c, Humpback whale tail. Nos. 583, 593c, 50c, Humpback whale, diff. Nos. 584, 593d, 80c, Striped dolphins. Nos. 585, 593e, 90c, Striped dolphins, diff. Nos. 586, 593f, $1, Striped dolphins, diff. Nos. 587, 593g, $1.10, Striped dolphin. Nos. 588, 593h, $1.20, Striped dolphins, diff. Nos. 589, 593i, $5, Striped dolphins, diff. Nos. 590, 593j, $6, Humpback whale tail, diff. Nos. 591, 593k, $7.50, Humpback whale, diff. Nos. 592, 593l, $10, Humpback whale, diff.

2012, June 22　　　**Perf. 14**
Stamps Without Dark Blue Frame Near Denomination
581-592 A124　Set of 12　55.00 55.00
Stamps With Dark Blue Frame All Around
593 A124　Sheet of 12, #a-l　55.00 55.00

Entombment of Christ, by Pietro Lorenzetti — A125

The Last Supper, by Lorenzetti A126

Madonna with St. Francis and St. John the Evangelist, by Lorenzetti A127

Deposition of Christ from the Cross, by Lorenzetti A128

The Flagellation of Christ, by Lorenzetti A129

Entry of Christ Into Jerusalem, by Lorenzetti A130

Perf. 14¾x14¼
2012, Nov. 16　　　**Litho.**
Stamps With White Frames
594　Horiz. pair　2.80 2.80
a. A125 80c multi　1.40 1.40
b. A126 80c multi　1.40 1.40
595　Horiz. pair　3.00 3.00
a. A127 90c multi　1.50 1.50
b. A128 90c multi　1.50 1.50
596　Horiz. pair　10.00 10.00
a. A129 $3 multi　5.00 5.00
b. A130 $3 multi　5.00 5.00
　　Nos. 594-596 (3)　15.80 15.80
Miniature Sheet
Stamps Without White Frame
597　Sheet of 6　16.00 16.00
a. A125 80c multi　1.40 1.40
b. A126 80c multi　1.40 1.40
c. A127 90c multi　1.50 1.50
d. A128 90c multi　1.50 1.50
e. A129 $3 multi　5.00 5.00
f. A130 $3 multi　5.00 5.00

Christmas.

Personalizable Stamp — A131

2012, Dec. 21　Litho.　Perf. 14x14¾
598 A131 $4 multi　6.75 6.75

Miniature Sheet

New Year 2013 (Year of the Snake) — A132

No. 599 — Snake with background color of: a, Green. b, Yellow, c, Pink. d, Violet.

2013, Feb. 21　Litho.　Perf. 14¾x14
599 A132 $1.20 Sheet of 4, #a-d　8.00 8.00

Cetaceans — A133

Various boats and: Nos. 600, 612a, 10c, Humpback whale. Nos. 601, 612b, 40c, Humpback whale, diff. Nos. 602, 612c, 60c, Humpback whale, diff. Nos. 603, 612d, 70c, Striped dolphin. Nos. 604, 612e, $1.50, Striped dolphin, diff. Nos. 605, 612f, $1.80, Striped dolphin, diff. Nos. 606, 612g, $2, Striped dolphin, diff. Nos. 607, 612h, $2.25, Striped dolphin, diff. Nos. 608, 612i, $2.50, Striped dolphin, diff. Nos. 609, 612j, Humpback whale, diff. Nos. 610, 612k, $4, Humpback whale, diff. Nos. 611, 612l, $20, Humpback whale, diff.

2013, June 5　Litho.　Perf. 14
Stamps With White Frames
600-611 A133　Set of 12　62.50 62.50
Miniature Sheet
Stamps Without White Frames
612 A133　Sheet of 12, #a-l　62.50 62.50

Souvenir Sheet

Birth of Prince George of Cambridge — A134

No. 613: a, $1.30, Duchess of Cambridge. b, $1.50, Duchess of Cambridge reviewing Scouts, Duchess and Duke of Cambridge kissing. c, $1.70, Duchess of Cambridge, diff.

2013, Aug. 1　Litho.　Perf. 13½
613 A134　Sheet of 3, #a-c　7.25 7.25

Souvenir Sheet

China International Collection Expo — A135

No. 614: a, $1.50, Painting by Paul Gauguin. b, $1.70, Beijing Exhibition Center.

2013, Sept. 26　Litho.　Perf. 12
614 A135　Sheet of 2, #a-b　5.50 5.50

Pres. John F. Kennedy (1917-63) A136

Designs: $2.50, Kennedy and quotation. $2.90, Kennedy.

2013, Nov. 8　Litho.　Perf. 14¼
615-616 A136　Set of 2　9.00 9.00

Christmas — A137

Religious paintings by: $1, William Brassey Hole. $1.30, Bernardino Luini.
No. 619 — Religious paintings by: a, $2, Gentile da Fabriano. b, $2.40, Marten de Vos. c, $2.60, Pietro Perugino.

2013, Nov. 18　Litho.　Perf. 13¼
617-618 A137　Set of 2　4.00 4.00
Souvenir Sheet
619　A137　Sheet of 3, #a-c　11.50 11.50

Miniature Sheet

New Year 2014 (Year of the Horse) — A138

No. 620 — Color of horse: a, $1, Purple. b, $1.30, White, horiz. c, $1.50, Dark blue. d, $1.70, Yellow, horiz.

2014, Jan. 10　Litho.　Perf. 13¾
620 A138　Sheet of 4, #a-d　9.00 9.00

Miniature Sheet

Easter — A139

No. 621 — Religious paintings by: a, 50c, Benvenuto Garofalo. b, $1, Tiziano Vecelli (Titian). c, $1.30, Piero della Francesca. d, $1.50, Peter Paul Rubens. e, $1.70, Ambrogio Borgognone.
$9.50, Painting by Paolo Veronese.

2014, Apr. 9　Litho.　Perf. 13¼
621 A139　Sheet of 5, #a-e, + label　10.50 10.50
Souvenir Sheet
622 A139 $9.50 multi　16.50 16.50

Worldwide Fund for Nature (WWF) A140

Various depictions of spotted reef crab: $1, $1.30, $1.70, $2.10.

2014, Nov. 28　Litho.　Perf. 14
623-626 A140　Set of 4　9.75 9.75
626a　Souvenir sheet of 4, #623-626　9.75 9.75

Nos. 623-626 were each printed in sheets of 4.

Souvenir Sheet

Christmas — A141

No. 627 — Religious paintings by: a, Fra Angelico. b, Pieter Breugel, the Elder. c, Paolo Schiavo.

Perf. 14¾x14¼

2014, Dec. 12   Litho.
627 A141 $1.50 Sheet of 3, #a-c   7.00 7.00

Souvenir Sheet

New Year 2015 (Year of the Sheep) — A142

No. 628 — Sheep with background color of: a, $3.80, Green. b, $4.10, Orange.

2015, Jan. 5   Litho.   **Perf. 13¼**
628 A142   Sheet of 2, #a-b   11.50 11.50

Miniature Sheet

Easter — A143

No. 629 — Paintings depicting Jesus Christ by: a, Bartolomé Esteban Murillo. b, Albrecht Altdorfer. c, John Singleton Copley. d, William Blake.

2015, Mar. 31   Litho.   **Perf. 14x14¼**
629 A143 $2 Sheet of 4, #a-d   12.50 12.50

Souvenir Sheet

Birth of Princess Charlotte of Cambridge — A144

No. 630: a, Duchess of Cambridge holding Princess Charlotte. b, Duke of Cambridge and Prince George.

Perf. 14¾x14¼

2015, June 23   Litho.
630 A144 $4.50 Sheet of 2,
           #a-b   12.00 12.00

New Year 2016 (Year of the Monkey) A145

Designs: $2.60, Monkey and red chop mark. $3, Monkey, diff.
No. 633: a, $3.80, Monkey and red chop mark. b, $4.10, Monkey, diff.

2015, Sept. 25   Litho.   **Perf. 13¼**
631-632 A145   Set of 2   7.25 7.25
Souvenir Sheet
633 A145   Sheet of 2, #a-b   10.50 10.50

No. 633 contains two 50x50mm diamond-shaped stamps.

Miniature Sheet

Queen Elizabeth II, Longest-Reigning British Monarch — A146

No. 634 — Various photographs of Queen Elizabeth II: a, $1.30. b, $1.50. c, $1.70. d, $2.

2015, Nov. 20   Litho.   **Perf. 14x14¼**
634 A146   Sheet of 4, #a-d   8.75 8.75

Souvenir Sheet

Christmas — A147

No. 635 — Details from *The Nativity*, by Lorenzo Monaco: a, Virgin Mary. b, Infant Jesus and farm animals, c, St. Joseph.

2015, Dec. 9   Litho.   **Perf. 13¼**
635 A147 $1 Sheet of 3, #a-c   4.00 4.00

Souvenir Sheet

Queen Elizabeth II, 90th Birthday — A148

No. 636 — Queen Elizabeth II: a, Without hat. b, With hat.

2016, May 10   Litho.   **Perf. 13¼**
636 A148 $3 Sheet of 2, #a-b   8.25 8.25

Marae Moana Marine Park — A149

Designs: 30c, Short-finned pilot whales. 50c, Whitetip reef shark. 80c, Common dolphins. $1, Emblem of Marae Moana Marine Park. $1.10, Humpback whales. $1.30, Blue shark. $1.50, Tiger shark. $1.70, Spinner dolphin. $2, Killer whale.

2016, May 27   Litho.   **Perf. 14¼x14¾**
637 A149   30c multi   .40   .40
638 A149   50c multi   .70   .70
639 A149   80c multi   1.10   1.10
640 A149 $1 multi   1.40   1.40
641 A149 $1.10 multi   1.75   1.75
642 A149 $1.30 multi   1.90   1.90
643 A149 $1.50 multi   2.10   2.10
644 A149 $1.70 multi   2.40   2.40
645 A149 $2 multi   2.75   2.75
     Nos. 637-645 (9)   14.50 14.50

New Year 2017 (Year of the Rooster) A150

Designs: $2.30, Rooster, green & orange tail feathers. $4.50, Rooster, green tail feathers.

2016, Aug. 10   Litho.   **Perf. 13½**
646-647 A150   Set of 2   10.00 10.00
647a   Souvenir sheet of 2,
       #646-647   10.00 10.00

Worldwide Fund for Nature (WWF) A151

Chatham albatrosses: Nos. 648, 652a, $1, Two on cliff, one in flight. Nos. 649, 652b, $1.70, Adult and juvenile. Nos. 650, 652c, $2, Bird in flight. Nos. 651, 652d, $2.40, Two adults and nest.

2016, Dec. 6   Litho.   **Perf. 14¾x14¼**
Stamps With White Frames
648-651 A151   Set of 4   10.00 10.00
Stamps Without White Frames
652 A151   Block or horiz.
       strip of 4, #a-d   10.00 10.00

For surcharges, see Nos. 682-687.

Christmas — A153

No. 653 — Stained-glass window depicting: a, Adoration of the Shepherds. b, Holy Family.
No. 654 — Stained-glass window depicting: a, Holy Family and cows. b, Holy Family, diff.

2016, Dec. 19   Litho.   **Perf. 13¼**
653 A152 50c Horiz. pair, #a-b   1.40 1.40
654 A153 $1 Horiz. pair, #a-b   2.75 2.75

Miniature Sheet

Easter — A154

No. 655 — Paintings of the Resurrection of Christ by: a, Gustave Doré. b, Gebhard Fugel. c, James Jacques Tissot. d, Master of Wittingau.

2017, Apr. 12   Litho.   **Perf. 13**
655 A154 $1 Sheet of 4, #a-d   5.50 5.50

Miniature Sheet

Pres. John F. Kennedy (1917-63) — A155

No. 656 — Pres. Kennedy: a, $1, With Wernher von Braun. b, $1, With others watching television coverage of first U.S. manned space flight. c, $2.50, With W. Averill Harriman and Dean Rusk. d, $2.50, Delivering speech on Nuclear Test Ban Treaty.

2017, July 3   Litho.   **Perf. 13**
656 A155   Sheet of 4, #a-d   10.50 10.50

Miniature Sheet

Reign of Queen Elizabeth II, 65th Anniv. — A156

A152

No. 657 — Queen Elizabeth II: a, Holding handbag. b, Standing near railing. c, Holding paper. d, Wearing turquoise green hat and jacket.

2017, July 17   Litho.   Perf. 13
657 A156 $2.50 Sheet of 4,
            #a-d   15.00 15.00

New Year 2018 (Year of the Dog) — A157

Designs: $3, Dog. $3.80, Figurine of dog.

2017, Nov. 1   Litho.   Perf. 13¼
658-659 A157 Set of 2   9.50 9.50
659a   Souvenir sheet of 2, #658-
               659   9.50 9.50

Christmas — A158

No. 660, $1: a, Moon and palm trees. b, Sailboat.
No. 661, $2.40: a, Scallop shell. b, Holly and sea turtle.

2017, Dec. 5   Litho.   Perf. 12½
Horiz. pairs, #a-b
660-661 A158 Set of 2   9.75 9.75

Butterflies — A159

No. 662: a, Great eggfly butterfly. b, Blue-spotted Charaxes butterfly. c, Karner blue butterfly. d, Monarch butterfly.

2017, Dec. 8   Litho.   Perf. 12½
662 A159 $2.50 Block of 4, #a-
           d   14.50 14.50

Miniature Sheet

Easter — A160

No. 663: a, $1, Tulip. b, $1, Church, chalice and bread. c, $2.40, Sun, cross and dove. d, $2.40, Easter eggs, shells and butterflies.

2018, Mar. 19   Litho.   Perf. 13
663 A160 Sheet of 4, #a-d   10.00 10.00

Birdpex Philatelic Exhibition, Mondorf-les-Bains, Luxembourg — A161

No. 664: a, $1, Hawaiian petrel. b, $4.80, Juan Fernandez petrels.

2018, May 4   Litho.   Perf. 13
664 A161 Horiz. pair, #a-b   8.25 8.25

Wedding of Prince Harry and Meghan Markle — A162

No. 665: a, Prince Charles bringing bride to groom. b, Couple kissing.
$8, Bride and groom on church steps.

2018, Aug. 2   Litho.   Perf. 13
665 A162 $4.80 Sheet of 2,
           #a-b   13.00 13.00

Souvenir Sheet
666 A162 $8 multi   11.00 11.00

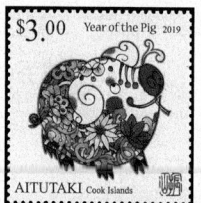

New Year 2019 (Year of the Pig) — A163

Pig facing: $3, Right. $3.80, Left.

2018, Dec. 10   Litho.   Perf. 13¼
667-668 A163 Set of 2   9.00 9.00

Birds of Prey A164

Designs: Nos. 669, 681a, 20c, Bonelli's eagle. Nos. 670, 681b, 30c, Pearl kite. Nos. 671, 681c, 40c, Black-breasted buzzard kite. Nos. 672, 681d, 50c, Brahminy kite. Nos. 673, 681e, $1, Oriental honey buzzard. Nos. 674, 681f, $2, Henst's goshawk. Nos. 675, 681g, $2.40, Cuban black hawk. Nos. 676, 681h, $2.60, Double-toothed kite. Nos. 677, 681i, $4.50, Crowned eagle. Nos. 678, 681j, $5, African marsh harrier. Nos. 679, 681k, $7.50, White-bellied sea eagle. Nos. 680, 681l, $10, Pacific baza.

2018, Dec. 27   Litho.   Perf. 13
Stamps With White Frames
669 A164 20c multi   .25   .25
670 A164 30c multi   .40   .40
671 A164 40c multi   .55   .55
672 A164 50c multi   .65   .65
673 A164 $1 multi   1.40 1.40
674 A164 $2 multi   2.75 2.75
  a.   Souvenir sheet of 6, #669-
        674   6.00 6.00
675 A164 $2.40 multi   3.25 3.25
676 A164 $2.60 multi   3.50 3.50
677 A164 $4.50 multi   6.00 6.00
678 A164 $5 multi   6.75 6.75
679 A164 $7.50 multi   10.00 10.00
680 A164 $10 multi   13.50 13.50
  a.   Souvenir sheet of 6, #675-
        680   43.00 43.00
  Nos. 669-680 (12)   49.00 49.00

Miniature Sheet
Stamps Without White Frames
681 A164 Sheet of 12, #a-l 49.00 49.00

Stamps on Nos. 674a and 680a have white frames on one or two sides. See Nos. 690-695.

Nos. 649-651 Surcharged

Methods and Perfs. As Before
2019, Aug. 5
682 A151 50c on $1.70 #649   .65   .65
683 A151 50c on $2 #650   .65   .65
684 A151 50c on $2.40 #651   .65   .65
685 A151 $1 on $1.70 #649   1.25 1.25
686 A151 $1 on $2 #650   1.25 1.25
687 A151 $1 on $2.40 #651   1.25 1.25
  Nos. 682-687 (6)   5.70 5.70

New Year 2020 (Year of the Rat) — A165

Rat facing: $3, Right. $3.80, Left.

2019, Oct. 11   Litho.   Perf. 13¼
688-689 A165 Set of 2   8.75 8.75

Birds of Prey Type of 2018

Designs: Nos. 690, 694a, $2.50, Long-crested eagle. Nos. 691, 694b, $3, Spanish imperial eagle. Nos. 692, 694c, $4, Tawny eagle. Nos. 693, 694d, $6, Verreaux's eagle.

2019, Nov. 15   Litho.   Perf. 13
690 A164 $2.50 multi   3.25 3.25
691 A164 $3 multi   4.00 4.00
692 A164 $4 multi   5.25 5.25
693 A164 $6 multi   8.00 8.00
  Nos. 690-693 (4)   20.50 20.50
Stamps Without White Frames
Stamp Size: 48x40mm
Perf. 13¼x13
694 A164 Block or vert. strip
           of 4, #a-d   20.50 20.50
  e.   Souvenir sheet of 4, #694a-
        694d   20.50 20.50

Nos. 694a-694d were printed in sheets of 8 containing two of each stamp. Stamps on No. 694e have white frames on two adjacent sides.

Owls A166

Designs: Nos. 695, 699a, $5.50, Barred owl. Nos. 696, 699b, $6.70, Little owl. Nos. 697, 699c, $22.40, Whiskered screech owl. Nos. 698, 699d, $29.90, Verreaux's eagle owl.

2019, Nov. 20   Litho.   Perf. 13
695 A166 $5.50 multi   7.25 7.25
696 A166 $6.70 multi   8.75 8.75
697 A166 $22.40 multi   29.00 29.00
698 A166 $29.90 multi   39.00 39.00
  Nos. 695-698 (4)   84.00 84.00
Stamps Without White Frames
Stamp Size: 48x40mm
Perf. 13¼x13
699 A166 Block or vert. strip
           of 4, #a-d   84.00 84.00
  e.   Souvenir sheet of 4, #699a-
        699d   84.00 84.00

Nos. 699a-699d were printed in sheets of 8 containing two of each stamp. Stamps on No. 699e have white frames on two adjacent sides.

SEMI-POSTAL STAMPS

Christmas Type of 1974

Designs: 1c+1c, like No. 104. 5c+1c, like No. 105. 8c+1c, like No. 106. 10c+1c, like No. 107. 25c+1c, like No. 108. 30c+1c, like No. 109.

1974, Dec. 2   Photo.   Perf. 13½
B1 A29 1c + 1c multicolored   .25   .25
B2 A29 5c + 1c multicolored   .25   .25
B3 A29 8c + 1c multicolored   .25   .25
B4 A29 10c + 1c multicolored .25   .25
B5 A29 25c + 1c multicolored .30   .30
B6 A29 30c + 1c multicolored .30   .30
  Nos. B1-B6 (6)   1.60 1.60

Surtax was for child welfare.

Nos. 117-120 Surcharged in Silver

1975, Dec. 19   Photo.   Perf. 14x13½
B7   A32 Strip of 3   .45   .45
  a.-c.   6c+1c any single   .25   .25
B8   A32 Strip of 3   .50   .50
  a.-c.   7c+1c any single   .25   .25
B9   A32 Strip of 3   1.00 1.00
  a.-c.   15c+1c any single   .30   .30
B10 A32 Strip of 3   1.50 1.50
  a.-c.   20c+1c any single   .45   .45
  Nos. B7-B10 (4)   3.45 3.45

Christmas. The surtax was for children's activities during holiday season.

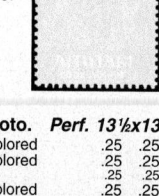

Nos. 135-142a Surcharged in Silver

1976, Nov. 19   Photo.   Perf. 13½x13
B11 6c + 1c multicolored   .25   .25
B12 6c + 1c multicolored   .25   .25
  a. A36 Pair, #B11-B12   .25
B13 7c + 1c multicolored   .25   .25
B14 7c + 1c multicolored   .25   .25
  a. A36 Pair, #B13-B14   .25
B15 15c + 1c multicolored   .25   .25
B16 15c + 1c multicolored   .25   .25
  a. A36 Pair, #B15-B16   .45   .45
B17 20c + 1c multicolored   .30   .30
B18 20c + 1c multicolored   .50   .50
  a. A36 Pair, #B17-B18   1.00 1.00
  b. Souvenir sheet of 8   2.00 2.00

Surtax was for child welfare. Stamps of No. B18b each surcharged 2c.

Nos. 152-159a Surcharged in Black

1977, Nov. 15   Perf. 13½x14
B19 6c + 1c multicolored   .25   .25
B20 6c + 1c multicolored   .25   .25
  a. A41 Pair, #B19-B20   .25
B21 7c + 1c multicolored   .25   .25
B22 7c + 1c multicolored   .25   .25
  a. A41 Pair, #B21-B22   .25
B23 15c + 1c multicolored   .25   .25
B24 15c + 1c multicolored   .25   .25
  a. A41 Pair, #B23-B24   .50   .50
B25 20c + 1c multicolored   .30   .30
B26 20c + 1c multicolored   .30   .30
  a. A41 Pair, #B25-B26   .65   .65
  b. Souvenir sheet of 8   2.50 2.50
  Nos. B19-B26 (8)   2.10 2.10

Surtax was for child welfare. Stamps of No. B26b each surcharged 2c.

Easter Type of 1978
Souvenir Sheets

Paintings: No. B27, like No. 163. No. B28, like No. 164. No. B29, like No. 165.

1978, Mar. 17 Photo.   Perf. 14
B27 A44 50c + 5c multicolored   .55   .55
B28 A44 50c + 5c multicolored   .55   .55
B29 A44 50c + 5c multicolored   .55   .55

Nos. B27-B29 contain one stamp 33x25mm.

Christmas Type of 1978
Souvenir Sheet

1978, Dec. 4 Photo.   Perf. 14½x13
B30 Sheet of 4   2.25 2.25
a. A46 15c + 2c like #167   .25   .25
b. A46 17c + 2c like #168   .30   .30
c. A46 30c + 2c like #169   .45   .45
d. A46 35c + 2c like #170   .60   .60

Year of the Child Type
Souvenir Sheet

1979, Oct. 1 Photo.   Perf. 14x13½
B31 Sheet of 3   1.25 1.25
a. A48 30c + 3c like #173   .30   .30
b. A48 35c + 3c like #174   .35   .35
c. A48 65c + 3c like #175   .45   .45

Easter Type of 1980
Souvenir Sheet

No. B32 shows entire painting in continuous design. Nos. B32a-B32c similar to Nos. 183-185. Size of Nos. B32a-B32c: 25x50mm.

1980, Apr. 3 Photo.   Perf. 13x13½
B32 Sheet of 3   1.90 1.90
a. A50 20c + 2c multicolored .45 .45
b. A50 30c + 2c multicolored .60 .60
c. A50 35c + 2c multicolored .75 .75

Christmas Type of 1980
Souvenir Sheet

1980, Nov. 21 Photo.   Perf. 13x13½
B33 Sheet of 4   1.50 1.50
a. A53 15c + 2c like #208   .25   .25
b. A53 20c + 2c like #209   .30   .30
c. A53 25c + 2c like #210   .35   .35
d. A53 35c + 2c like #211   .45   .45

Easter Type of 1981
Souvenir Sheet

1981, Mar. 31 Photo.   Perf. 13½
B34 Sheet of 3   1.65 1.65
a. A54 30c + 2c like #212   .35   .35
b. A54 40c + 2c like #213   .50   .50
c. A54 50c + 2c like #214   .65   .65

Nos. 247-249
Surcharged

1981, Nov. 23 Photo.   Perf. 13x13½
B35 A56 60 + 5c multi   .65   .65
B36 A56 80 + 5c multi   .70   .70
B37 A56 $1.40 + 5c multi .90   .90
Nos. B35-B37 (3)   2.25 2.25

Intl. Year of the Disabled. Surtax was for the handicapped.

Soccer Type of 1981
Souvenir Sheet

a-b, 12c+2c. c-d, 15c+2c. e-f, 20c+2c. g-h, 25c+2c.

1981, Nov. 30   Perf. 14
B38 A57 Sheet of 8, multi   6.00 6.00

No. B38 contains stamps with 2c surtax similar to Nos. 250-253. Surtax was for local sports.

Nos. 400-404
Surcharged

1986, Nov. 25 Litho.   Perf. 13½
B39 A79 75c + 10c multi   3.00 3.00
B40 A79 $1.35 + 10c multi 3.50 3.50
B41 A79 $1.95 + 10c multi 4.25 4.25
B42 A79 $2.75 + 10c multi 5.25 5.25
Nos. B39-B42 (4)   16.00 16.00
Souvenir Sheet
B43   Sheet of 4   16.50 16.50
a.-d. A79 $1.65 +10c on #404a-404d, each   4.00 4.00

State visit of Pope John Paul II.
For surcharges see Nos. B51-B54.

Nos. 394-395, 397 and 400-403 Surcharged in Silver or Black

1987, Apr. 29 Litho.   Perf. 13½, 14
B44 A79 75c + 50c #400   3.50 2.50
B45 A77 $1 + 50c #394 (B) 4.25 3.50
B46 A79 $1.35 + 50c #401 5.75 5.00
B47 A79 $1.95 + 50c #402 6.25 5.00
B48 A78 $2 + 50c #397   6.50 5.00
B49 A77 $2.75 + 50c #395 (B) 8.00 6.25
B50 A79 $2.75 + 50c #403 8.50 7.25
Nos. B44-B50 (7)   42.75 34.50

Nos. B39-B42
Surcharged in
Silver

1987, Apr. 29   Litho.   Perf. 13½
B51 A79 75c + 50c No. B39   4.00 4.00
B52 A79 $1.35 + 50c No. B40 4.50 4.50
B53 A79 $1.95 + 50c No. B41 4.75 4.75
B54 A79 $2.75 + 50c No. B42 6.00 6.00
Nos. B51-B54 (4)   19.25 19.25

No. 523 Surcharged in Silver

Souvenir Sheet
1998, Nov. 19   Litho.   Perf. 14
B55 A108 $4 + $1 multicolored 6.25 6.25

AIR POST STAMPS

Capt. Bligh Type of 1974

1974, Sept. 9   Litho.   Perf. 13
Size: 46x26mm
C1 A27 10c Bligh and "Bounty"   .75 .60
C2 A27 10c "Bounty" at sea   .75 .60
a. Pair, #C1-C2   1.75 1.75
C3 A27 25c Bligh and "Bounty"   .85 .75
C4 A27 25c Chart, 1856   .85 .75
a. Pair, #C3-C4   2.00 2.00
C5 A27 30c Cook and "Resolution"   1.00 1.00
C6 A27 30c Maps   1.00 1.00
a. Pair, #C5-C6   2.75 2.75
Nos. C1-C6 (6)   5.20 4.70

See note after No. 101.

OFFICIAL STAMPS

Nos. 83-90, 92-95, 150-151 Ovptd. or Srchd. in Black, Silver or Gold

1978-79   Photo.   Perf. 13x13½
O1 A25 1c multi   1.10 .25
O2 A25 2c multi   1.75 .25
O3 A25 3c multi   1.75 .25
O4 A25 4c multi (G)   1.75 .25
O5 A25 5c multi   1.75 .25
O6 A25 8c multi   1.75 .25
O7 A25 10c multi   2.00 .25
O8 A25 15c on 60c multi 3.50 .25
O9 A25 18c on 60c multi 3.50 .25
O10 A25 20c multi (G) 3.50 .25
O11 A40 50c multi   1.50 .70
O12 A25 60c multi   12.00 .80
O13 A25 $1 multi   12.00 1.00
O14 A26 $2 multi   11.00 .80
O15 A40 $4 on $1 multi (S) 2.50 .80
O16 A26 $5 multi   13.00 1.50
Nos. O1-O16 (16)   74.35 8.10

Overprint on 4c, 20c, $1 diagonal.
Issued: Nos. O14-O16, 2/20/79; others, 11/3/78.

Stamps of 1983-84 Ovptd. or Surcharged in Green

or Gold (#O29-O32)

1985, Aug. 9   Perf. 14, 13x13½
O17 A66 2c No. 322   2.10 2.10
O18 A66 5c No. 324   2.50 2.50
O19 A66 10c No. 325   3.00 3.00
O20 A66 12c No. 326   3.25 3.00
O21 A66 18c No. 327   4.00 3.50
O22 A66 20c on 24c No. 328 4.50 3.75
O23 A66 30c No. 329   3.50 2.50
O24 A66 40c on 36c No. 330 3.50 2.50
O25 A66 50c No. 332   3.50 2.50
O26 A66 55c on 48c No. 331 3.50 2.50
O27 A66 60c No. 333   4.00 2.75
O28 A66 65c on 72c No. 334 4.00 2.75
O29 A61 75c on 48c No. 276 2.50 2.10
O30 A61 75c on 48c No. 277 2.50 2.10
O31 A61 75c on 48c No. 278 2.50 2.10

O32 A61 75c on 48c No. 279 2.50 2.10
a. Block of 4, Nos. O29-O32 11.00 11.00
O33 A66 80c on 96c No. 335 4.00 3.75
Nos. O17-O33 (17)   55.35 45.50

Nos. 336-341 Overprinted Like Nos. O17-O21, O23, O25, O27 in Metallic Green

1986, Oct. 1   Perf. 14
O34 A66 $3 multi   8.50 6.50
O35 A66 $4.20 multi   11.00 8.50
O36 A66 $5.60 multi   12.00 10.00
O37 A66 $9.60 multi   15.00 12.00

1988-91   Perf. 14
O38 A66 $1.20 multi   5.00 2.50
O39 A66 $2.10 multi   7.50 4.00

Nos. 246C-246D
Surcharged in
Metallic Blue

O40 A55 $14 on $4 (B)   17.50 14.00
O41 A55 $18 on $5 (B)   22.50 19.00
Nos. O34-O41 (8)   99.00 76.50

Issue dates: July 2, 1991; others, June 15.

AJMAN

äj-ˈman

LOCATION — Oman Peninsula, Arabia, on Persian Gulf
GOVT. — Sheikdom under British Protection
AREA — 100 sq. mi.
POP. — 4,400
CAPITAL — Ajman

Ajman is one of six Persian Gulf sheikdoms to join the United Arab Emirates, which proclaimed its independence Dec. 2, 1971. See United Arab Emirates.

100 Naye Paise = 1 Rupee

> **Catalogue values for all unused stamps in this country are for Never Hinged items.**

Sheik Rashid bin Humaid al Naimi & Arab Stallion A1

Designs: 2np, 50np, Regal angelfish. 3np, 70np, Camel. 4np, 1r, Angelfish. 5np, 1.50r, Green turtle. 10np, 2r, Jewelfish. 15np, 3r, White storks. 20np, 5r, White-eyed gulls. 30np, 10r, Lanner falcon. 40np as 1np.

Photo. & Litho.

1964		Unwmk.		Perf. 14
		Size: 35x22mm		
1	A1	1np gold & multi	.25	.25
2	A1	2np gold & multi	.25	.25
3	A1	3np gold & multi	.25	.25
4	A1	4np gold & multi	.25	.25
5	A1	5np gold & multi	.25	.25
6	A1	10np gold & multi	.25	.25
7	A1	15np gold & multi	.25	.25
8	A1	20np gold & multi	.25	.25
9	A1	30np gold & multi	.25	.25
		Size: 42x27mm		
10	A1	40np gold & multi	.25	.25
11	A1	50np gold & multi	.25	.25
12	A1	70np gold & multi	.25	.25
13	A1	1r gold & multi	.40	.25
14	A1	1.50r gold & multi	.80	.35
15	A1	2r gold & multi	1.00	.50
		Size: 53x33½mm		
16	A1	3r gold & multi	1.50	1.00
17	A1	5r gold & multi	4.00	2.40
18	A1	10r gold & multi	7.50	3.75
		Nos. 1-18 (18)	18.20	11.25

Issued: Nos. 1-9, 6/20; Nos. 10-15, 9/7; Nos. 16-18, 11/4. Exist imperf. Value, set $30.

Pres. and Mrs. John F. Kennedy with Caroline — A2

Pres. Kennedy: 10np, As a boy in football uniform. 15np, Diving. 50np, As navy lieutenant, receiving Navy and Marine Corps Medal from Capt. Frederic L. Conklin. 1r, Sailing with Jacqueline Kennedy. 2r, With Eleanor Roosevelt. 5r, With Lyndon B. Johnson and Hubert H. Humphrey. 10r, Portrait.

1964, Dec. 15		Photo.	Perf. 13½x14
19	A2	10np grn & red lil	.25	.25
20	A2	15np Prus bl & vio	.25	.25
21	A2	50np org brn & dk bl	.25	.25
22	A2	1r brn & Prus grn	.50	.30
23	A2	2r red lil & dp ol	.75	.50
24	A2	3r grn & red brn	1.50	.75
25	A2	5r vio & brn	2.75	2.00
26	A2	10r dk bl & red brn	5.50	3.50
		Nos. 19-26 (8)	11.75	7.80

John F. Kennedy (1917-63). Exist imperf. Value, set $17.50. A souvenir sheet contains one each of Nos. 23-26. Value, perf or imperf, $25.

Runners at Start — A3

10np, 1.50r, Boxing. 25np, 2r, Judo. 50np, 5r, Gymnast on vaulting horse. 1r, 3r, Sailing yacht.

1965, Jan. 12		Photo.	Perf. 13½x14
27	A3	5np red brn, brt pink & Prus grn	.25	.25
28	A3	10np dk ol grn, bl gray & red brn	.25	.25
29	A3	15np dk vio, grn & sep	.25	.25
30	A3	25np bl sal pink & blk	.25	.25
31	A3	50np mar, bl & ind	.25	.25
32	A3	1r dk grn, lil & ultra	.50	.25
33	A3	1.50r lil, grn & brn	.75	.50
34	A3	2r red org, bis & dk bl	1.25	.70
35	A3	3r dk brn, grnsh bl & lil	2.00	1.25
36	A3	5r grn, yel & red brn	3.25	1.75
		Nos. 27-36 (10)	9.00	5.70

18th Olympic Games, Tokyo, Oct. 10-25, 1964. Exist imperf. Value, set $12. A souvenir sheet contains four stamps similar to Nos. 33-36 in changed colors. Values: perf $10; imperf $14.

Stanley Gibbons Catalogue, 1865, U.S. No. 1X2 — A4

Designs: 10np, Austria, Scarlet Mercury 1856. 15np, British Guiana 1c, 1856. 25np, Canada 12p, 1851. 50np, Hawaii 2c, 1851. 1r, Mauritius 2p, 1847. 3r, Switzerland, Geneva 10c, 1843. 5r, Tuscany 31, 1860. 5np, 15np, 50np and 3r show first edition of Stanley Gibbons Catalogue; 10np, 25np, 1r and 5r show 1965 Elizabethan Catalogue.

1965, May 6		Unwmk.	Perf. 13
37	A4	5np multi	.25	.25
38	A4	10np multi	.25	.25
39	A4	15np multi	.25	.25
40	A4	25np multi	.25	.25
41	A4	50np multi	.25	.25
42	A4	1r multi	.50	.25
43	A4	3r multi	1.50	.50
a.		Souv. sheet of 4, #38-39, 42-43	4.50	
44	A4	5r multi	3.00	1.10
a.		Souv. sheet of 4, #37, 40-41, 44	4.00	
		Nos. 37-44 (8)	6.25	3.10

Gibbons Catalogue Cent. Exhib., London, Feb. 17-20. Nos. 43a and 44a for 125th anniv. of 1st postage stamp. Exist imperf. Value, set $9. Sheets exist imperf. Value for both sheets, $7.

Stamps of Ajman were replaced in 1972 by those of United Arab Emirates.

AIR POST STAMPS

Type of Regular Issue, 1964

Designs: 15np, Arab stallion. 25np, Regal angelfish. 35np, Camel. 50np, Angelfish. 75np, Green turtle. 1r, Jewelfish. 2r, White storks. 3r, White-eyed gulls. 5r, Lanner falcon.

Photo. & Litho.

1965		Unwmk.	Perf. 14
		Size: 42x25½mm		
C1	A1	15np silver & multi	.25	.25
C2	A1	25np silver & multi	.25	.25
C3	A1	35np silver & multi	.25	.25
C4	Al	50np silver & multi	.50	.25
C5	A1	75np silver & multi	.75	.25
C6	A1	1r silver & multi	1.00	.25
		Size: 53x33½mm		
C7	A1	2r silver & multi	1.50	.75
C8	A1	3r silver & multi	3.00	1.00
C9	A1	5r silver & multi	4.50	1.75
		Nos. C1-C9 (9)	12.00	5.00

Issued: Nos. C1-C6, 11/15; Nos. C7-C9, 12/18. Exist imperf. Value, set $25.

AIR POST OFFICIAL STAMPS

Type of Regular Issue, 1964

Designs: 75np, Jewelfish. 2r, White storks. 3r, White-eyed gulls. 5r, Lanner falcon.

Photo. & Litho.

1965, Dec. 18		Unwmk.	Perf. 14
		Size: 42x25½mm		
CO1	A1	75np gold & multi	.75	.35
		Size: 53x33½mm		
CO2	A1	2r gold & multi	2.25	.50
CO3	A1	3r gold & multi	3.00	1.00
CO4	A1	5r gold & multi	5.00	1.40
		Nos. CO1-CO4 (4)	11.00	3.25

OFFICIAL STAMPS

Type of Regular Issue, 1964

25np, Arab stallion. 40np, Regal angelfish. 50np, Camel. 75np, Angelfish. 1r, Green turtle.

Photo. & Litho.

1965, Dec. 1		Unwmk.	Perf. 14
		Size: 42x25½mm		
O1	A1	25np gold & multi	.30	.25
O2	A1	40np gold & multi	.40	.25
O3	A1	50np gold & multi	.50	.30
O4	A1	75np gold & multi	.60	.35
O5	A1	1r gold & multi	.90	.40
		Nos. O1-O5 (5)	2.70	1.55

ALAOUITES

ˈal-au-ˌwītz

LOCATION — A division of Syria, in Western Asia
GOVT. — Under French Mandate
AREA — 2,500 sq. mi.
POP. — 278,000 (approx. 1930)
CAPITAL — Latakia

This territory became an independent state in 1924, although still administered under the French Mandate. In 1930, it was renamed Latakia, and Syrian stamps overprinted "Lattaquie" superseded the stamps of Alaouites. For these and subsequent issues, see Latakia and Syria.

100 Centimes = 1 Piaster

Issued under French Mandate
Stamps of France Surcharged

Nos. 1-6, 16-18   Nos. 7-15, 19-21

1925		Unwmk.	Perf. 14x13½
1	A16	0.10p on 2c vio brn	4.00	
2	A22	0.25p on 5c orange	4.00	4.00
3	A20	0.75p on 15c gray grn	7.25	7.25
4	A22	1p on 20c red brn	4.00	4.00
5	A22	1.25p on 25c blue	4.00	4.00
6	A22	1.50p on 30c red	14.50	14.50
7	A22	2p on 35c violet	4.75	4.75

8	A18	2p on 40c red & pale bl	5.50	5.50
9	A18	2p on 45c grn & bl	19.00	19.00
10	A18	3p on 60c vio & ultra	8.75	8.75
11	A18	3p on 60c lt vio	14.00	14.00
b.		Double surcharge	165.00	165.00
12b	A20	4p on 85c vermil-ion	4.00	4.00
c.		As "b," inverted surcharge	60.00	60.00
13	A18	5p on 1fr cl & ol grn	8.50	8.50
14	A18	10p on 2fr org & pale bl	13.00	13.00
15	A18	25p on 5fr bl & buff	16.00	16.00
		Nos. 1-15 (15)	131.75	131.75

Two types of surcharge exist on the 4p and on the 5p-25p. For detailed listings, see the *Scott Classic Specialized Catalogue of Stamps and Covers 1840-1940*. For overprints, see Nos. C1-C4.

Same Surcharges on Pasteur Stamps of France

16	A23	0.50p on 10c green	3.00	3.00
17	A23	0.75p on 15c green	3.75	3.75
18	A23	1.50p on 30c red	3.00	3.00
19	A23	2p on 45c red	3.75	3.75
20	A23	2.50p on 50c blue	5.25	5.25
21	A23	4p on 75c blue	9.00	9.00
		Nos. 16-21 (6)	27.75	27.75

Two types of overprints exist on No. 21. For detailed listings, see *Scott Classic Specialized Catalogue of Stamps and Covers 1840-1940*.

Inverted Surcharges

1a	A16	0.10p on 2c vio brn	50.00
2a	A22	0.25p on 5c orange	50.00
3a	A22	0.75p on 15c gray grn	50.00
4a	A22	1p on 20c red brn	50.00
5a	A22	1.25p on 25c blue	50.00
6a	A22	1.50p on 30c red	60.00
7a	A22	2p on 35c violet	50.00
8a	A18	2p on 40c red & pale bl	50.00
9a	A18	2p on 45c grn & bl	60.00
10a	A18	3p on 60c vio & ultra	60.00
11a	A20	3p on 60c lt vio	60.00
12a	A20	4p on 85c vermilion	60.00
13a	A18	5p on 1fr cl & ol grn	60.00
14a	A18	10p on 2fr org & pale bl	70.00
15a	A18	25p on 5fr bl & buff	70.00
16a	A23	0.50p on 10c green	40.00
17a	A23	0.75p on 15c green	40.00
18a	A23	1.50p on 30c red	45.00
19a	A23	2p on 45c red	40.00
20a	A23	2.50p on 50c blue	40.00
21a	A23	4p on 75c blue	40.00

Stamps of Syria, 1925, Overprinted in Red, Black or Blue

On A3, A5

On A4

1925, Mar. 1			Perf. 12½, 13½
25	A3	0.10p dk violet (R)	1.50	2.25
a.		Double overprint	42.50	42.50
b.		Inverted overprint	35.00	
c.		Black overprint	37.50	37.50
e.		"ALAOUITES" instead of "ALAOUITES"	30.00	30.00
26	A4	0.25p olive black (R)	2.25	3.00
a.		Inverted overprint	40.00	
b.		Blue overprint	50.00	50.00
27	A4	0.50p yellow green	1.75	1.75
a.		Inverted overprint	40.00	40.00
b.		Blue overprint	50.00	50.00
c.		Red overprint	50.00	50.00
d.		"ALAOUITE," instead of "ALAOUITES"	50.00	50.00
e.		Double overprint	50.00	50.00
28	A4	0.75p brown orange	2.00	2.25
a.		Inverted overprint	45.00	60.00
b.		Double overprint	47.50	65.00
29	A5	1p magenta	2.75	2.75
a.		Inverted overprint	40.00	47.50
30	A4	1.25p deep green	3.25	3.50
a.		Red overprint	50.00	50.00
b.		Double overprint		75.00
31	A4	1.50p rose red (Bl)	2.75	3.00
a.		Inverted overprint	45.00	45.00
b.		Black overprint	40.00	40.00
c.		As "b," inverted	80.00	

32	A4	2p dk brown (R)	2.75	3.50
a.		Blue overprint	65.00	65.00
b.		Inverted overprint	40.00	40.00
33	A4	2.50p pck blue (R)	4.25	4.50
a.		Black overprint	65.00	65.00
34	A4	3p orange brown	2.50	2.75
a.		Inverted overprint	40.00	40.00
b.		Blue overprint	70.00	70.00
c.		Double overprint		90.00
35	A4	5p violet	3.75	4.00
a.		Red overprint	70.00	70.00
b.		Inverted overprint	42.50	
36	A4	10p violet brown	5.50	6.00
37	A4	25p ultra (R)	9.00	10.00
		Nos. 25-37 (13)	44.00	49.25

For overprints see Nos. C5-C19.

Stamps of Syria, 1925, Surcharged in Black or Red

Nos. 38-42

Nos. 43-45

1926

38	A4	3.50p on 0.75p brn org	2.50	2.75
a.		Surcharged on face and back	25.00	25.00
39	A4	4p on 0.25p ol blk	2.50	2.50
40	A4	6p on 2.50p pck bl (R)	3.00	3.25
41	A4	12p on 1.25p dp grn	3.25	3.50
a.		Inverted surcharge	35.00	35.00
42	A4	20p on 1.25p dp grn	5.25	5.25
43	A4	4.50p on 0.75p brn org	5.25	3.25
a.		Inverted surcharge	60.00	60.00
b.		Double surcharge	55.00	55.00
44	A4	7.50p on 2.50p pck bl	4.75	3.25
45	A4	15p on 25p ultra	8.75	5.50
a.		Inverted surcharge	50.00	
		Nos. 38-45 (8)	35.25	29.25

Two types of overprints exist on No. 39. For detailed listings, see Scott Classic Specialized Catalogue of Stamps and Covers 1840-1940. For overprint, see No. C21.

Syria No. 199 Ovptd. in Red like No. 25

1928

46	A3	5c on 0.10p dk violet	2.00	1.75
a.		Double surcharge	50.00	

Syria Nos. 178 and 174 Surcharged like Nos. 43-45 in Red

47	A4	2p on 1.25p dp green	16.00	8.00
a.		Double surcharge	60.00	
b.		Inverted surcharge	50.00	50.00
48	A4	4p on 0.25p olive black	11.00	6.50
a.		Double surcharge	50.00	50.00
b.		Inverted surcharge	50.00	50.00

For overprint see No. C20.

49	A4	4p on 0.25p olive black	82.50	50.00
a.		Double impression	150.00	
		Nos. 46-49 (4)	111.50	66.25

AIR POST STAMPS

Nos. 8, 10, 13 & 14 with Additional Ovpt. in Black

1925, Jan. 1　Unwmk.　Perf. 14x13½

C1b	A18	2p on 40c	17.00	15.00
C2	A18	3p on 60c	22.50	20.00
a.		Inverted overprint	125.00	125.00
C3	A18	5p on 1fr	17.00	14.00
a.		Inverted overprint	37.50	37.50
C4	A18	10p on 2fr	22.00	15.00
a.		Inverted overprint	35.00	35.00
		Nos. C1-C4 (4)	78.50	64.00

Two types of overprints exist on Nos. C1-C4. For detailed listings, see Scott Classic Specialized Catalogue of Stamps and Covers 1840-1940.

Nos. 32, 34, 35 & 36 With Additional Ovpt. in Green

1925, Mar. 1　　　Perf. 13½

C5	A4	2p dark brown	7.50	6.00
a.		Inverted overprint	75.00	75.00
b.		Red overprint	125.00	
C6	A4	3p orange brown	7.50	6.00
a.		Inverted overprint	75.00	75.00
b.		Red overprint	100.00	
C7	A4	5p violet	7.50	6.00
a.		Inverted overprint	75.00	75.00
b.		Red overprint	100.00	
C8	A4	10p violet brown	7.50	6.00
a.		Inverted overprint	75.00	75.00
b.		Red overprint	100.00	
		Nos. C5-C8 (4)	30.00	24.00

Nos. 32, 34, 35 & 36 With Additional Ovpt. in Red

1926, May 1

C9	A4	2p dark brown	7.50	6.50
a.		Red overprint double	175.00	175.00
b.		Black overprint double	175.00	175.00
c.		Black overprint inverted	70.00	70.00
C10	A4	3p orange brown	7.50	6.50
a.		Black overprint inverted	70.00	70.00
C11	A4	5p violet	8.50	7.50
a.		Black overprint inverted	70.00	70.00
C12	A4	10p violet brown	8.50	7.50
a.		Black overprint inverted	70.00	70.00
		Nos. C9-C12 (4)	32.00	28.00

No. C9 has the original overprint in black.

Double or inverted overprints, original or plane, are known on most of Nos. C9-C12. Value, each $75. Value for example with both original and plane overprint inverted, each $150.

The red plane overprint was also applied to Nos. C5-C8. These are believed to have been essays, and were not regularly issued. Value, each $100.

Nos. 27c, 37 and Syria No. 177 With Addtl. Ovpt. of Airplane in Red or Black

1929, June-July

C17	A4	0.50p yel grn (R)	5.00	5.00
a.		Plane overprint double	250.00	
b.		Plane ovpt. on face and back	60.00	
c.		Pair with plane overprint Tête-bêche	325.00	
d.		Double overprint	225.00	225.00
e.		Overprint inverted	125.00	
f.		Plane only inverted	250.00	
C18	A5	1p magenta (Bk)	9.00	9.00
a.		Red overprint	50.00	

C19	A4	25p ultra (R)	52.50	40.00
a.		Plane overprint inverted	125.00	125.00
b.		Surcharge double	150.00	150.00
		Nos. C17-C19 (3)	66.50	54.00

Nos. 28 and 30 exist with additional overprint of airplane in red. These stamps were never issued. Value, each $100.

Nos. 47 and 45 With Additional Ovpt. of Airplane in Red

1929-30

C20	A4	2p on 1.25p ('30)	7.25	7.25
a.		Surcharge inverted	60.00	60.00
b.		Double surcharge	85.00	85.00
c.		Triple surcharge	200.00	
C21	A4	15p on 25p (Bk + R)	57.50	50.00
a.		Plane overprint inverted	225.00	225.00

POSTAGE DUE STAMPS

Postage Due Stamps of France, 1893-1920, Surcharged Like No. 1 (Nos. J1-J2) or No. 7 (Nos. J3-J5)

1925　Unwmk.　　Perf. 14x13½

J1	D2	0.50p on 10c choc	9.00	9.00
J2	D2	1p on 20c ol grn	9.00	9.00
J3	D2	2p on 30c red	9.50	9.50
J4	D2	3p on 50c vio brn	9.50	9.50
J5	D2	5p on 1fr red brn, straw	10.00	10.00
		Nos. J1-J5 (5)	47.00	47.00

Two types of overprints exist on No. J5. For detailed listings, see Scott Classic Specialized Catalogue of Stamps and Covers 1840-1940.

1925 Syria Postage Due Stamps Overprinted in Black, Blue or Red

1925　　　　　　　Perf. 13½

J6	D5	0.50p brown, yel	5.50	5.50
a.		Blue overprint	45.00	
b.		Red overprint	45.00	
c.		Overprint inverted	37.50	37.50
J7	D6	1p vio, rose (Bl)	5.00	5.00
a.		Black overprint	155.00	155.00
b.		Double overprint (Bk + Bl)	175.00	175.00
c.		Overprint inverted	40.00	40.00
J8	D5	2p blk, blue (Bl)	6.75	6.75
a.		Blue overprint	45.00	
J9	D5	3p blk, red org (Bl)	9.00	9.00
a.		Overprint inverted	35.00	
J10	D5	5p blk, bl grn (R)	11.00	11.00
a.		Overprint inverted	30.00	30.00
b.		Black overprint	45.00	
		Nos. J6-J10 (5)	37.25	37.25

The stamps of Alaouites were superseded in 1930 by those of Latakia.

ALBANIA

al-'bā-nē-ə

LOCATION — Southeastern Europe
GOVT. — Republic
AREA — 11,101 sq. mi.
POP. — 3,364,571 (1999 est.)
CAPITAL — Tirana

After the outbreak of World War I, the country fell into a state of anarchy when the Prince and all members of the International Commission left Albania. Subsequently General Ferrero in command of Italian troops declared Albania an independent country. A constitution was adopted and a republican form of government was instituted which continued until 1928 when, by constitutional amendment, Albania was declared to be a monarchy. The President of the republic, Ahmed Zogu, became king of the new state. Many unlisted varieties or surcharges and lithographed labels are said to have done postal duty in

Albania and Epirus during this unsettled period.

On April 7, 1939, Italy invaded Albania. King Zog fled but did not abdicate. The King of Italy acquired the crown.

Germany occupied Albania from September, 1943, until late 1944 when it became an independent state. The People's Republic began in January, 1946.

40 Paras = 1 Piaster = 1 Grossion
100 Centimes = 1 Franc (1917)
100 Qintar = 1 Franc
100 Qintar (Qindarka) = 1 Lek (1947)

> Catalogue values for unused stamps in this country are for Never Hinged items, beginning with Scott 458 in the regular postage section, Scott B34 in the semipostal section, and Scott C67 in the airpost section.

Watermarks

Wmk. 125 —　　Wmk. 220 —
Lozenges　　　Double Headed Eagle

Issues of 1908 Turkey Stamps Handstamped

Perf. 12, 13½ and Compound

1913, June　　　　Unwmk.

1	A19	2½pi violet brown	750.00	900.00

With Additional Overprint in Carmine

2	A19	10pa blue green	675.00	650.00

Handstamped on Issue of 1909

4	A21	5pa ocher	450.00	450.00
5	A21	10pa blue green	350.00	225.00
6	A21	20pa car rose	350.00	250.00
7	A21	1pi ultra	325.00	450.00
8	A21	2pi blue black	500.00	450.00
10	A21	5pi dark violet	1,400.	1,500.
11	A21	10pi dull red	5,000.	4,750.

For surcharge see No. 19.

Additional values of 25pi dark green and 50pi red brown were overprinted and sold only to dealers. Values, 25pi $8,000, 50pi $16,000.

With Additional Overprint in Blue or Carmine

13A	A21	10pa blue green	900.00	850.00
14	A21	20pa car rose (Bl)	800.00	850.00
15	A21	1pi brt blue (C)	1,900.	1,750.
15A	A21	2pi brt blue (C)	3,750.	3,500.

Handstamped on Newspaper Stamp of 1911

| 17 | A21 | 2pa olive green | 425.00 | 425.00 |

Handstamped on Postage Due Stamp of 1908

18	A19	1pi black, *dp*		
		rose	3,000.	2,500.
a.		Inverted overprint		

No. 18 was used for regular postage.

No. 6 Surcharged With New Value

19	A21	10pa on 20pa		
		car rose	1,250.	1,250.
a.		"11" instead of "10"		
b.		Inverted surcharge	3,250.	—
c.		Double surcharge		

A1

Handstamped on White Laid Paper Without Eagle and Value Issued Without Gum

1913, July　　　　　　　　　　*Imperf.*

20	A1	(1pi) black	325.00	525.00
		Cut to shape	190.00	275.00
a.		Sewing machine perf.	575.00	725.00

Value Typewritten in Violet Issued Without Gum

1913, Aug.　　　　　　　　　With Eagle

21	A1	10pa violet	12.00	12.00
		Double impression	—	—
22	A1	20pa red & black	16.00	13.50
		"2p para"	—	—
23	A1	1gr black	16.00	16.00
24	A1	2gr blue & violet	20.00	16.00
25	A1	5gr violet & blue	24.00	21.00
26	A1	10gr blue	24.00	21.00
		Nos. 21-26 (6)	112.00	99.50

Nos. 21-26 exist with the eagle inverted or omitted and with numerous errors in the figures of value and the spelling of the word "grosh."

A2

Handstamped on White Laid Paper Eagle and Value in Black Issued Without Gum

1913, Nov.　　　　　　　　　*Perf. 11½*

27	A2	10pa green	4.00	3.25
b.		Eagle and value in green	1,750.	1,750.
c.		10pa red (error)	32.50	32.50
d.		10pa violet (error)	32.50	32.50
29	A2	20pa red	6.00	4.75
b.		20pa green (error)	42.50	32.50
30	A2	30pa violet	6.00	4.75
a.		30pa ultramarine (error)	32.50	32.50
b.		30pa red (error)	32.50	32.50
31	A2	1gr ultramarine	8.00	7.25
a.		1gr green (error)	32.50	32.50
b.		1gr black (error)	32.50	32.50
c.		1gr violet (error)	32.50	32.50
33	A2	2gr black	12.00	8.00
a.		2gr violet (error)	40.00	40.00
b.		2gr blue (error)	40.00	40.00
		Nos. 27-33 (5)	36.00	28.00

The stamps of this issue are known with eagle or value inverted or omitted.
1st anniv. of Albanian independence.
Counterfeits exist.

Skanderbeg (George Castriota) — A3

1913, Dec.　　Typo.　　*Perf. 14*

35	A3	2q orange brn & buff	3.50	1.75
36	A3	5q green & blue grn	3.50	1.75
37	A3	10q rose red	3.50	1.75

38	A3	25q dark blue	3.50	1.75
39	A3	50q violet & red	8.50	3.50
40	A3	1fr deep brown	20.00	10.50
		Nos. 35-40 (6)	42.50	21.00

For overprints and surcharges see Nos. 41-52, 105, J1-J9.

Nos. 35-40 Handstamped in Black or Violet

1914, Mar. 7

41	A3	2q orange brn & buff	50.00	65.00
42	A3	5q grn & bl grn (V)	50.00	65.00
43	A3	10q rose red	50.00	65.00
44	A3	25q dark blue (V)	50.00	65.00
45	A3	50q violet & red	50.00	65.00
46	A3	1fr deep brown	50.00	65.00
		Nos. 41-46 (6)	300.00	390.00

Issued to celebrate the arrival of Prince Wilhelm zu Wied on Mar. 7, 1914.

Nos. 35-40 Surcharged in Black

a　　　　　　　　　b

1914, Apr. 2

47	A3 (a)	5pa on 2q	2.10	2.10
48	A3 (a)	10pa on 5q	2.10	2.10
49	A3 (a)	20pa on 10q	3.50	2.75
50	A3 (b)	1gr on 25q	3.50	3.50
51	A3 (b)	2gr on 50q	3.50	3.50
52	A3 (b)	5gr on 1fr	14.00	10.50
		Nos. 47-52 (6)	28.70	24.45

For overprints see Nos. 105, J6-J9.

Inverted Surcharge

47a	A3 (a)	5pa on 2q	24.00	24.00
48a	A3 (a)	10pa on 5q	22.50	22.50
49a	A3 (a)	20pa on 10q	24.00	24.00
50a	A3 (b)	1gr on 25q	24.00	24.00
51a	A3 (b)	2gr on 50q	28.00	28.00
52b	A3 (b)	5gr on 1fr	90.00	90.00
		Nos. 47a-52b (6)	212.50	212.50

Korce (Korytsa) Issues

A4

1914　　Handstamped　　*Imperf.*

52A	A4	10pa violet & red	200.00	200.00
c.		10pa black & red	325.00	325.00
53	A4	25pa violet & red	200.00	200.00
a.		25pa black & red	425.00	425.00

Nos. 52A-53a were handstamped directly on the cover, so the paper varies. They were also produced in sheets; these are rarely found. Nos. 52A-53a were issued by Albanian military authorities.
Counterfeits exists of Nos. 52A and 53.

A5

1917　Typo. & Litho.　*Perf. 11½*

54	A5	1c dk brown & grn	17.50	12.00
55	A5	2c red & green	17.50	12.00
56	A5	3c gray grn & grn	17.50	12.00

57	A5	5c green & black	16.00	8.00
58	A5	10c rose red & black	16.00	8.00
59	A5	25c blue & black	16.00	8.00
60	A5	50c violet & black	16.00	10.00
61	A5	1fr brown & black	16.00	10.00
		Nos. 54-61 (8)	132.50	80.00

A6

1917-18

62	A6	1c dk brown & grn	2.75	2.40
63	A6	2c red brown & grn	2.75	2.40
a.		"CTM" for "CTS"	72.50	120.00
64	A6	3c black & green	2.75	2.40
a.		"CTM" for "CTS"	80.00	135.00
65	A6	5c green & black	4.00	4.00
66	A6	10c dull red & black	4.00	4.00
67	A6	50c violet & black	7.25	6.50
68	A6	1fr red brn & black	20.00	17.50
		Nos. 62-68 (7)	43.50	39.20

Counterfeits abound of Nos. 54-68, 80-81.

No. 65 Surcharged in Red

1918

| 80 | A6 | 25c on 5c green & blk | 275.00 | 325.00 |

A7

1918

| 81 | A7 | 25c blue & black | 72.50 | 95.00 |

General Issue

A8　　　　　　　A9

Handstamped in Rose or Blue　　XVI MCMXIX

1919　　　　　　　　*Perf. 12½*

84	A8	(2)q on 2h brown	7.50	7.50
85	A8	5q on 16h green	7.50	7.50
86	A8	10q on 8h rose (Bl)	7.50	7.50
87	A8	25q on 64h blue	8.50	8.50
88	A9	25q on 64h blue	300.00	300.00
89	A8	50q on 32h violet	7.50	7.50
90	A8	1fr on 1.28k org, *bl*		
		Nos. 84-90 (7)	347.50	347.50

See Nos. J10-J13. Compare with types A10-A14. For overprints see Nos 91-104.

Handstamped in Rose or Blue

1919, Jan. 16

91	A8	(2)q on 2h brown	14.00	14.00
92	A8	5q on 16h green	10.50	10.50
93	A8	10q on 8h rose (Bl)	10.50	10.50
94	A8	25q on 64h blue	140.00	140.00
95	A9	25q on 64h blue	45.00	60.00
96	A8	50q on 32h violet		
97	A8	1fr on 1.28k org, *bl*	14.00	14.00
		Nos. 91-97 (7)	248.00	263.00

Handstamped in Violet

1919

98	A8	(2)q on 2h brown	17.50	17.50
99	A8	5q on 16h green	17.50	17.50
100	A8	10q on 8h rose	17.50	17.50
101	A8	25q on 64h blue	17.50	17.50
102	A9	25q on 64h blue	140.00	140.00
103	A8	50q on 32h violet	17.50	17.50
104	A8	1fr on 1.28k org, *bl*	17.50	17.50
		Nos. 98-104 (7)	245.00	245.00

No. 50 Overprinted in Violet

1919　　　　　　　　*Perf. 14*

| 105 | A3 | 1gr on 25q blue | 32.50 | 25.00 |

A10　　　　　　　A11

1919, June 5　　*Perf. 11½, 12½*

106	A10	10q on 2h brown	7.00	7.00
107	A11	15q on 8h rose	7.00	7.00
108	A11	20q on 16h green	7.00	7.00
109	A10	25q on 64h blue	7.00	7.00
110	A11	50q on 32h violet	7.00	7.00
111	A11	1fr on 96h orange	7.00	7.00
112	A10	2fr on 1.60k vio, *buff*	25.00	21.00
		Nos. 106-112 (7)	67.00	63.00

Nos. 106-108, 110 exist with inverted surcharge.

A12　　　　　　　A13

Surcharged in Black or Violet

1919

113	A12	10q on 8h car	7.00	7.00
114	A12	15q on 8h car (V)	7.00	7.00
115	A13	20q on 16h green	7.00	7.00
116	A13	25q on 32h violet	7.00	7.00
117	A13	50q on 64h blue	20.00	14.00
118	A13	1fr on 96h orange	8.50	7.00
119	A12	2fr on 1.60k vio, *buff*	14.00	10.50
		Nos. 113-119 (7)	70.50	59.50

A14

Overprinted in Blue or Black Without New Value

1920   *Perf. 12½*

120	A14	1q gray (Bl)	100.00 95.00
121	A14	10q rose (Bk)	14.00 32.50
a.		Double overprint	150.00 150.00
122	A14	20q brown (Bl)	45.00 40.00
123	A14	25q blue (Bk)	525.00 600.00
124	A14	50q brown vio (Bk)	60.00 80.00
		Nos. 120-124 (5)	744.00 847.50

Counterfeit overprints exist of Nos. 120-128.

Surcharged in Color Noted with New Value

125	A14	2q on 10q rose (R)	14.00 21.00
126	A14	5q on 10q rose (G)	14.00 17.50
127	A14	25q on 10q rose (Bl)	14.00 21.00
128	A14	50q on 10q rose (Br)	14.00 35.00
		Nos. 125-128 (4)	56.00 94.50

Stamps of type A14 (Portrait of the Prince zu Wied) were not placed in use without overprint or surcharge.

A15

Post Horn Overprinted in Black

1920   *Perf. 14x13*

129	A15	2q orange	10.50 8.50
130	A15	5q deep green	17.50 15.00
131	A15	10q red	32.50 32.50
132	A15	25q light blue	55.00 30.00
133	A15	50q gray green	12.50 10.50
134	A15	1fr claret	12.50 10.50
		Nos. 129-134 (6)	140.50 107.00

Type A15 was never placed in use without post horn or "Besa" overprint.

Stamps of Type A15
(No Post Horn)
Overprinted

1921

135	A15	2q orange	7.00 7.00
136	A15	5q deep green	7.00 7.00
137	A15	10q red	14.00 12.00
138	A15	25q light blue	25.00 21.00
139	A15	50q gray green	14.00 12.00
140	A15	1fr claret	14.00 12.00
		Nos. 135-140 (6)	81.00 71.00

For surcharge & overprints see Nos. 154, 156-157.

Stamps of these types, and with "TAKSE" overprint, were unauthorized and never placed in use. They are common.

Gjirokaster
A18

Korcha
A19

Designs: 5q, Kanina. 10q, Berati. 25q, Bridge at Vezirit. 50q, Rozafat. 2fr, Dursit.

1923   **Typo.**   *Perf. 12½, 11½*

147	A18	2q orange	.70 1.40
148	A18	5q yellow green	.70 1.10
149	A18	10q carmine	.70 1.10
150	A18	25q dark blue	.70 1.10
151	A18	50q dark green	.70 1.10
152	A19	1fr dark violet	.70 2.75
153	A19	2fr olive green	4.25 7.00
		Nos. 147-153 (7)	8.45 15.55

For overprints & surcharges see Nos. 158-185, B1-B8.

No. 135 Surcharged

1922   *Perf. 14x13*
154   A15   1q on 2q orange   3.25   8.50

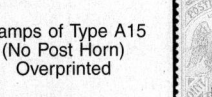

Stamps of Type A15
(No Post Horn)
Overprinted

1922

156	A15	5q deep green	5.00 8.00
157	A15	10q red	5.00 8.00

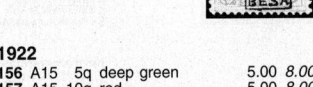

Nos. 147-151 Ovptd.
in Black and
Violet

1924, Jan.   *Perf. 12½*

158	A18	2q red orange	10.00 20.00
159	A18	5q yellow green	10.00 20.00
160	A18	10q carmine	7.50 14.50
161	A18	25q dark blue	7.50 14.50
162	A18	50q dark green	11.50 20.00
		Nos. 158-162 (5)	46.50 89.00

The words "Mbledhje Kushtetuese" are in taller letters on the 25q than on the other values. Opening of the Constituent Assembly. Counterfeits of Nos. 158 and 161 are plentiful.

No. 147
Surcharged

1924
163   A18   1q on 2q red orange   3.00   8.00

Nos. 163,
147-152
Overprinted

1924

164	A18	1q on 2q orange	2.75 7.25
165	A18	2q orange	2.75 7.25
166	A18	5q yellow green	2.75 7.25
167	A18	10q carmine	2.75 7.25
168	A18	25q dark blue	2.75 7.25
169	A18	50q dark green	6.25 14.00
170	A19	1fr dark violet	6.25 17.50
		Nos. 164-170 (7)	26.25 67.75

Issued to celebrate the return of the Government to the Capital after a revolution.

Nos. 163,
147-152
Overprinted

1925

171	A18	1q on 2q orange	3.25 8.00
172	A18	2q orange	3.25 8.00
173	A18	5q yellow green	3.25 8.00
174	A18	10q carmine	3.25 8.00
175	A18	25q dark blue	3.25 8.00
176	A18	50q dark green	3.25 12.00
177	A19	1fr dark violet	6.25 16.00
		Nos. 171-177 (7)	25.75 68.00

Proclamation of the Republic, Jan. 21, 1925. The date "1921" instead of "1925" occurs once in each sheet of 50. Counterfeits exist.

Nos. 163,
147-153
Overprinted

1925

178	A18	1q on 2q orange	1.10 1.60
a.		Inverted overprint	12.50 12.50
179	A18	2q orange	1.10 1.60
180	A18	5q yellow green	1.10 1.60
a.		Inverted overprint	12.50 12.50
181	A18	10q carmine	1.10 1.60
182	A18	25q dark blue	1.10 1.60
183	A18	50q dark green	1.10 1.60
184	A19	1fr dark violet	5.00 4.00
185	A19	2fr olive green	7.50 4.00
		Nos. 178-185 (8)	19.10 17.60

Counterfeits exist.

President Ahmed Zogu
A25   A26

1925   *Perf. 13½, 13½x13*

186	A25	1q orange	.25 .25
187	A25	2q red brown	.25 2.00
188	A25	5q green	.25 .25
189	A25	10q rose red	.25 .25
190	A25	15q gray brown	.75 2.00
191	A25	25q dark blue	.25 .25
192	A25	50q blue green	.85 1.50
193	A26	1fr red & ultra	1.75 2.00
194	A26	2fr green & orange	1.90 2.00
195	A26	3fr brown & violet	4.00 5.00
196	A26	5fr violet & black	4.50 6.75
		Nos. 186-196 (11)	15.00 22.25

No. 193 in ultramarine and brown, and No. 194 in green and brown were not regularly issued. Value, set $15.
For overprints & surcharges see Nos. 197-209, 238-248.

Nos. 186-196
Overprinted in Various
Colors

1927

197	A25	1q orange (V)	.60 1.00
198	A25	2q red brn (G)	.25 .30
199	A25	5q green (R)	1.25 .50
200	A25	10q rose red (Bl)	.25 .30
201	A25	15q gray brn (G)	7.00 14.00
202	A25	25q dk blue (R)	.50 .40
203	A25	50q blue grn (Bl)	.50 .40
204	A26	1fr red & ultra (Bk)	1.40 .55
205	A26	2fr green & org (Bk)	1.50 .80
206	A26	3fr brown & vio (Bk)	2.40 1.60
207	A26	5fr violet & blk (Bk)	3.50 2.75
		Nos. 197-207 (11)	19.15 22.60

No. 200 exists perf. 11.
For surcharges see Nos. 208-209, 238-240.

Nos. 200, 202
Surcharged in Black or
Red

1928

208	A25	1q on 10q rose red	.50 .55
a.		Inverted surcharge	4.00 4.00
209	A25	5q on 25q dk blue (R)	.50 .55
a.		Inverted surcharge	4.00 4.00

A27   King Zog
I — A28

Black Overprint

1928   *Perf. 14x13½*

210	A27	1q orange brown	5.00 9.50
211	A27	2q slate	5.00 9.50
212	A27	5q blue green	5.00 12.00
213	A27	10q rose red	4.00 12.00
214	A27	15q bister	15.00 47.50
215	A27	25q deep blue	6.00 12.00
216	A27	50q lilac rose	10.00 15.00

Red Overprint
Perf. 13½x14

217	A28	1fr blue & slate	10.00 12.00
		Nos. 210-217 (8)	60.00 129.50

Compare with types A29-A32.

A29   A30

Black or Red Overprint

1928   *Perf. 14x13½*

218	A29	1q orange brown	12.50 25.00
219	A29	2q slate (R)	12.50 25.00
220	A29	5q blue green	10.00 20.00
221	A29	10q rose red	10.00 16.00
222	A29	15q bister	15.00 27.50
223	A29	25q deep blue (R)	10.00 16.00
224	A29	50q lilac rose	10.00 16.00

Perf. 13½x14

225	A30	1fr blue & slate (R)	12.50 20.00
226	A30	2fr green & slate (R)	12.50 20.00
		Nos. 218-226 (9)	105.00 185.50

Proclamation of Ahmed Zogu as King of Albania.

A31   A32

Black Overprint

1928   *Perf. 14x13½*

227	A31	1q orange brown	.40 1.25
228	A31	2q slate	.40 1.25
229	A31	5q blue green	2.75 3.50
230	A31	10q rose red	.40 1.25
231	A31	15q bister	15.00 24.00
232	A31	25q deep blue	.40 1.00
233	A31	50q lilac rose	.75 2.00

Perf. 13½x14

234	A32	1fr blue & slate	1.50 2.50
235	A32	2fr green & slate	1.50 4.00
236	A32	3fr dk red & ol bis	7.50 12.00
237	A32	5fr dull vio & gray	7.50 16.00
		Nos. 227-237 (11)	38.10 69.00

The overprint reads "Kingdom of Albania."

Nos. 203, 202, 200
Surcharged in Black

1929   *Perf. 13½x13, 11½*
238 A25 1q on 50q blue green .40 *.55*
239 A25 5q on 25q dark blue .40 *.55*
240 A25 15q on 10q rose red .60 *1.00*
    Nos. 238-240 (3) 1.40 2.10

Nos. 186-189, 191-194
Overprinted in Black or
Red

1929   *Perf. 11½, 13½*
241 A25 1q orange 7.50 *20.00*
242 A25 2q red brown 7.50 *20.00*
243 A25 5q green 7.50 *20.00*
244 A25 10q rose red 7.50 *20.00*
245 A25 25q dark blue 7.50 *20.00*
246 A25 50q blue green (R) 10.00 *24.00*
247 A26 1fr red & ultra 14.00 *35.00*
248 A26 2fr green & orange 14.00 *35.00*
    Nos. 241-248 (8) 75.50 194.00

34th birthday of King Zog. The overprint
reads "Long live the King."

Lake
Butrinto — A33

King Zog
I — A34

Zog Bridge
A35

Ruin at Zog
Manor
A36

Perf. 14, 14½
1930, Sept. 1   **Photo.**   **Wmk. 220**
250 A33 1q slate .25 *.25*
251 A33 2q orange red .25 *.25*
252 A34 5q yellow green .25 *.25*
253 A34 10q carmine .25 *.25*
254 A34 15q dark brown .25 *.25*
255 A34 25q dark ultra .25 *.25*
256 A33 50q slate green .70 *.55*
257 A35 1fr violet 1.10 *1.00*
258 A35 2fr indigo 1.50 *1.10*
259 A36 3fr gray green 3.50 *2.25*
260 A36 5fr orange brown 4.50 *3.50*
    Nos. 250-260 (11) 12.80 9.90

2nd anniversary of accession of King Zog I.
For overprints see Nos. 261-270, 299-309,
J39. For surcharges see Nos. 354-360.

Nos. 250-259
Overprinted in Black

1934, Dec. 24
261 A33 1q slate 8.50 *12.00*
262 A33 2q orange red 8.50 *12.00*
263 A34 5q yellow green 8.50 *9.50*
264 A34 10q carmine 9.25 *12.00*
265 A34 15q dark brown 9.25 *12.00*
266 A34 25q dark ultra 9.25 *12.00*
267 A33 50q slate green 10.00 *16.00*
268 A35 1fr violet 11.00 *20.00*
269 A35 2fr indigo 12.00 *25.00*
270 A36 3fr gray green 15.00 *35.00*
    Nos. 261-270 (10) 101.25 165.50

Tenth anniversary of the Constitution.

Allegory of
Death of
Skanderbeg
A37

Albanian Eagle
in Turkish
Shackles
A38

5q, 25q, 40q, 2fr, Eagle with wings spread.

1937   **Unwmk.**   *Perf. 14*
271 A37 1q brown violet .25 *.25*
272 A38 2q brown .50 *.35*
273 A38 5q lt green .50 *.50*
274 A38 10q olive brown .50 *.80*
275 A38 15q rose red .80 *1.00*
276 A38 25q blue 1.50 *2.00*
277 A37 50q deep green 3.75 *3.25*
278 A38 1fr violet 9.00 *6.00*
279 A38 2fr orange brown 12.00 *9.00*
    Nos. 271-279 (9) 28.80 23.15

Souvenir Sheet
280   Sheet of 3 17.50 *150.00*
  a. A37 20q red violet 3.50 *6.25*
  b. A38 30q olive brown 3.50 *6.25*
  c. A38 40q red 3.50 *6.25*

25th anniv. of independence from Turkey,
proclaimed Nov. 28, 1912.

Queen
Geraldine
and King
Zog — A40

1938   *Perf. 14*
281 A40 1q slate violet .30 *.40*
282 A40 2q red brown .30 *.40*
283 A40 5q green .30 *.40*
284 A40 10q olive brown 1.10 *.80*
285 A40 15q rose red 1.10 *.80*
286 A40 25q blue 2.75 *2.00*
287 A40 50q Prus green 5.75 *4.00*
288 A40 1fr purple 11.50 *8.00*
    Nos. 281-288 (8) 23.10 16.80

Souvenir Sheet
289   Sheet of 4 32.50 *125.00*
  a. A40 20q dark red violet 7.75 *9.75*
  b. A40 30q brown olive 7.75 *9.75*

Wedding of King Zog and Countess Geraldine Apponyi, Apr. 27, 1938.
No. 289 contains 2 each of Nos. 289a,
289b.

Queen
Geraldine — A42

National
Emblems — A43

Designs: 10q, 25q, 30q, 1fr, King Zog.

1938
290 A42 1q dp red violet .25 *.55*
291 A43 2q red orange .25 *.55*
292 A42 5q deep green .50 *.50*
293 A42 10q red brown .50 *1.00*
294 A42 15q deep rose 1.00 *1.25*
295 A42 25q deep blue 1.40 *1.40*
296 A43 50q gray black 8.50 *6.00*
297 A42 1fr slate green 12.50 *9.00*
    Nos. 290-297 (8) 24.90 20.25

Souvenir Sheet
298   Sheet of 3 22.50 *75.00*
  b. A43 20q Prussian green 7.00 *12.00*
  c. A42 30q deep violet 7.00 *12.00*

10th anniv. of royal rule. They were on sale
for 3 days (Aug. 30-31, Sept. 1) only, during
which their use was required on all mail.
No. 298 contains Nos. 294, 298b, 298c.

King Victor
Emmanuel III — A56

1942   **Photo.**
324 A56 5q green 1.25 *2.00*
325 A56 10q brown 1.25 *2.00*
326 A56 15q rose red 1.25 *2.00*

Issued under Italian Dominion

Nos. 250-260
Overprinted in Black

1939   **Wmk. 220**   *Perf. 14*
299 A33 1q slate 1.25 *1.25*
300 A33 2q orange red 1.25 *1.25*
301 A34 5q yellow green 1.25 *1.25*
302 A34 10q carmine 1.25 *1.25*
303 A34 15q dark brown 2.00 *3.75*
304 A34 25q dark ultra 2.00 *3.75*
305 A33 50q slate green 2.50 *5.00*
306 A35 1fr violet 2.50 *5.00*
307 A35 2fr indigo 3.25 *9.50*
308 A36 3fr gray green 7.75 *22.50*
309 A36 5fr orange brown 10.00 *25.00*
    Nos. 299-309 (11) 35.00 79.50

Resolution adopted by the Natl. Assembly,
Apr. 12, 1939, offering the Albanian Crown to
Italy.

A46   A47

Native Costumes — A48

King Victor Emmanuel III
A49   A50

Native Costume — A51

Monastery
A52

Designs: 2fr, Bridge at Vezirit. 3fr, Ancient
Columns. 5fr, Amphitheater.

1939   **Unwmk.**   **Photo.**   *Perf. 14*
310 A46 1q blue gray 1.25 *.50*
311 A47 2q olive green 1.25 *.50*
312 A48 3q golden brown 1.25 *.50*
313 A49 5q green 1.25 *.25*
314 A50 10q brown 1.25 *.25*
315 A50 15q crimson 1.25 *.25*
316 A50 25q sapphire 2.00 *.80*
317 A50 30q brt violet 2.50 *1.40*
318 A51 50q dull purple 3.25 *3.25*
319 A49 65q red brown 5.00 *11.50*
320 A52 1fr myrtle green 7.50 *9.50*
321 A52 2fr brown lake 11.50 *19.00*
322 A52 3fr brown black 19.00 *35.00*
323 A52 5fr gray violet 25.00 *50.00*
    Nos. 310-323 (14) 83.25 132.70

For overprints and surcharges see Nos.
331-353.

327 A56 25q blue 1.25 *2.00*
328 A56 65q red brown 3.50 *4.00*
329 A56 1fr myrtle green 3.50 *4.00*
330 A56 2fr gray violet 3.50 *4.00*
    Nos. 324-330 (7) 15.50 20.00
Conquest of Albania by Italy, 3rd anniv.

No. 311 Surcharged in
Black

331 A47 1q on 2q olive green 1.60 *4.00*

**Issued under German
Administration**

Stamps of 1939
Overprinted in Carmine
or Brown

1943
332 A47 2q olive green 1.00 *4.00*
333 A48 3q golden brown 1.00 *4.00*
334 A49 5q green 1.00 *4.00*
335 A50 10q brown 1.00 *4.00*
336 A50 15q crimson (Br) 1.00 *4.00*
337 A50 25q sapphire 1.00 *4.00*
338 A50 30q brt violet 1.00 *4.00*
339 A49 65q red brown 1.50 *8.00*
340 A52 1fr myrtle green 6.25 *24.00*
341 A52 2fr brown lake 7.75 *80.00*
342 A52 3fr brown black 60.00 *200.00*

Surcharged with New Values
343 A48 1q on 3q gldn brn 1.00 *8.00*
344 A49 50q on 65q red brn 1.50 *12.00*
    Nos. 332-344 (13) 85.00 360.00

Proclamation of Albanian independence.
The overprint "14 Shtator 1943" on Nos. 324
to 328 is private and fraudulent.

Independent State

Nos. 312 to 317 and
319 to 321 Surcharged
with New Value and
Bars in Black or
Carmine, and:

1945
345 A48 30q on 3q gldn brn 3.00 *12.00*
346 A49 40q on 5q green 3.00 *12.00*
347 A50 50q on 10q brown 3.00 *12.00*
348 A50 60q on 15q crimson 3.00 *12.00*
349 A50 80q on 25q saph (C) 3.00 *12.00*
350 A50 1fr on 30q brt violet 3.00 *12.00*
351 A49 2fr on 65q red brn 3.00 *12.00*
352 A52 3fr on 1fr myr green 3.00 *12.00*
353 A52 5fr on 2fr brown lake 3.00 *12.00*
    Nos. 345-353 (9) 27.00 108.00

"DEMOKRATIKE" is not abbreviated on
Nos. 352 and 353.

Nos. 250, 251, 256
and 258 Surcharged
in Black or Carmine,
and

1945   **Wmk. 220**
354 A33 30q on 1q slate 2.00 *6.00*
355 A33 60q on 1q slate 2.00 *6.00*
356 A33 80q on 1q slate 2.00 *6.00*
357 A33 1fr on 1q slate 4.00 *12.00*
358 A33 2fr on 2q org red 5.00 *13.50*
359 A33 3fr on 50q sl grn 10.00 *25.00*
360 A35 5fr on 2fr indigo 12.50 *40.00*
    Nos. 354-360 (7) 37.50 108.50

Albanian Natl. Army of Liberation, 2nd anniv.
The surcharge on No. 360 is condensed to
fit the size of the stamp.

Country House,
Labinot — A57

40q, 60q, Bridge at Berat. 1fr, 3fr, Permet.

Perf. 11½
1945, Nov. 28   Unwmk.   Typo.
361 A57 20q bluish green   .30   1.20
362 A57 30q deep orange   .40   1.75
363 A57 40q brown   .40   1.75
364 A57 60q red violet   .60   2.50
365 A57 1fr rose red   1.50   5.00
366 A57 3fr dark blue   10.00 21.00
   Nos. 361-366 (6)   13.20 33.20

Counterfeits: lithographed; genuine: typographed.
For overprints and surcharges see Nos. 367-378, 418-423, B28-B33.

Nos. 361 to 366 Overprinted in Black

1946
367 A57 20q bluish green   .60   1.40
368 A57 30q deep orange   .80   1.75
369 A57 40q brown   1.00   2.10
370 A57 60q red violet   1.60   3.50
371 A57 1fr rose red   6.00 12.50
372 A57 3fr dark blue   10.00 21.00
   Nos. 367-372 (6)   20.00 42.25

Convocation of the Constitutional Assembly, Jan. 10, 1946.

People's Republic

#361-366 Overprinted in Black

1946   Perf. 11
373 A57 20q bluish green   .40   1.10
374 A57 30q deep orange   .60   1.40
375 A57 40q brown   1.00   2.75
376 A57 60q red violet   2.00   5.25
377 A57 1fr rose red   6.00 14.00
378 A57 3fr dark blue   10.00 21.00
   Nos. 373-378 (6)   20.00 45.50

Proclamation of the Albanian People's Republic.
Some values exist perf 11½.
For surcharges see Nos. 418-423.

Globe, Dove and Olive Branch — A60

Perf. 11½, Imperf.
1946, Mar. 8   Typo.
Denomination in Black
379 A60 20q lilac & dull red   .25   1.25
380 A60 40q dp lilac & dull red   .45   1.75
381 A60 50q violet & dull red   .90   2.50
382 A60 1fr lt blue & red   1.60   5.00
383 A60 2fr dk blue & red   2.00   8.00
   Nos. 379-383 (5)   5.20 18.50

International Women's Congress.
Counterfeits exist.

Athletes with Shot and Indian Club A61

Perf. 11½
1946, Oct. 6   Litho.   Unwmk.
384 A61 1q grnsh black   5.00   8.50
385 A61 2q green   5.00   8.50
386 A61 5q brown   5.00   8.50
387 A61 10q crimson   5.00   8.50
388 A61 20q ultra   5.00   8.50

389 A61 40q rose violet   5.00   8.50
390 A61 1fr deep orange   12.50 25.00
   Nos. 384-390 (7)   42.50 76.00

Balkan Games, Tirana, Oct. 6-13.

Qemal Stafa — A62

1947, May 5   Perf. 12½x11½
391 A62 20q brn & yel brn   5.00 11.00
392 A62 28q dk blue & blue   5.00 11.00
393 A62 40q brn blk & gray brn   5.00 11.00
  a. Souvenir sheet, #391-393   90.00 110.00
   Nos. 391-393 (3)   15.00 33.00

5th anniv. of the death of Qemal Stafa.

Young Railway Laborers A64

1947, May 16   Perf. 11½
395 A64 1q brn blk & gray brn   2.00   1.40
396 A64 4q dk green & green   2.00   1.40
397 A64 10q blk brn & bis brn   2.00   1.60
398 A64 15q dk red & red   2.00   1.60
399 A64 20q indigo & bl gray   4.00   3.00
400 A64 28q dk blue & blue   6.00   2.50
401 A64 40q brn vio & rose vio 12.50 14.50

Perf. 13x12½
402 A64 68q dk brn & org brn   15.00 25.00
   Nos. 395-402 (8)   45.50 51.00

Issued to publicize the construction of the Durres Elbasan Railway by Albanian youths. The 4q, 20q, 28q and 40q exist perf 13x12½.

Citizens Led by Hasim Zeneli A65

Enver Hoxha and Vasil Shanto — A66

Inauguration of Vithkuq Brigade — A67

Vojo Kushi — A68

1947, July 10   Litho.
403 A65 16q brn org & red brn   4.00   7.00
404 A66 20q org brn & dk brn   4.00   7.00
405 A67 28q blue & dk blue   4.00   7.00
406 A68 40q lilac & dk brn   4.00   7.00
   Nos. 403-406 (4)   16.00 28.00

4th anniv. of the formation of Albania's army, July 10, 1943.

Conference Building Ruins, Peza — A69

1947, Sept. 16
407 A69 2 l red violet   2.50   5.25
408 A69 2.50 l deep blue   2.50   5.25

Peza Conf., Sept. 16, 1942, 5th anniv.

Disabled Soldiers — A70

1947, Nov. 17   Perf. 12½x11½
408A A70 1 l red   7.00 11.00

Disabled War Veterans Cong., 11/14-20/47.

A71

A73

2 l, Banquet. 2.50 l, Peasants rejoicing.

Perf. 11½x12½, 12½x11½
1947, Nov. 17   Unwmk.
409 A71 1.50 l dull violet   3.50   7.00
410 A71 2 l brown   3.50   7.00
411 A71 2.50 l blue   3.50   7.00
412 A73 3 l rose red   3.50   7.00
   Nos. 409-412 (4)   14.00 28.00

Agrarian reform law of 11/17/46, 1st anniv.

Burning Farm Buildings A74

Designs: 2.50 l, Trench scene. 5 l, Firing line. 8 l, Winter advance. 12 l, Infantry column.

1947, Nov. 29   Perf. 11½x12½
413 A74 1.50 l red   2.00   3.00
414 A74 2.50 l rose brown   2.00   3.00
415 A74 5 l blue   4.00   6.00
416 A74 8 l purple   6.00   9.00
417 A74 12 l brown   10.00 14.00
   Nos. 413-417 (5)   24.00 35.00

3rd anniv. of Albania's liberation.

Nos. 373 to 378 Surcharged with New Value and Bars in Black
1948, Feb. 22   Perf. 11
418 A57 50q on 30q dp org   .25   .50
419 A57 1 l on 20q bluish grn   .40   .85
420 A57 2.50 l on 60q red vio   1.00   2.50
421 A57 3 l on 1fr rose red   1.40   3.25
422 A57 5 l on 3fr dk bl   3.00   5.25
423 A57 12 l on 40q brown   8.00 14.00
   Nos. 418-423 (6)   14.05 26.35

The two bars consist of four type squares each set close together.
Some values exist perf 11½.

Map, Train and Construction Workers — A75

1948, June 1   Litho.   Perf. 11½
424 A75 50q dk car rose   1.00   1.10
425 A75 1 l lt green & blk   1.00   1.10
426 A75 1.50 l deep rose   1.60   1.75
427 A75 2.50 l org brn & dk brn 2.50   2.25
428 A75 5 l dull blue   4.00   4.25
429 A75 8 l sal & dk brn   7.00   7.00
430 A75 12 l red vio & dk vio 12.00   8.50
431 A75 20 l olive gray   16.00 17.50
   Nos. 424-431 (8)   45.10 43.45

Issued to publicize the construction of the Durres-Tirana Railway.

Marching Soldiers A76

Design: 8 l, Battle scene.

1948, July 10
432 A76 2.50 l yellow brown   2.00   3.50
433 A76 5 l dark blue   2.75   5.00
434 A76 8 l violet gray   5.25   7.00
   Nos. 432-434 (3)   10.00 15.50

5th anniv. of the formation of Albania's army.

Bricklayer, Flag, Globe and "Industry" — A77

1949, May 1   Photo.   Perf. 12½x12
435 A77 2.50 l olive brown   .60   1.75
436 A77 5 l blue   1.20   1.75
437 A77 8 l violet brown   2.25   4.50
   Nos. 435-437 (3)   4.05   8.00

Issued to publicize Labor Day, May 1, 1949.

Map and Soldier — A78

1949, July 10   Unwmk.
438 A78 2.50 l brown   .60   1.75
439 A78 5 l light ultra   1.20   2.75
440 A78 8 l brown orange   2.25   5.25
   Nos. 438-440 (3)   4.05   9.75

6th anniv. of the formation of Albania's army.

Enver Hoxha — A79

1949, Oct. 16   Engr.   Perf. 12½
441 A79 50q purple   .25   .25
442 A79   1 l dull green   .25   .25
443 A79 1.50 l car lake   .25   .25
444 A79 2.50 l brown   .35   .25
445 A79   5 l violet blue   .80   .70
446 A79   8 l sepia   1.50   2.10
447 A79 12 l rose lilac   4.00   3.50
448 A79 20 l gray blue   4.75   5.25
    Nos. 441-448 (8)   12.15 12.55

Albanian Citizen and Spasski Tower, Kremlin — A80

1949, Sept. 10 Photo. Perf. 12½x12
449 A80 2.50 l orange brown   .60   1.50
450 A80   5 l deep ultra   1.50   3.50

Albanian-Soviet friendship.

Albanian Soldier and Flag — A81

Battle Scene — A82

1949, Nov. 29   Unwmk.   Perf. 12
451 A81 2.50 l brown   .40   1.10
452 A82   3 l dark red   .40   2.10
453 A81   5 l violet   1.25   2.75
454 A82   8 l black   2.50   5.25
    Nos. 451-454 (4)   4.55 11.20

Fifth anniversary of Albania's liberation.

Joseph V. Stalin — A83

1949, Dec. 21
455 A83 2.50 l dark brown   .40   1.40
456 A83   5 l violet blue   1.00   2.50
457 A83   8 l rose brown   2.75   6.00
    Nos. 455-457 (3)   4.15   9.90

70th anniv. of the birth of Joseph V. Stalin.

Canceled to Order
Beginning in 1950, Albania sold some issues in sheets canceled to order. Values in second column, when much less than unused, are for "CTO" examples. Postally used stamps are valued at slightly less than, or the same as, unused.

Symbols of UPU and Postal Transport A84

1950, July 1   Photo.   Perf. 12x12½
458 A84   5 l blue   2.00   1.40
459 A84   8 l rose brown   4.00   1.90
460 A84 12 l sepia   8.00   2.40
    Nos. 458-460 (3)   14.00   5.70

75th anniv. (in 1949) of the UPU.

Sami Frasheri — A85

Authors: 2.50 l, Andon Zako. 3 l, Naim Frasheri. 5 l, Kostandin Kristoforidhi.

1950, Nov. 5   Perf. 14
461 A85   2 l dark green   1.00   .40
462 A85 2.50 l red brown   1.40   .45
463 A85   3 l brown carmine   3.00   .65
464 A85   5 l deep blue   3.25   .80
    Nos. 461-464 (4)   8.65   2.30

"Jubilee of the Writers of the Renaissance."

Arms and Albanian Flags — A86

1951, Jan. 11   Engr.   Perf. 14x13½
465 A86 2.50 l brown carmine 1.60   .30
466 A86   5 l deep blue   3.25   .65
467 A86   8 l sepia   5.25   1.25
    Nos. 465-467 (3)   10.10   2.20

5th anniv. of the formation of the Albanian People's Republic.

Skanderbeg — A87

1951, Mar. 1
468 A87 2.50 l brown   1.75   .30
469 A87   5 l violet   3.25   .55
470 A87   8 l olive bister   5.25   1.10
    Nos. 468-470 (3)   10.25   1.95

483rd anniv. of the death of George Castriota (Skanderbeg).

Enver Hoxha and Congress of Permet — A88

1951, May 24   Photo.   Perf. 12
471 A88 2.50 l dark brown   .80   .25
472 A88   3 l rose brown   .80   .35
473 A88   5 l violet blue   2.00   .55
474 A88   8 l rose lilac   3.75   .85
    Nos. 471-474 (4)   7.35   2.00

Congress of Permet, 7th anniversary.

Child and Globe — A89

Weighing Baby — A90

1951, July 16
475 A89   2 l green   2.00   .80
476 A90 2.50 l brown   2.75   .95
477 A90   3 l red   3.75   1.25
478 A89   5 l blue   5.50   1.40
    Nos. 475-478 (4)   14.00   4.40

Intl. Children's Day, June 1, 1951.

Enver Hoxha and Birthplace of Albanian Communist Party — A91

1951, Nov. 8   Photo.   Perf. 14
479 A91 2.50 l olive brown   .55   .25
480 A91   3 l rose brown   .55   .40
481 A91   5 l dark slate blue 1.25   .65
482 A91   8 l black   2.50   .90
    Nos. 479-482 (4)   4.85   2.20

Albanian Communist Party, 10th anniv.

Battle Scene A92

Designs: 5 l, Schoolgirl. Agriculture and Industry." 8 l, Four portraits.

1951, Nov. 28   Perf. 12x12½
483 A92 2.50 l brown   .80   .25
484 A92   5 l blue   1.60   .50
485 A92   8 l brown carmine   3.60   .85
    Nos. 483-485 (3)   6.00   1.60

Albanian Communist Youth Org., 10th anniv.

Albanian Heroes (Haxhija, Lezha, Giylbegaj, Mazi and Deda) — A93

Designs: Nos. 486-489 each show 5 "Heroes of the People"; No. 490 shows 2 (Stafa and Shanto).

1950, Dec. 25   Unwmk.   Perf. 14
486 A93   2 l dark green   .75   .25
487 A93 2.50 l purple   1.10   .25
488 A93   3 l scarlet   2.25   .35
489 A93   5 l brt blue   3.75   .45
490 A93   8 l olive brown   7.50   1.25
    Nos. 486-490 (5)   15.35   2.55

6th anniv. of Albania's liberation.

Tobacco Factory, Shkoder A94

Composite, Lenin Hydroelectric Plant — A95

Designs: 1 l, Canal. 2.50 l, Textile factory. 3 l, "8 November" Cannery. 5 l, Motion Picture Studio, Tirana. 8 l, Stalin Textile Mill, Tirana. 20 l, Central Hydroelectric Dam.

1953, Aug. 1   Perf. 12x12½, 12½x12
491 A94 50q red brown   .45   .25
492 A94   1 l dull green   .85   .25
493 A94 2.50 l brown   .85   .25
494 A94   3 l rose brown   1.25   .25
495 A94   5 l blue   2.10   .25
496 A94   8 l brown olive   2.50   .25
497 A95 12 l deep plum   4.25   .40
498 A94 20 l slate blue   6.00   .60
    Nos. 491-498 (8)   18.25   2.50

Liberation Scene — A96

1954, Nov. 29   Perf. 12x12½
499 A96 50q brown violet   .25   .25
500 A96   1 l olive green   .55   .25
501 A96 2.50 l yellow brown   .80   .25
502 A96   3 l carmine rose   1.60   .25
503 A96   5 l gray blue   2.40   .25
504 A96   8 l rose brown   4.00   .65
    Nos. 499-504 (6)   9.60   1.90

10th anniversary of Albania's liberation.

School — A97

Pandeli Sotiri, Petro Nini Luarasi, Nuci Naci — A98

1956, Feb. 23   Unwmk.
505 A97   2 l rose violet   .40   .25
506 A98   3 l lt green   .55   .25
507 A98   5 l ultra   1.40   .40
508 A97 10 l brt grnsh blue   4.75   .75
    Nos. 505-508 (4)   7.10   1.65

Opening of the 1st Albanian school, 70th anniv.

Flags — A99

Designs: 5 l, Labor Party headquarters, Tirana. 8 l, Marx and Lenin.

1957, June 1   Engr.   Perf. 11½x11
509 A99 2.50 l brown   .40   .25
510 A99   5 l lt violet blue   1.25   .25
511 A99   8 l rose lilac   1.60   1.00
    Nos. 509-511 (3)   3.25   1.50

Albania's Labor Party, 15th anniv.

Congress Emblem A100

1957, Oct. 4   **Unwmk.**   **Perf. 11½**
512 A100 2.50 l gray brown .50 .25
513 A100 3 l rose red .50 .25
514 A100 5 l dark blue .50 .25
515 A100 8 l green 2.50 .65
Nos. 512-515 (4) 4.00 1.40

4th Intl. Trade Union Cong., Leipzig, 10/4-15.

Lenin and Cruiser "Aurora" A101

1957, Nov. 7   **Litho.**   **Perf. 10½**
516 A101 2.50 l violet brown .50 .25
517 A101 5 l violet blue 1.50 .25
518 A101 8 l gray 1.50 .35
Nos. 516-518 (3) 3.50 .85

40th anniv. of the Russian Revolution.

Albanian Fighter Holding Flag — A102

1957, Nov. 28   **Perf. 10½**
519 A102 1.50 l magenta .50 .25
520 A102 2.50 l brown 1.00 .25
521 A102 5 l blue 1.50 .35
522 A102 8 l green 4.00 .65
Nos. 519-522 (4) 7.00 1.50

Proclamation of independence, 45th anniv.

Naum Veqilharxhi — A103

1958, Feb. 1   **Unwmk.**
523 A103 2.50 l dark brown .45 .25
524 A103 5 l violet blue .90 .25
525 A103 8 l rose lilac 2.75 .60
Nos. 523-525 (3) 4.10 1.10

160th anniv. of the birth of Naum Veqilharxhi, patriot and writer.

Luigj Gurakuqi (1879-1925), Writer & Politician — A104

1958, Apr. 15   **Photo.**   **Perf. 10½**
526 A104 1.50 l dark green .45 .25
527 A104 2.50 l brown .45 .25
528 A104 5 l blue .45 .25
529 A104 8 l sepia 2.75 .60
Nos. 526-529 (4) 4.10 1.25

Transfer of the ashes of Luigj Gurakuqi.

Soldiers A105

2.50 l, 11 l, Airman, sailor, soldier and tank.

1958, July 10   **Litho.**
530 A105 1.50 l blue green .25 .25
531 A105 2.50 l dark red brown .25 .25
532 A105 8 l rose red .80 .30
533 A105 11 l bright blue 1.75 .50
Nos. 530-533 (4) 3.05 1.30

15th anniversary of Albanian army.

Cerciz Topulli and Mihal Grameno A106

Buildings and Tree A107

1958, July 1
534 A106 2.50 l dk olive bister .45 .25
535 A107 3 l green .45 .25
536 A106 5 l blue 1.40 .25
537 A107 8 l red brown 2.25 .40
Nos. 534-537 (4) 4.55 1.15

50th anniversary, Battle of Mashkullore.

Ancient Amphitheater and Goddess of Butrinto A108

1959, Jan. 25   **Litho.**   **Perf. 10½**
538 A108 2.50 l redsh brown .45 .25
539 A108 6.50 l lt blue green 1.40 .30
540 A108 11 l dark blue 2.75 .75
Nos. 538-540 (3) 4.60 1.30

Cultural Monuments Week.

Frederic Joliot-Curie and World Peace Congress Emblem — A109

1959, July 1   **Unwmk.**
541 A109 1.50 l carmine rose 1.75 .25
542 A109 2.50 l rose violet 3.50 .30
543 A109 11 l blue 9.00 1.50
Nos. 541-543 (3) 14.25 2.05

10th anniv. of the World Peace Movement.

Basketball — A110

Sports: 2.50 l, Soccer, 5 l, Runner. 11 l, Man and woman runners with torch and flags.

1959, Nov. 20   **Perf. 10½**
544 A110 1.50 l bright violet .90 .25
545 A110 2.50 l emerald .90 .25
546 A110 5 l carmine rose 1.75 .25
547 A110 11 l ultra 5.50 1.75
Nos. 544-547 (4) 9.05 2.50

1st Albanian Spartacist Games.

Fighter and Flags — A111

Designs: 2.50 l, Miner with drill standing guard. 3 l, Farm woman with sheaf of grain. 6.50 l, Man and woman in laboratory.

1959, Nov. 29
548 A111 1.50 l brt carmine .90 .25
549 A111 2.50 l red brown 1.20 .25
550 A111 3 l brt blue green 1.75 .30
551 A111 6.50 l bright red 3.50 .50
a. Souvenir sheet 9.00 13.50
Nos. 548-551 (4) 7.35 1.30

15th anniversary of Albania's liberation.
No. 551a contains one each of Nos. 548-551, imperf. and all in bright carmine. Inscribed ribbon frame of sheet and frame lines for each stamp are blue green.

Mother and Child, UN Emblem A112

1959, Dec. 5   **Unwmk.**
552 A112 5 l lt grnsh blue 4.50 1.00
a. Miniature sheet 6.50 9.50

10th anniv. (in 1958) of the signing of the Universal Declaration of Human Rights.
No. 552a contains one imperf. stamp similar to No. 552; ornamental border.

Woman with Olive Branch — A113

1960, Mar. 8   **Litho.**   **Perf. 10½**
553 A113 2.50 l chocolate .90 .25
554 A113 11 l rose carmine 3.25 .50

50th anniv. of Intl. Women's Day, Mar. 8.

Alexander Moissi — A114

1960, Apr. 20
555 A114 3 l deep brown .45 .25
556 A114 11 l Prus green 1.40 .35

80th anniversary of the birth of Alexander Moissi (Moisiu) (1880-1935), German actor.

Lenin — A115

1960, Apr. 22
557 A115 4 l Prus blue 1.40 .25
558 A115 11 l lake 3.50 .40

90th anniversary of birth of Lenin.

School Building — A116

1960, May 30   **Litho.**   **Perf. 10½**
559 A116 5 l green 1.75 .35
560 A116 6.50 l plum 1.75 .35

1st Albanian secondary school, 50th anniv.

Soldier on Guard Duty — A117

1960, May 12   **Unwmk.**   **Perf. 10½**
561 A117 1.50 l carmine rose .45 .25
562 A117 11 l Prus blue 2.25 .40

15th anniversary of the Frontier Guards.

Liberation Monument, Tirana, Family and Policeman — A118

1960, May 14
563 A118 1.50 l green .45 .25
564 A118 8.50 l brown 2.75 .40

15th anniversary of the People's Police.

Congress Site — A119

1960, Mar. 25
565 A119 2.50 l sepia .45 .25
566 A119 7.50 l dull blue 1.40 .25

40th anniversary, Congress of Louchnia.

Pashko Vasa — A120

Designs: 1.50 l, Jani Vreto. 6.50 l, Sami Frasheri. 11 l, Page of statutes of association.

1960, May 5
567 A120 1 l gray olive .45 .25
568 A120 1.50 l brown .45 .25
569 A120 6.50 l blue 1.40 .25
570 A120 11 l rose red 4.00 .35
Nos. 567-570 (4) 6.30 1.10

80th anniv. (in 1959) of the Association of Albanian Authors.

Albanian Fighter and Cannon — A121

1960, Aug. 2   **Litho.**   **Perf. 10½**
571 A121 1.50 l olive brown .45 .25
572 A121 2.50 l maroon .90 .35
573 A121 5 l dark red 1.75 .45
Nos. 571-573 (3) 3.10 1.05

Battle of Viona (against Italian troops), 40th anniv.

TU-104 Plane, Clock Tower, Tirana, and Kremlin, Moscow A122

1960, Aug. 18
574 A122   1 l redsh brown   .90 .25
575 A122 7.50 l brt grnsh blue   2.75 .35
576 A122 11.50 l gray   4.50 .60
    Nos. 574-576 (3)   8.15 1.20
TU-104 flights, Moscow-Tirana, 2nd anniv.

Rising Sun and
Federation
Emblem — A123

1960, Nov. 10   Unwmk.   *Perf. 10½*
577 A123 1.50 l ultra   .45 .25
578 A123 8.50 l red   1.75 .35
Intl. Youth Federation, 15th anniv.

Ali Kelmendi — A124

1960, Dec. 5   Litho.   *Perf. 10½*
579 A124 1.50 l pale gray grn   .45 .25
580 A124   11 l dull rose lake 1.75 .30
Ali Kelmendi, communist leader, 60th
birthday.

Flags of Russia and
Albania and Clasped
Hands — A125

1961, Jan. 10   Unwmk.   *Perf. 10½*
581 A125 2 l violet   .45 .25
582 A125 8 l dull red brown 1.75 .35
15th anniv. of the Albanian-Soviet Friendship Society.

Marx and
Lenin — A126

1961, Feb. 13   Litho.
583 A126 2 l rose red   .45 .25
584 A126 8 l violet blue   1.75 .25
Fourth Communist Party Congress.

Man from
Shkoder — A127

Costumes: 1.50 l, Woman from Shkoder.
6.50 l, Man from Lume. 11 l, Woman from
Mirdite.

1961, Apr. 28   *Perf. 10½*
585 A127   1 l slate   .90 .25
586 A127 1.50 l dull claret   .90 .25
587 A127 6.50 l ultra   3.50 .55
588 A127   11 l red   5.50 1.40
    Nos. 585-588 (4)   10.80 2.45

Otter — A128

Designs: 6.50 l, Badger. 11 l, Brown bear.

1961, June 25   Unwmk.   *Perf. 10½*
589 A128 2.50 l grayish blue   3.50 .25
590 A128 6.50 l blue green   7.25 .50
591 A128   11 l dark red brown 16.00 .85
    Nos. 589-591 (3)   26.75 1.60

Dalmatian
Pelicans — A129

1961, Sept. 30   *Perf. 14*
592 A129 1.50 l shown   4.50 .25
593 A129 7.50 l Gray herons   6.25 .60
594 A129   11 l Little egret   11.50 .75
    Nos. 592-594 (3)   22.25 1.60

Cyclamen — A130

1961, Oct. 27   Litho.
595 A130 1.50 l shown   1.75 .25
596 A130   8 l Forsythia   6.00 .50
597 A130   11 l Lily   7.00 .60
    Nos. 595-597 (3)   14.75 1.35

Milosh G.
Nikolla — A131

1961, Oct. 30   *Perf. 14*
598 A131 50q violet brown   .45 .25
599 A131 8.50 l Prus green   1.40 .35
50th anniv. of the birth of Milosh Gjergi
Nikolla, poet.

Flag with Marx and
Lenin — A132

1961, Nov. 8
600 A132 2.50 l vermilion   .55 .25
601 A132 7.50 l dull red brown 1.25 .35
20th anniv. of the founding of Albania's
Communist Party.

Worker, Farm
Woman and
Emblem — A133

1961, Nov. 23   Unwmk.   *Perf. 14*
602 A133 2.50 l violet blue   .45 .25
603 A133 7.50 l rose claret   1.75 .30
20th anniv. of the Albanian Workers' Party.

Yuri Gagarin and
Vostok 1 — A134

1962, Feb. 15   Unwmk.   *Perf. 14*
604 A134 50q blue   .90 1.40
605 A134 4 l red lilac   3.50 3.50
606 A134 11 l dk slate grn   9.00 10.00
    Nos. 604-606 (3)   13.40 14.90
1st manned space flight, made by Yuri A.
Gagarin, Soviet astronaut, Apr. 12, 1961.
Nos. 604-606 were overprinted with an overall yellow tint and with "POSTA AJRORE" (Air
Mail) in maroon or black in 1962. Value: set,
maroon ovpt., $90 mint, $130 used; set, black
ovpt., $300 mint, $400 used.

Petro Nini
Luarasi — A135

1962, Feb. 28   Litho.
607 A135 50q Prus blue   .45 .25
608 A135 8.50 l olive gray   3.50 .25
50th anniv. (in 1961) of the death of Petro
Nini Luarasi, Albanian patriot.

Malaria Eradication
Emblem — A136

1962, Apr. 30   Unwmk.   *Perf. 14*
609 A136 1.50 l brt green   .45 .25
610 A136 2.50 l brown red   .45 .25
611 A136 10 l red lilac   .90 .25
612 A136 11 l blue   .90 .35
    Nos. 609-612 (4)   2.70 1.10
WHO drive to eradicate malaria.
Souvenir sheets, perf. and imperf., contain
one each of Nos. 609-612. Value $30 each.
Nos. 609-612 imperf., value, set $25.

Camomile — A137

Medicinal plants.

1962, May 10
613 A137 50q shown   .45 .30
614 A137   8 l Linden   1.50 .60
615 A137 11.50 l Garden sage 2.50 .90
    Nos. 613-615 (3)   4.45 1.80
Value, imperf. set $30 mint, $40 used.

Woman
Diver — A138

2.50 l, Pole vault. 3 l, Mt. Fuji & torch, horiz.
9 l, Woman javelin thrower. 10 l, Shot putting.

1962, May 31   *Perf. 14*
616 A138 50q brt grnsh bl &
          blk   .25 .25
617 A138 2.50 l gldn brn & sepia .25 .25
618 A138   3 l blue & gray   .35 .25
619 A138   9 l rose car & dk
          brn   1.75 .25
620 A138 10 l olive & blk   1.75 .30
    Nos. 616-620 (5)   4.35 1.30
1964 Olympic Games, Tokyo. Value, imperf
set, $50 mint, $70 used. A 15 l (like 3 l) exists
in souv. sheet, perf. and imperf. Value, each
$35 mint, $50 used.

Globe and
Orbits — A139

Dog Laika and
Sputnik
2 — A140

Designs: 1.50 l, Rocket to the sun. 20 l,
Lunik 3 photographing far side of the moon.

1962, June   Unwmk.   *Perf. 14*
621 A139 50q violet & org   .45 .25
622 A140   1 l blue grn & brn   .90 .30
623 A140 1.50 l yellow & ver   1.25 .40
624 A139 20 l magenta & bl 9.00 5.50
    Nos. 621-624 (4)   11.60 6.45
Russian space explorations.
Nos. 621-624 exist imperf in changed colors. Value, mint $65, used $75.
Two miniature sheets exist, containing one
14-lek picturing Sputnik 1. The perforated 14-
lek is yellow and brown; the imperf. red and
brown. Value, each mint $65, used $75.

Soccer Game,
Map of South
America
A141

2.50 l, 15 l, Soccer game and globe as ball.

1962, July   Litho.
625 A141   1 l org & dk pur   .45 .25
626 A141 2.50 l emer & bluish
          grn   .90 .25
627 A141 6.50 l lt brn & pink   .90 .25
628 A141 15 l bluish grn & mar 2.25 .40
    Nos. 625-628 (4)   4.50 1.15
World Soccer Championships, Chile, 5/30-
6/17.
Exist imperforate in changed colors. Value,
mint $40, used $75.
Two miniature sheets exist, each containing
a single 20-lek in design similar to A141. The
perf. sheet is brown and green; the imperf.,
brown and orange. Value, mint $40, used $75.

Map of Europe and
Albania — A142

Designs: 1 l, 2.50 l, Map of Adriatic Sea and Albania and Roman statue.

1962, Aug.

630	A142	50q multicolored	.45	1.00
631	A142	1 l ultra & red	.90	2.75
632	A142	2.50 l blue & red	7.25	8.50
633	A142	11 l multicolored	10.00	17.50
		Nos. 630-633 (4)	18.60	29.75

Tourist propaganda. Imperforates in changed colors exist. Value, mint $35, used $70.

Miniature sheets containing a 7 l and 8 l stamp, perf. and imperf., exist. Value, mint $40, used $75.

Woman of Dardhe — A143

Regional Costumes: 1 l, Man from Devoll. 2.50 l, Woman from Lunxheri. 14 l, Man from Gjirokaster.

1962, Sept.

635	A143	50q car, bl & pur	.45	.25
636	A143	1 l red brn & ocher	.45	.25
637	A143	2.50 l vio, yel grn & blk	1.25	.60
638	A143	14 l red brn & pale grn	5.75	1.60
		Nos. 635-638 (4)	7.90	2.70

Exist imperf. Value, set, mint $40, used $60.

Chamois — A144

Animals: 1 l, Lynx, horiz. 1.50 l, Wild boar, horiz. 15 l, 20 l, Roe deer.

1962, Oct. 24   Unwmk.   Perf. 14

639	A144	50q sl grn & dk pur	.45	.25
640	A144	1 l orange & blk	1.75	.25
641	A144	1.50 l red brn & blk	2.25	.25
642	A144	15 l yel ol & red brn	17.50	1.00
		Nos. 639-642 (4)	21.95	1.75

Miniature Sheet

643	A144	20 l red & red brn	135.00	145.00

Imperfs. in changed colors, value Nos. 639-642 $75, No. 643 $125.

Ismail Qemali — A145

Designs: 1 l, Albania eagle. 16 l, Eagle over fortress formed by "RPSH."

1962, Dec. 28   Litho.

644	A145	1 l red & red brn	.45	.25
645	A145	3 l org brn & blk	3.00	.25
646	A145	16 l dk car rose & blk	5.25	.50
		Nos. 644-646 (3)	8.70	1.00

50th anniv. of independence. Imperfs. in changed colors, value, set $40 mint, $60 used.

Monument of October Revolution — A146

1963, Jan. 5   Unwmk.   Perf. 14

647	A146	5 l shown	1.00	.25
648	A146	10 l Lenin statue	2.50	.35

October Revolution (Russia, 1917), 45th anniv.

Henri Dunant, Cross, Globe and Nurse — A147

1963, Jan 25   Unwmk.   Perf. 14

649	A147	1.50 l rose lake, red & ultra	.45	.25
650	A147	2.50 l lt bl, red & blk	.90	.25
651	A147	6 l emerald, red & blk	1.75	.25
652	A147	10 l dull yel, red & blk	3.00	.60
		Nos. 649-652 (4)	6.10	1.35

Cent. of the Geneva Conf., which led to the establishment of the Intl. Red Cross in 1864. Imperfs. in changed colors, value, set $60.

Stalin and Battle of Stalingrad A148

1963, Feb. 2

653	A148	8 l dk green & slate	9.00	1.00

Battle of Stalingrad, 20th anniv. See No. C67.

Andrian G. Nikolayev — A149

Designs: 7.50 l, Vostoks 3 and 4 and globe, horiz. 20 l, Pavel R. Popovich. 25 l, Nikolayev, Popovich and globe with trajectories.

1963, Feb. 28   Litho.

654	A149	2.50 l vio bl & sepia	.45	.40
655	A149	7.50 l lt blue & blk	1.25	.80
656	A149	20 l violet & sepia	3.50	2.25
		Nos. 654-656 (3)	5.20	3.45

Miniature Sheet

657	A149	25 l vio bl & sepia	45.00	45.00

1st group space flight of Vostoks 3 and 4, Aug. 11-15, 1962. Imperfs in changed colors, value: Nos. 654-656 $45 mint or used; No. 657 perf. $45 mint or used; No. 657 imperf. $50 mint or used.

"Albania" Decorating Police Officer — A150

1963, Mar. 20   Unwmk.   Perf. 14

658	A150	2.50 l crim, mag & blk	.90	.25
659	A150	7.50 l org ver, dk red & blk	3.00	.25

20th anniversary of the security police.

Polyphylla Fullo — A151

Beetles: 1.50 l, Lucanus cervus. 8 l, Procerus gigas. 10 l, Cicindela albanica.

1963, Mar. 20

660	A151	50q ol grn & brn	1.00	.25
661	A151	1.50 l blue & brn	1.75	.25
662	A151	8 l dl rose & blk vio	7.50	1.25
663	A151	10 l brt citron & blk	9.75	1.40
		Nos. 660-663 (4)	20.00	3.15

1913 Stamp and Postmark A152

10 l, Stamps of 1913, 1937 and 1962.

1963, May 5

664	A152	5 l yel, buff, bl & blk	1.75	.25
665	A152	10 l car rose, grn & blk	3.00	.45

50th anniversary of Albanian stamps.

Boxer — A153

Designs: 3 l, Basketball baskets. 5 l, Volleyball. 6 l, Bicyclists. 9 l, Gymnast. 15 l, Hands holding torch, and map of Japan.

1963, May 25   Perf. 13½

666	A153	2 l yel, blk & red brn	.55	1.00
667	A153	3 l ocher, brn & bl	.60	2.00
668	A153	5 l gray bl, red brn & brn	1.00	2.75
669	A153	6 l gray, dk gray & grn	1.25	5.00
670	A153	9 l rose, red brn & bl	2.25	7.50
		Nos. 666-670 (5)	5.65	18.25

Miniature Sheet

671	A153	15 l lt bl, car, blk & brn	13.50	13.50

1964 Olympic Games in Tokyo. Value, imperfs. Nos. 666-670 $20, No. 671 $20.

Crested Grebe — A154

Birds: 3 l, Golden eagle. 6.50 l, Gray partridges. 11 l, Capercaillie.

1963, Apr. 20   Litho.   Perf. 14

672	A154	50q multicolored	1.25	.25
673	A154	3 l multicolored	2.75	.50
674	A154	6.50 l multicolored	6.50	1.25
675	A154	11 l multicolored	9.00	2.00
		Nos. 672-675 (4)	19.50	4.00

Soldier and Building A155

2.50 l, Soldier with pack, ship, plane. 5 l, Soldier in battle. 6 l, Soldier, bulldozer.

1963, July 10   Unwmk.   Perf. 12

676	A155	1.50 l brick red, yel & blk	.45	.25
677	A155	2.50 l bl, ocher & brn	.90	.25
678	A155	5 l bluish grn, gray & blk	1.25	.25
679	A155	6 l red brn, buff & bl	1.75	.25
		Nos. 676-679 (4)	4.35	1.00

Albanian army, 20th anniversary.

Maj. Yuri A. Gagarin A156

Designs: 5 l, Maj. Gherman Titov. 7 l, Maj. Andrian G. Nikolayev. 11 l, Lt. Col. Pavel R. Popovich. 14 l, Lt. Col. Valeri Bykovski. 20 l, Lt. Valentina Tereshkova.

1963, July 30
Portraits in Yellow and Black

680	A156	3 l brt purple	.90	.25
681	A156	5 l dull blue	.90	.25
682	A156	7 l gray	1.25	.25
683	A156	11 l deep claret	2.75	.35
684	A156	14 l blue green	4.00	.60
685	A156	20 l ultra	6.25	1.00
		Nos. 680-685 (6)	16.05	2.80

Man's conquest of space. Value, imperf. set $40.

Volleyball A157

1963, Aug. 31   Perf. 12x12½

686	A157	2 l shown	.45	.25
687	A157	3 l Weight lifting	.45	.25
688	A157	5 l Soccer	.90	.25
689	A157	7 l Boxing	1.25	.25
690	A157	8 l Rowing	3.00	.30
		Nos. 686-690 (5)	6.05	1.30

European championships. Imperfs. in changed colors, value set $35.

Papilio Podalirius A158

1963, Sept. 29   Litho.
Various Butterflies and Moths in Natural Colors

691	A158	1 l red	.45	.25
692	A158	2 l blue	.90	.25
693	A158	4 l dull lilac	1.75	.60
694	A158	5 l pale green	2.25	.60
695	A158	8 l bister	4.50	1.25
696	A158	10 l light blue	5.75	1.75
		Nos. 691-696 (6)	15.60	4.70

Oil Refinery, Cerrik — A159

2.50 l, Food processing plant, Tirana, horiz. 30 l, Fruit canning plant. 50 l, Tannery, horiz.

1963, Nov. 15   Unwmk.   Perf. 14

697	A159	2.50 l rose red, pnksh	.90	.25
698	A159	20 l slate grn, grnsh	3.50	.25
699	A159	30 l dull pur, grysh	9.00	.55
700	A159	50 l ocher, yel	9.00	.85
		Nos. 697-700 (4)	22.40	1.90

Industrial development in Albania. For surcharges see Nos. 841-846.

Flag and Shield — A160

1963, Nov. 24   *Perf. 12½x12*
701 A160 2 l grnsh bl, blk, ocher
      & red   .45 .25
702 A160 8 l blue, blk, ocher &
      red   1.75 .50

1st Congress of Army Aid Assn.

Chinese, Caucasian and Negro
Men — A161

1963, Dec. 10   *Perf. 12x11½*
703 A161 3 l bister & blk   .45 .25
704 A161 5 l bister & ultra   .90 .25
705 A161 7 l bister & vio   2.25 .30
    Nos. 703-705 (3)   3.60 .80

15th anniv. of the Universal Declaration of Human Rights.

Slalom Ascent — A162

Designs: 50q, Bobsled, horiz. 6.50 l, Ice hockey, horiz. 12.50 l, Women's figure skating. No. 709A, Ski jumper.

1963, Dec. 25   *Perf. 14*
706 A162 50q grnsh bl &
      blk   .45 .25
707 A162 2.50 l red, gray &
      blk   .60 .25
708 A162 6.50 l yel, blk &
      gray   1.20 .25
709 A162 12.50 l red, blk &
      yel grn   2.25 .55
    Nos. 706-709 (4)   4.50 1.30

Miniature Sheet
709A A162 12.50 l multi   25.00 25.00

9th Winter Olympic Games, Innsbruck, Jan. 29-Feb. 9, 1964. Imperfs. in changed colors, value 706-709 $75, No. 709A $50.

Lenin — A163

1964, Jan. 21   *Perf. 12½x12*
710 A163 5 l gray & bister   .90 .25
711 A163 10 l gray & ocher   2.00 .30

40th anniversary, death of Lenin.

Hurdling — A164

Designs: 3 l, Track, horiz. 6.50 l, Rifle shooting, horiz. 8 l, Basketball.

Perf. 12½x12, 12x12½
1964, Jan. 30   Litho.
712 A164 2.50 l pale vio & ultra   .45 .25
713 A164 3 l lt grn & red brn   .90 .35
714 A164 6.50 l blue & claret   1.25 1.00
715 A164 8 l lt blue & ocher   2.25 1.60
    Nos. 712-715 (4)   4.85 3.20

1st Games of the New Emerging Forces, GANEFO, Jakarta, Indonesia, Nov. 10-22, 1963.

Fish — A165

1964, Feb. 26   Unwmk.   *Perf. 14*
716 A165 50q Sturgeon   .45 .25
717 A165 1 l Gilthead   .90 .25
718 A165 1.50 l Striped mullet   1.25 .25
719 A165 2.50 l Carp   1.75 .25
720 A165 6.50 l Mackerel   2.75 .40
721 A165 10 l Lake Ohrid
      trout   4.50 .50
    Nos. 716-721 (6)   11.60 1.90

Wild Animals A166

1964, Mar. 28   *Perf. 12½x12*
722 A166 1 l Red Squirrel   .45 .25
723 A166 1.50 l Beech marten   .85 .25
724 A166 2 l Red fox   .85 .40
725 A166 2.50 l Hedgehog   1.25 .40
726 A166 3 l Hare   1.75 .60
727 A166 5 l Jackal   1.75 .60
728 A166 7 l Wildcat   3.50 .60
729 A166 8 l Wolf   4.50 .95
    Nos. 722-729 (8)   14.90 4.05

Lighting Olympic Torch — A167

5 l, Torch, globes. 7 l, 15 l, Olympic flag, Mt. Fuji. 10 l, National Stadium, Tokyo.

1964, May 18   *Perf. 12x12½*
730 A167 3 l lt yel grn, yel &
      buff   .45 .70
731 A167 5 l red & vio blue   .65 1.00
732 A167 7 l lt bl, ultra & yel   .90 1.50
733 A167 10 l orange, bl & vio   1.25 2.50
    Nos. 730-733 (4)   3.25 5.70

Miniature Sheet
734 A167 15 l lt bl, ultra & org   22.50 22.50

18th Olympic Games, Tokyo, Oct. 10-25, 1964. No. 734 contains one 49x62mm stamp. Imperfs. in changed colors, value Nos. 730-733 $17.50, No. 734 $22.50.
See No. 745.

Partisans — A168

5 l, Arms of Albania. 8 l, Enver Hoxha.

Perf. 12½x12
1964, May 24   Litho.   Unwmk.
735 A168 2 l orange, red & blk   1.25 .25
736 A168 5 l multicolored   3.00 .30
737 A168 8 l red brn, blk & red   6.25 .90
    Nos. 735-737 (3)   10.50 1.45

20th anniv. of the Natl. Anti-Fascist Cong. of Liberation, Permet, May 24, 1944. The label attached to each stamp, without perforations between, carries a quotation from the 1944 Congress.

Albanian Flag and Revolutionists A169

Perf. 12½x12
1964, June 10   Litho.   Unwmk.
738 A169 2.50 l red & gray   .45 .25
739 A169 5 l lilac rose & gray   1.25 .25

Albanian revolution of 1924, 40th anniv.

Full Moon — A170

Designs: 5 l, New moon. 8 l, Half moon. 11 l, Waning moon. 15 l, Far side of moon.

1964, June 27   *Perf. 12x12½*
740 A170 1 l purple & yel   .45 .25
741 A170 5 l violet & yel   .60 .25
742 A170 8 l blue & yel   .90 .30
743 A170 11 l green & yel   3.50 .45
    Nos. 740-743 (4)   5.45 1.25

Miniature Sheet
Perf. 12 on 2 sides
744 A170 15 l ultra & yel   15.00 15.00

No. 744 contains one stamp, size: 35x36mm, perforated at top and bottom. Imperfs. in changed colors, value Nos. 740-743 $16, No. 744 $15.

No. 733 with Added Inscription "Rimini 25-VI-64"
1964   *Perf. 12x12½*
745 A167 10 l orange, bl & vio   7.00 7.00

"Toward Tokyo 1964" Phil. Exhib. at Rimini, Italy, June 25-July 6.

Wren — A171

Birds: 1 l, Penduline titmouse. 2.50 l, Green woodpecker. 3 l, Tree creeper. 4 l, Nuthatch. 5 l, Great titmouse. 6 l, Goldfinch. 18 l, Oriole.

1964, July 31   *Perf. 12x12½*
746 A171 50q multi   .45 .25
747 A171 1 l orange & multi   .90 .25
748 A171 2.50 l multi   1.25 .40
749 A171 3 l blue & multi   1.75 .40
750 A171 4 l yellow & multi   2.25 .80
751 A171 5 l blue & multi   2.75 .80
752 A171 6 l lt vio & multi   3.00 1.25
753 A171 18 l pink & multi   5.50 2.75
    Nos. 746-753 (8)   17.85 6.90

Running and Gymnastics A172

Sport: 2 l, Weight lifting, judo. 3 l, Equestrian, bicycling. 4 l, Soccer, water polo. 5 l, Wrestling, boxing. 6 l, Pentathlon, hockey. 7 l, Swimming, sailing. 8 l, Basketball, volleyball. 9 l, Rowing, canoeing. 10 l, Fencing, pistol shooting. 20 l, Three winners.

Perf. 12x12½
1964, Sept. 25   Litho.   Unwmk.
754 A172 1 l lt bl, rose & emer
      er   .25 .25
755 A172 2 l bis brn, bluish
      grn & vio   .25 .25
756 A172 3 l vio, red org & ol
      bis   .25 .25
757 A172 4 l grnsh bl, ol &
      ultra   .45 .35
758 A172 5 l grnsh bl, car &
      pale lil   .45 .35
759 A172 6 l dk bl, org & lt bl   .70 .75
760 A172 7 l dk bl, lt ol & org   .70 .75
761 A172 8 l emer, gray & yel   .90 .75
762 A172 9 l bl, yel & lil rose   .90 .75
763 A172 10 l brt grn, org brn
      & yel   1.25 1.00
    Nos. 754-763 (10)   6.10 5.45

Miniature Sheet
Perf. 12
764 A172 20 l violet & lemon   15.00 15.00

18th Olympic Games, Tokyo, Oct. 10-25. No. 764 contains one stamp, size: 41x68mm. Imperfs in changed colors, value: Nos. 754-763, $17.50 mint, $25 used; No. 764, $20 mint, $25 used.

Arms of People's Republic of China — A173

Mao Tsetung and Flag A174

1964, Oct. 1   *Perf. 11½x12, 12x11½*
765 A173 7 l black, red & yellow 10.00 4.50
766 A174 8 l black, red & yellow 10.00 6.00

People's Republic of China, 15th anniv.

Karl Marx A175

Designs: 5 l, St. Martin's Hall, London. 8 l, Friedrich Engels.

1964, Nov. 5   *Perf. 12x11½*
767 A175 2 l red, lt vio & blk   .90 .45
768 A175 5 l gray blue   2.25 1.40
769 A175 8 l ocher, blk & red   4.00 1.75
    Nos. 767-769 (3)   7.15 3.60

Centenary of First Socialist International.

Jeronim de Rada — A176

1964, Nov. 15   *Perf. 12½x11½*
770 A176 7 l slate green   1.10 .35
771 A176 8 l dull violet   1.90 .60

Birth of Jeronim de Rada, poet, 150th anniv.

Arms of
Albania — A177

Factories
A178

Designs: 3 l, Combine harvester. 4 l, Woman chemist. 10 l, Hands holding Communist Party book, hammer and sickle.

Perf. 11½x12, 12x11½
1964, Nov. 29
772 A177 1 l multicolored   .45 .40
773 A178 2 l red, yel & vio bl   .80 .80
774 A178 3 l red, yel & brn   1.20 1.25
775 A178 4 l red, yel & gray
     grn   1.50 1.60
776 A177 10 l red, bl & blk   3.50 4.00
    Nos. 772-776 (5)   7.45 8.05

20th anniversary of liberation.

Planet
Mercury — A179

Planets: 2 l, Venus and rocket. 3 l, Earth, moon and rocket. 4 l, Mars and rocket. 5 l, Jupiter. 6 l, Saturn. 7 l, Uranus. 8 l, Neptune. 9 l, Pluto. 15 l, Solar system and rocket.

1964, Dec. 15   *Perf. 12x12½*
777 A179 1 l yellow & pur   .25 .25
778 A179 2 l multicolored   .50 .25
779 A179 3 l multicolored   .40 .40
780 A179 4 l multicolored   .40 .40
781 A179 5 l yel, dk pur &
     brn   .80 .60
782 A179 6 l lt grn, vio brn &
     yel   1.20 .60
783 A179 7 l yellow & grn   1.40 .90
784 A179 8 l yellow & vio   1.60 1.00
785 A179 9 l lt grn, yel & blk   1.75 1.25
    Nos. 777-785 (9)   8.30 5.65

Miniature Sheet
Perf. 12 on 2 sides
786 A179 15 l car, bl, yel &
     grn   25.00 35.00

No. 786 contains one stamp, size: 62x51mm, perforated at top and bottom. Imperfs. in changed colors. Value Nos. 777-785, $30; No. 786, $25.

European
Chestnut — A180

1965, Jan. 25   *Perf. 11½x12*
787 A180 1 l shown   .25 .25
788 A180 2 l Medlars   .35 .25
789 A180 3 l Persimmon   .55 .25
790 A180 4 l Pomegranate   .75 .40
791 A180 5 l Quince   1.50 .50
792 A180 10 l Orange   3.00 1.00
    Nos. 787-792 (6)   6.40 2.65

Symbols of
Industry — A181

Designs: 5 l, Books, triangle and compass. 8 l, Beach, trees and hotel.

1965, Feb. 20
793 A181 2 l blk, car rose &
     pink   7.50 7.00
794 A181 5 l yel, gray & blk   12.00 10.50
795 A181 8 l blk, vio bl & lt bl   15.00 13.00
    Nos. 793-795 (3)   34.50 30.50

Professional trade associations, 20th anniv.

Water
Buffalo
A182

Various designs: Water buffalo.

1965, Mar.   *Perf. 12x11½*
796 A182 1 l lt yel grn, yel &
     brn blk   .75 .35
797 A182 2 l lt grn, dk gray &
     blk   1.50 .65
798 A182 3 l yellow, brn & grn   2.25 1.10
799 A182 7 l brt grn, yel & brn
     blk   5.25 1.50
800 A182 12 l pale lil, dk brn &
     ind   9.00 1.75
    Nos. 796-800 (5)   18.75 5.35

Mountain View, Valbona — A183

1.50 l, Seashore. 3 l, Glacier and peak. 4 l, Gorge. 5 l, Mountain peaks. 9 l, Lake and hills.

1965, Mar.   Litho.   *Perf. 12*
801 A183 1.50 l multi   1.40 .35
802 A183 2.50 l multi   3.00 .70
803 A183 3 l multi, vert.   3.00 .70
804 A183 4 l multi, vert.   3.75 1.25
805 A183 5 l multi   4.75 1.50
806 A183 9 l multi   12.50 3.00
    Nos. 801-806 (6)   28.40 7.50

Frontier
Guard — A184

1965, Apr. 25   Unwmk.
807 A184 2.50 l lt blue & multi   1.25 .25
808 A184 12.50 l lt ultra & multi   7.25 .90

20th anniversary of the Frontier Guards.

Small-bore Rifle
Shooting,
Prone — A185

Designs: 2 l, Rifle shooting, standing. 3 l, Target over map of Europe, showing

Bucharest. 4 l, Pistol shooting. 15 l, Rifle shooting, kneeling.

1965, May 10
809 A185 1 l lil, car rose, blk &
     brn   .35 .25
810 A185 2 l bl, blk, brn & vio bl   .35 .25
811 A185 3 l pink & car rose   .70 .25
812 A185 4 l bis, blk & vio brn   1.40 .25
813 A185 15 l brt grn, brn & vio
     brn   4.25 .50
    Nos. 809-813 (5)   7.05 1.50

European Shooting Championships, Bucharest.

ITU Emblem,
Old and New
Communications
Equipment
A186

1965, May 17   *Perf. 12½x12*
814 A186 2.50 l brt grn, blk & lil
     rose   .75 .25
815 A186 12.50 l vio, blk & brt bl   4.25 .30

Centenary of the ITU.

Col. Pavel
Belyayev — A187

Designs: 2 l, Voskhod II. 6.50 l, Lt. Col. Alexei Leonov. 20 l, Leonov floating in space.

1965, June 15   *Perf. 12*
816 A187 1.50 l lt blue & brn   .25 .25
817 A187 2 l dk bl, lt vio &
     lt ultra   .25 .25
818 A187 6.50 l lilac & brn   .35 .25
819 A187 20 l chlky bl, yel &
     blk   3.25 .40
    Nos. 816-819 (4)   4.10 1.15

Miniature Sheet
Perf. 12 on 2 sides
820 A187 20 l brt bl, org &
     blk   11.00 11.00

Space flight of Voskhod II and 1st man walking in space, Lt. Col. Alexei Leonov. No. 820 contains one stamp, size: 51x59½mm, perforated at top and bottom. Imperf., brt grn background, value $12.

Marx and
Lenin — A188

1965, June 21   *Perf. 12*
821 A188 2.50 l dk brn, red & yel   .75 .25
822 A188 7.50 l sl grn, org ver &
     buff   3.00 .25

6th Conf. of Postal Ministers of Communist Countries, Peking, June 21-July 15.

Mother and
Child — A189

2 l, Pioneers. 3 l, Boy and girl at play, horiz. 4 l, Child on beach. 15 l, Girl with book.

Perf. 12½x12, 12x12½
1965, June 29   Litho.   Unwmk.
823 A189 1 l brt bl, rose lil & blk   .25 .25
824 A189 2 l salmon, vio & blk   .25 .25
825 A189 3 l green, org & vio   .35 .25
826 A189 4 l multicolored   .85 .25

827 A189 15 l lil rose, brn &
     ocher   3.25 .50
    Nos. 823-827 (5)   4.95 1.50

Issued for International Children's Day.

Statue of
Magistrate — A190

Designs: 1 l, Amphora. 2 l, Illyrian armor. 3 l, Mosaic, horiz. 15 l, Torso, Apollo statue.

1965, July 20   *Perf. 12*
828 A190 1 l lt ol, org & brn   .25 .25
829 A190 2 l gray grn, grn &
     brn   .55 .25
830 A190 3 l tan, brn, car & lil   .75 .25
831 A190 4 l green, bis & brn   1.60 .25
832 A190 15 l gray & pale claret   4.00 .65
    Nos. 828-832 (5)   7.15 1.65

Flowers — A191

1965, Aug. 11   *Perf. 12½x12*
833 A191 1 l Fuchsia   .25 .25
834 A191 2 l Cyclamen   .75 .25
835 A191 3 l Tiger lily   1.30 .25
836 A191 3.50 l Iris   1.60 .25
837 A191 4 l Dahlia   1.75 .25
838 A191 4.50 l Hydrangea   2.25 .25
839 A191 5 l Rose   2.40 .30
840 A191 7 l Tulips   3.25 .35
    Nos. 833-840 (8)   13.55 2.15

Nos. 698-700 Surcharged New Value and Two Bars
1965, Aug. 16   *Perf. 14*
841 A159 5q on 30 l   .60 .60
842 A159 15q on 30 l   .60 .60
843 A159 25q on 50 l   1.00 1.00
844 A159 80q on 50 l   2.00 2.00
845 A159 1.10 l on 20 l   3.00 3.00
846 A159 2 l on 20 l   5.00 5.00
    Nos. 841-846 (6)   12.20 12.20

White
Stork — A192

Migratory Birds: 20q, Cuckoo. 30q, Hoopoe. 40q, European bee-eater. 50q, European nightjar. 1.50 l, Quail.

1965, Aug. 31   *Perf. 12*
847 A192 10q yel, blk & gray   .40 .40
848 A192 20q brt pink, blk &
     dk bl   .80 .40
849 A192 30q violet, blk & bis   1.20 .60
850 A192 40q emer, blk yel &
     org   1.60 .80
851 A192 50q ultra, brn & red
     brn   2.00 .95
852 A192 1.50 l bis, red brn &
     dp org   6.00 2.75
    Nos. 847-852 (6)   12.00 5.90

"Homecoming," by Bukurosh
Sejdini — A193

1965, Sept. 26   Litho.   Perf. 12x12½
853 A193 25q olive black   1.75   .40
854 A193 65q blue black   5.25   1.60
855 A193 1.10 l black   7.50   3.25
    Nos. 853-855 (3)   14.50   5.25

Second war veterans' meeting.

Hunting — A194

1965, Oct. 6   Litho.   Unwmk.
856 A194 10q Capercaillie   .35   .25
857 A194 20q Deer   .65   .25
858 A194 30q Pheasant   .75   .25
859 A194 40q Mallards   1.25   .25
860 A194 50q Boar   1.40   .25
861 A194 1 l Rabbit   3.25   .55
    Nos. 856-861 (6)   7.65   1.80

Oleander — A195

Flowers: 20q, Forget-me-nots. 30q, Pink.
40q, White water lily. 50q, Bird's foot. 1 l, Corn
poppy.

1965, Oct. 26   Perf. 12½x12
862 A195 10q brt bl, grn & car
        rose   .25   .25
863 A195 20q org red, bl, brn &
        grn   .35   .25
864 A195 30q vio, car rose &
        grn   .45   .25
865 A195 40q emerald, yel &
        hlk   65   .30
866 A195 50q org brn, yel & grn 1.10   .40
867 A195 1 l yel grn, blk &
        rose red   2.50   1.60
    Nos. 862-867 (6)   5.30   3.05

Hotel Turizmi,
Fier — A196

Buildings: 10q, Hotel, Peshkopi. 15q, Sana-
torium, Tirana. 25q, Rest home, Pogradec.
65q, Partisan Sports Arena, Tirana. 80q, Rest
home, Mali Dajt. 1.10 l, Culture House, Tirana.
1.60 l, Hotel Adriatik, Durres. 2 l, Migjeni Theater, Shkoder. 3 l, Alexander Moissi House of
Culture, Durres.

1965, Oct. 27   Perf. 12x12½
868 A196   5q blue & blk   .25   .25
869 A196 10q ocher & blk   .25   .25
870 A196 15q dull grn & blk   .25   .25
871 A196 25q violet & blk   .25   .25
872 A196 65q lt brn & blk   .70   .50
873 A196 80q yel grn & blk   1.40   .50
874 A196 1.10 l lilac & blk   2.00   .50
875 A196 1.60 l lt vio bl & blk 2.75   1.40
876 A196   2 l dull rose & blk   3.50   1.40
877 A196   3 l gray & blk   6.25   2.50
    Nos. 868-877 (10)   17.60   7.80

Freighter
"Teuta" — A197

Ships: 20q, Raft. 30q, Sailing ship, 19th
cent. 40q, Sailing ship, 18th cent. 50q,
Freighter "Vlora." 1 l, Illyric galleys.

1965, Nov. 16
878 A197 10q brt grn & dk grn   .30   .25
879 A197 20q ol bis & dk grn   .30   .25
880 A197 30q lt & dp ultra   .40   .25
881 A197 40q vio & dp vio   .50   .25
882 A197 50q pink & dk red   1.50   .25
883 A197 1 l bister & brn   3.50   .45
    Nos. 878-883 (6)   6.50   1.70

Brown Bear — A198

Various Albanian bears. 50q, 55q, 60q,
horiz.

1965, Dec. 7   Perf. 11½x12
884 A198 10q bister & dk brn   .45   .25
885 A198 20q pale brn & dk brn   .55   .25
886 A198 30q bis, dk brn & car 1.10   .25
887 A198 35q pale brn & dk brn 1.30   .25
888 A198 40q bister & dk brn   1.60   .25
889 A198 50q bister & dk brn   2.75   .25
890 A198 55q bister & dk brn   3.25   .30
891 A198 60q pale brn, dk brn
        & car   6.00   .50
    Nos. 884-891 (8)   17.00   2.30

Basketball and
Players — A199

10q, Games' emblem (map of Albania and
basket). 30q, 50q, Players with ball (diff.
designs). 1.40 l, Basketball medal on ribbon.

1965, Dec. 15   Litho.   Perf. 12½x12
892 A199 10q blue, yel & car   .25   .25
893 A199 20q rose lil, lt brn &
        blk   .25   .25
894 A199 30q bis, lt brn, red &
        blk   .30   .25
895 A199 50q lt grn, lt brn &
        blk   1.20   .25
896 A199 1.40 l rose, blk, brn &
        yel   2.40   .50
    Nos. 892-896 (5)   4.40   1.50

7th Balkan Basketball Championships,
Tirana, Dec. 15-19.

Arms of Republic
and Smokestacks
A200

Arms and: 10q, Book. 30q, Wheat. 60q,
Book, hammer & sickle. 80q, Factories.

1966, Jan. 11   Litho.   Perf. 11½x12
Coat of Arms in Gold
897 A200 10q crimson & brn   .25   .25
898 A200 20q blue & vio bl   .25   .25
899 A200 30q org yel & brn   .50   .25
900 A200 60q yel grn & brt grn 1.20   .25
901 A200 80q crimson & brn   1.40   .25
    Nos. 897-901 (5)   3.60   1.25

Albanian People's Republic, 20th anniv.

Cow
A201

1966, Feb. 25   Perf. 12½x12, 12x12½
902 A201 10q shown   .25   .25
903 A201 20q Pig   .40   .25
904 A201 30q Ewe & lamb   .75   .30
905 A201 35q Ram   1.20   .30
906 A201 40q Dog   1.50   .30
907 A201 50q Cat, vert.   1.75   .30
908 A201 55q Horse, vert.   2.00   .40
909 A201 60q Ass, vert.   4.00   .60
    Nos. 902-909 (8)   11.85   2.70

Soccer Player and
Map of
Uruguay — A202

5q, Globe in form of soccer ball. 15q, Player,
map of Italy. 20q, Goalkeeper, map of France.
25q, Player, map of Brazil. 30q, Player, map of
Switzerland. 35q, Player, map of Sweden.
40q, Player, map of Chile. 50q, Player, map of
Great Britain. 70q, World Championship cup &
ball.

1966, Mar. 20   Litho.   Perf. 12
910 A202 5q gray & dp org   .25   .25
911 A202 10q lt brn, bl & vio   .25   .25
912 A202 15q cit, dk bl & brt bl .25   .25
913 A202 20q org, vio bl & brt bl .25   .25
914 A202 25q salmon & sepia   .25   .25
915 A202 30q lt yel grn & brn   .35   .25
916 A202 35q lt ultra & emer   .50   .25
917 A202 40q pink & brown   .55   .25
918 A202 50q pale grn, mag &
        rose red   .75   .25
919 A202 70q gray, brn, yel & blk 1.00   .30
    Nos. 910-919 (10)   4.40   2.55

World Cup Soccer Championship, Wembley, England, July 11-30.

Andon Zako
Cajupi — A203

1966, Mar. 27   Unwmk.
920 A203 40q bluish blk   .65   .25
921 A203 1.10 l dark green   2.00   .40

Andon Zako Cajupi, poet, birth centenary.

Painted
Lady — A204

Designs: 20q, Blue dragonfly. 30q, Cloud-
less sulphur butterfly. 35q, 40q, Splendid dragonfly. 50q, Machaon swallow-tail. 55q, Sulphur
butterfly. 60q, Whitemarbled butterfly.

1966, Apr. 21   Litho.   Perf. 11½x12
922 A204 10q multicolored   .45   .25
923 A204 20q yellow & multi   .55   .25
924 A204 30q yellow & multi   .75   .25
925 A204 35q sky blue & multi   1.10   .25
926 A204 40q multicolored   1.60   .25
927 A204 50q rose & multi   2.25   .25
928 A204 55q multicolored   2.75   .25
929 A204 60q multicolored   7.00   .35
    Nos. 922-929 (8)   16.45   2.10

WHO
Headquarters,
Geneva, and
Emblem — A205

Designs (WHO Emblem and): 35q, Ambulance and stretcher bearers, vert. 60q, Albanian mother and nurse weighing infant, vert.
80q, X-ray machine and hospital.

Perf. 12x12½, 12½x12
1966, May 3   Litho.
930 A205 25q lt blue & blk   .40   .25
931 A205 35q salmon & ultra   .75   .25
932 A205 60q lt grn, bl & red   1.20   .25
933 A205 80q yel, bl, grn & lt brn 1.50 .25
    Nos. 930-933 (4)   3.85   1.00

Inauguration of the WHO Headquarters,
Geneva.

Bird's Foot
Starfish
A206

Designs: 25q, Starfish. 35q, Brittle star. 45q,
But-thorn starfish. 50q, Starfish. 60q, Sea
cucumber. 70q, Sea urchin.

1966, May 10   Perf. 12x12½
934 A206 15q multicolored   .25   .25
935 A206 25q multicolored   .45   .30
936 A206 35q multicolored   .75   .40
937 A206 45q multicolored   1.00   .45
938 A206 50q multicolored   1.10   .55
939 A206 60q multicolored   1.60   .75
940 A206 70q multicolored   2.00   1.90
    Nos. 934-940 (7)   7.15   4.60

Luna
10 — A207

30q, 80q, Trajectory of Luna 10, earth &
moon.

1966, June 10   Perf. 12x12½
941 A207 20q blue, yel & blk   .35   .25
942 A207 30q yel grn, blk & bl   .70   .25
943 A207 70q vio, yel & blk   1.40   .25
944 A207 80q yel, vio, grn & blk 2.50   .50
    Nos. 941-944 (4)   4.95   1.25

Launching of the 1st artificial moon satellite,
Luna 10, Apr. 3, 1966.

Jules
Rimet
Cup and
Soccer
A208

Designs: Various scenes of soccer play.

1966, July 12   Litho.   Perf. 12x12½
Black Inscriptions
945 A208 10q ocher & lilac   .30   .25
946 A208 20q lt blue & cit   .35   .25
947 A208 30q brick red & Prus
        bl   .50   .25
948 A208 35q lt ultra & rose   .70   .25
949 A208 40q yel grn & lt red
        brn   .70   .25
950 A208 50q lt red brn & yel
        grn   .85   .25
951 A208 55q rose lil & yel grn .85   .25
952 A208 60q dp rose & ocher   1.75   .25
    Nos. 945-952 (8)   6.00   2.00

World Cup Soccer Championship, Wembley, England, July 11-30.

Water Level Map of
Albania — A209

30q, Water measure & fields. 70q, Turbine &
pylon. 80q, Hydrological decade emblem.

1966, July   **Perf. 12½x12**
953 A209 20q brick red, blk & org   .50   .25
954 A209 30q emer, blk & lt brn   .50   .25
955 A209 70q brt violet & blk   1.50   .25
956 A209 80q brt bl, org, yel &
       blk   2.50   .45
    Nos. 953-956 (4)   5.00 1.20

Hydrological Decade (UNESCO), 1965-74.

Greek Turtle — A210

Designs: 15q, Grass snake. 25q, European
pond turtle. 30q, Wall lizard. 35q, Wall gecko.
45q, Emerald lizard. 50q, Slowworm. 90q,
Horned viper (or sand viper).

1966, Aug. 10   Litho.   Perf. 12½x12
957 A210 10q gray & multi   .25   .25
958 A210 15q yellow & multi   .30   .25
959 A210 25q ultra & multi   .35   .25
960 A210 30q multicolored   .45   .25
961 A210 35q multicolored   .70   .25
962 A210 45q multicolored   .85   .25
963 A210 50q orange & multi   1.00   .30
964 A210 90q lilac & multi   1.75   .55
    Nos. 957-964 (8)   5.65 2.35

Persian
Cat
A211

Cats: 10q, Siamese, vert. 15q, European
tabby, vert. 25q, Black kitten. 60q, 65q, 80q,
Various Persians.

Perf. 12x12½, 12½x12
1966, Sept. 20   Litho.
965 A211 10q multicolored   .35   .25
966 A211 15q blk, sepia & car   .35   .25
967 A211 25q blk, dk & lt brn   .70   .25
968 A211 45q blk, org & yel   1.00   .25
969 A211 60q blk, brn & yel   1.75   .30
970 A211 65q multicolored   1.75   .40
971 A211 80q blk, gray & yel   2.50   .50
    Nos. 965-971 (7)   8.40 2.20

Pjeter Budi,
Writer — A212

1966, Oct. 5   Perf. 12x12½
972 A212 25q buff & slate grn   .50   .25
973 A212 1.75 l gray & dull claret   1.50   .45

UNESCO
Emblem
A213

Designs (UNESCO Emblem and): 15q,
Open book, rose and school. 25q, Male folk
dancers. 1.55 l, Jug, column and old building.

1966, Oct. 20   Litho.   Perf. 12
974 A213 5q lt gray & multi   .25   .25
975 A213 15q dp blue & multi   .25   .25
976 A213 25q gray & multi   .30   .25
977 A213 1.55 l multi   2.25   .50
    Nos. 974-977 (4)   3.05 1.25

20th anniv. of UNESCO.

A214

Designs: 15q, Hand holding book with pictures of Marx, Engels, Lenin and Stalin. 25q,
Map of Albania, hammer and sickle, symbols
of agriculture and industry. 65q, Symbolic
grain and factories. 95q, Fists holding rifle,
spade, axe, sickle and book.

1966, Nov. 1   Litho.   Perf. 11½x12
978 A214 15q vermilion & gold   .25   .25
979 A214 25q multicolored   .25   .25
980 A214 65q brn, brn org &
       gold   1.20   .25
981 A214 95q yellow & multi   1.50   .40
    Nos. 978-981 (4)   3.20 1.15

Albanian Communist Party, 5th Cong.

A215

Designs: 15q, Hammer and sickle, Party
emblem in sunburst. 25q, Partisan and sunburst. 65q, Steel worker and blast furnace.
95q, Combine harvester, factories, and pylon.

1966, Nov. 8
982 A215 15q orange & multi   .40   .25
983 A215 25q red & multi   .40   .25
984 A215 65q multicolored   1.20   .25
985 A215 95q blue & multi   1.20   .40
    Nos. 982-985 (4)   3.20 1.15

25th anniv. of the founding of the Albanian
Workers Party.

Russian Wolfhound — A216

Dogs: 15q, Sheep dog. 25q, English setter.
45q, English springer spaniel. 60q, Bulldog.
65q, Saint Bernard. 80q, Dachshund.

1966, Oct. 30   Litho.   Perf. 12½x12
986 A216 10q green & multi   .40   .25
987 A216 15q multicolored   .65   .25
988 A216 25q lilac & multi   .80   .25
989 A216 45q rose & multi   1.20   .35
990 A216 60q brown & multi   1.60   .40

991 A216 65q ultra & multi   1.75   .45
992 A216 80q blue grn & multi   3.25   .50
    Nos. 986-992 (7)   9.65 2.45

Ndre Mjeda — A217

1966   Perf. 12½x12
993 A217 25q brt bl & dk brn   .35   .25
994 A217 1.75 l brt grn & dk brn   2.40   .65

Birth Centenary of the priest Ndre Mjeda.

Proclamation
A218

Designs: 10q, Banner, man and woman
holding gun and axe, horiz. 1.85 l, man with
axe and banner and partisan with gun.

1966, Dec. 25   Perf. 11½x12, 12x11½
995 A218 5q lt brn, red & blk   .25   .25
996 A218 10q red, blk, gray &
       bl   .40   .25
997 A218 1.85 l red, blk & salm-
       on   2.40   .30
    Nos. 995-997 (3)   3.05   .80

Albanian Communist Party, 25th anniv.

Golden
Eagle — A219

Birds of Prey: 15q, European sea eagle.
25q, Griffon vulture. 40q, Common sparrowhawk. 50q, Osprey. 70q, Egyptian vulture.
90q, Kestrel.

1966, Dec. 20   Litho.   Perf. 11½x12
998 A219 10q gray & multi   .35   .25
999 A219 15q multicolored   .35   .25
1000 A219 25q citron & multi   .70   .25
1001 A219 40q multicolored   1.00   .25
1002 A219 50q multicolored   1.40   .30
1003 A219 70q yellow & multi   2.00   .40
1004 A219 90q multicolored   3.00   .50
    Nos. 998-1004 (7)   8.80 2.20

Hake
A220

Fish: 15q, Red mullet. 25q, Opah. 40q,
Atlantic wolf fish. 65q, Lumpfish. 80q, Swordfish. 1.15 l, Shorthorn sculpin.

1967, Jan. 20   Photo.   Perf. 12x11½
Fish in Natural Colors
1005 A220 10q blue   .35   .25
1006 A220 15q lt yellow grn   .35   .25
1007 A220 25q Prus blue   .65   .25
1008 A220 40q emerald   .65   .25
1009 A220 65q brt blue grn   1.00   .30
1010 A220 80q blue   1.60   .40
1011 A220 1.15 l brt green   2.50   .65
    Nos. 1005-1011 (7)   7.10 2.35

White
Pelican
A221

Designs: Various groups of pelicans.

1967, Feb. 22   Litho.   Perf. 12
1012 A221 10q pink & multi   .25   .25
1013 A221 15q pink & multi   .25   .25
1014 A221 25q pink & multi   1.00   .25
1015 A221 50q pink & multi   2.00   .25
1016 A221 2 l pink & multi   5.00   .75
    Nos. 1012-1016 (5)   8.50 1.75

Camellia
A222

Flowers: 10q, Chrysanthemum. 15q, Holly-
hock. 25q, Flowering Maple. 35q, Peony. 65q,
Gladiolus. 80q, Freesia. 1.15 l, Carnation.

Unwmk.
1967, Apr. 12   Litho.   Perf. 12
Flowers in Natural Colors
1017 A222 5q pale brown   .25   .25
1018 A222 10q lt lilac   .25   .25
1019 A222 15q gray   .25   .25
1020 A222 25q ultra   .45   .25
1021 A222 35q lt blue   .70   .25
1022 A222 65q lt blue grn   1.40   .25
1023 A222 80q lt bluish gray   1.75   .30
1024 A222 1.15 l dull yellow   2.10   .45
    Nos. 1017-1024 (8)   7.15 2.25

Congress Emblem
and Power
Station — A223

1967, Apr. 24   Litho.   Perf. 12
1025 A223 25q multi   .75   .25
1026 A223 1.75 l multi   2.25   .55

Cong. of the Union of Professional Workers,
Tirana, Apr. 24.

Rose — A224

Various Roses in Natural Colors.

1967, May 15   Perf. 12x12½
1027 A224 5q blue gray   .35   .25
1028 A224 10q brt blue   .35   .25
1029 A224 15q rose violet   .35   .25
1030 A224 25q lemon   .35   .25
1031 A224 35q brt grnsh blue   .70   .25
1032 A224 50q gray   1.00   .25
1033 A224 80q brown   1.00   .30
1034 A224 1.65 l gray green   2.75   .50
    Nos. 1027-1034 (8)   6.85 2.30

Seashore, Bregdet Borsh — A225

Views: 15q, Buthrotum, vert. 25q, Shore, Fshati Piqeras. 45q, Shore, Bregdet. 50q, Shore, Bregdet Himare. 65q, Ship, Sarande (Santi Quaranta). 80q, Shore, Dhermi. 1 l, Sunset, Bregdet, vert.

Perf. 12x12½, 12½x12

1967, June 10

1035	A225	15q multicolored	.40	.25
1036	A225	20q multicolored	.40	.25
1037	A225	25q multicolored	.80	.35
1038	A225	45q multicolored	.80	.35
1039	A225	50q multicolored	.80	.35
1040	A225	65q multicolored	1.50	.50
1041	A225	80q multicolored	1.50	.70
1042	A225	1 l multicolored	2.40	1.00
	Nos. 1035-1042 (8)		8.60	3.75

Fawn
A226

Roe Deer: 20q, Stag, vert. 25q, Doe, vert. 30q, Young stag and doe. 35q, Doe and fawn. 40q, Young stag, vert. 65q, Stag and doe, vert. 70q, Running stag and does.

Perf. 12½x12, 12x12½

1967, July 20   **Litho.**

1043	A226	15q multicolored	.35	.25
1044	A226	20q multicolored	.35	.25
1045	A226	25q multicolored	.70	.25
1046	A226	30q multicolored	.70	.25
1047	A226	35q multicolored	1.00	.25
1048	A226	40q multicolored	1.00	.25
1049	A226	65q multicolored	2.10	.35
1050	A226	70q multicolored	2.75	.55
	Nos. 1043-1050 (8)		8.95	2.40

Man and Woman from Madhe
A227

Regional Costumes: 20q, Woman from Zadrimes. 25q, Dancer and drummer, Kukesit. 45q, Woman spinner, Dardhes. 50q, Farm couple, Myseqese. 65q, Dancer with tambourine, Tirana. 80q, Man and woman, Dropullit. 1 l, Piper, Laberise.

1967, Aug. 25   **Perf. 12**

1051	A227	15q tan & multi	.40	.25
1052	A227	20q lt yellow grn	.40	.25
1053	A227	25q multicolored	.40	.25
1054	A227	45q sky blue & multi	.80	.25
1055	A227	50q lemon & multi	.80	.30
1056	A227	65q pink & multi	.80	.40
1057	A227	80q multicolored	1.60	.45
1058	A227	1 l gray & multi	1.60	.60
	Nos. 1051-1058 (8)		6.80	2.75

Fighters and Newspaper — A228

75q, Printing plant, newspapers, microphone. 2 l, People holding newspaper.

1967, Aug. 25   **Perf. 12½x12**

1059	A228	25q multicolored	.35	.25
1060	A228	75q pink & multi	1.00	.50
1061	A228	2 l multicolored	2.75	1.25
	Nos. 1059-1061 (3)		4.10	2.00

Issued for the Day of the Press.

Street Scene, by Kole
Idromeno — A229

Hakmarrja Battalion, by Sali
Shijaku — A230

Designs: 20q, David, fresco by Onufri, 16th century, vert. 45q, Woman's head, ancient mosaic, vert. 50q, Men on horseback from 16th century icon, vert. 65q, Farm Women, by Zef Shoshi. 80q, Street Scene, by Vangjush Mio. 1 l, Bride, by Kolé Idromeno, vert.

Perf. 12, 12x12½, (A230)

1967, Oct. 25   **Litho.**

1062	A229	15q multicolored	.45	.25
1063	A229	20q multicolored	.45	.25
1064	A230	25q multicolored	1.00	.25
1065	A229	45q multicolored	1.00	.25
1066	A229	50q multicolored	1.00	.25
1067	A230	65q multicolored	1.75	.25
1068	A230	80q multicolored	1.75	.30
1069	A230	1 l multicolored	4.00	.35
	Nos. 1062-1069 (8)		11.40	2.15

Lenin at Storming of Winter Palace — A231

Designs: 15q, Lenin and Stalin, horiz. 50q, Lenin and Stalin addressing meeting. 1.10 l, Storming of the Winter Palace, horiz.

1967, Nov. 7   **Perf. 12**

1070	A231	15q red & multi	.30	.25
1071	A231	25q slate grn & blk	.70	.25
1072	A231	50q brn, blk & brn vio	1.00	.25
1073	A231	1.10 l lilac, gray & blk	2.00	.30
	Nos. 1070-1073 (4)		4.00	1.05

50th anniv. of the Russian October Revolution.

Rabbit — A232

Designs: Various hares and rabbits. The 15q, 25q, 35q, 40q and 1 l are horizontal.

1967, Sept. 30

1074	A232	15q orange & multi	.25	.25
1075	A232	20q brt yel & multi	.35	.25
1076	A232	25q lt brn & multi	.35	.25
1077	A232	35q multicolored	.75	.25
1078	A232	40q yellow & multi	.75	.25
1079	A232	50q pink & multi	2.25	.25
1080	A232	65q multicolored	2.25	.35
1081	A232	1 l lilac & multi	3.00	.55
	Nos. 1074-1081 (8)		9.95	2.40

University, Torch and Book — A233

1967, Sept. 15   **Litho.**   **Perf. 12**

1082	A233	25q multi	.50	.25
1083	A233	1.75 l multi	3.00	.35

10th anniv. of the founding of the State University, Tirana.

Coat of Arms and Soldiers
A234

65q, Arms, Factory, grain, flag, gun, radio tower. 1.20 l, Arms, hand holding torch.

1967, Sept. 16   **Perf. 12x11½**

1084	A234	15q multi	.30	.25
1085	A234	65q multi	1.00	.25
1086	A234	1.20 l multi	2.25	.25
	Nos. 1084-1086 (3)		3.55	.75

25th anniversary of the Democratic Front.

Turkey
A235

Designs: 20q, Duck. 25q, Hen. 45q, Rooster. 50q, Guinea fowl. 65q, Goose, horiz. 80q, Mallard, horiz. 1 l, Chicks, horiz.

Perf. 12x12½, 12½x12

1967, Nov. 25   **Photo.**

1087	A235	15q gold & multi	.25	.25
1088	A235	20q gold & multi	.25	.25
1089	A235	25q gold & multi	.35	.25
1090	A235	45q gold & multi	1.00	.25
1091	A235	50q gold & multi	1.00	.25
1092	A235	65q gold & multi	1.00	.25
1093	A235	80q gold & multi	2.00	.35
1094	A235	1 l gold & multi	3.25	.45
	Nos. 1087-1094 (8)		9.10	2.30

Skanderbeg
A236

Designs: 10q, Arms of Skanderbeg. 25q, Helmet and sword. 30q, Kruje Castle. 35q, Petreles Castle. 65q, Berati Castle. 80q, Skanderbeg addressing national chiefs. 90q, Battle of Albulenes.

1967, Dec. 10   **Litho.**   **Perf. 12x12½**
Medallion in Bister and Dark Brown

1095	A236	10q gold & violet	.25	.25
1096	A236	15q gold & rose car	.25	.25
1097	A236	25q gold & vio bl	.30	.25
1098	A236	30q gold & dk blue	.40	.25
1099	A236	35q gold & maroon	.50	.25
1100	A236	65q gold & green	.80	.25
1101	A236	80q gold & gray brn	1.60	.30
1102	A236	90q gold & ultra	1.60	.35
	Nos. 1095-1102 (8)		5.70	2.15

500th anniv. of the death of Skanderbeg (George Castriota), national hero.

10th Winter Olympic Games, Grenoble, France, Feb. 6-18 — A237

Designs: 15q, 2 l, Winter Olympics emblem. 25q, Ice hockey. 30q, Women's figure skating. 50q, Slalom. 80q, Downhill skiing. 1 l, Ski jump.

1967-68

1103	A237	15q multicolored	.25	.25
1104	A237	25q multicolored	.25	.25
1105	A237	30q multicolored	.25	.25
1106	A237	50q multicolored	.30	.25
1107	A237	80q multicolored	.75	.25
1108	A237	1 l multicolored	1.60	.25
	Nos. 1103-1108 (6)		3.40	1.50

Miniature Sheet
Imperf

1109	A237	2 l red, gray & brt bl ('68)	4.50	4.50

Nos. 1103-1108 issued Dec. 29, 1967.

Skanderbeg Monument, Kruje — A238

Designs: 10q, Skanderbeg monument, Tirana. 15q, Skanderbeg portrait, Uffizi Galleries, Florence. 25q, engraved portrait of Gen. Tanush Topia. 35q, Portrait of Gen. Gjergj Arianti, horiz. 65q, Portrait bust of Skanderbeg by O. Paskali. 80q, Title page of "The Life of Skanderbeg." 90q, Skanderbeg battling the Turks, painting by S. Brota, horiz.

Perf. 12x12½, 12½x12

1968, Jan. 17   **Litho.**

1110	A238	10q multicolored	.35	.25
1111	A238	15q multicolored	.35	.25
1112	A238	25q blk, yel & lt bl	.75	.25
1113	A238	30q multicolored	.75	.25
1114	A238	35q lt vio, pink & blk	.75	.25
1115	A238	65q multicolored	1.50	.30
1116	A238	80q pink, blk & yel	2.25	.50
1117	A238	90q beige & multi	2.25	.65
	Nos. 1110-1117 (8)		8.95	2.70

500th anniv. of the death of Skanderbeg (George Castriota), national hero.

Carnation
A239

1968, Feb. 15   **Perf. 12**
Various Carnations in Natural Colors

1118	A239	15q green	.25	.25
1119	A239	20q dk brown	.25	.25
1120	A239	25q brt blue	.25	.25
1121	A239	50q gray olive	.70	.25
1122	A239	80q bluish gray	.90	.25
1123	A239	1.10 l violet gray	1.50	.40
	Nos. 1118-1123 (6)		3.85	1.65

"Electrification"
A240

65q, Farm tractor, horiz. 1.10 l, Cow & herd.

1968, Mar. 5   Litho.   Perf. 12
1124	A240	25q multi	.55	.25
1125	A240	65q multi	1.60	.30
1126	A240	1.10 l multi	2.25	.40
	Nos. 1124-1126 (3)		4.40	.95

Fifth Farm Cooperatives Congress.

Goat
A241

Various goats. 15q, 20q, 25q are vertical.

1968, Mar. 25   Perf. 12x12½, 12½x12
1127	A241	15q multi	.25	.25
1128	A241	20q multi	.25	.25
1129	A241	25q multi	.35	.25
1130	A241	30q multi	.35	.25
1131	A241	40q multi	.50	.25
1132	A241	50q multi	.50	.25
1133	A241	80q multi	1.50	.25
1134	A241	1.40 l multi	2.25	.40
	Nos. 1127-1134 (8)		5.95	2.15

Zef N.
Jubani — A242

1968, Mar. 30   Perf. 12
1135	A242	25q yellow & choc	.35	.25
1136	A242	1.75 l lt violet & blk	1.90	.50

Sesquicentennial of the birth of Zef N. Jubani, writer and scholar.

Physician and
Hospital — A243

Designs (World Health Organization Emblem and): 65q, Hospital and microscope, horiz. 1.10 l, Mother feeding child.

Perf. 12½x12, 12x12½
1968, Apr. 7   Litho.
1137	A243	25q green & claret	.25	.25
1138	A243	65q black, yel & bl	.90	.30
1139	A243	1.10 l black & dp org	1.10	.40
	Nos. 1137-1139 (3)		2.25	.95

20th anniv. of WHO.

Scientist
A244

Women: 15q, Militia member. 60q, Farm worker. 1 l, Factory worker.

1968, Apr. 14   Perf. 12
1140	A244	15q ver & dk red	.35	.25
1141	A244	25q blue grn & grn	.35	.25
1142	A244	60q dull yel & brn	1.10	.25
1143	A244	1 l lt vio & vio	1.90	.40
	Nos. 1140-1143 (4)		3.70	1.15

Albanian Women's Organization, 25th anniv.

Karl Marx
A245

Designs: 25q, Marx lecturing to students. 65q, "Das Kapital," "Communist Manifesto" and marching crowd. 95q, Full-face portrait.

1968, May 5   Litho.   Perf. 12
1144	A245	15q gray, dk bl & bis	.45	.25
1145	A245	25q brn vio, dk brn & dl yel	.60	.25
1146	A245	65q gray, blk, brn & car	1.25	.25
1147	A245	95q gray, ocher & blk	3.00	.50
	Nos. 1144-1147 (4)		5.30	1.25

Karl Marx, 150th birth anniversary.

Heliopsis
A246

Flowers: 20q, Red flax. 25q, Orchid. 30q, Gloxinia. 40q, Turk's-cap lily. 80q, Amaryllis. 1.40 l, Red magnolia.

1968, May 10   Perf. 12x12½
1148	A246	15q gold & multi	.25	.25
1149	A246	20q gold & multi	.25	.25
1150	A246	25q gold & multi	.30	.25
1151	A246	30q gold & multi	.35	.25
1152	A246	40q gold & multi	.35	.25
1153	A246	80q gold & multi	1.10	.40
1154	A246	1.40 l gold & multi	1.90	.60
	Nos. 1148-1154 (7)		4.50	2.25

Proclamation of Prizren — A247

25q, Abdyl Frasheri. 40q, House in Prizren.

1968, June 10   Litho.   Perf. 12
1155	A247	25q emerald & blk	.40	.25
1156	A247	40q multicolored	.75	.25
1157	A247	85q yellow & multi	1.10	.30
	Nos. 1155-1157 (3)		2.25	.80

League of Prizren against the Turks, 90th anniv.

Shepherd, by
A.
Kushi — A248

Paintings from Tirana Art Gallery: 20q, View of Tirana, by V. Mio, horiz. 25q, Mountaineer, by G. Madhi. 40q, Refugees, by A. Buza. 80q, Guerrillas of Shahin Matrakut, by S. Xega.

1.50 l, Portrait of an Old Man, by S. Papadhimitri. 1.70 l, View of Scutari, by S. Rrota. 2.50 l, Woman in Scutari Costume, by Z. Colombi.

1968, June 20   Perf. 12x12½
1158	A248	15q gold & multi	.25	.25
1159	A248	20q gold & multi	.25	.25
1160	A248	25q gold & multi	.25	.25
1161	A248	40q gold & multi	.25	.25
1162	A248	80q gold & multi	.55	.25
1163	A248	1.50 l gold & multi	1.40	.30
1164	A248	1.70 l gold & multi	2.25	.55
	Nos. 1158-1164 (7)		5.20	2.10

Miniature Sheet
Perf. 12½xImperf.
1165	A248	2.50 l multi	2.50	2.50

No. 1165 contains one stamp, size: 50x71mm.

Soldier and Guns — A249

25q, Sailor, warships. 65q, Aviator, planes, vert. 95q, Militiamen, woman.

1968, July 10   Litho.   Perf. 12
1166	A249	15q multicolored	.35	.25
1167	A249	25q multicolored	.35	.25
1168	A249	65q multicolored	1.50	.25
1169	A249	95q multicolored	2.25	.25
	Nos. 1166-1169 (4)		4.45	1.00

25th anniversary of the People's Army.

Squid
A250

Designs: 20q, Crayfish. 25q, Whelk. 50q, Crab. 70q, Spiny lobster. 80q, Shore crab. 90q, Norway lobster.

1968, Aug. 20
1170	A250	15q multicolored	.35	.25
1171	A250	20q multicolored	.35	.25
1172	A250	25q multicolored	.35	.25
1173	A250	50q multicolored	.35	.25
1174	A250	70q multicolored	.75	.30
1175	A250	80q multicolored	1.90	.35
1176	A250	90q multicolored	1.90	.40
	Nos. 1170-1176 (7)		5.95	2.05

Women's Relay Race — A251

Sport: 20q, Running. 25q, Women's discus. 30q, Equestrian. 40q, High jump. 50q, Women's hurdling. 80q, Soccer. 1.40 l, Woman diver. 2 l, Olympic stadium.

1968, Sept. 23   Photo.   Perf. 12
1177	A251	15q multicolored	.25	.25
1178	A251	20q multicolored	.25	.25
1179	A251	25q multicolored	.25	.25
1180	A251	30q multicolored	.25	.25
1181	A251	40q multicolored	.30	.25
1182	A251	50q multicolored	.30	.25
1183	A251	80q multicolored	.75	.25
1184	A251	1.40 l multicolored	1.50	.35
	Nos. 1177-1184 (8)		3.85	2.10

Souvenir Sheet
Perf. 12½ Horizontally
1185	A251	2 l multicolored	2.50	2.50

19th Olympic Games, Mexico City, Oct. 12-27. No. 1185 contains one rectangular stamp, size: 64x54mm. Value of imperfs., Nos. 1177-1184 $10.50, No. 1185 $7.50.

Enver
Hoxha — A252

1968, Oct. 16   Litho.   Perf. 12
1186	A252	25q blue gray	.40	.25
1187	A252	25q rose brown	.40	.25
1188	A252	80q violet	.80	.35
1189	A252	1.10 l brown	1.20	.50
	Nos. 1186-1189 (4)		2.80	1.35

Souvenir Sheet
Imperf
1190	A252	1.50 l rose red, bl vio & gold	75.00	75.00

60th birthday of Enver Hoxha, First Secretary of the Central Committee of the Communist Party of Albania.

Book and
Pupils
A253

1968, Nov. 14   Photo.
1191	A253	15q mar & slate grn	.35	.25
1192	A253	85q gray olive & sepia	2.25	.25

60th anniv. of the Congress of Monastir, Nov. 14-22, 1908, which adopted a unified Albanian alphabet.

Waxwing — A254

Birds: 20q, Rose-colored starling. 25q, Kingfishers. 50q, Long-tailed tits. 80q, Wallcreeper. 1.10 l, Bearded tit.

1968, Nov. 15   Litho.
Birds in Natural Colors
1193	A254	15q lt blue & blk	.25	.25
1194	A254	20q bister & blk	.25	.25
1195	A254	25q pink & blk	.40	.25
1196	A254	50q lt yel grn & blk	1.00	.25
1197	A254	80q bis brn & blk	2.00	.35
1198	A254	1.10 l pale grn & blk	3.00	.55
	Nos. 1193-1198 (6)		6.90	1.90

Mao Tse-tung — A255

1968, Dec. 26   Litho.   Perf. 12½x12
1199	A255	25q gold, red & blk	1.00	.40
1200	A255	1.75 l gold, red & blk	6.50	3.50

75th birthday of Mao Tse-tung.

Adem Reka and Crane — A256

Portraits: 10q, Pjeter Lleshi and power lines. 15q, Mohammed Shehu and Myrteza Kepi. 25q, Shkurte Vata and women railroad workers. 65q, Agron Elezi, frontier guard. 80q, Ismet Bruçaj and mountain road. 1.30 l, Fuat Cela, blind revolutionary.

1969, Feb. 10   Litho.   Perf. 12x12½
1201	A256	5q multicolored	.35	.25
1202	A256	10q multicolored	.35	.25
1203	A256	15q multicolored	.70	.25
1204	A256	25q multicolored	1.00	.25
1205	A256	65q multicolored	1.40	.25
1206	A256	80q multicolored	1.40	.25
1207	A256	1.30 l multicolored	2.10	.25
		Nos. 1201-1207 (7)	7.30	1.75

Contemporary heroine and heroes.

Meteorological Instruments — A257

Designs: 25q, Water gauge. 1.60 l, Radar, balloon and isobars.

1969, Feb. 25   Perf. 12
1208	A257	15q multicolored	.40	.25
1209	A257	25q ultra, org & blk	.40	.25
1210	A257	1.60 l rose vio, yel & blk	2.60	.60
		Nos. 1208-1210 (3)	3.40	1.10

20th anniv. of Albanian hydrometeorology.

Partisans, 1944, by F. Haxmiu — A258

Paintings: 5q, Student Revolutionists, by P. Mele, vert. 65q, Steel Mill, by C. Ceka. 80q, Reconstruction, by V. Kilica. 1.10 l, Harvest, by N. Jonuzi. 1.15 l, Terraced Landscape, by S. Kaceli. 2 l, Partisans' Meeting.

Perf. 12x12½, 12½x12
1969, Apr. 25   Litho.
Size: 31½x41½mm
1211	A258	5q buff & multi	.25	.25

Size: 51½x30½mm
1212	A258	25q buff & multi	.25	.25

Size: 40½x32mm
1213	A258	65q buff & multi	.30	.25

Size: 51½x30½mm
1214	A258	80q buff & multi	.35	.25
1215	A258	1.10 l buff & multi	.75	.25
1216	A258	1.15 l buff & multi	.75	.25
		Nos. 1211-1216 (6)	2.65	1.50

Miniature Sheet
Imperf
Size: 111x90mm
1217	A258	2 l ocher & multi	1.50	1.50

Leonardo da Vinci, Self-portrait A259

Designs (after Leonardo da Vinci): 35q, Lilies. 40q, Design for a flying machine, horiz. 1 l, Portrait of Beatrice. No. 1222, Portrait of a Noblewoman. No. 1223, Mona Lisa.

Perf. 12x12½, 12½x12
1969, May 2   Litho.
1218	A259	25q gold & sepia	.25	.25
1219	A259	35q gold & sepia	.35	.25
1220	A259	40q gold & sepia	.50	.25
1221	A259	1 l gold & sepia	1.40	.25
1222	A259	2 l gold & sepia	2.75	.55
		Nos. 1218-1222 (5)	5.25	1.55

Miniature Sheet
Imperf
1223	A259	2 l gold & multi	3.50	2.50

Leonardo da Vinci (1452-1519), painter, sculptor, architect and engineer.

First Congress Meeting Place A260

Designs: 1 l, Albanian coat of arms. 2.25 l, Two partisans with guns and flag.

1969, May 24   Perf. 12
1224	A260	25q lt grn, blk & red	.35	.25
1225	A260	2.25 l multi	2.75	1.00

Souvenir Sheet
1226	A260	1 l gold, bl, blk & red	35.00	35.00

25th anniversary of the First Anti-Fascist Congress of Permet, May 24, 1944.

Albanian Violet — A261

Designs: Violets and Pansies.

1969, June 30   Litho.   Perf. 12x12½
1227	A261	5q gold & multi	.25	.25
1228	A261	10q gold & multi	.25	.25
1229	A261	15q gold & multi	.30	.25
1230	A261	20q gold & multi	.35	.25
1231	A261	25q gold & multi	.35	.25
1232	A261	80q gold & multi	1.10	.35
1233	A261	1.95 l gold & multi	1.90	.65
		Nos. 1227-1233 (7)	4.50	2.25

Plum, Fruit and Blossoms A262

Designs: Blossoms and Fruits.

1969, Aug. 10   Litho.   Perf. 12
1234	A262	10q shown	.25	.25
1235	A262	15q Lemon	.25	.25
1236	A262	25q Pomegranate	.30	.25
1237	A262	50q Cherry	.75	.25
1238	A262	80q Peach	1.10	.25
1239	A262	1.20 l Apple	1.90	.40
		Nos. 1234-1239 (6)	4.55	1.65

Basketball A263

Designs: 10q, 80q, 2.20 l, Various views of basketball game. 25q, Hand aiming ball at basket and map of Europe, horiz.

1969, Sept. 15   Litho.   Perf. 12
1240	A263	10q multi	.35	.25
1241	A263	15q buff & multi	.35	.25
1242	A263	25q blue & multi	.35	.25
1243	A263	80q multi	1.10	.25
1244	A263	2.20 l multi	2.00	.50
		Nos. 1240-1244 (5)	4.15	1.50

16th European Basketball Championships, Naples, Italy, Sept. 27-Oct. 5.

Runner A264

Designs: 5q, Games' emblem. 10q, Woman gymnast. 20q, Pistol shooting. 25q, Swimmer at start. 80q, Bicyclist. 95q, Soccer.

1969, Sept. 30
1245	A264	5q multicolored	.25	.25
1246	A264	10q multicolored	.25	.25
1247	A264	15q multicolored	.30	.25
1248	A264	20q multicolored	.35	.25
1249	A264	25q multicolored	.35	.25
1250	A264	80q multicolored	1.00	.25
1251	A264	95q multicolored	1.40	.25
		Nos. 1245-1251 (7)	3.90	1.75

Second National Spartakiad.

Electronic Technicians, Steel Ladle — A265

25q, Mao Tse-tung with microphones. 1.40 l, Children holding Mao's red book.

1969, Oct. 1   Litho.   Perf. 12
1252	A265	25q multi, vert.	2.50	.60
1253	A265	85q multi	7.50	2.25
1254	A265	1.40 l multi, vert.	12.00	4.00
		Nos. 1252-1254 (3)	22.00	6.85

People's Republic of China, 20th anniv.

Enver Hoxha A266

Designs: 80q, Pages from Berat resolution. 1.45 l, Partisans with flag.

1969, Oct. 20   Litho.   Perf. 12
1255	A266	25q multicolored	.25	.25
1256	A266	80q gray & multi	.55	.25
1257	A266	1.45 l ocher & multi	1.60	.45
		Nos. 1255-1257 (3)	2.40	.95

25th anniv. of the 2nd reunion of the Natl. Antifascist Liberation Council, Berat.

Soldiers — A267

Designs: 30q, Oil refinery. 35q, Combine harvester. 45q, Hydroelectric station and dam. 55q, Militia woman, man and soldier. 1.10 l, Dancers and musicians.

1969, Nov. 29
1258	A267	25q multi	.30	.25
1259	A267	30q multi	.35	.25
1260	A267	35q multi	.50	.25
1261	A267	45q multi	.85	.25
1262	A267	55q multi	1.20	.30
1263	A267	1.10 l multi	2.00	.45
		Nos. 1258-1263 (6)	5.20	1.75

25th anniv. of the socialist republic.

Joseph V. Stalin, (1879-1953), Russian Political Leader — A268

1969, Dec. 21   Litho.   Perf. 12
1264	A268	15q lilac	.25	.25
1265	A268	25q slate blue	.40	.25
1266	A268	1 l brown	1.40	.25
1267	A268	1.10 l violet blue	1.60	.25
		Nos. 1264-1267 (4)	3.65	1.00

Head of Woman A269

Greco-Roman Mosaics: 25q, Geometrical floor design, horiz. 80q, Bird and tree, horiz. 1.10 l, Floor with birds and grapes, horiz. 1.20 l, Fragment with corn within oval design.

1969, Dec. 25   Perf. 12½x12

1268	A269	15q gold & multi	.25	.25
1269	A269	25q gold & multi	.25	.25
1270	A269	80q gold & multi	.75	.25
1271	A269	1.10 l gold & multi	1.00	.25
1272	A269	1.20 l gold & multi	1.50	.35
		Nos. 1268-1272 (5)	3.75	1.35

Cancellation of 1920 — A270

25q, Proclamation and congress site.

1970, Jan. 21   Litho.   Perf. 12

1273	A270	25q red, gray & blk	.35	.25
1274	A270	1.25 l dk grn, yel & blk	2.25	.25

Congress of Louchnia, 50th anniversary.

Worker, Student and Flag A271

1970, Feb. 11   Perf. 12½x12

1275	A271	25q red & multi	.35	.25
1276	A271	1.75 l red & multi	2.25	.50

Vocational organizations in Albania, 25th anniv.

Turk's-cap Lily — A272

Lilies: 5q, Cernum, vert. 15q, Madonna, vert. 25q, Royal, vert. 1.10 l, Tiger. 1.15 l, Albanian.

Perf. 11½x12, 12x11½

1970, Mar. 10   Litho.

1277	A272	5q multi	.25	.25
1278	A272	15q multi	.25	.25
1279	A272	25q multi	.75	.25
1280	A272	80q multi	1.50	.25
1281	A272	1.10 l multi	2.25	.25
1282	A272	1.15 l multi	2.60	.30
		Nos. 1277-1282 (6)	7.60	1.55

Lenin A273

Designs (Lenin): 5q, Portrait, vert. 25q, As volunteer construction worker. 95q, Addressing crowd. 1.10 l, Saluting, vert.

1970, Apr. 22   Litho.   Perf. 12

1283	A273	5q multi	.25	.25
1284	A273	15q multi	.25	.25
1285	A273	25q multi	.35	.25
1286	A273	95q multi	.90	.25
1287	A273	1.10 l multi	1.60	.25
		Nos. 1283-1287 (5)	3.35	1.25

Centenary of birth of Lenin (1870-1924).

Frontier Guard A274

1970, Apr. 25

1288	A274	25q multi	.35	.25
1289	A274	1.25 l multi	1.75	.50

25th anniversary of Frontier Guards.

Soccer Players — A275

Designs: 5q, Jules Rimet Cup and globes. 10q, Aztec Stadium, Mexico City. 25q, Defending goal. 65q, 80q, No. 1296, Two soccer players in various plays. No. 1297, Mexican horseman and volcano Popocatepetl.

1970, May 15   Litho.   Perf. 12½x12

1290	A275	5q multicolored	.25	.25
1291	A275	10q multicolored	.25	.25
1292	A275	15q multicolored	.25	.25
1293	A275	25q lt green & multi	.25	.25
1294	A275	65q pink & multi	.55	.25
1295	A275	80q lt blue & multi	.75	.40
1296	A275	2 l yellow & multi	1.50	.45
		Nos. 1290-1296 (7)	3.80	2.10

Souvenir Sheet
Perf 12 x Imperf

1297	A275	2 l multicolored	2.75	2.75

World Soccer Championships for the Jules Rimet Cup, Mexico City, May 31-June 21, 1970. No. 1297 contains one large horizontal stamp. Nos. 1290-1297 exist imperf. Value: Nos. 1290-1296, mint or used, $12; No. 1297, mint $10, used $5.

UPU Headquarters and Monument, Bern — A276

1970, May 30   Litho.   Perf. 12½x12

1298	A276	25q ultra, gray & blk	.25	.25
1299	A276	1.10 l org, buff & blk	1.00	.25
1300	A276	1.15 l grn, gray & blk	1.25	.30
		Nos. 1298-1300 (3)	2.50	.80

Inauguration of the new UPU Headquarters in Bern.

Bird and Grapes Mosaic A277

Mosaics, 5th-6th centuries, excavated near Pogradec: 10q, Waterfowl and grapes. 20q, Bird and tree stump. 25q, Bird and leaves. 65q, Fish. 2.25 l, Peacock, vert.

1970, July 10   Litho.   Perf. 12½x12, 12x11½

1301	A277	5q multi	.25	.25
1302	A277	10q multi	.25	.25
1303	A277	20q multi	.30	.25
1304	A277	25q multi	.35	.25
1305	A277	65q multi	.75	.25
1306	A277	2.25 l multi	2.60	.35
		Nos. 1301-1306 (6)	4.50	1.60

Fruit Harvest and Dancers A278

Designs: 25q, Contour-plowed fields and conference table. 80q, Cattle and newspapers. 1.30 l, Wheat harvest.

1970, Aug. 28   Litho.   Perf. 12x11½

1307	A278	15q brt violet & blk	.35	.25
1308	A278	25q dp blue & blk	.35	.25
1309	A278	80q dp brown & blk	1.00	.25
1310	A278	1.10 l org brn & blk	1.40	.25
		Nos. 1307-1310 (4)	3.10	1.00

25th anniv. of the agrarian reform law.

Attacking Partisans — A279

Designs: 25q, Partisans with horses and flag. 1.60 l, Partisans.

1970, Sept. 3   Perf. 12

1311	A279	15q org brn & blk	.25	.25
1312	A279	25q brn, yel & blk	.50	.25
1313	A279	1.60 l dp grn & blk	1.50	.35
		Nos. 1311-1313 (3)	2.25	.85

50th anniversary of liberation of Vlona.

Miners, by Nexhmedin Zajmi — A280

Paintings from the National Gallery, Tirana: 5q, Bringing in the Harvest, by Isuf Sulovari, vert. 15q, The Activists, by Dhimitraq Trebicka, vert. 65q, Instruction of Partisans, by Hasan Nallbani. 95q, Architectural Planning, by Vilson Kilica. No. 1319, Woman Machinist, by Zef Shoshi, vert. No. 1320, Partisan Destroying Tank, by Sali Shijaku, vert.

Perf. 12½x12, 12x12½

1970, Sept. 25   Litho.

1314	A280	5q multicolored	.25	.25
1315	A280	15q multicolored	.25	.25
1316	A280	25q multicolored	.25	.25
1317	A280	65q multicolored	.25	.25
1318	A280	95q multicolored	.95	.25
1319	A280	2 l multicolored	1.75	.35
		Nos. 1314-1319 (6)	3.70	1.60

Miniature Sheet
Imperf

1320	A280	2 l multicolored	2.50	1.50

Electrification Map of Albania — A281

Designs: 25q, Light bulb, hammer and sickle emblem, map of Albania and power graph. 80q, Linemen at work. 1.10 l, Use of electricity on the farm, in home and business.

1970, Oct. 25   Litho.   Perf. 12

1321	A281	15q multi	.25	.25
1322	A281	25q multi	.35	.25
1323	A281	80q multi	1.00	.25
1324	A281	1.10 l multi	1.20	.25
		Nos. 1321-1324 (4)	2.80	1.00

Albanian village electrification completion.

Friedrich Engels A282

Designs: 1.10 l, Engels as young man. 1.15 l, Engels addressing crowd.

1970, Nov. 28   Litho.   Perf. 12x12½

1325	A282	25q bister & dk bl	.35	.25
1326	A282	1.10 l bis & dp claret	.95	.25
1327	A282	1.15 l bis & dk ol grn	1.20	.30
		Nos. 1325-1327 (3)	2.50	.80

150th anniv. of the birth of Friedrich Engels (1820-95), German socialist, collaborator with Karl Marx.

Factories — A282a

Designs: 10q, Tractor factory, Tirana, horiz. 15q, Fertilizer factory, Fier, horiz. 20q, Superphosphate factory, Lac. 25q, Cement factory, Elbasan, horiz. 80q, Coking plant, Qyteti Stalin, horiz.

1970-71   Litho.   Perf. 12

1327A	A282a	10q multi	250.00	160.00
1327B	A282a	15q multi	250.00	160.00
1327C	A282a	20q multi	250.00	160.00
1327D	A282a	25q multi	250.00	160.00
1327E	A282a	80q multi	250.00	160.00
		Nos. 1327A-1327E (5)	1,250.	800.00

Issue dates: 15q, 12/4/70. 10q, 20q, 25q, 80q, 1/20/71.

Ludwig van Beethoven A283

Designs: 5q, Birthplace, Bonn. 25q, 65q, 1.10 l, various portraits. 1.80 l, Scene from Fidelio, horiz.

1970, Dec. 16   Litho.   Perf. 12

1328	A283	5q dp plum & gold	.25	.25
1329	A283	15q brt rose lil & sil	.25	.25
1330	A283	25q green & gold	.35	.25
1331	A283	65q magenta & sil	.85	.25
1332	A283	1.10 l dk blue & gold	1.75	.30
1333	A283	1.80 l black & sil	2.75	.50
		Nos. 1328-1333 (6)	6.20	1.80

Ludwig van Beethoven (1770-1827), composer.

Coat of Arms A284

Designs: 25q, Proclamation. 80q, Enver Hoxha reading proclamation. 1.30 l, Young people and proclamation.

1971, Jan. 11   Litho.   Perf. 12

1334	A284	15q lt bl, gold, blk & red	.25	.25
1335	A284	25q rose lil, blk, gold & gray	.25	.25

1336	A284	80q emerald, blk &		
		gold	.85	.25
1337	A284	1.30 l yel org, blk &		
		gold	1.20	.30
		Nos. 1334-1337 (4)	2.55	1.05

Declaration of the Republic, 25th anniv.

"Liberty" — A285

Designs: 50q, Women's brigade. 65q, Street battle, horiz. 1.10 l, Execution, horiz.

1971, Mar. 18   *Perf. 12x11½, 11½x12*   **Litho.**

1338	A285	25q dk bl & bl	.35	.25
1339	A285	50q slate green	.50	.25
1340	A285	65q dk brn & chest	.75	.25
1341	A285	1.10 l purple	1.25	.25
		Nos. 1338-1341 (4)	2.85	1.00

Centenary of the Paris Commune.

Black Men — A286

1.10 l, Men of 3 races. 1.15 l, Black protest.

1971, Mar. 21   *Perf. 12x12½*

1342	A286	25q blk & bis brn	.25	.25
1343	A286	1.10 l blk & rose car	.75	.25
1344	A286	1.15 l blk & ver	.90	.25
		Nos. 1342-1344 (3)	1.90	.75

Intl. year against racial discrimination.

Tulip — A287

Designs: Various tulips.

1971, Mar. 25

1345	A287	5q multi	.25	.25
1346	A287	10q yellow & multi	.25	.25
1347	A287	15q pink & multi	.30	.25
1348	A287	20q lt blue & multi	.35	.25
1349	A287	25q multi	.35	.25
1350	A287	80q multi	1.00	.25
1351	A287	1 l multi	1.75	.25
1352	A287	1.45 l citron & multi	2.10	.30
		Nos. 1345-1352 (8)	6.35	2.05

Horseman, by Dürer — A288

Art Works by Dürer: 15q, Three peasants. 25q, Dancing peasant couple. 45q, The bagpiper. 65q, View of Kalkrebut, horiz. 2.40 l, View of Trent, horiz. 2.50 l, Self-portrait.

1971, May 15   *Perf. 11½x12, 12x11½*   **Litho.**

1353	A288	10q blk & pale grn	.30	.25
1354	A288	15q black & pale lil	.30	.25
1355	A288	25q blk & pale bl	.35	.25
1356	A288	45q blk & pale		
		rose	.90	.25
1357	A288	65q black & multi	1.75	.25
1358	A288	2.40 l black & multi	5.50	.40
		Nos. 1353-1358 (6)	9.10	1.65

Miniature Sheet

Imperf

| 1359 | A288 | 2.50 l multi | 3.50 | 2.50 |

Albrecht Dürer (1471-1528), German painter and engraver.

Satellite Orbiting Globe — A289

Designs: 1.20 l, Government Building, Tirana, and Red Star emblem. 2.20 l, like 60q, 2.50 l, Flag of People's Republic of China forming trajectory around globe.

1971, June 10   **Litho.**   *Perf. 12x12½*

1360	A289	60q purple & multi	.80	.25
1361	A289	1.20 l ver & multi	1.60	.30
1362	A289	2.20 l green & multi	3.25	.50

Imperf

| 1363 | A289 | 2.50 l vio blk & multi | 5.00 | 2.75 |
| | | Nos. 1360-1363 (4) | 10.65 | 3.80 |

Space developments of People's Republic of China.

Mao Tse-tung A290

Designs: 1.05 l, House where Communist Party was founded, horiz. 1.20 l, Peking crowd with placards, horiz.

1971, July 1   *Perf. 12x12½, 12½x12*

1364	A290	25q silver & multi	.85	.25
1365	A290	1.05 l silver & multi	2.25	2.00
1366	A290	1.20 l silver & multi	3.25	2.25
		Nos. 1364-1366 (3)	6.35	4.50

50th anniv. of Chinese Communist Party.

Crested Titmouse — A291

1971, Aug. 15   **Litho.**   *Perf. 12½x12*

1367	A291	5q shown	.25	.25
1368	A291	10q European		
		serin	.30	.25
1369	A291	15q Linnet	.45	.25
1370	A291	25q Firecrest	.70	.25
1371	A291	45q Rock thrush	1.00	.25
1372	A291	60q Blue tit	1.75	.50
1373	A291	2.40 l Chaffinch	6.25	.75
	a.	Block of 7, #1367-1373 + label	17.50	15.00
		Nos. 1367-1373 (7)	10.70	4.50

Continuous design with bird's nest label at upper left.

Nos. 1367-1372 exist in blocks of 8, with two labels. Value: unused $55; used $25.

Olympic Rings and Running — A292

Designs (Olympic Rings and): 10q, Hurdles. 15q, Canoeing. 25q, Gymnastics. 80q, Fencing. 1.05 l, Soccer. 2 l, Runner at finish line. 3.60 l, Diving, women's.

1971, Sept. 15

1374	A292	5q green & multi	.25	.25
1375	A292	10q multicolored	.25	.25
1376	A292	15q blue & multi	.25	.25
1377	A292	25q violet & multi	.25	.25
1378	A292	80q lilac & multi	.75	.25
1379	A292	1.05 l multicolored	.95	.25
1380	A292	3.60 l multicolored	3.00	.50
		Nos. 1374-1380 (7)	5.70	2.00

Souvenir Sheet

Imperf

| 1381 | A292 | 2 l brt blue & multi | 2.50 | 1.50 |

20th Olympic Games, Munich, Aug. 26-Sept. 10, 1972.

Workers with Flags A293

Designs: 1.05 l, Party Headquarters, Tirana, and Red Star. 1.20 l, Rifle, star, flag and "VI."

1971, Nov. 1   **Perf. 12**

1382	A293	25q multi	.35	.25
1383	A293	1.05 l multi	1.00	.30
1384	A293	1.20 l multi, vert.	1.40	.30
		Nos. 1382-1384 (3)	2.75	.80

6th Congress of Workers' Party.

Factories and Workers A294

Designs: 80q, "XXX" and flag, vert. 1.55 l, Enver Hoxha and flags.

1971, Nov. 8

1385	A294	15q gold, sil, lil &		
		yel	.25	.25
1386	A294	80q gold, sil & red	.90	.25
1387	A294	1.55 l gold, sil, red &		
		brn	1.90	.30
		Nos. 1385-1387 (3)	3.05	.80

30th anniversary of Workers' Party.

Construction Work, by M. Fushekati — A295

Contemporary Albanian Paintings: 5q, Young Man, by R. Kuci, vert. 25q, Partisan, by D. Jukniu, vert. 80q, Fliers, by S. Kristo. 1.20 l, Girl in Forest, by A. Sadikaj. 1.55 l, Warriors with Spears and Shields, by S. Kamberi. 2 l, Freedom Fighter, by I. Lulani.

1971, Nov. 20   *Perf. 12x12½, 12½x12*

1388	A295	5q gold & multi	.25	.25
1389	A295	15q gold & multi	.25	.25
1390	A295	25q gold & multi	.25	.25
1391	A295	80q gold & multi	.75	.25
1392	A295	1.20 l gold & multi	.85	.25
1393	A295	1.55 l gold & multi	1.00	.30
		Nos. 1388-1393 (6)	3.35	1.55

Miniature Sheet

Imperf

| 1394 | A295 | 2 l gold & multi | 2.50 | 1.75 |

Young Workers' Emblem — A296

1971, Nov. 23   *Perf. 12x12½*

1395	A296	15q lt blue & multi	.25	.25
1396	A296	1.35 l grnsh gray &		
		multi	1.25	.30

Albanian Young Workers' Union, 30th anniv.

"Halili and Hajria" Ballet — A297

Scenes from "Halili and Hajria" Ballet: 10q, Brother and sister. 15q, Hajria before Sultan Suleiman. 50q, Hajria and husband. 80q, Execution of Halili. 1.40 l, Hajria killing her husband.

1971, Dec. 27   *Perf. 12½x12*

1397	A297	5q silver & multi	.25	.25
1398	A297	10q silver & multi	.25	.25
1399	A297	15q silver & multi	.25	.25
1400	A297	50q silver & multi	.60	.25
1401	A297	80q silver & multi	1.00	.50
1402	A297	1.40 l silver & multi	2.00	.90
		Nos. 1397-1402 (6)	4.35	2.40

Albanian ballet Halili and Hajria after drama by Kol Jakova.

Biathlon and Olympic Rings — A298

Designs (Olympic Rings and): 10q, Sledding. 15q, Ice hockey. 20q, Bobsledding. 50q, Speed skating. 1 l, Slalom. 2 l, Ski jump. 2.50 l, Figure skating, pairs.

1972, Feb. 10

1403	A298	5q lt olive & multi	.25	.25
1404	A298	10q lt violet & multi	.25	.25
1405	A298	15q multicolored	.25	.25
1406	A298	20q pink & multi	.25	.25
1407	A298	50q lt blue & multi	.50	.25
1408	A298	1 l ocher & multi	.80	.25
1409	A298	2 l lilac & multi	1.75	.40
		Nos. 1403-1409 (7)	4.05	1.90

Souvenir Sheet

Imperf

| 1410 | A298 | 2.50 l blue & multi | 2.75 | 1.75 |

11th Winter Olympic Games, Sapporo, Japan, Feb. 3-13.

Wild Strawberries A299

Wild Fruits and Nuts: 10q, Blackberries. 15q, Hazelnuts. 20q, Walnuts. 25q, Strawberry-tree fruit. 30q, Dogwood berries. 2.40 l, Rowan berries.

1972, Mar. 20   Litho.   Perf. 12

1411	A299	5q lt grn & multi	.25	.25
1412	A299	10q yellow & multi	.25	.25
1413	A299	15q lt vio & multi	.25	.25
1414	A299	20q pink & multi	.25	.25
1415	A299	25q multi	.25	.25
1416	A299	30q multi	.35	.25
1417	A299	2.40 l multi	3.00	.50
	Nos. 1411-1417 (7)		4.60	2.00

"Your Heart is Your Health" A300

World Health Day: 1.20 l, Cardiac patient and electrocardiogram.

1972, Apr. 7   Perf. 12x12½

1418	A300	1.10 l multicolored	1.25	.40
1419	A300	1.20 l rose & multi	1.40	.85

Worker and Student — A301

7th Trade Union Cong., May 8: 2.05 l, Assembly Hall, dancers and emblem.

1972, Apr. 24   Litho.   Perf. 11½x12½

1420	A301	25q multi	.50	.25
1421	A301	2.05 l blue & multi	2.00	.40

Qemal Stafa A302

Designs: 15q, Memorial flame. 25q, Monument "Spirit of Defiance," vert.

1972, May 5   Perf. 12½x12, 12x12½

1422	A302	15q gray & multi	.25	.25
1423	A302	25q sal rose, blk & gray	.30	.25
1424	A302	1.90 l dull yel & blk	1.75	.35
	Nos. 1422-1424 (3)		2.30	.85

30th anniversary of the murder of Qemal Stafa and of Martyrs' Day.

Camellia A303

Designs: Various camellias.

1972, May 10   Perf. 12x12½
Flowers in Natural Colors

1425	A303	5q lt blue & blk	.25	.25
1426	A303	10q citron & blk	.25	.25
1427	A303	15q grnsh gray & blk	.25	.25
1428	A303	25q pale sal & blk	.25	.25
1429	A303	45q gray & blk	.45	.25

1430	A303	50q sal pink & blk	.85	.25
1431	A303	2.50 l bluish gray & blk	3.25	.90
	Nos. 1425-1431 (7)		5.55	2.40

High Jump — A304

Designs (Olympic and Motion Emblems and): 10q, Running. 15q, Shot put. 20q, Bicycling. 25q, Pole vault. 50q, Hurdles, women's. 75q, Hockey. 2 l, Swimming. 2.50 l, Diving, women's.

1972, June 30   Litho.   Perf. 12½x12

1432	A304	5q multicolored	.25	.25
1433	A304	10q lt brn & multi	.25	.25
1434	A304	15q lt lil & multi	.25	.25
1435	A304	20q multicolored	.30	.25
1436	A304	25q lt vio & multi	.30	.25
1437	A304	50q lt grn & multi	.50	.25
1438	A304	75q multicolored	1.00	.25
1439	A304	2 l multicolored	3.00	.35
	Nos. 1432-1439 (8)		5.85	2.10

Miniature Sheet
Imperf

1440	A304	2.50 l multi	3.50	2.50

20th Olympic Games, Munich, Aug. 26-Sept. 11. Nos. 1432-1439 each issued in sheets of 8 stamps and one label (3x3) showing Olympic rings in gold.

Autobus A305

25q, Electric train. 80q, Ocean liner Tirana. 1.05 l, Automobile. 1.20 l, Trailer truck.

1972, July 25   Litho.   Perf. 12

1441	A305	15q org brn & multi	.25	.25
1442	A305	25q gray & multi	.35	.25
1443	A305	80q dp grn & multi	.50	.25
1444	A305	1.05 l multi	.70	.25
1445	A305	1.20 l multi	1.40	.25
	Nos. 1441-1445 (5)		3.20	1.25

Arm Wrestling A306

Folk Games: 10q, Piggyback ball game. 15q, Women's jumping. 25q, Rope game (srum). 90q, Leapfrog. 2 l, Women throwing pitchers.

1972, Aug. 18

1446	A306	5q multi	.25	.25
1447	A306	10q lt bl & multi	.25	.25
1448	A306	15q rose & multi	.25	.25
1449	A306	25q lt bl & multi	.25	.25
1450	A306	90q ocher & multi	.90	.25
1451	A306	2 l lt grn & multi	1.75	.30
	Nos. 1446-1451 (6)		3.65	1.55

1st National Festival of People's Games.

Mastheads — A307

30th Press Day: 25q, Printing press. 1.90 l, Workers reading paper.

1972, Aug. 25

1452	A307	15q lt bl & blk	.25	.25
1453	A307	25q red, grn & blk	.25	.25
1454	A307	1.90 l lt vio & blk	1.40	.40
	Nos. 1452-1454 (3)		1.90	.90

Map of Peza Area, Memorial Tablet A308

25q, Guerrillas with flag. 1.90 l, Peza Conference memorial.

1972, Sept. 16

1455	A308	15q shown	.25	.25
1456	A308	25q multicolored	.35	.25
1457	A308	1.90 l multicolored	1.90	.40
	Nos. 1455-1457 (3)		2.50	.90

30th anniversary, Conference of Peza.

Partisans, by Sotir Capo — A309

Paintings: 10q, Woman, by Ismail Lulani, vert. 15q, "Communists," by Lec Shkreli, vert. 20q, View of Nendorit, 1941, by Sali Shijaku, vert. 50q, Woman with Sheaf, by Zef Shoshi, vert. 1 l, Landscape with Children, by Dhimitraq Trebicka. 2 l, Women on Bicycles, by Vilson Kilica. 2.30 l, Folk Dance, by Abdurrahim Buza.

Perf. 12½x12, 12x12½

1972, Sept. 25   Litho.

1458	A309	5q gold & multi	.25	.25
1459	A309	10q gold & multi	.25	.25
1460	A309	15q gold & multi	.25	.25
1461	A309	20q gold & multi	.25	.25
1462	A309	50q gold & multi	.25	.25
1463	A309	1 l gold & multi	.70	.25
1464	A309	2 l gold & multi	1.75	.40
	Nos. 1458-1464 (7)		3.70	1.90

Miniature Sheet
Imperf

1465	A309	2.30 l gold & multi	2.50	1.75

No. 1465 contains one 41x68mm stamp.

Congress Emblem — A310

Design: 2.05 l, Young worker with banner.

1972, Oct. 23   Litho.   Perf. 12

1466	A310	25q silver, red & gold	.50	.25
1467	A310	2.05 l silver & multi	1.90	.50

Union of Working Youth, 6th Congress.

Hammer and Sickle — A311

Design: 1.20 l, Lenin as orator.

1972, Nov. 7   Litho.   Perf. 11½x12

1468	A311	1.10 l multi	1.00	.25
1469	A311	1.20 l multi	2.00	.30

Russian October Revolution, 55th anniv.

Ismail Qemali — A312

Designs: 15q, Albanian fighters, horiz. 65q, Rally, horiz. 1.25 l, Coat of arms.

Perf. 12x11½, 11½x12

1972, Nov. 29

1470	A312	15q red, brt bl & blk	.25	.25
1471	A312	25q yel, blk & red	.25	.25
1472	A312	65q red, sal & blk	.55	.25
1473	A312	1.25 l dl red & blk	1.75	.25
	Nos. 1470-1473 (4)		2.80	1.00

60th anniv. of independence.

Cock, Mosaic A313

Mosaics, 2nd-5th centuries, excavated near Buthrotium and Apollonia: 10q, Bird, vert. 15q, Partridges, vert. 25q, Warrior's legs. 45q, Nymph riding dolphin, vert. 50q, Fish, vert. 2.50 l, Warrior with helmet.

1972, Dec. 10   Perf. 12½x12, 12x12½

1474	A313	5q silver & multi	.25	.25
1475	A313	10q silver & multi	.25	.25
1476	A313	15q silver & multi	.25	.25
1477	A313	25q silver & multi	.25	.25
1478	A313	45q silver & multi	.40	.25
1479	A313	50q silver & multi	.55	.25
1480	A313	2.50 l silver & multi	2.10	.80
	Nos. 1474-1480 (7)		4.05	2.30

Nicolaus Copernicus A314

Designs: 10q, 25q, 80q, 1.20 l, Various portraits of Copernicus. 1.60 l, Heliocentric solar system.

1973, Feb. 19   Litho.   Perf. 12x12½

1481	A314	5q lil rose & multi	.25	.25
1482	A314	10q dull ol & multi	.25	.25
1483	A314	25q multicolored	.25	.25
1484	A314	80q lt violet & multi	.25	.25
1485	A314	1.20 l blue & multi	1.40	.30
1486	A314	1.60 l gray & multi	2.25	.40
	Nos. 1481-1486 (6)		4.65	1.70

500th anniversary of the birth of Nicolaus Copernicus (1473-1543), Polish astronomer.

Flowering Cactus — A315

Designs: Various flowering cacti.

1973, Mar. 25   Litho.   Perf. 12

1487	A315	10q multicolored	.30	.25
1488	A315	15q multicolored	.30	.25
1489	A315	20q beige & multi	.30	.25
1490	A315	25q gray & multi	.30	.25
1491	A315	30q beige & multi	4.25	1.50
1492	A315	65q gray & multi	1.40	.25
1493	A315	80q multicolored	1.40	.25
1494	A315	2 l multicolored	1.75	.60
a.		Block of 8, #1487-1494	16.00	8.00
		Nos. 1487-1494 (8)	10.00	3.60

A block containing Nos. 1487-1490, 1492-1494 and a label exists.

Guard and Factories — A316

1.80 l, Guard and guards with prisoner.

1973, Mar. 20   Litho.   Perf. 12½x12

1495	A316	25q ultra & blk	.35	.25
1496	A316	1.80 l	dk red & multi	2.00	.40

30th anniv. of the State Security Branch.

Common Tern — A317

Sea Birds: 15q, White-winged black terns, vert. 25q, Black-headed gull, vert. 45q, Great black-headed gull. 80q, Slender-billed gull, vert. 2.40 l, Sandwich terns.

1973, Apr. 30   Perf. 12½x12, 12x12½

1497	A317	5q gold & multi	.25	.25
1498	A317	15q gold & multi	.25	.25
1499	A317	25q gold & multi	.30	.25
1500	A317	45q gold & multi	.70	.25
1501	A317	80q gold & multi	1.40	.25
1502	A317	2.40 l	gold & multi	2.75	.55
		Nos. 1497-1502 (6)	5.65	1.80

Letters, 1913 Cancellation and Post Horn — A318

Design: 1.80 l, Mailman, 1913 cancel.

1973, May, 5   Litho.   Perf. 12x11½

1503	A318	25q red & multi	.70	.25
1504	A318	1.80 l	red & multi	2.75	.55

60th anniversary of Albanian stamps.

Farmer, Worker, Soldier A319

Design: 25q, Woman and factory, vert.

1973, June 4   Perf. 12

1505	A319	25q carmine rose	.35	.25
1506	A319	1.80 l	yel, dp org & blk	2.10	.50

7th Congress of Albanian Women's Union.

Creation of General Staff, by G. Madhi — A320

Designs: 40q, "August 1949," sculpture by Sh. Haderi, vert. 60q, "Generation after Generation," sculpture by H. Dule, vert. 80q, "Defend Revolutionary Victories," by M. Fushekati.

1973, July 10   Litho.   Perf. 12½x12

1507	A320	25q gold & multi	7.00	10.00
1508	A320	40q gold & multi	7.00	10.00
1509	A320	60q gold & multi	7.00	10.00
1510	A320	80q gold & multi	7.00	10.00
		Nos. 1507-1510 (4)	28.00	40.00

30th anniversary of the People's Army.

"Electrification," by S. Hysa — A321

Albanian Paintings: 10q, Woman Textile Worker, by N. Nallbani. 15q, Gymnasts, by M. Fushekati. 50q, Aviator, by F. Stamo. 80q, Fascist Prisoner, by A. Lakuriqi. 1.20 l, Workers with Banner, by P. Mele. 1.30 l, Farm Woman, by Zef Shoshi. 2.05 l, Battle of Tenda, by F. Haxhiu. 10q, 50q, 80q, 1.20 l, 1.30 l, vertical.

Perf. 12½x12, 12x12½

1973, Aug. 10

1511	A321	5q gold & multi	.25	.25
1512	A321	10q gold & multi	.25	.25
1513	A321	15q gold & multi	.25	.25
1514	A321	50q gold & multi	.65	.25
1515	A321	80q gold & multi	.75	.25
1516	A321	1.20 l	gold & multi	1.10	.25
1517	A321	1.30 l	gold & multi	2.25	.25
		Nos. 1511-1517 (7)	5.50	1.75

Souvenir Sheet

Imperf

1518	A321	2.05 l	multi	2.50	1.75

Mary Magdalene, by Caravaggio A322

Paintings by Michelangelo da Caravaggio: 10q, The Lute Player, horiz. 15q, Self-portrait. 50q, Boy Carrying Fruit and Flowers. 80q, Still Life, horiz. 1.20 l, Narcissus. 1.30 l, Boy Peeling Apple. 2.05 l, Man with Feathered Hat.

Perf. 12x12½, 12½x12

1973, Sept. 28

1519	A322	5q gold & multi	.25	.25
1520	A322	10q gold & multi	.25	.25
1521	A322	15q gold, blk & gray	.25	.25
1522	A322	50q gold & multi	.25	.25
1523	A322	80q gold & multi	.55	.25
1524	A322	1.20 l	gold & multi	.70	.30
1525	A322	1.30 l	gold & multi	1.40	.30
		Nos. 1519-1525 (7)	3.65	1.85

Souvenir Sheet

Imperf

1526	A322	2.05 l	multi	3.75	3.50

Michelangelo da Caravaggio (Merisi; 1573?-1609), Italian painter. No. 1526 contains one stamp, size: 63x73mm.

Soccer — A323

Designs: 5q-1.25 l, Various soccer scenes. 2.05 l, Ball in goal and list of cities where championships were held.

1973, Oct. 30   Litho.   Perf. 12½x12

1527	A323	5q multi	.25	.25
1528	A323	10q multi	.25	.25
1529	A323	15q multi	.25	.25
1530	A323	20q multi	.25	.25
1531	A323	25q multi	.25	.25
1532	A323	90q multi	.40	.25
1533	A323	1.20 l	multi	.80	.25
1534	A323	1.25 l	multi	1.25	.25
		Nos. 1527-1534 (8)	3.70	2.00

Minature Sheet

Imperf

1535	A323	2.05 l	multi	2.75	2.00

World Soccer Cup, Munich 1974.

Weight Lifter — A324

Designs: Various stages of weight lifting. 1.20 l, 1.60 l, horiz.

1973, Oct. 30   Litho.   Perf. 12

1536	A324	5q multi	.25	.25
1537	A324	10q multi	.25	.25
1538	A324	25q multi	.25	.25
1539	A324	90q multi	.25	.25
1540	A324	1.20 l	multi	.65	.25
1541	A324	1.60 l	multi	1.60	.25
		Nos. 1536-1541 (6)	3.25	1.50

Weight Lifting Championships, Havana, Cuba.

Cement Factory, Kavaje — A325

Harvester Combine A326

Skiers and Hotel — A326a

Mountain Lake — A326b

Designs: 10q, Ali Kelmendi truck factory and tank cars, horiz. 15q, Ballet. 25q, "Communication." 60q, Resort, horiz. 1 l, Mao Tse-tung textile mill. 1.20 l, Steel workers. 2.40 l, Welder

and pipe. 3 l, Skanderbeg Monument, Tirana. 5 l, Roman arches, Durres.

Perf. 12½x12, 12x12½

1973-74   Litho.

1543	A325	5q gold & multi	.25	.25
1544	A325	10q gold & multi	.25	.25
1545	A325	15q gold & multi	.40	.25
1545A	A326	20q gold & multi	.25	.25
1546	A325	25q gold & multi	.25	.25
1547	A326a	35q gold & multi	.30	.25
1548	A325	60q gold & multi	.80	.25
1549	A326b	80q gold & multi	1.40	.25
1549A	A325	1 l	gold & multi	.25	.25
1549B	A325	1.20 l	gold & multi	.95	.25
1549C	A326b	2.40 l	gold & multi	1.90	.35
1550	A326b	3 l	gold & multi	3.50	.35
1551	A325	5 l	gold & multi	3.50	.60
		Nos. 1543-1551 (13)	14.00	3.80

Issue dates: Nos. 1545-1546, 1549-1550, Dec. 5, 1973; others, 1974.

Mao Tse-tung — A327

80th birthday of Mao Tse-tung: 1.20 l, Mao Tse-tung addressing crowd.

1973, Dec. 26   Perf. 12

1552	A327	85q multicolored	11.00	1.25
1553	A327	1.20 l	multicolored	17.00	2.25

Old Man and Dog, by Gericault A328

Paintings by Jean Louis André Theodore Gericault: 10q, Horse's Head. 15q, Male Model. 25q, Head of Black Man. 1.20 l, Self-portrait. 2.05 l, Raft of the Medusa, horiz. 2.20 l, Battle of the Giants.

Perf. 12x12½, 12½x12

1974, Jan. 18   Litho.

1554	A328	10q gold & multi	.25	.25
1555	A328	15q gold & multi	.25	.25
1556	A328	20q gold & multi	.25	.25
1557	A328	25q gold & blk	.25	.25
1558	A328	1.20 l	gold & multi	1.40	.25
1559	A328	2.20 l	gold & multi	2.60	.40
		Nos. 1554-1559 (6)	5.00	1.65

Souvenir Sheet

Imperf

1560	A328	2.05 l	gold & multi	2.75	1.90

No. 1560 contains one 87x78mm stamp.

Lenin, by Pandi Mele — A329

Designs: 25q, Lenin with Sailors on Cruiser Aurora, by Dhimitraq Trebicka, horiz. 1.20 l, Lenin, by Vilson Kilica.

1974, Jan. 21 Perf. 12½x12, 12x12½
1561	A329	25q gold & multi	.90	.25
1562	A329	60q gold & multi	2.10	.25
1563	A329	1.20 l gold & multi	6.00	.55
		Nos. 1561-1563 (3)	9.00	1.05

50th anniv. of the death of Lenin.

Swimming Duck, Mosaic — A330

Designs: Mosaics from the 5th-6th Centuries A.D., excavated near Buthrotium, Pogradec and Apollonia.

1974, Feb. 20 Litho. Perf. 12½x12
1564	A330	5q shown	.25	.25
1565	A330	10q Bird, flower	.25	.25
1566	A330	15q Vase, grapes	.25	.25
1567	A330	25q Duck	.25	.25
1568	A330	40q Donkey, bird	.25	.25
1569	A330	2.50 l Sea horse	1.25	.40
		Nos. 1564-1569 (6)	2.50	1.65

Soccer — A331

Various scenes from soccer. 2.05 l, World Soccer Cup & names of participating countries.

1974, Apr. 25 Litho. Perf. 12½x12
1570	A331	10q gold & multi	.25	.25
1571	A331	15q gold & multi	.25	.25
1572	A331	20q gold & multi	.25	.25
1573	A331	25q gold & multi	.25	.25
1574	A331	40q gold & multi	.25	.25
1575	A331	80q gold & multi	.55	.25
1576	A331	1 l gold & multi	.70	.30
1577	A331	1.20 l gold & multi	1.20	.40
		Nos. 1570-1577 (8)	3.70	2.20

Souvenir Sheet

Imperf
1578	A331	2.05 l gold & multi	2.50	1.75

World Cup Soccer Championship, Munich, June 13-July 7. No. 1578 contains one stamp (60x60mm) with simulated perforations. Nos. 1570-1577 exist imperf, No. 1578 with simulated perfs omitted. Values $10 and $20, respectively.

Arms of Albania, Soldier — A332

Design: 1.80 l, Soldier and front page of 1944 Congress Book.

1974, May 24 Litho. Perf. 12
1579	A332	25q multicolored	.35	.25
1580	A332	1.80 l multicolored	1.40	.30

30th anniversary of the First Anti-Fascist Liberation Congress of Permet.

Medicinal Plants A333

10q, Bittersweet. 15q, Arbutus. 20q, Lilies of the valley. 25q, Autumn crocus. 40q, Borage, horiz. 80q, Soapwort, horiz. 2.20 l, Gentian, horiz.

1974, May 5 Perf. 12x12½
1581	A333	10q multicolored	.25	.25
1582	A333	15q multicolored	.25	.25
1583	A333	20q multicolored	.25	.25
1584	A333	25q multicolored	.25	.25
1585	A333	40q multicolored	.45	.25
1586	A333	80q multicolored	.85	.25
1587	A333	2.20 l multicolored	2.50	.45
		Nos. 1581-1587 (7)	4.80	1.95

Revolutionaries with Albanian Flag — A334

1.80 l, Portraits of 5 revolutionaries, vert.

Perf. 12½x12, 12x12½
1974, June 10
1588	A334	25q red, blk & lil	.35	.25
1589	A334	1.80 l yel, red & blk	1.40	.45

50th anniversary Albanian Bourgeois Democratic Revolution.

European Redwing — A335

Designs: Songbirds; Nos. 1597-1600 vert.

Perf. 12½x12, 12x12½
1974, July 15 Litho.
1594	A335	10q shown	.25	.25
1595	A335	15q European robin	.25	.25
1596	A335	20q Greenfinch	.25	.25
1597	A335	25q Bullfinch	.25	.25
1598	A335	40q Hawfinch	.35	.25
1599	A335	80q Blackcap	1.40	.25
1600	A335	2.20 l Nightingale	2.75	.50
		Nos. 1594-1600 (7)	5.50	2.00

Globe — A336

Cent. of UPU: 1.20 l, UPU emblem. 2.05 l, Jet over globe.

1974, Aug. 25 Litho. Perf. 12x12½
1601	A336	85q grn & multi	1.20	.25
1602	A336	1.20 l vio & ol grn	1.75	.25

Miniature Sheet

Imperf
1603	A336	2.05 l blue & multi	15.00	25.00

Widows, by Sali Shijaku — A337

Albanian Paintings: 15q, Drillers, by Danish Jukniu, vert. 20q, Workers with Blueprints, by Clirim Ceka. 25q, Call to Action, by Spiro Kristo, vert. 40q, Winter Battle, by Sabaudin Xhaferi. 80q, Comrades, by Clirim Ceka, vert. 1 l, Aiding the Partisans, by Guri Madhi. 1.20 l, Teacher with Pupils, by Kleo Nini Brezat. 2.05 l, Comrades in Arms, by Guri Madhi.

Perf. 12½x12, 12x12½
1974, Sept. 25
1604	A337	10q silver & multi	.25	.25
1605	A337	15q silver & multi	.25	.25
1606	A337	20q silver & multi	.25	.25
1607	A337	25q silver & multi	.25	.25
1608	A337	40q silver & multi	.30	.25
1609	A337	80q silver & multi	.70	.25
1610	A337	1 l silver & multi	1.00	.25
1611	A337	1.20 l silver & multi	1.40	.25
		Nos. 1604-1611 (8)	4.40	2.00

Miniature Sheet

Imperf
1612	A337	2.05 l silver & multi	2.50	1.75

Crowd on Tien An Men Square A338

Design: 1.20 l, Mao Tse-tung, vert.

1974, Oct. 1 Perf. 12
1613	A338	85q gold & multi	6.00	1.50
1614	A338	1.20 l gold & multi	9.50	2.50

25th anniversary of the proclamation of the People's Republic of China.

Women's Volleyball A339

Spartakiad Medal and: 15q, Women hurdlers. 20q, Women gymnasts. 25q, Mass exercises in Stadium. 40q, Weight lifter. 80q, Wrestlers. 1 l, Military rifle drill. 1.20 l, Soccer.

1974, Oct. 9 Perf. 12x12½
1615	A339	10q multi	.25	.25
1616	A339	15q multi	.25	.25
1617	A339	20q multi	.25	.25
1618	A339	25q gray & multi	.25	.25
1619	A339	40q multi	.25	.25
1620	A339	80q multi	.35	.25
1621	A339	1 l multi	.70	.25
1622	A339	1.20 l tan & multi	1.00	.25
		Nos. 1615-1622 (8)	3.30	2.00

National Spartakiad, Oct. 9-17.

View of Berat — A340

Designs: 80q, Enver Hoxha addressing Congress, bas-relief, horiz. 1 l, Hoxha and leaders leaving Congress Hall.

Perf. 12x12½, 12½x12
1974, Oct. 20 Litho.
1623	A340	25q rose car & blk	.35	.25
1624	A340	80q yel, brn & blk	1.00	.25
1625	A340	1 l dp lilac & blk	2.00	.30
		Nos. 1623-1625 (3)	3.35	.80

30th anniversary of 2nd Congress of Berat.

Anniversary Emblem, Factory Guards — A341

35q, Chemical industry. 50q, Agriculture. 80q, Arts. 1 l, Atomic diagram & computer. 1.20 l, Youth education. 2.05 l, Crowd & History Book.

1974, Nov. 29 Litho. Perf. 12½x12
1626	A341	25q green & multi	.25	.25
1627	A341	35q ultra & multi	.25	.25
1628	A341	50q brown & multi	.25	.25
1629	A341	80q multicolored	.35	.25
1630	A341	1 l violet & multi	.85	.25
1631	A341	1.20 l multicolored	1.00	.30
		Nos. 1626-1631 (6)	2.95	1.55

Miniature Sheet

Imperf
1632	A341	2.05 l gold & multi	1.75	1.50

30th anniv. of liberation from Fascism.

Artemis, from Apolloni A342

1974, Dec. 25 Photo. Perf. 12x12½
1633	A342	10q shown	.25	.25
1634	A342	15q Zeus statue	.25	.25
1635	A342	20q Poseidon statue	.30	.25
1636	A342	25q Illyrian helmet	.35	.25
1637	A342	40q Amphora	.70	.25
1638	A342	80q Agrippa	1.00	.25
1639	A342	1 l Demosthenes	1.40	.30
1640	A342	1.20 l Head of Bilia	2.00	.35
		Nos. 1633-1640 (8)	6.25	2.15

Miniature Sheet

Imperf
1641	A342	2.05 l Artemis & amphora	2.50	2.10

Archaeological discoveries in Albania.

Workers and Factories A343

25q, Handshake, tools and book, vert.

1975, Feb. 11 Litho. Perf. 12
1642	A343	25q brown & multi	.35	.25
1643	A343	1.80 l yellow & multi	1.40	.35

Albanian Trade Unions, 30th anniversary.

Chicory
A344

1975, Feb. 15
1644	A344	5q shown	.25	.25
1645	A344	10q Houseleek	.25	.25
1646	A344	15q Columbine	.25	.25
1647	A344	20q Anemone	.25	.25
1648	A344	25q Hibiscus	.25	.25
1649	A344	30q Gentian	.35	.25
1650	A344	35q Hollyhock	.35	.25
1651	A344	2.70 l Iris	1.10	.45
		Nos. 1644-1651 (8)	3.05	2.20

Protected flowers.

Jesus, from
Doni Madonna
A345

Works by Michelangelo: 10q, Slave, sculpture. 15q, Head of Dawn, sculpture. 20q, Awakening Giant, sculpture. 25q, Cumaenian Sybil, Sistine Chapel. 30q, Lorenzo di Medici, sculpture. 1.20 l, David, sculpture. 2.05 l, Self-portrait. 3.90 l, Delphic Sybil, Sistine Chapel.

1975, Mar. 20   Litho.   Perf. 12x12½
1652	A345	5q gold & multi	.25	.25
1653	A345	10q gold & multi	.25	.25
1654	A345	15q gold & multi	.25	.25
1655	A345	20q gold & multi	.25	.25
1656	A345	25q gold & multi	.25	.25
1657	A345	30q gold & multi	.25	.25
1658	A345	1.20 l gold & multi	.55	.25
1659	A345	3.90 l gold & multi	1.60	.50
		Nos. 1652-1659 (8)	3.65	2.25

Miniature Shoot
Imperf
1660	A345	2.05 l gold & multi	3.25	2.00

Michelangelo Buonarroti (1475-1564), Italian sculptor, painter and architect.

Two-wheeled Cart — A346

Albanian Transportation of the Past: 5q, Horseback rider. 15q, Lake ferry. 20q, Coastal three-master. 25q, Phaeton. 3.35 l, Early automobile on bridge.

1975, Apr. 15   Litho.   Perf. 12½x12
1661	A346	5q bl grn & multi	.25	.25
1662	A346	10q ol & multi	.25	.25
1663	A346	15q lil & multi	.25	.25
1664	A346	20q multi	.25	.25
1665	A346	25q multi	.25	.25
1666	A346	3.35 l ocher & multi	1.90	.50
		Nos. 1661-1666 (6)	3.15	1.75

Guard at Frontier
Stone — A347

Guardsman and
Militia — A348

1975, Apr. 25   Perf. 12
1667	A347	25q multi	.35	.25
1668	A348	1.80 l multi	1.40	.35

30th anniversary of Frontier Guards.

Posting Illegal Poster — A349

Designs: 60q, Partisans in battle. 1.20 l, Partisan killing German soldier, and Albanian coat of arms.

1975, May 9   Perf. 12½x12
1669	A349	25q multi	.25	.25
1670	A349	60q multi	.50	.25
1671	A349	1.20 l red & multi	1.00	.30
		Nos. 1669-1671 (3)	1.75	.80

30th anniversary of victory over Fascism.

European Widgeons — A350

Waterfowl: 5q, Anas penelope. 10q, Netta rufina. 15q, Anser albifrons. 20q, Anas acuta. 25q, Mergus serrator. 30q, Pata somateria. 35q, Cignus cignus. 2.70 l, Spatula clypeata.

1975, June 15   Litho.   Perf. 12
1672	A350	5q brt blue & multi	.25	.25
1673	A350	10q yel grn & multi	.25	.25
1674	A350	15q brt rose lil & multi	.25	.25
1675	A350	20q bl grn & multi	.25	.25
1676	A350	25q multicolored	.25	.25
1677	A350	30q multicolored	.30	.25
1678	A350	35q orange & multi	.45	.25
1679	A350	2.70 l multi	2.75	.90
		Nos. 1672-1679 (8)	4.75	2.65

Shyqyri
Kanapari, by
Musa
Qarri — A351

Albanian Paintings: 10q, Woman Saving Children in Sea, by Agim Faja. 15q, "November 28, 1912" (revolution), by Petrit Ceno, horiz. 20q, "Workers Unite," by Sali Shijaku. 25q, The Partisan Shota Galica, by Ismail Lulani. 30q, Victorious Resistance Fighters, 1943, by Nestor Jonuzi. 80q, Partisan Couple in Front of Red Flag, by Vilson Halimi. 2.05 l, Dancing Procession, by Abdurahim Buza.

2.25 l, Republic Day Celebration, by Fatmir Haxhiu, horiz.

**   Perf. 12x12½, 12½x12**

1975, July 15   Litho.
1680	A351	5q gold & multi	.25	.25
1681	A351	10q gold & multi	.25	.25
1682	A351	15q gold & multi	.25	.25
1683	A351	20q gold & multi	.25	.25
1684	A351	25q gold & multi	.25	.25
1685	A351	30q gold & multi	.25	.25
1686	A351	80q gold & multi	.30	.25
1687	A351	2.25 l gold & multi	1.40	.45
		Nos. 1680-1687 (8)	3.20	2.20

Miniature Sheet
Imperf
1688	A351	2.05 l gold & multi	2.25	2.25

Nos. 1680-1687 issued in sheets of 8 stamps and gold center label showing palette and easel.

Farmer
Holding
Reform
Law — A352

Design: 2 l, Produce and farm machinery.

1975, Aug. 28   Perf. 12
1689	A352	15q multicolored	.35	.25
1690	A352	2 l multicolored	1.75	.50

Agrarian reform, 30th anniversary.

Alcynonium
Palmatum
A353

Corals: 10q, Paramuricea chamaeleon. 20q, Coralium rubrum. 25q, Eunicella covalini. 3.70 l, Cladocora cespitosa.

1975, Sept. 25   Litho.   Perf. 12
1691	A353	5q blue, ol & blk	.30	.25
1692	A353	10q blue & multi	.30	.25
1693	A353	20q blue & multi	.30	.25
1694	A353	25q blue & blk	.30	.25
1695	A353	3.70 l blue & blk	3.00	.80
		Nos. 1691-1695 (5)	4.20	1.80

Bicycling
A354

Designs (Montreal Olympic Games Emblem and): 10q, Canoeing. 15q, Fieldball. 20q, Basketball. 25q, Water polo. 30q, Hockey. 1.20 l, Pole vault. 2.05 l, Fencing. 2.15 l, Montreal Olympic Games emblem and various sports.

1975, Oct. 20   Litho.   Perf. 12½
1696	A354	5q multi	.25	.25
1697	A354	10q multi	.25	.25
1698	A354	15q multi	.25	.25
1699	A354	20q multi	.40	.25
1700	A354	25q multi	.45	.25
1701	A354	30q multi	.55	.25
1702	A354	1.20 l multi	1.50	.30
1703	A354	2.05 l multi	2.75	.45
		Nos. 1696-1703 (8)	6.40	2.25

Miniature Sheet
Imperf
1704	A354	2.15 l org & multi	6.50	5.25

21st Olympic Games, Montreal, July 18-Aug. 8, 1976. Nos. 1696-1703 exist imperf. Value $10.

Power Lines
Leading to
Village
A355

Designs: 25q, Transformers and insulators. 80q, Dam and power station. 85q, Television set, power lines, grain and cogwheel.

1975, Oct. 25   Perf. 12x12½
1705	A355	15q ultra & yel	.25	.25
1706	A355	25q brt vio & pink	.25	.25
1707	A355	80q lt grn & gray	.60	.25
1708	A355	85q ocher & brn	1.40	.45
		Nos. 1705-1708 (4)	2.50	1.20

General electrification, 5th anniversary.

Child, Rabbit and Teddy Bear Planting
Tree — A356

Fairy Tales: 10q, Mother fox. 15q, Ducks in school. 20q, Little pigs building house. 25q, Animals watching television. 30q, Rabbit and bear at work. 35q, Working and playing ants. 2.70 l, Wolf in sheep's clothes.

1975, Dec. 25   Litho.   Perf. 12½x12
1709	A356	5q black & multi	.25	.25
1710	A356	10q black & multi	.25	.25
1711	A356	15q black & multi	.25	.25
1712	A356	20q black & multi	.30	.25
1713	A356	25q black & multi	.40	.25
1714	A356	30q black & multi	.50	.25
1715	A356	35q black & multi	.55	.25
1716	A356	2.70 l black & multi	3.00	.75
		Nos. 1709-1716 (8)	5.50	2.50

Arms,
People,
Factories
A357

Design: 1.90 l, Arms, government building, celebrating crowd.

1976, Jan. 11   Litho.   Perf. 12
1717	A357	25q gold & multi	.35	.25
1718	A357	1.90 l gold & multi	2.25	.35

30th anniversary of proclamation of Albanian People's Republic.

Ice Hockey,
Olympic
Games'
Emblem
A358

Designs: 10q, Speed skating. 15q, Biathlon. 50q, Ski jump. 1.20 l, Slalom. 2.15 l, Figure skating, pairs. 2.30 l, One-man bobsled.

1976, Feb. 4
1719	A358	5q silver & multi	.25	.25
1720	A358	10q silver & multi	.25	.25
1721	A358	15q silver & multi	.25	.25
1722	A358	50q silver & multi	.35	.25
1723	A358	1.20 l silver & multi	1.10	.25
1724	A358	2.30 l silver & multi	2.00	.40
	Nos. 1719-1724 (6)		4.20	1.65

Miniature Sheet
Perf. 12 on 2 sides x Imperf.
1725	A358	2.15 l silver & multi	3.25	2.00

12th Winter Olympic Games, Innsbruck, Austria, Feb. 4-15.

Meadow Saffron A359

Medicinal Plants: 10q, Deadly night-shade. 15q, Yellow gentian. 20q, Horse chestnut. 70q, Shield fern. 80q, Marshmallow. 2.30 l, Thorn apple.

1976, Apr. 10   Litho.   Perf. 12x12½
1726	A359	5q black & multi	.25	.25
1727	A359	10q black & multi	.25	.25
1728	A359	15q black & multi	.25	.25
1729	A359	20q black & multi	.25	.25
1730	A359	70q black & multi	.35	.25
1731	A359	80q black & multi	.60	.25
1732	A359	2.30 l black & multi	1.75	.35
	Nos. 1726-1732 (7)		3.70	1.85

Bowl and Spoon — A360

15q, Flask, vert. 20q, Carved handles, vert. 25q, Pistol and dagger. 80q, Wall hanging, vert. 1.20 l, Earrings and belt buckle. 1.40 l, Jugs, vert.

1976   Litho.   Perf. 12½x12, 12x12½
1733	A360	10q lilac & multi	.25	.25
1734	A360	15q gray & multi	.25	.25
1735	A360	20q multi	.25	.25
1736	A360	25q car & multi	.25	.25
1737	A360	80q yellow & multi	.25	.25
1738	A360	1.20 l multi	.75	.30
1739	A360	1.40 l tan & multi	1.50	.40
	Nos. 1733-1739 (7)		3.50	1.95

Natl. Ethnographic Conf., Tirana, June 28. For surcharge see No. 1873.

Founding of Cooperatives, by Zef Shoshi — A361

Paintings: 10q, Going to Work, by Agim Zajmi, vert. 25q, Crowd Listening to Loud-speaker, by Vilson Kilica. 40q, Woman Welder, by Sabaudin Xhaferi, vert. 50q, Factory, by Isuf Sulovari, vert. 1.20 l, 1942 Revolt, by Lec Shkreli, vert. 1.60 l, Coming Home from Work, by Agron Dine. 2.05 l, Honoring a Young Pioneer, by Andon Lakuriqi.

Perf. 12½x12, 12x12½
1976, Aug. 8   Litho.
1740	A361	5q gold & multi	.25	.25
1741	A361	10q gold & multi	.25	.25
1742	A361	25q gold & multi	.25	.25
1743	A361	40q gold & multi	.25	.25
1744	A361	50q gold & multi	.25	.25
1745	A361	1.20 l gold & multi	.75	.55
1746	A361	1.60 l gold & multi	1.00	.85
	Nos. 1740-1746 (7)		3.00	2.65

Miniature Sheet
Perf. 12 on 2 sides x Imperf.
1747	A361	2.05 l gold & multi	2.00	1.50

Red Flag, Agricultural Symbols — A362

Design: 1.20 l, Red flag and raised pickax.

1976, Nov. 1
1748	A362	25q multi	.30	.25
1749	A362	1.20 l multi	1.75	.50

7th Workers Party Congress.

Enver Hoxha, Partisans and Albanian Flag — A363

1.90 l, Demonstrators with Albanian flag.

1976, Oct. 28   Perf. 12x12½
1750	A363	25q multi	.40	.25
1751	A363	1.90 l multi	1.60	.65

Anti-Fascist demonstrations, 35th anniv.

Attacking Partisans, Meeting House A364

Designs (Red Flag and): 25q, Partisans, pickax and gun. 80q, Workers, soldiers, pickax and gun. 1.20 l, Agriculture and industry. 1.70 l, Dancers, symbols of science and art.

1976, Nov. 8   Litho.   Perf. 12x12½
1752	A364	15q gold & multi	.25	.25
1753	A364	25q gold & multi	.25	.25
1754	A364	80q gold & multi	.70	.25
1755	A364	1.20 l gold & multi	1.00	.25
1756	A364	1.70 l gold & multi	1.40	.25
	Nos. 1752-1756 (5)		3.60	1.25

35th anniv. of 1st Workers Party Congress.

Young Workers and Track A365

1.25 l, Young soldiers and Albanian flag.

1976, Nov. 23   Perf. 12
1757	A365	80q yellow & multi	1.25	.35
1758	A365	1.25 l carmine & multi	2.25	.50

Union of Young Communists, 35th anniv.

"Cuca e Maleve" Ballet A366

Scenes from ballet "Mountain Girl."

1976, Dec. 14   Perf. 12
1759	A366	10q gold & multi	.25	.50
1760	A366	15q gold & multi	.25	.50
1761	A366	20q gold & multi	.25	1.00
1762	A366	25q gold & multi	.30	2.00
1763	A366	80q gold & multi	.85	3.00
1764	A366	1.20 l gold & multi	1.00	4.00
1765	A366	1.40 l gold & multi	1.40	4.00
	Nos. 1759-1765 (7)		4.30	15.00

Miniature Sheet
Perf. 12 on 2 sides x Imperf.
1766	A366	2.05 l gold & multi	2.75	2.75

Bashtove Castle A367

Albanian Castles: 15q, Gjirokaster. 20q, Ali Pash Tepelene. 25q, Petrele. 80q, Berat. 1.20 l, Durres. 1.40 l, Kruje.

1976, Dec. 30   Litho.   Perf. 12
1767	A367	10q black & dull bl	.25	.25
1768	A367	15q black & grn	.25	.25
1769	A367	20q black & gray	.25	.25
1770	A367	25q black & brn	.35	.25
1771	A367	80q black & rose	1.00	.35
1772	A367	1.20 l black & vio	1.60	.50
1773	A367	1.40 l black & brn red	1.75	.55
	Nos. 1767-1773 (7)		5.45	2.40

Skanderbeg's Shield and Spear — A368

Skanderbeg's Weapons: 80q, Helmet, sword and scabbard. 1 l, Halberd, quiver with arrows, crossbow and spear.

1977, Jan. 28   Litho.   Perf. 12
1774	A368	15q silver & multi	1.25	.40
1775	A368	80q silver & multi	4.25	2.50
1776	A368	1 l silver & multi	6.50	5.00
	Nos. 1774-1776 (3)		12.00	7.90

Skanderbeg (1403-1468), national hero.

Ilia Qiqi, Messenger in Storm — A369

Modern Heroes: 10q, Ilia Dashi, sailor in battle. 25q, Fran Ndue Ivanaj, fisherman in storm. 80q, Zeliha Allmetaj, woman rescuing child. 1 l, Ylli Zaimi, rescuing goats from flood. 1.90 l, Isuf Plloci, fighting forest fire.

1977, Feb. 28   Litho.   Perf. 12x12½
1777	A369	5q brown & multi	.25	.25
1778	A369	10q ultra & multi	.25	.25
1779	A369	25q blue & multi	.40	.25
1780	A369	80q ocher & multi	.90	.35
1781	A369	1 l brown & multi	1.25	.45
1782	A369	1.90 l brown & multi	2.60	1.40
	Nos. 1777-1782 (6)		5.65	2.95

Polyvinylchloride Plant, Vlore — A370

6th Five-year plan: 25q, Naphtha fractioning plant, Ballsh. 65q, Hydroelectric station and dam, Fjerzes. 1 l, Metallurgical plant and blast furnace, Elbasan.

1977, Mar. 29   Litho.   Perf. 12½x12
1783	A370	15q silver & multi	.35	.25
1784	A370	25q silver & multi	.40	.25
1785	A370	65q silver & multi	1.10	.35
1786	A370	1 l silver & multi	1.60	.65
	Nos. 1783-1786 (4)		3.45	1.50

Qerime Halil Galica — A371

Design: 1.25 l, Qerime Halil Galica "Shota" and father Azem Galica.

1977, Apr. 20   Litho.   Perf. 12
1787	A371	80q dark red	1.10	.30
1788	A371	1.25 l gray blue	1.60	.70

"Shota" Galica, communist fighter.

Victory Monument, Tirana — A372

Red Star and: 80q, Clenched fist, Albanian flag. 1.20 l, Bust of Qemal Stafa, poppies.

1977, May 5   Litho.   Perf. 12
1789	A372	25q multi	.35	.25
1790	A372	80q multi	1.25	.45
1791	A372	1.20 l multi	2.00	.85
	Nos. 1789-1791 (3)		3.60	1.55

35th anniversary of Martyrs' Day.

Physician Visiting Farm, Mobile Clinic — A373

10q, Cowherd, cattle ranch. 20q, Militia woman helping with harvest, rifle, combine. 80q, Modern village, highway, power lines. 2.95 l, Tractor, greenhouses.

1977, June 18
1792	A373	5q multi	.25	.25
1793	A373	10q multi	.25	.25
1794	A373	20q multi	.30	.25
1795	A373	80q multi	1.00	.25
1796	A373	2.95 l multi	3.50	.75
	Nos. 1792-1796 (5)		5.30	1.75

"Socialist transformation of the villages."

Armed Workers, Flag and Factory — A374

1.80 l, Workers with proclamation and flags.

1977, June 20
1797	A374	25q multi	1.00	.25
1798	A374	1.80 l multi	1.50	.80

9th Labor Unions Congress.

Kerchief Dance — A375

Designs: Various folk dances.

1977, Aug. 20   Litho.   Perf. 12
1799	A375	5q multi	.25	.25
1800	A375	10q multi	.25	.25
1801	A375	15q multi	.25	.25
1802	A375	25q multi	.25	.25
1803	A375	80q multi	.25	.25
1804	A375	1.20 l multi	.70	.35
1805	A375	1.55 l multi	1.00	.45
	Nos. 1799-1805 (7)		2.95	2.05

Miniature Sheet
Perf. 12 on 2 sides x Imperf.
1806	A375	2.05 l multi	2.25	2.00

See Nos. 1836-1840, 1884-1888.

Attack A376

Designs: 25q, Enver Hoxha addressing Army. 80q, Volunteers and riflemen. 1 l, Volunteers, hydrofoil patrolboat and MiG planes. 1.90 l, Volunteers and Albanian flag.

1977, July 10   Litho.   Perf. 12
1807	A376	15q gold & multi	.35	.25
1808	A376	25q gold & multi	.35	.25
1809	A376	80q gold & multi	1.00	.35
1810	A376	1 l gold & multi	1.75	.50
1811	A376	1.90 l gold & multi	2.75	.90
	Nos. 1807-1811 (5)		6.20	2.25

"One People-One Army."

Armed Workers, Article 3 of Constitution A377

Design: 1.20 l, Symbols of farming and fertilizer industry, Article 25 of Constitution.

1977, Oct.
1812	A377	25q red, gold & blk	.40	.25
1813	A377	1.20 l red, gold & blk	1.50	.50

New Constitution.

Picnic — A378

Film Frames: 15q, Telephone lineman in winter. 25q, Two men and a woman. 80q, Workers. 1.20 l, Boys playing in street. 1.60 l, Harvest.

1977, Oct. 25   Litho.   Perf. 12½x12
1814	A378	10q blue green	.35	.35
1815	A378	15q multi	.35	.35
1816	A378	25q black	.35	.35
1817	A378	80q multi	1.40	1.40
1818	A378	1.20 l deep claret	2.00	2.00
1819	A378	1 l multi	2.25	2.25
	Nos. 1814-1819 (6)		6.70	6.70

Albanian films.

Farm Workers in Field, by V. Mio A379

Paintings by V. Mio: 10q, Landscape in Snow. 15q, Grazing Sheep under Walnut Tree in Spring. 25q, Street in Korce. 80q, Horseback Riders on Mountain Pass. 1 l, Boats on Shore. 1.75 l, Tractors Plowing Fields. 2.05 l, Self-portrait.

1977, Dec. 25   Litho.   Perf. 12½x12
1820	A379	5q gold & multi	.25	.25
1821	A379	10q gold & multi	.25	.25
1822	A379	15q gold & multi	.25	.25
1823	A379	25q gold & multi	.25	.25
1824	A379	80q gold & multi	.35	.25
1825	A379	1 l gold & multi	.60	.25
1826	A379	1.75 l gold & multi	1.00	.25
	Nos. 1820-1826 (7)		2.95	1.75

Miniature Sheet
Imperf.; Perf. 12 Horiz. between Vignette and Value Panel
1827	A379	2.05 l gold & multi	2.50	2.25

Pan Flute — A380

Folk Musical Instruments: 25q, Single-string goat's-head fiddle. 80q, Woodwind. 1.20 l, Drum. 1.70 l, Bagpipe. Background shows various woven folk patterns.

1978, Jan. 20   Perf. 12x12½
1828	A380	15q multi	.40	.25
1829	A380	25q multi	.75	.25
1830	A380	80q multi	2.00	1.00
1831	A380	1.20 l multi	3.50	2.00
1832	A380	1.70 l multi	9.00	3.50
	Nos. 1828-1832 (5)		15.65	7.00

Albanian Flag, Monument and People — A381

25q, Ismail Qemali, fighters, horiz. 1.65 l, People dancing around Albanian flag, horiz.

Perf. 12½x12, 12x12½
1977, Nov. 28
1833	A381	15q multi	.25	.25
1834	A381	25q multi	.30	.25
1835	A381	1.65 l multi	2.40	2.00
	Nos. 1833-1835 (3)		2.95	2.50

65th anniversary of independence.

Folk Dancing Type of 1977
Designs: Various dances.

1978, Feb. 15   Litho.   Perf. 12
1836	A375	5q multi	.25	.25
1837	A375	25q multi	.25	.25
1838	A375	80q multi	.75	.30
1839	A375	1 l multi	.75	.40
1840	A375	2.30 l multi	1.75	1.40
	Nos. 1836-1840 (5)		3.75	2.60

Nos. 1836-1840 have white background around dancers, Nos. 1799-1805 have pinkish shadows.

Tractor Drivers, by Dhimitraq Trebicka A382

Working Class Paintings: 80q, Steeplejack, by Spiro Kristo. 85q, "A Point in the Discussion," by Skender Milori. 90q, Oil rig crew, by Anesti Cini, vert. 1.60 l, Metal workers, by Ramadan Karanxha. 2.20 l, Political discussion, by Sotiraq Sholla.

1978, Mar. 25   Litho.   Perf. 12
1841	A382	25q multi	.30	.25
1842	A382	80q multi	.50	.25
1843	A382	85q multi	.60	.25
1844	A382	90q multi	.70	.30
1845	A382	1.60 l multi	1.25	.90
	Nos. 1841-1845 (5)		3.35	1.95

Miniature Sheet
Perf. 12 on 2 sides x Imperf.
1846	A382	2.20 l multi	6.00	3.50

Woman with Rifle and Pickax A383

1.95 l, Farm & Militia women, industrial plant.

1978, June 1   Litho.   Perf. 12
1847	A383	25q gold & red	.35	.25
1848	A383	1.95 l gold & red	5.25	1.50

8th Congress of Women's Union.

Children and Flowers — A384

Designs: 10q, Children with rifle, ax, book and flags. 25q, Dancing children in folk costume. 1.80 l, Children in school.

1978, June 1   Litho.
1849	A384	5q multi	.25	.25
1850	A384	10q multi	.25	.25
1851	A384	25q multi	.45	.25
1852	A384	1.80 l multi	3.00	.90
	Nos. 1849-1852 (4)		3.95	1.65

International Children's Day.

Spirit of Skanderbeg as Conqueror A385

10q, Battle at Mostar Bridge. 80q, Marchers, Albanian flag. 1.20 l, Riflemen in winter battle. 1.65 l, Abdyl Frasheri (1839-92). 2.20 l, Rifles, scroll, pen, League building. 2.60 l, League headquarters, Prizren.

1978, June 10   Litho.   Perf. 12
1853	A385	10q multi	.25	.25
1854	A385	25q multi	.25	.30
1855	A385	80q multi	1.25	.75
1856	A385	1.20 l multi	1.75	1.00
1857	A385	1.65 l multi	2.75	1.50
1858	A385	2.60 l multi	4.50	4.50
	Nos. 1853-1858 (6)		10.75	8.30

Miniature Sheet
Perf. 12 on 2 sides x Imperf.
1859	A385	2.20 l multi	3.00	2.25

Centenary of League of Prizren.

Guerrillas and Flag, 1943 — A386

Designs: 25q, Soldier, sailor, airman, militiaman, horiz. 1.90 l, Members of armed forces, civil guards, and Young Pioneers.

1978, July 10   Perf. 11½x12½
1860	A386	5q multi	.75	.25
1861	A386	25q multi	1.25	.25
1862	A386	1.90 l multi	6.50	3.50
	Nos. 1860-1862 (3)		8.50	4.00

35th anniversary of People's Army.

Woman with Machine Carbine — A387

25q, Man with target rifle, horiz. 95q, Man shooting with telescopic sights, horiz. 2.40 l, Woman target shooting with pistol.

Perf. 12½x12, 12x12½
1978, Sept. 20   Litho.
1863	A387	25q black & yel	.25	.25
1864	A387	80q orange & blk	.50	.35
1865	A387	95q red & blk	.75	.50
1866	A387	2.40 l carmine & blk	1.90	1.50
	Nos. 1863-1866 (4)		3.40	2.60

32nd National Rifle-shooting Championships, Sept. 20.

Kerchief Dance — A388

15q, Musicians. 25q, Fiddler with single-stringed instrument. 80q, Dancers, men. 1.20 l, Saber dance. 1.90 l, Singers, women.

1978, Oct. 6   Perf. 12
1867	A388	5q multi	.25	.25
1868	A388	15q multi	.25	.25
1869	A388	25q multi	.25	.25
1870	A388	80q multi	.25	.25
1871	A388	1.20 l multi	1.00	.90
1872	A388	1.90 l multi	2.00	1.25
	Nos. 1867-1872 (6)		4.00	2.50

National Folklore Festival.
See Nos. 2082-2085, 2289-2290.

No. 1736 Surcharged with New Value, 2 Bars and "RICCIONE 78"
1978   Litho.   Perf. 12½x12
1873	A360	3.30 l on 25q multi	12.00	12.00

Riccione 78 Philatelic Exhibition.

Enver Hoxha A389

1978, Oct. 16   Litho.   Perf. 12x12½
1874	A389	80q red & multi	.40	.35
1875	A389	1.20 l red & multi	.75	.35
1876	A389	2.40 l red & multi	1.50	1.00
	Nos. 1874-1876 (3)		2.65	1.70

Miniature Sheet
Perf. 12½ on 2 sides x Imperf.
1877	A389	2.20 l red & multi	3.50	2.00

70th birthday of Enver Hoxha, First Secretary of Central Committee of the Communist Party of Albania.

Woman and Wheat — A390

25q, Woman with egg crates. 80q, Shepherd, sheep. 2.60 l, Milkmaid, cows.

1978, Dec. 15   **Perf. 12x12½**
1878	A390	15q multicolored	.40	.40
1879	A390	25q multicolored	.55	.40
1880	A390	80q multicolored	2.00	1.50
1881	A390	2.60 l multicolored	7.50	5.00
		Nos. 1878-1881 (4)	10.45	7.30

Dora d'Istria — A391

Design: 1.10 l, Full portrait of Dora d'Istria, author; birth sesquicentennial.

1979, Jan. 22   **Litho.**   **Perf. 12**
1882	A391	80q lt grn & blk	1.10	.75
1883	A391	1.10 l vio brn & blk	1.90	1.50

Folk Dancing Type of 1977

Designs: Various folk dances.

1979, Feb. 25
1884	A375	15q multi	.35	.25
1885	A375	25q multi	.35	.25
1886	A375	80q multi	1.50	.75
1887	A375	1.20 l multi	1.75	1.00
1888	A375	1.40 l multi	2.00	1.40
		Nos. 1884-1888 (5)	5.95	3.65

Nos. 1884-1888 have white background. Denomination in UL on No. 1885, in UR on No. 1802; LL on No.1886, UL on No. 1803.

Tower House — A392

Traditional Houses: 15q, Stone gallery house, horiz. 80q, House with wooden galleries, horiz. 1.20 l, Galleried tower house. 1.40 l, 1.90 l, Tower houses, diff.

1979, Mar. 20
1889	A392	15q multi	.25	.25
1890	A392	25q multi	.25	.25
1891	A392	80q multi	.75	.25
1892	A392	1.20 l multi	1.00	.45
1893	A392	1.40 l multi	1.50	.65
		Nos. 1889-1893 (5)	3.75	1.85

Miniature Sheet
Perf. 12 on 2 sides x Imperf.
1894	A392	1.90 l multi	5.25	3.75

See Nos. 2015-2018.

Soldier, Factories, Wheat A393

1.65 l, Soldiers, workers and coat of arms.

1979, May 14   **Litho.**   **Perf. 12**
1895	A393	25q multi	.75	.35
1896	A393	1.65 l multi	3.50	2.00

Congress of Permet, 35th anniversary.

Albanian Flag A394

1979, June 4
1897	A394	25q multi	.75	.35
1898	A394	1.65 l multi	3.50	2.25

5th Congress of Albanian Democratic Front.

Alexander Moissi, (1880-1935), Actor — A395

1979, Apr 2
1899	A395	80q multi	1.00	.35
1900	A395	1.10 l multi, diff.	1.50	1.00

Vasil Shanto, (1913-44) A396

Design: 25q, 90q, Qemal Stafa (1921-42).

1979, May 5
1901	A396	15q multi	.25	.25
1902	A396	25q multi	.40	.25
1903	A396	60q multi	1.40	.60
1904	A396	90q multi	2.25	1.50
		Nos. 1901-1904 (4)	4.30	2.60

Shanto and Stafa, anti-Fascist fighters. For similar design see A410.

Winter Campaign, by Arben Basha — A397

Paintings of Military Scenes by: 25q, Ismail Lulani. 80q, Myrteza Fushekati. 1.20 l, Muhamet Deliu. 1.40 l, Jorgji Gjikopulli. 1.90 l, Fatmir Haxhiu.

1979, July 15   **Litho.**   **Perf. 12½x12**
1905	A397	15q multi	.25	.25
1906	A397	25q multi	.25	.25
1907	A397	80q multi	.75	.25
1908	A397	1.20 l multi	1.00	.45
1909	A397	1.40 l multi	1.50	.75
		Nos. 1905-1909 (5)	3.75	1.95

Miniature Sheet
Perf. 12 on 2 sides x Imperf.
1910	A397	1.90 l multi	2.75	2.00

Athletes Surrounding Flag — A398

1979, Oct. 1   **Litho.**   **Perf. 12**
1911	A398	15q shown	.25	.25
1912	A398	25q Shooting	.25	.25
1913	A398	80q Dancing	.70	.25
1914	A398	1.20 l Soccer	.85	.60
1915	A398	1.40 l High jump	1.20	.85
		Nos. 1911-1915 (5)	3.25	2.20

Liberation Spartakiad, 35th anniversary.

Literary Society Headquarters A399

Albanian Literary Society Centenary: 25q, Seal and charter. 80q, Founder. 1.55 l, 1879 Headquarters. 1.90 l, Founders.

1979, Oct. 12
1916	A399	25q multi	.25	.25
1917	A399	80q multi	.75	.35
1918	A399	1.20 l multi	1.00	.60
1919	A399	1.55 l multi	1.25	.75
		Nos. 1916-1919 (4)	3.25	1.95

Miniature Sheet
Perf. 12½ on 2 sides x Imperf.
1920	A399	1.90 l multi	2.50	2.00

Congress Statute, Coat of Arms — A400

1979, Oct. 20   **Photo.**   **Perf. 12x12½**
1921	A400	80q multi	.75	.75
1922	A400	1.65 l multi	3.00	2.50

2nd Congress of Berat, 35th anniversary.

Industry and Culture — A401

5q, Children Entering School, Books. 10q, Communications. 15q, Steel workers. 20q, Dancers, instruments. 25q, Newspapers, radio, television. 60q, Textile worker. 80q, Armed forces. 1.20 l, Industry. 1.60 l, Transportation. 2.40 l, Agriculture. 3 l, Medicine.

1979   **Litho.**   **Perf. 12½x12**
1923	A401	5q shown	.25	.25
1924	A401	10q multi	.25	.25
1925	A401	15q multi	.25	.25
1926	A401	20q multi	.25	.25
1927	A401	25q multi	.25	.25
1928	A401	60q multi	1.00	.25
1929	A401	80q multi	1.40	.25
1930	A401	1.20 l multi	2.40	.25
1931	A401	1.60 l multi	3.25	.40
1932	A401	2.40 l multi	5.00	.45
1932A	A401	3 l multi	6.75	.90
		Nos. 1923-1932A (11)	21.05	3.45

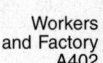

Workers and Factory A402

Worker, Red Flag and: 80q, Hand holding sickle and rifle. 1.20 l, Red star and open book. 1.55 l, Open book and cogwheel.

1979, Nov. 29
1933	A402	25q multi	.25	.25
1934	A402	80q multi	.75	.35
1935	A402	1.20 l multi	.90	.75
1936	A402	1.55 l multi	1.50	.90
		Nos. 1933-1936 (4)	3.40	2.25

35th anniversary of independence.

Joseph Stalin — A403

Design: 1.10 l, Stalin on dais, horiz.

1979, Dec. 21   **Litho.**   **Perf. 12**
1937	A403	80q red & dk bl	1.10	.75
1938	A403	1.10 l red & dk bl	1.50	1.50

Joseph Stalin (1879-1953), birth centenary.

Fireplace and Pottery, Korcar A404

Home Furnishings: 80q, Cupboard bed, dagger, pistol, ammunition pouch, Shkodar. 1.20 l, Stool, pot, chair, Mirdit. 1.35 l, Chimney, dagger, jacket, Gjirokaster.

1980, Feb. 27   **Litho.**   **Perf. 12**
1939	A404	25q multi	.25	.25
1940	A404	80q multi	.50	.50
1941	A404	1.20 l multi	1.10	.75
1942	A404	1.35 l multi	1.50	1.50
		Nos. 1939-1942 (4)	3.35	3.00

See Nos. 1985-1988.

Pipe, Painted Flask A405

80q, Leather handbags. 1.20 l, Carved eagle, embroidered rug. 1.35 l, Lace.

1980, Mar. 4
1943	A405	25q shown	.25	.25
1944	A405	80q multi	.50	.50
1945	A405	1.20 l multi	1.10	.75
1946	A405	1.35 l multi	1.50	1.50
		Nos. 1943-1946 (4)	3.35	3.00

Prof. Aleksander Xhuvanit Birth Centenary A406

1980, Mar. 14
1947	A406	80q multi	1.60	1.20
1948	A406	1 l multi	2.00	2.00

Revolutionaries on Horseback — A407

Insurrection at Kosove, 70th Anniversary: 1 l, Battle scene.

1980, Apr. 4
1949	A407	80q red & black	1.50	1.10
1950	A407	1 l red & black	2.25	1.90

Soldiers and Workers Laboring to Aid the Stricken Populations, by D. Jukniu and I. Lulani — A408

1980, Apr. 15   Litho.   Perf. 12½
1951	A408	80q lt blue & multi	1.50	1.10
1952	A408	1 l lt blue grn & multi	2.25	1.90

Lenin, 110th Birth Anniversary
A409

1980, Apr. 22
1953	A409	80q multi	1.50	1.10
1954	A409	1 l multi	2.25	1.90

Misto Mame and Ali Demi, War Martyrs A410

War Martyrs: 80q, Sadik Staveleci, Vojo Kusji, Hoxhi Martini. 1.20 l, Bule Naipi, Persefoni Kokedhima. 1.35 l, Ndoc Deda, Hydajet Lezha, Naim Gyylbegu, Ndoc Mazi, Ahmed Haxha.

1980, May 5
1955	A410	25q multi	.25	.25
1956	A410	80q multi	.70	.50
1957	A410	1.20 l multi	1.20	.70
1958	A410	1.35 l multi	1.40	1.40
	Nos. 1955-1958 (4)		3.55	2.85

See Nos. 2012A-2012D, 2025-2028, 2064-2067, 2122-2125, 2171-2174, 2207-2209.

Scene from "Mirela" A411

1980, June 7
1959	A411	15q shown	.25	.25
1960	A411	25q The Scribbler	.25	.25
1961	A411	80q Circus Bears	.80	.80
1962	A411	2.40 l Waterdrops	2.75	2.75
	Nos. 1959-1962 (4)		4.05	4.05

Carrying Iron Castings in the Enver Hoxha Tractor Combine, by S. Shijaku and M. Fushekati — A412

Paintings (Gallery of Figurative Paintings, Tirana): 80q, The Welder, by Harilla Dhima. 1.20 l, Steel Erectors, by Petro Kokushta. 1.35 l, Pandeli Lena, 1.80 l Communists, by Vilson Kilica.

1980, July 22
1963	A412	25q multi	.25	.25
1964	A412	80q multi	.70	.70
1965	A412	1.20 l multi	1.20	1.20
1966	A412	1.35 l multi	1.40	1.40
	Nos. 1963-1966 (4)		3.55	3.55

Imperf
1967	A412	1.80 l multi	2.50	2.50

No. 1967 measures 66x82mm and has a row of perforations above and below the vignette.

Gate, Parchment Miniature, 11th Cent. — A413

Bas reliefs of the Middle Ages: 80q, Eagle, 13th cent. 1.20 l, Heraldic lion, 14th cent. 1.35 l, Pheasant, 14th cent.

1980, Sept. 27   Litho.   Perf. 12
1968	A413	25q gold & blk	.25	.25
1969	A413	80q gold & blk	.55	.55
1970	A413	1.20 l gold & blk	1.20	1.20
1971	A413	1.35 l gold & blk	1.20	1.20
	Nos. 1968-1971 (4)		3.20	3.20

Divjaka National Park A414

1980, Nov. 6   Photo.
1972	A414	80q shown	.75	.60
1973	A414	1.20 l Lura	1.10	1.10
1974	A414	1.60 l Thethi	1.90	1.60
	Nos. 1972-1974 (3)		3.75	3.30

Souvenir Sheet
Perf. 12½ Horiz.
1975	A414	1.80 l Llogara Park	3.50	3.50

Citizens, Flag and Arms of Albania A415

1 l, People's Party Headquarters, Tirana.

1981, Jan. 11   Litho.   Perf. 12
1976	A415	80q multicolored	1.00	.70
1977	A415	1 l multicolored	1.40	.70

35th anniversary of the Republic.

Child's Bed A416

80q, Wooden bucket, brass bottle. 1.20 l, Shoes. 1.35 l, Jugs.

1981, Mar. 20   Litho.   Perf. 12
1978	A416	25q multicolored	.25	.25
1979	A416	80q multicolored	.50	.40
1980	A416	1.20 l multicolored	.80	.70
1981	A416	1.35 l multicolored	1.00	.90
	Nos. 1978-1981 (4)		2.55	2.25

A417

80q, Soldiers. 1 l, Sword combat. 1.80 l, Soldier with pistol.

1981, Apr. 20
1982	A417	80q multicolored	.70	.70
1983	A417	1 l multicolored	.85	.70

Souvenir Sheet
Perf. 12½ Vert.
1984	A417	1.80 l multicolored	3.25	2.75

Battle of Shtimje centenary.

Home Furnishings Type of 1980

25q, House interior, Labara. 80q, Labara, diff. 1.20 l, Mat. 1.35 l, Dibres.

1981, Feb. 25   Litho.   Perf. 12
1985	A404	25q multicolored	.25	.25
1986	A404	80q multicolored	.35	.25
1987	A404	1 l multicolored	.85	.40
1988	A404	1.35 l multicolored	1.00	.90
	Nos. 1985-1988 (4)		2.45	1.80

A419

Designs: Children's circus.

1981, June   Perf. 12
1989	A419	15q multi	.25	.25
1990	A419	25q multi	.50	.40
1991	A419	80q multi	.80	.65
1992	A419	2.40 l multi	1.00	.90
	Nos. 1989-1992 (4)		2.55	2.20

Soccer Players A420

1982 World Cup Soccer Elimination Games: Various soccer players.

1981, Mar. 31   Litho.   Perf. 12
1993	A420	25q multi	.75	.35
1994	A420	80q multi	2.60	1.50
1995	A420	1.20 l multi	3.75	2.60
1996	A420	1.35 l multi	4.50	3.00
	Nos. 1993-1996 (4)		11.60	7.45

Allies, by S. Hysa A421

Paintings: 80q, Warriors, by A. Buza. 1.20 l, Rallying to the Flag, Dec. 1911, by A. Zajmi, vert. 1.35 l, My Flag is My Heart, by L. Cefa, vert. 1.80 l, Circling the Flag in a Common Cause, by N. Vasia.

1981, July 10   Perf. 12½x12
1997	A421	25q multi	.25	.25
1998	A421	80q multi	.75	.35
1999	A421	1.20 l multi	.85	.75
2000	A421	1.35 l multi	1.50	.85
	Nos. 1997-2000 (4)		3.35	2.20

Souvenir Sheet
Perf. 12½ Horiz.
2001	A421	1.80 l multi	3.50	2.50

No. 2001 contains one 55x55mm stamp.

Rifleman A422

1981, Aug. 30   Perf. 12
2002	A422	25q shown	.25	.25
2003	A422	80q Weight lifting	.50	.35
2004	A422	1.20 l Volleyball	.75	.65
2005	A422	1.35 l Soccer	1.00	.75
	Nos. 2002-2005 (4)		2.50	2.00

Albanian Workers' Party, 8th Congress A423

80q, Flag, star. 1 l, Flag, hammer & sickle.

1981, Nov. 1
2006	A423	80q multicolored	.60	.45
2007	A423	1 l multicolored	.85	.75

Albanian Workers' Party, 40th Anniv. — A424

80q, Symbols of industrialization. 2.80 l, Fist, emblem. 1.80 l, Enver Hoxha, Memoirs.

1981, Nov. 8
2008	A424	80q multicolored	.35	.35
2009	A424	2.80 l multicolored	1.75	1.40

Souvenir Sheet
Perf. 12 Horiz.
2010	A424	1.80 l multicolored	3.75	3.75

Communist Youth Org., 40th Anniv. — A425

1981, Nov. 23
2011	A425	80q Star, ax, map	.75	.75
2012	A425	1 l Flags, star	1.50	1.40

War Martyrs Type of 1980

25q, Perlat Rexhepi (1919-42) and Branko Kadia (1921-42). 80q, Xheladin Beqiri (1908-44) and Hajdar Dushi (1916-44). 1.20 l, Koci Bako (1905-41), Vasil Laci (1923-41) and Mujo Ulqinaku (1898-1939). 1.35 l, Mine Peza (1875-1942) and Zoja Cure (1920-44).

1981, May 5   Litho.   Perf. 12
2012A	A410	25q silver & multi	.25	.25
2012B	A410	80q gold & multi	1.00	.35
2012C	A410	1.20 l silver & multi	1.25	.75
2012D	A410	1.35 l gold & multi	2.00	.85
	Nos. 2012A-2012D (4)		4.50	2.20

Fan S. Noli,
Writer, Birth
Centenary
A426

1982, Jan. 6   Litho.   Perf. 12
2013 A426 80q lt ol grn & gold 1.00 .50
2014 A426 1.10 l lt red brn &
            gold 1.25 .75

Traditional Houses Type of 1979
1982, Feb.   Perf. 12½x12
2015 A392 25q Bulqize .25 .25
2016 A392 80q Lebush 1.00 .70
2017 A392 1.20 l Bicaj 1.50 1.00
2018 A392 1.55 l Klos 2.00 1.25
      Nos. 2015-2018 (4) 4.75 3.20

TB Bacillus
Centenary
A428

1982, Mar. 24   Perf. 12
2019 A428 80q Globe 3.75 1.50
2020 A428 1.10 l Koch 5.25 2.50

Albanian League House, Prizren, by
K. Buza — A429

Kosova Landscapes: 25q, Castle at
Prizrenit, by G. Madhi. 1.20 l, Mountain Gorge
at Rogove, by K. Buza. 1.55 l, Street of the
Hadhji at Zekes, by G. Madhi. 25q, 1.20 l,
1.55 l vert.

Perf. 12x12½, 12½x12
1982, Apr. 15   Litho.
2021 A429 25q multi .45 .25
2022 A429 80q multi 1.40 1.00
2023 A429 1.20 l multi 2.25 1.25
2024 A429 1.55 l multi 3.25 1.50
      Nos. 2021-2024 (4) 7.35 4.00

War Martyrs Type of 1980
Designs: 25q, Hibe Palikuqi, Liri Gero. 80q,
Mihal Duri, Kajo Karafili. 1.20 l, Fato Dudumi,
Margarita Tutulani, Shejnaze Juka. 1.55 l,
Memo Meto, Gjok Doci.

1982, May   Perf. 12
2025 A410 25q multi .35 .25
2026 A410 80q multi .85 .60
2027 A410 1.20 l multi 1.25 .75
2028 A410 1.55 l multi 2.25 1.00
      Nos. 2025-2028 (4) 4.70 2.60

Loading Freighter — A430

Children's Paintings.
1982, June 15   Perf. 12½x12
2029 A430 15q shown .50 .25
2030 A430 80q Forest 1.00 .45
2031 A430 1.20 l City 1.50 .90
2032 A430 1.65 l Park 3.00 1.25
      Nos. 2029-2032 (4) 6.00 2.85

9th
Congress
of Trade
Unions
A431

80q, Workers, factories. 1.10 l, Emblem,
flag.

1982, June 6   Litho.   Perf. 12
2033 A431 80q multicolored 2.00 1.25
2034 A431 1.10 l multicolored 2.75 1.50

Alpine
Village
Festival,
by
Danish
Jukniu
A432

Industrial Development Paintings: 80q,
Hydroelectric Station Builders, by Ali Miruku.
1.20 l, Steel Workers, by Clirim Ceka. 1.55 l,
Oil drillers, by Pandeli Lena. 1.90 l, Trapping
the Furnace, by Jorgji Gjikopulli.

1982, July   Perf. 12½
2035 A432 25q multi .50 .25
2036 A432 80q multi 1.50 1.40
2037 A432 1.20 l multi 2.25 1.60
2038 A432 1.55 l multi 3.00 1.90
      Nos. 2035-2038 (4) 7.25 5.15

Souvenir Sheet
Perf. 12 Horiz.
2039 A432 1.90 l multi 4.00 2.75

No. 2039 contains one 54x48mm stamp.

Communist Party
Newspaper "Voice
of the People,"
40th Anniv. —
A432a

80q, Newspapers. 1.10 l, Paper, press.
1982, Aug. 25   Litho.   Perf. 12
2039A A432a 80q multi 75.00 70.00
2039B A432a 1.10 l multi 75.00 70.00

40th Anniv.
of
Democratic
Front
A433

80q, Glory to the Heroes of Peza Monument. 1.10 l, Marchers.

1982, Sept. 16   Perf. 12
2040 A433 80q multi 7.50 2.50
2041 A433 1.10 l multi 11.00 3.50

8th Youth
Congress — A434

1982, Oct. 4
2042 A434 80q multi 6.00 3.00
2043 A434 1.10 l multi 10.00 4.50

Handmade
Shoulder
Bags — A435

25q, Rug, horiz. 1.20 l, Wooden pots, bowls,
horiz. 1.55 l, Jug.

1982, Nov.
2044 A435 25q multi .45 .25
2045 A435 80q multi 1.00 .60
2046 A435 1.20 l multi 1.40 .85
2047 A435 1.55 l multi 2.25 1.10
      Nos. 2044-2047 (4) 5.10 2.80

70th Anniv. of Independence — A436

20q, Ishamil Qemali. 1.20 l, Partisans.
2.40 l, Partisans, diff.
1.90 l, Independence Monument, Tirana.

1982, Nov. 28
2048 A436 20q multicolored .35 .25
2049 A436 1 multicolored 1.75 .90
2050 A436 2.40 l multicolored 3.00 1.75
      Nos. 2048-2050 (3) 5.10 2.90

Souvenir Sheet
Perf. 12 Horiz.
2051 A436 1.90 l multicolored 5.00 3.50

Dhermi
Beach
A437

1982, Dec. 20
2052 A437 25q shown .25 .25
2053 A437 80q Sarande .75 .45
2054 A437 1.20 l Ksamil 1.00 .90
2055 A437 1.55 l Lukove 1.50 1.00
      Nos. 2052-2055 (4) 3.50 2.60

Handkerchief Dancers — A438

Folkdancers — 80q, With kerchief, drum.
1.20 l, With guitar, flute, tambourine. 1.55 l,
Women.

1983, Feb. 20   Litho.   Perf. 12
2056 A438 25q multi .25 .25
2057 A438 80q multi .60 .25
2058 A438 1.20 l multi 1.10 .75
2059 A438 1.55 l multi 1.50 1.10
      Nos. 2056-2059 (4) 3.45 2.35

A439

1983, Mar. 14   Litho.   Perf. 12
2060 A439 80q multi 1.50 .75
2061 A439 1.10 l multi 1.90 1.00

Karl Marx (1818-83).

A440

80q, Electricity generation. 1.10 l, Gas & oil
production.

1983, Apr. 20
2062 A440 80q multi 1.00 .60
2063 A440 1.10 l multi 1.25 .90

Energy development.

War Martyrs Type of 1980
Designs: 25q, Asim Zeneli (1916-43), Nazmi
Rushiti (1919-42). 80q, Shyqyri Ishmi (1922-
42), Shyqyri Alimerko (1923-43), Myzafer
Asqeriu (1918-42). 1.20 l, Qybra Sokoli (1924-
44), Qeriba Derri (1905-44), Ylbere Bilibashi
(1928-44). 1.55 l, Themo Vasi (1915-43), Abaz
Shehu (1905-42).

1983, May 5   Litho.   Perf. 12
2064 A410 25q multi .25 .25
2065 A410 80q multi .75 .30
2066 A410 1.20 l multi 1.25 .75
2067 A410 1.55 l multi 1.90 1.00
      Nos. 2064-2067 (4) 4.15 2.30

Women's
Union, 9th
Congress
A441

1983, June 1   Litho.   Perf. 12x12½
2068 A441 80q red & gold 1.40 .75
2069 A441 1.10 l blue & gold 1.75 1.00

Bicycling
A442

1983, June 20   Perf. 12
2070 A442 25q shown .25 .25
2071 A442 80q Chess .75 .25
2072 A442 1.20 l Gymnastics 1.25 .75
2073 A442 1.55 l Wrestling 1.50 1.00
      Nos. 2070-2073 (4) 3.75 2.25

40th Anniv. of
People's
Army — A443

20q, Armed services. 1.20 l, Soldier, gun
barrels. 2.40 l, Factory guard, crowd.

1983, July 10
2074 A443 20q multicolored .25 .25
2075 A443 1.20 l multicolored 1.50 .75
2076 A443 2.40 l multicolored 2.50 1.25
      Nos. 2074-2076 (3) 4.25 2.25

Sunny Day, by Myrteza
Fushekati — A444

Paintings: 80q, Messenger of the Grasp, by
Niko Progi. 1.20 l, 29 November 1944, by
Harilla Dhimo. 1.55 l, Fireworks, by Pandi
Mele. 1.90 l, Partisan Assault, by Sali Shijaku
and M. Fushekati.

1983, Aug. 28	Litho.		Perf. 12½x12	
2077	A444	25q multi	.25	.25
2078	A444	80q multi	.85	.40
2079	A444	1.20 l multi	1.00	.75
2080	A444	1.55 l multi	1.50	.85
	Nos. 2077-2080 (4)		3.60	2.25

Souvenir Sheet
Perf. 12

2081	A444	1.90 l multi	8.50	6.00

Folklore Festival Type of 1978

Gjirokaster Folklore Festival: folkdances:
25q, Sword dance. 80q, Kerchief dance.
1.20 l, Shepherd flautists. 1.55 l, Garland
dance.

1983, Oct. 6	Litho.		Perf. 12	
2082	A388	25q multicolored	.25	.25
2083	A388	80q multicolored	1.50	.90
2084	A388	1.20 l multicolored	1.50	.90
2085	A388	1.55 l multicolored	3.00	2.00
	Nos. 2082-2085 (4)		6.25	3.90

World Communications Year — A446

1983, Nov. 10				
2086	A446	60q multicolored	.50	.35
2087	A446	1.20 l multicolored	1.40	1.10

75th Birthday
of Enver
Hoxha
A447

1983, Oct. 16	Litho.		Perf. 12½	
2088	A447	80q multi	.90	.75
2089	A447	1.20 l multi	1.50	1.25
2090	A447	1.80 l multi	2.00	1.75
	Nos. 2088-2090 (3)		4.40	3.75

Souvenir Sheet
Perf. 12 Horiz.

2091	A447	1.90 l multi	3.00	3.00

The
Right to
a Joint
Triumph,
by J.
Keraj
A448

Era of Skanderbeg in Figurative Art: 80q,
The Heroic Center of the Battle of Krujes, by
N. Bakalli. 1.20 l, The Rights of the Enemy
after our Triumph, by N. Progri. 1.55 l, The
Discussion at Lezhes, by B. Ahmeti. 1.90 l,
Victory over the Turks, by G. Madhi.

1983, Dec. 10			Perf. 12½x12	
2092	A448	25q multi	.35	.25
2093	A448	80q multi	1.10	.75
2094	A448	1.20 l multi	1.50	.90
2095	A448	1.55 l multi	2.25	1.10
	Nos. 2092-2095 (4)		5.20	3.00

Souvenir Sheet
Perf. 12 Horiz.

2096	A448	1.90 l multi	7.50	7.50

Greco-Roman Ruins of Illyria — A449

80q, Amphitheater, Buthroxtum. 1.20 l, Col-
onnade, Apollonium. 1.80 l, Vaulted gallery,
amphitheater at Epidamnus.

1983, Dec. 28			Perf. 12	
2097	A449	80q multicolored	1.50	1.10
2098	A449	1.20 l multicolored	2.25	1.50
2099	A449	1.80 l multicolored	2.25	1.75
	Nos. 2097-2099 (3)		6.00	4.35

Archeological
Discoveries
A450

Designs: Apollo, 3rd cent. 25q, Tombstone,
Korce, 3rd cent. 80q, Apollo, diff. 1st cent.
1.10 l, Earthenware pot (child's head), Tren,
1st cent. 1.20 l, Man's head, Dyrrah, 2.20 l,
Eros with Dolphin, statue Bronze Dyrrah, 3rd
cent.

1984, Feb. 25			Perf. 12x12½	
2100	A450	15q multi	.25	.25
2101	A450	25q multi	.25	.25
2102	A450	80q multi	.80	.50
2103	A450	1.10 l multi	1.20	.75
2104	A450	1.20 l multi	1.60	.85
2105	A450	2.20 l multi	2.50	1.00
	Nos. 2100-2105 (6)		6.60	3.60

Clock
Towers — A451

1984, Mar. 30	Litho.		Perf. 12	
2106	A451	15q Gjirokaster	.25	.25
2107	A451	25q Kavaje	.25	.25
2108	A451	80q Elbasan	.80	.50
2109	A451	1.10 l Tirana	1.00	.75
2110	A451	1.20 l Peqin	1.25	.90
2111	A451	2.20 l Kruje	2.25	1.50
	Nos. 2106-2111 (6)		5.80	4.15

40th Anniv.
of
Liberation
A452

15q, Student & microscope. 25q, Guerrilla
with flag. 80q, Children with flag. 1.10 l, Soldier. 1.20 l, Workers with flag. 2.20 l, Militia at
dam.

1984, Apr. 20	Litho.		Perf. 12	
2112	A452	15q multi	.25	.25
2113	A452	25q multi	.25	.25
2114	A452	80q multi	.90	.45
2115	A452	1.10 l multi	1.20	.75
2116	A452	1.20 l multi	1.50	.90
2117	A452	2.20 l multi	2.25	1.10
	Nos. 2112-2117 (6)		6.35	3.70

Children — A453

15q, Children reading. 25q, Young pioneers.
60q, Gardening. 2.80 l, Kite flying.

1984, May	Litho.		Perf. 12	
2118	A453	15q multicolored	.45	.25
2119	A453	25q multicolored	1.00	.25
2120	A453	60q multicolored	1.75	.90
2121	A453	2.80 l multicolored	3.25	1.60
	Nos. 2118-2121 (4)		6.45	3.00

War Martyrs Type of 1980

Designs: 15q, Manush Almani, Mustafa
Matohiti, Kastriot Muco. 25q, Zaho Koka,
Reshit Collaku, Maliq Muco. 1.20 l, Lefter Talo,
Tom Kola, Fuat Babani. 2.20 l, Myslysm Shyri,
Dervish Hexali, Skender Caci.

1984, May 5	Litho.		Perf. 12	
2122	A410	15q multi	.50	.25
2123	A410	25q multi	1.10	.25
2124	A410	1.20 l multi	2.00	.90
2125	A410	2.20 l multi	3.50	2.00
	Nos. 2122-2125 (4)		7.10	3.40

A454

80q, Enver Hoxha. 1.10 l, Resistance
fighter.

1984, May 24	Litho.		Perf. 12	
2126	A454	80q multicolored	2.50	1.50
2127	A454	1.10 l multicolored	3.00	1.75

40th anniv. of Permet Congress.

A455

15q, Goalkeeper. 25q, Referee. 1.20 l, Map
of Europe. 2.20 l, Field diagram.

1984, June 12	Litho.		Perf. 12	
2128	A455	15q multicolored	1.20	.25
2129	A455	25q multicolored	1.20	.25
2130	A455	1.20 l multicolored	3.50	.75
2131	A455	2.20 l multicolored	4.25	1.50
	Nos. 2128-2131 (4)		10.15	2.75

European soccer championships.

Freedom Came, by Myrteza
Fushekati — A456

Paintings, Tirana Gallery of Figurative Art:
25q, Morning, by Zamir Mati, vert. 80q, My
Darling, by Agim Zajmi, vert. 2.60 l, For the
Partisans, by Arben Basha. 1.90 l, Eagle, by
Zamir Mati, vert.

1984, June 12			Perf. 12½	
2132	A456	15q multi	.40	.25
2133	A456	25q multi	.80	.35
2134	A456	2.00 l multi	2.00	1.10
2135	A456	2.60 l multi	3.25	1.75
	Nos. 2132-2135 (4)		6.45	3.45

Souvenir Sheet
Perf. 12 Horiz.

2136	A456	1.90 l multi	8.00	3.50

Flora — A457

15q, Moraceae L. 25q, Plantaginaceae L.
1.20 l, Hypericaceae L. 2.20 l, Leontopodium
alpinum.

1984, Aug. 20	Litho.		Perf. 12	
2137	A457	15q multicolored	2.25	.60
2138	A457	25q multicolored	3.00	1.10
2139	A457	1.20 l multicolored	8.25	3.50
2140	A457	2.20 l multicolored	17.00	6.50
	Nos. 2137-2140 (4)		30.50	11.70

AUSIPEX '84, Melbourne, Sept. 21-
30 — A458

Perf. 12 Horiz.

1984, Sept. 21				Litho.
2141	A458	1.90 l Sword dancers, emblem	4.00	4.00

A459

Forestry, logging, UNFAO emblem — 15q,
Beech trees, transport. 25q, Pine forest, logging cable. 1.20 l, Firs, sawmill. 2.20 l, For-
ester clearing woods.

1984, Sept. 25			Perf. 12	
2142	A459	15q multi	.80	.45
2143	A459	25q multi	1.25	.75
2144	A459	1.20 l multi	4.00	2.50
2145	A459	2.20 l multi	6.00	3.25
	Nos. 2142-2145 (4)		12.05	6.95

View of
Gjirokaster
A460

1984, Oct. 13   *Perf. 12½*
2146 A460 1.20 l multicolored   2.00 2.00
EURPHILA '84, Rome.

5th National
Spartakiad
A461

15q, Soccer. 25q, Women's track & field.
80q, Weight lifting. 2.20 l, Pistol shooting.
1.90 l, Opening ceremony, red flags.

1984, Oct. 19   *Perf. 12*
2147 A461   15q multicolored   .25 .25
2148 A461   25q multicolored   .30 .25
2149 A461   80q multicolored   .75 .30
2150 A461 2.20 l multicolored   2.10 1.50
   Nos. 2147-2150 (4)   3.40 2.30
Souvenir Sheet
Perf. 12 Horiz.
2151 A461 1.90 l multicolored   3.00 2.25

November
29
Revolution,
40th Anniv.
A462

80q, Industrial reconstruction. 1.10 l, Natl.
flag, partisans.
1.90 l, Gen. Enver Hoxha reading 1944
declaration.

1984, Nov. 29   *Perf. 12*
2152 A462   80q multicolored   2.00 .75
2153 A462 1.10 l multicolored   2.50 1.00
Souvenir Sheet
Perf. 12 Horiz.
2154 A462 1.90 l multicolored   4.00 4.00

Archaeological
Discoveries
from
Illyria — A463

Designs: 15q, Iron Age water container.
80q, Terra-cotta woman's head, 6th-7th cent.
B.C. 1.20 l, Aphrodite, bust, 3rd cent. B.C.
1.70 l, Nike, A.D. 1st-2nd cent. bronze statue.

1985, Feb. 25   *Perf. 12x12½*
2155 A463   15q multi   .40 .25
2156 A463   80q multi   1.50 .70
2157 A463 1.20 l multi   2.00 .90
2158 A463 1.70 l multi   3.00 1.50
   Nos. 2155-2158 (4)   6.90 3.40

Hysni Kapo
(1915-1980), Natl.
Labor Party
Leader — A464

1985, Mar. 4   *Perf. 12*
2159 A464   90q red & blk   1.40 1.00
2160 A464 1.10 l chlky bl & blk   1.75 1.50

OLYMPHILEX '85, Lausanne — A465

25q, Women's track & field. 60q, Weight lifting. 1.20 l, Soccer. 1.50 l, Women's pistol
shooting.

1985, Mar. 18
2161 A465   25q multicolored   .25 .25
2162 A465   60q multicolored   .65 .35
2163 A465 1.20 l multicolored   1.10 .90
2164 A465 1.50 l multicolored   2.00 1.00
   Nos. 2161-2164 (4)   4.00 2.50

Johann Sebastian
Bach — A466

80q, Portrait, manuscript. 1.20 l, Eisenach,
birthplace.

1985, Mar. 31
2165 A466   80q multicolored   16.00 8.00
2166 A466 1.20 l multicolored   20.00 10.00

Gen. Enver
Hoxha (1908-
1985)
A467

1985, Apr. 11   *Perf. 12½*
2167 A467   80q multicolored   2.00 1.90
Souvenir Sheet
Imperf
2168 A467 1.90 l multicolored   3.25 3.25

Natl.
Frontier
Guards,
40th Anniv.
A468

25q, Guardsman, family. 80q, At frontier
post.

1985, Apr. 25   *Perf. 12*
2169 A468   25q multicolored   1.25 .75
2170 A468   80q multicolored   3.00 2.25

War Martyrs Type of 1980

25q, Mitro Xhani (1916-44), Nimete
Progonati (1929-44), Kozma Nushi (1909-44).
40q, Ajet Xhindoli (1922-43), Mustafa Kacaci
(1903-44), Estref Caka Osaja (1919-44). 60q,
Celo Sinani (1929-44), Lt. Ambro Andoni

(1920-44), Meleq Gosnishti (1913-44). 1.20 l,
Thodhori Mastora (1920-44), Fejzi Micoli
(1919-45), Hysen Cino (1920-44).

1985, May 5
2171 A410   25q multi   .55 .35
2172 A410   40q multi   .85 .70
2173 A410   60q multi   1.40 .85
2174 A410 1.20 l multi   2.50 2.00
   Nos. 2171-2174 (4)   5.30 3.90

Victory over
Fascism
A469

25q, Rifle, red flag, inscribed May 9. 80q,
Hand holding rifle, globe, broken swastika.

1985, May 9
2175 A469 25q multi   22.50 35.00
2176 A469 80q multi   60.00 90.00
End of World War II, 40th anniv.

Primary
School,
by
Thoma
Malo
A470

Paintings, Tirana Gallery of Figurative Art:
80q, The Heroes, by Hysen Devolli, vert. 90q,
In Our Days, by Angjelin Dodmasej, vert. 1.20
l, Going Off to Sow, by Ksenofon Dilo. 1.90 l,
Foundry Workers, by Mikel Gurashi.

1985, June 25   *Perf. 12½*
2177 A470   25q multi   .25 .25
2178 A470   80q multi   1.00 .75
2179 A470   90q multi   1.25 1.00
2180 A470 1.20 l multi   1.60 1.25
   Nos. 2177-2180 (4)   4.10 3.25
Souvenir Sheet
Perf. 12 Horiz.
2181 A470 1.90 l multi   3.25 2.75

Basketball
Championships,
Spain — A471

Various plays.

1985, July 20   *Litho.*   *Perf. 12*
2182 A471   25q dull bl & blk   .30 .25
2183 A471   80q dull grn & blk   1.10 .35
2184 A471 1.20 l dl vio & blk   1.40 .90
2185 A471 1.60 l dl rose & blk   2.25 1.50
   Nos. 2182-2185 (4)   5.05 3.00

Fruits — A472

1985, Aug. 20
2186 A472   25q Oranges   .40 .25
2187 A472   80q Plums   2.00 1.00
2188 A472 1.20 l Apples   3.25 1.50
2189 A472 1.60 l Cherries   4.00 2.25
   Nos. 2186-2189 (4)   9.65 5.10

Architecture
A473

1985, Sept. 20
2190 A473   25q Kruja   .50 .50
2191 A473   80q Gjirokastra   2.50 1.25
2192 A473 1.20 l Berati   2.75 1.50
2193 A473 1.60 l Shkodera   3.75 1.75
   Nos. 2190-2193 (4)   9.50 5.00

Natl. Folk Theater
Festival — A474

Various scenes from folk plays.

1985, Oct. 6
2194 A474   25q multi   .50 .25
2195 A474   80q multi   1.50 .75
2196 A474 1.20 l multi   2.00 .90
2197 A474 1.60 l multi   2.50 1.40
Size: 56x82mm
Imperf
2198 A474 1.90 l multi   3.75 3.00
   Nos. 2194-2198 (5)   10.25 6.30

Socialist People's Republic, 40th
Anniv. — A475

25q, Natl. crest, vert. 80q, Proclamation,
1946.

1986, Jan. 11   *Litho.*   *Perf. 12½*
2199 A475 25q multicolored   1.50 .75
2200 A475 80q multicolored   3.00 1.50

A476

Designs: 25q, Dam, River Drin, Melgun.
80q, Bust of Enver Hoxha, dam power house.

1986, Feb. 20   *Perf. 12*
2201 A476 25q multi   5.50 2.00
2202 A476 80q multi   12.00 7.00
Enver Hoxha hydro-electric power station,
Koman.

A477

Flowers: 25q,   Gymnospermium
shqipetarum. 1.20 l, Leucojum valentinum.

1986, Mar. 20   Litho.   Perf. 12
2203	A477	25q multi	2.00	1.00
2204	A477	1.20 l multi	8.00	4.00
a.		Pair, #2203-2204	12.00	12.00

Nos. 2203-2204 exist imperf. Value, pair: mint $40, used $35.

A478

Famous Men — A479

Designs: 25q, Maxim Gorky, Russian author. 80q, Andre Marie Ampere, French physicist. 1.20 l, James Watt, English inventor of modern steam engine. 2.40 l, Franz Liszt, Hungarian composer.

1986, Apr. 20
2205		Strip of 4	12.00	8.00
a.	A478	25q dull red brown	.50	.50
b.	A478	80q dull violet	2.00	1.25
c.	A478	1.20 l blue green	3.50	2.00
d.	A478	2.40 l dull lilac rose	7.00	4.50

Size: 88x72mm
Imperf
2206	A479	1.90 l multi	7.00	4.00

No. 2206 has central area picturing Gorky, Ampere, Watt and Liszt, perf. 12½.

War Martyrs Type of 1980

25q, Ramiz Aranitasi (1923-43), Inajete Dumi (1924-44) and Laze Nuro Ferraj (1897-1944). 80q, Dine Kalenja (1919-44), Kozma Naska (1921-44), Met Hasa (1929-44) and Fahri Ramadani (1920-44). 1.20 l, Hiqmet Buzi (1927-44), Bajram Tusha (1922-42), Mumin Selami (1923-42) and Hajrfdin Bylyshi (1923-42).

1986, May 5   Perf. 12
2207	A410	25q multi	1.75	1.50
2208	A410	80q multi	4.50	2.50
2209	A410	1.20 l multi	7.25	5.00
		Nos. 2207-2209 (3)	13.50	9.00

A480

1986 World Cup Soccer Championships, Mexico — A481

25q, Globe, world cup. 1.20 l, Player, soccer ball.

1986, May 31   Litho.   Perf. 12
2210	A480	25q multicolored	.40	.30
2211	A480	1.20 l multicolored	2.00	1.50

Size: 97x64mm
Imperf
2212	A481	1.90 l multicolored	3.50	2.50
		Nos. 2210-2212 (3)	5.90	4.30

No. 2212 has central label, perf. 12½.

Transportation Workers' Day, 40th Anniv. — A482

1986, Aug. 10   Litho.   Perf. 12
2213	A482	1.20 l multi	11.00 6.50

Prominent Albanians A483

Designs: 30q, Naim Frasheri (1846-1900), poet. 60q, Ndre Mjeda (1866-1937), poet. 90q, Petro Nini Luarasi (1865-1911), poet, journalist. 1 l, Andon Zako Cajupi (1866-1930), poet. 1.20 l, Millosh Gjergj Nikolla Migjeni (1911-1938), novelist. 2.60 l, Urani Rumbo (1884-1936), educator.

1986, Sept. 20   Litho.   Perf. 12
2214	A483	30q multi	.70	.30
2215	A483	60q multi	1.25	1.60
2216	A483	90q multi	2.00	1.00
2217	A483	1 l multi	2.50	1.25
2218	A483	1.20 l multi	3.00	1.50
2219	A483	2.60 l multi	8.00	2.50
		Nos. 2214-2219 (6)	17.45	8.15

Albanian Workers' Party, 9th Congress, Tirana A484

1986, Nov. 3   Litho.   Perf. 12
2220	A484	30q multi	14.00 7.50

No. 2220 exists with country name misspelled "SHQIPERSIE." Value, mint, $150.

A485

Albanian Workers' Party, 45th Anniv.: 30q, Handstamp, signature of Hoxha. 1.20 l, Marx, Engels, Lenin and Stalin, party building.

1986, Nov. 8
2221	A485	30q multi	4.00	1.00
2222	A485	1.20 l multi	11.00	3.00

A486

Statue of Mother Albania.

1986, Nov. 29   Perf. 12x12½
2223	A486	10q peacock blue	.25	.25
2224	A486	20q henna brn	.25	.25
2225	A486	30q vermilion	.25	.25
2226	A486	50q dk olive bis	.25	.25
2227	A486	60q lt olive grn	.35	.25
2228	A486	80q rose	.25	.25
2229	A486	90q ultra	.50	.25
2230	A486	1.20 l green	1.00	.50
2231	A486	1.60 l red vio	1.25	.60
2232	A486	2.20 l myrtle grn	2.00	1.25
2233	A486	3 l brn org	2.50	1.75
2234	A486	6 l yel bister	5.00	3.25
		Nos. 2223-2234 (12)	13.85	9.10

For surcharges see Nos. 2435-2439.

Artifacts A487

Designs: 30q, Head of Aesoulapius, 5th cent. B.C. Byllis, marble. 80q, Aphrodite, 3rd cent. B.C., Fier, terracotta. 1 l, Pan, 3rd-2nd cent. B.C., Byllis, bronze. 1.20 l, Jupiter, A.D. 2nd cent., Tirana, limestone.

1987, Feb. 20
2235	A487	30q multi	1.00	.60
2236	A487	80q multi	2.00	1.00
2237	A487	1 l multi	3.00	1.40
2238	A487	1.20 l multi	4.00	2.50
		Nos. 2235-2238 (4)	10.00	5.50

A488

Gun, quill pen, book of the alphabet and: 30q, Monument, vert. 80q, School, Korca. 1.20 l, Students.

1987, Mar. 7   Perf. 12
2239	A488	30q multi	.40	.25
2240	A488	80q multi	1.25	.50
2241	A488	1.20 l multi	1.75	1.25
		Nos. 2239-2241 (3)	3.40	2.00

First Albanian school, cent.

A489

Famous Men: 30q, Victor Hugo, French author. 80q, Galileo Galilei, Italian mathematician, philosopher. 90q, Charles Darwin, British biologist. 1.30 l, Miguel Cervantes, Spanish novelist.

1987, Apr. 20
2242	A489	30q multi	.45	.25
2243	A489	80q multi	1.10	.50
2244	A489	90q multi	1.60	1.10
2245	A489	1.30 l multi	2.25	1.75
		Nos. 2242-2245 (4)	5.40	3.60

World Food Day — A490

30q, Forsythia europaea. 90q, Moltkia doerfleri. 2.10 l, Wulfenia baldacii.

1987, May 20
2246	A490	30q multicolored	.55	.30
2247	A490	90q multicolored	1.10	.75
2248	A490	2.10 l multicolored	2.40	2.10
		Nos. 2246-2248 (3)	4.05	3.15

10th Trade Unions Cong. — A491

1987, June 25
2249	A491	1.20 l multi	4.00 3.00

Sowing, by Bujar Asllani — A492

Paintings in the Eponymous Museum, Tirana: 30q, The Sustenance of Industry, by Myrteza Fushekati, vert. 80q, The Gifted Partisan, by Skender Kokobobo, vert. 1.20 l, At the Forging Block, by Clirim Ceka.

Perf. 12x12½, 12½x12

1987, July 20   Litho.
2250	A492	30q multi	.50	.40
2251	A492	80q multi	.80	.80
2252	A492	1 l shown	1.20	1.00
2253	A492	1.20 l multi	1.60	1.40
		Nos. 2250-2253 (4)	4.10	3.60

A493

OLYMPHILEX '87, Rome, Aug. 29-Sept. 6 — A494

1987, Aug. 29   Litho.   Perf. 12½
2254	A493	30q Hammer throw	.40	.40
2255	A493	90q Running	1.25	.80
2256	A493	1.10 l Shot put	1.25	1.00

Size: 85x60mm
2257	A494	1.90 l Runner, globe	2.00 2.00
		Nos. 2254-2257 (4)	4.90 4.20

Famous Men A495

Designs: 30q, Themistokli Germenji (1871-1917), author, politician. 80q, Bajram Curri (1862-1925), founder of the Albanian League. 90q, Aleks Stavre Drenova (1872-1947), poet. 1.30 l, Gjerasim D. Qiriazi (1861-1894), teacher, journalist.

1987, Sept. 30   **Perf. 12**

2258	A495	30q multi	.25	.25
2259	A495	80q multi	.90	.30
2260	A495	90q multi	1.10	.75
2261	A495	1.30 l multi	1.90	1.50
	Nos. 2258-2261 (4)		4.15	2.80

Albanian Labor Party Congress, Tirana
A496

1987, Oct. 22   **Litho.**   **Perf. 12**

2262	A496	1.20 l multi	5.00	3.50

Natl. Independence, 75th Anniv. — A497

1987, Nov. 27

2263	A497	1.20 l State flag	5.50	4.00

Postal Administration, 75th Anniv. — A498

1987, Dec. 5

2264	A498	90q P.O. emblem	5.00	3.50
2265	A498	1.20 l State seal	7.00	7.00

Art & Literature — A499

Portraits: 30q, Lord Byron (1788-1824), English Poet. 1.20 l, Eugene Delacroix (1798-1863), French painter.

1988, Mar. 10

2266	A499	30q org brn & blk	4.00	3.25
2267	A499	1.20 l pale vio & blk	16.00	12.50

WHO, 40th Anniv. — A500

1988, Apr. 7

2268	A500	90q multi	22.50	20.00
2269	A500	1.20 l multi	30.00	25.00

Flowers — A501

Designs: 30q, Sideritis raeseri. 90q, Lunaria telekiana. 2.10 l, Sanguisorba albanica.

1988, May 20   **Booklet Stamps**

2270	A501	30q multicolored	8.00	5.00
2271	A501	90q multicolored	16.00	11.00
2272	A501	2.10 l multicolored	24.00	16.00
a.		Bklt. pane of 3, plus label	50.00	50.00
	Nos. 2270-2272 (3)		48.00	32.00

10th Women's Federation Congress A502

1988, June 6

2273	A502	90q blk, red & dark org	21.00	19.00

European Soccer Championships — A503

Various athletes.
1.90 l, Goalie designs of Nos. 2274-2276.

1988, June 10

2274	A503	30q multicolored	2.00	2.00
2275	A503	80q multicolored	3.00	3.00
2276	A503	1.20 l multicolored	5.00	5.00

Size: 79x68mm

Imperf

2277	A503	1.90 l multicolored	12.00	12.00
	Nos. 2274-2277 (4)		22.00	22.00

League of Prizren, 110th Anniv. — A504

1988, June 10   **Litho.**   **Perf. 12**

2278	A504	30q Hands	40.00	40.00
2279	A504	1.20 l House	70.00	70.00

People's Army, 45th Anniv. — A505

1988, July 10

2280	A505	60q shown	40.00	40.00
2281	A505	90q Soldier statue	70.00	70.00

Famous Albanians A506

Designs: 30q, Mihal Grameno (1871-1931), author. 90q, Bajo Topulli (1868-1930), freedom fighter. 1 l, Murat Toptani (1868-1917), poet. 1.20 l, Jul Variboba, poet.

1988, Aug. 15

2282	A506	30q multi	15.00	15.00
2283	A506	90q multi	25.00	25.00
2284	A506	1 l multi	30.00	30.00
2284A	A506	1.20 l multi	40.00	40.00
	Nos. 2282-2284A (4)		110.00	110.00

Migjeni (1911-1938), Poet — A507

1988, Aug. 26   **Litho.**   **Perf. 12**

2285	A507	90q silver & brown	16.00	16.00

Ballads A508

1988, Sept. 5

2286	A508	30q Dede Skurra	10.00	8.00
2287	A508	90q Omeri Iri	25.00	21.00
2288	A508	1.20 l Gjergj Elez Alia	30.00	30.00
	Nos. 2286-2288 (3)		65.00	54.00

Folklore Festival Type of 1978

30q, Kerchief Dance. 1.20 l, Dancers with raised arm.

1988, Oct. 6

2289	A388	30q multi	30.00	30.00
2290	A388	1.20 l multi	110.00	90.00

Enver Hoxha Museum A510

Perf. 12x12½, 12½x12

1988, Oct. 16   **Litho.**

2291	A510	90q Portrait, vert.	4.00	4.00
2292	A510	1.20 l shown	6.00	6.00

Hoxha (1908-85), Communist leader.

Monastir Congress, 80th Anniv. A511

1988, Nov. 14   **Litho.**   **Perf. 12**

2293	A511	60q Scroll	22.50	20.00
2294	A511	90q Book, building	35.00	30.00

Locomotives, Map Showing Rail Network — A512

1989, Feb. 28   **Litho.**   **Perf. 12½x12**

2295	A512	30q 1947	.25	.25
2296	A512	90q 1949	.75	.35
2297	A512	1.20 l 1978	1.00	.60
2298	A512	1.80 l 1985	1.60	.75
2299	A512	2.40 l 1988	3.75	1.50
	Nos. 2295-2299 (5)		7.35	3.45

Archaeological Treasures — A513

30q, Illyrian grave. 90q, Warrior on horseback.

1989, Mar. 10   **Litho.**   **Perf. 12**

2300	A513	30q blk & tan	.25	.25
2301	A513	90q blk & dl grn	.90	.75
2302	A513	2.10 l shown	1.50	1.25
	Nos. 2300-2302 (3)		2.65	2.25

Folklore A514

1989, Apr. 5   **Litho.**   **Perf. 12x12½**

2303	A514	30q multicolored	.35	.25
2304	A514	90q multi, diff.	.75	.50
2305	A514	1 l multi, diff.	.75	.75
2306	A514	1.20 l multi, diff.	1.10	1.10
	Nos. 2303-2306 (4)		2.95	2.60

Flowers — A515

Designs: 30q, Aster albanicus. 90q, Orchis x paparisti. 2.10 l, Orchis albanica.

1989, May 10   **Perf. 12**

2307	A515	30q multicolored	.75	.30
2308	A515	90q multicolored	3.25	1.10
2309	A515	2.10 l multicolored	5.25	1.75
	Nos. 2307-2309 (3)		9.25	3.15

Famous People — A516

Designs: 30q, Johann Strauss the Younger (1825-1899), composer. 80q, Marie Curie (1867-1934), chemist. 1 l, Federico Garcia Lorca (1898-1936), poet. 1.20 l, Albert Einstein (1879-1955), physicist.

1989, June 3

2310	A516	30q gold & blk brn	.35	.25
2311	A516	80q gold & blk brn	.75	.45
2312	A516	1 l gold & blk brn	1.10	.90
2313	A516	1.20 l gold & blk brn	1.50	1.25
a.		Block of 4, #2310-2313	5.50	4.75
		Nos. 2310-2313 (4)	3.70	2.85

6th Congress of Albanian Democratic Front A517

1989, June 26

2314	A517	1.20 l multicolored	7.25	4.00

French Revolution, Bicent. — A518

90q, Storming of the Bastille. 1.20 l, Statue.

1989, July 7 Litho. Perf. 12½

2315	A518	90q multicolored	.65	.45
2316	A518	1.20 l shown	1.20	.75

Illyrian Ship A519

80q, Caravel. 90q, 3-masted schooner. 1.30 l, Modern cargo ship.

1989, July 25 Perf. 12

2317	A519	30q shown	.35	.25
2318	A519	80q multicolored	.70	.50
2319	A519	90q multicolored	.70	.70
2320	A519	1.30 l multicolored	1.00	1.00
		Nos. 2317-2320 (4)	2.75	2.45

A520

Famous Men: 30q, Pjeter Bogdani (1625-1689), writer. 80q, Gavril Dara (1826-1889), poet. 90q, Thimi Mitko (1820-1890), writer. 1.30 l, Kole Idromeno (1860-1939), painter.

1989, Aug. 30 Litho. Perf. 12

2321	A520	30q multicolored	.25	.25
2322	A520	80q multicolored	.50	.30
2323	A520	90q multicolored	.85	.60
2324	A520	1.30 l multicolored	1.25	.75
		Nos. 2321-2324 (4)	2.85	1.90

A521

1989, Sept. 29

2325	A521	90q shown	.70	.60
2326	A521	1.20 l Workers	1.00	.50

First Communist International, 125th anniv.

Spartakiad Games A522

1989, Oct. 27 Perf. 12x12½

2327	A522	30q Gymnastics	.25	.25
2328	A522	80q Soccer	.50	.25
2329	A522	1 l Cycling	.55	.45
2330	A522	1.20 l Running	.85	.75
		Nos. 2327-2330 (4)	2.15	1.70

Miniature Sheet

45th Anniv. of Liberation — A523

1989, Nov. 29 Perf. 12x12½

2331	A523	Sheet of 4	4.25	4.25
a.		30q Revolutionary	.50	.25
b.		80q "45"	1.00	.30
c.		1 l Coat of arms	1.00	.50
d.		1.20 l Workers	1.00	.85

Rupicapra Rupicapra A524

1990, Mar. 15 Perf. 12

2332	A524	10q Two adults	.25	.25
2333	A524	30q Adult, kid	.55	.25
2334	A524	80q Adult	1.60	.75
2335	A524	90q Adult head	1.60	1.00
a.		Block of 4, #2332-2335	5.00	5.00

World Wildlife Fund.

Tribal Masks A525

1990, Apr. 4 Perf. 12x12½

2336	A525	30q shown	.30	.30
2337	A525	90q multi, diff.	.65	.40
2338	A525	1 l multi, diff.	.90	.55
2339	A525	1.80 l multi, diff.	1.40	.80
		Nos. 2336-2339 (4)	3.25	2.05

Mushrooms A526

30q, Amanita caesarea. 90q, Lepiota procera. 1.20 l, Boletus edulis. 1.80 l, Clathrus cancelatus.

1990, Apr. 28 Litho. Perf. 12

2340	A526	30q multicolored	.25	.25
2341	A526	90q multicolored	.50	.40
2342	A526	1.20 l multicolored	.85	.60
2343	A526	1.80 l multicolored	1.20	1.00
		Nos. 2340-2343 (4)	2.80	2.45

First Postage Stamp, 150th Anniv. A527

1990, May 6 Perf. 12

2344	A527	90q shown	.45	.45
2345	A527	1.20 l Post rider	.90	.90
2346	A527	1.80 l Carriage	1.75	1.25
a.		Bklt. pane of 3, #2344-2346 + label	3.50	
		Nos. 2344-2346 (3)	3.10	2.60

World Cup Soccer, Italy A528

1990, June Litho. Perf. 12

2347	A528	30q multicolored	.30	.30
2348	A528	90q multi, diff.	.65	.65
2349	A528	1.20 l multi, diff.	1.10	.90

Size: 80x63mm

Imperf

2350	A528	3.30 l multi, diff.	3.25	3.25
		Nos. 2347-2350 (4)	5.30	5.10

Vincent Van Gogh, Death Cent. — A529

Self portraits and: 30q, Details from various paintings. 90q, Woman in field. 2.10 l, Asylum. 2.40 l, Self-portrait.

1990, July 27

2351	A529	30q multicolored	.40	.40
2352	A529	90q multicolored	.80	.80
2353	A529	2.10 l multicolored	1.75	1.75

Size: 87x73mm

Imperf

2354	A529	2.40 l multicolored	4.00	4.00
		Nos. 2351-2354 (4)	6.95	6.95

Albanian Folklore — A530

Scenes from medieval folktale of "Gjergj Elez Alia": 30q, Alia lying wounded. 90q, Alia being helped onto horse. 1.20 l, Alia fighting Bajloz. 1.80 l, Alia on horseback over severed head of Bajloz.

1990, Aug. 30 Perf. 12½x12

2355	A530	30q multicolored	.30	.30
2356	A530	90q multicolored	.70	.40
2357	A530	1.20 l multicolored	1.00	.80
2358	A530	1.80 l multicolored	1.50	1.00
		Nos. 2355-2358 (4)	3.50	2.50

Founding of Berat, 2400th Anniv. — A531

Designs: 30q, Xhamia E Plumbit. 90q, Kisha E Shen Triadhes. 1.20 l, Ura E Beratit. 1.80 l, Onufri-Piktor Mesjetar. 2.40 l, Nikolla-Piktor Mesjetar.

1990, Sept. 20 Perf. 12½

2359		Block of 5 + 4 labels	5.00	5.00
a.	A531	30q multi	.25	.25
b.	A531	90q multi	.25	.25
c.	A531	1.20 l multi	.60	.60
d.	A531	1.80 l multi	1.00	1.00
e.	A531	2.40 l multi	1.25	1.25

No. 2359 was sold in souvenir folders for 9.90 l.

Illyrian Heroes — A532

1990, Oct. 20 Perf. 12

2360	A532	30q Pirroja	.25	.25
2361	A532	90q Teuta	.50	.50
2362	A532	1.20 l Bato	.75	.75
2363	A532	1.80 l Bardhyli	1.00	1.00
		Nos. 2360-2363 (4)	2.50	2.50

Intl. Literacy Year A533

1990, Oct. 30

2364	A533	90q lt bl & multi	.65	.60
2365	A533	1.20 l pink & multi	.90	.90

Albanian Horseman by Eugene Delacroix A534

Designs: 1.20 l, Albanian Woman by Camille Corot. 1.80 l, Skanderbeg by unknown artist.

1990, Nov. 30 Perf. 12x12½

2366	A534	30q multicolored	.30	.30
2367	A534	1.20 l multicolored	.90	.70
2368	A534	1.80 l multicolored	1.25	1.00
		Nos. 2366-2368 (3)	2.45	2.00

A535

1.20 l, Boletini standing.

1991, Jan. 23 Litho. Perf. 12x12½

2369	A535	90q shown	.60	.50
2370	A535	1.20 l multicolored	.90	.70

Isa Boletini (1864-1916), freedom fighter.

A536

1991, Jan. 30   Litho.   *Perf. 12*
Background Color
2371 A536   90q   pale yellow   .60   .50
2372 A536   1.20 l pale gray   .90   .70

Arberi State, 800th anniv.

Pierre Auguste Renoir (1841-1919),
Painter — A537

Paintings: 30q, Girl Reading, 1876, vert.
90q, The Swing, 1876, vert. 1.20 l, Boating
Party, 1868-1869. 1.80 l, Flowers and grapes,
1878. 3 l, Self-portrait.

1991, Feb. 25   *Perf. 12½x12*
2373 A537   30q   multicolored   .50   .25
2374 A537   90q   multicolored   .75   .50
2375 A537   1.20 l multicolored   1.10   .90
2376 A537   1.80 l multicolored   1.75 1.40

Size: 95x75mm
Imperf
2377 A537   3 l   multicolored   4.00 4.00
     Nos. 2373-2377 (5)   8.10 7.05

Flowers — A538

30q, Cistus albanicus. 90q, Trifolium pilczii.
1.80 l, Lilium albanicum.

1991, Mar. 30   *Perf. 12*
2378 A538   30q   multicolored   .30   .30
2379 A538   90q   multicolored   .70   .70
2380 A538   1.80 l multicolored 1.40 1.00
     Nos. 2378-2380 (3)   2.40 2.00

Legend of
Rozafa
A539

Various scenes from legend.

1991, Sept. 30 Litho.   *Perf. 12x12½*
2381 A539   30q   multicolored   .30   .30
2382 A539   90q   multicolored   .50   .30
2383 A539   1.20 l multicolored 1.00   .70
2384 A539   1.80 l multicolored 1.40 1.20
     Nos. 2381-2384 (4)   3.20 2.50

For surcharges see Nos. 2586, 2604.

Wolfgang
Amadeus Mozart,
Death
Bicent. — A540

1991, Oct. 5   Litho.   *Perf. 12*
2385 A540   90q   Conducting   .75   .45
2386 A540   1.20 l Portrait   1.00   .70
2387 A540   1.80 l Playing piano 1.60 1.20

Size: 89x70mm
Imperf
2388 A540   3 l   Medal, score   5.00 5.00
     Nos. 2385-2388 (4)   8.35 7.35

Airplanes — A541

Designs: 30q, Glider, Otto Lilienthal, 1896.
80q, Avion III, Clement Ader, 1897. 90q, Flyer,
Wright Brothers, 1903. 1.20 l, Concorde.
1.80 l, Tupolev 114. 2.40 l, Dornier 31 E.

1992, Jan. 27   Litho.   *Perf. 12½x12*
2389 A541   30q   multicolored   .30   .30
2390 A541   80q   multicolored   .45   .35
2391 A541   90q   multicolored   .65   .55
2392 A541   1.20 l multicolored   .90   .65
2393 A541   1.80 l multicolored   .90   .65
2394 A541   2.40 l multicolored 1.40 1.20
     Nos. 2389-2394 (6)   4.60 3.70

No. 2393 misidentifies a Tupolev 144.

Explorers — A542

1992, Jan. 10
2395 A542   30q   Bering   .30   .30
2396 A542   90q   Columbus   .70   .30
2397 A542   1.80 l Magellan   1.50   .90
     Nos. 2395-2397 (3)   2.50 1.50

1992 Winter
Olympics,
Albertville
A543

30q, Ski jumping. 90q, Cross country skiing.
1.20 l, Pairs figure skating. 1.80 l, Luge.

1992, Feb. 15   Litho.   *Perf. 12½*
2398 A543   30q   multicolored   .30   .30
2399 A543   90q   multicolored   .50   .45
2400 A543   1.20 l multicolored   .75   .60
2401 A543   1.80 l multicolored 1.10 1.00
     Nos. 2398-2401 (4)   2.65 2.35

For surcharge see No. 2598.

Participation of Albania in Conference
on Security and Cooperation in
Europe, Berlin (1991) — A544

1992, Mar. 31   Litho.   *Perf. 12½x12*
2402 A544   90q   shown   .85   .85
2403 A544   1.20 l Flags, map 1.00 1.00
  a.   Pair, #2402-2403   3.50 3.50

   Dated 1991. Issued in sheets containing 2
No. 2403a, 3 each Nos. 2402-2403 + 2 labels.
No. 2402 was also issued in sheets of 16.

Albanian Admission to CEPT — A545

90q, Envelopes, CEPT emblem.

1992, Apr. 25   Litho.   *Perf. 12½*
2404 A545   90q blk, blue & red
                   lil   .85   .85
2405 A545   1.20 l blk, pur & red lil 1.00 1.00
  a.   Pair, #2404-2405   1.90 1.90

   Issued in sheets containing 2 No. 2405a, 3
each Nos. 2404-2405 and 2 labels.

Martyrs' Day — A546

90q, Freedom flame, vert. 4.10 l, Flowers.

1992, May 5   *Perf. 12x12½*
2406 A546   90q   multicolored   .50   .50
**   *Perf. 12½x12***
2407 A546   4.10 l multicolored   2.50 2.00

European Soccer Championships,
Sweden'92 — A547

Various stylized designs of soccer plays.

1992, June 10   Litho.   *Perf. 12*
2408 A547   30q   green & lt grn .40   .25
2409 A547   90q   blue & pink   .75   .50
2410 A547   10.80 l henna & tan 4.50 3.75

Size: 90x70mm
Imperf
2411 A547   5 l   tan, lt green &
                   pink   2.75 2.75
     Nos. 2408-2411 (4)   8.40 7.25

1992
Summer
Olympics,
Barcelona
A548

1992, June 14   Litho.   *Perf. 12*
2412 A548   30q   Tennis   .35   .35
2413 A548   90q   Baseball   1.00   .55
2414 A548   1.80 l Table tennis 2.00 1.50

Size: 90x70mm
Imperf
2415 A548   5 l   Torch bearer 3.25 3.25
     Nos. 2412-2415 (4)   6.60 5.65

United
Europe
A549

1992, July 10   Litho.   *Perf. 12*
2416 A549   1.20 l multicolored 1.00   .75

Horses
A550

30q, Native. 90q, Nonius. 1.20 l, Arabian,
vert. 10.60 l, Haflinger, vert.

1992, Aug. 10   Litho.   *Perf. 12*
2417 A550   30q   multicolored   .25   .25
2418 A550   90q   multicolored   .40   .40
2419 A550   1.20 l multicolored   .55   .55
2420 A550   10.60 l multicolored 4.25 4.25
     Nos. 2417-2420 (4)   5.45 5.45

For surcharge, see No. 2781.

Discovery
of America,
500th
Anniv.
A551

Map of North and South America and: 60q,
Columbus, sailing ships. 3.20 l, Columbus
meeting natives. 5 l, Map, Columbus.

1992, Aug. 20
2421 A551   60q blk, bl & gray   .50   .50
2422 A551   3.20 l blk, brn &
                    gray   3.50 3.50

Size: 90x70mm
Imperf
2423 A551   5 l   multi   70.00 70.00

Mother Theresa,
Infant — A552

1992, Oct. 4   Litho.   *Perf. 12x12½*
2424 A552   40q fawn   .30   .30
2425 A552   60q brown   .30   .30
2426 A552   1 l violet   .30   .30
2427 A552   1.80 l gray   .30   .30
2428 A552   2 l red   .30   .30
2429 A552   2.40 l green   .30   .30
2430 A552   3.20 l blue   .40   .40
2431 A552   5.60 l rose violet   .60   .60
2432 A552   7.20 l olive   1.00 1.00
2433 A552   10 l org brn   1.25 1.25
     Nos. 2424-2433 (10)   5.05 5.05

See Nos. 2472-2476.
For surcharge, see No. 2786.

A553

1993, Apr. 25   Litho.   Perf. 12
2434 A553 16 l multicolored   2.50 2.50
Visit of Pope John Paul II.

Nos. 2223-2226,
2229 Surcharged

1993, May 2   Litho.   Perf. 12x12½
2435 A486   3 l on 10q   .25   .25
2436 A486   6.50 l on 20q   .55   .55
2437 A486 13 l on 30q   1.50   1.50
2438 A486 20 l on 90q   2.25   2.25
2439 A486 30 l on 50q   3.00   3.00
      Nos. 2435-2439 (5)   7.55   7.55

Lef Nosi
(1873-1945),
Minister of
Posts
A554

1993, May 5   Litho.   Perf. 12
2440 A554 6.50 l ol brn & bister   .90   .90
First Albanian postage stamps, 80th anniv.

Europa
A555

Contemporary paintings by: 3 l, A. Zajmi,
vert. 7 l, E. Hila. 20 l, B. Ahmeti-Peizazh.

1993, May 28   Litho.   Perf. 12
2441 A555   3 l multicolored   .90   .90
2442 A555   7 l multicolored   3.50   3.50
Size: 116x122mm
2443 A555 20 l multicolored   6.50   6.50
      Nos. 2441-2443 (3)   10.90 10.90

1993 Mediterranean Games,
France — A556

3 l, Running. 16 l, Kayaking. 21 l, Cycling.
20 l, Mediterranean map.

1993, June 20   Litho.   Perf. 12
2444 A556   3 l multicolored   .30   .30
2445 A556 16 l multicolored   1.75   1.75
2446 A556 21 l multicolored   2.40   2.40
Size: 111x78mm
Imperf
2447 A556 20 l multicolored   3.25   3.25
      Nos. 2444-2447 (4)   7.70   7.70
For surcharge, see No. 2789.

Frang Bardhi,
Author, 350th
Death Anniv.
A557

1993, Aug. 20   Litho.   Perf. 12x12½
2448 A557 6.50 l shown   1.10   1.10
Size: 89x101mm
Imperf
2449 A557 20 l Writing at desk   3.50   3.50

A558

68 l, Mascot, ball, US map.

1994, July 17   Litho.   Perf. 12
2450 A558 42 l shown   1.10   1.10
2451 A558 68 l multicolored   1.60   1.60
1994 World Cup Soccer Championships, US.

A559

European Inventors, Discoveries: 50 l,
Gjovalin Gjadri, engineer. 100 l, Karl von
Ghega, Austrian engineer. 150 l, Sketch of
road project.

1994, Dec. 31   Litho.   Perf. 14
2452 A559   50 l multicolored   1.50   1.50
2453 A559 100 l multicolored   2.25   2.25
Size: 50x70mm
Imperf
2454 A559 150 l multicolored   3.75   3.75
      Nos. 2452-2454 (3)   7.50   7.50
      Europa (No. 2454).

Ali Pasa of Tepelene (Lion of Janina)
(1744-1822) — A560

1995, Jan. 28   Perf. 14
2455 A560 60 l shown   1.40   1.40
Size: 70x50mm
Imperf
2456 A560 100 l Tepelene Palace 1.50   1.50

Intl. Olympic Committee,
Cent. — A561

1995, Feb. 2   Imperf.
2457 A561 80 l multicolored   1.75   1.75

Karl Benz (1844-1929), Automobile
Pioneer — A562

Designs: 5 l, Automobile company emblem,
Benz. 10 l, Modern Mercedes Benz automobile. 60 l, First four-wheel Benz 1886 motor
car. 125 l, Pre-war Mercedes touring car.

1995, Jan. 21   Litho.   Perf. 14
2458 A562   5 l multicolored   .30   .30
2459 A562   10 l multicolored   .30   .30
2460 A562   60 l multicolored   .90   .90
2461 A562 125 l multicolored   3.00   3.00
      Nos. 2458-2461 (4)   4.50   4.50

Liberation,
50th Anniv.
(in 1994)
A563

1995, Jan. 28   Litho.   Perf. 14
2462 A563 50 l black, gray & red 1.25 1.25
      Dated 1994.

Miniature Sheet

Albania '93 — A564

Composers: a, 3 l, Wagner. b, 6.50 l, Grieg.
c, 11 l, Gounod. d, 20 l, Tchaikovsky.

1995, Jan. 26   Perf. 12
2463 A564 Sheet of 4, #a.-d.   2.50   2.50

Voskopoja Academy, 250th
Anniv. — A565

Buildings of Voskopoja.

1995, Feb. 2
2464   42 l multicolored   .90   .90
2465   68 l multicolored   2.25   2.25
   a.   A565 Pair, #2464-2465   3.50   3.50

Bleta
Apricula — A566

5 l, On flower. 10 l, Honeycomb, bee. 25 l,
Emerging from cell of honeycomb.

1995, Aug. 20   Litho.   Perf. 12
2466 A566   5 l multicolored   .30   .30
2467 A566 10 l multicolored   .30   .30
2468 A566 25 l multicolored   1.25   1.25
      Nos. 2466-2468 (3)   1.85   1.85

Peace &
Freedom — A567

Stylized hands reaching for: 50 l, Olive
branch. 100 l, Peace dove.
150 l, Stylized person.

1995, Aug. 10   Perf. 13½x14
2469 A567   50 l multicolored   1.75   1.75
2470 A567 100 l multicolored   3.50   3.50
Size: 80x60mm
Imperf
2471 A567 150 l multicolored   5.00   5.00
      Nos. 2469-2471 (3)   10.25 10.25
      Europa.
For surcharges, see Nos. B39-B40.

Mother Teresa Type of 1992
1994-95   Litho.   Perf. 12x12½
2472 A552   5 l violet   .30   .30
2473 A552 18 l orange   1.10   1.10
2474 A552 20 l rose lilac   .45   .45
2475 A552 25 l green   1.75   1.75
2476 A552 60 l olive   1.75   1.75
      Nos. 2472-2476 (5)   5.35   5.35

Issued: 20 l, 1994; 60 l, 1995; others, 7/94.

Arctic Explorers — A568

Designs: a, Fridtjof Nansen (1861-1930), Norway. b, James Cook (1728-79), England. c, Roald Amundsen (1872-1928), Norway. d, Robert F. Scott (1872-1928), Great Britain.

1995, Sept. 14   Litho.   Perf. 13½x14
2477 A568 25 l Block of 4, #a.-d.   3.50 3.50

For surcharges, see No. 2790.

UN, 50th Anniv. A569

100 l, Like #2478, flags streaming to right.

1995, Sept. 14   Litho.   Perf. 14x13½
2478 A569   2 l shown   .25 .25
2479 A569 100 l multicolored   1.90 1.90

For surcharge, see No. 2782.

Poets — A570

1995   Perf. 13½x14
2480 A570 25 l Paul Éluard   .65 .65
2481 A570 50 l Sergei Yesenin   1.25 1.25
  a.   Pair, #2480-2481   2.00 2.00

Entry into Council of Europe A571

Designs: 25 l, Doves flying from headquarters, Strasbourg. 85 l, Albanian eagle over map of Europe.

1995   Perf. 14x13½
2482 A571 25 l multicolored   .90 .90
2483 A571 85 l multicolored   3.25 3.25

For surcharge see No. 2583.

Jan Kukuzeli, Composer A572

Stylized figure: 18 l, Writing. 20 l, Holding hand to head. 100 l, Holding up scroll of paper.

1995, Oct. 17   Perf. 13½x14
2484 A572 18 l multicolored   .50 .50
2485 A572 20 l multicolored   .50 .50
Size: 74x74mm
2486 A572 100 l multicolored   2.50 2.50
    Nos. 2484-2486 (3)   3.50 3.50

For surcharge, see No. 2787.

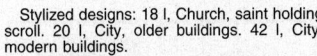

World Tourism Organization, 20th Anniv. — A573

Stylized designs: 18 l, Church, saint holding scroll. 20 l, City, older buildings. 42 l, City, modern buildings.

1995, Oct. 17
2487 A573 18 l multicolored   .50 .50
2488 A573 20 l multicolored   .65 .65
2489 A573 42 l multicolored   1.40 1.40
    Nos. 2487-2489 (3)   2.55 2.55

For surcharge, see No. 2788.

Fables of Jean de la Fontaine (1621-95) A574

Designs: 2 l, Raptor, turtle, wolf, goose, mouse, lion, rats. 3 l, Crow, goose, dog, foxes. 25 l, Insect, doves, frogs. 60 l, Drawings of Da la Fontaine, animals, birds.

1995, Aug. 20   Litho.   Perf. 14x13½
2490 A574   2 l multicolored   .25 .25
2491 A574   3 l multicolored   .25 .25
2492 A574 25 l multicolored   .50 .50
Imperf
Size: 73x56mm
2493 A574 60 l multicolored   2.00 2.00
    Nos. 2490-2493 (4)   3.00 3.00

For surcharges, see Nos. 2783, 2784, 2791.

Folklore Festival, Berat — A575

Stylized designs: 5 l, Men's choir. 50 l, Costumed woman seated in chair.

1995, Oct. 17   Litho.   Perf. 13½x14
2494 A575   5 l multicolored   .25 .25
2495 A575 50 l multicolored   1.20 1.20

Motion Pictures, Cent. — A576

1995, Nov. 17
2496 A576 10 l Louis Lumiere   .25 .25
2497 A576 85 l Auguste Lumiere   1.50 1.50
  a.   Pair, #2496-2497   2.00 2.00

Elvis Presley (1935-77) A577

1995, Nov. 20   Litho.   Perf. 14x13½
2498 A577   3 l orange & multi   .30 .30
2499 A577 60 l green & multi   1.75 1.75

For surcharge, see No. 2785.

A578

1995, Nov. 25   Perf. 13½x14
2500 A578 10 l 1925 Bank notes   .30 .30
2501 A578 25 l 1995 Bank notes   .80 .80

National Bank, 70th anniv.

A579

50 l, Maiden planting tree.

1995, Nov. 27   Litho.   Perf. 13½x14
2502 A579   5 l shown   .25 .25
2503 A579 50 l multicolored   1.50 1.50

Democracy, 5th anniv.

A580

Designs: 25 l, Soccer ball, British flag, map of Europe, stadium. 100 l, Soccer ball, player.

1996, June 4   Perf. 14
2504 A580 25 l multicolored   .50 .50
2505 A580 100 l multicolored   2.25 2.25

Euro '96, European Soccer Championships, Great Britain.
For surcharge, see No. 2792.

Mother Teresa — A581

150 l, Mother Teresa, diff.

1996, May 5   Perf. 13½x14
2506 A581   25 l blue & multi   .90 .90
2507 A581 100 l red & multi   2.25 2.25
Size: 52x74mm
Imperf
2508 A581 150 l multi   6.25 6.25
    Nos. 2506-2508 (3)   9.40 9.40

Europa. For overprints see Nos. 2551, 2582.

GSM Cellular Telephone Transmission A582

Designs: 10 l, Satellite transmitting signals. 60 l, Uses for cellular telephone, vert.

Perf. 13x13½, 13½x13
1996, Aug. 1   Litho.
2509 A582 10 l multicolored   .25 .25
2510 A582 60 l multicolored   1.50 1.50

1996 Summer Olympic Games, Atlanta — A583

Stylized designs: 5 l, Runners. 25 l, Throwers. 60 l, Jumpers. 100 l, Emblem, US flag.

1996, Aug. 3   Litho.   Perf. 13x14
2511 A583   5 l multicolored   .25 .25
2512 A583   25 l multicolored   .55 .55
2513 A583   60 l multicolored   1.50 1.50
Size: 52x37mm
Imperf
2514 A583 100 l multicolored   2.25 2.25
    Nos. 2511-2514 (4)   4.55 4.55

Gottfried Wilhelm Leibniz (1646-1716), Mathematician — A584

85 l, René Descartes (1596-1650), mathematician.

1996, Sept. 20   Litho.   Perf. 14
2515 A584 10 l multicolored   .40 .40
2516 A584 85 l multicolored   2.00 2.00

Paintings by Francisco Goya (1746-1828) A585

Designs: 10 l, The Naked Maja. 60 l, Dona Isabel Cobos de Porcel. 100 l, Self portrait.

1996, Sept. 25   Perf. 14x13½
2517 A585 10 l multicolored   .30 .30
2518 A585 60 l multicolored   1.40 1.40
Souvenir Sheet
2519 A585 100 l multicolored   2.00 2.00

Religious Engravings — A586

Designs: a, 5 l, Book cover showing crucifixion, angels. b, 25 l, Medallion of crucifixion. c, 85 l, Book cover depicting life of Christ.

1996, Nov. 5   Perf. 13x13½
2520 A586 Block of 3, #a.-c. +
            label   2.50 2.50

UNICEF, 50th
Anniv. — A587

Children's paintings: 5 l, Fairy princess. 10 l, Doll, sun. 25 l, Sea life. 50 l, House, people.

1996, Nov. 11   Perf. 13½
2521 A587 5 l   multicolored   .25   .25
2522 A587 10 l multicolored   .25   .25
2523 A587 25 l multicolored   .80   .80
2524 A587 50 l multicolored   1.20 1.20
      Nos. 2521-2524 (4)   2.50 2.50

Gjergj Fishta
(1871-1940),
Writer,
Priest — A588

60 l, Battle scene, portrait.

1996, Dec. 20   Perf. 13½x14
2525 A588 10 l shown   .25   .25
2526 A588 60 l multicolored   1.40 1.40

Omar
Khayyam — A589

1997, Mar. 6   Perf. 14
2527 A589 20 l shown   .40   .40
2528 A589 50 l Portrait, diff. 1.00 1.00

A590

1997, Mar. 20   Perf. 14x14½
2529 A590 20 l Portrait   .40   .40
2530 A590 60 l Printing press   1.20 1.20
  a. Pair, #2529-2530   1.75 1.75

Johannes Gutenberg (1397?-1468).

A591

The Azure Eye (Stories and Legends): 30 l, Dragon on rock looking at warrior, donkey. 100 l, Dragon drinking water from pond, warrior.

1997, May 5   Litho.   Perf. 13x14
2531 A591 30 l multicolored   .70   .70
2532 A591 100 l multicolored   2.25 2.25

Europa.

A592

1997, Apr. 10   Perf. 14
2533   10 l Pelicanus crispus .25   .25
2534   80 l Pelicans, diff.   1.40 1.40
  a. A592 Pair, #2533-2534   1.75 1.75

No. 2534a is a continuous design.

A593

1997, June 25   Litho.   Perf. 14
2535 A593 10 l blk & dark brn   .25   .25
2536 A593 25 l blk & blue blk   .75   .75

Souvenir Sheet
2537 A593 80 l gray brown   2.00 2.00

Faik Konica (1875-1942), writer and politician.
No. 2537 contains one 22x26mm stamp.

A594

1997 Mediterranean Games, Bari: 20 l, Man running. 30 l, Woman running, 3-man canoe.

100 l, Man breaking finish line, silhouettes of man and woman.

1997, June 13
2538 A594 20 l multicolored   .40   .40
2539 A594 30 l multicolored   .80   .80

            Size: 52x74mm
               Imperf
2540 A594 100 l multicolored   2.00 2.00

Skanderbeg — A595

1997, Aug. 25   Litho.   Perf. 13
2541 A595 5 l   red brn & red   .25   .25
2542 A595 10 l dp ol & ol   .25   .25
2543 A595 20 l dp grn & grn   .40   .40
2544 A595 25 l dp mag & red
                   lil   .50   .50
2545 A595 30 l dk vio & vio   .55   .55
2546 A595 50 l black   .80   .80
2547 A595 60 l brn & lt brn   1.00 1.00
2548 A595 80 l dk brown &
                   brn   1.50 1.50
2549 A595 100 l dk red brown
                   & red brn   1.75 1.75
2550 A595 110 l dark blue   1.90 1.90
      Nos. 2541-2550 (10)   8.90 8.90

No. 2507 Ovptd. in Silver "HOMAZH
          / 1910-1997"

1997   Perf. 13½x14
2551 A581 100 l red & multi   2.50 2.50

Religious Manuscripts — A596

Albanian Codex: a, 10 l, 11th cent. b, 25 l, 6th cent. c, 60 l, 6th cent., diff.

1997, Nov. 15   Litho.   Perf. 13x14
2552 A596 Block of 3, #a.-c. +
            label   2.25 2.25
            See No. 2575.

Post and Telecommunications
Administration, 85th Anniv. — A597

1997, Dec. 4   Perf. 13½
2553 A597 10 l multi   .25   .25
2554 A597 30 l multi, diff.   .75   .75

A598

1998, Mar. 25   Litho.   Perf. 14
2555 A598 30 l red brn & multi   .60   .60
2556 A598 100 l tan & multi   1.90 1.90
  a. Pair, #2555-2556   2.50 2.50

Nikete Dardani, musician.

A599

Legends of Pogradec Ohrid Lake: a, 30 l, Old man seated at table. b, 50 l, Three Graces. c, 60 l, Two women, fountain. d, 80 l, Iceman.

1998, Apr. 15
2557 A599 Block of 4, #a.-d.   3.50 3.50

A600

1998, May 5   Litho.   Perf. 13x14
2558 A600 60 l shown   1.50 1.50
2559 A600 100 l multi, diff.   2.00 2.00

            Size: 50x72mm
               Imperf
2560 A600 150 l multi, diff.   3.50 3.50

Europa (folk festivals).

A601

Albanian League of Prizren, 120th anniv.: a, 30 l, Abdyl Frasheri. b, 50 l, Sulejman Vokshi. c, 60 l, Iljaz Pashe Dibra. d, 80 l, Ymer Prizreni.

1998, June 10   Litho.   Perf. 13½x13
2561 A601 Block of 4, #a.-d.   2.75 2.75

1998 World Cup Soccer Championships, France — A602

Stylized soccer players.

1998, June 10   Perf. 13½
2562 A602 60 l multicolored   .90 .90
2563 A602 100 l multicolored   1.60 1.60
Size: 50x73mm
Imperf
2564 A602 120 l Mascot   2.25 2.25

European Youth Greco-Roman Wrestling Championships, Albania — A603

1998, July 5   Perf. 13½
2565 A603 30 l shown   .50 .50
2566 A603 60 l Wrestlers, diff.   1.00 1.00
  a.   Pair, #2565-2566   1.60 1.60

Eqerem Cabej (1908-1980), Albanian Etymologist — A604

1998, Aug. 7   Perf. 14
2567 A604 60 l yel brn & multi   .80 .80
2568 A604 80 l brn red & multi   1.20 1.20
  a.   Pair, #2567-2568   2.25 2.25

Paul Gauguin (1848-1903) A605

Paintings (details): 60 l, The Vision after the Sermon. 80 l, Ea Haere la Oe.

---

120 l, Stylized design to resemble self-portrait.

1998, Sept. 10   Perf. 13½
2569 A605 60 l multicolored   .90 .90
2570 A605 80 l multicolored   1.25 1.25
  a.   Pair, #2569-2570   2.25 2.25
Size: 50x73mm
Imperf
2571 A605 120 l multicolored   2.25 2.25

Epitaph of Gllavenica, 14th Cent. Depiction of Christ — A606

Designs: 30 l, Entire cloth showing artwork. 80 l, Closer view. 100 l, Upper portion of cloth, vert.

1998, Oct. 5   Perf. 14½x14
2572 A606 30 l multicolored   .50 .50
2573 A606 80 l multicolored   1.50 1.50
Souvenir Sheet
Perf. 13
2574 A606 100 l multicolored   1.75 1.75

No. 2574 contains one 25x29mm stamp.

Religious Manuscripts Type of 1997

Illustrations from Purple Codex, Gold Codex: a, 30 l, Manuscript, columns on sides, arched top. b, 50 l, Manuscript cover with embossed pictures of icons. c, 80 l, Manuscript picturing cathedral, birds.

1998, Oct. 15   Perf. 13x14
2575 A596 Block of 3, #a.-c. + label   3.00 3.00

Mikel Koliqi (1902-97), First Albanian Cardinal — A607

1998, Nov. 28   Perf. 14
2576 A607 30 l shown   .50 .50
2577 A607 100 l Portrait, facing   1.75 1.75
  a.   Pair, #2576-2577   2.50 2.50

Mother Teresa (1910-97) — A608

60 l, With child, horiz.

Perf. 14x13½, 13½x14
1998, Sept. 5   Photo.
2578 A608 60 l multicolored   1.50 1.50
2579 A608 100 l shown   2.50 2.50

See Italy Nos. 2254-2255.

Diana, Princess of Wales (1961-97) — A609

100 l, With Mother Teresa.

1998, Aug. 31   Litho.   Perf. 13½
2580 A609 60 l shown   2.00 2.00
2581 A609 100 l multicolored   3.00 3.00

No. 2508 Overprinted in Blue

1998, Oct. 23   Litho.   Imperf.
2582 A581 150 l multicolored   8.00 8.00

No. 2482 Surcharged

1999, Apr. 20   Litho.   Perf. 14x13½
2583 A571 150 l on 25 l multi   4.00 4.00

Famous Americans — A610

a, Washington. b, Lincoln. c, Martin Luther King, Jr.

1999, Mar. 15   Perf. 14
2584 A610 150 l Block of 3, #a.-c. + label   9.00 9.00

Monachus Albiventer — A611

Seals: a, 110 l, One looking left, one looking right. b, 150 l, Both looking right. c, 110 l, Mirror image of No. 2585b. d, 150 l, Mirror image of No. 2585a.

1999, Apr. 10
2585 A611 Sheet of 4, #a.-d.   10.00 10.00

No. 2382 Surcharged

1999, Apr. 24   Litho.   Perf. 12x12¼
2586 A539 150 l on 90 l multi   3.25 3.25

IBRA '99, Nuremburg.

A612

1999, Apr. 25   Litho.   Perf. 13½x13¾
2587 A612 10 l blue & multi   .75 .75
2588 A612 100 l green & multi   4.00 4.00
Souvenir Sheet
Perf. 13
2589 A612 250 l green & multi   5.00 5.00

NATO, 50th anniv. No. 2589 contains one 30x50mm stamp.

A613

Cartoon mouse: a, 80 l, Writing. b, 110 l, Holding chin. c, 150 l, Wearing bow tie. d, 60 l, Pointing.

1999, Apr. 30   Litho.   Perf. 13x13¾
2590 A613 Strip of 4, #a.-d.   8.50 8.50

Animated films.

Europa A614

1999, May 1   Litho.   Perf. 13¾x13
2591 A614 90 l Thethi Park   2.00 2.00
2592 A614 310 l Lura Park   4.50 4.50
Imperf
Size: 80x60mm
2592A A614 350 l Kombetare Park   9.00 9.00
  Nos. 2591-2592A (3)   15.50 15.50

Illyrian Coins
A615

Designs: a, 200 l, Kings of Illyria — Monumiou c. 300-280 BC cow suckling calf, square containing double stellate pattern, and Epidamos-Dyrrachium c. 623 BC, square with double stellate. b, 20 l, Damastion c. 395-380 BC siver drachm portable ingot, Byllis c. 238-168 BC AE13 serpent entwined around cornucopia, Skodra after 168 BC, AE17 war galley, and other war galley coin. c, 10l, Epirote Republic before 238 BC silver tetraobol with jugate busts of Zeus and Dione on obverse and thunderbolt within oak wreath reverse.

310 l, Kings of Illyria — Genthos c. 197-168 BC head wearing kausia.

1999, June 1   Litho.   Perf. 13¾x13¼
2593 A615   Strip of 3, #a.-c.   5.00 5.00
Souvenir Sheet
Perf. 13
2594 A615   310 l multicolored   6.50 6.50

Charlie
Chaplin — A616

Designs: 30 l, Holding cigarette. 50 l, Tipping hat. 250 l, Dancing.

1999, June 20   Litho.   Perf. 14x14¼
2595 A616   30 l multicolored   .75   .75
2596 A616   50 l multicolored   1.50 1.50
2597 A616   250 l multicolored   6.00 6.00
  a.   Booklet pane, 2 each
       #2595-2597, perf. 14¼
       vert.   70.00
       Complete booklet   70.00
       Nos. 2595-2597 (3)   8.25 8.25

In No. 2597a, the 30 l stamps are at the ends of the pane and the 250 l stamps are in the middle.

No. 2398
Surcharged

1999, July 2   Litho.   Perf. 12½
2598 A543   150 l on 30q multi   3.00 3.00

PhilexFrance 99.

Holocaust — A617

1999, July 6   Litho.   Perf. 14x14¼
2599 A617   30 l brown & multi   .60   .60
2600 A617   150 l gray & multi   3.25 3.25

First Manned Moon Landing, 30th
Anniv. — A618

No. 2601: a, 30 l, Astronaut, earth. b, 150 l, Lunar Module. c, 300 l, Astronaut, flag. 280 l, Lift-off.

1999, July 25   Litho.   Perf. 13¼x14
2601 A618   Strip of 3, #a.-c.   10.00 10.00
Souvenir Sheet
Perf. 13
2602 A618   280 l multicolored   6.00 6.00

No. 2602 contains one 25x29mm stamp.

UPU, 125th Anniv. — A619

Background colors: a, 20 l, aquamarine and brown. b, 60 l, bister and dark blue.

1999, Aug. 1   Litho.   Perf. 14x14¼
2603 A619   Pair, #a.-b.   2.00 2.00

No. 2383
Surcharged in
Brown, Symbol
in Red and
Green

1999   Method & Perf. as Before
2604 A539   150 l on 1.20 l multi   3.00 3.00

China 1999 World Philatelic Exhibition.

A620

Background colors: a, 10 l, Yellow. b, 20 l, Orange. c, 200 l, Green.

1999, Sept. 2   Litho.   Perf. 14x14¼
2605 A620   Strip of 3, #a.-c.   5.00 5.00

First Natl. Track & Field Championships, 70th anniv.

A621

30 l, Madonna and Child.

1999, Oct. 30   Perf. 14
2606 A621   30 l multicolored   .50   .50
2607 A621   300 l shown   6.00 6.00
  a.   Souv. sheet, 2 ea #2606-
       2607   12.00 12.00

Art by Onufri of Elbasan.

Famous Albanians — A622

Designs: a, 10 l, Bilal Golemi (1899-1955), veterinarian. b, 20 l, Azem Galica (1889-1924), freedom fighter. c, 50 l, Viktor Eftimiu (1889-1972), writer. d, 300 l, Lasgush Poradeci (1900-87), poet.

1999, Nov. 28   Litho.   Perf. 14¼x14
2608 A622   Block of 4, #a.-d.   8.00 8.00

Carnival
Masks — A623

1999, Dec. 1   Perf. 13¾
2609 A623   30 l shown   .50   .50
2610 A623   300 l Turkey head   6.50 6.50

Millennium
A624

2000, Mar. 27   Litho.   Perf. 13½x14
2611 A624   40 l red & multi   .75   .75
2612 A624   90 l blue & multi   2.00 2.00

Native Costumes — A625

a, 5 l, Librazhdi. b, 10 l, Malesia e Madhe woman. c, 15 l, Malesia e Madhe man. d, 20 l, Tropoje. e, 30 l, Dumrea. f, 35 l, Tirana man. g, 40 l, Tirana woman. h, 45 l, Arbereshe. i, 50 l, Gjirokaster. j, 55 l, Lunxheri. k, 70 l, Cameria. l, 90 l, Laberia.

2000, Mar. 28   Perf. 13x13¾
2613 A625   Booklet pane of 12   9.00 9.00
       Booklet, #2613   12.00

Gustave Mayer (1850-1900), Student
of Albanian Culture — A626

Colors: a, 50 l, olive green. b, 130 l, carmine lake.

2000, Mar. 30   Perf. 13½x14
2614 A626   Pair, #a-b   3.50 3.50

Cartoon Duck — A627

Duck with: a, 250 l, Top hat. b, 10 l, Ten-gallon hat. c, 30 l, Cap. d, 90 l, Bow.

2000, Apr. 6   Litho.   Perf. 13x13¾
2615 A627   Strip of 4, #a-d   7.50 7.50

Grand Prix Race
Cars — A628

Various cars.

2000, Apr. 10   Litho.   Perf. 14¼x14
2616   Bklt. pane of 10 + 2 la-
           bels   12.50 12.50
  a.-j.   A628 30 l any single   1.25 1.25
           Booklet, #2616   15.00

Holy Year
2000
A629

Designs: 15 l, Church with bell tower. 40 l, Church with conical roof. 90 l, Ruins. 250 l, Aerial view of ruins.

2000, Apr. 22   Litho.   Perf. 13¾x14
2617-2619 A629   Set of 3   4.00 4.00
Souvenir Sheet
Perf. 13¾
2620 A629   250 l multi   4.50 4.50

No. 2620 contains one 38x38mm stamp.

Europa, 2000
Common Design Type
2000, May 9   Perf. 13x13¾
2621 CD17   130 l multi   3.00 3.00
Souvenir Sheet
Perf. 13
2622 CD17   300 l Detail of #2621 8.00 8.00

No. 2622 contains one 25x29mm stamp.

Miniature Sheet

Wild Animals — A630

No. 2623: a, 10 l, Canis lupus. b, 40 l, Ursus arctos. c, 90 l, Sus scrofa. d, 220 l, Vulpes vulpes.

2000, May 17			Perf. 14¼x13¾	
2623	A630	Sheet of 4, #a-d	7.50	7.50

Gustav Mahler
(1860-1911),
Composer
A631

2000, May 30			Perf. 13½x14	
2624	A631	130 l multi	2.50	2.50

WIPA 2000 Stamp Exhibition, Vienna.

European Soccer
Championships — A632

10 l, Goalie. 120 l, Player heading ball. 260 l, Player kicking ball.

2000, June 1			Perf. 13¾x13¼	
2625-2626	A632	Set of 2	2.50	2.50
		Imperf		
		Size: 81x60mm		
2627	A632	260 l multi	5.00	5.00

Paintings by Pablo Picasso — A633

Various unnamed paintings or self-portraits: 30 l, Brown panel. 40 l, Green panel. 130 l, Self-portrait, with Espana 2000 philatelic exhibition emblem, vert. 250 l, Blue panel.

2000		Litho.	Perf. 13¾	
2628-2631	A633	Set of 4	6.50	6.50
		Souvenir Sheet		
		Perf. 13		
2632	A633	400 l Self-portrait	8.00	8.00

No. 2632 contains one 25x29mm stamp. Issued: 130 l, 10/6; others 6/7.

2000 Summer Olympics,
Sydney — A634

No. 2633: a, 10 l, Basketball. b, 40 l, Soccer. c, 90 l, Runner. d, 250 l, Cycling.

2000, July 1			Perf. 14x14¼	
2633	A634	Block of 4, #a-d	8.00	8.00

First Zeppelin Flight, Cent. — A635

No. 2634: a, 15 l, LZ-1 over Friedrichshafen. b, 30 l, Airship over Paris. c, 300 l, R34 over New York.
No. 2635, Ferdinand von Zeppelin.

2000, July 2			Perf. 13¾x13	
2634	A635	Sheet of 3, #a-c	7.50	7.50
		Souvenir Sheet		
		Perf. 13		
2635	A635	300 l multi	6.50	6.50

No. 2634 contains three 40x28mm stamps.

Flowers — A636

No. 2636: a, 50 l, Gentiana lutea. b, 70 l, Gentiana cruciata.

2000, Oct. 10			Perf. 13¼x14	
2636	A636	Pair, #a-b	2.75	2.75

Famous Albanians — A637

a, 30 l, Naim Frasheri, writer (1845-1900). b, 50 l, Bajram Curri, politician (1862-1925).

2000, Nov. 28			Perf. 14¼x13¾	
2637	A637	Pair, #a-b	2.00	2.00

UN High
Commissioner on
Refugees, 50th
Anniv. — A638

50 l, Mother & child. 90 l, Mother & child, diff.

2000, Dec. 14			Perf. 13¾x14¼	
2638-2639	A638	Set of 2	3.00	3.00

Famous Albanians — A639

No. 2640: a, Ahmed Myftar Dede. b, Sali Njazi Dede.

2001, Feb. 22		Litho.	Perf. 14¼x14	
2640	A639	90 l Horiz. pair, #a-b	4.50	4.50

Native Costumes — A640

No. 2641: a, Man from Tropoje. b, Woman from Lume. c, Woman from Mirdite. d, Man from Lume. e, Woman from Zadrime. f, Woman from Shpati. g, Man from Kruje. h, Woman from Macukulli. i, Woman from Dardhe. j, Man from Lushnje. k, Woman from Dropulli. l, Woman from Shmili.

2001, Mar. 15			Perf. 13x13¾	
2641	A640	20 l Sheet of 12, #a-l	5.00	5.00
		Booklet, #2641	7.00	7.00

See Nos. 2669, 2701, 2760, 2770.

Flowers — A641

No. 2642: a, 10 l, Magnolia grandiflora. b, 20 l, Rosa virginiana. c, 90 l, Dianthus barbatus. d, 140 l, Syringa vulgaris.

2001, Mar. 30			Perf. 14x14¼	
2642	A641	Block of 4, #a-d	5.00	5.00

Cartoon Dog — A642

Denominations: a, 50 l. b, 90 l. c, 140 l, d, 20 l.

2001, Apr. 6			Perf. 13x13¾	
2643	A642	Strip of 4, #a-d	5.00	5.00

Opera Composers — A643

Designs: No. 2644, 90 l, Vincenzo Bellini (1801-35). No. 2645, 90 l, Giuseppe Verdi (1813-1901).
300 l, Bellini and Verdi.

2001, Apr. 20			Perf. 13¾x13	
2644-2645	A643	Set of 2	3.50	3.50
		Souvenir Sheet		
		Perf. 13¾		
2646	A643	300 l multi	5.00	5.00

Europa
A644

Designs: 40 l, Waterfall, cliffs. 110 l, Waterfall, boulders. 200 l, Water, shoreline. 350 l, Ripples in water, vert.

2001, Apr. 29			Perf. 13¾x14	
2647-2649	A644	Set of 3	6.50	6.50
		Souvenir Sheet		
		Perf. 12¾x13		
2650	A644	350 l multi	8.00	8.00

No. 2650 contains one 25x29mm stamp.

Domestic Animals — A645

No. 2651: a, 10 l, Horse. b, 15 l, Donkey. c, 80 l, Cat. d, 90 l, Dog.
300 l, Cat.

2001, May 17			Perf. 14¼x14	
2651	A645	Sheet of 4, #a-d	4.00	4.00
		Souvenir Sheet		
		Perf. 12¾x13		
2652	A645	300 l shown	5.00	5.00

No. 2651 contains four 42x26mm stamps.

2001 Mediterranean Games, Tunis, Tunisia — A646

No. 2653: a, 10 l, Swimmer. b, 90 l, Runners. c, 140 l, Cyclists.
260 l, Discus thrower.

2001, June 1   **Perf. 14¼x14**
2653 A646   Vert. strip of 3, #a-c   5.00 5.00
Souvenir Sheet
Perf. 13x12¾
2654 A646   260 l multi   5.25 5.25
No. 2654 contains one 29x25mm stamp.

History of Aviation — A647

No. 2655: a, Clement Ader's flight of Eole, Oct. 9, 1890. b, Louis Blériot's flight of Blériot IX over English Channel, July 25, 1909. c, Charles Lindbergh's solo transatlantic flight of Spirit of St. Louis, May, 1927. d, Flight over Tirana, May 30, 1925. e, Antonov AN-10, 1956. f, First Concorde flight, Feb. 9, 1969. g, First Boeing 747 flight, Jan. 22, 1970. h, First flight of Space Shuttle Columbia, Apr. 12, 1981.

2001, June 20   **Perf. 13¾x13**
2655 A647 40 l   Sheet of 8, #a-h   8.00 8.00

Bridges — A648

No. 2656: a, 10 l, Tabakeve. b, 20 l, Kamares. c, 40 l, Golikut. d, 90 l, Mesit.
250 l, Tabakeve.

2001, July 20   **Perf. 13¾x13¼**
2656 A648   Sheet of 4, #a-d   3.25 3.25
Souvenir Sheet
Perf. 12¾x13
2657 A648   250 l shown   5.00 5.00
No. 2656 contains four 38x30mm stamps.

Coats of Arms — A649

Arms of: 20 l, Dimitri of Arber. 45 l, Balsha. 50 l, Muzaka. 90 l, George Castrioti (Skanderbeg).

2001, Sept. 12   **Perf. 12¾x13**
2658 A649 20 l multi   .50 .50
   a.   Booklet pane of 4   2.00
2659 A649 45 l multi   1.00 1.00
   a.   Booklet pane of 4   9.00
2660 A649 50 l multi   1.10 1.10
   a.   Booklet pane of 4   4.50
2661 A649 90 l multi   2.00 2.00
   a.   Booklet pane of 4   8.00
    Booklet, #2658a-2661a   24.00
    Nos. 2658-2661 (4)   4.60 4.60
See Nos. 2681-2684, 2709-2712, 2775, 2797-2800, 2801-2804.

Year of Dialogue Among Civilizations A650

Colors of denomination: 45 l, Green. 50 l, Black. 120 l, White.

2001, Oct. 6   **Perf. 13½x14**
2662-2664 A650   Set of 3   5.00 5.00

Nobel Prizes, Cent. — A651

Laureates: 10 l, Doctors Without Borders, Peace, 1999. 20 l, Wilhelm C. Roentgen, Physics, 1901. 90 l, Farid Murad, Physiology or Medicine, 1988. 200 l, Mother Teresa, Peace, 1979.

2001, Dec. 1   **Perf. 13¾x13¼**
2665-2668 A651   Set of 4   7.50 7.50

Costumes Type of 2001

No. 2669: a, Man from Gjakova. b, Woman from Prizren. c, Man from Shkoder. d, Woman from Shkoder. e, Man from Berat. f, Woman from Berat. g, Woman from Elbasan. h, Man from Elbasan. i, Woman from Vlore. j, Man from Vlore. k, Woman from Gjirokaster. l, Woman from Delvina.

2002, Mar. 20   Litho.   Perf. 13x13¾
2669 A640 30 l   Sheet of 12, #a-l   8.75 8.75
    Complete booklet, #2669   9.75

Cartoon Deer — A652

No. 2670: a, 50 l, Deer. b, 90 l, Deer and rabbit. c, 140 l, Deer, diff. d, 20 l, Deer and rabbit, diff.

2002, Apr. 8   **Perf. 13x13¾**
2670 A652   Horiz. strip of 4, #a-d   5.50 5.50

Fireplaces — A653

Fireplace color: a, 30 l, Deep brown. b, 40 l, Henna brown. 50 l, Orange brown. 90 l, Chestnut.

2002, Apr. 15   Litho.   Perf. 14
2671 A653   Sheet of 4, #a-d   4.00 4.00

Europa — A654

Designs: 40 l, High wire act. 90 l, Acrobats. 220 l, Contortionist. 350 l, Trained horse act.

2002, May 1   Litho.   Perf. 13x13¾
2672-2674 A654   Set of 3   7.50 7.50
Souvenir Sheet
Perf. 13¾
2675 A654 350 l multi   7.50 7.50
No. 2675 contains one 37x37mm stamp.

2002 World Cup Soccer Championships, Japan and Korea — A655

Emblem, soccer ball and stylized players: 20 l, 30 l, 90 l, 120 l
360 l, Stylized player and emblem.

2002, May 6   Litho.   Perf. 13¾x13¼
2676-2679 A655   Set of 4   5.00 5.00
Souvenir Sheet
Perf. 13
2680 A655 360 l multi   7.00 7.00
No. 2680 contains one 50x29mm stamp.

Arms Type of 2001
2002, May 12   **Perf. 13**
2681 A649 20 l   Gropa   .40 .40
   a.   Booklet pane of 4   1.75 —
2682 A649 45 l   Skurra   .90 .40
   a.   Booklet pane of 4   4.00 —
2683 A649 50 l   Bua   1.00 1.00
   a.   Booklet pane of 4   4.50 —
2684 A649 90 l   Topia   2.00 2.00
   a.   Booklet pane of 4   9.00 —
    Complete booklet, #2681a-2684a   20.00
    Nos. 2681-2684 (4)   4.30 3.80

Cacti — A656

No. 2685: a, Opuntia catingola. b, Neoporteria pseudoreicheana. c, Lobivia shaferi. d, Hylocereus undatus. e, Borzicactus madisoniorum.

2002, May 17   **Perf. 14**
2685 A656 50 l   Sheet of 5, #a-e   5.00 5.00

Blood Donation — A657

Letters "A," "B," and "O" with: No. 2686, 90 l, Stylized people. No. 2687, 90 l, Wings.

2002, June 16   **Perf. 13¾x14¼**
2686-2687 A657   Set of 2   4.00 4.00

Sportsmen A658

No. 2688: a, Naim Kryeziu, soccer player. b, Riza Lushta, soccer player. c, Ymer Pampuri, weight lifter.
300 l, Loro Borici, soccer player, vert.

2002, July 3   **Perf. 14¼x14**
2688   Horiz. strip of 3   3.50 3.50
   a.-c.   A658 50 l Any single   1.10 1.10
Size: 60x80mm
Imperf
2689 A658 300 l multi   6.00 6.00

Intl. Federation of Stamp Dealers Associations, 50th Anniv. A659

Designs: 50 l, Man, #2471. 100 l, Map of Albania, Europe, cube of blue spheres.

2002, Sept. 1   Litho.   Perf. 13¾x13¼
2690-2691 A659   Set of 2   3.00 3.00

Anti-Terrorism — A660

Designs: 100 l, Statue of Liberty. 150 l, World Trade Center on fire.
350 l, Statue of Liberty and World Trade Center, vert.

2002, Sept. 11   **Perf. 13¾x13**
2692-2693 A660   Set of 2   5.00 5.00
Souvenir Sheet
Perf. 13
2694 A660 350 l multi   7.00 7.00
No. 2694 contains one 29x50mm stamp.

Mediterranean Sealife — A661

No. 2695: a, Caretta caretta. b, Delphinus delphis. c, Prionace glauca. d, Balaenoptera physalus. e, Torpedo torpedo. f, Octopus vulgaris.

Perf. 14¼x14¾

2002, Sept. 12   Litho.
2695 A661 50 l Sheet of 6, #a-f   6.00 6.00

Famous Albanians — A662

No. 2696: a, Tefta Tashko Koço (1910-47), singer. b, Naim Frasheri (1923-75), actor. c, Kristaq Antoniu (1909-79), singer. d, Panajot Kanaçi (1923-96), choreographer.

2002, Oct. 6   **Perf. 13¾**
2696 A662 50 l Block of 4, #a-d   4.00 4.00

Independence, 90th Anniv. — A663

Designs: 20 l, Flags of Albania and other nations. 90 l, People, Albanian flag.

2002, Nov. 28   Litho.   **Perf. 13½x14**
2697-2698 A663 Set of 2   2.00 2.00

Post and Telecommunications Administration, 90th Anniv. — A664

Designs: 20 l, Satellite dish. 90 l, Telegraph, air mail envelope.

2002, Dec. 4
2699-2700 A664 Set of 2   2.00 2.00

Costumes Type of 2001

No. 2701: a, Woman from Kelmendi. b, Man from Zadrime. c, Woman from Zerqani. d, Man from Peshkopi. e, Man from Malesia e Tiranes. f, Woman from Malesia e Tiranes. g, Woman from Fushe Kruje. h, Man from Shpati. i, Woman from Myzeqe. j, Woman from Labinoti. k, Man from Korce. l, Man from Laberi.

2003, Apr. 1   Litho.   **Perf. 13¼**
2701 A640 30 l Sheet of 12, #a-l   8.00 8.00
    Booklet, #2701   10.00 10.00

Characterizations of Popeye — A665

No. 2702: a, 80 l, Popeye and Olive Oyl. b, 150 l, Popeye smoking pipe. c, 40 l, Popeye and Brutus. d, 50 l, Popeye walking.

2003, Apr. 6
2702 A665   Strip of 4, #a-d   7.00 7.00

Castles — A666

No. 2703: a, 10 l, Porto Palermo. b, 20 l, Petrela. c, 50 l, Kruja. d, 120 l, Preza.

2003, Apr. 15   Litho.   **Perf. 13¼**
2703 A666   Sheet of 4, #a-d   4.50 4.50

Europa — A667

Poster art: 150 l, Onufri. 200 l, Various posters. 350 l, Face from Onufri poster.

2003, Apr. 30   **Perf. 14**
2704-2705 A667   Set of 2   6.00 6.00
Souvenir Sheet
2706 A667 350 l multi   8.00 8.00

First Albanian Stamps, 90th Anniv. A668

Designs: 50 l, Stamped envelopes, sheets of stamps. 1000 l, Seal of Post, Telegraph and Telephone Ministry.

2003, May 12   **Perf. 13¼**
2707-2708 A668   Set of 2   22.50 22.50

Arms Type of 2001

Family arms: 10 l, Arianiti. 20 l, Jonima. 70 l, Dukagjini. 120 l, Kopili.

2003, May 12
2709 A649   10 l multi   .30 .30
   a.   Booklet pane of 4   1.25
2710 A649   20 l multi   .50 .50
   a.   Booklet pane of 4   2.25
2711 A649   70 l multi   1.50 1.50
   a.   Booklet pane of 4   7.00
2712 A649   120 l multi   2.50 2.50
   a.   Booklet pane of 4   11.00
    Complete booklet, #2709a, 2710a, 27111a, 2712a   24.00
    Nos. 2709-2712 (4)   4.80 4.80

Fruit — A669

No. 2713: a, 50 l, Punica gramatunil. b, 60 l, Citrus medica. c, 70 l, Cucumis melo. d, 80 l, Ficus.

Serpentine Die Cut 6¼
2003, May 17   **Self-Adhesive**
2713 A669   Sheet of 4, #a-d   5.50 5.50

Roman Emperors from Illyria and Coins Depicting Them — A670

No. 2714: a, Diocletian (c. 245-c. 313). b, Justinian I (483-565). c, Claudius II (214-70). d, Constantine I (the Great) (d. 337).

2003, June 20   Litho.   **Perf. 13¼**
2714 A670 70 l Block of 4, #a-d   6.00 6.00

Birds — A671

No. 2715: a, Ciconia ciconia. b, Aquilia chrysaetos. c, Bubo bubo. d, Tetrao urogallos.

2003, Aug. 20   **Perf. 14½x14¼**
2715 A671 70 l Sheet of 4, #a-d   6.00 6.00

First International Soccer Match in Albania, 90th Anniv. — A672

No. 2716: a, Denomination at right. b, Denomination at left.

2003, Sept. 2
2716 A672 80 l Horiz. pair, #a-b   3.50 3.50

Paintings by Edouard Manet — A673

Designs: 40 l, Lunch in the Workshop (detail). 100 l, The Fifer. 250 l, Manet, horiz.

2003, Sept. 20   **Perf. 14½x14¼**
2717-2718 A673   Set of 2   3.00 3.00
Souvenir Sheet
Perf. 14¼x14½
2719 A673 250 l multi   4.50 4.50

Sculptors — A674

No. 2720: a, Odhise Paskali. b, Janaq Paco. c, Llazar Nikolla. d, Murat Toptani.

2003, Oct. 6   **Perf. 13¼**
2720 A674 50 l Block of 4, #a-d   4.00 4.00

Beatification of Mother Teresa — A675

Sculptures of Mother Teresa: 40 l, Profile. 250 l, Front view. 350 l, Mother Teresa praying.

2003, Oct. 19   **Perf. 13¼**
2721-2722 A675   Set of 2   6.00 6.00
Souvenir Sheet
Perf.
2723 A675 350 l multi   7.00 7.00
No. 2723 contains one 40mm diameter stamp.

Natural Monuments — A676

Designs: 20 l, Divjaka Forest Park. 30 l, Fir trees, Hotova. 200 l, Fir tree, Drenova.

2003, Oct. 20   **Perf. 13¼**
2724-2726 A676   Set of 3   5.00 5.00

Tour de France Bicycle Race, Cent. A677

Designs: 50 l, Cyclist, "100," map of France. 100 l, Cyclists, French flag.

2003, Nov. 1   **Perf. 14¼x14½**
2727-2728 A677   Set of 2   3.00 3.00

Europa — A678

Various vacation spots with country name in: No. 2729, 200 l, White. No. 2730, 200 l, Light blue.
350 l, Orange.

2004, June 23	Litho.	Perf. 13½
2729-2730 A678	Set of 2	9.00 9.00
a. Booklet pane, 4 each #2729-2730, perf. 13½ on 3 sides		46.00 —
Complete booklet, #2730a		46.00

Souvenir Sheet
Perf. 14¼x13½

2731 A678	350 l multi	9.00 9.00

No. 2731 contains one 29x37mm stamp.
In No. 2730a, the two columns in the middle are tete-beche pairs of Nos. 2729-2730.

European Soccer Championships, Portugal — A679

Various players: 20 l, 40 l, 50 l, 200 l.
350 l, Player (37mm diameter stamp).

2004, June 24		Perf. 14
2732-2735 A679	Set of 4	7.00 7.00

Souvenir Sheet
Perf.

2736 A679	350 l multi	8.00 8.00

2004 Summer Olympics, Athens — A680

Designs: 10 l, Statue of discus thrower. 200 l, Bust. 350 l, Torch bearer.

2004, Aug. 12		Perf. 13½
2737-2738 A680	Set of 2	4.50 4.50

Souvenir Sheet
Perf. 13½x13¾

2739 A680	350 l multi	8.00 8.00

No. 2739 contains one 38x54mm stamp.

Prince Wilhelm zu Wied (1876-1945), Appointed Ruler of Albania A681

Designs: 40 l, With hat. 150 l, Without hat.

2004, Aug. 30	Litho.	Perf. 13½
2740-2741 A681	Set of 2	4.00 4.00

Characterizations of Bugs Bunny — A682

No. 2742 — Background color: a, 40 l, Orange. b, 50 l, Light blue. c, 80 l, Purple. d, 150 l, Green.

2004, Sept. 15		
2742 A682	Horiz. strip of 4, #a-d	7.00 7.00

Icons Painted by Nikolla Onufri A683

Various saints: 10 l, 20 l, 1000 l.

2004, Oct. 3		Perf. 14
2743-2745 A683	Set of 3	22.50 22.50

Souvenir Sheet
Perf. 13½x14¼

2746 A683	400 l Saint, diff.	9.00 9.00

Souvenir Sheet

Ladybugs — A684

No. 2747: a, With 12 spots, on flower. b, With 5 spots, on flower. c, With wings extended. d, On leaves.

2004, Oct. 10		Perf. 14
2747 A684	80 l Sheet of 4, #a-d	7.00 7.00

Entertainment Personalities — A685

No. 2748: a, Ndrek Luca (1924-93), actor. b, Jorgjia Truja (1909-94), singer, film director. c, Maria Kraja (1911-99), opera singer. d, Zina Andri (1924-80), actress, theater director.

2004, Oct. 12		Perf. 13¾x13½
2748 A685	50 l Block of 4, #a-d	4.50 4.50

Coats of Arms — A686

Designs: 20 l, Spani. 40 l, Gjuraj. 80 l, Zahariaj. 150 l, Dushmani.

2004, Oct. 25		Perf. 13¾x14
2749 A686	20 l multi	.50 .50
a. Booklet pane of 4		2.00
2750 A686	40 l multi	.80 .80
a. Booklet pane of 4		3.50

2751 A686	80 l multi	2.00 2.00
a. Booklet pane of 4		8.00 —
2752 A686	150 l multi	3.25 3.25
a. Booklet pane of 4		14.00 —
Complete booklet, #2749a-2752a		29.00
Nos. 2749-2752 (4)		6.55 6.55

Souvenir Sheet

Dahlias — A687

No. 2753: a, Pink flower with small petals, large bud in front. b, Bud in back. c, Small flower at right. d, Red flower with large petals, small bud in front.

2004, Nov. 1		Perf. 14
2753 A687	80 l Sheet of 4, #a-d	7.00 7.00

Art in National Gallery — A688

No. 2745 — Art by: a, Unknown artist (Madonna and Child). b, Mihal Anagnosti. c, Onufer Qiprioti. d, Cetiret. e, Onuferi. f, Kel Kodheli. g, Vangjush Mio. h, Abdurahim Buza. i, Mustafa Arapi. j, Guri Madhi. k, Janaq Paço. l, Zef Kolombi. m, Hasan Reçi. n, Vladimir Jani. o, Halim Beqiri. p, Edison Gjergo. q, Naxhi Bakalli. r, Agron Bregu. s, Edi Hila. t, Artur Muharremi. u, Rembrandt. v, Gazmend Leka. w, Damien Hirst. x, Edvin Rama. y, Ibrahim Kodra.

2004, Nov. 20		Perf. 14
2754	Sheet of 25	12.50 12.50
a.-y. A688 20 l Any single		.50 .50

NATO in Kosovo, 5th Anniv. — A689

NATO emblem and: 100 l, Pennants and stars. 200 l, Doves, UN flag.
350 l, Buildings, Albanian flag.

2004, Nov. 28		Perf. 14¼x13½
2755-2756 A689	Set of 2	7.00 7.00

Souvenir Sheet

2757 A689	350 l multi	8.00 8.00

Liberation From Nazi Occupation, 60th Anniv. — A690

Designs: 50 l, Two doves. 200 l, One dove.

2004, Nov. 29		Perf. 13¾x13½
2758-2759 A690	Set of 2	6.00 6.00

Native Costumes Type of 2001

No. 2760: a, Woman from Gramshi (showing back). b, Woman from Gramshi (showing front). c, Woman from Korça with blue skirt. d, Man from Kolonja. e, Woman from Korça with red dress. f, Woman from Librazhdi. g, Woman from Permeti. h, Woman from Pogradeci. i, Man from Skrapari. j, Woman from Skrapari. k, Woman from Tepelena. l, Woman from Vlora.

2004, Dec. 4		Perf. 13½
2760 A640	30 l Sheet of 12, #a-l	10.00 10.00
Complete booklet, #2760		11.50

Europa Stamps, 50th Anniv. (in 2006) — A691

Vignettes similar to: 200 l, #2558. 250 l, #2471, horiz. 500 l, #2675.

2005, Oct. 1	Litho.	Perf. 13¾
2761-2762 A691	Set of 2	10.00 10.00

Souvenir Sheet

2763 A691	500 l multi	12.00 12.00

No. 2763 contains one 38x38mm stamp.

A692

Europa — A693

2005, Oct. 5		Perf. 14x13¾
2764 A692	200 l multi	5.00 5.00
a. Perf. 13¼x13¾ on 2 or 3 sides		5.00 5.00
2765 A693	200 l multi	5.00 5.00
a. Perf. 13¼x13¾ on 2 or 3 sides		5.00 5.00

Souvenir Sheet
Perf. 12¾x13

2766 A633	350 l Stuffed cabbage	9.00 9.00
a. Booklet pane, #2766, 3 each #2764a, 2765a		40.00 —
Complete booklet, #2766a		55.00

No. 2766 contains one 25x30mm stamp. Serial number is at top right of sheet margin on No. 2766, and on binding stub on No. 2766a. No. 2766a sold for 1650 l.

Admission to the United Nations, 50th Anniv. — A694

2005, Oct. 19		Perf. 12¾
2767 A694	40 l multi	.80 .80

Cartoon Characters: — A695

No. 2768 — Tom & Jerry: a, 150 l, Tom. b, 40 l, Tom & Jerry. c, 50 l, Tom & Jerry, diff. d, 80 l, Jerry.

2005, Oct. 20		Perf. 14
2768 A695	Horiz. strip of 4, #a-d	6.00 6.00

Paintings
A696

Various unattributed paintings: a, Mountain, town and river. b, Castle and aqueduct. c, Crowd, minaret. d, Castle on mountain, people near river.

2005, Oct. 21
2769		Horiz. strip of 4	20.00	20.00
a.	A696	10 l multi	.30	.30
b.	A696	20 l multi	.30	.30
c.	A696	30 l multi	.60	.60
d.	A696	1000 l multi	17.50	17.50

Costumes Type of 2001

No. 2770: a, Man, Tirana. b, Woman, Bende Tirana. c, Woman, Zall Dajt. d, Man, Kavaje-Durres. e, Woman, Has. f, Man, Mat. g, Woman, Liqenas. h, Woman, Klenje. i, Woman, Maleshove. j, Woman, German. k, Woman, Kruje. l, Man, Reç.

2005, Oct. 24   Perf. 14x13¾
2770	A640	30 l Sheet of 12,		
		#a-l	8.00	8.00
		Complete booklet, #2770	13.00	

Complete booklet sold for 460 l.

2005 Mediterranean Games, Almería, Spain — A697

2005, Oct. 25   Perf. 14¼x13¾
2771		Horiz. strip of 3	3.50	3.50
a.	A697	20 l Runner in blocks	.40	.40
b.	A697	60 l Gymnastics	1.00	1.00
c.	A697	120 l Relay race	2.00	2.00

Souvenir Sheet
Perf. 12¾x13
2772	A697	300 l Diver	7.50	7.50

No. 2772 contains one 50x30mm stamp.

Rotary International, Cent. — A698

Rotary International emblem and: 30 l, Map of North America. 150 l, Rays and "100 Vjet," vert.

2005, Nov. 11   Perf. 13¾
2773-2774	A698	Set of 2	4.00	4.00

Arms Type of 2001

No. 2775 — Arms of: a, Bua Despots. b, Karl Topia. c, Dukagjini II. d, Engjej.

2005, Nov. 14   Perf. 12¾
2775		Horiz. strip of 4	5.00	5.00
a.	A649	10 l multi	.30	.30
b.	A649	30 l multi	.50	.50
c.	A649	100 l multi	1.50	1.50
d.	A649	150 l multi	2.50	2.50
e.		Booklet pane, 4 #2775a	1.30	—
f.		Booklet pane, 4 #2775b	2.50	—
g.		Booklet pane, 4 #2775c	7.00	—
h.		Booklet pane, 4 #2775d	11.00	—
		Complete booklet, #2775e-2775h	25.00	

Souvenir Sheet

Portulaca Flowers — A699

No. 2776: a, Yellow flowers. b, Three white flowers. c, Red and bright yellow flowers. d, Pink flower. e, Red flower.

2005, Nov. 17   Perf. 14
2776	A699	70 l Sheet of 5,		
		#a-e	9.00	9.00

Cycling in Albania, 80th Anniv. — A700

2005, Nov. 20   Perf. 13¼x13¾
2777		Strip of 3	6.00	6.00
a.	A700	50 l blue & multi	1.25	1.25
b.	A700	60 l red & multi	1.75	1.75
c.	A700	120 l bright red & multi	3.25	3.25

Souvenir Sheet

Skanderbeg (1405-68), National Hero — A701

No. 2778 — Various scenes of warriors in battle: a, 40 l (50x30mm). b, 50 l (50x30mm). c, 60 l (50x30mm). d, 70 l (50x30mm). e, 80 l (30mm diameter). f, 90 l (30mm diameter).

2005, Nov. 28   Perf. 13
2778	A701	Sheet of 6, #a-f	10.00	10.00

End of World War II, 60th Anniv. — A702

No. 2779: a, 50 l, Doves, roses, army helmet. b, 200 l, Statues, flags, dove.

2005, Nov. 29   Perf. 14x13¾
2779	A702	Horiz. pair, #a-b	5.25	5.25

Marubi Family Artists A703

No. 2780: a, Matia Kodheli-Marubi. b, Gege Marubi. c, Pjeter Marubi. d, Kel Marubi.

2005, Dec. 4
2780		Horiz. strip of 4	7.50	7.50
a.	A703	10 l multi	.30	.30
b.	A703	20 l multi	.50	.50
c.	A703	70 l multi	1.75	1.75
d.	A703	200 l multi	5.00	5.00

Nos. 2417, 2433, 2446, 2477, 2478, 2484, 2487, 2490-2492, 2498 and 2504 Surcharged

Methods and Perfs as Before
2006
2781	A550	on 30q #2417	2.00	2.00
2782	A569	on 2 l #2478	2.00	2.00
2783	A574	on 2 l #2490	2.00	2.00

2784	A574	on 3 l #2491	2.00	2.00
2785	A577	on 3 l #2498	2.00	2.00
2786	A552	on 10 l #2433	2.00	2.00
2787	A572	on 18 l #2484	2.00	2.00
2788	A573	on 18 l #2487	2.00	2.00
2789	A556	on 21 l #2446	2.00	2.00
2790	A568	on 25 l #2477		
		(block of 4, #a-d)	150.00	150.00
2791	A574	on 25 l #2492	2.00	2.00
2792	A580	on 25 l #2504	2.00	2.00
		Nos. 2781-2789,2791-2792		
		(11)	22.00	22.00

Location of surcharge varies.

Visit of Pres. George W. Bush to Albania — A704

No. 2793 — Photograph of Bush in: a, 20 l, Blue. b, 40 l, Green. c, 80 l, Full color.
200 l, Statue of Liberty, flags of US and Albania, horiz.

Perf. 13¼x13½
2007, June 10   Litho.
2793	A704	Horiz. strip of 3,		
		#a-c	3.25	3.25

Souvenir Sheet
Perf. 13½x13¼
2794	A704	200 l multi	4.00	4.00

Italian Delegation of Experts in Albania, 10th Anniv. — A705

Perf. 13¼x13½
2007, Sept. 15   Litho.
2795	A705	40 l multi	1.25	1.25

Granite Paper

Miniature Sheet

Albanian Flag — A706

No. 2796 — Various depictions of Albanian flag blowing in wind: a, 5 l. b, 10 l. c, 20 l. d, 30 l. e, 40 l. f, 50 l. g, 60 l. h, 70 l. i, 80 l. j, 100 l. k, 1000 l. l, 2000 l.

2007, Oct. 5   Litho.   Perf. 13¼x13
2796	A706	Sheet of 12,		
		#a-l	90.00	90.00

Arms Type of 2001

Arms of: 20 l, Despot Andrea II Muzaka. 40 l, Matrenga family. 80 l, Leke Dukagjini. 150 l, Konstantin Kastrioti.

2007, Oct. 15   Litho.   Perf. 12¾x13¼
2797	A649	20 l multi	1.50	1.50
2798	A649	40 l multi	3.00	3.00
2799	A649	80 l multi	5.50	5.50
2800	A649	150 l multi	10.00	10.00
a.		Vert. strip of 4, #2797-2800	150.00	—
		Nos. 2797-2800 (4)	20.00	20.00

Nos. 2797-2800 are dated 2006.

Arms Type of 2001

Arms of: 10 l, Lança family. 20 l, Riki family. 60 l, Kokini family. 100 l, Zako family.

2007, Oct. 17   Litho.   Perf. 12¾x13¼
2801	A649	10 l multi	.50	.50
2802	A649	20 l multi	1.00	1.00
2803	A649	60 l multi	3.00	3.00

2804	A649	100 l multi	5.50	5.50
a.		Vert. strip of 4, #2801-2804		
		Nos. 2801-2804 (4)	10.00	10.00

Europa — A707

Men and women and: No. 2805, 200 l, Flag of European Union, map of Europe. No. 2806, 200 l, Flag and map of Albania.
350 l, Men, women, flags of Albania and European Union, horiz.

2007, Oct. 23   Litho.   Perf. 13x13¼
2805-2806	A707	Set of 2	10.00	10.00

Souvenir Sheet
Perf. 13¼x13
2807	A707	350 l multi	9.00	9.00

No. 2807 contains one 30x25mm stamp. Dated 2006.

Europa — A708

Designs: 100 l, Scouts, flags, mountain. 150 l, Scouts, flags, mountain, diff. 250 l, Knot, horiz.

2007, Oct. 24   Perf. 13¼x13
2808-2809	A708	Set of 2	5.00	5.00

Souvenir Sheet
2810	A708	250 l multi	5.75	5.75

Scouting, cent. No. 2810 contains one 30x25mm stamp.

Pink Panther — A709

No. 2811 — Pink Panther: a, 150 l, Wearing uniform. b, 40 l, Wearing bowtie. c, 50 l, With inspector. d, 80 l, With elbow resting on orange panel.

2007, Oct. 25   Perf. 13
2811	A709	Horiz. strip of 4,		
		#a-d	7.00	7.00

Children's Art — A710

No. 2812 — Art by: a, 10 l, Arkida Lema. b, 40 l, Amarilda Prifti. c, 50 l, Iliaz Kasa. d, 80 l, Klaudia Mezini, horiz.

2007, Oct. 29   Perf. 13
2812	A710	Horiz. strip of 4, #a-d	7.00	7.00

Frescoes — A712

Designs: 70 l, sower, by David Selenices. 110 l, Floral mural, Et'hem Bey Mosque, Tirana.

2007, Oct. 31   Litho.   Perf. 13
2814-2815 A712 Set of 2   4.50 4.50

Miniature Sheet

Native Costumes — A713

No. 2816: a, German woman. b, Kurbin man. c, Golloborde woman. d, Kerrabe Malesi man. e, Gur i Bardhe woman. f, Martanesh woman. g, Puke woman. h, Serice Labinot woman. i, Shen Gjergj woman. j, Tirane Qytet woman. k, Zalle Dajt man. l, Zaranike Godolesh woman.

2008, Nov. 1   Litho.   Perf. 13
2816 A713 40 l, Sheet of 12,
          #a-l   12.00 12.00

Dated 2006. A sheet of 20 l stamps depicting native costumes with country name at left was issued on Nov. 2 in limited quantities to those with reservations to purchase the sheet, and later was sold at an inflated price. Value, $100.

Tourism
A714

No. 2817: a, Thethi National Park (Parku Kombetar Thethit). b, Lures Lake (Liqenet e Lures). c, Kanina Castle (Kalaja e Kanines). d, Karavasta Lagoon (Laguna e Karavastase).

2007, Nov. 5
2817   Horiz. strip of 4   7.00 7.00
  a. A714 40 l green & multi   1.00 1.00
  b. A714 50 l red violet & multi 1.25 1.25
  c. A714 60 l red & multi   1.50 1.50
  d. A714 70 l blue violet & multi 2.25 2.25

Trees of
Elbasan
A715

Designs: 70 l, Tree and pond. 90 l, Hollowed-out tree.

2007, Nov. 8   Perf. 13x13¼
2818-2819 A715 Set of 2   4.50 4.50

Dated 2006.

Pope Clement XI
(1649-1721)
A716

No. 2820: a, 30 l, Red background. b, 120 l, Blue background.

2007, Nov. 9   Perf. 13¼x13
2820 A716 Vert. pair, #a-b   4.50 4.50

Dated 2006.

Léopold Sédar
Senghor (1906-
2001), First
President of
Senegal — A717

Color of photograph: 40 l, Sepia. 80 l, Black.

2007, Nov. 10
2821-2822 A717 Set of 2   4.00 4.00

Dated 2006.

Albania as Balkan Soccer Champions,
60th Anniv. (in 2006) — A718

Background colors: 10 l, Buff and red. 80 l, Light and dark blue.

2007, Nov. 11   Perf. 13x13¼
2823-2824 A718 Set of 2   7.00 7.00

Dated 2006.

Miniature Sheet

Gjirokaster UNESCO World Heritage
Site — A719

No. 2825: a, 10 l, Cannons. b, 20 l, Wall decoration. c, 30 l, Building. d, 60 l, Bridge. e, 80 l, Aerial view of town. f, 90 l, Castle atop cliff.

2007, Nov. 12   Perf. 13¼x13
2825 A719 Sheet of 6, #a-f   9.00 9.00

Dated 2006.

Participation of
Albanian Military
in International
Missions, 10th
Anniv. (in
2006) — A720

Designs: 10 l, Soldier in gas mask. 100 l, Soldiers in raft.

2008, Nov. 13
2826-2827 A720 Set of 2   3.00 3.00

Dated 2006.

Mother Teresa
(1910-97), 1978
Nobel Peace
Laureate — A721

Background color: 60 l, Orange yellow. 130 l, Brown. 200 l, Red.

2007, Nov. 15   Perf. 13¼x13
2828-2829 A721 Set of 2   7.50 7.50
Souvenir Sheet
2830 A721 200 l multi   —

Statue of Gaia
Found Near
Durres — A722

No. 2831: a, 30 l, Small image of statue. b, 120 l, Large image of statue.

2007, Nov. 16   Litho.   Perf. 13¼x13
2831 A722 Vert. pair, #a-b   10.00 10.00

A 200 l souvenir sheet issued with this set was sold in limited quantities to those with reservations to purchase the sheet, and later was sold at an inflated price. Value, $100.

Prehistoric Cave
and Rock
Drawings
A723

Designs: 20 l, Rock drawings, Lepenice. 100 l, Rock drawing, Tren. 300 l, Cave drawing, Tren.

2007, Nov. 19   Perf. 13¼x13
2832-2833 A723 Set of 2   3.00 3.00
Souvenir Sheet
Perf. 13x13¼
2834 A723 300 l multi   6.00 6.00

Dated 2006.

Famous
Men
A724

No. 2835: a, Osman Kazazi (1917-99), resistance leader. b, Pjeter Arbnori (1935-2006), politician. c, Lasgush Poradeci (1899-1987), writer. d, Cesk Zadeja (1927-97), musician.

2007, Nov. 22   Perf. 13¼x13
2835   Horiz. strip of 4   5.50 5.50
  a. A724 10 l multi   .30   .30
  b. A724 20 l multi   .30   .30
  c. A724 60 l multi   1.25 1.25
  d. A724 100 l multi   2.00 2.00

Famous
Men — A725

No. 2836: a, Abdurrahim Buza (1905-87), painter. b, Aleks Buda (1911-93), historian. c, Thimi Mitko (1820-90), writer. d, Martin Camaj (1925-94), writer.

2007, Nov. 22   Perf. 13x13¼
2836   Horiz. strip of 4   5.75 5.75
  a.-d. A725 50 l Any single   1.25 1.25

Dated 2006.

2006 World Cup
Soccer
Championships,
Germany — A726

Stylized soccer players with background colors of: 30 l, Yellow. 60 l, Red. 120 l, Black. 350 l, Emblem of 2006 World Cup.

2007, Nov. 26
2837-2839 A726 Set of 3   10.00 10.00
Souvenir Sheet
2840 A726 350 l multi   15.00 15.00

Dated 2006.

Independence, 95th Anniv. — A727

Ismail Qemali (1844-1919), first Albanian Prime Minister and: 50 l, Heraldic eagle and years. 110 l, Text.

2007, Nov. 28   Perf. 13x13¼
2841-2842 A727 Set of 2   5.50 5.50

Vegetables
A728

No. 2843: a, Garlic. b, Onions. c, Peppers. d, Tomatoes.

2007, Dec. 3   Litho.   Perf. 12¾
2843   Horiz. strip of 4 + 3   12.50 12.50
labels
a.-d. A728 80 l Any single   3.00 3.00

Wulfenia
Baldacci
A729

2007, Dec. 4   Litho.   Perf. 13
2844   Horiz. pair + central   10.00 10.00
label
a.   A729 70 l lilac & multi   3.75 3.75
b.   A729 100 l buff & multi   5.25 5.25

Albanian Post and
Telecommunications Department, 95th
Anniv. — A730

Denomination in: 80 l, Red. 90 l, Black.

2007, Dec. 5   Perf. 13¼x13
2845-2846 A730 Set of 2   5.50 5.50

Miniature Sheet

Infrastructure Development — A731

No. 2847: a, 10 l, Trans-Balkan Road. b, 20 l, Port of Durres. c, 30 l, Road, Tirana. d, 40 l, Mother Teresa Terminal. e, 50 l, Road, Shkoder. f, 60 l, Tepelene-Gjirokaster Road. g, 70 l, Fier-Lushnje Road. h, 80 l, Kalimash-Morine Road.
150 l, Mother Teresa Air Terminal, Tirana.

2007, Dec. 7   Perf. 13¼x12¾
2847 A731 Sheet of 8, #a-h   9.50 9.50

Souvenir Sheet

2848 A731 150 l multi   4.50 4.50

Invitation to Join NATO — A732

No. 2849 — NATO emblem and: a, 40 l, Flags of member nations. b, 60 l, Heraldic eagles.

2008, Apr. 12 Litho. Perf. 13x13¼
2849 A732 Horiz. pair, #a-b   2.00 2.00

Children's Drawings — A733

No. 2850 — Dove and: a, 40 l, Black doves and flowers. b, 70 l, Boat on water.

2008, June 1   Litho.   Perf. 13x13¼
2850 A733 Horiz. pair, #a-b   3.00 3.00

UEFA Euro 2008 Soccer
Championships, Austria and
Switzerland — A734

No. 2851: a, 50 l, Map of Switzerland. b, 250 l, Map of Austria
200 l, Mascots, vert.

2008, June 16   Perf. 13x13¼
2851 A734 Horiz. pair, #a-b   10.00 10.00

Souvenir Sheet
Perf. 13¼x13
2852 A734 200 l multi   5.00 5.00

Prizren League, 130th Anniv. — A735

No. 2853: a, 100 l, Handwritten document. b, 150 l, Building, Albanian flag.

2008, June 27   Perf. 13¼x13
Granite Paper
2853 A735 Vert. pair, #a-b   7.50 7.50

First Albanian
Postage Stamps,
95th
Anniv. — A736

2008, June 30   Litho.
2854 A736 40 l multi   1.00 1.00

Famous
People of
Albanian
Heritage
A737

No. 2855: a, John Belushi (1949-82), actor. b, Gjon Mili (1904-84), photographer. c, Mimar Sinan (1489-1588), architect. d, Ibrahim Kodra (1918-2006), artist.

2008, July 9   Perf. 13x13¼
2855   Horiz. strip of 4   5.50 5.50
a.   A737 5 l multi   .30   .30
b.   A737 10 l multi   .30   .30
c.   A737 20 l multi   .30   .30
d.   A737 200 l multi   4.00 4.00

A738

Europa — A739

Hand holding quill pen and: 100 l, Map of Europe. 150 l, Map of Albania and Adriatic region.

2008, July 15   Perf. 13¼x13
Granite Paper (#2856-2857)
2856-2857 A738 Set of 2   6.50 6.50

Souvenir Sheet
Perf. 13¼x13
2858 A739 250 l multi   6.50 6.50

Poppies — A740

No. 2859: a, 50 l, Two poppies. b, 150 l, One poppy.

2008, July 30   Perf. 13¼x13
Granite Paper
2859 A740 Vert. pair, #a-b   5.00 5.00

2008 Summer
Olympics,
Beijing — A741

No. 2860: a, Soccer. b, Water polo. c, Running. d, Cycling.

2008, Aug. 8   Perf. 13x13¼
2860   Horiz. strip of 4   4.00 4.00
a.   A741 20 l multi   .60   .60
b.   A741 30 l multi   .80   .80
c.   A741 40 l multi   1.00 1.00
d.   A741 50 l multi   1.40 1.40

Landscapes — A742

No. 2861: a, 60 l, Osumit Canyon. b, 250 l, Komanit Lake.

2008, Aug. 25   Perf. 13
2861 A742 Horiz. pair, #a-b   9.00 9.00

King Zog (1895-1961) — A743

No. 2862 — Denomination color: a, 40 l, Black. b, 100 l, Red.

2008, Sept. 1   Perf. 13x13¼
2862 A743 Horiz. pair, #a-b   4.25 4.25

Freedom Fighters — A744

No. 2863: a, 40 l, Azem Hajdari (1963-98), assassinated politician. b, 200 l, Adem Jashari (1955-98), Kosovar independence leader.

2008, Sept. 12
2863 A744 Horiz. pair, #a-b   7.00 7.00

Independence of Kosovo — A745

No. 2864: a, 20 l, Ymer Prizreni (1820-87), political leader. b, 30 l, Isa Boletini (1864-1916), military leader. c, 40 l, Ibrahim Rugova (1944-2006), President of Kosovo. d, 50 l, Azem Galica (1889-1924), military leader. e, 70 l, Adem Jashari (1955-98), independence leader.

2008, Sept. 20   Perf. 13¼x13
2864 A745 Block of 5, #a-e, +   6.00 6.00
4 labels

Roman Emperors of Illyrian Origin — A746

No. 2865: a, 30 l, Decius (201-51). b, 200 l, Maximinus Thrax (173-238).

2008, Oct. 3   **Perf. 13**
2865 A746   Vert. pair, #a-b   6.50 6.50

Harry Potter — A747

No. 2866 — Harry Potter and: a, 20 l, Professor Dumbledore. b, 30 l, Kreacher. c, 50 l, Hermione Granger and friends. d, 100 l, Kreacher.

2008, Oct. 15   **Perf. 13x13¼**
2866 A747   Block of 4, #a-d   7.50 7.50
   A booklet containing a pane of Nos. 2866a-2866d sold for 550 l.

Monastir Congress, Cent. — A748

No. 2867: a, 40 l, Building. b, 100 l, Pages with handwritten Albanian alphabet.

2008, Nov. 14   **Perf. 13**
2867 A748   Horiz. pair, #a-b   4.50 4.50

Archaeology — A749

No. 2868: a, Ruins of synagogue, Sarande. b, Site at Orikumit. c, Site at Antigonese.

2008, Dec. 5   **Perf. 13**
2868   Horiz. strip of 3   4.50 4.50
   a.   A749 10 l multi   .30 .30
   b.   A749 50 l multi   1.75 1.75
   c.   A749 80 l multi   2.25 2.25

Universal Postal Union, 135th Anniv. — A750

No. 2869 — Emblems of Albania Post and UPU, world map and background color of: a, 100 l, Yellow bister. b, 200 l, Light blue, vert.

Perf. 13x13¼ (#2869a), 13¼x13 (#2869b)

2009, Oct. 9   **Litho.**
2869 A750   Pair, #a-b   6.50 6.50

Stan Laurel (1890-1965) and Oliver Hardy (1892-1957), Comedians A751

No. 2870 — Laurel and Hardy: a, 150 l, Holdings hats. b, 200 l, Wearing hats. 300 l, Laurel and Hardy wearing mortarboards, horiz.

2009, Oct. 16   **Litho.**   **Perf. 13¼x13**
2870 A751   Vert. pair, #a-b   10.00 10.00
        Souvenir Sheet
        Perf. 13x13¼
2871 A751   300 l multi   8.00 8.00

Weight Lifting — A752

No. 2872 — Various weight lifters and: a, 10 l, Oval with latitudinal and longitudinal lines. b, 60 l, Olympic rings. c, 120 l, Circles and stars. d, 150 l, Double-headed eagle of Albanian arms.

2009, Oct. 21   **Perf. 13¼x13**
2872 A752   Block of 4, #a-d   10.00 10.00

European Court of Human Rights, 50th Anniv. A753

2009, Oct. 30   **Perf. 13**
2873 A753   200 l multi   5.50 5.50

Council of Europe, 60th Anniv. A754

2009, Nov. 2
2874 A754   150 l multi   4.00 4.00

Albanian Painters — A755

No. 2875: a, 40 l, Abidin Dino (1913-93). b, 50 l, Lin Delija (1926-94). c, 60 l, Lika Janko (1928-2001). d, 150 l, Artur Tashko (1901-94).

2009, Nov. 11
2875 A755   Block of 4, #a-d   9.00 9.00

Traffic Safety — A756

No. 2876 — Traffic officer: a, 5 l, Holding matador's red cape. 1000 l, Stopping traffic.

2009, Nov. 16   **Perf. 13¼x13**
2876 A756   Horiz. pair, #a-b   20.00 20.00

Diplomatic Relations Between Albania and People's Republic of China, 60th Anniv. — A757

2009, Nov. 23   **Perf. 13**
2877 A757   20 l multi   .50 .50

Albanian Iso-polyphonic Singers, UNESCO Intangible Cultural Heritage — A758

No. 2878: a, 40 l, Singers. b, 250 l, Musicians.

2009, Nov. 25   **Perf. 13¼x13**
2878 A758   Horiz. pair, #a-b   6.00 6.00

End of World War II, 65th Anniv. — A759

No. 2879 — Double-headed eagle and: a, 70 l, Soldier. b, 200 l, Bombers.

2009, Nov. 29   **Perf. 13x13¼**
2879 A759   Horiz. pair, #a-b   6.00 6.00

Legend of Mujit and Halitit — A760

No. 2880: a, 30 l, Man being held against giant's breasts. b, 200 l, Man and woman on horse.

2009, Dec. 5
2880 A760   Horiz. pair, #a-b   6.00 6.00

Religious Art and Buildings — A761

No. 2881: a, Mosque, Berat. b, Church, Korçe. c, Church, Lezhe.

2009, Dec. 9   **Perf. 13¼x13**
2881   Horiz. strip of 3   8.00 8.00
   a.   A761 90 l multi   1.75 1.75
   b.   A761 100 l multi   2.00 2.00
   c.   A761 120 l multi   2.50 2.50

Europa A762

Designs: 200 l, Planets, dish antenna. 250 l, Spacecraft and exploration vehicle on Mars. 350 l, Satellite above planet.

2009, Dec. 11   **Perf. 13x13¼**
2882 A762 200 l multi   5.00 5.00
2883 A762 250 l multi   6.00 6.00
        Souvenir Sheet
        Perf. 13¼x13
2884 A762 350 l multi   9.00 9.00
   a.   Booklet pane, #2882-2884   22.50 —
      Complete booklet, #2884a   22.50

   Intl. Year of Astronomy. No. 2884 contains one 30x25mm stamp.

Archaeological Sites — A763

No. 2885: a, 30 l, Fort, Tirana. b, 250 l, Tomb, Kamenica.

2009, Dec. 16   **Perf. 13**
2885 A763   Horiz. pair, #a-b   6.00 6.00

National Theater A764

No. 2886 — Scenes from plays: a, Shi ne Plazh. b, Pallati 176. c, Apologjia e Vertete e Sokratit.

2009, Dec. 21
2886 Horiz. strip of 3   8.00 8.00
  a. A764 20 l multi   .40 .40
  b. A764 80 l multi   1.60 1.60
  c. A764 200 l multi   4.00 4.00

Central State Archives, 60th
Anniv. — A765

No. 2887: a, 40 l, Book, handwritten manuscript. b, 60 l, Scroll.

2009, Dec. 28
2887 A765   Horiz. pair, #a-b   2.50 2.50

Albanian-Italian Friendship — A766

2010, Apr. 12   **Litho.**   *Perf. 13*
2888 A766 40 l multi   .80 .80

Mother Teresa
(1910-97),
Humanitarian
A767

2010, Aug. 26
2889 A767 100 l multi   1.90 1.90
See Kosovo No. 154, Macedonia No. 529.

Visaless
Entry Into
Europe for
Albanians
A768

2010, Nov. 8   *Perf. 13x13¼*
2890 A768 40 l multi   .80 .80

National Library. 50th Anniv. — A769

No. 2891: a, 10 l, Man reading book. b, 1000 l, Man at computer.

2011, Feb. 18
2891 A769   Horiz. pair, #a-b   20.00 20.00
Dated 2010.

Student's Protest Movement, 20th
Anniv. — A770

No. 2892: a, 40 l, Protestors, man at microphone. b, 60 l, Toppling of Enver Hoxha statue.
200 l, Students giving "V" for victory hand sign, vert.

2011, Feb. 20   *Perf. 13*
2892 A770   Horiz. pair, #a-b   2.00 2.00
Souvenir Sheet
2893 A770 200 l multi   4.00 4.00
Dated 2010.

Europa — A771

No. 2894 — Characters from children's stories: a, 100 l, Sun, donkey and rooster. b, 150 l, Bird and cat in balloons, girl.
250 l, Girl, stack of books, horiz.

2011, Feb. 25   *Perf. 13¼x13*
2894 A771   Vert. pair, #a-b   4.50 4.50
Souvenir Sheet
Perf. 13x13¼
2895 A771 250 l multi   4.50 4.50
Dated 2010.

Underwater Archaeology — A772

No. 2896: a, 50 l, Close-up of underwater artifact. b, 250 l, Items on seabed.

2011, Mar. 2   *Perf. 13¼x13*
2896 A772   Horiz. pair, #a-b   6.00 6.00
Dated 2010.

2010 World Cup Soccer
Championships, South Africa — A773

No. 2897 — Emblem, ball and players: a, 80 l. b, 120 l.
200 l, Two players.

2011, Mar. 10   *Perf. 13¼x13*
2897 A773   Horiz. pair, #a-b   4.00 4.00
Souvenir Sheet
2898 A773 200 l multi   4.00 4.00
Dated 2010.

Albanian Peacekeeping Force — A774

No. 2899: a, 50 l, Helicopter, soldiers. b, 200 l, Soldier, tank.

2011, Mar. 21
2899 A774   Horiz. pair, #a-b   5.25 5.25
Dated 2010.

Lushnja Congress, 90th
Anniv. — A775

No. 2900: a, 70 l, Document and seal. b, 150 l, Building.

2011, Mar. 23
2900 A775   Horiz. pair, #a-b   4.50 4.50
Dated 2010.

National
Cultural
Heritage
Day — A776

No. 2901: a, House, Gjirokaster. b, Apron, Dumre. c, Fortress, Tirana. d, Lute, Shkoder. 200 l, Woman, Zadrime.

2011, Mar. 31   *Perf. 13x13¼*
2901 Horiz. strip of 4   5.75 5.75
  a. A776 10 l multi   .25 .25
  b. A776 70 l multi   1.40 1.40
  c. A776 80 l multi   1.60 1.60
  d. A776 120 l multi   2.50 2.50
Souvenir Sheet
2902 A776 200 l multi   4.25 4.25
Dated 2010.

Items Made of Silver — A777

No. 2903: a, Pendant. b, Purse. c, Butterfly. d, Decorated case and cylinder with tip. 200 l, Open case and cylinder.

2011, Apr. 6   *Perf. 13*
2903 A777   Block of 4, #a-d   4.25 4.25
Souvenir Sheet
2904 A777 200 l multi   4.25 4.25
Dated 2010.

Durres-Kukes Road — A778

No. 2905 — Road design and: a, 40 l, Hills. b, 60 l, Construction equipment. c, 90 l, Tunnel. d, 150 l, Bridge.

2011, Apr. 11   *Perf. 13x13¼*
2905 A778   Block of 4, #a-d   7.00 7.00
Dated 2010.

Miniature Sheet

Historic Center of Berati UNESCO
World Heritage Site — A779

No. 2906: a, 10 l, Building. b, 20 l, Buildings on hillside, street light. c, 30 l, Bridge. d, 50 l, Archway, fence on wall, buildings. e, 60 l, Buildings on hillside. 80 l, Church.

2011, Apr. 11   *Perf. 13x13¼*
2906 A779   Sheet of 6, #a-f   5.25 5.25

Europa — A780

Map of Europe with tree trunks and hills in: 200 l, Brown. 250 l, Green.

2011, July 30   *Perf. 13¼x13*
2907 A780 200 l multi   4.25 4.25
Souvenir Sheet
2908 A780 250 l multi   5.25 5.25
Intl. Year of Forests.

Boxing — A781

No. 2909: a, 50 l, Boxers, boxer with red shirt at left. b, 100 l, Boxers, boxer with red shirt at right.
250 l, Boxer throwing punch.

2011, Aug. 26
2909 A781   Horiz. pair, #a-b   3.00 3.00
Souvenir Sheet
2910 A781 250 l multi   5.00 5.00

Multi-party Elections, 20h Anniv. — A782

2011, Sept. 1   **Perf. 13x13¼**
2911 A782 150 l multi   3.00 3.00

Ismail Kadare, Writer A783

2011, Sept. 12   **Perf. 13**
2912 A783 40 l multi   .80 .80

Tourism — A784

No. 2913: a, 80 l, Valbona River and mountains. b, 120 l, Rocks in Valbona River.

2011, Sept. 27
2913 A784   Horiz. pair, #a-b   4.00 4.00

Albanian Red Cross, 90th Anniv. — A785

No. 2914 — Emblem and: a, 70 l + 10 l, Aid to pregnant woman, first aid. b, 120 l, Woman receiving two bags.

2011, Oct. 4
2914 A785   Horiz. pair, #a-b   4.00 4.00

Carrier Pigeons — A786

No. 2915 — Globe and: a, 10 l, Pigeon with mail bag. b, 1000 l, Pigeon without mail bag.

2011, Oct. 9
2915 A786   Horiz. pair, #a-b   19.50 19.50

Mosaics — A787

No. 2916 — Mosaic from: a, 20 l, St. Michael's Basilica, Arapaj. b, 60 l, Church, Antigone. c, 120 l, Mesaplikut Basilica.

2011, Oct. 14   **Litho.**
2916 A787   Horiz. strip of 3,
     #a-c   4.00 4.00

Forum of States on Adriatic and Ionian Seas A788

2011, Nov. 18   **Perf. 13x13¼**
2917 A788 90 l multi   1.75 1.75

Flowers — A789

No. 2918: a, 30 l, Gymnospermium shqipetarum. b, 70 l, Viola kosaninii. c, 100 l, Aster albanicus subsp. paparisoi.

2011, Dec. 5   **Perf. 13¼x13**
2918 A789   Horiz. strip of 3,
     #a-c   4.00 4.00

Academy of Arts, 45th Anniv. — A790

2011, Dec. 15   **Perf. 13**
2919 A790 250 l multi   4.75 4.75

Nudes — A791

No. 2920 — Nude: a, 10 l, Painting by Vangjush Mio. b, 90 l, Painting by Abdurrahim Buza. c, 100 l, Scupllure by Janaq Paço. 250 l, Nude sculpture by Paço, diff.

2011, Dec. 22   **Perf. 13x13¼**
2920 A791   Horiz. strip of 3, #a-
     c   3.75 3.75
    Souvenir Sheet
2921 A791 250 l multi   4.75 4.75

Democracy in Albania, 20th Anniv. — A792

2012, Mar. 22   **Perf. 13**
2922 A792 100 l multi   1.90 1.90

Europa — A793

No. 2923 — Various tourist attractions: a, 30 l. b, 250 l.

2012, Sept. 21   **Perf. 13x13¼**
2923 A793   Horiz. pair, #a-b   5.25 5.25

2012 European Soccer Championships, Poland and Ukraine — A794

No. 2924 — Emblem, soccer ball, flags of European nations and large flag of: a, 100 l, Poland. b, 200 l, Ukraine.

2012, Sept. 28   **Perf. 13**
2924 A794   Horiz. pair, #a-b   5.75 5.75

Kin Dushi (1922-94), Writer A795

2012, Oct. 3   **Perf. 13x13¼**
2925 A795 150 l multi   2.75 2.75

Albanian Membership in Universal Postal Union, 90th Anniv. — A796

2012, Oct. 9   **Perf. 13¼x12¾**
2926 A796 250 l multi   4.75 4.75

Revolts Against Ottoman Rule, Cent. — A797

No. 2927: a, 10 l, Rebel leader, row of rebels. b, 1000 l, Rebels.

2012, Oct. 19   **Perf. 13**
2927 A797   Horiz. pair, #a-b   18.50 18.50

    Souvenir Sheet

Rock Art — A798

No. 2928 — Rock art at: a, 20 l, Rubik. b, 60 l, Boville. c, 150 l, Lepenice.

2012, Oct. 29   **Perf. 13¼x13**
2928 A798   Sheet of 3, #a-c   4.25 4.25

Linguists Who Have Studied Albanian Language A799

No. 2929: a, Eric Hamp. b, Norbert Jokl (1877-1942). c, Holger Pedersen (1867-1953).

2012, Nov. 16   **Perf. 13**
2929   Horiz. strip of 3   3.50 3.50
   a.   A799 50 l multi   .95 .95
   b.   A799 60 l multi   1.10 1.10
   c.   A799 70 l multi   1.40 1.40
    See No. 2947.

Dancers A800

No. 2930 — Dancers from: a, Tropoje. b, Tirana. c, Cameri. d, Lushnje.

2012, Nov. 23   **Perf. 13x13¼**
2930   Horiz. strip of 4   6.25 6.25
   a.   A800 20 l multi   .40 .40
   b.   A800 40 l multi   .75 .75
   c.   A800 120 l multi   2.25 2.25
   d.   A800 150 l multi   2.75 2.75

Independence, Cent. — A801

2012, Nov. 23   **Perf. 13¼x13**
2931 A801 40 l black & red   .75 .75

Declaration of Independence, Cent. — A802

No. 2932: a, People, Albanian flag. b, People, Albanian flag, diff. c, Flags, United Nations Headquarters. d, Flags, NATO emblem.

2012, Nov. 28   **Perf. 13x13¼**
2932   Horiz. strip of 4   5.50 5.50
   a.   A802 50 l multi   .95 .95
   b.   A802 60 l multi   1.10 1.10
   c.   A802 70 l multi   1.40 1.40
   d.   A802 100 l multi   1.90 1.90
   e.   Booklet pane of 4, #2932a-2932d   5.50
    Complete booklet, #2932e   5.50

Albanian Army, Cent. — A803

No. 2933: a, 90 l, Soldiers in traditional costumes. b, 150 l, Soldiers wearing helmets.

2012, Dec. 4   **Litho.**
2933 A803   Horiz. pair, #a-b   4.50 4.50

Albanian Post, Telegraph and
Telephone Administration,
Cent. — A804

No. 2934 — Telephone, poles, wires, and: a,
80 l, Envelopes, mailbox. b, 200 l, Letter in
open envelope.

2012, Dec. 5		Perf. 13	
2934 A804	Horiz. pair, #a-b	5.25	5.25
c.	Booklet pane of 2, #2934a-2934b, + 2 labels	5.25	—
	Complete booklet, #2934c	5.25	

Marine Life and Plants — A805

No. 2935: a, 10 l, Fish, sea grasses, diver.
b, 250 l, Fish, sea grasses, coral.

2012, Dec. 14		Perf. 13x12¾	
2935 A805	Horiz. pair, #a-b	5.00	5.00
c.	Booklet pane of 2, #2935a-2935b	5.00	—
	Complete booklet, #2935c	5.00	

First Handstamped Envelope of
Albania, Cent. — A806

No. 2936: a, 120 l, Front of addressed handstamped envelope. b, 150 l, Back of envelope,
handstamp.

2013, May 5		Perf. 13	
2936 A806	Horiz. pair, #a-b	5.25	5.25
c.	Booklet pane of 2, #2936a-2936b	5.25	—
	Complete booklet, #2936c	5.25	

World Track and Field Championships,
Moscow — A807

No. 2937: a, 30 l, Runner. b, 200 l, High
jumper.
250 l, Pole vaulter.

2013, Aug. 27		Perf. 13	
2937 A807	Horiz. pair, #a-b	4.50	4.50
Souvenir Sheet			
2938 A807	250 l multi	4.75	4.75

Vedat Kokona (1913-98),
Lexicographer — A808

2013, Aug. 30	Litho.	Perf. 13	
2939 A808	150 l multi	3.00	3.00

Europa — A809

No. 2940 — Globe, parcels, envelopes and:
a, 80 l, Postal van and truck. b, 200 l, Airplane,
train and ship.

2013, Oct. 4	Litho.	Perf. 13¼x13	
2940 A809	Horiz. pair, #a-b	5.50	5.50
c.	Booklet pane of 2, #2940a-2940b	5.50	—
	Complete booklet, #2940c	5.50	

Albanian Police, Cent. — A810

No. 2941 — Flag and: a, 10 l, Policewoman.
b, 250 l, Policeman.

2013, Oct. 18	Litho.	Perf. 13¼x13	
2941 A810	Horiz. pair, #a-b	5.00	5.00

Flowers
A811

No. 2942: a, Scilla albanica. b, Gymnospermium maloi. c, Tulipa albanica.

2013, Oct. 30	Litho.	Perf. 13x13¼	
2942	Horiz. strip of 3	5.00	5.00
a.	A811 20 l multi	.40	.40
b.	A811 90 l multi	1.75	1.75
c.	A811 175 l multi	2.75	2.75

17th Mediterranean Games, Mersin,
Turkey — A812

No. 2943: a, 40 l, Diving, swimming, synchronized swimming. b, 150 l, Volleyball,
weight lifting, cycling.
200 l, Rowing, horiz.

2013, Nov. 6	Litho.	Perf. 13¼x13	
2943 A812	Horiz. pair, #a-b	4.75	4.75
Souvenir Sheet			
Perf. 13x13¼			
2944 A812	200 l multi	4.00	4.00

International Red Cross, 150th
Anniv. — A813

No. 2945 — Red cross and: a, 40 l, Aid
workers helping injured man, feeding woman.
b, 150 l, Worker giving bags of goods to man.
250 l, Aid workers assisting injured man.

2013, Nov. 15	Litho.	Perf. 13	
2945 A813	Horiz. pair, #a-b	3.75	3.75
Souvenir Sheet			
2946 A813	250 l multi	5.00	5.00

Linguists Type of 2012

No. 2947 — Historians: a, Milan Sufflay
(1879-1931). b, Konstantin Jiracek (1854-
1918). c, Ludwig von Thallóczy (1854-1916).

2013, Nov. 25			
2947	Horiz. strip of 3	5.25	5.25
a.	A799 10 l multi	.25	.25
b.	A799 100 l multi	2.00	2.00
c.	A799 150 l multi	3.00	3.00

Recent Archaeological Finds — A814

No. 2948: a, Bronze foot, 2nd-3rd cent. b,
Bronze fibula with horse design, 7th-8th cent.
c, Marble statue of an aristocrat, 2nd cent. d,
Relief of Heraclius and Apollo, 2nd cent.

2013, Dec. 3	Litho.	Perf. 13	
2948	Horiz. strip of 4	6.50	6.50
a.	A814 20 l multi	.35	.35
b.	A814 90 l multi	1.75	1.75
c.	A814 100 l multi	2.00	2.00
d.	A814 120 l multi	2.40	2.40

Nikolla Naço
(1843-1913),
Newspaper
Editor — A815

2013, Dec. 18	Litho.	Perf. 13¼x13	
2949 A815	200 l multi	4.00	4.00

2014 World Cup Soccer
Championships, Brazil — A816

No. 2950: a, Mascot. b, Mascot holding soccer ball. c, Mascot dribbling soccer ball.
140 l, Emblem, vert.

2014, July 9	Litho.	Perf. 13	
2950	Horiz. strip of 3	3.25	3.25
a.	A816 10 l multi	.25	.25
b.	A816 50 l multi	1.00	1.00
c.	A816 100 l multi	2.00	2.00
Souvenir Sheet			
2951 A816	140 l multi	2.75	2.75

Visit to Albania
of Pope
Francis — A817

2014, Sept. 21	Litho.	Perf. 13	
2952 A817	100 l multi	1.90	1.90

Europa — A818

No. 2953: a, 100 l, Gajdja (bagpipes). b,
150 l, Lodra (drum).

2014, Oct. 9	Litho.	Perf. 13¼x13	
2953 A818	Horiz. pair, #a-b	4.50	4.50
c.	Souvenir sheet of 2, #2953a-2953b + central label	4.50	4.50
	Complete booklet, #2953c	4.50	

Kuçi Assembly, 400th Anniv. — A819

No. 2954: a, 80 l, Participants examining
document. b, 150 l, Participants.
200 l, Participants, diff.

2014, Oct. 14	Litho.	Perf. 13x13¼	
2954 A819	Horiz. pair, #a-b	4.25	4.25
Souvenir Sheet			
2955 A819	200 l multi	3.75	3.75

Souvenir Sheet

Relations Between Albania and
Kuwait — A820

No. 2956: a, 100 l, Shiekh Sabah, emir of
Kuwait. b, Handshake, flags of Albania and
Kuwait.

2014, Nov. 11	Litho.	Perf. 13¼x13	
2956 A820	100 l Sheet of 2, #a-b	3.50	3.50

Sulejman Pashe
Delvina (1884-
1933), Prime
Minister — A821

2014, Nov. 18	Litho.	Perf. 13¼x13	
2957 A821	150 l multi	2.75	2.75

Reptiles and Amphibians — A822

No. 2958: a, 80 l, Caretta caretta. b, 170 l,
Hyla arborea.

2014, Nov. 22	Litho.	Perf. 13	
2958 A822	Horiz. pair, #a-b	4.50	4.50

Miniature Sheet

Coronation of Prince William of Wied, Cent. — A823

No. 2959: a, 60 l, Princess Sophie (1885-1936), wife of Prince William. b, 70 l, Crown, arms of Albania. c, 80 l, Star with eagle in circle. d, 90 l, Prince William of Wied (1876-1945).

2014, Nov. 26 Litho. Perf. 13¼x13
2959 A823 Sheet of 4, #a-d 5.50 5.50

World War II Liberation of Albania, 70th Anniv. — A824

2014, Nov. 29 Litho. Perf. 13
2960 A824 40 l multi .70 .70

Archaeological Items From Dyrrachium (Dürres) A825

No. 2961 — Depictions of Artemis: a, 50 l, Statue, 4th cent. B.C. b, 60 l, Bust, 4th cent. B.C. c, 70 l, Marble bust, 4th cent. B.C. d, 90 l, Bronze statue, 3rd cent. B.C.

2014, Dec. 5 Litho. Perf. 13
2961 Horiz. strip of 4 4.75 4.75
  a. A825 50 l multi .90 .90
  b. A825 60 l multi 1.00 1.00
  c. A825 70 l multi 1.25 1.25
  d. A825 90 l multi 1.60 1.60

Albanian Candidacy for European Union Membership — A826

2014, Dec. 8 Litho. Perf. 13x13¼
2962 A826 40 l multi .70 .70

William Shakespeare (1564-1616), Writer — A827

2014, Dec. 12 Litho. Perf. 13
2963 A827 150 l multi 2.60 2.60

Wooden Handicrafts — A828

No. 2964: a, 40 l, Chair, Mirdite. b, 50 l, Cradle, Rreshen. c, 60 l, Shepherd's crook, Laberi. d, 70 l, Spoons, Tirana. 180 l, Ceiling decorations, Leuse.

2014, Dec. 19 Litho. Perf. 13
2964 A828 Block of 4, #a-d 4.00 4.00
Souvenir Sheet
2965 A828 180 l multi 3.25 3.25

Icons in Museums — A829

No. 2966 — Icon from: a, 10 l, Himare. b, 30 l, Dhermi. c, 40 l, Dhermi, diff. d, 70 l, Vuno. e, 90 l, Deme. f, 100 l, Vuno, diff.

2014, Dec. 24 Litho. Perf. 13¼x13
2966 A829 Sheet of 6, #a-f 6.00 6.00
  g. Booklet pane of 6, #2966a-
    2966f 6.00
    Complete booklet, #2966g 6.00

No. 2966g has a decorative, curved pane margin.

Elez Isufi (1861-1924), Guerrilla Leader — A830

2014, Dec. 29 Litho. Perf. 13¼x13
2967 A830 1000 l multi 17.50 17.50

Europa — A831

2015, Sept. 2 Litho. Perf. 13¼x13
2968 A831 130 l multi 2.10 2.10
Souvenir Sheet
2969 A831 250 l multi 4.00 4.00
  a. Booklet pane of 2, #2968-2969 6.25
    Complete booklet, #2969a 6.25

National Parks A832

No. 2970: a, Shebenik-Jabllanice National Park. b, Bredhi i Hotoves National Park. c, Dajti National Park.

2015, Sept. 16 Litho. Perf. 13¼x13
2970 Horiz. strip of 3 5.00 5.00
  a. A832 50 l multi .80 .80
  b. A832 100 l multi 1.60 1.60
  c. A832 150 l multi 2.50 2.50

Early Locomotives and Their Inventors — A833

No. 2971: a, 50 l, New Castle, Richard Trevithick (1771-1833). b, 60 l, Salamanca, Matthew Murray (1765-1826). c, 90 l, Rocket, Robert Stephenson (1803-59). d, 100 l, Locomotion, George Stephenson (1781-1848).

Perf. 13¼x12¾
2015, Sept. 27 Litho.
2971 A833 Block of 4, #a-d 5.00 5.00
  Locomotives, 190th anniv.

Famous Men — A834

No. 2972: a, 40 l, Dhimiter Shuteriqi (1915-2003), writer. b, 50 l, Zef Skiroi (1865-1927), poet. c, 60 l, Mahir Domi (1915-2000), linguist. d, 100 l, Gaqo Avrazi (1915-85), composer.

2015, Sept. 28 Litho. Perf. 13¼x13
2972 A834 Block of 4, #a-d 4.00 4.00

Albanian Soccer Federation, 85th Anniv. — A835

No. 2973 — Federation emblem and: a, 5 l, Soccer ball, goaltender and net. b, 10 l, Grass. c, 1000 l, Soccer ball and player making scissor kick.

2015, Oct. 8 Litho. Perf. 13¼x13
2973 A835 Horiz. strip of 3,
    #a-c 16.00 16.00

Famous Men — A836

No. 2974: a, Nicéphore Niépce (1765-1833), inventor of photography. b, Carl Patsch (1865-1945), historian. c, Boris Pasternak (1890-1960), 1958 Nobel laureate in Literature. d, Norman Wisdom (1915-2010), comedian and actor.

2015, Oct. 9 Litho. Perf. 13
2974 Horiz. strip of 4 4.25 4.25
  a. A836 10 l multi .25 .25
  b. A836 80 l multi .95 .95
  c. A836 80 l multi 1.25 1.25
  d. A836 100 l multi 1.60 1.60

United Nations, 70th Anniv. A837

2015, Oct. 24 Litho. Perf. 13¼x13
2975 A837 180 l multi 3.00 3.00

Ceramic Vessels — A838

No. 2976 — Various vessels: a, 50 l. b, 60 l. c, 70 l. d, 120 l. 200 l, Various ceramic vessels, diff.

2015, Nov. 6 Litho. Perf. 13
2976 A838 Block of 4, #a-d 4.75 4.75
Souvenir Sheet
2977 A838 200 l multi 3.25 3.25

Recent Archaeological Discoveries — A839

No. 2978: a, 10 l, Ivory mirror handle, 4th-5th cent. B.C. b, 30 l, Marble statue of officer, 1st cent. B.C. c, 60 l, Bronze utensil handle, 6th-7th cent. B.C. d, 150 l, Bronze statue of Hermes, 1st cent. B.C.

2015, Nov. 16 Litho. Perf. 13
2978 A839 Block of 4, #a-d 4.00 4.00

International Telecommunication Union, 150th Anniv. — A840

2015, Dec. 5 Litho. Perf. 13
2979 A840 2500 l multi 40.00 40.00

Marine Life — A841

No. 2980: a, 5 l, Sabella spallanzanii. b, 150 l, Antedon mediterranea. 250 l, Cotylorhiza tuberculata.

2015, Dec. 23   Litho.   Perf. 13¼x13
2980 A841   Horiz. pair, #a-b   2.50 2.50
Souvenir Sheet
2981 A841 250 l multi   4.00 4.00

2016 European Soccer Championships, France — A842

No. 2982 — Emblem and player with denomination at: a, 70 l, UL. b, 100 l, UR.

2016, June 10   Litho.   Perf. 13x13¼
2982 A842   Horiz. pair, #a-b   2.75 2.75

Europa A843

2016, July 9   Litho.   Perf. 13x13¼
2983 A843 200 l multi   3.25 3.25
Think Green Issue.

Flowers — A844

No. 2984: a, Tulipa kosovarica. b, Campanula comosiformis. c, Solenanthus albanicus.

2016, July 27   Litho.   Perf. 13¼x13
2984   Horiz. strip of 3   4.00 4.00
a.   A844 20 l multi   .35 .35
b.   A844 30 l multi   .50 .50
c.   A844 190 l multi   3.00 3.00

Balkanfila 2016 Intl. Stamp Exhibition, Tirana — A845

2016, Aug. 9   Litho.   Perf. 13x13¼
2985 A845 250 l multi   4.25 4.25

Famous Men — A846

No. 2986: a, Ndre Mjeda (1866-1937), poet. b, Kole Jakova (1916-2002), writer. c, Jusuf Vrioni (1916-2001), diplomat and translator.

2016, Aug. 17   Litho.   Perf. 13x13¼
2986   Horiz. strip of 3   3.50 3.50
a.   A846 10 l multi   .25 .25
b.   A846 50 l multi   .80 .80
c.   A846 150 l multi   2.40 2.40

Albania, 2015-17 Member of United Nations Human Rights Council A847

2016, Aug. 29   Litho.   Perf. 13x13¼
2987 A847 1000 l multi   16.50 16.50

Albanian Literary Commission, Cent. — A848

2016, Sept. 1   Litho.   Perf. 13
2988 A848 60 l multi   1.00 1.00

Canonization of St. Teresa of Calcutta (Mother Teresa) — A849

2016, Sept. 4   Litho.   Perf. 13x13¼
2989 A849 120 l multi   2.00 2.00
a.   Booklet pane of 1   2.00
    Complete booklet, #2989a   2.00

Carved Stone Containers — A850

No. 2990 — Various containers: a, 10 l. b, 80 l. c, 130 l. d, 180 l. 250 l, Bowl with lid.

2016, Sept. 27   Litho.   Perf. 13
2990 A850   Block of 4, #a-d   6.50 6.50
Souvenir Sheet
2991 A850 250 l multi   4.25 4.25

Miguel de Cervantes (1547-1616), Writer — A851

Designs: 140 l, Cervantes, Don Quixote on horse, windmill. 200 l, Don Quixote and Sancho Panza, vert.

2016, Oct. 9   Litho.   Perf. 13x13¼
2992 A851 140 l multi   2.25 2.25
Souvenir Sheet
2993 A851 200 l multi   3.25 3.25

Dritero Agolli (1931-2017), Writer — A852

2016, Oct. 13   Litho.   Perf. 13
2994 A852 120 l multi   2.00 2.00

Autonomous Republic of Korçe, Cent. — A853

No. 2995: a, 5 l, Themistokli Germenji (1871-1917), prefect, flag and building. b, 2500 l, Soldiers and civilians.

2016, Dec. 10   Litho.   Perf. 13
2995 A853   Horiz. pair, #a-b   39.00 39.00

Flora — A854

No. 2996: a, 150 l, Ajuga reptans. b, 250 l, Vaccinium myrtillus.

2017, Nov. 1   Litho.   Perf. 13¼x13
2996 A854   Horiz. pair, #a-b   7.00 7.00

Berat Castle Ruins A855

2017, Nov. 18   Litho.   Perf. 13¼x13
2997 A855 200 l multi   3.75 3.75
Souvenir Sheet
2998 A855 250 l multi   4.50 4.50
Europa.

Divjake-Karavasta National Park — A856

No. 2999: a, 40 l, Various birds. b, 1000 l, Flamingo and water buffalos.

2017, Nov. 24   Litho.   Perf. 13¼x13
2999 A856   Horiz. pair, #a-b   18.50 18.50

Famous Albanians A857

No. 3000: a, Musine Kokalari (1917-83), writer. b, Zef Kolombi (1907-49), painter. c, Prenke Jakova (1917-69), composer. d, Dom Nikolle Kaçorri (1862-1917), politician.

2017, Dec. 5   Litho.   Perf. 13x13¼
3000   Horiz. strip of 4   4.00 4.00
a.   A857 10 l multi   .25 .25
b.   A857 40 l multi   .75 .75
c.   A857 70 l multi   1.25 1.25
d.   A857 90 l multi   1.75 1.75

Famous Men A858

No. 3001: a, Ferdinand von Zeppelin (1838-1917), manufacturer of Zeppelin airships. b, Edgar Degas (1834-1917), painter. c, Stefan Zweig (1881-1942), writer.

2017, Dec. 12   Litho.   Perf. 13
3001   Horiz. strip of 3   4.75 4.75
a.   A858 20 l multi   .40 .40
b.   A858 90 l multi   1.75 1.75
c.   A858 140 l multi   2.60 2.60

2017 World Aquatics Championships, Budapest, Hungary — A859

No. 3002: a, 60 l, Swimming, water polo, synchronized swimming. b, 90 l, Synchronized swimming and various swimming strokes.

2017, Dec. 15   Litho.   Perf. 13¼x13
3002 A859   Horiz. pair, #a-b   2.75 2.75

International Immigration Day — A860

No. 3003 — Emigrants, ship, emblem of Pan-Albanian Federation of America and: a, 60 l, Statue of Liberty. b, 250 l, Map of Europe.

2017, Dec. 18   Litho.   Perf. 13¼x13
3003 A860   Horiz. pair, #a-b   5.75 5.75

Lynx
A861

Lynx facing: 120 l, Right. 1.90 l, Left.

2017, Dec. 21 Litho. Perf. 13x13¼
3004 A861 120 l multi 2.25 2.25
Souvenir Sheet
3005 A861 190 l multi 3.50 3.50

Glassware — A862

No. 3006: a, 5 l, Three bottles with caps. b, 40 l, Vase and three small glasses. c, 90 l, Pitcher with lid and two bowls. d, 130 l, Two pitchers.
200 l, Five glasses and two vases.

2017, Dec. 23 Litho. Perf. 13
3006 A862 Block of 4, #a-d 4.75 4.75
Souvenir Sheet
3007 A862 200 l multi 3.75 3.75

Albanian
Art — A863

Inscriptions: 30 l, Portreti i Skenderbeut (Portrait of Skanderbeg). 40 l, Skice, studim (Study sketch), horiz. 50 l, Kaloresi (Cavalry), horiz. 80 l, Leningradi ne shi (Leningrad in the Rain), horiz. 90 l, Skice, studim (Study sketch of girl). 100 l, Ne gjume (Asleep). 180 l, Rrobaqepesja (Seamstress). 190 l, Varrimi i shokut (Burial of a Friend).

2017, Dec. 27 Litho. Perf. 13
3008-3015 A863 Set of 8 14.00 14.00

European
Day of
Personal
Data
Protection
A864

2017, Dec. 28 Litho. Perf. 13x13¼
3016 A864 2500 l multi 45.00 45.00

Year of Skanderbeg — A865

2018, May 5 Litho. Perf. 13
3017 A865 250 l multi 4.75 4.75
Skanderbeg (1405-68), Albanian national hero.

Europa
A866

Designs: 200 l, Gorica Bridge, Berat. 250 l, Mesi Bridge, Shkoder.

2018, Oct. 25 Litho. Perf. 13x13¼
3018 A866 200 l multi 3.75 3.75
Souvenir Sheet
3019 A866 250 l multi 4.50 4.50
a. Booklet pane of 2, #3018-3019 8.25
Complete booklet, #3019a 8.25

Souvenir Sheet

Skanderbeg (1405-68), Albanian
National Hero — A867

No. 3020: a, 150 l, 16th cent. engraving of Skanderbeg by Dominicus Custos. b, 250 l, Skanderbeg with sword.

2018, Nov. 6 Litho. Perf. 13x13¼
3020 A867 Sheet of 2, #a-b 7.50 7.50

Famous Men — A868

No. 3021: a, 90 l, Claude Debussy (1862-1918), composer. b, 180 l, Gustav Klimt (1862-1918), painter.

2018, Nov. 16 Litho. Perf. 13
3021 A868 Horiz. pair, #a-b 5.00 5.00

Flowers — A869

No. 3022: a, 40 l, Abelmoschus esculentus. b, 1000 l, Hypericum perforatum.

2018, Dec. 7 Litho. Perf. 13¼x13
3022 A869 Horiz. pair, #a-b 19.50 19.50

Fish — A870

No. 3023: a, 5 l, Acipenser sturio. b, 190 l, Salmo trutta.

2018, Dec. 14 Litho. Perf. 13¼x13
3023 A870 Horiz. pair, #a-b 3.75 3.75

Historical Anniversaries — A871

No. 3024: a, Publication of *Dottrina Christiana,* 400th anniv. b, Fourteen Points of Pres. Woodrow Wilson, cent. c, Committee for the National Defense of Kosovo, cent.

2018, Dec. 14 Litho. Perf. 13¼x13
3024 Horiz. strip of 3 5.75 5.75
a. A871 50 l multi .90 .90
b. A871 120 l multi 2.25 2.25
c. A871 140 l multi 2.60 2.60

Tourism — A872

No. 3025: a, 40 l, Hills and waterfall near Permët. b, 2500 l, Katiu Bridge near Permet.

2018, Dec. 22 Litho. Perf. 13
3025 A872 Horiz. pair, #a-b 47.50 47.50

Embroidery Patterns — A873

No. 3026 — Various embroidery patterns: a, 40 l. b, 80 l. c, 90 l. d, 130 l.
200 l, Embroidery pattern, diff.

2018, Dec. 27 Litho. Perf. 13
3026 A873 Block of 4, #a-d 6.25 6.25
Souvenir Sheet
3027 A873 200 l multi 3.75 3.75

Albanian
Art — A874

Designs: 10 l, Erdhi Liria (Freedom came). 20 l, Fshatarja (Rustic scene of farmwoman drinking) (43x31mm). 30 l, Portret Punetoreje (Work portrait) (31x43mm). 40 l, Toke e Begate (Prosperous Land). 60 l, Vagonisti (Miner pushing rail car) (31x43mm). 70 l, Te Korrurat (Harvested), horiz. 90 l, Vijtja (Woman and plants) (31x43mm). 100 l, Mik-pritja (Woman holding dish) (40x40mm).

2018, Dec. 29 Litho. Perf. 13
3028-3035 A874 Set of 8 7.75 7.75

Albanian Parliamentarism,
Cent. — A875

Designs: 200 l, Republic of Albania Assembly Building.
No. 3037: a, Congress of Lushnja Building, 1920. b, National Council Building, 1920-25. c, Albanian parliamentarism centenary emblem. d, Chamber of Deputies Building, 1925-44.

2020, Jan. 21 Litho. Perf. 13¼x13
3036 A875 200 l multi 3.75 3.75
Miniature Sheet
3037 Sheet of 5, #3036, 3037a-3037d, + 4 labels 6.50 6.50
a. A875 20 l multi .35 .35
b. A875 30 l multi .55 .55
c. A875 40 l multi .75 .75
d. A875 60 l multi 1.10 1.10

Souvenir Sheet

Liberation of Albania, 75th
Anniv. — A876

No. 3038: a, 50 l, Mother Albania statue, Tirana. b, 250 l, Poppies.

2020, Feb. 10 Litho. Perf. 13x13¼
3038 A876 Sheet of 2, #a-b 5.50 5.50

SEMI-POSTAL STAMPS

Nos. 148-151
Surcharged in Red and Black

1924, Nov. 1
B1 A18 5q + 5q yel grn 11.00 30.00
B2 A18 10q + 5q carmine 11.00 30.00
B3 A18 25q + 5q dark blue 11.00 30.00
B4 A18 50q + 5q dark grn 11.00 30.00
Nos. B1-B4 (4) 44.00 120.00

Nos. B1 to B4 with Additional Surcharge in Red and Black

1924
B5 A18 5q + 5q + 5q yel
grn 11.00 26.00
B6 A18 10q + 5q + 5q car 11.00 26.00
B7 A18 25q + 5q + 5q dk bl 11.00 26.00
B8 A18 50q + 5q + 5q dk
grn 11.00 26.00
Nos. B5-B8 (4) 44.00 104.00

Issued under Italian Dominion

Nurse and Child — SP1

Unwmk.
1943, Apr. 1   **Photo.**   **Perf. 14**

B9	SP1	5q + 5q dark grn	.75	1.50
B10	SP1	10q + 10q olive brn	.75	1.50
B11	SP1	15q + 10q rose red	.75	1.50
B12	SP1	25q + 15q saphire	.75	2.75
B13	SP1	30q + 20q violet	.75	2.75
B14	SP1	50q + 25q dk org	1.00	2.75
B15	SP1	65q + 30q grnsh blk	1.40	4.00
B16	SP1	1fr + 40q chestnut	3.00	5.25
	Nos. B9-B16 (8)		9.15	22.00

The surtax was for the control of tuberculosis.

For surcharges see Nos. B24-B27.

Issued under German Administration

War Victims SP2

1944, Sept. 22

B17	SP2	5g + 5(q) dp grn	2.50	17.00
B18	SP2	10g + 5(q) dp brn	2.50	17.00
B19	SP2	15g + 5(q) car lake	2.50	17.00
B20	SP2	25q + 10(q) dp blue	2.50	17.00
B21	SP2	1fr + 50q dk olive	2.50	17.00
B22	SP2	2fr + 1(fr) purple	2.50	17.00
B23	SP2	3fr + 1.50(fr) dk org	2.50	17.00
	Nos. B17-B23 (7)		17.50	119.00

Surtax for victims of World War II.

Independent State

Nos. B9 to B12 Surcharged in Carmine

1945, May 4   **Unwmk.**   **Perf. 14**

B24	SP1	30q +15q on 5q+5q	8.25	13.00
B25	SP1	50q +25q on 10q+10q	8.25	13.00
B26	SP1	1fr +50q on 15q+10q	21.00	27.50
B27	SP1	2fr +1fr on 25q+15q	29.00	37.50
	Nos. B24-B27 (4)		66.50	91.00

The surtax was for the Albanian Red Cross.

People's Republic

Nos. 361 to 366 Overprinted in Red (cross) and Surcharged in Black

1946, July 16   **Perf. 11**

B28	A57	20q + 10q bluish grn	17.50	30.00
B29	A57	30q + 15q dp org	17.50	30.00
B30	A57	40q + 20q brown	17.50	30.00
B31	A57	60q + 30q red vio	17.50	30.00
B32	A57	1fr + 50q rose red	17.50	30.00
B33	A57	3fr + 1.50fr dk bl	17.50	30.00
	Nos. B28-B33 (6)		105.00	180.00

To honor and benefit the Congress of the Albanian Red Cross.

Counterfeits: lithographed; genuine: typographed.

> **Catalogue values for unused stamps in this section, from this point to the end of the section, are for Never Hinged items.**

SP3

First Aid and Red Cross: 25q+5q, Nurse carrying child on stretcher. 65q+25q, Symbolic blood transfusion. 80q+40q, Mother and child.

1967, Dec. 1   **Litho.**   **Perf. 11½x12**

B34	SP3	15q + 5q blk, red & brn	.80	.35
B35	SP3	25q + 5q multi	1.60	.80
B36	SP3	65q + 25q multi	5.50	2.75
B37	SP3	80q + 40q multi	8.00	4.00
	Nos. B34-B37 (4)		15.90	7.90

6th congress of the Albanian Red Cross.

SP4

1996, Aug. 5   **Litho.**   **Perf. 13½x13**

B38	SP4	50 l +10 l multi	1.50	1.50

Albanian Red Cross, 75th anniv.

Nos. 2469-2470 Surcharged

Methods and Perfs as Before
2001, Mar. 12

B39	A567	80 l +10 l on 50 l multi	4.50	4.50
B40	A567	130 l +20 l on 100 l multi	7.50	7.50

AIR POST STAMPS

Airplane Crossing Mountains AP1

Wmk. 125
1925, May 30   **Typo.**   **Perf. 14**

C1	AP1	5q green	2.25	3.50
C2	AP1	10q rose red	2.25	3.50
C3	AP1	25q deep blue	2.25	3.50
C4	AP1	50q dark green	3.50	6.00
C5	AP1	1fr dk vio & blk	6.25	10.50
C6	AP1	2fr ol grn & vio	10.50	17.50
C7	AP1	3fr brn org & dk grn	12.50	17.50
	Nos. C1-C7 (7)		39.50	62.00

Nos. C1-C7 exist imperf. Value $3,000.

For overprint see Nos. C8-C28.

Nos. C1-C7 Overprinted

1927, Jan. 18

C8	AP1	5q green	5.25	10.50
a.	Dbl. overprint, one invtd.		50.00	
C9	AP1	10q rose red	5.25	10.50
a.	Inverted overprint		45.00	
b.	Dbl. overprint, one invtd.		50.00	
C10	AP1	25q deep blue	4.75	9.50
C11	AP1	50q dark grn	3.25	6.50
a.	Inverted overprint		45.00	
C12	AP1	1fr dk vio & blk	3.25	6.50
a.	Inverted overprint		45.00	
b.	Double overprint		45.00	
C13	AP1	2fr ol grn & vio	7.50	10.50
C14	AP1	3fr brn org & dk grn	10.50	15.00
	Nos. C8-C14 (7)		39.75	69.00

Nos. C1-C7 Overprinted

1928, Apr. 21

C15	AP1	5q green	5.25	10.50
a.	Inverted overprint		70.00	
C16	AP1	10q rose red	5.25	10.50
C17	AP1	25q deep blue	5.25	10.50
C18	AP1	50q dark green	10.00	21.00
C19	AP1	1fr dk vio & blk	55.00	110.00
C20	AP1	2fr ol grn & vio	55.00	110.00
C21	AP1	3fr brn org & dk grn	55.00	110.00
	Nos. C15-C21 (7)		190.75	382.50

First flight across the Adriatic, Valona to Brindisi, Apr. 21, 1928.

The variety "SHQYRTARE" occurs once in the sheet for each value. Value 3 times normal.

Nos. C1-C7 Overprinted in Red Brown

1929, Dec. 1

C22	AP1	5q green	6.00	8.75
C23	AP1	10q rose red	6.00	8.75
C24	AP1	25q deep blue	6.00	8.75
C25	AP1	50q dk grn	125.00	175.00
C26	AP1	1fr dk vio & blk	250.00	200.00
C27	AP1	2fr ol grn	250.00	375.00
C28	AP1	3fr brn org & dk grn	250.00	375.00
	Nos. C22-C28 (7)		893.00	1,151.

Excellent counterfeits exist.

King Zog and Airplane over Tirana AP2

AP3

1930, Oct. 8   **Photo.**   **Unwmk.**

C29	AP2	5q yellow green	1.00	1.75
C30	AP2	15q rose red	1.00	1.75
C31	AP2	20q slate blue	1.00	1.75
C32	AP2	50q olive green	2.00	2.75
C33	AP3	1fr dark blue	3.00	5.25
C34	AP3	2fr olive brown	10.00	17.50
C35	AP3	3fr purple	22.50	17.50
	Nos. C29-C35 (7)		40.50	48.25

For overprints and surcharges see Nos. C36-C45.

Nos. C29-C35 Overprinted

1931, July 6

C36	AP2	5q yellow grn	5.25	10.50
a.	Double overprint		140.00	
C37	AP2	15q rose red	5.25	10.50
C38	AP2	20q slate blue	5.25	10.50
C39	AP2	50q olive grn	5.25	10.50
C40	AP3	1fr dark blue	30.00	60.00
C41	AP3	2fr olive brn	30.00	60.00
C42	AP3	3fr purple	30.00	60.00
a.	Inverted overprint		275.00	
	Nos. C36-C42 (7)		111.00	222.00

1st air post flight from Tirana to Rome.

Only a very small part of this issue was sold to the public. Most of the stamps were given to the Aviation Company to help provide funds for conducting the service.

Issued under Italian Dominion

Nos. C29-C30 Overprinted in Black

1939, Apr. 19   **Unwmk.**   **Perf. 14**

C43	AP2	5q yel green	2.50	7.00
C44	AP2	15q rose red	2.50	7.00

No. C32 With Additional Surcharge

C45	AP2	20q on 50q ol grn	5.00	11.50
a.	Inverted overprint		—	—
	Nos. C43-C45 (3)		10.00	25.50

See note after No. 309.

King Victor Emmanuel III and Plane over Mountains AP4

1939, Aug. 4   **Photo.**

C46	AP4	20q brown	32.50	15.00

Shepherds AP5

Map of Albania Showing Air Routes — AP6

Designs: 20q, Victor Emmanuel III and harbor view. 50q, Woman and river valley. 1fr, Bridge at Vezirit. 2fr, Ruins. 3fr, Women waving to plane.

1940, Mar. 20   **Unwmk.**

C47	AP5	5q green	1.25	1.25
C48	AP6	15q rose red	1.25	1.90
C49	AP6	20q deep blue	2.50	3.25
C50	AP6	50q brown	3.25	9.50
C51	AP5	1fr myrtle green	6.50	12.50
C52	AP6	2fr brown black	9.50	19.00
C53	AP6	3fr rose violet	16.00	25.00
	Nos. C47-C53 (7)		40.25	72.40

People's Republic

Vuno-Himare
AP12

Albanian Towns: 1 l, 10 l, Rozafat-Shkoder.
2 l, 20 l, Keshtjelle-Butrinto.

1950, Dec. 15   Engr.   Perf. 12½x12

C54	AP12	50q gray black	.25	.80
C55	AP12	1 l red brown	.25	.80
C56	AP12	2 l ultra	.50	1.60
C57	AP12	5 l deep green	1.75	3.25
C58	AP12	10 l deep blue	4.50	5.50
C59	AP12	20 l purple	9.00	8.00
	Nos. C54-C59 (6)		16.25	19.95

Nos. C56-C58 Surcharged with New Value and Bars in Red or Black

1952-53

C60	AP12	50q on 2 l (R)	90.00	150.00
C61	AP12	50q on 5 l	22.50	30.00
C62	AP12	2.50 l on 5 l (R)	150.00	175.00
C63	AP12	2.50 l on 10 l	25.00	45.00
	Nos. C60-C63 (4)		287.50	400.00

Issued: Nos. C60, C62, 12/26/52; Nos. C61, C63, 3/14/53.

> Catalogue values for unused stamps in this section, from this point to the end of the section, are for Never Hinged items.

Banner with
Lenin, Map of
Stalingrad and
Tanks — AP13

1963, Feb. 2   Litho.   Perf. 14

C67	AP13	7 l grn & dp car	9.00	3.50

20th anniversary, Battle of Stalingrad.

Sputnik
and Sun
AP14

Designs: 3 l, Lunik 4. 5 l, Lunik 3 photographing far side of the Moon. 8 l, Venus space probe. 12 l, Mars 1.

1963, Oct. 31   Unwmk.   Perf. 12

C68	AP14	2 l org, yel & blk	.35	.35
C69	AP14	3 l multi	.70	.35
C70	AP14	5 l rose lil, yel & blk	1.00	.35
C71	AP14	8 l multi	1.75	.70
C72	AP14	12 l blue & org	3.50	2.75
	Nos. C68-C72 (5)		7.30	4.50

Russian interplanetary explorations.

Nos. C68 and C71 Overprinted "Riccione 23-8-1964"

1964, Aug. 23

C73	AP14	2 l org, yel & blk	7.00	14.00
C74	AP14	8 l multicolored	14.00	21.00

Intl. Space Exhib. in Riccione, Italy.

Plane
over
Berat
AP15

1975, Nov. 25   Litho.   Perf. 12

C75	AP15	20q multi	.25	.25
C76	AP15	40q Gjirokaster	.30	.25
C77	AP15	60q Sarande	.55	.30
C78	AP15	90q Durres	1.10	.35
C79	AP15	1.20 l Kruje	1.40	.70
C80	AP15	2.40 l Boga	2.75	1.40
C81	AP15	4.05 l Tirana	4.25	2.10
	Nos. C75-C81 (7)		10.60	5.35

SPECIAL DELIVERY STAMPS

Issued under Italian Dominion

King Victor
Emmanuel
III — SD1

1940   Unwmk.   Photo.   Perf. 14

E1	SD1	25q bright violet	4.50	7.50
E2	SD1	50q red orange	11.50	18.00

Issued under German Administration

No. E1
Overprinted
in Carmine

1943

E3	SD1	25q bright violet	12.50	24.00

Proclamation of Albanian independence.

POSTAGE DUE STAMPS

Nos. 35-39
Handstamped in
Various Colors

1914, Feb. 23   Unwmk.   Perf. 14

J1	A3	2q org brn & buff (Bl)	10.50	4.50
a.		Violet ovpt.	30.00	30.00
b.		Black ovpt.	30.00	30.00
J2	A3	5q green (R)	10.50	4.50
a.		Violet ovpt.	37.50	37.50
b.		Blue ovpt.	30.00	30.00
J3	A3	10q rose red (Bl)	15.00	4.50
a.		Violet ovpt.	30.00	26.00
J4	A3	25q dark blue (R)	17.50	4.50
J5	A3	50q vio & red (Bk)	26.00	14.00
	Nos. J1-J5 (5)		79.50	32.00

The two parts of the overprint are hand-stamped separately. Stamps exist with one or both handstamps inverted, double or omitted.

Nos. 48-51
Overprinted in Black

1914, Apr. 16

J6	A3 (a)	10pa on 5q green	5.25	4.50
J7	A3 (a)	20pa on 10q rose red	5.25	4.50
J8	A3 (b)	1gr on 25q blue	5.25	4.50
J9	A3 (b)	2gr on 50q vio & red	5.25	4.50
	Nos. J6-J9 (4)		21.00	18.00

Same Design as
Regular Issue of
1919, Overprinted

1919, Feb. 10   Perf. 11½, 12½

J10	A8	(4)q on 4h rose	13.00	10.50
J11	A8	(10)q on 10k red, grn	13.00	10.50
J12	A8	20q on 2k org, gray	13.00	10.50
J13	A8	50q on 5k brn, yel	13.00	10.50
	Nos. J10-J13 (4)		52.00	42.00

Nos. J10-J12 exist with overprint in red. Value, each $50.

Fortress at
Scutari — D3

Post Horn Overprinted in Black

1920, Apr. 1   Perf. 14x13

J14	D3	4q olive green	.75	4.50
J15	D3	10q rose red	1.50	6.50
J16	D3	20q bister brn	1.50	6.50
J17	D3	50q black	4.00	17.50
	Nos. J14-J17 (4)		7.75	35.00

D5

Background of Red Wavy Lines

1922   Perf. 12½, 11½

J23	D5	4q black, red	1.10	4.50
J24	D5	10q black, red	1.10	4.50
J25	D5	20q black, red	1.10	4.50
J26	D5	50q black, red	1.10	4.50
	Nos. J23-J26 (4)		4.40	18.00

Nos. J23-J26
Overprinted in White

1925

J27	D5	4q black, red	1.90	4.50
J28	D5	10q black, red	1.90	4.50
J29	D5	20q black, red	1.90	4.50
J30	D5	50q black, red	1.90	4.50
	Nos. J27-J30 (4)		7.60	18.00

The 10q with overprint in gold was a trial printing. It was not put in use.

D7

Overprinted "QIND. AR" in Red

1926, Dec. 24   Perf. 13½x13

J31	D7	10q dark blue	.75	3.50
J32	D7	20q green	.75	3.50
J33	D7	30q red brown	1.50	7.00
J34	D7	50q dark brown	2.75	13.00
	Nos. J31-J34 (4)		5.75	27.00

Coat of Arms — D8

Wmk. Double Headed Eagle (220)

1930, Sept. 1   Photo.   Perf. 14, 14½

J35	D8	10q dark blue	6.75	21.00
J36	D8	20q rose red	2.75	13.00
J37	D8	30q violet	2.75	13.00
J38	D8	50q dark green	2.75	13.00
	Nos. J35-J38 (4)		15.00	60.00

Nos. J36-J38 exist with overprint "14 Shtator 1943" (see Nos. 332-344) which is private and fraudulent on these stamps.

No. 253 Overprinted

1936   Perf. 14

J39	A34	10q carmine	15.00	45.00
a.		Hyphens on each side of "Takse" ('39)	100.00	200.00

Issued under Italian Dominion

Coat of Arms — D9

1940   Unwmk.   Photo.   Perf. 14

J40	D9	4q red orange	37.50	75.00
J41	D9	10q bright violet	37.50	75.00
J42	D9	20q brown	37.50	75.00
J43	D9	30q dark blue	37.50	75.00
J44	D9	50q carmine rose	37.50	75.00
	Nos. J40-J44 (5)		187.50	375.00

CENTRAL ALBANIA

After the departure of Prince Wilhelm of Wied Oct. 2, 1914, Essad Pasha established a regime in Durres, which, with Serbian support, soon included much of central Albania. The regime issued stamps, overprinted on previously issued Albanian regular postage, postage due, and revenue stamps, and on unissued stamps commissioned in 1913 by an earlier government, which were in use during 1915/1916. Essad's Central Albania collapsed with the Austro-Hungarian invasion of the area in the spring of 1916.

Albania Nos. 35-37,
47-52 Handstamped in
Black, Blue, Red
or Violet

1915   Perf. 14

1	A3	2q orange brn & buff	28.00	27.00
2	A3	5q green & bl grn	60.00	60.00
3	A3	10q rose red	40.00	37.50
4	A3	25q dark blue	55.00	55.00
5	A3	50q violet & red	55.00	65.00
6	A3(a)	5pa on 2q org brn & buff	40.00	37.50
7	A3(a)	10pa on 5q grn & bl grn	17.00	17.00
8	A3(a)	20pa on 10q rose red	17.00	17.00
9	A3(b)	1gr on 25q dk bl	17.00	17.00
10	A3(b)	2gr on 50q vio & red	17.00	17.00
11	A3(b)	5gr on 1r dp brown	37.50	50.00
	Nos. 1-11 (11)		383.50	410.00

Crescent Handstamp in Black or Violet on Unissued Stamps of Albania

12	A1	2pa orange	9.25	6.25
13	A1	5pa violet	9.25	8.75
14	A1	10pa green	9.25	9.25
15	A1	20pa red	9.25	6.25
16	A1	40pa blue	12.00	6.25
17	A1	100pa pink	28.00	11.50
18	A1	5pi black	80.00	32.00
	Nos. 12-18 (7)		157.00	80.25

Handstamp on Albania Fiscal Stamps

19	A2	10pa green	11.00	11.50
20	A2	20pa red	11.00	8.75
21	A2	50pa blue	7.50	6.25
22	A2	3pi pink	7.50	6.25
23	A2	6pi chocolate	17.00	13.50
		Nos. 19-23 (5)	54.00	46.25

POSTAGE DUE STAMPS
Large "T" Handstamp on Albania Nos. 47-52

J1	A3	2q orange brn & buff	45.00	42.50
J2	A3(a)	10pa on 5q grn & bl grn	28.00	27.00
J3	A3(a)	20pa on 10q rose	28.00	27.00
J4	A3(b)	1gr on 25q dk bl	28.00	27.00
J5	A3(b)	2gr on 50q vio & red	28.00	27.00
		Nos. J1-J5 (5)	157.00	150.50

ALEXANDRETTA

ˌa-lig-ˌʒan-ˈdre-tə

LOCATION — A political territory in northern Syria, bordering on Turkey
GOVT. — French mandate
AREA — 10,000 sq. mi. (approx.)
POP. — 270,000 (approx.)

Included in the Syrian territory mandated to France under the Versailles Treaty. In 1938 the name was changed to Hatay in 1938. The following year France returned the territory to Turkey in exchange for certain concessions. See Hatay.

100 Centimes = 1 Piaster

Stamps of Syria, 1930-36, Overprinted or Surcharged in Black or Red

a

b

c

d

e

1938		**Unwmk.**	**Perf. 12x12½**	
1	A6 (a)	0.10p vio brn	3.50	3.50
2	A6 (a)	0.20p brn org	3.50	3.00
		Perf. 13½		
3	A9 (b)	0.50p vio (R)	4.50	3.50
4	A10 (b)	1p bis brn	4.50	3.00
5	A9 (b)	2p dk vio (R)	5.75	3.50
6	A13 (b)	3p yel grn	9.00	7.00
7	A10 (b)	4p yel org	10.00	7.00
8	A16 (b)	6p grnsh blk (R)	12.00	8.00
9	A18 (b)	25p vio brn	25.00	25.00
10	A15 (c)	0.75p org red	9.00	9.00
11	A10 (d)	2.50p on 4p yel org	7.50	4.00
12	AP2 (e)	12.50p on 15p org red	20.00	15.00
		Nos. 1-12 (12)	114.25	91.50
		Set, never hinged	275.00	

Issue dates: Nos. 1-9, Apr. 14, Nos. 10-12, Sept. 2.

Nos. 4, 7, 10-12 Ovptd. in Black

1938, Nov. 10

13	A15	75c	60.00	60.00
a.		Overprint inverted	500.00	
14	A10	1p	37.50	37.50
a.		"Sandjah d'Alexandrette" omitted	325.00	
15	A10	2.50p on 4p	32.50	32.50
16	A10	4p	37.50	37.50
a.		"Sandjah d'Alexandrette" omitted	325.00	
17	AP2	12.50p on 15p	80.00	80.00
a.		"Sandjah d'Alexandrette" omitted	1,500.	
		Nos. 13-17 (5)	247.50	247.50
		Set, never hinged	500.00	

Death of Kemal Ataturk, pres. of Turkey.

AIR POST STAMPS

Air Post Stamps of Syria, 1937, Overprinted Type "b" in Red or Black

1938, Apr. 14		**Unwmk.**	**Perf. 13**	
C1	AP14	½p dark vio (R)	4.50	5.00
C2	AP15	1p black (R)	4.50	5.50
C3	AP14	2p blue grn (R)	5.50	7.50
C4	AP15	3p deep ultra	6.00	8.00
C5	AP14	5p rose lake	11.00	18.00
C6	AP15	10p red brown	11.50	20.00
C7	AP14	15p lake brown	14.50	23.50
C8	AP15	25p dk blue (R)	20.00	31.00
		Nos. C1-C8 (8)	77.50	118.50
		Set, never hinged	225.00	

POSTAGE DUE STAMPS

Postage Due Stamps of Syria, 1925-31, Ovptd. Type "b" in Black or Red

1938, Apr. 14		**Unwmk.**	**Perf. 13½**	
J1	D5	0.50p brown, yel	6.50	5.75
J2	D6	1p violet, rose	7.50	6.50
J3	D5	2p blk, blue (R)	8.50	8.00
J4	D5	3p blk, red org	10.00	9.00
J5	D5	5p blk, bl grn (R)	16.00	14.50
J6	D7	8p blk, gray bl (R)	22.50	20.00
		Nos. J1-J6 (6)	71.00	63.75
		Set, never hinged	225.00	

On No. J2, the overprint is vertical, reading up, other denominations, horizontal.
Stamps of Alexandretta were discontinued in 1938 and replaced by those of Hatay.

ALGERIA

al-ˈjir-ē-ə

LOCATION — North Africa
GOVT. — Republic
AREA — 919,595 sq. mi.
POP. — 29,300,000 (1998 est.)
CAPITAL — Algiers

The former French colony of Algeria became an integral part of France on Sept. 1, 1958, when French stamps replaced Algerian stamps. Algeria

---

became an independent country July 3, 1962.

100 Centimes = 1 Franc
100 Centimes = 1 Dinar (1964)

> Catalogue values for unused stamps in this country are for Never Hinged items, beginning with Scott 109 in the regular postage section, Scott B27 in the semi-postal section, Scott C1 in the air-post section, Scott CB1 in the air-post semi-postal section, and Scott J25 in the postage due section.

Stamps of France Overprinted in Red, Blue or Black

a

b

c

d

1924-26		**Unwmk.**	**Perf. 14x13½**	
1	A16(a)	1c dk gray (R)	.40	.40
2	A16(a)	2c violet brn	.40	.40
3	A16(a)	3c orange	.40	.40
4	A16(a)	4c yel brn (Bl)	.40	.40
5	A22(a)	5c orange (Bl)	.40	.40
6	A16(a)	5c green ('25)	.80	.40
7	A23(a)	10c green	.80	.40
b.		Booklet pane of 10	—	
		Complete booklet, 2 #7b	300.00	
8	A22(a)	10c green ('25)	.80	.40
a.		Pair, one without overprint	1,500.	
9	A20(a)	15c slate grn	.40	.40
10	A23(a)	15c green ('25)	1.20	.40
11	A22(a)	15c red brn (Bl) ('26)	.40	.40
12	A22(a)	20c red brn (Bl)	.40	.40
a.		Pair, one without overprint	1,500.	
13	A22(a)	25c blue (R)	.80	.40
a.		Booklet pane of 10	—	
		Complete booklet, 2 #13a	1,450.	
b.		Pair, one without overprint	1,750.	
14	A23(a)	30c red (Bl)	2.40	.80
15	A22(a)	30c cerise ('25)	.80	.80
a.		"ALGERIE" double	225.00	150.00
16	A22(a)	30c lt bl (R) ('25)	.80	.80
a.		Booklet pane of 10	—	
		Complete booklet, 2 #16a	550.00	
17	A22(a)	35c violet	.80	.80
18	A18(a)	40c red & pale bl	1.20	.80
19	A22(a)	40c ol brn (R) ('25)	1.20	.80
20	A18(b)	45c grn & bl (R)	.80	.80
a.		Double overprint	350.00	
21	A23(a)	45c red (Bl) ('25)	1.25	.80
22	A23(a)	50c blue (R)	.80	.80

23	A20(a)	60c lt violet	1.20	.80
a.		Inverted overprint	2,900.	
24	A20(a)	65c rose (Bl)	1.20	.80
25	A23(a)	75c blue (R)	1.25	.75
a.		Double overprint	300.00	300.00
26	A20(a)	80c ver ('26)	2.00	1.20
27	A20(a)	85c ver (Bl)	1.20	1.20
28	A18(b)	1fr cl & ol grn	2.00	1.20
a.		Olive green omitted	325.00	325.00
29	A22(a)	1.05fr ver ('26)	1.60	1.60
30	A18(c)	2fr org & pale bl	2.40	1.60
31	A18(b)	3fr vio & bl ('26)	5.50	2.40
a.		Blue omitted	325.00	
32	A18(d)	5fr bl & buff (R)	16.00	12.00
		Nos. 1-32 (32)	52.80	36.35

No. 15 was issued precanceled only. Values for precanceled stamps in first column are for those which have not been through the post and have original gum. Values in second column are for postally used, gumless stamps. For surcharges see Nos. 75, P1.

Street in Kasbah, Algiers
A1

Mosque of Sidi Abd-er-Rahman
A2

La Pêcherie Mosque — A3

Marabout of Sidi Yacoub
A4

1926-39		**Typo.**	**Perf. 14x13½**	
33	A1	1c olive	.25	.25
a.		Imperforate	110.00	
34	A1	2c red brown	.25	.25
35	A1	3c orange	.25	.25
36	A1	5c blue green	.25	.25
37	A1	10c brt violet	.40	.25
a.		Booklet pane of 10	—	
		Complete booklet, 2 #37a	400.00	
38	A2	15c orange brn	.40	.25
a.		Imperforate	110.00	
b.		Booklet pane of 10	—	
		Complete booklet, 2 #38b	350.00	
39	A2	20c green	.40	.25
40	A2	20c deep rose	.25	.25
a.		Imperforate	120.00	
41	A2	25c blue grn	.40	.25
42	A2	25c blue ('27)	.80	.40
a.		Imperforate	120.00	
43	A2	25c vio bl ('39)	.25	.25
44	A2	30c blue	.40	.40
a.		Imperforate	120.00	
45	A2	30c bl grn ('27)	1.25	.80
46	A2	35c dp violet	1.60	1.20
47	A2	40c olive green	.40	.25
a.		Booklet pane of 10	—	
		Complete booklet, 2 #47a	325.00	
b.		Imperforate	120.00	
48	A3	45c violet brn	.80	.40
49	A3	50c blue	.40	.40
a.		Booklet pane of 10	—	
		Complete booklet, 2 #49a	400.00	
b.		Imperforate	125.00	
c.		Vert. pair, #49 and 49b	225.00	
50	A3	50c dk red ('30)	.40	.25
a.		Booklet pane of 10	—	
		Complete booklet, 2 #50a	450.00	
b.		Imperforate	120.00	
51	A3	60c yellow grn	.40	.40
52	A3	65c blk brn ('27)	3.25	2.40
53	A1	65c ultra ('38)	.40	.40
a.		Booklet pane of 10	—	
		Complete booklet, 2 #53a	160.00	
54	A4	75c carmine	1.20	.80
a.		Imperforate	125.00	
b.		Vert. pair, #54 and 54a	225.00	
55	A3	75c blue ('29)	4.75	.80
56	A3	80c orange red	1.20	.80
57	A3	90c red ('27)	8.00	4.00
58	A4	1fr gray grn & red brn	1.20	.80
a.		Imperforate	175.00	
59	A3	1.05fr lt brown	1.20	.80
60	A3	1.10fr mag ('27)	8.00	4.00
61	A4	1.25fr dk bl & ultra	1.60	1.20
62	A4	1.50fr dk bl & ultra ('27)	5.50	.80
a.		Imperforate	400.00	
63	A4	2fr prus bl & blk brn	4.75	1.20
a.		Imperforate	125.00	
64	A4	3fr violet & org	8.00	1.60
65	A4	5fr red & violet	16.00	4.75

66	A4	10fr ol brn & rose		
		('27)	80.00	47.50
a.		Imperforate	725.00	
67	A4	20fr vio & grn ('27)	8.00	8.00
		Nos. 33-67 (35)	162.60	86.85

A 90c red, design A1, was prepared but not issued. Values: unused $950, never hinged $1,350.

Type A4, 50c blue and rose red, inscribed "CENTENAIRE-ALGERIE" is France No. 255.

See design A24. For stamps and types surcharged see Nos. 68-74, 131, 136, 187, B1-B13, J27, P2.

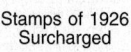

Stamps of 1926 Surcharged

1927

68	A2	10c on 35c dp violet	.25	.25
69	A2	25c on 30c blue	.25	.25
70	A2	30c on 25c blue grn	.40	.25
71	A3	65c on 60c yel grn	1.60	1.20
72	A3	90c on 80c org red	1.40	.95
73	A3	1.10fr on 1.05fr lt brn	1.00	.50
74	A4	1.50fr on 1.25fr dk bl & ultra	3.25	1.50
		Nos. 68-74 (7)	8.15	4.90

Bars cancel the old value on Nos. 68, 69, 73, 74.

No. 4 Surcharged

1927

75	A16	5c on 4c yellow brown	.40	.40
a.		Blue surcharge	1,250.	1,400.

Bay of Algiers — A5

1930, May 4   **Engr.**   **Perf. 12½**

78	A5	10fr red brown	21.00	21.00
a.		Imperf., pair	150.00	

Cent. of Algeria and for Intl. Phil. Exhib. of North Africa, May, 1930.

One example of No. 78 was sold with each 10fr admission.

Travel across the Sahara — A6

Arch of Triumph, Lambese — A7

Admiralty Building, Algiers — A8

Kings' Tombs near Touggourt — A9

El-Kebir Mosque, Algiers — A10

Oued River at Colomb-Bechar — A11

Sidi Bon Medine Cemetery at Tlemcen — A13

View of Ghardaia — A12

1936-41   **Engr.**   **Perf. 13**

79	A6	1c ultra	.25	.40
80	A11	2c dk violet	.25	.40
81	A7	3c dk blue grn	.25	.40
82	A12	5c red violet	.40	.25
83	A8	10c emerald	.25	.40
84	A9	15c red	.25	.40
85	A13	20c dk blue grn	.40	.40
86	A10	25c rose vio	1.20	.80
87	A12	30c yellow grn	.80	.40
88	A9	40c brown vio	.40	.40
89	A13	45c deep ultra	2.00	1.20
		On cover		4.50
90	A8	50c red	1.00	.40
91	A6	65c red brn	8.00	4.00
92	A6	65c rose car ('37)	.80	.80
93	A6	70c red brn ('39)	.40	.40
94	A11	75c slate bl	.80	.40
95	A7	90c henna brn	2.40	1.60
96	A10	1fr brown	.80	.80
97	A8	1.25fr lt violet	1.20	.80
98	A8	1.25fr car rose ('39)	.80	.80
99	A11	1.50fr turq blue	2.40	.80
99A	A11	1.50fr rose ('40)	.80	.80
100	A12	1.75fr henna brn	.40	.40
101	A7	2fr dk brown	.80	.40
102	A6	2.25fr yellow grn	20.00	13.50
103	A12	2.50fr dk ultra ('41)	.80	.80
104	A13	3fr magenta	1.20	.80
105	A10	3.50fr pck blue	6.50	4.00
106	A8	5fr slate blue	1.60	.80
107	A11	10fr henna brn	1.20	.80
108	A9	20fr turq blue	1.60	1.20
		Nos. 79-108 (31)	60.15	38.95

See Nos. 124-125, 162.

Nos. 82 and 100 with surcharge "E. F. M. 30frs" (Emergency Field Message) were used in 1943 to pay cable tolls for US and Canadian servicemen.

For other surcharges see Nos. 122, B27.

> **Catalogue values for unused stamps in this section, from this point to the end of the section, are for Never Hinged items.**

Algerian Pavilion — A14

1937   **Perf. 13**

109	A14	40c brt green	2.00	1.20
110	A14	50c rose carmine	2.00	.80
111	A14	1.50fr blue	2.75	1.20
112	A14	1.75fr brown black	2.75	1.60
		Nos. 109-112 (4)	9.50	4.80

Paris International Exposition.

Constantine in 1837 — A15

1937

113	A15	65c deep rose	1.20	.80
114	A15	1fr brown	12.00	1.60
115	A15	1.75fr blue green	1.60	.80
116	A15	2.15fr red violet	1.60	.80
		Nos. 113-116 (4)	16.40	4.00

Taking of Constantine by the French, cent.

Ruins of a Roman Villa — A16

1938

117	A16	30c green	2.00	.80
118	A16	65c ultra	.80	.80
119	A16	75c rose violet	2.00	.80
120	A16	3fr carmine rose	5.50	4.00
121	A16	5fr yellow brown	8.00	5.50
		Nos. 117-121 (5)	18.30	11.90

Centenary of Philippeville.

No. 90 Surcharged in Black

1938

122	A8	25c on 50c red	.80	.40
a.		Double surcharge	100.00	60.00
b.		Inverted surcharge	72.50	47.50
c.		Pair, one without surcharge	400.00	

Types of 1936 Numerals of Value on Colorless Background

1939

124	A7	90c henna brown	1.20	.40
125	A10	2.25fr blue green	1.20	.80

For surcharge see No. B38.

American Export Liner Unloading Cargo — A17

1939

126	A17	20c green	4.00	1.60
127	A17	40c red violet	4.00	1.60
128	A17	90c brown black	2.40	.80
129	A17	1.25fr rose	9.50	4.00
130	A17	2.25fr ultra	4.00	2.40
		Nos. 126-130 (5)	23.90	10.40

New York World's Fair.

Type of 1926, Surcharged in Black

Two types of surcharge:
I — Bars 6mm
II — Bars 7mm

1939-40   **Perf. 14x13½**

131	A1	1fr on 90c crimson (I)	.80	.40
a.		Booklet pane of 10	—	
		Complete booklet, 2 #131a	625.00	
b.		Double surcharge (I)	175.00	
c.		Inverted surcharge (I)	87.50	
d.		Pair, one without surch. (I)	1,800.	
e.		Type II ('40)	8.00	1.60
f.		Inverted surcharge (II)	95.00	
g.		Pair, one without surch. (II)	1,800.	

View of Algiers — A18

1941   **Typo.**

132	A18	30c ultra	.50	.30
133	A18	70c sepia	.50	.30
134	A18	1fr carmine rose	.50	.30
		Nos. 132-134 (3)	1.50	.90

See No. 163.

Marshal Pétain — A19

1941   **Engr.**   **Perf. 13**

135	A19	1fr dark blue	.50	.30

For stamp and type surcharged see Nos. B36-B37.

No. 53 Surcharged in Black

1941   **Perf. 14x13½**

136	A1	50c on 65c ultra	.70	.25
a.		Booklet pane of 10	120.00	
		Complete booklet, 2 #136a	95.00	
b.		Inverted surcharge	225.00	
c.		Pair, one without surch.		

Marshal Pétain — A20

1942   **Perf. 14x13**

137	A20	1.50fr orange red	.30	.25

Four other denominations of type A20 exist but were not placed in use. Values: 4fr, $1,300; 5fr, $1,100; 10fr, 20fr, each $600.

Constantine A21

Oran A22

Arms of Algiers — A23

Engraver's Name at Lower Left

1942-43   **Photo.**   **Perf. 12**

138	A21	40c dark vio ('43)	.70	.40
139	A22	60c rose ('43)	.55	.25
140	A21	1.20fr yel grn ('43)	.30	.25
141	A23	1.50fr car rose	.30	.25
142	A22	2fr sapphire	.80	.25
143	A21	2.40fr rose ('43)	.55	.25
144	A23	3fr sapphire	.95	.25
145	A21	4fr blue ('43)	.70	.25
146	A22	5fr yel grn ('43)	.65	.30
		Nos. 138-146 (9)	5.50	2.45

For type surcharged see No. 166.

No. 142 exists in green and violet. Value, each $60.

Imperforates

Nearly all of Algeria Nos. 138-285, B39-B96, C1-C12 and CB1-CB3 exist imperforate. See note after France No. 395.

Without Engraver's Name

1942-45   **Typo.**   **Perf. 14x13½**

147	A23	10c dull brn vio ('45)	.30 .25
148	A22	30c dp bl grn ('45)	.30 .25
149	A21	40c dull brn vio ('45)	.30 .25
150	A21	60c rose ('45)	.30 .25
151	A21	70c deep bl ('45)	.30 .25
152	A23	80c dk bl grn ('43)	1.25 .90
153	A21	1.20fr dp bl grn ('45)	.50 .30
154	A23	1.50fr brt rose ('43)	.30 .25
155	A22	2fr dp blue ('45)	.30 .25
156	A21	2.40fr rose ('45)	.80 .65
157	A23	3fr dp blue ('45)	.55 .40
158	A22	4.50fr brown vio ('45)	.30 .25
		Nos. 147-158 (12)	5.50 4.25

For surcharge see No. 190.

La Pêcherie
Mosque — A24

1942   **Typo.**

159	A24	50c dull red	.55 .25
a.		Booklet pane of 10	
		Complete booklet, 2 #159a	325.00

1942   **Photo.**   **Perf. 12**

160	A24	40c gray green	.55 .25
161	A24	50c red	.55 .25

Types of 1936-41, Without "RF"

1942   **Engr.**   **Perf. 13**

162	A11	1.50fr rose	.55 .25

   Typo.   **Perf. 14x13½**

163	A18	30c ultra	.55 .25

"One Aim Alone" A25   "Victory" A26

1943   **Litho.**   **Perf. 12**

164	A25	1.50fr deep rose	.55 .25
165	A26	1.50fr dark blue	.55 .25

Type of 1942-3 Surcharged with New Value in Black

1943   **Photo.**

166	A22	2fr on 5fr red orange	.30 .25
a.		Surcharge omitted	325.00

Summer Palace, Algiers A27

1944, Dec. 1   **Litho.**

167	A27	15fr slate	2.00 1.75
168	A27	20fr lt blue grn	2.00 .80
169	A27	50fr dk carmine	1.60 .80
170	A27	100fr deep blue	4.00 2.50
171	A27	200fr dull bis brn	5.50 2.75
		Nos. 167-171 (5)	15.10 8.60

Marianne A28   Gallic Cock A29

1944-45

172	A28	10c gray	.55 .30
173	A28	30c red violet	.30 .25
174	A29	40c rose car ('45)	.50 .30
175	A28	50c red	.50 .30
176	A28	80c emerald	.30 .25
177	A29	1fr green ('45)	.30 .25
178	A28	1.20fr rose lilac	.30 .25
179	A28	1.50fr dark blue	.30 .25
a.		Double impression	70.00
180	A29	2fr red	.30 .25
a.		Double impression	85.00
181	A29	2fr dk brown ('45)	.30 .25
182	A28	2.40fr rose red	.55 .25
183	A28	3fr purple	.55 .40
184	A29	4fr ultra ('45)	.30 .25
185	A28	4.50fr olive blk	.95 .70
186	A29	10fr grnsh blk ('45)	1.90 .95
		Nos. 172-186 (15)	7.90 5.20

No. 38 Surcharged in Black

1944   **Perf. 14x13½**

187	A2	30c on 15c orange brn	1.20 .50
a.		Inverted surcharge	70.00

This stamp exists precanceled only. See note below No. 32.

No. 154 Surcharged

1945

190	A23	50c on 1.50fr brt rose	.55 .40
a.		Inverted surcharge	72.50

Stamps of France, 1944, Overprinted Type "a" of 1924 in Black

1945-46

191	A99	80c yellow grn	.65 .25
192	A99	1fr grnsh blue	.50 .25
193	A99	1.20fr violet	.70 .25
194	A99	2fr violet brown	.90 .25
195	A99	2.40fr carmine rose	1.20 .40
196	A99	3fr orange	1.00 .30
		Nos. 191-196 (6)	4.95 1.70

Stamps of France, 1945-47, Overprinted in Black, Red or Carmine

1945-47

197	A145	40c lilac rose	.30 .25
198	A145	50c violet bl (R)	.30 .25
199	A145	60c brt ultra (R)	.95 .25
200	A146	1fr rose red ('47)	.50 .25
201	A146	1.50fr rose lilac ('47)	.50 .25
202	A147	2fr myr grn (R) ('46)	.30 .25
203	A147	3fr deep rose	.70 .25
204	A147	4.50fr ultra (C) ('47)	2.00 .25
205	A147	5fr lt green ('46)	.50 .25
206	A147	10fr ultra	1.75 .50
		Nos. 197-206 (10)	7.80 2.75

France No. 383 Surcharged and Overprinted in Black

1946

207	A99	2fr on 1.50fr henna brn	.50 .25
a.		Without "2F"	525.00

France Nos. 562 and 564 Overprinted in Carmine or Blue

1947

208	A153	10c dp ultra & blk (C)	.30 .25
209	A155	50c brown, yel & red (Bl)	.80 .30

Constantine A30   Algiers A31

Arms of Oran — A32

Perf. 14x13½

1947-49   **Unwmk.**   **Typo.**

210	A30	10c dk grn & brt red	.30 .25
211	A31	50c black & orange	.30 .25
212	A32	1fr ultra & yellow	.30 .25
213	A30	1.30fr blk & grnsh bl	1.90 1.25
214	A31	1.50fr pur & org yel	.50 .25
215	A32	2fr blk & brt grn	.30 .25
216	A30	2.50fr blk & brt red	1.20 .80
217	A31	3fr vio brn & grn	.55 .25
218	A32	3.50fr lt grn & rose lil	.55 .25
219	A31	4fr dk brn & brt grn	.45 .25
220	A31	4.50fr ultra & scar	.55 .25
221	A31	5fr blk & grnsh bl	.30 .25
222	A32	6fr brown & scarlet	1.00 .30
223	A32	8fr choc & ultra ('48)	.65 .25
224	A30	10fr car & choc ('48)	1.00 .40
225	A31	15fr black & red ('49)	1.10 .25
		Nos. 210-225 (16)	10.95 5.75

See Nos. 274-280, 285.

Peoples of the World A33

1949, Oct. 24   **Engr.**   **Perf. 13**

226	A33	5fr green	2.75 2.00
227	A33	15fr scarlet	3.50 2.00
228	A33	25fr ultra	6.00 5.25
		Nos. 226-228 (3)	12.25 9.25

75th anniv. of the UPU.

Grapes — A34

25fr, Dates. 40fr, Oranges and lemons.

1950, Feb. 25

229	A34	20fr multicolored	2.75 .80
230	A34	25fr multicolored	3.25 1.25
231	A34	40fr multicolored	7.25 1.60
		Nos. 229-231 (3)	13.25 3.65

Apollo of Cherchell — A35

Designs: 12fr, 18fr, Isis statue, Cherchell. 15fr, 20fr, Child with eagle.

1952   **Unwmk.**   **Perf. 13**

240	A35	10fr gray black	.65 .25
241	A35	12fr orange brn	1.25 .40
242	A35	15fr deep blue	1.10 .25
243	A35	18fr rose red	1.10 .40
244	A35	20fr deep green	1.60 .25
245	A35	30fr deep blue	1.90 .95
		Nos. 240-245 (6)	7.60 2.50

War Memorial, Algiers — A38

1952, Apr. 11

246	A38	12fr dark green	2.00 .80

Issued to honor the French Africa Army.

Fossilized Nautilus — A39

Phonolite Dike A40

1952, Aug. 11

247	A39	15fr brt crimson	6.50 2.75
248	A40	30fr deep ultra	3.50 1.60

19th Intl. Geological Cong., Algiers, 9/8-15.

French and Algerian Soldiers and Camel — A41

1952, Nov. 30

249	A41	12fr chestnut brown	2.50 1.75

50th anniv. of the establishment of the Sahara Companies.

Eugène Millon A42

François C. Maillot — A43

Portrait: 50fr, Alphonse Laveran.

1954, Jan. 4   **Unwmk.**   **Engr.**   **Perf. 13**

250	A42	25fr dk grn & choc	2.00 .80
251	A43	40fr org brn & brn car	3.00 1.20
252	A42	50fr ultra & indigo	3.00 .80
		Nos. 250-252 (3)	8.00 2.80

Military Health Service.

Oranges — A44

1954, May 8
253 A44 15fr indigo & blue 2.00 1.20
3rd Intl. Cong. on Agronomy, Algiers, 1954.

Type of France, 1954 Overprinted type "a" in Black
Unwmk.
1954, June 6   Engr.   Perf. 13
254 A240 15fr rose carmine 2.00 1.20
Liberation of France, 10th anniversary.

Darguinah Hydroelectric Works — A45

1954, June 19
255 A45 15fr lilac rose 1.60 1.20
Opening of Darguinah hydroelectric works.

Patio of Bardo Museum — A46

1954   Typo.   Perf. 14x13½
257 A46 12fr red brn & brn org .80 .30
258 A46 15fr dk blue & blue .70 .25
See Nos. 267-271.

Type of France, 1954, Overprinted type "a" in Carmine
1954   Engr.   Perf. 13
260 A247 12fr dark green 2.00 1.00
150th anniv. of the 1st Legion of Honor awards at Camp de Boulogne.

St. Augustine — A47

1954, Nov. 11
261 A47 15fr chocolate 1.60 1.25
1600th anniv. of the birth of St. Augustine.

Aesculapius Statue and El Kattar Hospital, Algiers A48

1955, Apr. 3   Unwmk.   Perf. 13
262 A48 15fr red 1.60 .80
Issued to publicize the 30th French Congress of Medicine, Algiers, April 3-6, 1955.

Chenua Mountain and View of Tipasa A49

1955, May 31
263 A49 50fr brown carmine 1.50 .95
2000th anniv. of the founding of Tipasa.

Type of France, 1955 Overprinted type "a" in Red
1955, June 13
264 A251 30fr deep ultra 2.00 1.20
Rotary Intl., 50th anniv.

Marianne — A50

1955, Oct. 3   Typo.   Unwmk.
265 A50 15fr carmine .80 .25
See No. 284.

Great Kabylia Mountains A51

1955, Dec. 17   Engr.   Perf. 13
266 A51 100fr indigo & ultra 6.50 .80

Bardo Type of 1954, "Postes" and "Algerie" in White
Perf. 14x13½
1955-57   Unwmk.   Typo.
267 A46 10fr dk brn & lt brn .80 .25
268 A46 12fr red brn & brn org ('56) .40 .25
269 A46 18fr crimson & ver ('57) 1.00 .30
270 A46 20fr grn & yel grn ('57) .90 .50
271 A46 25fr purple & brt purple 1.00 .25
Nos. 267-271 (5) 4.10 1.55

Marshal Franchet d'Esperey A52

1956, May 25   Engr.   Perf. 13
272 A52 15fr sapphire & indigo 2.00 1.20
Birth cent. of Marshal Franchet d'Esperey.

Marshal Jacques Leclerc A53

1956, Nov. 29
273 A53 15fr red brown & sepia 2.00 1.60
Death of Marshal Leclerc.
For design surcharged see No. B90.

Type of 1947-49 and

Arms of Bône — A54

Arms: 2fr, Tizi-Quzou. 3fr, Mostaganem. 5fr, Tlemcen. 10fr, Setif. 12fr, Orleansville.

1956-58   Typo.   Perf. 14x13½
274 A54 1fr green & ver .30 .25
275 A54 2fr ver & ultra ('58) 1.00 .55
276 A54 3fr ultra & emer ('58) 1.40 .30
277 A54 5fr ultra & yellow .80 .25
278 A31 6fr red & grn ('57) 1.40 .40
279 A54 10fr dp cl & emer ('58) 1.50 .90
280 A54 12fr ultra & red ('58) 1.75 .90
Nos. 274-280 (7) 8.15 3.95

Nos. 275 and 279 are inscribed "Republique Francaise." See No. 285.

View of Oran — A55

1956-58   Engr.   Perf. 13
281 A55 30fr dull purple 1.20 .40
282 A55 35fr car rose ('58) 2.40 .80

Electric Train Crossing Bridge A56

1957, Mar. 25
283 A56 40fr dk blue grn & emer 2.40 .55

Marianne Type of 1955 Inscribed "Algerie" Vertically
Perf. 14x13½
1957, Dec. 2   Typo.   Unwmk.
284 A50 20fr ultra .95 .25

Arms Type of 1947-49 Inscribed "Republique Francaise"
1958, July
285 A31 6fr red & green 37.50 28.00

Independent State
France Nos. 939, 968, 945-946 & 1013 Ovptd. in Black or Red

No. 286   No. 287

No. 288   No. 289

No. 290

1962, July 2
Typographed Overprint
286 A336 10c brt green .75 .45
287 A349 25c lake & gray .75 .45
288 A339 45c brt vio & ol gray 7.00 3.75
289 A339 50c sl grn & lt claret 7.00 3.75
290 A372 1fr dk bl, sl & bis 4.25 1.75
Nos. 286-290 (5) 19.75 10.15

Handstamped Overprint
286a A336 10c bright green .75 .45
287a A349 25c lake & gray .75 .45
288a A339 45c brt vio & ol gray 29.00 22.50
289a A339 50c sl grn & lt claret 29.00 22.50
290a A372 1fr dk bl, sl & bis 6.00 3.00
Nos. 286a-290a (5) 65.50 48.90

Post offices were authorized to overprint their stock of these 5 French stamps. The size of the letters was specified as 3x6mm each, but various sizes were used. The post offices

had permission to make their own rubber stamps. Typography, pen or pencil were also used. Many types exist. Colors of hand-stamped overprints include black, red, blue, violet. "EA" stands for Etat Algérien.

Mosque, Tlemcen — A57

Roman Gates of Lodi, Médéa A58

5c, Kerrata Gorge. 10c, Dam at Foum el Gherza. 95c, Oil field, Hassi Messaoud.

1962, Nov. 1   Engr.   Perf. 13
291 A57 5c Prus grn, grn & choc .25 .25
292 A58 10c ol blk & dk bl .25 .25
293 A57 25c sl grn, brn & ver .50 .25
294 A57 95c dk bl, blk & bis 2.75 .95
295 A58 1fr green & blk 2.40 1.50
Nos. 291-295 (5) 6.15 3.20

The designs of Nos. 291-295 are similar to French issues of 1959-61 with "Republique Algerienne" replacing "Republique Francaise."

Flag, Rifle, Olive Branch — A59

Design: Nos. 300-303, Broken chain, dove, and rifle added to design A59.

1963, Jan. 6   Litho.   Perf. 12½
Flag in Green and Red
296 A59 5c bister brown .25 .25
297 A59 10c blue .25 .25
298 A59 25c vermilion 1.75 .25
299 A59 95c violet 1.35 .75
300 A59 1fr green 1.20 .35
301 A59 2fr brown 3.00 .75
302 A59 5fr lilac 5.25 3.00
303 A59 10fr gray 20.00 14.00
Nos. 296-303 (8) 33.05 19.60

Nos. 296-299 for the successful revolution and Nos. 300-303 the return of peace.

Men of Various Races, Wheat Emblem and Globe A60

1963, Mar. 21   Engr.   Perf. 13
304 A60 25c maroon, dl grn & yel .65 .25
FAO "Freedom from Hunger" campaign.

Map of Algeria and Emblems — A61

1963, July 5   Unwmk.   Perf. 13
305 A61 25c bl, dk brn, grn & red .65 .25
1st anniv. of Algeria's independence.

Physicians from 13th Century Manuscript — A62

1963, July 29   **Engr.**
306 A62 25c brn red, grn & bis   2.00 .55
2nd Congress of the Union of Arab physicians.

Orange and Blossom — A63

1963   **Perf. 14x13**
307 A63 8c gray grn & org   .25 .25
308 A63 20c slate & org red   .25 .25
309 A63 40c grnsh bl & org   .70 .30
310 A63 55c ol grn & org red   1.00 .30
    Nos. 307-310 (4)   2.20 1.35
Nos. 307-310 issued precanceled only. See note below No. 32.

Scales and Scroll A64

1963, Oct. 13   Unwmk.   Perf. 13
311 A64 25c blk, grn & rose red   .65 .35
Issued to honor the new constitution.

Guerrillas — A65

1963, Nov. 1
312 A65 25c dk brn, yel grn & car   .65 .35
9th anniversary of Algerian revolution.

Centenary Emblem — A66

1963, Dec. 8   Photo.   Perf. 12
313 A66 25c lt vio bl, yel & dk red   .90 .60
Centenary of International Red Cross.

UNESCO Emblem, Scales and Globe — A67

1963, Dec. 16   Unwmk.   Perf. 12
314 A67 25c lt blue & blk   .65 .25
15th anniv. of the Universal Declaration of Human Rights.

Workers — A68

1964, May 1   Engr.   Perf. 13
315 A68 50c dull red, red org & bl   1.25 .40
Issued for the Labor Festival.

Map of Africa and Flags A69

1964, May 25   Unwmk.   Perf. 13
316 A69 45c blue, orange & car   1.00 .35
Africa Day on the 1st anniv. of the Addis Ababa charter on African unity.

Ramses II Battling the Hittites (from Abu Simbel) — A70

Design: 30c, Two statues of Ramses II.

1964, June 28   Engr.   Perf. 13
317 A70 20c choc, red & vio bl   .90 .40
318 A70 30c brn, red & grnsh bl   1.05 .55
UNESCO world campaign to save historic monuments in Nubia.

A71

5c, 25c, 85c, Tractors. 10c, 30c, 65c, Men working with lathe. 12c, 15c, 45c, Electronics center & atom symbol. 20c, 50c, 95c, Draftsman & bricklayer.

1964-65   Typo.   Perf. 14x13½
319 A71 5c red lilac   .25 .25
320 A71 10c brown   .25 .25
321 A71 12c emerald ('65)   .45 .25
322 A71 15c dk blue ('65)   .30 .25
323 A71 20c yellow   .45 .25
324 A71 25c red   .45 .25
325 A71 30c purple ('65)   .35 .25
326 A71 45c rose car   .65 .25
327 A71 50c ultra   .65 .25
328 A71 65c orange   .70 .25
329 A71 85c green   1.40 .25
330 A71 95c car rose   1.75 .35
    Nos. 319-330 (12)   7.65 3.10
For surcharges see Nos. 389, 424.

A72

1964, Aug. 30   Engr.   Perf. 13
331 A72 85c Communications tower   1.90 .75
Inauguration of the Hertzian cable telephone line Algiers-Annaba.

Industrial & Agricultural Symbols — A73

1964, Sept. 26   Typo.   Perf. 13½x14
332 A73 25c lt ultra, yel & red   .60 1.25
1st Intl. Fair at Algiers, Sept. 26-Oct. 11.

Gas Flames and Pipes — A74

1964, Sept. 27
333 A74 30c violet, blue & yel   .85 .50
Arzew natural gas liquification plant opening.

Planting Trees — A75

1964, Nov. 29   Unwmk.
334 A75 25c slate grn, yel & car   .50 .25
National reforestation campaign.

Children and UNICEF Emblem — A76

1964, Dec. 13   Perf. 13½x14
335 A76 15c pink, vio bl & lt grn   .50 .25
Issued for Children's Day.

Decorated Camel Saddle — A77

1965, May 29   Typo.   Perf. 13½x14
336 A77 20c blk, red, emer & brn   .70 .25
Handicrafts of Sahara.

ICY Emblem A78

1965, Aug. 29   Engr.   Perf. 13
337 A78 30c blk, mar & bl grn   .90 .40
338 A78 60c blk, brt bl & bl grn   1.25 .50
International Cooperation Year, 1965.

ITU Emblem A79

1965, Sept. 19
339 A79 60c purple, emer & buff   .90 .50
340 A79 95c dk brn, mar & buff   1.25 .55
Cent. of the ITU.

Musicians A80

Miniatures by Mohammed Racim: 60c, Two female musicians. 5d, Algerian princess and antelope.

1965, Dec. 27   Photo.   Perf. 11½
341 A80 30c multicolored   1.75 .65
342 A80 60c multicolored   2.50 1.25
343 A80 5d multicolored   14.00 7.50
    Nos. 341-343 (3)   18.25 9.40

Bulls, Painted in 6000 B.C. — A81

Wall Paintings from Tassili-N-Ajjer, c. 6000 B.C.: No. 345, Shepherd, vert. 2d, Fleeing ostriches. 3d, Two girls, vert.

1966, Jan. 29   Photo.   Perf. 11½
344 A81 1d brn, bis & red brn   4.50 2.75
345 A81 1d gray, blk, ocher & dk brn   4.50 2.75
346 A81 2d brn, ocher & red brn   10.00 4.75
347 A81 3d buff, blk, ocher & brn red   10.00 4.75
    Nos. 344-347 (4)   29.00 15.00
See Nos. 365-368.

Pottery — A82

Handicrafts from Great Kabylia: 50c, Weaving, woman at loom, horiz. 70c, Jewelry.

1966, Feb. 26   Engr.   Perf. 13
348 A82 40c Prus bl, brn red & blk   .50 .35
349 A82 50c dk red, ol & ocher   .75 .40
350 A82 70c vio bl, blk & red   1.25 .55
    Nos. 348-350 (3)   2.50 1.30

Weather Balloon, Compass Rose and
Anemometer — A83

1966, Mar. 23   Engr.   Unwmk.
351 A83 1d claret, brt bl & grn   1.25   .50
World Meteorological Day.

Book, Grain,
Cogwheel and
UNESCO
Emblem — A84

Design: 60c, Grain, cogwheel, book and
UNESCO emblem.

1966, May 2   Typo.   Perf. 13x14
352 A84 30c yellow bis & blk   .45   .25
353 A84 60c dk red, gray & blk   .70   .40
Literacy as basis for development.

WHO Headquarters, Geneva — A85

1966, May 30   Engr.   Perf. 13
354 A85 30c multicolored   .45   .35
355 A85 60c multicolored   .85   .40
Inauguration of the WHO Headquarters,
Geneva.

Algerian Scout
Emblem — A86

Arab Jamboree
Emblem — A87

1966, July 23   Photo.   Perf. 12x12½
356 A86 30c multicolored   1.25   .60
357 A87 1d multicolored   1.75   .65
No. 356 commemorates the 30th anniv. of
the Algerian Mohammedan Boy Scouts. No.
357, the 7th Arab Boy Scout Jamboree, held
at Good Daim, Libya, Aug. 12.

Map of Palestine
and
Victims — A88

1966, Sept. 26   Typo.   Perf. 10½
358 A88 30c red & black   .60   .25
Deir Yassin Massacre, Apr. 9, 1948.

Abd-el-Kader — A89

1966, Nov. 2   Photo.   Perf. 11½
359 A89 30c multicolored   .25   .25
360 A89 95c multicolored   1.05   .40
Transfer from Damascus to Algiers of the
ashes of Abd-el-Kader (1807?-1883), Emir of
Mascara. See Nos. 382-387.

UNESCO
Emblem — A90

1966, Nov. 19   Typo.   Perf. 10½
361 A90 1d multicolored   1.05   .40
20th anniv. of UNESCO.

Horseman
A91

Miniatures by Mohammed Racim: 1.50d,
Woman at her toilette. 2d, The pirate Barba-
rossa in front of the Admiralty.

1966, Dec. 17   Photo.   Perf. 11½
Granite Paper
362 A91   1d multicolored   3.25   1.50
363 A91 1.50d multicolored   5.25   1.75
364 A91   2d multicolored   6.50   3.50
    Nos. 362-364 (3)   15.00   6.75

Wall Paintings Type of 1966
Wall Paintings from Tassili-N-Ajjer, c. 6000
B.C.: 1d, Cow. No. 366, Antelope. No. 367,
Archers. 3d, Warrior, vert.

1967, Jan. 28   Photo.   Perf. 11½
365 A81 1d brn, bis & dl vio   3.25   1.90
366 A81 2d brn, ocher & red
        brn   5.00   3.75
367 A81 2d brn, yel & red brn   5.00   3.75
368 A81 3d blk, gray, yel & red
        brn   7.00   5.25
    Nos. 365-368 (4)   20.25   14.65

Bardo
Museum
A92

La Kalaa
Minaret — A93

Design: 1.30d, Ruins at Sedrata.

1967, Feb. 27   Photo.   Perf. 13
369 A92 35c multicolored   .40   .25
370 A93 95c multicolored   .90   .50
371 A92 1.30d multicolored   1.50   .65
    Nos. 369-371 (3)   2.80   1.40

Moretti and
International
Tourist Year
Emblem
A94

Design: 70c, Tuareg riding camel, Tassili,
and Tourist Year Emblem, vert.

1967, Apr. 29   Litho.   Perf. 14
372 A94 40c multi   .70   .40
373 A94 70c multi   1.40   .60
International Tourist Year, 1967.

Spiny-tailed
Agamid
A95

Designs: 20c, Ostrich, vert. 40c, Slender-
horned gazelle, vert. 70c, Fennec.

1967, June 24   Photo.   Perf. 11½
374 A95 5c bister & blk   .70   .70
375 A95 20c ocher, blk & pink   1.40   .70
376 A95 40c ol bis, blk & red brn   2.10   1.00
377 A95 70c gray, blk & dp org   2.75   1.75
    Nos. 374-377 (4)   6.95   4.15

Dancers — A96

Typographed and Engraved
1967, July 4   Perf. 10½
378 A96 50c gray vio, yel & blk   .90   .40
National Youth Festival.

Map of the Mediterranean and Sport
Scenes — A97

1967, Sept. 2   Typo.   Perf. 10½
379 A97 30c black, red & blue   .65   .40
Issued to publicize the 5th Mediterranean
Games, Tunis, Sept. 8-17.

Skiers — A98

Olympic
Emblem
and Sports
A99

1967, Oct. 21   Engr.   Perf. 13
380 A98 30c brt blue & ultra   .90   .40
381 A99 95c brn org, pur & brt
        grn   1.65   .75
Issued to publicize the 10th Winter Olympic
Games, Grenoble, Feb. 6-18, 1968.

Abd-el-Kader Type of 1966
Lithographed, Photogravure
1967-71   Perf. 13½, 11½
382 A89 5c dull pur ('68)   .25   .25
383 A89 10c green   .25   .25
383A A89 10c sl grn (litho., '69)   .25   .25
383B A89 25c orange ('71)   .30   .25
384 A89 30c black ('68)   .35   .25
385 A89 30c lt violet ('68)   .45   .25
386 A89 50c rose claret   .75   .25
387 A89 70c violet blue   .85   .30
    Nos. 382-387 (8)   3.45   2.05
No. 383, 50c and 70c, issued Nov. 13, 1967,
are on granite paper, photo. The 5c, No.383A,
25c and 30c are litho., perf. 13½; others, perf.
11½.
The three 1967 stamps (No. 383, 50c, 70c)
have numerals thin, narrow and close
together; the Arabic inscription at lower right is
2mm high. The 5 litho. stamps are redrawn,
with numerals thicker and spaced more widely;
Arabic at lower right 3mm high.

Boy Scouts
Holding
Jamboree
Emblem
A100

1967, Dec. 23   Engr.   Perf. 13
388 A100 1d multicolored   1.90   .70
12th Boy Scout World Jamboree, Farragut
State Park, Idaho, Aug. 1-9.

No. 324 Surcharged
1967   Typo.   Perf. 14x13½
389 A71 30c on 25c red   .65   .25

Mandolin — A101

1968, Feb. 17   Photo.   Perf. 12½x13
390 A101 30c shown   .55   .25
391 A101 40c Lute   .75   .40
392 A101 1.30d Rebec   2.75   1.10
    Nos. 390-392 (3)   4.05   1.75

Nememcha
Rug — A102

Algerian Rugs: 70c, Guergour. 95c, Djebel-
Amour. 1.30d, Kalaa.

1968, Apr. 13   Photo.   Perf. 11½
393 A102 30c multi   .95   .60
394 A102 70c multi   1.75   .95
395 A102 95c multi   3.00   2.00
396 A102 1.30d multi   3.50   1.50
    Nos. 393-396 (4)   9.20   5.05

Human
Rights
Flame
A103

1968, May 18   Typo.   Perf. 10½
397 A103 40c blue, red & yel   .65   .80
International Human Rights Year, 1968.

WHO
Emblem
A104

1968, May 18
398 A104 70c blk, lt bl & yel   .80   .40
20th anniv. of the WHO.

Welder — A105

1968, June 15   Engr.   Perf. 13
399 A105 30c gray, brn & ultra   .45   .25
Algerian emigration to Europe.

Athletes, Olympic
Flame and
Rings — A106

50c, Soccer player. 1d, Mexican pyramid,
emblem, Olympic flame, rings & athletes,
horiz.

Perf. 12½x13, 13x12½
1968, July 4   Photo.
400 A106 30c green, red & yel   .65   .50
401 A106 50c rose car & multi   .95   .60
402 A106 1d dk grn, org, brn &
red   1.60   .95
Nos. 400-402 (3)   3.20 2.05
19th Olympic Games, Mexico City, 10/12-27.

Scouts and
Emblem — A107

1968, July 4   Perf. 13
403 A107 30c multicolored   .65   .25
8th Arab Boy Scout Jamboree, Algiers, 1968.

Barbary
Sheep — A108

1968, Oct. 19   Photo.   Perf. 11½
404 A108 40c shown   .90   .40
405 A108 1d Red deer   2.10   .65

Hunting Scenes,
Djemila — A109

Design: 95c, Neptune's chariot, Timgad,
horiz. Both designs are from Roman mosaics.

Perf. 12½x13, 13x12½
1968, Nov. 23   Photo.
406 A109 40c gray & multi   .60   .25
407 A109 95c gray & multi   1.35   .55

"Industry" — A110

Designs: No. 409, Miner with drill. 95c,
"Energy" (circle and rays).

1968, Dec. 14   Perf. 11½
408 A110 30c dp orange & sil   .45   .25
409 A110 30c brown & multi   .45   .25
410 A110 95c silver, red & blk   1.25   .40
Nos. 408-410 (3)   2.15   .90
Issued to publicize industrial development.

Opuntia Ficus
Indica — A111

Flowers: 40c, Carnations. 70c, Roses. 95c,
Bird-of-paradise flower.

1969, Jan.   Photo.   Perf. 11½
Flowers in Natural Colors
411 A111 25c pink & blk   .65   .45
412 A111 40c yellow & blk   1.10   .60
413 A111 70c gray & blk   1.65   .75
414 A111 95c brt blue & blk   2.90 1.10
Nos. 411-414 (4)   6.30 2.90
See Nos. 496-499.

Irrigation Dam at Djorf Torba-Oued
Guir — A112

Design: 1.50d, Truck on Highway No. 51
and camel caravan.

1969, Feb. 22   Photo.   Perf. 11½
415 A112 30c multi   .55   .25
416 A112 1.50d multi   1.90   .75
Public works in the Sahara.

Mail Coach
A113

1969, Mar. 22   Photo.   Perf. 11½
417 A113 1d multicolored   2.60   .75
Issued for Stamp Day, 1969.

Capitol,
Timgad — A114

1d, Septimius Temple, Djemila, horiz.

1969, Apr. 5   Photo.   Perf. 13x12½
418 A114 30c gray & multi   .55   .25
419 A114 1d gray & multi   1.35   .50
Second Timgad Festival, Apr. 4-8.

ILO Emblem
A115

1969, May 24   Photo.   Perf. 11½
420 A115 95c dp car, yel & blk   1.15   .45
50th anniv. of the ILO.

Arabian
Saddle — A116

Algerian Handicrafts: 30c, Bookcase. 60c,
Decorated copper plate.

1969, June 28 Photo.   Perf. 12x12½
Granite Paper
421 A116 30c multicolored   .45   .25
422 A116 60c multicolored   .85   .35
423 A116 1d multicolored   1.50   .65
Nos. 421-423 (3)   2.80 1.25

No. 321 Surcharged

1969   Typo.   Perf. 14x13½
424 A71 20c on 12c emerald   .50   .25

Pan-African
Culture Festival
Emblem — A117

1969, July 19   Photo.   Perf. 12½
425 A117 30c multicolored   .60   .25
1st Pan-African Culture Festival, Algiers,
7/21-8/1.

African
Development
Bank
Emblem — A118

1969, Aug. 23   Typo.   Perf. 10½
426 A118 30c dull blue, yel & blk   .60   .25
5th anniv. of the African Development Bank.

Astronauts and
Landing Module on
Moon — A119

Perf. 12½x11½
1969, Aug. 23   Photo.
427 A119 50c gold & multi   1.10   .50
Man's 1st landing on the moon, July 20,
1969. US astronauts Neil A. Armstrong and
Col. Edwin E. Aldrin, Jr., with Lieut. Col.
Michael Collins piloting Apollo 11.

Algerian Women, by Dinet — A120

1.50d, The Watchmen, by Etienne Dinet.

1969, Nov. 29   Photo.   Perf. 14½
428 A120 1d multi   2.00   .80
429 A120 1.50d multi   2.50 1.25

Mother and
Child — A121

1969, Dec. 27   Photo.   Perf. 11½
430 A121 30c multicolored   .65   .40
Issued to promote mother and child
protection.

Agricultural
Growth
Chart,
Tractor and
Dam
A122

30c, Transportation and development. 50c,
Abstract symbols of industrialization.

1970, Jan. 31   Photo.   Perf. 12½
Size: 37x23mm
431 A122 25c dk brn, yel & org   .30   .25

Litho.   Perf. 14
Size: 49x23mm
432 A122 30c blue & multi   1.00   .25

Photo. **Perf. 12½**
Size: 37x23mm
433 A122 50c rose lilac & blk .60 .25
　Nos. 431-433 (3) 1.90 .75
　Four-Year Development Plan.

Old and New Mail
Delivery — A123

1970, Feb. 28 **Photo.** **Perf. 11½**
Granite Paper
434 A123 30c multicolored .70 .25
　Issued for Stamp Day.

Spiny
Lobster — A124

　Designs: 40c, Mollusks. 75c, Retepora cel-
lulosa. 1d, Red coral.

1970, Mar. 28
435 A124 30c ocher & multi .55 .25
436 A124 40c multicolored .80 .40
437 A124 75c ultra & multi 1.35 .55
438 A124 1d lt blue & multi 2.10 .80
　Nos. 435-438 (4) 4.80 2.00

Oranges,
EXPO '70
Emblem
A125

　Designs (EXPO '70 Emblem and): 60c,
Algerian pavilion. 70c, Grapes.

1970, Apr. 25 **Photo.** **Perf. 12½x12**
439 A125 30c lt blue, grn & org .65 .25
440 A125 60c multicolored .65 .40
441 A125 70c multicolored 1.30 .60
　Nos. 439-441 (3) 2.60 1.25
　EXPO '70 International Exhibition, Osaka,
Japan, Mar. 15-Sept. 13, 1970.

Olives, Oil
Bottle — A126

1970, May 16 **Photo.** **Perf. 12½x12**
442 A126 1d yellow & multi 2.00 .80
　Olive Year, 1969-1970.

Common Design Types
pictured following the introduction.

UPU Headquarters Issue
Common Design Type
1970, May 30 **Perf. 13**
Size: 36x26mm
443 CD133 75c multicolored 1.10 .40

Saber — A127

　Designs: 40c, Guns, 18th century, horiz. 1d,
Pistol, 18th century, horiz.

1970, June 27 **Photo.** **Perf. 12½**
444 A127 40c yellow & multi 1.10 .60
445 A127 75c red & multi 1.50 .80
446 A127 1d multicolored 2.10 1.10
　Nos. 444-446 (3) 4.70 2.50

Map of
Arab
Countries
and Arab
League
Flag
A128

Typographed and Engraved
1970, July 25 **Perf. 10½**
447 A128 30c grn, ocher & lt bl .55 .25
　25th anniversary of the Arab League.

Vladimir
Lenin — A129

1970, Aug. 29 **Litho.** **Perf. 11½x12**
448 A129 30c brown & buff 2.50 .40
　Lenin (1870-1924), Russian communist
leader.

Exhibition Hall and Algiers Fair
Emblem — A130

1970, Sept. 11 **Engr.** **Perf. 14x13½**
449 A130 60c lt olive green .65 .30
　New Exhibition Hall for Algiers Intl. Fair.

Education Year Emblem, Blackboard,
Atom Symbol — A131

Koran
Page — A132

1970, Oct. 24 **Photo.** **Perf. 14**
450 A131 30c pink, blk, gold & lt
　　bl .50 .25
451 A132 3d multicolored 4.00 1.75
　Issued for International Education Year.

Great
Mosque,
Tlemcen
A133

　Design: 40c, Ketchaoua Mosque, Algiers,
vert. 1d, Mosque, Sidi-Okba, vert.

1970-71 **Litho.** **Perf. 14**
456 A133 30c multicolored .40 .25
457 A133 40c sepia & lemon
　　('71) .50 .25
458 A133 1d multicolored 1.00 .40
　Nos. 456-458 (3) 1.90 .90

Symbols of
the Arts
A134

1970, Dec. 26 **Photo.** **Perf. 13x12½**
459 A134 1d grn, lt grn & org 1.00 .50

Main Post
Office,
Algiers
A135

1971, Jan. 23 **Perf. 11½**
460 A135 30c multicolored 1.00 .40
　Stamp Day, 1971.

Hurdling
A136

　40c, Vaulting, vert. 75c, Basketball, vert.

1971, Mar. 7 **Photo.** **Perf. 11½**
461 A136 20c lt blue & slate .45 .25
462 A136 40c lt ol grn & slate .55 .40
463 A136 75c salmon pink &
　　slate .95 .60
　Nos. 461-463 (3) 1.95 1.25
　Mediterranean Games, Izmir, Turkey, Oct.
1971.

Symbolic
Head — A137

1971, Mar. 27 **Perf. 12½**
464 A137 60c car rose, blk & sil .65 .30
　Intl. year against racial discrimination.

Emblem
and
Technicians
A138

1971, Apr. 24 **Photo.** **Perf. 12½x12**
465 A138 70c cl, org & bluish blk .75 .30
　Founding of the Institute of Technology.

Woman from
Aurès — A139

　Regional Costumes: 70c, Man from Oran.
80c, Man from Algiers. 90c, Woman from
Amour Mountains.

1971, Oct. 16 **Perf. 11½**
466 A139 50c gold & multi 1.10 .50
467 A139 70c gold & multi 1.40 .80
468 A139 80c gold & multi 1.75 .95
469 A139 90c gold & multi 2.10 1.00
　Nos. 466-469 (4) 6.35 3.25
　See Nos. 485-488, 534-537.

UNICEF Emblem,
Birds and
Plants — A140

1971, Dec. 6 **Perf. 11½**
470 A140 60c multicolored .75 .50
　25th anniv. of UNICEF.

Lion
of St.
Mark
A141

　1.15d, Bridge of Sighs, Venice, vert.

1972, Jan. 24 **Litho.** **Perf. 12**
471 A141 80c multi 1.10 .55
472 A141 1.15d multi 2.25 .95
　UNESCO campaign to save Venice.

Javelin — A142

Designs: 25c, Bicycling, horiz. 60c, Wrestling. 1d, Gymnast on rings.

1972, Mar. 25   Photo.   Perf. 11½
473 A142 25c maroon & multi   .40   .25
474 A142 40c ocher & multi   .50   .25
475 A142 60c ultra & multi   1.10   .50
476 A142 1d rose & multi   1.50   .55
Nos. 473-476 (4)   3.50   1.55

20th Olympic Games, Munich, 8/26-9/11.

Book and Book Year Emblem — A143

1972, Apr. 15
477 A143 1.15d bister, brn & red   .80   .50

International Book Year 1972.

Mailmen — A144

1972, Apr. 22
478 A144 40c gray & multi   .70   .25

Stamp Day 1972.

Flowers — A145

1972, May 27
479 A145 50c Jasmine   .65   .40
480 A145 60c Violets   .65   .50
481 A145 1.15d Tuberose   1.75   .65
Nos. 479-481 (3)   3.05   1.55

Olympic Stadium, Chéraga A146

1972, June 10
482 A146 50c gray, choc & grn   .70   .40

New Day, Algerian Flag — A147

1972, July 5
483 A147 1d green & multi   1.15   .60

10th anniversary of independence.

Festival Emblem — A148

1972, July 5   Litho.   Perf. 10½
484 A148 40c grn, dk brn & org   .60   .25

1st Arab Youth Festival, Algiers, July 5-11.

Costume Type of 1971

Regional Costumes: 50c, Woman from Hoggar. 60c, Kabyle woman. 70c, Man from Mzab. 90c, Woman from Tlemcen.

1972, Nov. 18   Photo.   Perf. 11½
485 A139 50c gold & multi   1.40   .65
486 A139 60c gold & multi   1.75   .65
487 A139 70c gold & multi   1.90   .95
488 A139 90c gold & multi   2.25   1.10
Nos. 485-488 (4)   7.30   3.35

Mailing a Letter — A149

1973, Jan. 20   Photo.   Perf. 11
489 A149 40c orange & multi   .60   .25

Stamp Day.

Ho Chi Minh, Map of Viet Nam — A150

1973, Feb. 17   Photo.   Perf. 11½
490 A150 40c multicolored   .90   .35

To honor the people of Viet Nam.

Embroidery from Annaba A151

Designs: 60c, Tree of Life pattern from Algiers. 80c, Constantine embroidery.

1973, Feb. 24
491 A151 40c gray & multi   .55   .30
492 A151 60c blue and multi   .80   .50
493 A151 80c dk red, gold & blk   1.25   .65
Nos. 491-493 (3)   2.60   1.45

Stylized Globe and Wheat — A152

1973, Mar. 26   Photo.   Perf. 11½
494 A152 1.15d brt rose lil, org & grn   .80   .35

World Food Program, 10th anniversary.

Soldier and Flag A153

1973, Apr. 23   Photo.   Perf. 14x13½
495 A153 40c multicolored   .60   .25

Honoring the National Service.

Flower Type of 1969

30c, Opuntia ficus indica. 40c, Roses. 1d, Carnations. 1.15d, Bird-of-paradise flower.

1973, May 21   Photo.   Perf. 11½
Flowers in Natural Colors
496 A111 30c pink & blk   .75   .25
497 A111 40c gray & blk   .90   .40
498 A111 1d yellow & multi   2.00   .65
499 A111 1.15d multi   3.25   .95
Nos. 496-499 (4)   6.90   2.25

For overprints and surcharges see Nos. 518-519, 531.

OAU Emblem — A154

1973, May 28   Photo.   Perf. 12½x13
500 A154 40c multicolored   .60   .25

Org. for African Unity, 10th anniv.

Desert and Fruitful Land, Farmer and Family A155

1973, June 18   Perf. 11½
501 A155 40c gold & multi   .70   .25

Agricultural revolution.

Map of Africa, Scout Emblem — A156

1973, July 16   Litho.   Perf. 10½
502 A156 80c purple   .80   .40

24th Boy Scout World Conference (1st in Africa), Nairobi, Kenya, July 16-21.

Algerian PTT Emblem A157

1973, Aug. 6   Perf. 14
503 A157 40c blue & orange   .60   .25

Adoption of new emblem for Post, Telegraph and Telephone System.

Conference Emblem — A158

Perf. 13½x12½
1973, Sept. 5   Photo.
504 A158 40c dp rose & multi   .40   .30
505 A158 80c blue grn & multi   .75   .40

4th Summit Conference of Non-aligned Nations, Algiers, Sept. 5-9.

Port of Skikda A159

1973, Sept. 29   Photo.   Perf. 11½
506 A159 80c ocher, blk & ultra   .70   .40

New port of Skikda.

Young Workers — A160

1973, Oct. 22   Photo.   Perf. 13
507 A160 40c multicolored   .60   .25

Voluntary work service.

Arms of Algiers A161

1973, Dec. 22 **Photo.** *Perf. 13*
508 A161 2d gold & multi 2.75 1.40
Millennium of Algiers.

Infant — A162

1974, Jan. 7 **Litho.** *Perf. 10½x11*
509 A162 80c orange & multi .70 .50
Fight against tuberculosis.
No. 509 exists with 1973 year date. Value $60.

Man and Woman, Industry and Transportation — A163

1974, Feb. 18 **Photo.** *Perf. 11½*
510 A163 80c multicolored .85 .40
Four-year plan.

A164

1974, Feb. 25 **Photo.** *Perf. 11½*
511 A164 1.50d multi 2.75 1.40
Millennium of the birth of abu-al-Rayhan al-Biruni (973-1048), philosopher and mathematician.

Map and Colors of Algeria, Tunisia, Morocco A165

1974, Mar. 4 **Photo.** *Perf. 13*
512 A165 40c gold & multi .60 .25
Maghreb Committee for Coordination of Posts and Telecommunications.

Hand Holding Rifle — A166

1974, Mar. 25 *Perf. 11½*
513 A166 80c red & black .70 .25
Solidarity with the struggle of the people of South Africa.

Mother and Children — A167

1974, Apr. 8 *Perf. 13½*
514 A167 85c multicolored .70 .25
Honoring Algerian mothers.

Village A168

Designs: 80c, Harvest. 90c, Tractor and sun. Designs after children's drawings.

1974, June 15 **Size: 45x26mm**
515 A168 70c multicolored .65 .25
Size: 48x33mm
516 A168 80c multicolored .85 .40
517 A168 90c multicolored 1.05 .60
Nos. 515-517 (3) 2.55 1.25

Nos. 498-499 Overprinted

1974, June 22 **Photo.** *Perf. 11½*
518 A111 1d multi 1.65 .80
519 A111 1.15d multi 2.25 1.25
1974 Flower Show.

Stamp Vending Machine — A169

1974, Oct. 7 **Photo.** *Perf. 13*
520 A169 80c multicolored .85 .25
Stamp Day 1974.

UPU Emblem and Globe A170

1974, Oct. 14 *Perf. 14*
521 A170 80c multicolored 1.00 .40
Centenary of Universal Postal Union.

"Revolution" — A171

Soldiers and Mountains A172

Raising New Flag — A173

Design: 1d, Algerian struggle for independence (people, sun and fields).

1974, Nov. 4 **Photo.** *Perf. 14*
522 A171 40c multicolored .50 .25
523 A172 70c multicolored .70 .25
524 A173 95c multicolored .90 .35
525 A171 1d multicolored 1.15 .40
Nos. 522-525 (4) 3.25 1.25
20th anniv. of the start of the revolution.

"Horizon 1980" — A174

1974, Nov. 23 **Photo.** *Perf. 13*
526 A174 95c ocher, dk red & blk .70 .40
10-year development plan, 1971-1980.

Ewer and Basin — A175

1974, Dec. 21 *Perf. 11½*
527 A175 50c shown .55 .30
528 A175 60c Coffee pot .75 .40
529 A175 95c Sugar bowl 1.00 .55
530 A175 1d Bath tub 1.40 .65
Nos. 527-530 (4) 3.70 1.90
17th century Algerian copperware.

No. 497 Surcharged in Black

1975, Jan. 4
531 A111 50c on 40c multi 2.50 .55

Mediterranean Games' Emblem — A176

1975, Jan. 27 *Perf. 13½*
532 A176 50c purple, yel & grn .45 .25
533 A176 1d orange, bl & mar .80 .35
Mediterranean Games, Algiers, 1975.

Costume Type of 1971

Regional Costumes: No. 534, Woman from Hoggar. No. 535, Woman from Algiers. No. 536, Woman from Oran. No. 537, Man from Tlemcen.

1975, Feb. 22 **Photo.** *Perf. 11½*
534 A139 1d gold & multi 1.50 .75
535 A139 1d gold & multi 1.50 .75
536 A139 1d gold & multi 1.50 .75
537 A139 1d gold & multi 1.50 .75
Nos. 534-537 (4) 6.00 3.00

Map of Arab Countries, ALO Emblem A177

1975, Mar. 10 **Litho.** *Perf. 10½x11*
538 A177 50c red brown .60 .30
Arab Labor Organization, 10th anniversary.

Blood Transfusion A178

1975, Mar. 15 *Perf. 14*
539 A178 50c car rose & multi .75 .40
Blood donation and transfusions.

Post Office, Al-Kantara — A179

1975, May 10 **Photo.** *Perf. 11½*
Granite Paper
540 A179 50c multicolored .65 .25
Stamp Day 1975.

Policeman and Map of Algeria — A180

1975, June 1 **Photo.** *Perf. 13*
541 A180 50c multicolored 1.00 .40
Natl. Security and 10th Natl. Police Day.

Ground Receiving Station A181

Designs: 1d, Map of Algeria with locations of radar sites, transmission mast and satellite. 1.20d, Main and subsidiary stations.

1975, June 28 **Photo.** *Perf. 13*
542 A181 50c blue & multi .50 .25
543 A181 1d blue & multi .85 .25
544 A181 1.20d blue & multi 1.10 .40
Nos. 542-544 (3) 2.45 .90
National satellite telecommunications network.

Revolutionary with Flag — A182

1975, Aug. 20 **Photo.** *Perf. 11½*
545 A182 1d multicolored .65 .35
August 20th Revolutionary Movement (Skikda), 20th anniversary.

Swimming and Games' Emblem A183

Perf. 13x13½, 13½x13
1975, Aug. 23 **Photo.**
546 A183 25c shown .25 .25
547 A183 50c Judo, map .40 .25
548 A183 70c Soccer, vert. .60 .30
549 A183 1d Running, vert. .80 .40
550 A183 1.20d Handball, vert. 1.00 .60
a. Souv. sheet, #546-550, perf 13 6.75 6.75
Nos. 546-550 (5) 3.05 1.80
7th Mediterranean Games, Algiers, 8/23-9/46.
No. 550a sold for 4.50d. Exists imperf., same value.

Setif, Guelma, Kherrata — A184

1975 **Litho.** *Perf. 13½x14*
551 A184 5c orange & blk .25 .25
552 A184 10c emerald & brn .25 .25
553 A184 25c dl blue & blk .25 .25
554 A184 30c lemon & blk .40 .25
555 A184 50c brt grn & blk .40 .25

556 A184 70c fawn & blk .45 .25
557 A184 1d vermilion & blk .75 .35
Nos. 551-557 (7) 2.75 1.85
30th anniv. of victory in World War II. Issued: 50c, 1d, Nov. 3; others, Dec. 17. For surcharge see No. 611.

Map of Maghreb and APU Emblem A185

1975, Nov. 20 **Photo.** *Perf. 11½*
558 A185 1d multicolored .70 .40
10th Cong. of Arab Postal Union, Algiers.

Mosaic, Bey Constantine's Palace A186

Dey-Alger Palace — A187

Famous buildings: 2d, Prayer niche, Medersa Sidi-Boumediene, Tlemcen.

1975, Dec. 22
559 A186 1d lt blue & multi 1.05 .40
560 A186 2d buff & multi 2.10 .95
561 A187 2.50d buff & blk 2.75 1.40
Nos. 559-561 (3) 5.90 2.75

Al-Azhar University A188

Perf. 11½x12½
1975, Dec. 29 **Litho.**
562 A188 2d multicolored 2.10 .80
Millennium of Al-Azhar University.

Red-billed Firefinch — A189

Birds: 1.40d, Black-headed bush shrike, horiz. 2d, Blue tit. 2.50d, Blackbellied sandgrouse, horiz.

1976, Jan. 24 **Photo.** *Perf. 11½*
563 A189 50c multi 1.75 .70
564 A189 1.40d multi 3.00 1.25
565 A189 2d multi 3.50 1.40
566 A189 2.50d multi 4.00 2.00
Nos. 563-566 (4) 12.25 5.35
See Nos. 595-598.

Telephones 1876 and 1976 — A190

1976, Feb. 23 **Photo.** *Perf. 13½x13*
567 A190 1.40d rose, dk & lt bl 1.00 .55
Centenary of first telephone call by Alexander Graham Bell, Mar. 10, 1876.

Map of Africa with Angola and its Flag — A191

1976, Feb. 23 *Perf. 11½*
568 A191 50c brown & multi .60 .25
Algeria's solidarity with the People's Republic of Angola.

A192

Sahraoui flag and child, map of former Spanish Sahara.

1976, Mar. 15 **Photo.** *Perf. 11½*
569 A192 50c multicolored .55 .25
Algeria's solidarity with Sahraoui Arab Democratic Republic, former Spanish Sahara.

Stamp Day — A193

1976, Mar. 22
570 A193 1.40d Mailman 1.25 .40

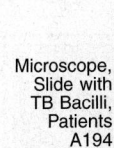

Microscope, Slide with TB Bacilli, Patients A194

1976, Apr. 26 *Perf. 13x13½*
571 A194 50c multicolored 1.05 .30
Fight against tuberculosis.

"Setif, Guelma, Kherrata" — A195

1976, May 24 **Photo.** *Perf. 13½x13*
572 A195 50c blue & yellow .60 .25
a. Booklet pane of 6 8.00
b. Booklet pane of 10 12.00
No. 572 was issued in booklets only.

Ram's Head over Landscape A196

1976, June 17 **Photo.** *Perf. 11½*
573 A196 50c multicolored .70 .25
Livestock breeding.

People Holding Torch, Map of Algeria — A197

1976, June 29 **Photo.** *Perf. 14x13½*
574 A197 50c multicolored .60 .25
National Charter.

Palestine Map and Flag — A198

1976, July 12 *Perf. 11½*
Granite Paper
575 A198 50c multicolored .65 .25
Solidarity with the Palestinians.

Map of Africa — A199

1976, Oct. 3 **Litho.** *Perf. 10½x11*
576 A199 2d dk blue & multi 1.50 .65
2nd Pan-African Commercial Fair, Algiers.

Blind
Brushmaker
A200

The
Blind,
by
Dinet
A201

1976, Oct. 23 Photo. *Perf. 14½*
577 A200 1.20d blue & multi .95 .50
578 A201 1.40d gold & multi .95 .65
Rehabilitation of the blind.

"Constitution 1976" — A202

1976, Nov. 19 Photo. *Perf. 11½*
579 A202 2d multicolored 1.50 .65
New Constitution.

Soldiers Planting
Seedlings
A203

1976, Nov. 25 Litho. *Perf. 12*
580 A203 1.40d multicolored 1.50 .55
Green barrier against the Sahara.

Ornamental Border and
Inscription — A204

1976, Dec. 18 Photo. *Perf. 11½*
Granite Paper
581 A204 2d multicolored 1.50 .65
Re-election of Pres. Houari Boumediene.
See No. 627.

Map with Charge
Zones and
Dials — A205

1977, Jan. 22 *Perf. 13*
582 A205 40c silver & multi .50 .25
Inauguration of automatic national and international telephone service.

People and
Buildings — A206

1977, Jan. 29 Photo. *Perf. 11½*
583 A206 60c on 50c multi .60 .25
2nd General Population and Buildings Census. No. 583 was not issued without the typographed red brown surcharge, date, and bars.

Sahara
Museum,
Uargla
A207

1977, Feb. 12 Litho. *Perf. 14*
584 A207 60c multicolored .60 .40

El-Kantara
Gorge — A208

Perf. 12½x13½
1977, Feb. 19 Photo.
585 A208 20c green & yellow .25 .25
a. Bklt. pane, 3 #585, 4 #586 + label 6.00
b. Bklt. pane, 5 #585, 2 #587 + label 7.00
586 A208 60c brt lilac & yel .25 .25
587 A208 1d brown & yellow .65 .25
Nos. 585-587 (3) 1.15 .75

National Assembly — A209

1977, Feb. 27 *Perf. 11½*
588 A209 2d multicolored 1.30 .55

People and
Flag — A210

Soldier and
Flag — A211

Perf. 13½, 11½ (3d)
1977, Mar. 12 Photo.
589 A210 2d multicolored 1.30 .55
590 A211 3d multicolored 2.10 .80
Solidarity with the peoples of Zimbabwe (Rhodesia), 2d; Namibia, 3d.

Winter, Roman
Mosaic
A212

The Seasons from Roman Villa, 2nd century A.D.: 1.40d, Fall. 2d, Summer. 3d, Spring.

1977, Apr. 21 Photo. *Perf. 11½*
Granite Paper
591 A212 1.20d multi 1.50 .75
592 A212 1.40d multi 1.50 .75
593 A212 2d multi 2.40 1.15
594 A212 3d multi 3.25 1.50
a. Souv. sheet, #591-594 12.00 12.00
Nos. 591-594 (4) 8.65 4.15
No. 594a sold for 8d and exists imperf.

Bird Type of 1976
Birds: 60c, Tristram's warbler. 1.40d, Moussier's redstart, horiz. 2d, Temminck's horned lark, horiz. 3d, Eurasian hoopoe.

1977, May 21 Photo. *Perf. 11½*
595 A189 60c multi 1.30 .65
596 A189 1.40d multi 1.90 .90
597 A189 2d multi 3.00 1.30
598 A189 3d multi 4.25 1.90
Nos. 595-598 (4) 10.45 4.75

Horseman — A213

Design: 5d, Attacking horsemen, horiz.

1977, June 25 Photo. *Perf. 11½*
599 A213 2d multicolored 2.00 .80
600 A213 5d multicolored 5.00 2.00

Flag Colors, Games
Emblem — A214

Wall
Painting,
Games
Emblem
A215

1977, Sept. 24 Photo. *Perf. 11½*
601 A214 60c multi .55 .25
602 A215 1.40d multi 1.30 .60
3rd African Games, Algiers 1978.

Village
and
Tractor
A216

1977, Nov. 12 *Perf. 14x13*
603 A216 1.40d multi 1.00 .40
Socialist agricultural village.

Almohades Dirham, 12th
Century — A217

Ancient Coins: 1.40d, Almohades coin, 12th century. 2d, Almoravides dinar, 11th century.

1977, Dec. 17 Photo. *Perf. 11½*
604 A217 60c ultra, sil & blk .55 .40
605 A217 1.40d grn, gold & brn 1.30 .60
606 A217 2d red brn, gold & brn 1.75 .90
Nos. 604-606 (3) 3.60 1.90

Flowering
Trees — A218

1978, Feb. 11 Photo. *Perf. 11½*
607 A218 60c Cherry .55 .25
608 A218 1.20d Peach 1.05 .70
609 A218 1.30d Almond 1.20 .70
610 A218 1.40d Apple 1.45 .80
Nos. 607-610 (4) 4.25 2.50

No. 555 Surcharged
in Black

1978, Feb. 11 Litho. *Perf. 13½x14*
611 A184 60c on 50c .80 .25

Children
with Traffic
Signs and
Car — A219

1978, Apr. 29 Photo. *Perf. 11½*
612 A219 60c multicolored .80 .25
Road safety and protection of children.

Sports and
Games
Emblems
A220

Designs (Games Emblem and): 40c, Volleyball. 60c, Rowing, vert. 1.20d, Basketball. 1.30d, Hammer throwing, vert. 1.40d, Map of Africa and boxers, vert.

1978, July 13 Photo. *Perf. 11½*
613 A220 40c multi .25 .25
614 A220 60c multi .45 .25
615 A220 1.20d multi 1.00 .40

616 A220 1.30d multi .... 1.00 .50
617 A220 1.40d multi .... 1.40 .60
　　　Nos. 613-617 (5) 4.10 2.00

3rd African Games, Algiers, July 13-28.

TB Patient Returning to
Family — A221

1978, Oct. 5　Photo.　Perf. 13½x14
618 A221 60c multicolored ...... .70 .25

Anti-tuberculosis campaign.

Holy
Kaaba — A222

1978, Oct. 28　Photo.　Perf. 11½
619 A222 60c multicolored ...... .80 .25

Pilgrimage to Mecca.

National
Servicemen
Building
Road — A223

1978, Nov. 4
620 A223 60c multicolored ...... .80 .25

African Unity Road from El Goleah to In
Salah, inauguration.

Fibula — A224

Jewelry: 1.35d, Pendant. 1.40d, Ankle ring.

1978, Dec. 21　Photo.　Perf. 12x11½
621 A224 1.20d multi .... 1.20 .50
622 A224 1.35d multi .... 1.45 .60
623 A224 1.40d multi .... 1.75 .75
　　　Nos. 621-623 (3) 4.40 1.85

Pres. Boumediene
A225

1979, Jan. 7　Photo.　Perf. 12x11½
624 A225 60c green, red &
　　　　　brown .... .55 .25

Houari Boumediene, pres. of Algeria 1965-
1978.

Torch and
Books
A226

1979, Jan. 27　Photo.　Perf. 11½
625 A226 60c multicolored ...... .55 .25

Natl. Front of Liberation Party Cong.

Pres. Boumediene — A227

1979, Feb. 4　Photo.　Perf. 11½
626 A227 1.40d multi .... 1.25 .55

40 days after death of Pres. Houari
Boumediène.

Ornamental Type of 1976

Proclamation of new President.

1979, Feb. 10
627 A204 2d multicolored .... 1.50 .40

Election of Pres. Chadli Bendjedid.

A229

1979, Apr. 18　Photo.　Perf. 11½
628 A229 60c multicolored ...... .50 .25

Sheik Abdul-Hamid Ben Badis (1889-1940).

A230

Designs: 1.20d, Telephone dial, map of
Africa. 1.40d, Symbolic Morse key and waves.

1979, May 19　Photo.　Perf. 13½x14
629 A230 1.20d multi .... .85 .30
630 A230 1.40d multi .... 1.05 .50

Telecom '79 Exhib., Geneva, Sept. 20-26.

Harvest, IYC
Emblem
A231

1.40d, Dancers and IYC emblem, vert.

Perf. 11½x11, 11x11½
1979, June 21
631 A231　60c multi .... .55 .25
632 A231 1.40d multi .... 1.10 .50

International Year of the Child.

Nuthatch — A232

1979, Oct. 20　Photo.　Perf. 11½
633 A232 1.40d multicolored ... 2.40 1.25

A233

Designs: 1.40d, Flag, soldiers and workers.
3d, Revolutionaries and emblem.

1979, Nov. 1　Photo.　Perf. 12½
634 A233 1.40d multi .... 1.00 .30
　　　　Size: 37x48mm
　　　　　Perf. 11½
635 A233　3d multi .... 1.90 .85

November 1 revolution, 25th anniversary.

Hegira,
1500
Anniv.
A234

1979, Dec. 2　Photo.　Perf. 11½
636 A234　3d multicolored .... 2.00 .75

Camels, Lion,
Men and
Slave — A235

Dionysian Procession (Setif Mosaic): 1.35d,
Elephants, tigers and women. 1.40d, Men in
tiger-drawn cart. No. 639a has continuous
design.

Granite Paper
1980, Feb. 16　Photo.　Perf. 11½
637 A235 1.20d multi .... 1.50 .40
638 A235 1.35d multi .... 1.50 .55
639 A235 1.40d multi .... 1.75 .80
　a.　Strip of 3, #637-639 .... 5.75 5.75

Science
Day — A236

1980, Apr. 19　Photo.　Perf. 12
640 A236 60c multicolored ...... .65 .25

Dam and
Workers
A237

1980, June 17　Photo.　Perf. 11½
641 A237 60c multicolored ...... .60 .25

Extraordinary Congress of the National Liberation Front Party.

Olympic
Sports,
Moscow
'80
Emblem
A238

50c, Flame, rings, vert.

1980, June 28
642 A238 50c multicolored ...... .45 .25
643 A238 1.40d shown .... .90 .50

22nd Summer Olympic Games, Moscow,
July 19-Aug. 3.

20th Anniversary of OPEC — A239

60c, Men holding OPEC emblem, vert.

Perf. 11x10½, 10½x11
1980, Sept. 15　　　　Engr.
644 A239 60c multicolored ...... .60 .25
645 A239 1.40d shown .... 1.40 .50

Aures
Valley
A240

1980, Sept. 25　Litho.　Perf. 13½x14
646 A240 50c shown .... .45 .25
647 A240　1d El Oued Oasis ... .85 .25
648 A240 1.40d Tassili Rocks .. 1.25 .40
649 A240　2d View of Algiers . 2.10 .70
　　　Nos. 646-649 (4) 4.65 1.60

World Tourism Conf., Manila, Sept. 27.

Avicenna (980-1037), Philosopher and Physician
A241

1980, Oct. 25 **Photo.** *Perf. 12*
650 A241 2d multicolored   2.25 .80

Ruins of El Asnam
A242

1980, Nov. 13 **Photo.** *Perf. 12*
651 A242 3d multicolored   2.10 .55

Earthquake relief.

Crown
A243

No. 652, Necklace, vert. No. 653, Earrings, bracelet, vert. No. 654, Crown.

Granite Paper
1980, Dec. 20 **Photo.** *Perf. 12*
652 A243 60c multi   .60 .25
653 A243 1.40d multi   1.00 .50
654 A243 2d multi   1.50 .65
Nos. 652-654 (3)   3.10 1.40

See Nos. 705-707.

1980-1984 Five-Year Plan — A244

1981, Jan. 29 **Litho.** *Perf. 14*
655 A244 60c multicolored   .60 .25

Basket Weaving — A245

Granite Paper
1981, Feb. 19 **Photo.** *Perf. 12½*
656 A245 40c shown   .40 .25
657 A245 60c Rug weaving   .50 .25
658 A245 1d Coppersmith   .80 .25
659 A245 1.40d Jeweler   1.10 .45
Nos. 656-659 (4)   2.80 1.20

Cedar Tree
A246

Arbor Day: 1.40d, Cypress tree, vert.

Granite Paper
1981, Mar. 19 **Photo.** *Perf. 12*
660 A246 60c multi   .40 .25
661 A246 1.40d multi   1.10 .60

Mohamed Bachir el Ibrahimi (1869-1965)
A247

Children Going to School
A248

1981, Apr. 16 **Granite Paper**
662 A247 60c multicolored   .60 .25
663 A248 60c multicolored   .60 .25

Science Day.

12th International Hydatidological Congress, Algiers — A249

1981, Apr. 23 *Perf. 14x13½*
664 A249 2d multicolored   2.00 .50

13th World Telecommunications Day — A250

1981, May 14 **Photo.** *Perf. 14x13½*
665 A250 1.40d multi   1.25 .25

Disabled People and Hand Offering Flower — A251

1.20d, Symbolic globe, vert.

Perf. 12½x13, 13x12½
1981, June 20 **Litho.**
666 A251 1.20d multicolored   .95 .25
667 A251 1.40d shown   1.10 .30

Intl. Year of the Disabled.

Papilio Machaon
A252

1.20d, Rhodocera rhamni. 1.40d, Charaxes jasius. 2d, Papilio podalirius.

1981, Aug. 20 **Photo.** *Perf. 11½*
Granite Paper
668 A252 60c multi   .90 .35
669 A252 1.20d multicolored   1.60 .50
670 A252 1.40d multicolored   2.00 .90
671 A252 2d multicolored   2.50 .90
Nos. 668-671 (4)   7.00 2.65

Monk Seal — A253

1981, Sept. 17 *Perf. 14x13½*
672 A253 60c shown   .90 .40
673 A253 1.40d Macaque   1.90 .80

World Food Day — A254

1981, Oct. 16 **Photo.** *Perf. 14x14½*
674 A254 2d multicolored   1.25 .50

Cave Drawings of Tassili — A255

Various cave drawings. 1.60d, 2d horiz.

1981, Nov. 21 *Perf. 11½*
675 A255 60c multi   .60 .25
676 A255 1d multi   1.20 .40
677 A255 1.60d multi   1.65 .55
678 A255 2d multi   2.25 .80
Nos. 675-678 (4)   5.70 2.00

Galley, 17-18th Cent.
A256

1981, Dec. 17 **Photo.** *Perf. 11½*
679 A256 60c shown   .70 .50
680 A256 1.60d Ship, diff.   1.90 .95

1982 World Cup Soccer
A257

Designs: Various soccer players.

Perf. 13x12½x 12½x13
1982, Feb. 25
681 A257 80c multi, vert.   .65 .25
682 A257 2.80d multi   2.00 .80

TB Bacillus Centenary
A258

1982, Mar. 20 **Photo.** *Perf. 14½x14*
683 A258 80c multi   .60 .25

Painted Stand
A259

1982, Apr. 24 **Photo.** *Perf. 11½*
Granite Paper
684 A259 80c Mirror, vert.   .50 .25
685 A259 2d shown   1.25 .45
Size: 48x33mm
686 A259 2.40d Chest   1.75 .60
Nos. 684-686 (3)   3.50 1.30

Djamaael Djadid Mosque, Algiers
A260

No. 688, Sidi Boumediene Mosque, Tlemcen. No. 689, Garden of Dey, Algiers.

1982, May 15 **Litho.** *Perf. 14*
Size: 32x22mm
687 A260 80c brown   .50 .25
a. Size: 30½x21mm   3.50 .75
688 A260 2.40d purple   1.50 .50
689 A260 3d slate   2.00 .60
a. Size: 30½x21mm   5.00 1.25
Nos. 687-689 (3)   4.00 1.35

See Nos. 731-734, 745-747, 774, 778-783.

A261

Medicinal plants: No. 690, Callitris articulata. No 691, Artemisia herba-alba. No. 692, Ricinus communis. No. 693, Thymus fontanesii.

1982, May 27 **Photo.** *Perf. 11½*
Granite Paper
690 A261 50c multi   .40 .25
691 A261 80c multi   .60 .25
692 A261 1d multi   .90 .40
693 A261 2.40d multi   1.75 .75
Nos. 690-693 (4)   3.65 1.65

A262

No. 694, Riflemen. No. 695, Soldiers, horiz. No. 696, Symbols, citizens, horiz. No. 697, Emblem.

1982, July 5   **Granite Paper**
694 A262 50c multi   .45 .25
695 A262 80c multi   .55 .25
696 A262 2d multi   1.40 .75
    Nos. 694-696 (3)   2.40 1.25
     Souvenir Sheet
697 A262 5d multi   5.50 5.50
    Independence, 20th anniv.
    No. 697 contains one 32x39mm stamp.

Soummam
Congress
A263

1982, Aug. 20   **Litho.**
698 A263 80c Congress building   .60 .25

Scouting
Year — A264

1982, Oct. 21   **Photo.**
     Granite Paper
699 A264 2.80d multi   2.00 .60

Palestinian
Child — A265

1982, Nov. 25   **Litho.**   **Perf. 10½**
700 A265 1.60d multi   .95 .30

Chlamydotis
Undulata — A266

    Protected birds: No. 701, Geronticus
eremita, horiz. No. 702, Chlamydotis Undulata. No. 703, Aguila rapax, horiz. No. 704,
Gypaetus barbatus.

     Perf. 15x14, 14x15
1982, Dec. 23   **Photo.**
701 A266 50c mutli   .75 .55
702 A266 80c multi   1.15 .75
703 A266 2d multi   2.10 1.50
704 A266 2.40d multi   2.75 1.90
    Nos. 701-704 (4)   6.75 4.70

     Jewelry Type of 1980
1983, Feb. 10   **Perf. 11½**
     Granite Paper
705 A243 50c Picture frame   .35 .25
706 A243 1d Flaska   .60 .40
707 A243 2d Brooch, horiz.   1.25 .65
    Nos. 705-707 (3)   2.20 1.30

A267

    80c, Abies numidica, vert. 2.80d, Acacia
raddiana.

1983, Mar. 17   **Photo.**
     Granite Paper
708 A267 80c multicolored   .70 .25
709 A267 2.80d multicolored   2.25 .80
    Intl. Arbor Day.

Various
Minerals — A268

    1.20d, 2.40d horiz.
     Granite Paper
     Perf. 12x12½, 12½x12
1983, Apr. 21   **Photo.**
710 A268 70c multi   1.25 .35
711 A268 80c multi   1.40 .50
712 A268 1.20d multi   1.60 .65
713 A268 2.40d multi   2.50 1.25
    Nos. 710-713 (4)   6.75 2.75

30th Anniv.
of Intl.
Customs
Cooperation
Council
A269

1983, May 14   **Photo.**   **Perf. 11½**
     Granite Paper
714 A269 80c multi   .70 .25

Emir Abdelkader Death
Centenary — A270

1983, May 22   **Photo.**   **Perf. 12**
     Granite Paper
715 A270 4d multi   2.40 .90

Local Mushrooms
A271

    No. 716, Amanita muscaria. No. 717, Ama-
nita phalloides. No. 718, Pleurotus eryngii. No.
719, Tefezia leonis.

1983, July 21   **Perf. 14x15**
716 A271 50c multi   1.00 .35
717 A271 80c multi   1.45 .75
718 A271 1.40d multi   3.00 1.10
719 A271 2.80d multi   4.50 2.10
    Nos. 716-719 (4)   9.95 4.30

A272

1983, Sept. 1   **Photo.**   **Perf. 11½**
720 A272 80c multi   .70 .25
    ibn-Khaldun, historian, philosopher.

World Communications Year — A273

    80c, Post Office, Algiers. 2.40d, Telephone,
circuit box.

     Perf. 11½x12½
1983, Sept. 22   **Litho.**
721 A273 80c multicolored   .55 .25
722 A273 2.40d multicolored   1.40 .60

Goat and
Tassili
Mountains
A274

    80c, Tuaregs in native costume. 2.40d, Ani-
mals, rock painting. 2.80d, Rock formation.

1983, Oct. 20   **Litho.**   **Perf. 12½x13**
723 A274 50c shown   .40 .25
724 A274 80c multicolored   .50 .25
725 A274 2.40d multicolored   1.40 .55
726 A274 2.80d multicolored   1.75 .75
    Nos. 723-726 (4)   4.05 1.80

Sloughi
Dog — A275

     Perf. 14x14½, 14½x14
1983, Nov. 24   **Photo.**
727 A275 80c shown   1.10 .35
728 A275 2.40d Sloughi, horiz.   2.75 .95

Natl. Liberation Party, 5th
Congress — A276

    80c, Symbols of development. 5d, Emblem.

1983, Dec. 19   **Photo.**   **Perf. 11½**
729 A276 80c multicolored   .80 .40
     Souvenir Sheet
730 A276 5d multicolored   5.00 5.00
    No. 730 contains one 32x38mm stamp.

     View Type of 1982
    10c, View of Oran, 1830. 1d, Sidi Abder-
ahman and Taalibi Mosques. 2d, Bejaia, 1830.
4d, Constantine, 1830.

1984, Jan. 26   **Litho.**   **Perf. 14**
     Size: 32x22mm
731 A260 10c multicolored   .25 .25
   a.   Size: 30½x21mm   .80 .40
732 A260 1d multicolored   .50 .25
   a.   Size: 30½x21mm   1.50 .80
733 A260 2d multicolored   1.00 .50
   a.   Size: 30½x21mm   3.00 1.50
734 A260 4d multicolored   2.50 .65
   a.   Size: 30½x21mm   6.00 1.50
    Nos. 731-734 (4)   4.25 1.65

Pottery
A278

     Perf. 11½x12, 12x11½
1984, Feb. 23   **Photo.**
     Granite Paper
735 A278 80c Jug, vert.   .50 .25
736 A278 1d Platter   .65 .40
737 A278 2d Oil lamp, vert.   1.40 .60
738 A278 2.40d Pitcher   1.75 .75
    Nos. 735-738 (4)   4.30 2.00

Fountains of Old
Algiers — A279

    Various fountains.

1984, Mar. 22   **Photo.**   **Perf. 11½**
     Granite Paper
739 A279 50c multi   .25 .25
740 A279 80c multi   .55 .40
741 A279 2.40d multi   1.40 .65
    Nos. 739-741 (3)   2.20 1.30

1984 Summer
Olympics — A280

1984, May 19   **Photo.**   **Perf. 11½**
     Granite Paper
742 A280 1d multi   1.25 .40

Brown Stallion
A281

1984, June 14   **Photo.**   **Perf. 11½**
     Granite Paper
743 A281 80c shown   .80 .40
744 A281 2.40d White mare   2.10 .95

     View Type of 1982
1984   **Litho.**   **Perf. 14**
     Size: 32x22mm
745 A260 5c Mustapha Pacha   .50 .25
   a.   Size: 30½x21mm   .80 .40
746 A260 20c Bab Azzoun   .50 .25
   d.   Size: 30½x21mm   1.00 .60
746A A260 30c Algiers   .50 .25
   d.   Size: 30½x21mm   1.50 .50
746B A260 40c Kolea   .50 .25
746C A260 50c Algiers   .50 .25
   e.   Size: 30½x21mm   1.50 .50
747 A260 70c Mostaganem   .60 .25
   a.   Size: 30½x21mm   2.00 1.00
    Nos. 745-747 (6)   3.10 1.50

    Issued: Nos. 745, 746, 747, 7/19; Nos.
746A-746C, 10/20.

Lute
A282

    Native musical instruments.

1984, Sept. 22　Litho.　Perf. 15x14
748	A282	80c shown	.60 .25
749	A282	1d Drum	.90 .40
750	A282	2.40d Fiddle	1.75 .75
751	A282	2.80d Bagpipe	2.00 .95
		Nos. 748-751 (4)	5.25 2.35

30th Anniv. of Algerian
Revolution — A284

80c, Partisans. 5d, Algerian flags, vert.

1984, Nov. 3　Photo.　Perf. 11½x12
757	A284	80c multicolored	.85 .25

Souvenir Sheet
758	A284	5d multicolored	5.50 5.50

M'Zab
Valley
A285

80c, Map of valley. 2.40d, Town of M'Zab,
vert.

1984, Dec. 15　Perf. 15x14, 14x15
759	A285	80c multicolored	.75 .25
760	A285	2.40d multicolored	1.75 .60

18th and 19th
Century
Metalware — A286

1985, Jan. 26　Photo.　Perf. 11½
761	A286	80c Coffee pot	.60 .25
762	A286	2d Bowl, horiz.	1.25 .65
763	A286	2.40d Covered bowl	1.75 .85
		Nos. 761-763 (3)	3.60 1.75

Fish
A287

50c, Thunnus thynnus. 80c, Sparus aurata.
2.40d, Epinephelus guaza. 2.80d, Mustelus
mustelus.

1985, Feb. 23　Photo.　Perf. 15x14
764	A287	50c multicolored	.50 .25
765	A287	80c multicolored	.90 .40
766	A287	2.40d multicolored	2.25 1.10
767	A287	2.80d multicolored	2.75 1.25
		Nos. 764-767 (4)	6.40 3.00

National
Games
A288

1985, Mar. 28　Perf. 11½x12
Granite Paper
768	A288	80c Doves, emblem	.80 .25

Environmental Conservation — A289

1985, Apr. 25　Perf. 13½
769	A289	80c Stylized trees	.70 .25
770	A289	1.40d Stylized waves	1.00 .40

View Type of 1982 and

The Casbah — A290

View of	Street Scene
Constantine	in Algiers
A290a	A290b

Designs: 2.50d, Djamaael Djadid Mosque,
Algiers. 2.90d, like No. 746. 5d, like No. 746A.
1.50d, like No. 746B. 4.20d, like No. 764.

Perf. 13½x12½, 13 (#774, 4.20d),
Perf. 13½x14 (#775)
Perf. 14½x14 (2d)

Photo., Litho. (2d, 6,20d, 7.50d,
#775)

1985-94
771	A290	20c dk blue & buff	.25 .25
772	A290	80c sage grn &	
		buff	.60 .25
773	A290a	1d dk olive grn	.50 .25
a.		Bklt. pane of 5 + label	4.00
774	A260	1.50d dull red	.55 .25
775	A290b	1.50d red brn & brn	.40 .25
a.		Booklet pane of 6	2.75
776	A290b	2d dk bl & lt bl	.40 .25
a.		Booklet pane of 5 + label	3.00
777	A290	2.40d chestnut &	
		buff	1.75 .25
a.		Bklt. pane of 5 (20c, 3 80c, 2.40d) + label	5.75
778	A260	2.50d bluish green	1.00 .25
779	A260	2.90d slate	1.25 .25
780	A260	4.20d gray green	1.40 .35
781	A260	5d dp bis & blk	2.10 .40

Perf. 14
782	A260	6.20d like #731	1.10 .30
783	A260	7.50d like #745	1.75 .30
		Nos. 771-783 (13)	13.05 3.60

Nos. 771-772, 777 issued only in booklet
panes.
Issued: 20c, 80c, 2.40d, 6/1/85; 1d, 1/26/89;
2.50d, 2.90d, 5d, 2/23/89; No. 774, 4.20d,
3/21/91; No. 775, 5/20/92; 6.20d, 7.50d,
4/22/92; 2d, 10/21/93; No. 776a, 10/21/94.
See No. 1010.

UN, 40th
Anniv. — A291

1985, June 26　Photo.　Perf. 14
784	A291	1d Dove, emblem, 40	.90 .25

Natl. Youth
Festival — A292

1985, July 5　Litho.　Perf. 13½
785	A292	80c multicolored	.70 .25

Intl. Youth
Year
A293

80c, Silhouette, globe, emblem, vert. 1.40d,
Doves, globe.

1985, July 5
786	A293	80c multicolored	.60 .25
787	A293	1.40d multicolored	.90 .40

World Map,
OPEC — A294

1985, Sept. 14　Photo.　Perf. 12½x13
788	A294	80c multicolored	.80 .25

Organization of Petroleum Exporting Countries, 25th anniv.

Family
Planning — A295

1985, Oct. 3　Litho.　Perf. 14
789	A295	80c Mother and sons	.60 .25
790	A295	1.40d Weighing infant	.90 .40
791	A295	1.70d Breast-feeding	1.30 .50
		Nos. 789-791 (3)	2.80 1.15

El-Meniaa
Township — A296

80c, Chetaibi Bay, horiz. 2.40d, Bou Noura
Town, horiz.

1985, Oct. 24　Engr.　Perf. 13
792	A296	80c multicolored	.50 .25
793	A296	2d shown	1.40 .40
794	A296	2.40d multicolored	1.60 .60
		Nos. 792-794 (3)	3.50 1.25

The Palm
Grove, by N.
Dinet — A297

1985, Nov. 21　Photo.　Perf. 11½x12
Granite Paper
795	A297	2d multicolored	1.50 .75
796	A297	3d multi, diff.	2.10 1.10

Tapestries
A298

Various designs.

1985, Dec. 19　Granite Paper
797	A298	80c multi	.70 .50
798	A298	1.40d multi	1.40 .75
799	A298	2.40d multi	2.00 1.25
800	A298	2.80d multi	2.50 1.75
		Nos. 797-800 (4)	6.60 4.25

Wildcats
A299

80c, Felis margarita. 1d, Felis caracal. 2d,
Felis sylvestris. 2.40d, Felis serval, vert.

1986, Jan. 23　Perf. 12x11½, 11½x12
Granite Paper
801	A299	80c multicolored	1.40 .60
802	A299	1d multicolored	1.75 .70
803	A299	2d multicolored	2.50 .90
804	A299	2.40d multicolored	3.50 1.60
		Nos. 801-804 (4)	9.15 3.80

UN Child Survival
Campaign
A300

80c, Oral vaccine. 1.40d, Mother, child, sun.
1.70d, Three children.

1986, Feb. 13　Litho.　Perf. 13½
805	A300	80c multicolored	.55 .25
806	A300	1.40d multicolored	1.10 .65
807	A300	1.70d multicolored	1.60 .85
		Nos. 805-807 (3)	3.25 1.75

Algerian General
Worker's Union,
30th Anniv. — A301

1986, Feb. 24　Perf. 12½
Granite Paper
808	A301	2d multicolored	1.50 .60

National Charter — A302

Granite Paper

1986, Mar. 6 **Photo.** *Perf. 11½*
809 A302 4d multicolored 3.00 1.25

Natl. Day of the Disabled — A303

1986, Mar. 15 *Perf. 12½x13*
810 A303 80c multicolored .70 .30

A304

1986, Apr. 17 **Litho.** *Perf. 14x15*
811 A304 80c multicolored .75 .40
Anti-Tuberculosis campaign.

A305

2d, Soccer ball, sombrero. 2.40d, Soccer players.

1986, Apr. 24 *Perf. 14*
812 A305 2d multicolored 1.50 .55
813 A305 2.40d multicolored 1.75 .65
1986 World Cup Soccer Championships, Mexico.

Inner Courtyards — A306

Granite Paper

1986, May 15 **Photo.** *Perf. 11½*
814 A306 80c multicolored .70 .30
815 A306 2.40d multi, diff. 1.90 .95
816 A306 3d multi, diff. 2.40 1.25
  Nos. 814-816 (3) 5.00 2.50

Blood Donation Campaign A307

1986, June 26 **Litho.** *Perf. 13½*
817 A307 80c multicolored 1.40 .40

Southern District Radio Communication Inauguration A308

1986, July *Perf. 13*
818 A308 60c multicolored .50 .25

Mosque Gateways A309

2d, Door. 2.40d, Ornamental arch.

Granite Paper

1986, Sept. 27 **Photo.** *Perf. 12x11½*
819 A309 2d multicolored 1.40 .60
820 A309 2.40d multicolored 1.60 .85

Intl. Peace Year A310

Perf. 13½x14½
1986, Oct. 16 **Photo.**
821 A310 2.40d multi 1.60 .60

Folk Dancing A311

1986, Nov. 22 **Litho.** *Perf. 14x13½*
822 A311 80c Woman, scarf .70 .25
823 A311 2.40d Woman, diff. 1.75 .70
824 A311 2.80d Man, sword 1.90 .80
  Nos. 822-824 (3) 4.35 1.75

Flowers — A312

80c, Narcissus tazetta. 1.40d, Iris unguicularis. 2.40d, Capparis spinosa. 2.80d, Gladiolus segetum.

1986, Dec. 18 **Photo.** *Perf. 14*
825 A312 80c multicolored .70 .30
826 A312 1.40d multicolored 1.25 .60
827 A312 2.40d multicolored 1.75 1.00
828 A312 2.80d multicolored 2.10 1.25
  Nos. 825-828 (4) 5.80 3.15
  See Nos. 936-938.

Abstract Paintings by Mohammed Issia Khem — A313

2d, Man and woman, vert. 5d, Man and books.

Perf. 11½x12, 12x11½
1987, Jan. 29 **Litho.**
829 A313 2d multicolored 1.50 .85
830 A313 5d multicolored 3.25 2.00

Jewelry from Aures A314

Granite Paper

1987, Feb. 27 **Photo.** *Perf. 12*
831 A314 1d Earrings .75 .45
832 A314 1.80d Bracelets 1.20 .70
833 A314 2.90d Nose rings 1.75 1.10
834 A314 3.30d Necklace 2.10 1.25
  Nos. 831-834 (4) 5.80 3.50
  Nos. 831-833 vert.

Petroglyphs, Atlas — A315

1987, Mar. 26 **Litho.** *Perf. 12x11½*
Granite Paper
835 A315 1d Man and woman 1.10 .70
836 A315 2.90d Goat 2.50 1.40
837 A315 3.30d Horse, bull 2.75 1.40
  Nos. 835-837 (3) 6.35 3.50

Syringe as an Umbrella — A316

Granite Paper

1987, Apr. 7 *Perf. 11½*
838 A316 1d multicolored .80 .25
Child Immunization Campaign, World Health Day.

Volunteers A317

1987, Apr. 23 *Perf. 10½*
839 A317 1d multicolored .55 .30

Third General Census — A318

1987, May 21 *Perf. 13½*
840 A318 1d multicolored .70 .30

Algerian Postage, 25th Anniv. — A319

War Orphans' Fund label (1fr + 9fr) of 1962.

Granite Paper

1987, July 5 **Photo.** *Perf. 11½x12*
841 A319 1.80d multicolored 2.75 .70

A320

A321

1987, July 5 **Granite Paper**
842 A320 1d multicolored .60 .25
Souvenir Sheet
843 A321 5d multicolored 5.50 5.50
Natl. independence, 25th anniv.

Amateur Theater Festival, Mostaganem A322

Granite Paper

1987, July 20   *Perf. 12x11½*
844 A322 1d Actors on stage .55 .25
845 A322 1.80d Theater   .95 .60
   a.   Pair, #844-845   1.50 1.50

No. 845a has continuous design.

Mediterranean Games,
Latakia — A323

1987, Aug. 6   *Perf. 13x12½, 12½x13*
846 A323 1d Discus   .60 .30
847 A323 2.90d Tennis, vert.   1.50 .85
848 A323 3.30d Team handball 1.75 1.00
   Nos. 846-848 (3)   3.85 2.15

Birds — A324

1d, Phoenicopterus ruber roseus. 1.80d,
Porphyrio porphyrio. 2.50d, Elanus caeruleus.
2.90d, Milvus milvus.

1987   Litho.   *Perf. 13½*
849 A324 1d multicolored   .85 .50
850 A324 1.80d multicolored   1.40 1.00
851 A324 2.50d multicolored   2.25 1.25
852 A324 2.90d multicolored   2.50 1.50
   Nos. 849-852 (4)   7.00 4.25

Agriculture
A325

No. 853, Planting. No. 854, Reservoir. No.
855, Harvesting crop, vert. No. 856, Produce,
vert.

Perf. 10½x11, 11x10½
1987, Nov. 26   Litho.
853 A325 1d multicolored   .65 .25
854 A325 1d multicolored   .65 .25
855 A325 1d multicolored   .65 .25
856 A325 1d multicolored   .65 .25
   Nos. 853-856 (4)   2.60 1.00

African Telecommunications
Day — A326

1987, Dec. 7   *Perf. 10½*
857 A326 1d multicolored   .90 .25

Transportation — A327

1987, Dec. 18   Litho. *Perf. 10½x11*
858 A327 2.90d shown   1.50 .70
859 A327 3.30d Diesel train   3.00 1.50

Algerian
Universities
A328

Various campuses.

1987, Dec. 26 *Perf. 10½x11, 11x10½*
860 A328 1d shown   .50 .25
861 A328 2.50d multi, diff.   1.30 .50
862 A328 2.90d multi, diff.   1.50 .60
863 A328 3.30d multi, diff., vert. 1.75 .70
   Nos. 860-863 (4)   5.05 2.05

Intl. Rural Development Fund, 10th
Anniv. — A329

1988, Jan. 27   *Perf. 10½x11*
864 A329 1d multicolored   .80 .25

Autonomy of
State-owned
Utilities — A330

1988, Feb. 27 Litho. *Perf. 11x10½*
865 A330 1d multicolored   .60 .25

Intl. Women's
Day — A331

1988, Mar. 10 Litho. *Perf. 11x10½*
866 A331 1d multicolored   .70 .25

Arab Scouts, 75th
Anniv. — A332

1988, Apr. 7   Litho.   *Perf. 10½*
867 A332 2d multicolored   1.20 .50

1988 Summer
Olympics,
Seoul — A333

1988, July 23   Litho.   *Perf. 10½*
868 A333 2.90d multicolored   1.60 .85

Hot
Springs — A334

2.90d, Caverns, horiz. 3.30d, Gazebo, fountain, horiz.

1988, July 16
869 A334 1d shown   .45 .25
870 A334 2.90d multicolored   1.50 .60
871 A334 3.30d multicolored   1.75 .70
   Nos. 869-871 (3)   3.70 1.55

World
Wildlife
Fund
A335

Barbary apes, Macaca sylvanus: 50c, Adult.
90c, Family. 1d, Close-up, vert. 1.80d, Seated
on branch, vert.

1988, Sept. 17 Litho. *Perf. 10½*
872 A335 50c multicolored   1.00 .45
873 A335 90c multicolored   1.25 .65
874 A335 1d multicolored   1.75 .90
875 A335 1.80d multicolored   3.00 1.60
   Nos. 872-875 (4)   7.00 3.60

Intl. Literacy
Day — A336

1988, Sept. 10 Photo. *Perf. 10½*
876 A336 2.90d multicolored   1.50 .85

WHO, 40th
Anniv. — A337

1988, Oct. 15
877 A337 2.90d multicolored   1.50 .70

Fight
Apartheid
A338

1988, Nov. 19 Litho. *Perf. 10½x11*
878 A338 2.50d multicolored   1.25 .50

Natl. Front
Congress — A339

1988, Nov. 29   *Perf. 11x10½*
879 A339 1d multicolored   .60 .25

Agriculture
A340

No. 880, Irrigation. No. 881, Orchard, fields,
livestock.

1988, Dec. 24   *Perf. 10½*
880 A340 1d multicolored   .55 .25
881 A340 1d multicolored   .55 .25

Natl. Goals — A342

No. 887, Ancient fort. No. 888, Telecommunications. No. 889, Modern buildings.

1989, Mar. 9   Litho. *Perf. 11½*
        Granite Paper
886 A342 1d shown   .50 .25
887 A342 1d multicolored   .50 .25
888 A342 1d multicolored   .50 .25
889 A342 1d multicolored   .50 .25
   Nos. 886-889 (4)   2.00 1.00

   Nos. 887-889 horiz.

Airports — A343

2.90d, Oran Es Senia, horiz. 3.30d,
Tebessa, horiz.

1989, Mar. 23 *Perf. 10½x11, 11x10½*
890 A343 2.90d multicolored   1.20 .55
891 A343 3.30d multicolored   1.40 .70
892 A343 5d shown   2.10 1.25
   Nos. 890-892 (3)   4.70 2.50

Development of the South — A344

1d, Irrigation. 1.80d, Building. 2.50d, Fossil
fuel extraction, vert.

1989, Apr. 24   Litho. *Perf. 13½*
893 A344 1d multicolored   .50 .25
894 A344 1.80d multicolored   .70 .40
895 A344 2.50d multicolored   1.05 .55
   Nos. 893-895 (3)   2.25 1.20

Eradicate
Locusts
A345

1989, May 25   *Perf. 10½*
896 A345 1d multicolored   .50 .25

National
Service — A346

1989, May 11   Litho.   Perf. 13½
897 A346 2d multicolored   1.40   .70

1st Moon
Landing,
20th Anniv.
A347

4d, Astronaut, lunar module, Moon's
surface.

1989, July 23   Litho.   Perf. 13½
898 A347 2.90d shown   1.25   .60
899 A347   4d multi, vert.   1.60   .90

Interparliamentary Union,
Cent. — A348

1989, Sept. 4   Perf. 10½
900 A348 2.90d gold, brt rose lil
          & blk   1.20   .40

Produce
A349

1989, Sept. 23   Litho.   Perf. 11½
Granite Paper
901   Strip of 3   4.00 4.00
  a. A349 2d multi, diff.   .75   .50
  b. A349 3d multi, diff.   1.20   .65
  c. A349 5d shown   1.90 1.20

Fish — A350

1d, Sarda sarda. 1.80d, Zeus faber. 2.90d,
Pagellus bogaraveo. 3.30d, Xiphias gladius.

1989, Oct. 27   Litho.   Perf. 13½
902 A350 1d multicolored   .70   .30
903 A350 1.80d multicolored   1.25   .50
904 A350 2.90d multicolored   1.90   .70
905 A350 3.30d multicolored   2.25   .90
      Nos. 902-905 (4)   6.10 2.40

Algerian
Revolution, 35th
Anniv. — A351

1989, Nov. 4   Litho.   Perf. 13½
906 A351 1d multicolored   .50   .25

African
Development
Bank, 25th
Anniv. — A352

1989, Nov. 18   Perf. 10½
907 A352 1d multicolored   .50   .25

Mushrooms
A353

No. 908, Boletus satanas. No. 909, Psalliota
xanthoderma. No. 910, Lepiota procera. No.
911, Lactarius deliciosus.

1989, Dec. 16   Perf. 13½
908 A353   1d mutli   1.00   .30
909 A353 1.80d multi   1.50   .75
910 A353 2.90d multi   2.40 1.00
911 A353 3.30d multi   3.25 1.25
      Nos. 908-911 (4)   8.15 3.30

A354

1990, Jan. 18   Litho.   Perf. 10½
912 A354 1d multicolored   .50   .25

Pan-African Postal Union, 10th anniv.

Energy
Conservation
A355

1990, Feb. 22   Litho.   Perf. 14
913 A355 1d multicolored   .60   .25

A356

1990, Mar. 2   Photo.   Perf. 11½
914 A356 3d multicolored   1.30   .60

African Soccer Championships.

A357

1990, May 17   Litho.   Perf. 13½
917 A357 2.90d shown   1.10   .60
918 A357   5d Trophy   2.00 1.10

World Cup Soccer Championships, Italy.

Rural Electrification — A358

1990, June 21
919 A358 2d multicolored   .90   .30

Youth
A359

Youth Holding
Rainbow — A360

1990, July 6   Perf. 13½
920 A359 2d multicolored   .85   .30
921 A360 3d multicolored   1.25   .50

Maghreb Arab
Union — A361

1990   Perf. 14x13½
922 A361 1d multicolored   .50   .25

Vocations
A362

1990, Apr. 26   Litho.   Perf. 12½
923 A362   2d Craftsmen   .75   .40
924 A362 2.90d Auto mechanics   1.00   .60
925 A362 3.30d Deep sea fishing 1.75   .75
      Nos. 923-925 (3)   3.50 1.75

Organization of Petroleum Exporting
Countries (OPEC), 30th
Anniv. — A363

1990   Perf. 13½
926 A363 2d multicolored   1.50   .30

Savings
Promotion
A364

1990, Oct. 31   Litho.   Perf. 14
927 A364 1d multicolored   .50   .25

Namibian Independence — A365

1990, Nov. 8
928 A365 3d multicolored   1.00   .30

Farm
Animals — A366

1990, Nov. 29   Perf. 13½
929 A366   1d Duck   .50   .25
930 A366   2d Rabbit, horiz.   1.00   .40
931 A366 2.90d Turkey   1.30   .65
932 A366 3.30d Rooster, horiz.   1.60   .85
      Nos. 929-932 (4)   4.40 2.15

Anti-French Riots,
30th
Anniv. — A367

1990, Dec. 11
933 A367 1d multicolored   .65   .25

A368

1990, Dec. 20 — Perf. 14
934 A368 1d multicolored .40 .25

Fight against respiratory diseases.

Constitution, 2nd Anniv. — A369

1991, Feb. 24 Litho. Perf. 13½
935 A369 1d multicolored .55 .25

Flower Type of 1986

2d, Jasminum fruticans. 4d, Dianthus crinitus. 5d, Cyclamen africanum.

1991, May 23 Litho. Perf. 13½
Size: 26x36mm
936 A312 2d multicolored .80 .30
937 A312 4d multicolored 1.90 .70
938 A312 5d multicolored 2.25 1.00
Nos. 936-938 (3) 4.95 2.00

Children's Drawings A370

1991, June 3 Litho. Perf. 13½
939 A370 3d shown 1.20 .50
940 A370 4d Children playing 1.20 .50

Maghreb Arab Union Summit — A371

1991, June 10
941 A371 1d multicolored .45 .25

Geneva Convention on Refugees, 40th Anniv. — A372

1991, July 28 Litho. Perf. 14½x13½
942 A372 3d multicolored 1.00 .35

Postal Service A373

4.20d, Expo emblem, vert.

1991, Oct. 12 — Perf. 14
943 A373 1.50d shown .60 .25
944 A373 4.20d multicolored 1.25 .50

Telecom '91, 6th World Forum and Exposition on Telecommunications, Geneva, Switzerland (No. 944).

Butterflies A374

2d, Zerynthia rumina. 4d, Melitaea didyma. 6d, Vanessa atalanta. 7d, Nymphalis polychloros.

Granite Paper
1991, Nov. 21 Litho. Perf. 11½
945 A374 2d multicolored .85 .35
946 A374 4d multicolored 1.20 .50
947 A374 6d multicolored 1.65 .75
948 A374 7d multicolored 2.00 1.10
Nos. 945-948 (4) 5.70 2.70

A375

3d, Necklace. 4d, Jewelry of Southern Tuaregs. 5d, Brooch. 7d, Rings, horiz.

Granite Paper
1991, Dec. 21 — Perf. 12
949 A375 3d multicolored .75 .30
950 A375 4d multicolored .85 .45
951 A375 5d multicolored 1.00 .70
952 A375 7d multicolored 1.75 1.10
Nos. 949-952 (4) 4.35 2.55

Algerian Women — A376

1992, Mar. 8 Litho. Perf. 14
953 A376 1.50d multicolored .50 .25

Gazelles A377

Designs: 1.50d, Gazella dorcas. 6.20d, Gazella cuvieri. 8.60d, Gazella dama.

1992, May 13 — Perf. 14½x13
954 A377 1.50d multicolored .50 .35
955 A377 6.20d multicolored 1.10 .75
956 A377 8.60d multicolored 1.75 1.10
Nos. 954-956 (3) 3.35 2.20

1992 Summer Olympics, Barcelona A379

1992, June 24 Litho. Perf. 14
958 A379 6.20d Runners 1.25 .50

Independence, 30th Anniv. — A381

1992, July 7 Litho. Perf. 14
960 A381 5d multicolored 1.00 .30

Medicinal Plants — A382

No. 961, Ajuga iva. No. 962, Rhamnus alaternus. No. 963, Silybum marianum. No. 964, Lavandula stoechas.

1992, Sept. 23 Litho. Perf. 14
961 A382 1.50d multi .50 .25
962 A382 5.10d multi 1.20 .50
963 A382 6.20d multi 1.30 .60
964 A382 8.60d multi 1.60 .85
Nos. 961-964 (4) 4.60 2.20

Post Office Modernization A383

1992, Oct. 10 Litho. Perf. 14
965 A383 1.50d multicolored .40 .25

Marine Life — A384

Designs: 1.50d, Hippocampus hippocampus. 2.70d, Caretta caretta. 6.20d, Muraena helena. 7.50d, Palinurus elephas.

1992, Dec. 23
966 A384 1.50d multicolored .60 .25
967 A384 2.70d multicolored .90 .25
968 A384 6.20d multicolored 1.90 .65
969 A384 7.50d multicolored 2.10 .85
Nos. 966-969 (4) 5.50 2.00

Pres. Mohammad Boudiaf (1919-92) — A385

Granite Paper
1992, Nov. 3 Litho. Perf. 11½
970 A385 2d green & multi .35 .25
971 A385 8.60d blue & multi 1.60 .85

Coins A386

1.50d, Numidia, 2nd cent. BC. 2d, Dinar, 14th cent. 5.10d, Dinar, 11th cent. 6.20d, Abdelkader, 19th cent.

Granite Paper
1992, Dec. 16 Litho. Perf. 11½
972 A386 1.50d multicolored .30 .25
973 A386 2d multicolored .40 .25
974 A386 5.10d multicolored .90 .35
975 A386 6.20d multicolored 1.15 .50
Nos. 972-975 (4) 2.75 1.35

Door Knockers — A387

1993, Feb. 17 Litho. Perf. 14
976 A387 2d Algiers .30 .25
977 A387 5.60d Constantine .80 .40
978 A387 8.60d Tlemcen 1.50 .65
Nos. 976-978 (3) 2.60 1.30

Flowering Trees — A388

4.50d, Neflier (medlar), horiz. 8.60d, Cognassier (quince). 11d, Abricotier (apricot).

Granite Paper
1993, Mar. 17 Perf. 12x11½, 11½x12
979 A388 4.50d multicolored .85 .40
980 A388 8.60d multicolored 1.75 .75
981 A388 11d multicolored 2.25 1.00
Nos. 979-981 (3) 4.85 2.15

Natl. Coast Guard Service, 20th Anniv. A389

1993, Apr. 3 Litho. Perf. 14
982 A389 2d multicolored 1.10 .30

Traditional Grain Processing A390

1993, May 19 Litho. Perf. 14
983 A390 2d Container .45 .25
984 A390 5.60d Millstone .90 .50
985 A390 8.60d Press 1.40 .65
Nos. 983-985 (3) 2.75 1.40

Royal Mausoleums — A391

1993, June 16   Litho.   Perf. 14
986 A391   8.60d Mauretania   1.25   .60
987 A391   12d El Khroub   2.00   .85

Ports
A392

1993, Oct. 20   Litho.   Perf. 14x13½
988 A392   2d Annaba   .35   .25
989 A392   8.60d Arzew   1.50   .55

Varanus
Griseus
A393

Design: 2d, Chamaeleo vulgaris, vert.

Perf. 13½x14, 14x13½
1993, Nov. 20
990 A393   2d multicolored   .50   .25
991 A393   8.60d multicolored   1.75   .80

Tourism
A394

1993, Dec. 18   Litho.   Perf. 14x13½
992 A394   2d Tipaza   .35   .25
993 A394   8.60d Kerzaz   1.10   .50

A395

1994, Jan. 2   Perf. 13½x14
994 A395   2d multicolored   .60   .25
   SONATRACH (Natl. Society for Research,
Transformation, and Commercialization of
Hydrocarbons), 30th anniv.

Chahid
Day — A396

1994, Feb. 18   Litho.   Perf. 13½x14
995 A396   2d multicolored   .60   .25

1994 World Cup Soccer
Championships, US — A397

1994, Mar. 16   Perf. 14x13½
996 A397   8.60d multicolored   2.25   .85

Orchids — A398

5.60d, Orchis simia lam. 8.60d, Ophrys
lutea cavan. 11d, Ophrys apifera huds.

1994, Apr. 20   Litho.   Perf. 11½
Granite Paper
997 A398   5.60d multicolored   1.50   .60
998 A398   8.60d multicolored   1.75   .85
999 A398   11d multicolored   2.75 1.25
   Nos. 997-999 (3)   6.00 2.70

Ancient
Petroglyphs
A399

3d, Inscriptions. 10d, Man on horse.

1994, May 21   Litho.   Perf. 13x14
1000 A399   3d multicolored   .95   .25
1001 A399   10d multicolored   2.10   .75

A400

1994, June 25
1002 A400   12d multicolored   1.90   .65
   Intl. Olympic Committee, cent.

World Population
Day — A401

1994, July 13
1003 A401   3d multicolored   .50   .25

Views of Algiers Type of 1992
Design: 3d, like No. 775.

1994, July 13   Litho.   Perf. 14
1010 A290b 3d dk blue & lt blue   .75   .25

Jewelry
from
Saharan
Atlas
Region
A402

Perf. 13½x14, 14x13½
1994, Oct. 18   Litho.
1019 A402   3d Fibules, vert.   .60   .25
1020 A402   5d Belt   .90   .30
1021 A402   12d Bracelets   2.40   .85
   Nos. 1019-1021 (3)   3.90 1.40

Algerian
Revolution, 40th
Anniv. — A403

1994, Nov. 3   Litho.   Perf. 13½x14
1022 A403   3d multicolored   .40   .25

A404

1994, Nov. 16   Litho.   Perf. 13½x14
1023 A404   3d Ladybugs   .50   .25
1024 A404   12d Beetles   2.00   .75

Fight
Against
AIDS
A405

1994, Dec. 1   Litho.   Perf. 14x13½
1025 A405   3d multicolored   1.00   .25

Folk
Dances — A406

1994, Dec. 17   Litho.   Perf. 13½x14
1026 A406   3d Algeroise   .40   .30
1027 A406   10d Constantinoise 1.20   .75
1028 A406   12d Alaoui   1.40   .90
   Nos. 1026-1028 (3)   3.00 1.95
   See Nos. 1170-1172.

Minerals — A407

1994, Sept. 21
1029 A407   3d Gres lite-erode   .60   .25
1030 A407   5d Cipolin   1.00   .50
1031 A407   10d Marne a turitella 2.40   .95
   Nos. 1029-1031 (3)   4.00 1.70

World Tourism Organization, 20th
Anniv. — A408

1995, Jan. 28   Litho.   Perf. 14x13½
1032 A408   3d multicolored   .40   .25

Honey
Bees — A409

1995, Feb. 22   Perf. 13½x14, 14x13½
1033 A409   3d shown   .40   .30
1034 A409   13d On flower, horiz. 1.60   .90

Flowers — A410

Granite Paper
1995, Mar. 29   Photo.   Perf. 11½
1035 A410   3d Dahlias   .50   .30
1036 A410   10d Zinnias   1.50   .80
1037 A410   13d Lilacs   1.75   .90
   Nos. 1035-1037 (3)   3.75 2.00

Decorative
Stonework — A411

Various patterns.

1995, Apr. 19   Perf. 14
1039 A411   3d brown   .60   .30
1040 A411   4d green   .75   .30
1041 A411   5d deep claret   .90   .30
   Nos. 1039-1041 (3)   2.25   .90

End of
World
War II,
50th
Anniv.
A413

1995, May 3   Perf. 14x13½
1048 A413   3d multicolored   .70   .30

Souvenir Sheet

VE Day, 50th Anniv. — A414

1995, May 10   Litho.   Perf. 13½x14
1049 A414 13d multicolored   7.00 7.00

Volleyball,
Cent. — A415

1995, June 14
1050 A415 3d multicolored   .65   .30

Environmental
Protection — A416

3d, Air water pollution. 13d, Air pollution.

1995, June 5
1051 A416 3d multicolored   .40   .30
1052 A416 13d multicolored   1.60   .85

General
Electrification
A417

1995, July 5   Litho.   Perf. 13½x14
1053 A417 3d multicolored   .65   .30

UN, 50th
Anniv.
A418

1995, Oct. 24   Perf. 14x13½
1054 A418 13d multicolored   2.50 1.00

Pottery — A419

10d, Pot, Lakhdaria. 20d, Pitcher, Aokas. 21d, Jar, Larbaa Nath Iraten. 30d, Vase, Ouadhia.

1995, Nov. 14   Litho.   Perf. 14
1055 A419 10d dark brown   1.00   .50
1056 A419 20d dull maroon   2.10 1.00
1057 A419 21d golden brown   2.10 1.00
1058 A419 30d dark rose brown   3.25 1.25
    Nos. 1055-1058 (4)   8.45 3.75

Aquatic
Birds
A420

1995, Dec. 20 Litho.   Perf. 14x13½
1059 A420 3d Tadorna tadorna   .70   .25
1060 A420 5d Gallinago gallinago 1.20   .40

1996
Summer
Olympics,
Atlanta
A421

1996, Jan. 24   Litho.   Perf. 14x13½
1061 A421 20d multicolored   2.10 1.00

Touareg
Leather
Crafts
A422

Perf. 14x13½, 13½x14
1996, Feb. 14   Litho.
1062 A422 5d shown   1.00   .30
1063 A422 16d Saddle bag, vert. 1.50 1.00

Pasteur Institute
of Algeria — A423

1996, Mar. 20 Litho.   Perf. 13½x14
1064 A423 5d multicolored   .75   .25

Youm El
Ilm — A424

Designs: 16d, Dove, stylus, vert. 23d, Open book showing pencil, stylus, compass, satellite in earth orbit, vert.

Perf. 14x13½, 13½x14
1996, Apr. 16   Litho.
1065 A424 5d multicolored   .55   .30
1066 A424 16d multicolored   1.40   .80
1067 A424 23d multicolored   2.50 1.25
    Nos. 1065-1067 (3)   4.45 2.35

Minerals
A425

Mineral, region: 10d, Iron, Djebel-Ouenza. 20d, Gold, Tirek-Amesmessa.

1996, May 6   Litho.   Perf. 14x13½
1068 A425 10d multicolored   1.15   .55
1069 A425 20d multicolored   2.10 1.00

Butterflies
A426

Designs: 5d, Pandoriana pandora. 10d, Coenonympha pamphilus. 20d, Cynthia cardui. 23d, Melanargia galathea.

1996, June 12   Litho.   Perf. 11½
Granite Paper
1070 A426 5d multicolored   .75   .30
1071 A426 10d multicolored   1.25   .60
1072 A426 20d multicolored   2.75 1.00
1073 A426 23d multicolored   3.00 1.50
    Nos. 1070-1073 (4)   7.75 3.40

Civil
Protection
A427

5d, Giving medical aid, ambulance. 23d, Prevention of natural disasters, vert.

Perf. 14x13½, 13½x14
1996, Oct. 9   Litho.
1074 A427 5d multicolored   .60   .30
1075 A427 23d multicolored   2.75 1.25

World Day
Against Use
of Illegal
Drugs
A428

1996, June 26 Litho.   Perf. 14x13½
1076 A428 5d multicolored   .70   .30

UNICEF, 50th
Anniv. — A429

Stylized designs: 5d, Two children, wreath, pencils, flowers. 10d, Five children, pencil, key, flower, flag, hypodermic.

1996, Nov. 20 Litho.   Perf. 13½x14
1077 A429 5d multicolored   .40   .30
1078 A429 10d multicolored   .80   .45

4th General
Census
A430

1997, Feb. 12 Litho.   Perf. 14x13½
1079 A430 5d multicolored   .50   .30

Protest at
Ouargla, 35th
Anniv. — A431

1997, Feb. 27   Perf. 13½x14
1080 A431 5d multicolored   .50   .30

Interior Courts of
Algerian
Dwellings
A432

Designs: 5d, Palace of Hassan Pasha. 10d, Khedaouj El-Amia, Algiers. 20d, Palace of Light. 30d, Abdellatif Villa.

1996, Dec. 18 Litho.   Perf. 13½x14
1081 A432 5d multicolored   .40   .25
1082 A432 10d multicolored   .80   .45
1083 A432 20d multicolored   1.75 1.00
1084 A432 30d multicolored   2.50 1.40
    Nos. 1081-1084 (4)   5.45 3.10

Paintings
by Ismail
Samsom
(1934-88)
A433

20d, Woman with Pigeons. 30d, Interrogation.

1996, Dec. 25   Perf. 14
1085 A433 20d multicolored   1.25 1.00
1086 A433 30d multicolored   1.75 1.50

Victory Day,
35th Anniv.
A434

1997, Mar. 19   Perf. 14x13½
1087 A434 5d multicolored   .50   .25

Flowers — A435

Designs: 5d, Ficaria verna. 16d, Lonicera arborea. 23d, Papaver rhoeas.

1997, Apr. 23   Litho.   Perf. 13½x14
1088 A435 5d multicolored   .50   .30
1089 A435 16d multicolored   1.40   .90
1090 A435 23d multicolored   2.00 1.50
    Nos. 1088-1090 (3)   3.90 2.70

World Day to Stop Smoking — A436

1997, May 31   Litho.   Perf. 13½x14
1091 A436 5d multicolored   .65   .25

Legislative Elections — A437

1997, June 4
1092 A437 5d multicolored   .45   .25

Scorpions A438

Designs: 5d, Buthus occitanus tunetanus. 10d, Androctonus australis hector.

1997, June 18   Perf. 14x13½
1093 A438 5d multicolored   .55   .30
1094 A438 10d multicolored   .95   .60

Natl. Independence, 35th Anniv. — A439

Designs: 5d, Crowd celebrating, flags. 10d, Doves, broken chain, "35," flag.

1997, July 5   Litho.   Perf. 14x13½
1095 A439 5d multicolored   .50   .25
Souvenir Sheet
Perf. 14
1096 A439 10d multicolored   2.75 2.75
No. 1096 contains one 30x40mm stamp.

Wood Carvings — A440

Designs: 5d, Inscription, Nedroma Mosque. 23d, Door, Ketchaoua Mosque.

1997, Jan. 15   Litho.   Perf. 13½x14
1097 A440 5d multicolored   .50   .30
1098 A440 23d multicolored   1.75 1.10

Moufdi Zakaria (1908-77), poet. — A441

1997, Aug. 17   Litho.   Perf. 13½x14
1099 A441 5d multicolored   .50   .25

Textile Patterns A442

1997, Sept. 17   Litho.   Perf. 14
1100 A442 3d Dokkali   .40   .30
1101 A442 5d Tellis   .50   .30
1102 A442 10d Bou-Taleb   .90   .60
1103 A442 20d Ddil   1.75 1.25
     Nos. 1100-1103 (4)   3.55 2.45

Natl. Police Force, 25th Anniv. A443

1997, Oct. 6   Perf. 14x13½
1104 A443 5d multicolored   .60   .25

Express Mail Service A444

1997, Oct. 9
1105 A444 5d multicolored   .60   .25

Local Elections — A445

1997, Oct. 23   Perf. 13½x14
1106 A445 5d multicolored   .50   .25

Lighthouses A446

5d, Tenes. 10d, Cape Caxine, vert.

Perf. 14x13½, 13½x14
1997, Nov. 5   Litho.
1107 A446 5d multicolored   .65   .25
1108 A446 10d multicolored   1.50   .70

New Airpost Service, 1st Anniv. A447

1997, Nov. 17   Perf. 14x13½
1109 A447 5d multicolored   .60   .25

Shells A448

Designs: 5d, Chlamys varia. 10d, Bolinus brandaris. 20d, Hinia reticulata, vert.

Perf. 14x13½, 13½x14
1997, Dec. 17   Litho.
1110 A448 5d multicolored   .90   .25
1111 A448 10d multicolored   1.50   .60
1112 A448 20d multicolored   3.00 1.20
     Nos. 1110-1112 (3)   5.40 2.05

A449

1997, Dec. 25   Perf. 13½x14
1113 A449 5d multicolored   .60   .25
Election of the Natl. Council.

A450

Completion of Government Reforms: a, Natl. flag, people, book, ballot box. b, People, open book, torch. c, Ballot box. d, Flag, rising sun, flower. e, Ballots, building, flag.

1997, Dec. 30   Litho.   Perf. 13½x14
1114 A450 5d Strip of 5, #a.-e.   2.50 2.50

Bombing of Sakiet Sidi Youcef, 40th Anniv. A451

1998, Feb. 8   Litho.   Perf. 14x13½
1115 A451 5d multicolored   .70   .25

National Archives A452

1998, Feb. 16
1116 A452 5d multicolored   .50   .25

Intl. Women's Day A453

1998, Mar. 8   Litho.   Perf. 14x13½
1117 A453 5d multicolored   .50   .25

Expo '98, Lisbon A454

1998, Jan. 21   Litho.   Perf. 14x13½
1118 A454 5d shown   .50   .25
Size: 80x75mm
Imperf
1119 A454 24d Mosaic   3.25 3.25

1998 World Cup Soccer Championships, Paris — A455

1998, Apr. 15   Litho.   Perf. 13½x14
1120 A455 24d multi   2.40 1.25

Algiers Casbah A456

Designs: 5d, Aerial view, vert. 10d, Buildings, vert. 24d, Aerial view, diff.

1998, Apr. 22   Perf. 13½x14, 14x13½
1121 A456 5d multi   .40   .25
1122 A456 10d multi   .75   .60
1123 A456 24d multi   1.75 1.25
     Nos. 1121-1123 (3)   2.90 2.10

Zaatcha Resistance — A457

1998, May 20   Perf. 13¼x13
1124 A457 5d multi   .50   .25

Tourism A458

5d, Mountains, farm, desert, vert. 10d, Youths, modes of transportation. 24d, Taghit.

Perf. 13½x14, 14x13½
1998, June 4   Litho.
1125 A458 5d multi   .40   .25
1126 A458 10d multi   .80   .50
1127 A458 24d multi   1.75 1.25
     Nos. 1125-1127 (3)   2.95 2.00

Arab Post Day
A459

1998, Aug. 3 Litho. Perf. 14x13½
1128 A459 5d multi .75 .25

Interpol, 75th Anniv.
A460

1998, Sept. 7 Litho. Perf. 14x13½
1129 A460 5d multi .60 .25

Creation of Provisional Government, 40th Anniv. — A461

1998, Sept. 19 Perf. 13¼x13
1130 A461 5d multi .50 .25

Natl. Diplomacy Day
A462

1998, Oct. 8 Perf. 14
1131 A462 5d multi .50 .25

Algerian Olympic Committee, 35th Anniv.
A463

1998, Oct. 18 Perf. 14x13½
1132 A463 5d multi .60 .25

Birds
A464

Designs: 5d, Pandion haliaetus. 10d, Larus audouinii. 24d, Phalacrocorax aristotelis, vert. 30d, Phalacrocorax carbo, vert.

Perf. 14x13½, 13½x14
1998, Nov. 11
1133 A464 5d multi .70 .25
1134 A464 10d multi 1.40 .60
1135 A464 24d multi 2.75 1.25
1136 A464 30d multi 3.50 1.75
Nos. 1133-1136 (4) 8.35 3.85

See Nos. 1204-1207, 1325-1326.

Universal Declaration of Human Rights, 50th Anniv.
A465

1998, Dec. 10 Litho. Perf. 14x13½
1137 A465 5d Profiles, emblem .60 .25
1138 A465 24d shown 2.25 1.00

Spinning and Weaving Tools
A466

Designs: 5d, Comb, vert. 10d, Cards. 20d, Spindle, vert. 24d, Loom, vert.

1999, Jan. 20 Perf. 13½x14, 14x13½
1139 A466 5d multi .55 .25
1140 A466 10d multi 1.00 .50
1141 A466 20d multi 2.10 1.00
1142 A466 24d multi 2.50 1.25
Nos. 1139-1142 (4) 6.15 3.00

Natl. Chahid Day — A467

1999, Feb. 18 Perf. 13x13¼
1143 A467 5d multi .50 .25

Flowering Trees
A468

1999, Mar. 17 Perf. 14x13½, 13½x14
1144 A468 5d Pear .50 .25
1145 A468 10d Plum .90 .50
1146 A468 24d Orange, vert. 2.10 1.25
Nos. 1144-1146 (3) 3.50 2.00

Presidential Elections
A469

1999, Apr. 15 Perf. 13x13¼
1147 A469 5d multi .50 .25

Handicrafts
A470

Designs: 5d, Tlemcen mosaic, 14th cent., vert. 10d, Mosaic, Al Qal'a of Beni Hammad, 11th cent., vert. 20d, Cradle. 24d, Table.

1999, Apr. 18 Perf. 13¼x14, 14x13¼
1148 A470 5d multi .55 .25
1149 A470 10d multi .90 .60
1150 A470 20d multi 1.75 1.00
1151 A470 24d multi 2.10 1.25
Nos. 1148-1151 (4) 5.30 3.10

7th African Games, Johannesburg — A471

Stylized athletes and: 5d, Map of Africa, vert. 10d, South African flag.

1999, May 12 Perf. 13¼x14, 14x13¼
1152 A471 5d multi .45 .25
1153 A471 10d multi .80 .50

Rocks — A472

1999, June 6 Perf. 13¼x14
1154 A472 5d Gneiss .45 .25
1155 A472 20d Granite 1.60 1.00
1156 A472 24d Schist 2.00 1.25
Nos. 1154-1156 (3) 4.05 2.50

A473

1999, July 12 Perf. 13x13¼
1157 A473 5d multi .50 .25

Organization of African Unity, 35th summit.

A474

1999, July 12 Perf. 13¼x14
1158 A474 5d multi .50 .25

Organization of African Unity Convention on Refugees.

Police Day — A475

1999, July 22 Perf. 13x13¼
1159 A475 5d multicolored 1.00 .25

Intl. Year of Culture and Peace (in 2000)
A476

1999, Sept. 14 Litho. Perf. 14
1160 A476 5d multi .50 .25

Fish
A477

Designs: 5d, Dentex dentex. 10d, Mullus surmuletus. 20d, Dentex gibbosus. 24d, Diplodus sargus.

1999, Sept. 15 Perf. 14x13¼
1161 A477 5d multi .65 .25
1162 A477 10d multi 1.25 .50
1163 A477 20d multi 2.25 1.00
1164 A477 24d multi 3.25 1.25
Nos. 1161-1164 (4) 7.40 3.00

Civil Peace Referendum
A478

1999, Sept. 16 Perf. 13¼x14
1165 A478 5d multi .50 .25

UPU, 125th Anniv.
A479

1999, Oct. 9 Perf. 14x13¼
1166 A479 5d multi .55 .25

World Post Day
A480

1999, Oct. 9 Litho. Perf. 14x13½
1167 A480 5d multi .55 .25

Intl. Rural Women's Day
A481

1999, Oct. 14 Litho. Perf. 14x13¼
1168 A481 5d multi .55 .25

Designs: No. 1222, 5d, Jacks. No. 1223, 5d, Hopscotch. No. 1224, 5d, Top spinning. No. 1225, 5d, Marbles.

2001, June 2
1222-1225 A502 Set of 4 2.50 .90

Natl. Asthma Day — A503

2001, June 9
1226 A503 5d multi .50 .25

14th Mediterranean Games, Tunis, Tunisia — A504

Designs: No. 1227, 5d, Map, "50." No. 1228, 5d, Runners, emblem.

2001, July 25 Litho. Perf. 14
1227-1228 A504 Set of 2 1.00 .50

15th World Festival of Youth and Students — A505

2001, Aug. 8
1229 A505 5d multi .50 .25

Natl. Mujahedeen Day — A506

2001, Aug. 20 Perf. 13¼x14
1230 A506 5d multi .50 .25

Intl. Teachers' Day — A507

2001, Oct. 6 Litho. Perf. 13¼x14
1231 A507 5d multi .50 .25

Year of Dialogue Among Civilizations A508

2001, Oct. 9
1232 A508 5d multi .75 .30

Natl. Emigration Day — A509

2001, Oct. 17 Perf. 14x13¼
1233 A509 5d multi .50 .25

19th Cent. Revolt Leaders — A510

Designs: No. 1234, 5d, Sheik El-Mokrani, 1871-73. No. 1235, 5d, Sheik Bouamama, 1881-1908.

2001, Nov. 1 Perf. 13¼x14
1234-1235 A510 Set of 2 1.10 .50

Jewelry From Aurès Region — A511

Designs: No. 1236, 5d, Fibula. No. 1237, 5d, Earring. 24d, Pendant.

2002, Jan. 23
1236-1238 A511 Set of 3 3.00 3.00

2002 World Cup Soccer Championships, Japan and Korea — A512

Designs: 5d, Goalie, ball, net, pagoda. 24d, Oriental man, ball, vert.

2002, Feb. 27 Perf. 14x13¼, 13¼x14
1239-1240 A512 Set of 2 2.75 2.00

Ceasefire With French Forces, 40th Anniv. — A513

2002, Mar. 19 Perf. 13x13½
1241 A513 5d multi .70 .40

Villages A514

Designs: No. 1242, 5d, Sidi-Ouali. No. 1243, 5d, Casbah of Ighzar.

2002, Apr. 17 Litho. Perf. 14x13¼
1242-1243 A514 Set of 2 1.00 .80

World Basketball Championships, Indianapolis A515

2002, May 15 Perf. 13¼x14
1244 A515 5d multi .75 .45

Children's Day — A516

Children's art: No. 1245, 5d, Shown. No. 1246, 5d, Two girls, one waving.

2002, June 1 Perf. 14x13¼
1245-1246 A516 Set of 2 1.00 .80

Mohamed Temmam (1915-88), Artist — A517

Designs: No. 1247, 10d, Self-portrait. No. 1248, 10d, Tailor.

2002, June 8 Perf. 13x13¼
1247-1248 A517 Set of 2 2.00 1.50

Independence, 40th Anniv. — A518

Designs: 5d, Emblem. 24d, People with flag.

2002, July 5 Litho. Perf. 14
1249-1250 A518 Set of 2 2.50 2.00

Rocks and Minerals A519

Designs: No. 1251, 5d, Conglomerate rock. No. 1252, 5d, Galena. No. 1253, 5d, Calcite, vert. No. 1254, 5d, Feldspar, vert.

2002, July 24
1251-1254 A519 Set of 4 2.00 2.00

Lighthouses A520

Designs: 5d, Cherchell. 10d, Cap de Fer. 24d, Ile de Rachgoun.

2002, Sept. 11
1255-1257 A520 Set of 3 3.25 3.25

Reorganization of Postal Service — A521

2002, Oct. 9
1258 A521 5d multi .50 .50

Pottery — A522

Designs: No. 1259, 5d, Oil lamp. No. 1260, 5d, Jar with handles, Iraten. No. 1261, 5d, Jar, Miliana. No. 1262, 5d, Cooking pot and couscousier, Lakhdaria.

2002, Oct. 23
1259-1262 A522 Set of 4 2.00 2.00

Intl. Day for Tolerance A523

2002, Nov. 16 Litho. Perf. 14
1263 A523 24d multi 2.00 2.00

Shells A524

Designs: No. 1264, 5d, Acanthocardia aculeata. No. 1265, 5d, Venus verrucosa. No. 1266, 5d, Epitonium commune. No. 1267, 5d, Xenophora crispa.

2002, Dec. 4 Litho. Perf. 14
1264-1267 A524 Set of 4 2.50 2.50

Medicinal Plants — A525

Designs: 5d, Eucalyptus globulus. 10d, Malva sylvestris. 24d, Laurus nobilis.

2002, Dec. 21
1268-1270 A525 Set of 3 3.25 3.25

Algeria — France Year A526

Designs: 5d, Eiffel Tower, Paris and Martyr's Monument, Algiers, vert. 24d, Flags of Algeria and France.

2003, Feb. 19
1271-1272 A526 Set of 2 2.50 2.50

10th Arab Games A527

2003, Feb. 26
1273 A527 5d multi .40 .40

Intl. Year of Water A528

Designs: 5d, El Maadjen, Relizane. 10d, Well, M'zab Valley. 24d, Kesria, Timimoun.

2003, Mar. 22 Litho. Perf. 14
1274-1276 A528 Set of 3 3.50 3.50

Vandal Tablets A529

Designs: 10d, Slave sale document, 494. 24d, Tablet for calculations, 493, vert.

Perf. 13x13¼, 13¼x13
2003, Apr. 23 Litho.
1277-1278 A529 Set of 2 3.00 3.00
Portions of the designs were applied by a thermographic process producing a shiny, raised effect.

Natl. Students Day — A530

2003, May 19 Litho. Perf. 14
1279 A530 5d multi .40 .40

Snails — A531

Designs: 5d, Rumina decollata. 24d, Heix aspersa.

2003, May 21 Litho. Perf. 14
1280-1281 A531 Set of 2 2.50 2.50

African Union, 1st Anniv. — A532

2003, July 9 Perf. 13¼x14
1282 A532 5d multi .50 .50

Seaweeds — A533

Designs: 5d, Ulva lactuca. 24d, Gymnogongrus crenulatus.

2003, July 30 Litho. Perf. 14
1283-1284 A533 Set of 2 2.50 2.50

Roman Mosaics — A534

Designs: 5d, Farm Work. 10d, Ulysses and the Sirens. 24d, Hunting Scene.

2003, Sept. 17 Perf. 13½x14
1285-1287 A534 Set of 3 3.00 3.00

Algerian Olympic Committee, 40th Anniv. A535

2003, Oct. 18 Litho. Perf. 14x13½
1288 A535 5d multi .50 .50

World Diabetes Prevention Day — A536

2003, Nov. 14 Perf. 13½x14
1289 A536 5d multi .50 .50

Architectural Decorations A537

Designs: 5d, Door, Hassan Pacha Palace, Algiers. 10d, Window, Hassan Pacha Palace. 24d, Ceiling, Djamaa Edjedid, Algiers.

2003, Dec. 17 Litho. Perf. 13x13¼
1290-1292 A537 Set of 3 3.00 3.00

Algeria — People's Republic of China Diplomatic Relations, 45th Anniv. A538

2003, Dec. 22 Perf. 12
1293 A538 5d multi .50 .50

2004 Summer Olympics, Athens — A539

Olympic rings, Parthenon and: 5d, Hurdler. 10d, Torch bearer.

2004, Feb. 29 Perf. 13¼x14
1294-1295 A539 Set of 2 1.25 1.25

Intl. Women's Day — A540

2004, Mar. 8
1296 A540 5d multi .50 .50

Arbor Day A541

Trees: 5d, Olive. 10d, Date palm, vert.

Perf. 14x13¼, 13¼x14
2004, Mar. 21 Litho.
1297-1298 A541 Set of 2 1.25 1.25

Numidian Kings — A542

Designs: No. 1299, 5d, Massinissa (r. 203 BC-148 BC). No. 1300, 5d, Micipsa (r. 148 BC-118 BC). No. 1301, 5d, Jugurtha (r. 118 BC-105 BC). No. 1302, 5d, Juba I (r. 63 BC-50 to 46 BC). No. 1303, 5d, Juba II (r. 29 BC- 25 BC).

2004, Mar. 31 Litho. Perf. 13¼x14
1299-1303 A542 Set of 5 2.25 2.25

2004 Presidential Elections — A543

Litho. & Embossed
2004, Apr. 8 Perf. 13¼x13
1304 A543 24d multi 2.25 2.25

FIFA (Fédération Internationale de Football Association), Cent. — A544

"100" and: 5d, Goalie. 24d, Soccer balls, world map.

Perf. 14, 14x13¼ (24d)
2004, May 21 Litho.
1305-1306 A544 Set of 2 2.50 2.50

Dromedary A545

2004, June 9 Litho. Perf. 14x13¼
1307 A545 24d multi 2.25 2.25

Blood Donation Day — A546

2004, June 14 Perf. 14
1308 A546 5d multi .50 .50

Professional Training — A547

2004, June 23
1309 A547 5d multi .50 .50

Intl. Chess Federation (FIDE), 80th Anniv. — A548

2004, July 21   Litho.   Perf. 14
1310 A548 5d multi   1.20   .50

CNEP Bank, 40th Anniv. A549

Bank emblems and: 5d, Bank notes. 24d, Algiers.

2004, Aug. 10   Litho.   Perf. 14
1311-1312 A549 Set of 2   2.50   2.50

Roses — A550

2004, Oct. 20   Litho.   Perf. 14
Color of Rose
1313 A550 15d yellow   1.00   1.00
1314 A550 20d yellow, diff.   2.00   2.00
1315 A550 30d red   3.00   3.00
1316 A550 50d pink   4.00   4.00
     Nos. 1313-1316 (4)   10.00   10.00

Sixth Pan-African Conference of Red Cross and Red Crescent, Algiers — A551

2004, Sept. 8   Litho.   Perf. 14
1317 A551 24d multi   2.25   2.25

Sahara Desert Landmarks A552

Designs: 5d, In Téhaq. 24d, Ekanassay, vert.

Perf. 14, 14¼x14 (24d)
2004, Sept. 15
1318-1319 A552 Set of 2   2.50   2.50

Revolutionary Committee of Unity and Action, 50th Anniv. — A553

2004, Nov. 1   Litho.   Perf. 13¼x13
1320 A553 15d multi   1.75   1.75

Souvenir Sheet

Start of Algerian Revolution, 50th Anniv. — A554

2004, Nov. 1   Litho.   Perf. 13½x13
1321 A554 30d multi   2.50   2.50

Launch of ALSAT 1 Satellite, 2nd Anniv. A555

2004, Nov. 28   Litho.   Perf. 14x13½
1322 A555 30d multi   2.50   2.50

Environmental Protection — A556

2004, Dec. 22
1323 A556 15d multi   1.25   1.25

Rabah Bitat (1925-2000), Politician — A557

2004, Dec. 29   Litho.   Perf. 14x13½
1324 A557 15d multi   1.25   1.25

Bird Type of 1998
Designs: 10d, Columba palumbus. 15d, Columba livia.

2005, Jan. 26   Litho.   Perf. 14x13½
1325-1326 A464 Set of 2   2.25   2.25

Flowers — A559

Designs: 15d, Echium australis. 30d, Borago officinalis.

2005, Feb. 23   Litho.   Perf. 13½x14
1327-1328 A559 Set of 2   3.50   3.50

Day of the Handicapped — A560

2005, Mar. 14   Perf. 14x13½
1329 A560 15d multi   1.10   1.10

Arab League Emblem and Algerian Flag A561

Inscription commemorating: 15d, 17th Arab Summit, Algiers. 30d, Arab League, 60th anniv., vert.

2005, Mar. 22   Perf. 14x13½, 13½x14
1330-1331 A561 Set of 2   3.50   3.50

National Reconciliation — A562

2005, Apr. 8   Perf. 14x13½
1332 A562 15d multi   1.25   1.25

Madrases A563

Madras in: 10d, Algiers. 15d, Constantine. 30d, Tlemcen.

2005, Apr. 16
1333-1335 A563 Set of 3   4.50   4.50
     Science Day.

Intl. Day of Intellectual Property A564

2005, Apr. 26
1336 A564 15d multi   1.25   1.25

Intl. Day of Work Safety and Health — A565

2005, Apr. 28   Perf. 13½x14
1337 A565 15d multi   1.25   1.25

Massacres of May 8, 1945, 60th Anniv. A566

2005, May 8   Litho.   Perf. 14x13¼
1338 A566 15d multi   1.25   1.25

15th Mediterranean Games, Almeria, Spain — A567

Games emblem and: 15d, Medal, stylized athletes. 30d, Mediterranean Sea and "2005," horiz.

2005, May 28   Perf. 13¼x14, 14x13¼
1339-1340 A567 Set of 2   3.50   3.50

Poets — A568

Designs: 10d, Lakhdar Ben Khlouf. 15d, Mohamed Ben M'sayeb. 20d, Si Mohand-Ou-M'hand. 30d, Aissa El-Djermouni.

2005, June 8   Litho.   Perf. 13x13½
1341-1344 A568 Set of 4   6.50   6.50

World Day Against Drug Abuse A569

2005, June 26   Perf. 14x13½
1345 A569 15d multi   1.50   1.50

General Algerian Muslim Student's Union, 50th Anniv. — A570

2005, July 9   Litho.   Perf. 13½x14
1346 A570 15d multi   1.25   1.25

Leopards A571

Leopard: 15d, Sitting. 30d, Standing.

2005, July 21   Perf. 14x13½
1347-1348 A571 Set of 2   3.50   3.50

World Summit on the Information Society, Tunis — A572

2005, July 27 **Perf. 13½x14**
1349 A572 15d multi 1.75 1.75

Moudjahid Day — A573

2005, Aug. 20
1350 A573 15d multi 1.25 1.25

Uprising at Constantine and Philippeville, 50th anniv.

Intl. Year of Sports and Physical Education A574

2005, Sept. 7 **Litho.** **Perf. 13¼x14**
1351 A574 30d multi 2.40 2.40

Forts A575

Designs: 10d, Lighthouse Fort, Algiers. 15d, Cap Matifou Fort, Algiers. 30d, Santa Cruz Fort, Oran.

2005, Sept. 15 **Perf. 14x13¼**
1352-1354 A575 Set of 3 4.50 4.50

September 29, 2005 Referendum — A576

2005 **Litho.** **Perf. 14x13½**
1355 A576 15d multi 1.15 1.15

Acquisition of Control of Broadcasting, 43rd Anniv. — A577

2005, Oct. 28
1356 A577 30d multi 2.25 2.25

Personal Effects of Emir Abdelkader (1808-83) A578

Designs: 15d, Saddle. 30d, Boots. 40d, Vest, vert. 50d, Signet, vert.

2005, Nov. 1 **Perf. 14x13½, 13½x14**
1357-1360 A578 Set of 4 10.50 10.50

Miguel de Cervantes (1547-1616), Writer — A579

2005, Nov. 16 **Litho.** **Perf. 13½x14**
1361 A579 30d multi 2.25 2.25

Public Destruction of Mines — A580

2005, Nov. **Litho.** **Perf. 13½x14**
1362 A580 30d multi 2.25 2.25

World AIDS Day — A581

2005, Dec. 1 **Litho.** **Perf. 13½x14**
1363 A581 30d multi 2.50 2.50

Numidian Kings — A582

Designs: 15d, Ptolemy of Mauretania, ruler from 23-40 A.D. 30d, Syphax, ruler from 220-203 B.C.

2005, Dec. 14 **Litho.** **Perf. 13¼x14**
1364-1365 A582 Set of 2 3.25 3.25

Birds — A584

Designs: 10d, Ciconia ciconia. 15d, Ciconia nigra. 20d, Platalea leucorodia. 30d, Grus grus.

2006, Jan. 25 **Perf. 13x13½**
1367-1370 A584 Set of 4 5.50 5.50

2006 Winter Olympics, Turin A585

2006, Feb. 1 **Perf. 14x13¼**
1371 A585 15d multi 1.10 1.10

General Union of Algerian Workers, 50th Anniv. — A586

2006, Feb. 24 **Perf. 13¼x14**
1372 A586 15d multi 1.10 1.10

2006 World Cup Soccer Championships, Germany A587

2006, Mar. 22
1373 A587 30d multi 2.25 2.25

Opening of New Algiers Airport A588

2006, Apr. 8 **Perf. 14x13¼**
1374 A588 30d multi 2.25 2.25

Student's Day, 50th Anniv. — A589

2006, May 19 **Perf. 13x13½**
1375 A589 20d multi 1.40 1.40

World Environment Day — A590

2006, June 5 **Perf. 14**
1376 A590 30d multi 2.25 2.25

Soummam Congress, 50th Anniv. — A591

2006, Aug. 20 **Perf. 13x13½**
1377 A591 20d multi 1.50 1.50

16th Arab Scholars' Games — A592

2006, Sept. 2 **Perf. 13¼x14**
1378 A592 30d multi 2.25 2.25

Intl. Year of Deserts and Desertifcation — A593

Designs: No. 1379, 15d, Oasis. No. 1380, 15d, Oasis, sand dunes and water.

2006, Sept. 20 **Litho.** **Perf. 14**
1379-1380 A593 Set of 2 2.25 2.25

World Teachers Day A594

2006, Oct. 5
1381 A594 20d multi 1.40 1.40

Arbor Day — A595

Trees: 20d, Atlas pistachio. 30d, Pomagranate.

2006, Oct. 25
1382-1383 A595 Set of 2 3.75 3.75

Sino-African Cooperation Summit, Beijing — A596

2006, Nov. 4   *Perf. 12*
1384 A596 30d multi   2.25 2.25

19th Century Powder Flasks — A597

Background color: 15d, Pink. 20d, Pale green.

2006, Nov. 22 Litho.   *Perf. 13½x14*
1385-1386 A597 Set of 2   3.00 3.00

Transitory Arab Parliament, 1st Anniv. — A598

2006, Dec. 17   *Perf. 13½x13*
1387 A598 15d multi   1.10 1.10

El Moudjahid Newspaper, 50th Anniv. — A599

2006, Dec. 18   *Perf. 14*
1388 A599 30d multi   2.25 2.25

Desalinization of Sea Water — A600

2006, Dec. 20
1389 A600 20d multi   1.50 1.50

A601

Algiers, 2007 Arab Cultural Capital — A602

2007, Jan. 12 Litho.   *Perf. 13½x13*
1390 A601 15d multi   1.25 1.25
1391 A602 30d multi   2.25 2.25

Lighthouses — A603

Lighthouse at: 15d, Ilot d'Arzew. 20d, Cap Sigli. 38d, Ras-afia.

2007, Feb. 14 Litho.   *Perf. 14*
1392-1394 A603 Set of 3   5.25 5.25

Employment of Women — A604

2007, Mar. 8 Litho.   *Perf. 14*
1395 A604 15d multi   1.25 1.25

Sheikh Mohamed Ameziane Belhaddad (1790-1873), Leader of 1871 Rebellion A605

2007, Apr. 8   *Perf. 13x13¼*
1396 A605 15d multi   1.25 1.25

Ksars A606

Village scenes: No. 1397, 15d, Kenadsa. No. 1398, 15d, Temacine, vert.

2007, Apr. 21   *Perf. 13¼x13, 13x13¼*
1397-1398 A606 Set of 2   2.25 2.25

2nd Afro-Asiatic Games, Algiers A607

2007, May 18 Litho.   *Perf. 14*
1399 A607 15d multi   1.10 1.10

9th All-African Games, Algiers — A608

2007, May 18
1400 A608 15d multi   1.10 1.10

Gardens — A609

Designs: 15d, Landon Gardens, Biskra. 20d, Ibn Badis Gardens, Oran. 38d, Essai du Hamma Gardens, Algiers.

2007, June 5   *Perf. 13½x13*
1401-1403 A609 Set of 3   5.50 5.50

National Gendarmerie, 45th Anniv. — A610

Designs: 15d, Gendarmerie emblem. 38d, Gendarmerie emblem, gendarme and automobile.

2007, June 25 Litho.   *Perf. 14*
1404-1405 A610 Set of 2   4.00 4.00

Independence, 45th Anniv. — A611

Designs: 15d, People, flags and dove. 20d, Anniversary emblem, vert.

2007, July 5   *Perf. 13¼x13*
1406 A611 15d multi   1.25 1.25
          Imperf
       Size: 60x77mm
1407 A611 20d multi   3.00 3.00

Ceramics A612

Designs: No. 1408, 15d, Jar with handles. No. 1409, 15d, Glazed jar without handles. 20d, Censer. 38d, Lamp, horiz.

2007, Aug. 5 Litho.   *Perf. 14*
1408-1411 A612 Set of 4   6.00 6.00

Endangered Animals — A613

Designs: 15d, Striped hyena. 38d, White-tailed fox.

2007, Sept. 12   *Perf. 13¼x13*
1412-1413 A613 Set of 2   3.25 3.25

Theaters A614

Theater in: No. 1414, 15d, Setif. No. 1415, 15d, Oran. 20d, Annaba, horiz. 38d, Algiers.

    Perf. 13x13¼, 13¼x13
2007, Oct. 24   **Litho.**
1414-1417 A614 Set of 4   5.75 5.75

Encyclopedia of Algerian Postage Stamps A615

2007, Nov. 1   *Perf. 13x13¼*
1418 A615 15d multi   1.40 1.40

Bey Ahmed of Constantine (1784-1850), Leader of 1836-48 Resistance Against French A616

2007, Nov. 7
1419 A616 15d multi   1.25 1.25

National Artisan's Day — A617

2007, Nov. 9   *Perf. 13¼x14*
1420 A617 15d multi   1.40 1.40

Tilapia
A618

2007, Dec. 12   **Litho.**   **Perf. 14**
1421   A618   15d multi   1.50   1.50

Miniature Sheet

Emir Abdelkader (1808-83) — A619

No. 1422: a, Abdelkader seated. b, Abdelkader standing. c, Abdelkader, diff.

2007, Dec. 15
1422   A619   Sheet of 3   5.00   5.00
a.-b.   15d Either single   1.10   1.10
c.   38d multi   2.75   2.75

Fifth
General
Census
A620

2008, Jan. 16   **Perf. 14x13¼**
1423   A620   15d multi   1.25   1.25

French Air
Raid on Sakiet
Sidi Youssef,
Tunisia, 50th
Anniv. — A621

2008, Feb. 8   **Litho.**   **Perf. 13x13¼**
1424   A621   15d multi   1.25   1.25

Miniature Sheet

Fountains — A621a

2008, Feb. 23   **Perf. 14**
1425   A621a   Sheet of 4   5.50   5.50
a.   10d Ain de la Grande Rue   .65   .65
b.   15d Ain Bir Djebbah   1.00   1.00
c.   20d Ain Sidi Abdellah   1.35   1.35
d.   38d Ain Bir Chebana   2.60   2.60

Miniature Sheet

Water and Sustainable
Development — A622

No. 1428: a, Issakarssen Wetlands. b, Reghaia Wetlands. c, Guerbes Wetlands. d, Emblem of Expo Zaragoza 2008.

2008, Mar. 22   **Litho.**   **Perf. 14**
1428   A622   Sheet of 4, #a-d   5.50   5.50
a.   10d multi   .65   .65
b.   15d multi   1.00   1.00
c.   20d multi   1.35   1.35
d.   38d multi   2.60   2.60

Souvenir Sheet

National Liberation Front Soccer Team,
50th Anniv. — A623

2008, Apr. 12   **Litho.**   **Perf.**
1429   A623   38d multi   2.75   2.75
No. 1429 contains one 36mm diameter stamp.

Writers
A624

No. 1430: a, Redha Houhou (1911-56). b, Abdelhamid Benhadouga (1925-96). c, Malek Bennabi (1905-73). d, Kateb Yacine (1929-89).

2008, Apr. 16   **Litho.**   **Perf. 14x13½**
1430   Horiz. strip of 4   4.25   4.25
a.-d.   A624 15d Any single   1.00   1.00

Children and New
Technologies
A625

2008, June 1   **Perf. 13½x14**
1431   A625   15d multi   1.05   1.05

Souvenir Sheet

Baya Mahieddine (1931-98),
Artist — A626

No. 1432: a, 15d, Mahieddine. b, 38d, Painting by Mahieddine.

2008, June 8   **Perf. 14**
1432   A626   Sheet of 2, #a-b   4.00   4.00

Kassamen,
Algerian
National
Anthem, by
Moufdi Zakaria
A627

2008, July 3   **Perf. 13x13¼**
1433   A627   15d multi   1.05   1.05

Railway
Stations
A628

Station in: 10d, Algiers. 15d, Constantine. 20d, Oran. 38d, Skikda.

2008, July 9   **Perf. 14x13½**
1434-1437   A628   Set of 4   5.00   5.00

Ferhat Abbas
(1899-1985),
President of
First Algerian
Temporary
Government
A629

2008, Sept. 19   **Perf. 13x13¼**
1438   A629   15d multi   1.10   1.10

2008
Summer
Olympics,
Beijing
A630

Designs: No. 1439, 15d, Fencing. No. 1440, 15d, Wrestling.

2008, July 23   **Litho.**   **Perf. 14x13½**
1439-1440   A630   Set of 2   2.10   2.10

National
Popular
Army
A631

2008, Nov. 1
1441   A631   15d multi   1.05   1.05

12th Session of
Government
Postage Stamp
Printers
Assoc.,
Algiers — A632

2008, Nov. 5   **Perf. 13x13¼**
1442   A632   15d multi   1.05   1.05

Miniature Sheet

Bridges in Constantine — A633

No. 1443: a, 10d, Sidi M'Cid Bridge. b, 15d, Sidi Rached Bridge. c, 20d, El Kantara Bridge. d, 38d, La Medersa Bridge.

2008, Nov. 26   **Perf. 14**
1443   A633   Sheet of 4, #a-d   5.00   5.00

Universal
Declaration
of Human
Rights,
60th Anniv.
A634

2008, Dec. 10   **Perf. 14x13½**
1444   A634   15d multi   1.05   1.05

Cities
A635

Designs: 10d, Tebessa. 15d, Saida. 20d, Miliana. 38d, Biskra.

2008, Dec. 18   **Perf. 13¼x13**
1445-1448   A635   Set of 4   5.00   5.00

Diplomatic
Relations
Between
Algeria and
People's
Republic of
China, 50th
Anniv.
A636

2008, Dec. 20   **Perf. 12**
1449   A636   15d multi   1.10   1.10

Louis Braille (1809-52), Educator of the Blind — A637

2009, Jan. 4   *Perf. 13½x14*
1450 A637 15d multi   1.10 1.10

Mausoleums A638

Mausoleum of: 15d, Sidi Abderrahmane, Algiers. 20d, Sidi Ibrahim El Atteuf, Ghardaia, horiz.

2009, Feb. 25   *Perf. 13½x14, 14x13½*
1451-1452 A638 Set of 2   2.25 2.25

Natl. Day of the Handicapped A639

Designs: 15d, Silhouettes of man with raised arm and man in wheelchair. 20d, Athlete in wheelchair, hand prints.

2009, Mar. 14   *Perf. 13½x14*
1453-1454 A639 Set of 2   2.25 2.25

Protection of Polar Regions and Glaciers — A640

2009, Mar. 28   **Litho.**
1455 A640 38d multi   2.75 2.75

Presidential Elections A641

2009, Apr. 9   *Perf. 13x13¼*
1456 A641 15d multi   1.00 1.00

Items in National Museum A642

Designs: 15d, Wooden sandals. 20d, Fragment of silver brooch. 30d, Vest.

2009, Apr. 18   *Perf. 14x13½*
1457-1459 A642 Set of 3   4.50 4.50

University of Algiers, Cent. A643

2009, May 11
1460 A643 15d multi   1.00 1.00

Jewelry of Southern Algeria — A644

Designs: 1d, Silver fibulas. 5d, Amulet necklace. 9d, Pectoral jewelry and chain. 10d, Circular fibula.

2009, May 13   *Perf. 13¾*
1461-1464 A644 Set of 4   1.75 1.75

Protection of Children From Cyberspace Dangers — A645

2009, May 17   *Perf. 14x13½*
1465 A645 15d multi   1.10 1.10

16th Mediterranean Games, Pescara, Italy — A646

Designs: 15d, Sailboarding. 20d, Equestrian, horiz.

Perf. 13½x14, 14x13½
2009, June 3   **Litho.**
1466-1467 A646 Set of 2   2.40 2.40

Roman Era Archaeological Sites — A647

Designs: 15d, Madaure archaeological site. 20d, Khemissa archaeological site. 30d, Old Theater, Guelma.

2009, June 14   *Perf. 13½x14*
1468-1470 A647 Set of 3   4.25 4.25

Second Panafrican Cultural Festival of Algiers — A648

Designs: 15d, Shown. 20d, Map of Africa, antelope, geometric designs.

2009, July 4   *Perf. 13¼x13*
1471-1472 A648 Set of 2   2.25 2.25

"The Child of Today, the Man of Tomorrow" A649

"I Love My Country" — A650

2009, June 26   *Perf. 13½x14*
1473 A649 15d multi   1.00 1.00
1474 A650 20d multi   1.25 1.25

Algerian Electricity and Gas Company, 40th Anniv. — A651

2009, July 28
1475 A651 15d multi   1.00 1.00

Traffic Safety — A652

2009, Aug. 6
1476 A652 15d multi   1.00 1.00

Fishing Ports — A653

Designs: 15d, Bouharoun. 20d, Béni Saf. 30d, Stora.

2009, Sept. 2   **Litho.**   *Perf. 13½x13*
1477-1479 A653 Set of 3   4.25 4.25

Protection of the Aged — A654

2009, Oct. 10   *Perf. 13½x14*
1480 A654 15d multi   1.00 1.00

National Armed Forces — A655

2009, Nov. 1   **Litho.**   *Perf. 13x13¼*
1481 A655 15d multi   1.00 1.00

Olive Oil Production — A656

Designs: 15d, Picking olives. 20d, Pressing olives, vert.

Perf. 13¼x13, 13x13¼
2009, Nov. 25
1482-1483 A656 Set of 2   2.40 2.40

Folktales A657

No. 1484: a, Loundja, la Fille de l'Ogre. b, Badra. c, La Fée Colombe. d, La Rose Rouge.

2009, Dec. 7   **Litho.**   *Perf. 13x13¼*
1484   Block or strip of 4   4.25 4.25
a.-d.   A657 15d Any single   .95 .95

Birds of Prey A658

Designs: 15d, Aquila chrysaetos. 20d, Falco biarmicus, vert. 30d, Falco peregrinus, vert.

2010, Jan. 27   *Perf. 13¼x13, 13x13¼*
1485-1487 A658 Set of 3   4.50 4.50

Victims of French Nuclear Testing in
Algeria — A659

2010, Feb. 10   *Perf. 13¼x13*
1488 A659 15d multi   1.60 1.60

Forts
A660

Designs: 15d, Fort de l'Empereur, Bordj
Moulay Hassan, Algiers. 20d, Gouraya Fort,
Béjaia.

2010, Feb. 15
1489-1490 A660   Set of 2   2.50 2.50

Expo 2010, Shanghai — A661

Designs: 15d, Stylized people, flowers,
buildings. 38d, Algeria Pavilion.

2010, Mar. 24   **Litho.**   *Perf. 13¼x13*
1491-1492 A661   Set of 2   3.75 3.75

16th Intl.
Conference on
Liquified Gas,
Oran — A662

Conference emblem, world map and: 15d,
Gas plant. 20d, Port, horiz.

2010, Apr. 18   *Perf. 13x13½, 13½x13*
1493-1494 A662   Set of 2   2.50 2.50

May 8, 1945
Massacres, 65th
Anniv. — A663

2010, May 8   *Perf. 13¼*
1495 A663 15d multi   1.00 1.00

2010 World Cup Soccer
Championships, South Africa — A664

Designs: No. 1496, 15d, World Cup trophy,
flags of participating countries. No. 1497, 15d,
Player, crowd holding Algerian flags.
No. 1498: a, Fox playing soccer. b, Player,
soccer ball.

2010, May 8   *Perf. 13x13¼*
1496-1497 A664   Set of 2   2.00 2.00
Souvenir Sheet
Imperf
1498 A664 15d Sheet of 2, #a-b   2.00 2.00

Ahellil of Gourara UNESCO World
Intangible Cultural Heritage — A665

2010, June 2   *Perf. 13¼x13*
1499 A665 15d multi   1.15 1.15

Martyr's
Sanctuary,
Algiers — A666

2010, June 20
1500 A666 (15d) multi   1.10 1.10

African Year of
Peace and
Security
A667

2010, July 19   *Perf. 13x13¼*
1501 A667 15d multi   1.10 1.10

Caves
A668

Designs: No. 1502, 15d, Béni Add Cave,
Ain Fezza. No. 1503, 15d, Ziama Cave,
Mansouriah.

2010, July 25   *Perf. 13¼x13*
1502-1503 A668   Set of 2   2.10 2.10

Organization of the Petroleum
Exporting Countries, 50th
Anniv. — A669

Designs: 15d, Emblem. 38d, Emblem, world
map, oil tanker.

2010, Sept. 14   **Litho.**   *Perf. 13¼x13*
1504-1505 A669   Set of 2   3.75 3.75

Mosques
A670

Designs: 15d, El Hanafi Mosque, Blida. 20d,
Sidi Ali Dib Mosque, Skikda. 30d, Grand
Mosque, Nedroma.

2010, Sept. 15   *Perf. 13x13¼*
1506-1508 A670   Set of 3   4.50 4.50

Dates
A671

Date varieties: No. 1509, 15d, Degla Beida.
No. 1510, 15d, Akerbuch. No. 1511, 15d,
Ghars, vert. No. 1512, 15d, Deglet Nour, vert.

2010, Oct. 6   *Perf. 13¼x13, 13x13¼*
1509-1512 A671   Set of 4   4.50 4.50

Handcrafted
Items — A672

Designs: 15d, Candlestick holder. 20d, Qua-
noun (musical instrument). 30d, Leather-cov-
ered chest with handles, horiz.

Perf. 13¼x14, 14x13¼
2010, Nov. 30   **Litho.**
1513-1515 A672   Set of 3   4.50 4.50

Trees
A673

Designs: 15d, Cork oak. 20d, Carob tree.
30d, Soapberry tree. 38d, Argan tree.

2011, Jan. 29   *Perf. 13¼x13*
1516-1519 A673   Set of 4   6.25 6.25

Tlemcen, 2011
Capital of
Islamic Culture
A674

Designs: 15d, Minaret of Mansoura. 20d,
Door knocker, Side Boumedienne Mosque.

2011, Feb. 15   **Litho.**   *Perf. 13x13¼*
1520-1521 A674   Set of 2   2.10 2.10

Snakes
A675

Designs: No. 1522, 15d, Couleuvre a
diademe (diadem snake). No. 1523, 15d,
Vipere a cornes (Saharan horned viper).

2011, Mar. 13
1522-1523 A675   Set of 2   2.00 2.00

First Economic
Census — A676

2011, Apr. 12   *Perf. 13½x14*
1524 A676 15d multi   .90 .90

18th Cent. Tableware From
Algiers — A677

Designs: 15d, Couscous dish. 30d, Butter
dish.

2011, Apr. 19   *Perf. 13¼x13*
1525-1526 A677   Set of 2   2.75 2.75

Telecenters — A678

2011, May 17   *Perf. 14x13½*
1527 A678 15d multi   1.10 1.10

Campaign Against Human Immunodeficiency Virus — A679

2011, June 30   *Perf. 13½x14*
1528 A679 15d multi   1.10 1.10

Benyoucef Benkhedda (1920-2003), Politician A680

2011, Sept. 19   *Perf. 13x13¼*
1529 A680 15d multi   .90 .90

A681

Comic Strips — A682

2011, Sept. 25   *Perf. 13¼x14*
1530 A681 15d multi   .90 .90
1531 A682 15d multi   .90 .90

World Post Day A683

Main post office in: No. 1532, 15d, Constantine. No. 1533, 15d, Oran.

2011, Oct. 9   *Perf. 14x13¼*
1532-1533 A683 Set of 2   1.90 1.90

Paris Massacre of Algerian Protestors, 50th Anniv. — A684

2011, Oct. 17   *Perf. 13x13¼*
1534 A684 15d multi   .90 .90

Algerian Press Service, 50th Anniv. A685

2011, Oct. 25   *Perf. 14x13¼*
1535 A685 15d multi   .90 .90

Army Museum — A686

2011, Nov. 1   *Perf. 13¼x13*
1536 A686 15d multi   .90 .90

Souvenir Sheet

Algiers Metro — A687

No. 1537: a, Train at station, people on platform. b, Train in tunnel.

2011, Nov. 14   *Perf. 14*
1537 A687 15d Sheet of 2, #a-b   2.00 2.00

Sheep — A688

Sheep breeds: No. 1538, 15d, Ouled Djallal. No. 1539, 15d, El Hamra.

2011, Nov. 16   *Perf. 13¼x13*
1538-1539 A688 Set of 2   2.00 2.00

Ornamental Plants — A689

Designs: 15d, Bougainvillea. 20d, Glycine (wisteria). 30d, Mimosa, horiz. 38d, Galant de nuit (night-blooming cestrum), horiz.

2011, Dec. 26   *Perf. 13x13¼, 13¼x13*
1540-1543 A689 Set of 4   6.25 6.25

Ceasefire Between Algeria and France, 50th Anniv. — A690

2012, Mar. 19   Litho.   *Perf. 13x13¼*
1544 A690 15d multi   .90 .90

Expo 2012, Yeosu, South Korea — A691

2012, Mar. 21   *Perf. 13¼x13*
1545 A691 15d multi   .90 .90

Wainscoting A692

Designs: 15d, Door, Dar Aziza, Algiers. 20d, Ceiling, Dar Aziza. 30d, Window, Hassen Pacha Palace, Algiers.

2012, Mar. 26   *Perf. 13x13¼*
1546-1548 A692 Set of 3   3.75 3.75

Snails — A693

Designs: 15d, Theba pisana. 20d, Eobania vermiculata.

2012, Mar. 28
1549-1550 A693 Set of 2   2.10 2.10

Ulemas A694

Designs: 15d, Sheikh Larbi Djedri Tebessi (1895-1957). 20d, Sheikh Embarek El-Mili (1898-1945). 30d, Sheikh Ahmed Hamani (1915-98).

2012, Apr. 16   Litho.   *Perf. 13x13¼*
1551-1553 A694 Set of 3   3.75 3.75

City Scenes A695

Designs: 15d, Casbah of Dellys. 20d, Saracen Gate, Bejaia. 30d, Casbah of Constantine.

2012, June 26
1554-1556 A695 Set of 3   3.75 3.75

2012 Summer Olympics, London A696

Designs: 15d, Judo, London Eye. 38d, Rowing, Tower Bridge, vert.

Perf. 14x13¼, 13¼x14
2012, June 27
1557-1558 A696 Set of 2   1.40 1.40

Algerian Armed Forces, 50th Anniv. A697

Designs: No. 1559, 15d, Gendarme on motorcycle. No. 1560, 15d, Tank. No. 1561, 15d, Missiles. No. 1562, 15d, Airplane in flight. No. 1563, 15d, Member of Republican Guard on horse. No. 1564, 15d, Naval vessel.

2012, July 5   *Perf. 14*
Stamps With Year and Inscriptions At Bottom
1559-1564 A697 Set of 6   2.25 2.25
1561a   Souvenir sheet of 3, #1559-1561, with year and inscriptions at bottom of stamp removed   1.10 1.10
1564a   Souvenir sheet of 3, #1562-1564, with year and inscriptions at bottom of stamp removed   1.10 1.10

Souvenir Sheet

Algerian Independence, 50th Anniv. — A698

2012, July 5   *Imperf.*
1565 A698 15d multi   .40 .40

Wheat Varieties
A699

Designs: 15d, Bousselam. 20d, Mohamed Ben Bachir. 30d, Hedba 03.

2012, Sept. 29   **Perf. 13x13¼**
1566-1568 A699 Set of 3   1.75 1.75

Algerian Radio and Television, 50th Anniv. — A700

2012, Oct. 28   **Perf. 13¼x13**
1569 A700 15d multi   .40 .40

Postage Stamps of Independent Algeria, 50th Anniv. — A701

2012, Nov. 1
1570 A701 15d multi   .40 .40

Medicinal Plants — A702

Designs: 15d, Globularia vulgaris. 20d, Glycyrrhiza glabra. 30d, Menyanthes trifoliata.

2012, Dec. 11   **Litho.**   **Perf. 13x13¼**
1571-1573 A702 Set of 3   1.75 1.75

Diplomatic Relations Between Algeria and Russia, 50th Anniv. — A703

2012, Dec. 18   **Litho.**   **Perf. 13¼x13**
1574 A703 15d multi   .40 .40

Roman Mosaics
A704

Mosaic depicting: 15d, Muse. 20d, Hunting scene.

2012, Dec. 18   **Litho.**   **Perf. 13x13¼**
1575-1576 A704 Set of 2   .90 .90

Yennayer Festival (Berber New Year) — A705

2013, Jan. 12   **Litho.**   **Perf. 13x13¼**
1577 A705 15d multi   .40 .40

Lighthouses — A706

Designs: 15d, Srigina Island Lighthouse. 20d, Cap Bougaroun Lighthouse. 30d, Cap Ivi Lighthouse.

2013, Feb. 27   **Litho.**   **Perf. 13¼x13**
1578-1580 A706 Set of 3   3.75 3.75

Fruit and Blossoms — A707

Designs: 15d, Apricots. 20d, Cherries.

2013, Mar. 3   **Litho.**   **Perf. 13¼x13**
1581-1582 A707 Set of 2   1.90 1.90

First Chinese Medical Team in Algeria, 50th Anniv. — A708

2013, Apr. 16   **Litho.**   **Perf. 12**
1583 A708 15d multi   .40 .40
Souvenir Sheet
1584 A708 50d multi   1.25 1.25

National Copyright Office, 40th Anniv. — A709

2013, Apr. 26   **Litho.**   **Perf. 13x13¼**
1585 A709 15d multi   .40 .40

National Administration School — A710

2013, Apr. 29   **Litho.**   **Perf. 13¼x13**
1586 A710 15d multi   .40 .40

Roman Pottery — A711

Designs: No. 1587, 15d, Two-handled urn with lid, denomination at LL (shown). No. 1588, 15d, Two-handled urn without lid, denomination at LL. No. 1589, 15d, Single-handled urn without lid, denomination at LR.

2013, May 5   **Litho.**   **Perf. 13x13¼**
1587-1589 A711 Set of 3   1.25 1.25

Improvements in Road Safety With Global Positioning Satellite Technology
A712

2013, May 17   **Litho.**   **Perf. 13x13¼**
1590 A712 15d multi   .40 .40

Algerian Insurance and Re-insurance Company, 50th Anniv. — A713

2013, June 8   **Litho.**   **Perf. 13x13¼**
1591 A713 15d multi   .40 .40

Police Day — A714

2013, July 22   **Litho.**   **Perf. 13x13¼**
1592 A714 15d multi   .40 .40

Marine Life — A715

Designs: No. 1593, 15d, Paracentrotus lividus. No. 1594, 15d, Bathynectes maravigna. No. 1595, 15d, Haliotis tuberculata.

2013, Aug. 3   **Litho.**   **Perf. 13¼x13**
1593-1595 A715 Set of 3   1.25 1.25

Flowers A716

Designs: No. 1596, 15d, Carnations. No. 1597, 15d, Petunias.

2013, Aug. 5   **Litho.**   **Perf. 13x13¼**
1596-1597 A716 Set of 2   .75 .75

22nd African Regional Conference of Interpol, Oran — A717

2013, Sept. 10   **Litho.**   **Perf. 13¼x13**
1598 A717 38d multi   .95 .95

Algerian Olympic Committee, 50th Anniv. A718

Olympic rings, "50," and: 15d, Stylized bird. 30d, Stylized bird and torch, vert.

2013, Oct. 28   **Litho.**   **Perf. 14**
1599-1600 A718 Set of 2   1.10 1.10

Transportation — A719

Designs: 15d, Cable cars, Constantine. 20d, Tram, Oran.

2013, Oct. 30 **Litho.** **Perf. 13¼x13**
1601-1602 A719 Set of 2 .90 .90

Diplomatic Relations Between Algeria and People's Republic of China, 55th Anniv. — A720

2013, Dec. 20 **Litho.** **Perf. 12**
1603 A720 15d multi .40 .40

Fish Farming A721

Designs: 15d, Floating cages. 20d, Clenopharyngodon idella.

2013, Dec. 24 **Litho.** **Perf. 14**
1604-1605 A721 Set of 2 .90 .90

Sonatrach (State-owned Oil and Gas Corporation), 50th Anniv. — A722

2013, Dec. 31 **Litho.** **Perf. 13x13¼**
1606 A722 15d multi .40 .40

Souvenir Sheet
1607 A722 50d multi 1.40 1.40
No. 1607 contains one 35x48mm stamp.

Flowers — A723

Designs: 15d, Ornithogalum arabicum. 20d, Bellis sylvestris. 30d, Calendula arvensis.

2014, Jan. 29 **Litho.** **Perf. 14**
1608-1610 A723 Set of 3 1.75 1.75

Constitutional Council Building, Algiers, 25th Anniv. — A724

2014, Feb. 23 **Litho.** **Perf. 13¼x13**
1611 A724 15d multi .40 .40

Coins A725

Obverse and reverse of Almohad dinar from: 15d, 524-58. 20d, 580-95.

2014, Feb. 26 **Litho.** **Perf. 13¼x13**
1612-1613 A725 Set of 2 .90 .90

Supreme Court, 50th Anniv. — A726

2014, Mar. 2 **Litho.** **Perf. 14**
1614 A726 15d multi .40 .40

National Day of Handicapped Persons A727

2014, Mar. 14 **Litho.** **Perf. 13x13¼**
1615 A727 15d multi .40 .40

Intl. Day of Anti-Personnel Mine Victims — A728

2014, Apr. 4 **Litho.** **Perf. 13x13¼**
1616 A728 15d multi .40 .40

2014 Presidential Election — A729

2014, Apr. 16 **Litho.** **Perf. 13¼x13**
1617 A729 15d multi .40 .40

19th Century Kitchen Tools — A730

Designs: 15d, Coffee mill, Algiers. 20d, Tuareg sugar hammer, horiz. 30d, Tuareg sugar shears, horiz.

Perf. 13x13¼, 13¼x13
2014, Apr. 28 **Litho.**
1618-1620 A730 Set of 3 1.75 1.75

Amazigh High Commission, 19th Anniv. — A731

2014, May 27 **Litho.** **Perf. 13¼x14**
1621 A731 15d multi .40 .40

17th Ministerial Conference of the Non-Aligned Movement, Algiers — A732

Designs: No. 1622, 15d, Stylized dove with olive branch, globe with Algeria highlighted. No. 1623, 15d, Conference emblem.

2014, May 28 **Litho.** **Perf. 13x13¼**
1622-1623 A732 Set of 2 .75 .75
1623a Souvenir sheet of 2, #1622-1623 .75 .75

2014 World Cup Soccer Championships, Brazil — A733

Algerian soccer player dribbling ball with country name in: 15d, White. 38d, Green.

2014, June 26 **Litho.** **Perf. 13x13¼**
1624-1625 A733 Set of 2 1.40 1.40

Olympic Complex, Oran — A734

2014, July 5 **Litho.** **Perf. 13¼x13**
1626 A734 15d multi .40 .40

Traditional Women's Veils — A735

Designs: 15d, Haik. 30d, M'laya.

2014, Aug. 27 **Litho.** **Perf. 13x13¼**
1627-1628 A735 Set of 2 1.10 1.10

Prehistoric Art — A736

Designs: 15d, Painting on rock of horse-drawn chariot. 20d, Head of ram. 30d, Baetulus, vert.

2014, Sept. 1 **Litho.** **Perf. 14**
1629-1631 A736 Set of 3 1.60 1.60

Souvenir Sheet

Rugs — A737

No. 1632: a, Rug from Serbia ("Radomir Bojanic" inscribed at LR). b, Rug from Algeria (Arabic script at LR)

2014, Oct. 7 **Litho.** **Perf. 13¼x14**
1632 A737 15d Sheet of 2, #a-b .75 .75
See Serbia No. 647.

World Post Day — A738

2014, Oct. 9 **Litho.** **Perf. 13¼x14**
1633 A738 15d multi .35 .35

Algerian War of Independence, 60th Anniv. — A739

2014, Nov. 1 Litho.
1634 A739 15d multi .35 .35

Sheikh Abdelkrim Dali (1914-78), Musician A740

2014, Nov. 16 Litho. *Perf. 13x13¼*
1635 A740 15d multi .35 .35

Bridges — A741

Designs: No. 1636, 15d, Saleh Bey Viaduct, Constantine. No. 1637, 15d, Highway bridge and Algerian flag, vert.

Perf. 13¼x13, 13x13¼
2014, Nov. 19 Litho.
1636-1637 A741 Set of 2 .70 .70

Intl. Year of Solidarity With the Palestinian People — A742

2014, Dec. 13 Litho. *Perf. 13¼x13*
1638 A742 15d multi .35 .35

Expo 2015, Milan — A743

Designs: 15d, Globe, hand holding wheat stalks, silhouettes of people. 38d, Stylized fish and fruit, horiz.

2014, Dec. 22 Litho. *Perf. 14*
1639-1640 A743 Set of 2 1.25 1.25

Bordj el Kifan, Algiers — A744

2015 Litho. *Perf. 14x13¾*
1641 A744 4d pale orange .25 .25
1642 A744 10d lt blue .25 .25
1643 A744 25d green .55 .55
Issued: 4d, 10d, 8/5; 25d, 1/4.

Algerian Customs — A745

2015, Jan. 26 Litho. *Perf. 13¼x13*
1644 A745 25d multi .55 .55

Intl. Day of the Fight Against Cancer A746

2015, Feb. 4 Litho. *Perf. 14*
1645 A746 25d multi .55 .55

World Consumer Rights Day — A747

World map, bar code and: 25d, Shopping cart. 30d, Umbrella.

2015, Mar. 15 Litho. *Perf. 13½x14*
1646-1647 A747 Set of 2 1.25 1.25

A748

A749

Constantine, 2015 Capital of Arab Culture — A750

Perf. 13x13¼, 13¼x13
2015, Apr. 16 Litho.
1648 A748 10d multi .25 .25
1649 A749 25d multi .55 .55
Souvenir Sheet
1650 A750 60d purple & blk 1.25 1.25

Diplomatic Relations Between Algeria and Mexico, 50th Anniv. — A751

2015, Apr. 23 Litho. *Perf. 13x13¼*
1651 A751 25d multi .55 .55

Mosques A752

El Aatiq Mosque in: No. 1652, 25d, Ghardaia. No. 1653, 25d, Metlili, vert.

Perf. 14x13½, 13½x14
2015, May 28 Litho.
1652-1653 A752 Set of 2 1.00 1.00

World Refugee Day — A753

2015, June 20 Litho. *Perf. 13½x14*
1654 A753 25d multi .50 .50

Traditional Costumes A754

Man and woman from: 25d, Algiers. 30d, Kabylie.

2015, July 15 Litho. *Perf. 13x13¼*
1655-1656 A754 Set of 2 1.10 1.10

Famous Men A755

Designs: No. 1657, 25d, Abdelhamid Benhadouga (1925-96), writer. No. 1658, 25d, M'hamed Issiakhem (1928-85), painter. No. 1659, 25d, Ismail Samsom (1934-88), painter, vert. No. 1660, 25d, Mouloud Feraoun (1913-62), writer, vert.

Perf. 14x13½, 13½x14
2015, Sept. 21 Litho.
1657-1660 A755 Set of 4 1.90 1.90

Day of Algerian Diplomacy — A756

2015, Oct. 8 Litho. *Perf. 13¼x13*
1661 A756 25d multi .50 .50

United Nations, 70th Anniv. A757

2015, Oct. 24 Litho. *Perf. 14x13½*
1662 A757 25d multi .50 .50

Algerian Revolution, 61st Anniv. — A758

2015, Nov. 1 Litho. *Perf. 13½x14*
1663 A758 25d multi .50 .50

A759

Energy A760

2015, Nov. 11 Litho. *Perf. 14x13½*
1664 A759 10d multi .25 .25
1665 A760 25d multi .50 .50

A761

Arab Family Day
A762

2015, Dec. 7   Litho.   Perf. 13½x14
1666 A761 25d multi   .50   .50
        Perf. 14x13½
1667 A762 30d multi   .60   .60

International Year of Light — A763

2015, Dec. 20   Litho.   Perf. 13½x14
1668 A763 25d multi   .50   .50

International Telecommunication Union, 150th Anniv. — A764

2015, Dec. 22   Litho.   Perf. 14x13½
1669 A764 25d multi   .50   .50

Fish
A765

Designs: 25d, Scorpaena scrofa. 50d, Mugil cephalus.

2016, Jan. 20   Litho.   Perf. 14x13½
1670-1671 A765 Set of 2   1.40 1.40

Medicinal Plants — A766

Designs: 10d, Persicaria hydropiper. 25d, Eupatorium cannabinum.

2016, Feb. 10   Litho.   Perf. 13½x14
1672-1673 A766 Set of 2   .65   .65

Campaign Against Domestic Violence
A767

2016, Feb. 24   Litho.   Perf. 14x13½
1674 A767 25d multi   .45   .45

Southern Algeria Development
A768

2016, Mar. 16   Litho.   Perf. 13½x14
1675 A768 25d multi   .50   .50

Beni Haroun Dam — A769

2016, Mar. 22   Litho.   Perf. 13¼x13
1676 A769 25d multi   .50   .50

World Autism Day
A770

Children's art: 25d, City. 50d, Flowers.

2016, Apr. 2   Litho.   Perf. 13¼x13
1677-1678 A770 Set of 2   1.40 1.40

Museums — A771

Designs: No. 1679, 25d, Ahmed Zabana National Public Museum, Oran. No. 1680, 25d, Cirta National Public Museum, Constantine. No. 1681, 25d, Nasreddine Dinet National Public Museum, Boussaada.

2016, Apr. 18   Litho.   Perf. 13¼x13
1679-1681 A771 Set of 3   1.40 1.40

Gun
A772

Gorgon's Mask — A773

2016, May 18   Litho.   Perf. 13¼x13
1682 A772 25d multi   .45   .45
        Perf. 13x13¼
1683 A773 50d multi   .90   .90

2016 Summer Olympics, Rio de Janeiro
A774

Statue of Christ the Redeemer, Rio de Janeiro, and: 10d, Weight lifting. 25d, Boxing. 50d, Statue of Christ the Redeemer, soccer.

2016, June 1   Litho.   Perf. 13x13¼
1684-1685 A774 Set of 2   .65   .65
        Souvenir Sheet
1686 A774 50d multi   .90   .90

Harbors
A775

Harbor of: 10d, El Djamila. 25d, Sidi Fredj. 50d, Tigzirt.

2016, June 22   Litho.   Perf. 14x13½
1687-1689 A775 Set of 3   1.60 1.60

Dances
A776

Designs: 10d, Baba Merzoug-Karkabo. 25d, El Baroude. 50d, El Hadra.

2016, July 20   Litho.   Perf. 14x13½
1690-1692 A776 Set of 3   1.60 1.60

Cities
A777

Designs: No. 1693, 25d, Mostaganem. No. 1694, 25d, Djelfa.

2016, Aug. 3   Litho.   Perf. 13¼x13
1693-1694 A777 Set of 2   .95   .95

Soummam Conference, 60th Anniv. — A778

2016, Aug. 20   Litho.   Perf. 13x13¼
1695 A778 25d multi   .45   .45

Architecture — A779

Designs: 25d, Faculty of Medicine Building, Laghouat. 50d, Faculty of Law Building, Algiers.

2016, Sept. 7   Litho.   Perf. 13¼x13
1696-1697 A779 Set of 2   1.40 1.40

Emblem of Professional Education and Job Training
A780

"Professional Training, the Key for Employment" — A781

2016, Oct. 5   Litho.   Perf. 14
1698 A780 10d multi   .25   .25
1699 A781 25d multi   .45   .45

Institute of Diplomacy and International Relations — A782

2016, Oct. 24   Litho.   Perf. 14x13½
1700 A782 25d multi   .45   .45

Mohammed Aissa Messaoudi (1931-94), Journalist
A783

2016, Oct. 28   Litho.   Perf. 13x13¼
1701 A783 25d multi   .45   .45

"Taxation To Build the Algeria of Tomorrow" A784

Land Registry A785

2016, Nov. 9   Litho.   Perf. 13½x14
1702 A784 10d multi   .25   .25

Perf. 14x13½
1703 A785 25d multi   .45   .45

Atlas Lion A786

2016, Dec. 14   Litho.   Perf. 13¼x13
1704 A786 50d multi   .90   .90

Modernization of Justice System — A787

2017, Jan. 15   Litho.   Perf. 13¼x13
1705 A787 25d multi   .45   .45

Spas A788

Designs: 5d, Hammam Essalihine. 20d, Hammam Bouhadjar. 25d, Hammam Zelfana.

2017, Jan. 29   Litho.   Perf. 14x13¼
1706-1708 A788   Set of 3   .95   .95

Berber as an Official Language in Algeria, 1st Anniv. — A789

2017, Feb. 7   Litho.   Perf. 13x13¼
1709 A789 25d multi   .45   .45

Campaign Against Food Wastage A790

Prevention of Food Poisoning — A791

2017, Mar. 15   Litho.   Perf. 14x13¼
1710 A790 25d multi   .45   .45

Perf. 13¼x14
1711 A791 25d multi   .45   .45

International Trisomy 21 (Down Syndrome) Day — A792

2017, Mar. 21   Litho.   Perf. 13¼x13
1712 A792 25d multi   .45   .45

Souvenir Sheet

Tinhinan Jewelry — A793

No. 1713: a, 10d, Necklace. b, 20d, Gold bracelets. c, 20d, Gold pendant.

2017, Apr. 18   Litho.   Perf. 14
1713 A793   Sheet of 3, #a-c   .95   .95

Second Session of the Specialized Technical Committee on Social Development, Labor and Employment of the African Union — A794

2017, Apr. 26   Litho.   Perf. 13¼x14
1714 A794 25d multi   .45   .45

Theaters — A795

Theater in: No. 1715, 25d, Sidi Bel Abbes. No. 1716, 25d, Tizi Ouzou. No. 1717, 25d, Bejaia.

2017, May 18   Litho.   Perf. 13¼x14
1715-1717 A795   Set of 3   .95   .95

Warda Al-Jazairia (1939-2012), Singer — A796

Fadila Dziria (1917-70), Singer — A797

2017, June 8   Litho.   Perf. 13x13¼
1718 A796 50d multi   .95   .95
1719 A797 50d multi   .95   .95

Miniature Sheet

Waterfalls — A798

No. 1720: a, Oued El Bared Waterfall, Setif. b, Tifrit Waterfall, Saida. c, Sidi Ouadah Waterfall, Tiaret. d, Lakhdaria Waterfall, Bouira.

2017, June 24   Litho.   Perf. 14x13¼
1720 A798 25d Sheet of 4, #a-d   1.90   1.90

Miniature Sheet

Battles — A799

No. 1721: a, Battle of Bir El Gharama, 1881. b, Battle of Bir Teskift, 1957. c, Battle of Djbel Bouk'hil, 1961. d, Battle of Kheng Ennetah, 1832. e, Battle of Ain Zana, 1959.

2017, July 5   Litho.   Perf. 14x13¼
1721 A799 25d Sheet of 5, #a-e   2.40   2.40

Souvenir Sheet

Algerian Police Force, 55th Anniv. — A800

2017, July 23   Litho.   Perf. 14
1722 A800 25d multi   .50   .50

Road Safety A801

2017, Aug. 6   Litho.   Perf. 14x13¼
1723 A801 25d multi   .45   .45

Dangers of the Internet — A802

2017, Aug. 6   Litho.   Perf. 13¼x14
1724 A802 25d multi   .45   .45

Algiers Architecture — A803

Designs: No. 1725, 25d, International Conference Center. No. 1726, 25d, Opera House.

2017, Sept. 10   Litho.   Perf. 13¼x13
1725-1726 A803   Set of 2   .90   .90

National Office of Weights and Measures, 31st Anniv. — A804

2017, Sept. 29   Litho.   Perf. 13¼x14
1727 A804 25d multi   .45   .45

Fruits and Vegetables A805

Designs: No. 1728, 25d, Citrouilles (squashes). No. 1729, 25d, Aubergines (eggplants). No. 1730, 25d, Clementines. No. 1731, 25d, Pêches (peaches).

2017, Oct. 16   Litho.   Perf. 14
1728-1731 A805   Set of 4   1.75   1.75

Blood Donation — A806

2017, Oct. 25   Litho.   Perf. 13¼x13
1732 A806 25d multi   .45   .45

Diplomatic Relations Between Algeria and Viet Nam, 55th Anniv. A807

2017, Oct. 28 Litho. Perf. 14x13¼
1733 A807 25d multi .45 .45

Souvenir Sheet

National Liberation Front Proclamation of November 1, 1954 — A808

No. 1734: a, House from which proclamation was made, and printing press. b, Printing press.

2017, Nov. 1 Litho. Perf. 14x13¼
1734 A808 25d Sheet of 2, #a-b .90 .90

Fidel Castro (1926-2016), President of Cuba — A809

2017, Nov. 26 Litho. Perf. 13x13¼
1735 A809 25d multi .45 .45

Mouloud Mammeri (1917-89), Writer — A810

Litho. & Engr.
2017, Dec. 28 Perf. 13x13¼
1736 A810 50d black .90 .90

Campaign Against Violence — A811

2018, Jan. 2 Litho. Perf. 14¼
1737 A811 25d multi + label .45 .45

National Day of Municipalities — A812

2018, Jan. 18 Litho. Perf. 13¼x13
1738 A812 25d multi .45 .45

New Cities A813

Designs: No. 1739, 25d, Ali Mendjeli. No. 1740, 25d, Sidi Abdellah.

2018, Jan. 28 Litho. Perf. 14x13¼
1739-1740 A813 Set of 2 .90 .90

International Mother Language Day — A814

2018, Feb. 21 Litho. Perf. 13x13¼
1741 A814 25d multi .45 .45

International Decade of Water for Sustainable Development — A815

Foggaras (water systems) in Adrar Province: No. 1742, 25d, Foggara El Beidha, Tidikelt Region. No. 1743, 25d, Foggara El Kbira, Gourara Region. No. 1744, 25d, Foggara Armoul, Touât Region.

2018, Mar. 22 Litho. Perf. 14x13¼
1742-1744 A815 Set of 3 1.40 1.40

National Service, 50th Anniv. — A816

2018, Apr. 8 Litho. Perf. 13x13¼
1745 A816 25d multi .45 .45

2018 World Cup Soccer Championships, Russia — A817

2018, Apr. 21 Litho. Perf. 14x13¼
1746 A817 25d multi .45 .45

Historical Sites A818

Designs: 5d, Jedar near Tiaret. 10d, Ruins of Tiddis, vert. 20d, Cedias Mausoleum, Khenchela, vert. 25d, El Mokrani Castle, Bordj Bou Arreridj.

Perf. 14x13¼, 13¼x14
2018, May 12 Litho.
1747-1750 A818 Set of 4 1.10 1.10

International Day of Living Together in Peace — A819

2018, May 16 Litho. Perf. 13x13¼
1751 A819 25d multi .45 .45

International Day of Biological Diversity — A820

2018, May 22 Litho. Perf. 14
1752 A820 25d multi .45 .45

Couscous — A821

2018, June 12 Litho. Perf. 13¼x13
1753 A821 25d multi .45 .45

United Nations Day for Public Service A822

2018, June 23 Litho. Perf. 13x13¼
1754 A822 25d multi .45 .45

Freedom Fighters — A823

Designs: 10d, Cherif Boubaghla (?-1854). 20d, Sheikh Amoud (1859-1929), vert. 25d, Bennacer Ben Chohra (1804-84), vert.

Perf. 13¼x13, 13x13¼
2018, July 5 Litho.
1755-1757 A823 Set of 3 .95 .95

Blaoui el Houari (1926-2017), Singer — A824

2018, July 19 Litho. Perf. 13x13¼
1758 A824 50d multi .85 .85

Souvenir Sheet

Nelson Mandela (1918-2013), President of South Africa — A825

2018, July 18 Litho. Perf. 13¼
1759 A825 100d multi 1.75 1.75

A826

Third African Youth Games, Algeria — A827

2018, July 19 Litho. Perf. 13¼x14
1760 A826 25d multi .45 .45
1761 A827 25d multi .45 .45

Zaouia (Islamic School) A828

Dome of Zaouia, Map of Algeria, Muslim Man and Calligrapher A829

2018, Sept. 1 Litho. Perf. 14
1762 A828 25d multi

Perf. 13¼
1763 A829 25d multi

Sbiba Festival — A830

No. 1764: a, Four Tuareg dancers. b, Tuareg dancers and festival attendees.

2018, Sept. 27 Litho. Perf. 14x13½
1764 A830 25d Horiz. pair, #a-b — —

Honeycomb, Bees and Eucalyptus Blossoms — A831

Honeycomb, Bees and Jujube Blossoms — A832

2018, Oct. 16 Litho. Perf. 14¼
1765 A831 25d multi — —
1766 A832 25d multi — —

National Press Day — A833

2018, Oct. 22 Litho. Perf. 13x13½
1767 A833 25d multi — —

Green City — A834

2018, Oct. 25 Litho. Perf. 13x13½
1768 A834 25d multi — —

Mostefa Ben Boulaid (1917-56), Revolution Leader — A835

Mourad Didouche (1927-55), Revolution Leader — A836

Larbi Ben M'hidi (1923-57), Revolution Leader — A837

Colonel Amirouchené Ait Hamouda (1926-59), Revolution Leader — A838

Colonel Youcef Zighoud (1921-56), Revolution Leader — A839

2018, Nov. 1 Litho. Perf. 13½x14
1769 A835 25d multi — —
1770 A836 25d multi — —
1771 A837 25d multi — —
1772 A838 25d multi — —
1773 A839 25d multi — —

Martyrs of the Algerian Revolution.

Souvenir Sheet

Proclamation Declaring the Formation of the State of Palestine, 30th Anniv. — A840

2018, Nov. 15 Litho. Perf. 13½x13
1774 A840 70d multi

Women's Entrepreneurship Day — A841

2018, Nov. 21 Litho. Perf. 14x13¼
1775 A841 25d multi .45 .45

Launch of Alcomsat-1, 1st Anniv. — A842

2018, Dec. 11 Litho. Perf. 13½x14
1776 A842 25d multi — —

World Arabic Language Day — A843

2018, Dec. 18 Litho. Perf. 13x13½
1777 A843 50d multi

Diplomatic Relations Between Algeria and People's Republic of China, 60th Anniv. — A844

2018, Dec. 20 Litho. Perf. 13½x13
1778 A844 25d multi — —

Pres. Houari Boumédiène (1932-78) A845

2018, Dec. 27 Litho. Perf. 13½
1779 A845 50d multi

International Year of the Periodic Table of Elements — A846

2019, Jan. 2 Litho. Perf. 13¼x13
1780 A846 25d multi .45 .45

Women in Health Services in the Algerian Revolution — A847

No. 1781: a, Female health care worker treating standing soldier in forest. b, Male and female health care workers treating soldiers sitting against rock face.

2019, Feb. 18 Litho. Perf. 14x13½
1781 A847 25d Horiz. pair, #a-b — —

Mar. 8, 1974, Crash of Airplane Carrying Algerian Journalists in Hanoi, Viet Nam — A848

2019, Mar. 8   Litho.   Perf. 13½x13
1782 A848 25d multi

International Labor Organization, Cent. — A849

2019, Mar. 9   Litho.   Perf. 13½x13
1783 A849 25d multi

Emiliano Zapata (1879-1919), Leader of Mexican Revolution — A850

2019, Apr. 10   Litho.   Perf. 13½x13
1784 A850 25d multi

Souvenir Sheet

Science Day — A851

2019, Apr. 16   Litho.   Imperf.
1785 A851 50d multi

Souvenir Sheet

Protected Species — A852

No. 1786: a, Oryx dammah. b, Cobra from North Africa.

2019, May 11   Litho.   Perf. 14x13½
1786 A852 25d Sheet of 2, #a-b

2019 Africa Cup of Nations Soccer Tournament, Egypt — A853

2019, May 15   Litho.   Perf.
1787 A853 25d multi

Traditional Costumes A854

Designs: No. 1788, 25d, Woman wearing Tlemcenian scarf. No. 1789, 25d, Man wearing burnous of Southern Algeria. No. 1790, 25d, Woman wearing Kabyle dress. No. 1791, 25d, Man wearing clothing of Aurès.

2019, July 8   Litho.   Perf. 13x13½
1788-1791 A854   Set of 4

National Society for Electricity and Gas (Sonelgaz), 50th Anniv. — A855

2019, July 28   Litho.   Perf. 13x13½
1792 A855 25d multi

Ahmed Zabana (1926-56), Revolution Leader — A856

Ali Ammar (1930-57), Revolution Leader — A857

Malika Gaid (1933-58), Revolutionary Hero and Nurse — A858

Hassiba Ben Bouali (1938-57), Revolutionary Hero — A859

Ourida Meddad (1938-57), Revolutionary Hero — A860

2019, Oct. 3   Litho.   Perf. 13½x14
1793   Vert. strip of 5
a. A856 25d multi
b. A857 25d multi
c. A858 25d multi
d. A859 25d multi
e. A860 25d multi

Martyrs of the Algerian Revolution.

Mohamed Seddik Ben Yahia (1932-82), Politician A861

2019, Oct. 8   Litho.   Perf. 13x13½
1794 A861 50d multi

Dome of the Rock, Jerusalem, Doves and Palestinian Authority Flag — A862

2019, Oct. 9   Litho.   Perf. 13½x13
1795 A862 100d multi

Jerusalem, capital of the Palestinian Authority.

World Organ Donation and Transplantation Day — A863

2019, Oct. 20   Litho.   Perf. 14x13½
1796 A863 25d multi

24th Algiers International Book Fair — A864

2019, Nov. 2   Litho.   Perf. 13x13½
1797 A864 25d multi

Souvenir Sheet

National Handicrafts Day — A865

No. 1798: a, Southern milk churn. b, Central milk churn.

2019, Nov. 11   Litho.   Perf. 14x13½
1798 A865 50d Sheet of 2, #a-b

Algerian Sign Language Dictionary A866

2019, Dec. 5   Litho.   Perf. 13x13½
1799 A866 25d multi

Stone Engravings, Sfissifa Station — A867

Ain El Haneche Archaeological Site — A868

Abou Al Mouhajir Dinar Mosque, Mila — A869

2020, Jan. 25   Litho.   Perf. 13½x13
1800 A867 25d multi — —
1801 A868 25d multi — —
1802 A869 25d multi — —
Archaeological sites and treasures.

SEMI-POSTAL STAMPS

Regular Issue of 1926
Surcharged in Black or Red

1927   Unwmk.   Perf. 14x13½
B1 A1 5c +5c bl grn 1.60 1.60
B2 A1 10c +10c lilac 1.60 1.60
B3 A2 15c +15c org brn 1.60 1.60
B4 A2 20c +20c car rose 1.60 1.60
B5 A2 25c +25c bl grn 1.60 1.60
B6 A2 30c +30c lt bl 1.60 1.60
B7 A2 35c +35c dp vio 1.60 1.60
B8 A2 40c +40c ol grn 1.60 1.60
B9 A2 50c +50c dp bl (R) 1.60 1.60
  a. Double surcharge 425.00 425.00
B10 A3 80c +80c red org 1.60 1.60
B11 A4 1fr +1fr gray grn & red brn 1.60 1.60
B12 A4 2fr +2fr Prus bl & blk brn 32.50 32.50
B13 A4 5fr +5fr red & vio 42.50 42.50
  Nos. B1-B13 (13) 92.60 92.60
The surtax was for the benefit of wounded soldiers. Government officials speculated in this issue.

Railroad Terminal, Oran SP1

Ruins at Djemila SP2 / Mosque of Sidi Abd-er-Rahman SP3

Designs: 10c+10c, Rummel Gorge, Constantine. 15c+15c, Admiralty Buildings, Algiers. 25c+25c, View of Algiers. 30c+30c, Trajan's Arch, Timgad. 40c+40c, Temple of the North, Djemila. 75c+75c Mansourah Minaret, Tlemcen. 1f+1f, View of Ghardaia. 1.50f+1.50f, View of Tolga. 2f+2f, Tuareg warriors. 3f+3f, Kasbah, Algiers.

1930   Engr.   Perf. 12½
B14 SP1 5c +5c orange 12.00 12.00
B15 SP1 10c +10c ol grn 12.00 12.00
B16 SP1 15c +15c dk brn 12.00 12.00
B17 SP1 25c +25c black 12.00 12.00
B18 SP1 30c +30c dk red 12.00 12.00
B19 SP1 40c +40c ap grn 12.00 12.00
B20 SP2 50c +50c ultra 9.50 9.50
B21 SP2 75c +75c red pur 9.50 9.50
B22 SP2 1fr +1fr org red 9.50 9.50
B23 SP2 1.50fr +1.50fr deep ultra 9.50 9.50
B24 SP2 2fr +2fr dk car 9.50 9.50
B25 SP2 3fr +3fr dk grn 9.50 9.50
B26 SP3 5fr +5fr grn & car 24.00 24.00
  a. Center inverted 750.00
  Nos. B14-B26 (13) 153.00 153.00
Centenary of the French occupation of Algeria. The surtax on the stamps was given to the funds for the celebration.
Nos. B14-B26 exist imperf. Value, set in pairs, $800.

> Catalogue values for unused stamps in this section, from this point to the end of the section, are for Never Hinged items.

No. 102 Surcharged in Red

1938   Perf. 13
B27 A6 65c +35c on 2.25fr yel grn 1.60 1.20
  a. Inverted surcharge 350.00
  b. Pair, one without surcharge 1,875.
20th anniversary of Armistice.
No. 79 with surcharge is considered an essay. Values: unused $260, never hinged $350.

René Caillié, Charles Lavigerie and Henri Duveyrier SP14

1939   Engr.
B28 SP14 30c +20c dk bl grn 2.40 2.40
B29 SP14 90c +60c car rose 2.40 2.40
B30 SP14 2.25fr +75c ultra 20.00 16.00
B31 SP14 5fr +5fr brn blk 40.00 32.50
  Nos. B28-B31 (4) 64.80 53.30
Pioneers of the Sahara.

French and Algerian Soldiers SP15

1940   Photo.   Perf. 12
B32 SP15 1fr +1fr bl & car 1.60 1.20
  a. Double surcharge 260.00
B33 SP15 1fr +2fr brn rose & blk 1.60 1.20
B34 SP15 1fr +4fr dp grn & red 2.40 2.00
B35 SP15 1fr +9fr brn & car 4.00 2.75
  Nos. B32-B35 (4) 9.60 7.15
The surtax was used to assist the families of mobilized men.
Nos. B32-B35 exist without surcharge. Value set, $325.

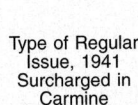

Type of Regular Issue, 1941 Surcharged in Carmine

1941   Engr.   Perf. 13
B36 A19 1fr +4fr black .65 .30

No. 135 Surcharged in Carmine

B37 A19 1fr +4fr dark blue .65 .30
The surtax was for National Relief.

No. 124 Surcharged in Black

1942
B38 A7 90c +60c henna brn .55 .25
  a. Double surcharge 175.00
The surtax was used for National Relief. The stamp could also be used as 1.50 francs for postage.

Mother and Child — SP16

1943, Dec. 1   Litho.   Perf. 12
B39 SP16 50c +4.50fr brt pink 1.00 1.30
B40 SP16 1.50fr +8.50fr lt grn 1.00 1.30
B41 SP16 3fr +12fr dp bl 1.00 1.30
B42 SP16 5fr +15fr vio brn 1.00 1.40
  Nos. B39-B42 (4) 4.00 5.30
The surtax was for the benefit of soldiers and prisoners of war.

Planes over Fields SP17

Unwmk.
1945, July 2   Engr.   Perf. 13
B43 SP17 1.50fr +3.50fr lt ultra, red org & blk 1.10 .85
The surtax was for the benefit of Algerian airmen and their families.

France No. B192 Overprinted Type "a" of 1924 in Black
1945
B44 SP146 4fr +6fr dk vio brn 1.10 .85
The surtax was for war victims of the P.T.T.

Overprinted in Blue on Type of France, 1945
1945, Oct. 15
B45 SP150 2fr +3fr dk brn 1.10 .85
For Stamp Day.

Overprinted in Blue on Type of France, 1946
1946, June 29
B46 SP160 3fr +2fr red 1.60 1.25
For Stamp Day.

Children Playing by Stream SP18

Girl — SP19 / Athlete — SP20

Repatriated Prisoner and Bay of Algiers SP21

1946, Oct. 2   Engr.   Perf. 13
B47 SP18 3fr +17fr dark grn 2.75 2.25
B48 SP19 4fr +21fr red 2.75 2.25
B49 SP20 8fr +27fr rose lilac 7.25 6.25
B50 SP21 10fr +35fr dark blue 3.25 2.50
  Nos. B47-B50 (4) 16.00 13.25

Type of France, 1947, Overprinted type "a" of 1924 in Carmine
1947, Mar. 15
B51 SP172 4.50fr +5.50fr dp ultra 1.75 1.25
For Stamp Day.

Same on Type of France, 1947, Surcharged Like No. B36 in Carmine
1947, Nov. 13
B52 A173 5fr +10fr dk Prus grn 1.60 1.25

Type of France, 1948, Overprinted in Dark Green — f

1948, Mar. 6
B53 SP176 6fr +4fr dk grn 1.75 1.25
For Stamp Day.

Type of France, 1948, Overprinted In Blue

1948, May
B54 A176 6fr +4fr red 1.60 1.25

Battleship Richelieu and the Admiralty, Algiers SP22

Aircraft Carrier Arromanches — SP23

Unwmk.
1949, Jan. 15   Engr.   Perf. 13
B55 SP22 10fr +15fr dp blue 10.00 8.00
B56 SP23 18fr +22fr red 10.00 8.00
The surtax was for naval charities.

Type of France, 1949, Overprinted in Blue — g

1949, Mar. 26
B57 SP180 15fr +5fr lilac rose 3.25 2.25
For Stamp Day, Mar. 26-27.

Type of France, 1950, Overprinted type "f" in Green

1950, Mar. 11
B58 SP183 12fr +3fr blk brn   3.25 2.75
For Stamp Day, Mar. 11-12.

Foreign Legionary — SP24

1950, Apr. 30
B59 SP24 15fr +5fr dk grn   3.00 2.40

Charles de Foucauld and Gen. J. F. H. Laperrine SP25

1950, Aug. 21   Unwmk.   Perf. 13
B60 SP25 25fr +5fr brn ol & brn blk   8.00 6.25
50th anniversary of the presence of the French in the Sahara.

Emir Abd-el-Kader and Marshal T. R. Bugeaud — SP26

1950, Aug. 21
B61 SP26 40fr +10fr org brn & blk brn   8.00 6.25
Unveiling of a monument to Emir Abd-el-Kader at Cacheron.

Col. Colonna d'Ornano and Fine Arts Museum, Algiers SP27

1951, Jan. 11
B62 SP27 15fr +5fr blk brn, vio brn & red brn   1.40 1.25
Death of Col. Colonna d'Ornano, 10th anniv.

Type of France, 1951, Overprinted type "a" of 1924 in Black

1951, Mar. 10
B63 SP186 12fr +3fr brown   2.75 2.50
For Stamp Day.

Type of France, 1952, Overprinted type "g" in Dark Blue

1952, Mar. 8   Unwmk.   Perf. 13
B64 SP190 12fr +3fr dk bl   2.75 2.50
For Stamp Day.

French Military Medal — SP28

Unwmk.

1952, July 5   Engr.   Perf. 13
B65 SP28 15fr +5fr grn, yel & brn 3.50 2.75
Centenary of the creation of the French Military Medal.

Type of France 1952, Surcharged type "g" and Surtax in Black

1952, Sept. 15
B66 A222 30fr +5fr dp ultra   4.00 3.25
10th anniv. of the defense of Bir-Hakeim.

View of El Oued SP29

Design: 12fr+3fr, View of Bou-Noura.

1952, Nov. 15   Engr.
B67 SP29 8fr +2fr ultra & red   3.25 3.00
B68 SP29 12fr +3fr red   6.50 4.75
The surtax was for the Red Cross.

Type of France, 1953, Overprinted type "a" of 1924 in Black

1953, Mar. 14   Engr.
B69 SP193 12fr +3fr purple   2.50 2.40
For Stamp Day. Surtax for Red Cross.

Victory of Cythera — SP30

Unwmk.

1953, Dec. 18   Engr.   Perf. 13
B70 SP30 15fr +5fr blk brn & brn 1.60 1.25
The surtax was for army welfare work.

Type of France, 1954, Overprinted type "a" of 1924 in Black

1954, Mar. 20   Unwmk.   Perf. 13
B71 SP196 12fr +3fr scarlet   2.25 2.00
For Stamp Day.

Soldiers and Flags — SP31

1954, Mar. 27
B72 SP31 15fr +5fr dk brn   2.00 1.25
The surtax was for old soldiers.

Foreign Legionary — SP32

1954, Apr. 30
B73 SP32 15fr +5fr dk grn   3.00 2.50
The surtax was for the welfare fund of the Foreign Legion.

Nurses and Verdun Hospital, Algiers SP33

15fr+5fr, J. H. Dunant & ruins at Djemila.

1954, Oct. 30
B74 SP33 12fr +3fr indigo & red   6.50 5.50
B75 SP33 15fr +5fr pur & red   7.50 6.25
The surtax was for the Red Cross.

Earthquake Victims and Ruins — SP34

First Aid — SP35

Design: Nos. B80-B81, Removing wounded.

1954, Dec. 5
B76 SP34 12fr +4fr dk vio brn   3.50 2.75
B77 SP34 15fr +5fr dp bl   3.50 2.75
B78 SP35 18fr +6fr lil rose   4.50 3.50
B79 SP35 20fr +7fr violet   4.50 3.50
B80 SP35 25fr +8fr rose brn   4.50 3.50
B81 SP35 30fr +10fr brt bl grn   4.50 3.50
        Nos. B76-B81 (6)   25.00 19.50
The surtax was for victims of the Orleansville earthquake disaster of September 1954.

Type of France, 1955, Overprinted type "a" of 1924 in Black

1955, Mar. 19
B82 SP199 12fr +3fr dp ultra   2.75 2.25
For Stamp Day, Mar. 19-20.

Women and Children — SP36

1955, Nov. 5
B83 SP36 15fr +5fr blue & indigo 1.40 1.25
The tax was for war victims.

Cancer Victim — SP37

1956, Mar. 3   Unwmk.   Perf. 13
B84 SP37 15fr +5fr dk brn   2.00 1.60
The surtax was for the Algerian Cancer Society. The male figure in the design is Rodin's "Age of Bronze."

Type of France, 1956, Overprinted type "a" of 1924 in Black

1956, Mar.
B85 SP202 12fr +3fr red   2.50 2.00
For Stamp Day, Mar. 17-18.

Foreign Legion Rest Home SP38

1956, Apr. 29
B86 SP38 15fr +5fr dk bl grn   2.50 2.00
Honoring the French Foreign Legion.

Type of France, 1957, Overprinted type "f" in Black

1957, Mar. 16   Engr.   Perf. 13
B87 SP204 12fr +3fr dull purple   2.00 1.60
For Stamp Day and to honor the Maritime Postal Service.

Fennec SP39

Design: 15fr+5fr, Stork flying over roofs.

1957, Apr. 6
B88 SP39 12fr +3fr red brn & red 9.00 7.25
B89 SP39 15fr +5fr sepia & red   9.00 7.25
The surtax was for the Red Cross.

Regular Issue of 1956 Srchd. in Dark Blue

1957, June 18
B90 A53 15fr +5fr scar & rose red   2.50 1.60
17th anniv. of General de Gaulle's appeal for a Free France.

The Giaour, by Delacroix — SP40

On the Banks of the Oued, by Fromentin SP41

Design: 35fr+10fr, Dancer, by Chasseriau.

Unwmk.

1957, Nov. 30   Engr.   Perf. 13
B91 SP40 15fr +5fr dk car   8.00 7.00
B92 SP41 20fr +5fr grn   8.00 7.00
B93 SP40 35fr +10fr dk bl   9.00 7.25
        Nos. B91-B93 (3)   25.00 21.25
Surtax for army welfare organizations.

Type of France Overprinted type "f" in Blue

1958, Mar. 15   Unwmk.   Perf. 13
B94 SP206 15fr +5fr org brn   2.00 1.60
For Stamp Day.

Bird-of-Paradise Flower — SP42

1958, June 14   Engr.   Perf. 13
B95 SP42 20fr +5fr grn, org & vio 5.50 4.00
The surtax was for Child Welfare.

Arms & Marshal's Baton — SP43

1958, July 20
B96 SP43 20fr +5fr ultra, car & grn   2.50 2.00
Marshal de Lattre Foundation.

Independent State

Clasped Hands, Wheat, Olive Branch — SP44

1963, May 27   Unwmk.   Perf. 13
B97 SP44 50c +20c sl grn, brt grn & car   1.10 .65
Surtax for the Natl. Solidarity Fund.

Burning Books — SP45

1965, June 7   Engr.   Perf. 13
B98 SP45 20c +5c ol grn, red & blk   .50 .40
Burning of the Library of Algiers, 6/7/62.

Soldiers and Woman Comforting Wounded Soldier — SP46

1966, Aug. 20   Photo.   Perf. 11½
B99 SP46 30c +10c multi   1.25 .70
B100 SP46 95c +10c multi   1.75 1.25
Day of the Moudjahid (Moslem volunteers).

Red Crescent, Boy and Girl — SP47

1967, May 27   Litho.   Perf. 14
B101 SP47 30c +10c brt grn, brn & car   .85 .50
Algerian Red Crescent Society.

SP48

Flood Victims — SP48a

1969, Nov. 15   Typo.   Perf. 10½
B102 SP48 30c +10c multi   .70 .50

Litho.
B103 SP48a 95c +25c multi   1.60 .95

Red Crescent Flag SP49

1971, May 17   Engr.   Perf. 10½
B104 SP49 30c +10c slate grn & car   .70 .40
Algerian Red Crescent Society.

Intl. Children's Day — SP50

1989, June 1   Litho.   Perf. 10½x11
B105 SP50 1d +30c multi   .70 .55
Surtax for child welfare.

Solidarity with Palestinians SP51

1990, Dec. 9   Litho.   Perf. 10½x11
B106 SP51 1d +30c multi   .70 .45

Natl. Solidarity with Education SP52

1995, Sept. 20   Litho.   Perf. 13x14
B107 SP52 3d +50c multi   .60 .30

Red Crescent Society SP53

1998, May 2   Litho.   Perf. 13x13¼
B108 SP53 5d +1d multi   .50 .30

World Children's Day SP54

No. B110, Flower, child, adult, vert.

1998, June 1   Perf. 14x13½, 13½x14
B109 SP54 5d +1d shown   .50 .25
B110 SP54 5d +1d multi   .50 .25

Flood Victim Relief — SP55

2001, Dec. 24   Litho.   Perf. 13¼x14
B111 SP55 5d +5d multi   1.00 .75

Earthquake Relief — SP56

2003, Dec. 3   Litho.   Perf. 13¼x14
B112 SP56 5d +5d multi   .90 .90

TeleFood SP57

Children's drawings with: No. B113, 5d+1d, Blue frame. No. B114, 5d+1d, Pink frame.

Perf. 14, 14x13½ (#B114)
2004, Oct. 16   Litho.
B113-B114 SP57   Set of 2   1.00 1.00

AIR POST STAMPS

Catalogue values for unused stamps in this section are for Never Hinged items.

Plane over Algiers Harbor AP1

Two types of 20fr:
Type I — Monogram "F" without serifs. "POSTE" indented 3mm.
Type II — Monogram "F" with serifs. "POSTE" indented 4½mm.

Unwmk.
1946, June 20   Engr.   Perf. 13
C1 AP1 5fr red   .30 .25
C2 AP1 10fr deep blue   .30 .25
C3 AP1 15fr deep green   1.20 .40
C4 AP1 20fr brown (II)   1.10 .25
C4A AP1 20fr brown (I)   225.00 140.00
C5 AP1 25fr violet   1.40 .25
C6 AP1 40fr gray black   1.60 .65
Nos. C1-C4,C5-C6 (6)   5.90 2.05
For surcharges see Nos. C7, CB1-CB2.

No. C1 Surcharged in Black

1947, Jan. 18
C7 AP1 (4.50fr) on 5fr red   .35 .25
a.   Inverted surcharge   800.00 600.00
b.   Double surcharge   1,000. 700.00
c.   Pair, one without surcharge   1,200.

Storks over Mosque — AP2

Plane over Village AP3

1949-53
C8 AP2 50fr green   4.50 .90
C9 AP3 100fr brown   3.50 .65
C10 AP2 200fr bright red   10.50 5.25
C11 AP3 500fr ultra ('53)   32.50 20.00
Nos. C8-C11 (4)   51.00 26.80

Beni Bahdel Dam — AP4

1957, July 1   Unwmk.   Perf. 13
C12 AP4 200fr dark red   9.50 2.00

Independent State

Caravelle over Ghardaia — AP5

Designs: 2d, Caravelle over El Oued. 5d, Caravelle over Tipasa.

1967-68   Engr.   Perf. 13
C13 AP5 1d lil, org brn & emer   1.40   .60
C14 AP5 2d brt bl, org brn &
          emer   3.25 1.40
C15 AP5 5d brt bl, grn & org
          brn ('68)   8.50 3.25
     Nos. C13-C15 (3)   13.15 5.25

Plane over Casbah, Algiers — AP6

Designs: 3d, Plane over Oran. 4d, Plane over Rhumel Gorge.

1971-72   Photo.   Perf. 12½
C16 AP6 2d grysh blk & multi   2.50 1.00
C17 AP6 3d violet & blk   3.75 1.60
C18 AP6 4d blk & multi   4.25 2.00
     Nos. C16-C18 (3)   10.50 4.60

Issued: 2d, 6/12/71; 3d, 4d, 2/28/72.

Storks and
Plane — AP7

1979, Mar. 24   Photo.   Perf. 11½
C19 AP7 10d multi   6.50 2.50

Plane Approaching Coastal
City — AP8

1991, Apr. 26   Litho.   Perf. 13½
C20 AP8 10d shown   3.00 1.50
C21 AP8 20d Plane over city   6.00 3.00

Plane Over
Djidjelli
Corniche — AP9

1993, Sept. 25   Engr.   Perf. 13½x14
C22 AP9 50d blue, grn & brn   6.75 3.25

AIR POST SEMI-POSTAL STAMPS

Catalogue values for unused
stamps in this section are for
Never Hinged items.

No. C2
Surcharged
in Carmine

1947, June 18   Perf. 13
CB1 AP1 10fr +10fr deep blue   2.50 1.75
7th anniv. of Gen. Charles de Gaulle's
speech in London, June 18, 1940.

No. C1
Surcharged
in Blue

1948, June 18
CB2 AP1 5fr +10fr red   2.50 1.75
8th anniv. of Gen. Charles de Gaulle's
speech in London, June 18, 1940.

Monument, Clock
Tower and
Plane — SPAP1

1949, Nov. 10   Engr.   Unwmk.
CB3 SPAP1 15fr +20fr dk brn   7.00 5.25
25th anniv. of Algeria's 1st postage stamps.

POSTAGE DUE STAMPS

D1

**   Perf. 14x13½**
1926-27   Typo.   Unwmk.
J1   D1 5c light blue   .40   .30
J2   D1 10c dk brn   .40   .30
J3   D1 20c olive grn   .80   .30
J4   D1 25c car rose   .80   .65
J5   D1 30c rose red   1.20   .50
J6   D1 45c blue grn   1.60   .65
J7   D1 50c brn vio   .80   .25
J8   D1 60c green ('27)   3.25   .90
J9   D1 1fr red brn, *straw*   .40   .30
J10 D1 2fr lil rose ('27)   .80   .30
J11 D1 3fr deep blue ('27)   .80   .30
     Nos. J1-J11 (11)   11.25 4.75
See Nos. J25-J26, J28-J32. For surcharges,
see Nos. J18-J20.

D2

1926-27
J12 D2 1c olive grn   .40   .40
J13 D2 10c violet   1.60   .80
J14 D2 30c bister   1.60   .80
J15 D2 60c dull red   1.20   .80
J16 D2 1fr brt vio ('27)   20.00 4.00
J17 D2 2fr lt bl ('27)   16.00 1.60
     Nos. J12-J17 (6)   40.80 8.40
See note below France No. J51.
For surcharges, see Nos. J21-J24.

Stamps of 1926
Surcharged

1927
J18 D1 60c on 20c olive grn   2.00   .80
J19 D1 2fr on 45c blue grn   2.75 1.60
J20 D1 3fr on 25c car rose   1.60   .80
     Nos. J18-J20 (3)   6.35 3.20

Recouvrement Stamps
of 1926 Surcharged

1927-32
J21 D2 10c on 30c bis ('32)   5.50 4.00
J22 D2 1fr on 1c olive grn   4.00 1.60
J23 D2 1fr on 60c dl red ('32)   24.00 12.00
J24 D2 2fr on 10c violet   16.00 12.00
     Nos. J21-J24 (4)   49.50 18.40

Catalogue values for unused
stamps in this section, from this
point to the end of the section, are
for **Never Hinged** items.

Type of 1926, Without "R F"
1942   Typo.   Perf. 14x13½
J25 D1 30c dark red   1.25 1.25
J26 D1 2fr magenta   1.75 *2.75*

Type of 1926
Surcharged in Red

1944   Perf. 14x13½
J27 A2 50c on 20c yel grn   1.00   .70
  a.   Inverted surcharge   27.50
  b.   Double surcharge   70.00
No. J27 was issued precanceled only. See
note after No. 32.

Type of 1926
1944   Litho.   Perf. 12
J28 D1 1.50fr brt rose lilac   1.00   .50
J29 D1 2fr greenish blue   1.25   .90
J30 D1 5fr rose carmine   1.25 1.10
     Nos. J28-J30 (3)   3.50 2.50

Type of 1926
1947   Typo.   Perf. 14x13½
J32 D1 5fr green   2.50 1.25

France Nos. J80-J81
Overprinted in Carmine
or Black

1947
J33 D5 10c sepia (C)   .50   .25
J34 D5 30c bright red violet   .65   .25

D3

**   Perf. 14x13**
1947-55
**   Unwmk.   Engr.**
J35 D3 20c red   .70   .35
J36 D3 60c ultra   1.00   .45
J37 D3 1fr dk org brn   .50   .35
J38 D3 1.50fr dull green   1.50 1.10
J39 D3 2fr red   .70   .45
J40 D3 3fr violet   .75   .45
J41 D3 5fr ultra ('49)   1.10   .35
J42 D3 6fr black   .85   .45
J43 D3 10fr lil rose   1.40   .45
J44 D3 15fr ol grn ('55)   1.40 1.25
J45 D3 20fr brt grn   1.10   .85
J46 D3 30fr red org ('55)   2.50 1.50

J47 D3 50fr indigo ('51)   4.75 2.75
J48 D3 100fr brt bl ('53)   17.50 8.50
     Nos. J35-J48 (14)   35.75 19.15

Independent State

France Nos. J93-J97
Overprinted in Black

**   Perf. 14x13½**
1962, July 2   Typo.   Unwmk.
Handstamped Overprint
J49 D6 5c bright pink   7.00 7.00
J50 D6 10c red orange   7.00 7.00
J51 D6 20c olive bister   7.00 7.00
J52 D6 50c dark green   10.00 10.00
J53 D6 1fr deep green   14.00 14.00
     Nos. J49-J53 (5)   45.00 45.00
Typographed Overprint
J49a D6 5c bright pink   23.00 17.00
J50a D6 10c red orange   23.00 17.00
J51a D6 20c olive bister   23.00 17.00
J52a D6 50c dark green   50.00 35.00
J53a D6 1fr deep green   70.00 55.00
     Nos. J49a-J53a (5)   189.00 141.00
See note after No. 290.

Scales — D4

1963, June 25   Perf. 14x13½
J54 D4 5c car rose & blk   .25   .25
J55 D4 10c olive & car   .25   .25
J56 D4 20c ultra & blk   .55   .30
J57 D4 50c bister brn & grn   1.25   .80
J58 D4 1fr lilac & org   2.25 2.00
     Nos. J54-J58 (5)   4.55 3.60

**No. J58 Surcharged with New Value
& 3 Bars**
1968, Mar. 28   Typo.   Perf. 14x13½
J59 D4 60c on 1fr lilac & org   1.25 1.00

Grain — D5

1972-93   Litho.   Perf. 13½x14
J60 D5 10c bister   .25   .25
J61 D5 20c deep brown   .25   .25
J62 D5 40c orange   .25   .25
J63 D5 50c dk vio blue   .30   .25
J64 D5 80c dk olive gray   .75   .30
J65 D5 1d green   .90   .55
  a.   yel green, perf. 14 ¼x14   .25   .25
J66 D5 2d blue   1.75 1.00
  a.   Prus bl, perf. 14 ¼x14   .25   .25
J67 D5 3d violet   .50   .25
J68 D5 4d lilac rose   .65   .35
     Nos. J60-J68 (9)   5.60 3.45
Issued: 3d, 4d, 1/21/93; others, 10/21/72.
Nos. J65a is inscribed "B ALGERIE" at bot-
tom right. No. J66a is inscribed "B ALGERIE"
or "BC ALGERIE."

Main Post Office,
Algiers — D6

2006, Mar. 28   Litho.   Perf. 13¾x14
J69 D6 5d green   .90   .90
J70 D6 10d blue   1.60 1.60

NEWSPAPER STAMPS

Nos. 1 and 33
Surcharged in Red

1924-26		Unwmk.	Perf. 14x13½	
P1	A16	½c on 1c dk gray	.40	.40
a.		Triple surcharge	300.00	
P2	A1	½c on 1c olive ('26)	.40	.40

ALLENSTEIN

ˈa-lən-ˌshtīn

LOCATION — In East Prussia
AREA — 4,457 sq. mi.
POP. — 540,000 (estimated 1920)
CAPITAL — Allenstein

Allenstein, a district of East Prussia, held a plebiscite in 1920 under the Versailles Treaty, voting to join Germany rather than Poland. Later that year, Allenstein became part of the German Republic.

100 Pfennig = 1 Mark

Stamps of Germany, 1906-20, Overprinted

Perf. 14, 14½, 14x14½, 14½x14

1920				Wmk. 125
1	A16	5pf green	.45	1.20
2	A16	10pf carmine	.45	1.20
3	A22	15pf dk vio	.45	1.20
4	A22	15pf vio brn	5.50	12.00
5	A16	20pf bl vio	.45	1.75
6	A16	30pf org & blk, buff	.45	1.75
7	A16	40pf lake & blk	.45	1.20
8	A16	50pf pur & blk, buff	.45	1.20
9	A16	75pf grn & blk	.45	1.20
10	A17	1m car rose	1.60	5.00
a.		Double overprint	250.00	1,000.
11	A17	1.25m green	1.60	5.25
a.		Double overprint	—	—
12	A17	1.50m yel brn	1.00	4.00
13	A21	2.50m lilac rose	2.50	10.50
14	A19	3m blk vio	2.50	5.25
a.		Double overprint	300.00	1,050.
		Never hinged	575.00	—
b.		Inverted overprint	—	—
		Nos. 1-14 (14)	18.30	52.70
		Set, never hinged	52.00	

Overprinted

15	A16	5pf green	.40	1.00
16	A16	10pf carmine	.40	1.00
17	A22	15pf dark vio	.40	1.00
18	A22	15pf vio brn	20.00	40.00
19	A16	20pf blue vio	.65	1.50
20	A16	30pf org & blk, buff	.40	1.00
21	A16	40pf lake & blk	.40	1.00
22	A16	50pf pur & blk, buff	.40	1.00
23	A16	75pf grn & blk	.65	1.50
24	A17	1m car rose	1.60	3.00
a.		Inverted overprint	600.00	800.00
		Never hinged	800.00	
25	A17	1.25m green	1.60	3.00
26	A17	1.50m yel brn	1.25	3.00
27	A21	2.50m lilac rose	2.75	7.50
28	A19	3m blk vio	1.75	3.00
a.		Inverted overprint	400.00	975.00
		Never hinged	725.00	
b.		Double overprint	200.00	600.00
		Never hinged	600.00	
		Nos. 15-28 (14)	32.65	68.50
		Set, never hinged	80.00	

The 40pf carmine rose (Germany No. 124) exists with this oval overprint, but it is doubtful whether it was regularly issued. Value $110 hinged, $210 never hinged.

ANDORRA, SPANISH ADMINISTRATION

an-'dor-ə

LOCATION — On the southern slope of the Pyrenees Mountains between France and Spain.
GOVT. — Co-principality
AREA — 179 sq. mi.
POP. — 72,766 (July 1, 1996)
CAPITAL — Andorra la Vella

Andorra was subject to the joint control of France and the Spanish Bishop of Urgel and paid annual tribute to both. In 1993, Andorra became a constitutional coprincipality, governed by its own parliament.

100 Centimos = 1 Peseta
100 Centimes = 1 Franc
100 Cents = 1 Euro (2002)

Catalogue values for unused stamps in the Spanish Administration for this country are for Never Hinged items, beginning with Scott 50 in the regular postage section and Scott C2 in the airpost section; for the French Administration of this country, Never Hinged items begin at Scott 78 for regular postage, Scott B1 for the semi-postal section, Scott C1 for the airpost section, and Scott J21 for the postage due section.

A majority of the Spanish Andorra stamps issued to about 1950 are poorly centered. The fine examples that are valued will be somewhat off center. Very poorly centered examples (perfs cutting design) sell for less. Well centered very fine stamps are scarce and sell for approximately twice the values shown (Nos. 1-24, E1-E3), or 50% more (Nos. 25-49, E4-E5).

Stamps of Spain, 1922-26, Overprinted in Red or Black

Perf. 13½x12½, 12½x11½, 14

1928   Unwmk.

No.	Type	Description		
1	A49	2c olive green	.55	.55

Control Numbers on Back

2	A49	5c car rose (Bk)	.80	.80
3	A49	10c green	.80	.80
4	A49	15c slate blue	3.25	3.25
5	A49	20c violet	3.25	3.50
6	A49	25c rose red (Bk)	3.25	3.50
b.		Inverted ovpt., perf 14	130.00	
7	A49	30c black brown	18.00	16.50
b.		Inverted ovpt., perf 12½x11½	130.00	50.00
8	A49	40c deep blue	18.00	11.00
9	A49	50c orange (Bk)	18.00	14.50
c.		Inverted ovpt., perf 14	130.00	—
10	A49a	1p blue blk	23.00	23.50
11	A49a	4p lake (Bk)	150.00	175.00
12	A49a	10p brown (Bk)	275.00	275.00
a.		Double overprint	700.00	
		Nos. 1-12 (12)	513.90	527.90
		Set, never hinged	1,200.	

Counterfeit overprints exist.
Nos. 1-12 perf 14 are worth much more. See the *Scott Classic Specialized Catalogue.*

La Vall
A1

St. Juan de Caselles
A2

St. Julia de Loria — A3

St. Coloma — A4

General Council — A5

1929, Nov. 25   Engr.   Perf. 14

13	A1	2c olive green	1.10	.60

Control Numbers on Back

14	A2	5c carmine lake	3.50	1.25
15	A3	10c yellow green	3.50	4.50
16	A4	15c slate green	3.50	4.50
17	A3	20c violet	3.50	4.50
18	A4	25c carmine rose	7.75	6.25
19	A1	30c olive green	115.00	175.00
20	A2	40c dark blue	4.50	3.00
21	A3	50c deep orange	5.50	4.50
22	A5	1p slate	12.50	14.50
23	A5	4p deep rose	90.00	110.00
24	A5	10p bister brown	100.00	140.00
		Nos. 13-24 (12)	350.35	468.60
		Set, never hinged	800.00	

Nos. 13-24 exist imperforate. Value, $800.

1931-38   Perf. 11½

13a	A1	2c	6.25	.80

Control Numbers on Back

14a	A2	5c	10.00	2.25
15a	A3	10c	10.00	2.00
16a	A4	15c	30.00	25.00
17a	A3	20c	10.00	6.00
18a	A4	25c	10.00	6.00
19a	A1	30c ('33)	175.00	65.00
20a	A2	40c ('35)	17.00	13.00
22a	A5	1p ('38)	40.00	25.00
		Nos. 13a-22a (9)	308.25	145.05
		Set, never hinged	500.00	

Without Control Numbers

1936-43   Perf. 11½x11

25	A1	2c red brown ('37)	2.00	1.60
26	A2	5c dark brown	2.00	1.60
27	A3	10c blue green	13.00	3.25
a.		10c yellow green	150.00	80.00
		Never hinged	200.00	
28	A4	15c blue green ('37)	7.50	3.50
a.		15c yellow green	8.00	5.75
29	A3	20c violet	7.00	3.50
30	A4	25c deep rose ('37)	3.25	3.25
31	A1	30c carmine	5.50	3.25
31A	A2	40c dark blue	750.00	—
		Never hinged	1,250.	
32	A1	45c rose red ('37)	2.00	1.60
33	A3	50c deep orange	10.00	5.75
34	A1	60c deep blue ('37)	7.00	3.50
34A	A5	1p slate	1,000.	—
		Never hinged	2,000.	
35	A5	4p deep rose ('43)	40.00	47.50
36	A5	10p bister brn ('43)	52.50	57.50
		Nos. 25-31,32-34,35-36 (12)	151.75	135.80
		Set, never hinged	325.00	

Exist imperforate. Value hinged, $275.
Beware of counterfeits of Nos. 31A and 34A. Purchase of stamps with certificates is strongly advised.

Edelweiss — A6

Provost — A7

Coat of Arms — A8

Plaza of Ordino — A9

Chapel of Meritxell — A10

Map — A11

1948-53   Unwmk.   Photo.   Perf. 12½

37	A6	2c brn olive ('51)	.35	.35
38	A6	5c orange ('53)	.35	.35
39	A6	10c blue ('53)	.35	.35

		Engr.	Perf. 9½x10	
40	A7	20c brown vio	4.25	2.75
41	A7	25c org, perf. 12½ ('53)	3.00	2.10
42	A8	30c dk slate grn	4.25	3.25
43	A9	50c deep green	5.00	4.75
44	A10	75c dark blue	6.50	4.75
45	A9	90c dp car rose	3.50	3.50
46	A10	1p brt orange ver	5.00	4.25
47	A8	1.35c dk blue vio	3.50	3.50

		Perf. 10		
48	A11	4p ultra ('53)	4.75	8.50
49	A11	10p dk vio brn ('51)	11.00	11.00
		Nos. 37-49 (13)	51.80	49.40
		Set, never hinged	120.00	

Catalogue values for unused stamps in this section, from this point to the end of the section, are for Never Hinged items.

Bridge of St. Anthony — A12

Madonna of Meritxell, 8th Century — A13

Designs: 70c, Aynos pasture. 1p, View of Canillo. 2p, St. Coloma. 2.50p, Arms of Andorra. 3p, Old Andorra, horiz. 5p, View of Ordino, horiz.

1963-64   Unwmk.   Engr.   Perf. 13

50	A12	25c dk gray & sepia	.30	.25
51	A12	70c dk sl grn & brn blk	.40	.35
52	A12	1p slate & dull pur	.85	.45
53	A12	2p violet & dull pur	.85	.50
54	A12	2.50p rose claret	.85	.70
55	A12	3p blk & grnsh gray	1.60	.80
56	A12	5p dk brn & choc	2.50	1.25
57	A13	6p sepia & car	3.50	2.75
		Nos. 50-57 (8)	10.85	7.05

Issued: 25c-2p, 7/20/63; 2.50p-6p, 2/29/64.

Narcissus — A14

1966, June 10   Engr.   Perf. 13

58	A14	50c shown	.85	.50
59	A14	1p Pinks	.85	.50
60	A14	5p Jonquils	2.50	1.50
61	A14	10p Hellebore	1.75	1.00
		Nos. 58-61 (4)	5.95	3.50

Common Design Types pictured following the introduction.

Europa Issue 1972
Common Design Type

1972, May 2   Photo.   Perf. 13
Size: 25½x38mm

62	CD15	8p multicolored	60.00	60.00

Encamp Valley — A15

Tourist publicity: 1.50p, Massana (village). 2p, Skiing on De La Casa Pass. 5p, Pessons Lake, horiz.

1972, July 4   Photo.   Perf. 13

63	A15	1p multicolored	.50	.40
64	A15	1.50p multicolored	.75	.40
65	A15	2p multicolored	2.25	1.00
66	A15	5p multicolored	3.00	1.10
		Nos. 63-66 (4)	6.50	2.90

Butterfly Stroke A16

Design: 2p, Volleyball, vert.

1972, Oct.   Photo.   Perf. 13

67	A16	2p lt blue & multi	.35	.35
68	A16	5p multicolored	.55	.55

20th Olympic Games, Munich, 8/26-9/11.

St. Anthony Singers A17

1.50p, Les Caramelles (boys' choir). 2p, Nativity scene. 5p, Man holding giant cigar, vert. 8p, Hermit of Meritxell, vert. 15p, Marratxa dancers.

1972, Dec. 5   Photo.   Perf. 13

69	A17	1p multicolored	.35	.25
70	A17	1.50p multicolored	.35	.25
71	A17	2p multicolored	.45	.35
72	A17	5p multicolored	.60	.45
73	A17	8p multicolored	.90	.50
74	A17	15p multicolored	1.75	1.10
		Nos. 69-74 (6)	4.40	2.90

Andorran customs. No. 71 is for Christmas.

Europa Issue 1973
Common Design Type and

Symbol of Unity A18

1973, Apr. 30   Photo.   Perf. 13

75	A18	2p ultra, red & blk	.40	.25

Size: 37x25mm

76	CD16	8p tan, red & blk	1.25	.85

Nativity — A19

Christmas: 5p, Adoration of the Kings. Designs are from altar panels of Meritxell Parish Church.

1973, Dec. 14   Photo.   Perf. 13

77	A19	2p multicolored	.40	.30
78	A19	5p multicolored	1.25	1.00

Virgin of Ordino — A20

Europa: 8p, Les Banyes Cross.

1974, Apr. 29   Photo.   Perf. 13
79 A20 2p multicolored   .90 .70
80 A20 8p slate & brt blue   2.75 1.75

Cupboard — A21

Crowns of Virgin and Child of Roser — A22

1974, July 30   Photo.   Perf. 13
81 A21 10p multicolored   2.00 1.60
82 A22 25p dark red & multi   3.75 3.25

UPU Monument, Bern A23

1974, Oct. 9   Photo.   Perf. 13
83 A23 15p multicolored   1.75 1.75
Centenary of Universal Postal Union.

Nativity A24

Christmas: 5p, Adoration of the Kings.

1974, Dec. 4   Photo.   Perf. 13
84 A24 2p multicolored   .80 .70
85 A24 5p multicolored   1.90 1.60

Mail Delivery, Andorra, 19th Century — A25

1975, Apr. 4   Photo.   Perf. 13
86 A25 3p multicolored   .45 .45
Espana 75 Intl. Philatelic Exhibition, Madrid, 4/4-13.

12th Century Painting, Ordino Church — A26

Design: 12p, Christ in Glory, 12th century Romanesque painting, Ordino church.

1975, Apr. 28   Photo.   Perf. 13
87 A26 3p multicolored   1.25 .70
88 A26 12p multicolored   2.25 1.40

Urgel Cathedral and Document — A27

1975, Oct. 4   Photo.   Perf. 13
89 A27 7p multicolored   1.75 1.25
Millennium of consecration of Urgel Cathedral, and Literary Festival 1975.

Nativity, Ordino A28

Christmas: 7p, Adoration of the Kings, Ordino.

1975, Dec. 3   Photo.   Perf. 13
90 A28 3p multicolored   .40 .40
91 A28 7p multicolored   .85 .85

Caldron and CEPT Emblem — A29

Europa: 12p, Chest and CEPT emblem.

1976, May 3   Photo.   Perf. 13
92 A29 3p bister & multi   .40 .25
93 A29 12p yel & multi, horiz.   1.00 .50

Slalom and Montreal Olympic Emblem — A30

Design: 15p, One-man canoe and Montreal Olympic emblem, horiz.

1976, July 9   Photo.   Perf. 13
94 A30 7p multicolored   .45 .25
95 A30 15p multicolored   .90 .40
21st Olympic Games, Montreal, Canada, July 17-Aug. 1.

Nativity A31

Christmas: 25p, Adoration of the Kings. Wall paintings in La Massana Church.

1976, Dec. 7   Photo.   Perf. 13
96 A31 3p multicolored   .50 .25
97 A31 25p multicolored   1.00 .35

View of Ansalonge — A32

Europa: 12p, Xuclar, valley, mountains.

1977, May 2   Litho.   Perf. 13
98 A32 3p multicolored   .35 .25
99 A32 12p multicolored   .90 .40

Cross of Terme — A33

Christmas: 12p, Church of St. Miguel d'Engolasters.

1977, Dec. 2   Photo.   Perf. 13x12½
100 A33 5p multicolored   .45 .35
101 A33 12p multicolored   1.10 .65

Souvenir Sheet

A34

Designs: 5p, Map of Post Offices. 10p, Mail delivery. 20p, Post Office, 1928. 25p, Andorran coat of arms.

1978, Mar. 31   Photo.   Perf. 13x13½
102 A34   Sheet of 4   1.60 1.60
  a.   5p multicolored   .35 .35
  b.   10p multicolored   .35 .35
  c.   20p multicolored   .35 .35
  d.   25p multicolored   .35 .35
Spanish postal service in Andorra, 50th anniv.

La Vall — A35

Europa: 12p, St. Juan de Caselles.

1978, May 2   Perf. 13
103 A35 5p multicolored   .40 .25
104 A35 12p multicolored   .90 .40

Crown, Bishop's Mitre and Staff A36

1978, Sept. 24   Photo.   Perf. 13
105 A36 5p brown, car & yel   .85 .40
700th anniversary of the signing of treaty establishing Co-Principality of Andorra.

Holy Family — A37

Christmas: 25p, Adoration of the Kings. Both designs after frescoes in the Church of St. Mary d'Encamp.

1978, Dec. 5   Photo.   Perf. 13
106 A37 5p multicolored   .25 .25
107 A37 25p multicolored   .65 .35

Young Woman — A38

Designs: 5p, Young man. 12p, Bridegroom and bride riding mule.

1979, Feb. 14   Photo.   Perf. 13
108 A38 3p multicolored   .25 .25
109 A38 5p multicolored   .25 .25
110 A38 12p multicolored   .40 .30
  Nos. 108-110 (3)   .90 .80

Old Mail Truck A39

Europa: 12p, Stampless covers of 1846 & 1854.

1979, Apr. 30   Engr.   Perf. 13
111 A39 5p yel grn & dk blue   .40 .25
112 A39 12p dk red & violet   .85 .40

Children Holding Hands A40

1979, Oct. 18   Photo.   Perf. 13
113 A40 19p multicolored   .90 .35
International Year of the Child.

St. Coloma's Church — A41

Christmas: 25p, Agnus Dei roundel, St. Coloma's Church.

1979, Nov. 28　Photo.　Perf. 13½
114 A41 8p multicolored .25 .25
115 A41 25p multicolored .70 .40

Bishop Pere d'Arg A42

Bishops of Urgel: 5p, Josep Caixal. 13p, Joan Bennloch.

1979, Dec. 27　　　　Engr.
116 A42 1p dk blue & brown .30 .25
117 A42 5p rose lake & purple .30 .25
118 A42 13p brown & dk green .30 .30
　　Nos. 116-118 (3) .90 .80

See Nos. 132-133, 159, 175, C4.

Antoni Fiter, Magistrate — A43

Europa: 19p, Francesc Cairat, magistrate.

1980, Apr. 28　Photo.　Perf. 13x13½
119 A43 8p bister, blk & brn .35 .25
120 A43 19p lt green & blk .85 .40

Boxing, Moscow '80 Emblem A44

1980, July 23　Photo.　Perf. 13½x13
121 A44 5p Downhill skiing .25 .25
122 A44 8p shown .25 .25
123 A44 50p Target shooting .80 .40
　　Nos. 121-123 (3) 1.30 .90

12th Winter Olympic Games, Lake Placid, NY, Feb. 12-24 (5p); 22nd Summer Olympic Games, Moscow, July 19-Aug. 3.

Nativity A45

1980, Dec. 12　Litho.　Perf. 13
124 A45 10p Nativity, vert. .25 .25
125 A45 22p shown .65 .30

Christmas 1980.

Children Dancing at Santa Anna Feast A46

Europa: 30p, Going to church on Aplec de la Verge de Canolich Day.

1981, May 7　Photo.　Perf. 13
126 A46 12p multicolored .40 .25
127 A46 30p multicolored .85 .40

50th Anniv. of Police Force A47

1981, July 2　Photo.　Perf. 13½x13
128 A47 30p multicolored .85 .35

Intl. Year of the Disabled A48

1981, Oct. 8　Photo.　Perf. 13½
129 A48 50p multicolored 1.25 .40

Christmas 1981 A49

Designs: Encamp Church retable.

1981, Dec. 3　Photo.　Perf. 13½
130 A49 12p Nativity .40 .25
131 A49 30p Adoration .80 .40

Bishops of Urgel Type of 1979
1981, Dec. 12　　　Engr.　Perf. 13½
132 A42 7p Salvador Casanas .30 .25
133 A42 20p Josep de Boltas .55 .25

Natl. Arms — A51

1982, Feb. 17　Photo.　Perf. 13x13½
134 A51 1p bright pink .25 .25
135 A51 3p bister brown .25 .25
136 A51 7p red orange .25 .25
137 A51 12p lake .25 .25
138 A51 15p ultra .30 .25
139 A51 20p blue green .40 .40
140 A51 30p crimson rose .80 .40

Perf. 13½x12½
1982, Sept. 30　　　　Engr.
Size: 25½x30½mm
141 A51 50p dark green 1.00 .40
142 A51 100p dark blue 1.75 .80
　　Nos. 134-142 (9) 5.25 3.25

For type A51 without "PTA" see Nos. 192-198.

Europa 1982 A52

14p, New Reforms, 1866, vert. 33p, Reform of Institutions, 1981.

1982, May 12　Photo.　Perf. 13
143 A52 14p multicolored .35 .25
144 A52 33p multicolored 1.00 .40

1982 World Cup — A53

Designs: Various soccer players.

1982, June 13　Photo.　Perf. 13x13½
145 A53 14p multicolored 1.05 1.05
146 A53 33p multicolored 1.90 1.90
a. Pair, #145-146 + label 3.25 3.25

A54

Anniversaries: 9p, Permanent Spanish and French delegations, cent. 14p, 50th anniv. of Andorran stamps, horiz. 23p, St. Francis of Assisi (1182-1226). 33p, Anyos Pro-Vicarial District membership centenary (Relacio sobre la Vall de Andorra titlepage).

1982, Sept. 7　　　Engr.　Perf. 13
147 A54 9p dk blue & brown .30 .25
148 A54 14p black & green .80 .25
149 A54 23p dk blue & brown .60 .25
150 A54 33p black & olive grn .60 .40
　　Nos. 147-150 (4) 2.30 1.30

A55

A55a

Christmas: 14p, Madonna and Child, Andorra la Vieille Church, vert. 33p, El Tio de Nadal (children in traditional costumes striking hollow tree).

Perf. 13x13½, 13½x13
1982, Dec. 9　　　　　　Photo.
151 A55 14p multicolored .40 .25
152 A55a 33p multicolored .85 .40

Europa 1983 A56

16, La Cortinada Church, architect, 12th cent. 38p, Water mill, 16th cent.

1983, June 7　Photo.　Perf. 13
153 A56 16p multicolored .40 .25
154 A56 38p multicolored .85 .40

Local Mushrooms — A57

16p, Lactarius sanguifluus.

1983, July 20　Photo.　Perf. 13x12½
155 A57 16p multicolored .80 .60

See Nos. 165, 169, 172.

Universal Suffrage, 50th Anniv. A58

Photogravure and Engraved
1983, Sept. 6　　　　Perf. 13
156 A58 10p multicolored .40 .25

Visit of Monsignor Jacinto Verdaguer Bishop and Co-Prince A59

1983, Sept. 6
157 A59 50p multicolored 1.00 .55

Christmas 1983 — A60

Saint Cerni de Nagol, Romanesque fresco, Church of San Cerni de Nagol.

1983, Nov. 24　Photo.　Perf. 13½
158 A60 16p multicolored .45 .25

Bishops of Urgel Type of 1979
26p, Joan J. Laguarda Fenollera.

1983, Dec. 7　　　Engr.　Perf. 13
159 A42 26p multicolored .80 .40

1984 Winter Olympics A62

1984, Feb. 17　Litho.　Perf. 13½x14
160 A62 16p Ski jumping .80 .25

ESPANA '84 — A63

1984, Apr. 27　Photo.　Perf. 13
161 A63 26p Emblems .80 .40

Europa
(1959-84)
A64

1984, May 5   Engr.
162 A64 16p brown   .60   .25
163 A64 38p blue   .90   .40

1984
Summer
Olympics
A65

1984, Aug. 9   Litho.   Perf. 13½x14
164 A65 40p Running   1.25   .60

Mushroom Type of 1983

11p, Morchella esculenta.

1984, Sept. 27 Photo. Perf. 13x12½
165 A57 11p multicolored   7.25 2.00

Christmas
1984
A66

1984, Dec. 6   Photo.   Perf. 13½
166 A66 17p Nativity carving   .50   .25

Europa
1985
A67

18p, Mossen Enric Arfany, composer, natl.
hymn score. 45p, Musician Playing Viol,
Romanesque fresco detail, La Cortinada
Church, vert.

1985, May 3   Engr.   Perf. 13½
167 A67 18p dk vio, grn & choco-
          late   .45   .25
168 A67 45p green & chocolate   1.40   .40

Mushroom Type of 1983
Perf. 13½x12½

1985, Sept. 19   Photo.
169 A57 30p Gyromitra esculenta 1.10   .40

Pal Village — A68

1985, Nov. 7   Engr.   Perf. 13½
170 A68 17p brt ultra & dk blue   .50   .25

Christmas
1985
A69

Fresco: Angels Playing Trumpet and Psal-
tery, St. Bartholomew Chapel.

1985, Dec. 11   Photo.   Perf. 13½x13
171 A69 17p multicolored   .50   .25

Mushroom Type of 1983
Perf. 13½x12½

1986, Apr. 10   Photo.
172 A57 30p Marasmius oreades   .90   .40

Europa
1986 — A70

1986, May 5   Engr.   Perf. 13
173 A70 17p Water   .40   .30
174 A70 45p Soil and air   1.60   .60

Bishops of Urgel Type of 1979

1986, Sept. 11   Engr.   Perf. 13½
175 A42 35p Justi Guitart   .80   .40

Christmas — A72

Santa Roma de Les Bons Church bell.

1986, Dec. 11   Litho.   Perf. 14
176 A72 19p multicolored   .50   .25

A73

Contemporary Natl. Coat of Arms.

1987, Mar. 27   Photo.   Perf. 14
177 A73 48p multicolored   .90   .40

Visit of the co-princes: the Bishop of Urgel
and president of France, September 26, 1986.

Europa
1987
A74

Modern architecture: 19p, Meritxell Sanctuary interior. 48p, Sanctuary exterior, vert.

1987, May 15   Engr.   Perf. 14x13½
178 A74 19p dark blue & brown   .40   .40
179 A74 48p dark blue & brown   1.60   .40

Souvenir Sheet

1992 Summer Olympics,
Barcelona — A75

20p, House of the Valleys. 50p, Bell tower,
Chapel of the Archangel Michael, and torchbearer.

1987, July 20   Photo.   Perf. 14
180 A75 Sheet of 2   4.00 4.00
  a.   20p multicolored   1.20 1.20
  b.   50p multicolored   2.25 2.25

Local
Mushrooms — A76

1987, Sept. 11   Perf. 13½x12½
181 A76 100p Boletus edulis   2.25 1.25

Christmas
A77

Design: Detail from a Catalan manuscript,
De Nativitat, by R. Llull.

1987, Nov. 18   Litho.   Perf. 14
182 A77 20p multicolored   .50   .25

Lance and
Arrowhead
(Bronze
Age)
A78

1988, Mar. 25   Photo.   Perf. 14
183 A78 50p multicolored   .90   .40

Europa
1988 — A79

Transport and communications: 20p, Les
Bons, a medieval road. 45p, Trader and pack
mules, early 20th cent.

1988, May 5   Engr.   Perf. 14x13½
184 A79 20p dark bl & dark red   .45   .25
185 A79 45p dark bl & dark red   1.50   .40

Pyrenean
Mastiff — A80

1988, July 26   Litho.   Perf. 14x13½
186 A80 20p multicolored   1.50   .60

Bishop of Urgel
and Seigneur of
Caboet Confirming
Co-Principality,
700th
Anniv. — A81

1988, Oct. 24   Litho.   Perf. 14x13½
187 A81 20p gold, blk & int blue   .60   .30

Christmas
1988
A82

1988, Nov. 30 Litho.   Perf. 14x13½
188 A82 20p multicolored   .50   .25

Arms Type of 1982 Without "PTA"
1988, Dec. 2   Photo.   Perf. 13½x13½
192 A51 20p brt blue green   .50   .25

Size: 25x30½mm
Perf. 13½x12½
Engr.
194 A51 50p grnsh black   1.00   .40
196 A51 100p dark blue   2.25   .80
198 A51 500p dark brown   8.25 3.00
    Nos. 192-198 (4)   12.00 4.45

Europa
1989
A83

Perf. 14x13½, 13½x14
1989, May 8   Litho. & Engr.
200 A83 20p Leapfrog, vert.   .55   .40
201 A83 45p Tug of war   1.50   .80

Santa
Roma
Church,
Les Bons
A84

Litho. & Engr.
1989, June 20   Perf. 13½x14
202 A84 50p blk, dp bl & grn bl 1.25   .40

Anniv.
Emblem — A85

1989, Oct. 26   Litho.   Perf. 14x13½
203 A85 20p multicolored   .80   .40

Intl. Red Cross and Red Crescent societies,
125th annivs.; Year for the Protection of
Human Life.

Christmas — A86

The Immaculate Conception.

1989, Dec. 1
204 A86 20p multicolored   .50   .25

Europa
1990
A87

Post offices.

Perf. 13½x14, 14x13½
1990, May 17   **Photo.**
205 A87 20p shown   .55   .25
206 A87 50p Post office, vert.   1.40   .40

Gomphidius Rutilus — A88

1990, June 21   Litho.   Perf. 13x13½
207 A88 45p multicolored   1.50   .60

Plandolit House — A89

Litho. & Engr.
1990, Oct. 17   **Perf. 13x12½**
208 A89 20p brown & org yel   .50   .25

Christmas — A90

1990, Nov. 26   Litho.   Perf. 14x13½
209 A90 25p lake, brn & bister   .60   .30

4th Games of the Small European States A91

1991, Apr. 29   Photo.   Perf. 13½x14
210 A91 25p Discus   .60   .30
211 A91 45p High jump, runner   1.00   .40

Europa — A92

Perf. 14x13½, 13½x14
1991, May 10   **Litho.**
212 A92 25p Olympus-1 satellite   .70   .40
213 A92 55p Olympus-1, horiz.   2.50   .80

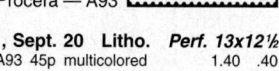
Macrolepiota Procera — A93

1991, Sept. 20   Litho.   Perf. 13x12½
214 A93 45p multicolored   1.40   .40

Christmas — A94

1991, Nov. 29   Photo.   Perf. 14x13½
215 A94 25p multicolored   1.00   .40

Woman Carrying Water Pails A95

1992, Feb. 14   Photo.   Perf. 13½x14
216 A95 25p multicolored   .80   .40

European Discovery of America, 500th Anniv. A96

Perf. 14x13½, 13½x14
1992, May 8   **Photo.**
217 A96 27p Santa Maria, vert.   .65   .40
218 A96 45p King Ferdinand   2.25   .40

Europa.

1992 Summer Olympics, Barcelona A97

1992, July 22   Photo.   Perf. 13½x14
219 A97 27p Kayak   .80   .40

Nativity Scene, by Fra Angelico — A98

1992, Nov. 18   Photo.   Perf. 14
220 A98 27p multicolored   .80   .40

Natl. Automobile Museum A99

Litho. & Engr.
1992, Sept. 10   **Perf. 13½x14**
221 A99 27p 1894 Benz   1.00   .40

Cantharellus Cibarius — A100

1993, Mar. 25   Photo.   Perf. 13½x14
222 A100 28p multicolored   1.00   .40

Contemporary Paintings — A101

Europa: 28p, Upstream, by John Alan Morrison. 45p, Rhythm, by Angel Calvente, vert.

Perf. 13½x14, 14x13½
1993, May 20   **Litho.**
223 A101 28p multicolored   .75   .40
224 A101 45p multicolored   1.50   .80

Art and Literature Society, 25th Anniv. — A102

1993, Sept. 23   Litho.   Perf. 14
225 A102 28p multicolored   .80   .40

Christmas — A103

Litho. & Engr.
1993, Nov. 25   **Perf. 14x13½**
226 A103 28p multicolored   .80   .40

Souvenir Sheet

Constitution, 1st Anniv. — A104

1994, Mar. 14   Photo.   Perf. 14
227 A104 29p multicolored   1.00   .75

Sir Alexander Fleming (1881-1955), Co-discoverer of Penicillin — A105

1994, May 6   Photo.   Perf. 13½x14
228 A105 29p Portrait   .60   .40
229 A105 55p AIDS virus   1.50   .80

Europa.

Hygrophorus Gliocyclus — A106

1994, Sept. 27   Photo.   Perf. 14
230 A106 29p multicolored   1.00   .50

Christmas — A107

1994, Nov. 29   Photo.   Perf. 14x13½
231 A107 29p multicolored   1.00   .50

Nature Conservation in Europe — A108

1995, Mar. 23   Photo.   Perf. 14
232 A108 30p Farm in valley   .70   .45
233 A108 60p Stone fence, valley   1.35   .75

Europa A109

1995, May 8   Photo.   Perf. 14
234 A109 60p multicolored   1.60   .80

Christmas — A110

1995, Nov. 8   Photo.   Perf. 14
235 A110 30p Flight to Egypt   1.00   .40

Entrance Into Council of Europe A111

1995, Nov. 10
236 A111 30p multicolored   1.10   .40

Mushrooms — A112

30p, Ramaria aurea. 60p, Tuber melanosporum.

1996, Apr. 30   Photo.   *Perf. 14*
237 A112 30p multicolored   .90   .35
238 A112 60p multicolored   1.60   .80

Isabelle Sandy (1884-1975), Writer — A113

1996, May 7
239 A113 60p brown & violet   *1.75   .80*
Europa.

Intl. Museum Day A114

Design: Antique coal-heated iron.

1996, Sept. 12   Photo.   *Perf. 14*
240 A114 60p multicolored   1.10   .55

Christmas A115

The Annunciation, by Andrew Martin, 1753, St. Eulalia d'Encamp Church.

1996, Nov. 26   Photo.   *Perf. 14*
241 A115 30p multicolored   .90   .40

Museums of Andorra A116

Early bicycles designed by: 32p, Karl Drais, 1818. 65p, Pierre Michaux, 1861.

1997, Apr. 28   Photo.   *Perf. 14*
242 A116 32p multicolored   .70   .35
243 A116 65p multicolored   1.40   .70
See Nos. 248-249.

A117

Europa (Stories and Legends): Hikers watching family of bears crossing over river on fallen tree.

1997, May 6   Photo.   *Perf. 14*
244 A117 65p multicolored   *1.75   .80*

UNESCO — A118

1997, Sept. 30   Photo.   *Perf. 14*
245 A118 32p multicolored   .80   .35

Christmas — A119

1997, Nov. 25   Photo.   *Perf. 14*
246 A119 32p multicolored   .75   .35

1998 Winter Olympic Games, Nagano A120

1998, Feb. 23   Photo.   *Perf. 14*
247 A120 35p Slalom skier   .80   .35

Museums of Andorra Type of 1997

Early bicycles: 35p, Kangaroo, 1878. 70p, Hirondelle, 1889.

1998, Apr. 24   Photo.   *Perf. 13½x14*
248 A116 35p multicolored   .60   .35
249 A116 70p multicolored   1.25   .70

Harlequins, Canillas Carnival A121

1998, May 22   Photo.   *Perf. 14*
250 A121 70p multicolored   *1.50   .70*
Europa.

Manual Digest, 250th Anniv. — A122

1998, Sept. 30   Photo.   *Perf. 14*
251 A122 35p multicolored   .70   .40

Inauguration of the Postal Museum of Andorra — A123

1998, Nov. 19   Photo.   *Perf. 14*
252 A123 70p multicolored   1.25   .75

Christmas A124

1998, Nov. 26
253 A124 35p multicolored   .80   .40

Museums of Andorra A125

Early bicycles designed by: 35p, Salvo, 1878, vert. 70p, Rudge, 1883.

1999, Jan. 29   Photo.   *Perf. 14*
254 A125 35p multicolored   .70   .40
255 A125 70p multicolored   1.10   .75

Council of Europe, 50th Anniv. A126

1999, Apr. 29   Photo.   *Perf. 14*
256 A126 35p multicolored   .80   .40

Incles Valley A127

1999, May 6
257 A127 70p multicolored   1.60   .80
Europa.

Transporting Mail on Horseback — A128

1999, Feb. 18   Photo.   *Perf. 14*
258 A128 35p black & sepia   1.00   .50

Restoration of Casa Rull, Sispony, La Massana A129

1999, Sept. 22   Photo.   *Perf. 13½x14*
259 A129 35p multicolored   .90   .45

Christmas — A130

1999, Nov. 10   Engr.   *Perf. 14x13½*
260 A130 35p orange brn & brn   .90   .45

St. Coloma's Church — A131

1999, Nov. 12   Photo.
261 A131 35p multicolored   .80   .40
European heritage.

Europa, 2000
Common Design Type
2000, May 11   Photo.   *Perf. 13¾*
262 CD17 70p multicolored   *1.75   .80*

Angonella Lakes A132

2000, June 29   Photo.   *Perf. 13¾x14*
263 A132 35p multicolored   .90   .45

Casa Lacruz A133

2000, July 20   Photo.   *Perf. 13¾x14*
264 A133 35p multicolored   .90   .45

China, Areny-Plandolit Museum — A134

2000, July 27   *Perf. 14x13¾*
265 A134 70p multicolored   1.50   .75

2000 Summer Olympics, Sydney — A135

2000, Sept. 29   Photo.   *Perf. 14x13½*
266 A135 70p multicolored   1.50   .75

European Convention on Human Rights, 50th Anniv. A136

2000, Nov. 3   *Perf. 13½x14*
267 A136 70p multicolored   1.60 .75

Natl. Archives, 25th Anniv. — A137

2000, Nov. 14   *Perf. 14x13½*
268 A137 35p multicolored   .80 .40

Christmas — A138

2000, Nov. 22
269 A138 35p multicolored   1.00 .40

Rec de Solà — A139

2001, Mar. 30 Photo.   *Perf. 14x13¾*
270 A139 40p multicolored   .80 .60

Europa A140

2001, May 16   *Perf. 13¾x14*
271 A140 75p multicolored   1.50 .85

Casa Palau, Sant Julià de Lòria — A141

2001, June 20 Photo.   *Perf. 14x13¾*
272 A141 75p multi   1.25 .75

Chapel of the Virgin of Meritxell, 25th Anniv. of Rebuilding — A142

2001, Sept. 7 Photo.   *Perf. 14x13¾*
273 A142 40p multi   .90 .60

Natl. Auditorium, 10th Anniv. A143

2001, Sept. 20   *Perf. 13¾x14*
274 A143 75p multi   1.50 1.00

Christmas A144

2001, Nov. 20 Photo.   *Perf. 13¾x14*
275 A144 40p multi   1.00 .55

100 Cents = 1 Euro (€)

Coat of Arms — A145

2002, Jan. 2 Photo.   *Perf. 12¾x13¼*
276 A145 25c brown orange   .85 .60
277 A145 50c claret   1.40 1.10

Birds A146

Designs: 25c, Prunella collaris. 50c, Montifringilla nivalis.

2002, Mar. 27   *Perf. 13¾x14*
278-279 A146 Set of 2   2.50 2.00

Intl. Year of Mountains A147

2002, Apr. 5
280 A147 50c multi   1.75 1.10

Europa A148

2002, May 9
281 A148 50c multi   14.00 3.50

Architectural Heritage — A149

Designs: €1.80, Casa Fusilé, Escaldes-Engordany. €2.10, Farga Rossell Centre, La Massana.

2002, June 14 Photo.   *Perf. 14x13¾*
282-283 A149 Set of 2   11.00 9.00

Historic Automobiles A150

Designs: 25c, Pinette. 50c, Rolls-Royce, horiz.

2002, Oct. 8   *Perf. 14x13¾, 13¾x14*
284-285 A150 Set of 2   2.25 2.00

Christmas A151

2002, Nov. 26   *Perf. 13¾x14*
286 A151 25c multi   .90 .70

Artistic Heritage — A152

Various religious murals from Santa Coloma Church: a, 25c. b, 75c. c, 50c.

2002, Nov. 28   *Perf. 14x13¾*
287 A152 Horiz. strip of 3, #a-c 4.25 3.50

Sassanat Bridge A153

    Perf. 13½x13¾
2003, Feb. 27   **Photo.**
288 A153 26c multi   1.40 .60

Constitution, 10th Anniv. — A154

2003, Mar. 14 Photo.   *Perf. 13¾x14*
289 A154 76c multi   2.50 1.75

Europa — A155

2003, Apr. 24   *Perf. 14x13¾*
290 A155 76c multi   2.25 1.10

Oenanthe Oenanthe — A156

2003, June 11 Photo.   *Perf. 14x13¾*
291 A156 26c multi   1.25 .90

Admission to United Nations, 10th Anniv. A157

2003, July 28 Photo.   *Perf. 13¾x14*
292 A157 76c multi   2.50 1.75

Automobiles — A158

Designs: 51c, 1908 Carter, vert. 76c, 1928 Peugeot.

2003, Oct. 15   *Perf. 14x13¾, 13¾x14*
293-294 A158 Set of 2   7.00 7.00

Christmas A159

2003, Nov. 20   *Perf. 13¾x14*
295 A159 26c multi   .90 .60

Coat of Arms — A160

2004, Jan. 2   *Perf. 12¾x13¼*
296 A160 27c bright blue   .70 .60
297 A160 52c olive green   1.40 1.25
298 A160 77c red orange   2.00 1.75
    Nos. 296-298 (3)   4.10 3.60

See Nos. 308-310, 319-320, 327-328.

Art by
Joaquim
Mir
A161

Designs: 27c, Fira del Bestiar. 52c,
L'Escorxador, vert.

2004   *Perf. 13¾x14, 14x13¾*
299-300 A161   Set of 2   2.25 1.75
   Issued: 27c, 2/20; 52c, 3/18.

Europa — A162

2004, Apr. 29   Photo.   *Perf. 14x13¾*
301 A162 77c black   2.00 1.60

Fringilla
Coelebs
A163

2004, June 15   Photo.   *Perf. 13¾x14*
302 A163 27c multi   1.00 .60

Automobiles — A164

Designs: €1.90, 1939 Simca 508-C. €2.19,
1955 Messerschmitt KR-1.

2004, Oct. 15   Photo.   *Perf. 13¾x14*
303-304 A164   Set of 2   11.00 9.50

Postal
Code — A165

2004, Oct. 25   *Perf. 14x13¾*
305 A165 52c multi   1.60 1.25

Admission
to Council
of Europe,
10th
Anniv.
A166

2004, Nov. 10   *Perf. 13¾x14*
306 A166 52c multi   1.50 1.25

Christmas
A167

2004, Nov. 22
307 A167 27c multi   1.00 .75

Arms Type of 2004
2005, Jan. 28   Litho.   *Perf. 12¾x13¼*
308 A160 28c blue   .70 .65
309 A160 53c yel green   1.35 1.25
310 A160 78c brt pink   2.00 1.75
    Nos. 308-310 (3)   4.05 3.65

Selection of Madriu-Peralita-Claror
Valley as UNESCO World Heritage
Site — A168

2005, Mar. 7   Photo.   *Perf. 14x13¾*
311 A168 28c multi   .90 .90

Endless,
Sculpture
by Mark
Brusse
A169

2005, Mar. 14   *Perf. 13¾x14*
312 A169 53c multi   1.50 1.10

Europa
A170

2005, Apr. 15   Photo.   *Perf. 13¾x14*
313 A170 78c multi   2.50 1.60

9th Games of
Small European
States — A171

2005, May 20   Photo.   *Perf. 14x13¾*
314 A171 €1.95 multi   5.50 4.25

Caritas Andorra,
25th
Anniv. — A172

2005, June 15
315 A172 28c multi   .70 .70

Cinclus
Cinclus
A173

2005, July 11   Photo.   *Perf. 13¾x14*
316 A173 €2.21 multi   6.25 6.25

Christmas
A174

2005, Nov. 2   Photo.   *Perf. 13¾x14*
317 A174 28c blk & org   1.00 .65

2006
Winter
Olympics,
Turin
A175

2006, Feb. 6
318 A175 29c multi   1.00 .70

Arms Type of 2004
2006, Mar. 1   Litho.   *Perf. 12¾x13¼*
319 A160 29c yel brown   .75 .65
320 A160 57c blue   1.50 1.25

Earth, Fire, Water
and Wind,
Sculpture by
Satoru
Sato — A176

2006, Apr. 10   Photo.   *Perf. 14x13¾*
321 A176 78c multi   2.50 1.75

Europa
A177

2006, May 16   *Perf. 13¾x14*
322 A177 57c multi   1.75 1.75

Perdix
Perdix
A178

2006, June 6
323 A178 €2.39 multi   6.75 6.75

Fulbright Scholarships — A179

2006, Aug. 8   Photo.   *Perf. 13¾x14*
324 A179 57c multi   1.75 1.45

UNESCO, 60th
Anniv., Andorran
National
UNESCO
Committee, 10th
Anniv. — A180

2006, Oct. 2   *Perf. 14x13¾*
325 A180 €2.33 multi   6.50 6.50

Christmas
A181

2006, Nov. 2   Photo.   *Perf. 13¾x14*
326 A181 29c multi   1.00 .80

Arms Type of 2004
2007, Jan. 19   Litho.   *Perf. 12¾x13¼*
327 A160 30c red   .75 .75
328 A160 58c gray   1.50 1.50

Santa Eulalia
d'Encamp
Church, by
Francesc
Galobardes
A182

2007, Feb. 12   Photo.   *Perf. 14x13¾*
329 A182 30c multi   .80 .80

Europa — A183

2007, Apr. 23   Photo.   *Perf. 14x13¾*
330 A183 58c multi   1.60 1.60
    Scouting, cent.

Jordino Family,
Sculptures by
Rachid
Khimoune — A184

2007, May 21
331 A184 €2.43 multi   6.75 6.75

Tetrao
Urogallus
A185

2007, July 4   Photo.   *Perf. 13¾x14*
332 A185 €2.49 multi   7.00 7.00

Casa de la Vall, by Francesc
Galobardes — A186

2007, Sept. 10
333 A186 78c multi   2.25 2.25

Andorran
Red Cross,
25th Anniv.
A187

2007, Oct. 15   Photo.   Perf. 13¾x14
334 A187 30c black & red   .90 .90

Christmas
A188

2007, Nov. 2
335 A188 30c multi   .90 .90

Gypaetus
Barbatus
A189

2008, Jan. 24   Photo.   Perf. 13¾
336 A189 31c multi   .90 .90

Carro Votiu,
Sculpture by
Jordi
Casamajor
A190

2008, Jan. 24   Perf. 12¾x13
337 A190 60c multi   1.60 1.60

Constitution, 15th
Anniv. — A191

2008, Mar. 12   Photo.   Perf. 14x13¾
338 A191 31c multi   .90 .90

Europa — A192

2008, Apr. 23
339 A192 60c black & deep blue   1.90 1.90

Andorran Science
Society, 25th
Anniv. — A193

2008, May 14
340 A193 78c blue & black   2.25 2.25

Souvenir Sheet

Expo Zaragoza 2008 — A194

2008, June 13   Photo.   Perf. 13¾
341 A194 €2.60 multi   7.50 7.50

2008 Summer
Olympics,
Beijing — A195

2008, July 8   Litho.   Perf. 14x13¾
342 A195 60c multi   1.90 1.90

Vall del
Comapedrosa
A196

2008, Sept. 15
343 A196 €2.44 multi   6.25 6.25

Sispony, by Carme Massana — A197

2008, Oct. 13   Photo.   Perf. 12¾
344 A197 31c multi   .90 .90

La Missa del
Gallo, by Sergi
Mas — A198

2008, Nov. 11
345 A198 31c multi   .90 .90

Christmas.

Narcissus
A199

Die Cut Perf. 13
2009, Jan. 17   Litho.
Self-Adhesive
346 A199 32c multi   .85 .85

Andorran School,
25th
Anniv. — A200

2009, Feb. 9   Perf. 14x13¾
347 A200 62c multi   1.60 1.60

Mercè Rodoreda
(1908-83),
Writer — A201

2009, Mar. 6
348 A201 78c black   2.00 2.00

Council of Europe,
60th
Anniv. — A202

2009, Apr. 6   Litho.   Perf. 14x13¾
349 A202 32c multi   1.00 1.00

Europa — A203

2009, Apr. 23
350 A203 62c multi   1.75 1.75

Intl. Year of Astronomy.

Souvenir Sheet

Madrid Bridge — A204

2009, May 18   Photo.
351 A204 €2.70 multi   6.50 6.50

Eurasian
Sparrowhawk
A205

2009, Sept. 10   Photo.   Perf. 14x13¾
352 A205 €2.47 multi   6.75 6.75

Paintings
A206

Designs: 62c, El Tarter, by Francesc
Galobardes. 78c, Contrallum a Canillo, by
Carme Massana.

2009, Oct. 8   Photo.   Perf. 13¾x14
353-354 A206   Set of 2   4.00 4.00

Christmas
A207

2009, Nov. 2   Litho.
355 A207 32c multi   .95 .95

Pyrenees
Iris
A208

Die Cut Perf. 13
2010, Jan. 12   Litho.
Self-Adhesive
356 A208 34c multi   .90 .90

Jacint Verdaguer
(1845-1902),
Poet — A209

Litho. & Engr.
2010, Feb. 8   Perf. 14x13¾
357 A209 64c black & red   1.75 1.75

Paris Bridge, Andorra la Vella — A210

2010, Mar. 5 **Litho.**
358 A210 €2.75 multi 7.00 7.00

Europa — A211

2010, May 6 **Photo.** *Perf. 13¼x13¾*
359 A211 64c multi 1.75 1.75

Bonfire A212

2010, June 1 *Perf. 13¾x13¼*
360 A212 64c multi 1.60 1.60

2010 World Cup Soccer Championships, South Africa — A213

2010, June 1
361 A213 78c multi 1.90 1.90

Recycling A214

Perf. 13¾x13¼
2010, Sept. 6 **Photo.**
362 A214 €2.49 multi 7.00 7.00

Churches — A215

Nos. 363: a, Sant Joan de Caselles Church. b, Sant Romà de Les Bons Church, horiz.

Perf. 13¼x13, 13x13¼
2010, Oct. 6 **Engr.**
363 A215 78c Sheet of 2, #a-b 4.50 4.50
See Andorra, French Administration No. 679.

Christmas A216

2010, Nov. 2 **Photo.** *Perf. 13¾x13¼*
364 A216 34c multi .95 .95

Escaldes-Engordany Parish, 2011 Capital of Catalan Culture — A217

Die Cut Perf. 13
2011, Jan. 12 **Litho.**
Self-Adhesive
365 A217 35c multi .95 .95

Miquel Marti i Pol (1929-2003), Writer — A218

2011, Feb. 7 *Perf. 14x13¾*
366 A218 65c black & gray 1.75 1.75

Europa — A219

2011, Apr. 4
367 A219 65c multi 1.75 1.75
Intl. Year of Forests.

Casa Farràs A220

2011, May 3 *Perf. 13¾x14*
368 A220 80c multi 2.40 2.40

Painted Keystone, Sant Esteve Church A221

2011, June 1
369 A221 €2.55 multi 7.00 7.00

Venice Biennale A222

Artwork by: 80c, Helena Guàrdia. €2.55, Francisco Sánchez.

2011, July 1
370-371 A222 Set of 2 9.25 9.25

Equality of the Sexes — A223

2011, Sept. 8 *Perf. 14x13¾*
372 A223 80c multi 2.25 2.25

America Issue, Mailbox A224

2011, Oct. 11 *Perf. 13¾x14*
373 A224 80c multi 2.25 2.25

Christmas A225

2011, Nov. 3
374 A225 35c multi 1.10 1.10
a. Tete-beche pair 2.50 2.50

Rossell Forge Interpretive Center, La Massana, 10th Anniv. — A226

2012, Jan. 9 **Litho.** *Die Cut Perf. 13*
Self-Adhesive
375 A226 36c multi 1.10 1.10

Agustí Bartra (1908-82), Poet — A227

2012, Feb. 27 *Perf. 14x13¾*
376 A227 51c black 1.40 1.40

Europa A228

2012, Apr. 4 *Perf. 13¾x14*
377 A228 70c multi 1.90 1.90

CIAM Building, Escaldes-Engordany — A229

2012, May 3
378 A229 85c multi 2.25 2.25

Wood Carving, Sant Marti de la Cortinada Church, Ordino — A230

2012, June 1 *Perf. 14x13¾*
379 A230 85c multi 2.25 2.25

A231

Art — A232

2012, July 2 *Perf. 13¾x14*
380 A231 €2.90 multi 7.50 7.50
Perf. 14x13¾
381 A232 €2.90 multi 7.50 7.50

Civic Values — A233

2012, Sept. 10 *Perf. 14x13¾*
382 A233 85c multi 2.25 2.25

America Issue,
Cosmological
Legend — A234

2012, Oct. 11
383 A234 85c multi　　　1.75 1.75

Christmas — A235

2012, Nov. 5
384 A235 36c multi　　　.95 .95

Salvador Espriu
(1913-85),
Poet — A236

2013, Jan. 10　*Die Cut Perf. 13*
Self-Adhesive
385 A236 37c multi　　　1.00 1.00

A237

2013, Feb. 21　*Perf. 13¾x14*
386 A237 75c multi　　　2.00 2.00
　Road between Andorra and La Seu d'Urgell,
Spain, cent.

Areny-Plandolit
Museum,
Ordino — A238

2013, Mar. 4　*Perf. 14x13¾*
387 A238 52c multi　　　1.40 1.40

Souvenir Sheet

Winter Jazz Festival — A239

2013, Apr. 1　　*Perf. 13¼x13¾*
388 A239 €2.72 multi　　　7.00 7.00

Europa
A240

2013, Apr. 23　　*Perf. 13¾x13¼*
389 A240 75c multi　　　2.00 2.00

Women in Portuguese
Costumes — A241

2013, May 6　　*Perf. 13½x13¼*
390 A241 90c multi　　　2.40 2.40

Casa dels
Russos
A242

2013, June 3
391 A242 75c multi　　　2.00 2.00

Souvenir Sheet

School Correspondence — A243

　　　　Perf. 13¼x13¾
2013, Sept. 16　　　**Litho.**
392 A243 €2.72 multi　　　7.50 7.50

Diversity and Anti-
Discrimination — A244

2013, Oct. 3　**Litho.**　*Perf. 13¾x13¼*
393 A244 90c multi　　　2.50 2.50

A245

Christmas — A246

2013, Nov. 4　**Litho.**　*Perf. 13¼x13¾*
394 A245 37c multi　　　1.00 1.00
395 A246 75c multi　　　2.00 2.00

14th Intl. Winter
Road Conference,
Andorra — A247

2014, Jan. 13　**Litho.**　*Perf. 13¼x13¾*
396 A247 38c multi　　　1.10 1.10

Coat of
Arms — A248

2014, Feb. 3　**Litho.**　*Perf. 13¼x13¾*
397　　Vert. strip of 5　　　4.50 4.50
　a.　A248 1c gray　　　.25　.25
　b.　A248 2c brown　　　.25　.25
　c.　A248 5c blue　　　.25　.25
　d.　A248 50c dull green　　1.40 1.40
　e.　A248 €1 red　　　2.75 2.75

Sculpture by
Samantha
Bosque — A249

2014, Mar. 3　**Litho.**　*Perf. 13¼x13¾*
398 A249 54c multi　　　1.50 1.50

Closure of
Radio
Andorra,
30th
Anniv.
A250

2014, Apr. 7　**Litho.**　*Perf. 13¾x13¼*
399 A250 92c multi　　　2.60 2.60

Accordion — A251

2014, Apr. 23　**Litho.**　*Perf. 13¼x13¾*
400 A251 76c multi　　　2.10 2.10
　　Europa.

Andorra
Ultra Trail,
Vallnord
A252

2014, June 9　**Litho.**　*Perf. 13¾x13¼*
401 A252 76c red & black　　2.10 2.10

Filipinos in
Andorra
A253

2014, July 7　**Litho.**　*Perf. 13¾x13¼*
402 A253 92c multi　　　2.50 2.50

Intl. Year
of Family
Farming
A254

　　　　Perf. 13¾x13¼
2014, Sept. 15　　　**Litho.**
403 A254 76c multi　　　2.00 2.00

Souvenir Sheet

Mural in Sant Martí de la Cortinada
Church — A255

2014, Oct. 6　**Litho.**　*Perf. 13¼x13¾*
404 A255 €2.72 multi　　　6.75 6.75

Christmas
A256

2014, Nov. 5 Litho. Perf. 13¾x13¼
405 A256 38c multi .95 .95

Casa
Felipó — A257

Perf. 13¼x13¾
2014, Nov. 10 Litho.
406 A257 €2.72 multi 6.75 6.75

Virgin of
Meritxell — A258

2015, Jan. 13 Litho. Perf. 14x13¾
407 A258 A multi .95 .95
No. 407 sold for 42c on day of issue.

Chamois
A259

2015, Feb. 9 Litho. Perf. 13¾x14
408 A259 €1 multi 2.25 2.25

Higher
Education
in
Andorra,
25th
Anniv.
A260

2015, Mar. 2 Litho. Perf. 13¾x13¼
409 A260 55c multi 1.25 1.25

Europa
A261

2015, Apr. 23 Litho. Perf. 13¾x13¼
410 A261 90c multi 2.10 2.10

Between,
Sculpture
by Agustí
Roqué
A262

2015, May 1 Litho. Perf. 13¾x13¼
411 A262 €2.84 multi 6.50 6.50
Venice Biennale.

2015 World Motorcycling Trial Grand
Prix, Andorra — A263

Perf. 13¾x13¼
2015, June 10 Litho.
412 A263 €1 multi 2.25 2.25

English
Community in
Andorra — A264

2015, July 8 Litho. Perf. 13¼x13¾
413 A264 90c multi 2.00 2.00

Joan Martí
Alanis
(1929-2009),
Bishop of Urgel
and Co-
Prince — A265

2015, Sept. 8 Litho. Perf. 13¼x13¾
414 A265 42c multi .95 .95

Age of Majority at
18, 30th
Anniv. — A266

2015, Sept. 8 Litho. Perf. 13¾
415 A266 €1 multi 2.25 2.25

Souvenir Sheet

Hotel Rosaleda, Encamp — A267

2015, Oct. 15 Litho. Perf. 13¼x13¾
416 A267 €2.84 multi 6.25 6.25

Christmas
A268

2015, Nov. 2 Litho. Perf. 13¾x13¼
417 A268 42c multi .95 .95

Dolors Parella i
Fivaller (d. 1855),
Murdered
Baroness — A269

2015, Nov. 4 Litho. Perf. 13¼x13¾
418 A269 90c multi 1.90 1.90

Coat of
Arms — A270

2016, Jan. 13 Litho. Perf. 14x13½
419 A270 A magenta & black 1.00 1.00
No. 419 sold for 45c on day of issue. See
No. 431.

Dog from Retable
in Church of Sant
Cristòfol,
d'Anyós — A271

2016, Feb. 9 Litho. Perf. 14x13½
420 A271 €1.30 multi 3.00 3.00

Interpretive Center
for Romanesque
Art, Pal, 10th
Anniv. — A272

2016, Mar. 2 Litho. Perf. 13¼x13¾
421 A272 57c multi 1.25 1.25
No. 421 has two die cut openings in the
interior of the arches.

Europa
A273

2016, Apr. 22 Litho. Perf. 13¾x13¼
422 A273 €1.15 multi 2.75 2.75
Think Green Issue.

Anima Compartida, by Joan
Xandri — A274

2016, May 11 Litho. Perf. 13¾x13¼
423 A274 €2.95 multi 6.75 6.75
2015 Venice Biennale.

Andorra la Vella, 2016 Ibero-American
Capital of Culture — A275

Perf. 13¾x13¼
2016, June 10 Litho.
424 A275 €1.30 multi 3.00 3.00

French
Community in
Andorra — A276

2016, July 8 Litho. Perf. 13¼x13¾
425 A276 €1.15 multi 2.60 2.60

Tree of
Science
A277

2016, Sept. 8 Litho. Perf. 13¾x13¼
426 A277 45c blk & brn 1.00 1.00
Ramon Llull (c. 1232-c. 1315), philosopher.

Reforms of 1866,
150th
Anniv. — A278

2016, Sept. 8 Litho. Perf. 13¼x13¾
427 A278 €1.30 multi 3.00 3.00

Souvenir Sheet

Vilanova Clinic — A279

2016, Oct. 14 Litho. Perf. 13¼x13¾
428 A279 €2.95 multi 6.50 6.50

Christmas — A280

2016, Nov. 4 Litho. Perf. 13¼x13¾
429 A280 45c Pastorets .95 .95

Montserrat Palau Martí (1916-2004),
Ethnologist — A281

2016, Nov. 8 Litho.   Perf. 13¾x13¼
430 A281 €1.15 multi   2.50 2.50

Coat of Arms Type of 2016
2017, Jan. 13 Litho.   Perf. 14x13½
431 A270 A blue & black   1.10 1.10
No. 431 sold for 50c on day of issue.

Argentine
Community in
Andorra — A282

Perf. 13¼x13¾
2017, Feb. 24   Litho.
432 A282 €1.25 multi   2.75 2.75

La Veu Silenciada (The Silenced
Voice), by Neus Mola — A283

Perf. 13¼ Horiz. at Top
2017, Mar. 9   Litho.
433 A283 €3.15 multi + label   6.75 6.75
No. 433 was sold folded.

Castell de les
Bons — A284

2017, Apr. 21 Litho.   Perf. 13¼x13¾
434 A284 €1.25 multi   2.75 2.75
Europa.

Pere Canturri
(1935-2015),
Historian and
Governmental
Minister — A285

2017, Apr. 28 Litho.   Perf. 13¼x13¾
435 A285 60c multi   1.40 1.40

Souvenir Sheet

Sculptures — A286

No. 436: a, Lost Origin, by Zoe. b, Ompha-
los, by Jordi Casamajor.

2017, May 11 Litho.   Perf. 13¼x13¾
436 A286   Sheet of 2   2.50 2.50
a.   50c multi   1.10 1.10
b.   60c multi   1.40 1.40

Birch Tree
and Leaf
A287

2017, June 5 Litho.   Perf. 13¾x13¼
437 A287 €1.35 multi   3.25 3.25

Estany
d'Encamp
A288

2017, July 8 Litho.   Perf. 13¾x13¼
438 A288 €1.25 multi   3.00 3.00

Julià Reig i
Ribó
(1911-96),
Politician
A289

2017, Sept. 8 Litho.   Perf. 13¾x13¼
439 A289 €1.35 multi   3,25 3.25

Pilar Riberaygua (1953-2002), Artist
and Gallery Owner — A290

Perf. 13¾x13¼
2017, Sept. 22   Litho.
440 A290 €1.25 multi   3.00 3.00

Souvenir Sheet

Arajol Chalet — A291

2017, Oct. 14 Litho.   Perf. 13¼x13¾
441 A291 €3.15 multi   7.50 7.50

Bulls, Sant
Miquel del
Prats
Altarpiece
Detail
A292

2017, Nov. 3 Litho.   Perf. 13¾x13¼
442 A292 €1.35 multi   3.25 3.25

Christmas
A293

Die Cut Perf. 13
2017, Nov. 8   Litho.
On Wood Veneer
Self-Adhesive
443 A293 50c multi   1.25 1.25

Coat of
Arms — A294

2018, Jan. 2 Litho.   Perf. 14x13¾
444 A294 A multi   1.40 1.40
No. 444 sold for 55c on day of issue.

Dante Alighieri (c.
1265-1321),
Writer — A295

2018, Feb. 24   Litho.   Perf. 13¾
445 A295 €1.35 multi   3.25 3.25
Italian Community in Andorra.

Souvenir Sheet

Andorran Constitution, 25th
Anniv. — A296

2018, Mar. 14 Litho.   Perf. 13x13½
446 A296 €3.30 multi   8.25 8.25

Escaldes-Engordany Parish, 40th
Anniv. — A297

2018, Apr. 6 Litho.   Perf. 13x13½
447 A297 55c multi   1.40 1.40

Engordany
Bridge
A298

2018, Apr. 23 Litho.   Perf. 14¼x14
448 A298 €1.35 multi   3.25 3.25
Europa. Stone grit is affixed to portions of
the design.

Roser Jordana Mallol (1942-2014),
Promoter of Andorran Tourism — A299

2018, May 16 Litho.   Perf. 13½x13
449 A299 €1.35 multi   3.25 3.25

Walnuts
and Leaf
of Walnut
Tree
A300

2018, May 25 Litho.   Perf. 13½x13
450 A300 €1.45 multi   3.50 3.50

Bilateral Relationships Between
Andorra and Spain, 25th
Anniv. — A301

2018, June 5 Litho.   Perf. 13½x13
451 A301 €1.35 multi   3.25 3.25

Summer Solstice Festival, UNESCO Intangible Cultural Heritage — A302

2018, June 22 **Litho.** **Perf. 13½x13**
452 A302 €1.45 multi 3.50 3.50

European Year of Cultural Heritage — A303

2018, July 5 **Litho.** **Perf. 13¼x13¾**
453 A303 €1.45 multi 3.50 3.50

Privada Tutelar Foundation, 10th Anniv. — A304

2018, Aug. 9 **Litho.** **Perf. 13¼x13¾**
454 A304 65c multi 1.50 1.50

View of Escaldes From Els Vilars A305

2018, Sept. 17 **Litho.** **Perf. 13½x13**
455 A305 €1.45 multi 3.50 3.50

Cultural Guide Courses, 25th Anniv. A306

2018, Oct. 10 **Litho.** **Perf. 13¾x13¼**
456 A306 €1.45 multi 3.50 3.50

Souvenir Sheet

Christmas Diorama (unfolded) — A307

2018, Nov. 8 **Litho.** **Perf. 13¾**
457 A307 €3.30 multi 7.50 7.50
No. 457 was sold with a fold in the sheet margin so the stamp would appear through the holes in the illustration printed on the back of the sheet margin.

Flag of Andorra A308

2019, Jan. 4 **Litho.** **Perf. 13½x13**
458 A308 A multi 1.40 1.40
No. 458 sold for 60c on day of issue. Compare with No. 472.

Tradition of Burning of Christmas Trees A309

2019, Jan. 24 **Litho.** **Perf. 13½x13**
459 A309 €1.40 multi 3.25 3.25

General Council of the Valleys, 600th Anniv. A310

2019, Feb. 11 **Litho.** **Perf. 13½x13**
460 A310 €3.50 multi 8.00 8.00

A311

Design: Maria Lluisa de Riba (1908-93), last heir of Rossell family, and Rossell house, Ordino.

2019, Mar. 8 **Litho.** **Perf. 13½x13**
461 A311 €1.50 multi 3.50 3.50

European Robin — A312

2019, Apr. 26 **Litho.** **Perf. 13¼x13½**
462 A312 €1.40 multi 3.25 3.25
Europa.

Souvenir Sheet

Andorran Foods — A313

No. 463: a, Chickory. b, Escudella.

2019, May 11 **Litho.** **Perf. 13x13¾**
463 A313 Sheet of 2 6.75 6.75
a. €1.40 multi 3.25 3.25
b. €1.50 multi 3.50 3.50

Souvenir Sheet

Hydroelectric Power in Andorra, 90th Anniv. — A314

Litho. With Lenticular Lens Affixed
2019, May 31 **Perf. 14½x14¾**
464 A314 €4 multi 9.00 9.00

Holly Leaves and Berries A315

Litho. With Foil Application
2019, July 8 **Perf. 13¾x13¼**
465 A315 70c multi 1.60 1.60

La Purito Cycling Tour, 5th Anniv. A316

2019, Aug. 4 **Litho.** **Perf. 13¾x13¼**
466 A316 70c multi 1.60 1.60

Goddess of Oxygen, by Philippe Shangti — A317

2019, Sept. 8 **Litho.** **Perf. 13x13½**
467 A317 €1.50 multi 3.25 3.25
Venice Art Biennale.

Molleres de Meritxell, by Francesc Galobardes A318

2019, Sept. 22 **Litho.** **Perf. 13½x13**
468 A318 €1.40 multi 3.25 3.25

The Firebird — A319

2019, Oct. 14 **Litho.** **Perf. 13x13½**
469 A319 70c multi 1.60 1.60
Russian community in Andorra.

Admission of Andorra to Council of Europe, 25th Anniv. — A320

2019, Nov. 8 **Litho.** **Perf. 13**
470 A320 €1.40 multi + label 3.25 3.25
See Andorra (French Administration) No. 815.

Christmas — A321

2019, Nov. 8 **Engr.** **Perf. 13x13½**
471 A321 60c black 1.40 1.40

Flag of Andorra A322

2020, Jan. 3 **Litho.** **Perf. 13½x13**
472 A322 A multi 1.50 1.50
No. 472 sold for 65c on day of issue. Compare with No. 458.

27th Ibero-American Summit of Heads of State and Government, Andorra — A323

Perf. 13¼x13½
2020, Feb. 11   Litho.
473   A323   75c multi   1.75   1.75

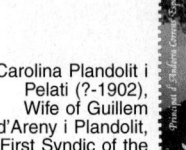

Carolina Plandolit i Pelati (?-1902), Wife of Guillem d'Areny i Plandolit, First Syndic of the General Council — A324

2020, Mar. 6   Litho.   **Perf. 13x13½**
474   A324   €1.55 multi   3.50   3.50

Wolf and Protective Collar for Sheepdogs A325

2020, Mar. 19   Litho.   **Perf. 13x13½**
475   A325   €1.45 multi   3.25   3.25

Cal Pal Manor House, La Cortinada A326

2020, May 14   Litho.   **Perf. 13¾x13¼**
476   A326   75c multi   1.75   1.75

Postal Carriers and Map of Andorra-La Seu d'Urgell, Spain Postal Route — A327

2020, May 14   Litho.   **Perf. 13¼x13¾**
477   A327   €1.45 multi   3.25   3.25
     Europa.

Andorran Woman Suffrage Decree, 50th Anniv. — A328

2020, May 29   Litho.   **Perf. 13¼**
478   A328   €3.80 multi   8.50   8.50

Beyondwalls, Painting on Land by Saype — A329

Perf. 13¾x13¼
2020, June 30   Litho.
479   A329   €1.45 multi   3.25   3.25
     2019 L'Andart Biennale.

Linden Leaf and Blossom A330

2020, July 8   Litho.   **Perf. 13½x13¼**
480   A330   €1.45 multi   3.50   3.50

Collada dels Meners — A331

2020, Aug. 4   Litho.   **Perf. 13x13½**
481   A331   €1.40 multi   3.50   3.50

Diplomatic Relations Between Andorra and Liechtenstein, 25th Anniv. — A332

2020, Sept. 8   Litho.   **Perf. 13¾x13¼**
482   A332   €1.55 multi   3.75   3.75

Pep Aguareles (1965-2019), Photographer — A333

2020, Oct. 9   Litho.   **Perf. 13¾x13¼**
483   A333   €1.45 multi   3.50   3.50

Chinese Community in Andorra — A334

2020, Oct. 21   Litho.   **Perf. 13¼**
484   A334   €3.80 multi   9.00   9.00

AIR POST STAMPS

A set of 12 stamps, inscribed "CORREU AER / SOBRETAXA" was authorized in 1932 for a proposed private air service between Andorra and Barcelona. These stamps were prepared but not issued. Value, set $40. The stamps were also overprinted "FRANQUICIA DEL CONSELL" for official use. Value, set $140.

Catalogue values for unused stamps in this section are for Never Hinged items.

AP1

Unwmk.
1951, June 27   Engr.   **Perf. 11**
C1   AP1   1p dark violet brown   25.00   4.25

AP2

Litho. & Engr.
1983, Oct. 20   **Perf. 13**
C2   AP2   20p brown & bis brn   .40   .25
   Jaime Sansa Nequi, Episcopal Church official.

AP3

1984, Oct. 25   Photo.   **Perf. 13**
C3   AP3   20p multicolored   .40   .25
   Pyrenees Art Center.

Bishops of Urgel Type of 1979
1985, June 13   Engr.   **Perf. 13½**
C4   A42   20p Ramon Iglesias   .40   .25

SPECIAL DELIVERY STAMPS

Special Delivery Stamp of Spain, 1905 Overprinted

1928   Unwmk.   **Perf. 14**
Without Control Number on Back
E1   SD1   20c red   80.00   *95.00*
     Never hinged   150.00
With Control Number on Back
E2   SD1   20c pale red   55.00   *55.00*
     Never hinged   95.00

Eagle over Mountain Pass — SD2

1929   **Perf. 14**
With Control Number on Back
E3   SD2   20c scarlet   25.00   20.00
     Never hinged   35.00

   Perf 11½ examples are numbered A000.000 and are specimens. Value, $400.

1937   **Perf. 11½x11**
Without Control Number on Back
E4   SD2   20c red   7.75   *9.50*
     Never hinged   8.75

Arms and Squirrel — SD3

1949   Unwmk.   Engr.   **Perf. 10x9½**
E5   SD3   25c red   5.75   4.50
     Never hinged   8.25

ANDORRA, FRENCH ADMINISTRATION

Stamps and Types of
France, 1900-1929,
Overprinted

Perf. 14x13½

1931, June 16   **Unwmk.**

1	A16	1c gray	1.00	1.00
a.	Double overprint		1,800.	2,500.
b.	Double overprint		1,800.	
2	A16	2c red brown	1.40	1.40
3	A16	3c orange	1.40	1.40
4	A16	5c green	2.10	2.40
5	A16	10c lilac	3.50	3.75
6	A22	15c red brown	5.50	5.50
7	A22	20c red violet	7.75	8.25
8	A22	25c yellow brn	9.50	10.00
9	A22	30c green	9.00	9.50
10	A22	40c ultra	10.00	12.00
11	A20	45c lt violet	40.00	40.00
12	A20	50c vermilion	45.00	45.00
a.	Pair, one without over-print		475.00	
13	A20	65c gray green	20.00	20.00
14	A22	75c rose lilac	14.00	14.00
15	A22	90c red	26.00	30.00
16	A17	1fr dull blue	30.00	34.00
17	A22	1.50fr light blue	40.00	42.50

Overprinted

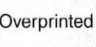

18	A18	2fr org & pale bl	24.00	30.00
19	A18	3fr brt vio & rose	100.00	120.00
20	A18	5fr dk bl & buff	130.00	135.00
21	A18	10fr grn & red	275.00	275.00
22	A18	20fr mag & grn	375.00	450.00
		Nos. 1-22 (22)	1,170.	1,291.

See No. P1 for ½c on 1c gray.
Nos. 9, 15 and 17 were not issued in France
without overprint.

Chapel of
Meritxell
A50

Bridge of
St. Anthony
A51

St. Miguel
d'Engolasters
A52

Gorge of St.
Julia
A53

Old
Andorra
A54

1932-43   **Engr.**   **Perf. 13**

23	A50	1c gray blk	.55	.55
24	A50	2c violet	.95	.80
25	A50	3c brown	.80	.65
26	A50	5c blue green	.95	.90
27	A51	10c dull lilac	1.30	1.30

28	A50	15c deep red	1.90	1.75
29	A51	20c lt rose	12.00	9.75
30	A52	25c brown	5.75	5.25
31	A51	25c brn car ('37)	11.00	14.00
32	A51	30c emerald	4.25	3.75
33	A51	40c ultra	12.00	9.75
34	A51	40c brn blk ('39)	1.45	1.40
35	A51	45c lt red	12.00	9.75
36	A51	45c bl grn ('39)	6.75	5.50
37	A52	50c lilac rose	13.50	13.00
38	A51	50c lt vio ('39)	6.50	5.75
38A	A51	50c grn ('40)	2.00	1.90
39	A51	55c lt vio ('38)	23.00	16.50
40	A51	60c yel brn ('38)	1.50	1.25
41	A52	65c yel grn	55.00	55.00
42	A51	65c blue ('38)	17.00	13.50
43	A51	70c red ('39)	2.75	2.10
44	A52	75c violet	11.50	7.75
45	A51	75c ultra ('39)	5.00	4.75
46	A51	80c green ('38)	29.00	21.00
46A	A53	80c bl grn ('40)	.50	.60
47	A51	90c deep rose	6.25	5.25
48	A53	90c dk grn ('39)	4.25	4.25
49	A53	1fr blue grn	20.00	13.50
50	A53	1fr scarlet ('38)	31.00	22.00
51	A53	1fr dp ultra ('39)	.50	.50
51A	A53	1.20fr brt vio ('42)	.50	.50
52	A50	1.25fr rose car ('33)	55.00	42.50
52A	A50	1.25fr rose ('38)	6.00	3.50
52B	A50	1.30fr sepia ('40)	.50	.50
53	A54	1.50fr ultra	25.00	16.00
53A	A53	1.50fr crim ('40)	.50	.50
54	A53	1.75fr violet ('33)	105.00	120.00
55	A53	1.75fr dk bl ('38)	50.00	47.50
56	A53	2fr red violet	11.50	9.50
56A	A50	2fr rose red ('40)	1.60	1.60
56B	A50	2fr dk bl grn ('42)	.50	.50
57	A50	2.15fr dk vio ('38)	60.00	55.00
58	A50	2.25fr ultra ('39)	9.00	8.00
58A	A50	2.40fr red ('42)	.65	.50
59	A50	2.50fr gray blk ('39)	9.75	7.75
59A	A50	2.50fr dp ultra ('40)	2.40	2.10
60	A53	3fr orange brn	14.00	9.00
60A	A50	3fr red brn ('40)	.50	.50
60B	A50	4fr sl bl ('42)	.50	.50
60C	A50	4.50fr dp vio ('42)	1.75	1.60
61	A54	5fr brown	.95	.70
62	A54	10fr violet	.95	.70
62B	A54	15fr dp ultra ('42)	1.20	1.00
63	A54	20fr rose lake	1.25	.85
63A	A51	50fr turq bl ('43)	1.75	1.50
		Nos. 23-63A (56)	661.65	586.00

A 20c ultra exists but was not issued. Value:
unused, $20,000; never hinged $30,000.

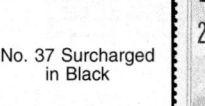

No. 37 Surcharged
in Black

1935, Sept. 18

64	A52	20c on 50c lil rose	18.50	17.00
a.	Double surcharge		6,500.	

Coat of Arms — A55

1936-42   **Perf. 14x13**

65	A55	1c black ('37)	.25	.25
66	A55	2c blue	.25	.25
67	A55	3c brown	.25	.25
68	A55	5c rose lilac	.25	.25
69	A55	10c ultra ('37)	.25	.25
70	A55	15c red violet	2.75	2.25
71	A55	20c emerald ('37)	.25	.25
72	A55	30c cop red ('38)	.60	.70
72A	A55	30c blk brn ('42)	.25	.40
73	A55	35c Prus grn ('38)	70.00	70.00
74	A55	40c cop red ('42)	.60	.60
75	A55	50c Prus grn ('42)	.60	.60
76	A55	60c turq bl ('42)	.60	.60
77	A55	70c vio ('42)	.60	.60
		Nos. 65-77 (14)	77.50	77.25
		Set, never hinged	135.00	

**Catalogue values for unused
stamps in this section, from this
point to the end of the section, are
for Never Hinged items.**

Coat of Arms — A56

1944

78	A56	10c violet	.30	.30
79	A56	30c deep magenta	.30	.30
80	A56	40c dull blue	.30	.30
81	A56	50c orange red	.30	.30
82	A56	60c black	.30	.30
83	A56	70c brt red violet	.30	.30
84	A56	80c blue green	.30	.30
		Nos. 78-84 (7)	2.10	2.10

See No. 114.

St. Jean de
Caselles
A57

La Maison
des Vallees
A58

Old Andorra
A59

Provost
A60

1944-47   **Perf. 13**

85	A57	1fr brown violet	.25	.25
86	A57	1.20fr blue	.25	.25
87	A57	1.50fr red	.25	.25
88	A57	2fr dk blue grn	.25	.25
89	A58	2.40fr rose red	.25	.25
90	A58	2.50fr rose red ('46)	7.25	.80
91	A58	3fr sepia	.25	.25
92	A58	4fr ultra	.40	.25
93	A59	4.50fr brown blk	.40	.25
94	A58	4.50fr dk bl grn ('47)	9.50	5.50
95	A59	5fr ultra	.35	.25
96	A59	5fr Prus grn ('46)	1.40	.50
97	A59	6fr rose car ('45)	.35	.25
98	A59	10fr Prus green	.35	.25
99	A59	10fr ultra ('46)	2.40	.40
100	A60	15fr rose lilac	.95	.40
101	A60	20fr deep blue	.95	.40
102	A60	25fr lt rose red ('46)	5.50	1.90
103	A60	40fr dk green ('46)	5.50	2.00
104	A60	50fr sepia	1.75	1.40
		Nos. 85-104 (20)	38.55	16.05

1948-49

105	A58	4fr lt blue grn	1.60	.80
106	A59	6fr violet brn	.80	.40
107	A58	8fr indigo	1.25	1.20
108	A59	12fr bright red	1.25	1.20
109	A59	12fr blue grn ('49)	1.50	.75
110	A59	17fr crimson ('49)	1.00	.55
111	A60	18fr deep blue	5.00	2.40
112	A60	20fr dark violet	3.50	2.00
113	A60	25fr ultra ('49)	2.50	1.20
		Nos. 105-113 (9)	18.40	10.50

1949-51   **Perf. 14x13, 13**

114	A56	1fr deep blue	.95	.65
115	A57	3fr red ('51)	7.25	4.75
116	A57	4fr sepia	2.50	2.25
117	A58	5fr emerald	3.75	2.75
118	A58	5fr purple ('51)	13.50	4.75
119	A58	6fr blue grn ('51)	7.25	3.25
120	A58	8fr brown	.95	.75
121	A59	15fr blk brn ('51)	16.00	3.00
122	A59	18fr rose red ('51)	30.00	15.00
123	A60	30fr ultra ('51)	40.00	22.50
		Nos. 114-123 (10)	122.15	59.65

Les Escaldres
Spa — A61

St. Coloma
Belfry
A62

Designs: 15fr-25fr, Gothic cross. 30fr-75fr,
Village of Les Bons.

1955-58   **Unwmk.**   **Engr.**   **Perf. 13**

124	A61	1fr dk gray bl	.25	.25
125	A61	2fr dp green	.35	.25
126	A61	3fr red	.35	.25
127	A61	5fr chocolate	.35	.25
128	A62	6fr dk bl grn	.80	.80
129	A62	8fr rose brown	.80	.80
130	A62	10fr brt violet	1.25	.80
131	A62	12fr indigo	1.60	.80
132	A61	15fr red	1.60	.85
133	A61	18fr blue grn	2.00	.85
134	A61	20fr dp purple	3.50	2.00
135	A61	25fr sepia	3.50	2.00
136	A62	30fr deep blue	40.00	19.50
137	A62	35fr Prus bl ('57)	12.00	7.25
138	A62	40fr dk green	47.50	28.00
139	A62	50fr cerise	4.50	3.25
140	A62	65fr purple ('58)	12.00	6.50
141	A62	70fr chestnut ('57)	7.25	6.50
142	A62	75fr violet blue	65.00	45.00
		Nos. 124-142 (19)	204.60	125.90

Issued: 35fr, 70fr, 8/19; 65fr, 2/10; others,
2/15.

Coat of Arms — A63

Gothic
Cross,
Meritxell
A64

65c, 85c, 1fr, Engolasters Lake.

1961, June 19   **Typo.**   **Perf. 14x13**

143	A63	5c brt green & blk	.25	.25
144	A63	10c red, pink & blk	.25	.25
145	A63	15c blue & black	.25	.25
146	A63	20c yellow & brown	.40	.30

		Engr.		**Perf. 13**
147	A64	25c violet, bl & grn	.60	.30
148	A64	30c mar, ol grn & brn	.70	.50
149	A64	45c indigo, bl & grn	17.50	16.00
150	A64	50c pur, lt brn & ol grn	1.50	1.25
151	A64	65c bl, ol & brn	22.00	18.50
152	A64	85c rose lil, vio bl & brn	22.00	18.50
153	A64	1fr grnsh bl, ind & brn	1.50	1.25
		Nos. 143-153 (11)	66.95	57.35

See Nos. 161-166A.

Imperforates

Most stamps of Andorra, French
Administration, from 1961 onward exist
imperforate in issued and trial colors,
and also in small presentation sheets in
issued colors.

Common Design Types
pictured following the introduction.

Telstar Issue
Common Design Type

1962, Sept. 29   **Engr.**
154 CD111 50c ultra & purple   2.00 1.60

1st television connection of the US and Europe through the Telstar satellite, 7/11-12.

"La Sardane" A66

Charlemagne Crossing Andorra — A67

1fr, Louis le Debonnaire giving founding charter.

1963, June 22   Unwmk.   Perf. 13
155 A66 20c lil rose, cl & ol grn   5.00 5.00
156 A67 50c sl grn & dk car rose   8.50 8.50
157 A67 1fr red brn, ultra & dk grn   14.00 14.00
   Nos. 155-157 (3)   27.50 27.50

Old Andorra Church and Champs-Elysées Palace — A68

1964, Jan. 20   **Engr.**
158 A68 25c vio brn, grn & blk   2.00 1.60

"PHILATEC," Intl. Philatelic and Postal Techniques Exhib., Paris, June 5-21, 1964.

Bishop of Urgel and Seigneur of Caboet Confirming Co-Principality, 1288 — A69

Design: 60c, Napoleon re-establishing Co-principality, 1806.

1964, Apr. 25   **Engr.**   *Perf. 13*
159 A69 60c dk brn, red brn & sl grn   22.50 22.50
160 A69 1fr brt bl, org brn & blk   22.50 22.50

Arms Type of 1961

1964, May 16   Typo.   Perf. 14x13
161 A63 1c dk blue & gray   .25 .25
162 A63 2c black & orange   .25 .25
163 A63 12c purple, emer & yel   .90 .90
164 A63 18c black, lil & pink   1.00 1.00
   Nos. 161-164 (4)   2.40 2.40

Scenic Type of 1961

Designs: 40c, 45c, Gothic Cross, Meritxell. 60c, 90c, Pond of Engolasters.

1965-71   **Engr.**   *Perf. 13*
165   A64 40c dk brn, org brn & sl grn   1.00 .80
165A A64 45c vio bl, ol bis & slate   1.10 .80
166   A64 60c org brn & dk brn   1.60 1.25
166A A64 90c ultra, bl grn & bister   2.00 1.00
   Nos. 165-166A (4)   5.70 3.85

Issued: 40c, 60c, Apr. 24, 1965. 45c, June 13, 1970. 90c, Aug. 28, 1971.

Syncom Satellite over Pleumeur-Bodou Station — A70

1965, May 17   **Unwmk.**
167 A70 60c dp car, lil & bl   6.50 4.75
   Cent. of the ITU.

Andorra House, Paris — A71

1965, June 5
168 A71 25c dk bl, org brn & ol gray   1.25 .80

Ski Lift — A72

Design: 25c, Chair lift, vert.

1966, Apr. 2   Engr.   Perf. 13
169 A72 25c brt bl, grn & dk brn   1.60 1.25
170 A72 40c mag, brt ultra & sep   2.40 1.60
   Winter sports in Andorra.

FR-1 Satellite — A73

1966, May 7   *Perf. 13*
171 A73 60c brt bl, grn & dk grn   2.10 1.60
   Issued to commemorate the launching of the scientific satellite FR-1, Dec. 6, 1965.

Europa Issue, 1966
Common Design Type

1966, Sept. 24   Engr.   Perf. 13
Size: 21½x35½mm
172 CD9 60c brown   3.00 3.00

Folk Dancers, Sculpture by Josep Viladomat — A74

1967, Apr. 29   Engr.   Perf. 13
173 A74 30c ol grn, dp grn & slate   1.25 .80
   Cent. (in 1966) of the New Reform, which reaffirmed and strengthened political freedom in Andorra.

Europa Issue, 1967
Common Design Type

1967, Apr. 29
Size: 22x36mm
174 CD10 30c bluish blk & lt bl   4.25 1.75
175 CD10 60c dk red & brt pink   6.50 4.50

Telephone Encircling the Globe — A75

1967, Apr. 29
176 A75 60c dk car, vio & blk   2.00 1.25
   Automatic telephone service.

Injured Father at Home A76

1967, Sept. 23   Engr.   Perf. 13
177 A76 2.30fr ocher, dk red brn & brn red   9.75 7.50
   Introduction of Social Security System.

Jesus in Garden of Gethsemane — A77

Designs (from 16th century frescoes in La Maison des Vallees): 30c, The Kiss of Judas. 60c, The Descent from the Cross (Pieta).

1967, Sept. 23
178 A77 25c black & red brn   .80 .80
179 A77 30c purple & red lilac   .80 .80
180 A77 60c indigo & Prus blue   1.60 1.25
   Nos. 178-180 (3)   3.20 2.85
   See Nos. 185-187.

Downhill Skier — A78

1968, Jan. 27   Engr.   Perf. 13
181 A78 40c org, ver & red lil   1.60 1.25
   10th Winter Olympic Games, Grenoble, France, Feb. 6-18.

Europa Issue, 1968
Common Design Type

1968, Apr. 27   Engr.   Perf. 13
Size: 36x22mm
182 CD11 30c gray & brt bl   6.50 3.00
183 CD11 60c brown & lilac   10.00 7.00

High Jump A79

1968, Oct. 12   Engr.   Perf. 13
184 A79 40c brt blue & brn   1.50 1.25
   19th Olympic Games, Mexico City, Oct. 12-27.

Fresco Type of 1967

Designs (from 16th century frescoes in La Maison des Vallees): 25c, The Scourging of Christ. 30c, Christ Carrying the Cross. 60c, The Crucifixion. (All horiz.)

1968, Oct. 12
185 A77 25c dk grn & gray grn   .85 .80
186 A77 30c dk brown & lilac   .85 .80
187 A77 60c dk car & vio brn   1.75 1.25
   Nos. 185-187 (3)   3.45 2.85

Europa Issue, 1969
Common Design Type

1969, Apr. 26   Engr.   Perf. 13
188 CD12 40c rose car, gray & dl bl   7.50 3.50
189 CD12 70c indigo, dl red & bl   11.00 8.50

10th anniv. of the Conf. of European Postal and Telecommunications Administrations.

Kayak on Isere River — A80

1969, Aug. 2   Engr.   Perf. 13
190 A80 70c dk sl grn, ultra & ind   2.50 2.75
   Intl. Canoe & Kayak Championships, Bourg-Saint-Maurice, Savoy, July 31-Aug. 6.

Drops of Water & Diamond — A80a

1969, Sept. 27   Engr.   Perf. 13
191 A80a 70c blk, dp ultra & grnsh bl   3.25 4.00
   European Water Charter.

St. John, the Woman and the Dragon A81

The Revelation (From the Altar of St. John, Caselles): 40c, St. John Hearing Voice from Heaven on Patmos. 70c, St. John and the Seven Candlesticks.

1969, Oct. 18
192 A81 30c brn, dp pur & brn red   .75 .75
193 A81 40c gray, dk brn & brn ol   1.10 1.10

194 A81 70c dk red, maroon &
brt rose lilac 1.40 1.40
Nos. 192-194 (3) 3.25 3.25
See Nos. 199-201, 207-209, 214-216.

Field Ball — A82

1970, Feb. 21 Engr. Perf. 13
195 A82 80c multi 2.00 2.00
Issued to publicize the 7th International
Field Ball Games, France, Feb. 26-Mar. 8.

Europa Issue, 1970
Common Design Type
1970, May 2 Engr. Perf. 13
Size: 36x22mm
196 CD13 40c orange 6.00 2.50
197 CD13 80c violet blue 14.00 6.00

Shot Put — A83

1970, Sept. 11 Engr. Perf. 13
198 A83 80c bl & dk brn 2.00 2.00
1st European Junior Athletic Championships, Colombes, France, Sept. 11-13.

Altar Type of 1969
The Revelation (from the Altar of St. John,
Caselles): 30c, St. John recording angel's
message. 40c, Angel erecting column symbolizing faithful in heaven. 80c, St. John's trial in
kettle of boiling oil.

1970, Oct. 24
199 A81 30c dp car, dk brn & brt
pur .90 .90
200 A81 40c violet & slate grn 1.10 1.10
201 A81 80c ol, dk bl & car rose 1.90 1.90
Nos. 199-201 (3) 3.90 3.90

Ice Skating A84

1971, Feb. 20 Engr. Perf. 13
202 A84 80c dk red, red lil & pur 2.00 2.00
World Figure Skating Championships,
Lyons, France, Feb. 23-28.

Capercaillie — A85

Nature protection: No. 204, Brown bear.

1971, Apr. 24 Photo. Perf. 13
203 A85 80c multicolored 3.25 3.25
Engr.
204 A85 80c blue, grn & brn 2.40 2.40

Europa Issue, 1971
Common Design Type
1971, May 8 Engr. Perf. 13
Size: 35½x22mm
205 CD14 50c rose red 8.00 2.25
206 CD14 80c lt blue green 12.00 5.50

Altar Type of 1969
The Revelation (from the Altar of St. John,
Caselles): 30c, St. John preaching, Rev. 1:3.
50c, "The Sign of the Beast . . ." Rev. 16:1-2.
90c, The Woman, Rev. 17:1.

1971, Sept. 18
207 A81 30c dl grn, ol & brt grn 1.25 1.00
208 A81 50c rose car, org & ol
brn 1.60 1.25
209 A81 90c blk, dk pur & bl 2.40 2.00
Nos. 207-209 (3) 5.25 4.25

Europa Issue 1972
Common Design Type
1972, Apr. 29 Photo. Perf. 13
Size: 21½x37mm
210 CD15 50c brt mag & multi 7.50 2.50
211 CD15 90c multicolored 13.50 4.50

Golden Eagle A86

1972, May 27 Engr.
212 A86 60c dk grn, olive & plum 5.00 3.25
Nature protection.

Shooting A87

1972, July 8
213 A87 1fr dk purple 3.75 2.00
20th Olympic Games, Munich, 8/26-9/11.

Altar Type of 1969
The Revelation (from the Altar of St. John,
Caselles): 30c, St. John, bishop and servant.
50c, Resurrection of Lazarus. 90c, Angel with
lance and nails.

1972, Sept. 16 Engr. Perf. 13
214 A81 30c dk ol, gray & red lil 1.25 .85
215 A81 50c vio blue & slate 1.50 1.25
216 A81 90c dk Prus bl & sl grn 2.40 2.40
Nos. 214-216 (3) 5.15 4.50

De Gaulle as Coprince of Andorra — A88

90c, De Gaulle in front of Maison des
Vallées.

1972, Oct. 23 Engr. Perf. 13
217 A88 50c violet blue 2.00 2.00
218 A88 90c dk carmine 3.00 3.00
a. Pair, #217-218 + label 6.00 6.00
Visit of Charles de Gaulle to Andorra, 5th
anniv.
See Nos. 399-400.

Europa Issue 1973
Common Design Type
1973, Apr. 28 Photo. Perf. 13
Size: 36x22mm
219 CD16 50c violet & multi 9.00 3.00
220 CD16 90c dk red & multi 11.00 8.00

Virgin of Canolich A89

1973, June 16 Engr. Perf. 13
221 A89 1fr ol, Prus bl & vio 2.25 1.60

Lily — A90

45c, Iris. 50c, Columbine. 65c, Tobacco.
No. 226, Pinks. No. 227, Narcissuses.

1973-74 Photo. Perf. 13
222 A90 30c car rose & multi .80 .80
223 A90 45c yel grn & multi .40 .40
224 A90 50c buff & multi 1.75 1.75
225 A90 65c gray & multi .40 .40
226 A90 90c ultra & multi 1.50 1.50
227 A90 90c grnsh bl & multi 1.25 1.25
Nos. 222-227 (6) 6.10 6.10
Issued: 30c, 50c, No. 226, 7/7/73. 45c, 65c,
No. 227, 4/6/74.
See Nos. 238-240.

Blue Titmouse — A91

Nature protection: 60c, Citril finch and mistletoe. 80c, Eurasian bullfinch. 1fr, Lesser
spotted woodpecker.

1973-74 Photo. Perf. 13
228 A91 60c buff & multi 4.00 1.75
229 A91 80c gray & multi 4.00 2.25
230 A91 90c gray & multi 2.75 1.25
231 A91 1fr yel grn & multi 2.75 1.60
Nos. 228-231 (4) 13.50 6.85
Issued: 90c, 1fr, 10/27/73. 60c, 80c, 9/21/74.

Europa Issue

Virgin of Pal — A92

90c, Virgin of Santa Coloma. Statues are
polychrome 12th cent. carvings by rural
artists.

1974, Apr. 27 Engr. Perf. 13
232 A92 50c multicolored 9.00 3.00
233 A92 90c multicolored 12.50 7.00

Arms of Andorra and Cahors Bridge — A93

1974, Aug. 24 Engr. Perf. 13
234 A93 1fr blue, vio & org 1.00 .80
First anniv. of meeting of the co-princes of
Andorra: Pres. Georges Pompidou of France
and Msgr. Juan Marti Alanis, Bishop of Urgel.

Mail Box, Chutes and Globe — A94

1974, Oct. 5 Engr. Perf. 13
235 A94 1.20fr multi 1.25 1.25
Centenary of Universal Postal Union.

Coronation of St. Marti, 16th Century — A95

Europa: 80c, Crucifixion, 16th cent., vert.

Perf. 11½x13, 13x11½
1975, Apr. 26 Photo.
236 A95 80c gold & multi 4.50 3.00
237 A95 1.20fr gold & multi 6.50 4.00

Flower Type of 1973
Designs: 60c, Gentian. 80c, Anemone.
1.20fr, Autumn crocus.

1975, May 10 Photo. Perf. 13
238 A90 60c olive & multi .50 .40
239 A90 80c brt rose & multi 1.25 .80
240 A90 1.20fr green & multi 1.25 .80
Nos. 238-240 (3) 3.00 2.00

Abstract Design — A96

1975, June 7 Engr. Perf. 13
241 A96 2fr bl, magenta & emer 1.75 1.50
ARPHILA 75 International Philatelic Exhibition, Paris, June 6-16.

A97

1975, Aug. 23　Engr.　Perf. 13
242 A97 80c violet bl & blk　　1.00 1.00
　　Georges Pompidou (1911-74), pres. of
France and co-prince of Andorra (1969-74).

A98

1975, Nov. 8　Engr.　Perf. 13
243 A98 1.20fr Costume, IWY
　　　Emblem　　　　1.25 1.00
　　International Women's Year.

Skier and
Snowflake
A99

1976, Jan. 31　Engr.　Perf. 13
244 A99 1.20fr multicolored　　1.50 1.10
　　12th Winter Olympic Games, Innsbruck,
Austria, Feb. 4-15.

Telephone and
Satellite — A100

1976, Mar. 20　Engr.　Perf. 13
245 A100 1fr multicolored　　　1.00 1.00
　　Centenary of first telephone call by Alexander Graham Bell, Mar. 10, 1976.

Catalan
Forge
A101

　　Europa: 1.20fr, Woolen worker.

1976, May 8　Engr.　Perf. 13
246 A101　80c multi　　　3.25 1.00
247 A101　1.20fr multi　　4.75 1.75

Thomas
Jefferson — A102

1976, July 3　Engr.　Perf. 13
248 A102 1.20fr multi　　　1.25 1.00
　　American Bicentennial.

Trapshooting
A103

1976, July 17　Engr.　Perf. 13
249 A103 2fr multi　　　　1.75 1.40
　　21st Olympic Games, Montreal, Canada,
July 17-Aug. 1.

Meritxell Sanctuary and Old
Chapel — A104

1976, Sept. 4　Engr.　Perf. 13
250 A104 1fr multi　　　　1.00 1.00
　　Dedication of rebuilt Meritxell Church, Sept.
8, 1976.

Apollo — A105

　　Design: 1.40fr, Morio butterfly.

1976, Oct. 16　Photo.　Perf. 13
251 A105　80c black & multi　1.90 1.25
252 A105　1.40fr salmon & multi　3.25 2.00
　　Nature protection.

Ermine — A106

1977, Apr. 2　Photo.　Perf. 13
253 A106 1fr vio bl, gray & blk　1.60 1.25
　　Nature protection.

St. Jean de
Caselles — A107

　　Europa: 1.40fr, Sant Vicens Castle.

1977, Apr. 30　Engr.　Perf. 13
254 A107　1fr multi　　　3.00 1.25
255 A107 1.40fr multi　　4.75 2.00

Manual Digest,
1748, Arms of
Andorra — A108

1977, June 11　Engr.　Perf. 13
256 A108 80c grn, bl & brn　　.90 .90
　　Establishment of Institute of Andorran
Studies.

St.
Romanus
of
Caesarea
A109

1977, July 23　Engr.　Perf. 12½x13
257 A109 2fr multi　　　　1.75 1.50
　　Design from altarpiece in Church of St.
Roma de les Bons.

General
Council
Chamber
A110

Guillem d'Arény
Plandolit — A111

1977, Sept. 24　Engr.　Perf. 13
258 A110 1.10fr multi　　　1.40 1.00
259 A111　2fr car & dk brn　1.40 1.00
　　Andorran heritage.　Guillem d'Arény
Plandolit started Andorran reform movement
in 1866.

Squirrel — A112

1978, Mar. 18　Engr.　Perf. 13
260 A112 1fr multi　　　　.90 .75

Flag and Valira
River
Bridge — A113

1978, Apr. 8
261 A113 80c multi　　　　.65 .65
　　Signing of the treaty establishing the Co-Principality of Andorra, 700th anniv.

Pal Church
A114

　　Europa: 1.40fr, Charlemagne's Castle,
Charlemagne on horseback, vert.

1978, Apr. 29　Engr.　Perf. 13
262 A114　1fr multi　　　3.00 1.50
263 A114 1.40fr multi　　　5.50 2.75

Virgin of
Sispony
A115

1978, May 20　Engr.　Perf. 12x13
264 A115 2fr multi　　　　1.50 1.25

Visura
Tribunal
A116

1978, June 24　Engr.　Perf. 13
265 A116 1.20fr multi　　　1.00 .50

Preamble of 1278 Treaty — A117

1978, Sept. 2　Engr.　Perf. 13x12½
266 A117 1.70fr multi　　　1.00 .75
　　700th anniversary of the signing of treaty
establishing Co-Principality of Andorra.

Pyrenean Chamois — A118

1979, Mar. 26   **Engr.**   *Perf. 13*
267 A118 1fr multi   .65 .65

White Partridges — A119

1979, Apr. 7   **Photo.**   *Perf. 13*
268 A119 1.20fr multi   1.50 .75

Nature protection. See Nos. 288-289.

French Mailman, 1900 — A120

Europa: 1.70fr, 1st French p.o. in Andorra.

1979, Apr. 28   **Engr.**   *Perf. 13*
269 A120 1.20fr multi   2.00 .75
270 A120 1.70fr multi   4.00 1.25

Falcon, Pre-Roman Painting A121

1979, June 2   **Engr.**   *Perf. 12½x13*
271 A121 2fr multi   1.10 .90

Child with Lambs, Church, IYC Emblem. — A122

1979, July 7   **Photo.**   *Perf. 13*
272 A122 1.70fr multi   1.20 .85

International Year of the Child.

Trobada Monument A123

1979, Sept. 29   **Engr.**   *Perf. 13*
273 A123 2fr multi   1.25 1.00

Co-Principality of Andorra, 700th anniv

Judo Hold — A124

1979, Nov. 24   **Engr.**   *Perf. 13*
274 A124 1.30fr multi   .90 .75

World Judo Championships, Paris, Dec. 1979.

Farm House, Cortinada — A125

1980, Jan. 26   **Engr.**   *Perf. 13*
275 A125 1.10fr multi   .75 .60

Cross-Country Skiing — A126

1980, Feb. 9
276 A126 1.80fr ultra & lil rose   1.50 1.10

13th Winter Olympic Games, Lake Placid, NY, Feb. 12-24.

A128

1980, Aug. 30   **Engr.**   *Perf. 13*
278 A128 1.20fr multi   .75 .75

World Bicycling championships.

A129

Europa: 1.30fr, Charlemagne (742-814). 1.80fr, Napoleon I (1769-1821).

1980, Apr. 26   **Engr.**   *Perf. 13*
279 A129 1.30fr multi   1.75 .60
280 A129 1.80fr gray grn & brn   2.00 1.00

Pyrenees Lily — A130

1.10fr, Dog-toothed violet.

1980   **Photo.**
281 A130 1.10fr multicolored   .75 .55
282 A130 1.30fr shown   .75 .65

Nature protection. Issue dates: 1.10fr, June 21; 1.30fr, May 17.

De La Vall House, 400th Anniversary of Restoration A131

1980, Sept. 6   **Engr.**
283 A131 1.40fr multi   .75 .65

Angel, Church of St. Cerni de Nagol, Pre-Romanesque Fresco — A132

1980, Oct. 25   *Perf. 13x12½*
284 A132 2fr multi   1.25 1.25

Bordes de Mereig Mountain Village A133

1981, Mar. 21   **Engr.**   *Perf. 13*
285 A133 1.40fr bl gray & dk brn   .80 .80

Europa Issue

Ball de l'Ossa, Winter Game A134

2fr, El Contrapas dance.

1981, May 16   **Engr.**
286 A134 1.40fr shown   1.50 .50
287 A134 2fr multicolored   1.75 1.00

Bird Type of 1979

1.20fr, Phylloscopus bonelli. 1.40fr, Tichodroma muraria.

1981, June 20   **Photo.**
288 A119 1.20fr multicolored   .65 .65
289 A119 1.40fr multicolored   1.00 .65

World Fencing Championship, Clermont-Ferrand, July 2-13 — A135

1981, July 4   **Engr.**
290 A135 2fr bl & blk   .90 .80

St. Martin, 12th Cent. Tapestry A136

1981, Sept. 5   **Engr.**   *Perf. 12x13*
291 A136 3fr multi   1.25 1.00

Intl. Drinking Water Decade — A137

1981, Oct. 17   *Perf. 13*
292 A137 1.60fr multi   .75 .50

Intl. Year of the Disabled — A138

1981, Nov. 7
293 A138 2.30fr multi   1.00 .65

Europa 1982 A139

1.60fr, Creation of Andorran govt., 1982. 2.30fr, Land Council, 1419.

1982, May 8   **Engr.**   *Perf. 13*
294 A139 1.60fr multi   1.50 .70
295 A139 2.30fr multi   2.00 .70

1982 World Cup — A140

Various soccer players.

1982, June 12   **Engr.**   *Perf. 13*
296   1.60fr red & dk brn   .80 .65
297   2.60fr red & dk brn   1.10 .95
  a. A140 Pair, #296-297 + label   2.25 2.25

Souvenir Sheet

No. 52 — A141

1982, Aug. 21   **Engr.**
298 A141 5fr blk & rose car   2.40 2.40
1st Andorran Stamp Exhib., 8/21-9/19.

Horse, Roman Wall Painting — A142

1982, Sept. 4 Photo.   Perf. 13x12½
299 A142 3fr multi   1.25 1.00

Wild Cat — A143

1982, Oct. 9   Engr.   Perf. 13
300 A143 1.80fr shown   1.10 .85
301 A143 2.60fr Pine trees   .90 .75

TB Bacillus Centenary — A144

1982, Nov. 13
302 A144 2.10fr Koch, lungs   .85 .65

St. Thomas Aquinas (1225-74) — A145

1982, Dec. 4
303 A145 2fr multi   .85 .65

Manned Flight Bicentenary A146

1983, Feb. 26   Engr.
304 A146 2fr multi   .90 .75

Nature Protection A147

1983, Apr. 16   Engr.   Perf. 13
305 A147 1fr Birch trees   .40 .30
306 A147 1.50fr Trout   .75 .55
See Nos. 325-326.

Catalane Gold Works A148

1983, May 7   Engr.   Perf. 13
307 A148 1.80fr Exterior   1.00 .50
308 A148 2.60fr Interior   1.60 .80
Europa.

30th Anniv. of Customs Cooperation Council — A149

3fr, Letter of King Louis XIII.

1983, May 14
309 A149 3fr multicolored   1.25 1.00

First Arms of Valleys of Andorra A150

1983, Sept. 3   Engr.   Perf. 13
310 A150 5c olive grn & red   .25 .25
311 A150 10c grn & olive grn   .25 .25
312 A150 20c brt pur & red   .25 .25
313 A150 30c brn vio & red   .35 .35
314 A150 40c dk bl & vio   .35 .35
315 A150 50c gray & red   .25 .25
316 A150 1fr deep magenta   .25 .25
317 A150 2fr org red & red brn   .90 .40
318 A150 5fr dk brn & red   .25 .80
    Nos. 310-318 (9)   4.10 3.15
See Nos. 329-335, 380-385, 464-465.

Painting, Cortinada Church A151

1983, Sept. 24   Perf. 12x13
319 A151 4fr multi   1.75 1.00

Plandolit House — A152

1983, Oct. 15   Photo.   Perf. 13
320 A152 1.60fr dp ultra & brn   .75 .55

1984 Winter Olympics A153

1984, Feb. 18   Engr.
321 A153 2.80fr multicolored   1.25 .90

Pyrenees Region Work Community (Labor Org.) A154

1984, Apr. 28   Engr.   Perf. 13
322 A154 3fr brt blue & sepia   1.20 .90

Europa (1959-84) A155

1984, May 5   Engr.
323 A155 2fr brt grn   1.60 .80
324 A155 2.80fr rose car   2.75 1.40

Nature Protection Type of 1983

1984, July 7   Engr.   Perf. 13
325 A147 1.70fr Chestnut tree   .80 .40
326 A147 2.10fr Walnut tree   1.00 .65

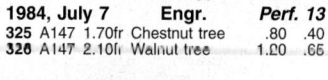

Pyrenees Art Center — A155a

1984, Sept. 7   Engr.
327 A155a 3fr multi   1.40 1.00

Romanesque Fresco, Church of St. Cerni de Nagol — A156

1984, Nov. 17   Perf. 12x13
328 A156 5fr multi   2.25 1.90

First Arms Type of 1983

1984-87   Engr.   Perf. 13
329 A150 1.90fr emerald   3.25 .80
330 A150 2.20fr red orange   1.25 .40
  a. Bklt. pane, 2 #329, 6 #330 15.00
331 A150 3fr bl grn & red
          brn   1.50 1.00
332 A150 4fr brt org & brn   3.50 1.25
333 A150 10fr brn org & blk   3.50 1.60
334 A150 15fr grn & dk grn   5.00 2.40

---

335 A150 20fr brt bl & red
           brn   7.00 2.75
    Nos. 329-335 (7)   25.00 10.20
Nos. 329-330 issued in booklets only.
Issued: 3fr, 20fr, 12/1/84; 10fr, 2/9/85; 4fr, 15fr, 4/19/86; 1.90fr, 2.20fr, 3/28/87.

Saint Julia Valley A157

1985, Apr. 13   Engr.
336 A157 2fr multi   1.00 .60

Europa 1985 — A158

2.10fr, Le Val D'Andorre. 3fr, Instruments.

1985, May 4   Engr.
337 A158 2.10fr multicolored   1.75 .75
338 A158 3fr multicolored   4.00 1.25

Intl. Youth Year — A159

1985, June 8   Engr.
339 A159 3fr multicolored   1.25 .90

Wildlife Conservation — A160

1.80fr, Anas platyrhynchos. 2.20fr, Cardue-lis carduelis.

1985, Aug. 3   Photo.
340 A160 1.80fr multicolored   1.00 .65
341 A160 2.20fr multicolored   1.40 .85

Two Saints, Medieval Fresco in St. Cerni de Nagol Church A161

1985, Sept. 14 Engr. Perf. 12½x13
342 A161 5fr multicolored   2.00 1.75

Postal Museum
Inauguration
A162

1986, Mar. 22   Engr.   Perf. 13
343 A162 2.20fr like No. 269   1.00 .65

Europa
1986
A163

1986, May 3   Engr.   Perf. 13
344 A163 2.20fr Ansalonga   2.50 .90
345 A163 3.20fr Isard   5.00 1.60

1986 World Cup
Soccer
Championships,
Mexico — A164

1986, June 14
346 A164 3fr multi   1.50 1.00

Angonella
Lake
A165

1986, June 28
347 A165 2.20fr multi   1.00 .70

Manual Digest Frontispiece,
1748 — A166

1986, Sept. 6   Engr.
348 A166 5fr chnt brn, gray ol &
        blk   2.25 1.40

Intl. Peace
Year
A167

1986, Sept. 27
349 A167 1.90fr bl gray & grnsh
        bl   1.00 .65

St. Vincenc
d'Enclar — A168

1986, Oct. 18   Engr.   Perf. 13½x13
350 A168 1.90fr multicolored   .95 .65

Contemporary
Natl. Coat of
Arms — A169

1987, Mar. 27   Litho.   Perf. 12½x13
351 A169 2.20fr multi   1.60 1.60

Visit of the French co-prince.

Europa
1987
A170

2.20fr, Meritxell Sanctuary. 3.40fr, Pleta
D'Ordino.

1987, May 2   Engr.   Perf. 13
352 A170 2.20fr multicolored   2.00 .80
353 A170 3.40fr multicolored   4.50 2.00

Ransol
Village — A171

1987, June 13   Photo.
354 A171 1.90fr multicolored   1.25 1.00

Nature
A172

1.90fr, Cavall rogenc. 2.20fr, Graellsia
isabellae.

1987, July 4
355 A172 1.90fr multicolored   1.25 .80
356 A172 2.20fr multicolored   1.60 1.25

Aryalsu, Romanesque Painting, La
Cortinada Church — A173

Litho. & Engr.
1987, Sept. 5   Perf. 12½x13
357 A173 5fr multi   2.50 1.60

Hiker
Looking at
Map
A174

1987, Sept. 19   Engr.   Perf. 13
358 A174 2fr olive, grn & dark
        brn vio   1.00 .60

Medieval
Iron Key, La
Cortinada
A175

1987, Oct. 17   Litho.
359 A175 3fr multi   1.25 1.00

Andorran Coat of
Arms — A176

Booklet Stamp
1988, Feb. 6   Engr.   Perf. 13
360 A176 2.20fr red   1.00 .50
a.   Bklt. pane of 5   5.00
    Complete bklt., 2 #360a   10.00
    See Nos. 386-388.

Shoemaker's Last
from Roc de
l'Oral — A177

1988, Feb. 13   Photo.
361 A177 3fr multi   1.50 1.10

Rugby
A178

1988, Mar. 19   Engr.   Perf. 13½x13
362 A178 2.20fr blk, org, turq grn 1.20 .95

Europa
1988 — A179

Transport and communication: 2.20fr,
Broadcast tower. 3.60fr, Computer graphics.

1988, Apr. 30   Engr.   Perf. 13
363 A179 2.20fr multicolored   1.75 .90
364 A179 3.60fr multicolored   3.75 1.10

Hot Springs,
Escaldes — A180

1988, May 14   Engr.
365 A180 2.20fr Prus blue, org
        brn & emer   1.25 .80

Tor D'Ansalonga Farmhouse,
Ansalonga Pass — A181

1988, June 11   Engr.
366 A181 2fr multi   1.10 .65

Sheepdog — A182

1988, July 2   Photo.
367 A182   2fr shown   1.50 .60
368 A182 2.20fr Hare   1.50 .60

Roman Fresco, 8th Cent., St. Steven's
Church, Andorre-La-Vieille — A183

1988, Sept. 3   Engr.   Perf. 13x12½
369 A183 5fr multicolored   2.25 1.50

French Revolution,
Bicent. — A184

1989, Jan. 1   Litho.   Perf. 13
370 A184 2.20fr red & vio bl   1.00 1.00

Poble de
Pal Village
A185

1989, Mar. 4   Engr.   Perf. 13
371 A185 2.20fr indigo & lilac   1.00 .65

Europa
1989
A186

Children's games: 2.20fr, Human tower. 3.60fr, The handkerchief.

1989, Apr. 29   Engr.   Perf. 13
372 A186 2.20fr multi   2.00   .80
373 A186 3.60fr multi   2.50 1.75

Red Cross
A187

1989, May 6
374 A187 3.60fr multi   1.75 1.25

Visigothic — Merovingian Age Cincture from a Column, St. Vicenc D'Anclar — A188

1989, June 3   Photo.
375 A188 3fr multi   1.40 1.10

Wildlife
A189

1989, Sept. 16   Engr.   Perf. 13
376 A189 2.20fr Wild boar   1.25   .90
377 A189 3.60fr Newt   2.00 1.25

Scene of Salome from the Retable of St. Michael of Mosquera, Encamp — A190

1989, Oct. 14   Perf. 13x13½
378 A190 5fr multi   2.50 1.25

La Margineda Bridge A191

1990, Feb. 26   Engr.   Perf. 13
379 A191 2.30fr multi   1.25   .60

Tourism.

Arms Types of 1983 and 1988

1990-93   Engr.   Perf. 13
380 A150 2.10fr green   1.00   .40
381 A150 2.20fr green   1.25   .40
382 A150 2.30fr vermilion   1.00   .40
383 A150 2.40fr green   1.40   .80
384 A150 2.50fr vermilion   1.25   .40
385 A150 2.80fr vermilion   1.60   .40
   Nos. 380-385 (6)   7.50 2.80

Booklet Stamps
Perf. 13

386 A176 2.30fr red   1.00   .40
 a.   Booklet pane of 5   5.00
387 A176 2.50fr vermilion   1.25   .40
 a.   Booklet pane of 5   6.25
388 A176 2.80fr red   1.25   .40
 c.   Booklet pane of 5   6.25
   Nos. 386-388 (3)   3.50 1.20

Issued: 2.20fr, #384, 10/26/91; #387, 10/21/91; 2.40fr, 2.80fr, 8/9/93; 2.10fr, 2.30fr, 1990.

Llorts Mines A193

1990, Apr. 21   Engr.   Perf. 12½x13
390 A193 3.20fr multicolored   1.75 1.00

Europa A194

Designs: 2.30fr, Early post office. 3.20fr, Modern post office.

1990, May 5   Perf. 13
391 A194 2.30fr blk & scar   2.00   .75
392 A194 3.20fr scar & vio   3.00 1.50

Otter A195

1990, May 25   Perf. 12x13
393 A195 2.30fr Roses, vert.   1.10   .55
394 A195 3.20fr shown   1.75 1.00

Censer of St. Roma of Les Bons A196

1990, June 25   Perf. 12½x13
395 A196 3fr multicolored   1.25   .65

Tobacco Drying Sheds, Les Bons A197

1990, Sept. 15   Engr.   Perf. 12½x13
396 A197 2.30fr multi   1.00   .65

St. Coloma (Detail) A198

1990, Oct. 8   Perf. 12½x13
397 A198 5fr multi   2.50 1.50

Coin from Church of St. Eulalia d'Encamp A199

1990, Oct. 27   Litho.   Perf. 13
398 A199 3.20fr multi   1.40   .75

De Gaulle Type of 1972 Dated 1990
1990, Oct. 23   Engr.   Perf. 13
399 A88 2.30fr vio bl   1.00   .65
400 A88 3.20fr dk car   1.25 1.10
 a.   Pair, #399-400 + label   2.50 2.50

Birth centenary of De Gaulle.

4th Games of the Small European States — A200

1991, Apr. 8   Photo.   Perf. 13
401 A200 2.50fr multicolored   1.00   .60

Chapel of St. Roma Dels Vilars A201

1991, Mar. 9   Engr.   Perf. 13
402 A201 2.50fr multicolored   1.10   .65

Europa — A202

2.50fr, TV satellite. 3.50fr, Telescope, horiz.

1991, Apr. 27   Perf. 13x12½, 12½x13
403 A202 2.50fr multicolored   2.75 1.75
404 A202 3.50fr multicolored   4.50 2.25

Bottles from Tombs of St. Vincenc d'Enclar A203

1991, May 11   Photo.   Perf. 13
405 A203 3.20fr multicolored   1.50 1.00

Farm Animals A204

1991, June 22   Engr.   Perf. 13
406 A204 2.50fr Sheep   1.25   .80
407 A204 3.50fr Cow   2.00 1.25

Petanque World Championships — A205

1991, Sept. 14   Engr.   Perf. 13
408 A205 2.50fr multicolored   1.25   .95

Wolfgang Amadeus Mozart, Death Bicent. A206

1991, Oct. 5
409 A206 3.40fr multicolored   1.75 1.10

Virgin and Child of St. Julia and St. Germa A207

1991, Nov. 16   Engr.   Perf. 12½x13
410 A207 5fr multicolored   2.00 1.00

Church of St. Andrew of Arinsal A209

1992 Winter Olympics, Albertville — A208

1992, Feb. 10   Litho.   Perf. 13
411 A208 2.50fr Slalom skiing   1.25 1.00
412 A208 3.40fr Figure skating 1.25 1.00
 a.   Pair, #411-412 + label   2.75 2.75

1992, Mar. 21   Engr.   Perf. 12x13
413 A209 2.50fr black & tan   .75   .50

Discovery of America, 500th Anniv. A210

2.50fr, Columbus' fleet. 3.40fr, Landing in New World.

1992, Apr. 25   Perf. 13
414 A210 2.50fr multicolored   2.50 1.00
415 A210 3.40fr multicolored   5.00 2.00

Europa.

1992 Summer
Olympics,
Barcelona — A211

1992, June 8   **Litho.**   **Perf. 13**
416 A211 2.50fr Kayaking   1.25 1.00
417 A211 3.40fr Shooting   1.25 1.00
   a.   Pair, #416-417 + label   2.75 2.75

European
Globeflower — A212

Design: 3.40fr, Vulture, horiz.

1992, July 6
418 A212 2.50fr multicolored   1.25 .65
419 A212 3.40fr multicolored   1.75 1.00

Martyrdom
of St.
Eulalia
A213

1992, Sept. 14   **Photo.**   **Perf. 13**
420 A213 4fr multicolored   1.50 .95

Sculpture
by Mauro
Staccioli
A214

1992, Oct. 5   **Engr.**   **Perf. 12½x13**
421 A214 5fr multicolored   2.00 1.00
Ordino Arcalis '91.

Tempest in a Tea Cup, by Dennis
Oppenheim — A215

1992, Nov. 14   **Engr.**   **Perf. 13x12½**
422 A215 5fr multicolored   2.00 1.00

Skiing in Andorra — A216

Ski resorts: No. 423: a, 2.50fr, Soldeu El
Tarter. b, 3.40fr, Arinsal.

No. 424: a, 2.50fr, Pas de la Casa-Grau
Roig. b, 2.50fr, Ordino Arcalis. c, 3.40fr, Pal.

1993, Mar. 13   **Litho.**   **Perf. 13**
423 A216 Pair, #a.-b. + label   2.60 2.60
424 A216 Strip of 3, #a.-c.   3.75 3.75

Sculptures — A217

Europa: 2.50fr, "Estructures Autogener-
adores," by Jorge du Bon, vert. 3.40fr, Sculpture, "Fisicromia per Andorra," by Carlos Cruz-
Diez.

1993, May 15   **Engr.**   **Perf. 12½x13**
425 A217 2.50fr multicolored   1.60 1.25
     Litho.
        Perf. 14x13½
426 A217 3.40fr multicolored   2.00 1.50

Butterflies
A218

2.50fr, Polymmatus icarus. 4.20fr,
Nymphalidae.

1993, June 28   **Litho.**   **Perf. 13**
427 A218 2.50fr multicolored   1.20 .65
428 A218 4.20fr multicolored   1.90 1.40

Tour de France
Bicycle
Race — A219

1993, July 20   **Litho.**   **Perf. 13**
429 A219 2.50fr multicolored   1.25 .65

Andorra
School,
10th Anniv.
A220

1993, Sept. 20   **Litho.**   **Perf. 13**
430 A220 2.80fr multicolored   1.25 1.00

Un Lloc
Paga, by
Michael
Warren
A221

1993, Oct. 18   **Engr.**   **Perf. 12½x13**
431 A221 5fr blue & black   2.00 1.50

Sculpture,
by Erik
Dietman
A222

1993, Nov. 8   **Engr.**   **Perf. 12½x13**
432 A222 5fr multicolored   2.00 1.50

1994 Winter
Olympics,
Lillehammer
A223

1994, Feb. 21   **Litho.**   **Perf. 13**
433 A223 3.70fr multicolored   2.25 1.50

1st Anniversary of
the
Constitution — A224

Designs: 2.80fr, Monument, by Emili
Armengol. 3.70fr, Stone tablet with inscription.

1994, Mar. 15   **Litho.**   **Perf. 13**
434 A224 2.80fr multicolored   1.25 1.00
435 A224 3.70fr multicolored   1.25 1.00
   a.   Pair, #434-435 + label   2.75 2.75

European
Discoveries
A225

Europa: 2.80fr, Discovery of AIDS virus.
3.70fr, Radio diffusion.

1994, May 7   **Litho.**   **Perf. 13**
436 A225 2.80fr multicolored   1.75 .90
437 A225 3.70fr multicolored   2.75 1.25

1994 World Cup Soccer
Championships, US — A226

1994, June 20
438 A226 3.70fr multicolored   2.00 1.25

Tourist
Sports — A227

Designs: No. 439, Mountain climbing. No.
440, Fishing. No. 441, Horseback riding. No.
442, Mountain biking.

1994, July 11
439 A227 2.80fr multicolored   1.20 1.00
440 A227 2.80fr multicolored   1.20 1.00
   a.   Pair, #439-440 + label   2.50 2.50
441 A227 2.80fr multicolored   1.20 1.00
442 A227 2.80fr multicolored   1.20 1.00
   a.   Pair, #441-442 + label   2.50 2.50
     Nos. 439-442 (4)   4.80 4.00

Butterflies
A228

2.80fr, Iphiclides podalirus. 4.40fr, Aglais
urticae.

1994, Sept. 5   **Litho.**   **Perf. 13**
443 A228 2.80fr multicolored   1.60 .65
444 A228 4.40fr multicolored   2.25 .95

A229

1994, Oct. 22   **Litho.**   **Perf. 13**
445 A229 2.80fr multicolored   1.10 .65
Meeting of the Co-Princes, 1st anniv.

A230

1995, Feb. 27   **Litho.**   **Perf. 13**
446 A230 2.80fr multicolored   1.50 .50
European Nature Conservation Year

1995 World Cup Rugby
Championships — A231

1995, Apr. 24   **Litho.**   **Perf. 13**
447 A231 2.80fr multicolored   1.50 .75

Peace &
Freedom
A232

Europa: 2.80fr, Dove with olive branch.
3.70fr, Flock of doves.

1995, Apr. 29
448 A232 2.80fr multicolored   1.90 .75
449 A232 3.70fr multicolored   3.00 1.00

Caritas in
Andorra,
15th Anniv.
A233

1995, May 15   **Litho.**   **Perf. 13**
450 A233 2.80fr multicolored   1.40 .65

Caldea Health
Spa — A234

1995, June 26   **Litho.**   **Perf. 13**
451 A234 2.80fr multicolored   1.20   .65

Ordino Natl.
Auditorium
A235

1995, July 10   **Litho. & Engr.**
452 A235 3.70fr black & buff   1.50 1.00

Virgin of Meritxell — A236

1995, Sept. 11   **Litho.**   **Perf. 14**
453 A236 4.40fr multicolored   1.75   .95

Protection
of Nature
A237

Butterflies: 2.80fr, Papallona llimonera, vert.
3.70fr, Papallona melanargia galathea.

1995, Sept. 25   **Perf. 13**
454 A237 2.80fr multicolored   1.50 1.00
455 A237 3.70fr multicolored   1.75 1.25

UN, 50th
Anniv. — A238

2.80fr, Flag, emblem. 3.70fr, Emblem, "50,"
flag.

1995, Oct. 21   **Litho.**   **Perf. 13**
456 A238 2.80fr multicolored   1.25 1.00
457 A238 3.70fr multicolored   1.25 1.00
   a.   Pair, #456-457 + label   2.75 2.75

Andorra's
Entrance
into Council
of Europe
A239

1995, Nov. 4
458 A239 2.80fr multicolored   1.40   .65

World Skiing Championships, Ordino
Arcalis — A240

1996, Jan. 29   **Litho.**   **Perf. 13**
459 A240 2.80fr multicolored   1.10   .65

Basketball in
Andorra — A241

1996, Jan. 29   **Litho.**   **Perf. 13**
460 A241 3.70fr multicolored   1.50   .95

Our Lady of
Meritxell
Special
School,
25th Anniv.
A242

1996, Feb. 17   **Litho.**   **Perf. 13**
461 A242 2.80fr multicolored   1.10   .65

Songbirds
A243

3fr, Pit riog. 3.80fr, Mallarenga carbonera.

1996, Mar. 25
462 A243   3fr   multicolored   1.25   .65
463 A243 3.80fr multicolored   1.75 1.40

First Arms Type of 1983

1996, Apr. 17   **Engr.**   **Perf. 13**
464 A150 2.70fr green   .95   .65
465 A150   3fr   red   1.20   .35

Cross of St. James
d'Engordany
A244

1996, Apr. 20   **Litho.**
466 A244 3fr multicolored   1.25   .65

Censer of
St. Eulalia
d'Encamp
A245

1996, Apr. 20
467 A245 3.80fr multicolored   1.50 1.20

Europa — A246

3fr, Ermessenda de Castellbo.

1996, May 6
468 A246 3fr multicolored   *1.90 1.00*

Chess — A247

1996, June 8   **Litho.**   **Perf. 13**
469 A247 4.50fr multicolored   1.90 1.00

1996
Summer
Olympic
Games,
Atlanta
A248

1996, June 29   **Litho.**   **Perf. 13**
470 A248 3fr multicolored   1.50   .70

Arms of the Community
of Canillo — A249

Sorpontino Dio Cut 7 Vcrt.

1996, June 10   **Litho.**
     Self-Adhesive
471 A249 (3fr) multicolored   1.20   .45
   a.   Booklet of 10   12.00

Natl.
Children's
Choir, 5th
Anniv.
A250

1996, Sept. 14   **Perf. 13**
472 A250 3fr multicolored   1.20   .60

Livestock
Fair
A251

1996, Oct. 26   **Engr.**   **Perf. 12x13**
473 A251 3fr multicolored   1.20   .60

Churches
A252

Designs: No. 474, St. Romá de Les Bons.
No. 475, St. Coloma.

1996, Nov. 16   **Litho.**   **Perf. 13**
474 A252 6.70fr multicolored   2.75 1.40
475 A252 6.70fr multicolored   2.75 1.40

A253

1997, Jan. 7   **Litho.**   **Perf. 13**
476 A253 3fr multicolored   1.20   .60
Pres. Francois Mitterrand (1916-96).

A254

***Sawtooth Die Cut 7 Vert. x Straight
Die Cut***

1997, Feb. 24   **Litho.**
     Self-Adhesive
477 A254 (3fr) Arms of Encamp   1.50   .45
   a.   Booklet pane of 10   15.00

By its nature, No. 477a is a complete booklet. The peelable paper backing serves as a
booklet cover.

A255

1997, Mar. 22   **Perf. 13**
478 A255 3fr Volleyball   1.25   .60

"The White
Lady" — A256

1997, June 10   **Litho.**   **Perf. 13**
479 A256 3fr multicolored   *1.75   .90*
Europa (Stories and Legends).

Oreneta
Cuablanca
A257

1997, May 31   **Litho.**   **Perf. 13**
480 A257 3.80fr multicolored   2.40 1.25

Paintings of
Mills
A258

1997, Sept. 15   **Litho.**   **Perf. 13**
481 A258   3fr Cal Pal, vert.   1.25   .60
482 A258 4.50fr Mas d'en Sole   2.00 1.00

Religious Artifacts A259

Designs: 3fr, Monstrance of St. Iscle and St. Victoria. 15.50fr, Altar piece of St. Pierre d'Alxirivall.

1997, Oct. 27
483 A259 3fr multicolored 1.40 .60
484 A259 15.50fr multicolored 5.50 2.75
a. Pair, #483-484 + label 7.50 7.50

Legends — A260

Designs: No. 485, Legend of Meritxell. No. 486, The cross of seven arms. 3.80fr, The fountain of Esmelicat.

1997, Nov. 22 Litho. Perf. 13
485 A260 3fr multicolored 1.40 .60
486 A260 3fr multicolored 1.40 .60
487 A260 3.80fr multicolored 2.00 1.00
a. Strip of 3, #485-487 5.00 5.00

Chapel of St. Miguel d'Engolasters — A261

1997, Nov. 28 Litho. Perf. 13
488 A261 3fr multicolored 1.20 .60

Monaco Intl. Philatelic Exhibition.

Happy Anniversary — A262

1998, Jan. 3 Litho. Perf. 13
489 A262 3fr Juggling candles 1.20 .60

1998 Winter Olympic Games, Nagano — A263

1998, Feb. 14
490 A263 4.40fr multicolored 2.00 1.00

Arms of Ordino — A264

Serpentine Die Cut Vert.
1998, Mar. 7 Self-Adhesive Litho.
Booklet Stamp
491 A264 (3fr) multicolored 1.25 .30
a. Booklet pane of 10 12.50
Complete booklet, #491a 12.50

See Nos. 504, 518, 531.

Mesa de Vila Church — A265

1998, Mar. 28 Perf. 13
492 A265 4.50fr multicolored 2.25 2.00

Rotary Club of Andorra, 20th Anniv. — A265a

1998, Apr. 11
493 A265a 3fr multicolored 1.20 .60

Finch A266

1998 Litho. Perf. 13
494 A266 3.80fr multicolored 2.00 1.00

1998 World Cup Soccer Championships, France — A267

1998, June 6 Litho. Perf. 13
495 A267 3fr multicolored 1.60 1.25

For overprint see No. 499.

Music Festival A268

1998, June 20 Litho. Perf. 13
496 A268 3fr multicolored *1.50 .90*

Europa.

Expo '98, Lisbon A269

1998, July 6
497 A269 5fr multicolored 2.25 1.40

Chalice, House of the Valleys — A270

1998, Sept. 19 Litho. Perf. 13
498 A270 4.50fr multicolored 2.25 1.00

No. 495 Overprinted

1998, Nov. 16
499 A267 3fr multicolored 2.75 1.50

Early Maps of Andorra A271

1998, Nov. 16
500 A271 3fr 1717, vert. 2.00 1.25
501 A271 15.50fr 1777 8.00 3.50

Inauguration of the Postal Museum — A272

1998, Nov. 19 Litho. Perf. 13
502 A272 3fr multicolored 1.20 .60

Manual Digest, 250th Anniv. A273

1998, Dec. 7
503 A273 3.80fr multicolored 1.50 1.00

Arms Type of 1998
Self-Adhesive
Serpentine Die Cut Vert.
1999, Jan. 18 Booklet Stamp
504 A264 (3fr) La Massana 1.25 .55
a. Booklet pane of 10 12.50

No. 504a is a complete booklet.

Recycling A274

1999, Mar. 13 Litho. Perf. 13
505 A274 5fr multicolored 2.25 1.40

Sorteny Valley — A275

1999, Apr. 10
506 A275 3fr multicolored *2.00 1.25*

Europa.

Council of Europe, 50th Anniv. A276

1999, May 5 Litho. Perf. 13
507 A276 3.80fr multicolored 1.60 1.00

First Stage Coach — A277

1999, May 15
508 A277 2.70fr multi 1.60 1.25

1999 European National Soccer Championships — A278

1999, June 10 Photo. Perf. 13
509 A278 4.50fr multicolored 2.25 1.50

PhilexFrance 99 — A279

1999, July 2 Litho. Perf. 13x13¼
510 A279 3fr multicolored 1.20 .60

Historic View of Pal — A280

Perf. 13x13¼, 13¼x13
1999, July 10 Litho.
511 A280 3fr shown 1.20 .60
512 A280 3fr Different view, vert. 1.40 .60

International Federation of
Photographic Art, 50th Anniv. — A281

1999, July 24   **Litho.**   *Perf. 13*
513 A281 4.40fr multicolored   2.25 1.00

Casa Rull,
Sispony
A282

1999, Sept. 6   **Litho.**   *Perf. 13x13¼*
514 A282 15.50fr multicolored   6.00 3.50

Chest With Six Locks — A283

1999, Oct. 9   **Litho.**   *Perf. 13x13¼*
515 A283 6.70fr multicolored   2.75 1.50

Christmas
A284

1999, Nov. 27   **Litho.**   *Perf. 13*
516 A284 3fr multicolored   1.20 .60

Year 2000
A285

2000, Jan. 5   **Litho.**   *Perf. 13x13¼*
517 A285 3fr multicolored   1.20 .60

Arms Type of 1998
Self-Adhesive
Serpentine Die Cut 6½ Vert.
2000, Feb. 26   **Booklet Stamp**
518 A264 (3fr) Andorra-la-Vielle   1.25 .40
   a.   Booklet pane of 10   12.50

No. 518a is a complete booklet.

Snowboarding
A286

2000, Mar. 17   **Litho.**   *Perf. 13*
519 A286 4.50fr multi   2.00 1.00

Montserrat
Caballé
Chant
Competition
A287

2000, Apr. 3   *Perf. 13x13¼*
520 A287 3.80fr multi   2.00 1.00

Campanula
Cochlearifolia
A288

2000, Apr. 17   **Litho.**   *Perf. 13*
521 A288 2.70fr multi   1.20 .60

Europa, 2000
Common Design Type
2000, May 9   *Perf. 13½x13*
522 CD17 3fr multi   2.00 1.00

Festivals
A289

No. 523: a, Canòlic. b, Meritxell.

2000, May 27   **Litho.**   *Perf. 13*
523   Pair + central label   3.00 3.00
  a.-b.   A289 3fr Any single   1.25 .60

Pardal
Comú — A290

2000, July 7   **Litho.**   *Perf. 13*
524 A290 4.40fr multi   2.00 1.00

A291

2000, Sept. 11   **Litho.**   *Perf. 13*
525 A291 5fr multi   2.00 1.00

2000 Summer Olympics, Sydney.

World Tourism
Day — A292

2000, Sept. 28
526 A292 3fr multi   1.20 .60

Expo 2000,
Hanover
A293

2000, Oct. 6   **Litho.**   *Perf. 13*
527 A293 3fr multi   1.20 .60

"Europe, A
Common
Heritage"
A294

2000, Nov. 4   **Litho.**   *Perf. 13½x13*
528 A294 3.80fr multi   1.60 1.00

Prehistoric Pottery of Prats — A295

2000, Dec. 16   *Perf. 13x13¼*
529 A295 6.70fr multi   3.00 1.50

National Archives,
25th Anniv. — A296

2000, Dec. 22   *Perf. 13*
530 A296 15.50fr multi   7.50 4.50

Arms Type of 1998
Serpentine Die Cut 6½ Vert.
2001, Feb. 19   **Litho.**
Booklet Stamp
Self-Adhesive
531 A264 (3fr) Sant Julià de
      Lòria   1.25 .40
  a.   Booklet, 10 #531   12.50

Canillo Aliga
Mountain
Station — A297

2001, Feb. 10   **Litho.**   *Perf. 13*
532 A297 4.50fr multi   2.00 1.00

Casa
Cristo
Museum
A298

2001, Feb. 17   *Perf. 13¼x13*
533 A298 6.70fr multi   2.75 1.50

Andorran Heritage — A299

No. 534: a, Legend of Engolasters Lake. b,
Foundation of Andorra.

2001, Mar. 23   *Perf. 13*
534 A299 3fr Pair, #a-b, with cen-
     tral label   3.00 3.00

Intl. Book
Day — A300

2001, Apr. 23   **Litho.**   *Perf. 13*
535 A300 3.80fr multi   1.75 1.00

Europa — A301

2001, Apr. 28
536 A301 3fr multi   *2.00 1.00*

A302

3fr, Raspberries, vert.

2001, May 12
537 A302   3fr multicolored   1.20 .60
538 A302   4.40fr shown   2.00 1.00

European Language Year
A303

2001, June 16 Litho. *Perf. 13*
539 A303 3.80fr multi 1.75 1.00

Escaldes-Engordany Jazz Festival — A304

2001, July 7
540 A304 3fr multi 1.60 .70

General Council's Kitchen
A305

2001, Aug. 10
541 A305 5fr multi 2.50 1.50

Chapel of the Virgin of Meritxell, 25th Anniv. of Rebuilding — A306

2001, Sept. 7 Litho. *Perf. 13*
542 A306 3fr multi 1.60 .80

Hotel Pla — A307

2001, Oct. 12
543 A307 15.50fr multi 6.50 3.00

Cross of Terme — A308

2001, Nov. 17 Litho. *Perf. 13½x13*
544 A308 2.70fr multi 1.25 .75

100 Cents = 1 Euro (€)

National Arms — A309

Legends
A310   A311

Designs: 10c, Legend of Meritxell. 20c, Fountain of Esmelicat. 50c, The Cross with Seven Arms. €1, The Founding of Andorra. €2, Legend of Engolasters Lake. €5, The White Lady.

Perf. 13¼ (A309), 13¼x13
2002, Jan. 2 Photo. (A309), Litho.
545 A309 1c yel & multi .25 .25
546 A309 2c tan & multi .25 .25
547 A309 5c bl & multi .25 .25
548 A310 10c multi .25 .25
549 A310 20c multi .50 .40
550 A309 (46c) red & multi 1.00 .40
551 A310 50c multi 2.25 .80
552 A311 €1 multi 2.50 1.00
553 A311 €2 multi 4.50 1.50
554 A311 €5 multi 12.00 5.00
  Nos. 545-554 (10) 23.75 10.10

See Nos. 577, 618, 635, 661-666, 680.

Traffic Safety Education in Schools — A312

2002, Jan. 25 Litho. *Perf. 13½x13*
555 A312 69c multi 2.25 1.00

2002 Winter Olympics, Salt Lake City — A313

2002, Feb. 2 Litho. *Perf. 13*
556 A313 58c multi 1.50 .75

Hotel Rosaleda A314

2002, Mar. 16 Litho. *Perf. 13*
557 A314 46c multi 2.25 1.00

World Day for Water — A315

2002, Mar. 22 Litho. *Perf. 13*
558 A315 67c multi 1.60 1.00

Europa — A316

2002, May 10 Litho. *Perf. 13*
559 A316 46c multi 2.00 .40

Bilberries — A317

2002, July 6 Litho. *Perf. 13*
560 A317 46c multi 1.60 .80

Seated Nude, Sculpture by Josep Viladomat — A318

2002, Aug. 24 Litho. *Perf. 13¼x13*
561 A318 €2.36 multi 6.50 3.25

Envalira Tunnel A319

2002, Sept. 2 *Perf. 13*
562 A319 46c multi 1.75 .80

Piper of Ordino — A320

2002, Sept. 27
563 A320 41c multi 1.75 .80
  See No. 578.

Detail of Santa Coloma Wall Painting — A321

2002, Nov. 16 Litho. *Perf. 13*
564 A321 €1.02 multi 3.00 1.75

Comú d'Escaldes — Engordany Coat of Arms — A322

Serpentine Die Cut 6¾ Vert.
2003, Jan. 20 Photo.
Booklet Stamp
Self-Adhesive
565 A322 (46c) multi 1.40 .50
  a. Booklet pane of 10 14.00

Legend of the Margineda Pine — A323

2003, Feb. 10 Litho. *Perf. 13*
566 A323 69c multi 2.00 1.00
  See No. 579.

Constitution, 10th Anniv. A324

2003, Mar. 14 Litho. *Perf. 13x13½*
567 A324 €2.36 multi 6.50 3.50

Buildings, Les Bons — A325

2003, Mar. 31 *Perf. 13*
568 A325 67c multi 2.25 1.25

Hotel Mirador A326

2003, Apr. 12 Litho. *Perf. 13*
569 A326 €1.02 multi 3.00 2.00

Europa — A327

2003, May 17
570 A327 46c multi 1.75 .80

Falles de
San Joan
A328

2003, June 23   Litho.   Perf. 13
571 A328 50c multi   1.60   .80

A329

2003, July 5
572 A329 50c multi   1.75   .80

Tour de France bicycle race, cent.

A330

2003, Aug. 8
573 A330 90c multi   2.50 1.50

World Track and Field Championships, Paris.

Sparassis
Crispa
A331

Currants
A332

2003, Sept. 15   Litho.   Perf. 13
574 A331 45c multi   1.50 1.00
575 A332 75c multi   2.25 1.00

Telephones
in Andorra,
Cent.
A333

2003, Oct. 30   Litho.   Perf. 13
576 A333 50c multi   1.75   .65

Types of 2002-03 Inscribed "Postes"
2003, Nov. 29   Photo.   Perf. 13x13¼
577 A309 (45c) green & multi   1.30   .80
Litho.
Perf. 13
578 A320 75c multi   3.25 2.00
579 A323 90c multi   3.25 2.25
      Nos. 577-579 (3)   7.80 5.05

Maternity,
by Paul
Gauguin
A334

2003, Nov. 29   Litho.   Perf. 13¼x13
580 A334 75c multi   3.00 1.75

St. Anthony's
Auction — A335

2004, Jan. 17   Litho.   Perf. 13
581 A335 50c multi   1.25   .60

Children of the
World — A336

2004, Mar. 20   Litho.   Perf. 13
582 A336 50c multi   1.25   .60

Hotel
Valira
A337

2004, Apr. 17   Litho.   Perf. 13
583 A337 €1.11 multi   3.00 2.50

Europa — A338

2004, May 7   Litho.   Perf. 13
584 A338 50c multi   1.40   .60

A339

2004, May 15
585 A339 45c multi   1.25   .65

Legend of the Castle of St. Vincent.

A340

2004, June 26
586 A340 75c multi   1.75   .90

Madriu-Peralita-Claror Valley, UNESCO
World Heritage Site candidate.

Poblet de
Fontenada
A341

2004, July 3
587 A341 50c multi   1.40   .60

2004
Summer
Olympics,
Athens
A342

2004, Aug. 7   Litho.   Perf. 13
588 A342 90c multi   2.50 1.75

Margineda Bridge — A343

No. 589: a, €1, Black and white sketch. b,
€2, Full color painting.

2004, Oct. 2
589 A343   Horiz. pair, #a-b, +
            central label   8.00 8.00

Postal
Code — A344

2004, Oct. 23   Perf. 13¼x13
590 A344 50c multi   1.40   .60

Admission to
Council of
Europe, 10th
Anniv. — A345

2004, Nov. 6
591 A345 €2.50 multi   6.50 4.00

Christmas — A346

2004, Dec. 4   Perf. 13
592 A346 50c multi   1.40   .60

The Magi
A347

2005, Jan. 5
593 A347 50c multi   1.50   .65

Selection of Madriu-Peralita-Claror
Valley as UNESCO World Heritage
Site — A348

2005, Jan. 22
594 A348 50c multi   1.40   .60

Legend of
Rat Pass
A349

2005, Feb. 12
595 A349 48c multi   1.50   .65

Aegolius
Funereus — A350

2005, Apr. 6   Litho.   Perf. 13
596 A350 90c multi   2.50 2.25

Europa
A351

2005, May 7   Litho.   Perf. 13x13¼
597 A351 55c multi   1.60 1.40

Souvenir Sheet

9th Games of Small European
States — A352

No. 598: a, 53c, Shooting. b, 55c, Track and field. c, 82c, Swimming. d, €1, Basketball.

2005, May 28   *Perf. 13¼x13*
598   A352   Sheet of 4, #a-d   8.00   8.00

Bordes d'Ensegur — A353

2005, June 11   Litho.   *Perf. 13*
599   A353   €2.50 multi   6.50   5.00

Police Motorcycle — A354

2005, July 2
600   A354   53c multi   1.50   1.20

Prats de Santa Coloma, by J. Mir — A355

2005, Aug. 10   *Perf. 13x13¼*
601   A355   82c multi   2.25   1.75

Calones Hostel A356

2005, Sept. 10   Litho.   *Perf. 13*
602   A356   €1.98 multi   6.00   4.50

Josep Alsina Photography Business — A357

2005, Oct. 8   Litho.   *Perf. 13¼x13*
603   A357   53c multi   1.40   .65

Rotary International, Cent. — A358

2005, Nov. 5   *Perf. 13*
604   A358   55c multi   1.40   .65

Adoration of the Shepherds, by Antoni Viladomat — A359

2005, Dec. 7   Litho.   *Perf. 13*
605   A359   €1.22 multi   3.50   3.00

Animals A360

Designs: No. 606, 53c, Ursus arctos. No. 607, 53c, Rupicapra pyrenaica, vert.

2006, Jan. 16
606-607   A360   Set of 2   3.00   2.50
See Nos. 619-620, 633-634, 648-649, 670-671.

2006 Winter Olympics, Turin — A361

No. 608: a, 55c, Alpine skiing. b, 75c, Cross-country skiing.

2006, Feb. 4
608   A361   Horiz. pair, #a-b, +
central label   3.50   3.50

Tobacco Museum — A362

2006, Mar. 4   Litho.   *Perf. 13*
609   A362   82c multi   2.00   1.50

Decree of Napoleon I, Bicent. — A363

2006, Mar. 27
610   A363   53c multi   1.40   .65

Legend of the Bear Cave — A364

2006, Apr. 10   Litho.   *Perf. 13*
611   A364   48c multi   2.00   1.00

Europa A365

2006, May 9   Litho.   *Perf. 13x13¼*
612   A365   53c multi   1.40   .65

Sorteny Valley Nature Park — A366

2006, June 10   *Perf. 13*
613   A366   55c multi   1.40   .65

Pablo Casals (1876-1973), Cellist — A367

2006, July 31   Litho.   *Perf. 13*
614   A367   90c multi   2.25   2.10

Ford Model T — A368

2006, Sept. 2   Litho.   *Perf. 13*
615   A368   85c multi   2.25   2.10

Montserrat Procession, by Josp Borrell — A369

2006, Nov. 4   Litho.   *Perf. 13¼x13*
616   A369   €1.30 multi   3.25   3.00

Retable, St. Martin's Church, Cortinada A370

2006, Dec. 2   *Perf. 13*
617   A370   54c multi   1.40   .65

Arms Type of 2002 Inscribed "Postes"

2007, Jan. 13   *Perf. 13x13¼*
618   A309   60c multi   1.50   .75

Animals Type of 2006

Designs: 54c, Marmota marmota, vert. 60c, Sciurus vulgaris.

2007, Jan. 20   *Perf. 13*
619-620   A360   Set of 2   3.00   2.50

Legend of the Wolf's Testament — A371

2007, Feb. 24
621   A371   49c multi   1.40   .65

Predelle, Prats A372

2007, Mar. 17   Litho.   *Perf. 13¼x13*
622   A372   €1.30 multi   3.50   3.25
Compare with types A383, A396, A414 and A420.

National Arms — A373

Serpentine Die Cut 11
2007, Apr. 2   Litho.
Booklet Stamp
Self-Adhesive
623   A373   (54c) multi   1.60   1.60
a.   Booklet pane of 10   16.00
b.   Booklet pane of 12   21.00
Issued: No. 623b, 3/1/16. Stamps in No. 623b sold for 80c on day of issue.

Rose A374

2007, Apr. 23   Photo.   *Perf. 13¼*
624   A374   86c multi   2.25   2.00
Values are for stamps with surrounding selvage.

Europa — A375

2007, May 5   Litho.   Perf. 13¼x13
625 A375 54c multi   1.75 1.60
Scouting, cent.

Joining of Meritxell and
Sabart — A376

No. 626: a, Madonna and Child. b, Priest.

2007, June 2   Litho.   Perf. 13
626 A376 54c Horiz. pair, #a-b, +
              central label   3.00 3.00

Engine
A377

2007, July 10
627 A377 60c multi   1.50 1.25

2007 Rugby
World Cup,
France
A378

2007, Sept. 1   Litho.   Perf. 13¼
628 A378 85c multi   2.00 1.50
Values are for stamps with surrounding
selvage.

Comapedrosa
Valley — A379

2007, Oct. 6   Litho.   Perf. 13¼x13
629 A379 €3.04 multi   7.50 6.50

Prehistoric
People — A380

Prehistoric people at: 60c, Margineda
Grotto. 85c, Cedre.

2007, Nov. 10
630-631 A380   Set of 2   4.00 3.50

Retable,
St.
Martin's
Church,
Cortinada
A381

2007, Dec. 3   Litho.   Perf. 13
632 A381 54c multi   1.40 .65

Animals Type of 2006

Designs: 54c, Vulpes vulpes. 60c, Sus
scrofa, vert.

2008, Jan. 28
633-634 A360   Set of 2   3.50 3.00

**Arms Type of 2002 Inscribed
"Postes"**
2008, Mar. 1   Photo.   Perf. 13x13¼
635 A309 65c blue & multi   1.50 1.00

Legend of the
Treasure of the
Fountain of
Manegó — A382

2008, Mar. 8   Litho.   Perf. 13
636 A382 50c multi   1.25 .75

Predelle,
Prats
A383

2008, Apr. 12   Perf. 13¼x13
637 A383 €1.33 multi   3.50 3.50
Compare with Types A372, A396, A414 and
A420.

Cartercar
Automobile
A384

2008, May 3   Litho.   Perf. 13
638 A384 65c multi   1.75 1.50

Europa
A385

2008, May 17
639 A385 55c multi   1.50 .75

Miniature Sheet

2008 Summer Olympics,
Beijing — A386

No. 640: a, Kayaking. b, Running. c, Swimming. d, Judo.

2008, June 16   Litho.   Perf. 13x13½
640 A386 55c Sheet of 4, #a-d   6.00 6.00
Olympex 2008 Philatelic Exhibition, Beijing
(#640d).

Narcissus
Poeticus — A387

2008, June 18   Perf. 13¼x13
641 A387 55c multi   1.50 .75
No. 641 is impregnated with a narcissus
scent.

Vall
d'Incles
A388

2008, July 5   Perf. 13
642 A388 €2.80 multi   7.50 7.50

Universal
Male
Suffrage,
75th Anniv.
A389

2008, Aug. 30   Litho.   Perf. 13
643 A389 55c multi   1.40 .75

Sustainable Development — A390

2008, Oct. 4   Litho.   Perf. 13
644 A390 88c multi   2.00 1.25

Roc
d'Enclar — A391

2008, Nov. 8   Perf. 13¼
645 A391 85c multi   2.00 1.25

Retable of St. Mark
and St.
Mary — A392

2008, Dec. 13   Perf. 13
646 A392 55c multi   1.40 .75

Louis Braille (1809-52), Educator of
the Blind — A393

2009, Jan. 24   Engr.
647 A393 88c multi   2.00 1.25

Animals Type of 2006

Designs: 55c, Equus mulus, vert. 65c, Bos
taurus.

2009, Feb. 14   Litho.   Perf. 13
648-649 A360   Set of 2   2.75 2.00

Legend of the
Devils of
Aixirvall — A394

2009, Mar. 7
650 A394 51c multi   1.40 .75

Souvenir Sheet

Protection of Polar Regions and
Glaciers — A395

No. 651: a, 56c, Emperor penguins. b, 85c,
Boat off shore in polar regions, vert.

Perf. 13x13¼, 13¼x13 (85c)
2009, Mar. 27   Litho. & Engr.
651 A395 Sheet of 2, #a-b, +
              label   3.50 3.50

Predelle,
Prats
A396

2009, Apr. 18   Litho.   Perf. 13¼x13
652 A396 €1.35 multi   3.50 3.50
Compare with types A372, A383, A414 and
A420.

Europa
A397

2009, May 2   **Perf. 13**
653 A397 56c multi   1.40   .75
   Intl. Year of Astronomy.

Early
Renault
Automobile
A398

2009, May 16
654 A398 70c multi   1.75 1.00

St. Joan de Caselles, by Maurice
Utrillo — A399

2009, May 23   **Perf. 13x13¼**
655 A399 90c multi   2.25 1.50

Cercle des
Pessons
A400

2009, June 13   Litho.   Perf. 13
656 A400 €2.80 multi   7.50 6.00

Tour de France
Bicycle
Race — A401

2009, July 11
657 A401 56c multi   1.40   .75

Arts and Letters
Circle, 40th
Anniv. — A402

2009, Oct. 3   Litho.   Perf. 13
658 A402 51c multi   1.40   .75

Romanesque
Art — A403

2009, Nov. 7   **Perf. 13¼x13**
659 A403 85c multi   2.00 1.50

Epiphany — A404

2009, Dec. 12   **Perf. 13**
660 A404 56c multi   1.40   .75

**Arms Type of 2002 Inscribed
"POSTES"**

2010, Jan. 4   Photo.   Perf. 13x13¼
661 A309   1c yel & multi   .25   .25
662 A309   5c lt bl & multi   .25   .25
663 A309   10c org & multi   .25   .25
664 A309   20c lilac & multi   .45   .45
665 A309   50c ol grn & multi 1.25 1.25
666 A309 (70c) dk bl & multi 1.60 1.60
   Nos. 661-666 (6)   4.05 4.05

2010
Winter
Olympics,
Vancouver
A405

2010, Jan. 23   Photo.   Perf. 13x13¼
667 A405 85c multi   2.00 1.50

Casamanya Peak — A406

2010, Feb. 15   Litho.   Perf. 13
668 A406 €2.80 multi   6.50 5.00

Rights of the Child
Convention, 20th
Anniv. — A407

2010, Mar. 2   **Photo.**
669 A407 56c multi   1.40   .75

Animals Type of 2006
   Designs: 56c, Gyps fulvus, vert. 90c, Ovis
aries.

2010, Mar. 8   Litho.   Perf. 13
670-671 A360   Set of 2   3.00 2.25

Andorran Embassy, Brussels — A408

2010, Apr. 12   Engr.   Perf. 13
672 A408 70c multi + label   1.75 1.75

Legend of
Charlemagne's
Chair — A409

2010, Apr. 26   Litho.   Perf. 13
673 A409 51c multi   1.25   .65

Europa
A410

**Litho. & Embossed with Foil
Application**
2010, May 10   **Perf. 13¼**
674 A410 56c multi   1.40 1.00

Radio
Andorra
Building
A411

2010, May 25   Litho.   Perf. 13
675 A411 56c multi   1.40 1.00

Still Life,
by Carme
Massana
A413

2010, July 12   **Perf. 13¼x13**
677 A413 95c multi   2.50 2.50

Predelle,
Prats
A414

2010, Sept. 6   Litho.   Perf. 13¼x13
678 A414 €1.40 multi   3.75 3.75
   Compare with types A372, A383, A396 and
A420.

Souvenir Sheet

Churches — A415

No. 679: a, Sant Joan de Caselles Church.
b, Sant Romà de Les Bons Church, horiz.

Perf. 13¼x13, 13x13¼
2010, Oct. 4   **Engr.**
679 A415 58c Sheet of 2, #a-b   3.25 3.25
   See Andorra, Spanish Administration No.
363.

**Arms Type of 2002 Inscribed
"POSTES"**

2010, Oct. 18   Photo.   Perf. 13x13¼
680 A309 (58c) red & multi   1.75 1.75

Feudal
Andorra — A416

681 A416 87c multi   2.40 2.40

Christmas — A417

2010, Nov. 29   **Perf. 13**
682 A417 58c multi   1.60 1.60

1985
Ferrari 328
GTS
A412

2010, June 21   Litho.   Perf. 13
676 A412 70c multi   1.75 1.75

Legend of St. Joan de Caselles — A418

2011, Feb. 12   **Litho.**   *Perf. 13*
683   A418   €2.80 multi   8.00 8.00

Francophonia — A419

2011, Mar. 19   *Perf. 13x13¼*
684   A419   87c multi   2.50 2.50

Predelle, Prats A420

2011, Apr. 9   *Perf. 13¼x13*
685   A420   €1.40 multi   4.00 4.00

Compare with types A372, A383, A386 and A414.

Europa — A421

Silk-Screened on Wood Veneer
2011, May 7   *Serpentine Die Cut 11*
Self-Adhesive
686   A421   58c black & white   1.75 1.75

Intl. Year of Forests.

Councilor, by Francesc Borràs (1891-1968) — A422

2011, May 21   **Litho.**   *Perf. 13*
687   A422   95c multi   2.75 2.75

Placeta de Sant Esteve — A423

2011, June 4   **Engr.**
688   A423   58c multi   1.75 1.75

Soriano-Pedroso Automobile — A424

2011, June 18   **Litho.**
689   A424   75c multi   2.10 2.10

Rugby A425

2011, July 9   **Photo.**   *Perf. 13*
690   A425   89c multi   2.40 2.40

Values are for stamps with surrounding selvage.

Souvenir Sheet

Dance of the Seven Parishes, Plaza Benlloch — A426

2011, July 16   **Litho. & Engr.**
691   A426   €1.45 multi   4.25 4.25

Flora — A427

Designs: 60c, Rhododendron ferrugineum. €1, Rosa sempervirens, horiz.

2011, Sept. 4   **Litho.**   *Perf. 13*
692-693   A427   Set of 2   4.50 4.50

See Nos. 706-707, 720-721, 751, 782.

Council of the Land A428

2011, Sept. 24   *Perf. 13x13¼*
694   A428   89c multi   2.50 2.50

Leaf and Coat of Arms — A429

2011, Oct. 1   **Photo.**   *Perf. 13x13¼*
695   A429   (57c) multi   1.60 1.60

Angel From Santa Eulalia d'Encamp Retable — A430

2011, Nov. 26   **Litho.**   *Perf. 13*
696   A430   60c multi   1.60 1.60

Legend of the Shop of the Sorceresses A431

2012, Jan. 14
697   A431   €2.78 multi   7.50 7.50

Women's World Cup Alpine Skiing Races, Soldeu A432

2012, Feb. 11   *Perf. 13x13¼*
698   A432   89c multi   2.40 2.40

Massana Valley, by Joaquim Mir (1873-1940) — A433

2012, Mar. 3
699   A433   €1 multi   2.60 2.60

Souvenir Sheet

Restoration of Casa de la Vall, 50th Anniv. — A434

No. 700 — Casa de la Vall in: a, 1962. b, 2012.

2012, Mar. 10   **Litho. & Engr.**
700   A434   60c Sheet of 2, #a-b   3.25 3.25

Bugatti 37 Race Car A435

2012, Apr. 14   **Litho.**   *Perf. 13*
701   A435   77c multi   2.10 2.10

Souvenir Sheet

Europa — A436

2012, May 5   **Litho.**   *Perf. 13¼x13*
702   A436   77c multi   2.00 2.00

Noi. 702 has die cut opening in center of stamp.

Placeta de la Consòrcia, Andorra la Vella — A437

2012, June 8   **Engr.**   *Perf. 13x12¾*
703   A437   60c multi   1.50 1.50

Judo — A438

2012, July 6   **Litho.**   *Perf. 13*
704   A438   77c multi   1.90 1.90

Souvenir Sheet

Marratxa Dance — A439

Litho. & Engr.
2012, July 20 *Perf. 13x13¼*
705 A439 €1.45 multi 3.75 3.75

Flora Type of 2011

Designs: 60c, Sempervivum montanum. €1, Eryngium bourgatii.

2012, Sept. 14 **Litho.** *Perf. 13*
706-707 A427 Set of 2 4.25 4.25

Woman Suffrage, 42nd Anniv. — A440

2012, Oct. 5 *Perf. 13¼x13*
708 A440 89c multi 2.25 2.25

Andorran Presidency of the Council of Europe — A441

2012, Oct. 26
709 A441 €1 multi 2.60 2.60

King Henri IV of France (1553-1610), Co-Prince of Andorra — A442

2012, Nov. 8 **Engr.** *Perf. 13x13¼*
710 A442 60c multi 1.60 1.60
a. Sheet of 10, 5 each #710, France #4297 16.00 16.00
See France No. 4297.

Angel From Roser d'Ordino Retable — A443

2012, Nov. 23 **Litho.** *Perf. 13*
711 A443 57c multi 1.50 1.50

Legend of Moixella — A444

2013, Jan. 12
712 A444 €2.78 multi 7.50 7.50

Souvenir Sheet

Bear Ball, Encamp — A445

Litho. & Engr.
2013, Feb. 23 *Perf. 13x13¼*
713 A445 €1.55 multi 4.00 4.00

Constitution, 20th Anniv. — A446

2013, Mar. 16 **Litho.** *Perf. 13*
714 A446 63c multi 1.60 1.60

Cord 810 Phaeton A447

2013, Apr. 13
715 A447 95c multi 2.50 2.50

Plaça Rebés, Andorra la Vella — A448

2013, May 11 **Engr.** *Perf. 12¾*
716 A448 63c multi 1.75 1.75

Europa A449

2013, May 18 **Litho.** *Perf. 13¼*
717 A449 80c multi 2.25 2.25

Retable, Church of Sant Miquel, Prats A450

2013, July 6 **Litho.** *Perf. 13¼x13*
718 A450 €1.05 multi 2.75 2.75

Andorran School, 30th Anniv. A451

2013, July 27 **Litho.** *Perf. 13*
719 A451 63c multi 1.75 1.75

Flora Type of 2011

Designs: 58c, Papaver rhoeas. €1.05, Paeonia mascula, horiz.

2013, Sept. 7 **Litho.** *Perf. 13*
720-721 A427 Set of 2 4.50 4.50

First French School in Canillo, Cent. — A452

2013, Oct. 2 **Litho.** *Perf. 13¼*
722 A452 63c multi 1.75 1.75

Andorran Presidency of the Working Community of the Pyrenees — A453

2013, Oct. 5 **Litho.** *Perf. 13¼*
723 A453 95c multi 2.60 2.60

El Pas de la Casa, Painting by Véronique Bandry A454

2013, Oct. 26 **Litho.** *Perf. 13¼x13*
724 A454 €1.55 multi 4.25 4.25

Angel, Saint Joan de Sispony Church — A455

2013, Nov. 12 **Litho.** *Perf. 13*
725 A455 58c multi 1.60 1.60
Christmas.

Legend of the Canòlich Sanctuary — A456

2014, Jan. 11 **Litho.** *Perf. 13*
726 A456 €3.50 multi 9.50 9.50

Schools in Partnership With UNESCO — A457

2014, Feb. 15 **Litho.** *Perf. 13¼*
727 A457 66c multi 1.90 1.90

1917 Hispano Guadalajara Automobile — A458

2014, Mar. 29 **Litho.** *Perf. 13*
728 A458 98c multi 2.75 2.75

Cyanistes Caeruleus A459

2014, May 3 **Engr.** *Perf. 13¼*
729 A459 66c multi 1.90 1.90

Bagpipes A460

2014, May 24 **Litho.** *Perf. 13¼*
730 A460 83c multi 2.25 2.25
Europa.

Madriu-Perafita-Claror Valley — A461

2014, June 16　Litho.　*Perf. 13*
731 A461 98c multi　　　　2.75 2.75

Buildings in Engordany — A462

2014, June 16　Engr.　*Perf. 13x12¾*
732 A462 66c multi　　　　1.90 1.90

Fixats en la Contemporaneitat, by
Javier Balmaseda — A463

2014, July 11　Litho.　*Perf. 13x13¼*
733 A463 €1.65 multi　　　　4.50 4.50

Souvenir Sheet

Santa Anna Ball — A464

Litho. & Engr.
2014, July 25　　　*Perf. 13x13¼*
734 A464 €1.65 multi　　　　4.50 4.50

Electricity
Museum,
Encamp
A465

2014, July 25　Litho.　*Perf. 13x13¼*
735 A465 €1.10 multi　　　　3.00 3.00

Pitavola
Butterfly
A466

2014, Sept. 6　Litho.　*Perf. 13*
736 A466 83c multi　　　　2.10 2.10

Detail
From Sant
Miquel de
Prats
Retable
A467

2014, Sept. 27　Litho.　*Perf. 13¼x13*
737 A467 €1.10 multi　　　　2.75 2.75

Skis and Ski
Poles — A468

2014, Oct. 18　Litho.　*Perf. 13¼*
738 A468 83c multi　　　　2.10 2.10

Esteve Albert
(1914-95),
Writer — A469

2014, Nov. 9　Engr.　*Perf. 13¼*
739 A469 66c ochre & blk　　　　1.75 1.75

Christmas
A470

2014, Nov. 29　Litho.　*Perf. 13*
740 A470 66c multi　　　　1.75 1.75

Instinct of Conservation, by Javier
Balmaseda — A471

2015, Jan. 3　Litho.　*Perf. 13x13¼*
741 A471 €1.90 multi　　　　4.50 4.50

Legend of the First
Snow — A472

2015, Feb. 7　Litho.　*Perf. 13*
742 A472 €3.67 multi　　　　8.25 8.25

Citroen DS
21 — A473

2015, Mar. 20　Litho.　*Perf. 13*
743 A473 €1.20 multi　　　　2.75 2.75

Departure of French Gendarmes Led
by Col. René Baulard, 75th Anniv.
A474

2015, Apr. 11　Litho.　*Perf. 13*
744 A474 76c multi　　　　1.75 1.75

Europa — A475

2015, May 9　Litho.　*Perf. 13¼*
745 A475 95c multi　　　　2.10 2.10

Trobada
Monument
A476

2015, June 13　Engr.　*Perf. 13¼*
746 A476 €1.25 multi　　　　2.75 2.75

Comapedrosa, Highest Peak in
Andorra — A477

2015, June 20　Litho.　*Perf. 13¼*
747 A477 76c multi　　　　1.75 1.75

Inside, by Agustí Roqué — A478

2015, July 4　Litho.　*Perf. 13x13¼*
748 A478 €3.05 multi　　　　6.75 6.75
Venice Biennale.

Souvenir Sheet

Contrapas Dance — A479

Litho. & Engr.
2015, July 18　　　*Perf. 13x13¼*
749 A479 €1.90 multi　　　　4.25 4.25

UCI Mountain
Bike and Trials
World
Championships,
Vallnord — A480

2015, Aug. 29　Litho.　*Perf. 13¼x13*
750 A480 €1.20 multi　　　　2.75 2.75

Flora Type of 2011 and

Parnassius
Apollo
A481

Design: 76c, Thymus vulgaris, vert.

2015, Oct. 2　Engr.　*Perf. 13*
751 A427 76c multi　　　　1.60 1.60
752 A481 95c multi　　　　2.25 2.25

Ramon d'Areny-Plandolit, Philatelist,
and Maximum Cards — A482

2015, Nov. 7　Engr.　*Perf. 13x12½*
753 A482 €1.25 multi　　　　2.75 2.75

Live
Nativity
Scene,
Engordany
A483

2015, Nov. 27　Litho.　*Perf. 13*
754 A483 76c multi　　　　1.60 1.60
Christmas.

2014 Andorran Coinage — A484

No. 755: a, 1-cent, 2-cent, 5-cent and 2-euro coins. b, 10-cent, 20-cent, 50-cent and 1-euro coins.

2016, Jan. 8 Litho. Perf. 13
755 A484 80c Horiz. pair, #a-b 3.50 3.50

Women's Alpine Skiing World Cup Race at Soldeu-El Tarter — A485

2016, Feb. 27 Litho. Perf. 13¼
756 A485 €1.25 multi 2.75 2.75

Donzella Cremada Rock Carving — A486

2016, Mar. 19 Litho. Perf. 13
757 A486 €3.77 multi 8.75 8.75

Reforms of 1866, 150th Anniv. — A487

2016, Apr. 23 Litho. Perf. 13¼
758 A487 €1 multi 2.40 2.40

The Republic, Statue by Josep Viladomat (1899-1989) and Escaldes-Engordany Art Center — A488

2016, Apr. 6 Engr. Perf. 13¼
759 A488 80c multi 1.90 1.90

Europa A489

2016, May 8 Litho. Perf. 13¼
760 A489 €1 multi 2.25 2.25

Think Green Issue.

Dancing Giants of Andorra Festival — A490

2016, June 10 Litho. Perf. 13¼
761 A490 80c multi 1.90 1.90

Souvenir Sheet

Sardana Dance — A491

Litho. & Engr.
2016, July 15 Perf. 13x13¼
762 A491 €1.60 multi 3.75 3.75

Intimitat Compartida, by Joan Xandri — A492

2016, July 29 Litho. Perf. 13x13¼
763 A492 €3.20 multi 7.25 7.25

2015 Venice Biennale.

Clipol Bus A493

2016, Sept. 2 Litho. Perf. 13
764 A493 €1.25 multi 2.75 2.75

Isabelle Sandy (1884-1975), Writer — A494

2016, Oct. 7 Engr. Perf. 13¼
765 A494 €1.60 multi 3.50 3.50

Lavender A495

Catalan Sheepdog A496

Litho. & Engr.
2016, Nov. 5 Perf. 13
766 A495 80c multi 1.75 1.75
767 A496 €1 multi 2.25 2.25

Angels Painted by Antoni Viladomat i Manalt (1678-1755) — A497

2016, Nov. 25 Litho. Perf. 13
768 A497 80c multi 1.75 1.75

Legend of the Cave of Arans — A498

2017, Jan. 13 Litho. Perf. 13
769 A498 €3.95 multi 8.50 8.50

Opening of Carmen Thyssen Museum, Escaldes-Engordany — A499

2017, Feb. 3 Litho. Perf. 13¼x13
770 A499 €1.30 multi 2.75 2.75

Philandorre Philatelic Association, 40th Anniv. — A500

2017, Mar. 9 Engr. Perf. 13
771 A500 85c multi + label 1.90 1.90

Comic Festival, La Massana A501

2017, Apr. 7 Litho. Perf. 13¼
772 A501 €1.70 multi 3.75 3.75

Sant Vincenç d'Enclar Castle — A502

2017, May 6 Litho. Perf. 13¼
773 A502 €1.10 multi 2.50 2.50

Europa.

Castellars Making Human Tower — A503

2017, May 26 Litho. Perf. 13¼
774 A503 85c multi 1.90 1.90

Maria Assumpta D'Areny Plandolit (1860-92), Daughter of Andorran Reformer Guillem d'Areny Plandolit — A504

2017, June 21 Engr. Perf. 13¼
775 A504 €1.10 multi 2.50 2.50

Souvenir Sheet

Stick Dancing — A505

Litho. & Engr.
2017, July 8 Perf. 13x13¼
776 A505 €1.70 multi 4.00 4.00

Murmuri, by Eve Ariza — A506

2017, July 22 Litho. Perf. 13
777 A506 €3.40 multi 8.00 8.00

2017 Venice Art Biennale.

Roc del Quer, Canillo — A507

2017, Sept. 2 Photo. Perf. 13x12¾
778 A507 €1.30 multi 3.00 3.00

Photograph of 1967 Visit of French President Charles de Gaulle to Andorra, by Fèlix Peig Ballart (1917-2007) — A508

2017, Sept. 15 Litho. Perf. 13¼
779 A508 85c multi 2.00 2.00

Pere Canturri (1935-2015), Historian and Governmental Minister — A509

2017, Oct. 7 **Litho.** *Perf. 13¼*
780 A509 €1.10 multi 2.60 2.60

Peugeot 172 M — A510

2017, Nov. 10 **Litho.** *Perf. 13*
781 A510 85c multi 2.10 2.10

Flora Type of 2011 and

Salamandra Salamandra — A511

Design: 85c, Cerastium pyrenaicum, horiz.

2017, Nov. 13 **Engr.** *Perf. 13*
782 A427 85c multi 2.10 2.10
783 A511 €1.10 multi 2.60 2.60

Christmas A512

2017, Nov. 24 **Litho.** *Perf. 13*
784 A512 85c multi 2.10 2.10

Legend of the Snow Maiden — A513

2018, Jan. 12 **Litho.** *Perf. 13*
785 A513 €4.05 multi 10.00 10.00

Tenth Conference on Snow and Mountain Tourism, Escaldes-Engordany — A514

2018, Feb. 2 **Litho.** *Perf. 13¼*
786 A514 €1.30 multi 3.25 3.25

Andorran Constitution, 25th Anniv. — A515

2018, Mar. 9 **Engr.** *Perf. 13¼*
787 A515 95c multi 2.40 2.40

Casa de la Vall, by Joan Miró (1893-1983) — A516

2018, Apr. 6 **Litho.** *Perf. 13x13¼*
788 A516 €1.20 multi 3.00 3.00

Caramelles (Singers) — A517

2018, Apr. 20 **Litho.** *Perf. 13¼*
789 A517 95c multi 2.25 2.25

Tosca Bridge — A518

2018, May 4 **Engr.** *Perf. 13¼*
790 A518 €1.20 multi 3.00 3.00
Europa.

Souvenir Sheet

Summer Solstice Festival, UNESCO Intangible Cultural Heritage — A519

2018, June 8 **Litho.** *Perf. 13x13¼*
791 A519 €1.90 multi 4.50 4.50

Escaldes-Engordany Parish, 40th Anniv. — A520

2018, June 14 **Litho.** *Perf. 13¼*
792 A520 80c multi 1.90 1.90

Pompeu Fabra (1868-1948), Linguist — A521

2018, July 20 **Engr.** *Perf. 13*
793 A521 €1.30 multi 3.00 3.00

Church of Santa Coloma and Icon — A522

2018, Aug. 10 **Engr.** *Perf. 13*
794 A522 €1.20 multi 2.75 2.75
European Year of Cultural Heritage.

Sweet Candies Caramels, Sculpture by Laurence Jenkell — A523

2018, Sept. 14 **Litho.** *Perf. 13x13¼*
795 A523 €1.20 multi 2.75 2.75

Otter A524

2018, Sept. 28 **Litho.** *Perf. 13*
796 A524 95c multi 2.25 2.25

Lídia Armengol i Vila (1948-91), Politician — A525

2018, Oct. 5 **Engr.** *Perf. 13¼*
797 A525 €1.20 choc & org red 2.75 2.75

Citroen CX — A526

2018, Nov. 9 **Litho.** *Perf. 13*
798 A526 €1.90 multi 4.50 4.50

Detail From Retable of Santa Creu de Canillo Church — A527

2018, Nov. 17 **Litho.** *Perf. 13*
799 A527 95c multi 2.25 2.25

Andorra Coat of Arms — A528

2019, Jan. 2 **Photo.** *Perf. 13x13¼*
800 A528 (€1.30) multi 3.00 3.00

Legend of the White Horse of Solana — A529

2019, Jan. 4 **Litho.** *Perf. 13*
801 A529 €4.18 multi 9.75 9.75

Escudelle of St. Anthony Festival, 50th Anniv. A530

2019, Jan. 17 **Litho.** *Perf. 13x13¼*
802 A530 88c multi 2.10 2.10

General Council of Andorra, 600th Anniv. A531

2019, Feb. 11   Litho.   Perf. 13x13¼
803   A531   €1.05 multi   2.40 2.40

2019 Finals of World Alpine Skiing Championships, Soldeu — A532

2019, Mar. 9   Litho.   Perf. 13¼
804   A532   €1.30 multi   3.00 3.00

Estanyó del Querol Lake — A533

2019, Apr. 13   Litho.   Perf. 13
805   A533   €1.05 multi   2.40 2.40

Lagopus Muta A534

2019, May 10   Engr.   Perf. 13x13¼
806   A534   €1.30 multi   3.00 3.00
Europa.

Andorra Hydroelectric Forces (Electric Company), 90th Anniv. — A535

2019, May 31   Litho.   Perf. 13x13¼
807   A535   €1.05 multi   2.40 2.40

Andorra, by Eduard Arranz Bravo A536

2019, July 5   Litho.   Perf. 13¼x13
808   A536   €1.05 black & red   2.40 2.40

Julia Bonet Fité (1922-2011), Businesswoman, and Her Perfume Shop — A537

2019, July 19   Engr.   Perf. 13x13¼
809   A537   €1.30 multi   3.00 3.00

Artifacts From La Margineda Archaeological Site — A538

2019, Aug. 9   Engr.   Perf. 13x13¼
810   A538   €2.10 multi   4.75 4.75

Renault 4CV A539

2019, Sept. 6   Litho.   Perf. 13¼
811   A539   €1.05 multi   2.40 2.40

Argynnis Pandora A540

Ursus Arctos A541

2019, Oct. 4   Litho.   Perf. 13
812   A540   €1.05 multi   2.40 2.40
Engr.
813   A541   €1.30 dark brown   3.00 3.00

Detail From Retable of Santa Creu de Canillo Church — A542

2019, Nov. 2   Litho.   Perf. 13
814   A542   €1.05 multi   2.40 2.40

Admission of Andorra to Council of Europe, 25th Anniv. — A543

2019, Nov. 8   Litho.   Perf. 13
815   A543   €1.30 multi + label   3.00 3.00
See Andorra (Spanish Administration) No. 470.

Envalira Pass A544

2020, Jan. 4   Litho.   Perf. 13
816   A544   €4.30 multi   9.50 9.50

Victoria Zorzano (1908-98), Radio Announcer A545

2020, Feb. 8   Engr.   Perf. 13¼
817   A545   €1.40 multi   3.25 3.25

International Francophone Organization, 50th Anniv. — A546

2020, Mar. 20   Litho.   Perf. 13¼x13
818   A546   €1.16 multi   2.50 2.50

Hiking Boots — A547

2020, Apr. 4   Litho.   Perf. 13¼x13
819   A547   €1.16 multi   2.60 2.60
Andorra GR7 long-distance hiking trail.

Map of 19th Century Andorra la Vella-L'Ospitalet, France Postal Route — A548

2020, May 11   Litho.   Perf. 13x13¼
820   A548   €1.40 multi   3.25 3.25
Europa.

Espai Columba Museum, 1st Anniv. A549

2020, June 12   Litho.   Perf. 13x13¼
821   A549   €1.16 multi   2.60 2.60

Oncorhynchus Mykiss — A550

2020, June 19   Litho.   Perf. 13
822   A550   €1.16 multi   2.60 2.60

L'Orri del Cubil Archaeological Site — A551

2020, July 3   Engr.   Perf. 13
823   A551   €2.32 brown & black   5.50 5.50

Esbalçat Pond — A552

2020, Aug. 21   Litho.   Perf. 13
824   A552   €1.16 multi   2.75 2.75

Comte de Foix Secondary School, 40th Anniv. A553

2020, Sept. 11   Engr.   Perf. 13¼
825   A553   €1.96 black & red   4.50 4.50

Jacques Chirac (1932-2019), President of France and Co-Prince of Andorra — A554

2020, Sept. 26   Litho.   Perf. 13¼
826   A554   €1.16 multi   2.75 2.75

Abies Alba
A555

2020, Oct. 2   **Litho.**   *Perf. 13*
827   A555   €1.40 multi   3.25   3.25

SEMI-POSTAL STAMP

Catalogue values for unused stamps in this section are for Never Hinged items.

Virgin of St. Coloma — SP1

Unwmk.
1964, July 25   **Engr.**   *Perf. 13*
B1   SP1   25c + 10c multi   24.00   24.00
The surtax was for the Red Cross.

AIR POST STAMPS

Catalogue values for unused stamps in this section are for Never Hinged items.

Chamois
AP1

Unwmk.
1950, Feb. 20   **Engr.**   *Perf. 13*
C1   AP1   100fr indigo   87.50   60.00

East Branch of Valira River — AP2

1955-57
C2   AP2   100fr dark green   16.00   10.50
C3   AP2   200fr cerise   32.50   16.00
C4   AP2   500fr dp bl ('57)   120.00   65.00
    Nos. C2-C4 (3)   168.50   91.50

No. C3 in dark green was not regularly issued. Value, $3,500.

D'Inclès Valley
AP3

1961-64   **Unwmk.**   *Perf. 13*
C5   AP3   2fr red, ol gray & cl   1.25   1.25
C6   AP3   3fr bl, mar & slate grn   1.60   1.60
C7   AP3   5fr rose lil & red org   3.25   2.40
C8   AP3   10fr bl grn & slate grn   4.75   4.50
    Nos. C5-C8 (4)   10.85   9.75

Issued: 10fr, 4/25/64; others, 6/19/61.

POSTAGE DUE STAMPS

Postage Due Stamps of France, 1893-1931, Overprinted

On Stamps of 1893-1926
1931-33   **Unwmk.**   *Perf. 14x13½*
J1   D2   5c blue   2.40   2.40
J2   D2   10c brown   2.40   2.40
J3   D2   30c rose red   1.60   1.60
J4   D2   50c violet brn   2.40   2.40
J5   D2   60c green   34.00   34.00
J6   D2   1fr red brn, *straw*   2.40   2.40
J7   D2   2fr brt violet   16.00   16.00
J8   D2   3fr magenta   3.25   3.25
    Nos. J1-J8 (8)   64.45   64.45

On Stamps of 1927-31
J9   D4   1c olive grn   3.25   3.25
J10   D4   10c rose   5.50   *6.50*
J11   D4   60c red   27.50   26.50
J12   D4   1fr Prus grn ('32)   110.00   *120.00*
J13   D4   1.20fr on 2fr bl   80.00   80.00
J14   D4   2fr ol brn ('33)   200.00   *225.00*
J15   D4   5fr on 1fr vio   120.00   120.00
    Nos. J9-J15 (7)   546.25   581.25

D5   D6

1935-41   **Typo.**
J16   D5   1c gray green   3.25   3.25
J17   D6   5c light blue ('37)   6.75   6.75
J18   D6   10c brown ('41)   4.00   *5.50*
J19   D6   2fr violet ('41)   11.00   8.75
J20   D6   5fr red orange ('41)   19.00   11.00
    Nos. J16-J20 (5)   44.00   35.25

Catalogue values for unused stamps in this section, from this point to the end of the section, are for Never Hinged items.

Wheat Sheaves — D7

1943-46   *Perf. 14x13½*
J21   D7   10c sepia   .80   .70
J22   D7   30c brt red vio   .90   .70
J23   D7   50c blue grn   1.25   1.10
J24   D7   1fr brt ultra   1.10   .90
J25   D7   1.50fr rose red   6.75   5.50
J26   D7   2fr turq blue   1.75   1.60
J27   D7   3fr brown org   2.00   1.90
J28   D7   4fr dp vio ('45)   6.25   5.50
J29   D7   5fr brt pink   4.25   3.75
J30   D7   10fr red org ('45)   6.50   5.50
J31   D7   20fr olive brn ('46)   7.75   6.50
    Nos. J21-J31 (11)   39.30   33.65

Inscribed: "Timbre Taxe"

1946-53
J32   D7   10c sepia ('46)   1.60   1.60
J33   D7   1fr ultra   .80   .80
J34   D7   2fr turq blue   1.25   1.25
J35   D7   3fr orange brn   2.75   2.75
J36   D7   4fr violet   3.50   3.50
J37   D7   5fr brt pink   2.75   2.75
J38   D7   10fr red orange   4.75   4.75
J39   D7   20fr olive brn   8.00   8.00
J40   D7   50fr dk green ('50)   47.50   47.50
J41   D7   100fr dp green ('53)   120.00   120.00
    Nos. J32-J41 (10)   192.90   192.90

Inscribed: "Timbre Taxe"
1961, June 19   *Perf. 14x13½*
J42   D7   5c rose pink   4.00   4.00
J43   D7   10c red orange   8.00   8.00
J44   D7   20c olive   12.00   12.00
J45   D7   50c dark slate green   24.00   24.00
    Nos. J42-J45 (4)   48.00   48.00

D8

1964-71   **Typo.**   *Perf. 14x13½*
J46   D8   5c Centaury ('65)   .25   .25
J47   D8   10c Gentian ('65)   .25   .25
J48   D8   15c Corn poppy   .25   .25
J49   D8   20c Violets ('71)   .30   .25
J50   D8   30c Forget-me-not   .40   .30
J51   D8   40c Columbine ('71)   .55   .40
J52   D8   50c Clover ('65)   .65   .55
    Nos. J46-J52 (7)   2.65   2.25

D9

1985, Oct. 21   **Engr.**   *Perf. 13*
J53   D9   10c Holly   .25   .25
J54   D9   20c Blueberries   .25   .25
J55   D9   30c Raspberries   .25   .25
J56   D9   40c Bilberries   .25   .25
J57   D9   50c Blackberries   .25   .25
J58   D9   1fr Broom   .40   .40
J59   D9   2fr Rosehips   .95   .65
J60   D9   3fr Nightshade   1.25   .95
J61   D9   4fr Nabiu   1.50   1.25
J62   D9   5fr Strawberries   1.90   1.50
    Nos. J53-J62 (10)   7.25   6.00

NEWSPAPER STAMP

France No. P7 Overprinted

1931   **Unwmk.**   *Perf. 14x13½*
P1   A16   ½c on 1c gray   1.25   1.25
   a.   Double overprint   2,750.
      Never Hinged   3,600.

ANGOLA
aŋ'gō-lə

LOCATION — S.W. Africa between Zaire and Namibia.
GOVT. — Republic
AREA — 481,351 sq. mi.
POP. — 11,177,537 (1999 est.)
CAPITAL — Luanda

Angola was a Portuguese overseas territory until it became independent November 11, 1975, as the People's Republic of Angola.

1000 Reis = 1 Milreis
100 Centavos = 1 Escudo (1913, 1954)
100 Centavos = 1 Angolar (1932)
10 Lweys = 1 Kwanza (1977)

Catalogue values for unused stamps in this country are for Never Hinged items, beginning with Scott 328 in the regular postage section, Scott C26 in the air-post section, Scott J31 in the postage due section, and Scott RA7 in the postal tax section.

Watermark

Wmk. 232 — Maltese Cross

Portuguese Crown — A1

Perf. 12½, 13½
1870-77   **Typo.**   **Unwmk.**
Thin to Medium Paper
1   A1   5r gray black   3.25   2.00
2   A1   10r yellow   30.00   20.00
3   A1   20r bister   3.00   2.25
4   A1   25r red   15.00   10.00
5   A1   40r blue ('77)   275.00   175.00
6   A1   50r green   70.00   15.00
7   A1   100r lilac   6.50   3.50
8   A1   200r orange ('77)   4.50   2.00
9   A1   300r choc ('77)   6.00   3.50

1881-85   *Perf. 12½, 13½*
10   A1   10r green ('83)   8.50   4.75
11   A1   20r carmine rose ('85)   21.00   14.00
12   A1   25r violet ('85)   12.50   5.00
13   A1   40r buff ('82)   13.00   4.75
15   A1   50r blue   45.00   10.00
    Nos. 10-15 (5)   100.00   38.50

Two types of numerals are found on #2, 11, 13, 15.
The cliche of 40r in plate of 20r error, was discovered before the stamps were issued. All examples were defaced by a blue pencil mark. Values, $2,100 unused; in pair with 20r, $2,400.
In perf. 12½, Nos. 1-4, 4a and 6, as well as 7a, were printed in 1870 on thicker paper and 1875 on normal paper. Stamps of the earlier printing sell for 2 to 5 times more than those of the 1875 printing.
Some reprints of the 1870-85 issues are on a smooth white chalky paper, ungummed and perf. 13½. Value, each $17.50.
Other reprints of these issues are on thin ivory paper with shiny white gum and clear-cut perf. 13½. Value, each $24.

King Luiz — A2

1886   **Embossed**   *Perf. 12½*
16   A2   5r black   14.00   6.50
17   A2   10r green   14.00   6.50
18   A2   20r rose   19.00   12.50
19   A2   25r red violet   15.00   4.00
20   A2   40r chocolate   17.50   7.50
21   A2   50r blue   21.00   4.00

22	A2	100r yellow brn	30.00	10.00
23	A2	200r gray violet	40.00	13.00
24	A2	300r orange	40.00	14.00
		Nos. 16-24 (9)	210.50	78.00

For surcharges see Nos. 61-69, 172-174, 208-210.

Reprints of 5r, 20r & 100r have cleancut perf. 13½.

King Carlos — A3

1893-94 Typo. Perf. 11½, 12½, 13½

25	A3	5r yellow	3.75	1.50
26	A3	10r redsh violet	5.00	3.00
27a	A3	15r chocolate	7.00	3.00
28	A3	20r lavender	7.00	3.00
29c	A3	25r green	7.00	3.75
30b	A3	50r light blue	10.00	4.00
31	A3	75r carmine	20.00	12.00
32	A3	80r lt green	20.00	9.00
33	A3	100r brown, buff	20.00	9.00
34	A3	150r car, rose	30.00	17.50
35	A3	200r dk blue, lt bl	30.00	17.50
36	A3	300r dk blue, sal	35.00	17.50

For surcharges see Nos. 70-81, 175-179, 213-216, 234.

No. P1 Surcharged in Blue

1894, Aug. Perf. 13½

37	N1	25r on 2½r brown	75.00	60.00
a.		Double surcharge, one inverted	175.00	
b.		Perf. 11½	110.00	85.00
c.		Perf. 12½	90.00	67.50
d.		As 'c,' double surcharge, one inverted	140.00	125.00

King Carlos — A5

1898-1903 Perf. 11½
Name and Value in Black except 500r

38	A5	2½r gray	.65	.50
39	A5	5r orange	.65	.50
40	A5	10r yellow grn	.65	.50
41	A5	15r violet brn	3.25	1.60
42	A5	15r gray green ('03)	1.60	1.40
43	A5	20r gray violet	.70	.50
44	A5	25r sea green	1.60	.75
45	A5	25r car ('03)	.85	.45
46	A5	50r blue	2.75	1.00
47	A5	50r brown ('03)	8.00	3.75
48	A5	65r dull blue ('03)	8.50	5.75
49	A5	75r rose	11.00	6.00
50	A5	75r red violet ('03)	3.00	2.00
51	A5	80r violet	10.00	3.00
52	A5	100r dk blue, blue	2.00	1.40
53	A5	115r org brn, pink ('03)	11.00	7.50
54	A5	130r brn, straw ('03)	11.00	7.50
55	A5	150r brn, straw	11.00	6.00
56	A5	200r red vio, pink	7.50	1.75
57	A5	300r dk blue, rose	6.50	5.00
58	A5	400r dull bl, straw ('03)	12.50	3.50
59	A5	500r blk & red, bl ('01)	16.00	5.00
60	A5	700r vio, yelsh ('01)	35.00	17.00
		Nos. 38-60 (23)	165.70	82.35

For surcharges and overprints see Nos. 83-102, 113-117, 159-171, 181-183, 217-218, 221-225.

Stamps of 1886-94 Surcharged in Black or Red

Two types of surcharge:

I — 3mm between numeral and REIS.
II — 4½mm spacing.

1902 Perf. 12½

61	A2	65r on 40r choc	12.00	6.50
62	A2	65r on 300r org, I	12.00	6.50
a.		Type II	12.00	6.50
63	A2	115r on 10r green	10.00	5.00
a.		Inverted surcharge	90.00	50.00
b.		Perf. 13½	75.00	45.00
64	A2	115r on 200r gray vio	10.00	5.00
65	A2	130r on 50r blue	13.00	5.00
66	A2	130r on 100r brown	8.50	5.00
67	A2	400r on 20r rose	110.00	65.00
a.		Perf. 13½	175.00	92.50
68	A2	400r on 25r violet	22.50	12.00
69	A2	400r on 5r black (R)	20.00	13.00
a.		Double surcharge	75.00	50.00
		Nos. 61-69 (9)	218.00	123.00

For surcharges see Nos. 172-174, 208-210.

Perf. 11½, 12½, 13½

70	A3	65r on 5r yel, I, perf. 11½	11.00	6.50
a.		Type II	11.00	7.00
71	A3	65r on 10r red vio, I, perf. 12½	7.25	5.50
a.		Type II	7.25	5.50
b.		Perf. 11½, I	12.00	7.00
c.		Perf. 11½, I	12.00	7.00
72	A3	65r on 20r lav, perf. 11½	11.00	6.50
73	A3	65r on 25r green, perf. 12½	15.00	9.00
b.		Perf. 13½	7.00	5.00
74	A3	115r on 80r lt grn, perf. 12½	15.00	9.00
75	A3	115r on 100r brn, buff, perf. 12½	15.00	7.25
b.		Perf. 13½	80.00	40.00
76	A3	115r on 150r car, rose, perf.	17.50	13.00
a.		Perf. 13½	25.00	15.00
b.		Perf. 12½	24.00	15.00
77	A3	130r on 15r choc, perf. 12½	6.50	5.50
b.		Type II	8.00	4.50
78	A3	130r on 75r carmine, perf. 11½	60.00	50.00
a.		Perf. 13½	70.00	55.00
b.		Perf. 12½	15.00	11.00
79	A3	130r on 300r dk bl, sal, perf. 12½	20.00	15.00
a.		Perf. 13½	35.00	12.50
80	A3	400r on 50r lt bl, I, perf. 12½	11.00	5.50
a.		Perf. 11½	32.50	15.00
c.		Type II	9.00	6.00
81	A3	400r on 200r bl, bl, perf. 12½	11.00	8.00
a.		Perf. 13½	375.00	225.00
82	N1	400r on 2½r brn, I, perf. 12½	1.75	1.60
a.		Type II	1.75	1.60
		Nos. 70-82 (13)	202.00	142.35

For surcharges see Nos. 175-180, 211-216, 234-235.

Reprints of Nos. 65, 67, 68 and 69 have clean-cut perforation 13½.

For detailed listings of perforation and paper varieties, see *Scott Classic Specialized Catalogue of Stamps and Covers 1840-1940.*

Stamps of 1898 Overprinted — a

1902 Perf. 11½

83	A5	15r brown	2.50	1.75
84	A5	25r sea green	2.00	1.00
85	A5	50r blue	4.50	2.00
86	A5	75r rose	7.00	5.25
		Nos. 83-86 (4)	16.00	10.00

For surcharge see No. 116.

No. 48 Surcharged in Black

1905

87	A5	50r on 65r dull blue	6.00	3.00

For surcharge see No. 183.

Stamps of 1898-1903 Overprinted in Carmine or Green — b

1911

88	A5	2½r gray	.60	.50
89	A5	5r orange yel	.60	.50
90	A5	10r light green	.60	.50
91	A5	15r gray green	.85	.70
92	A5	20r gray violet	.90	.75
93	A5	25r car (G)	.90	.75
94	A5	50r brown	3.25	1.75
95	A5	75r lilac	6.75	3.25
96	A5	100r dk blue, bl	6.75	3.50
97	A5	115r org brn, pink	3.75	1.75
98	A5	130r brn, straw	3.75	1.75
99	A5	200r red lil, pnksh	4.50	2.40
100	A5	400r dull bl, straw	4.50	1.75
101	A5	500r blk & red, bl	4.50	2.25
102	A5	700r violet, yelsh	4.50	2.50
		Nos. 88-102 (15)	46.70	24.60

Inverted and double overprints of Nos. 88-102 were made intentionally.

For surcharges see Nos. 217-218, 221-222, 224.

King Manuel II — A6

Overprinted in Carmine or Green

1912 Perf. 11½x12

103	A6	2½r violet	.75	.50
104	A6	5r black	.75	.50
105	A6	10r gray green	.75	.50
106	A6	20r carmine (G)	.75	.50
107	A6	25r violet brown	.75	.50
108	A6	50r dk blue	1.75	1.40
109	A6	75r bister brown	2.00	1.75
110	A6	100r brown, lt green	3.75	2.25
111	A6	200r dk green, salmon	3.75	2.40
112	A6	300r black, azure	3.75	2.40
		Nos. 103-112 (10)	18.75	12.70

For surcharges see Nos. 219-220, 226-227.

No. 91 Surcharged in Black

1912, June Perf. 11½

113	A5	2½r on 15r gray green	6.00	3.75
114	A5	5r on 15r gray green	6.75	3.75
115	A5	10r on 15r gray green	5.25	3.75
		Nos. 113-115 (3)	18.00	11.25

Inverted and double surcharges of Nos. 113-115 were made intentionally.

Nos. 86 and 50 Surcharged in Black and Overprinted in Violet — c

1912

116	A5	25r on 75r rose	110.00	60.00
117	A5	25r on 75r red violet	7.50	6.00
a.		"REUPBLICA"	135.00	70.00
b.		"25" omitted	135.00	70.00
c.		"REPUBLICA" omitted	135.00	70.00

Ceres — A7

With Imprint

1914 Chalky Paper Perf. 15x14
Name and Value in Black

118	A7	¼c olive brown	2.00	.90
119	A7	½c black	2.00	.90
120	A7	1c blue green	2.00	.90
121	A7	1½c lilac brown	4.00	2.25
122	A7	2c carmine	7.00	3.25
123	A7	2½c violet	1.40	.60
124	A7	5c blue	3.00	1.60
125	A7	7½c yellow brn	4.00	2.40
126	A7	8c slate	4.00	2.40
127	A7	10c orange brn	4.00	2.40
128	A7	15c brown rose	6.00	2.50
129	A7	20c yel green	3.00	1.60
130	A7	30c brown, green	3.00	2.40
131	A7	40c brown, pink	3.00	2.40
132	A7	50c orange, sal	11.00	8.25
133	A7	1e green, blue	8.00	4.75
		Nos. 118-133 (16)	67.40	39.50

1915-22 Ordinary Paper

134	A7	¼c olive brown	.45	.45
135	A7	½c black	.45	.45
136	A7	1c blue green	.45	.45
137	A7	1c yellow green ('18)	.45	.45
138	A7	1½c lilac brown	.45	.45
139	A7	2c carmine	.55	.45
140	A7	2½c dark violet	.45	.45
141	A7	3c orange	27.50	24.00
142	A7	4c dull rose ('21)	.45	.45
143	A7	5c blue	1.75	1.40
144	A7	6c lilac ('21)	.45	.45
145	A7	7c ultra ('21)	.45	.45
146	A7	7½c yellow brn ('20)	.55	.45
147	A7	8c slate	.60	.45
148	A7	10c orange brn ('18)	.55	.45
149	A7	12c olive brown ('21)	1.50	1.00
150	A7	15c plum ('20)	.55	.45
151	A7	15c brown rose ('21)	.55	.45
152	A7	20c yel green ('18)	6.75	5.00
153	A7	30c gray green ('21)	1.00	.65
154	A7	80c pink ('21)	1.75	1.00
155	A7	2e dark violet ('22)	3.50	3.00
		Nos. 134-155 (22)	51.25	42.90

1921-26 Perf. 12x11½

156	A7	¼c olive brown ('24)	.45	.45
157	A7	½c black	.45	.45
158	A7	1c blue green ('24)	.45	.45
158C	A7	1½c lilac brown ('24)	.45	.45
158D	A7	2c carmine ('24)	.45	.45
158E	A7	2c gray ('25)	.75	.55
158F	A7	2½c lt violet ('24)	.45	.45
158G	A7	3c orange	.45	.45
158H	A7	4c dull rose	.45	.45
158I	A7	4½c gray	.45	.45
158J	A7	5c blue ('24)	.45	.45
158K	A7	6c lilac	.45	.45
158L	A7	7c ultra	.45	.45
158M	A7	7½c yellow brown ('24)	.55	.45
158N	A7	8c slate ('24)	.55	.45
158O	A7	10c orange brn ('24)	.45	.40
158P	A7	12c olive brn	.75	.60
158Q	A7	12c dp green ('25)	.75	.50
158R	A7	15c plum ('24)	.45	.35
158S	A7	20c yel green	1.75	1.60
158T	A7	24c ultra ('25)	1.60	1.20
158U	A7	25c choc ('25)	1.60	1.20
158V	A7	30c gray grn	.75	.60
158W	A7	40c turq blue	1.20	.70
158X	A7	50c lt violet ('25)	1.40	.70
158Y	A7	60c dk blue ('22)	1.50	1.00
158Z	A7	60c dp rose ('26)	75.00	47.50
159A	A7	80c pink ('22)	1.75	1.00
159B	A7	1e rose ('22)	1.75	1.00
		Nos. 156-159B (29)	97.95	65.20

Glazed Paper

1921-25 Perf. 12x11½

159C	A7	1e rose	1.75	1.75
159D	A7	1e deep blue ('25)	3.25	1.60
159E	A7	2e dark violet ('22)	2.25	1.25
159F	A7	5e buff ('25)	14.00	11.50
159G	A7	10e pink ('25)	30.00	25.00
159H	A7	20e pale turq ('25)	100.00	70.00
		Nos. 159C-159H (6)	151.25	111.10

For surcharges see Nos. 228-229, 236-239.

Stamps of 1898-1903 Overprinted type "c" in Red or Green

1914 Perf. 11½, 12

159	A5	10r yel green (R)	7.50	5.50
160	A5	15r gray green (R)	6.75	5.00
161	A5	20r gray violet (G)	2.75	2.00
163	A5	75r red violet (G)	2.00	1.40
164	A5	100r blue, blue (R)	4.50	3.75
165	A5	115r org brn, pink (R)	150.00	
167	A5	200r red vio, pnksh (G)	2.75	1.75
169	A5	400r dl bl, straw (R)	50.00	50.00
170	A5	500r blk & red, bl (R)	6.75	6.25
171	A5	700r vio, yelsh (G)	35.00	27.00

Inverted and double overprints were made intentionally. No. 165 was not regularly issued. Red overprints on the 20r, 75r, 200r were not regularly issued. The 130r was not regularly issued without surcharge (No. 225).

On Nos. 63-65, 74-76, 78-79, 82
Perf. 11½, 12½, 13½

172	A2	115r on 10r (R)	17.00	17.00
a.		Perf. 13½	17.00	17.00
173	A2	115r on 200r (R)	22.50	22.50
174	A2	130r on 50r (R)	110.00	110.00
175	A3	115r on 80r (R)	210.00	200.00
176	A3	115r on 100r (R)	225.00	175.00
a.		Perf. 11½	300.00	300.00
b.		Perf. 13½	900.00	850.00
177	A3	115r on 150r (G)	225.00	175.00
a.		Perf. 11½	250.00	200.00
b.		Perf. 13½	750.00	700.00
178	A3	130r on 75r (G)	8.25	7.50
a.		Perf. 12½	9.00	7.50
179	A3	130r on 300r (G)	10.50	8.25
a.		Perf. 12½	17.50	16.00
180	N1	400r on 2½r (R)	1.10	4.00
a.		Perf. 11½	5.25	
b.		Perf. 13½		.85
		Nos. 172-180 (9)	829.35	719.25

Nos. 85-87
Overprinted in Red or Green

On Stamps of 1902
Perf. 11½, 12

181	A5	50r blue (R)	2.50	2.25
182	A5	75r rose (G)	6.00	4.50

On No. 87

183	A5	50r on 65r dull blue (R)	5.50	1.75
		Nos. 181-183 (3)	14.00	10.75

Inverted and double surcharges of Nos. 181-183 were made intentionally.

Common Design Types pictured following the introduction.

Vasco da Gama Issue of Various Portuguese Colonies

Common Design Types CD20-CD27 Srchd.

On Stamps of Macao

1913			**Perf. 12½ to 16**	
184	¼c on ½a blue grn		2.25	
185	½c on 1a red		2.25	1.75
186	1c on 2a red violet		2.40	1.75
187	2½c on 4a yel green		1.75	1.25
188	5c on 8a dk blue		1.75	1.25
189	7½c on 12a vio brn		8.00	5.50
190	10c on 16a bister brn		2.75	2.00
191	15c on 24a bister		3.75	2.50
	Nos. 184-191 (8)		24.90	15.50

On Stamps of Portuguese Africa
Perf. 14 to 15

192	¼c on 2½r blue grn	1.25	.85
193	½c on 5r red	1.25	.85
194	1c on 10r red violet	1.25	.85
195	2½c on 25r yel grn	1.25	.85
196	5c on 50r dk blue	1.25	.85
197	7½c on 75r vio brn	7.50	6.75
198	10c on 100r bister brn	3.00	2.00
199	15c on 150r bister	3.50	2.25
	Nos. 192-199 (8)	20.25	15.25

On Stamps of Timor

200	¼c on ½a blue grn	2.25	1.75
201	½c on 1a red	2.25	1.75
202	1c on 2a red vio	2.40	1.75
203	2½c on 4a yel grn	1.75	1.25
204	5c on 8a dk blue	1.75	1.25
205	7½c on 12a vio brn	8.00	5.50
206	10c on 16a bis brn	2.75	2.00
207	15c on 24a bister	3.50	2.25
	Nos. 200-207 (8)	24.90	17.25
	Nos. 184-207 (24)	70.05	48.00

Provisional Issue of 1902 Overprinted in Carmine

1915		**Perf. 11½, 12½, 13½**	
208	A2 115r on 10r green	2.00	2.00
a.	Perf. 12½	2.50	2.25
209	A2 115r on 200r gray vio	2.25	1.90
210	A2 130r on 100r brown	1.90	1.60

211	A3 115r on 80r lt green	2.50	2.25
212	A3 115r on 100r brn, buff	2.25	2.00
a.	Perf. 11½	100.00	90.00
b.	Perf. 13½	16.00	13.50
213	A3 115r on 150r car, rose	1.60	1.60
a.	Perf. 12½	3.75	3.25
b.	Perf. 13½	2.60	2.00
214	A3 130r on 15r choc	1.60	1.60
a.	Perf. 12½	8.25	6.75
215	A3 130r on 75r carmine	3.25	3.25
a.	Perf. 12½	5.00	4.25
b.	Perf. 12½	3.25	2.00
216	A3 130r on 300r dk bl, sal	2.00	2.00
a.	Perf. 13½	3.75	13.45
	Nos. 208-216 (9)	19.35	16.95

Stamps of 1911-14 Surcharged in Black

d

e

On Stamps of 1911

1919		**Perf. 11½**	
217	A5 (d) ½c on 75r red lilac	3.25	2.60
218	A5 (d) 2½c on 100r blue, grysh	3.50	2.60

On Stamps of 1912
Perf. 11½x12

219	A6 (e) ½c on 75r bis brn	2.00	1.50
220	A6 (e) 2½c on 100r brn, lt grn	3.50	2.60

On Stamps of 1914

221	A5 (d) ½c on 75r red lil	2.25	1.90
222	A5 (d) 2½c on 100r bl, grysh	2.60	2.25
	Nos. 217-222 (6)	17.10	13.45

Inverted and double surcharges were made for sale to collectors.

Nos. 163, 98 and Type of 1914 Surcharged in Black

1921			
223	A5 (c) 00.5c on 75r	400.00	350.00
224	A5 (b) 4c on 130r (#98)	3.00	3.00
225	A5 (c) 4c on 130r brn, straw	7.50	7.50
a.	Without surcharge	240.00	

Nos. 109 and 108 Surcharged with New Values and Bars in Black

226	A6 00.5c on 75r	2.25	1.90
227	A6 1c on 50r	2.50	2.50

Nos. 146 and 150 Surcharged with New Values and Bars in Black

228	A7 00.5c on 7½c	2.50	2.25
229	A7 04c on 15c	3.00	3.00
	Nos. 224-229 (6)	20.75	20.15
	Nos. 223-229 (7)	420.75	370.15

The 04c surcharge exists on the 15c brown rose, perf 12x11½, No. 158R.
Some authorities question the status of No. 223.

Nos. 81-82 Surcharged

1925		**Perf. 12½**	
234	A3 40c on 400r on 200r bl, bl	1.50	1.10
a.	Perf. 13½	11.00	7.50
235	N1 40c on 400r on 2½r brn	1.10	1.10
a.	Perf. 13½	1.10	1.10

Nos. 158Y, 159A, 159D-159E Surcharged

1931		**Perf. 12x 11½**	
236	A7 50c on 60c deep rose	2.25	2.00
237	A7 70c on 80c pink	4.50	3.00
238	A7 70c on 1e deep blue	4.00	3.00
239	A7 1.40e on 2e dark violet	2.50	2.00
	Nos. 236-239 (4)	13.25	10.00

Ceres — A14

Perf. 12x11½

1932-46		**Typo.**	**Wmk. 232**	
243	A14	1c bister brn	.30	.25
244	A14	5c dk brown	.35	.30
245	A14	10c dp violet	.35	.30
246	A14	15c black	.35	.30
247	A14	20c gray	.40	.30
248	A14	30c myrtle grn	.40	.30
249	A14	35c yel grn ('46)	7.50	4.50
250	A14	40c dp orange	.40	.30
251	A14	45c lt blue	1.75	1.25
252	A14	50c lt brown	.30	.25
253	A14	60c olive grn	1.00	.30
254	A14	70c orange brn	1.10	.30
255	A14	80c emerald	.75	.25
256	A14	85c rose	5.50	2.00
257	A14	1a claret	1.10	.30
258	A14	1.40a dk blue	11.50	1.75
258A	A14	1.75a dk blue ('46)	16.00	5.25
259	A14	2a dull vio	5.25	.55
260	A14	5a pale yel grn	10.50	1.75
261	A14	10a olive bis	20.00	5.25
262	A14	20a orange	52.50	5.25
		Nos. 243-262 (21)	137.30	31.00
		Set, never hinged	175.00	

For surcharges see Nos. 263-267, 271-273, 294A-300, J31-J36.

Surcharged in Black

5½mm between bars and new value.

1934			
263	A14 10c on 45c lt bl	3.50	2.50
264	A14 20c on 85c rose	3.50	2.50
265	A14 30c on 1.40a dk bl	3.50	2.50
266	A14 70c on 2a dl vio	4.50	3.25
267	A14 80c on 5a pale yel grn	7.00	2.75
	Nos. 263-267 (5)	22.00	13.50
	Set, never hinged	37.50	

See Nos. 294A-300.

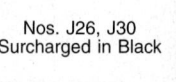

Nos. J26, J30 Surcharged in Black

1935		**Unwmk.**	**Perf. 11½**	
268	D2	5c on 6c lt brown	2.50	1.60
269	D2	30c on 50c gray	2.50	1.60
270	D2	40c on 50c gray	2.50	1.60
		Nos. 268-270 (3)	7.50	4.80
		Set, never hinged	14.00	

No. 255 Surcharged in Black

1938		**Wmk. 232**	**Perf. 12x11½**	
271	A14	5c on 80c emerald	1.10	.55
272	A14	10c on 80c emerald	1.60	.75
273	A14	15c on 80c emerald	2.25	.75
		Nos. 271-273 (3)	4.95	2.05
		Set, never hinged	8.25	

Vasco da Gama Issue
Common Design Types
Engr.; Name & Value Typo. in Black
Perf. 13½x13

1938, July 26			**Unwmk.**	
274	CD34	1c gray green	.25	.25
275	CD34	5c orange brn	.30	.30
276	CD34	10c dk carmine	.40	.30
277	CD34	15c dk violet brn	.40	.30
278	CD34	20c slate	.40	.30
279	CD35	30c rose violet	.55	.40
280	CD35	35c brt green	1.00	.75
281	CD35	40c brown	.40	.25
282	CD35	50c brt red vio	.55	.25
283	CD36	60c gray black	1.10	.30
284	CD36	70c brown vio	1.10	.30
285	CD36	80c orange	1.10	.30
286	CD36	1a red	1.10	.30
287	CD37	1.75a blue	2.10	1.00
288	CD37	2a brown car	3.25	1.50
289	CD37	5a olive grn	13.50	1.50
290	CD38	10a blue vio	28.00	1.90
291	CD38	20a red brown	40.00	4.25
		Nos. 274-291 (18)	95.50	14.45
		Set, never hinged	150.00	

For surcharges see Nos. 301-304.

Marble Column and Portuguese Arms with Cross — A20

1938, July 29		**Perf. 12½**	
292	A20 80c blue green	3.75	2.25
293	A20 1.75a deep blue	20.00	6.00
294	A20 20a dk red brown	60.00	27.00
	Nos. 292-294 (3)	83.75	35.25
	Set, never hinged	140.00	

Visit of the President of Portugal to this colony in 1938.

Stamps of 1932 Surcharged with New Value and Bars

8mm between bars and new value.

1941-45		**Wmk. 232**	**Perf. 12x11½**	
294A	A14 5c on 80c emer ('45)		.85	.55
295	A14 10c on 45c lt blue		1.75	1.25
296	A14 15c on 45c lt blue		1.75	1.25
297	A14 20c on 85c rose		1.75	1.25
298	A14 35c on 85c rose		1.75	1.25
299	A14 50c on 1.40a dk blue		1.75	1.25
300	A14 60c on 1a claret		9.00	7.50
	Nos. 294A-300 (7)		18.60	14.30
	Set, never hinged		32.50	

Nos. 285 to 287 Surcharged in Black or Red

1945		**Unwmk.**	**Perf. 13½x13**	
301	CD36	5c on 80c org	.85	.55
302	CD36	50c on 1a red	.85	.55
303	CD37	50c on 1.75a bl (R)	.85	.55
304	CD37	50c on 1.75a bl	.85	.55
		Nos. 301-304 (4)	3.40	2.20
		Set, never hinged	5.00	

Sao Miguel Fort, Luanda — A21

John IV — A22

Designs: 10c, Our Lady of Nazareth Church, Luanda. 50c, Salvador Correia de Sa e Bene vides. 1a, Surrender of Luanda. 1.75a, Diogo Cao. 2a, Manuel Cerveira Pereira. 5a, Stone Cliffs, Yelala. 10a, Paulo Dias de Novais. 20a, Massangano Fort.

Perf. 14½

1948, May   Unwmk.   Litho.

305	A21	5c dk violet	.30	.30
306	A21	10c dk brown	.75	.30
307	A22	30c blue grn	.30	.30
308	A22	50c vio brown	.30	.30
309	A21	1a carmine	.70	.30
310	A22	1.75a slate blue	1.00	.45
311	A22	2a green	1.00	.55
312	A21	5a gray black	2.50	1.10
313	A22	10a rose lilac	8.25	1.50
314	A21	20a gray blue	17.50	5.25
a.		Sheet of 10, #305-314	140.00	100.00
		Never hinged	200.00	
		Nos. 305-314 (10)	32.60	10.35
		Set, never hinged	50.00	

300th anniv. of the restoration of Angola to Portugal. No. 314a sold for 42.50a.

Lady of Fatima Issue
Common Design Type

1948, Dec.

315	CD40	50c carmine	1.50	.75
316	CD40	3a ultra	6.00	2.25
317	CD40	6a red orange	18.00	5.25
318	CD40	9a dp claret	42.50	9.00
		Nos. 315-318 (4)	68.00	17.25
		Set, never hinged	110.00	

Our Lady of the Rosary at Fatima, Portugal.

Chiumbe River — A24

Black Rocks — A25

Designs: 50c, View of Luanda. 2.50a, Sa da Bandeira. 3.50a, Mocamedes. 15a, Cubal River. 50a, Duke of Bragança Falls.

1949   Unwmk.   Perf. 13½

319	A24	20c dk slate blue	.55	.30
320	A25	40c black brown	.55	.30
321	A24	50c rose brown	.55	.30
322	A24	2.50a blue violet	3.00	.75
323	A24	3.50a slate gray	3.00	.90
323A	A24	15a dk green	18.00	2.75
324	A24	50a dp green	110.00	7.50
		Nos. 319-324 (7)	135.65	12.80
		Set, never hinged	225.00	

Sailing Vessel — A26

1949, Aug.   Perf. 14

325	A26	1a chocolate	6.75	.75
326	A26	4a dk Prus green	17.50	2.75
		Set, never hinged	37.50	

Centenary of founding of Mocamedes.

UPU Symbols — A27

1949, Oct.

327	A27	4a dk grn & lt grn	10.50	3.00
		Never hinged	16.00	

75th anniv. of the UPU.

> **Catalogue values for unused stamps in this section, from this point to the end of the section, are for Never Hinged items.**

Stamp of 1870 — A28

1950, Apr. 2   Perf. 11½x12

328	A28	50c yellow green	1.75	.55
329	A28	1a red	1.75	.85
330	A28	4a black	6.25	1.25
a.		Sheet of 3, #328-330	40.00	40.00
		Nos. 328-330 (3)	9.75	2.65

Angola's first philatelic exhibition, marking the 80th anniversary of Angola's first stamps. No. 330a contains Nos. 328, 329 (inverted), 330, perf. 11½ and sold for 6.50a. All examples carry an oval exhibition cancellation in the margin but the stamps were valid for postage.

Holy Year Issue
Common Design Types

1950, May   Perf. 13x13½

331	CD41	1a dull rose vio	1.60	.35
332	CD42	4a black	6.00	1.00

Dark Chanting Goshawk — A31

European Bee Eater — A32

10c, Racquet-tailed roller. 15c, Bateleur eagle. 50c, Giant kingfisher. 1a, Yellow-fronted barbet. 1.50a, Openbill (stork). 2a, Southern ground hornbill. 2.50a, African skimmer. 3a, Shikra. 3.50a, Denham's bustard. 4a, African golden oriole. 4.50a, Long-tailed shrike. 5a, Red-shouldered glossy starling. 6a, Sharp-tailed glossy starling. 7a, Red-shouldered widow bird. 10a, Half-colored kingfisher. 12.50a, White-crowned shrike. 15a, White-winged babbling starling. 20a, Yellow-billed hornbill. 25a, Amethyst starling. 30a, Orange-breasted shrike. 40a, Secretary bird. 50a, Rosy-faced lovebird.

Photogravure and Lithographed

1951   Unwmk.   Perf. 11½
Birds in Natural Colors

333	A31	5c lt blue	.55	.25
334	A32	10c aqua	.55	.25
335	A32	15c salmon pink	.75	.25
336	A32	20c pale yellow	.75	.40
337	A31	50c gray blue	.75	.25
338	A31	1a lilac	.75	.25
339	A31	1.50a gray buff	.75	.25
340	A31	2a cream	4.00	.25
341	A32	2.50a gray	1.50	.25
342	A32	3a lemon yel	1.10	.25
343	A31	3.50a lt gray	1.50	.25

344	A31	4a rose buff	1.75	.25
345	A32	4.50a rose lilac	1.75	.25
346	A31	5a green	7.50	.55
347	A31	6a blue	10.50	1.50
348	A31	7a orange	11.50	2.00
349	A31	10a lilac rose	45.00	2.75
350	A32	12.50a slate gray	13.00	3.75
351	A31	15a pale olive	11.50	3.75
352	A31	20a pale bis brn	110.00	9.00
353	A31	25a lilac rose	40.00	6.75
354	A32	30a pale salmon	40.00	9.00
355	A31	40a yellow	57.50	11.50
356	A31	50a turquoise	140.00	22.50
		Nos. 333-356 (24)	502.95	76.45
		Set, hinged	225.00	

Holy Year Extension Issue
Common Design Type

1951, Oct.   Litho.   Perf. 14

357	CD43	4a orange + label	5.25	1.50

Sheets contain alternate vertical rows of stamps and labels bearing quotations from Pope Pius XII or the Patriarch Cardinal of Lisbon. Stamp without label attached sells for less.

Medical Congress Issue
Common Design Type

Design: Medical examination

1952, June   Perf. 13½

358	CD44	1a vio blue & brn blk	1.50	.50

Head of Christ — A35

1952, Oct.   Unwmk.   Perf. 13

359	A35	10c dk blue & buff	.25	.25
360	A35	50c dk ol grn & ol gray	1.10	.35
361	A35	2a rose vio & cream	3.75	1.30
		Nos. 359-361 (3)	5.10	1.90

Exhibition of Sacred Missionary Art, Lisbon, 1951.

Leopard — A36

Sable Antelope — A37

Animals: 20c, Elephant. 30c, Eland. 40c, African crocodile. 50c, Impala. 1a, Mountain zebra. 1.50a, Sitatunga. 2a, Black rhinoceros. 2.30a, Gemsbok. 2.50a, Lion. 3a, Buffalo. 3.50a, Springbok. 4a, Brindled gnu. 5a, Hartebeest. 7a, Wart hog. 10a, Defassa waterbuck. 12.50a, Hippopotamus. 15a, Greater kudu. 20a, Giraffe.

1953, Aug. 15   Perf. 12½

362	A36	5c multicolored	.25	.25
363	A37	10c multicolored	.25	.25
364	A37	20c multicolored	.25	.25
365	A37	30c multicolored	.25	.25
366	A36	40c multicolored	.25	.25
367	A37	50c multicolored	.25	.25
368	A37	1a multicolored	.35	.25
369	A37	1.50a multicolored	.40	.25
370	A36	2a multicolored	.40	.25
371	A37	2.30a multicolored	.45	.25
372	A37	2.50a multicolored	.50	.25
373	A36	3a multicolored	.55	.25
374	A37	3.50a multicolored	.55	.25
375	A37	4a multicolored	20.00	.40
376	A37	5a multicolored	1.00	.35
377	A37	7a multicolored	1.50	.35
378	A37	10a multicolored	3.00	.35
379	A37	12.50a multicolored	7.50	3.00
380	A37	15a multicolored	10.00	3.00
381	A37	20a multicolored	13.00	1.90
		Nos. 362-381 (20)	60.70	12.60
		Set, hinged	20.00	

Stamp of Portugal and Arms of Colonies — A38

1953, Nov.   Photo.   Perf. 13
Stamp and Arms Multicolored

382	A38	50c gray & dark gray	1.25	.60

Cent. of Portugal's 1st postage stamps.

Map and Plane — A39

Typographed and Lithographed
1954, May 27   Perf. 13½

383	A39	35c multicolored	.25	.25
384	A39	4.50e multicolored	1.10	.65

Visit of Pres. Francisco H C. Lopes.

Sao Paulo Issue
Common Design Type

1954   Litho.

385	CD46	1e bister & gray	.80	.50

Map of Angola — A41

1955, Aug.   Unwmk.   Perf. 13½

386	A41	5c multicolored	.25	.25
387	A41	20c multicolored	.25	.25
388	A41	50c multicolored	.25	.25
389	A41	1e multicolored	.25	.25
390	A41	2.30e multicolored	.50	.35
391	A41	4e multicolored	2.50	.25
392	A41	10e multicolored	2.50	.25
393	A41	20e multicolored	4.25	.45
		Nos. 386-393 (8)	10.75	2.30

For overprints see Nos. 593, 598, 604.

Artur de Paiva — A42

1956, Oct. 9   Perf. 13½x12½

394	A42	1e blk, dk bl & ocher	.60	.30

Cent. of the birth of Col. Artur de Paiva.

Man of Malange — A43

Various Costumes in Multicolor;
Inscriptions in Black Brown

1957, Jan. 1   Photo.   Perf. 11½
Granite Paper

395	A43	5c gray	.25	.25
396	A43	10c orange yel	.25	.25
397	A43	15c lt blue grn	.25	.25
398	A43	20c pale rose vio	.25	.25
399	A43	30c brt rose	.25	.25
400	A43	40c blue gray	.25	.25
401	A43	50c pale olive	.25	.25
402	A43	80c lt violet	.45	.40

403	A43	1.50e buff	2.50	.40
404	A43	2.50e lt yel grn	3.25	.25
405	A43	4e salmon	2.00	.25
406	A43	10e salmon pink	3.00	.50
		Nos. 395-406 (12)	12.95	3.55

Jose M. Antunes — A44

1957, Apr.   **Perf. 13½**
407 A44   1e aqua & brown   .90   .45

Birth cent. of Father Jose Maria Antunes.

Fair Emblem, Globe and Arms — A45

1958, July   **Litho.**   **Perf. 12x11½**
408 A45   1.50e multicolored   .75   .35

World's Fair, Brussels, Apr. 17-Oct. 19.

Tropical Medicine Congress Issue
Common Design Type

Design: Securidaca longipedunculata.

1958, Dec. 15   **Perf. 13½**
409 CD47 2.50e multicolored   3.50   1.10

Medicine Man — A47

Designs: 1.50e, Early government doctor. 2.50e, Modern medical team.

1958, Dec. 18   **Perf. 11½x12**
410 A47   1e blue blk & brown   .45   .25
411 A47   1.50e gray, blk & brown   1.40   .50
412 A47   2.50e multicolored   2.25   1.10
     Nos. 410-412 (3)   4.10   1.85

75th anniversary of the Maria Pia Hospital, Luanda.

Welwitschia Mirabilis A48

1959, Oct. 1   **Litho.**   **Perf. 14½**
Various Views of Plant and Various Frames
413 A48   1.50e lt brn, grn & blk   1.10   .65
414 A48   2.50e multicolored   1.75   .85
415 A48   5e multicolored   3.00   1.00
416 A48   10e multicolored   4.50   2.10
     Nos. 413-416 (4)   10.35   4.60

Centenary of discovery of Welwitschia mirabilis, desert plant.

Map of West Africa, c. 1540, by Jorge Reinel — A49

1960, June 25   **Perf. 13½**
417 A49 2.50e multicolored   .55   .25

500th anniv. of the death of Prince Henry the Navigator.

Distributing Medicines A50

1960, Oct.   **Litho.**   **Perf. 14½**
418 A50 2.50e multicolored   .65   .35

10th anniv. of the Commission for Technical Co-operation in Africa South of the Sahara (C.C.T.A.).

Girl of Angola — A51

Various portraits.

1961, Nov. 30   **Unwmk.**   **Perf. 13**
419	A51	10c multicolored	.25	.25
420	A51	15c multicolored	.25	.25
421	A51	30c multicolored	.25	.25
422	A51	40c multicolored	.25	.25
423	A51	60c multicolored	.25	.25
424	A51	1.50e multicolored	.25	.25
425	A51	2e multicolored	1.00	.25
426	A51	2.50e multicolored	1.00	.25
427	A51	3e multicolored	3.50	.30
428	A51	4e multicolored	1.50	.25
429	A51	5e multicolored	1.10	.30
430	A51	7.50e multicolored	1.50	.90
431	A51	10e multicolored	1.20	.70
432	A51	15e multicolored	2.00	.90
432A	A51	25e multicolored	2.40	1.25
432B	A51	50e multicolored	2.75	2.75
		Nos. 419-432B (16)	20.45	9.35

Sports Issue
Common Design Type

Sports: 50c, Flying. 1e, Rowing. 1.50e, Water polo. 2.50e, Hammer throwing. 4.50e, High jump. 15e, Weight lifting.

1962, Jan. 18   **Perf. 13½**
Multicolored Design
433	CD48	50c lt blue	.25	.25
434	CD48	1e olive bister	1.10	.25
435	CD48	1.50e salmon	.75	.30
436	CD48	2.50e lt green	.90	.30
437	CD48	4.50e pale blue	.75	.60
438	CD48	15e yellow	1.75	1.50
		Nos. 433-438 (6)	5.50	3.20

For overprint see No. 608.

Anti-Malaria Issue
Common Design Type

Design: Anopheles funestus.

1962, April   **Litho.**   **Perf. 13½**
439 CD49 2.50e multicolored   1.75   .90

Gen. Norton de Matos — A54

1962, Aug. 8   **Unwmk.**   **Perf. 14½**
440 A54 2.50e multicolored   .65   .40

50th anniv. of the founding of Nova Lisboa.

Locusts — A56

1963, June 2   **Litho.**   **Perf. 14**
447 A56 2.50e multicolored   1.60   .95

15th anniv. of the Intl. Anti-Locust Organ.

Arms of Luanda A57

Vila de Santo Antonio do Zaire — A58

Coats of Arms (Provinces and Cities): 10c, Massangano. 15c, Sanza-Pombo. 25c, Ambriz. 30c, Muxima. 40c, Ambrizete. 50c, Carmona. 60c, Catete. 70c, Quibaxe. No. 458, Salazar. No. 459, Maquela do Zombo. 1.20e, Bembe. No. 461, Malanje. No. 462, Caxito. 1.80e, Dondo. 2e, Henrique de Carvalho. No. 465, Moçamedes. No. 466, Damba. 3e, Novo Redondo. 3.50e, S. Salvador do Congo. 4e, Cuimba. 5e, Luso. 6.50e, Negage. 7e, Quitexe. 7.50e, S. Filipe de Benguela. 8e, Mucaba. 9e, 31 de Janeiro. 10e, Lobito. 11e, Nova Caipemba. 12.50e, Gabela. 14e, Songo. 15e Sá da Bandeira. 17e, Quimbele. 17.50e, Silva Porto. 20e, Nova Lisboa. 22.50e, Cabinda. 25e, Noqui. 30e, Serpa Pinto. 35e, Santa Cruz. 50e, General Freire.

1963   **Perf. 13½**
Arms in Original Colors; Red and Violet Blue Inscriptions
448	A57	5c tan	.25	.25
449	A57	10c lt blue	.25	.25
450	A58	15c salmon	.25	.25
451	A58	20c olive	.25	.25
452	A58	25c lt blue	.25	.25
453	A57	30c buff	.25	.25
454	A57	40c gray	.25	.25
455	A57	50c lt green	.25	.25
456	A58	60c brt yellow	.25	.25
457	A58	70c dull rose	.25	.25
458	A57	1e pale lilac	.65	.25
459	A58	1e dull yellow	.30	.25
460	A57	1.20e rose	.30	.25
461	A57	1.50e pale salmon	.90	.25
462	A58	1.50e lt green	.75	.25
463	A58	1.80e yel olive	.75	.55
464	A57	2e lt yel green	.65	.25
465	A57	2.50e lt gray	2.50	.30
466	A58	2.50e dull blue	2.25	.25
467	A58	3e yel olive	.75	.25
468	A57	3.50e gray	.90	.25
469	A58	4e citron	.60	.30
470	A57	5e citron	.75	.30
471	A58	6.50e tan	.65	.40
472	A58	7e rose lilac	.90	.75
473	A57	7.50e pale lilac	1.00	.75
474	A58	8e lt aqua	.90	.75
475	A58	9e yellow	1.10	1.00
476	A57	10e dp salmon	1.20	.80
477	A58	11e dull yel grn	1.25	1.25
478	A57	12.50e pale blue	1.50	1.25
479	A58	14e lt gray	1.50	1.25
480	A57	15e lt blue	1.50	1.25
481	A58	17e pale blue	1.60	1.50
482	A57	17.50e dull yellow	2.40	2.25
483	A57	20e lt aqua	2.40	1.75
484	A57	22.50e gray	2.50	2.40
485	A58	25e citron	2.10	1.50
486	A57	30e yellow	3.00	2.50
487	A58	35e grysh blue	3.25	3.00
488	A58	50e dp yellow	4.50	2.25
		Nos. 448-488 (41)	47.80	32.80

Pres. Américo Rodrigues Thomaz — A59

1963, Sept. 16   **Litho.**
489 A59 2.50e multicolored   .65   .30

Visit of the President of Portugal.

Airline Anniversary Issue
Common Design Type

1963, Oct. 5   **Unwmk.**   **Perf. 14½**
490 CD50 1e lt blue & multi   1.00   .35

Cathedral of Sá da Bandeira — A61

Malange Cathedral A62

Churches: 20c, Landana. 30c, Luanda Cathedral. 40c, Gabela. 50c, St. Martin's Chapel, Baia dos Tigres. 1.50e, St. Peter, Chibia. 2e, Church of Our Lady, Benguela. 2.50e, Church of Jesus, Luanda. 3e, Camabatela. 3.50e, Mission, Cabinda. 4e, Vila Folgares. 4.50e, Church of Our Lady, Lobito. 5e, Church of Cabinda. 7.50e, Cacuso Church, Malange. 10e, Lubango Mission. 12.50e, Huila Mission. 15e, Church of Our Lady, Luanda Island.

1963, Nov. 1   **Litho.**
Multicolored Design and Inscription
491	A61	10c gray blue	.25	.25
492	A61	20c pink	.25	.25
493	A61	30c lt blue	.25	.25
494	A61	40c tan	.25	.25
495	A61	50c lt green	.25	.25
496	A62	1e buff	.25	.25
497	A61	1.50e lt vio blue	.25	.25
498	A62	2e pale rose	.35	.25
499	A61	2.50e gray	.35	.25
500	A62	3e buff	.35	.25
501	A61	3.50e olive	.55	.25
502	A62	4e buff	.55	.25
503	A62	4.50e pale blue	.75	.30
504	A61	5e tan	.75	.30
505	A62	7.50e gray	1.00	.55
506	A61	10e dull yellow	1.40	.75
507	A62	12.50e bister	1.60	1.25
508	A62	15e pale gray vio	2.40	1.40
		Nos. 491-508 (18)	11.80	7.55

National Overseas Bank Issue
Common Design Type

Design: Antonio Teixeira de Sousa.

1964, May 16   **Perf. 13½**
509 CD51 2.50e multicolored   .90   .30

Commerce Building and Arms of Chamber of Commerce A64

1964, Nov.   **Litho.**   **Perf. 12**
510 A64 1e multicolored   .45   .25

Luanda Chamber of Commerce centenary.

ITU Issue
Common Design Type

1965, May 17   **Unwmk.**   **Perf. 14½**
511 CD52 2.50e gray & multi   1.25   .65

Plane over Luanda Airport — A65

1965, Dec. 3   **Litho.**   **Perf. 13**
512 A65 2.50e multicolored   1.25   .60

25th anniv. of DTA, Direccao dos Transportes Aereos.

Harquebusier, 1539 — A66

50c, Harquebusier, 1539. 1e, Harquebusier, 1640. 1.50e, Infantry officer, 1777. 2e, Standard bearer, infantry, 1777. 2.50e, Infantry soldier, 1777. 3e, Cavalry officer, 1783. 4e, Cavalry soldier, 1783. 4.50e, Infantry officer, 1807. 5e, Infantry soldier, 1807. 6e, Cavalry officer, 1807. 8e, Cavalry soldier, 1807. 9e, Infantry soldier, 1873.

1966, Feb. 25 — Litho. — Perf. 14½

513	A66	50c multicolored	.25	.25
514	A66	1e multicolored	.25	.25
515	A66	1.50e multicolored	.25	.25
516	A66	2e multicolored	.25	.25
517	A66	2.50e multicolored	.40	.25
518	A66	3e multicolored	.40	.25
519	A66	4e multicolored	.60	.25
520	A66	4.50e multicolored	.65	.25
521	A66	5e multicolored	.65	.30
522	A66	6e multicolored	1.10	.65
523	A66	8e multicolored	1.50	1.10
524	A66	9e multicolored	1.60	1.25
		Nos. 513-524 (12)	7.90	5.30

National Revolution Issue
Common Design Type

Design: St. Paul's Hospital and Commercial and Industrial School.

1966, May 28 — Litho. — Perf. 12

525	CD53	1e multicolored	.50	.25

Emblem of Holy Ghost Society — A68

1966 — Litho. — Perf. 13

526	A68	1e blue & multi	.50	.25

Centenary of the Holy Ghost Society.

Navy Club Issue
Common Design Type

Designs: 1e, Mendes Barata and cruiser Dom Carlos I. 2.50e, Capt. Augusto de Castilho and corvette Mindelo.

1967, Jan. 31 — Litho. — Perf. 13

527	CD54	1e multicolored	.75	.25
528	CD54	2.50e multicolored	1.00	.50

Fatima Basilica — A70

1967, May 13 — Litho. — Perf. 12½x13

529	A70	50c multicolored	.45	.25

50th anniv. of the apparition of the Virgin Mary to 3 shepherd children at Fatima.

Angola Map, Manuel Cerveira Pereira — A71

1967, Aug. 15 — Litho. — Perf. 12½x13

530	A71	50c multicolored	.45	.25

350th anniv. of the founding of Benguela.

Administration Building, Carmona — A72

1967 — Litho. — Perf. 12

531	A72	1e multicolored	.45	.25

50th anniv. of the founding of Carmona.

Military Order of Valor — A73

50c, Ribbon of the Three Orders. 1.50e, Military Order of Avis. 2e, Military Order of Christ. 2.50e, Military Order of St. John of Espada. 3e, Order of the Empire. 4e, Order of Prince Henry. 5e, Order of Benemerencia. 10e, Order of Public Instruction. 20e, Order for Industrial & Agricultural Merit.

1967, Oct. 31 — Perf. 14

532	A73	50c lt gray & multi	.25	.25
533	A73	1e lt green & multi	.25	.25
534	A73	1.50e yellow & multi	.25	.25
535	A73	2e multicolored	.25	.25
536	A73	2.50e multicolored	.25	.25
537	A73	3e lt olive & multi	.35	.25
538	A73	4e gray & multi	.50	.25
539	A73	5e multicolored	.60	.25
540	A73	10e lilac & multi	1.00	.50
541	A73	20e lt blue & multi	2.25	1.20
		Nos. 532-541 (10)	5.95	3.70

Our Lady of Hope — A74

1e, Belmonte Castle, horiz. 1.50e, St. Jerome's Convent. 2.50e, Cabral's Armada.

1968, Apr. 22 — Litho. — Perf. 14

542	A74	50c yellow & multi	.25	.25
543	A74	1e gray & multi	.50	.25
544	A74	1.50e lt blue & multi	.60	.25
545	A74	2.50e buff & multi	1.00	.35
		Nos. 542-545 (4)	2.35	1.10

500th anniv. of the birth of Pedro Alvares Cabral, navigator who took possession of Brazil for Portugal.

Francisco Inocencio de Souza Coutinho — A75

1969, Jan. 7 — Litho. — Perf. 14

546	A75	2e multicolored	.45	.25

Founding of Novo Redondo, 200th anniv.

Admiral Coutinho Issue
Common Design Type

Design: Adm. Gago Coutinho and his first ship.

1969, Feb. 17 — Litho. — Perf. 14

547	CD55	2.50e multicolored	.85	.35

Compass Rose — A77

1969, Aug. 29 — Litho. — Perf. 14

548	A77	1e multicolored	.45	.25

500th anniv. of the birth of Vasco da Gama (1469-1524), navigator.

Administration Reform Issue
Common Design Type

1969, Sept. 25 — Litho. — Perf. 14

549	CD56	1.50e multicolored	.35	.25

Portal of St. Jeronimo's Monastery — A79

1969, Dec. 1 — Litho. — Perf. 14

550	A79	3e multicolored	.45	.25

500th anniv. of the birth of King Manuel I.

Angolasaurus Bocagei — A80

Fossils and Minerals: 1e, Ferrometeorite. 1.50e, Dioptase crystals. 2e, Gondwanidium. 2.50e, Diamonds. 3e, Estromatolite. 3.50e, Procarcharodon megalodon. 4e, Microceratodus angolensis. 4.50e, Moscovite. 5e, Barite. 6e, Nostoceras. 10e, Rotula orbiculus angolensis.

1970, Oct. 31 — Litho. — Perf. 13

551	A80	50c tan & multi	.25	.25
552	A80	1e multicolored	.25	.25
553	A80	1.50e multicolored	.30	.25
554	A80	2e multicolored	.30	.25
555	A80	2.50e lt gray & multi	.30	.25
556	A80	3e multicolored	.35	.25
557	A80	3.50e blue & multi	.50	.30
558	A80	4e lt gray & multi	.50	.30
559	A80	4.50e gray & multi	.50	.30
560	A80	5e gray & multi	.75	.30
561	A80	6e pink & multi	1.50	.90
562	A80	10e lt blue & multi	2.10	1.20
		Nos. 551-562 (12)	7.60	4.80

Marshal Carmona Issue
Common Design Type

1970, Nov. 15 — Perf. 14

563	CD57	2.50e multicolored	.45	.25

Arms of Malanje, Cotton Boll and Field — A82

1970, Nov. 20 — Perf. 13

564	A82	2.50e multicolored	.55	.35

Centenary of the municipality of Malanje.

Mail Ships and Angola No. 1 A83

4.50e, Steam locomotive and Angola No. 4.

1970, Dec. 1 — Perf. 13½

565	A83	1.50e multicolored	.40	.30
566	A83	4.50e multicolored	1.75	.75

Cent. of stamps of Angola. See No. C36. For overprint see No. 616B.

Map of Africa, Diagram of Seismic Tests — A84

1971, Aug. 22 — Litho. — Perf. 13

567	A84	2.50e multicolored	.45	.25

5th Regional Conference of Soil and Foundation Engineers, Luanda, Aug. 22-Sept. 5.

Galleon on Congo River — A85

1972, May 25 — Litho. — Perf. 13

568	A85	1e brt grn & multi	.65	.25

4th centenary of the publication of The Lusiads by Luiz Camoens.

Olympic Games Issue
Common Design Type

1972, June 20 — Perf. 14x13½

569	CD59	50c multicolored	.65	.25

Lisbon-Rio de Janeiro Flight Issue
Common Design Type

1972, Sept. 20 — Litho. — Perf. 13½

570	CD60	1e multicolored	.35	.25

WMO Centenary Issue
Common Design Type

1973, Dec. 15 — Litho. — Perf. 13

571	CD61	1e dk gray & multi	.45	.25

Radar Station A89

1974, June 25 — Litho. — Perf. 13

572	A89	2e multicolored	.45	.25

Establishment of satellite communications network via Intelsat among Portugal, Angola and Mozambique.
For overprint see No. 616A.

Harpa Doris — A90

Designs: Sea shells: 30c, Murex melanamathos. 50c, Venus foliaceo lamellosa. 70c, Lathyrus filosus. 1e, Cymbium cisium. 1.50e, Cassis tesselata. 2e, Cypraea stercoraria. 2.50e, Conus prometheus. 3e, Strombus latus. 3.50e, Tympanotonus fuscatus. 4e, Cardium costatum. 5e, Natica fulminea. 6e, Lyropecten nodosus. 7e, Tonna galea. 10e, Donax rugosus. 25e, Cymatium trigonum. 30e, Olivancilaria acuminata. 35e, Semifusus morio. 40e, Clavatula lineata. 50e, Solarium granulatum.

1974, Oct. 25 — Litho. — Perf. 12x12½

573	A90	25c shown	.25	.25
574	A90	30c multicolored	.25	.25
575	A90	50c multicolored	.30	.25
576	A90	70c multicolored	.35	.25
577	A90	1e multicolored	.35	.25
578	A90	1.50e multicolored	.40	.25
579	A90	2e multicolored	.40	.25
580	A90	2.50e multicolored	.45	.25
581	A90	3e multicolored	.65	.25
582	A90	3.50e multicolored	.65	.45
583	A90	4e multicolored	.65	.45
584	A90	5e multicolored	.75	.45
585	A90	6e multicolored	1.25	.45
586	A90	7e multicolored	1.25	.45
587	A90	10e multicolored	1.00	.45
588	A90	25e multicolored	2.25	.90

589	A90	30e multicolored	2.50	.90
590	A90	35e multicolored	3.00	.90
591	A90	40e multicolored	3.50	1.10
592	A90	50e multicolored	5.00	1.75
	Nos. 573-592 (20)		25.20	10.50

For overprints see Nos. 605-607, 617-630.

No. 386 Overprinted in Blue

1974, Dec. 21   Litho.   Perf. 13½

593	A41	5c multicolored	.30	.25

Youth philately.

Republic

Star and Hand Holding Rifle — A91

1975, Nov. 11   Litho.   Perf. 13x13½

594	A91	1.50e red & multi	.50	.25

Independence in 1975.

Diquiche Mask — A92

Design: 3e, Bui ou Congolo mask.

1976, Feb. 6   Perf. 13½

595	A92	50c lt blue & multi	.25	.25
596	A92	3e multicolored	.55	.25

Workers — A93

1976, May 1   Litho.   Perf. 12

597	A93	1e red & multi	.35	.25

International Workers' Day.

No. 392 Overprinted

1976, June 15   Litho.   Perf. 13½

598	A41	10e multicolored	1.10	.75

Stamp Day.

President Agostinho Neto — A94

1976, Nov. 11   Litho.   Perf. 13

599	A94	50c yel & dk brown	.25	.25
600	A94	2e lt gray & plum	.25	.25
601	A94	3e gray & indigo	.40	.25
602	A94	5e buff & brown	.40	.25
603	A94	10e tan & sepia	.55	.25
a.	Souv. sheet of 1, imperf.		4.00	4.00
	Nos. 599-603 (5)		1.85	1.25

First anniversary of independence.

Nos. 393, 588-589, 592 Overprinted

1977, Feb. 9   Perf. 13½, 12x12½

604	A41	20e multicolored	1.75	.50
605	A90	25e multicolored	2.25	.60
606	A90	30e multicolored	2.60	.75
607	A90	50e multicolored	4.25	1.25
	Nos. 604-607 (4)		10.85	3.10

Overprint in 3 lines on No. 604, in 2 lines on others.

No. 438 Overprinted

1976, Dec. 31   Perf. 13½

608	CD48	15e multicolored	2.00	.65

Child and WHO Emblem — A95

1977   Litho.   Perf. 10½

609	A95	2.50k blk & lt blue	.65	.25

Campaign for vaccination against poliomyelitis.

Map of Africa, Flag of Angola — A96

1977   Photo.

610	A96	6k blk, red & blue	.60	.35

First Congress of Popular Movement for the Liberation of Angola.

Anti-Apartheid Emblem — A97

1979, June 20   Litho.   Perf. 13½

611	A97	1k multicolored	.25	.25

Anti-Apartheid Year.

Human Rights Emblem — A98

1979, June 15   Litho.   Perf. 13½

612	A98	2.50k multicolored	.35	.25

Declaration of Human Rights, 30th anniv. (in 1975).

Child Flowers, Globe, IYC Emblem — A99

1980, May 1   Litho.   Perf. 14x14½

613	A99	3.50k multicolored	.45	.25

International Year of the Child (1979).

Running, Moscow '80 Emblem — A100

1980, Dec. 15   Litho.   Perf. 13½

614	A100	9k shown	.70	.25
615	A100	12k Swimming, horiz.	.80	.25

22nd Summer Olympic Games, Moscow, July 19-Aug. 3.

5th Anniv. of Independence A101

1980, Nov. 11

616	A101	5.50k multicolored	.45	.25

Nos. 572, 566 Overprinted

1980-81   Litho.   Perf. 13½x13

616A	A89	2e multi (bar only)	1.25	.25
616B	A83	4.50e multicolored	2.75	1.50

Issued: 2e, 5/17/81; 4.50e, 6/15/80.
See No. C37.

Nos. 577-580, 582-591 Overprinted

1981, June 15   Litho.   Perf. 12x12½

617	A90	1e multicolored	.25	.25
618	A90	1.50e multicolored	.25	.25
619	A90	2e multicolored	.25	.25
620	A90	2.50e multicolored	.25	.25
621	A90	3.50e multicolored	.25	.25
622	A90	4e multicolored	.30	.25
623	A90	5e multicolored	.35	.25
624	A90	6e multicolored	.40	.25
625	A90	7e multicolored	.55	.25
626	A90	10e multicolored	.65	.30

627	A90	25e multicolored	1.40	.50
628	A90	30e multicolored	1.75	.75
629	A90	35e multicolored	2.00	.90
630	A90	40e multicolored	2.50	1.25
	Nos. 617-630 (14)		11.15	5.95

Man Walking with Canes, Tchibinda Ilunga Statue — A102

1981, Sept. 5   Litho.   Perf. 13½

631	A102	9k multicolored	.50	.30

Turipex '81 tourism exhibition.

M.P.L.A. Workers' Party Congress A103

1980, Dec. 23   Litho.   Perf. 14

632	A103	50 l Millet	.25	.25
633	A103	5k Coffee	.35	.25
634	A103	7.50k Sunflowers	.40	.25
635	A103	13.50k Cotton	.65	.30
636	A103	14k Oil	.80	.35
637	A103	16k Diamonds	.95	.45
	Nos. 632-637 (6)		3.40	1.85

People's Power — A104

1980, Nov. 11

638	A104	40k lt blue & blk	1.75	.65

Natl. Heroes' Day — A105

4.50k, Former Pres. Neto. 50k, Neto, diff.

1980, Sept. 17   Perf. 14x13½

639	A105	4.50k multicolored	.25	.25
640	A105	50k multicolored	2.75	.75

Soweto Uprising, 5th Anniv. A106

1981

641	A106	4.50k multicolored	.35	.25

2nd Central African Games A107

50 l, Bicycling, tennis. 5k, Judo, boxing. 6k, Basketball, volleyball. 10k, Handball, soccer.

1981, Sept. 3   Litho.   Perf. 13½
642 A107   50 l multicolored   .25   .25
643 A107   5k multicolored   .65   .25
644 A107   6k multicolored   .85   .25
645 A107   10k multicolored   1.40   .25
Nos. 642-645 (4)   3.15   1.10

Souvenir Sheet
Imperf
646 A107   15k multicolored   3.00   3.00

Charaxes Kahldeni A108

1k, Abantis zambesiaca. 5k, Catacroptera cloanthe. 9k, Myrina ficedula, vert. 10k, Colotis danae. 15k, Acraea acrita. 100k, Precis hierta.

1982, Feb. 26   Litho.   Perf. 13½
647 A108   50 l shown   .25   .25
648 A108   1k multicolored   .25   .25
649 A108   5k multicolored   .40   .25
650 A108   9k multicolored   1.00   .25
651 A108   10k multicolored   1.00   .25
652 A108   15k multicolored   1.25   .40
653 A108   100k multicolored   8.00   3.00
a.   Souvenir sheet   12.00   12.00
Nos. 647-653 (7)   12.15   4.65

No. 653a contains Nos. 647-653, imperf., and sold for 30k (stamps probably not valid individually).

5th Anniv. of UN Membership — A109

5.50k, The Silence of the Night, by Musseque Catambor. 7.50k, Cotton picking, Catete.

1982, Sept. 22   Litho.
654 A109   5.50k multicolored   .40   .25
655 A109   7.50k multicolored   .55   .25

20th Anniv. of Engineering Laboratory A110

1982, Dec. 21   Litho.   Perf. 14
656 A110   9k Lab   .65   .30
657 A110   13k Worker, vert.   .65   .40
658 A110   100k Equipment, vert.   6.75   3.50
Nos. 656-658 (3)   8.05   4.20

Local Flowers — A111

5k, Dichrostachys glomerata. 12k, Amblygonocarpus obtusangulus. 50k, Albizzia versicolor.

1983, Feb. 18   Perf. 13½
659 A111   5k multicolored   .40   .25
660 A111   12k multicolored   .75   .30
661 A111   50k multicolored   3.50   1.40
Nos. 659-661 (3)   4.65   1.95

Women's Org., First Congress A112

1983   Litho.   Perf. 13½
662 A112   20k multicolored   1.25   .50

Africa Day — A113

1983, June 30   Perf. 13
663 A113   6.5k multicolored   .65   .35

World Communications Year — A114

1983, June 30   Litho.   Perf. 13½
664 A114   6.5k M'pungi   .75   .35
665 A114   12k Mondu   1.25   .55

BRASILIANA '83 Stamp Exhibition, Rio de Janeiro, July 29-Aug. 7 — A115

Crop-eating insects: 4.50k, Antestiopsis lineaticollis. 6.5k, Stephanoderes hampei ferr. 10k, Zonocerus variegatus.

1983, July 29   Litho.   Perf. 13
666 A115   4.5k multicolored   .50   .25
667 A115   6.5k multicolored   .55   .35
668 A115   10k multicolored   1.00   .60
Nos. 666-668 (3)   2.05   1.20

25th Anniv. of Economic Commission for Africa — A116

1983, Aug. 2
669 A116   10k Map, emblem   .70   .50

185th Anniv. of Post Office A117

50 l, Mail collection, vert. 3.5k, Unloading mail plane. 5k, Sorting mail. 15k, Mailing letter, vert. 30k, Post office box delivery.

1983, Dec. 7   Litho.   Perf. 13½
670 A117   50 l multicolored   .25   .25
671 A117   3.5k multicolored   .35   .25
672 A117   5k multicolored   .55   .40
673 A117   15k multicolored   1.50   .90

674 A117   30k multicolored   2.90   1.60
a.   Min. sheet of 3, #671-672, 674   8.00   8.00
Nos. 670-674 (5)   5.55   3.40

No. 674a sold for 100k.

Local Butterflies A118

50 l, Parasa karschi. 1k, Diaphone angolensis. 3.5k, Choeropasis jucunda. 6.5k, Hespagarista rendalli. 15k, Euchromia guineensis. 17.5k, Mazuca roseistriga. 20k, Utetheisa callima.

1984, Jan. 20   Litho.   Perf. 13½
675 A118   50 l multicolored   .25   .25
676 A118   1k multicolored   .30   .25
677 A118   3.5k multicolored   .55   .25
678 A118   6.5k multicolored   .95   .35
679 A118   15k multicolored   1.60   .90
680 A118   17.5k multicolored   1.90   1.00
681 A118   20k multicolored   2.75   1.25
Nos. 675-681 (7)   8.30   4.25

A119

1984, Apr. 11   Litho.   Perf. 13½
682 A119   30k multicolored   2.50   1.75

First Natl. Worker's Union Congress, Apr. 11-16.

Local Birds — A120

10.50k, Bucorvus leadbeateri. 14k, Gypohierax angolensis. 16k, Ardea goliath. 19.50k, Pelecanus onocrotalus. 22k, Platalea alba. 26k, Balearica pavonina.

1984, Oct. 24   Litho.   Perf. 13½
683 A120   10.50k multicolored   .80   .40
684 A120   14k multicolored   1.00   .50
685 A120   16k multicolored   1.20   .65
686 A120   19.50k multicolored   1.60   .65
687 A120   22k multicolored   1.75   .75
688 A120   26k multicolored   2.50   1.00
Nos. 683-688 (6)   8.85   3.95

Local Animals A121

1k, Tragelaphus strepsiceros. 4k, Antidorcas marsupialis angolensis. 5k, Pan troglodytes. 10k, Syncerus caffer. 15k, Hippotragus niger variani. 20k, Orycteropus afer. 25k, Crocuta crocuta.

1984, Nov. 12
689 A121   1k multicolored   .35   .25
690 A121   4k multicolored   .45   .25
691 A121   5k multicolored   .60   .25
692 A121   10k multicolored   1.75   .30
693 A121   15k multicolored   2.10   .45
694 A121   20k multicolored   2.50   .60
695 A121   25k multicolored   3.00   .65
Nos. 689-695 (7)   10.75   2.75

Angolese Monuments A122

5k, San Pedro da Barra. 12.5k, Nova Oeiras. 18k, M'Banza Kongo. 26k, Massangano. 39k, Escravatura Museum.

1985, Feb. 21   Litho.   Perf. 13½
696 A122   5k multicolored   .35   .25
697 A122   12.5k multicolored   .90   .50
698 A122   18k multicolored   1.20   .75
699 A122   26k multicolored   1.90   .90
700 A122   39k multicolored   2.60   1.50
Nos. 696-700 (5)   6.95   3.90

United Workers' Party, 25th Anniv. A123

1985, May   Litho.   Perf. 12
701 A123   77k XXV, red flags   7.00   4.00

Printed in sheets of 5.

A124

1k, Flags. 11k, Oil drilling platform, Cabinda. 57k, Conference.

1985, May
702 A124   1k multicolored   .25   .25
703 A124   11k multicolored   1.00   .80
704 A124   57k multicolored   2.60   1.25
a.   Strip of 3, #702-704   4.50   4.50

Southern African Development Council, 5th anniv.

Medicinal plants — A125

No. 705, Lonchocarpus sericeus. No. 706, Gossypium. No. 707, Cassia occidentalis. No. 708, Gloriosa superba. No. 709, Cochlospermum angolensis.

Lithographed and Typographed
1985, July 5   Perf. 11
705 A125   1k multi   .30   .25
706 A125   4k multi   .40   .30
707 A125   11k multi   1.00   .70
708 A125   25.50k multi   2.00   1.00
709 A125   55k multi   3.50   2.50
Nos. 705-709 (5)   7.20   4.75

ARGENTINA '85 exhibition.

5th Natl. Heroes Day A126

Natl. flag and: 10.50k, Portrait of Agostinho Neto, party leader. 36.50k, Neto working.

1985   Litho.   Perf. 13½
710 A126 10.50k multicolored   12.00   7.50
711 A126 36.50k multicolored   16.00 10.00

Ministerial Conference of Non-Aligned
Countries, Luanda — A127

1985, Sept. 4   Photo.   Perf. 11
712 A127 35k multicolored   2.50 1.75

UN, 40th
Anniv.
A128

1985, Oct. 29   Litho.   Perf. 11
713 A128 12.50k multicolored   1.25   .75

Industry and Natural
Resources — A129

1985, Nov. 11
714 A129   50 l Cement Factory   .25   .25
715 A129   5k Logging   .35   .25
716 A129   7k Quartz   .50   .40
717 A129   10k Iron mine   .85   .50
  a. Souvenir sheet of 4, #714-717,
       imperf.   3.50 3.50
       Nos. 714-717 (4)   1.95 1.40

  Natl. independence, 10th anniv.

2nd Natl. Workers' Party Congress
(MPLA) — A130

1985, Nov. 28   Perf. 13½
718 A130 20k multicolored   1.50 1.00

Demostenes de Almeida Clington
Races, 30th Anniv. — A131

Various runners.

1985, Dec. 13
719 A131   50 l multicolored   .25   .25
720 A131   5k multicolored   .40   .25
721 A131 6.50k multicolored   .60   .25
722 A131   10k multicolored   .80   .30
       Nos. 719-722 (4)   2.05 1.05

1986 World Cup
Soccer
Championships,
Mexico — A132

Map, soccer field and various plays.

1986, May 6   Litho.   Perf. 11½x11
723 A132   50 l multi   .25   .25
724 A132 3.50k multi   .40   .25
725 A132   5k multi   .65   .25
726 A132   7k multi   .80   .25
727 A132   10k multi   1.25   .40
728 A132   18k multi   2.10   .60
       Nos. 723-728 (6)   5.45 2.00

Struggle
Against
Portugal,
25th Anniv.
A133

1986, May 6   Perf. 11x11½
729 A133 15k multicolored   1.40   .50

First Man in
Space, 25th
Anniv.
A134

  50 l, Skylab, US. 1k, Spacecraft. 5k, A. Leonov space-walking. 10k, Lunokhod on Moon.
13k, Apollo-Soyuz link-up.

1986, Aug. 21   Litho.   Perf. 11x11½
730 A134   50 l multicolored   .25   .25
731 A134   1k multicolored   .25   .25
732 A134   5k multicolored   .40   .25
733 A134   10k multicolored   .90   .35
734 A134   13k multicolored   .95   .40
       Nos. 730-734 (5)   2.75 1.50

Admission
of Angola to
UN, 10th
Anniv.
A135

1986, Dec. 1   Litho.   Perf. 11x11½
735 A135 22k multi   1.60 1.10

Liberation Movement, 30th
Anniv. — A136

  Angolese at work, fighting and: No. 736a,
"1956." No. 736b, Congress emblem, "1980."
No. 736c, Labor Party emblem, "1985."

1986, Dec. 3   Perf. 11½x11
736   A136 Strip of 3   1.50 1.50
  a.-c.   5k any single   .45   .25

Agostinho
Neto
University,
10th Anniv.
A137

1986, Dec. 30   Litho.   Perf. 11x11½
737 A137   50 l Mathematics   .25   .25
738 A137   1k Law   .50   .35
739 A137   10k Medicine   .85   .60
       Nos. 737-739 (3)   1.60 1.20

Tribal
Hairstyles — A138

1987, Apr. 15   Litho.   Perf. 11½x11
740 A138   1k Ouioca   .25   .25
741 A138 1.50k Luanda   .35   .25
742 A138   5k Humbe   .65   .25
743 A138   7k Muila   .80   .25
744 A138   20k Muila, diff.   2.00   .45
745 A138   30k Dilolo   3.75   .80
       Nos. 740-745 (6)   7.80 2.25

Landscapes
A139

Perf. 11½x12, 12x11½
1987, July 7   Litho.
746 A139   50 l Pambala Shore   .25   .25
747 A139 1.50k Dala Waterfalls .25   .25
748 A139 3.50k Black Stones   .25   .25
749 A139   5k Cuango River   .45   .25
750 A139   10k Luanda coast   .95   .35
751 A139   20k Hills of Leba   1.90   .45
       Nos. 746-751 (6)   4.05 1.80

  Nos. 746-747, 749 and 751 horiz.

Lenin — A140

1987, Nov. 25   Perf. 12x12½
752 A140 15k multi   1.25   .45
  October Revolution, Russia, 70th anniv.

2nd Congress of
the Organization
of Angolan
Women
(OMA) — A141

  10k, Soldier, nurse, technician, student.

1988, May 30   Litho.   Perf. 13x13½
753 A141   2k shown   .25   .25
754 A141 10k multicolored   .65   .25

Victory
Carnival, 10th
Anniv.
A142

  Various carnival scenes.

1988, June 15   Litho.   Perf. 13½x13
755 A142   5k shown   .40   .25
756 A142 10k multi, diff.   .70   .30

Augusto N'Gangula (1956-1968),
Youth Pioneer Killed by Portuguese
Colonial Army — A143

Agostinho Neto Pioneers' Organization
(OPA), 25th Anniv. — A144

1989, Oct. 2   Litho.   Perf. 12x11½
757 A143 12k multicolored   1.10   .65
758 A144 15k multicolored   1.40   .80
       Pioneer Day.

10th Natl. Soccer Championships,
Benguela, May 1 — A145

1989, Oct. 16
759 A145 5k shown   .50   .40
760 A145 5k Luanda, 3 years   .50   .40
761 A145 5k Luanda, 5 years   .50   .40
  a.   Strip of 3, #759-761   1.60 1.60
       Nos. 759-761 (3)   1.50 1.20

Intl. Fund for
Agricultural
Development,
10th
Anniv. — A146

1990, Feb. 15   Litho.   Perf. 11½x12
762 A146 10k multicolored   1.10   .45

Ingombotas' Houses — A147

  Architecture: 2k, Alta Train Station. 5k,
National Museum of Anthropology. 15k, Ana
Joaquina Palace. 23k, Iron Palace. 36k, Mete-
orological observatory, vert. 50k, People's
Palace.

1990, Feb. 20   Perf. 12x11½, 11½x12
763 A147   1k shown   .25   .25
764 A147   2k multicolored   .25   .25
765 A147   5k multicolored   .40   .25
766 A147 15k multicolored   1.10   .60
767 A147 23k multicolored   1.90   .90
768 A147 36k multicolored   3.00 1.25
769 A147 50k multicolored   4.00 1.75
       Nos. 763-769 (7)   10.90 5.25

Luanda and
Benguela
Railways
A148

  Various maps and locomotives.

1990, Mar. 1   *Perf. 12x11½*
770 A148 5k shown .... .40 .25
771 A148 12k Garrat T (left) ..... 1.25 .45
772 A148 12k Garrat T (right) .... 1.25 .45
   a.   Pair, #771-772 .... 2.75 2.75
773 A148 14k Mikado .... 1.25 .75
    Nos. 770-773 (4) 4.15 1.90

Souvenir Sheet
774 A148 25k Diesel electric 3.00 3.00

No. 772a has a continuous design.

Southern Africa Development
Coordinating Conf. (SADCC), 10th
Anniv. — A149

1990, Apr. 1   **Litho.**   *Perf. 14*
775 A149 5k shown .... .40 .25
776 A149 9k Floating oil rig ...... 1.00 .45

Pan-African
Postal
Union
(PAPU),
10th Anniv.
A150

10k, Simulated stamp, map.

1990, Apr. 6
777 A150 4k shown .... .45 .25
778 A150 10k multicolored .... 1.00 .65

Paintings by
Raul
Indipwo
A151

6k, Tres Gracas. 9k, Muxima, vert.

1990, Apr. 24
779 A151 6k multicolored .... .45 .25
780 A151 9k multicolored .... 1.00 .35

Stamp World London 90.

Hippotragus Niger Variani, Adult Male
and Female — A152

1990, May 9   *Perf. 14x13½*
781 A152 5k Adult male 1.50 1.50
782 A152 5k shown 1.50 1.50
783 A152 5k Adult female 1.50 1.50
784 A152 5k Female, calf 1.50 1.50
    Nos. 781-784 (4) 6.00 6.00

World Wildlife Fund. Various combinations
available in blocks or strips of four.

Rosa de
Porcelana
A153

1990, June 2   **Litho.**   *Perf. 14*
785 A153 5k shown .... .40 .25
786 A153 8k Cravo burro .... .80 .35
787 A153 10k Alamandra .... .95 .45
    Nos. 785-787 (3) 2.15 1.05

Souvenir Sheet
788 A153 40k Hibiscus 5.00 5.00

Belgica '90.

Miniature Sheet

Intl. Literacy Year — A154

Various animals and forest scenes.

1990, July 26   **Litho.**   *Perf. 14*
789 A154   Sheet of 30 ...... 10.00 10.00
   a.-ad.   1k any single .... .30 .30
790 A154 5k Zebra 1.00 1.00
791 A154 5k Butterfly 1.00 1.00
792 A154 5k Horse 1.00 1.00
   a.   Block of 3, #790-792 + la-
        bel 4.00 4.00

People's
Assembly,
10th Anniv.
A155

1990, Nov. 11   *Perf. 14*
793 A155 10k multicolored .... .90 .90

3rd Natl. Labor
Congress
A156

1990   **Litho.**   *Perf. 13½*
794 A156 14k multicolored .... 1.00 .50

War of Independence, 30th
Anniv. — A157

Uniforms: No. 795, Machete, 1961. No. 796,
Rifle, 1962-63. No. 797, Rifle, 1968. No. 798,
Automatic rifle, 1972.

1991, Feb. 28   **Litho.**   *Perf. 14*
795 A157 6k multicolored .... .65 .25
   a.   Perf. 13½ vert. .... 1.20 .75
796 A157 6k multicolored .... .65 .25
   a.   Perf. 13½ vert. .... 1.20 .75
797 A157 6k multicolored .... .65 .25
   a.   Perf. 13½ vert. .... 1.20 .75
798 A157 6k multicolored .... .65 .25
   a.   Perf. 13½ vert. .... 1.20 .75
   b.   Bklt. pane of 4, #795a-798a   6.00
    Nos. 795-798 (4) 2.60 1.00

Musical Instruments — A158

Designs: a, Marimba. b, Mucupela. c,
Ngoma la Txina. d, Kissange.

1991, Apr. 5   **Litho.**   *Perf. 14*
799 A158 6k Block or strip of 4,
            #799a-799d 2.50 2.50

Tourism
A159

Designs: 3k, Iona National Park. 7k,
Kalandula Waterfalls. 35k, Lobito Bay. 60k,
Weltwitschia Mirabilis plant.

1991, June 25   **Litho.**   *Perf. 14*
800 A159 3k multi .... .25 .25
801 A159 7k multi .... .40 .40
802 A159 35k multi .... 1.90 .80
803 A159 60k multi 3.25 1.50
    Nos. 800-803 (4) 5.80 2.95

Souvenir Sheet

Design: 30k, Map details.

1991, June 25   **Litho.**   *Perf. 13¼*
803A A159 30k multi 4.00 4.00

Dogs
A160

1991, July 5   **Litho.**   *Perf. 14*
804 A160 5k Kabir of dembos .... .50 .50
805 A160 7k Ombua .... .55 .55
806 A160 11k Kabir massongo .... .90 .40
807 A160 12k Kawa tchowe .... .90 .50
    Nos. 804-807 (4) 2.85 1.95

1992
Summer
Olympics,
Barcelona
A161

1991, July 26   *Perf. 13*
808 A161 4k Judo .... .25 .25
809 A161 6k Sailing .... .25 .25
810 A161 10k Running .... .45 .25
811 A161 100k Swimming 3.50 2.25
    Nos. 808-811 (4) 4.45 3.00

Navigation
Aids
A162

1991, Nov. 8   **Litho.**   *Perf. 12*
812 A162 5k Quadrant .... .25 .25
813 A162 15k Astrolabe .... .55 .55
814 A162 20k Cross-staff ...... .75 .40
815 A162 50k Portolano 1.75 1.00
    Nos. 812-815 (4) 3.30 2.20

Iberex '91.

Rays
A163

1992, Mar. 30   **Litho.**   *Perf. 14*
816 A163 40k Myliobatis aquila ... .90 .30
817 A163 50k Aetobatus narinari . .90 .40
818 A163 66k Manta birostris .... 1.10 .50
819 A163 80k Raja miraletus ..... 1.50 .65
    Nos. 816-819 (4) 4.40 1.85

Souvenir Sheet
Perf. 13½
820 A163 25k Manta birostris,
            diff. 5.00 5.00

Quioca
Masks — A164

1992, Apr. 30   **Litho.**   *Perf. 13½*
821 A164 60k Kalelwa .... .25 .25
822 A164 100k Mukixe Wa Kino .. .45 .35
823 A164 150k Cikunza .... .75 .55
824 A164 250k Mukixi Wa
           Mbwesu .... 1.20 .70
    Nos. 821-824 (4) 2.65 1.85

See Nos. 854-857, 868-871, 883-886, 895-
898.

Lubrapex
'92 — A165

Medicinal Plants: 200k, Ptaeroxylon obli-
quum. 300k, Spondias mombin. 500k, Parinari
curatellifolia. 600k, Cochlospermum
angolense.

1992, May 8   *Perf. 14*
825 A165 200k brown & pale yel .. .75 .55
826 A165 300k brown & pale yel .. 1.10 .90
827 A165 500k brown & pale yel .. 2.00 1.60
828 A165 600k brown & pale yel .. 2.10 1.75
   a.   Block or strip of 4, #825-828   6.00 6.00

Evangelization of Angola, 500th
Anniv. — A166

150k, King, missionaries. 420k, Ruins of
M'banza Congo. 470k, Maxima Church. 500k,
Faces of people.

1992, May 10   *Perf. 13½*
829 A166 150k multicolored ...... .55 .45
830 A166 420k multicolored 1.60 1.25
831 A166 470k multicolored 1.75 1.40
832 A166 500k multicolored 2.00 1.60
    Nos. 829-832 (4) 5.90 4.70

Traditional Houses — A167

150k, Dimbas. 330k, Cokwe. 360k, Mbali. 420k, Ambwelas. 500k, Upper Zambezi.

Perf. 14, 13½ Vert. (#832A)
1992, May 22
832A	A167	150k multi	1.25	1.00
b.		Bklt. pane of 4, #832A, 833a-835a	7.50	
833	A167	330k multi	1.40	1.10
a.		Perf. 13½ vert.	1.60	1.60
834	A167	360k multi	1.60	1.25
a.		Perf. 13½ vert.	1.60	1.60
835	A167	420k multi	2.00	1.60
a.		Perf. 13½ vert.	2.00	2.00
836	A167	500k multi	2.00	1.60
		Nos. 832A-836 (5)	8.25	6.55

Expo '92, Seville.

Agapornis Roseicollis A168

150k, Two birds on branch. 200k, Birds feeding. 250k, Hand holding bird. 300k, Bird on perch.

1992, June 2 **Perf. 12x11½**
837	A168	150k multicolored	1.00	.50
838	A168	200k multicolored	1.40	.65
839	A168	250k multicolored	1.75	.80
840	A168	300k multicolored	2.10	1.00
a.		Strip of 4, #837-840	6.50	6.50

Expo '92, Seville.

Souvenir Sheet

Visit of Pope John Paul II to Angola — A169

Abstract paintings: a, 340k, The Crucifixion. b, 370k, The Resurrection.

1992, June 4 **Litho.** **Perf. 13½**
841	A169	Sheet of 2, #a.-b. + 2 labels	4.00	4.00

1992 Summer Olympics, Barcelona A170

1992, July 30 **Perf. 14**
842	A170	120k Hurdles	.55	.40
843	A170	180k Cycling	.80	.55
844	A170	240k Roller hockey	.95	.75
845	A170	360k Basketball	1.50	1.10
		Nos. 842-845 (4)	3.80	2.80

Native Fishing — A171

1992, Aug. 5 **Perf. 11½x12**
846	A171	65k Building traps	.50	.25
847	A171	90k Using nets	.65	.35
848	A171	100k Laying traps	.80	.40
849	A171	120k Fisherman in boats	.95	.50
		Nos. 846-849 (4)	2.90	1.50

Souvenir Sheet

Discovery of America, 500th Anniv. — A172

1992, Sept. 18 **Litho.** **Perf. 12**
850	A172	500k multicolored	4.00	4.00

Genoa '92.

First Free Elections in Angola — A173

Designs: 120k, People voting. 150k, Map, ballot box, peace doves. 200k, People, dove, hand dropping ballot into ballot box.

1992, Oct. 27 **Litho.** **Perf. 11½x12**
851	A173	120k multicolored	.35	.25
852	A173	150k multicolored	.40	.30
853	A173	200k multicolored	.55	.40
		Nos. 851-853 (3)	1.30	.95

Quioca Mask Type of 1992
1992, Nov. 6 **Perf. 13½**
854	A164	72k Cihongo	.25	.25
855	A164	80k Mbwasu	.35	.25
856	A164	120k Cinhanga	.40	.35
857	A164	210k Kalewa	.75	.65
		Nos. 854-857 (4)	1.75	1.50

Inauguration of Express Mail Service — A174

1992, Dec. 14 **Litho.** **Perf. 12x11½**
858	A174	450k Truck	1.40	1.20
859	A174	550k Airplane	1.75	1.40

Meteorological Instruments A175

1993, Mar. 23 **Litho.** **Perf. 11½x12**
860	A175	250k Weather balloon	.95	.80
861	A175	470k Actinometer	1.90	1.40
862	A175	500k Rain gauge	1.90	1.60
		Nos. 860-862 (3)	4.75	3.80

Seashells A176

210k, Trochita trochiformis. 330k, Strombus latus. 400k, Aporrhais pesgallinae. 500k, Fusos aff. albinus. 1000k, Pusionella nifat.

1993, Apr. 6 **Perf. 12x11½**
863	A176	210k multicolored	.75	.75
864	A176	330k multicolored	1.10	1.10
865	A176	400k multicolored	1.50	1.50
866	A176	500k multicolored	1.75	1.75
		Nos. 863-866 (4)	5.10	5.10

Souvenir Sheet
867	A176	1000k multicolored	4.00	4.00

Quioca Art Type of 1992
1993, June 7 **Litho.** **Perf. 12**
868	A164	72k Men with vehicles	.25	.25
869	A164	210k Cavalier	.75	.50
870	A164	420k Airplane	1.50	.90
871	A164	600k Men carrying stretcher	2.00	1.25
		Nos. 868-871 (4)	4.50	2.90

Flowering Plants — A177

360k, Sansevieria cylindrica. 400k, Euphorbia tirucalli. 500k, Opuntia ficus-indica. 600k, Dracaena aubryana.

1993, June 28 **Perf. 11½x12**
872	A177	360k multicolored	1.20	.90
873	A177	400k multicolored	1.40	1.00
874	A177	500k multicolored	1.50	1.00
875	A177	600k multicolored	2.00	1.40
		Nos. 872-875 (4)	6.10	4.30

Souvenir Sheet

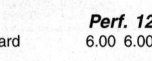

Africa Day — A178

1993, May 31 **Perf. 12**
876	A178	1500k Leopard	6.00	6.00

Tribal Pipes — A179

1993, Aug. 16 **Litho.** **Perf. 11½x12**
877	A179	72k Vimbundi	.25	.25
878	A179	200k Vimbundi, diff.	.75	.40
879	A179	420k Mutopa	1.40	.90
880	A179	600k Pexi	2.00	1.25
		Nos. 877-880 (4)	4.40	2.80

Souvenir Sheet

Union of Portuguese Speaking Capitals — A180

1993, July 30 **Perf. 12x11½**
881	A180	1500k multicolored	5.50	5.50

Turtles — A181

Designs: a, 180k, Chelonia mydas (b). b, 450k, Eretmochelys imbricata. c, 550k, Dermochelys coriacea. d, 630k, Caretta caretta.

1993, July 9 **Litho.** **Perf. 12½x12**
882	A181	Block of 4, #a.-d.	7.00	7.00

Quioca Art Type of 1992
1993, Sept. 1 **Litho.** **Perf. 12**
883	A164	300k Leopard	.95	.65
884	A164	600k Malhado	1.90	1.25
885	A164	800k Birds	2.50	1.60
886	A164	1000k Chickens	3.25	2.10
		Nos. 883-886 (4)	8.60	5.75

Mushrooms A182

300k, Tricholoma georgii. 500k, Amanita phalloides. 600k, Amanita vaginata. 1000k, Macrolepiota procera.

1993, Dec. 5 **Litho.** **Perf. 12**
887	A182	300k multicolored	.95	.55
a.		Perf. 11½ vert.	1.60	1.60
888	A182	500k multicolored	1.60	.95
a.		Perf. 11½ vert.	2.40	2.40
889	A182	600k multicolored	1.90	1.20
a.		Perf. 11½ vert.	3.25	3.25
890	A182	1000k multicolored	3.25	2.00
a.		Perf. 11½ vert.	4.75	4.75
b.		Booklet pane of 4, #887a-890a	12.00	
		Nos. 887-890 (4)	7.70	4.70

A183

Natl. Culture Day: 500k, Cinganji, wood carving of dancer. 1000k, Ohunya yo soma, staff with woman's face. 1200k, Ongende, sculpture of man on donkey. 2200k, Upi, corn pestle.

1994, Jan. 10   Litho.   Perf. 12
891	A183	500k	multicolored	.80	.50
892	A183	1000k	multicolored	1.50	.95
893	A183	1200k	multicolored	2.00	1.25
894	A183	2200k	multicolored	3.50	2.25
		Nos. 891-894 (4)		7.80	4.95

Hong Kong '94.

Quioca Art Type of 1992
1994, Feb. 21   Litho.   Perf. 12
895	A164	500k	Bird on flower	.50	.40
896	A164	2000k	Plant with roots	2.25	1.60
897	A164	2500k	Feto	2.75	2.00
898	A164	3000k	Plant	3.50	2.40
		Nos. 895-898 (4)		9.00	6.40

Social Responsibilities of AIDS — A184

500k, Mass of people. 1000k, Witchdoctor receiving AIDS through needle, people being educated. 3000k, Stylized man, woman.

1994, May 5   Litho.   Perf. 12
899	A184	500k	multicolored	.55	.40
900	A184	1000k	multicolored	1.10	.55
901	A184	3000k	multicolored	3.50	2.40
		Nos. 899-901 (3)		5.15	3.35

1994 World Cup Soccer Championships, US — A185

500k, Large arrows, small ball. 700k, Small arrows, large ball. 2200k, Ball in goal. 2500k, Ball, foot.

1994, June 17   Perf. 14
902	A185	500k	multicolored	.55	.40
903	A185	700k	multicolored	.80	.55
904	A185	2200k	multicolored	2.50	1.75
905	A185	2500k	multicolored	3.00	2.00
		Nos. 902-905 (4)		6.85	4.70

Dinosaurs A186

1000k, Brachiosaurus. 3000k, Spinosaurus. 5000k, Ouranosaurus. 10,000k, Lesothosaurus. 19,000k, Lesothosaurus, map of Africa.

1994, Aug. 16   Perf. 12
906	A186	1000k	multi	.25	.25
907	A186	3000k	multi	.75	.55
908	A186	5000k	multi	1.25	.95
909	A186	10,000k	multi	2.50	2.00
		Nos. 906-909 (4)		4.75	3.75

Souvenir Sheet
910	A186	19,000k	multi	7.50	7.50

PHILAKOREA '94. SINGPEX '94. No. 910 contains one 44x34mm stamp.

Tourism A187

2000k, Birds. 4000k, Wild animals. 8000k, Native women. 10,000k, Native men.

1994, Sept. 27   Litho.   Perf. 12x11½
911	A187	2000k	multi	.50	.40
912	A187	4000k	multi	.95	.80
913	A187	8000k	multi	2.00	1.60
914	A187	10,000k	multi	2.50	2.00
		Nos. 911-914 (4)		5.95	4.80

Post Boxes — A188

Designs: 5000k, Letters, bundled mail wall box. 7500k, Wall box for letters. 10,000k, Pillar box. 21,000k, Multi-function units.

1994, Oct. 7   Perf. 14½
915	A188	5000k	multicolored	.75	.40
916	A188	7500k	multicolored	1.00	.55
917	A188	10,000k	multicolored	1.40	.90
918	A188	21,000k	multicolored	3.00	1.75
		Nos. 915-918 (4)		6.15	3.50

Cotton Pests — A189

Insects: 5000k, Heliothis armigera. 6000k, Bemisia tabasi. 10,000k, Dysdercus. 27,000k, Spodoptera exigua.

1994, Nov. 11   Litho.   Perf. 14
919	A189	5000k	multicolored	.80	.40
920	A189	6000k	multicolored	1.00	.50
921	A189	10,000k	multicolored	1.60	.90
922	A189	27,000k	multicolored	4.00	2.10
		Nos. 919-922 (4)		7.40	3.90

Intl. Olympic Committee, Cent. A190

1994, Dec. 15
923	A190	27,000k	multicolored	4.50	4.50

Tribal Culture A191

Designs: 10,000k. Rubbing sticks to start fire. 15,000k, Extracting sap from tree. 20,000k, Smoking tribal pipe. 25,000k, Shooting bow & arrow. 28,000k, Mothers, children. 30,000k, Cave art.

1995, Jan. 6   Litho.   Perf. 14
924	A191	10,000k	multicolored	.50	.35
925	A191	15,000k	multicolored	.75	.50
926	A191	20,000k	multicolored	1.00	.65
927	A191	25,000k	multicolored	1.25	.80
928	A191	28,000k	multicolored	1.25	.90
929	A191	30,000k	multicolored	1.50	1.20
		Nos. 924-929 (6)		6.25	4.40

Traditional Ceramics A192

Designs: No. 930, Pitcher with bust of a woman as stopper. No. 931, Cone-shaped vase. No. 932, Bird-shaped vase. No. 933, Pitcher with bust of a man as stopper.

1995, Jan. 2   Litho.   Perf. 14½
930	A192	(2)	2nd class natl.	.55	.25
931	A192	(1)	1st class natl.	.80	.35
932	A192	(2)	2nd class intl.	1.10	.55
933	A192	(1)	1st class intl.	1.50	1.25
		Nos. 930-933 (4)		3.95	2.40

Rotary Intl., 90th Anniv. A193

a, Immunizing boy against polio. b, Medical examination. c, Immunizing girl against polio. No. 936, Dove over map.

1995, Feb. 23   Litho.   Perf. 14
934		Strip of 3		6.00	6.00
a.-c.	A193	27,000k any single		2.00	1.25
935		Strip of 3		6.00	6.00
a.-c.	A193	27,000k any single		2.00	1.25

Souvenir Sheet
936	A193	81,000k	multicolored	7.50	7.50
a.		English inscription		7.50	7.50

No. 934 has Portuguese inscriptions. No. 935 has English inscriptions. Both were issued in sheets of 9 stamps.
No. 936 contains Portuguese inscription in sheet margin.

Rotary Intl., 90th Anniv. — A194

Litho. & Embossed
1995, Feb. 23   Perf. 11½x12
937	A194	81,000k	gold	50.00	

World Telecommunications Day — A195

Designs: No. 938, 1957 Sputnik 1. No. 939, Shuttle, Intelsat satellite.

1995   Litho.   Perf. 14
938	A195	27,000k	multicolored	2.00	2.00
939	A195	27,000k	multicolored	2.00	2.00
a.		Souvenir sheet, #938-939		4.50	4.50

Independence, 20th Anniv. — A196

1995, Nov. 11   Litho.   Perf. 14
940	A196	2900k	multicolored	1.60	1.60

4th World Conference on Women, Beijing — A197

Designs: 375k, Women working in fields. 1106k, Woman teaching, girls with book.

1265k, Woman in industry, career woman. 2900k, Woman in native headdress, vert. 1500k, Native mother, children, vert.

1996, Jan. 29   Litho.   Perf. 14
941	A197	375k	multicolored	.25	.25
942	A197	1106k	multicolored	.80	.80
943	A197	1265k	multicolored	1.50	1.50
944	A197	2900k	multicolored	3.00	3.00
		Nos. 941-944 (4)		5.55	5.55

Souvenir Sheet
945	A197	1500k	multicolored	2.75	2.75

UN Assistance Programs — A198

Designs: 200k, Boy, highlift moving supplies. 1265k, Supply ship arriving. No. 948, Two high lifts. No. 949, Tractor-trailer traveling past vultures, native girl. No. 950, Man, ship.

1996   Litho.   Perf. 14
946	A198	200k	multicolored	.25	.25
947	A198	1265k	multicolored	1.00	1.00
948	A198	2583k	multicolored	2.25	2.25
949	A198	2583k	multicolored	2.50	2.50
		Nos. 946-949 (4)		6.00	6.00

Souvenir Sheet
950	A198	1265k	multicolored	6.50	6.50

Flora and Fauna A199

1500k, Verdant hawkmoth. 4400k, Water lily. 5100k, Panther toad. 6000k, African wild dog.
1500k: a, Western honey buzzard. b, Bateleuer. c, Common kestrel.
4400k; d, Red-crested turaco. e, Giraffe. f, Elephant.
5100k: g, Hippopotamus. h, Cattle egret. i, Lion.
6000k: j, Helmeted turtle. k, African pygmy goose. l, Egyptian plover.
12,000k, Spotted hyena.

1996, Apr. 20   Litho.   Perf. 14
951-954	A199	Set of 4		5.00	5.00
955	A199	Sheet of 12, #a.-l.		10.00	10.00

Souvenir Sheet
956	A199	12,000k	multicolored	3.00	3.00

Sheets of 12, #a-i.

Birds — A200

Fowl, each 5500k: No. 957a, California quail. b, Greater prairie chicken. c, Painted quail. d, Golden pheasant. e, Roulroul partridge. f, Ceylon sourfowl. g, Himalayan snowcock. h, Temminicks tragopan. i, Lady Amherst's pheasant. j, Great curassow. k, Red-legged partridge. l, Impeyan pheasant.
Hummingbirds, each 5500k: No. 958a, Anna's. b, Blue-throated. c, Broad-tailed. d, Costa's. e, White-eared. f, Calliope. g, Violet-crowned. h, Rufous. i, Crimson topaz. j, Broad-billed. k, Frilled coquette. l, Ruby-throated.
No. 959, 12,000k, Ring-necked pheasant. No. 960, 12,000k, Racquet-tail hummingbird.

1996, Apr. 20
957-958 A200 Set of 2   20.00 20.00
Souvenir Sheets
959-960 A200 Set of 2   5.50 5.50

Lubrapex '96 — A201

Wild animals: a, 180k, Lions attacking zebra. b, 450k, Zebras, lions, diff. c, 180k, Zebras grazing, lions stalking. d, 450k, Panthera leo. e, 550k, Cheetah. f, 630k, Cheetah running. g, 550k, Cheetah chasing antilope. h, 630k, Cheetah attacking antelope. i, 180k, Antilope (gnu) being attacked by wild dogs. j, 450k, Antelope, wild dogs. k, 180k, Pack of wild dogs. l, 450k, Licaon pictus. m, 550k, Panthera pardus. n, 630k, Oryx. o, 550k, Oryx, diff. p, 630k, Leopard attacking oryx.

1996, Apr. 27
961 A201 Sheet of 16, #a.-p.   9.00 9.00

Sheets of 6, #a.-f.

Ships — A202

Designs, each 6000k: No. 962a, Styrbjorn, Sweden, 1789. b, Constellation, US, 1797. c, Taureau, France, 1865. d, Bomb Ketch, France, 1682. e, Sardegna, Italy, 1881. f, HMS Glasgow, England, 1867.
No. 963a, Essex, US, 1812. b, HMS Inflexible, England, 1881. c, HMS Minotaur, England, 1863. d, Napoleon, France, 1854. e, Sophia Amalia, Denmark, 1650. f, Massena, France, 1887.
No. 964, 12,000k, HMS Tremendous, England, 1806, vert. No. 965, 12,000k, Royal Prince, England, 1666.

1996, May 4
962-963 A202 Set of 2   12.00 12.00
Souvenir Sheets
964-965 A202 Set of 2   10.00 10.00

UN, 50th Anniv. (in 1995) A203

Designs: No. 966, Boys pumping water. No. 967, Man, woman with girl.
8000k, Unloading supplies from ship.

1996, Apr. 27   Litho.   Perf. 14
966 A203 3500k multicolored   1.25 1.25
967 A203 3500k multicolored   1.25 1.25
Souvenir Sheet
968 A203 8000k multicolored   2.75 2.75

Sonangol, 20th Anniv. A204

Face in traditional mask, costume, native birds, and: No. 969, Oil derricks. No. 970, Oil storage tanks, ship. 2500k, Refinery equipment. 5000k, Cargo shipment, jet.

1996, May 12
969 A204 1000k multicolored   .25   .25
970 A204 1000k multicolored   .25   .25
971 A204 2500k multicolored   1.60 1.60
972 A204 5000k multicolored   2.75 2.75
        Nos. 969-972 (4)   4.85 4.85

Brapex '96 — A205

Designs: No. 973, Slaves in hold. No. 974, Slaves fleeing ship as it's overturned. No. 975, Slave boats approaching ship. No. 976, Slaves talking with captain.
50,000k, like No. 975.

1996, Oct. 19   Litho.   Perf. 14
973 A205 20,000k multicolored   2.25 2.25
974 A205 20,000k multicolored   2.25 2.25
975 A205 30,000k multicolored   3.00 3.00
976 A205 30,000k multicolored   3.00 3.00
        Nos. 973-976 (4)   10.50 10.50
Souvenir Sheet
977 A205 50,000k multicolored   8.00 8.00

Churches — A206

Designs: 5,000k, Mission, Huila. No. 979, Church of the Nazarene. No. 980, Church of Our Lady of Pó Pulo. 25,000k, St. Adriáo Church.

1996, Dec. 6   Litho.   Perf. 14
978 A206 5,000k multicolored   .40   .40
979 A206 10,000k multicolored   .90   .90
980 A206 10,000k multicolored   .90   .90
981 A206 25,000k multicolored   2.10 2.10
        Nos. 978-981 (4)   4.30 4.30

1996 Summer Olympic Games, Atlanta A207

5,000k, Handball, vert. 10,000k, Swimming. 25,000k, Track & field, vert. 35,000k, Shooting. 65,000k, Basketball.

1996, Dec. 9
982 A207 5,000k multi   .60   .60
983 A207 10,000k multi   1.25 1.25
984 A207 25,000k multi   3.25 3.25
985 A207 35,000k multi   4.50 4.50
        Nos. 982-985 (4)   9.60 9.60
Souvenir Sheet
986 A207 65,000k multi   6.00 6.00

MPLA (Liberation Movement), 40th Anniv. — A208

1996, Dec. 10   Litho.   Perf. 14
987 A208 30,000k Dolphins, map   3.50 3.50

Trains — A209

Trains — A209a

No. 988: a, AVE, Spain. b, Bullet Train, Japan. c, GM F7 Warbonnet, US. d, Deltic, Great Britain. e, Eurostar, France/Great Britain. f, ETR 450, Italy.
No. 989: a, Class E1300, Morocco. b, ICE, Germany. c, X2000, Sweden. d, TGV Duplex, France.
No. 989E, each 250,000k: f, Steam engine. g, Garrat. h, General Electric.
No. 990, 110,000k, Canadian Pacific 4-4-0, Canada. No. 991, 110,000k, Via Rail Canadian, Canada.

1997, May 29   Litho.   Perf. 14
Sheets of 6, 4 or 3
988 A209 100,000k #a.-f.   8.00 8.00
989 A209 140,000k #a.-d.   8.00 8.00
989E A209a Sheet of 3, #f.-h.   14.00 14.00
Souvenir Sheets
Perf. 13½
990-991 A209 Set of 2   8.00 8.00

Nos. 990-991 contain one 38x50 or 50x38mm stamp, respectively.
PACIFIC 97.

Horses — A210

No. 992: a, Thoroughbred. b, Palomino, appaloosa. c, Arabians. d, Arabian colt. e, Thoroughbred colt. f, Mustang. g, Mustang, diff. h, Furioso.
No. 993: a, Thoroughbred. b, Arabian, palomino. c, Arabian, chincoteague. d, Pintos. e, Przewalski's horse. f, Thoroughbred colt. g, Arabians. h, New forest pony.
No. 994: a, Selle Francais. b, Fjord. c, Percheron. d, Italian heavy draft. e, Shagya Arab. f, Avelignese. g, Czechoslovakian warmblood. h, New forest pony.
215,000k, Thoroughbreds. 220,000k, Thoroughbreds, diff.

1997, July 5   Litho.   Perf. 14
Sheets of 8
992 A210 100,000k #a.-h.   8.50 8.50
993 A210 120,000k #a.-h.   10.00 10.00
994 A210 140,000k #a.-h.   12.50 12.50
Souvenir Sheets
995 A210 215,000k multi   6.00 6.00
996 A210 220,000k multi   6.00 6.00
        PACIFIC 97.

1998 World Cup Soccer Championships, France — A211

Winners holding World Cup trophy: No. 997: a, Uruguay, 1930. b, Germany, 1954. c, Brazil, 1970. d, Argentina, 1986. e, Brazil, 1994.
Winning team pictures: No. 998a, Germany, 1954. b, Uruguay, 1958. c, Italy, 1938. d, Brazil, 1962. e, Brazil, 1970. f, Uruguay, 1930.
220,000k, Angolan team members standing. 250,000k, 1997 Angolan team picture.

1997, July 5   Litho.   Perf. 14
Sheets of 5 or 6
997 A211 100,000k #a.-e. +
         label   9.00 9.00
998 A211 100,000k #a.-f.   10.00 10.00
Souvenir Sheets
999 A211 220,000k multi   5.50 5.50
1000 A211 250,000k multi   5.50 5.50

ENSA (Security System), 20th Anniv. — A212

"Star" emblem, and stylized protection of "egg," each 240,000k: No. 1001, Industry. No. 1002, Recreation. No. 1003, Homes, shelters. No. 1004, Accident prevention.
350,000k, Emblem.

1998   Litho.   Perf. 13½
1001-1004 A212 Set of 4   8.00 8.00
Souvenir Sheet
Perf. 13½x13
1005 A212 350,000k multi   4.00 4.00

No. 1005 contains one 60x40mm stamp.

GURN (Natl. Unity & Reconciliation Government), 1st Anniv. — A213

Emblem, portion of country map and: 100,000k, a, Sea, swordfish, ships, oil derrick. b, Sea, ships, swordfish. c, Sea, swordfish, ships, mining car on railroad track. d, Sea, power lines.
200,000k: e, Train on track, antelope. f, Mining cars on track, tractor pulling cart. g, Railroad track across rivers, tractor plowing. h,

Power lines. i, UR corner of map, crystals. j, Train on track. k, Elephant, tree. l, Trunk of tree, bottom edge of map.

1998
1006 A213 Sheet of 12, #a.-l. 18.00 18.00

Souvenir Sheet

Education in Angola — A214

1998
1007 A214 400,000k multi 6.00 6.00

Diana, Princess of Wales (1961-97) — A215

Various portraits, each 100,000k, color of sheet margin: No. 1008, pale green. No. 1009, pale yellow.
400,000k, Wearing protective clothing.

1998, May 21   Litho.   Perf. 14
Sheets of 6, #a.-f.
1008-1009 A215 Set of 2 20.00 20.00
Souvenir Sheet
1010 A215 400,000k multi 5.00 5.00
See No. 1028.

Expo '98, Lisbon A216

Marine life: No. 1011, 100,000k, Anemones. No. 1012, 100,000k, Sea urchin. No. 1013, 100,000k, Sea horses. No. 1014, 100,000k, Coral (Caravela). No. 1015, 240,000k, Sea slug. No. 1016, 240,000k, Worms (Tunicados).

1998, May 21   Perf. 13½
1011-1016 A216 Set of 6 10.00 10.00

Butterflies — A217

No. 1017, each 120,000k: a, Metamorpha stelene. b, Papilio glaucus. c, Danaus plexippus. d, Catonephele numili. e, Plebejus argus. f, Hypolimnas bolina.
No. 1018, each 120,000k: a, Terinos terpander. b, Bematistes aganice. c, Hebomoia

glaucippe. d, Colias eurytheme. e, Pereute leucodrosime. f, Lycaena dispar.
No. 1019, each 120,000k, horiz.: a, Dynastor napolean. b, Zeuxidia amethystus. c, Battus philenor. d, Phoebis philea. e, Danaus chrysippus. f, Glaucopsyche alexis.
Each 250,000k: No. 1020, Euphaedra neophron. No. 1021, Thecla betulae, horiz. No. 1022, Uraneis ucubis, armillaria staminea.

1998, May 21   Perf. 14
Sheets of 6, #a.-f.
1017-1019 A217 Set of 3 20.00 20.00
Souvenir Sheets
1020-1022 A217 Set of 3 16.00 16.00

Cats and Dogs — A218

Cats, each 140,000k: No. 1023a, British tortoiseshell. b, Chinchilla. c, Russian blue. d, Black Persian (longhair). e, British red tabby. f, Birman.
Dogs, each 140,000k: No. 1024a, West Highland terrier. b, Irish setter. c, Dachshund. d, St. John water dog. e, Shetland sheep dog. f, Dalmatian.
Each 500,000k: No. 1025, Turkish van (swimming cat). No. 1026, Labrador retriever.

1998, May 21   Litho.   Perf. 14x13½
Sheets of 6, #a.-f.
1023-1024 A218 Set of 2 15.00 15.00
Souvenir Sheets
1025-1026 A218 Set of 2 12.00 12.00

Wild Animals — A219

100,000k: a, Panthera leo. b, Hippopotamus amphibius. c, Loxodonta africana. d, Giraffa camelopardalis.
220,000k: e, Syncerus caffer-caffer. f, Gorilla gorilla. g, Ceratotherim simum. h, Oryx gazella.

1998, July 24   Litho.   Perf. 14
1027 A219 Sheet of 8, #a.-h. 12.00 12.00

Diana, Princes of Wales Type of 1998

Pictures showing Diana's campaign to ban land mines, each 150,000k: a, With girl. b, With two boys. c, Wearing protective clothing.

1998, Aug. 31   Litho.   Perf. 14
1028 A215 Strip of 3, #a.-c. 7.00 7.00
No. 1028 was issued in sheets of 6 stamps.

Intl. Year of the Ocean — A220

Marine life: No. 1029a, Pagurites. b, Callinectes marginatus. c, Thais forbesi. d, Ostrea tulipa. e, Balanus amohitrite. f, Uca tangeri.
No. 1030: a, Littorina angulifera. b, Semifusus morio. c, Thais coronata. d, Cerithium atratum (red branch). e, Ostrea tulipa. f, Cerithium atratum (green branch).
Each 300,000k: No. 1031, Goniopsis, horiz. No. 1032, Unidentified shell.

1998, Sept. 4   Sheets of 6
1029 A220 100,000k #a.-f. 5.00 5.00
1030 A220 170,000k #a.-f. 7.00 7.00
Souvenir Sheets
1031-1032 A220 Set of 2 11.00 11.00

Souvenir Sheet

Battle Against Polio in Angola — A221

1998, Aug. 28   Litho.   Perf. 13½
1033 A221 500,000k multicolored 3.75 3.75

Traditional Boats A222

Designs: No. 1034, 250,000k, Boat, Bimba. No. 1035, 250,000k, Canoe with sail, Ndongo. 500,000k, Constructing boat, Ndongo.

1998, Sept. 4   Perf. 14
1034-1036 A222 Set of 3 7.50 7.50

Titanic — A223

Views of Titanic, each 350,000k: a, Under tow. b, Stern. c, Starboard side at night. d, At dock.

1998, Sept. 4
1037 A223 Sheet of 4, #a.-d. 9.00 9.00
No. 1037c is 76x30mm, No. 1037d is 38x61mm.

Angolan Food A224

Various vegetables, fruits: No. 1038, 100,000k, 4 fruits. No. 1039, 100,000k, Squash sliced in half. No. 1040, 120,000k, Ears of corn. No. 1041, 120,000k, Green beans. No. 1042, 140,000k, Fruit with red seeds sliced in half. No. 1043, 140,000k, Sliced bananas.

1998
1038-1043 A224 Set of 6 7.00 7.00
Portugal '98.

Airplanes A225

No. 1044, IL-62 M. No. 1045, B737 100.
No. 1046: a, Ultralight. b, Gyroplane. c, Business jet. d, onvertible plane (e). e, Chuterplane (a, b, d). f, Twin rotors (e). g, Skycrane. h, Aerospatiale Concorde (i). i, Flying boat.
No. 1047: a, Pedal power (b). b, Sail plane (a, e). c, Aerobatic (f). d, Hang gliding (g). e, Balloon (h). f, Glidercraft (e, i). g, Model airplane. h, Air racing (i). i, Solar cells.
No. 1048, 1,000,000k, Boeing 777. No. 1049, 1,000,000k, Columbia Space Shuttle, vert. No. 1049A, 1,000,000k, Boeing 737-200. No. 1049B, 1,000,000k, Boeing 747-300.

1998-99   Litho.   Perf. 14
1044 A225 200,000k multi 1.75 1.75
1045 A225 200,000k multi 1.75 1.75
Sheets of 9
1046 A225 150,000k #a.-i. 5.00 5.00
1047 A225 250,000k #a.-i. 8.00 8.00
Souvenir Sheets
1048-1049B A225 Set of 4 26.00 26.00
Nos. 1048-1049B each contain one 85x28mm stamp.
Issued: Nos. 1049A-1049B, 3/25/99; others 12/24/98.

Dinosaurs — A226

Designs, vert., each 120,000k: No. 1050, Parasaurolophus. No. 1051, Maiasaura. No. 1052, Iguanodon. No. 1053, Elaphosaurus.
No. 1054, vert. 120,000k: a, Brontosaurus. b, Plateosaurus. c, Brachiosaurus. d, Anatosaurus. e, Tyrannosaurus. f, Carnotaurus. g, Corythosaurus. h, Stegosaurus. i, Iguanodon, diff.
No. 1055, 120,000k: a, Hadrosaurus. b, Ouranosaurus. c, Hypsilophodon. d, Brachiosaurus. e, Shunosaurus. f, Amargasaurus. g, Tuojiangosaurus. h, Monoclonius. i, Struthiosaurus.
Each 550,000k: No. 1056, Triceratops, vert. No. 1057, Tyrannosaurus, vert.

1998, Dec. 28
1050-1053 A226 Set of 4 7.00 6.00
Sheets of 9, #a.-i.
1054-1055 A226 Set of 2 17.00 17.00
Souvenir Sheets
1056-1057 A226 Set of 2 8.00 8.00

World Wildlife Fund — A227

Lesser flamingo: a, Facing left. b, Body facing forward. c, Head and neck. d, With wings spread.

Strip of 4

1999		**Litho.**		**Perf. 14**
1058	A227	300,000k #a.-d.	5.00	5.00

No. 1058 was issued in sheets of 16 stamps.

Fauna
A228

Designs, each 300,000k: No. 1059, Equis caballus przewalski. No. 1060, Sphenisciciformes, vert. No. 1061, Haliaeetus leucocephalus, vert. No. 1062, Anodorhynchus hyacinthinus.

No. 1063, 300,000k: a, Vulpes velox hebes. b, Odocoileus. c, Pongo pygmaeus. d, Leontopitecus rosalia. e, Panthera tigris. f, Tragelaphus eurycerus.

No. 1064, 300,000k: a, Tremarctos ornatus. b, Aphelocoma. c, Otus insularis. d, Balaeniceps rex. e, Lepidochelys kempii. f, Lutra canadensis.

Each 1,000,000k: No. 1065, Ailuropoda melanoleuca, vert. No. 1066, Ursus arctos horribilis.

1999

1059-1062	A228	Set of 4	5.00	5.00
Sheets of 6, #a.-f.				
1063-1064	A228	Set of 2	15.00	15.00
Souvenir Sheets				
1065-1066	A228	Set of 2	12.00	12.00

These Flora and Fauna stamps, formerly Nos. 1067-1078, were not authorized by Angola postal authorities.

Other items inscribed "Angola" that were not authorized but which have appeared on the market include sheets with the themes of Disney and History of Animation, Millennium, Animals, Trains, Flora, Muhammad Ali & Lennox Lewis, Bruce Lee, Albert Einstein / Moon Landing, Elvis Presley and other entertainers, Great Personalities, John Kennedy and Marilyn Monroe, Martin Luther King, Jr., Payne Stewart, Colin Montgomerie, Babe Ruth, Cardinal John O'Connor, Pope John Paul II / Mother Teresa and Queen Elizabeth II / Winston Churchill.

World Telecommunications
Day — A230

1999, May 17		**Litho.**		**Perf. 14**
1079	A230	500,000k multi	.75	.75

Souvenir Sheet

Waterfalls — A231

a, Andulo. b, Chiumbo. c, Ruacaná. d, Coemba.

1999, June 5			**Sheet of 4**	
1080	A231	500,000k #a.-d.	3.00	3.00

A232

African Men's Basketball Championships — No. 1081: a, Poster. b, Basketball, hoop, tan background. c, Basketball, hoop, green background. d, Welwitschia plant holding basketball.

2,500,000k, Similar to No. 1081c.

1999, July 29		**Sheet of 4**	**Perf. 13½**	
1081	A232	1,500,000k #a.-d.	4.00	4.00
Souvenir Sheet				
Perf. 13x13½				
1082	A232	2,500,000k multi	2.50	2.50

No. 1082 contains one 40x30mm stamp.
Stamps have one "0" too many in the denominations. Correct denominations would be 1.500.000.00

A233

1999, Aug. 17				**Perf. 14**
1083	A233	1,000,000k multi	1.25	1.25

Southern African Development Community. Issued in sheets of 4. Value $5.

Tribal Kings — A234

No. 782: a, Ekuikui II. b, Mvemba Nzinga. c, Mwata Yamvu Naweji II. d, Njinga Mbande. 1,000,000k, Mandume Ndemufayo.

1999, Sept. 17			**Sheet of 4**	
1084	A234	500,000k #a.-d.	7.50	7.50
Souvenir Sheet				
1085	A234	1,000,000k multi	4.00	4.00

A235

Queen Mother (b. 1900) — No. 1086: a, With King George VI. b, Wearing brooch. c, Wearing tiara. d, Wearing hat.
500,000k, Wearing academic gown.

Sheet of 4

1999, Sept. 17		**Litho.**		**Perf. 14**
1086	A235	200,000k #a.-d.	8.00	8.00
Souvenir Sheet				
Perf. 13¾				
1087	A235	500,000k multi	5.50	5.50

No. 1087 contains one 38x51mm stamp.

Ships — A236

No. 1088, each 950,000k: a, Egyptian bark, 1300 B.C. b, Flemish carrack, 1480. c, Beagle, 1830. d, North Star, 1852. e, Fram, 1892. f, Unyon Maru, 1909. g, Juan Sebastian de Elcano, 1927. h, Tovarishch, 1933.

No. 1089, each 950,000k: a, Bucentauro, 1728. b, Clermont, 1807. c, Savannah, 1819. d, Dromedary, 1844. e, Iberia, 1881. f, S.S. Gluckauf, 1886. g, City of Paris, 1888. h, Mauretania, 1906.

No. 1090, each 950,000k: a, Gloire, 1859. b, L'Ocean, 1868. c, Dandalo, 1876, stern of HMS Dreadnought, 1906. d, Bow of Dreadnought. e, Bismarck, 1939, stern of USS Cleveland, 1946. f, Bow of Cleveland. g, USS Boston, 1942, stern of USS Long Beach, 1959. h, Bow of Long Beach.

Each 5,000,000k: No. 1091, Chinese junk. No. 1092, Madre de Deus, 1609. No. 1093, Catamaran, 1861. No. 1094, Natchez, 1870.

1999, Sept. 23		**Litho.**		**Perf. 14**
Sheets of 8				
1088-1090	A236	Set of 3	27.00	27.00
Souvenir Sheets				
1091-1094	A236	Set of 4	22.00	22.00

Mushrooms
A237

No. 1095, Amanita caesarea. No. 1096, Psalliota xanthoderma. No. 1097, Hygrocybe conica. No. 1098, Boletus chrysenteron. No. 1099, Coprinus comatus. No. 1100, Boletus luteus.

No. 1101: a, Morchella crassipes. b, Boletus rufescens. c, Amanita phalloides. d, Collybia iocephala. e, Tricholoma aurantium. f, Cortinarius violaceus. g, Mycena polygramma. h, Psalliota augusta.

No. 1102: a, Amanita muscaria. b, Boletus aereus. c, Coprinus comatus. d, Amanita

---

rubescens. e, Cortinarius collinitus. f, Boletus satanas. g, Lepiota procera. h, Clitocybe geotropa.

No. 1103: a, Russula nigricans. b, Boletus granulatus. c, Mycena strobilinoides. d, Amanita caesarea. e, Amanita muscaria. f, Boletus, crocipodius. g, Russula virescens. h, Lactarius deliciosus.

No. 1104, Psalliota haemorrhoidaria.
No. 1105, Mycena lilacifolia.

1999, Sept. 23		**Litho.**		**Perf. 14**
1095	A237	1,250,000k multi	1.25	1.00
1096	A237	1,250,000k multi	1.25	1.00
1097	A237	1,250,000k multi	1.25	1.00
1098	A237	1,250,000k multi	1.25	1.00
1099	A237	1,250,000k multi	1.25	1.00
1100	A237	1,250,000k multi	1.25	1.00
Nos. 1095-1100 (6)			7.50	6.00
Sheets of 8				
1101	A237	1,000,000k #a-h	8.00	8.00
1102	A237	1,000,000k #a-h	8.00	8.00
1103	A237	1,000,000k #a-h	8.00	8.00
Souvenir Sheets				
1104	A237	5,000,000k multi	5.50	5.50
1105	A237	5,000,000k multi	5.50	5.50

A238

First Manned Moon Landing, 30th Anniv.
A239

No. 1107: a, Astronaut spacewalking. b, Mariner 8. c, Viking 10. d, GINGA satellite. e, Soyuz 19. f, Voyager.

No. 1108, vert.: a, Space telescope. b, Space shuttle Atlantis. c, Uhuru satellite. d, Mir space station. e, Gemini 7. f, Venera 7.

No. 1109: a, Mercury, Venus. b, Jupiter. c, Neptune, Pluto. d, Earth, Mars. e, Saturn. f, Uranus.

No. 1110: a, Explorer 17. b, Intelsat 4A. c, GOES-D Satellite. d, Intelsat 2. e, Navstar. f, S.M.S.

No. 1111, 6,000,000k, Lunar rover, vert. No. 1112, 6,000,000k, Apollo 17 astronaut on moon, vert. No. 1113, 12,000,000k, Neil Armstrong, vert. No. 1114, 12,000,000k, Space shuttle Columbia. No. 1115, 12,000,000k, SBS-4, vert.

Perf. 13¾ (A238), 14 (A239)				
1999, Nov. 15				**Litho.**
Sheets of 6, #a.-f.				
1107-1108	A238	3,500,000k	10.00	10.00
1109-1110	A239	3,500,000k	10.00	10.00
Souvenir Sheets				
1111-1112	A238	Set of 2	8.00	8.00
1113-1115	A239	Set of 3	16.00	16.00

Hokusai Paintings — A240

No. 1116, each 3,500,000k: a, Night attack. b, Usigafuchi No Kudan. c, Drawing of man and bowl. d, Wildlife. e, Pheasant. f, People on bridge.

No. 1117, each 3,500,000k: a, Tree and shoreline. b, Kabuki theater. c, Hen. d, Cooper. e, Trip to Enoshima. f, Sumida River landscape.

Each 12,000,000k: No. 1118, Yama-uba and Kintori, vert. No. 1119, Woman, vert.

1999, Dec. 13   Litho.   Perf. 13¾
Sheets of 6, #a.-f.
1116-1117 A240 Set of 2   18.00 18.00
Souvenir Sheets
1118-1119 A240 Set of 2   12.00 12.00

On Dec. 13, the date of issue of these stamps, Angola devalued its currency, with approximately 1,000,000k being the equivalent of 1k after the devaluation.

Souvenir Sheets

PhilexFrance 99 — A241

No. 1120, 4-8-4 Linder Compound express. No. 1121, Hovertrain prototype.

2000, Mar. 13   Litho.   Perf. 13¾
1120-1121 A241 12k Set of 2   11.00 11.00

A242

Wildlife — A243

1.50k, Zebra. 2k, Fruit bat. 3k, California condor. 5.50k, Lion.
No. 1126, horiz.: a, Equus zebra. b, Ploceus xanthops. c, Lycaon protus. d, Acinonyx jubatus. e, Oryx gazella. f, Nursing Otocyon megalotis. g, Giraffa camelopardalis. h, Canis adustus. i, Perodicticus potto. j, Panthera leo. k, Coracius caudata. l, Pair of Otocyon megalotis.
No. 1127, horiz.: a, Struthio camelus. b, Felis lybica. c, Aepyceros melampus. d, Cercopithecus aethiops. e, Diceros bicornis. f, Papio sp. g, Felis caracal. h, Sagittarius serpentarius. i, Phacochoerus aethiopicus. j, Arctocephalus pusillus. k, Alcedo cristata. l, Hippopotamus amphibius.
No. 1128, 3.50k: a, Deer. b, Turkey. c, Beaver. d, Frog. e, Manatee. f, Trout.
No. 1129, 3.50k: a, Macaque. b, Toucan. c, Bothriopsis bilineata. d, Hyla leucopyliata. e, Tamarin. f, Eagle.
No. 1130, 3.50k, vert.: a, Mountain gorilla. b, Rhinoceros. c, Water buffalo. d, Chameleon. e, Cobra. f, Meerkats.
No. 1131, 3.50k, vert.: a, Kangaroo. b, Koala. c, Kingfishers. d, Frog on tree root. e, Three fish. f, Turtle.
No. 1132, 12k, Sloth. No. 1133, 12k, Lemur, vert. No. 1134, 12k, Cheetah, vert. No. 1135, 12k, Orangutan, vert. No. 1136, 12k, Cercopithecus aethiops, diff. No. 1137, 12k, Loxodonta africana.

2000, Apr. 7   Perf. 14
1122-1125 A242 Set of 4   6.00 6.00
1126 A243 1.50k Sheet of 12, #a-l   9.00 9.00
1127 A243 2k Sheet of 12, #a-l   13.00 13.00

Sheets of 6, #a-f
1128-1131 A242 Set of 4   40.00 40.00
Souvenir Sheets
1132-1135 A242 Set of 4   24.00 24.00
1136-1137 A243 Set of 2   12.00 12.00

Birds of Prey
A244

1.50k, Harpy eagle. 2k, Unidentified bird. 3k, Vulture, vert. 5.50k, King vulture, vert.
No. 1142, 3.50k: a, Accipiter gentilis. b, Surnia ulula. c, Falco peregrinus. d, Otus asio. e, Haliacetus vocifer. f, Herpetotheres cachinnans.
No. 1143, 3.50k: a, Falco sparverius. b, Pulsetrix perspicillata. c, Elemus leucurus. d, Ninox novaeseelandiae. e, Polemaetus bellicosus. f, Polyborus plancus.
No. 1144, 6.50k: a, Verreaux's eagle. b, Aguia gigante. c, Aguia peixe.
No. 1145, 6.50k, vert.: a, Aguia despeida. b, Aguia dourada. c, Aguia devoradora de macacos.
No. 1146, 12k, King vulture, diff. No. 1147, 12k, Falcon, vert. No. 1148, 15k, Sagittarius serpentarius. No. 1149, 15k, Aquila chrysaetos.

2000, Apr. 10
1138-1141 A244 Set of 4   5.50 5.50
Sheets of 6, #a-f
1142-1143 A244 Set of 2   19.00 19.00
Sheets of 3, #a-c
1144-1145 A244 Set of 2   18.00 18.00
Souvenir Sheets
1146-1147 A244 Set of 2   12.00 12.00
1148-1149 A244 Set of 2   13.00 13.00

Millennium — A245

Highlights of the 16th Century: a, Paintings by Lai-Ji. b, The Last Judgment, by Luca Signorelli. c, Garden of Earthly Delights by Hieronymus Bosch. d, The Prince, written by Niccolò Machiavelli. e, Utopia, written by Sir Thomas More. f, Martin Luther. g, Charles I of Spain becomes Holy Roman Emperor Charles V. h, The School of Athens, by Raphael. i, Juan Sebastián de Elcano circumnavigates globe. j, Henry VIII of England. k, Spanish conquest of Aztecs and Incas. l, Placentia Cathedral. m, Potatoes introduced to Europe. n, Heliocentric theory of Copernicus. o, Portuguese reach Japan. p, Death of Albrecht Dürer (60x40mm). q, Bartolomé de Las Casas promotes rights for Indians.

2000, Oct. 2   Litho.   Perf. 12¾x12½
1150 A245 2.50k Sheet of 17, #a-q, + label   24.00 24.00

War Damage in Angola
A246

Designs: No. 1151, 3k, B.N.A. Building, Kuito. No. 1152, 3k, Kunje St., Kuito. No. 1153, 4k, Post office. No. 1154, 4k, Police headquarters. No. 1155, 5k, Apartment house. No. 1157, 6k, Child waving from upper floor of apartment house. No. 1158, 6k, Building, man carrying pack.

2000, Sept. 29   Litho.   Perf. 14
1151-1158 A246 Set of 8   18.00 18.00

Popes — A247

No. 1159, 3k: a, Nicholas II, 1059-61. b, Paschal II, 1099-1118. c, Sergius IV, 1009-1012. d, Victor II, 1055-57. e, Victor III, 1086-87. f, Urban III, 1185-87.
No. 1160, 3k: a, Innocent II, 1130-43. b, John XIII, 965-72. c, Agapetus II, 946-55. d, John XV, 985-96. e, John XVIII, 1003-09. f, Lucius II, 1144-45.
No. 1161, 3k: a, Celestine II, 1143-44. b, Clement II, 1046-47. c, Clement III, 1187-91. d, Gelasius II, 1118-19. e, Benedict VII, 974-83. f, Gregory V, 996-99.
No. 1162, 12k, Leo IX, 1049-54. No. 1163, 12k, Gregory VII, 1073-85. No. 1164, 12k, Leo XIII, 1878-1903.

2000, Oct. 2   Perf. 12x12¼
Sheets of 6, #a-f
1159-1161 A247 Set of 3   27.00 27.00
Souvenir Sheets
1162-1164 A247 Set of 3   18.00 18.00

Monarchs — A248

No. 1165, 3k: a, Henry II, King of Germany and Holy Roman Emperor, 1002-24. b, Marina Mniszek, wife of false Russian czar Dmitri, 1605-06. c, Ivan IV of Russia, 1533-84. d, Ivan III of Russia, 1462-1505.
No. 1166, 3k: a, Charles II of Great Britain, 1660-85. b, Lady Jane Grey of England, 1533. c, Leopold III of Belgium, 1934-51. d, Louis XV of France, 1715-74.
No. 1167, 3k: a, James I of Great Britain, 1603-25. b, James II of Great Britain, 1685-88. c, James IV of Scotland, 1567-1625. d, Brian Boru of Ireland, 1002-14. e, Wilhelm I, King of Prussia and German Emperor, 1861-88. f, Edward VI of England, 1547-53.
No. 1168, 12k, Feodor I of Russia, 1584-98. No. 1169, 12k, False Russian czar Dmitri, 1605-06. No. 1170, 12k, William IV of Great Britain, 1830-37.

2000, Oct. 2   Sheets of 4, #a-d
1165-1166 A248 Set of 2   12.50 12.50
1167 A248 Sheet of 6, #a-f   9.50 9.50
Souvenir Sheets
1168-1170 A248 Set of 3   18.00 18.00

Children's Drawings
A249

Various designs. Denominations: 3k, 4k, 5k.

2000, Nov. 7   Perf. 14
1171-1173 A249 Set of 3   4.75 4.75

Post Office Buildings
A250

Designs: No. 1174, 5k, Former Secretary of Communications Building, Luanda. No. 1175, 5k, Mbanza Congo Post Office. No. 1176, 5k, Namibe Post Office. No. 1177, 8k, Facade of Luanda Post Office. No. 1178, 8k, Luanda Post Office, diff. No. 1179, 8k, Lobito Post Office.

2000, Sept. 29   Litho.   Perf. 14
1174-1179 A250 Set of 6   8.50 8.50

National Radio and Television, 25th Anniv. — A251

No. 1180, 9.50k: a, Woman at computer in newsroom. b, Reporter with tape recorder reporting on tank battle. c, Rescuing victims from airplane crash.
No. 1181, 9.50k: a, People and equipment in newsroom. b, Cameraman filming tank battle. c, Refugees.
No. 1182, 20k, Reporter with tape recorder. No. 1183, 20k, Cameraman, vert.

Perf. 13¼x13½, 13½x13¼
2000, Dec. 7   Sheets of 3, #a-c
1180-1181 A251 Set of 2   12.00 12.00
Souvenir Sheets
1182-1183 A251 Set of 2   8.00 8.00

Souvenir Sheet

Independence, 25th Anniv. — A252

No. 1184: a, Tank, rifle, dove. b, Dove, hoe, tractor.

2001, Feb. 13   Litho.   Perf. 14¼x14
1184 A252 12k Sheet of 2, #a-b   5.00 5.00

Africa Day
A253

Designs: No. 1185, 10k, Shown. No. 1186, 10k, Xylophone.
30k, Map, musical instruments, native with mask, elephant, satellite dishes and computer.

2001, May 25   Perf. 13x13¼
1185-1186 A253 Set of 2   4.00 4.00
Souvenir Sheet
1187 A253 30k multi   6.00 6.00

Flowers
A254

Butterfly and: 8k, Nicolaia speciosa. 9k, Allamanda cathartica. No. 1190, 10k, Welwitschia mirabilis. No. 1191, 10k, Tagetes patula. 30k, Welwitschia mirabilis.

2001, June 9
1188-1191 A254 Set of 4   7.75 7.75
Souvenir Sheet
1192 A254 30k multi   6.50 6.50

Belgica 2001 Intl. Stamp Exhibition, Brussels (No. 1192).

Souvenir Sheet

Total Solar Eclipse, June 21 — A255

2001, June 21
1193 A255 30k multi   6.50 6.50

Fish
A256

Designs: 11k, Protopterus annectens. 17k, Protopterus amphibius. 18k, Tilapia ruweti. 36k, Tilapia rendalli.

     Perf. 13½x13¼
2001, Sept. 28   **Litho.**
1194-1196 A256 Set of 3   7.75 7.75
Souvenir Sheet
     Perf. 13x13¼
1197 A256 36k multi   6.00 6.00

Traditional
Dances and
Costumes
A257

Designs: No. 1198, 11k, Massemba. No. 1199, 11k, Ovambo Efundula. 17k, Macolo Batuque. No. 1201, 18k, Humbi Puberty. No. 1202, 18k, Mukixi. 36k, Carneval.

2001, Nov. 12   **Perf. 13x13¼**
1198-1202 A257 Set of 5   11.00 11.00
Souvenir Sheet
1203 A257 36k multi   5.50 5.50

Souvenir Sheet

Handmade Weaving — A258

No. 1204: a, 17k, Banda. b, 18k, Kijinga.

2001, Dec. 7
1204 A258 Sheet of 2, #a-b   5.25 5.25

Minerals
A259

Designs: No. 1205, 11k, Hematite. No. 1206, 11k, Malachite. No. 1207, 18k, Psilomelane. No. 1208, 18k, Diamond.

2001, Dec. 14   **Perf. 13½x13¼**
1205-1208 A259 Set of 4   8.50 8.50

Masks — A260

Designs: 10k, Mwana Mpwevo. No. 1210, 11k, Mukixi. No. 1211, 11k, Mbunda. 17k, Mwana Pwo. 18k, Likisi-Cinganji. 36k, Ndemba, horiz.

2002, Jan. 8   **Perf. 13¼x13½**
1209-1213 A260 Set of 5   10.00 10.00
Souvenir Sheet
     Perf. 13x13¼
1214 A260 36k multi   5.50 5.50

2002 World Cup Soccer
Championships, Japan and
Korea — A261

Two players and: 35k, Ball in air. 37k, Ball on ground.

2002, June 28   **Perf. 13x13¼**
1215-1216 A261 Set of 2   11.00 11.00
1216a   Souvenir sheet, #1215-
     1216   10.00 10.00

Meeting of
African
Committee
of
International
Socialists
A262

Designs: No. 1217, 10k, Fight against poverty (red and orange map of Africa). No. 1218, 10k, Abolition of the death penalty (man with target on chest). No. 1219, 10k, End to violence against women (stylized woman). No. 1220, 10k, Fight against poverty (masks). No. 1221, 10k, Annulment of foreign debt (map of Africa with dollar sign)

2002, July 12
1217-1221 A262 Set of 5   7.50 7.50
1221a   Souvenir sheet, #1218-
     1221   6.00 6.00

National Peace and
Reconciliation — A263

2002, Oct. 9
1222 A263 35k multi   2.75 2.75

Reptiles
A264

Designs: 21k, Pithon anchietae. 35k, Lacerta sp. 37k, Naja nigricollis. 40k, Crocodylus niloticus.

2002, Oct. 15   **Perf. 13x13¼**
1223-1226 A264 Set of 4   10.00 10.00

Lighthouses
and Buoys
A265

Designs: No. 1227, 45k, Tafe. No. 1228, 45k, Red buoy, Luanda Bay. No. 1229, 45k, Green buoy, Luanda Bay. No. 1230, 45k, Cabeça da Cobra. No. 1231, 45k, Barra do Dande. No. 1232, 45k, Moita Seca.

2002, Nov. 22
1227-1232 A265 Set of 6   20.00 20.00

Souvenir Sheet

Dec. 4, 2002 Total Solar
Eclipse — A266

No. 1233: a, 21k, Sun partially eclipsed. b, 35k, Sun mostly eclipsed. c, 37k, Sun totally eclipsed.

2002, Dec. 4
1233 A266 Sheet of 3, #a-c   7.00 7.00

Angola -
Italy
Friendship
A267

António Manuel, Prince of N'Funta and Ambassador of Congo to Rome (d. 1608), and: 35k, Lion. 45k, Plaque with Italian inscription.

2002, Dec. 6
1234-1235 A267 Set of 2   6.00 6.00
1235a   Souvenir sheet, #1234-
     1235   6.00 6.00

Pottery
A268

Designs: 27k, Omolingui. 45k, Mulondo. 47k, Ombya yo Tuma. 51k, Sanga.

2002, Dec. 7   **Litho.**
1236-1238 A268 Set of 3   8.50 8.50
Souvenir Sheet
1239 A268 51k multi   4.00 4.00

United Nations 3rd Meeting on
Science, Technology and
Development — A269

2003, May 30   **Perf. 13x13¼**
1240 A269 50k multi   3.75 3.75

Powered
Flight, Cent.
A270

2003, Aug. 21   Litho.   Perf. 13x13½
1241 A270 25k multi   1.90 1.90

Printed in sheets of 3 stamps + label.

Poets
A271

Designs: No. 1242, 27k, António Jacinto (1924-91) and poem. No. 1243, 45k, Agostinho Neto (1922-79) and poem. No. 1244: a, 27k, Jacinto. b, 45k, Neto.

2003, Sept. 18   Litho.   Perf. 13x13¼
1242-1243 A271 Set of 2   5.00 5.00
Souvenir Sheet
1244 A271 Sheet of 2, #a-b   5.00 5.00

Hippotragus
Niger
A272

Designs: 27k, Pair with curved horns. 45k, Pair with straight horns. 47k, With herd in background.

2003, Oct. 9
1245-1247 A272 Set of 3   8.50 8.50

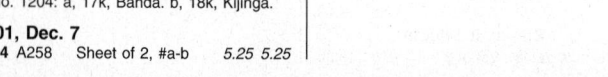

Women's Hairstyles — A273

No. 1248: a, Mbunda. b, Soyo. c, Huila. d, Humbi. e, Cabinda. f, Quipungu.

2003, Nov. 10   **Perf. 13¼x13**
1248 A273 25k Sheet of 6, #a-
     f   10.00 10.00

Whales
A274

Designs: 27k, Balaenoptera edeni. 45k, Cephalorhynchus heavisidii.
No. 1251: a, 47k, Giobiocephaia melaena.

2003, Dec. 5   Perf. 14¾x14¼
1249-1250 A274   Set of 2   5.00 5.00

Souvenir Sheet
1251 A274   Sheet, #1249,
                1251a   5.50 5.50

Christmas — A275

No. 1252, 27k: a, The Ascension, attributed to Jorge Afonso. b, Adoration of the Shepherds, by André Reinoso.
No. 1253, 45k: a, Adoration of the Shepherds, detail showing Holy Family, by Josefa de Obidos. b, Adoration of the Shepherds, detail showing angels, by de Obidos.

2003, Dec. 5   Perf. 13¼x13¾
Horiz. Pairs, #a-b
1252-1253 A275   Set of 2   10.00 10.00
1253c   Souvenir sheet, #1252a-
             1252b, 1253a-1253b   10.00 10.00

Chess — A276

No. 1254: a, Chess pieces. b, Chess pieces and board.

2003, Dec. 10
1254 A276 45k Horiz. pair, #a-b   6.50 6.50

Eagles
A277

Designs: No. 1255, 20k, Aquila rapax. No. 1256, 20k, Polemaetus bellicosus. No. 1257, 25k, Haliaeetus vocifer. No. 1258, 25k, Terathopius ecaudatus.
45k, Aquila verreauxi.

2003, Dec. 10   Perf. 14¾x14¼
1255-1258 A277   Set of 4   6.50 6.50
Souvenir Sheet
1259 A277 45k multi   3.25 3.25

Election of Pope John Paul II, 25th Anniv. — A278

No. 1260: a, Portrait. b, Pope waving.

2003, Dec. 15   Perf. 13¼x13¾
1260 A278 27k Horiz. pair, #a-b,
            + central label   4.00 4.00

Flora
A279

Designs: No. 1261, 27k, Psidium guayava. No. 1262, 27k, Adansonia digitata. No. 1263, 45k, Cymbopogon citratus. No. 1264, 45k, Carica papaya.

2004, Aug. 17 Litho.   Perf. 14x13½
1261-1264 A279   Set of 4   6.00 6.00
1264a   Souvenir sheet, #1261-
             1264   6.00 6.00

2004 Summer Olympics, Athens — A280

Designs: No. 1265, 27k, Handball. No. 1266, 27k, Basketball. No. 1267, 45k, Track. No. 1268, 45k, Volleyball.

2004, Sept. 30   Perf. 13¾
1265-1268 A280   Set of 4   6.00 6.00

Marine Mammals A281

No. 1269: a, Megaptera novaeangliae. b, Cephalorhynchus heavisidii. c, Tursiops truncatus.
99k, Megaptera novaeangliae, diff.

2004, Oct. 9   Perf. 14x13½
1269   Horiz. strip of 3   4.00 4.00
a.-b.   A281 27k Either single   1.10 1.10
c.   A281 45k multi   1.75 1.75
Souvenir Sheet
1270 A281 99k multi   4.00 4.00

A sheetlet of eight hexagonal 15k depicting the national birds of South African Postal Operators Association (SAPOA) countries was produced in extremely limited quantities. Sheetlet inscribed Angola, value $300.

Trains A282

Designs: No. 1271, 27k, shown. No. 1272, 27k, Benguela Locomotive 225. No. 1273, 27k, Moçamedes locomotive.

2004, Nov. 30   Perf. 13¾
1271-1273 A282   Set of 3   3.25 3.25

Fire Fighting A283

Telephone, emergency number and: No. 1274, 27k, Fire fighter with hose. No. 1275, 27k, Fire truck. 45k, Fire truck, diff.

2004, Nov. 30
1274-1276 A283   Set of 3   4.00 4.00
1276a   Souvenir sheet, #1274-
             1276   4.00 4.00

FIFA (Fédération Internationale de Football Association), Cent. — A284

2004, Dec. 7
1277 A284 45k multi   1.90 1.90

Christmas — A285

No. 1278: a, 27k, Magi. b, 45k Holy Family.

2004, Dec. 14 Litho.   Perf. 13¾
1278 A285   Horiz. pair, #a-b   3.00 3.00

Worldwide Fund for Nature (WWF) — A286

No. 1279 — Colobus angolensis: a, Pair of adults. b, Adult and juvenile. c, Close-up of adult's face. d, Adult on rock.

2004, Dec. 29 Litho.   Perf. 13¾
1279 A286 27k Block of 4, #a-d   4.00 4.00

Rotary International, Cent. — A287

Woman and: 45k, City. 51k, Ostriches.

2005, Feb. 23 Litho.   Perf. 13x13¼
1280-1281 A287   Set of 2   4.00 4.00
1281a   Souvenir sheet, #1280-
             1281   4.00 4.00

Basketry A288

Designs: No. 1282, 27k, Kinda Kya Kuzambuila. No. 1283, 27k, Ngyendu. No. 1284, 45k, Ngombo Ya Cisuka. No. 1285, 45k, Silo.
90k, Kinda Kya Kuzambuila, diff.

2005, Sept. 6 Litho.   Perf. 12x12½
1282-1285 A288   Set of 4   12.00 12.00
Souvenir Sheet
1286 A288 90k multi   20.00 20.00
Expo 2005, Aichi, Japan.

Independence, 30th Anniv. — A289

Designs: 27k, Capanda Hydroelectric Dam. 45k, Presidents Agostinho Neto and José Eduardo dos Santos, Angolan flag and dove.

2005, Nov. 8   Litho.   Perf. 12x12½
1287-1288 A289   Set of 2   5.50 5.50

Souvenir Sheet

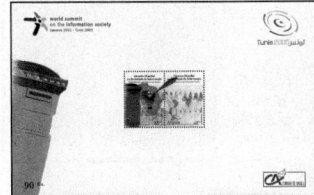
World Summit on the Information Society, Tunis — A290

No. 1289: a, Mail box, map of Africa, dish antenna, Angolan. b, Computer, world map, dish antenna.

2005, Nov. 14   Litho.   Perf. 12
1289 A290 45k Sheet of 2, #a-
              b   20.00 20.00

Souvenir Sheet

23rd Ministerial Conference of the African Oil Producing Countries — A291

Design: 51p, Off-shore oil rig.

2006, Apr. 24 Litho.   Perf. 12x12½
1294 A291 51k multi   —   —

Four additional stamps were issued in this set. The editors would like to examine any examples.

A292

2006 World Cup Soccer Championships, Germany — A293

2006, Aug. 30   Perf. 12x11¾
1295 A292 45k shown   3.00 3.00
1296 A293 45k shown   3.00 3.00
Souvenir Sheet
1297 A293 90k Player dribbling   4.50 4.50
Nos. 1295-1297 lack country name.

Community of Portuguese Language Nations, 10th Anniv. — A294

Anniversary emblem, emblem of 2006 Lubrapex Intl. Stamp Exhibition and: 27k,

Dogs. No. 1299, 45k, Vultures. No. 1300, 45k, Parrots.

2006, Oct. 30   Litho.   Perf. 12x11¾
1298-1300 A294   Set of 3   6.00 6.00

Nos. 1298-1300 lack country name.

National Bank of Angola, 30th Anniv. A295

Designs: No. 1301, 27k, Bird in flight, people in boat, ship, Katanga cross currency. No. 1302, 27k, Men, cowrie shells. No. 1303, 45k, Early automobile, coins. No. 1304, 45k, Building, banknotes.
90k, Dome, luggage

2006, Nov. 7
1301-1304 A295   Set of 4   7.50 7.50
Souvenir Sheet
1305 A295 90k multi   7.00 7.00

José Sayovo, First Angolan Paralympian Gold Medalist — A296

2006, Dec. 29   Litho.   Perf. 12x11¾
1306 A296 45k multi   1.10 1.10

Peace, 5th Anniv. A297

2007, Apr. 20   Litho.   Perf. 13x13½
1307 A297 51k multi   1.75 1.75

52nd Venice Art Biennale A298

Designs: 65k, Entire painting. 155k, Painting detail.

2007, Apr. 20   Perf. 13x13½
1308 A298 65k multi   1.90 1.90
Souvenir Sheet
Perf. 13½x13
1309 A298 155k multi   4.50 4.50

No. 1309 contains one 60x40mm stamp.

Souvenir Sheet

Africa Day — A299

2007, Apr. 20   Perf. 13½x13
1310 A299 130k multi   3.75 3.75

Scouting, Cent. — A300

No. 1311: a, 30k, Scouts sitting in fleur-de-lis pattern. b, 30k, Scouts sitting at desks. c, 55k, Scouts sitting on ground. d, 65k, Scouts saluting.
130k, Group of scouts standing on steps.

2007, June 1   Perf. 13x13½
1311 A300   Sheet of 4, #a-d   5.50 5.50
Souvenir Sheet
Perf. 13½x13
1312 A300 130k multi   4.00 4.00

No. 1312 contains one 60x40mm stamp.

Souvenir Sheet

Southern African Development Community, 27th Anniv. — A301

2007, Aug. 17   Perf. 12½x13
1313 A301 150k multi   8.00 8.00

Souvenir Sheet

Sports — A302

Perf. 13¼ Syncopated
2007, Sept. 20
1314 A302 130k multi   4.00 4.00

Souvenir Sheet

World Post Day — A303

No. 1315 — Post office at: a, Malange. b, Huamba.

2007, Oct. 9   Perf. 12¾x13½
1315 A303 45k Sheet of 2, #a-b   2.75 2.75

Sea Turtles — A304

No. 1316: a, 27k, Caretta caretta. b, 27k, Chelonia mydas. c, 45k, Eretmochelys imbricata. d, 45k, Lepidochelys olivacea.
130k, Dermochelys coriacea, vert.

2007, Nov. 11   Perf. 13x13¼
1316 A304   Sheet of 4, #a-d   4.50 4.50
Souvenir Sheet
Perf. 13¼ Syncopated
1317 A304 130k multi   4.00 4.00

No. 1317 contains one 38x39mm stamp.

Angolan Cuisine A305

Various unnamed Angolan dishes: 37k, 40k, 59k, 153k.

2008, May 30   Perf. 13x13½
1318-1320 A305   Set of 3   7.00 7.00
Souvenir Sheet
1321 A305 153k multi   13.00 13.00

Water Resources A306

Designs: No. 1322, 37k, Kuebe River. No. 1323, 37k, Kuanza Rapids. No. 1324, 40k, Kuanza River. No. 1325, 40k, Mouth of Mbridge River.
153k, Kalandula Waterfalls.

2008, June 30   Perf. 13x13½
1322-1325 A306   Set of 4   8.00 8.00
Souvenir Sheet
1326 A306 153k multi   8.00 8.00

Miniature Sheet

Lwini Fund, 10th Anniv. — A307

No. 1327: a, 37k, Land mine removal, vert. b, 40k, Wooden box and books. c, 40k, Princess Diana and Angolan woman. d, 59k, Children in wheelchairs. e, 59k, Men making baskets.

Perf. 13½x13, 13x13½ (37k)
2008, June 30
1327 A307   Sheet of 5, #a-e, + label   10.00 10.00

Water Jugs — A308

Designs: No. 1328, 37k, Jug with head on top. No. 1329, 37k, Two-handled jug. No. 1330, 40k, Jug with handle and spout. No. 1331, 40k, Jug with woman on top.

2008, July 30   Perf. 13½x13
1328-1331 A308   Set of 4   8.50 8.50

Mangroves on Chiloango River A309

Designs: No. 1332, 37k, Roots. No. 1333, 37k, Trees along river. 59k, Roots, diff.

2008, Aug. 30   Perf. 13x13½
1332-1334 A309   Set of 3   7.00 7.00

Miniature Sheet

2008 Summer Olympics, Beijing — A310

No. 1335: a, Basketball. b, Handball. c, Running. d, Canoeing.

2008, Sept. 20   Perf. 12¾x13½
1335 A310 30k Sheet of 4, #a-d   5.00 5.00

Coffee — A311

Designs: 37k, Coffee berries. No. 1337, 45k, Woman picking berries, horiz. No. 1338, 45k, Tree with berries.

Perf. 13¼x13, 13x13¼
2009, Dec. 7   Litho.
Granite Paper
1336-1338 A311   Set of 3   4.00 4.00

Pres. Antonio Agostinho Neto (1922-79) — A312

Pres. Neto: 40k, Behind lectern. 50k, In army uniform.
150k, Pres. Neto with school children, horiz.

2009, Dec. 7   **Granite Paper**
1339-1340 A312 Set of 2   2.75 2.75
Souvenir Sheet
1341 A312 150k multi   4.25 4.25

Souvenir Sheet

Pope Benedict XVI — A313

2009, Dec. 7   **Perf. 13¼x13**
Granite Paper
1342 A313 100k multi + label   4.00 4.00

2010 Africa Cup of Nations Soccer Tournament, Angola — A314

Stadiums in: No. 1343, 40k, Benguela. No. 1344, 40k, Cabinda. No. 1345, 50k, Luanda. No. 1346, 50k, Huilá.

2010, Jan. 8   **Perf. 13x13¼**
Granite Paper
1343-1346 A314 Set of 4   5.00 5.00

Africa Day A315

Designs: 40k, People from Uige and Zaire Provinces. 60k, People from Lunda and Moxico Provinces. 120k, People from Luanda Province.

2010   **Perf. 13x13¼**
1348-1349 A315 Set of 2   2.75 2.75
Souvenir Sheet
Perf. 13¼ Syncopated
1350 A315 120k multi   3.75 3.75

Expo 2010, Shanghai. No. 1350 contains one 50x39mm stamp.

African Women's Day — A316

Designs: No. 1351, 60k, Kwanhama woman. No. 1352, 60k, Quipungo woman. 150k, Mucubal woman.

2010   **Perf. 13¼x13**
1351-1352 A316 Set of 2   3.25 3.25
Souvenir Sheet
Perf. 13¼ Syncopated
1353 A316 150k multi   4.00 4.00

Expo 2010, Shanghai. No. 1353 contains one 39x50mm stamp.

Intl. Children's Day A317

Children, flowers and wildlife with background color of: No. 1354, 40k, Green. No. 1355, 40k, Orange. No. 1356, 60k, Blue. No. 1357, 60k, Green. 150k, Orange.

2010   **Perf. 13x13¼**
1354-1357 A317 Set of 4   5.00 5.00
Souvenir Sheet
Perf. 13¼ Syncopated
1358 A317 150k multi   4.25 4.25

Expo 2010, Shanghai. No. 1358 contains one 50x39mm stamp.

Organization of Petroleum Exporting Countries, 50th Anniv. — A318

50th anniversary emblem with Angolan flag and: 40k, Antelope. 50k, Statue. 60k, Offshore oil drilling platform. 150k, Off-shore oil drilling platform and other equipment.

2010, Oct.   **Perf. 13x13¼**
1359-1361 A318 Set of 3   3.25 3.25
Souvenir Sheet
Perf. 13½ Syncopated
1362 A318 150k multi   3.25 3.25

No. 1362 contains one 50x39mm stamp.

Portuguese Agency for External Investment and Commerce, 20th Anniv. — A319

2010, Nov.   **Perf. 13x13¼**
1363 A319 60k multi   1.40 1.40

Worldwide Fund for Nature (WWF) A320

No. 1364: a, Two Cercopithecus cephus, one on rock at left. b, Three Cercopithecus ascanius. c, Two Cercopithecus ascanius. d, Two Cercopithecus cephus, one on branch at right.
350k, Cercopithecus cephus and Cercopithecus ascanius, vert.

2011, Aug. 31   **Perf. 13x13¼**
1364 Strip of 4, #a-d   9.00 9.00
  a.-d. A320 100k Any single   2.25 2.25
  e. Souvenir sheet of 8, 2 each #1364a-1364d   18.00 18.00
Souvenir Sheet
Perf. 13¼
1365 A320 350k multi   7.50 7.50

No. 1365 contains one 39x45mm stamp.

A321

A322

A323

Southern African Development Community, 31st Anniv. — A324

Design: 150k, Emblem and map of Africa, diff.

2011, Aug. 12   **Perf. 13x13¼**
1366 A321 50k multi   1.10 1.10
1367 A322 50k multi   1.10 1.10
1368 A323 50k multi   1.10 1.10
1369 A324 50k multi   1.10 1.10
  Nos. 1366-1369 (4)   4.40 4.40
Souvenir Sheet
Perf. 13½
1370 A324 150k multi   3.25 3.25

Peonies — A325

No. 1371: a, Paeonia daurica. b, Paeonia mlokosewitschii. c, Paeonia veitchii. d, Paeonia broteri.
350k, Paeonia officinalis salmonea.

2011, Apr. 31   **Perf. 13¼x13**
1371 Horiz. strip of 4   9.00 9.00
  a.-d. A325 100k Any single   2.25 2.25
  e. Souvenir sheet of 4, #1371a-1371d   9.00 9.00
Souvenir Sheet
Perf. 13½
1372 A325 350k multi   7.50 7.50

China 2011 International Stamp Exhibition, Wuxi. No. 1372 contains one 39x45mm stamp.

National Bank of Angola, 35th Anniv. A326

Emblem and: 40k, Ornamental planter. 50k, Crest on exterior wall. No. 1375, 60k, Roof ornament. No. 1376, 60k, Windows near corner of building.
150k, Aerial view of building.

2011, Nov. 4   **Perf. 13x13¼**
1373-1376 A326 Set of 4   4.50 4.50
Souvenir Sheet
Perf. 13x13¼ Syncopated
1377 A326 150k multi   3.25 3.25

No. 1377 contains one 50x39mm stamp.

Fauna, Flora and Mushrooms A344

Designs: No. 1420, 300k, Adult and juvenile Diceros bicornis. No. 1421, 300k, Adult Diceros bicornis facing right. No. 1422, 300k, One Ceratotherium simum. No. 1423, 300k, Two Ceratotherium simum. No. 1424, 300k, Head of Giraffa camelopardalis angolensis. No. 1425, 300k, Front view of Giraffa camelopardalis angolensis drinking water. No. 1426, 300k, Side view of Giraffa camelopardalis angolensis with head lowered. No. 1427, 300k, Six adult and juvenile Giraffa camelopardalis angolensis. No. 1428, 300k, Galagoides demidoff. No. 1429, 300k, Allenopithecus nigroviridis. No. 1430, 300k, Lophocebus aterrimus. No. 1431, 300k, Colobus angolensis. No. 1432, 300k, Hypsignathus monstrosus. No. 1433, 300k, Mops condylurus. No. 1434, 300k, Epomops franqueti. No. 1435, 300k, Epomophorus crypturus. No. 1436, 300k, Acinonyx jubatus. No. 1437, 300k, Panthera pardus pardus. No. 1438, 300k, Caracal caracal. No. 1439, 300k, Panthera leo bleyenberghi. No. 1440, 300k, Loxodonta africana walking left. No. 1441, 300k, Loxodonta africana facing right. No. 1442, 300k, Two Loxodonta africana with hindquarters touching. No. 1443, 300k, Two Loxodonta africana facing right. No. 1444, 300k, Stenella attenuata. No. 1445, 300k, Stenella longirostris. No. 1446, 300k, Stenella frontalis. No. 1447, 300k, Lagenodelphis hosei. No. 1448, 300k, Globicephala macrorhynchus. No. 1449, 300k, Megaptera novaeangliae. No. 1450, 300k, Eubalaena australis. No. 1451, 300k, Kogia breviceps. No. 1452, 300k, Treron calvus. No. 1453, 300k, Oena capensis. No. 1454, 300k, Columba guinea. No. 1455, 300k, Streptopelia capicola. No. 1456, 300k, Bubo africanus. No. 1457, 300k, Bubo leucostictus. No. 1458, 300k, Otus senegalensis. No. 1459, 300k, Scotopelia peli. No. 1460, 300k, Agapornis pullarius. No. 1461, 300k, Poicephalus meyeri reichenowi. No. 1462, 300k, Poicephalus robustus. No. 1463, 300k, Poicephalus rueppellii. No. 1464, 300k, Halcyon senegalensis. No. 1465, 300k, Corythornis cristatus. No. 1466, 300k, Ispidina picta. No. 1467, 300k, Ceryle rudis. No. 1468, 300k, Merops variegatus. No. 1469, 300k, Merops albicollis. No. 1470, 300k, Merops bullockoides. No. 1471, 300k, Merops nubicoides. No. 1472, 300k, Dendropicos fuscescens. No. 1473, 300k, Campethera abingoni. No. 1474, 300k, Dendropicos elliotii. No. 1475, 300k, Chloropicus xantholophus. No. 1476, 300k, Tockus leucomelas. No. 1477, 300k, Bycanistes fistulator. No. 1478, 300k, Lophoceros alboterminatus. No. 1479, 300k, Bucorvus leadbeateri. No. 1480, 300k, Sylvietta ruficapilla. No. 1481, 300k, Acrocephalus gracilirostris. No. 1482, 300k, Sylvietta rufescens. No. 1483, 300k, Hylia prasina. No. 1484, 300k, Tricholaema leucomelas and Pogoniulus subsulphureus. No. 1485, 300k, Pogoniulus chrysoconus. No. 1486, 300k, Trachyphonus vaillantii. No. 1487, 300k, Lybius minor. No. 1488, 300k, Centropus monachus. No. 1489, 300k, Chrysococcyx klaas. No. 1490, 300k, Chrysococcyx caprius. No. 1491, 300k, Clamator glandarius. No. 1492, 300k, Ardea purpurea. No. 1493, 300k, Pelecanus onocrotalus. No. 1494, 300k, Hydroprogne caspia. No. 1495, 300k, Sarkidiornis melanotos. No. 1496, 300k, Haliaeetus vocifer. No. 1497, 300k, Aquila nipalensis. No. 1498, 300k, Aquila rapax. No. 1499, 300k, Gypohierax angolensis. No. 1500, 300k, Papilio phorcas congoanus. No. 1501, 300k, Hypolycaena antifaunus. No. 1502, 300k, Charaxes numenes. No. 1503, 300k, Charaxes eupale. No. 1504, 300k, Barbus fasciolatus. No. 1505, 300k, Schilbe mystus. No. 1506, 300k, Trachinus araneus. No. 1507, 300k, Synodontis woosnami and Chelonia mydas. No. 1508, 300k, Euspira grossularia. No. 1509, 300k, Tonna galea. No. 1510, 300k, Cardium costatum. No. 1511, 300k, Marginella glabella. No. 1512, 300k, Osteolaemus tetraspis, head at LL. No. 1513, 300k, Osteolaemus tetraspis, head at LR. No. 1514, 300k, Crocodylus niloticus, head at right. No. 1515, 300, Crocodylus niloticus, head at left. No. 1516, 300k, Dendroaspis jamesoni. No. 1517, 300k, Bitis caudalis. No. 1518, 300k, Bitis arietans. No. 1519, 300k, Naja anchietae. No. 1520, 300k, Caretta caretta. No.1521, 3 00k, Dermochelys coriacea. No. 1522, 300k,

Lepidochelys olivacea. No. 1523, 300k, Eretmochelys imbricata. No. 1524, 300k, Diplodocus longus and amethyst. No. 1525, 300k, Rhamphorhynchus longicaudus and pyroxenite. No. 1526, 300k, Hatzegopteryx thambema and quartz. No. 1527, 300k, Yangchuanosaurus shangyouensis, atacamite and libethenite. No. 1528, 300k, Adult Diceros bicornis facing left. No. 1529, 300k, Hippotragus niger variani. No. 1530, 300k, Lycaon pictus. No. 1531, 300k, Gyps africanus. No. 1532, 300k, Laelia purpurata "Miss Scarlet." No. 1533, 300k, Cymbidium "Sandy Tiger." No. 1534, 300k, Laeliocattleya "Trick or Treat Sweety." No. 1535, 300k, Brassolaeliocattleya Momilani Rainbow "The Gypsy." No. 1536, 300k, Amanita muscaria. No. 1537, 300k, Coprinellus micaceus. No. 1538, 300k, Amanita rubescens. No. 1539, 300k, Agaricus xanthodermus.

No. 1540, 1200k, Adult and juvenile Ceratotherium simum. No. 1541, 1200k, Giraffa camelopardalis angolensis, diff. No. 1542, 1200k, Ceratopithecus ascanius. No. 1543, 1200k, Cistugo seabrae. No. 1544, 1200k, Leptailurus serval. No. 1545, 1200k, Loxodonta africana facing left. No. 1546, 1200k, Steno bredanensis. No. 1547, 1200k, Balaenoptera musculus. No. 1548, 1200k, Spilogelia senegalensis. No. 1549, 1200k, Bubo lacteus. No. 1550, 1200k, Psittacus erithacus. No. 1551, 1200k, Halcyon leucocephala. No. 1552, 1200k, Merops malimbicus. No. 1553, 1200k, Campethera bennettii. No. 1554, 1200k, Bycanistes bucinator. No. 1555, 1200k, Hyliota flavigaster. No. 1556, 1200k, Trachyphonus purpuratus. No. 1557, 1200k, Chrysococcyx cupreus. No. 1558, 1200k, Netta rufina. No. 1559, 1200k, Terathopius ecaudatus. No. 1560, 1200k, Junonia sp. No. 1561, 1200k, Synodontis nigromaculatus. No. 1562, 1200k, Architectonica perspectiva. No. 1563, 1200k, Crocodylus niloticus, diff. No. 1564, 1200k, Bitis caudalis, diff. No. 1565, 1200k, Chelonia mydas. No. 1566, 1200k, Austroraptor cabazai and rhodochrosite. No. 1567, 1200k, Mecistops cataphractus. No. 1568, 1200k, Laelia anceps "SanBar Bounty." No. 1569, 1200k, Gliophorus psittacinus.

2018, Dec. 10   Litho.   Perf. 13x13¼
1420-1539 A344   Set of 120   235.00   235.00
Souvenir Sheets
1540-1569 A344   Set of 30   235.00   235.00

A345

A346

A347

Personalized Stamps — A348

2019, May 15   Litho.   Perf. 12¾x13¼
1570 A345 500k multi   3.00   3.00
1571 A346 500k multi   3.00   3.00

1572 A347 500k multi   3.00   3.00
     Perf. 13¼x12¾
1573 A348 500k multi   3.00   3.00
   Nos. 1570-1573 (4)   12.00   12.00

The vignette portions of Nos. 1570-1573 could be personalized.

First Man on the Moon, 50th Anniv. — A349

No. 1574: a, Apollo 11 Lunar Module approaching Moon's surface. b, Neil Armstrong's first step on the Moon. c, Armstrong and Buzz Aldrin on Moon. d, Lunar Module leaving Moon.
1200k, Armstrong and U.S. flag on Moon.

Litho. With Foil Application
2019, May 15   Perf. 13¼
1574 A349   300k Sheet of 4, #a-
     d   7.25   7.25
     Souvenir Sheet
1575 A349 1200k multi   7.25   7.25
No. 1575 contains one 45x51mm stamp.

A350

No. 1576, 300k, The Floor Scrapers, by Gustave Caillebotte (1848-94). No. 1577, 300k, The Luncheon on the Grass, by Edouard Manet (1832-83). No. 1578, 300k, Pont Boieldieu in Rouen, Rainy Weather, by Camille Pissarro (1830-1903). No. 1579, 300k, Dance at Le Moulin de la Galette, by Pierre-Auguste Renoir (1841-1919).

No. 1580, 300k, Oshkosh Striker 8x8 fire truck. No. 1581, 300k, 1980 Seagrave fire truck. No. 1582, 300k, Spartan KME fire truck. No. 1583, 300k, American LaFrance Pioneer fire truck.

No. 1584, 300k, U-127 class 4-6-0 locomotive. No. 1585, 300k, London North Eastern Railway class A4 2509 Silver Link. No. 1586, 300k, London North Eastern Railway class A3 4472 Flying Scotsman. No. 1587, 300k, South African class 25NC 4-8-4 locomotive. No. 1588, 300k, South African class 33-400 locomotive. No. 1589, 300k, South African class GMA 4-8-2+2-8-4 locomotive. No. 1590, 300k, South African class 43-000 locomotive. No. 1591, 300k, South African class 26 4-8-4 locomotive.

No. 1592, 300k, Prototype Russian rescue vehicle, vert. No. 1593, 300k, 1991 Land Rover Defender ambulance, vert. No. 1594, 300k, RMMV Survivor R, vert. No. 1595, 300k, Scania P 93ML fire truck, vert.

No. 1596, 300k, BMW R1200GS motorcycle, vert. No. 1597, 300k, KTM 950 Adventure motorcycle, vert. No. 1598, 300k, Suzuki TL1000R motocycle, vert. No. 1599, 300k, 2009 Yamaha R1 motorcycle, vert.

No. 1600, 300k, Fairchild Republic A-10 Thunderbolt II, vert. No. 1601, 300k, McDonnell Douglas F/A-18 Hornet, vert. No. 1602, 300k, Alenia Aermacchi M-346 Master, vert. No. 1603, 300k, Lockheed F-117 Nighthawk, vert.

No. 1604, 300k, Pres. John F. Kennedy (1917-63) and Apollo mission emblem, vert. No. 1605, 300k, Apollo 11 Command and Service Modules, Apollo 11 emblems and "50," vert. No. 1606, 300k, Saturn V SA-506 rocket, vert. No. 1607, 300k, Neil Armstrong (1930-2012), first man on Moon, vert.

No. 1608, 300k, Thalassa and flag of Netherlands, vert. No. 1609, 300k, Juan Sebastián de Elcano and flag of Spain, vert. No. 1610, 300k, Christian Radich and flag of Norway, vert. No. 1611, 300k, Gorch Fock and flag of Germany, vert.
No. 1612, 300k, Portland Head Lighthouse, Maine, and flag of United States, vert. No. 1613, 300k, Portland Bill Lighthouse, and flag of Great Britain, vert. No. 1614, 300k, Slettnes Lighthouse, and flag of Norway, vert. No. 1615, 300k, Rubjerg Knude Lighthouse, and flag of Denmark, vert.
No. 1616, 300k, Equus quagga and flag of Botswana, vert. No. 1617, 300k, Loxodonta africana and flag of Central African Republic, vert. No. 1618, 300k, Aquila chrysaetos and flag of Egypt, vert. No. 1619, 300k, Panthera leo and flag of Kenya, vert.
No. 1620, 300k, World map, child and parched land, vert. No. 1621, 300k, Sea level measurement posts, vert. No. 1622, 300k, Corals in acidified ocean, vert. No. 1623, 300k, Polar bears on ice, vert.
No. 1624, 300k, Egyptian Mau cat, vert. No. 1625, 300k, Siamese cat, vert. No. 1626, 300k, Russian Blue cat and flag of Russia, vert. No. 1627, 300k, Japanese bobtail cats, vert.
No. 1628, 300k, Cyclostoma purum, vert. No. 1629, 300k, Tegula gallina, vert. No. 1630, 300k, Calyptraea spirata and Labyrinthus plicatus, vert. No. 1631, 300k, Hindsia nivea and Micrarionta kelletti, vert.
No. 1632, 300k, Ichthyosaurus communis, vert. No. 1633, 300k, Liopleurodon ferox, vert. No. 1634, 300k, Eromangasaurus australis, vert. No. 1635, 300k, Dinichthys terrelli, vert.
No. 1636, 300k, Parasaurolophus walkeri, vert. No. 1637, 300k, Ceratops horridus, vert. No. 1638, 300k, Tyrannosaurus rex and Charles Darwin (1809-82), naturalist, vert. No. 1639, 300k, Darwin, map and dinosaur skeleton, vert.
No. 1640, 300k, Two Girl Scouts and tent, vert. No. 1641, 300k, Boy and Girl Scout at campfire, vert. No. 1642, 300k, Boy and Girl Scout with map and flag, vert. No. 1643, 300k, Three Scouts and campfire, vert.
No. 1644, 300k, Pope John Paul II (1920-2005) with arms raised, vert. No. 1645, 300k, Pope John Paul II holding cross, vert. No. 1646, 300k, Pope John Paul II and bishop, vert. No. 1647, 300k, Pope John Paul II standing in automobile, vert.
No. 1648, 300k, Princess Diana (1961-97) in wedding dress, vert. No. 1649, 300k, Princess Diana with Indian children, vert. No. 1650, 300k, Princess Diana riding horse, vert. No. 1651, 300k, Princess Diana holding roses, coat of arms, vert.
No. 1652, 300k, Nelson Mandela (1918-2013), President of South Africa, prison and his prisoner number, vert. No. 1653, 300k, Nobel medal, Mandela wearing tribal costume, vert. No. 1654, 300k, Mandela and election campaign crowd, vert. No. 1655, 300k, Mandela casting ballot, flag and coat of arms of South Africa, vert.
No. 1656, 300k, Mohandas K. Gandhi (1869-1948), Indian nationalist leader, his signature and Taj Mahal, vert. No. 1657, 300k, Taj Mahal, Gandhi holding walking stick, vert. No. 1658, 300k, Gandhi, flag and emblem of India, vert. No. 1659, 300k, Gandhi and crowd, vert.
No. 1660, 300k, Henri Dunant (1828-1910), founder of International Red Cross, and Red Cross volunteers and flag, vert. No. 1661, 300k, Dodge WC54 ambulance and Red Cross tent, vert. No. 1662, 300k, Barkas V 901/2 ambulance and AW139 helicopter, vert. No. 1663, 300k, World War I Red Cross nurses, vert.
No. 1664, 300k, Sick child and mosquito, vert. No. 1665, 300k, Child, hand with hypodermic needle and mosquito, vert. No. 1666, 300k, Children under mosquito netting, vert. No. 1667, 300k, Man spraying insecticide, mosquito, vert.
No. 1668, 300k, Rotary International emblem and Rotary founder Paul P. Harris (1868-1947), seated, vert. No. 1669, 300k, Rotary International emblem and Harris, standing, vert. No. 1670, 300k, Rotary International emblem, Harris and his wife, Jean (1881-1963), vert. No. 1671, 300k, Rotary International emblem, Harris and Luther Burbank (1849-1926), botanist.
No. 1672, 300k, 2018 Nobel laureates in Physiology or Medicine, Tasuku Honjo and James P. Allison, vert. No. 1673, 300k, 2018 Nobel laureates in Chemistry, George P. Smith, Frances H. Arnold, and Sir Gregory P. Winter, vert. No. 1674, 300k, 2018 Nobel laureates in Physics, Arthur Ashkin, Gérard A. Mourou, and Donna T. Strickland, vert. No. 1675, 300k, 2018 Nobel laureates in Economics, William D. Nordhaus and Paul M. Romer, vert.
No. 1676, 300k, Magnus Carlsen, World chess champion, flag and reversed map of Norway, vert. No. 1677, 300k, Fabiano Caruana, second-ranked chess player in world, flag and map of United States, vert. No. 1678, 300k, Ding Liren, fourth-ranked chess player in world, flag and map of People's Republic of China, vert. No. 1679, 300k, Sergey Karjakin, youngest chess player to

achieve Grand Master status, flag and map of Russia, vert.
No. 1680, 300k, Omakola, vert. No. 1681, 300k, Tambor falante, vert. No. 1682, 300k, Lamelofone, vert. No. 1683, 300k, Mucupela, vert.
No. 1684, 300k, Pig with tulip, vert. No. 1685, 300k, Pig with pear, vert. No. 1686, 300k, Pig balancing on ball, vert. No. 1687, 300k, Pig jumping rope, vert.
No. 1688, 1200k, Water Lilies, by Claude Monet (1840-1926). No. 1689, 1200k, Mount Arlington, New Jersey 1939 Model VC fire truck. No. 1690, 1200k, Great Western Railway class 7800 locomotive. No. 1691, 1200k, South African class 19D 4-8-2 locomotive. No. 1692, 1200k, Canadair CL-415 firefighting airplane, vert. No. 1693, 1200k, Gilera CX motorcycle, vert. No. 1694, 1200k, Dornier Alpha Jet and Lockheed Martin F-35 Lightning II, vert. No. 1695, 1200k, Apollo 11 Command, Service and Lunar Modules and medal, vert. No. 1696, 1200k, Dar Mlodziedzy and flag of Poland, vert. No. 1697, 1200k, Split Rock Lighthouse, Minnesota, and flag of United States, vert. No. 1698, 1200k, Hippotragus niger and flag of Angola, vert. No. 1699, 1200k, Thermometer and changing landscape, vert. No. 1700, 1200k, Peterbald cat, vert. No. 1701, 1200k, Succinea putris, Fusus kelletii, and Labyrinthus leucodon, vert. No. 1702, 1200k, Helicoprion beswsonowi, vert. No. 1703, 1200k, Darwin and Stegosaurus stenops, vert. No. 1704, 1200k, Two Scouts, tent and lantern, vert. No. 1705, 1200k, Pope John Paul II holding cross, diff., vert. No. 1706, 1200k, Princess Diana and Queen Elizabeth II, vert. No. 1707, 1200k, Mandela standing in automobile, vert. No. 1708, 1200k, Gandhi holding microphone, vert. No. 1709, 1200k, Dunant and horse drawn ambulance, vert. No. 1710, 1200k, Plasmodium malariae and medical worker, vert. No. 1711, 1200k, Rotary International emblem and bust of Harris, vert. No. 1712, 1200k, Dove and 2018 Nobel Peace laureates, Denis Mukwege and Nadia Murad, vert. No. 1713, 1200k, Shakhriyar Mamedyarov, third-ranked chess player in world, flag and map of Azerbaijan, vert. No. 1714, 1200k, Balafon and marimba, vert. No. 1715, 1200k, Pig blowing bubbles, vert.

    Perf. 13x13¼, 13¼x13
2019, May 15   Litho.
1576-1687 A350   Set of 112   200.00   200.00
     Souvenir Sheets
1688-1715 A350   Set of 28   200.00   200.00

SEMI-POSTAL STAMPS

Angolan Red Cross — SP1

No. B1, Mother and child. No. B2, Zebra and foal.

1991, Sept. 19   Litho.   Perf. 14
B1 SP1 20k +5k multi   1.25   1.25
B2 SP1 40k +5k multi   2.25   2.25

AIR POST STAMPS

Plane Over Globe
Common Design Type
    Perf. 13½x13
1938, July 26   Engr.   Unwmk.
   Name and Value in Black
C1 CD39 10c red orange   .60   .40
C2 CD39 20c purple   .60   .40
C3 CD39 50c orange   .60   .40
C4 CD39 1a ultra   .60   .40
C5 CD39 2a lilac brn   1.25   .40
C6 CD39 3a dk green   2.50   .60
C7 CD39 5a red brown   6.00   .90
C8 CD39 9a rose carmine   9.25   1.90
C9 CD39 10a magenta   12.50   3.00
   Nos. C1-C9 (9)   33.90   8.40
Set, Never Hinged   47.50

No. C7 exists with overprint "Exposicao Internacional de Nova York, 1939-1940" and Trylon and Perisphere. Value; used & unused $110., never hinged, $160.

AP2

1947, Aug.　Litho.　Rough Perf. 10½
C10	AP2	1a red brown	16.00	5.25
C11	AP2	2a yellow grn	18.00	6.75
C12	AP2	3a orange	18.00	6.75
C13	AP2	3.50a orange	32.50	6.75
C14	AP2	5a olive grn	110.00	30.00
C15	AP2	6a rose	110.00	29.00
C16	AP2	9a red	375.00	300.00
C17	AP2	10a green	250.00	115.00
C18	AP2	20a blue	350.00	125.00
C19	AP2	50a black	450.00	300.00
C20	AP2	100a yellow	625.00	575.00
		Nos. C10-C20 (11)	2,355.	1,500.

Planes Circling Globe — AP3

1949, May 1　Photo.　Perf. 11½
C21	AP3	1a henna brown	.75	.25
C22	AP3	2a red brown	1.50	.25
C23	AP3	3a plum	2.00	.25
C24	AP3	6a dull green	4.00	.85
C25	AP3	9a violet brown	5.50	2.25
		Nos. C21-C25 (5)	13.75	3.85
		Set, Never Hinged	21.00	

Catalogue values for unused stamps in this section, from this point to the end of the section, are for Never Hinged items.

Cambambe Dam AP4

Designs: 1.50e, Oil refinery, vert. 3e, Salazar Dam. 4e, Capt. Teófilo Duarte Dam. 4.50e, Craveiro Lopes Dam. 5e, Cuango Dam. 6e, Quanza River Bridge. 7e, Capt. Teófilo Duarte Bridge. 8.50e, Oliveira Salazar Bridge. 12.50e, Capt. Silva Carvalho Bridge.

Perf. 11½x12, 12x11½
1965, July 12　Litho.　Unwmk.
C26	AP4	1.50e multicolored	2.50	.25
C27	AP4	2.50e multicolored	1.50	.25
C28	AP4	3e multicolored	2.50	.25
C29	AP4	4e multicolored	1.00	.25
C30	AP4	4.50e multicolored	1.00	.25
C31	AP4	5e multicolored	1.60	.25
C32	AP4	6e multicolored	1.60	.25
C33	AP4	7e multicolored	2.50	.25
C34	AP4	8.50e multicolored	3.25	1.40
C35	AP4	12.50e multicolored	3.75	1.60
		Nos. C26-C35 (10)	21.20	5.00

Stamp Centenary Type

Design: 2.50e, Boeing 707 jet & Angola #2.

1970, Dec. 1　Litho.　Perf. 13½
C36	A83	2.50e multicolored	1.40	.35
a.		Souv. sheet of 3, #565-566, C36	13.00	13.00

No. C36a sold for 15e.

No. C36 Ovptd.

1980, June 15　Litho.　Perf. 13½
C37	A83	2.50e multicolored	1.40	.45

POSTAGE DUE STAMPS

D1

1904　Unwmk.　Typo.　Perf. 11½x12
J1	D1	5r yellow grn	.50	.45
J2	D1	10r slate	.50	.45
J3	D1	20r yellow brn	.95	.50
J4	D1	30r orange	.95	.50
J5	D1	50r gray brown	1.15	.85
J6	D1	60r red brown	11.50	5.50
J7	D1	100r lilac	2.25	2.75
J8	D1	130r dull blue	2.25	2.75
J9	D1	200r carmine	13.50	7.50
J10	D1	500r gray violet	12.00	6.00
		Nos. J1-J10 (10)	45.55	27.25
		Set, never hinged	100.00	

Postage Due Stamps of 1904 Overprinted in Carmine or Green

1911
J11	D1	5r yellow grn	.35	.30
J12	D1	10r slate	.35	.30
J13	D1	20r yellow brn	.35	.30
J14	D1	30r orange	.50	.30
J15	D1	50r gray brown	.50	.30
J16	D1	60r red brown	1.55	1.00
J17	D1	100r lilac	1.60	1.00
J18	D1	130r dull blue	1.75	1.40
J19	D1	200r carmine (G)	2.25	1.40
J20	D1	500r gray violet	2.60	2.60
		Nos. J11-J20 (10)	11.80	8.90
		Set, never hinged	70.00	

D2

1921　Perf. 11½
J21	D2	½c yellow green	.35	.30
J22	D2	1c slate	.35	.30
J23	D2	2c orange brown	.35	.30
J24	D2	3c orange	.35	.30
J25	D2	5c gray brown	.35	.30
J26	D2	6c lt brown	.45	.30
J27	D2	10c red violet	.65	.50
J28	D2	13c dull blue	1.10	.95
J29	D2	20c carmine	1.10	.95
J30	D2	50c gray	1.10	.95
		Nos. J21-J30 (10)	6.15	5.15
		Set, never hinged	8.00	

For surcharges see Nos. 268-270.

Catalogue values for unused stamps in this section, from this point to the end of the section, are for Never Hinged items.

Stamps of 1932 Surcharged in Black

1948　Wmk. 232　Perf. 12x11½
J31	A14	10c on 20c gray	.50	.30
J32	A14	20c on 30c myrtle grn	.95	.50
J33	A14	30c on 50c lt brown	1.30	.80
J34	A14	40c on 1a claret	1.90	1.20
J35	A14	50c on 2a dull vio	3.25	2.10
J36	A14	1a on 5a pale yel grn	3.50	2.50
		Nos. J31-J36 (6)	11.40	7.40

Common Design Type
Photogravure and Typographed
1952　Unwmk.　Perf. 14
Numeral in Red, Frame Multicolored
J37	CD45	10c red brown	.35	.25
J38	CD45	30c olive green	.35	.25
J39	CD45	50c chocolate	.35	.25
J40	CD45	1a dk vio blue	.95	.50
J41	CD45	2a red brown	1.15	.65
J42	CD45	5a black brown	1.15	.65
		Nos. J37-J42 (6)	4.30	2.55

NEWSPAPER STAMP

N1

1893　Typo.　Unwmk.　Perf. 11½
P1	N1	2½r brown	4.00	1.60
a.		Perf. 12½	4.00	1.40
b.		Perf. 13½	3.50	1.40

No. P1 was also used for ordinary postage. For surcharges see Nos. 37, 82, 180, 235.

POSTAL TAX STAMPS

Pombal Issue
Common Design Types
1925, May 8　Unwmk.　Perf. 12½
RA1	CD28	15c lilac & black	1.10	1.10
RA2	CD29	15c lilac & black	1.10	1.10
RA3	CD30	15c lilac & black	1.10	1.10
		Nos. RA1-RA3 (3)	3.30	3.30

"Charity" — PT1

1929　Litho.　Perf. 11
Without Gum
RA4	PT1	50c dark blue	8.25	2.25

Coat of Arms — PT2

1939　Without Gum　Perf. 10½
RA5	PT2	50c turq green	3.50	.35
RA6	PT2	1a red	5.50	2.25

A 1.50a, type PT2, was issued for fiscal use. Value, $7.50.

Catalogue values for unused stamps in this section, from this point to the end of the section, are for Never Hinged items.

Old Man — PT3

Designs: 1e, Boy. 1.50e, Girl.

Imprint: "Foto-Lito-E.G.A.-Luanda"
Heads in dark brown
1955　Unwmk.　Perf. 13
RA7	PT3	50c dk ocher	.50	.25
RA8	PT3	1e orange ver	.75	.60
RA9	PT3	1.50e brt yel grn	1.00	.60
		Nos. RA7-RA9 (3)	2.25	1.45

A 2.50e, type PT3 showing an old woman, was issued for revenue use. Value $2.
See Nos. RA16, RA19-RA21, RA25-RA27.

No. RA7 Surcharged in Red or Black

1957-58　Head in dark brown
RA11	PT3	10c on 50c dk ocher (R)	.35	.30
RA12	PT3	10c on 50c dk ocher ('58)	.35	.30
RA13	PT3	30c on 50c dk ocher	.35	.30
		Nos. RA11-RA13 (3)	1.05	.90

Mother and Child — PT4

Design: 30c, Boy and girl.

1959　Litho.　Perf. 13
RA14	PT4	10c orange & blk	.30	.25
RA15	PT4	30c slate & blk	.30	.25

Type of 1955 Redrawn

Design: 1e, Boy.

1961, Nov.　Perf. 13
RA16	PT3	1e salmon pink & dk brn	.35	.30

Denomination in italics.

Yellow, White and Black Men — PT5

1962, July 1　Typo.　Perf. 10½
Without Gum
RA17	PT5	50c multicolored	.35	.25
RA18	PT5	1e multicolored	.50	.25

Issued for the Provincial Settlement Committee (Junta Provincial do Povoamento). The tax was used to promote Portuguese settlement in Angola, and to raise educational and living standards of recent immigrants.
Denominations higher than 1e were used for revenue purposes.

Head Type of 1955

Designs: 50c, Old man. 1e, Boy. 1.50e, Girl.

Without Imprint
Heads in dark brown
1964-65　Litho.　Perf. 11½
RA19	PT3	50c orange	.35	.25
RA20	PT3	1e dull red org ('65)	.35	.25
RA21	PT3	1.50e yel grn ('65)	.35	.25
		Nos. RA19-RA21 (3)	1.05	.85

No. RA20 is the second redrawing of 1e, with bolder lettering. Space between "Assistencia" and denomination on RA20-RA21 is ½mm; on the 1955 issue space is 2¼mm and 1¾mm, respectively.

Map of Angola, Industrial and Farm Workers — PT6

1965, Sept. 1   Litho.   *Perf. 13*

RA22	PT6	50c multicolored	.25	.25
RA23	PT6	1e multicolored	.30	.25

The 2e was used for revenue purposes. Value 50c.

Head Type of 1955

Designs: 50c, Old man. 1e, Boy. 1.50e, Girl.

Imprint: "I.N.A." or "INA" (1e)

1966   Heads in dark brown

RA25	PT3	50c dull orange	.30	.25
RA26	PT3	1e dull brick red	.30	.25
RA27	PT3	1.50e lt yel green	.35	.35
		Nos. RA25-RA27 (3)	.95	.85

Woman Planting Tree — PT7

1972   Litho.   *Perf. 13*

RA28	PT7	50c shown	.25	.25
RA29	PT7	1e Workers	.30	.25
RA30	PT7	2e Produce	.30	.25
		Nos. RA28-RA30 (3)	.85	.75

POSTAL TAX DUE STAMPS

Pombal Issue

Common Design Types

1925, May 8   Unwmk.   *Perf. 12½*

RAJ1	CD28	30c lilac & black	1.10	1.10
RAJ2	CD29	30c lilac & black	1.10	1.10
RAJ3	CD30	30c lilac & black	1.10	1.10
		Nos. RAJ1-RAJ3 (3)	3.30	3.30

See note after Portugal No. RAJ4.

ANGRA

ˈaŋ-grə

LOCATION — An administrative district of the Azores, consisting of the islands of Terceira, Sao Jorge and Graciosa.
GOVT. — A district of Portugal
AREA — 275 sq. mi.
POP. — 70,000 (approx.)
CAPITAL — Angra do Heroismo

1000 Reis = 1 Milreis

King Carlos — A1

1892-93   Typo.   Unwmk.   *Perf. 12½*

1	A1	5r yellow	5.00	2.10
a.		*Perf 11½*	15.50	8.50
b.		*Perf 13½*	4.25	2.10
2	A1	10r redsh violet	5.00	2.10
a.		*Perf 13½*	5.00	3.00
3	A1	15r chocolate	5.00	3.50
a.		*Perf 13½*	5.00	3.50
4	A1	20r lavender	5.00	3.50
a.		*Perf 13½*	5.00	3.50
5	A1	25r green	7.00	1.40
a.		*Perf 13½*	12.00	6.50
b.		*Perf 11½*	8.50	3.50
7	A1	50r blue	11.50	6.50
a.		*Perf 13½*	15.50	7.00
8	A1	75r carmine	12.00	7.00
9	A1	80r yellow green	15.50	13.00
10	A1	100r brown, *yel*, perf 13½ ('93)	52.50	17.50
a.		*Perf 12½*	200.00	135.00
11	A1	150r car, *rose* ('93)	67.50	47.50
a.		*Perf 13½*	77.50	57.50
12	A1	200r dk blue, *bl* ('93)	67.50	47.50
		Never hinged	120.00	
a.		*Perf 13½*	77.50	57.50
13	A1	300r dk blue, *sal* ('93)	67.50	47.50
		Never hinged	120.00	
a.		*Perf 13½*	77.50	57.50
		Nos. 1-13 (12)	321.00	199.10

Reprints of 50r, 150r, 200r and 300r, made in 1900, are perf. 11½ and ungummed. Value, each $75. Reprints of all values, made in

1905, have shiny white gum and clean-cut perf. Value, each $30.

King Carlos — A2

Name and Value in Black except Nos. 26 and 35

1897-1905   *Perf. 11½*

14	A2	2½r gray	.75	.50
15	A2	5r orange	.75	.50
a.		*Diagonal half used as 2½r on newspaper or circular*		28.00
16	A2	10r yellow grn	.75	.50
17	A2	15r brown	11.50	5.75
18	A2	15r gray grn ('99)	1.40	.70
19	A2	20r gray violet	3.00	1.50
20	A2	25r sea green	4.25	1.40
21	A2	25r car rose ('99)	.75	.70
22	A2	50r dark blue	7.00	2.10
23	A2	50r ultra ('05)	17.00	11.50
24	A2	65r slate bl ('98)	2.10	.70
25	A2	75r rose	4.25	2.10
26	A2	75r gray brn & car, *straw* ('05)	15.50	10.50
27	A2	80r violet	3.00	1.40
28	A2	100r dk blue, *bl*	3.50	2.00
29	A2	115r org brn, *pink* ('98)	3.50	2.10
30	A2	130r gray brn, *straw* ('98)	3.50	2.10
31	A2	150r lt brn, *straw*	3.50	2.00
32	A2	180r sl, *pnksh* ('98)	4.25	3.50
33	A2	200r red vio, *pnksh*	7.75	5.00
34	A2	300r blue, *rose*	10.50	7.00
35	A2	500r blk & red, *bl*	21.00	14.00
a.		*Perf. 12½*	32.00	18.50
		Nos. 14-35 (22)	129.50	77.55

Azores stamps were used in Angra from 1906 to 1931, when they were superseded by those of Portugal.

ANGUILLA

aŋˌgwi-lə

LOCATION — In the West Indies southeast of Puerto Rico
GOVT. — British territory
AREA — 60 sq. mi.
POP. — 10,663 (est. 1997)
CAPITAL — The Valley

Anguilla separated unilaterally from the Associated State of St. Kitts-Nevis-Anguilla in 1967, formalized in 1980 following direct United Kingdom intervention some years before. A British Commissioner exercises executive authority.

100 Cents = 1 Eastern Caribbean Dollar

> **Catalogue values for all unused stamps in this country are for Never Hinged items.**

St. Kitts-Nevis Nos. 145-160 Overprinted

On Type A14

On Type A15

Wmk. 314

1967, Sept. 4   Photo.   *Perf. 14*

1	A14	½c blue & dk brn	75.00	21.00
2	A15	1c multicolored	85.00	9.00
3	A14	2c multicolored	75.00	2.90
4	A14	3c multicolored	75.00	7.00
5	A14	4c multicolored	90.00	5.25
6	A15	5c multicolored	375.00	40.00
7	A15	6c multicolored	160.00	16.00
8	A15	10c multicolored	90.00	9.00
9	A14	15c multicolored	180.00	14.00
10	A15	20c multicolored	375.00	21.00
11	A14	25c multicolored	300.00	40.00
12	A15	50c multicolored	5,500.	725.00
13	A14	60c multicolored	6,500.	1,850.
14	A14	$1 multicolored	4,500.	625.00
15	A15	$2.50 multicolored	3,500.	375.00
16	A14	$5 multicolored	4,000.	400.00
		Nos. 1-16 (16)	25,880.	4,160.

Counterfeit overprints exist.

Mahogany Tree, The Quarter A1

Designs: 2c, Sombrero Lighthouse. 3c, St. Mary's Church. 4c, Valley Police Station. 5c, Old Plantation House, Mt. Fortune. 6c, Valley Post Office. 10c, Methodist Church, West End. 15c, Wall-Blake Airport. 20c, Plane over Sandy Ground. 25c, Island Harbor. 40c, Map of Anguilla. 60c, Hermit crab and starfish. $1, Hibiscus. $2.50, Coconut harvest. $5, Spiny lobster.

**   *Perf. 12½x13***

1967-68   Litho.   Unwmk.

17	A1	1c orange & multi	.25	.80
18	A1	2c gray green & blk	.25	1.00
19	A1	3c emerald & blk	.25	.25
20	A1	4c brt blue & blk	.25	.25
21	A1	5c lt blue & multi	.25	.25
22	A1	6c ver & black	.25	.25
23	A1	10c multicolored	.25	.25
24	A1	15c multicolored	2.10	.25
25	A1	20c multicolored	1.25	1.75
26	A1	25c multicolored	.60	.25
27	A1	40c blue & multi	1.00	.50
28	A1	60c yellow & multi	4.50	4.00
29	A1	$1 lt green & multi	1.75	2.75
30	A1	$2.50 multicolored	2.00	5.50
31	A1	$5 multicolored	2.75	3.50
		Nos. 17-31 (15)	17.70	21.55

Issued: 1c, 5c, 10c, 20c, 25c, 40c, 11/27/67; 3c, 4c, 15c, 60c, $1, $5, 2/10/68; 2c, 6c, $2.50, 3/21/68.
For overprints see Nos. 53-67, 78-82.

Sailboats A2

Designs: 15c, Boat building. 25c, Schooner Warspite. 40c, Yacht Atlantic Star.

1968, May 11   *Perf. 14*

32	A2	10c rose & multi	.35	.25
33	A2	15c olive & multi	.40	.25
34	A2	25c lilac rose & multi	.60	.25
35	A2	40c dull blue & multi	.65	.35
		Nos. 32-35 (4)	2.00	1.10

Purple-throated Carib — A3

Anguillan Birds: 15c, Bananaquit. 25c, Black-necked stilt, horiz. 40c, Royal tern, horiz.

1968, July 8

36	A3	10c dull yel & multi	.75	.25
37	A3	15c yel green & multi	1.00	.25
38	A3	25c multicolored	1.40	.25
39	A3	40c multicolored	1.75	.35
		Nos. 36-39 (4)	4.90	1.10

Girl Guide Badge — A4

10c, Girl Guide badge, horiz. 25c, Badge and Headquarters, horiz. 40c, Merit Badges.

1968, Oct. 14   *Perf. 13x13½, 13½x13*

40	A4	10c lt green & multi	.25	.25
41	A4	15c lt blue & multi	.25	.25
42	A4	25c multicolored	.25	.25
43	A4	40c multicolored	.30	.25
		Nos. 40-43 (4)	1.05	1.00

Anguillan Girl Guides, 35th anniversary.

Three Kings A5

Christmas: 10c, Three Kings seeing Star, vert. 15c, Holy Family, vert. 40c, Shepherds seeing Star. 50c, Holy Family and donkey.

1968, Nov. 18

44	A5	1c lilac rose & black	.25	.25
45	A5	10c blue & black	.25	.25
46	A5	15c brown & black	.25	.25
47	A5	40c brt ultra & black	.25	.25
48	A5	50c green & black	.30	.25
		Nos. 44-48 (5)	1.30	1.25

Bagging Salt — A6

Salt Industry: 15c, Packing salt. 40c, Salt pond. 50c, Loading salt.

1969, Jan. 4   *Perf. 13*

49	A6	10c red & multi	.25	.25
50	A6	15c lt blue & multi	.30	.25
51	A6	40c emerald & multi	.30	.25
52	A6	50c purple & multi	.35	.25
		Nos. 49-52 (4)	1.20	1.00

Nos. 17-31 Overprinted

1969, Jan. 9   *Perf. 12½x13*

53	A1	1c orange & multi	.25	.25
54	A1	2c gray green & blk	.25	.25
55	A1	3c emerald & blk	.25	.25
56	A1	4c brt blue & blk	.25	.25
57	A1	5c lt blue & multi	.25	.25
58	A1	6c vermilion & blk	.25	.25
59	A1	10c multicolored	.25	.25
60	A1	15c multicolored	.25	.30
61	A1	20c multicolored	.30	.35
62	A1	25c multicolored	.40	.50
63	A1	40c blue & multi	.70	.70
64	A1	60c yellow & multi	.80	.80
65	A1	$1 lt green & multi	1.25	1.50
66	A1	$2.50 multicolored	3.75	4.50
67	A1	$5 multicolored	8.25	9.50
		Nos. 53-67 (15)	17.45	19.90

Crucifixion, School of Quentin Massys A7

Easter: 40c, The Last Supper, ascribed to Roberti.

1969, Mar. 31   Litho.   Perf. 13½
68	A7	25c multicolored	.25	.25
69	A7	40c multicolored	.35	.25

Amaryllis A8

1969, June 10   Perf. 14
70	A8	10c shown	.25	.25
71	A8	15c Bougainvillea	.35	.35
72	A8	40c Hibiscus	.55	.55
73	A8	50c Cattleya orchid	1.75	1.25
		Nos. 70-73 (4)	2.90	2.40

Turban and Star Shells A9

Sea Shells: 15c, Spiny oysters. 40c, Scotch, royal and smooth bonnets. 50c, Triton trumpet.

1969, Sept. 22
74	A9	10c multicolored	.25	.25
75	A9	15c multicolored	.35	.35
76	A9	40c multicolored	.70	.35
77	A9	50c multicolored	.80	.40
		Nos. 74-77 (4)	2.10	1.30

No. 17 Ovptd.

No. 25 Ovptd.

No. 26 Ovptd.

No. 27 Ovptd.

No. 28 Ovptd.

1969, Oct. 27   Perf. 12½x13
78	A1	1c orange & multi	.25	.25
79	A1	20c multicolored	.25	.25
80	A1	25c multicolored	.25	.25
81	A1	40c blue & multi	.50	.25
82	A1	60c yellow & multi	.75	.30
		Nos. 78-82 (5)	2.00	1.30

Red Goatfish A10

Designs: 15c, Blue-striped grunts. 40c, Mutton grouper. 50c, Banded butterfly-fish.

1969, Dec. 1   Perf. 14
83	A10	10c multicolored	.40	.25
84	A10	15c multicolored	.50	.25
85	A10	40c multicolored	.95	.45
86	A10	50c multicolored	1.25	.60
		Nos. 83-86 (4)	3.10	1.55

Morning Glory — A11

1970, Feb. 23
87	A11	10c shown	.40	.25
88	A11	15c Blue petrea	.55	.25
89	A11	40c Hibiscus	.75	.30
90	A11	50c Flamboyant	.95	.35
		Nos. 87-90 (4)	2.65	1.15

The Way to Calvary, by Tiepolo — A12

Easter: 20c, Crucifixion, by Masaccio, vert. 40c, Descent from the Cross, by Rosso Fiorentino, vert. 60c, Jesus Carrying the Cross, by Murillo.

1970, Mar. 26   Perf. 13½
91	A12	10c multicolored	.25	.25
92	A12	20c multicolored	.25	.25
93	A12	40c multicolored	.30	.25
94	A12	60c multicolored	.40	.30
		Nos. 91-94 (4)	1.20	1.05

Anguilla Map, Scout Badge A13

Designs: 15c, Cub Scouts practicing first aid. 40c, Monkey bridge. 50c, Scout Headquarters, The Valley, and Lord Baden-Powell.

1970, Aug. 10   Perf. 13
95	A13	10c multicolored	.25	.25
96	A13	15c multicolored	.25	.25
97	A13	40c multicolored	.30	.25
98	A13	50c multicolored	.40	.30
		Nos. 95-98 (4)	1.20	1.05

Anguilla Boy Scouts, 40th anniversary.

Boat Building A14

Designs: 2c, Road construction. 3c, Blowing Point dock. 4c, Radio announcer. 5c, Cottage Hospital extension. 6c, Valley secondary school. 10c, Hotel extension. 15c, Sandy Ground. 20c, Supermarket and movie house. 25c, Bananas and mangoes. 40c, Wall-Blake airport. 60c, Sandy Ground jetty. $1, Administration building. $2.50, Cow and calf. $5, Sandy Hill Bay.

1970, Nov. 23   Litho.   Perf. 14
99	A14	1c multicolored	.30	.40
100	A14	2c multicolored	.30	.40
101	A14	3c multicolored	.30	.25
102	A14	4c multicolored	.30	.50
103	A14	5c multicolored	.50	.50
104	A14	6c multicolored	.40	.50
105	A14	10c multicolored	.40	.30
106	A14	15c multicolored	.40	.30
107	A14	20c multicolored	.75	.30
108	A14	25c multicolored	.40	1.00
109	A14	40c multicolored	4.00	3.00
110	A14	60c multicolored	.70	3.00
111	A14	$1 multicolored	1.25	1.25
112	A14	$2.50 multicolored	1.75	4.00
113	A14	$5 multicolored	3.75	4.00
		Nos. 99-113 (15)	15.50	19.70

Adoration of the Shepherds, by Guido Reni — A15

Christmas: 20c, Virgin and Child, by Benozzo Gozzoli. 25c, Nativity, by Botticelli. 40c, Santa Margherita Madonna, by Mazzola. 50c, Adoration of the Kings, by Tiepolo.

1970, Dec. 11   Perf. 13½
114	A15	1c multicolored	.25	.25
115	A15	20c multicolored	.25	.25
116	A15	25c multicolored	.30	.25
117	A15	40c multicolored	.45	.35
118	A15	50c multicolored	.50	.40
		Nos. 114-118 (5)	1.75	1.50

Angels Weeping over the Dead Christ, by Guercino — A16

Easter: 10c, Ecce Homo, by Correggio, vert. 15c, Christ Appearing to St. Peter, by Carracci, vert. 50c, The Supper at Emmaus, by Caravaggio.

1971, Mar. 29
119	A16	10c pink & multi	.25	.25
120	A16	15c lt blue & multi	.25	.25
121	A16	40c yel green & multi	.40	.25
122	A16	50c violet & multi	.50	.25
		Nos. 119-122 (4)	1.40	1.00

Hypolimnas Misippus — A17

Butterflies: 15c, Junonia lavinia. 40c, Agraulis vanillae. 50c, Danaus plexippus.

1971, June 21   Perf. 14x14½
123	A17	10c multicolored	2.00	1.00
124	A17	15c multicolored	2.00	1.25
125	A17	40c multicolored	2.50	1.50
126	A17	50c multicolored	2.50	2.00
		Nos. 123-126 (4)	9.00	5.75

Magnanime and Aimable in Battle — A18

Ships: 15c, HMS Duke and Agamemnon against Glorieux. 25c, HMS Formidable and Namur against Ville de Paris. 40c, HMS Canada. 50c, HMS St. Albans and wreck of Hector.

1971, Aug. 30   Litho.   Perf. 14
127	A18	10c multicolored	1.10	1.10
128	A18	15c multicolored	1.40	1.40
129	A18	25c multicolored	1.50	1.50
130	A18	40c multicolored	1.60	1.60
131	A18	50c multicolored	1.75	1.75
a.		Strip of 5, #127-131	8.25	8.25
		Nos. 127-131 (5)	7.35	7.35

West Indies sea battles.

Ansidei Madonna, by Raphael — A19

Christmas: 25c, Mystic Nativity, by Botticelli. 40c, Virgin and Child, School of Seville, inscribed Murillo. 50c, Madonna of the Iris, ascribed to Dürer.

1971, Nov. 29   Perf. 14x13½
132	A19	20c green & multi	.30	.30
133	A19	25c blue & multi	.30	.30
134	A19	40c lilac rose & multi	.35	.40
135	A19	50c violet & multi	.40	.60
		Nos. 132-135 (4)	1.35	1.60

Map of Anguilla and St. Maarten, by Jefferys, 1775 — A20

Maps of Anguilla by: 15c, Samuel Fahlberg, 1814. 40c, Thomas Jefferys, 1775, horiz. 50c, Capt. E. Barnett, 1847, horiz.

1972, Jan. 24   Perf. 14x13½, 13½x14
136	A20	10c lt blue & multi	.25	.25
137	A20	15c lt green & multi	.35	.30
138	A20	40c lt green & multi	.55	.40
139	A20	50c lt ultra & multi	.80	.40
		Nos. 136-139 (4)	1.95	1.35

Jesus Buffeted, Stained-glass Window — A21

Easter (19th cent. Stained-glass Windows, Bray Church): 15c, Jesus Carrying the Cross.

25c, Crucifixion. 40c, Descent from the Cross. 50c, Burial.

1972, Mar. 14   *Perf. 14x13½*
140	A21	10c multicolored	.30	.30
141	A21	15c multicolored	.35	.35
142	A21	25c multicolored	.35	.35
143	A21	40c multicolored	.40	.40
144	A21	50c multicolored	.50	.50
a.		Strip of 5, #140-144	2.50	2.50
		Nos. 140-144 (5)	1.90	1.90

Spear Fishing — A22

Sandy Ground — A23

2c, Loblolly tree, vert. 4c, Ferry, Blowing Point, vert. 5c, Agriculture. 6c, St. Mary's Church, vert. 10c, St. Gerard's Church. 15c, Cottage Hospital. 20c, Public Library. 25c, Sunset, Blowing Point. 40c, Boat building. 60c, Hibiscus. $1, Man-o-war bird. $2.50, Frangipani. $5, Brown pelican. $10, Green-back turtle.

1972-75   *Perf. 13½*
145	A22	1c shown	.25	.25
146	A23	2c multicolored	.25	.50
147	A23	3c shown	.25	.50
148	A23	4c multicolored	1.75	.25
149	A23	5c multicolored	.25	1.25
150	A23	6c multicolored	.35	.50
151	A23	10c multicolored	.35	.50
152	A23	15c multicolored	.35	.40
153	A23	20c multicolored	.35	.45
154	A23	25c multicolored	.50	2.00
155	A22	40c multicolored	5.00	1.25
156	A23	60c multicolored	4.25	4.25
157	A23	$1 multicolored	10.00	8.50
158	A23	$2.50 multicolored	6.00	11.00
159	A23	$5 multicolored	18.00	19.00
160	A22	$10 multicolored	17.00	20.00
		Nos. 145-160 (16)	61.90	70.60

Issued: $10, 5/20/75; others 10/30/72.
For overprints see Nos. 229-246.

Common Design Types
pictured following the introduction.

Silver Wedding Issue, 1972
Common Design Type

Design: Queen Elizabeth II, Prince Philip, schooner and dolphin.

Perf. 14x14½
1972, Nov. 20   **Photo.**   **Wmk. 314**
161	CD324	25c olive & multi	.55	.75
162	CD324	40c maroon & multi	.55	.75

Flight into Egypt — A24

20c, Star of Bethlehem. 25c, Nativity. 40c, Three Kings. 50c, Adoration of the Kings.

Perf. 13½
1972, Dec. 4   **Litho.**   **Unwmk.**
163	A24	1c shown	.25	.25
164	A24	20c multicolored	.25	.25
165	A24	25c multicolored	.25	.25
166	A24	40c multicolored	.25	.25

167	A24	50c multicolored	.25	.25
a.		Vert. strip of 4, #164-167	1.40	1.40
		Nos. 163-167 (5)	1.25	1.25

Christmas.

Betrayal of Jesus — A25

10c, Man of Sorrow. 20c, Jesus Carrying Cross. 25c, Crucifixion. 40c, Descent from Cross. 50c, Resurrection.

1973, Mar. 26
168	A25	1c shown	.25	.25
169	A25	10c multicolored	.25	.25
170	A25	20c multicolored	.25	.25
171	A25	25c multicolored	.25	.25
172	A25	40c multicolored	.25	.25
173	A25	50c multicolored	.25	.35
a.		Souvenir sheet of 6	1.10	1.50
b.		Vert. strip of 5, #169-173	1.00	1.00
		Nos. 168-173 (6)	1.50	1.60

Easter. No. 173a contains 6 stamps similar to Nos. 168-173 with bottom panel in lilac rose.

Santa Maria A26

20c, Old West Indies map. 40c, Map of voyages. 70c, Sighting land. $1.20, Columbus landing.

1973, Sept. 10
174	A26	1c multicolored	.25	.25
175	A26	20c multicolored	1.60	1.60
176	A26	40c multicolored	1.90	1.90
177	A26	70c multicolored	2.00	2.00
178	A26	$1.20 multicolored	2.75	2.75
a.		Souvenir sheet of 5, #174-178	8.00	8.00
b.		Horiz. strip of 5, #174-178	8.00	8.00
		Nos. 174-178 (5)	8.50	8.50

Discovery of West Indies by Columbus.

Princess Anne's Wedding Issue
Common Design Type
1973, Nov. 14   **Wmk. 314**   *Perf. 13½*
179	CD325	60c blue grn & multi	.25	.25
180	CD325	$1.20 lilac & multi	.30	.30

Wedding of Princess Anne and Capt. Mark Phillips, Nov. 14, 1973.

Adoration of the Shepherds, by Guido Reni — A27

Paintings: 10c, Virgin and Child, by Filippino Lippi. 20c, Nativity, by Meester Van de Brunswijkse Diptiek. 25c, Madonna of the Meadow, by Bellini. 40c, Virgin and Child, by Cima. 50c, Adoration of the Kings, by Geertgen Tot Sint Jans.

1973, Dec. 2   **Unwmk.**
181	A27	1c multicolored	.25	.25
182	A27	10c multicolored	.25	.25
183	A27	20c multicolored	.25	.25
184	A27	25c multicolored	.25	.25
185	A27	40c multicolored	.25	.25
186	A27	50c multicolored	.25	.25
a.		Souvenir sheet of 6, #181-186	1.50	1.50
b.		Horiz. strip of 5, #182-186	1.00	1.00
		Nos. 181-186 (6)	1.50	1.50

Christmas.

Crucifixion, by Raphael — A28

Easter (Details from Crucifixion by Raphael): 15c, Virgin Mary and St. John. 20c, The Two Marys. 25c, Left Angel. 40c, Right Angel. $1, Christ on the Cross.

1974, Mar. 30
187	A28	1c lilac & multi	.25	.25
188	A28	15c gray & multi	.25	.25
189	A28	20c salmon & multi	.25	.25
190	A28	25c yel green & multi	.25	.25
191	A28	40c orange & multi	.25	.25
192	A28	$1 lt blue & multi	.25	.25
a.		Souvenir sheet of 6, #187-192	1.50	1.75
b.		Vert. strip of 5, #188-192	1.00	1.00
		Nos. 187-192 (6)	1.50	1.50

Churchill Making Victory Sign — A29

20c, Roosevelt, Churchill, US, British flags. 25c, Churchill broadcasting during the war. 40c, Blenheim Palace. 60c, Churchill Statue & Parliament. $1.20, Chartwell.

1974, June 24
193	A29	1c multicolored	.25	.25
194	A29	20c multicolored	.25	.25
195	A29	25c multicolored	.25	.25
196	A29	40c multicolored	.30	.30
197	A29	60c multicolored	.35	.35
198	A29	$1.20 multicolored	.50	.50
a.		Souvenir sheet of 6, #193-198	1.75	1.75
b.		Horiz. strip of 5, #194-198	2.00	2.00
		Nos. 193-198 (6)	1.90	1.90

Sir Winston Spencer Churchill (1874-1965).

UPU Emblem, Map of Anguilla — A30

1974, Aug. 27
199	A30	1c black & ultra	.25	.25
200	A30	20c black & orange	.25	.25
201	A30	25c black & yellow	.25	.25
202	A30	40c black & brt lilac	.25	.25
203	A30	60c black & lt green	.30	.30
204	A30	$1.20 black & blue	.45	.45
a.		Souvenir sheet of 6	1.60	2.00
b.		Horiz. strip of 5, #200-204	1.50	1.50
		Nos. 199-204 (6)	1.75	1.75

UPU, centenary. No. 204a contains one each of Nos. 199-204 with second row (40c, 60c, $1.20) perf. 15 at bottom.

Fishermen Seeing Star — A31

Christmas: 20c, Nativity. 25c, King offering gift. 40c, Star over map of Anguilla. 60c, Family looking at star. $1.20, Two angels with star and "Peace."

1974, Dec. 16   **Litho.**   *Perf. 14½*
205	A31	1c brt blue & multi	.25	.25
206	A31	20c dull grn & multi	.25	.25
207	A31	25c gray & multi	.25	.25
208	A31	40c car & multi	.25	.25
209	A31	60c dp blue & multi	.25	.25

210	A31	$1.20 ultra & multi	.25	.25
a.		Souvenir sheet of 6, #205-210	1.60	2.25
b.		Horiz. strip of 5, #206-210	1.25	1.25
		Nos. 205-210 (6)	1.50	1.50

Virgin Mary, St. John, Mary Magdalene A32

Paintings from Isenheim Altar, by Matthias Grunewald: 10c, Crucifixion. 15c, John the Baptist. 20c, St. Sebastian and Angels. $1, Burial of Christ, horiz. $1.50, St. Anthony, the Hermit.

1975, Mar. 25   *Perf. 13½*
211	A32	1c multicolored	.25	.25
212	A32	10c multicolored	.25	.25
213	A32	15c multicolored	.25	.25
214	A32	20c multicolored	.25	.25
215	A32	$1 multicolored	.25	.35
216	A32	$1.50 multicolored	.30	.45
a.		Souvenir sheet of 6	1.60	2.00
b.		Horiz. strip of 5, #212-216	1.25	1.25
		Nos. 211-216 (6)	1.55	1.80

Easter. No. 216a contains 6 stamps similar to Nos. 211-216 with simulated perforations.

Statue of Liberty, N.Y. Skyline — A33

10c, Capitol, Washington, DC. 15c, Congress voting independence. 20c, Washington, map & his battles. $1, Boston Tea Party. $1.50, Bicentennial emblem, historic US flags.

1975, Nov. 10
217	A33	1c multicolored	.25	.25
218	A33	10c multicolored	.25	.25
219	A33	15c multicolored	.25	.25
220	A33	20c multicolored	.25	.25
221	A33	$1 multicolored	.50	.40
222	A33	$1.50 multicolored	.60	.60
a.		Souvenir sheet of 6	1.75	2.50
b.		Horiz. strip of 5, #218-222	2.00	2.00
		Nos. 217-222 (6)	2.10	2.00

American Bicentennial. No. 222a contains one each of Nos. 217-222 with second row (20c, $1, $1.50) perf. 15 at bottom.

Virgin and Child with St. John, by Raphael — A34

Paintings, Virgin and Child by: 10c, Cima. 15c, Dolci. 20c, Durer. $1, Bellini. $1.50, Botticelli.

1975, Dec. 8   *Perf. 14x13½*
223	A34	1c ultra & multi	.25	.25
224	A34	10c Prus blue & multi	.25	.25
225	A34	15c plum & multi	.25	.25
226	A34	20c car rose & multi	.25	.25
227	A34	$1 brt grn & multi	.30	.25
228	A34	$1.50 blue grn & multi	.45	.40
a.		Souvenir sheet of 6, #223-228	2.25	2.75
b.		Horiz. strip of 5, #224-228	1.75	1.50
		Nos. 223-228 (6)	1.75	1.65

Christmas.

Nos. 145-146, 148, 150-160 Surcharged and/or Overprinted

(a)

(b)

1976		Litho.		Perf. 13½	
229	A22	(a)	1c #145	.35	.50
230	A22	(b)	2c on 1c #145	.35	.50
231	A23	(a)	2c #146	7.75	1.75
232	A22	(b)	3c on 40c #155	.90	.75
233	A23	(a)	4c #148	1.10	1.25
234	A22	(a)	5c on 40c #155	.35	.65
235	A23	(a)	6c #150	.35	.65
236	A23	(b)	10c on 20c #153	.35	.65
237	A23	(a)	10c #151	8.25	5.50
238	A22	(a)	15c #152	.35	1.25
239	A23	(a)	20c #153	.35	.60
240	A23	(a)	25c #154	.35	.60
241	A22	(a)	40c #155	1.10	.80
242	A22	(a)	60c #156	.75	.80
243	A23	(a)	$1 #157	6.75	2.50
244	A23	(a)	$2.50 #158	2.25	2.50
245	A23	(a)	$5 #159	8.50	10.00
246	A22	(a)	$10 #160	3.25	7.00
			Nos. 229-246 (18)	43.40	38.25

Nos. 229-246 exist with second "o" of "Constitution" in italic type. Value, set $175.

Flowering Trees — A35

1976, Feb. 16			Perf. 13½x14	
247	A35	1c Almond	.25	.25
248	A35	10c Clusia rosea	.25	.25
249	A35	15c Calabash	.25	.25
250	A35	20c Cordia	.25	.25
251	A35	$1 Papaya	.50	.40
252	A35	$1.50 Flamboyant	.70	.55
a.		Souvenir sheet of 6, #247-252	2.50	2.50
b.		Horiz. strip of 5, #248-252	2.50	2.50
		Nos. 247-252 (6)	2.20	1.95

The Three Marys — A36

Designs: 10c, Crucifixion. 15c, Two soldiers. 20c, Annunciation. $1, Altar tapestry, 1470, Monastery of Rheinau, Switzerland, horiz. $1.50, "Noli me Tangere" (Jesus and Mary Magdalene). Designs of vertical stamps show details from tapestry shown on $1 stamp.

1976, Apr. 5			Perf. 14x13½, 13½x14	
253	A36	1c multicolored	.25	.25
254	A36	10c multicolored	.25	.25
255	A36	15c multicolored	.25	.25
256	A36	20c multicolored	.25	.25
257	A36	$1 multicolored	.45	.45
258	A36	$1.50 multicolored	.55	.55
a.		Souvenir sheet of 6	2.25	2.75
b.		Horiz. strip of 5, #254-258	2.25	2.25
		Nos. 253-258 (6)	2.00	2.00

Easter. No. 258a contains 6 stamps similar to Nos. 253-258 with simulated perforations.

Le Desius and La Vaillante Approaching Anguilla — A37

Sailing Ships: 3c, Sailboat leaving Anguilla for Antigua to get help. 15c, HMS Lapwing in battle with frigate Le Desius and brig La Vaillante. 25c, La Vaillante aground off St. Maarten. $1, Lapwing. $1.50, Le Desius burning.

1976, Nov. 8		Litho.	Perf. 13½x14	
259	A37	1c multicolored	.25	.25
260	A37	3c multicolored	1.40	.50
261	A37	15c multicolored	1.50	.70
262	A37	25c multicolored	1.50	.95
263	A37	$1 multicolored	2.00	1.40
264	A37	$1.50 multicolored	2.25	1.90
a.		Souvenir sheet of 6, #259-264	7.75	7.75
b.		Strip of 5, #260-264	9.50	9.50
		Nos. 259-264 (6)	8.90	5.70

Bicentenary of Battle of Anguilla between French and British ships.

Christmas Carnival — A38

Children's Paintings: 3c, 3 children dreaming of Christmas gifts. 15c, Caroling. 25c, Candlelight procession. $1, Going to Church on Christmas Eve. $1.50, Airport, coming home for Christmas.

1976, Nov. 22				
265	A38	1c multicolored	.25	.25
266	A38	3c multicolored	.25	.25
267	A38	15c multicolored	.25	.25
268	A38	25c multicolored	.25	.25
269	A38	$1 multicolored	.30	.30
270	A38	$1.50 multicolored	.40	.40
a.		Souvenir sheet of 6, #265-270	2.25	2.25
b.		Strip of 5, #266-270	1.75	1.75
		Nos. 265-270 (6)	1.70	1.70

Christmas. For overprints and surcharges see Nos. 305-310a.

Prince Charles and HMS Minerva, 1973 — A39

Designs: 40c, Prince Philip landing at Road Bay, 1964. $1.20, Homage to Queen at Coronation. $2.50, Coronation regalia and map of Anguilla.

1977, Feb. 9				
271	A39	25c multicolored	.25	.25
272	A39	40c multicolored	.25	.25
273	A39	$1.20 multicolored	.25	.25
274	A39	$2.50 multicolored	.35	.30
a.		Souvenir sheet of 4, #271-274	1.00	1.50
		Complete booklet, 2 each #271-274	3.00	
		Complete booklet, 2 each #271-274 with vert. selvage at right	5.00	
		Nos. 271-274 (4)	1.10	1.05

25th anniv. of reign of Queen Elizabeth II. The booklets with thin vert. selvage at right were from a separate printing.
For overprints see Nos. 297-300.

Yellow-crowned Night Heron — A40

Designs: 2c, Great barracuda. 3c, Queen conch. 4c, Spanish bayonet (Yucca). 5c, Trunkfish. 6c, Cable and telegraph building. 10c, American sparrow hawk. 15c, Ground orchids. 20c, Parlorfish. 22c, Lobster fishing boat. 35c, Boat race. 50c Sea bean (flowers). $1, Sandy Island with palms. $2.50, Manchineel (fruit). $5, Ground lizard. $10, Red-billed tropic bird.

1977-78		Litho.	Perf. 13½x14	
275	A40	1c multicolored	.35	1.00
276	A40	2c multicolored	.35	2.50
277	A40	3c multicolored	2.00	3.50
278	A40	4c multicolored	.40	.70
279	A40	5c multicolored	1.75	.45
280	A40	6c multicolored	.35	.45
281	A40	10c multicolored	5.50	4.50
282	A40	15c multicolored	3.75	2.00
283	A40	20c multicolored	3.75	1.00
284	A40	22c multicolored	.60	1.00
285	A40	35c multicolored	1.50	1.00
286	A40	50c multicolored	1.00	.90
287	A40	$1 multicolored	.70	.90
288	A40	$2.50 multicolored	1.10	1.00
289	A40	$5 multicolored	2.25	2.25
290	A40	$10 multicolored	9.00	6.50
		Nos. 275-290 (16)	34.35	29.65

Issued: Nos. 275-280, 290, 4/18/77; others 2/20/78.

For overprints and surcharges see Nos. 319-324, 337-342, 387-390, 402-404, 407-415, 417-423.

Crucifixion, by Quentin Massys — A41

Easter (Paintings): 3c, Betrayal of Christ, by Ugolino. 22c, Way to Calvary, by Ugolino. 30c, The Deposition, by Ugolino. $1, Resurrection, by Ugolino. $1.50, Crucifixion, by Andrea del Castagno.

1977, Apr. 25				
291	A41	1c multicolored	.25	.25
292	A41	3c multicolored	.25	.25
293	A41	22c multicolored	.25	.25
294	A41	30c multicolored	.35	.30
295	A41	$1 multicolored	.60	.55
296	A41	$1.50 multicolored	.90	.80
a.		Souvenir sheet of 6, #291-296	2.50	2.50
b.		Strip of 5, #292-296	2.50	2.50
		Nos. 291-296 (6)	2.60	2.40

Nos. 271-274, 274a Overprinted

1977, Oct. 26		Litho.	Perf. 13½x14	
297	A39	25c multicolored	.25	.25
298	A39	40c multicolored	.25	.25
299	A39	$1.20 multicolored	.40	.50
300	A39	$2.50 multicolored	.75	1.00
a.		Souvenir sheet of 4	1.40	2.00
		Nos. 297-300 (4)	1.65	2.00

Visit of Queen Elizabeth II to West Indies.

Suzanne Fourment in Velvet Hat, by Rubens — A42

Rubens Paintings: 40c, Helena Fourment with her Children. $1.20, Rubens with his wife. $2.50, Marchesa Brigida Spinola-Doria.

1977, Nov. 1			Perf. 14x13½	
301	A42	25c black & multi	.25	.25
302	A42	40c black & multi	.30	.30
303	A42	$1.20 multicolored	.80	.80
304	A42	$2.50 black & multi	1.10	1.35
a.		Souvenir sheet of 4, #301-304	2.50	2.75
		Nos. 301-304 (4)	2.45	2.70

Peter Paul Rubens, 400th birth anniv. Nos. 301-304 printed in sheets of 5 stamps and blue label with Rubens' portrait.
For overprint, see Nos. 311-314.

Nos. 265-270b Ovptd. & Srchd.

1977, Nov. 7			Perf. 13½x14	
305	A38	1c multicolored	.25	.25
306	A38	5c on 3c multi	.25	.25
307	A38	12c on 15c multi	.25	.25
308	A38	18c on 25c multi	.30	.30
309	A38	$1 multicolored	.60	.60
310	A38	$2.50 on $1.50 multi	1.25	1.25
a.		Souvenir sheet of 6, #305-310	3.50	3.50
b.		Strip of 5, #306-310	3.00	3.00
		Nos. 305-310 (6)	2.90	2.90

Christmas. Stamps and souvenir sheets have "1976" and old denomination obliterated with variously shaped rectangles.

Nos. 301-304a Ovptd. in Gold

1978, Mar. 6			Perf. 14x13½	
311	A42	25c black & multi	.25	.25
312	A42	40c black & multi	.25	.25
313	A42	$1.20 black & multi	.60	.60
314	A42	$2.50 black & multi	.70	.70
a.		Souvenir sheet of 4, #311-314	2.25	2.50
		Nos. 311-314 (4)	1.80	1.80

Buckingham Palace — A43

Designs: 50c, Coronation procession. $1.50, Royal family on balcony. $2.50, Royal coat of arms.

1978, Apr. 6			Perf. 14	
315	A43	22c multicolored	.25	.25
316	A43	50c multicolored	.25	.25
317	A43	$1.50 multicolored	.40	.40
318	A43	$2.50 multicolored	.60	.60
a.		Souvenir sheet of 4, #315-318	1.60	1.60
		Complete booklet, 2 each #315-318	3.25	
		Complete booklet, 2 each #315-318 with thin vert. selvage at right	4.00	
		Nos. 315-318 (4)	1.50	1.50

25th anniv. of coronation of Queen Elizabeth II.
The booklets with thin vert. selvage at right were from a separate printing.

Nos. 284-285 and 288 Ovptd. and Surcharged

1978, Aug. 14　Litho.　Perf. 13½x14

319	A40	22c multicolored	.50	.50
320	A40	35c multicolored	.70	.70
321	A40	$1.50 on $2.50 multi	1.30	1.30
		Nos. 319-321 (3)	2.50	2.50

Valley Secondary School, 25th anniv. Surcharge on No. 321 includes heavy bar over old denomination.

Nos. 286-287, 289 Ovptd. and Surcharged

1978, Aug. 14

322	A40	50c multicolored	1.00	1.00
323	A40	$1 multicolored	1.25	1.25
324	A40	$1.20 on $5 multi	2.00	2.00
		Nos. 322-324 (3)	4.25	4.25

Road Methodist Church, centenary. Surcharge on No. 324 includes heavy bar over old denomination.

Mother and Child — A44

Christmas: 12c, Christmas masquerade. 18c, Christmas dinner. 22c, Serenade. $1, Star over manger. $2.50, Family going to church.

1978, Dec. 11　Litho.　Perf. 13½

325	A44	5c multicolored	.25	.25
326	A44	12c multicolored	.25	.25
327	A44	18c multicolored	.25	.25
328	A44	22c multicolored	.25	.25
329	A44	$1 multicolored	.30	.30
330	A44	$2.50 multicolored	.60	.60
a.		Souvenir sheet of 6, #325-330	2.00	2.25
		Nos. 325-330 (6)	1.00	1.00

Type A44 in Changed Colors with IYC Emblem and Inscription

1979, Jan. 15　Litho.　Perf. 13½

331	A44	5c multicolored	.25	.25
332	A44	12c multicolored	.25	.25
333	A44	18c multicolored	.25	.25
334	A44	22c multicolored	.25	.25
335	A44	$1 multicolored	.30	.30
336	A44	$2.50 multicolored	.50	.50
a.		Souvenir sheet of 6, #331-336	2.75	3.25
		Nos. 331-336 (6)	1.80	1.80

Intl. Year of the Child. For overprint see No. 416.

Nos. 275-278, 280-281 Surcharged

1979, Feb. 8　Litho.　Perf. 13½x14

337	A40	12c on 2c multi	.60	.50
338	A40	14c on 4c multi	.50	.60
339	A40	18c on 3c multi	1.10	.90
340	A40	25c on 6c multi	.70	.55
341	A40	38c on 10c multi	2.75	1.10
342	A40	40c on 1c multi	3.00	1.10
		Nos. 337-342 (6)	8.65	4.75

No. 338 exists with surcharge inverted. Value, $30.

Valley Methodist Church A45

Church Interiors: 12c, St. Mary's Anglican Church, The Valley. 18c, St. Gerard's Roman Catholic Church, The Valley. 22c, Road Methodist Church. $1.50, St. Augustine's Anglican Church, East End. $2.50, West End Methodist Church.

1979, Mar. 30　Litho.　Perf. 14

343	A45	5c multicolored	.25	.25
344	A45	12c multicolored	.25	.25
345	A45	18c multicolored	.25	.25
346	A45	22c multicolored	.25	.25
347	A45	$1.50 multicolored	.40	.40
348	A45	$2.50 multicolored	.60	.60
a.		Souvenir sheet of 6	2.25	2.25
b.		Strip of 6, #343-348	2.00	2.00
		Nos. 343-348 (6)	2.00	2.00

Easter. No. 348a contains Nos. 343-348 in 2 horizontal rows of 3.

US No. C3a A46

No. 350, Cape of Good Hope #1. No. 351, Penny Black. No. 352, Germany #C36. No. 353, US #245. No. 354, Great Britain #93.

1979, Apr. 23　Litho.　Perf. 14

349	A46	1c multicolored	.25	.25
350	A46	1c multicolored	.25	.25
351	A46	22c multicolored	.25	.25
352	A46	35c multicolored	.25	.25
353	A46	$1.50 multicolored	.50	.50
354	A46	$2.50 multicolored	.75	.75
a.		Souvenir sheet of 6, #349-353	2.00	2.75
		Complete booklet, 2 each #349-354	4.50	
		Nos. 349-354 (6)	2.25	2.25

Sir Rowland Hill (1795-1879), originator of penny postage.

Wright's Flyer A — A47

History of Aviation: 12c, Louis Bleriot landing at Dover, 1909. 18c, Vickers Vimy, 1919. 22c, Spirit of St. Louis, 1927. $1.50, LZ127 Graf Zeppelin, 1928. $2.50, Concorde, 1979.

1979, May 21　Litho.　Perf. 14

355	A47	5c multicolored	.25	.25
356	A47	12c multicolored	.30	.25
357	A47	18c multicolored	.35	.25
358	A47	22c multicolored	.40	.30
359	A47	$1.50 multicolored	.95	.95
360	A47	$2.50 multicolored	3.50	1.50
a.		Souvenir sheet of 6, #355-360	6.50	6.50
		Nos. 355-360 (6)	5.75	3.50

Map of Anguilla, Map and View of Sombrero Island A48

Map of Anguilla, Map and View of: 12c, Anguillita Island. 18c, Sandy Island. 25c, Prickly Pear Cays. $1, Dog Island. $2.50, Scrub Island.

1979　　　　　Litho.　　Perf. 14

361	A48	5c multicolored	.25	.25
362	A48	12c multicolored	.25	.25
363	A48	18c multicolored	.25	.25
364	A48	25c multicolored	.25	.25
365	A48	$1 multicolored	.45	.55
366	A48	$2.50 multicolored	.70	.95
a.		Souvenir sheet of 6, #361-366	3.00	3.00
		Nos. 361-366 (6)	2.15	2.50

Anguilla's Outer Islands.

Red Poinsettia — A49

35c, Kalanchoe. $1.50, Cream poinsettia. $2.50, White poinsettia.

1979, Oct. 22　Litho.　Perf. 14½

367	A49	22c shown	.25	.25
368	A49	35c multicolored	.25	.25
369	A49	$1.50 multicolored	.40	.40
370	A49	$2.50 multicolored	.65	.65
a.		Souvenir sheet of 4, #367-370	2.50	2.50
		Nos. 367-370 (4)	1.55	1.55

Christmas.

Booths and Frames A50

Designs: 50c, Earls Court Exhibition Hall. $1.50, Penny Black, Great Britain #2. $2.50, Exhibition emblem.

1979, Dec. 10　Litho.　Perf. 13

371	A50	35c multicolored	.25	.25
372	A50	50c multicolored	.25	.25
373	A50	$1.50 multicolored	.40	.40
374	A50	$2.50 multicolored	.70	.70
b.		Souvenir sheet of 4, #371-374	1.75	1.75
		Complete booklet, 2 each #371-374	4.00	
		Nos. 371-374 (4)	1.60	1.60

Perf. 14½

371a	A50	35c	.25	.25
372a	A50	50c	.25	.25
373a	A50	$1.50	.45	.45
374a	A50	$2.50	.80	.80
c.		Souvenir sheet of 4, #371-374	2.00	2.00
		Nos. 371a-374a (4)	1.75	1.75

London 1980 Intl. Stamp Exhibition, May 6-14, 1980.

Lake Placid and Olympic Rings — A51

Olympic Rings and: 18c, Ice Hockey. 35c, Figure skating. 50c, Bobsledding. $1, Downhill skiing. $2.50, Luge.

1980, Jan.　Litho.　Perf. 13½, 14½

375	A51	5c multicolored	.25	.25
376	A51	18c multicolored	.25	.25
377	A51	35c multicolored	.25	.25
378	A51	50c multicolored	.30	.25
379	A51	$1 multicolored	.45	.65
380	A51	$2.50 multicolored	.80	1.10
a.		Souvenir sheet of 6, #375-380	2.25	3.00
		Nos. 375-380 (6)	2.30	2.75

13th Winter Olympic Games, Lake Placid, NY, Feb. 12-24.

Salt Field A52

12c, Tallying salt. 18c, Unloading salt flats. 22c, Storage pile. $1, Bagging and grinding. $2.50, Loading onto boats.

1980, Apr. 14　Litho.　Perf. 14

381	A52	5c multicolored	.25	.25
382	A52	12c multicolored	.25	.25
383	A52	18c multicolored	.25	.25
384	A52	22c multicolored	.25	.25
385	A52	$1 multicolored	.40	.40
386	A52	$2.50 multicolored	.85	.85
a.		Souvenir sheet of 6, #381-386	2.25	2.25
		Nos. 381-386 (6)	2.25	2.25

Salt industry.

Nos. 281, 288 Overprinted

1980, Apr. 16　　　　Perf. 13½x14

387	A40	10c multicolored	3.25	.30
388	A40	$2.50 multicolored	3.25	2.00

Nos. 283, 289 Overprinted

1980, Apr. 16　　　　Perf. 13½x14

389	A40	20c multicolored	2.50	.30
390	A40	$5 multicolored	6.00	3.00

Rotary International, 75th anniversary.

Big Ben, Great Britain No. 643, London 1980 Emblem — A53

Designs: $1.50, Canada No. 756. $2.50, Statue of Liberty, US No. 1632.

1980, May

391	A53	50c multicolored	.45	.45
392	A53	$1.50 multicolored	.65	.65
393	A53	$2.50 multicolored	1.15	1.15
a.		Souvenir sheet of 3, #391-393	2.25	2.25
		Nos. 391-393 (3)	2.25	2.25

London 1980 International Stamp Exhibition, May 6-14.

Queen Mother Elizabeth, 80th Birthday — A54

1980, Aug. 4   Litho.   *Perf. 14*
394	A54	35c multicolored	.55 .35
395	A54	50c multicolored	.70 .40
396	A54	$1.50 multicolored	1.25 1.00
397	A54	$3 multicolored	1.50 1.50
a.		Souvenir sheet of 4, #394-397	5.00 4.25
		Nos. 394-397 (4)	4.00 3.25

Pelicans — A55

22c, Great gray herons. $1.50, Swallows. $3, Hummingbirds.

1980, Nov. 10   Litho.   *Perf. 14*
398	A55	5c multicolored	.40 .25
399	A55	22c multicolored	1.10 .30
400	A55	$1.50 multicolored	2.40 .95
401	A55	$3 multicolored	3.00 2.10
a.		Souvenir sheet of 4, #398-401	12.00 12.00
		Nos. 398-401 (4)	6.90 3.60

Christmas. For overprints see Nos. 405-406.

Nos. 275, 278, 280-290, 334, 400-401
Overprinted

Perf. 13½x14, 14 (A55)
1980, Dec. 18   Litho.
402	A40	1c #275	.25 .80
403	A40	2c on 4c #278	.25 .80
404	A40	5c on 15c #282	1.25 .80
405	A55	5c on $1.50 #400	1.25 .80
406	A55	5c on $3 #401	1.25 .80
407	A40	10c #281	1.90 .80
408	A40	12c on $1 #287	.30 .80
409	A40	14c on $2.50 #288	.30 .80
410	A40	15c #282	1.50 .80
411	A40	18c on $5 #289	.35 .80
412	A40	20c #283	.35 .80
413	A40	22c #284	.35 .80
414	A40	25c on 15c #282	1.50 .95
415	A40	35c #285	.40 .95
416	A44	38c on 22c #334	.40 .95
417	A40	40c on 1c #275	.40 .95
418	A40	50c #286	.45 1.10
419	A40	$1 #287	.60 1.40
420	A40	$2.50 #288	1.50 3.50
421	A40	$5 #289	2.75 4.50
422	A40	$10 #290	5.50 6.50
423	A40	$10 on 6c #280	5.50 6.50
		Nos. 402-423 (22)	28.30 36.90

Petition for Separation, 1825 — A56

22c, Referendum ballot, 1967. 35c, Airport blockade, 1967. 50c, Anguilla flag. $1, Separation celebration, 1980.

1980, Dec. 18   *Perf. 14*
424	A56	18c multicolored	.25 .25
425	A56	22c multicolored	.25 .25
426	A56	35c multicolored	.30 .30
427	A56	50c multicolored	.35 .35
428	A56	$1 multicolored	.60 .80
a.		Souvenir sheet of 5, #424-428	1.75 2.00
		Nos. 424-428 (5)	1.75 1.95

Separation from St. Kitts-Nevis.

Nelson's Dockyard, by R. Granger Barrett A57

Ship Paintings: 35c, Agamemnon, Vanguard, Elephant, Captain and Victory, by Nicholas Pocock. 50c, Victory, by Monamy Swaine. $3, Battle of Trafalgar, by Clarkson Stanfield. $5, Lord Nelson, by L.F. Abbott and Nelson's arms.

1981, Mar. 2   Litho.   *Perf. 14*
429	A57	22c multicolored	2.10 .90
430	A57	35c multicolored	2.40 1.25
431	A57	50c multicolored	2.75 1.50
432	A57	$3 multicolored	3.75 5.50
		Nos. 429-432 (4)	11.00 9.15

Souvenir Sheet
433	A57	$5 multicolored	4.75 4.75

Lord Horatio Nelson (1758-1805), 175th death anniversary (1980).

Minnie Mouse A58

Easter: Various Disney characters in Easter outfits.

1981, Mar. 30   Litho.   *Perf. 13½*
434	A58	1c multicolored	.25 .25
435	A58	2c multicolored	.25 .25
436	A58	3c multicolored	.25 .25
437	A58	5c multicolored	.25 .25
438	A58	7c multicolored	.25 .25
439	A58	9c multicolored	.25 .25
440	A58	10c multicolored	.25 .25
441	A58	$2 multicolored	1.50 1.50
442	A58	$3 multicolored	2.00 2.00
		Nos. 434-442 (9)	5.25 5.25

Souvenir Sheet
443	A58	$5 multicolored	5.50 5.50

Prince Charles, Lady Diana, St. Paul's Cathedral A59

$2.50, Althorp. $3, Windsor Castle. $5, Buckingham Palace.

1981, June 15   Litho.   *Perf. 14*
444	A59	50c shown	.25 .25
a.		Souvenir sheet of 2	.30 .30
b.		Wmk. 380	.25 .25
c.		Booklet pane of 4 #444b	1.00 1.00
445	A59	$2.50 multicolored	.45 .60
a.		Souvenir sheet of 2	1.60 1.60
446	A59	$3 multicolored	.55 .75
a.		Souvenir sheet of 2	2.00 2.00
b.		Wmk. 380	1.25 1.25
c.		Booklet pane of 4 #446b	5.00 5.00
		Complete booklet, #444c, 446c	6.00
		Nos. 444-446 (3)	1.25 1.60

Souvenir Sheet
447	A59		1.50 1.50

Royal Wedding. Nos. 444a-446a contain stamps in different colors.

Boys Climbing Tree A60

10c, Boys sailing boats. 15c, Children playing instruments. $3, Children with animals. $4, Boys playing soccer, vert.

1981   Litho.   *Perf. 14*
448	A60	5c multicolored	.25 .25
449	A60	10c multicolored	.30 .30
450	A60	15c multicolored	.40 .45
451	A60	$3 multicolored	2.75 3.50
		Nos. 448-451 (4)	3.70 4.50

Souvenir Sheet
452	A60	$4 multicolored	4.25 4.25

UNICEF, 35th anniv.
Issued: 5c-15c, July 31; $3-$4, Sept. 30.

"The Children were Nestled all Snug in their Beds" — A61

Christmas: Scenes from Walt Disney's The Night Before Christmas.

1981, Nov. 2   Litho.   *Perf. 13½*
453	A61	1c multicolored	.25 .25
454	A61	2c multicolored	.25 .25
455	A61	3c multicolored	.25 .25
456	A61	5c multicolored	.30 .25
457	A61	7c multicolored	.30 .25
458	A61	10c multicolored	.30 .25
459	A61	12c multicolored	.30 .25
460	A61	$2 multicolored	3.25 2.10
461	A61	$3 multicolored	3.25 2.50
		Nos. 453-461 (9)	8.45 6.35

Souvenir Sheet
462	A61	$5 multicolored	7.00 7.00

Red Grouper — A62

No. 473

5c, Ferries, Blowing Point. 10c, Racing boats. 15c, Majorettes. 20c, Launching boat, Sandy Hill. 25c, Coral. 30c, Little Bay cliffs. 35c, Fountain Cave. 40c, Sandy Isld. 45c, Landing, Sombrero. 60c, Seine fishing. 75c, Boat race, Sandy Ground. $1, Bagging lobster, Island Harbor. $5, Pelicans. $7.50, Hibiscus. $10, Queen triggerfish.

1982, Jan. 1   Litho.   *Perf. 14*
463	A62	1c multi	.25 .90
464	A62	5c multi	.35 .90
465	A62	10c multi	.25 .90
466	A62	15c multi	.25 .90
467	A62	20c multi	.45 .90
468	A62	25c multi	1.75 .90
469	A62	30c multi	.35 1.10
470	A62	35c multi	1.75 1.25
471	A62	40c multi	.35 1.10
472	A62	45c multi	.55 1.25
473	A62	50c on 45c, #472	.60 .55
474	A62	60c multi	3.50 3.50
475	A62	75c multi	1.10 2.50
476	A62	$1 multi	2.25 2.50
477	A62	$5 multi	18.00 18.00
478	A62	$7.50 multi	14.00 20.00
479	A62	$10 multi	18.00 20.00
		Nos. 463-479 (17)	64.00 77.15

For overprints & surcharges see Nos. 507-510, 546A-546D, 578-582, 606-608, 640-647.

Easter — A63

Butterflies on flowers: 10c, Zebra, anthurium. 35c, Caribbean buckeye. 75c, Monarch, allamanda. $3, Red rim, orchid. $5, Flambeau, amaryllis.

**1982, Apr. 5   **
480	A63	10c multicolored	1.00 .25
481	A63	35c multicolored	1.75 .55
482	A63	75c multicolored	2.00 .80
483	A63	$3 multicolored	3.50 2.40
		Nos. 480-483 (4)	8.25 4.00

Souvenir Sheet
484	A63	$5 multicolored	5.75 5.75

Princess Diana, 21st Birthday — A64

Designs: Portraits, 1961-1981.

1982, May 17
485	A64	10c 1961	.60 .25
486	A64	30c 1968	1.35 .25
487	A64	40c 1970	.70 .30
488	A64	60c 1974	.70 .40
489	A64	$2 1981	1.10 1.50
490	A64	$3 1981	5.00 2.10
a.		Souvenir sheet of 6, #485-490	9.75 9.75
		Complete booklet, 4 each #485, 487-489	10.00
		Nos. 485-490 (6)	9.45 4.80

Souvenir Sheet
491	A64	$5 1981	9.75 9.75

For overprints see Nos. 639A-639G.

1982 World Cup — A65

Various Disney characters playing soccer.

1982, Aug. 3   Litho.   *Perf. 11*
492	A65	1c multicolored	.25 .25
493	A65	3c multicolored	.25 .25
494	A65	4c multicolored	.25 .25
495	A65	5c multicolored	.25 .25
496	A65	7c multicolored	.25 .25
497	A65	8c multicolored	.25 .25
498	A65	10c multicolored	.25 .25
499	A65	$2.50 multicolored	2.50 2.25
500	A65	$3 multicolored	2.50 2.25
		Nos. 492-500 (9)	6.75 6.25

Souvenir Sheet
Perf. 14
501	A65	$5 multicolored	8.00 8.00

Scouting Year A66

1982, July 5

502	A66	10c Pitching tent	.60	.50
503	A66	35c Marching band	1.00	.70
504	A66	75c Sailing	1.40	1.25
505	A66	$3 Flag bearers	3.75	2.75
		Nos. 502-505 (4)	6.75	5.20

Souvenir Sheet

506	A66	$5 Camping	6.25	6.25

Nos. 465, 474-475, 477 Overprinted

1982, Oct. 18   Litho.   Perf. 14

507	A62	10c multicolored	.30	.30
508	A62	60c multicolored	.70	.70
509	A62	75c multicolored	.90	.90
510	A62	$5 multicolored	5.00	5.00
		Nos. 507-510 (4)	6.90	6.90

12th Commonwealth Games, Brisbane, Australia, Sept. 30-Oct. 9.

Christmas — A67

Scenes from Walt Disney's Winnie the Pooh.

1982, Nov. 29

511	A67	1c multicolored	.25	.25
512	A67	2c multicolored	.25	.25
513	A67	3c multicolored	.25	.25
514	A67	5c multicolored	.40	.25
515	A67	7c multicolored	.40	.25
516	A67	10c multicolored	.50	.25
517	A67	12c multicolored	.60	.30
518	A67	20c multicolored	1.35	.35
519	A67	$5 multicolored	8.50	8.50
		Nos. 511-519 (9)	12.50	10.65

Souvenir Sheet

520	A67	$5 multicolored	11.50	11.50

Commonwealth Day (Mar. 14) — A68

10c, Carnival procession. 35c, Flags. 75c, Economic cooperation. $2.50, Salt pond. $5, Map showing Commonwealth.

1983, Feb. 28   Litho.   Perf. 14

521	A68	10c multicolored	.25	.25
522	A68	35c multicolored	.45	.50
523	A68	75c multicolored	.85	1.00
524	A68	$2.50 multicolored	5.25	5.25
		Nos. 521-524 (4)	6.80	7.00

Souvenir Sheet

525	A68	$5 multicolored	7.00	7.00

Easter — A69

Ten Commandments.

1983, Mar. 31   Litho.   Perf. 14

526	A69	1c multicolored	.25	.25
527	A69	2c multicolored	.25	.25
528	A69	3c multicolored	.25	.25
529	A69	10c multicolored	.25	.25
530	A69	35c multicolored	.55	.30
531	A69	60c multicolored	1.00	.50
532	A69	75c multicolored	1.10	.55
533	A69	$2 multicolored	2.75	2.10
534	A69	$2.50 multicolored	3.00	2.10
535	A69	$5 multicolored	4.25	3.25
		Nos. 526-535 (10)	13.65	9.80

Souvenir Sheet

536	A69	$5 Moses Taking Tablets	4.50	4.50

Local Turtles and World Wildlife Fund Emblem — A70

1983, Aug. 10   Litho.   Perf. 13½

537	A70	10c Leatherback	5.00	2.10
538	A70	35c Hawksbill	8.25	3.25
539	A70	75c Green	12.00	4.75
540	A70	$1 Loggerhead	13.50	6.50
		Nos. 537-540 (4)	38.75	16.60

Souvenir Sheet

541	A70	$5 Leatherback, diff.	30.00	8.25

1983, Aug. 10   Litho.   Perf. 12

537a	A70	10c Leatherback	3.50	2.40
538a	A70	35c Hawksbill	11.00	4.75
539a	A70	75c Green	14.50	10.50
540a	A70	$1 Loggerhead	22.00	13.00
		Nos. 537a-540a (4)	51.00	30.65

Manned Flight Bicentenary A71

10c, Montgolfiere, 1783. 60c, Blanchard & Jeffries, 1785. $1, Giffard's airship, 1852. $2.50, Lilienthal's glider, 1890. $5, Wright Brothers' plane, 1909.

1983, Aug. 22   Perf. 14

542	A71	10c multicolored	.60	.40
543	A71	60c multicolored	1.90	.90
544	A71	$1 multicolored	2.00	1.10
545	A71	$2.50 multicolored	3.00	3.00
		Nos. 542-545 (4)	7.50	5.40

Souvenir Sheet

546	A71	$5 multicolored	6.50	6.50

Nos. 465, 471, 476-477 Overprinted

10c, Racing boats. 40c, Sandy Isld. $1, Bagging lobster, Island Harbor. $5, Pelicans.

1983, Oct. 24   Litho.   Perf. 14

546A	A62	10c multicolored	.30	.25
546B	A62	40c multicolored	.45	.35
546C	A62	$1 multicolored	1.00	.65
546D	A62	$2 multicolored	7.75	3.75
		Nos. 546A-546D (4)	9.50	5.00

Jiminy Cricket A72

Various Disney productions: 2c, Jiminy Cricket, kettle. 3c, Jiminy Cricket, toys. 4c, Mickey and Morty. 5c, Scrooge McDuck. 6c, Minnie and Goofy. 10c, Goofy and Elf. $2, Scrooge McDuck, diff. $3, Disney characters. $5, Scrooge McDuck.

1983, Nov. 14   Perf. 13½

547	A72	1c shown	.25	.25
548	A72	2c multicolored	.25	.25
549	A72	3c multicolored	.25	.25
550	A72	4c multicolored	.25	.25
551	A72	5c multicolored	.25	.25
552	A72	6c multicolored	.25	.25
553	A72	10c multicolored	.25	.25
554	A72	$2 multicolored	4.50	3.25
555	A72	$3 multicolored	5.00	3.00
		Nos. 547-555 (9)	11.25	8.00

Souvenir Sheet

556	A72	$5 multicolored	8.00	8.00

Boys' Brigade Centenary — A73

10c, Anguilla company, banner. $5, Marching with drummer.

1983, Sept. 12   Litho.   Perf. 14

557	A73	10c multicolored	.50	.35
558	A73	$5 multicolored	3.75	3.25
a.		Souvenir sheet of 2, #557-558	4.75	4.75

1984 Olympics, Los Angeles — A74

Mickey Mouse Competing in Decathlon.

1984, Feb. 20   Litho.   Perf. 14

559	A74	1c 100-meter run	.25	.25
560	A74	2c Long jump	.25	.25
561	A74	3c Shot put	.25	.25
562	A74	4c High jump	.25	.25
563	A74	5c 400-meter run	.25	.25
564	A74	6c Hurdles	.25	.25
565	A74	10c Discus	.25	.25
566	A74	$1 Pole vault	3.25	3.00
567	A74	$4 Javelin	6.75	4.75
		Nos. 559-567 (9)	11.75	9.50

Souvenir Sheet

568	A74	$5 1500-meter run	12.50	12.50

1984, Apr. 24   Perf. 12½x12

559a	A74	1c	.25	.25
560a	A74	2c	.25	.25
561a	A74	3c	.25	.25
562a	A74	4c	.25	.25
563a	A74	5c	.25	.25
564a	A74	6c	.25	.25
565a	A74	10c	.25	.25
566a	A74	$1	4.75	3.75
567a	A74	$4	6.25	9.50
		Nos. 559a-567a (9)	12.75	15.00

Souvenir Sheet

568a	A74	$5 With Olympic rings emblem	11.00	11.00

Nos. 559a-567a inscribed with Olympic rings emblem. Printed in sheets of 5 plus label.

Easter A75

Ceiling and Wall Frescoes, La Stanze della Segnatura, by Raphael (details).

1984, Apr. 19   Litho.   Perf. 13½x14

569	A75	10c Justice	.25	.25
570	A75	25c Poetry	.30	.30
571	A75	35c Philosophy	.40	.40
572	A75	40c Theology	.40	.40
573	A75	$1 Abraham & Paul	.90	.90
574	A75	$2 Moses & Matthew	1.75	1.75
575	A75	$3 John & David	2.50	2.50
576	A75	$4 Peter & Adam	3.00	3.00
		Nos. 569-576 (8)	9.50	9.50

Souvenir Sheet

577	A75	$5 Astronomy	5.25	5.25

Nos. 463, 469, 477-479 Surcharged

1984   Litho.   Perf. 14

578	A62	25c on $7.50 #478	.85	.45
579	A62	35c on 30c #469	.70	.55
580	A62	60c on 1c #463	.75	.60
581	A62	$2.50 on $5 #477	3.75	1.90
582	A62	$2.50 on $10 #479	2.75	1.90
		Nos. 578-582 (5)	8.80	5.40

Issue dates: 25c, May 17, others, Apr. 24.

Ausipex '84 — A76

Australian stamps.

1984, July 16   Litho.   Perf. 13½

583	A76	10c No. 2	.60	.45
584	A76	75c No. 18	1.75	1.40
585	A76	$1 No. 130	2.25	1.90
586	A76	$2.50 No. 178	3.50	3.50
		Nos. 583-586 (4)	8.10	7.25

Souvenir Sheet

587	A76	$5 Nos. 378, 379	6.75	6.75

Slavery Abolition Sesquicentennial — A77

Abolitionists and Vignettes: 10c, Thomas Fowell Buxton, planting sugar cane. 25c, Abraham Lincoln, cotton field. 35c, Henri Christophe, armed slave revolt. 60c, Thomas Clarkson, addressing Anti-Slavery Society. 75c, William Wilberforce, Slave auction. $1, Olaudah Equiano, slave raid on Benin coast. $2.50, General Gordon, slave convoy in Sudan. $5, Granville Sharp, restraining ship captain from boarding slave.

1984, Aug. 1   Perf. 12

588	A77	10c multicolored	.25	.25
589	A77	25c multicolored	.45	.45
590	A77	35c multicolored	.55	.55
591	A77	60c multicolored	.70	.70
592	A77	75c multicolored	.90	.90
593	A77	$1 multicolored	1.00	1.00
594	A77	$2.50 multicolored	1.90	1.90
595	A77	$5 multicolored	3.75	3.75
a.		Miniature sheet of 8, #588-595	9.50	11.00
		Nos. 588-595 (8)	9.50	9.50

For overprints see Nos. 688-695a.

Christmas — A78

Various Disney characters and celebrations.

Perf. 14, 12½x12 ($2)

1984, Nov. 12			Litho.	
596	A78	1c multicolored	.25	.25
597	A78	2c multicolored	.25	.25
598	A78	3c multicolored	.25	.25
599	A78	4c multicolored	.25	.25
600	A78	5c multicolored	.25	.25
601	A78	10c multicolored	.25	.25
602	A78	$1 multicolored	3.75	3.00
603	A78	$2 multicolored	4.75	5.00
604	A78	$4 multicolored	6.00	9.50
		Nos. 596-604 (9)	16.00	19.00

Souvenir Sheet

605	A78	$5 multicolored	8.50	8.50

Nos. 464-465, 477 Ovptd. or Srchd.

1984, Aug. 13				
606	A62	5c #464	.35	.25
607	A62	20c on 10c #465	.50	.30
608	A62	$5 #477	7.00	4.25
		Nos. 606-608 (3)	7.85	4.80

Intl. Civil
Aviation
Org., 40th
Anniv.
A79

60c, Icarus, by Hans Erni. 75c, Sun Princess, by Sadiou Diouf. $2.50, Anniv. emblem, vert.
$5, Map of the Caribbean.

1984, Dec. 3			Litho.	Perf. 14
609	A79	60c multicolored	.90	1.00
610	A79	75c multicolored	1.40	1.60
611	A79	$2.50 multicolored	4.00	4.25
		Nos. 609-611 (3)	6.30	6.85

Souvenir Sheet

612	A79	$5 multicolored	6.00	7.00

Audubon Birth
Bicent. — A80

Illustrations by artist and naturalist J. J. Audubon (1785-1851) — 10c, Hirundo rustica. 60c, Mycteria americana. 75c, Sterna dougallii. $5, Pandion haliaetus.
No. 617, Vireo solitarus, horiz. No. 618, Piranga ludoviciana, horiz.

1985, Apr. 30			Litho.	Perf. 14
613	A80	10c multicolored	1.25	1.00
614	A80	60c multicolored	2.10	2.10
615	A80	75c multicolored	2.10	2.10
616	A80	$5 multicolored	7.75	7.75
		Nos. 613-616 (4)	13.20	12.95

Souvenir Sheets

617	A80	$4 multicolored	7.00	7.00
618	A80	$4 multicolored	7.00	7.00

Queen Mother 85th
Birthday — A81

Photographs: 10c, Visiting the children's ward at King's College Hospital. $2, Inspecting Royal Marine Volunteer Cadets at Deal. $3, Outside Clarence House in London. $5, In an open carriage at Ascot.

1985, July 2				
619	A81	10c multicolored	.25	.25
620	A81	$2 multicolored	1.00	1.00
621	A81	$3 multicolored	1.75	1.75
		Nos. 619-621 (3)	3.00	3.00

Souvenir Sheet

622	A81	$5 multicolored	2.75	2.75

Nos. 619-621 printed in sheetlets of 5.

Birds
A82

5c, Brown pelican. 10c, Turtle dove. 15c, Man-o-war. 20c, Antillean crested hummingbird. 25c, White-tailed tropicbird. 30c, Caribbean elaenia. No. 629, 35c, Black-whiskered vireo. No. 629A, 35c, Lesser Antillean bullfinch ('86). 40c, Yellow-crowned night heron. 45c, Pearly-eyed thrasher. 50c, Laughing bird. 65c, Brown booby. 80c, Gray kingbird. $1, Audubon's shearwater. $1.35, Roseate tern. $2.50, Bananaquit. $5, Belted kingfisher. $10, Green heron.

1985-86			Litho.	Perf. 13½x14
623	A82	5c multi	3.00	2.00
624	A82	10c multi	3.00	2.00
625	A82	15c multi	3.00	2.00
626	A82	20c multi	3.00	2.00
627	A82	25c multi	3.00	2.50
628	A82	30c multi	3.00	2.50
629	A82	35c multi	13.00	10.00
629A	A82	35c multi	3.00	2.50
630	A82	40c multi	3.00	2.50
631	A82	45c multi	3.00	2.50
632	A82	50c multi	3.00	2.50
633	A82	65c multi	3.00	2.50
634	A82	80c multi	4.00	5.00
635	A82	$1 multi	4.00	5.00
636	A82	$1.35 multi	3.00	5.00
637	A82	$2.50 multi	10.00	11.00
638	A82	$5 multi	7.75	13.50
639	A82	$10 multi	13.00	17.50
		Nos. 623-639 (18)	87.75	92.50

Issued: 25c, 65c, $1.35, $5, 7/22; 45c, 50c, 80c, $1, $10, 9/30; 5c-20c, 30c, No. 629, 40c, $2.50, 11/11; No. 629A, 3/10.
For overprints & surcharges see Nos. 678-682, 713-716, 723-739, 750-753, 764-767, 783-786.

**Nos. 485-491
Overprinted**

1985, Oct. 31			Litho.	Perf. 14
639A	A64	10c multicolored	.25	.25
639B	A64	30c multicolored	.25	.25
639C	A64	40c multicolored	.30	.30
639D	A64	60c multicolored	.45	.45
639E	A64	$2 multicolored	1.50	1.50
639F	A64	$3 multicolored	3.50	3.50
h.		Souv. sheet of 6, #639A-639F	4.25	4.25
		Complete booklet, 4 each #639A, 639C-639E	11.00	
		Nos. 639A-639F (6)	6.25	6.25

Souvenir Sheet

639G	A64	$5 multicolored	4.50	4.50

Nos. 464, 469, 475 and 477 Ovptd.

1985, Oct. 14			Litho.	Perf. 14
640	A62	5c multicolored	.45	.25
641	A62	30c multicolored	.75	.55
642	A62	75c multicolored	1.10	.90
643	A62	$5 multicolored	10.50	10.50
		Nos. 640-643 (4)	12.80	12.20

Nos. 465 and 469 Ovptd. or Srchd.

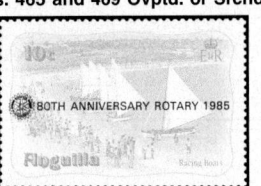

1985, Nov. 18				
644	A62	10c multicolored	.65	.25
645	A62	35c on 30c multi	1.40	.50

Nos. 476, 469 Srchd. or Ovptd.

1985, Nov. 18				
646	A62	$1 multicolored	2.25	1.25
647	A62	$5 on 30c multi	6.75	6.75

Brothers Grimm — A83

Christmas: Disney characters in Hansel and Gretel.

1985, Nov. 11			Litho.	Perf. 14
648	A83	5c multicolored	.55	.55
649	A83	50c multicolored	1.75	.80
650	A83	90c multicolored	2.25	1.25
651	A83	$4 multicolored	4.00	4.00
		Nos. 648-651 (4)	8.55	6.60

Souvenir Sheet

652	A83	$5 multicolored	8.00	8.00

Mark Twain (1835-1910),
Author — A84

Disney characters in Huckleberry Finn.

1985, Nov. 11				
653	A84	10c multicolored	.70	.35
654	A84	60c multicolored	2.25	1.10
654A	A84	$1 multicolored	3.00	1.60
655	A84	$3 multicolored	4.00	4.00
		Nos. 653-655 (4)	9.95	7.05

Souvenir Sheet

656	A84	$5 multicolored	9.00	9.00

Christmas. No. 654A printed in sheets of 8.

Statue of
Liberty
Centennial
A85

10c, Danmark, Denmark. 20c, Eagle, USA. 60c, Amerigo Vespucci, Italy. 75c, Sir Winston Churchill, G.B. $2, Nippon Maru, Japan. $2.50, Gorch, Germany.
$5, Statue of Liberty, vert.

1985, Nov. 25				
657	A85	10c multicolored	.85	.70
658	A85	20c multicolored	1.25	.95
659	A85	60c multicolored	1.60	1.60
660	A85	75c multicolored	1.60	1.50
661	A85	$2 multicolored	1.60	3.00
662	A85	$2.50 multicolored	2.10	3.00
		Nos. 657-662 (6)	9.00	10.75

Souvenir Sheet

663	A85	$5 multicolored	9.00	9.00

Easter — A86

Stained glass windows.

1986, Mar. 27			Litho.	Perf. 14
664	A86	10c multicolored	.25	.25
665	A86	25c multicolored	.50	.50
666	A86	45c multicolored	.90	.90
667	A86	$4 multicolored	4.25	5.25
		Nos. 664-667 (4)	5.90	6.90

Souvenir Sheet

668	A86	$5 multi, horiz.	7.00	7.00

Halley's
Comet
A87

A88

Designs: 5c, Johannes Hevelius (1611-1687), Mayan temple observatory. 10c, US Viking probe landing on Mars, 1976. 60c, Theatri Cosmicum (detail), 1668. $4, Sighting, 1835. $5, Comet over Anguilla.

1986, Mar. 24				
669	A87	5c multicolored	.45	.45
670	A87	10c multicolored	.50	.50
671	A87	60c multicolored	1.50	1.10
672	A87	$4 multicolored	6.25	6.25
		Nos. 669-672 (4)	8.70	8.30

Souvenir Sheet

673	A88	$5 multicolored	5.50	6.25

Queen Elizabeth II, 60th Birthday
Common Design Type

20c, Inspecting guards, 1946. $2, Garter
Ceremony, 1985. $3, Trooping the color.
$5, Christening, 1926.

1986, Apr. 21

674	CD339	20c multicolored		.25	.25
675	CD339	$2 multicolored		1.50	1.50
676	CD339	$3 multicolored		2.25	2.25
		Nos. 674-676 (3)		4.00	4.00

Souvenir Sheet

677	CD339	$5 multicolored	4.00	4.00

Nos. 623, 631, 635, 637 and 639 Ovptd.

1986, May 22   *Perf. 13½x14*

678	A82	5c multicolored	.90	1.10
679	A82	45c multicolored	2.00	.75
680	A82	$1 multicolored	3.50	1.60
681	A82	$2.50 multicolored	3.50	4.25
682	A82	$10 multicolored	10.00	11.00
		Nos. 678-682 (5)	19.90	18.70

Wedding of Prince
Andrew and Sarah
Ferguson — A89

1986, July 23   **Litho.**   *Perf. 14*

683	A89	10c Couple	.25	.25
684	A89	35c Andrew	.30	.30
685	A89	$2 Sarah	1.10	1.60
686	A89	$3 Couple, diff.	1.75	2.75
		Nos. 683-686 (4)	3.40	4.90

Souvenir Sheet

687	A89	$6 Westminster Abbey	5.25	6.00

Perf. 12

683a	A89	10c Couple	.40	.25
684a	A89	35c Andrew	.65	.30
685a	A89	$2 Sarah	1.60	1.25
686a	A89	$3 Couple, diff.	2.00	1.90
		Nos. 683a-686a (4)	4.65	3.70

Souvenir Sheet

687a	A89	$6 Westminster Abbey	5.25	6.00

Nos. 588-595 Overprinted

1986, Sept. 29   **Litho.**   *Perf. 12*

688	A77	10c multicolored	.65	.35
689	A77	25c multicolored	1.00	.55
690	A77	35c multicolored	1.25	.65
691	A77	60c multicolored	2.00	.95
692	A77	75c multicolored	2.00	1.25
693	A77	$1 multicolored	2.00	1.40
694	A77	$2.50 multicolored	3.50	5.00
695	A77	$5 multicolored	4.75	6.50
a.		Miniature sheet, #688-695	19.00	20.00
		Nos. 688-695 (8)	17.15	16.65

Ships
A90

1986, Nov. 29   **Litho.**   *Perf. 14*

696	A90	10c Trading Sloop	1.75	.45
697	A90	45c Lady Rodney	3.25	.60
698	A90	80c West Derby	4.50	3.00
699	A90	$3 Warspite	7.75	6.00
		Nos. 696-699 (4)	17.25	10.05

Souvenir Sheet

700	A90	$6 Boat Race Day, vert.	20.00	20.00

Christmas.

Discovery of
America, 500th
Anniv. (in
1992) — A91

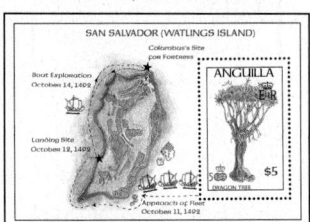

Dragon Tree — A92

5c, Christopher Columbus, astrolabe. 10c,
Aboard ship. 35c, Santa Maria. 80c, Ferdinand, Isabella. $4, Indians. No. 707, Carib-
bean manatee.

1986, Dec. 22

701	A91	5c multi	.85	.85
702	A91	10c multi	1.40	.90
703	A91	35c multi	2.75	1.60
704	A91	80c multi, horiz.	2.00	2.25
705	A91	$4 multi	4.50	5.00
		Nos. 701-705 (5)	11.50	10.60

Souvenir Sheets

706	A92	$5 shown	9.00	9.00
707	A92	$5 multi, horiz.	9.00	9.00

Butterflies
A93

10c, Monarch. 80c, White peacock. $1,
Zebra. $2, Caribbean buckeye.
$6, Flambeau.

1987, Apr. 14   **Litho.**   *Perf. 14*

708	A93	10c multicolored	2.00	.90
709	A93	80c multicolored	5.50	2.75
710	A93	$1 multicolored	6.50	3.25
711	A93	$2 multicolored	10.00	11.00
		Nos. 708-711 (4)	24.00	17.90

Souvenir Sheet

712	A93	$6 multicolored	20.00	20.00

Easter.

Nos. 629A, 631, 634 and 639 Ovptd in Red

1987, May 25   **Litho.**   *Perf. 13½x14*

713	A82	35c on No. 629A	2.25	1.00
714	A82	45c on No. 631	2.25	1.10
715	A82	80c on No. 634	3.25	1.60
716	A82	$10 on No. 639	12.00	16.00
		Nos. 713-716 (4)	19.75	19.70

Separation from St. Kitts and Nevis,
20th Anniv. — A94

10c, Old goose iron, electric iron. 35c, Old
East End School, Albena Lake-Hodge Comprehensive College. 45c, Old market place,
People's Market. 80c, Old ferries & modern
ferry at Blowing Point. $1, Old & new cable &
wireless offices. $2, Public meeting at Bur-
rowes Park, House of Assembly.

1987, May 25   *Perf. 14*

717	A94	10c multicolored	.75	.50
718	A94	35c multicolored	.85	.65
719	A94	45c multicolored	1.00	.80
720	A94	80c multicolored	2.25	1.00
721	A94	$1 multicolored	1.75	1.25
722	A94	$2 multicolored	2.50	2.75
a.		Souvenir sheet of 6, #717-722	12.50	12.50
		Nos. 717-722 (6)	9.10	6.95

Nos. 623, 625-628, 629A-639 Ovptd. in Red or Srchd. in Red & Black

1987, Sept. 4   **Litho.**   *Perf. 13½x14*

723	A82	5c No. 623	3.50	3.00
724	A82	10c on 15c No. 625	3.50	3.00
725	A82	15c No. 625	3.50	3.00
726	A82	20c No. 626	3.50	3.00
727	A82	25c No. 627	3.50	3.00
728	A82	30c No. 628	3.50	3.00
729	A82	35c No. 629A	3.50	3.00
730	A82	40c No. 630	3.50	3.00
731	A82	45c No. 631	3.50	3.00
732	A82	50c No. 632	3.50	3.00
733	A82	65c No. 633	3.75	3.25
734	A82	80c No. 634	3.50	3.00
735	A82	$1 No. 635	4.00	4.00
736	A82	$1.35 No. 636	4.75	4.75
737	A82	$2.50 No. 637	6.00	6.00
738	A82	$5 No. 638	7.50	9.00
739	A82	$10 No. 639	11.00	13.50
		Nos. 723-739 (17)	75.00	74.00

Cricket World Cup — A95

Various action scenes.

1987, Oct. 5   *Perf. 14*

740	A95	10c multicolored	1.75	.90
741	A95	35c multicolored	2.50	.90
742	A95	45c multicolored	2.50	.95
743	A95	$2.50 multicolored	5.00	7.50
		Nos. 740-743 (4)	11.75	10.25

Souvenir Sheet

744	A95	$6 multicolored	15.00	15.00

Sea
Shells,
Crabs
A96

10c, West Indian top shell. 35c, Ghost crab.
50c, Spiny Caribbean vase. $2, Great land
crab.
$6, Queen conch.

1987, Nov. 2

745	A96	10c multicolored	1.75	.70
746	A96	35c multicolored	2.25	1.10
747	A96	50c multicolored	4.00	2.10
748	A96	$2 multicolored	6.00	10.50
		Nos. 745-748 (4)	14.00	14.40

Souvenir Sheet

749	A96	$6 multicolored	14.00	14.00

Christmas.

Nos. 629A, 635-636 and 639 Ovptd. in Scarlet

1987, Dec. 14   **Litho.**   *Perf. 13½x14*

750	A82	35c multicolored	.30	.30
751	A82	$1 multicolored	.70	.75
752	A82	$1.35 multicolored	1.00	1.00
753	A82	$10 multicolored	7.00	8.50
		Nos. 750-753 (4)	9.00	10.55

Easter
(Lilies) — A97

30c, Crinum erubescens. 45c, Hymenocallis
caribaea. $1, Crinum macowanii. $2.50, Hem-
erocallis fulva.

$6, Lilium longiflorum.

1988, Mar. 28   **Litho.**   *Perf. 14*

754	A97	30c multicolored	.65	.35
755	A97	45c multicolored	.85	.35
756	A97	$1 multicolored	2.25	1.00
757	A97	$2.50 multicolored	2.50	4.00
		Nos. 754-757 (4)	6.25	5.70

Souvenir Sheet

758	A97	$6 multicolored	5.75	7.25

1988 Summer
Olympics,
Seoul — A98

1988, July 25   **Litho.**   *Perf. 14*

759	A98	35c 4x100-Meter relay	.70	.35
760	A98	45c Windsurfing	.80	.50
761	A98	50c Tennis	2.25	1.60
762	A98	80c Basketball	5.00	4.25
		Nos. 759-762 (4)	8.75	6.70

Souvenir Sheet

763	A98	$6 Women's 200 meters	5.75	5.75

Nos. 629A, 634-635 and 637 Ovptd.

1988, Dec. 14 Litho. Perf. 13½x14
764	A82	35c multicolored	1.90	.85
765	A82	80c multicolored	2.75	1.75
766	A82	$1 multicolored	2.75	2.10
767	A82	$2.50 multicolored	4.75	5.75
	Nos. 764-767 (4)		12.15	10.45

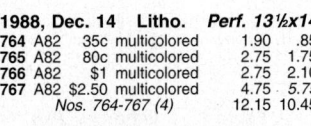

Marine Life — A99

35c, Common sea fan. 80c, Coral crab. $1, Grooved brain coral. $1.60, Old wife. $6, West Indies spiny lobster.

1988, Nov. 28 Litho. Perf. 14
768	A99	35c multicolored	1.50	.45
769	A99	80c multicolored	2.25	.95
770	A99	$1 multicolored	3.25	1.60
771	A99	$1.60 multicolored	3.50	4.50
	Nos. 768-771 (4)		10.50	7.50

Souvenir Sheet
772	A99	$6 multicolored	6.75	6.75

Christmas.

Lizards — A100

1989, Feb. 20 Litho. Perf. 13½x14
773	A100	45c Wood slave	1.50	.70
774	A100	80c Slippery back	2.40	1.25
775	A100	$2.50 Iguana	5.50	6.50
	Nos. 773-775 (3)		9.40	8.45

Souvenir Sheet
776	A100	$6 Tree lizard	16.00	16.00

Easter — A101

Paintings: 35c, Christ Crowned with Thorns, by Hieronymus Bosch (c. 1450-1516. 80c, Christ Bearing the Cross, by David. $1, The Deposition, by David. $1.60, Pieta, by Rogier van der Weyden (1400-1464). $6, Crucified Christ with the Virgin Mary and Saints, by Raphael.

1989, Mar. 23 Litho. Perf. 14x13½
777	A101	35c multicolored	.50	.35
778	A101	80c multicolored	.90	.75
779	A101	$1 multicolored	1.00	.80
780	A101	$1.60 multicolored	1.60	2.25
	Nos. 777-780 (4)		4.00	4.15

Souvenir Sheet
781	A101	$6 multicolored	4.50	5.00

University of the West Indies, 40th Anniv. — A102

1989, Apr. 24 Litho. Perf. 14x13½
782	A102	$5 Coat of arms	3.50	4.50

Nos. 634-636 and 638 Ovptd.

1989, July 3 Litho. Perf. 13½X14
783	A82	80c multicolored	2.75	1.25
784	A82	$1 multicolored	2.75	1.60
785	A82	$1.35 multicolored	3.25	2.50
786	A82	$5 multicolored	9.25	12.00
	Nos. 783-786 (4)		18.00	17.35

Christmas — A103

Well-known and historic houses: 5c, Lone Star, 1930. 35c, Whitehouse, 1906. 45c, Hodges House. 80c, Warden's Place. $6, Wallblake House, 1787.

1989, Dec. 4 Litho. Perf. 13½x14
787	A103	5c multicolored	.45	1.10
788	A103	35c multicolored	.75	.55
789	A103	45c multicolored	.90	.65
790	A103	80c multicolored	1.60	2.10
	Nos. 787-790 (4)		3.70	4.40

Souvenir Sheet
791	A103	$6 multicolored	5.00	5.00

Fish A104

5c, Blear eye. 10c, Redman. 15c, Speckletail. 25c, Grunt. 30c, Amber jack. 35c, Red hind. 40c, Goatfish. 45c, Old wife. 50c, Butter fish. 65c, Shell fish. 80c, Yellowtail snapper. $1, Katy. $1.35, Mutton grouper. $2.50, Doctor fish. $5, Angelfish. $10, Barracuda.

1990, Apr. 2 Litho. Perf. 13½x14
792	A104	5c multicolored	1.10	1.50
793	A104	10c multicolored	1.10	1.50
794	A104	15c multicolored	1.10	.90
795	A104	25c multicolored	1.25	1.10
796	A104	30c multicolored	1.25	1.10
797	A104	35c multicolored	1.25	1.10
798	A104	40c multicolored	1.50	1.10
799	A104	45c multicolored	1.50	.80
800	A104	50c multicolored	1.75	1.25
801	A104	65c multicolored	2.25	1.25
802	A104	80c multicolored	2.10	1.50
803	A104	$1 multicolored	2.25	1.50
804	A104	$1.35 multicolored	2.50	2.25
805	A104	$2.50 multicolored	4.00	4.75
806	A104	$5 multicolored	5.75	7.75
807	A104	$10 multicolored	9.25	11.50
	Nos. 792-807 (16)		39.90	40.85

Inscribed "1992"
792a	A104	5c Blear eye	.90	1.25
793a	A104	10c Redman	.90	1.25
797a	A104	35c Red hind	1.00	1.00
	Nos. 792a-797a (3)		2.80	3.50

For overprints and surcharge see Nos. 821-824, 849. For booklet see No. 890.

Easter — A105

35c, Last Supper. 45c, Trial. $1.35, Calvary. $2.50, Empty tomb. $6, The Resurrection.

1990, Apr. 2 Perf. 14x13½
811	A105	35c multicolored	1.25	.25
812	A105	45c multicolored	1.25	.35
813	A105	$1.35 multicolored	3.00	3.00
814	A105	$2.50 multicolored	3.75	3.75
	Nos. 811-814 (4)		9.25	7.35

Souvenir Sheet
815	A105	$6 multicolored	11.50	11.50

See Nos. 834-838.

Cape of Good Hope No. 7 — A106

Stamps of Great Britain and exhibition emblem: 25c, No. 1, vert. 50c, No. 2, vert. $2.50, No. 93. $6, Nos. 1-2.

1990, Apr. 30 Perf. 14
816	A106	25c multicolored	1.00	.40
817	A106	50c multicolored	1.75	.70
818	A106	$1.50 shown	3.00	3.00
819	A106	$2.50 multicolored	4.00	4.75
	Nos. 816-819 (4)		9.75	8.85

Souvenir Sheet
820	A106	$6 multicolored	13.00	15.00

Stamp World London '90, Penny Black 150th anniv.

Nos. 803-806 Overprinted

a

b

c

d

$1, Katy. $1.35, Mutton grouper. $2.50, Doctor fish. $5, Angelfish.

1990, Sept. 24 Litho. Perf. 13½x14
821	A104(a)	$1 multi	2.25	1.40
822	A104(b)	$1.35 multi	2.50	1.60
823	A104(c)	$2.50 multi	6.00	6.00
824	A104(d)	$5 multi	11.50	11.50
	Nos. 821-824 (4)		22.25	20.50

Birds A107

10c, Laughing gull. 35c, Brown booby. $1.50, Bridled tern. $3.50, Brown pelican. $6, Least tern.

1990, Dec. 3 Perf. 14
825	A107	10c multicolored	.95	.55
826	A107	35c multicolored	1.60	.55
827	A107	$1.50 multicolored	2.25	2.75
828	A107	$3.50 multicolored	5.00	5.00
	Nos. 825-828 (4)		9.80	8.85

Souvenir Sheet
829	A107	$6 multicolored	10.00	11.50

Christmas.

Flags A108

50c, Mermaid. 80c, New Anguilla official. $1, Three dolphins. $5, Governor's official.

1990, Nov. 5 Litho. Perf. 13½x14
830	A108	50c multicolored	1.75	.65
831	A108	80c multicolored	2.75	1.25
832	A108	$1 multicolored	2.90	1.50
833	A108	$5 multicolored	8.25	9.50
	Nos. 830-833 (4)		15.65	12.90

Nos. 811-815 Inscribed or Overprinted

1991, Apr. 30 Litho. Perf. 14x13½
834	A105	35c like #811	1.25	.75
835	A105	45c like #812	1.50	.75
836	A105	$1.35 like #813	3.00	3.00
837	A105	$2.50 like #814	4.75	5.25
	Nos. 834-837 (4)		10.50	9.75

Souvenir Sheet
838	A105	$6 like #815	13.50	13.50

Easter. "1990" obliterated by black bar in souvenir sheet margin.

Christmas — A109

5c, Angel, vert. 35c, Santa, vert. $1, Palm trees, poinsettias. $5, Homes, holly.

Perf. 14x13½, 13½x14
1991, Dec.   **Litho.**
839	A109	5c multicolored	.75	.90
840	A109	35c multicolored	2.00	.75
841	A109	80c shown	3.00	2.75
842	A109	$1 multicolored	3.00	2.75
	Nos. 839-842 (4)		8.75	7.15

Souvenir Sheet
843	A109	$5 multicolored	10.00	10.00

Easter
A110

Designs: 35c, Church, angels holding palms, vert. 45c Church, angels singing, vert. 80c, Village. $1, People going to church, vert. $5, People at beach, sailboats.

1992		Litho.		Perf. 14	
844	A110	35c	multicolored	1.00	.65
845	A110	45c	multicolored	1.25	.65
846	A110	80c	multicolored	2.25	1.10
847	A110	$1	multicolored	2.25	1.60
848	A110	$5	multicolored	6.25	12.00
		Nos. 844-848 (5)		13.00	16.00

No. 796 Surcharged

1992, June 10 Litho. Perf. 13½x14

849	A104	$1.60 on 30c #796	4.00	2.75

No. 849 inscribed "1992."

Independence,
25th
Anniv. — A111

80c, Official seal, flag. $1, Official seal. $1.60, Flags, airport. $2, First seal. $10, Nos. 1, 8-11, 15-16.

1992, Aug. 10		Litho.		Perf. 14	
850	A111	80c	multicolored	2.50	1.50
851	A111	$1	multicolored	2.50	1.60
852	A111	$1.60	multicolored	4.75	4.75
853	A111	$2	multicolored	4.75	4.75
		Nos. 850-853 (4)		14.50	12.50

Souvenir Sheet

854	A111	$10	multicolored	15.00	15.00

No. 854 contains one 85x85mm stamp.
For booklet see No. 970.

Sailboat Racing — A112

Designs: 20c, On course. 35c, Stylized boat poster. 45c, Start of race. No. 858, Blue Bird, 1971, vert. No. 859, Construction plans for Blue Bird, vert. $1, Stylized boat poster, diff. $6, Like Nos. 855 & 857.

		Perf. 13½x14, 14x13½			
1992, Oct. 12				**Litho.**	
855	A112	20c	multicolored	1.90	.60
856	A112	35c	multicolored	2.40	.50
857	A112	45c	multicolored	2.75	.50
858	A112	80c	multicolored	3.75	4.25
859	A112	80c	multicolored	3.75	4.25
a.		Pair, #858-859		8.00	10.00
860	A112	$1	multicolored	3.75	2.50
		Nos. 855-860 (6)		18.30	12.60

Souvenir Sheet

861	A112	$6	multicolored	10.00	12.50

No. 861 contains one 96x31mm stamp.

Discovery
of
America,
500th
Anniv.
A113

80c, Landfall. $1, Columbus, vert. $2, Fleet. $3, Pinta. $6, Map of voyage, vert.

1992, Dec. 15		Litho.		Perf. 14	
862	A113	80c	multicolored	3.00	1.75
863	A113	$1	multicolored	3.00	1.75
864	A113	$2	multicolored	4.75	5.50
865	A113	$3	multicolored	5.50	7.00
		Nos. 862-865 (4)		16.25	16.00

Souvenir Sheet

866	A113	$6	multicolored	15.00	15.00

Christmas
A114

Various Christmas trees and: 20c, Mucka Jumbie on stilts. 70c, Masquerading house to house. $1.05, Christmas baking, old oven style. $2.40, $5, Collecting presents.

1992, Dec. 7					
867	A114	20c	multicolored	.90	.65
868	A114	70c	multicolored	2.00	.95
869	A114	$1.05	multicolored	2.25	1.75
870	A114	$2.40	multicolored	4.25	6.00
		Nos. 867-870 (4)		9.40	9.35

Souvenir Sheet

871	A114	$5 Sheet of 1 + 3 labels		7.00	7.00

Labels on No. 871 are similar to Nos. 867-869, but without denomination.

Easter — A115

Children's drawings: 20c, Kite flying. 45c, Cliff top village service. 80c, Morning devotion on Sombrero. $1.50, Hilltop church service. $5, Good Friday kites.

1993, Mar. 29		Litho.		Perf. 14	
872	A115	20c	multicolored	1.75	.90
873	A115	45c	multicolored	2.75	.90
874	A115	80c	multicolored	4.00	2.10
875	A115	$1.50	multicolored	4.50	7.00
		Nos. 872-875 (4)		13.00	10.90

Souvenir Sheet

876	A115	$5	multicolored	9.00	9.00

No. 876 contains one 42x56mm stamp.

Native
Industries
A116

20c, Salt. 80c, Tobacco, $1, Cotton. $2, Sugar cane.

1993, June 23		Litho.		Perf. 14	
877	A116	20c	multicolored	3.25	1.10
878	A116	80c	multicolored	3.00	1.75
879	A116	$1	multicolored	3.00	1.75
880	A116	$2	multicolored	4.25	6.50
		Nos. 877-880 (4)		13.50	11.10

Souvenir Sheet

881	A116	$6 Fishing	14.00	14.00

Coronation of
Queen Elizabeth
II, 40th
Anniv. — A117

Designs: 80c, Lord Great Chamberlain presents the spurs of chivalry. $1, The benediction. $2, Queen Elizabeth II, coronation photograph. $3, St. Edward's Crown. $6, Queen, Prince Philip in Gold State Coach.

1993, Aug. 16		Litho.		Perf. 14	
882	A117	80c	multicolored	2.25	1.00
883	A117	$1	multicolored	2.50	1.10
884	A117	$2	multicolored	3.25	3.25
885	A117	$3	multicolored	3.75	4.75
		Nos. 882-885 (4)		11.75	10.10

Souvenir Sheet

886	A117	$6	multicolored	14.00	16.00

Anguilla Carnival — A118

20c, Pan musician. 45c, Pirates. 80c, Stars. $1, Playing mas. $2, Masqueraders. $3, Commandos. $5, Carnival fantasy.

1993, Aug. 23		Litho.		Perf. 14	
887	A118	20c	multicolored	.70	.50
888	A118	45c	multicolored	1.25	.50
889	A118	80c	multicolored	2.40	1.10
890	A118	$1	multicolored	2.40	1.25
		Booklet, 5 ea #796, 890		14.00	
891	A118	$2	multicolored	3.75	5.50
892	A118	$3	multicolored	4.00	6.25
		Nos. 887-892 (6)		14.50	15.10

Souvenir Sheet

893	A118	$5	multicolored	14.00	14.00

Christmas
A119

Traditional Christmas customs: 20c, Mucka Jumbies. 35c, Serenaders. 45c, Baking. $3, Five-fingers Christmas tree. $4, Mucka Jumbies and serenaders.

1993, Dec. 7		Litho.		Perf. 14x13½	
894	A119	20c	multicolored	1.10	.90
895	A119	35c	multicolored	1.50	.90
896	A119	45c	multicolored	1.75	.90
897	A119	$3	multicolored	5.75	8.00
		Nos. 894-897 (4)		10.10	10.70

Souvenir Sheet
Perf. 14

898	A119	$4	multicolored	5.75	5.75

No. 898 contains one 54x42mm stamp.

Mail
Delivery — A120

Designs: 20c, Traveling Branch mail van, Sandy Ground, horiz. 45c, Mail boat, Betsy R, The Forest. 80c, Old post office, horiz. $1, Mail by jeep, Island Harbor. $4, New post office, 1993, horiz.

1994, Feb. 11		Litho.		Perf. 14	
899	A120	20c	multicolored	2.00	.95
900	A120	45c	multicolored	2.75	.95
901	A120	80c	multicolored	3.50	1.90
902	A120	$1	multicolored	3.50	1.90
903	A120	$4	multicolored	5.50	8.75
		Nos. 899-903 (5)		17.25	14.45

Royal
Visits — A121

45c, Princess Alexandra. 50c, Princess Alice. 80c, Prince Philip. $1, Prince Charles. $2, Queen Elizabeth II.

1994, Feb. 18					
904	A121	45c	multicolored	2.00	.80
905	A121	50c	multicolored	2.25	.80
906	A121	80c	multicolored	3.00	1.75
907	A121	$1	multicolored	3.50	1.75
908	A121	$2	multicolored	4.75	5.50
a.		Souvenir sheet of 4, #904-908		15.00	15.00
		Nos. 904-908 (5)		15.50	10.60

Easter — A122

Stained glass windows: 20c, Crucifixion. 45c, Empty tomb. 80c, Resurrection. $3, Risen Christ with disciples.

1994, Apr. 6		Litho.		Perf. 14x15	
909	A122	20c	multicolored	.90	.65
910	A122	45c	multicolored	1.10	.80
911	A122	80c	multicolored	2.10	1.10
912	A122	$3	multicolored	5.50	6.25
		Nos. 909-912 (4)		9.60	8.80

Christmas — A123

Designs: 20c, Adoration of the shepherds. 30c, Magi, shepherds. 35c, The Annunciation. 45c, Nativity Scene. $2.40, Flight into Egypt.

1994, Nov. 22		Litho.		Perf. 14	
913	A123	20c	multicolored	1.00	.80
914	A123	30c	multicolored	1.25	.80
915	A123	35c	multicolored	1.25	.80
916	A123	45c	multicolored	1.50	.80
917	A123	$2.40	multicolored	5.00	6.00
		Nos. 913-917 (5)		10.00	9.20

1994 World Cup Soccer
Championships, US — A124

Soccer player and: 20c, Pontiac Silverdome, Detroit. 70c, Foxboro Stadium, Boston. $1.80, RFK Memorial Stadium, Washington. $2.40, Soldier Field, Chicago. $6, Two players.

1994, Oct. 3   Litho.   Perf. 13½x14

918	A124	20c multicolored	1.00	.50
919	A124	70c multicolored	1.50	1.10
920	A124	$1.80 multicolored	3.00	3.25
921	A124	$2.40 multicolored	3.50	4.00
		Nos. 918-921 (4)	9.00	8.85

Souvenir Sheet

922	A124	$6 multicolored	13.00	13.00

Easter
A125

Turtle dove: 45c, One on tree branch. 50c, One on nest, one on branch. $5, Mother with young.

1995, Apr. 10   Litho.   Perf. 14

923	A125	20c multicolored	.70	.60
924	A125	45c multicolored	1.10	.90
925	A125	50c multicolored	1.25	1.10
926	A125	$5 multicolored	7.00	10.00
		Nos. 923-926 (4)	10.05	12.60

UN,
50th
Anniv.
A126

Secretaries general and: 20c, Trygve Lie (1946-53), general assembly. 80c, UN flag, UN headquarters with "50" (no portrait). $1, Dag Hammarskjold (1953-61), charter, U Thant (1961-71). $5, UN complex, New York, vert. (no portrait).

Perf. 13½x14, 14x13½

1995, June 26   Litho.

927	A126	20c multicolored	.40	.40
928	A126	80c multicolored	.80	.80
929	A126	$1 multicolored	1.00	1.00
930	A126	$5 multicolored	5.00	5.00
		Nos. 927-930 (4)	7.20	7.20

Caribbean Development Bank, 25th
Anniv. — A127

Designs: 45c, Emblem, map of Anguilla. $5, Local headquarters along waterfront.

1995, Aug. 15   Litho.   Perf. 13½x14

931	A127	45c multicolored	2.50	2.50
932	A127	$5 multicolored	4.75	4.75
a.		Pair, #931-932	7.50	7.50

Whales — A128

20c, Blue whale. 45c, Right whale, vert. $1, Sperm whale. $5, Humpback whale.

Perf. 13½x14, 14x13½

1995, Nov. 24   Litho.

933	A128	20c multicolored	2.75	.95
934	A128	45c multicolored	3.00	.80
935	A128	$1 multicolored	3.75	2.10
936	A128	$5 multicolored	8.50	10.50
		Nos. 933-936 (4)	18.00	14.35

Christmas
A129

10c, Palm tree. 25c, Fish net floats. 45c, Sea shells. $5, Fish.

1995, Dec. 12   Perf. 14½

937	A129	10c multicolored	.80	.80
938	A129	25c multicolored	1.10	.65
939	A129	45c multicolored	1.25	.65
940	A129	$5 multicolored	9.50	12.00
		Nos. 937-940 (4)	12.65	14.10

Corals
A130

20c, Deep water gorgonia. 80c, Common sea fan. $5, Venus sea fern.

1996, June 21   Litho.   Perf. 14x14½

941	A130	20c multicolored	2.00	.95
942	A130	80c multicolored	3.25	1.40
943	A130	$5 multicolored	9.00	11.00
		Nos. 941-943 (3)	14.25	13.35

A131

1996 Summer Olympic Games, Atlanta: 20c, Running. 80c, Javelin, wheelchair basketball. $1, High jump. $3.50, Olympic torch, Greek, US flags.

1996, Dec. 12   Litho.   Perf. 14

944	A131	20c multicolored	.95	.75
945	A131	80c multicolored	3.25	1.50
946	A131	$1 multicolored	2.25	1.50
947	A131	$3.50 multicolored	6.00	6.00
		Nos. 944-947 (4)	12.45	9.75

A132

Battle for Anguilla, bicent.: 60c, Sandy Hill Fort, HMS Lapwing. 75c, French troops

destroy church, horiz. $1.50, HMS Lapwing defeats Valiant, Decius, horiz. $4, French troops land, Rendezvous Bay.

1996, Dec. 12

948	A132	60c multicolored	1.25	1.25
949	A132	75c multicolored	1.25	1.25
950	A132	$1.50 multicolored	2.50	2.50
951	A132	$4 multicolored	4.00	5.00
		Nos. 948-951 (4)	9.00	10.00

Fruits
and
Nuts
A133

10c, Gooseberry. 20c, West Indian cherry. 40c, Tamarind. 50c, Pomme-surette. 60c, Sea almond. 75c, Sea grape. 80c, Banana. $1, Genip. $1.10, Coco plum. $1.25, Pope. $1.50, Papaya. $2, Sugar apple. $3, Soursop. $4, Pomegrante. $5, Cashew. $10, Mango.

1997, Apr. 30   Litho.   Perf. 14

952	A133	10c multicolored	.50	.75
953	A133	20c multicolored	.60	.40
954	A133	40c multicolored	.75	.40
955	A133	50c multicolored	1.00	.50
956	A133	60c multicolored	1.00	.60
957	A133	75c multicolored	1.25	.80
958	A133	80c multicolored	1.25	.90
959	A133	$1 multicolored	1.50	1.25
960	A133	$1.10 multicolored	1.50	1.75
961	A133	$1.25 multicolored	1.75	1.90
962	A133	$1.50 multicolored	2.00	2.25
963	A133	$2 multicolored	2.50	3.00
964	A133	$3 multicolored	4.00	4.00
965	A133	$4 multicolored	5.25	5.50
966	A133	$5 multicolored	6.25	6.50
967	A133	$10 multicolored	10.00	10.50
		Nos. 952-967 (16)	41.10	41.00

Iguanas — A134

World Wildlife Fund: a, 20c, Baby iguanas emerging from eggs, juvenile iguana. b, 50c, Adult on rock. c, 75c, Two iguanas on tree limbs. d, $3, Adult up close, adult on tree branch.

1997, Oct. 13   Litho.   Perf. 13½x14

968	A134	Strip of 4, #a.-d.	10.00	10.00

Diana, Princess of Wales (1961-
97) — A135

Designs: a, 15c, In red & white. b, $1, In yellow. c, $1.90, Wearing tiara. d, $2.25, Wearing blouse with Red Cross emblem.

1998, Apr. 14   Litho.   Perf. 14

969	A135	Strip of 4, #a.-d.	9.50	9.50

No. 969 was issued in sheets of 16 stamps.

Fountain
Cavern
Carvings
A136

30c, Rainbow Deity (Juluca). $1.25, Lizard. $2.25, Solar Chieftan. $2.75, Creator.

1997, Nov. 17   Litho.   Perf. 14x14½

970	A136	30c multicolored	.55	.55
		Booklet, 5 ea #851, 970	12.00	
971	A136	$1.25 multicolored	1.25	1.25
972	A136	$2.25 multicolored	2.10	2.10
973	A136	$2.75 multicolored	2.75	2.75
		Nos. 970-973 (4)	6.65	6.65

1998 Intl.
Arts
Festival
A137

Paintings: 15c, "Treasure Island." 30c, "Posing in the Light." $1, "Pescadores de Anguilla." $1.50, "Fresh Catch." $1.90, "The Bell Tower of St. Mary's."

1998, Aug. 24   Litho.   Perf. 14

974	A137	15c multi	.65	.65
975	A137	30c multi, vert.	.80	.80
976	A137	$1 multi, vert.	1.40	1.40
		Booklet, 5 ea #975-976	10.00	
977	A137	$1.50 multi, vert.	1.40	1.60
978	A137	$1.90 multi, vert.	1.75	2.00
		Nos. 974-978 (5)	6.00	6.45

Christmas
A138

Paintings of "Hidden beauty of Anguilla": 15c, Woman cooking over open fire, girl seated on steps. $1, Person looking over fruits and vegetables. $1.50, Underwater scene. $3, Cacti growing along shore.

1998, Nov. 18

979	A138	15c multicolored	.50	.50
980	A138	$1 multicolored	1.00	1.00
981	A138	$1.50 multicolored	1.40	1.40
982	A138	$3 multicolored	2.10	2.10
		Nos. 979-982 (4)	5.00	5.00

Royal
Air
Force,
80th
Anniv.
A139

Designs: 30c, Sopwith Camel, Bristol F2B. $1, Supermarine Spitfire II, Hawker Hurricane Mk1. $1.50, Avro Lancaster. $1.90, Harrier GR7, Panavia Tornado F3.

1998, Dec. 31   Litho.   Perf. 13½
Granite Paper (No. 983)

983	A139	30c multicolored	1.25	.60
984	A139	$1 multicolored	2.00	1.00
985	A139	$1.50 multicolored	2.50	2.25
986	A139	$1.90 multicolored	4.00	3.25
		Booklet, 5 ea #983-984	16.50	
		Nos. 983-986 (4)	9.75	7.10

University of the West Indies, 50th
Anniv. — A140

Designs: $1.50, Anguilla campus. $1.90, Anguilla campus, torchbearer, University arms.

1998, Dec. 31   Litho.   Perf. 13¼
Granite Paper (#988)

987-988	A140	Set of 2	3.00	3.50

First Manned Moon Landing, 30th
Anniv. — A141

Designs: 30c, Lift-off of Apollo 11, Command and Service Modules in lunar orbit. $1, Buzz Aldrin on Moon, footprint. $1.50, Lunar Module leaving Moon. $1.90, Splashdown.

1999, May 6 — Litho. — Perf. 13¾

989	A141	30c multi	.80	.50
990	A141	$1 multi	1.40	.90
991	A141	$1.50 multi	1.50	1.75
992	A141	$1.90 multi	2.50	3.25
	Nos. 989-992 (4)		6.20	6.40

Heroes of Anguilla's Revolution A142

Designs: 30c, Albena Lake Hodge (1920-85). $1, Collins O. Hodge (1926-78). $1.50, Edwin W. Rey (1906-80). $1.90, Walter G. Hodge (1920-89).

1999, July 5 — Perf. 14½x14¼

993	A142	30c multi	.50	.30
994	A142	$1 multi	.90	.60
995	A142	$1.50 multi	1.25	1.25
996	A142	$1.90 multi	1.90	2.00
	Nos. 993-996 (4)		4.55	4.15

Modern Architecture A143

Designs: No. 997, 30c, Library and resource center. No. 998, 65c, Parliamentary building and court house. No. 999, $1, Caribbean Commercial Bank. No. 999A, $1.50, Police headquarters. No. 1000, $1.90, Post office.

1999 — Litho. — Perf. 14x14½

997-1000	A143	Set of 5	7.50 7.50

Christmas and Millennium Celebrations — A144

Designs: 30c, Fireworks display and barbecue. $1, Globe, musicians. $1.50, Family dinner. $1.90, Decorated tree.

1999 — Litho. — Perf. 13¼

1001	A144	30c multi	.55	.50
1002	A144	$1 multi	1.40	.90
1003	A144	$1.50 multi	2.10	2.10
1004	A144	$1.90 multi	2.25	3.75
	Nos. 1001-1004 (4)		6.30	7.25

Beaches — A145

1005, 15c, Shoal Bay. 1006, 30c, Maundys Bay. 1007, $1, Rendezvous Bay. 1008, $1.50, Meads Bay. 1009, $1.90, Little Bay. 1010, $2, Sandy Ground.

1999 — Perf. 12

1005-1010	A145	Set of 6	8.25	8.25
1010a		Sheet of 6, #1005-1010	8.25	8.25
1010b		As "a," with show emblem in margin	8.25	8.00

The Stamp Show 2000, London (No. 1010b). Issued: No. 1010b, 5/22/00.

Easter A146

Toys: 25c, Banjo. 30c, Top. $1.50, Slingshot. $1.90, Roller. $2.50, Killy ban.
No. 1016: a, 75c, Rag doll. b, $1, Kite. c, $1.25, Cricket ball. d, $4, Pond boat.

2000 — Perf. 13¼

1011	A146	25c multi	.25	.25
1012	A146	30c multi	.35	.35
1013	A146	$1.50 multi	1.25	1.25
1014	A146	$1.90 multi	1.60	2.25
1015	A146	$2.50 multi	2.60	3.00
	Nos. 1011-1015 (5)		6.05	7.10

Souvenir Sheet

1016	A146	Sheet of 4, #a-d	6.25	6.25

100th Test Match at Lord's Ground — A147

$2, Lanville Harrigan. $4, Cardigan Connor. $6, Lord's Ground, horiz.

2000, May 5 — Litho. — Perf. 13¾x13¼

1017-1018	A147	Set of 2	7.75 7.75

Souvenir Sheet

1018A	A147	$6 multi	12.00 12.00

Prince William, 18th Birthday — A148

Prince William and: 30c, Queen Elizabeth II, Princes Philip and Charles. $1, Princess Diana, Princes Harry and Charles. $1.90, Princes Harry and Charles. $2.25, Princes Charles and Harry, in winter wear.
$8, Prince William, vert.

2000, July 20 — Perf. 13¼

1019-1022	A148	Set of 4	9.25 9.25

Souvenir Sheet

1023	A148	$8 multicolored	9.50 9.50

Queen Mother, 100th Birthday — A149

Queen Mother and: 30c, Prince William. $1.50, Anguilla shoreline. $1.90, Clarence House. $5, Castle of Mey.

2000, Aug. 4

1024-1027	A149	Set of 4	8.75 8.75

Intl. Arts Festival A150

Artwork: 15c, Anguilla Montage, by Weme Caster. 30c, Serenity, by Damien Carty. 65c, Inter-island Cargo, by Paula Walden. $1.50, Rainbow City Where Spirits Find Form, by Fiona Percy. $1.90, Sailing Silver Seas, by Valerie Carpenter.
$7, Historic Anguilla, by Melsadis Fleming.

2000, Sept. 21 — Perf. 14¼x14½

1028-1032	A150	Set of 5	5.75 5.75

Souvenir Sheet

Perf. 14¼

1033	A150	$7 multi	7.25 7.25

No. 1033 contains one 43x28mm stamp.

Christmas A151

Flower and Garden Show flower arrangements by: 15c, Rowena Carty. 25c, Yvonda Hodge. 30c, Carty, diff. $1, Simon Rogers. $1.50, Lady Josephine Gumbs. $1.90, Carty, diff.

2000, Nov. 22 — Perf. 13¼

1034-1039	A151	Set of 6	6.75 6.75

Natl. Bank of Anguilla, 15th Anniv. — A152

Designs: 30c, Soccer team in annual primary school tournament. $1, Sponsored sailboat, De Chan, vert. $1.50, Bank's crest, vert. $1.90, New bank building.

2000, Nov. 27

1040-1043	A152	Set of 4	5.25 5.25

Ebenezer Methodist Church, 170th Anniv. — A153

Church in: 30c, Sepia tones. $1.90, Full color.

2000, Dec. 4

1044-1045	A153	Set of 2	2.75 2.75

UN Women's Human Rights Campaign — A154

Designs: 25c, Soroptimist Day Care Center. 30c, Britannia Idalia Gumbs, vert. $2.25, Woman, vert.

2001 — Litho. — Perf. 13¼

1046-1048	A154	Set of 3	4.00 4.00

American Revolution, 225th Anniv. — A155

Designs: 30c, John Paul Jones, USS Ranger. $1, George Washington, Battle of Yorktown. $1.50, Thomas Jefferson, Submission of Declaration of Independence. $1.90, John Adams, Adams and Benjamin Franklin signing peace treaty.

2001, July 4 — Litho. — Perf. 13¼

1049-1052	A155	Set of 4	8.75 8.75

Birds A156

Designs: 30c, White-cheeked pintail. $1, Black-faced grassquits, vert. $1.50, Brown noddy. $2, Black-necked stilts, vert. $3, Snowy plovers.
No. 1058: a, 25c, Snowy egret. b, 65c, Red-billed tropicbird. $1.35, Greater yellowlegs. $2.25, Sooty tern.

2001, Aug. 7

1053-1057	A156	Set of 5	14.00 14.00

Souvenir Sheet

1058	A156	Sheet of 4, #a-d	11.00 11.00

Year of Dialogue Among Civilizations A157

2001, Oct. 9 — Perf. 13¼x13

1059	A157	$1.90 multi	3.00 3.00

Christmas — A158

Musical instruments: 15c, Triangle. 25c, Maracas. 30c, Guiro, vert. $1.50, Marimba. $1.90, Tambu, vert. $2.50, Bath pan, vert.
No. 1066, vert.: a, 75c, Banjo. b, $1, Quatro. c, $1.25, Ukulele. d, $3, Cello.

2001, Nov. 5 — Litho. — Perf. 13¼

1060-1065	A158	Set of 6	10.00 10.00

Souvenir Sheet

1066	A158	Sheet of 4, #a-d	9.00 9.00

Sombrero Lighthouse — A159

Designs: 30c, Lighhouse in 1960s, vert. $1.50, Comparison of old and new lighthouses. $1.90, New lighthouse, 2001, vert.

2002, Apr. 2   Litho.   *Perf. 13¼*
1067-1069 A159   Set of 3   7.00 7.00

Social Security Board, 20th Anniv. — A160

Social Security: 30c, Community service, vert. 75c, Benefits all ages, vert. $2.50, Benefits employees.

2002, May 28   Litho.   *Perf. 13¼*
1070-1072 A160   Set of 3   5.00 5.00

Royal Navy Ships A161

Designs: 30c, HMS Antrim, 1967. 50c, HMS Formidable, 1939. $1.50, HMS Dreadnought, 1906. $2, HMS Warrior, 1860.
$7, HMS Ark Royal, 1981, vert.

2002, June 24   Litho.   *Perf. 13¼*
1073-1076 A161   Set of 4   6.25 6.25
    Souvenir Sheet
1077 A161 $7 multi   10.00 10.00

Reign of Queen Elizabeth II, 50th Anniv. — A162

Designs: 30c, Holding baby. $1.50, Wearing white dress. $1.90, Wearing tiara. $5, Wearing yellow hat.
$8, At desk.

2002, Oct. 14   Litho.   *Perf. 13¼*
1078-1081 A162   Set of 4   8.50 8.50
    Souvenir Sheet
1082   A162 $8 multi   10.00 10.00

Pan-American Health Organization, Cent. — A163

Designs: 30c, The Valley Health Center. $1.50, Emblem, "100."

2002, Nov. 11
1083-1084 A163   Set of 2   2.75 2.75

Ships A164

15c, Finance. 30c, Tiny Gull. 65c, Lady Laurel. 75c, Spitfire. $1, Liberator. $1.35, Excelsior. $1.50, Rose Millicent. $1.90, Betsy R. $2, Sunbeam R. $2.25, New London. $3, Ismay. $10, Warspite.

2003, June 10   Litho.   *Perf. 14*
1085 A164 15c multi   .50 .50
1086 A164 30c multi   .60 .30
1087 A164 65c multi   1.00 .65
1088 A164 75c multi   1.00 .75
1089 A164 $1 multi   1.25 1.00
1090 A164 $1.35 multi   1.50 1.50
1091 A164 $1.50 multi   1.75 1.60
1092 A164 $1.90 multi   2.00 1.90
1093 A164 $2 multi   2.25 2.00
1094 A164 $2.25 multi   3.00 2.50
1095 A164 $3 multi   3.25 3.25
1096 A164 $10 multi   10.00 11.00
   Nos. 1085-1096 (12)   28.10 26.95

Artifacts — A165

Designs: 30c, Stone pestle. $1, Frog-shaped shell ornament. $1.50, Pottery. $1.90, Mask.

2003, Aug. 18   Litho.   *Perf. 13¼*
1097-1100 A165   Set of 4   5.75 5.75

Hotels A166

Designs: 75c, Frangipani Beach Club. $1, Pimms, Cap Juluca. $1.35, Cocoloba Beach Resort. $1.50, Malliouhana Hotel. $1.90, Carimar Beach Club. $3, Covecastles.

2003   Litho.   *Perf. 13¼*
1101-1106 A166   Set of 6   9.50 9.50

2002 International Arts Festival — A167

Paintings: 15c, Eudice's Garden, by Eunice Summer. 30c, Hammocks, by Lisa Davenport. $1, Conched Out, by Richard Shaffett. $1.50, Island Rhythms, by Carol Gavin. $1.90, Party at the Beach, by Jean-Pierre Ballagny. $3, Shoal Bay Before Luis, by Jacqueline Mariethoz, vert.

Perf. 13½x13¼, 13¼x13½
2004, Aug. 23   Litho.
1107-1112 A167   Set of 6   12.50 12.50

2004 Summer Olympics, Athens — A168

2004 Athens Olympics emblem and: 30c, Runners. $1, Yachting. $1.50, Gymnastics. $1.90, Acropolis, Pierre de Coubertin, Dimitrios Vikelas, horiz.

Perf. 13½x13¼, 13¼x13½
2004, Sept. 20   Litho.
1113-1116 A168   Set of 4   7.00 7.00

Goats A169

Various goats: 30c, 50c, $1, $1.50, $1.90, $2.25. $1, $1.90 are vert.

Perf. 13¼x13½, 13½x13¼
2004, Oct. 4
1117-1122 A169   Set of 6   10.50 10.50

Development of the Telephone A170

Types of telephones: 30c, Cordless. $1, Touch-tone. $1.50, Cellular. $1.90, Rotary dial, horiz. $3.80, Magneto.

Perf. 13¼x13, 13x13¼
2004, Nov. 8   Litho.
1123-1127 A170   Set of 5   8.75 8.75

Christmas A171

Santa Claus: 30c, Baking with rock oven. $1.50, Climbing coconut tree. $1.90, With string band. $3.80, Delivering gifts by donkey. $8, Delivering gifts by boat.

2004, Nov. 15   *Perf. 13x13¼*
1128-1131 A171   Set of 4   7.25 7.25
    Souvenir Sheet
1132 A171 $8 multi   7.50 7.50

World AIDS Day — A172

Children's drawings by: 30c, Owean Hodge. $1.50, Lydia Fleming. $1.90, Nina Rodriguez.
No. 1136: a, 15c, Kenswick Richardson. b, 75c, Toniquewah Ruan. c, $1, Elizabeth Anne Orchard. d, $2, Tricia Watty-Beard.

2005, Jan. 18   *Perf. 13*
1133-1135 A172   Set of 3   5.00 5.00
    Souvenir Sheet
1136 A172   Sheet of 4, #a-d   5.00 5.00

Rotary International, Cent. — A173

Designs: 30c, Emblem of Anguilla Rotary Club. $1, Pelican and palm tree. $1.50, Rotary

International founder Paul Harris. $1.90, Children at playground.

Perf. 14¾x14¼
2005, Mar. 23   Litho.
1137-1140 A173   Set of 4   4.75 4.75

Dogs A174

Designs: 30c, Dog in field. $1.50, Two dogs sitting, vert. $1.90, Dog sitting, vert. $2.25, Dog.

Perf. 14¼x14¾, 14¾x14¼
2005, June 1
1141-1144 A174   Set of 4   5.50 5.50

Commercial Airplanes — A175

Designs: 30c, Air Anguilla Cessna 402. 40c, LIAT DHC Dash 8. 60c, Winair Foxtrot-DHC Twin Otter. $1, Anguilla Airways Piper Aztec. $1.50, St. Thomas Air Transport Piper Aztec. $1.90, Carib Air Service Piper Aztec.

2006, Mar. 13   Litho.   *Perf. 13¼*
1145-1150 A175   Set of 6   7.00 7.00

Butterflies — A176

Designs: 30c, Appias drusillia. $1.50, Danaus plexippus megalippe. $1.90, Phoebis sennae. $2.75, Papilio demoleus.
No. 1155: a, 40c, Aphrissa statira. b, 60c, Eurema elathea. c, $1, Danaus plexippus megalippe, diff. d, $3, Agraulis vanillae.

2006, Oct. 9   Litho.   *Perf. 13¼*
1151-1154 A176   Set of 4   7.25 7.25
    Miniature Sheet
1155 A176   Sheet of 4, #a-d   5.75 5.75

Anguilla Soroptomist Club, 25th Anniv. — A177

Designs: $1.90, Soroptomist International emblem. $2.75, Alecia Ballin.

2007, Jan. 29
1156-1157 A177   Set of 2   5.25 5.25

Bronze Devotional Medallions From El Buen Consuelo Shipwreck A178

Medallions depicting: 30c, St. Bruno. $1.50, Our Lady of Sorrows. $1.90, Five Wounds of Jesus. $2.75, Virgin and Child.

2007, Mar. 19	Litho.	Perf. 13¼
1158-1161 A178	Set of 4	6.25 6.25

Anguilla Revolution, 40th Anniv. — A179

Participants: 30c, Hyacinth Carty. $1, Edward Duncan. $1.50, Connell Harrigan. $1.90, Rev. Leonard Carty. $2.25, Jeremiah Gumbs. $3.75, Atlin Harrigan.

2007, July 18	Litho.	Perf. 13¼
1162-1167 A179	Set of 6	10.00 10.00

Historical Architecture — A180

Designs: 30c, Building with lean-to and gabled roof, by Melsadis Fleming. $1, Building with lean-to and gabled roof, by Daryl Thompson. $1.25, Building with double-hipped roof, by Fleming. $1.50, Building with hipped roof, by Susan Croft. $1.90, Building with double-gabled roof, by Fleming. $2.40, Building with double-hipped roof, by Fleming, diff. $2.75, Building with hipped roof, by Fleming. $3.75, Building with gabled roof, by Fleming.

2008, Oct. 6		Perf. 14x14¾
1168-1175 A180	Set of 8	10.00 10.00

Traditional Household Items — A181

Designs: 30c, Three-legged pot. $1, Mortar and pestle. $1.50, Gas and coal irons. $1.90, Oil and gas lamps. $2, Coal pots. $2.25, Enamel and aluminum utensils.

2009, June 18		Perf. 13¼
1176-1181 A181	Set of 6	6.75 6.75

Wild Flowers — A182

Designs: 30c, Tabebulia heterophylla. $1, Argemone mexicana. $1.50, Catharanthus roseus. $1.90, Datura stramonium. $2, Centrosena virginiatum. $2.25, Tetramicra canaliculata.

2009, Sept. 12		
1182-1187 A182	Set of 6	6.75 6.75

Endemic Flora and Fauna — A183

Designs: $1.50, Sombrero Island ground lizard. $2, Little Scrub Island ground lizard. $2.25, Anguilla bush.

2010, Aug. 10		Perf. 13¼
1188-1190 A183	Set of 3	4.50 4.50

Wedding of Prince William and Catherine Middleton A184

Designs: $4, Couple. $5, Couple, horiz. $6, Couple, diff. $10, Couple and royal arms, horiz.

2011, June 20	Litho.	Perf. 13¼
1191-1194 A184	Set of 4	18.50 18.50

Anguilla Revolutionary Coins — A185

Designs: 15c, 1967 Liberty dollar counterstruck on Panamanian balboa. 40c, 1967 Liberty dollar counterstruck on Mexican peso. $2.50, Obverse and reverse of 1968 silver $25 coin commemorating first year of Independence. $5, Ship, reverse of 1969 $4 coin.

2012, Feb. 28		Perf. 13½x13¼
1195-1198 A185	Set of 4	6.00 6.00

Royal Anguilla Police Force, 40th Anniv. — A186

Designs: 30c, Old Valley Police Station. $1, Police on parade. $1.50, Police headquarters. $1.90, Past and present police crests. $5, Lt.

Col. Claudius M. Roberts, first Chief of Police, vert.

2012, Nov. 26		Perf. 13¼
1199-1203 A186	Set of 5	7.25 7.25

Methodism on Anguilla, 200th Anniv. — A187

Designs: 40c, Old Methodist Manse, Sandy Ground. 65c, Map of Anguilla, 200th anniversary emblem. $10, Montage of Ebenezer and Bethel Churches, by Aileen Lamond-Smith.

2013, Nov. 11	Litho.	Perf. 13¼
1204-1206 A187	Set of 3	8.25 8.25

Ship Captains — A188

Captains: 15c, George Richardson (1919-2003). 50c, James Woods (1908-98). 75c, Fritz Ericson Hughes (1891-1970). $1.35, Christopher John Connor (1925-94). $2, Herchel Gumbs (1884-1965). $2.25, Zilphus Fleming (1915-92). $2.50, Walter Hodge (1920-89). $5, John Franklin (1912-98).

2013, Nov. 25	Litho.	Perf. 13¼
1207-1214 A188	Set of 8	11.00 11.00
1214a	Sheet of 8, #1207-1214	11.00 11.00

See Nos. 1219-1226.

Secondary Education , 60th Anniv. — A189

Designs: 15c, Boy's shirt and tie, 1950s. $1.35, Girl's uniform, 1950s. $2, James T. Thom, first principal of Valley Secondary School. $2.50, Valley Secondary School crest.

2013, Dec. 31	Litho.	Perf. 13¼
1215-1218 A189	Set of 4	4.50 4.50

Ship Captains Type of 2013

Designs: 50c, Harry S. Franklin (1926-2006). 65c, John A. Edwards (1910-75). 75c, Amos Richardson (1924-2004). 80c, George Joshua Gumbs (1926-2012). $2, Ivan Richardson (1917-67). $2.50, Edward Camile Connor (1910-2000). $3, Henry E. Richardson (1890-1990). $6, Malcolm C. Wathey (1905-84).

2014, July 7	Litho.	Perf. 13¼
1219-1226 A188	Set of 8	12.00 12.00
1226a	Souvenir sheet of 8, #1219-1226	12.00 12.00

Day Around the Island Boat Race Winning Sailboats — A190

Designs: 50c, Real Deal, champion in 2011, 2012. 60c, Superstar, champion in 2004, 2007, 2009, horiz. 80c, Nathalie, champion in 1993, 1994, 1995. $1.35, UFO, champion in 1997, 1998, 2003, 2005, horiz. $3, De Tree, champion in 2001, 2006, 2008, 2010, 2013, horiz. $10, De Chan, champion in 1982-84, 1986, 1991-92, 1996, 2002.

No. 1233: a, 15c, Sonic, champion in 2014. b, 40c, Satellite, champion in 2000. c, 65c, Viagra, champion in 1999. d, 75c, Saga Boy, champion in 1990. e, $4, Wasp, champion in 1987.

2015, May 29	Litho.	Perf. 13¼
1227-1232 A190	Set of 6	12.00 12.00
Souvenir Sheet		
1233 A190	Sheet of 5, #a-e	4.50 4.50

Summer Festival — A191

Designs: 50c, Calypso Show. $1, August Monday Beach Party, horiz. $1.40, Jouvert, horiz. $1.80, Woman in butterfly costume, horiz. $2.10, Parade, horiz. $3, Queen Show.

2016, Aug. 2	Litho.	Perf. 13¼
1234-1239 A191	Set of 6	7.25 7.25

National Symbols — A192

Designs: 50c, Ground lizard (national animal). 75c, White cedar flowers (national flower). $1.40, Peas and rice (national dish). $1.80, Turtle doves (national bird). $2.10, Boat racing (national sport). $3, Turquoise, white and orange (national colors). $5, White cedar tree (national tree), vert. $10, National flag.

2016, Oct. 10	Litho.	Perf. 13¼
1240-1247 A192	Set of 8	18.50 18.50

ANJOUAN

'an-jü-wän

LOCATION — One of the Comoro Islands in the Mozambique Channel between Madagascar and Mozambique.
GOVT. — French colony.
AREA — 89 sq. mi.
POP. — 20,000 (approx. 1912)
CAPITAL — Mossamondu
See Comoro Islands.

100 Centimes = 1 Franc

Navigation and Commerce — A1

Perf. 14x13½

1892-1907   Typo.   Unwmk.
Name of Colony in Blue or Carmine

1	A1	1c black, *blue*	1.75	1.75
2	A1	2c brown, *buff*	2.75	1.75
3	A1	4c claret, *lav*	5.50	4.00
4	A1	5c green, *grnsh*	9.50	6.25
5	A1	10c blk, *lavender*	11.50	6.75
6	A1	10c red ('00)	37.50	30.00
7	A1	15c blue, quadrille paper	17.00	11.50
8	A1	15c gray, *lt gray* ('00)	32.50	22.50
9	A1	20c red, *green*	17.50	11.00
10	A1	25c black, *rose*	17.50	14.00
11	A1	25c blue ('00)	32.50	22.50
12	A1	30c brn, *bister*	35.00	22.50
13	A1	35c blk, *yel* ('06)	18.00	10.00
14	A1	40c red, *straw*	37.50	32.50
15	A1	45c blk, *gray grn* ('07)	150.00	115.00
16	A1	50c car, *rose*	45.00	32.50
17	A1	50c brn, *az* ('00)	32.50	32.50
18	A1	75c vio, *orange*	37.50	27.50
19	A1	1fr brnz grn, *straw*	90.00	77.50
		Nos. 1-19 (19)	631.00	482.00

Perf. 13½x14 stamps are counterfeits.

Issues of 1892-1907 Surcharged in Black or Carmine

1912

20	A1	5c on 2c brn, *buff*	1.25	1.25
21	A1	5c on 4c cl, *lav* (C)	1.40	*1.50*
a.		Pair, one without surcharge	*1,000.*	*1,100.*
22	A1	5c on 15c blue (C)	1.40	1.40
a.		Pair, one without surcharge	*1,100.*	*1,000.*
23	A1	5c on 20c red, *green*	1.40	1.40
a.		Pair, one without surcharge	*1,100.*	*1,100.*
24	A1	5c on 25c blk, *rose* (C)	1.50	*1.75*
25	A1	5c on 30c brn, *bis* (C)	2.00	*2.10*
26	A1	10c on 40c red, *straw*	2.00	*2.25*
27	A1	10c on 45c black, *gray green* (C)	2.40	2.40
28	A1	10c on 50c car, *rose*	6.00	*6.50*
29	A1	10c on 75c vio, *org*	4.00	*4.50*
30	A1	10c on 1fr brnz grn, *straw*	5.50	*5.75*
a.		Pair, one without surcharge	*1,250.*	*1,200.*
		Nos. 20-30 (11)	28.85	30.80

Two spacings between the surcharged numerals are found on Nos. 20-30. See the *Scott Classic Specialized Catalogue of Stamps and Covers* for detailed listings.

Nos. 20-30 were available for use in Madagascar and the Comoro archipelago.

The stamps of Anjouan were superseded by those of Madagascar, and in 1950 by those of Comoro Islands.

ANNAM & TONKIN

a-'nam and 'tän-'kin

LOCATION — In French Indo-China bordering on the China Sea on the east and Siam on the west.
GOVT. — French Protectorate
AREA — 97,503 sq. mi.
POP. — 14,124,000 (approx. 1890)
CAPITAL — Annam: Hue; Tonkin: Hanoi

For administrative purposes, the Protectorates of Annam, Tonkin, Cambodia, Laos and the Colony of Cochin-China were grouped together and were known as French Indo-China.

100 Centimes = 1 Franc

Catalogue values for unused stamps are for examples without gum as most stamps were issued in that condition.

Stamps of French Colonies, 1881-86 Handstamped Surcharged in Black

Perf. 14x13½

1888, Jan. 21   Unwmk.

1	A9	1c on 2c brn, *buff*	47.50	*50.00*
a.		Inverted surcharge	200.00	200.00
b.		Sideways surcharge	200.00	210.00
2	A9	1c on 4c claret, *lav*	37.50	45.00
a.		Inverted surcharge	200.00	210.00
b.		Double surcharge	275.00	225.00
c.		Sideways surcharge	200.00	210.00
3	A9	5c on 10c blk, *lav*	47.50	37.50
a.		Inverted surcharge	200.00	200.00
b.		Double surcharge	225.00	225.00
4	A9	5c on 2c brn, *buff*	8,500.	

Hyphen between "A" and "T"

7	A9	1c on 2c brn, *buff*	325.00	*425.00*
a.		Inverted surcharge	750.00	775.00
b.		Sideways surcharge	750.00	775.00
c.		Pair, Nos. 1, 7	9,000.	
8	A9	1c on 4c claret, *lav*	525.00	*625.00*
9	A9	5c on 10c blk, *lav*	220.00	*240.00*

A 5c on 2c with surcharge in blue was prepared but not issued.

In these surcharges there are different types of numerals and letters.

There are numerous other errors in the placing of the surcharges, including double one inverted, double both inverted, double one sideways, and pair one without surcharge. Such varieties command substantial premiums.

These stamps were superseded in 1892 by those of Indo-China.

ANTIGUA

an-'tēg-wə

LOCATION — In the West Indies, southeast of Puerto Rico
GOVT. — Independent state
AREA — 171 sq. mi.
POP. — 64,246 (est. 1999)
CAPITAL — St. John's

Antigua was one of the presidencies of the former Leeward Islands colony until becoming a Crown Colony in 1956. It became an Associated State of the United Kingdom in 1967 and an independent nation on November 1, 1981, taking the name of Antigua and Barbuda.

Antigua stamps were discontinued in 1890 and resumed in 1903. In the interim, stamps of Leeward Islands were used. Between 1903-1956, stamps of Antigua and Leeward Islands were used concurrently.

12 Pence = 1 Shilling
20 Shillings = 1 Pound
100 Cents = 1 Dollar (1951)

> Catalogue values for unused stamps in this country are for Never Hinged items, beginning with Scott 96.

Watermark

Wmk. 5 — Star

Values for unused stamps are for examples with original gum as defined in the catalogue introduction. Any exceptions will be noted. Very fine examples of Nos. 1-8, 11, 18-20 will have perforations touching the design on at least one frameline due to the narrow spacing of the stamps on the plates. Stamps with perfs clear of the framelines on all four sides are extremely scarce and will command higher prices.

Queen Victoria — A1

1862   Engr.   Unwmk.

Rough Perf. 14-16

1	A1	6p blue green	950.00	600.00
a.		Perf. 11-13	8,500.	
b.		Perf. 11-13x14-16	3,750.	
c.		Perf. 11-13 compound with 14-16	3,750.	

There is a question whether Nos. 1a-1c ever did postal duty.
Values for No. 1 are for stamps with perfs. cutting into the design. Values for No. 1b are for examples without gum.

1863-67   Wmk. 5

2	A1	1p dull rose	135.00	60.00
a.		Vert. pair, imperf. btwn.	37,500.	
b.		Imperf., pair		2,750.
c.		1p lilac rose	150.00	82.50
3	A1	1p vermilion ('67)	275.00	32.50
a.		Horiz. pair, imperf. btwn.	37,500.	
4	A1	6p green	775.00	30.00
a.		6p yellow green	4,750.	120.00
b.		Pair, imperf. btwn.	—	

1872   Wmk. 1   Perf. 12½

5	A1	1p lake	220.00	22.50
6	A1	1p vermilion	225.00	26.50
7	A10	6p blue green	600.00	12.50

Queen Victoria — A2

1873-79   Perf. 14

8	A1	1p lake	250.00	12.50
a.		Half used as ½p on cover		9,500.

Typo.

9	A2	2½p red brown ('79)	700.00	210.00
10	A2	4p blue ('79)	290.00	18.00

Engr.

11	A1	6p blue green ('76)	450.00	22.50

1882-87   Typo.   Wmk. 2

12	A2	½p green	5.00	20.00
13	A2	2½p red brown	225.00	67.50
14	A2	2½p ultra ('87)	8.50	17.00
15	A2	4p blue	350.00	19.00
16	A2	4p brown org ('87)	2.50	3.75
17	A2	1sh violet ('86)	190.00	175.00

Engr.

18	A1	1p carmine ('84)	2.60	4.50
19	A1	6p deep green	77.50	150.00

No. 18 was used for a time in St. Christopher and is identified by the "A12" cancellation.

1884   Perf. 12

20	A1	1p rose red	65.00	20.00

Seal of the Colony — A3   King Edward VII — A4

1903   Typo.   Wmk. 1   Perf. 14

21	A3	½p blue grn & blk	4.00	7.50
a.		Bluish paper ('09)	100.00	100.00
22	A3	1p car & black	14.00	1.50
a.		Bluish paper ('09)	92.50	92.50
23	A3	2p org brn & vio	8.25	27.50
24	A3	2½p ultra & black	18.00	25.00
25	A3	3p ocher & gray green	12.00	24.00
26	A3	6p black & red vio	35.00	60.00
27	A3	1sh violet & ultra	57.50	70.00
28	A3	2sh pur & gray green	95.00	125.00
29	A3	2sh6p red vio & blk	30.00	75.00
30	A4	5sh pur & gray green	115.00	165.00
		Nos. 21-30 (10)	388.75	580.50

The 2½p, 1sh and 5sh exist on both ordinary and chalky paper.

1908-20   Wmk. 3

31	A3	½p green	5.25	5.25
32	A3	1p scarlet ('15)	8.00	3.75
33	A3	2p org brn & dull vio ('12)	5.25	35.00
34	A3	2½p ultra	24.00	19.00
35	A3	3p ocher & grn green ('12)	7.00	21.00
36	A3	6p blk & red vio ('11)	8.25	47.50
37	A3	1sh vio & ultra	27.50	80.00
38	A3	2sh vio & green ('12)	110.00	130.00
		Nos. 31-38 (8)	195.25	341.50

Nos. 33, 35 to 38 are on chalky paper.
For overprints see Nos. MR1-MR3.

George V — A6

1913

41	A6	5sh violet & green	100.00	160.00

St. John's Harbor — A7

1921-29   Wmk. 4

42	A7	½p green	3.25	.60
43	A7	1p rose red	4.50	.60
44	A7	1p dp violet ('23)	8.75	1.75
45	A7	1½p orange ('22)	6.50	6.00
46	A7	1½p rose red ('26)	10.00	2.00
47	A7	1½p fawn ('29)	3.25	.75
48	A7	2p gray	4.50	.90
49	A7	2½p ultra ('27)	17.00	5.00
50	A7	2½p orange ('23)	2.75	20.00

Chalky Paper

51	A7	3p violet, yel	16.00	8.00
52	A7	6p vio & red vio	8.50	6.00
53	A7	1sh black, emer ('29)	6.50	5.00
54	A7	2sh vio & ultra, blue ('27)	12.00	65.00
55	A7	2sh6p blk & red, blue ('27)	52.50	47.50
56	A7	3sh grn & vio ('22)	52.50	105.00
57	A7	4sh blk & red ('22)	52.50	77.50
		Nos. 42-57 (16)	261.00	351.60

Wmk. 3
Chalky Paper

58	A7	3p violet, yel ('22)	5.00	15.00
59	A7	4p black & red, yel ('22)	2.50	6.50
60	A7	1sh black, emerald ('22)	4.75	10.50
61	A7	2sh vio & ultra, bl ('22)	14.50	37.50
62	A7	2sh6p blk & red, bl ('22)	19.00	70.00
63	A7	5sh grn & red, yel ('22)	9.25	60.00
64	A7	£1 vio & black, red ('22)	300.00	425.00
		Nos. 58-64 (7)	355.00	624.50

Old Dockyard, English Harbour — A8

Govt. House, St. John's — A9

Nelson's "Victory," 1805 — A10

Sir Thomas Warner's Ship, 1632 — A11

Perf. 12½
1932, Jan. 27   Engr.   Wmk. 4

67	A8	½p green	4.75	8.75
68	A8	1p scarlet	6.50	9.00
69	A8	1½p lt brown	4.75	5.50
70	A9	2p gray	9.00	27.50
71	A9	2½p ultra	8.75	9.75
72	A9	3p orange	8.75	14.00
73	A10	6p violet	16.00	14.00
74	A10	1sh olive green	21.00	32.50
75	A10	2sh6p claret	57.50	82.50
76	A11	5sh red brown & black	125.00	160.00
		Nos. 67-76 (10)	262.00	363.50
		Set, never hinged	650.00	

Tercentenary of the colony.
Forged cancellations abound, especially dated "MY 18 1932."

Common Design Types pictured following the introduction.

Silver Jubilee Issue
Common Design Type
1935, May 6   Perf. 13½x14

77	CD301	1p car & blue	2.25	4.00
78	CD301	1½p gray blk & ultra	2.50	1.50
79	CD301	2½p blue & brn	6.50	1.75
80	CD301	1sh brt vio & ind	9.00	16.00
		Nos. 77-80 (4)	20.25	23.25
		Set, never hinged	32.50	

Coronation Issue
Common Design Type
1937, May 12   Perf. 11x11½

81	CD302	1p carmine	.50	2.75
82	CD302	1½p brown	.35	2.50
83	CD302	2½p deep ultra	1.00	2.75
		Nos. 81-83 (3)	1.85	8.00
		Set, never hinged	2.75	

English Harbour — A14   Nelson's Dockyard — A15

Fort James — A16   St. John's Harbor — A17

1938-51   Engr.   Perf. 12½

84	A14	½p yel green	.30	1.50
85	A15	1p scarlet	2.25	2.50
86	A15	1½p red brown ('43)	1.80	2.75
87	A14	2p gray	.70	1.00
88	A15	2½p ultra ('43)	.75	.90
89	A16	3p pale orange ('44)	.75	1.10
90	A17	6p purple	2.75	1.25
91	A17	1sh brown & blk	3.50	2.00
92	A16	2sh6p dp claret ('42)	16.00	20.00
93	A17	5sh grayish olive green ('44)	9.00	11.00
94	A15	10sh red vio ('48)	11.00	35.00
95	A16	£1 Prussian blue ('48)	22.50	60.00
		Nos. 84-95 (12)	71.30	139.00
		Set, never hinged	105.00	

See Nos. 107-113, 115-116, 118-121, 136-142, 144-145.
For overprint see Nos. 125-126.

> Catalogue values for unused stamps in this section, from this point to the end of the section, are for Never Hinged items.

Peace Issue
Common Design Type
1946, Nov. 1   Wmk. 4   Perf. 13½x14

96	CD303	1½p brown	.25	.25
97	CD303	3p dp orange	.25	.55

Silver Wedding Issue
Common Design Types
1949, Jan. 3   Photo.   Perf. 14x14½

98	CD304	2½p bright ultra	.55	2.75

Engraved; Name Typographed
Perf. 11½x11

| 99 | CD305 | 5sh dk brown olive | 13.00 | 13.00 |

UPU Issue
Common Design Types
Perf. 13½, 11x11½
1949, Oct. 10   **Wmk. 4**
Engr.; Name Typo. on 3p and 6p

100	CD306	2½p deep ultra	.40	.70
101	CD307	3p orange	1.60	3.25
102	CD308	6p purple	.80	2.25
103	CD309	1sh red brown	.80	1.50
		Nos. 100-103 (4)	3.60	7.70

University Issue
Common Design Types
Perf. 14x14½
1951, Feb. 16   **Engr.**   **Wmk. 4**

| 104 | CD310 | 3c chocolate & blk | .45 | 1.75 |
| 105 | CD311 | 12c purple & blk | .90 | 2.00 |

Coronation Issue
Common Design Type
1953, June 2   *Perf. 13½x13*

| 106 | CD312 | 2c dk green & blk | .40 | .75 |

Types of 1938 with Portrait of Queen Elizabeth II

Martello Tower — A24

Perf. 13x13½, 13½x13
1953-56   **Wmk. 4**

107	A16	½c dk red brn ('56)	.35	.35
108	A14	1c gray	.30	1.75
109	A15	2c deep green	.30	.25
110	A15	3c yellow & blk	.35	.25
111	A14	4c rose red (shades)	1.25	.25
112	A15	5c dull vio & blk	2.40	.45
113	A16	6c orange	2.40	.25
114	A24	8c deep blue	2.60	.25
115	A17	12c violet	2.60	.25
116	A17	24c chocolate & blk	4.50	.25
117	A24	48c dp bl & rose lil	9.50	3.25
118	A24	60c claret	8.50	.75
119	A17	$1.20 olive green	3.75	.90
120	A15	$2.40 magenta	17.00	11.50
121	A16	$4.80 greenish blue	22.00	27.50
		Nos. 107-121 (15)	77.95	48.20

See No. 143. For overprint see Nos. 125-126.

West Indies Federation
Common Design Type
Perf. 11½x11
1958, Apr. 22   **Engr.**   **Wmk. 314**

122	CD313	3c green	1.50	.30
123	CD313	6c blue	1.90	2.75
124	CD313	12c carmine rose	2.40	.75
		Nos. 122-124 (3)	5.80	3.80

Nos. 110 and 115 Overprinted in Red or Black: "Commemoration Antigua Constitution 1960"
Perf. 13x13½, 13½x13
1960, Jan. 1   **Wmk. 4**

| 125 | A15 | 3c yellow & black | .25 | .25 |
| 126 | A17 | 12c violet (Blk) | .25 | .25 |

Constitutional reforms effective Jan. 1, 1960.

Lord Nelson and Nelson's Dockyard A26

Perf. 11½x11
1961, Nov. 14   **Wmk. 314**

| 127 | A26 | 20c brown & lilac | 1.60 | 1.60 |
| 128 | A26 | 30c dk blue & green | 1.75 | 2.75 |

Completion of the restoration of Lord Nelson's headquarters, English Harbour.

Stamp of 1862 and Royal Mail Steam Packet in English Harbour
A27

1962, Aug. 1   **Engr.**   *Perf. 13*

129	A27	3c dull green & pur	.70	.25
130	A27	10c dull green & ultra	.80	.25
131	A27	12c dull green & blk	.90	.25
132	A27	50c dull grn & brn org	1.50	2.25
		Nos. 129-132 (4)	3.90	3.00

Centenary of first Antigua postage stamp.

Freedom from Hunger Issue
Common Design Type
Perf. 14x14½
1963, June 4   **Photo.**   **Wmk. 314**

| 133 | CD314 | 12c green | .35 | .35 |

Red Cross Centenary Issue
Common Design Type
1963, Sept. 2   **Litho.**   *Perf. 13*

| 134 | CD315 | 3c black & red | .25 | .75 |
| 135 | CD315 | 12c ultra & red | .75 | 1.25 |

Types of 1938-53 with Portrait of Queen Elizabeth II
Perf. 13x13½, 13½x13
1963-65   **Engr.**   **Wmk. 314**

136	A16	½c brown ('65)	2.50	.85
137	A14	1c gray ('65)	1.25	1.00
138	A15	2c deep green	.70	.30
139	A15	3c orange yel & blk	.40	.30
140	A14	4c brown red	.35	3.00
141	A15	5c dull vio & black	.30	.25
142	A16	6c orange	.60	.35
143	A24	8c deep blue	.35	.25
144	A17	12c violet	1.00	.25
145	A17	24c choc & black	5.00	.80
		Nos. 136-145 (10)	12.45	7.35

For surcharge see No. 152.

Shakespeare Issue
Common Design Type
Perf. 14x14½
1964, Apr. 23   **Photo.**   **Wmk. 314**

| 151 | CD316 | 12c red brown | .35 | .25 |

No. 144 Surcharged with New Value and Bars
Perf. 13½x13
1965, Apr. 1   **Engr.**   **Wmk. 314**

| 152 | A17 | 15c on 12c violet | .30 | .30 |

ITU Issue
Common Design Type
Perf. 11x11½
1965, May 17   **Litho.**   **Wmk. 314**

| 153 | CD317 | 2c blue & ver | .25 | .25 |
| 154 | CD317 | 50c orange & vio bl | 1.20 | 1.10 |

Intl. Cooperation Year Issue
Common Design Type
1965, Oct. 25   *Perf. 14½*

| 155 | CD318 | 4c blue grn & claret | .25 | .25 |
| 156 | CD318 | 15c lt vio & green | .30 | .25 |

Churchill Memorial Issue
Common Design Type
1966, Jan. 24   **Photo.**   *Perf. 14*
Design in Black, Gold and Carmine Rose

157	CD319	½c bright blue	.25	2.00
158	CD319	4c green	.30	.25
159	CD319	25c brown	1.25	.30
160	CD319	35c violet	1.25	.50
		Nos. 157-160 (4)	3.05	3.05

Royal Visit Issue
Common Design Type
1966, Feb. 4   **Litho.**   *Perf. 11x12*
Portraits in Black

| 161 | CD320 | 6c violet blue | 1.75 | 1.10 |
| 162 | CD320 | 15c dark car rose | 1.75 | 1.50 |

World Cup Soccer Issue
Common Design Type
1966, July 1   **Wmk. 314**   *Perf. 14*

| 163 | CD321 | 6c multicolored | .25 | .60 |
| 164 | CD321 | 35c multicolored | .55 | .25 |

WHO Headquarters Issue
Common Design Type
1966, Sept. 20   *Perf. 14*

| 165 | CD322 | 2c multicolored | .25 | .25 |
| 166 | CD322 | 15c multicolored | .90 | .30 |

Nelson's Dockyard A35

Designs: 1c, Old post office, St. John's. 2c, Health Center. 3c, Teachers' Training College. 4c, Martello Tower, Barbuda. 5c, Ruins of officers quarters, Shirley Heights. 6c, Government House, Barbuda. 10c, Princess Margaret School. 15c, Air terminal. 25c, General post office. 35c, Clarence House. 50c, Government House. 75c, Administration building. $1, Court House, St. John's. $2.50, Magistrates' Court. $5, St. John's Cathedral.

Perf. 11½x11
1966, Nov. 1   **Engr.**   **Wmk. 314**

167	A35	½c green & blue	.25	1.10
168	A35	1c purple & rose	.25	.30
169	A35	2c slate & org	.25	.25
170	A35	3c rose red & blk	.30	.30
171	A35	4c dull vio & brn	1.00	.25
172	A35	5c vio bl & olive	.25	.25
173	A35	6c dp org & pur	1.00	.30
174	A35	10c brt grn & rose red	.25	.25
175	A35	15c brn & blue	1.50	.25
		Complete booklet, 4 ea. #172, 174, 175	11.00	
176	A35	25c slate & brn	.55	.25
177	A35	35c dp rose & sep	1.50	.55
178	A35	50c green & black	2.00	2.25
179	A35	75c Prus bl & vio blue	3.50	2.25
180	A35	$1 dp rose & olive	8.00	2.50
181	A35	$2.50 black & rose	6.50	8.00
182	A35	$5 ol grn & dl vio	9.00	6.50
		Nos. 167-182 (16)	36.10	25.55

For surcharge see No. 231.

1969   *Perf. 13½*

167a	A35	½c	.25	2.25
168a	A35	1c	.25	1.25
169a	A35	2c	.25	.65
170a	A35	3c	.25	.25
171a	A35	4c	.25	.25
172b	A35	5c	.25	.25
173a	A35	6c	.25	.90
174b	A35	10c	.25	.25
175b	A35	15c	.55	.25
176a	A35	25c	.45	.25
177a	A35	35c	.60	1.00
178a	A35	50c	.75	2.25
180a	A35	$1	1.25	5.00
181a	A35	$2.50	1.50	8.00
182a	A35	$5	11.50	24.00
		Nos. 167a-182a (15)	18.60	46.80

The ½c, 3c, 6c are on ordinary paper. The 15c through $5 on glazed paper. The others exist on both papers.

UNESCO Anniversary Issue
Common Design Type
1966, Dec. 1   **Litho.**   *Perf. 14*

183	CD323	4c "Education"	.25	.25
184	CD323	25c "Science"	.40	.25
185	CD323	$1 "Culture"	1.25	2.00
		Nos. 183-185 (3)	1.90	2.50

Independent State

Flag of Antigua, Spiny Lobster, Maps of Antigua and Barbuda
A37

Designs: 15c, 35c, Flag of Antigua. 25c, Flag and Premier's Office Building.

1967, Feb. 27   **Photo.**   *Perf. 14*

186	A37	4c multicolored	.25	.25
187	A37	15c multicolored	.25	.25
188	A37	25c multicolored	.25	.25
189	A37	35c multicolored	.25	.25
		Nos. 186-189 (4)	1.00	1.00

Antigua's independence, Feb. 27, 1967.

Gilbert Memorial Church, Antigua — A38

25c, Nathaniel Gilbert's House. 35c, Map of the Caribbean and Central America.

Perf. 14x13½
1967, May 18   **Photo.**   **Wmk. 314**

190	A38	4c brt red & black	.25	.25
191	A38	25c emerald & black	.25	.25
192	A38	35c ultra & black	.25	.25
		Nos. 190-192 (3)	.75	.75

Attainment of autonomy by the Methodist Church in the Caribbean and the Americas, and the opening of headquarters near St. John's, Antigua, May 1967.

Antiguan and British Royal Arms — A39

1967, July 21   *Perf. 14½x14*

| 193 | A39 | 15c dark green & multi | .25 | .25 |
| 194 | A39 | 35c deep blue & multi | .25 | .25 |

Granting of a new coat of arms to the State of Antigua; 300th anniv. of the Treaty of Breda.

Sailing Ship, 17th Century A40

Design: 6c, 35c, Map of Barbuda from Jan Blaeu's Atlas, 1665.

Perf. 11½x11
1967, Dec. 14   **Engr.**   **Wmk. 314**

195	A40	4c dark blue	.35	.25
196	A40	6c deep plum	.35	1.25
197	A40	25c green	.50	.25
198	A40	35c black	.50	.30
		Nos. 195-198 (4)	1.70	2.05

Resettlement of Barbuda, 300th anniv.

Dow Hill Antenna — A41

Designs: 15c, Antenna and rocket blasting off. 25c, Nose cone orbiting moon. 50c, Re-entry of space capsule.

Perf. 14½x14
1968, Mar. 29   **Photo.**   **Wmk. 314**

199	A41	4c dk blue, org & black	.25	.25
200	A41	15c dk blue, org & black	.25	.25
201	A41	25c dk blue, org & black	.25	.25
202	A41	50c dk blue, org & black	.25	.35
		Nos. 199-202 (4)	1.00	1.10

Dedication of the Dow Hill tracking station in Antigua for the NASA Apollo project.

Beach and Sailfish
A42

Designs: ½c, 50c, Limbo dancer, flames and dancing girls. 15c, Three girls on a beach and water skier. 35c, Woman scuba diver, corals and fish.

1968, July 1   Photo.   Perf. 14

203	A42	½c red & multi	.25	.25
204	A42	15c sky blue & multi	.25	.25
205	A42	25c blue & multi	.30	.25
206	A42	35c brt blue & multi	.30	.25
207	A42	50c multicolored	.50	1.10
		Nos. 203-207 (5)	1.60	2.10

Issued for tourist publicity.

St. John's Harbor, 1768
A43

St. John's Harbor: 15c, 1829. 25c, Map of deep-sea harbor, 1968. 35c, Dock, 1968. 2c, Like $1.

Engr. & Litho.; Engr. ($1)
1968, Oct. 31   Wmk. 314   Perf. 13

208	A43	2c dp car & lt blue	.25	.30
209	A43	15c sepia & yel grn	.35	.25
210	A43	25c dk blue & yel	.45	.25
211	A43	35c dp green & sal	.50	.25
212	A43	$1 black	.85	1.75
		Nos. 208-212 (5)	2.40	2.80

Opening of St. John's deep-sea harbor.

Mace and Parliament
A44

Mace and: 15c, Mace bearer. 25c, House of Representatives, interior. 50c, Antigua coat of arms and great seal.

1969, Feb. 3   Photo.   Perf. 12½

213	A44	4c crimson & multi	.25	.25
214	A44	15c crimson & multi	.25	.25
215	A44	25c crimson & multi	.25	.25
216	A44	50c crimson & multi	.30	1.40
		Nos. 213-216 (4)	1.05	2.15

300th anniversary of Antigua Parliament.

CARIFTA Cargo — A45

4c, 15c, Ship, plane and trucks, horiz.

Perf. 13½x13, 13x13½
1969, Apr. 14   Litho.   Wmk. 314

217	A45	4c blk & brt lilac rose	.25	.25
218	A45	15c blk & brt grnsh blue	.25	.25
219	A45	25c bister & black	.25	.25
220	A45	35c tan & black	.25	.25
		Nos. 217-220 (4)	1.00	1.00

1st anniv. of CARIFTA (Caribbean Free Trade Area).

Map of Redonda Island
A46

25c, View of Redonda from the sea & seagulls.

1969, Aug. 1   Photo.   Perf. 13x13½

221	A46	15c ultra & multi	.25	.25
222	A46	25c multicolored	.25	.25
223	A46	50c salmon & multi	.40	.60
		Nos. 221-223 (3)	.90	1.10

Centenary of Redonda phosphate industry.

Adoration of the Kings, by Gugliemo Marcillat
A47

Christmas: 10c, 50c, Holy Family, by anonymous German artist, 15th century.

1969, Oct. 15   Litho.   Perf. 13x14

224	A47	6c bister brn & multi	.25	.25
225	A47	10c fawn & multi	.25	.25
226	A47	35c gray olive & multi	.25	.25
227	A47	50c gray blue & multi	.30	.25
		Nos. 224-227 (4)	1.05	1.00

Arms of Antigua — A48

Coil Stamps
Wmk. 314 upright
1970, Jan. 30   Photo.   Perf. 14½x14

228	A48	5c bright blue	.25	.25
a.		Wmk. 373 ('77)	7.00	
229	A48	10c bright green	.25	.25
a.		Wmk. 373, invtd. ('77)	—	2.00
230	A48	25c deep magenta	.25	.25
a.		Wmk. 373 ('77)	12.50	
		Nos. 228-230 (3)	.75	.75

Glazed Paper
1973, Mar. 5   Wmk. 314 sideways

228b	A48	5c bright blue	1.00	2.00
229b	A48	10c bright green	1.00	2.00
230b	A48	25c deep magenta	1.25	1.75
		Nos. 228b-230b (3)	3.25	5.75

No. 176 Surcharged

1970, Jan. 2   Engr.   Perf. 11½x11

231	A35	20c on 25c slate & brn	.35	.25

Sikorsky S-38
A49

Aircraft: 20c, Dornier DO-X. 35c, Hawker Siddeley 748. 50c, Douglas C-124C Globemaster II. 75c, Vickers VC 10.

1970, Feb. 16   Litho.   Perf. 14½

232	A49	5c brt green & multi	.60	.25
233	A49	20c ultra & multi	1.00	.25
234	A49	35c blue grn & multi	1.25	.25
235	A49	50c blue & multi	1.25	1.50
236	A49	75c vio blue & multi	1.60	2.25
		Nos. 232-236 (5)	5.70	4.50

40th anniversary of air service.

Dickens and Scene from "Pickwick Papers"
A50

Charles Dickens (1812-1870), English novelist and Scene from: 5c, "Nicholas Nickleby." 35c, "Oliver Twist." $1, "David Copperfield."

Wmk. 314
1970, May 19   Litho.   Perf. 14

237	A50	5c olive & sepia	.25	.25
238	A50	20c aqua & sepia	.25	.25
239	A50	35c violet & sepia	.25	.25
240	A50	$1 scarlet & sepia	.60	.75
		Nos. 237-240 (4)	1.35	1.50

Carib Indian and War Canoe
A51

Ships: 1c, Columbus and "Nina." 2c, Sir Thomas Warner's arms and sailing ship. 3c, Viscount Hood and "Barfleur." 4c, Sir George Rodney and "Formidable." 5c, Capt. Horatio Nelson and "Boreas." 6c, King William IV and "Pegasus." 10c, Capt. Cuthbert Collingwood and "Pelican." 15c, Capt. Cuthbert Collingwood and "Pelican." 20c, Admiral Nelson and "Victoria." 25c, Paddle steamer "Solent" and Steam Packet Company emblem. 35c, King George V and corvette "Canada." 50c, Cruiser "Renown" and royal badge. 75c, S.S. "Federal Maple" and maple leaf. $1, Racing yacht "Sol-Quest" and Gallant 53 class emblem. $2.50, Missile destroyer "London" and her emblem. $5, Tug "Pathfinder" and arms of Antigua.

Wmk. 314 Sideways
1970, Aug. 19   Litho.   Perf. 14

241	A51	½c ocher & multi	.25	1.25
242	A51	1c Prus bl & multi	.30	1.25
243	A51	2c yel grn & multi	.35	3.00
244	A51	3c ol bis & multi	.35	3.00
245	A51	4c bl gray & multi	.40	2.75
246	A51	5c fawn & multi	.50	.40
247	A51	6c rose lil & multi	1.40	4.25
248	A51	10c brn org & multi	.80	.25
249	A51	15c ultra & multi	7.00	1.00
250	A51	20c ol grn & multi	1.15	.40
251	A51	25c olive & multi	1.25	.40
252	A51	35c dull red brn & multi	1.60	.80
253	A51	50c lt brn & multi	3.50	5.75
254	A51	75c beige & multi	4.50	5.75
255	A51	$1 Prus green & multi	4.50	1.75
256	A51	$2.50 gray & multi	6.25	7.25
257	A51	$5 yel & multi	2.75	6.00
		Nos. 241-257 (17)	36.85	45.25

1972-74   Wmk. 314 Upright

241a	A51	½c	.30	.45
242a	A51	1c	.40	1.25
244a	A51	3c	.80	1.75
245a	A51	4c	.55	2.00
246a	A51	5c	.60	.40
247a	A51	6c	.90	2.75
248a	A51	10c	.60	.60
249a	A51	15c	6.25	.90
254a	A51	75c	6.25	3.00
255a	A51	$1	2.75	1.75
256a	A51	$2.50	2.50	6.50
257a	A51	$5	3.50	10.00
		Nos. 241a-257a (12)	25.40	31.35

For surcharge see No. 368.

1975, Jan. 21   Wmk. 373

257b	A51	$5 yellow & multi	4.00	12.00

Nativity, by Albrecht Dürer — A52

Christmas: 10c, 50c, Adoration of the Magi, by Albrecht Dürer.

Engr. & Litho.
1970, Oct. 28   Perf. 13½x14

258	A52	3c brt grnsh blue & blk	.25	.25
259	A52	10c pink & plum	.25	.25
260	A52	35c brick red & black	.25	.25
261	A52	50c lilac & violet	.30	.25
		Nos. 258-261 (4)	1.05	1.00

Private, 4th West India Regiment, 1804 — A53

Military Uniforms: ½c, Drummer Boy, 4th King's Own Regiment, 1759. 20c, Grenadier Company Officer, 60th Regiment, The Royal American, 1809. 35c, Light Company Officer, 93rd Regiment, The Sutherland Highlanders, 1826-1834. 75c, Private, 3rd West India Regiment, 1851.

Perf. 14x13½
1970, Dec. 1   Litho.   Wmk. 314

262	A53	½c lake & multi	.25	.25
263	A53	10c brn org & multi	.45	.25
264	A53	20c Prus grn & multi	.90	.25
265	A53	35c dl pur & multi	1.10	.25
266	A53	75c dk ol grn & multi	2.25	2.75
a.		Souv. sheet, #262-266 + label	6.50	7.00
		Nos. 262-266 (5)	4.95	3.75

See Nos. 274-278, 283-287, 307-311, 329-333.

Market Woman Voting — A54

Voting by: 20c, Businessman. 35c, Mother (and child). 50c, Workman.

Perf. 14½x14
1971, Feb. 1   Photo.   Wmk. 314

267	A54	5c brown	.25	.25
268	A54	20c olive black	.25	.25
269	A54	35c rose magenta	.25	.25
270	A54	50c violet blue	.25	.25
		Nos. 267-270 (4)	1.00	1.00

Adult suffrage, 20th anniversary.

Last Supper, from The Small Passion, by Dürer — A55

Woodcuts by Albrecht Dürer: 35c, Crucifixion from Eichstatt Missal. 75c, Resurrection from The Great Passion.

Perf. 14x13½
1971, Apr. 7   Litho.   Wmk. 314

271	A55	5c gray, red & black	.25	.25
272	A55	35c gray, violet & black	.25	.25
273	A55	75c gray, gold & black	.25	.25
		Nos. 271-273 (3)	.75	.75

Easter.

Uniform Type of 1970

Military Uniforms: ½c, Private, Suffolk Regiment, 1704. 10c, Grenadier, South Staffordshire, 1751. 20c, Fusilier, Royal Northumberland, 1778. 35c, Private, Northamptonshire, 1793, 75c, Private, East Yorkshire, 1805.

1971, July 12		Litho.	Wmk. 314	
274	A53	½c gray grn & multi	.25	.25
275	A53	10c bluish blk & multi	.45	.25
276	A53	20c dk pur & multi	1.15	.25
277	A53	35c dk ol & multi	1.40	.25
278	A53	75c brown & multi	1.75	2.75
a.		Souv. sheet, #274-278 + label	7.00	8.00
		Nos. 274-278 (5)	5.00	3.75

Virgin and Child, by Veronese — A56

Christmas: 5c, 50c, Adoration of the Shepherds, by Bonifazio Veronese.

1971, Oct. 4			Perf. 14x13½	
279	A56	3c multicolored	.25	.25
280	A56	5c multicolored	.25	.25
281	A56	35c multicolored	.25	.25
282	A56	50c multicolored	.40	.30
		Nos. 279-282 (4)	1.15	1.05

Uniform Type of 1970

Military Uniforms: ½c, Officer, King's Own Borderers Regiment, 1815. 10c, Sergeant, Buckinghamshire Regiment, 1837. 20c, Private, South Hampshire Regiment, 1853. 35c, Officer, Royal Artillery, 1854. 75c, Private, Worcestershire Regiment, 1870.

1972, July 1				
283	A53	½c ol brn & multi	.25	.25
284	A53	10c dp grn & multi	.60	.25
285	A53	20c brt vio & multi	1.10	.25
286	A53	35c mar & multi	1.35	.25
287	A53	75c dk vio bl & multi	1.75	3.00
a.		Souvenir sheet of 5, #283-287 + label	7.50	8.50
		Nos. 283-287 (5)	5.05	4.05

Reticulated Helmet Cowrie — A57

Sea Shells: 5c, Measled cowrie. 35c, West Indian fighting conch. 50c, Hawkwing conch.

1972, Aug. 1			Perf. 14½x14	
288	A57	3c multicolored	.55	.25
289	A57	5c ver & multi	.55	.25
290	A57	35c lt vio & multi	1.60	.25
291	A57	50c rose red & multi	1.75	2.75
		Nos. 288-291 (4)	4.45	3.50

St. John's Cathedral, 1745-1843 — A58

Christmas: 50c, Interior of St. John's. 75c, St. John's rebuilt.

1972, Nov. 6		Litho.	Perf. 14	
292	A58	35c org brn & multi	.25	.25
293	A58	50c vio & multi	.30	.30
294	A58	75c multicolored	.50	.55
a.		Souv. sheet, #292-294, perf 15	1.00	1.25
		Nos. 292-294 (3)	1.05	1.10

Silver Wedding Issue, 1972
Common Design Type

1972, Nov. 20		Photo.	Perf. 14x14½	
295	CD324	20c ultra & multi	.25	.25
296	CD324	35c steel blue & multi	.25	.25

Map of Antigua, Batsman Driving Ball — A60

Designs: 35c, Batsman and wicketkeeper. $1, Emblem of Rising Sun Cricket Club.

1972, Dec. 15			Perf. 13½x14	
297	A60	5c multicolored	.25	.25
298	A60	35c multicolored	.75	.30
299	A60	$1 multicolored	2.25	2.50
a.		Souvenir sheet of 3, #297-299	5.25	6.25
		Nos. 297-299 (3)	3.25	3.05

Rising Sun Cricket Club, St. John's, 50th anniv.

Map of Antigua and Yacht — A61

1972, Dec. 29			Perf. 14½	
300	A61	35c shown	.25	.25
301	A61	50c Racing yachts	.25	.25
302	A61	75c St. John's G.P.O.	.35	.25
303	A61	$1 Statue of Liberty	.40	.25
a.		Souvenir sheet of 2, #301, 303	1.10	1.25
		Nos. 300-303 (4)	1.25	1.00

Opening of Antigua and Barbuda Information Office in New York City.

Window with Episcopal Coat of Arms — A62

Stained glass windows from Cathedral of St. John: 35c, Crucifixion. 75c, Arm of Rt. Rev. D.G. Davis, 1st bishop of Antigua.

1973, Apr. 16		Litho.	Perf. 13½	
304	A62	5c yellow & multi	.25	.25
305	A62	35c brt lilac & multi	.25	.25
306	A62	75c blue & multi	.30	.25
		Nos. 304-306 (3)	.80	.75

Easter.

Uniform Type of 1970

Military Uniforms: ½c, Private, Col. Zacharia Tiffin's Regiment, 1701. 10c, Private, 63rd Regiment, 1759. 20c, Officer, 35th Sussex Regiment, 1828. 35c, Private, 2nd West India Regiment, 1853. 75c, Sergeant, Princess of Wales Regiment, Hertfordshire, 1858.

1973, July 1			Perf. 14x13½	Wmk. 314	
307	A53	½c dp ultra & multi	.25	.25
308	A53	10c rose lilac & multi	.35	.25
309	A53	20c gray & multi	.50	.25
310	A53	35c multicolored	.70	.25
311	A53	75c multicolored	1.50	1.25
a.		Souv. sheet, #307-311 + label	4.00	3.75
		Nos. 307-311 (5)	3.30	2.25

Butterfly Costumes — A63

Designs: 20c, Carnival revelers. 35c, Costumed group. 75c, Carnival Queen.

1973, July 30			Perf. 13½x14	Unwmk.	
312	A63	5c multicolored	.25	.25
313	A63	20c multicolored	.25	.25
314	A63	35c multicolored	.25	.25
315	A63	75c multicolored	.30	.25
a.		Souvenir sheet of 4, #312-315	1.10	1.25
		Nos. 312-315 (4)	1.05	1.00

Carnival, July 29-Aug. 7.

Virgin of the Porridge, by David — A64

Christmas: 5c, Adoration of the Kings, by Stomer. 20c, Virgin of the Grand Duke, by Raphael. 35c, Nativity with God the Father and Holy Ghost, by Tiepolo. $1, Madonna and Child, by Murillo.

1973, Oct. 15		Photo.	Perf. 14½	Unwmk.	
316	A64	3c brt blue & multi	.25	.25
317	A64	5c emerald & multi	.25	.25
318	A64	20c gold & multi	.25	.25
319	A64	35c violet & multi	.25	.25
320	A64	$1 red & multi	.35	.55
a.		Souvenir sheet of 5, #316-320	1.40	1.60
		Nos. 316-320 (5)	1.35	1.55

Princess Anne and Mark Phillips — A65

Design: $2, different border.

1973, Nov. 14		Litho.	Perf. 13½	
321	A65	35c dull ultra & multi	.25	.25
322	A65	$2 yel grn & multi	.25	.25
a.		Souvenir sheet of 2, #321-322	.65	.65

Wedding of Princess Anne and Capt. Mark Phillips.
Nos. 321-322 were issued in sheets of 5 plus label.

Nos. 321-322 and 322a Ovptd.

1973, Dec. 15		Litho.	Perf. 13½	
323	A65	35c multicolored	.25	.25
324	A65	$2 multicolored	.40	.40
a.		Souvenir sheet of 2, #323-324	.65	.65

Visit of Princess Anne and Mark Phillips to Antigua, Dec. 16. Same overprint in sheet margins of Nos. 323-324 and 324a.
Overprint lithographed. Also exists typographed.

Arms of Antigua and U.W.I. A66

Designs: 20c, Dancers. 35c, Antigua campus. 75c, Chancellor Sir Hugh Wooding.

1974, Feb. 18			Wmk. 314	
325	A66	5c multicolored	.25	.25
326	A66	20c multicolored	.25	.25
327	A66	35c multicolored	.25	.25
328	A66	75c multicolored	.25	.25
		Nos. 325-328 (4)	1.00	1.00

University of the West Indies, 24th anniv.

Uniform Type of 1970

Military Uniforms: ½c, Officer, 59th Foot, 1797. 10c, Gunner, Royal Artillery, 1800. 20c, Private, 1st West India Regiment, 1830. 35c, Officer, Gordon Highlanders, 1843. 75c, Private, Royal Welsh Fusiliers, 1846.

1974, May 1			Perf. 14x13½	
329	A53	½c dull grn & multi	.25	.25
330	A53	10c ocher & multi	.40	.25
331	A53	20c multicolored	.75	.25
332	A53	35c gray bl & multi	.90	.25
333	A53	75c dk gray & multi	1.25	1.75
a.		Souvenir sheet of 5, #329-333	3.25	2.50
		Nos. 329-333 (5)	3.55	2.75

English Mailman and Coach, Helicopter — A67

UPU, Cent.: 1c, English bellman, 1846; Orinoco mailboat, 1851; telecommunications satellite. 2c, English mailtrain guard, 1852; Swiss post passenger bus, 1906; Italian hydrofoil. 5c, Swiss messenger, 16th century; Wells Fargo coach, 1800; Concorde. 20c, German position, 1820; Japanese mailmen, 19th century; carrier pigeon. 35c, Contemporary Antiguan mailman; radar station; aquaplane. $1, Medieval French courier; American train, 1884; British Airways jet.

1974, July 15		Litho.	Perf. 14½	
334	A67	½c multicolored	.25	.25
335	A67	1c multicolored	.25	.25
336	A67	2c multicolored	.25	.25
337	A67	5c multicolored	.55	.40
338	A67	20c multicolored	.30	.25
339	A67	35c multicolored	.40	.25
340	A67	$1 multicolored	1.50	2.00
a.		Souvenir sheet of 7, #334-340 + label, perf. 13	4.00	3.65
		Nos. 334-340 (7)	3.50	3.65

For surcharges see Nos. 365-367.

Traditional Steel Band A68

Carnival 1974 (Steel Bands): 5c, Traditional players, vert. 35c, Modern steel band. 75c, Modern players, vert.

1974, Aug. 1,		Wmk. 314	Perf. 14	
341	A68	5c rose red, dk red & blk	.25	.25
342	A68	20c ocher, brn & blk	.25	.25
343	A68	35c yel grn, grn & blk	.25	.25
344	A68	75c dl bl, dk bl & blk	.25	1.00
a.		Souvenir sheet of 4, #341-344	.75	1.25
		Nos. 341-344 (4)	1.00	1.75

For surcharge see No. 364.

Soccer — A69

Designs: Games' emblem and soccer.

1974, Sept. 23		Unwmk.	Perf. 14½	
345	A69	5c multicolored	.25	.25
346	A69	35c multicolored	.25	.25
347	A69	75c multicolored	.25	.25

348 A69 $1 multicolored .30 .30
  a. Souvenir sheet of 4 1.10 1.10
  Nos. 345-348 (4) 1.05 1.05

World Cup Soccer Championship, Munich, June 13-July 7. Nos. 345-348 issued in sheets of 5 plus label showing Soccer Cup. No. 348a contains one each of Nos. 345-348, perf. 13½, and 2 labels.

For overprints and surcharges see Nos. 361-363.

Winston Churchill (1874-1965) at Harrow — A70

Designs: 35c, St. Paul's during bombing and Churchill portrait. 75c, Churchill's coat of arms and catafalque. $1, Churchill during Boer war, warrant for arrest and map of his escape route.

1974, Oct. 20   Unwmk.   Perf. 14½
349 A70 5c multicolored .25 .25
350 A70 35c multicolored .25 .25
351 A70 75c multicolored .25 .60
352 A70 $1 multicolored .30 1.00
  a. Souvenir sheet of 4, #349-352 1.10 1.60
  Nos. 349-352 (4) 1.05 2.10

Virgin and Child, by Giovanni Bellini — A71

Christmas — Paintings of the Virgin and Child: 1c, Raphael. 2c, Van der Weyden. 3c, Giorgione. 5c, Andrea Mantegna. 20c, Alvise Vivarini. 35c, Bartolommeo Montagna. 75c, Lorenzo Costa.

1974, Nov. 18   Litho.   Perf. 14½
353 A71 ½c shown .25 .25
354 A71 1c multicolored .25 .25
355 A71 2c multicolored .25 .25
356 A71 3c multicolored .25 .25
357 A71 5c multicolored .25 .25
358 A71 20c multicolored .25 .25
359 A71 35c multicolored .25 .25
360 A71 75c multicolored .35 1.00
  a. Souv. sheet, #357-360, perf 13½ 1.00 1.50
  Nos. 353-360 (8) 2.10 2.75

Nos. 346-348
Overprinted

No. 344
Surcharged and
Overprinted

1974, Oct. 16   Litho.   Perf. 14½, 14
361 A69 35c multicolored .30 .30
362 A69 75c multicolored .45 .35
363 A69 $1 multicolored .55 .45
364 A68 $5 on 75c multi 1.75 2.50
  Nos. 361-364 (4) 3.05 3.60

Earthquake of Oct. 8, 1974.

Nos. 338-340 and 254a Surcharged

1974-75   Wmk. 314   Perf. 14½
365 A67 50c on 20c 1.25 2.00
366 A67 $2.50 on 35c 2.75 6.00
367 A67 $5 on $1 6.00 7.50
  Perf. 14
368 A51 $10 on 75c 2.75 8.00
  Nos. 365-368 (4) 12.75 23.50

Carib War Canoe, English Harbour A72

Designs (Nelson's Dockyard): 15c, Raising ship, 1770. 35c, Lord Nelson and "Boreas." 50c, Yachts arriving for Sailing Week, 1974. $1, "Anchorage" in Old Dockyard, 1970.

1975, Mar. 17   Unwmk.   Perf. 14½
369 A72 5c multicolored .30 .25
370 A72 15c multicolored .90 .25
371 A72 35c multicolored 1.25 .25
372 A72 50c multicolored 1.50 1.75
373 A72 $1 multicolored 1.75 2.10
  Nos. 369-373 (5) 5.70 4.60

Souvenir Sheet
Perf. 13½
373A A72 Sheet of 5, #369-373 6.00 6.00

Stamps in No. 373A are 43x28mm.

Lady of the Valley Church A73

Churches of Antigua: 20c, Gilbert Memorial. 35c, Grace Hill Moravian. 50c, St. Phillip's. $1, Ebenezer Methodist.

1975, May 19   Litho.   Perf. 14½
374 A73 5c multicolored .25 .25
375 A73 20c multicolored .25 .25
376 A73 35c multicolored .25 .25
377 A73 50c multicolored .25 .25
378 A73 $1 multicolored .25 .45
  a. Souvenir sheet of 3, #376-378, perf. 13½ 1.00 1.40
  Nos. 374-378 (5) 1.25 1.45

Antigua, Senex's Atlas, 1721, and Hevelius Sextant, 1640 A74

Maps of Antigua: 20c, Jeffery's Atlas, 1775, and 18th century engraving of ship. 35c, Barbuda and Antigua, 1775 and 1975. $1, St. John's and English Harbour, 1973.

1975, July 21   Wmk. 314
379 A74 5c multicolored .35 .25
380 A74 20c multicolored .65 .25
381 A74 35c multicolored .85 .25
382 A74 $1 multicolored 1.75 2.10
  a. Souvenir sheet of 4, #379-382 4.50 3.50
  Nos. 379-382 (4) 3.60 2.85

Bugler and Sunset A75

Nordjamb 75 Emblem and: 20c, Black and white Scouts, tents and flags. 35c, Lord Baden-Powell and tents. $2, Dahomey dancers.

Unwmk.
1975, Aug. 26   Litho.   Perf. 14
383 A75 15c multicolored .30 .30
384 A75 20c multicolored .35 .25
385 A75 35c multicolored .50 .30

---

386 A75 $2 multicolored 2.00 2.25
  a. Souvenir sheet of 4, #383-386 4.00 4.00
  Nos. 383-386 (4) 3.15 3.05

Nordjamb 75, 14th Boy Scout Jamboree, Lillehammer, Norway, July 29-Aug. 7.

Eurema Elathea A76

Butterflies: 1c, Danaus plexippus. 2c, Phoebis philea. 5c, Marpesia petreus thetys. 20c, Eurema proterpia. 35c, Papilio polydamas. $2, Vanessa cardui.

1975, Oct. 30   Litho.   Perf. 14
387 A76 ½c multicolored .25 .25
388 A76 1c multicolored .25 .25
389 A76 2c multicolored .25 .25
390 A76 5c multicolored .30 .25
391 A76 20c multicolored 1.25 .50
392 A76 35c multicolored 1.75 .75
393 A76 $2 multicolored 5.00 8.00
  a. Miniature sheet of 4, #390-393 9.50 10.00
  Nos. 387-393 (7) 9.05 10.25

Virgin and Child, by Correggio — A77

Christmas: Virgin and Child paintings.

1975, Nov. 17   Unwmk.
394 A77 ½c shown .25 .25
395 A77 1c El Greco .25 .25
396 A77 2c Durer .25 .25
397 A77 3c Antonello .25 .25
398 A77 5c Bellini .25 .25
399 A77 10c Durer .25 .25
400 A77 35c Bellini .40 .25
401 A77 $2 Durer .75 .90
  a. Souvenir sheet of 4, #398-401 2.00 2.00
  Nos. 394-401 (8) 2.65 2.65

West Indies Team A78

Designs: 5c, Batsman I.V.A. Richards and cup, vert. 35c, Bowler A.M.E. Roberts and cup, vert.

1975, Dec. 15   Litho.   Perf. 14
402 A78 5c multicolored 1.10 .55
403 A78 35c multicolored 2.00 .55
404 A78 $2 multicolored 4.25 7.75
  Nos. 402-404 (3) 7.35 8.55

World Cricket Cup, victory of West Indies team.

A number of unissued items, imperfs., part perfs., missing color varieties, etc., were made available when the Format International inventory was liquidated. Imperfs of some or all of the Antigua stamps in the following sets are included: #405-422, 503-507, 515-517, 703-707, 745-749, 755-759, 808-816, 819-826, 905-909, 934-937.

See footnote after #962.

Antillean Crested Hummingbird — A79

Irrigation System, Diamond Estate — A80

Designs: 1c, Imperial parrot. 2c, Zenaida dove. 3c, Loggerhead kingbird. 4c, Red-necked pigeon. 5c, Rufous-throated solitaire. 6c, Orchid tree. 10c, Bougainvillea. 15c, Geiger tree. 20c, Flamboyant. 25c, Hibiscus. 35c, Flame of the Woods. 50c, Cannon at Fort James. 75c, Premier's Office. $1, Potworks Dam. $5, Government House. $10, Coolidge International Airport.

1976, Jan. 19   Litho.   Perf. 15
405 A79 ½c multicolored .35 .60
406 A79 1c multicolored 1.25 .50
407 A79 2c multicolored 1.25 .50
408 A79 3c multicolored 1.25 .55
409 A79 4c multicolored 1.25 2.00
410 A79 5c multicolored 1.75 .25
411 A79 6c multicolored .30 2.00
412 A79 10c multicolored .30 .25
413 A79 15c multicolored .35 .25
414 A79 20c multicolored .35 .35
415 A79 25c multicolored .35 .25
416 A79 35c multicolored .35 .35
417 A79 50c multicolored .50 .50
418 A79 75c multicolored .60 1.75
419 A79 $1 multicolored .75 .95
  Perf. 13½x14
420 A80 $2.50 rose & multi 1.50 4.50
421 A80 $5 lilac & multi 2.50 5.50
422 A80 $10 multicolored 4.25 7.50
  Nos. 405-422 (18) 19.20 28.55

Inscribed "1978"
1978
405a A79 ½c multicolored .90 1.10
406a A79 1c multicolored 1.50 1.10
407a A79 2c multicolored 1.50 1.10
408a A79 3c multicolored 1.50 1.10
409a A79 4c multicolored 1.75 1.10
410a A79 5c multicolored 2.00 1.10
411a A79 6c multicolored .35 1.25
412a A79 10c multicolored .35 .35
413a A79 15c multicolored .30 .35
414a A79 20c multicolored .30 1.00
415a A79 25c multicolored .35 .55
416a A79 35c multicolored .35 .55
417a A79 50c multicolored .55 1.00
418a A79 75c multicolored .55 1.10
419a A79 $1 multicolored .75 1.25
  Perf. 13½x14
420a A80 $2.50 rose & multi 1.75 5.50
421a A80 $5 lilac & multi 1.90 6.50
422a A80 $10 multicolored 6.50 8.50
  Nos. 405a-422a (18) 23.15 34.30

For overprints see Nos. 607-617.

Some Antigua issues from the 1970s were overprinted "Redonda." Other stamps inscribed "Redonda," but lacking any mention of Antigua, were also created in the 1970s and 1980s. These stamps are not listed because Redonda is uninhabited and has no need for stamps of its own.

Privates, Clark's Illinois Regiment — A81

1c, Riflemen, Pennsylvania Militia. 2c, Decorated American powder horn. 5c, Water bottle of Maryland troops. 35c, "Liberty Tree" and "Rattlesnake" flags. $1, American privateer Montgomery. $2.50, Congress Flag. $5, Continental Navy sloop Ranger.

1976, Mar. 17   Litho.   Perf. 14½
423 A81 ½c multicolored .25 .25
424 A81 1c multicolored .25 .25
425 A81 2c multicolored .25 .25
426 A81 5c multicolored .25 .25
427 A81 35c multicolored .45 .25
428 A81 $1 multicolored 1.25 .30
429 A81 $5 multicolored 2.25 2.75
  Nos. 423-429 (7) 4.95 4.30

Souvenir Sheet
Perf. 13
430 A81 $2.50 multicolored   1.90   1.90

American Bicentennial.

High
Jump,
Olympic
Rings
A82

Olympic Rings and: 1c, Boxing. 2c, Pole vault. 15c, Swimming. 30c, Running. $1, Bicycling. $2, Shot put.

1976, July 12   Litho.   Perf. 14½

431	A82	½c yellow & multi	.25	.25
432	A82	1c purple & multi	.25	.25
433	A82	2c emerald & multi	.25	.25
434	A82	15c brt blue & multi	.25	.25
435	A82	30c olive & multi	.30	.25
436	A82	$1 orange & multi	.40	.25
437	A82	$2 red & multi	1.10	1.10
a.		Souvenir sheet of 4	2.25	2.25
		Nos. 431-437 (7)	2.80	2.60

21st Olympic Games, Montreal, Canada, July 17-Aug. 1. No. 437a contains one each of Nos. 434-437, perf. 13½.

Water
Skiing
A83

Water Sports: 1c, Sailfish sailing. 2c, Snorkeling. 20c, Deep-sea fishing. 50c, Scuba diving. $2, Swimming.

1976, Aug. 26   Perf. 14

438	A83	½c yel grn & multi	.25	.25
439	A83	1c sepia & multi	.25	.25
440	A83	2c gray & multi	.25	.25
441	A83	20c multi	.25	.25
442	A83	50c brt vio & multi	.40	.40
443	A83	$2 lt gray & multi	1.10	1.10
a.		Souvenir sheet of 3, #441-443	2.00	2.00
		Nos. 438-443 (6)	2.50	2.50

French Angelfish — A84

1976, Oct. 4   Litho.   Perf. 13½x14

444	A84	15c shown	.45	.25
445	A84	30c Yellowfish grouper	.70	.25
446	A84	50c Yellowtail snappers	.85	.45
447	A84	90c Shy hamlet	1.30	.75
		Nos. 444-447 (4)	3.30	1.70

The
Annunciation
A85

Christmas: 10c, Flight into Egypt. 15c, Three Kings. 50c, Shepherds and star. $1, Kings presenting gifts to Christ Child.

1976, Nov. 15   Litho.   Perf. 14

448	A85	8c multicolored	.25	.25
449	A85	10c multicolored	.25	.25
450	A85	15c multicolored	.25	.25
451	A85	50c multicolored	.25	.25
452	A85	$1 multi	.25	.25
		Nos. 448-452 (5)	1.25	1.25

Mercury
and UPU
Emblem
A86

Designs: 1c, Alfred Nobel, symbols of prize categories. 10c, Viking spacecraft. 50c, Vivi Richards (batsman) and Andy Roberts (bowler). $1, Alexander G. Bell, telephones, 1876 and 1976. $2, Schooner Freelance.

1976, Dec. 28   Litho.   Perf. 14

453	A86	½c multicolored	.25	.25
454	A86	1c multicolored	.25	.25
455	A86	10c multicolored	.35	.25
456	A86	50c multicolored	3.50	1.75
457	A86	$1 multicolored	.90	1.75
458	A86	$2 multicolored	2.10	4.00
a.		Souvenir sheet of 4, #455-458	8.25	8.25
		Nos. 453-458 (6)	7.35	8.25

Special 1976 Events: UN Postal Admin., 25th anniv. (½c); Nobel Prize, 75th anniv. (1c); Viking Space Mission to Mars (10c); World Cricket Cup victory (50c); Telephone cent. ($1); Operation Sail, American Bicent. ($2).

Royal
Family — A87

Designs: 10c, Queen Elizabeth, Prince Philip and their children. 30c, Elizabeth II and Prince Philip touring Antigua. 50c, Queen enthroned. 90c, Queen wearing crown. $2.50, Queen and Prince Charles. $5, Queen and Prince Philip.

1977, Feb. 7   Perf. 13½x14

459	A87	10c multicolored	.25	.25
460	A87	30c multicolored	.25	.25
461	A87	50c multicolored	.25	.25
462	A87	90c multicolored	.25	.25
463	A87	$2.50 multicolored	.25	.50
		Nos. 459-463 (5)	1.25	1.50

Souvenir Sheet

464	A87	$5 multicolored	.70	.85
		Complete booklet, 6 #461 var., 1 #464 var., self-adhesive and in changed colors	3.75	

Reign of Queen Elizabeth II, 25th anniv. Nos. 459-463 were printed in sheets of 40. Sheets of 5 plus label, perf. 12, probably were not sold by the Antigua Post Office.
For overprints see Nos. 477-482.

Scouts
Camping
A88

Boy Scout Emblem and: 1c, Scouts on hike. 2c, Rock climbing. 10c, Cutting logs. 30c, Map and compass reading. 50c, First aid. $2, Scouts on raft.

1977, May 23   Litho.   Perf. 14

465	A88	½c multicolored	.25	.25
466	A88	1c multicolored	.25	.25
467	A88	2c multicolored	.25	.25
468	A88	10c multicolored	.25	.25
469	A88	30c multicolored	.30	.25
470	A88	50c multicolored	.50	.35
471	A88	$2 multicolored	1.00	2.00
a.		Souvenir sheet of 3, #469-471	3.25	3.75
		Nos. 465-471 (7)	2.80	3.60

Caribbean Boy Scout Jamboree, Jamaica.

Carnival Queen
Holding
Horseshoe — A89

30c, Carnival Queen in feather costume. 50c, Butterfly costume. 90c, Carnival Queen with ornaments. $1, Carnival King, Queen.

1977, July 18   Litho.   Perf. 14

472	A89	10c multicolored	.25	.25
473	A89	30c multicolored	.25	.25
474	A89	50c multicolored	.25	.25
475	A89	90c multicolored	.35	.30
476	A89	$1 multicolored	.40	.40
a.		Souvenir sheet of 4, #473-476	1.50	1.75
		Nos. 472-476 (5)	1.50	1.45

21st Summer Carnival.

Nos. 459-464
Overprinted

ROYAL VISIT
28th OCTOBER 1977

Perf. 13½x14, 12

1977, Oct. 17   Litho.

477	A87	10c multicolored	.25	.25
478	A87	30c multicolored	.25	.25
479	A87	50c multicolored	.25	.25
480	A87	90c multicolored	.30	.30
481	A87	$2.50 multicolored	.45	.40
		Nos. 477-481 (5)	1.50	1.45

Souvenir Sheet

482	A87	$5 multicolored	1.75	1.75

Visit of Queen Elizabeth II, Oct. 28.

Virgin and Child,
by Cosimo
Tura — A90

Virgin and Child by: 1c, $2, Carlo Crivelli (different). 2c, 25c, Lorenzo Lotto (different). 8c, Jacopo da Pontormo. 10c, Tura.

1977, Nov. 15   Litho.   Perf. 14

483	A90	½c multicolored	.25	.25
484	A90	1c multicolored	.25	.25
485	A90	2c multicolored	.25	.25
486	A90	8c multicolored	.25	.25
487	A90	10c multicolored	.25	.25
488	A90	25c multicolored	.25	.25
489	A90	$2 multicolored	.50	1.00
a.		Souvenir sheet of 4, #486-489	1.40	2.50
		Nos. 483-489 (7)	2.00	2.50

Christmas.

Pineapple
A91

10th anniv. of Statehood: 15c, Flag of Antigua. 50c, Police band. 90c, Prime Minister V. C. Bird. $2, Coat of Arms.

1977, Dec. 28   Litho.   Perf. 13x13½

490	A91	10c multicolored	.25	.25
491	A91	15c multicolored	.50	.25
492	A91	50c multicolored	2.00	.75
493	A91	90c multicolored	.50	.75

494	A91	$2 multicolored	.90	1.50
a.		Souv. sheet of #491-494, perf 14	3.50	3.50
		Nos. 490-494 (5)	4.15	3.50

Wright
Glider III,
1902
A92

1c, Flyer I in air, 1903. 2c, Weight and derrick launch system and wing engine, 1903. 10c, Orville Wright, vert. 50c, Flyer III, 1905. 90c, Wilbur Wright, vert. $2, Wright Model B, 1910. $2.50, Flyer I, 1903, on ground.

1978, Mar. 28   Perf. 14

495	A92	½c multicolored	.25	.25
496	A92	1c multicolored	.25	.25
497	A92	2c multicolored	.25	.25
498	A92	10c multicolored	.35	.25
499	A92	50c multicolored	.55	.25
500	A92	90c multicolored	.80	.30
501	A92	$2 multicolored	.80	.80
		Nos. 495-501 (7)	3.25	2.35

Souvenir Sheet

502	A92	$2.50 multicolored	2.10	2.75

1st powered flight by Wright brothers, 75th anniv.

Sunfish
Regatta
A93

Sailing Week 1978: 50c, Fishing and work boat race. 90c, Curtain Bluff race. $2, Powerboat rally. $2.50, Guadeloupe-Antigua race.

1978, Apr. 29   Litho.   Perf. 14½

503	A93	10c multicolored	.30	.25
504	A93	50c multicolored	.40	.25
505	A93	90c multicolored	.70	.40
506	A93	$2 multicolored	1.25	.75
		Nos. 503-506 (4)	2.65	1.65

Souvenir Sheet

507	A93	$2.50 multicolored	2.25	2.25

25th Anniv. of the
Coronation of
Queen Elizabeth
II — A94

Designs: 10c, Elizabeth II and Prince Philip. 30c, Coronation. 50c, State coach. 90c, Elizabeth II and Archbishop. $2.50, Elizabeth II. $5, Elizabeth II, Prince Philip, Prince Charles and Princess Anne as children.

1978, June 2   Litho.   Perf. 14, 12

508	A94	10c multicolored	.25	.25
509	A94	30c multicolored	.25	.25
510	A94	50c multicolored	.25	.25
511	A94	90c multicolored	.25	.25
512	A94	$2.50 multicolored	.30	.30
		Nos. 508-512 (5)	1.30	1.30

Souvenir Sheet

513	A94	$5 multicolored	1.25	1.25

25th anniv. of coronation of Queen Elizabeth II.
Nos. 508-512 were printed in sheets of 50 (2 panes of 25), perf. 14, and in sheets of 3 plus label, perf. 12, with frames in changed colors.

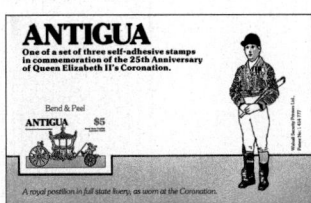

Glass Coach — A95

Royal Coaches: 50c, Irish state coach. $5, Coronation coach.

1978, June 2   Litho.   Imperf.
Self-adhesive

514		Souvenir booklet	2.50	
	a.	A95 Bklt. pane, 3 each 25c, 50c	1.00	
	b.	A95 Bklt. pane, 1 $5	1.40	

25th anniversary of coronation of Queen Elizabeth II. No. 514 contains 2 booklet panes printed on peelable paper backing showing royal processions.

Soccer — A96

Designs: Various soccer scenes. Stamps in souvenir sheet horizontal.

1978, Aug. 18   Litho.   Perf. 15

515	A96	10c multicolored	.25	.25
516	A96	15c multicolored	.25	.25
517	A96	$3 multicolored	1.60	1.75
		Nos. 515-517 (3)	2.10	2.25

Souvenir Sheet

518		Sheet of 4	3.75	3.75
	a.	A96 25c multicolored	.25	.25
	b.	A96 30c multicolored	.40	.40
	c.	A96 50c multicolored	.70	.70
	d.	A96 $2 multicolored	2.00	2.00

11th World Cup Soccer Championship, Argentina, June 1-25.

Purple Wreath — A97

1978, Oct.   Litho.   Perf. 14

519	A97	25c shown	.25	.25
520	A97	50c Sunflowers	.40	.25
521	A97	90c Frangipani	.70	.30
522	A97	$2 Passionflower	1.50	1.75
		Nos. 519-522 (4)	2.85	2.55

Souvenir Sheet

523	A97	$2.50 Red hibiscus	2.00	2.50

St. Ildefonso Receiving Chasuble, by Rubens A98

Christmas: 25c, Flight of St. Barbara, by Rubens. $2, Madonna and Child with Ss. Joseph and John and a Dono, by Sebastiano del Piombo. $4, Annunciation, by Rubens.

1978, Oct. 30   Litho.   Perf. 14

524	A98	8c multicolored	.25	.25
525	A98	25c multicolored	.25	.25
526	A98	$2 multicolored	.65	.55
		Nos. 524-526 (3)	1.15	1.05

Souvenir Sheet

527	A98	$4 multicolored	1.90	1.90

No. 526 is incorrectly attributed to Rubens.

Antigua #2 — A99

Designs: 50c, Great Britain Penny Black, 1840. $1, Woman posting letter in pillar box, and coach. $2, Mail train, ship, plane and Concorde. $2.50, Rowland Hill.

1979, Aug. 27   Litho.   Perf. 14

528	A99	25c multicolored	.25	.25
529	A99	50c multicolored	.25	.25
530	A99	$1 multicolored	.35	.25
531	A99	$2 multicolored	.85	.50
		Nos. 528-531 (4)	1.70	1.25

Souvenir Sheet

532	A99	$2.50 multicolored	1.15	1.15

Sir Rowland Hill (1795-1879), originator of penny postage.

Nos. 528-531 were printed in sheets of 50 (2 panes of 25), perf. 14, and in sheets of 5 plus label, perf. 12, with frames in changed colors.

For overprints, see Nos. 571A-571D.

Crucifixion, by Dürer — A100

Designs (after Dürer): 10c, Deposition. $2.50, Crucifixion. $4, Man of Sorrows.

1979, Mar. 15

533	A100	10c multicolored	.25	.25
534	A100	50c multicolored	.50	.25
535	A100	$4 multicolored	1.10	1.10
		Nos. 533-535 (3)	1.85	1.60

Souvenir Sheet

536	A100	$2.50 multicolored	1.25	1.25

Easter.

Child Playing with Sailboat — A101

IYC emblem, child's hand holding toy: 50c, Rocket. 90c, Automobile. $2, Train. $5, Plane.

1979, Apr. 9   Litho.   Perf. 14

537	A101	25c multicolored	.25	.25
538	A101	50c multicolored	.25	.25
539	A101	90c multicolored	.40	.30
540	A101	$2 multicolored	1.00	1.00
		Nos. 537-540 (4)	1.90	1.80

Souvenir Sheet

541	A101	$5 multicolored	1.90	1.90

International Year of the Child.

Yellowjacks — A102

Sport Fish: 50c, Bluefin tunas. 90c, Sailfish. $2.50, Barracuda. $3, Wahoos.

1979, May   Litho.   Perf. 14½

542	A102	30c multicolored	.30	.25
543	A102	50c multicolored	.40	.30
544	A102	90c multicolored	.85	.40
545	A102	$3 multicolored	2.50	2.00
		Nos. 542-545 (4)	4.05	2.95

Souvenir Sheet

546	A102	$2.50 multicolored	2.25	2.25

Capt. Cook and his Birthplace at Marton — A103

Capt. James Cook (1728-1779) and: 50c, HMS Endeavour. 90c, Marine timekeeper. $2.50, HMS Resolution. $3, Landing at Botany Bay.

1979, July 2   Litho.   Perf. 14

547	A103	25c multicolored	.55	.30
548	A103	50c multicolored	.85	.40
549	A103	90c multicolored	.60	.75
550	A103	$3 multicolored	1.45	2.75
		Nos. 547-550 (4)	3.45	4.20

Souvenir Sheet

551	A103	$2.50 multicolored	2.75	2.75

Holy Family — A104

Stained-glass Windows: 25c, Flight into Egypt. 50c, Shepherd and star. $3, Angel with trumpet. $4, Three Kings offering gifts.

1979, Oct. 1   Litho.   Perf. 14

552	A104	8c multicolored	.25	.25
553	A104	25c multicolored	.25	.25
554	A104	50c multicolored	.30	.30
555	A104	$4 multicolored	.80	2.25
		Nos. 552-555 (4)	1.60	3.05

Souvenir Sheet
Perf. 12x12½

556	A104	$3 multicolored	1.25	1.75

Christmas.

Javelin, Olympic Rings — A105

1980, Feb. 7   Litho.   Perf. 14

557	A105	10c shown	.25	.25
558	A105	25c Running	.30	.30
559	A105	$1 Pole vault	.50	.50
560	A105	$2 Hurdles	.60	1.50
		Nos. 557-560 (4)	1.65	2.55

Souvenir Sheet

561	A105	$3 Boxing, horiz.	1.25	1.25

22nd Summer Olympic Games, Moscow, July 19-Aug. 3.

Disney Characters and IYC Emblem A106

Transportation scenes: ½c, Mickey, plane. 1c, Donald, car. 2c, Goofy driving taxi. 3c, Mickey, Minnie in sidecar. 4c, Huey, Dewey and Louie. 5c, Grandma Duck. 10c, Mickey in

jeep. $1, Chip and Dale sailing. $4, Donald on train.
$2.50, Goofy in glider.
½c, 2c, 3c, 4c, 5c, $1, $2.50, horiz.

1980, Mar. 24   Litho.   Perf. 11

562	A106	½c multicolored	.25	.25
563	A106	1c multicolored	.25	.25
564	A106	2c multicolored	.25	.25
565	A106	3c multicolored	.25	.25
566	A106	4c multicolored	.25	.25
567	A106	5c multicolored	.25	.25
568	A106	10c multicolored	.25	.25
569	A106	$1 multicolored	1.25	1.50
570	A106	$4 multicolored	3.00	6.00
		Nos. 562-570 (9)	6.00	9.25

Souvenir Sheet

571	A106	$2.50 multicolored	7.50	7.50

Nos. 528-531 in Changed Colors & Overprinted

1980, May 6   Litho.   Perf. 12

571A	A99	25c multicolored	.35	.35
571B	A99	50c multicolored	.45	.45
571C	A99	$1 multicolored	.75	.75
571D	A99	$2 multicolored	3.00	3.00
		Nos. 571A-571D (4)	4.55	4.55

London '80 Intl. Stamp Exhib., May 6-14.
For overprints see Barbuda Nos. 423-426.

Birth of Venus, by Botticelli — A106a

10c, David, by Donatello. 50c, Reclining Couple, sarcophagus, Cerveteri. 90c, The Garden of Earthly Delights, by Hieronymus Bosch. $1, Portinari Altarpiece, by Hugo van der Goes. $4, Eleanora of Toledo and her Son Giovanni de Medici, by Bronzino. $5, The Holy Family, by Rembrandt.

Perf. 13½x14, 14x13½
1980, June 23   Litho.

572	A106a	10c multi, vert.	.25	.25
573	A106a	30c multi	.40	.25
574	A106a	50c multi	.55	.40
575	A106a	90c multi	.70	.70
576	A106a	$1 multi	.80	.80
577	A106a	$4 multi, vert.	2.00	3.00
		Nos. 572-577 (6)	4.70	5.40

Souvenir Sheet
Perf. 14

578	A106a	$5 multicolored	3.00	3.00

Anniversary Emblem, Intl. Headquarters, Evanston, IL — A107

50c, Antigua club banner. 90c, Map of Antigua. $3, Paul. P. Harris, emblem. $5, Emblems, Antigua flags.

1980, July 21   Litho.   Perf. 14

579	A107	30c shown	.35	.25
580	A107	50c multicolored	.40	.40
581	A107	90c mutlicolored	.60	.60
582	A107	$3 multicolored	1.90	2.75
		Nos. 579-582 (4)	3.25	4.00

Souvenir Sheet

583	A107	$5 multicolored	2.00	2.00

Rotary International, 75th anniv.

A108

1980, Sept. 15
| 584 | A108 | 10c multicolored | .25 | .25 |
| 585 | A108 | $2.50 multicolored | 1.25 | 1.50 |

Souvenir Sheet
Perf. 12
| 586 | A108 | $3 multicolored | 1.25 | 2.00 |

Queen Mother Elizabeth, 80th birthday.

A109

No. 587, Ringed Kingfisher. No. 588, Plain pigeon. No. 889, Green-throated carib. No. 890, Black-necked stilt.
No. 591, Roseate tern.

1980, Nov. 3   Litho.   Perf. 14
587	A109	10c multicolored	.90	.30
588	A109	30c multicolored	1.25	.50
589	A109	$1 multicolored	1.75	1.75
590	A109	$2 multicolored	2.50	3.75
		Nos. 587-590 (4)	6.40	6.30

Souvenir Sheet
| 591 | A109 | $2.50 multicolored | 6.75 | 6.75 |

Maleficent and Diablo — A110

Christmas: Various scenes from Walt Disney's Sleeping Beauty. $4 vert.

1980, Dec. 23   Perf. 11, 13½x14 ($4)
592	A110	½c multicolored	.25	.25
593	A110	1c multicolored	.25	.25
594	A110	2c multicolored	.25	.25
595	A110	4c multicolored	.25	.25
596	A110	8c multicolored	.25	.25
597	A110	10c multicolored	.25	.25
598	A110	25c multicolored	.30	.30
599	A110	$2 multicolored	2.25	2.25
600	A110	$2.50 multicolored	2.50	2.50
		Nos. 592-600 (9)	6.55	6.55

Souvenir Sheet
| 601 | A110 | $4 multicolored | 6.50 | 6.50 |

Sugar-cane Railway Diesel Locomotive No. 15 — A111

50c, Narrow-gauge steam locomotive. 90c, Diesels #1, #10. $3, Hauling sugar-cane. $2.50, Sugar factory, train yard.

1981, Jan. 12   Perf. 14
602	A111	25c shown	.25	.25
603	A111	50c multicolored	.40	.40
604	A111	90c multicolored	.75	.75
605	A111	$3 multicolored	2.10	2.10
		Nos. 602-605 (4)	3.50	3.50

Souvenir Sheet
| 606 | A111 | $2.50 multicolored | 2.60 | 2.60 |

Nos. 411-412, 414-422 Overprinted

1981, Mar. 31   Litho.
607	A79	6c multicolored	.25	.25
608	A79	10c multicolored	.25	.25
609	A79	20c multicolored	.25	.25
610	A79	25c multicolored	.25	.25
611	A79	35c multicolored	.30	.30
612	A79	50c multicolored	.50	.50
613	A79	75c multicolored	.60	.60
614	A79	$1 multicolored	.85	1.25
615	A80	$2.50 multicolored	1.50	2.25
616	A80	$5 multicolored	2.60	3.75
617	A80	$10 multicolored	5.25	7.00
		Nos. 607-617 (11)	12.60	16.65

Pipes of Pan, by Picasso — A112

Paintings by Pablo Picasso (1881-1973): 50c, Seated Harlequin. 90c, Paulo as Harlequin. $4, Mother and Child. $5, Three Musicians.

1981, May 5   Litho.   Perf. 14
618	A112	10c multicolored	.25	.25
619	A112	50c multicolored	.40	.40
620	A112	90c multicolored	.75	.75
621	A112	$4 multicolored	2.10	2.10
		Nos. 618-621 (4)	3.50	3.50

Souvenir Sheet
Perf. 14x14½
| 622 | A112 | $5 multicolored | 2.25 | 2.75 |

Royal Wedding Issue
Common Design Type

1981, June 16   Litho.   Perf. 14
623	CD331a	25c Couple	.25	.25
624	CD331a	50c Glamis Castle	.25	.25
625	CD331a	$4 Charles	.80	.80
		Nos. 623-625 (3)	1.30	1.30

Souvenir Sheet
626	CD331	$5 Glass coach	1.25	1.25
627	CD331	Booklet	4.00	
a.		Pane of 6 (2x25c, 2x$1, 2x$2), Charles	2.50	
b.		Pane of 1, $5, Couple	1.50	

No. 627 contains imperf., self-adhesive stamps.
Nos. 623-625 also printed in sheets of 5 plus label, perf. 12 in changed colors.
For surcharges see Nos. 792, 795, 802, 805.

Campfire Sing A113

1981, Oct. 28   Litho.   Perf. 15
628	A113	10c Irene Joshua	.25	.25
629	A113	50c shown	.40	.25
630	A113	90c Sailing	.65	.55
631	A113	$2.50 Milking cow	1.60	2.00
		Nos. 628-631 (4)	2.90	3.05

Souvenir Sheet
| 632 | A113 | $5 Flag raising | 5.25 | 5.25 |

Girl Guides, 50th anniv.

A114

10c, Arms. 50c, Flag. 90c, Prime Minister Bird. $2.50, St. John's Cathedral, horiz. $5, Map.

1981, Nov. 1   Litho.   Perf. 15
633	A114	10c multicolored	.30	.25
634	A114	50c multicolored	.85	.50
635	A114	90c multicolored	.55	.55
636	A114	$2.50 multicolored	1.40	2.25
		Nos. 633-636 (4)	3.10	3.55

Souvenir Sheet
| 637 | A114 | $5 multicolored | 4.25 | 3.25 |

Independence.
No. 637 contains one 41x41mm stamp.

A115

Christmas (Virgin and Child Paintings by): 8c, Holy Night, by Jacques Stella (1596-1657). 30c Julius Schnorr von Carolsfeld (1794-1872). $1, Alonso Cano (1601-1667). $3, Lorenzo de Credi (1459-1537). $5, Holy Family, by Pieter von Avont (1600-1652).

1981, Nov. 16
638	A115	8c multicolored	.30	.25
639	A115	30c multicolored	.50	.25
640	A115	$1 multicolored	1.20	1.20
641	A115	$3 multicolored	1.75	3.25
		Nos. 638-641 (4)	3.75	4.95

Souvenir Sheet
| 642 | A115 | $5 multicolored | 3.75 | 4.50 |

On No. 639, the artist's name is misspelled as "Carolfeld."

Intl. Year of the Disabled A116

1981, Dec. 1   Litho.   Perf. 15
643	A116	10c Swimming	.25	.25
644	A116	50c Discus	.30	.30
645	A116	90c Archery	.45	.55
646	A116	$2 Baseball	1.00	1.40
		Nos. 643-646 (4)	2.00	2.50

Souvenir Sheet
| 647 | A116 | $4 Basketball | 4.50 | 3.25 |

1982 World Cup Soccer A117

Designs: Various soccer players.

1982, Apr. 15   Litho.   Perf. 14
648	A117	10c multicolored	.30	.25
649	A117	50c multicolored	.45	.30
650	A117	90c multicolored	.90	.65
651	A117	$4 multicolored	3.00	3.50
		Nos. 648-651 (4)	4.65	4.70

Souvenir Sheet
| 652 | A117 | $5 multicolored | 6.75 | 7.50 |

Also issued in sheetlets of 5 + label in changed colors, perf. 12.

A118

No. 653, A-300 Airbus. No. 654, Hawker-Siddeley 748. No. 655, De Havilland Twin Otter DCH6. No. 656, Britten-Norman Islander.
No. 657, Jet, horiz.

1982, June 17   Litho.   Perf. 14½
653	A118	10c multicolored	.25	.25
654	A118	50c multicolored	.35	.35
655	A118	90c multicolored	.65	.65
656	A118	$2.50 multicolored	1.75	1.75
		Nos. 653-656 (4)	3.00	3.00

Souvenir Sheet
| 657 | A118 | $5 multicolored | 4.00 | 4.00 |

Coolidge Intl. Airport opening.

A119

No. 658, Cordia, vert. No. 659, Golden spotted mongoose. No. 660, Corallita, vert. No. 661, Bulldog bats.
No. 662, Caribbean monk seals.

1982, June 28   Litho.   Perf. 14½
658	A119	10c multicolored	.35	.25
659	A119	50c multicolored	.70	.40
660	A119	90c multicolored	1.10	.75
661	A119	$3 multicolored	2.50	3.25
		Nos. 658-661 (4)	4.65	4.65

Souvenir Sheet
| 662 | A119 | $5 multicolored | 7.75 | 7.75 |

Charles Darwin's death centenary.

Princess Diana Issue
Common Design Type

90c, Greenwich Palace. $1, Wedding. $4, Diana.
$5, Diana, diff.

1982, July 1   Litho.   Perf. 14½x14
663	CD332	90c multicolored	.70	.50
664	CD332	$1 multicolored	.80	.60
665	CD332	$4 multicolored	3.00	2.50
		Nos. 663-665 (3)	4.50	3.60

Souvenir Sheet
| 666 | CD332 | $5 multicolored | 3.75 | 3.75 |

For overprints and surcharges see Nos. 672-675, 797, 799, 803, 806.

Scouting Year A120

Independence Day celebration: 10c, Decorating buildings. 50c, Helping woman. 90c, Princess Margaret. $2.20, Cub Scout giving directions.
$5, Baden-Powell.

1982, July 15   Perf. 14
667	A120	10c multicolored	.30	.25
668	A120	50c multicolored	.60	.45
669	A120	90c multicolored	.85	.65
670	A120	$2.20 multicolored	1.50	2.50
		Nos. 667-670 (4)	3.25	3.85

Souvenir Sheet
| 671 | A120 | $5 multicolored | 5.75 | 5.75 |

Nos. 663-666
Overprinted

1982, Aug. 30   Litho.   Perf. 14½x14
672 CD332 90c multicolored .... .45 .45
673 CD332 $1 multicolored .... .55 .55
674 CD332 $4 multicolored 1.90 1.90
   Nos. 672-674 (3) 2.90 2.90
Souvenir Sheet
675 CD332 $5 multicolored 2.60 2.60
For surcharges see Nos. 798, 800, 804, 807.

Roosevelt
Driving by
"The Little
White
House"
A121

25c, Washington as blacksmith. 45c, Churchill, Roosevelt, Stalin. 60c, Washington crossing Delaware, vert. $1, Roosevelt on train, vert. $3, Roosevelt, vert.
No. 682, Washington, vert. No. 683, Eleanor and Franklin.

1982, Sept. 20   Perf. 15
676 A121 10c shown .... .25 .25
677 A121 25c multicolored .... .40 .25
678 A121 45c multicolored .... 1.40 .35
679 A121 60c multicolored .... .95 .35
680 A121 $1 multicolored .... 1.35 .90
681 A121 $3 multicolored 1.30 2.50
   Nos. 676-681 (6) 5.65 4.60
Souvenir Sheets
682 A121 $4 multicolored 3.50 3.50
683 A121 $4 multicolored 3.50 3.50
George Washington's 250th birth anniv. and Franklin D. Roosevelt's birth centenary.

Christmas — A122

Raphael Paintings: 10c, Annunciation. 30c, Adoration of the Magi. $1, Presentation at the Temple. $4, Coronation of the Virgin.
$5, Marriage of the Virgin.

1982, Nov.   Litho.   Perf. 14
684 A122 10c multicolored .... .25 .25
685 A122 30c multicolored .... .25 .25
686 A122 $1 multicolored .... .50 .50
687 A122 $4 multicolored 2.25 2.25
   Nos. 684-687 (4) 3.25 3.25
Souvenir Sheet
688 A122 $5 multicolored 3.25 3.25

500th Birth Anniv. of Raphael — A123

45c, Galatea taking Reins of Dolphins, vert. 50c, Sea Nymphs carried by Tritons, vert. 60c, Winged Angel Steering Dolphins. $4, Cupids Shooting Arrows.
$5, Galatea.

1983, Jan. 28.   Litho.   Perf. 14½
689 A123 45c multicolored .... .30 .30
690 A123 50c multicolored .... .40 .40
691 A123 60c multicolored .... .45 .45
692 A123 $4 multicolored 2.00 2.00
   Nos. 689-692 (4) 3.15 3.15
Souvenir Sheet
693 A123 $5 multicolored 3.00 3.00

A124

1983, Mar. 14   Perf. 14
694 A124 25c Pineapple crop ...... .25 .25
695 A124 45c Carnival .... .25 .25
696 A124 60c Tourists, sailboat .. .35 .35
697 A124 $3 Control Tower 1.00 1.50
   Nos. 694-697 (4) 1.85 2.35
Commonwealth Day.

World Communications Year — A125

15c, TV screen, camera. 50c, Police radio, car. 60c, Long distance phone call. $3, Dish antenna, planets.
$5, Comsat satellite.

1983, Apr. 5   Litho.   Perf. 14
698 A125 15c multicolored .... .50 .25
699 A125 50c multicolored 2.10 1.25
700 A125 60c multicolored 2.10 1.40
701 A125 $3 multicolored 4.00 5.00
   Nos. 698-701 (4) 8.70 7.90
Souvenir Sheet
702 A125 $5 multicolored 2.75 3.25

Imperforates
See note following No. 404.

Bottlenose
Dolphin
A126

50c, Finback whale. 60c, Bowhead whale. $3, Spectacled porpoise.
$5, Unicorn whale.

1983, May 9   Litho.   Perf. 15
703 A126 15c shown .... .75 .25
704 A126 50c multicolored 1.60 1.25
705 A126 60c multicolored 1.75 1.25
706 A126 $3 multicolored 3.25 4.25
   Nos. 703-706 (4) 7.35 7.00
Souvenir Sheet
707 A126 $5 multicolored 8.50 8.50

Cashew
Nut
A127

1983, July 11   Perf. 14
708 A127 1c shown .... .25 1.10
709 A127 2c Passion fruit .... .25 1.10
710 A127 3c Mango .... .25 1.10
711 A127 5c Grapefruit .... .25 1.10
712 A127 10c Pawpaw .... .40 .25
713 A127 15c Breadfruit .... .75 .25
714 A127 20c Coconut .... .45 .25
715 A127 25c Oleander .... .75 .35
716 A127 30c Banana .... .55 .40
717 A127 40c Pineapple .... .75 .40
718 A127 45c Cordia .... .85 .55
719 A127 50c Cassia .... .90 .60
720 A127 60c Poui 1.75 1.00
721 A127 $1 Frangipani 2.25 1.50
722 A127 $2 Flamboyant 3.50 3.75
723 A127 $2.50 Lemon 3.75 6.00
724 A127 $5 Lignum vitae 5.00 12.00
725 A127 $10 Arms 8.00 17.00
   Nos. 708-725 (18) 30.65 48.70

1985   Perf. 12½x12
708a A127 1c .... .25 1.10
709a A127 2c .... .25 1.10
710a A127 3c .... .25 1.10
711a A127 5c .... .30 1.10
712a A127 10c .... .35 .25
713a A127 15c .... .50 .25
714a A127 20c .... .60 .25
715a A127 25c .... .60 .25
716a A127 30c .... .70 .30
717a A127 40c .... .75 .30
718a A127 45c .... .80 .45
719a A127 50c .... 1.20 .45
720a A127 60c 1.75 1.10
721a A127 $1 .... 2.00 1.25
722a A127 $2 .... 3.75 4.25
723a A127 $2.50 .... 4.25 6.00
724a A127 $5 .... 6.75 12.00
725a A127 $10 .... 11.00 17.00
   Nos. 708a-725a (18) 36.05 48.50
   Issue dates: $2-$5, Dec; others Mar.

Manned Flight Bicentenary — A128

30c, Dornier DoX. 50c, Supermarine S-6B. 60c, Curtiss F9C, USS Akron. $4, Pro Juventute balloon.
$5, Graf Zeppelin.

1983, Aug. 15   Perf. 15
726 A128 30c multicolored .... 1.00 .30
727 A128 50c multicolored .... 1.25 .60
728 A128 60c multicolored .... 1.40 .75
729 A128 $4 multicolored 3.25 5.75
   Nos. 726-729 (4) 6.90 7.40
Souvenir Sheet
730 A128 $5 multicolored 3.50 3.50

Christmas — A129

Raphael Paintings: 10c, Angel flying with scroll. 30c, Angel, diff. $1, Inscribing tablet. $4, Angel showing tablet.
$5, Vision of Ezekiel.
10c, 30c, $1, $4, Sybils and Angels details.

1983, Oct. 4   Litho.   Perf. 14
731 A129 10c multicolored .... .35 .25
732 A129 30c multicolored .... .65 .40
733 A129 $1 multicolored 1.50 1.25
734 A129 $4 multicolored 2.75 4.75
   Nos. 731-734 (4) 5.25 6.65
Souvenir Sheet
735 A129 $5 multicolored 1.60 2.10

Methodist Church,
Anniv. — A130

Designs: 15c, John Wesley founder of Methodism. 50c, Nathaniel Gilbert, Antiguan founder. 60c, St. John's Methodist Church Steeple. $3, Ebenezer Methodist Church.

1983, Nov.   Litho.   Perf. 14
736 A130 15c multicolored .... .25 .25
737 A130 50c multicolored .... .75 .45
738 A130 60c multicolored .... .80 .60
739 A130 $3 multicolored 2.25 3.75
   Nos. 736-739 (4) 4.05 5.05

1984 Olympics,
Los
Angeles — A131

1984, Jan.   Litho.   Perf. 15
740 A131 25c Discus .... .25 .25
741 A131 50c Gymnastics .... .30 .25
742 A131 90c Hurdling .... .60 .60
743 A131 $3 Bicycling 4.00 3.00
   Nos. 740-743 (4) 5.15 4.10
Souvenir Sheet
744 A131 $5 Volleyball, horiz. ... 3.50 4.00

Booker
Vanguard
A132

1984, June 4   Litho.   Perf. 15
745 A132 45c shown .... 1.00 .45
746 A132 50c Canberra .... 1.20 .70
747 A132 60c Yachts .... 1.40 .90
748 A132 $4 Fairwind 3.00 6.75
   Nos. 745-748 (4) 6.60 8.80
Souvenir Sheet
749 A132 $5 Man-of-war, vert. ... 2.75 3.50

Local
Flowers — A133

1984, June 25   Litho.   Perf. 15
755 A133 15c multicolored .... .50 .25
756 A133 50c multicolored .... 1.00 .75
757 A133 60c multicolored 1.00 1.00
758 A133 $3 multicolored 3.50 5.50
   Nos. 755-758 (4) 6.00 7.50
Souvenir Sheet
759 A133 $5 multicolored 3.50 3.50

US
Presidents — A134

1984, July 18   Litho.   Perf. 14
760 A134 10c Lincoln .... .25 .25
761 A134 20c Truman .... .25 .25
762 A134 30c Eisenhower .... .30 .25
763 A134 40c Reagan .... .50 .45
764 A134 90c Lincoln, diff. ..... .90 .80
765 A134 $1.10 Truman, diff. 1.25 1.10
766 A134 $1.50 Eisenhower, diff. 1.60 1.75
767 A134 $2 Reagan, diff. 1.75 2.00
   Nos. 760-767 (8) 6.80 6.85

Slavery Abolition
Sesquicentennial — A135

40c, Moravian Mission. 50c, Antigua Courthouse, 1823. 60c, Sugar cane planting. $3, Boiling House, Delaps' Estate.

1984, Aug. 1
768	A135	40c multicolored	.85	.45
769	A135	50c multicolored	.90	.60
770	A135	60c multicolored	1.00	.70
771	A135	$3 multicolored	3.75	4.75
	Nos. 768-771 (4)		6.50	6.50

Souvenir Sheet
772	A135	$5 multicolored	6.25	6.25

Song Birds — A136

40c, Rufous-sided towhee. 50c, Parula warbler. 60c, House wren. $2, Ruby-crowned kinglet. $3, Yellow-shafted flicker. $5, Yellow-breasted chat.

1984, Aug. 15   **Perf. 15**
773	A136	40c multicolored	1.65	.70
774	A136	50c multicolored	1.50	.90
775	A136	60c multicolored	1.75	1.75
776	A136	$2 multicolored	2.00	3.50
777	A136	$3 multicolored	2.25	4.75
	Nos. 773-777 (5)		9.15	11.60

Souvenir Sheet
778	A136	$5 multicolored	4.75	5.75

AUSIPEX '84 — A137

$1, Grass skiing. No. 780, $5, Australian rules football. No. 781, $5, Boomerang.

1984, Sept. 21   **Perf. 15**
779	A137	$1 multicolored	1.25	1.50
780	A137	$5 multicolored	4.00	4.75

Souvenir Sheet
781	A137	$5 multicolored	3.25	3.25

The Blue Dancers, by Degas — A137a

Paintings by Correggio: 25c, Virgin and Infant with Angels and Cherubs. 60c, The Four Saints. 90c, Saint Catherine. $3, The Campori Madonna. No. 790, St. John the Baptist. Paintings by Degas: 50c, The Pink Dancers. 70c, Two Dancers. $4, Dancers at the Bar. No. 791, Folk Dancers.

1984, Oct.   **Litho.**   **Perf. 15**
782	A137a	15c multicolored	.35	.25
783	A137a	25c multicolored	.40	.25
784	A137a	50c multicolored	.85	.50
785	A137a	60c multicolored	.85	.40
786	A137a	70c multicolored	1.05	.70
787	A137a	90c multicolored	1.05	.75
788	A137a	$3 multicolored	2.40	4.00
789	A137a	$4 multicolored	2.60	4.50
	Nos. 782-789 (8)		9.55	11.35

Souvenir Sheets
790	A137a	$5 multi, horiz.	3.00	3.00
791	A137a	$5 multi, horiz.	3.00	3.00

Nos. 623-626, 663-666, 672-675, 694-697 Surcharged in Black or Gold

(CD331)

(A124)

(CD332)

1984, June   **Perf. 14, 14½x14**
792	CD331	$2 on 25c #623	3.00	3.50
793	A124	$2 on 25c #694	2.25	1.50
794	A124	$2 on 45c #695	2.25	1.50
795	CD331	$2 on 50c #624	3.00	3.50
796	A124	$2 on 60c #696	2.25	2.75
797	CD332	$2 on 90c #663 (G)	2.50	2.75
798	CD332	$2 on 90c #672 (G)	2.50	2.75
799	CD332	$2 on $1 #664 (G)	2.50	2.75
800	CD332	$2 on $1 #673 (G)	2.50	2.75
801	A124	$2 on $3 #697	2.25	1.50
802	CD331	$2 on $4 #625	3.00	3.50
803	CD332	$2 on $4 #665 (G)	2.50	2.75
804	CD332	$2 on $4 #674 (G)	2.50	2.75
	Nos. 792-804 (13)		33.00	34.25

Souvenir Sheets
805	CD331	$2 on $5 #626	8.00	8.00
806	CD332	$2 on $5 #666	6.75	6.75
807	CD332	$2 on $5 #675	6.75	6.75

Nos. 797-800, 803-804 exist with silver surcharge.

Christmas 1984 and 50th Anniv. of Donald Duck A138

Scenes from various Donald Duck comics.

1984, Nov.   **Litho.**   **Perf. 11**
808	A138	1c multicolored	.25	.25
809	A138	2c multicolored	.25	.25
810	A138	3c multicolored	.25	.25
811	A138	4c multicolored	.25	.25
812	A138	5c multicolored	.25	.25
813	A138	10c multicolored	.25	.25
814	A138	$1 multicolored	1.75	1.10
815	A138	$2 multicolored	2.00	2.75
816	A138	$5 multicolored	3.75	5.50
	Nos. 808-816 (9)		9.00	10.85

Souvenir Sheets   **Perf. 14**
817	A138	$5 multi, horiz.	6.75	6.75
818	A138	$5 Donald on beach	6.75	6.75

20th Century Leaders A139

No. 819, John F. Kennedy (1917-1963), vert. No. 820, Winston Churchill (1874-1965), vert. No. 821, Mahatma Gandhi (1869-1948), vert. No. 822, Mao Tse-Tung (1883-1976), vert. No. 823, Kennedy in Berlin. No. 824, Churchill in Paris. No. 825, Gandhi in Great Britain. No. 826, Mao in Peking. No. 827, Flags of Great Britain, India, China, USA.

1984, Nov. 19   **Litho.**   **Perf. 15**
819	A139	60c multicolored	1.15	1.40
820	A139	60c multicolored	1.15	1.40
821	A139	60c multicolored	1.15	1.40
822	A139	60c multicolored	1.15	1.40
823	A139	$1 multicolored	1.25	1.60
824	A139	$1 multicolored	1.25	1.60
825	A139	$1 multicolored	1.25	1.60
826	A139	$1 multicolored	1.25	1.60
	Nos. 819-826 (8)		9.60	12.00

Souvenir Sheet
827	A139	$5 multicolored	9.25	9.25

Statue of Liberty Centennial A140

25c, Torch on display, 1885. 30c, Restoration, 1984-1986, vert. 50c, Bartholdi supervising construction, 1876. 90c, Statue on Liberty Island. $1, Dedication Ceremony, 1886, vert. $3, Operation Sail, 1976, vert. $5, Port of New York.

1985, Jan. 7
828	A140	25c multicolored	.25	.25
829	A140	30c multicolored	.25	.25
830	A140	50c multicolored	.40	.30
831	A140	90c multicolored	.70	.50
832	A140	$1 multicolored	1.50	1.10
833	A140	$3 multicolored	2.00	2.75
	Nos. 828-833 (6)		5.10	5.15

Souvenir Sheet
834	A140	$5 multicolored	4.50	4.50

Traditional Scenes A141

15c, Ceramics, Arawak pot shard. 50c, Tatooing, body design. 60c, Harvesting Manioc, god Yocahu. $3, Caribs in battle, war club. $5, Tainos worshiping.

1985, Jan. 21
835	A141	15c multicolored	.30	.25
836	A141	50c multicolored	.40	.40
837	A141	60c multicolored	.55	.50
838	A141	$3 multicolored	1.75	2.50
	Nos. 835-838 (4)		3.00	3.65

Souvenir Sheet
839	A141	$5 multicolored	2.75	2.75

Invention of the Motorcycle, Cent. — A142

10c, Triumph 2HP Jap, 1903. 30c, Indian Arrow, 1949. 60c, BMW R100RS, 1976. $4, Harley Davidson Model II, 1916. $5, Laverda Jota, 1975.

1985, Mar. 7   **Perf. 14**
840	A142	10c multicolored	.60	.40
841	A142	30c multicolored	1.10	.50
842	A142	60c multicolored	1.40	1.25
843	A142	$4 multicolored	5.50	7.25
	Nos. 840-843 (4)		8.60	9.40

Souvenir Sheet
844	A142	$5 multicolored	6.00	7.00

John J. Audubon, 200th Birth Anniv. A143

90c, Horned grebe. $1, Least petrel. $1.50, Great blue heron. $3, Double-crested cormorant. $5, White-tailed tropic bird, vert.

1985, Mar. 25   **Perf. 14**
845	A143	90c multicolored	1.75	1.10
846	A143	$1 multicolored	2.00	1.10
847	A143	$1.50 multicolored	2.75	3.00
848	A143	$3 multicolored	4.50	5.75
	Nos. 845-848 (4)		11.00	10.95

Souvenir Sheet
849	A143	$5 multicolored	10.00	10.00

See Nos.910-914.

Butterflies A144

25c, Polygrapha cyanea. 60c, Leodonta dysoni. 90c, Junea doraete. $4, Prepona xenagoras. $5, Caerois gerdrudtus.

1985, Apr. 16   **Perf. 14**
850	A144	25c multicolored	1.25	.25
851	A144	60c multicolored	2.25	1.10
852	A144	90c multicolored	3.00	1.25
853	A144	$4 multicolored	7.50	10.00
	Nos. 850-853 (4)		14.00	12.60

Souvenir Sheet
854	A144	$5 multicolored	6.50	6.50

Cessna 172 A145

90c, Fokker DVII. $1.50, Spad VII. $3, Boeing 747. $5, Twin Otter, Coolidge Intl. Airport.

1985, Apr. 30
855	A145	30c shown	1.25	.25
856	A145	90c multicolored	2.50	1.25
857	A145	$1.50 multicolored	3.50	3.25
858	A145	$3 multicolored	5.25	7.00
	Nos. 855-858 (4)		12.50	11.75

Souvenir Sheet
859	A145	$5 multicolored	5.25	5.25

40th anniv. of the ICAO. Nos. 855, 858-859 show the ICAO and UN emblems.

Maimonides (1135-1204), Judaic Philosopher and Physician — A146

1985, June 17   **Litho.**   **Perf. 14**
860	A146	$2 yellow green	3.75	3.25

Souvenir Sheet
861	A146	$5 deep brown	6.75	5.00

Intl. Youth
Year
A147

25c, Agriculture. 50c, Hotel management.
60c, Environmental studies. $3, Windsurfing.
$5, Youths, national flag.

1985, July 1

862	A147	25c multicolored	.25	.25
863	A147	50c multicolored	.35	.30
864	A147	60c multicolored	1.00	.75
865	A147	$3 multicolored	2.10	5.00
		Nos. 862-865 (4)	3.70	6.30

Souvenir Sheet

866	A147	$5 multicolored	3.25	3.25

Queen Mother,
85th
Birthday — A148

Designs: 90c, $1, Attending a church ser-
vice. No. 867A, $1.50, Touring the London
Gardens, children in a sandpit. $2.50, $3, Photograph (1979). $5, With Prince Edward at the
wedding of Prince Charles and Lady Diana
Spencer.

Perf. 14, 12x12½ (90c, $1, $3)

1985, July 15

866A	A148	90c multi ('86)	.55	.55
867	A148	$1 multi	.60	.60
867A	A148	$1 multi ('86)	.60	.60
868	A148	$1.50 multi	.90	.90
869	A148	$2.50 multi	1.40	1.40
869A	A148	$3 multi ('86)	1.60	1.60
		Nos. 866A-869A (6)	5.65	5.65

Souvenir Sheet

870	A148	$5 multicolored	4.00	4.00

Nos. 866A, 867A, 869A issued in sheets of
5 plus label on Jan. 13, 1986.

Marine
Life — A149

15c, Fregata magnificens. 45c, Diploria
labyrinthi-formis. 60c, Oreaster reticulatus. $3,
Gymnothorax moringa.
$5, Acropora palmata.

1985, Aug. 1   ***Perf. 14***

871	A149	15c multicolored	1.00	.25
872	A149	45c multicolored	2.00	.85
873	A149	60c multicolored	2.25	1.60
874	A149	$3 multicolored	7.00	8.50
		Nos. 871-874 (4)	12.25	11.20

Souvenir Sheet

875	A149	$5 multicolored	8.75	8.75

Johann Sebastian
Bach — A150

1985, Aug. 26   Litho.   *Perf. 14*

876	A150	25c Bass trombone	1.10	.40
877	A150	50c English horn	1.40	.90
878	A150	$1 Violino piccolo	2.75	1.50
879	A150	$3 Bass rackett	6.00	6.75
		Nos. 876-879 (4)	11.25	9.55

Souvenir Sheet

880	A150	$5 Portrait	5.75	5.75

Girl
Guides,
75th
Anniv.
A151

Public service and growth-oriented activities: 15c, Public service. 45c, Guides meeting.
60c, Lord and Lady Baden-Powell. $3, Nature
study.
$5, Barn swallow.

1985, Sept. 10

881	A151	15c multicolored	.75	.25
882	A151	45c multicolored	1.25	.40
883	A151	60c multicolored	1.60	.60
884	A151	$3 multicolored	4.25	4.25
		Nos. 881-884 (4)	7.85	5.50

Souvenir Sheet

885	A151	$5 multicolored	5.50	8.00

State Visit of Elizabeth II, Oct.
24 — A152

1985, Oct. 24   Litho.   *Perf. 14½*

886	A152	60c National flags	.90	.45
887	A152	$1 Elizabeth II, vert.	1.35	.90
888	A152	$4 HMY Britannia	3.25	6.50
		Nos. 886-888 (3)	5.50	7.85

Souvenir Sheet

889	A152	$5 Map of Antigua	3.50	3.50

Mark Twain — A153

Disney characters in Roughing It: 25c, Cow-
boys and Indians. 50c, Canoeing. $1.10, Pony
Express. $1.50, Buffalo hunt in Missouri. $2,
Nevada silver mine.
$5, Stagecoach on Kansas plains.

1985, Nov. 4   *Perf. 14*

890	A153	25c multicolored	1.00	.25
891	A153	50c multicolored	1.25	.40
892	A153	$1.10 multicolored	2.00	1.25
893	A153	$1.50 multicolored	2.50	3.50
894	A153	$2 multicolored	3.25	4.25
		Nos. 890-894 (5)	10.00	9.65

Souvenir Sheet

895	A153	$5 multicolored	8.75	8.75

Jacob and Wilhelm Grimm, Fabulists
and Philologists — A154

Disney characters in Spindle, Shuttle and
Needle.

1985, Nov. 11

896	A154	30c multicolored	1.00	.35
897	A154	60c multicolored	1.50	.70
898	A154	70c multicolored	1.75	1.25
899	A154	$1 multicolored	2.00	1.60
900	A154	$3 multicolored	4.50	7.00
		Nos. 896-900 (5)	10.75	10.90

Souvenir Sheet

900A	A154	$5 multicolored	8.75	8.75

UN
40th
Anniv.
A155

Stamps of UN and portraits: 40c, No. 18 and
Benjamin Franklin. $1, No. 391 and George
Washington Carver, agricultural chemist. $3,
No. 299 and Charles Lindbergh. $5, Marc
Chagall, artist, vert.

1985, Nov. 18   *Perf. 13½x14*

901	A155	40c multicolored	.90	.50
902	A155	$1 multicolored	1.75	1.25
903	A155	$3 multicolored	4.25	7.00
		Nos. 901-903 (3)	6.90	8.75

Souvenir Sheet
Perf. 14x13½

904	A155	$5 multicolored	6.75	6.75

Christmas — A156

Religious paintings: 10c, Madonna and
Child, by De Landi. 25c, Madonna and Child,
by Bonaventura Berlinghieri (d. 1244). 60c,
The Nativity, by Fra Angelico (1400-1455). $4,
Presentation in the Temple, by Giovanni di
Paolo Grazia (c.1403-1482). $5, The Nativity,
by Antoniazzo Romano.

1985, Dec. 30   *Perf. 15*

905	A156	10c multicolored	.30	.25
906	A156	25c multicolored	.60	.25
907	A156	60c multicolored	.85	.45
908	A156	$4 multicolored	1.90	4.00
		Nos. 905-908 (4)	3.65	4.95

Souvenir Sheet

909	A156	$5 multicolored	3.50	3.75

Audubon Type of 1985

Illustrations of North American ducks: 60c,
Mallard. 90c, Dusky duck. $1.50, Common
pintail. $3, Widgeon.
$5, Common eider.

1986, Jan. 6   *Perf. 12½x12*

910	A143	60c multicolored	1.90	1.00
911	A143	90c multicolored	2.40	1.50
912	A143	$1.50 multicolored	3.00	3.50
913	A143	$3 multicolored	4.00	5.75
		Nos. 910-913 (4)	11.30	11.75

Souvenir Sheet
Perf. 14

914	A143	$5 multicolored	7.25	7.25

1986 World Cup Soccer
Championships, Mexico — A157

1986, Mar. 17   Litho.   *Perf. 14*

915	A157	30c shown	1.30	.25
916	A157	60c Heading the ball	1.50	.60
917	A157	$1 Referee	1.90	1.40
918	A157	$4 Goal	5.25	7.50
		Nos. 915-918 (4)	9.95	9.75

Souvenir Sheet

919	A157	$5 Action	7.50	7.50

Nos. 916-917 vert.
For overprints see Nos. 963-967.

A158

Halley's Comet — A159

Designs: 5c, Edmond Halley, Greenwich
Observatory. 10c, Me 163B Komet. German
WWII fighter plane. 60c, Montezuma sighting
comet, 1517. $4, Pocahontas saving Capt.
John Smith's life, 1607 sighting as sign for
Powhatan Indians to raid Jamestown. $5,
Comet over Antigua.

1986, Mar. 24

920	A158	5c multicolored	.30	.25
921	A158	10c multicolored	.35	.25
922	A158	60c multicolored	1.40	.50
923	A158	$4 multicolored	4.25	5.75
		Nos. 920-923 (4)	6.30	6.75

Souvenir Sheet

924	A159	$5 multicolored	4.50	4.50

For overprints see Nos. 973-977.

Queen Elizabeth II, 60th Birthday
Common Design Type

60c, Wedding, 1947. $1, Trooping the color.
$4, Visiting Scotland.
$5, Held by Queen Mary, 1927.

1986, Apr. 21

925	CD339	60c multicolored	.40	.45
926	CD339	$1 multicolored	.60	.60
927	CD339	$4 multicolored	1.75	1.90
		Nos. 925-927 (3)	2.75	2.95

Souvenir Sheet

928	CD339	$5 multicolored	2.75	3.25

Boats — A160

30c, Tugboat. 60c, Fishing boat. $1, Sail-
boat 2056. $4, Lateen-rigged sailboat.
$5, Boatbuilding.

1986, May 15

929	A160	30c multicolored	.25	.25
930	A160	60c multicolored	.45	.30
931	A160	$1 multicolored	.80	.50
932	A160	$4 multicolored	3.00	3.00
		Nos. 929-932 (4)	4.50	4.05

Souvenir Sheet

933	A160	$5 multicolored	3.25	4.00

A number of unissued items,
imperfs., part perfs., missing color varieties, etc., were made available when
the Format International inventory was
liquidated. Imperfs of some or all of the
Antigua stamps in the following sets are
included: Nos. 405-422, 503-507, 515-
517, 703-707, 745-749, 755-759, 808-
816, 819-826, 905-909, 934-937.
See footnote after No. 962.

AMERIPEX '86 — A161

American trains.

			Perf. 15	
1986, May 22			**Perf. 15**	
934	A161	25c Hiawatha	1.10	.30
935	A161	50c Grand Canyon	1.35	.60
936	A161	$1 Powhattan Arrow	1.75	1.75
937	A161	$3 Empire State	3.00	5.50
		Nos. 934-937 (4)	7.20	8.15

Souvenir Sheet
938	A161	$5 Daylight	8.00	10.00

Wedding of Prince Andrew and Sarah Ferguson
Common Design Type

			Perf. 14	
1986, July 23			**Perf. 14**	
939	CD340	45c Couple	.30	.30
940	CD340	60c Prince Andrew	.45	.45
941	CD340	$4 Princes Andrew, Philip	2.75	3.75
		Nos. 939-941 (3)	3.50	4.50

Souvenir Sheet
942	CD340	$5 Couple, diff.	3.50	4.25

Conch
Shells — A162

15c, Say fly-specked cerith. 45c, Gmelin smooth scotch bonnet. 60c, Linne West Indian crown conch. $3, Murex ciboney.
$5, Atlantic natica.

		Litho.	Perf. 15	
1986, Aug. 6		**Litho.**	**Perf. 15**	
943	A162	15c multicolored	.75	.35
944	A162	45c multicolored	1.75	1.25
945	A162	60c multicolored	1.90	1.90
946	A162	$3 multicolored	5.75	9.50
		Nos. 943-946 (4)	10.15	13.00

Souvenir Sheet
947	A162	$5 multicolored	7.25	8.00

Flowers
A163

10c, Water lily. 15c, Queen of the night. 50c, Cup of gold. 60c, Beach morning glory. 70c, Golden trumpet. $1, Air plant. $3, Purple wreath. $4, Zephyr lily.
No. 956, Dozakie. No. 957, Four o'clock.

		Litho.	Perf. 15	
1986, Aug. 25		**Litho.**	**Perf. 15**	
948	A163	10c multicolored	.30	.25
949	A163	15c multicolored	.30	.25
950	A163	50c multicolored	.50	.45
951	A163	60c multicolored	.65	.55
952	A163	70c multicolored	.75	.65
953	A163	$1 multicolored	.85	1.10
954	A163	$3 multicolored	1.90	2.75
955	A163	$4 multicolored	2.40	3.50
		Nos. 948-955 (8)	7.65	9.50

Souvenir Sheets
956	A163	$4 multicolored	2.75	3.25
957	A163	$5 multicolored	3.50	4.00

Fungi — A164

10c, Hygrocybe occidentalis scarletina. 50c, Trogia buccinalis. $1, Collybia subpruinosa. $4, Leucocoprinus brebissonii.
$5, Pyrrhoglossum pyrrhum.

1986, Sept. 15				
958	A164	10c multicolored	.30	.25
959	A164	50c multicolored	.65	.55
960	A164	$1 multicolored	1.35	1.25
961	A164	$4 multicolored	3.25	4.50
		Nos. 958-961 (4)	5.55	6.55

Souvenir Sheet
962	A164	$5 multicolored	11.00	11.00

An unissued $3 stamp and No. 961 inscribed "4$" were made available when the Format International inventory was liquidated.

Nos. 915-919 Ovptd. in Gold in 2 or 3 lines

WINNERS
Argentina 3 W Germany 2

			Perf. 14	
1986, Sept. 15			**Perf. 14**	
963	A157	30c multicolored	1.10	.35
964	A157	60c multicolored	1.60	.70
965	A157	$1 multicolored	2.00	1.10
966	A157	$4 multicolored	3.50	4.50
		Nos. 963-966 (4)	8.20	6.65

Souvenir Sheet
967	A157	$5 multicolored	5.00	5.00

Automobile, Cent. — A165

Carl Benz and classic automobiles: 10c, 1933 Auburn Speedster. 15c, 1986 Mercury Sable. 50c, 1959 Cadillac. 60c, 1950 Studebaker. 70c, 1939 Lagonda V-12. $1, 1930 Adler Standard. $3, 1956 DKW. $4, 1936 Mercedes 500K.
No. 972, 1921 Mercedes Knight. No. 972A, 1896 Daimler.

1986, Oct. 20				
968	A165	10c multicolored	.25	.25
968A	A165	15c multicolored	.30	.25
969	A165	50c multicolored	.55	.25
970	A165	60c multicolored	.70	.30
970A	A165	70c multicolored	.80	.40
970B	A165	$1 multicolored	1.10	.55
970C	A165	$3 multicolored	2.75	2.75
971	A165	$4 multicolored	3.25	3.25
		Nos. 968-971 (8)	9.70	8.00

Souvenir Sheets
972	A165	$5 multicolored	4.25	4.25
972A	A165	$5 multicolored	4.25	4.25

Nos. 920-924 Ovptd. in Black or Silver

HALLEY'S COMET 1985-6

		Litho.	Perf. 14	
1986, Oct. 22		**Litho.**	**Perf. 14**	
973	A158	5c multicolored	4.75	.25
974	A158	10c multicolored	.25	.25
975	A158	60c multicolored	1.25	.60
976	A158	$4 multicolored	5.50	4.00
		Nos. 973-976 (4)	11.75	5.10

Souvenir Sheet
977	A159	$5 multicolored (S)	6.00	6.50

Christmas — A166

Disney characters as children: 25c, Mickey. 30c, Mickey, Minnie. 40c, Aunt Matilda, Goofy. 60c, Goofy, Pluto. 70c, Pluto, Donald, Daisy. $1.50, Stringing popcorn. $3, Grandma Duck, Minnie. $4, Donald, Pete. No. 986, Playing with presents. No. 987, Reindeer.

			Perf. 11	
1986, Nov. 4			**Perf. 11**	
978	A166	25c multicolored	.55	.25
979	A166	30c multicolored	.70	.30
980	A166	40c multicolored	.75	.35
981	A166	60c multicolored	.90	.65
982	A166	70c multicolored	1.10	1.00
983	A166	$1.50 multicolored	1.75	2.25
984	A166	$3 multicolored	2.75	4.25
985	A166	$4 multicolored	3.25	4.25
		Nos. 978-985 (8)	11.75	13.30

Souvenir Sheets
Perf. 14
986	A166	$5 multicolored	6.50	7.00
987	A166	$5 multicolored	6.50	7.00

Nos. 985 printed in sheets of 8.

Coat of Arms A167   Natl. Flag A168

		Litho.	Perf. 14x14½	
1986, Nov. 25		**Litho.**	**Perf. 14x14½**	
988	A167	10c bright blue	1.00	.90
989	A168	25c orange	1.75	1.25

Marc Chagall (1887-1985), Artist A169

Designs: No. 990, The Profile, 1957. No. 991, Portrait of the Artist's Sister, 1910. No. 992, Bride with Fan, 1911. No. 993, David in Profile, 1914. No. 994, Fiancee with Bouquet, 1977. No. 995, Self-portrait with Brushes, 1909. No. 996, The Walk, 1973. No. 997, Candles, 1938. No. 998, Fall of Icarus, 1975. No. 999, Myth of Orpheus, 1977.

		Litho.	Perf. 13½x14	
1987, Mar. 30		**Litho.**	**Perf. 13½x14**	
990	A169	10c multicolored	.45	.25
991	A169	30c multicolored	.60	.30
992	A169	40c multicolored	.80	.35
993	A169	60c multicolored	.90	.40
994	A169	90c multicolored	1.00	.55
995	A169	$1 multicolored	1.00	.60
996	A169	$3 multicolored	2.50	2.50
997	A169	$4 multicolored	2.75	2.75

Size: 110x95mm
Imperf
998	A169	$5 multicolored	5.75	5.75
999	A169	$5 multicolored	5.75	5.75
		Nos. 990-999 (10)	21.50	19.20

A170

America's Cup — A171

30c, Canada I, 1981. 60c, Gretel II, 1970. $1, Sceptre, 1958. $3, Vigilant, 1893.
$5, Australia II, Liberty, 1983.

			Perf. 15	
1987, Feb. 5			**Perf. 15**	
1000	A170	30c multicolored	.55	.25
1001	A170	60c multicolored	.70	.35
1002	A170	$1 multicolored	1.00	1.00
1003	A170	$3 multicolored	2.50	3.00
		Nos. 1000-1003 (4)	4.75	4.60

Souvenir Sheet
1004	A171	$5 multicolored	5.00	5.00

Fish, World Wildlife Fund A172

Marine Birds A173

15c, Bridled burrfish. 30c, Brown noddy. 40c, Nassau grouper. 50c, Laughing gull. 60c, French angelfish. $1, Porkfish. $2, Royal tern. $3, Sooty tern.
No. 1013, Banded butterfly fish. No. 1014, Brown booby.

		Litho.	Perf. 14	
1987, Feb. 23		**Litho.**	**Perf. 14**	
1005	A172	15c multicolored	3.00	.45
1006	A173	30c multicolored	6.00	.50
1007	A172	40c multicolored	3.75	.60
1008	A173	50c multicolored	6.75	1.40
1009	A173	60c multicolored	4.00	1.40
1010	A172	$1 multicolored	4.00	1.60
1011	A173	$2 multicolored	9.00	5.50
1012	A173	$3 multicolored	9.00	7.50
		Nos. 1005-1012 (8)	45.50	18.95

Souvenir Sheets
1013	A172	$5 multicolored	10.00	10.00
1014	A173	$5 multicolored	10.00	10.00

The 30c, 50c, $2, $3 and Nos. 1013-1014 do not picture the WWF emblem.
For overprints see Nos. 1137-1139A.

Statue of Liberty, Cent. A174

Photographs by Peter B. Kaplan: 15c, Lee Iacocca. 30c, Statue at dusk. 45c, Crown, head. 50c, Iacocca, torch. 60c, Crown observatory. 90c, Interior restoration. $1, Head. $2, Statue at sunset. $3, Men on scaffold, flag. $5, Statue at night.

			Perf. 14	
1987, Apr. 20			**Perf. 14**	
1015	A174	15c multicolored	.25	.25
1016	A174	30c multicolored	.25	.25
1017	A174	45c multicolored	.35	.35
1018	A174	50c multicolored	.40	.40
1019	A174	60c multicolored	.40	.40
1020	A174	90c multicolored	.55	.55
1021	A174	$1 multicolored	.65	.65
1022	A174	$2 multicolored	1.25	1.50
1023	A174	$3 multicolored	1.40	2.00
1024	A174	$5 multicolored	2.40	3.50
		Nos. 1015-1024 (10)	7.90	9.85

Nos. 1015-1018, 1021-1022, 1024 vert.

Walt Disney Animated Characters and Epcot Center, Walt Disney World — A189

25c, The Living Seas. 30c, World of Motion. 40c, Spaceship Earth. 60c, Universe of Energy. 70c, Journey to Imagination. $1.50, The Land. $3, Communicore. $4, Horizons. No. 1125, Epcot Center. No. 1126, The Contemporary Resort Hotel.

1988, May 3   Perf. 14x13½, 13½x14

1116A	A189	1c like 25c	.25	.25
1116B	A189	2c like 30c	.25	.25
1116C	A189	3c like 40c	.25	.25
1116D	A189	4c like 60c	.25	.25
1116E	A189	5c like 70c	.25	.25
1116F	A189	10c like $1.50	.25	.25
1117	A189	25c multi	.45	.25
1118	A189	30c multi	.45	.25
1119	A189	40c multi	.55	.25
1120	A189	60c multi	.75	.35
1121	A189	70c multi	.85	.40
1122	A189	$1.50 multi	1.60	1.60
1123	A189	$3 multi	2.25	2.75
1124	A189	$4 multi	2.25	2.75
		Nos. 1116A-1124 (14)	10.65	10.10

Souvenir Sheets

1125	A189	$5 multi	4.00	4.00
1126	A189	$5 multi	4.00	4.00

30c, 40c, $1.50, $3 and No. 1126 are vert.

Flowering Trees — A190

1988, May 16   Perf. 14

1127	A190	10c Jacaranda	.30	.25
1128	A190	30c Cordia	.30	.25
1129	A190	50c Orchid tree	.45	.40
1130	A190	90c Flamboyant	.55	.50
1131	A190	$1 African tulip tree	.65	.60
1132	A190	$2 Potato tree	1.25	1.60
1133	A190	$3 Crepe myrtle	1.50	2.00
1134	A190	$4 Pitch apple	1.75	2.75
		Nos. 1127-1134 (8)	6.75	8.35

Souvenir Sheets

1135	A190	$5 Cassia	3.25	3.75
1136	A190	$5 Chinaberry	3.25	3.75

Nos. 1135-1136 are continuous designs.

Nos. 1011-1012, 1014 and 1013 Ovptd. in Black for Philatelic Exhibitions

a

b

c

d

1988, May 9   Litho.   Perf. 14

1137	A173 (a)	$2 multi	8.00	8.00
1138	A173 (b)	$3 multi	8.50	8.50

Souvenir Sheets

1139	A173 (c)	$5 multi	14.00	14.00
1139A	A172 (d)	$5 multi	14.00	14.00

1988 Summer Olympics, Seoul A192

40c, Gymnastic rings, vert. 60c, Weight lifting, vert. $1, Water polo. $3, Boxing. $5, Torch-bearer, vert.

1988, June 10

1140	A192	40c multicolored	.35	.30
1141	A192	60c multicolored	.40	.30
1142	A192	$1 multicolored	.80	.45
1143	A192	$3 multicolored	1.60	2.25
		Nos. 1140-1143 (4)	3.15	3.30

Souvenir Sheet

1144	A192	$5 multicolored	3.50	3.50

Butterflies A193

1c, Monarch. 2c, Jamaican clearwing. 3c, Yellow-barred ringlet. 5c, Cracker. 10c, Jamaican mestra. 15c, Mimic. 20c, Silver spot. 25c, Zebra. 30c, Fiery sulphur. 40c, Androgeus swallowtail. 45c, Giant brimstone. 50c, Orbed sulphur. 60c, Blue-backed skipper. $1, Common white skipper. $2, Baracoa skipper. $2.50, Mangrove skipper. $5, Silver king. $10, Pygmy skipper. $20, Parides lycimenes.

1988-90   Litho.   Perf. 14

1145	A193	1c multi	.50	1.10
1146	A193	2c multi	.65	1.10
1147	A193	3c multi	.65	1.10
1148	A193	5c multi	.80	1.10
1149	A193	10c multi	.95	.35
1150	A193	15c multi	1.25	.35
1151	A193	20c multi	1.40	.35
1152	A193	25c multi	1.40	.35
1153	A193	30c multi	1.40	.35
1154	A193	40c multi	1.40	.35
1155	A193	45c multi	1.40	.35
1156	A193	50c multi	1.50	.45
1157	A193	60c multi	1.60	.60
1158	A193	$1 multi	2.00	1.00
1159	A193	$2 multi	3.00	3.50
1160	A193	$2.50 multi	4.00	4.75
1161	A193	$5 multi	5.00	7.00
1161A	A193	$10 multi	7.00	12.00
1162	A193	$20 multi	18.00	21.00
		Nos. 1145-1162 (19)	53.90	57.15

Issued: $20, Feb. 19, 1990; others, Aug. 29.

John F. Kennedy A194

30c, First family. 60c, Motorcade, Mexico. $1, Funeral procession. $4, Aboard PT109.

$5, Taking Oath of Office.

1988, Nov. 22   Litho.   Perf. 14

1162A	A194	1c like 30c	.25	.25
1162B	A194	2c like $4	.25	.25
1162C	A194	3c like $1	.25	.25
1162D	A194	4c like 60c	.25	.25
1163	A194	30c multi	.35	.25
1164	A194	60c multi	.70	.40
1165	A194	$1 multi	.75	.75
1166	A194	$4 multi	2.25	3.25
		Nos. 1162A-1166 (8)	5.05	5.65

Souvenir Sheet

1167	A194	$5 multi	3.75	3.75

Miniature Sheet

Christmas, Mickey Mouse 60th Anniv. — A195

Walt Disney characters: No. 1168: a, Morty and Ferdie. b, Goofy. c, Chip-n-Dale. d, Huey and Dewey. e, Minnie Mouse. f, Pluto. g, Mickey Mouse. h, Donald Duck and Louie.
No. 1169, Goofy driving Mickey and Minnie in a horse-drawn carriage. No. 1170, Characters on roller skates, caroling.

1988, Dec. 1   Perf. 13½x14, 14x13½

1168	A195	Sheet of 8	9.00	9.00
a.-h.		$1 any single	.95	.95

Souvenir Sheets

1169	A195	$7 multicolored	5.25	5.25
1170	A195	$7 multi, horiz.	5.25	5.25

1988, Dec. 1   Litho.   Perf. 14

1171	A195	10c like No. 1168e	.25	.25
1172	A195	25c like No. 1168f	.25	.25
1173	A195	30c like No. 1168g	.30	.30
1174	A195	70c like No. 1168h	.60	.60
		Nos. 1171-1174 (4)	1.40	1.40

Arawak Indian Whip Dance — A196

UPAE and discovery of America emblems and: a, Five adults. b, Eight adults. c, Seven adults. d, Three adults, three children.

1989, May 16   Litho.   Perf. 14

1175		Strip of 4	5.00	5.00
a.-d.	A196	$1.50 any single	.90	.90

Souvenir Sheet

1176	A196	$6 Arawak chief	4.00	4.00

Discovery of America 500th anniv. (in 1992), pre-Columbian societies and customs.

Jet Flight, 50th Anniv. A197

Various jet aircraft: 10c, DeHavilland Comet 4. 30c, Messerschmitt Me262. 40c, Boeing 707. 60c, Canadair F-86 Sabre. $1, Lockheed F-104 Starfighter. $2, McDonnell Douglas DC-10. $3, Boeing 747. $4, McDonnell F-4 Phantom.
No. 1185, Grumman F-14 Tomcat. No. 1186, Concorde.

1989, May 29   Litho.   Perf. 14x13½

1177	A197	10c multicolored	1.10	.35
1178	A197	30c multicolored	1.60	.35
1179	A197	40c multicolored	1.60	.35
1180	A197	60c multicolored	1.90	.50
1181	A197	$1 multicolored	2.10	.75
1182	A197	$2 multicolored	3.00	2.75
1183	A197	$3 multicolored	3.25	4.25
1184	A197	$4 multicolored	3.25	4.25
		Nos. 1177-1184 (8)	17.80	13.55

Souvenir Sheets

1185	A197	$7 multicolored	6.00	7.00
1186	A197	$7 multicolored	6.00	7.00

Caribbean Cruise Ships A198

25c, TSS Festivale. 45c, M.S. Southward. 50c, M.S. Sagafjord. 60c, MTS Daphne. 75c, M.V. Cunard Countess. 90c, M.S. Song of America. $3, M.S. Island Princess. $4, S.S. Galileo.
No. 1195, S.S. Norway. No. 1196, S.S. Oceanic.

1989, June 20   Litho.   Perf. 14

1187	A198	25c multi	1.30	.35
1188	A198	45c multi	1.50	.35
1189	A198	50c multi	1.50	.35
1190	A198	60c multi	1.50	.40
1191	A198	75c multi	1.75	1.00
1192	A198	90c multi	2.00	1.10
1193	A198	$3 multi	4.00	5.50
1194	A198	$4 multi	4.00	6.00
		Nos. 1187-1194 (8)	17.55	15.05

Souvenir Sheets

1195	A198	$6 multi	4.50	5.50
1196	A198	$6 multi	4.50	5.50

Paintings by Hiroshige — A199

Designs: 25c, Fish Swimming by Duck Half-submerged in Stream. 45c, Crane and Wave. 50c, Sparrows and Morning Glories. 60c, Crested Blackbird and Flowering Cherry. $1, Great Knot Sitting among Water Grass. $2, Goose on a Bank of Water. $3, Black Paradise Flycatcher and Blossoms. $4, Sleepy Owl Perched on a Pine Branch. No. 1205, Bullfinch Flying Near a Clematis Branch. No. 1206, Titmouse on a Cherry Branch.

1989, July 3   Perf. 14x13½

1197	A199	25c multicolored	.90	.30
1198	A199	45c multicolored	1.10	.40
1199	A199	50c multicolored	1.25	.40
1200	A199	60c multicolored	1.25	.50
1201	A199	$1 multicolored	1.60	.65
1202	A199	$2 multicolored	2.50	2.50
1203	A199	$3 multicolored	3.00	3.00
1204	A199	$4 multicolored	3.00	3.00
		Nos. 1197-1204 (8)	14.60	10.75

Souvenir Sheets

1205	A199	$5 multicolored	6.00	6.00
1206	A199	$5 multicolored	6.00	6.00

Hirohito (1901-1989) and enthronement of Akihito as emperor of Japan.

PHILEXFRANCE '89 — A200

Walt Disney characters, French landmarks: 1c, Helicopter over the Seine. 2c, Arc de Triomphe. 3c, Painting Notre Dame Cathedral. 4c, Entrance to the Metro. 5c, Fashion show. 10c, Follies. No. 1213, Shopping stalls on the Seine. $6, Sidewalk cafe, Left Bank. No. 1215, Hot air balloon Ear Force One. No. 1216, Dining.

1989, July 7   Perf. 14x13½

1207	A200	1c multicolored	.25	.25
1208	A200	2c multicolored	.25	.25
1209	A200	3c multicolored	.25	.25

1210	A200	4c multicolored	.25	.25
1211	A200	5c multicolored	.25	.25
1212	A200	10c multicolored	.25	.25
1213	A200	$5 multicolored	7.50	7.50
1214	A200	$6 multicolored	7.50	7.50
		Nos. 1207-1214 (8)	16.50	16.50

Souvenir Sheets

1215	A200	$5 multicolored	6.25	6.25
1216	A200	$5 multicolored	6.25	6.25

1990 World Cup Soccer Championships, Italy — A201

Natl. flag, various actions of a defending goalie.

1989, Aug. 21   **Perf. 14**

1217	A201	15c multicolored	.75	.25
1218	A201	25c multicolored	.80	.25
1219	A201	$1 multicolored	1.25	1.00
1220	A201	$4 multicolored	2.50	4.75
		Nos. 1217-1220 (4)	5.30	6.25

Souvenir Sheets

1221	A201	$5 2 players, horiz.	3.75	4.25
1222	A201	$5 3 players, horiz.	3.75	4.25

For overprints see Nos. 1344-1349.

Mushrooms — A202

10c, Lilac fairy helmet. 25c, Rough psathyrella, vert. 50c, Golden tops. 60c, Blue cap, vert. 75c, Brown cap, vert. $1, Green gill, vert. $3, Red pinwheel. $4, Red chanterelle. No. 1231, Slender stalk. No. 1232, Paddy straw mushroom.

1989, Oct. 12   **Litho.**   **Perf. 14**

1223	A202	10c multi	.75	.35
1224	A202	25c multi	1.05	.30
1225	A202	50c multi	1.50	.50
1226	A202	60c multi	1.50	.60
1227	A202	75c multi	1.75	1.10
1228	A202	$1 multi	1.75	1.25
1229	A202	$3 multi	2.75	3.75
1230	A202	$4 multi	2.75	3.75
		Nos. 1223-1230 (8)	13.80	11.60

Souvenir Sheets

1231	A202	$6 multi	8.50	8.50
1232	A202	$6 multi	8.50	8.50

Nos. 1224, 1226-1228, 1231 vert.

Wildlife A203

25c, Hutia. 45c, Caribbean monk seal. 60c, Mustache bat, vert. $4, Manatee, vert. $5, West Indies giant rice rat.

1989, Oct. 19   **Litho.**   **Perf. 14**

1233	A203	25c multi	.80	.35
1234	A203	45c multi	2.25	.75
1235	A203	60c multi	1.50	.75
1236	A203	$4 multi	3.25	5.25
		Nos. 1233-1236 (4)	7.80	7.10

Souvenir Sheet

1237	A203	$5 multi	8.50	9.00

American Philatelic Soc. Emblem, Stamps on Stamps and Walt Disney Characters Promoting Philately A204

Designs: 1c, Israel #150, printing press. 2c, Italy #1238, first day cancel. 3c, US #143L4, Pony Express recruits. 4c, Denmark #566, early radio broadcast. 5c, German Democratic Republic #702, television. 10c, Great Britain #1, stamp collector. $4, Japan #1414, integrated circuits. $6, Germany #B667, boom box. No. 1246, US #1355, C3a, and Jenny biplane over Disneyland, horiz. No. 1247, US #940, 1421 and stamps for the wounded.

1989, Nov. 2   **Perf. 13½x14, 14x13½**

1238	A204	1c multicolored	.25	.25
1239	A204	2c multicolored	.25	.25
1240	A204	3c multicolored	.25	.25
1241	A204	4c multicolored	.25	.25
1242	A204	5c multicolored	.25	.25
1243	A204	10c multicolored	.25	.25
1244	A204	$4 multicolored	4.00	5.50
1245	A204	$5 multicolored	5.00	6.50
		Nos. 1238-1245 (8)	10.50	13.50

Souvenir Sheets

1246	A204	$5 multicolored	5.50	6.50
1247	A204	$5 multicolored	5.50	6.50

Locomotives and Walt Disney Characters — A205

25c, John Bull, 1831. 45c, Atlantic, 1832. 50c, William Crook's, 1861. 60c, Minnetonka, 1869. $1, Thatcher Perkins, 1863. $2, Pioneer, 1848. $3, Peppersass, 1869. $4, Gimbels Flyer. No. 1256, #6100 Class S-1 & 1835 Thomas Jefferson. No. 1257, Jupiter & #119.

Perf. 14x13½, 13½x14

1989, Nov. 17

1248	A205	25c multi	.85	.40
1249	A205	45c multi	.95	.40
1250	A205	50c multi	.95	.40
1251	A205	60c multi	.95	.60
1252	A205	$1 multi	1.20	.75
1253	A205	$2 multi	1.75	2.25
1254	A205	$3 multi	2.25	3.75
1255	A205	$4 multicolored	2.40	3.75
		Nos. 1248-1255 (8)	11.30	12.30

Souvenir Sheets

1256	A205	$6 multi	12.00	12.00
1257	A205	$6 multi	12.00	12.00

New York World's Fair, 50th anniv., and World Stamp Expo '89, Washington, DC.

1st Moon Landing, 20th Anniv. A206

10c, Apollo 11 liftoff. 45c, Aldrin walking on Moon. $1, Eagle ascending from Moon. $4, Recovery after splashdown. $5, Armstrong.

1989, Nov. 24   **Litho.**   **Perf. 14**

1258	A206	10c multicolored	.55	.25
1259	A206	45c multicolored	1.40	.25
1260	A206	$1 multicolored	1.60	.85
1261	A206	$4 multicolored	2.50	4.50
		Nos. 1258-1261 (4)	6.05	5.85

Souvenir Sheet

1262	A206	$5 multicolored	5.50	5.50

Nos. 1258-1259 and 1262, vert.

Souvenir Sheet

Smithsonian Institution, Washington, DC — A207

1989, Nov. 17   **Litho.**   **Perf. 14**

1263	A207	$4 multicolored	3.00	3.00

World Stamp Expo '89.

Christmas — A208

Religious paintings: 10c, The Small Cowper Madonna. 25c, Madonna of the Goldfinch. 30c, The Alba Madonna. 50c, Bologna Altarpiece (attendant). 60c, Bologna Altarpiece (heralding angel). 70c, Bologna Altarpiece (archangel). $4, Bologna Altarpiece (saint holding ledger). No. 1271, Madonna of Foligno. No. 1272, The Marriage of the Virgin. No. 1273, Bologna Altarpiece (Madonna and Child). Bologna Altarpiece by Giotto. Other paintings by Raphael.

1989, Dec. 11   **Litho.**   **Perf. 14**

1264	A208	10c multicolored	.35	.25
1265	A208	25c multicolored	.45	.25
1266	A208	30c multicolored	.45	.25
1267	A208	50c multicolored	.70	.40
1268	A208	60c multicolored	.75	.45
1269	A208	70c multicolored	.85	.50
1270	A208	$4 multicolored	2.75	4.25
1271	A208	$5 multicolored	2.75	4.25
		Nos. 1264-1271 (8)	9.05	10.60

Souvenir Sheets

1272	A208	$5 multicolored	5.00	6.00
1273	A208	$5 multicolored	5.00	6.00

America Issue — A210

UPAE, discovery of America 500th anniv. emblems and marine life: 10c, Star-eyed hermit crab. 20c, Spiny lobster. 25c, Magnificent banded fanworm. 45c, Cannonball jellyfish. 60c, Red-spiny sea star. $2, Peppermint shrimp. $3, Coral crab. $4, Branching fire coral. No. 1283, Common sea fan. No. 1284, Portuguese man-of-war.

1990, Mar. 26   **Litho.**   **Perf. 14**

1275	A210	10c multicolored	.50	.25
1276	A210	20c multicolored	.75	.25
1277	A210	25c multicolored	.80	.25
1278	A210	45c multicolored	.95	.30
1279	A210	60c multicolored	1.10	.50
1280	A210	$2 multicolored	1.90	2.25
1281	A210	$3 multicolored	2.10	3.50
1282	A210	$4 multicolored	2.10	3.50
		Nos. 1275-1282 (8)	10.20	10.80

Souvenir Sheets

1283	A210	$5 multicolored	4.25	4.25
1284	A210	$5 multicolored	4.25	4.25

Orchids — A211

No. 1285, Vanilla mexicana. No. 1286, Epidendrum ibaguense. No. 1287, Epidendrum secundum. No. 1288, Maxillaria conferta. No. 1289, Oncidium altissimum. No. 1290, Spiranthes lanceolata. No. 1291, Tonopsis utricularioides. No. 1292, Epidendrum nocturnum. No. 1293, Octomeria graminifolia. No. 1294, Rodriguezia lanceolata.

1990, Apr. 17   **Perf. 14**

1285	A211	15c multicolored	.80	.35
1286	A211	45c multicolored	1.10	.35
1287	A211	50c multicolored	1.25	.40
1288	A211	60c multicolored	1.40	.40
1289	A211	$1 multicolored	1.50	.85
1290	A211	$2 multicolored	2.00	2.25
1291	A211	$3 multicolored	2.25	3.25
1292	A211	$5 multicolored	3.25	4.25
		Nos. 1285-1292 (8)	13.55	12.10

Souvenir Sheets

1293	A211	$6 multicolored	4.00	4.00
1294	A211	$6 multicolored	4.00	4.00

EXPO '90, Osaka.

Fish A212

10c, Flamefish. 15c, Coney. 50c, Squirrelfish. 60c, Sergeant major. $1, Yellowtail snapper. $2, Rock beauty. $3, Spanish hogfish. $4, Striped parrotfish. No. 1303, Blackbar soldierfish. No. 1304, Foureye butterflyfish.

1990, May 21   **Perf. 14**

1295	A212	10c multicolored	.80	.45
1296	A212	15c multicolored	1.10	.45
1297	A212	50c multicolored	1.50	.55
1298	A212	60c multicolored	1.60	.55
1299	A212	$1 multicolored	1.75	.75
1300	A212	$2 multicolored	2.50	2.75
1301	A212	$3 multicolored	3.00	3.50
1302	A212	$4 multicolored	3.25	3.50
		Nos. 1295-1302 (8)	15.50	12.50

Souvenir sheets

1303	A212	$5 multicolored	5.50	5.50
1304	A212	$5 multicolored	5.50	5.50

Victoria and Elizabeth II — A213

1990, May 3   **Litho.**   **Perf. 15x14**

1305	A213	45c green	1.00	.30
1306	A213	60c bright rose	1.40	.50
1307	A213	$5 bright ultra	4.00	5.25
		Nos. 1305-1307 (3)	6.40	6.05

Souvenir Sheet

1308	A213	$6 black	5.00	6.00

Penny Black, 150th anniv.

Royal Mail Transport A214

Designs: 50c, Steam packet Britannia, 1840. 75c, Railway mail car, 1892. $4, Centaurus seaplane, 1938. $6, Subway, 1927.

1990, May 3   *Perf. 13½*
1309	A214	50c red & deep green	1.25	.30
1310	A214	75c red & vio brn	1.50	1.00
1311	A214	$4 red & brt ultra	4.00	*5.25*
		Nos. 1309-1311 (3)	6.75	6.55

Souvenir Sheet
1312	A214	$6 red & black	5.50	*6.25*

Stamp World London '90.

Miniature Sheet

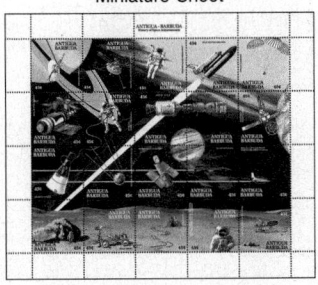

Space Achievements — A215

Designs: a, *Voyager 2* passing Saturn. b, *Pioneer 11* photographing Saturn. c, Manned maneuvering unit. d, *Columbia* space shuttle. e, Splashdown of Apollo 10 command module. f, *Skylab*. g, Ed White space walking, Gemini 4 mission. h, Apollo module, Apollo-Soyuz mission. i, Soyuz module, Apollo-Soyuz mission. j, *Mariner 1* passing Venus. k, Gemini 4 module. l, *Sputnik*. m, Hubble Space Telescope. n, X-15 rocket plane. o, Bell X-1 breaking sound barrier. p, Astronaut, Apollo 17 mission. r, American lunar rover. r, Lunar module, Apollo 14 mission. s, First men on the Moon, Apollo 11 mission. t, Lunokhod, Soviet lunar rover.

1990, June 11   **Litho.**   *Perf. 14*
1313	A215	Sheet of 20	16.00	16.00
a.-t.		45c any single	.75	.75

Mickey Production Studios — A216

Walt Disney characters in Hollywood: 45c, Minnie Mouse reading script. 50c, Director Mickey Mouse, take 1 of Minnie. 60c, Make-up artist Daisy Duck. $1, Clarabelle as Cleopatra. $2, Mickey, Goofy, Donald Duck. $3, Goofy destroying set. $4, Mickey, Donald editing film. No. 1322, Mickey directs surfing film. No. 1323, Minnie, Daisy, Clarabelle in musical.

1990, Sept. 3   **Litho.**   *Perf. 14x13½*
1314	A216	25c shown	.70	.25
1315	A216	45c multicolored	.80	.25
1316	A216	50c multicolored	.90	.25
1317	A216	60c multicolored	1.10	.30
1318	A216	$1 multicolored	1.25	.60
1319	A216	$2 multicolored	1.75	2.10
1320	A216	$3 multicolored	2.25	3.25
1321	A216	$4 multicolored	2.25	3.25
		Nos. 1314-1321 (8)	11.00	10.25

Souvenir Sheets
1322	A216	$5 multicolored	4.50	4.50
1323	A216	$5 multicolored	4.50	4.50

A217

1990, Aug. 27   **Litho.**   *Perf. 14*
1324	A217	15c multicolored	.40	.25
1325	A217	35c multi, diff.	.65	.25
1326	A217	75c multi, diff.	1.10	.65
1327	A217	$3 multi, diff.	2.00	*3.00*
		Nos. 1324-1327 (4)	4.15	4.15

Souvenir Sheet
1328	A217	$6 multi, diff.	5.00	5.00

Queen Mother, 90th birthday.

A218

No. 1329, 20-Kilometer Walk. No. 1330, Triple jump. No. 1331, 10,000 meter run. No. 1332, Javelin.

No. 1333, Opening ceremony, Los Angeles, 1984.

1990, Oct. 1   **Litho.**   *Perf. 14*
1329	A218	50c multicolored	.90	.30
1330	A218	75c multicolored	1.10	.60
1331	A218	$1 multicolored	1.35	.70
1332	A218	$5 multicolored	3.50	*5.50*
		Nos. 1329-1332 (4)	6.85	*7.10*

Souvenir Sheet
1333	A218	$6 multicolored	5.75	*7.25*

1992 Summer Olympics, Barcelona.

Intl. Literacy Year — A219

Walt Disney characters in scenes from books by Charles Dickens: 15c, Huey and Dewey, Christmas Stories. 45c, Donald Duck, Bleak House. 50c, Dewey, Bad Pete, Oliver Twist. 60c, Daisy Duck, Old Curiosity Shop. $1, Little Nell. $2, Scrooge McDuck, Pickwick Papers. $3, Mickey and Minnie Mouse, Dombey and Son. $5, Minnie, Our Mutual Friend. No. 1342, Mickey and friends, David Copperfield. No. 1343, Pinocchio, Oliver Twist.

1990, Oct. 15   **Litho.**   *Perf. 14*
1334	A219	15c multicolored	.75	.25
1335	A219	45c multicolored	1.00	.35
1336	A219	50c multicolored	1.10	.40
1337	A219	60c multicolored	1.25	.45
1338	A219	$1 multicolored	1.40	.70
1339	A219	$2 multicolored	2.00	2.25
1340	A219	$3 multicolored	2.25	3.25
1341	A219	$5 multicolored	2.75	4.25
		Nos. 1334-1341 (8)	12.50	11.90

Souvenir Sheets
1342	A219	$6 multicolored	6.00	6.00
1343	A219	$6 multicolored	6.00	6.00

Nos. 1217-1222 Overprinted

1990, Nov. 11
1344	A201	15c multicolored	.85	.30
1345	A201	25c multicolored	.85	.30
1346	A201	$1 multicolored	1.75	1.50
1347	A201	$4 multicolored	3.50	*5.00*
		Nos. 1344-1347 (4)	6.95	*7.10*

Souvenir Sheets
1348	A201	$5 on #1221	5.50	5.50
1349	A201	$5 on #1222	5.50	5.50

Overprint on Nos. 1348-1349 is 32x13mm.

Birds A220

10c, Pearly-eyed thrasher. 25c, Purple-throated carib. 50c, Common yellowthroat. 60c, American kestrel. $1, Yellow-bellied sapsucker. $2, Purple gallinule. $3, Yellow-crowned night heron. $4, Blue-hooded euphonia.

No. 1358, Brown pelican. No. 1359, Frigate bird.

1990, Nov. 19
1350	A220	10c multicolored	.50	.35
1351	A220	25c multicolored	.60	.40
1352	A220	50c multicolored	.70	.45
1353	A220	60c multicolored	1.10	.75
1354	A220	$1 multicolored	1.25	.80
1355	A220	$2 multicolored	2.25	*2.50*
1356	A220	$3 multicolored	2.50	3.00
1357	A220	$4 multicolored	2.75	*3.25*
		Nos. 1350-1357 (8)	11.65	11.50

Souvenir Sheets
1358	A220	$6 multicolored	7.00	8.75
1359	A220	$6 multicolored	7.00	8.75

Christmas — A221

Paintings: 25c, Madonna and Child with Saints by del Piombo. 30c, Virgin and Child with Angels by Grunewald, vert. 40c, Holy Family and a Shepherd by Titian. 60c, Virgin and Child by Fra Filippo Lippi, vert. $1, Jesus, St. John and Two Angels by Rubens. $2, Adoration of the Shepherds by Catena. $4, Adoration of the Magi by Giorgione. $5, Virgin and Child Adored by a Warrior by Catena. No. 1368, Allegory of the Blessings of Jacob by Rubens, vert. No. 1369, Adoration of the Magi by Fra Angelico, vert.

Perf. 14x13½, 13½x14

1990, Dec. 10   **Litho.**
1360	A221	25c multicolored	.85	.40
1361	A221	30c multicolored	.85	.40
1362	A221	40c multicolored	1.00	.45
1363	A221	60c multicolored	1.25	.50
1364	A221	$1 multicolored	1.50	1.00
1365	A221	$2 multicolored	2.25	*2.50*
1366	A221	$4 multicolored	3.50	*5.00*
1367	A221	$5 multicolored	3.50	*5.00*
		Nos. 1360-1367 (8)	14.70	15.25

Souvenir Sheets
1368	A221	$6 multicolored	4.25	4.25
1369	A221	$6 multicolored	4.25	4.25

Peter Paul Rubens (1577-1640), Painter — A222

Entire paintings or different details from: 25c, Rape of the Daughters of Leucippus. 45c, $2, $4, Bacchanal. 50c, $1, $3, Rape of the Sabine Women. 60c, Battle of the Amazons. No. 1378, Rape of Hippodameia. No. 1379, Battle of the Amazons.

1991, Jan. 21   **Litho.**   *Perf. 14*
1370	A222	25c multicolored	1.00	.30
1371	A222	45c multicolored	1.25	.45
1372	A222	50c multicolored	1.25	.50
1373	A222	60c multicolored	1.50	.65
1374	A222	$1 multicolored	1.75	1.00
1375	A222	$2 multicolored	2.00	*2.50*
1376	A222	$3 multicolored	2.50	3.75
1377	A222	$4 multicolored	2.75	4.75
		Nos. 1370-1377 (8)	14.00	13.90

Souvenir Sheets
1378	A222	$6 multicolored	4.50	*5.25*
1379	A222	$6 multicolored	4.50	*5.25*

World War II Milestones A223

Designs: 10c, US troops enter Germany, Sept. 11, 1944. 15c, All axis forces surrender in North Africa, May 12, 1943. 25c, US troops invade Kwajalein, Jan. 31, 1944. 45c, Roosevelt and Churchill meet in Casablanca, Jan. 14, 1943. 50c, Marshal Badoglio signs agreement with allies, Sept. 1, 1943. $1, Mountbatten appointed Supreme Allied Commander, Southeast Asia Command, Aug. 25, 1943. $2, Major Greek tactical victory, Koritza, Nov. 22, 1940. $4, Britain and USSR sign mutual assistance pact, July 12, 1941. $5, Operation Torch, Nov. 8, 1942. No. 1389, Japanese attack on Pearl Harbor, Dec. 7, 1941. No. 1390, American bombing attack on Schweinfurt, Oct. 14, 1943.

1991, Mar. 11   **Litho.**   *Perf. 14*
1380	A223	10c multicolored	1.10	.60
1381	A223	15c multicolored	1.25	.50
1382	A223	25c multicolored	1.25	.50
1383	A223	45c multicolored	2.50	.65
1384	A223	50c multicolored	1.50	.65
1385	A223	$1 multicolored	2.75	1.50
1386	A223	$2 multicolored	3.00	2.75
1387	A223	$4 multicolored	3.00	*4.00*
1388	A223	$5 multicolored	3.25	*4.00*
		Nos. 1380-1388 (9)	19.60	15.15

Souvenir Sheets
1389	A223	$6 multicolored	6.75	*7.25*
1390	A223	$6 multicolored	6.75	*7.25*

Cog Railways of the World A224

Designs: 25c, Prince Regent, Middleton Colliery, 1812. 30c, Snowdon Mountain Railway, Wales. 40c, 1st Railcar at Hell Gate, Manitou and Pike's Peak Railway. 60c, PNKA Rack Railway, Amberawa, Java. $1, Green Mountain Railway, Mt. Desert Island, Maine, 1883. $2, Cog locomotive, Pike's Peak, 1891. $4, Vitznau-Rigi Cog Railway, Lake Lucerne. $5, Leopoldina Railway, Brazil. No. 1399, Electric Cog Donkey Engines, Panama Canal. No. 1400, Gornergratbahn, 1st electric cog railway in Switzerland, vert.

1991, Mar. 18   **Litho.**   *Perf. 14*
1391	A224	25c multicolored	1.10	.35
1392	A224	30c multicolored	1.25	.35
1393	A224	40c multicolored	1.25	.45
1394	A224	60c multicolored	1.50	.50
1395	A224	$1 multicolored	2.00	.75
1396	A224	$2 multicolored	2.75	2.75
1397	A224	$4 multicolored	3.25	*4.25*
1398	A224	$5 multicolored	3.25	*4.25*
		Nos. 1391-1398 (8)	16.35	13.65

Souvenir Sheets
1399	A224	$6 multicolored	7.00	7.00
1400	A224	$6 multicolored	7.00	7.00

Butterflies A225

10c, Zebra. 35c, Southern daggertail. 50c, Red anartia. 75c, Malachite. $1, Polydamas swallowtail. $2, Orion. $4, Mimic. $5, Cracker. Caterpillars: No. 1409, Monarch, vert. No. 1410, Painted lady, vert.

1991, Apr. 15   **Litho.**   *Perf. 14*
1401	A225	10c multicolored	.70	.35
1402	A225	35c multicolored	1.10	.35
1403	A225	50c multicolored	1.25	.45
1404	A225	75c multicolored	1.50	.85
1405	A225	$1 multicolored	1.75	1.00

1406	A225	$2 multicolored	2.25	2.50
1407	A225	$4 multicolored	3.00	4.00
1408	A225	$5 multicolored	3.00	4.00
		Nos. 1401-1408 (8)	14.55	13.50

Souvenir Sheets

| 1409 | A225 | $6 multicolored | 7.25 | 8.50 |
| 1410 | A225 | $6 multicolored | 7.25 | 8.50 |

Voyages of Discovery A226

Designs: 10c, Hanno, Phoenicia, c. 450 B.C. 15c, Pytheas, Greece, 325 B.C. 45c, Eric the Red, Viking, A.D. 985. 60c, Leif Erikson, Viking, A.D. 1000. $1, Scylax, Greece, A.D. 518. $2, Marco Polo, A.D. 1259. $4, Queen Hatsheput, Egypt, 1493 B.C. $5, St. Brendan, Ireland, 500 A.D. No. 1419, Columbus, bareheaded. No. 1420, Columbus, wearing hat.

1991, Apr. 22

1411	A226	10c multicolored	.80	.35
1412	A226	15c multicolored	.90	.35
1413	A226	45c multicolored	1.25	.40
1414	A226	60c multicolored	1.40	.55
1415	A226	$1 multicolored	1.75	.90
1416	A226	$2 multicolored	2.25	2.75
1417	A226	$4 multicolored	3.00	4.00
1418	A226	$5 multicolored	3.00	4.00
		Nos. 1411-1418 (8)	14.35	13.30

Souvenir Sheets

| 1419 | A226 | $6 multicolored | 4.25 | 4.75 |
| 1420 | A226 | $6 multicolored | 4.25 | 4.75 |

Discovery of America, 500th anniv. (in 1992).

Paintings by Vincent Van Gogh A227

Designs: 5c, Portrait of Camille Roulin. 10c, Portrait of Armand Roulin. 15c, Young Peasant Woman with Straw Hat Sitting in the Wheat. 25c, Portrait of Adeline Ravoux. 30c, The Schoolboy (Camille Roulin). 40c, Portrait of Doctor Gachet. 50c, Portrait of a Man. 75c, Two Children. $2, Portrait of Postman Joseph Roulin. $3, The Seated Zouave. $4, L'arlesienne: Madame Ginoux with Books. No. 1432, Self Portrait, November/December 1888. No. 1433, Flowering Garden. No. 1434, Farmhouse in Provence. $6, The Bridge at Trinquetaille.

1991, May 13   **Perf. 13½**

1421	A227	5c multicolored	.60	.75
1422	A227	10c multicolored	.60	.55
1423	A227	15c multicolored	.70	.45
1424	A227	25c multicolored	.80	.45
1425	A227	30c multicolored	.80	.45
1426	A227	40c multicolored	.90	.45
1427	A227	50c multicolored	1.00	.45
1428	A227	75c multicolored	1.60	.75
1429	A227	$2 multicolored	2.50	2.50
1430	A227	$3 multicolored	3.00	2.75
1431	A227	$4 multicolored	3.50	4.25
1432	A227	$5 multicolored	3.50	4.25
		Nos. 1421-1432 (12)	19.50	18.05

Size: 102x76mm
Imperf

1433	A227	$5 multicolored	5.00	6.00
1434	A227	$5 multicolored	5.00	6.00
1435	A227	$6 multicolored	6.00	7.00

Phila Nippon '91 — A228

Walt Disney characters demonstrating Japanese martial arts: 10c, Mickey as champion sumo wrestler, vert. 15c, Goofy using tonfa. 45c, Ninja Donald in full field dress. 60c, Mickey using weapon in kung fu, vert. $1, Goofy tries kendo, vert. $2, Mickey, Donald demonstrating special technique of aikido. $4, Mickey flips Donald with judo throw. $5, Mickey demonstrates yabusame (target shooting from running horse), vert. No. 1444, Mickey using karate. No. 1445, Mickey demonstrating tamashiwara (powerbreaking), vert.

Perf. 13½x14, 14x13½
1991, June 29   **Litho.**

1436	A228	10c multicolored	.70	.25
1437	A228	15c multicolored	.80	.25
1438	A228	45c multicolored	1.35	.45
1439	A228	60c multicolored	1.75	.60
1440	A228	$1 multicolored	2.25	1.25
1441	A228	$2 multicolored	2.75	3.00
1442	A228	$4 multicolored	3.50	4.75
1443	A228	$5 multicolored	3.50	4.75
		Nos. 1436-1443 (8)	16.60	15.30

Souvenir Sheets

| 1444 | A228 | $6 multicolored | 5.50 | 6.50 |
| 1445 | A228 | $6 multicolored | 5.50 | 6.50 |

Royal Family Birthday, Anniversary
Common Design Type

1991, July 8   **Litho.**   **Perf. 14**

1446	CD347	10c multicolored	.50	.25
1447	CD347	15c multicolored	.35	.25
1448	CD347	20c multicolored	.35	.25
1449	CD347	40c multicolored	1.00	.30
1450	CD347	$1 multicolored	1.25	.75
1451	CD347	$2 multicolored	1.75	1.75
1452	CD347	$4 multicolored	2.75	2.75
1453	CD347	$5 multicolored	4.50	4.50
		Nos. 1446-1453 (8)	12.45	10.80

Souvenir Sheets

| 1454 | CD347 | $4 | Elizabeth, Philip | 3.75 | 3.75 |
| 1455 | CD347 | $4 | Charles, Diana, sons | 5.50 | 5.50 |

10c, 40c, $1, $5, No. 1455, Charles and Diana, 10th wedding anniversary. Others, Queen Elizabeth II, 65th birthday.

Walt Disney Characters Playing Golf — A229

Designs: 10c, Daisy Duck teeing off. 15c, Goofy using 3-Wood. 45c, Mickey using 3-Iron. 60c, Mickey missing ball using 6-Iron. $1, Donald trying 8-Iron to get out of pond. $2, Minnie using 9-Iron. $4, Donald digging hole with sand wedge. $5, Goofy trying new approach with putter. No. 1464, Grandma Duck using pitching wedge. No. 1465, Mickey cheering Minnie as she uses her 5-Wood, horiz.

Perf. 13½x14, 14x13½
1991, Aug. 7   **Litho.**

1456	A229	10c multicolored	.75	.40
1457	A229	15c multicolored	.85	.40
1458	A229	45c multicolored	1.25	.40
1459	A229	60c multicolored	1.75	.50
1460	A229	$1 multicolored	2.00	1.10
1461	A229	$2 multicolored	2.50	2.75
1462	A229	$4 multicolored	3.25	4.00
1463	A229	$5 multicolored	3.50	4.00
		Nos. 1456-1463 (8)	15.85	13.55

Souvenir Sheets

| 1464 | A229 | $6 multicolored | 6.25 | 6.50 |
| 1465 | A229 | $6 multicolored | 6.25 | 6.50 |

1992 Summer Olympics, Barcelona A230

Archie Comics, 50th anniv.: 10c, Moose receiving gold medal. 25c, Archie, Veronica, Mr. Lodge, polo match, horiz. 40c, Archie & Betty, fencing. 60c, Archie, women's volleyball. $1, Archie, tennis. $2, Archie, marathon race. $4, Archie, judging women's gymnastics, horiz. $5, Archie, Betty, Veronica, basketball. No. 1474, Archie, soccer. No. 1475, Archie, Betty, baseball, horiz.

Perf. 13½x14, 14x13½
1991, Aug. 19

1466	A230	10c multicolored	.65	.30
1467	A230	25c multicolored	1.00	.30
1468	A230	40c multicolored	1.25	.35
1469	A230	60c multicolored	1.50	.45
1470	A230	$1 multicolored	1.75	1.00
1471	A230	$2 multicolored	2.50	2.50
1472	A230	$4 multicolored	3.75	3.75
1473	A230	$5 multicolored	3.75	5.00
		Nos. 1466-1473 (8)	16.15	13.65

Souvenir Sheets

| 1474 | A230 | $6 multicolored | 6.00 | 6.75 |
| 1475 | A230 | $6 multicolored | 6.00 | 6.75 |

Charles de Gaulle, Birth Cent. A231

Charles de Gaulle: 10c, and Pres. Kennedy, families, 1961. 15c, and Pres. Roosevelt, 1945. 45c, and Chancellor Adenauer, 1962, vert. 60c, Liberation of Paris, 1944, vert. $1, Crossing the Rhine, 1945. $2, In Algiers, 1944. $4, and Pres. Eisenhower, 1960. $5, Returning from Germany, 1968, vert. No. 1484, and Churchill at Casablanca, 1943. No. 1485, and Citizens.

1991, Sept. 11   **Litho.**   **Perf. 14**

1476	A231	10c multicolored	.80	.35
1477	A231	15c multicolored	.90	.35
1478	A231	45c multicolored	1.25	.40
1479	A231	60c multicolored	1.50	.50
1480	A231	$1 multicolored	1.75	.90
1481	A231	$2 multicolored	2.50	3.00
1482	A231	$4 multicolored	3.25	4.25
1483	A231	$5 multicolored	3.25	4.25
		Nos. 1476-1483 (8)	15.20	14.00

Souvenir Sheets

| 1484 | A231 | $6 multicolored | 6.75 | 6.75 |
| 1485 | A231 | $6 multicolored | 6.75 | 6.75 |

Independence, 10th Anniv. — A232

Designs: 10c, Island maps, government building. $6, Old P. O., St. Johns, #1 & #635.

1991, Oct. 28

| 1486 | A232 | 10c multicolored | .85 | .50 |

Souvenir Sheet

| 1487 | A232 | $6 multicolored | 6.75 | 8.00 |

No. 1487 contains one 50x38mm stamp.

Miniature Sheet

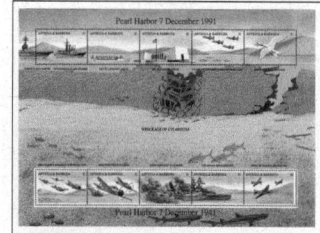

Attack on Pearl Harbor, 50th Anniv. — A233

Designs: No. 1488a, Bow of Nimitz class carrier, Ticonderoga class cruiser. b, Tourist boat to Arizona Memorial. c, USS Arizona Memorial. d, Aircraft salute to missing men. e, White tern. f, Japanese Kate torpedo bombers. g, Japanese Zero fighters. h, Battleship row in flames. i, USS Nevada breaking out. j, Zeros returning to carriers.

1991, Dec. 9   **Perf. 14½x15**

| 1488 | A233 | $1 Sheet of 10, #a.-j. | 22.50 | 22.50 |

Inscription for No. 1488f incorrectly describes torpedo bombers as Zekes.

3rd Antigua Methodist Cub Scout Pack, 60th Anniv. A234

Designs: $2, Lord Robert Baden-Powell, scouts, vert. $3.50, Scouts around campfire. $5, Antigua & Barbuda flag, Jamboree emblem, vert.

1991, Dec. 9   **Perf. 14**

1489	A234	75c multicolored	1.50	.90
1490	A234	$2 multicolored	6.00	5.00
1491	A234	$3.50 multicolored	5.00	5.00
		Nos. 1489-1491 (3)	12.50	10.90

Souvenir Sheet

| 1492 | A234 | $5 multicolored | 5.00 | 5.00 |

17th World Scout Jamboree, Korea.

Wolfgang Amadeus Mozart, Death Bicent. A235

Portrait of Mozart and: $1.50, Scene from opera, Don Giovanni. $4, St. Peter's Cathedral, Salzburg.

1991, Dec. 9

| 1493 | A235 | $1.50 multicolored | 3.50 | 3.50 |
| 1494 | A235 | $4 multicolored | 6.75 | 6.75 |

Anniversaries and Events — A236

Designs: $2, Otto Lilienthal's glider No. 5. $2.50, Locomotive cab, vert.

1991, Dec. 9   **Litho.**   **Perf. 14**

| 1495 | A236 | $2 multicolored | 3.50 | 2.75 |
| 1496 | A236 | $2.50 multicolored | 6.50 | 4.00 |

First glider flight, cent. (No. 1495). Trans-Siberian Railway, cent. (No. 1496).

Brandenburg Gate, Bicent. — A237

25c, Demonstrators in autos, German flag. $2, Statue. $3, Portions of decorative frieze.

1991, Dec. 9   **Litho.**   **Perf. 14**

1499	A237	25c multicolored	.25	.25
1500	A237	$2 multicolored	1.10	1.75
1501	A237	$3 multicolored	2.00	3.00
		Nos. 1499-1501 (3)	3.35	5.00

Souvenir Sheet

| 1502 | A237 | $4 multicolored | 4.75 | 4.75 |

Christmas
A238

Paintings by Fra Angelico: 10c, The Annunciation. 30c, Nativity. 40c, Adoration of the Magi. 60c, Presentation in the Temple. $1, Circumcision. $3, Flight into Egypt. $4, Massacre of the Innocents. $5, Christ Teaching in the Temple. No. 1511, Adoration of the Magi, diff. No. 1512, Adoration of the Magi (Cook Tondo).

1991, Dec. 12				Perf. 12	
1503	A238	10c	multicolored	.40	.25
1504	A238	30c	multicolored	.65	.25
1505	A238	40c	multicolored	.80	.30
1506	A238	60c	multicolored	1.00	.45
1507	A238	$1	multicolored	1.25	.75
1508	A238	$3	multicolored	2.50	3.00
1509	A238	$4	multicolored	2.75	3.50
1510	A238	$5	multicolored	3.00	3.75
		Nos. 1503-1510 (8)		12.35	12.25

Souvenir Sheets

1511	A238	$6	multicolored	7.00	8.00
1512	A238	$6	multicolored	7.00	8.00

Queen Elizabeth II's Accession to the Throne, 40th Anniv.
Common Design Type

Queen Elizabeth II and various island scenes.

1992, Feb. 6		Litho.		Perf. 14	
1513	CD348	10c	multicolored	.90	.30
1514	CD348	30c	multicolored	1.10	.30
1515	CD348	$1	multicolored	1.25	.75
1516	CD348	$5	multicolored	2.75	3.75
		Nos. 1513-1516 (4)		6.00	5.10

Souvenir Sheets

1517	CD348	$6	Beach	4.50	5.00
1518	CD348	$6	Flora	4.50	5.00

Mushrooms
A239

10c, Amanita caesarea. 15c, Collybia fusipes. 30c, Boletus aereus. 40c, Laccaria amethystina. $1, Russula virescens. $2, Tricholoma auratum. $4, Calocybe gambosa. $5, Panus tigrinus.
No. 1527, Auricularia auricula. No. 1528, Clavariadelphus truncatus.

1992		Litho.		Perf. 14	
1519	A239	10c	multicolored	.75	.35
1520	A239	15c	multicolored	.90	.35
1521	A239	30c	multicolored	1.25	.35
1522	A239	40c	multicolored	1.25	.45
1523	A239	$1	multicolored	2.00	1.00
1524	A239	$2	multicolored	2.75	2.75
1525	A239	$4	multicolored	3.50	4.00
1526	A239	$5	multicolored	3.50	4.00
		Nos. 1519-1526 (8)		15.90	13.25

Souvenir Sheet

1527	A239	$6	multicolored	6.50	7.00
1528	A239	$6	multicolored	6.50	7.00

Issued: 10c, 30c, $1, $5, No. 1528, May 18; others, Mar.

Disney Characters at Summer Olympics, Barcelona
A240

Designs: 10c, Mickey presenting gold medal to mermaid for swimming. 15c, Dewey and Huey watching Louie in kayak. 30c, Uncle McScrooge, Donald yachting. 50c, Donald, horse trying water polo. $1, Big Pete weight lifting. $2, Donald, Goofy fencing. $4, Mickey, Donald playing volleyball. $5, Goofy vaulting over horse.
No. 1537, $6, Mickey playing basketball, horiz. No. 1538, $6, Minnie Mouse on uneven parallel bars, horiz. No. 1539, $6, Mickey, Goofy, and Donald judging Minnie's floor exercise, horiz. No. 1540, $6, Mickey running after soccer ball.

1992, Mar. 16				Perf. 13	
1529	A240	10c	multicolored	.65	.25
1530	A240	15c	multicolored	.75	.25
1531	A240	30c	multicolored	.95	.30
1532	A240	50c	multicolored	1.50	.50
1533	A240	$1	multicolored	1.75	.85
1534	A240	$2	multicolored	2.75	2.75
1535	A240	$4	multicolored	3.50	4.25
1536	A240	$5	multicolored	3.50	4.25
		Nos. 1529-1536 (8)		15.35	13.40

Souvenir Sheets

1537-1540	A240	Set of 4		16.50	16.50

Dinosaurs
A241

10c, Pteranodon. 15c, Brachiosaurus. 30c, Tyrannosaurus rex. 50c, Parasaurolophus. $1, Deinonychus. $2, Triceratops. $4, Protoceratops. $5, Stegosaurus.
No. 1549, Apatosaurus. No. 1550, Allosaurus.

1992, Apr. 6				Perf. 14	
1541	A241	10c	multicolored	.70	.35
1542	A241	15c	multicolored	.75	.35
1543	A241	30c	multicolored	.95	.35
1544	A241	50c	multicolored	1.10	.45
1545	A241	$1	multicolored	1.50	.80
1546	A241	$2	multicolored	2.25	2.25
1547	A241	$4	multicolored	2.50	3.25
1548	A241	$5	multicolored	2.50	3.25
		Nos. 1541-1548 (8)		12.25	11.05

Souvenir Sheets

1549	A241	$6	multicolored	5.50	5.50
1550	A241	$6	multicolored	5.50	5.50

Nos. 1541-1544 are vert.

Easter — A242

Paintings: 10c, Supper at Emmaus, by Caravaggio. 15c, The Vision of St. Peter, by Francisco de Zurbaran. 30c, $1, Christ Driving the Money Changers from the Temple, by Tiepolo (detail on $1). 40c, Martyrdom of St. Bartholomew (detail), by Jusepe de Ribera. $2, Crucifixion (detail), by Albrecht Altdorfer. $4, $5, The Deposition (diff. detail), by Fra Angelico. No. 1559, Crucifixion, by Albrecht Altdorfer, vert. No. 1560, The Last Supper, by Vicente Juan Masip.

1992, Apr. 15				Perf. 14x13½	
1551	A242	10c	multicolored	.55	.25
1552	A242	15c	multicolored	.75	.25
1553	A242	30c	multicolored	1.00	.35
1554	A242	40c	multicolored	1.25	.50
1555	A242	$1	multicolored	2.25	1.00
1556	A242	$2	multicolored	3.25	3.25
1557	A242	$4	multicolored	4.25	4.75
1558	A242	$5	multicolored	4.25	4.75
		Nos. 1551-1558 (8)		17.55	15.10

Souvenir Sheet
Perf. 13½x14

1559	A242	$6	multicolored	5.50	6.50
1560	A242	$6	multicolored	5.50	6.50

Spanish Art — A243

Designs: 10c, The Miracle at the Well, by Alonso Cano. 15c, The Poet Luis de Gongora y Argote, by Velazquez. 30c, The Painter Francisco Goya, by Vincente Lopez Portana. 40c, Maria de Las Nieves Michaela Fourdiniere, by Luis Paret y Alcazar. $1, Charles III Eating before His Court, by Paret y Alcazar, horiz. $2, A Rain Shower in Granada, by Antonio Munoz Degrain, horiz. $4, Sarah Bernhardt, by Santiago Rusinol y Prats. $5, The Hermitage Garden, by Joaquin Mir Trinxet. No. 1569, Olympus: Battle with the Giants, by Francisco Bayeu y Subias. No. 1570, The Ascent of Monsieur Boucle's Montgolfier Balloon in the Gardens of Aranjuez, by Antonio Carnicero.

1992, May 11					
1561	A243	10c	multicolored	.45	.25
1562	A243	15c	multicolored	.65	.30
1563	A243	30c	multicolored	.90	.35
1564	A243	40c	multicolored	.90	.50
1565	A243	$1	multicolored	1.50	1.25
1566	A243	$2	multicolored	2.25	4.00
1567	A243	$4	multicolored	3.50	4.00
1568	A243	$5	multicolored	4.25	4.50

Size: 120x95mm
Imperf

1569	A243	$6	multicolored	7.50	8.50
1570	A243	$6	multicolored	7.50	8.50
		Nos. 1561-1570 (10)		29.40	32.15

Granada '92.

Discovery of America, 500th Anniv.
A244

Designs: 15c, San Salvador Island. 30c, Martin Alonzo Pinzon, captain of Pinta. 40c, Columbus, signature, coat of arms. $1, Pinta. $2, Nina. $4, Santa Maria. No. 1577, Sea monster. No. 1578, Map, sailing ship.

1992, May 25		Litho.		Perf. 14	
1571	A244	15c	multicolored	.35	.25
1572	A244	30c	multicolored	.45	.25
1573	A244	40c	multicolored	.60	.35
1574	A244	$1	multicolored	2.25	1.75
1575	A244	$2	multicolored	2.50	3.00
1576	A244	$4	multicolored	3.00	5.75
		Nos. 1571-1576 (6)		9.15	11.35

Souvenir Sheets

1577	A244	$6	multicolored	6.00	6.75
1578	A244	$6	multicolored	6.00	6.75

World Columbian Stamp Expo '92, Chicago.

Hummel Figurines — A245

Designs 15c, No. 1587a, $1.50, Boy sitting on rock pointing to flower in cap. 30c, No. 1587b, $1.50, Girl sitting on fence. 40c, No. 1587c, $1.50, Boy holding binoculars. 50c, No. 1587d, $1.50, Boy carrying umbrella. $1, No. 1588a, $1.50, Two boys looking up at direction marker. $2, No. 1588b, $1.50, Boy carrying basket on back, walking with stick. $4, No. 1588c, $1.50, Two girls, goat. $5, No. 1588d, $1.50, Boy carrying walking stick.

1993, Jan. 6		Litho.		Perf. 14	
1579	A245	15c	multicolored	.40	.25
1580	A245	30c	multicolored	.65	.25
1581	A245	40c	multicolored	.80	.30
1582	A245	50c	multicolored	.90	.40
1583	A245	$1	multicolored	1.50	.75
1584	A245	$2	multicolored	1.75	2.25
1585	A245	$4	multicolored	2.75	3.50
1586	A245	$5	multicolored	2.75	3.50
		Nos. 1579-1586 (8)		11.50	11.20

Souvenir Sheets

1587	A245	$1.50	Sheet of 4, #a.-d.	7.00	7.00
1588	A245	$1.50	Sheet of 4, #a.-d.	7.00	7.00

Hummingbirds and Flowers — A246

Designs: 10c, Antillean crested, wild plantain. 25c, Green mango, parrot's plantain. 45c, Purple-throated carib, lobster claws. 60c, Antillean mango, coral plant. $1, Vervain, cardinal's guard. $2, Rufous breasted hermit, heliconia. $4, Blue-headed, red ginger. $5, Green-throated carib, ornamental banana. No. 1597, Bee, jungle flame. No. 1598, Western streamertails, bignonia.

1992, Aug. 10		Litho.		Perf. 14	
1589	A246	10c	multicolored	.45	.45
1590	A246	25c	multicolored	.60	.30
1591	A246	45c	multicolored	.80	.35
1592	A246	60c	multicolored	.90	.45
1593	A246	$1	multicolored	1.25	.75
1594	A246	$2	multicolored	2.00	2.00
1595	A246	$4	multicolored	3.25	5.75
1596	A246	$5	multicolored	3.50	5.75
		Nos. 1589-1596 (8)		12.75	15.80

Souvenir Sheets

1597	A246	$6	multicolored	6.00	6.50
1598	A246	$6	multicolored	6.00	6.50

Genoa '92.

Discovery of America, 500th Anniv. — A247

1992, Aug. 24		Litho.		Perf. 14½	
1599	A247	$1	Coming ashore	1.00	.75
1600	A247	$2	Natives, ships	1.75	2.10

Organization of East Caribbean States.

Souvenir Sheet

Madison Square Garden, NYC — A248

1992, Oct. 28		Litho.		Perf. 14	
1601	A248	$6	multicolored	5.00	6.75

Postage Stamp Mega-Event, Jacob Javits Center, New York City.

Elvis Presley (1935-1977) — A249

Various pictures of Elvis Presley.

1992, Oct. 26   **Perf. 13½x14**
1602 A249 $1 Sheet of 9, #a.-
    i.   15.00 13.00

Inventors and Pioneers A250

Designs: 10c, Ts'ai Lun, paper. 25c, Igor I. Sikorsky, 4-engine airplane. 30c, Alexander Graham Bell, telephone. 40c, Johannes Gutenberg, printing press. 60c, James Watt, steam engine. $1, Anton van Leeuwenhoek, microscope. $4, Louis Braille, Braille printing. $5, Galileo, telescope. No. 1607, Phonograph. No. 1608, Steamboat.

1992, Oct. 19   **Litho.**   **Perf. 14**
1603 A250 10c multicolored   .25   .25
1604 A250 25c multicolored   1.50   .35
1605 A250 30c multicolored   .60   .40
1605A A250 40c multicolored   .60   .40
1605B A250 60c multicolored   3.75   1.00
1605C A250 $1 multicolored   2.00   1.50
1605D A250 $4 multicolored   4.50   5.75
1606 A250 $5 multicolored   4.75   5.75
   Nos. 1603-1606 (8)   17.95 15.40

Souvenir Sheet
1607 A250 $6 multicolored   5.75   6.50
1608 A250 $6 multicolored   5.75   6.50

Christmas A251

Details from Paintings: 10c, Virgin and Child with Angels, by School of Piero Della Francesca. 25c, Madonna Degli Alberelli, by Giovanni Bellini. 30c, Madonna and Child with St. Anthony Abbot and St. Sigismund, by Neroccio di Landi. 40c, Madonna and the Grand Duke, by Raphael. 60c, The Nativity, by George de la Tour. $1, Holy Family, by Jacob Jordaens. $4, Madonna and Child Enthroned, by Margaritone. $5, Madonna and Child on a Curved Throne, by Byzantine artist. No. 1617, Madonna and Child, by Domenico Ghirlandaio (both names misspelled). No. 1618, The Holy Family, by Pontormo.

1992, Nov. 16   **Perf. 13½x14**
1609 A251 10c multicolored   .65   .25
1610 A251 25c multicolored   1.00   .25
1611 A251 30c multicolored   1.10   .25
1612 A251 40c multicolored   1.25   .30
1613 A251 60c multicolored   1.50   .60
1614 A251 $1 multicolored   1.75   1.00
1615 A251 $4 multicolored   3.75   4.50
1616 A251 $5 multicolored   3.75   4.50
   Nos. 1609-1616 (8)   14.75 11.65

Souvenir Sheet
1617 A251 $6 multicolored   5.75   6.50
1618 A251 $6 multicolored   5.75   6.50

A252

A253

Anniversaries and Events: 10c, Cosmonauts. 40c, Graf Zeppelin, Goodyear blimp. 45c, Right Rev. Daniel C. Davis, St. John's Cathedral. 75c, Konrad Adenauer. $1, Bus Mosbacher, Weatherly. $1.50, Rain forest. No. 1625, Felis tigris. No. 1626, Flag, emblems, plant. No. 1627, Women acting on stage. $2.25, Women carrying baskets of food on their heads. $3, Lions Club emblem, club member. No. 1630, West German, NATO flags. No. 1631, China's Long March Booster Rocket. No. 1632, Dr. Hugo Eckener.
No. 1633, $6, The Hindenburg. No. 1634, $6, Brandenburg Gate, German flag. No. 1635, $6, Monarch butterfly. No. 1636, $6, Hermes Shuttle, Columbus Space Station.

1992, Dec. 14   **Litho.**   **Perf. 14**
1619 A252 10c multicolored   .80   .50
1620 A252 40c multicolored   1.75   .55
1621 A253 45c multicolored   .75   .35
1622 A252 75c multicolored   .90   .60
1623 A252 $1 multicolored   1.25   .75
1624 A252 $1.50 multicolored   1.75   1.10
1625 A252 $2 multicolored   4.25   2.00
1626 A253 $2 multicolored   2.75   1.50
1627 A253 $2 multicolored   2.50   1.75
1628 A252 $2.25 multicolored   2.50   2.50
1629 A252 $3 multicolored   3.75   3.75
1630 A252 $4 multicolored   5.00   5.00
1631 A252 $4 multicolored   5.50   5.50
1632 A252 $6 multicolored   5.00   5.00
   Nos. 1619-1632 (14)   38.45 30.85

Souvenir Sheets
1633-1636 A252 Set of 4   22.00 27.50

Intl. Space Year (Nos. 1619, 1631, 1636). Count Zeppelin, 75th anniv. of death (Nos. 1620, 1632-1633). Diocese of Northeast Caribbean and Aruba District, 150th anniv. (No. 1621). Konrad Adenauer, 25th anniv. of death (Nos. 1622, 1630, 1634). 1962 winner of America's Cup (No. 1623). Earth Summit, Rio (Nos. 1624-1625, 1635). Inter-American Institute for Cooperation on Agriculture, 50th anniv. (No. 1626). Cultural Development, 40th anniv. (No. 1627). WHO Intl. Conf. on Nutrition, Rome (No. 1628). Lions Club, 75th anniv. (No. 1629).
Issued: Nos. 1619, 1621-1623, 1626-1631, 1634, 1636, Nov.; Nos. 1624-1625, 1635, Dec. 14.

Euro Disney, Paris — A254

Disney characters: 10c, Golf course. 25c, Davy Crockett Campground. 30c, Cheyenne Hotel. 40c, Santa Fe Hotel. $1, New York Hotel. $2, In car, map showing location. $4, Pirates of the Caribbean. $5, Adventureland.
No. 1645, $6, Mickey Mouse on map with star, vert. No. 1646, $6, Roof turret at entrance, Mickey Mouse in uniform. No. 1646A, $6, Mickey Mouse, colored spots on poster, vert. No. 1646B, $6, Mickey on poster, vert., diff.

1992-93   **Litho.**   **Perf. 14x13½**
1637 A254 10c multicolored   .70   .25
1638 A254 25c multicolored   .90   .25
1639 A254 30c multicolored   .90   .25
1640 A254 40c multicolored   1.00   .30
1641 A254 $1 multicolored   2.00   .75
1642 A254 $2 multicolored   2.75   2.75

1643 A254 $4 multicolored   3.75   5.00
1644 A254 $5 multicolored   3.75   5.00
   Nos. 1637-1644 (8)   15.75 14.55

Souvenir Sheets
Perf. 13½x14
1645-1646B A254 Set of 4   17.00 20.00

Issued: Nos. 1638-1639, 1642-1643, 1646-1646B, 2/22/93; others, 12/1992.

Miniature Sheets

Louvre Museum, Bicent. — A255

Details or entire paintings, by Peter Paul Rubens: No. 1647a, Destiny of Marie de' Medici. b, Birth of Marie de'Medici. c, Marie's Education. d, Destiny of Marie de'Medici, diff. e, Henry IV Receives the Portrait. f, The Meeting at Lyons. g, The Marriage. h, The Birth of Louis XIII.
No. 1648a, The Capture of Juliers. b, The Exchange of Princesses. c, The Happiness of the Regency. d, The Majority of Louis XIII. e, The Flight from Blois. f, The Treaty of Angouleme. g, The Peace of Angers. h, The Queen's Reconciliation with Her Son.
$6, Helene Fourment Au Carosse.

1993, Mar. 22   **Litho.**   **Perf. 12**
1647 A255 $1 Sheet of 8, #a.-h.,
    + label   7.25 7.25
1648 A255 $1 Sheet of 8, #a.-h.,
    + label   7.25 7.25

Souvenir Sheet
Perf. 14½
1649 A255 $6 multicolored   7.75 7.75

No. 1649 contains one 55x88mm stamp.
Nos. 1647-1649 exist imperf. Values about double those of normal sheets.

Flowers — A256

15c, Cardinal's guard. 25c, Giant granadilla. 30c, Spider flower. 40c, Gold vine. $1, Frangipani. $2, Bougainvillea. $4, Yellow oleander. $5, Spicy jatropha.
No. 1658, Bird lime tree. No. 1659, Fairy lily.

1993, Mar. 15   **Litho.**   **Perf. 14**
1650 A256 15c multicolored   .95   .30
1651 A256 25c multicolored   1.10   .30
1652 A256 30c multicolored   1.10   .35
1653 A256 40c multicolored   1.10   .35
1654 A256 $1 multicolored   2.10   .90
1655 A256 $2 multicolored   2.75   2.75
1656 A256 $4 multicolored   3.75   4.50
1657 A256 $5 multicolored   3.75   4.50
   Nos. 1650-1657 (8)   16.60 13.95

Souvenir Sheets
1658 A256 $6 multicolored   5.25   6.50
1659 A256 $6 multicolored   5.25   6.50

Endangered Species — A257

Designs: No. 1660a, St. Lucia parrot. b, Cahow. c, Swallow-tailed kite. d, Everglades kite. e, Imperial parrot. f, Humpback whale. g, Puerto Rican plain pigeon. h, St. Vincent parrot. i, Puerto Rican parrot. j, Leatherback turtle. k, American crocodile. l, Hawksbill turtle.
No. 1662, West Indian manatee.

1993, Apr. 5
1660 A257 $1 Sheet of 12,
    #a.-l.   15.00 15.00

Souvenir Sheets
1661 A257 $6 like #1660f   4.75   5.50
1662 A257 $6 multicolored   4.75   5.50

Philatelic Publishing Personalities — A258

Portrait, stamp: No. 1663, J. Walter Scott (1842-1919), US "#C3a," Antigua #1. No. 1664, Theodore Champion, France #8, Antigua #1. No. 1665, E. Stanley Gibbons (1856-1913), cover of his first price list and catalogue, Antigua #1. No. 1666, Hugo Michel (1866-1944), Bavaria #1, Antigua #1. No. 1667, Alberto (1877-1944) and Giulio (1902-1987) Bolaffi, Sardinia #1, Great Britain #3. No. 1668, Richard Borek (1874-1947), Brunswick #24, Bavaria #1.
Front pages, Mekeel's Weekly Stamp News: No. 1669a, Jan. 7, 1890. b, Feb. 12, 1993.

1993, June 14
1663 A258 $1.50 multicolored   1.90   1.60
1664 A258 $1.50 multicolored   1.90   1.60
1665 A258 $1.50 multicolored   1.90   1.60
1666 A258 $1.50 multicolored   1.90   1.60
1667 A258 $1.50 multicolored   1.90   1.60
1668 A258 $1.50 multicolored   1.90   1.60
   Nos. 1663-1668 (6)   11.40 9.60

Souvenir Sheet
1669 A258 $3 Sheet of 2,
    #a.-b.   6.25   7.00

Mekeel's Weekly Stamp News, cent. (in 1891; No. 1669).

Miniature Sheets

Coronation of Queen Elizabeth II, 40th Anniv. — A259

No. 1670 — Coronation: a, 30c, Official photograph. b, 40c, Crown of Queen Elizabeth, the Queen Mother. c, $2, Dignitaries attending ceremony. d, $4, Queen, Prince Edward.
No. 1671, $1 — First decade, 1953-1963: a, Wedding photograph of Princess Margaret and Antony Armstrong-Jones. b, Queen opening Parliament, Prince Philip. c, Queen holding infant. d, Royal family. e, Queen Elizabeth II, formal portrait. f, Queen, Charles de Gaulle. g, Queen, Pope John XXIII. h, Queen inspecting troops.
No. 1672, $1 — Second decade, 1963-1973: a, Investiture of Charles as Prince of Wales. b, Queen opening Parliament, Prince Philip, diff. c, Queen holding infant, diff. d, Queen, Prince Philip, children. e, Wearing blue robe, diadem. f, Prince Philip, Queen

seated. g, Prince Charles, Queen at microphone. h, Queen conversing, model airplane.

No. 1673, $1 — Third decade, 1973-1983: a, Wedding photograph of Prince Charles and Princess Diana. b, Queen opening Parliament, Prince Philip, diff. c, Princess Diana with infant. d, Princess Anne with infant. e, Portrait of Queen. f, Queen waving, Prince Philip. g, Queen, Pope John Paul II. h, Wedding portrait of Mark Phillips and Princess Anne.

No. 1674, $1 — Fourth decade, 1983-1993: a, Wedding photograph of Sarah Ferguson and Prince Andrew. b, Queen opening Parliament, Prince Philip, diff. c, Princess Diana holding infant, diff. d, Sarah Ferguson, infant. e, Queen wearing blue dress. f, Queen waving from carriage, Prince Philip. g, Queen wearing military uniform. h, Queen Mother.

$6, Portrait, by Denis Fildes.

1993, June 2   Litho.   Perf. 13½x14
1670 A259   Sheet, 2 each #a.-d.   8.50 8.50
Sheets of 8, #a-h
1671-1674 A259   Set of 4   34.00 34.00
Souvenir Sheet
Perf. 14
1675 A259 $6 multicolored   5.00 5.00
No. 1675 contains one 28x42mm stamp.

Wedding of Japan's Crown Prince Naruhito and Masako Owada: Cameo photos of couple and: 40c, Crown Prince. $3, Princess.
$6, Princess wearing white coat, vert.

1993, Aug. 16   Litho.   Perf. 14
1676 A260   40c multicolored   .65 .40
1677 A260 $3 multicolored   2.25 3.25
Souvenir Sheet
1678 A260 $6 multicolored   6.00 6.00

Picasso (1881-1973) — A261

Paintings: 30c, Cat and Bird, 1939. 40c, Fish on a Newspaper, 1957. $5, Dying Bull, 1934.
$6, Woman with a Dog, 1953.

1993, Aug. 16   Litho.   Perf. 14
1679 A261   30c multicolored   .90 .40
1680 A261   40c multicolored   .90 .40
1681 A261 $5 multicolored   3.75 3.75
Nos. 1679-1681 (3)   5.55 4.55
Souvenir Sheet
1682 A261 $6 multicolored   5.75 5.75

Copernicus (1473-1543) A262

Designs: 40c, Astronomical devices. $4, Photograph of supernova.
$5, Copernicus.

1993, Aug. 16
1683 A262   40c multicolored   .65 .50
1684 A262 $4 multicolored   3.25 3.25
Souvenir Sheet
1685 A262 $5 multicolored   5.25 5.25

Willy Brandt (1913-1992), German Chancellor — A263

Designs: 30c, Helmut Schmidt, George Leber, Brandt. $4, Brandt, newspaper headlines.
$6, Brandt at Warsaw Ghetto Memorial, 1970.

1993, Aug. 16
1686 A263   30c multicolored   .75 .35
1687 A263 $4 multicolored   3.75 3.75
Souvenir Sheet
1688 A263 $6 multicolored   5.50 5.50

Polska '93 A264

Paintings: $1, Study of a Woman Combing Her Hair, by Wladyslaw Slewinski, 1897. $3, Artist's Wife with Cat, by Konrad Krzyzanowski, 1912.
$6, General Confusion, by S. I. Witkiewicz, 1930, vert.

1993, Aug. 16
1689 A264 $1 multicolored   .90 .90
1690 A264 $3 multicolored   2.25 2.25
Souvenir Sheet
1691 A264 $6 multicolored   5.50 5.50

Inauguration of Pres. William J. Clinton — A265

Designs: $5, Pres. Clinton driving car. $6, Pres. Clinton, inauguration ceremony, vert.

1993, Aug. 16
1692 A265 $5 multicolored   3.25 3.25
Souvenir Sheet
1693 A265 $6 multicolored   5.00 5.00
No. 1693 contains one 43x57mm stamp.

1994 Winter Olympics, Lillehammer, Norway — A266

15c, Irina Rodnina, Alexei Ulanov, gold medalists, pairs figure skating, 1972. $5, Alberto Tomba, gold medal, giant slalom, 1988, 1992.
$6, Yvonne van Gennip, Andrea Ehrig, gold, bronze medalists, speedskating, 1988.

1993, Aug. 16
1694 A266   15c multicolored   1.00 .30
1695 A266 $5 multicolored   3.25 3.25
Souvenir Sheet
1696 A266 $6 multicolored   5.50 5.50

1994 World Cup Soccer Championships, US — A267

English soccer players: No. 1697, $2, Gordon Banks. Nos. 1698, $2, Bobby Moore. No. 1699, $2, Peter Shilton. No. 1700, $2, Nobby Stiles. No. 1701, $2, Bryan Robson. No. 1702, $2, Geoff Hurst. No. 1703, $2, Gary Lineker. No. 1704, $2, Bobby Charlton. No. 1705, $2, Martin Peters. No. 1706, $2, John Barnes. No. 1707, $2, David Platt. No. 1708, $2, Paul Gascoigne.
No. 1709, $6, Bobby Moore. No. 1710, $6, Player holding 1990 Fair Play Winners Trophy.

1993, July 30   Litho.   Perf. 14
1697-1708 A267   Set of 12   18.00 18.00
Souvenir Sheets
1709-1710 A267   Set of 2   10.00 10.00
Nos. 1697-1708 issued in sheets of five plus label identifying player.

Aviation Anniversaries — A268

Designs: 30c, Dr. Hugo Eckener, Dr. Wm. Beckers, zeppelin over Lake George, NY. No. 1712, Chicago Century of Progress Exhibition seen from zeppelin. No. 1713, George Washington, Blanchard's balloon, vert. No. 1714, Gloster E.28/39, first British jet plane. $4, Pres. Wilson watching take-off of first scheduled air mail plane. No. 1716, Hindenburg over Ebbets Field, Brooklyn, NY, 1937. No. 1717, Gloster Meteor in combat.
No. 1718, Eckener, vert. No. 1719, Alexander Hamilton, Pres. Washington, John Jay, gondola of Blanchard's balloon. No. 1720, PBY-5.

1993, Oct. 11
1711 A268   30c multicolored   1.00 .60
1712 A268   40c multicolored   1.00 1.00
1713 A268   40c multicolored   1.00 1.00
1714 A268   40c multicolored   1.00 1.00
1715 A268 $4 multicolored   4.00 4.00
1716 A268 $4 multicolored   4.00 4.00
1717 A268 $4 multicolored   4.00 4.00
Nos. 1711-1717 (7)   16.00 15.60
Souvenir Sheets
1718 A268 $6 multicolored   5.25 5.25
1719 A268 $6 multicolored   6.00 6.00
1720 A268 $6 multicolored   6.00 6.00
Dr. Hugo Eckener, 125th anniv. of birth (Nos. 1711-1712, 1716, 1718). First US balloon flight, bicent. (Nos. 1713, 1715, 1719). Royal Air Force, 75th anniv. (Nos. 1714, 1717, 1720).
No. 1720 contains one 57x43mm stamp.

Mickey Mouse Movie Posters A269

Nos. 1721-1729: 10c, The Musical Farmer, 1932. 15c, Little Whirlwind, 1941. 30c, Pluto's Dream House, 1940. 40c, Gulliver Mickey, 1934. 50c, Alpine Climbers, 1936. $1, Mr. Mouse Takes a Trip, 1940. $2, The Nifty Nineties, 1941. $4, Mickey Down Under, 1948. $5, The Pointer, 1939.
No. 1730, $6, The Simple Things, 1953. No. 1731, $6, The Prince and the Pauper, 1990.

1993, Oct. 25   Litho.   Perf. 13½x14
1721-1729 A269   Set of 9   15.00 15.00
Souvenir Sheets
1730-1731 A269   Set of 2   13.00 13.00

St. John's Lodge #492, 150th Anniv. A270

Designs: 10c, W.K. Heath, Grand Inspector 1961-82, vert. 30c, Present Masonic Hall. 40c, 1st Masonic Hall. 60c, J.L.E. Jeffery, Grand Inspector 1953-61, vert.

1993, Aug. 16   Litho.   Perf. 14
1732-1735 A270   Set of 4   10.00 10.00

First Ford Engine and Benz's First 4-Wheel Car, Cent. A271

30c, Lincoln Continental. 40c, 1914 Mercedes racing car. $4, 1966 Ford GT40. $5, 1954 Mercedes Benz gull wing coupe, street version.
No. 1740, $6, Mustang emblem. No. 1741, $6, US #1286A, Germany #471.

1993, Oct. 11   Litho.   Perf. 14
1736-1739 A271   Set of 4   9.00 9.00
Souvenir Sheets
1740-1741 A271   Set of 2   11.00 11.00

Christmas — A272

Nos. 1742-1750, Disney characters in The Nutcracker: 10c, 15c, 20c, 30c, 40c, 50c, 60c, $3, $6.
No. 1751, $6, Minnie and Mickey. No. 1752, $6, Mickey, vert.

1993, Nov. 8   Perf. 14x13½, 13½x14
1742-1750 A272   Set of 9   13.00 13.00
Souvenir Sheets
1751-1752 A272   Set of 2   11.50 11.50

Fine Art — A273

Paintings by Rembrandt: No. 1753, 15c, Hannah and Samuel. No. 1755, 30c, Isaac & Rebecca (The Jewish Bride). No. 1756, 40c, Jacob Wrestling with the Angel. No. 1760, $5, Moses with the Tablets of the Law.
Paintings by Matisse: No. 1754, 15c, Guitarist. No. 1757, 60c, Interior with a Goldfish Bowl. No. 1758, $1, Portrait of Mlle. Yvonne Landsberg. No. 1759, $4, The Toboggan, Plate XX from Jazz.
No. 1761, $6, The Blinding of Samson by the Philistines, by Rembrandt. No. 1762, $6, The Three Sisters, by Matisse.

1993, Nov. 22   Perf. 13½x14
1753-1760 A273   Set of 8   10.50 10.50
Souvenir Sheets
1761-1762 A273   Set of 2   11.50 11.50

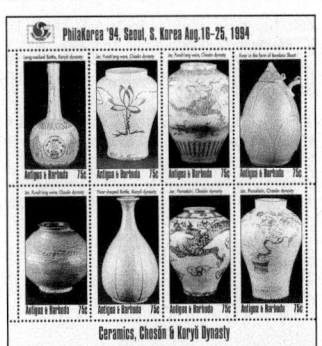

A274

Hong Kong '94 — A275

Stamps, fishing boats at Shau Kei Wan: No. 1763, Hong Kong #370, bow of boat. No. 1764, Stern of boat, #1300.

Museum of Qin figures, Shaanxi Province, Tomb of Qin First Emperor: No. 1765a, Inside museum. b, Cavalryman, horse. c, Warriors in battle formation. d, Painted bronze horses, chariot. e, Pekingese dog (not antiquity). f, Chin warrior figures, horses.

1994, Feb. 18 Litho. *Perf. 14*

1763 A274 40c multicolored .70 .70
1764 A274 40c multicolored .70 .70
a. Pair, #1763-1764 1.60 1.60

Miniature Sheet

1765 A275 40c Sheet of 6, #a.-f. 5.75 5.75

Nos. 1763-1764 issued in sheets of 5 pairs. No. 1764a is a continuous design.

New Year 1994 (Year of the Dog) (No. 1765e).

Hong Kong '94 — A276

Disney characters: 10c, Mickey's "Pleasure Junk." 15c, Mandarin Minnie. 30c, Donald, Daisy journey by house boat. 50c, Mickey, Birdman of Mongkok. $1, Pluto encounters a good-luck dog. $2, Minnie, Daisy celebrate Bun Festival. $4, Goofy, the noodle maker. $5, Goofy pulls Mickey in a rickshaw.

No. 1774, $5, Mickey celebrating New Year with Dragon Dance, horiz. No. 1775, $5, View of Hong Kong Harbor, horiz.

1994, Feb. 18 Litho. *Perf. 13½x14*

1766-1773 A276 Set of 8 14.00 14.00

Souvenir Sheets

Perf. 14x13½

1774-1775 A276 $5 Set of 2 11.00 11.00

Sierra Club, Cent. — A277

No. 1776: a, Bactrian camel, emblem UR. b, Bactrian camel, emblem UL. c, African elephant, emblem UL. d, African elephant, emblem UR. e, Leopard, blue background. f, Leopard, emblem UR. g, Leopard, emblem UL. h, Club emblem.

No. 1777: a, Sumatran rhinoceros, lying on ground. b, Sumatran rhinoceros, looking straight ahead. c, Ring-tailed lemur standing. d, Ring-tailed lemur sitting on branch. e, Red-fronted brown lemur on branch. f, Red-fronted brown lemur. g, Red-fronted brown lemur, diff.

No. 1778, $1.50, Sumatran rhinoceros, horiz. No. 1779, $1.50, Ring-tailed lemur, horiz. No. 1780, $1.50, Bactrian camel, horiz. No. 1781, $1.50, African elephant, horiz.

1994, Mar. 1 Litho. *Perf. 14*

1776 A277 $1.50 Sheet of 8, #a.-h. 12.00 12.00
1777 A277 $1.50 Sheet of 8, #a.-g, #1776h 12.00 12.00

Souvenir Sheets

1778-1781 A277 Set of 4 6.50 6.50

New Year 1994 (Year of the Dog) — A278

Small breeds of dogs: No. 1782a, West highland white terrier. b, Beagle. c, Scottish terrier. d, Pekingese. e, Dachshund. f, Yorkshire terrier. g, Pomeranian. h, Poodle. i, Shetland sheepdog. j, Pug. k, Shih tzu. l, Chihuahua.

Large breeds of dogs: No. 1783a, Mastiff. b, Border collie. c, Samoyed. d, Airedale terrier. e, English setter. f, Rough collie. g, Newfoundland. h, Weimaraner. i, English springer spaniel. j, Dalmatian. k, Boxer. l, Old English sheepdog.

No. 1784, $6, Welsh corgi. No. 1785, $6, Labrador retriever.

1994, Apr. 5 *Perf. 14*

1782 A278 50c Sheet of 12, #a.-l. 7.75 7.75
1783 A278 75c Sheet of 12, #a.-l. 11.50 11.50

Souvenir Sheets

1784-1785 A278 Set of 2 11.50 11.50

Orchids — A279

Designs: 10c, Spiranthes lanceolata. 20c, Ionopsis utricularioides. 30c, Tetramicra canaliculata. 50c, Oncidium picturatum. $1, Epidendrum difforme. $2, Epidendrum ciliare. $4, Epidendrum ibaguense. $5, Epidendrum nocturnum.

No. 1794, $6, Encyclia cochleata. No. 1795, $6, Rodriguezia lanceolata.

1994, Apr. 11 *Perf. 14*

1786-1793 A279 Set of 8 17.50 17.50

Souvenir Sheets

1794-1795 A279 Set of 2 11.00 *13.00*

Butterflies — A280

Designs: 10c, Monarch. 15c, Florida white. 30c, Little sulphur. 40c, Troglodyte. $1, Common long-tail skipper. $2, Caribbean buckeye. $4, Polydamas swallowtail. $5, Zebra.

No. 1804, $6, Cloudless sulphur. No. 1805, $6, Hanno blue.

1994, June 27 *Perf. 14*

1796-1803 A280 Set of 8 18.50 18.50

Souvenir Sheets

1804-1805 A280 Set of 2 11.00 *13.00*

Marine Life — A281

No. 1806: a, Bottlenose dolphin. b, Killer whale (a). c, Spinner dolphin (b). d, Ocean sunfish (a). e, Caribbean reef shark, short fin pilot whale (d, f). f, Butterfly fish. g, Moray eel. h, Trigger fish. i, Red lobster (h).

No. 1807, $6, Blue marlin, horiz. No. 1808, $6, Sea horse.

1994, July 21 Litho. *Perf. 14*

1806 A281 50c Sheet of 9, #a.-i. 7.75 7.75

Souvenir Sheets

1807-1808 A281 Set of 2 13.00 13.00

Intl. Year of the Family A282

1994, Aug. 4

1809 A282 90c multicolored 1.10 1.10

D-Day, 50th Anniv. A283

Designs: 40c, Short Sunderland attacks U-boat. $2, Lockheed P-38 Lightning attacks train. $3, B-26 Marauders of 9th Air Force.

$6, Hawker Typhoon Fighter Bombers.

1994, Aug. 4

1810-1812 A283 Set of 3 7.00 7.00

Souvenir Sheet

1813 A283 $6 multicolored 7.50 7.50

A284

Intl. Olympic Committee, Cent. — A285

Designs: 50c, Edwin Moses, US, hurdles, 1984. $1.50, Steffi Graf, Germany, tennis, 1988. $6, Johann Olav Koss, Norway, speed skating, 1994.

1994, Aug. 4

1814 A284 50c multicolored .40 .30
1815 A284 $1.50 multicolored 2.00 2.00

Souvenir Sheet

1816 A285 $6 multicolored 6.00 6.00

English Touring Cricket, Cent. A286

35c, M.A. Atherton, England, Wisden Trophy. 75c, I.V.A. Richards, Leeward Islands, vert. $1.20, R.B. Richardson, Leeward Islands, Wisden Trophy.

$3, First English team, 1895.

1994, Aug. 4

1817-1819 A286 Set of 3 6.00 6.00

Souvenir Sheet

1820 A286 $3 multicolored 3.00 3.00

First Manned Moon Landing, 25th Anniv. — A287

No. 1821, $1.50: a, Edwin E. Aldrin, Jr. b, First footprint on Moon. c, Neil A. Armstrong. d, Aldrin descending to lunar surface. e, Aldrin deploys ALSEP (spelled ALSET in error on stamp). f, Aldrin, US flag, Tranquility Base.

No. 1822, $1.50: a, Scientific research, Tranquility Base. b, Plaque on Moon. c, Eagle ascending to docking. d, Command module in lunar orbit. e, US No. C76 made from die carried to Moon. f, Pres. Nixon, Apollo 11 crew.

$6, Armstrong, Aldrin, Postmaster General Blount.

1994, Aug. 4 Sheets of 6, #a-f

1821-1822 A287 Set of 2 22.50 22.50

Souvenir Sheet

1823 A287 $6 multicolored 5.25 5.25

A288

PHILAKOREA '94 — A289

40c, Entrance bridge, Songgwangsa Temple. 90c, Song-op Folk Village, Cheju. $3, Panoramic view, Port Sogwip'o.

Ceramics, Koryo & Choson Dynasties: No. 1827a, Long-necked bottle. b, Jar. c, Jar, diff. d, Ewer in form of bamboo shoot. e, Jar, diff. f, Pear-shaped bottle. g, Porcelain jar with dragon design. h, Porcelain jar with bonsai design.

$4, Ox, ox herder, vert.

1994, Aug. 4   Perf. 14, 13½ (#1827)
1824-1826 A288   Set of 3   3.00 3.00
1827 A289 75c Sheet of 8, #a.-h. 6.25 6.25
Souvenir Sheet
1828 A288 $4 multicolored   4.50 4.50

Stars of Country & Western Music — A290

No. 1829, 75c: a, Patsy Cline. b, Tanya Tucker. c, Dolly Parton. d, Anne Murray. e, Tammy Wynette. f, Loretta Lynn. g, Reba McEntire. h, Skeeter Davis.

No. 1830, 75c: a, Travis Tritt. b, Dwight Yoakam. c, Billy Ray Cyrus. d, Alan Jackson. e, Garth Brooks. f, Vince Gill. g, Clint Black. h, Eddie Rabbit.

No. 1831, 75c: a, Hank Snow. b, Gene Autry. c, Jimmie Rogers. d, Ernest Tubb. e, Eddy Arnold. f, Willie Nelson. g, Johnny Cash. h, George Jones.

No. 1832, $6, Kitty Wells, horiz. No. 1833, $6, Hank Williams, Sr. No. 1834, $6, Hank Williams, Jr.

1994, Aug. 18   Litho.   Perf. 14
Sheets of 8, #a-h
1829-1831 A290   Set of 3   15.50 15.50
Souvenir Sheets
1832-1834 A290   Set of 3   15.50 15.50

1994 World Cup Soccer Championships, US — A291

Designs: 15c, Hugo Sanchez, Mexico. 35c, Juergen Klinsmann, Germany. 65c, Antigua player. $1.20, Cobi Jones, US. $4, Roberto Baggio, Italy. $5, Bwalya Kalusha, Zambia.

No. 1841, $6, FIFA World Cup Trophy, vert. No. 1842, $6, Maldive Islands player, vert.

1994, Sept. 19
1835-1840 A291   Set of 6   13.50 13.50
Souvenir Sheets
1841-1842 A291   Set of 2   8.75 8.75

Order of the Caribbean Community — A292

First award recipients: 65c, Sir Shridath Ramphal, statesman, Guyana. 90c, William Demas, economist, Trinidad & Tobago. $1.20, Derek Walcott, writer, St. Lucia.

1994, Sept. 26
1843-1845 A292   Set of 3   3.50 3.50

Herman E. Sieger (1902-54) A293

Germany No. C35, Graf Zeppelin, Sieger.

1994, June 6   Litho.   Perf. 14
1846 A293 $1.50 multicolored   4.00 4.00

Birds A294

Designs: 10c, Magnificent frigate birds. 15c, Bridled quail dove. 30c, Magnificent frigate bird hatchling. 40c, Purple-throated carib. No. 1851, $1, Antigua broad-wing hawk, vert. No. 1852, $1, Magnificent frigate bird, vert. $3, Magnificent frigate bird, white head. $4, Yellow warbler.

No. 1855, $6, West Indian Whistling duck. No. 1856, $6, Magnificent frigate bird, diff., vert.

1994, Dec. 12   Litho.   Perf. 14
1847-1854 A294   Set of 8   11.00 11.00
Souvenir Sheets
1855-1856 A294   Set of 2   9.25 9.25

World Wildlife Fund (Nos. 1847, 1849, 1852-1853).

Christmas A295

Paintings of Madonnas: 15c, The Virgin and Child by the Fireside, by Robert Campin. 35c, The Reading Madonna, by Giorgione. 40c, Madonna and Child, by Giovanni Bellini. 45c, The Litta Madonna, by da Vinci. 65c, The Virgin and Child Under the Apple Tree, by Lucas Cranach the Elder. 75c, Madonna and Child, by Master of the Female Half-Lengths. $1.20, An Allegory of the Church, by Alessandro Allori. $5, Madonna and Child Wreathed with Flowers, by Jacob Jordaens.

No. 1865, $6, The Virgin Enthroned with Child, by Bohemian Master. No. 1866, $6, Madonna and Child with (painting's) Commissioners, by Palma Vecchio.

1994, Dec. 12   Perf. 13½x14
1857-1864 A295   Set of 8   14.00 14.00
Souvenir Sheets
1865-1866 A295   Set of 2   9.50 9.50

Birds — A296

Designs: 15c, Magnificent frigate bird. 25c, Blue-hooded euphonia. 35c, Meadowlark. 40c, Red-billed tropic bird. 45c, Greater flamingo. 60c, Yellow-faced grassquit. 65c, Yellow-billed cuckoo. 70c, Purple-throated carib. 75c, Bananaquit. 90c, Painted bunting. $1.20, Red-legged honeycreeper. $2, Jacana. $5, Greater antillean bullfinch. $10, Caribbean elaenia. $20, Trembler.

1995, Feb. 6   Perf. 14½x14
1867 A296   15c multicolored   .25   .25
1868 A296   25c multicolored   .25   .25
1869 A296   35c multicolored   .25   .25
1870 A296   40c multicolored   .30   .30
1871 A296   45c multicolored   .40   .40
1872 A296   60c multicolored   .45   .45
1873 A296   65c multicolored   .60   .60
1874 A296   70c multicolored   .60   .60
1875 A296   75c multicolored   .65   .65
1876 A296   90c multicolored   .80   .80
1877 A296 $1.20 multicolored   1.00   1.00
1878 A296 $2 multicolored   1.75   1.75
1879 A296 $5 multicolored   4.75   4.75
1880 A296 $10 multicolored   9.50   9.50
1881 A296 $20 multicolored   19.00 19.00
Nos. 1867-1881 (15)   40.55 40.55

See Nos. 2693-2694.

Prehistoric Animals A297

Designs, vert: 15c, Pachycephalosaurus. 20c, Afrovenator. 65c, Centrosaurus. 90c, Pentaceratops. $1.20, Tarbosaurus. $5, Styracosaur.

No. 1888: a, Kronosaur. b, Ichthyosaur. c, Plesiosaur. d, Archelon. e, Two tyrannosaurs. f, One tyrannosaur. g, One parasaurolophus. h, Two parasaurolophuses. i, Oviraptor. j, Protoceratops with eggs. k, Pteranodon, protoceratops. l, Protoceratops.

No. 1889, $6, Carnotaurus. No. 1890, $6, Corythosaurus.

1995, May 15   Litho.   Perf. 14
1882-1887 A297   Set of 6   7.50 7.50
1888 A297 75c Sheet of 12, #a.-l.   8.50 8.50
Souvenir Sheets
1889-1890 A297   Set of 2   14.50 14.50

1996 Summer Olympics, Atlanta A298

Gold medalists: 15c, Al Oerter, US, discus. 20c, Greg Louganis, US, diving. 65c, Naim Suleymanoglu, Turkey, weight lifting. 90c, Louise Ritter, US, high jump. $1.20, Nadia Comaneci, Romania, gymnastics. $5, Olga Bondarenko, USSR, 10,000-meter run.

No. 1897, $6, Lutz Hessilch, Germany, 1000-meter sprint cycling, vert. No. 1898, $6, US team, eight-oared shell, 800-, 1500-meters.

1995, June 6   Litho.   Perf. 14
1891-1896 A298   Set of 6   7.25 7.25
Souvenir Sheets
1897-1898 A298   Set of 2   13.00 13.00

End of World War II, 50th Anniv. A299

No. 1899: a, Chiang Kai-Shek. b, Gen. MacArthur. c, Gen. Chennault. d, Brigadier Orde C. Wingate. e, Gen. Stilwell. f, Field Marshall William Slim.

No. 1900: a, Map of Germany showing battle plan. b, Tanks, infantry advance. c, Red Army at gates of Berlin. d, German defenses smashed. e, Airstrikes on Berlin. f. German soldiers give up. g, Berlin falls to Russians. h, Germany surrenders.

$3, Plane, ship, Adm. Chester Nimitz. $6, Gen. Konev at command post outside Berlin, vert.

1995, July 20
1899 A299 $1.20 Sheet of 6, #a.-f. + label   7.00 7.00
1900 A299 $1.20 Sheet of 8, #a.-h. + label   10.50 10.50
Souvenir Sheets
1901 A299 $3 multicolored   4.00 4.00
1902 A299 $6 multicolored   6.00 6.00

UN, 50th Anniv. — A300

No. 1903: a, 75c, Earl of Halifax, signatures. b, 90c, Virginia Gildersleeve. c, $1.20, Harold Stassen.

$6, Franklin D. Roosevelt.

1995, July 20   Litho.   Perf. 14
1903 A300   Strip of 3, #a.-c.   2.25 3.00
Souvenir Sheet
1904 A300 $6 multicolored   4.25 4.25

No. 1903 is a continuous design.

FAO, 50th Anniv. — A301

No. 1905 — Street market scene: a, 75c, Two women, bananas. b, 90c, Women, crates, produce. c, $1.20, Women talking, one with box of food on head.

$6, Tractor.

1995, July 20
1905 A301   Strip of 3, #a.-c.   2.25 3.00
Souvenir Sheet
1906 A301 $6 multicolored   4.25 4.25

No. 1905 is a continuous design.

Rotary Intl., 90th Anniv. — A302

1995, July 20
1907 A302 $5 shown   4.50 4.50
Souvenir Sheet
1908 A302 $6 Natl. flag, Rotary emblem   4.50 4.50

Queen Mother, 95th Birthday — A303

No. 1909: a, Drawing. b, White & dark pink hat. c, Formal portrait. d, Blue green hat, dress.

$6, Light blue dress, pearls.

1995, July 20   *Perf. 13½x14*
1909 A303 $1.50 Strip or block of
    4, #a.-d.   5.75 5.75

Souvenir Sheet

1910 A303 $6 multicolored   5.75 5.75

No. 1909 was issued in sheets of 2 each.
Sheets of 1909-1910 exist with black frame
overprinted in margin, with text "In
Memoriam/1900-2002."

Ducks — A304

No. 1911: a, Ring-necked duck. b, Ruddy
duck. c, Green-winged teal (d). d, Wood duck.
e, Hooded merganser (f). f, Lesser scaup (g).
g, West Indian tree duck (h, k, l). h, Fulvous
whistling duck (l). i, Bahama pintail. j, Shoveler
(i). k, Masked duck (l). l, American widgeon.
$6, Blue-winged teal.

1995, Aug. 31   Litho.   *Perf. 14*
1911 A304 75c Sheet of 12,
    #a.-l.   12.00 12.00

Souvenir Sheet

1912 A304 $6 multicolored   7.50 7.50

Bees
A305

Designs: 90c, Mining bee. $1.20, Solitary
bee. $1.65, Leaf-cutter. $1.75, Honey bee.
$6, Solitary mining bee.

1995, Sept. 7
1913-1916 A305   Set of 4   7.50 7.50

Souvenir Sheet

1917 A305 $6 multicolored   6.50 6.50

Domestic Cats — A306

Designs: a, Somali. b, Persian. c, Devon
rex. d, Turkish angora. e, Himalayan. f, Maine
coon. g, Nonpedigree. h, American wirehair. i,
British shorthair. j, American curl. k, Black
nonpedigree. l, Birman.
$6, Siberian, vert.

1995, Sept. 7
1918 A306 45c Sheet of 12,
    #a.-l.   9.00 9.00

Souvenir Sheet

1919 A306 $6 multicolored   7.00 7.00

Tourism
A307

Stylized paintings depicting: a, Caring. b,
Marketing. c, Working. d, Enjoying life.

1995, July 31   Litho.   *Perf. 14*
1920 A307 $2 Sheet of 4, #a.-d.   6.75 6.75

Greenbay
Moravian Church,
150th
Anniv. — A308

Designs: 20c, 1st structure, wood & stone.
60c, 1st stone, concrete building, 3/67. 75c,
$2, Present structure. 90c, John A. Buckley,
1st minister of African descent. $1.20, John
Ephraim Knight, longest serving minister. $6,
Front of present structure.

1995, Sept. 4
1921-1926 A308   Set of 6   9.00 9.00

Souvenir Sheet

1927 A308 $6 multicolored   5.50 5.50

Flowers — A309

No. 1928: a, Narcissus. b, Camellia. c, Iris.
d, Tulip. e, Poppy. f, Peony. g, Magnolia. h,
Oriental lily. i, Rose. j, Pansy. k, Hydrangea. l,
Azaleas.
$6, Bird of paradise, calla lily.

1995, Sept. 7
1928 A309 75c Sheet of 12,
    #a.-l.   9.25 9.25

Souvenir Sheet

1929 A309 $6 multicolored   5.50 5.50

1995 Boy Scout Jamboree,
Netherlands — A310

No. 1930, $1.20: a, Explorer tent. b, Camper
tent. c, Wall tent.
No. 1931, $1.20: a, Trail tarp. b, Miner's. c,
Voyager.
No. 1932, $6, Scout with camping equip-
ment, vert. No. 1933, $6, Scout making camp
fire.

1995, Oct. 5   **Strips of 3, #a-c**
1930-1931 A310   Set of 2   9.00 9.00

Souvenir Sheets

1932-1933 A310   Set of 2   10.00 10.00

For overprints see Nos. 1963-1966.

Trains
A311

Designs: 35c, Gabon. 65c, Canadian. 75c,
US. 90c, British high-speed. No. 1938, $1.20,
French high-speed. No. 1939, $6, American
high-speed (Amtrak).
No. 1940: a, Australian diesel. b, Italian
high-speed. c, Thai diesel. d, US steam. e,
South African steam. f, Natal steam. g, US war
train. h, British steam. i, British steam, diff.
No. 1941, $6, Australian diesel, vert. No.
1942, $6, Asian steam, vert.

1995, Oct. 23   Litho.   *Perf. 14*
1934-1939 A311   Set of 6   10.50 10.50
1940 A311 $1.20 Sheet of 9,
    #a.-i.   12.50 12.50

Souvenir Sheets

1941-1942 A311   Set of 2   14.00 14.00

Birds — A312

No. 1943: a, Purple-thoated carib. b, Antillean crested hummingbird. c, Bananaquit (d).
d, Mangrove cuckoo. e, Troupial. f, Green-
throated carib (e, g). g, Yellow warbler (h). h,
Blue-hooded Euphonia. i, Scally-breasted
thrasher. j, Burrowing owl (i). k, Caribbean
crackle (k). l, Adelaide's warbler.
$6, Purple gallinule.

1995, Aug. 31
1943 A312 75c Sheet of 12,
    #a.-l.   11.50 11.50

Souvenir Sheet

1944 A312 $6 multicolored   7.50 7.50

Miniature Sheets of 9

Establishment of Nobel Prize Fund,
Cent. — A313

No. 1945, $1: a, S.Y. Agnon, literature,
1966. b, Kipling, literature, 1907. c, Aleksandr
Solzhenitsyn, literature, 1970. d, Jack Stein-
berger, physics, 1988. e, Andrei Sakharov,
peace, 1975. f, Otto Stern, physics, 1943. g,
Steinbeck, literature, 1962. h, Nadine
Gordimer, literature, 1991. i, Faulkner, literature, 1949.
No. 1946, $1: a, Hammarskjold, peace,
1961. b, Georg Wittig, chemistry, 1979. c, Wilhelm Ostwald, chemistry, 1909. d, Koch, physiology or medicine, 1945. e, Karl Ziegler,
chemistry, 1963. f, Fleming, physiology or
medicine, 1945. g, Hermann Staudinger,
chemistry, 1953. h, Manfred Eigen, chemistry,
1967. i, Arno Penzias, physics, 1978.
No. 1947, $6, Elie Wiesel, peace, 1986,
vert. No. 1948, $6, Dalai Lama, peace, 1989,
vert.

Sheets of 9, #a-i, + label
1995, Nov. 8
1945-1946 A313   Set of 2   20.00 20.00

Souvenir Sheets

1947-1948 A313   Set of 2   10.00 10.00

Christmas
A314

Details or entire paintings: 15c, Rest on the
Flight into Egypt, by Veronese. 35c, Madonna
with The Child, by Van Dyck. 65c, Sacred
Conversation Piece, by Veronese. 75c, Vision
of Saint Anthony, by Van Dyck. 90c, The Virgin

and the Infant, by Van Eyck. No. 1954, The
Immaculate Conception, by Tiepolo.
$5, Christ Appearing to His Mother, by Van
Der Weyden. $6, Infant Jesus and the Young
St. John, by Murillo.

1995, Dec. 18   Litho.   *Perf. 13½x14*
1949-1954 A314   Set of 6   7.00 7.00

Souvenir Sheets

1955 A314 $5 multicolored   4.00 4.00
1956 A314 $6 multicolored   5.50 5.50

Elvis Presley
(1935-77)
A315

Nos. 1957-1958, Various portraits depicting
Presley's life.

1995, Dec. 8   *Perf. 14*
1957 A315 $1 Sheet of 9, #a.-
    i.   11.00 11.00

Souvenir Sheet

1958 A315 $6 multicolored   7.25 7.25

John Lennon
(1940-80),
Entertainer — A316

45c, 50c, 65c, 75c, Various portraits of
Lennon.

1995, Dec. 8
1959-1962 A316   Set of 4   3.00 3.00

Souvenir Sheet

1962A A316 $6 like 75c   6.75 6.75

Nos. 1959-1962 were each issued in miniature sheets of 16.
No. 1962A has a continuous design.

Nos. 1930-1933 Ovptd.

1995, Dec. 14
1963 A310 $1.20 Strip of 3, #a-c
    (#1930)   3.50 3.50
1964 A310 $1.20 Strip of 3, #a-c
    (#1931)   3.50 3.50

Souvenir Sheets

1965 A310 $6 multi (#1932)   6.50 6.50
1966 A310 $6 multi (#1933)   6.50 6.50

Size and location of overprint varies.

Mushrooms — A317

No. 1967, 75c: a, Hygrophoropsis auran-
tiaca. b, Hygrophorus bakerensis. c,
Hygrophorus conicus. d, Hygrophorus
miniatus.
No. 1968, 75c: a, Suillus brevipes. b, Suillus
luteus. c, Suillus granulatus. d, Suillus
caerulescens.
No. 1969, $6, Conocybe filaris. No. 1970,
$6, Hygrocybe flavescens.

1996, Apr. 22 Litho. Perf. 14
Strips of 4, #a-d
1967-1968 A317 Set of 2 6.25 6.25
Souvenir Sheets
1969-1970 A317 Set of 2 9.00 9.00

Nos. 1967-1968 were each issued in sheets of 12 stamps.

Sailing Ships A318

Designs: 15c, Resolution. 25c, Mayflower. 45c, Santa Maria. No. 1970D, 75c, Aemilia, Holland, 1630. No. 1970E, 75c, Sovereign of the Seas, England, 1637. 90c, HMS Victory, England, 1765.
No. 1971 — Battleships: a, Aemila, Holland, 1630. b, Sovereign of the Seas, England, 1637. c, Royal Louis, France, 1692. d, HMS Royal George, England, 1715. e, Le Protecteur, France, 1761. f, HMS Victory, England, 1765.
No. 1972 — Ships of exploration: a, Santa Maria. b, Victoria. c, Golden Hinde. d, Mayflower. e, Griffin. f, Resolution.
No. 1973, $6, Grande Hermine. No. 1974, $6 USS Constitution, 1797.

1996, Apr. 25
1970A-1970F A318 Set of 6 3.50 3.50
1971 A318 $1.20 Sheet of 6, #a.-f. 8.50 8.50
1972 A318 $1.50 Sheet of 6, #a.-f. 10.00 10.00
Souvenir Sheets
1973-1974 A318 Set of 2 11.50 11.50

1996 Summer Olympics, Atlanta A319

Designs: 65c, Florence Griffith Joyner, women's track, vert. 75c, Olympic Stadium, Seoul, 1988. 90c, Allison Jolly, yachting. $1.20, 2000m Tandem cycling.
No. 1979, 90c — Medalists: a, Wolfgang Nordwig, pole vault. b, Shirley Strong, women's 100m hurdles. c, Sergei Bubka, pole vault. d, Filbert Bayi, 3000m steeplechase. e, Victor Saneyev, triple jump. f, Silke Renk, women's javelin. g, Daley Thompson, decathlon. h, Bob Richards, pole vault. i, Parry O'Brien, shot put.
No. 1980, 90c — Diving medalists: a, Ingrid Kramer, women's platform. b, Kelly McCormick, women's springboard. c, Gary Tobian, men's springboard. d, Greg Louganis, men's diving. e, Michelle Mitchell, women's platform. f, Zhou Jihong, women's platform. g, Wendy Wyland, women's platform. h, Xu Yanmei, women's platform. i, Fu Mingxia, women's platform.
$5, Bill Toomey, decathlon. $6, Mark Lenzi, men's springboard.

1996, May 6
1975-1978 A319 Set of 4 2.50 2.50
Sheets of 9, #a-i
1979-1980 A319 90c Set of 2 12.50 12.50
Souvenir Sheets
1981 A319 $5 multicolored 4.50 4.50
1982 A319 $6 multicolored 5.50 5.50

Sea Birds A320

No. 1983, 75c: a, Black skimmer. b, Black-capped petrel. c, Sooty tern. d, Royal tern.
No. 1984, 75c: a, Pomarina jaegger. b, White-tailed tropicbird. c, Northern gannet. d, Laughing gull.
$5, Great frigatebird. $6, Brown pelican.

1996, May 13
Vertical Strips of 4, #a-d
1983-1984 A320 Set of 2 5.50 5.50
Souvenir Sheets
1985 A320 $5 multicolored 4.50 4.50
1986 A320 $6 multicolored 5.50 5.50

Nos. 1983-1984 were each issued in sheets of 12 stamps with each strip in sheet having a different order.

Disney Characters In Scenes from Jules Verne's Science Fiction Novels — A321

Designs: 1c, Around the World in Eighty Days. 2c, Journey to the Center of the Earth. 5c, Michel Strogoff. 10c, From the Earth to the Moon. 15c, Five Weeks in a Balloon. 20c, Around the World in Eighty Days, diff. $1, The Mysterious Island. $2, From the Earth to the Moon, diff. $3, Captain Grant's Children. $5, Twenty Thousand Leagues Under the Sea.
No. 1997, $6, Twenty Thousand Leagues Under the Sea, diff. No. 1998, $6, Journey to the Center of the Earth, diff.

1996, June 6 Litho. Perf. 14x13½
1987-1996 A321 Set of 10 12.50 12.50
Souvenir Sheets
1997-1998 A321 Set of 2 12.50 12.50

Bruce Lee (1940-73), Martial Arts Expert — A322

Various portraits.

1996, June 13 Perf. 14
1999 A322 75c Sheet of 9, #a.-i. 6.50 6.50
Souvenir Sheet
2000 A322 $5 multicolored 5.75 5.75
China '96 (No. 1999).

Queen Elizabeth II, 70th Birthday — A323

Designs: a, In blue dress, pearls. b, Carrying bouquet of flowers. c, In uniform.
$6, Painting as younger woman.

1996, July 17 Perf. 13½x14
2001 A323 $2 Strip of 3, #a.-c. 4.00 4.00
Souvenir Sheet
2002 A323 $6 multicolored 4.75 4.75
No. 2001 was issued in sheets of 9 stamps.

Traditional Cavalry — A324

No. 2003: a, Ancient Egyptian. b, 13th cent. English. c, 16th cent. Spanish. d, 18th cent. Chinese.
$6, 19th cent. French.

1996, July 24 Litho. Perf. 14
2003 A324 60c Block of 4, #a.-d. 2.50 2.50
Souvenir Sheet
2004 A324 $6 multicolored 4.75 4.75
No. 2003 was issued in sheets of 16 stamps.

UNICEF, 50th Anniv. — A325

Designs: 75c, Girl. 90c, Children. $1.20, Woman holding baby. $6, Girl, diff.

1996, July 30
2005-2007 A325 Set of 3 3.00 3.00
Souvenir Sheet
2008 A325 $6 multicolored 4.50 4.50

Jerusalem, 3000th Anniv. — A326

Site, flower: 75c, Tomb of Zachariah, verbascum sinuatum. 90c, Pool of Siloam, hyacinthus orientalis. $1.20, Hurva Synagogue, ranunculus asiaticus.
$6, Model of Herod's Temple.

1996, July 30
2009-2011 A326 Set of 3 2.25 2.25
Souvenir Sheet
2012 A326 $6 multicolored 6.50 6.50

Radio, Cent. A327

Entertainers: 65c, Kate Smith. 75c, Dinah Shore. 90c, Rudy Vallee. $1.20, Bing Crosby. $6, Jo Stafford.

1996, July 30
2013-2016 A327 Set of 4 3.50 3.50
Souvenir Sheet
2017 A327 $6 multicolored 4.50 4.50

Christmas A328

Details or entire paintings, by Filippo Lippi: 60c, Madonna Enthroned. 90c, Adoration of the Child and Saints. $1, Annunciation. $1.20, Birth of the Virgin. $1.60, Adoration of the Child. $1.75, Madonna and Child.
No. 2024, $6, Madonna and Child, diff. No. 2025, $6, Circumcision.

1996, Nov. 25 Perf. 13½x14
2018-2023 A328 Set of 6 7.50 7.50
Souvenir Sheets
2024-2025 A328 Set of 2 10.50 10.50

Disney Pals — A329

Designs: 1c, Goofy, Wilbur. 2c, Donald, Goofy. 5c, Donald, Panchito, Jose Carioca. 10c, Mickey, Goofy. 15c, Dale, Chip. 20c, Pluto, Mickey. $1, Daisy, Minnie at ice cream shop. $2, Daisy, Minnie. $3, Gus Goose, Donald.
No. 2035, $6, Donald, vert. No. 2036, $6, Goofy.

1997, Feb. 17 Litho. Perf. 14x13½
2026-2034 A329 Set of 9 5.50 5.50
Souvenir Sheets
Perf. 13½x14, 14x13½
2035-2036 A329 Set of 2 9.50 9.50

Salute to Broadway A330

No. 2037 — Stars, show: a, Robert Preston, The Music Man. b, Michael Crawford, Phantom of the Opera. c, Zero Mostel, Fiddler on the Roof. d, Patti Lupone, Evita. e, Raul Julia,

Threepenny Opera. f, Mary Martin, South Pacific. g, Carol Channing, Hello Dolly. h, Yul Brynner, The King and I. i, Julie Andrews, My Fair Lady.
$6, Mickey Rooney, Sugar Babies.

1997 *Perf. 14*
2037 A330 $1 Sheet of 9, #a.-i. 8.00 8.00
Souvenir Sheet
2038 A330 $6 multicolored 5.50 5.50

Butterflies — A331

Designs: 90c, Charaxes porthos. $1.20, Aethiopana honorius. $1.60, Charaxes hadrianus. $1.75, Precis westermanni.
No. 2043, $1.10: a, Charaxes protoclea. b, Byblia ilithyia. c, Black-headed tchagra (bird). d, Charaxes nobilis. e, Pseudacraea boisduvali. f, Charaxes smaragdalis. g, Charaxes lasti. h, Pseudacraea poggei. i, Graphium colonna.
No. 2044, $1.10: a, Carmine bee-eater (bird). b, Pseudacraea eurytus. c, Hypolimnas monteironis. d, Charaxes anticlea. e, Graphium leonidas. f, Graphium illyris. g, Nepheronia argia. h, Graphium policenes. i, Papilio dardanus.
No. 2045, $6, Euxanthe tiberius, horiz. No. 2046, $6, Charaxes lactitinctus, horiz. No. 2047, $6, Euphaedra neophron.

1997, Mar. 10
2039-2042 A331 Set of 4 5.50 5.50
Sheets of 9, #a-i
2043-2044 A331 Set of 2 18.50 18.50
Souvenir Sheets
2045-2047 A331 Set of 3 14.50 14.50

UNESCO, 50th Anniv. — A332

World Heritage Sites: 60c, Convent of the Companions of Jesus, Morelia, Mexico. 90c, Fortress, San Lorenzo, Panama, vert. $1, Canaima Natl. Park, Venezuela, vert. $1.20, Huascarán Natl. Park, Peru, vert. $1.60, Church of San Francisco, Guatemala, vert. $1.75, Santo Domingo, Dominican Republic, vert.
No. 2054, vert, each $1.10: a-c, Guanajuato, Mexico. d, Jesuit missions of the Chiquitos, Bolivia. e, Huascarán Natl. Park, Peru. f, Jesuit missions, La Santisima, Paraguay. g, Cartagena, Colombia. h, Old Havana fortification, Cuba.
No. 2055, each $1.65: a, Tikal Natl. Park, Guatemala. b, Rio Platano Reserve, Honduras. c, Ruins of Copán, Honduras. d, Church of El Carmen, Antigua, Guatemala. e, Teotihuacán, Mexico.
No. 2056, $6, Teotihuacán, Mexico, diff. No. 2057, $6, Tikal Natl. Park, Guatemala, diff.

1997, Apr. 10 *Litho.* *Perf. 14*
2048-2053 A332 Set of 6 4.75 4.75
2054 A332 Sheet of 8, #a.-h.
+ label 8.00 8.00
2055 A332 Sheet of 5, #a.-e.
+ label 7.50 7.50
Souvenir Sheets
2056-2057 A332 Set of 2 9.75 9.75

Endangered Species — A333

No. 2058, each $1.20: a, Red bishop. b, Yellow baboon. c, Superb starling. d, Ratel. e, Hunting dog. f, Serval.
No. 2059, each $1.65: a, Okapi. b, Giant forest squirrel. c, Masked weaver. d, Common genet. e, Yellow-billed stork. f, Red-headed agama.
No. 2060, $6, Malachite kingfisher. No. 2061, $6, Gray crowned crane. No. 2062, $6, Bat-eared fox.

1997, Apr. 24
2058 A333 Sheet of 6, #a.-f. 7.50 7.50
2059 A333 Sheet of 6, #a.-f. 9.00 9.00
Souvenir Sheets
2060-2062 A333 Set of 3 17.00 17.00

Charlie Chaplin (1889-1977), Comedian, Actor — A334

Various portraits.

1997, Feb. 24 *Litho.* *Perf. 14*
2063 A334 $1 Sheet of 9, #a.-i. 6.75 6.75
Souvenir Sheet
2064 A334 $6 multicolored 5.25 5.25

Paul P. Harris (1868-1947), Founder of Rotary, Intl. — A335

Designs: $1.75, Service above self, James Grant, Ivory Coast, 1994, portrait of Harris.
$6, Group study exchange, New Zealand.

1997, June 12 *Litho.* *Perf. 14*
2065 A335 $1.75 multicolored 1.60 1.60
Souvenir Sheet
2066 A335 $6 multicolored 4.50 4.50

Heinrich von Stephan (1831-97) A336

No. 2067, each $1.75, Portrait of Von Stephan and: a, Kaiser Wilhelm I. b, UPU emblem. c, Pigeon Post.
$6, Von Stephan, Basel messenger, 1400's.

1997, June 12
2067 A336 Sheet of 3, #a.-c. 3.50 3.50
Souvenir Sheet
2068 A336 $6 multicolored 5.00 5.00
PACIFIC 97.

Queen Elizabeth II, Prince Philip, 50th Wedding Anniv. A337

No. 2069: a, Queen. b, Royal arms. c, Queen, Prince in royal attire. d, Queen, King riding in open carriage. e, Balmoral Castle. f, Prince Philip.
$6, Early portrait of Queen, King in royal attire.

1997, June 12
2069 A337 $1 Sheet of 6, #a.-f. 6.25 6.25
Souvenir Sheet
2070 A337 $6 multicolored 5.25 5.25

Grimm's Fairy Tales A338

Scenes from "Cinderella", each $1.75: No. 2071: a, Mother, stepsisters. b, Cinderella, fairy godmother. c, Cinderella, Prince Charming.
$6, Prince trying shoe on Cinderella.

1997, June 13 *Perf. 13½x14*
2071 A338 Sheet of 3, #a.-c. 4.75 4.75
Souvenir Sheet
2072 A338 $6 multicolored 5.25 5.25

Chernobyl Disaster, 10th Anniv. A339

Designs: $1.65, UNESCO. $2, Chabad's Children of Chernobyl.

1997, June 12
2073 A339 $1.65 multicolored 1.50 1.50
2074 A339 $2 multicolored 1.75 1.75

Mushrooms — A340

Designs: 45c, Marasmius rotula. 65c, Cantharellus cibarius. 70c, Lepiota cristata. 90c, Auricularia mesenterica. $1, Pholiota alnicola. $1.65, Leccinum aurantiacum.
No. 2081, each $1.75: a, Entoloma serrulatum. b, Panaeolus sphinctrinus. c, Volvariella bombycina. d, Conocybe percincta. e, Pluteus cervinus. f, Russula foetens.
No. 2082, $6, Panellus serotinus. No. 2083, $6, Amanita cothurnata.

1997, Aug. 12 *Litho.* *Perf. 14*
2075-2080 A340 Set of 6 4.00 4.00

2081 A340 Sheet of 6, #a.-f. 8.00 8.00
Souvenir Sheets
2082-2083 A340 Set of 2 10.00 10.00

Orchids — A341

Designs: 45c, Odontoglossum cervantesii. 65c, Medford star. 75c, Motes resplendent. 90c, Debutante. $1, Apple blossom. $2, Dendrobium.
No. 2090, $1.65: a, Angel lace. b, Precious stones. c, Orange theope butterfly. d, Promenaea xanthina. e, Lycaste macrobulbon. f, Amesiella philippinensis. g, Machu Picchu. h, Zuma urchin.
No. 2091, $1.65: a, Sophia Martin. b, Dogface butterfly. c, Mini purple. d, Showgirl. e, Mem. Dorothy Bertsch. f, Black II. g, Leeanum. h, Paphiopedilum macranthum.
No. 2092, $6, Seine. No. 2093, $6, Paphiopedilum gratrixianum.

1997, Aug. 19 *Litho.* *Perf. 14*
2084-2089 A341 Set of 6 5.75 5.75
Sheets of 8, #a-h
2090-2091 A341 Set of 2 17.00 17.00
Souvenir Sheets
2092-2093 A341 Set of 2 10.00 10.00

1998 World Cup Soccer Championships, France — A342

Designs: 60c, Maradona, Argentina, 1986. 75c, Fritz Walter, W. Germany, 1954. 90c, Zoff, Italy, 1982. $1.20, Moore, England, 1966. $1.65, Alberto, Brazil, 1970. $1.75, Matthäus, W. Germany.
No. 2100, vert: a, Ademir, Brazil, 1950. b, Eusebio, Portugal, 1966. c, Fontaine, France, 1958. d, Schillaci, Italy, 1990. e, Leonidas, Brazil, 1938. f, Stabile, Argentina, 1930. g, Nejedly, Czechoslovakia, 1934. h, Muller, W. Germany, 1970.
No. 2101, $6, Players, W. Germany, 1990. No. 2102, $6, Bebeto, Brazil, vert.

1997, Oct. 6 *Litho.* *Perf. 14*
2094-2099 A342 Set of 6 5.25 5.25
2100 A342 $1 Sheet of 8, #a.-
h., + label 5.25 5.25
Souvenir Sheets
2101-2102 A342 Set of 2 8.50 8.50

Domestic Animals A343

No. 2103, $1.65 — Dogs: a, Dachshund. b, Staffordshire terrier. c, Sharpei. d, Beagle. e, Norfolk terrier. f, Golden retriever.
No. 2104, $1.65 — Cats: a, Scottish fold. b, Japanese bobtail. c, Tabby manx. d, Bicolor American shorthair. e, Sorrel abyssinian. f, Himalayan blue point.
No. 2105, $6, Siberian husky, vert. No. 2106, $6, Red tabby American shorthair kitten, vert.

1997, Oct. 27 *Litho.* *Perf. 14*
Sheets of 6, #a-f
2103-2104 A343 Set of 2 18.00 18.00
Souvenir Sheets
2105-2106 A343 Set of 2 10.00 10.00

Early Trains
A344

No. 2107, $1.65: a, Original Trevithick drawing, 1804. b, "Puffing Billy," William Hedley, 1860. c, Crampton locomotive, Northern Railway, France, 1858. d, Twenty-five ton locomotive, Lawrence Machine Shop, 1860's. e, First locomotive, "Mississippi," built in England. f, "Coppernob," locomotive by Edward Bury, Furness Railway.

No. 2108, $1.65: a, "Jenny Lind," by David Joy for E.B. Wilson. b, "Atlantic" type locomotive, by Schenectady Locomotive Works, 1899. c, British built tank engine, Japan, by Kisons of Leeds, 1881. d, Express freight locomotive, 4-8-2 type, Pennsylvania Railroad. e, Four-cylinder locomotive, by Karl Golsdorf, Austria. f, "E" series 0-10-0 locomotive, produced by Lugansk Works, Russia, 1930.

No. 2109, $6, "Patente" George Stephenson, 1843. No. 2110, $6, Brunel's Trestle, Lynher River.

1997, Nov. 10   Sheets of 6, #a-f
2107-2108   A344   Set of 2   19.00 19.00
Souvenir Sheets
2109-2110   A344   Set of 2   10.00 10.00

Christmas
A345

Entire paintings or details: 15c, The Angel Leaving Tobias and His Family, by Rembrandt. 25c, The Resurrection, by Martin Knoller. 60c, Astronomy, by Raphael. 75c, Music-making Angel, by Melozzo da Forli. 90c, Amor, by Parmigianino. $1.20, Madonna and Child with Saints John the Baptist, Anthony, Stephen and Jerome, by Rosso Fiorentino.

No. 2117, $6, The Portinari Altarpiece, by Hugo Van Der Goes. No. 2118, $6, The Wedding of Tobiolo, by Gianantonio and Francesco Guardi.

1997, Dec. 2   Litho.   Perf. 14
2111-2116   A345 $6 Set of 6   3.75 3.75
Souvenir Sheets
2117-2118   A345 $6 Set of 2   9.00 9.00

Diana, Princess of Wales (1961-97) — A346

Various portraits, color of sheet margin: No. 2119, $1.65, Pale green. No. 2120, $1.65, Pale pink.
No. 2121, $6,With her sons (in margin). No. 2122, $6, With Pope John Paul II (in margin).

1998, Jan. 19   Litho.   Perf. 14
Sheets of 6, #a-f
2119-2120   A346   Set of 2   12.50 12.50
Souvenir Sheets
2121-2122   A346   Set of 2   9.00 9.00

Fish
A347

Designs: 75c, Yellow damselfish. 90c, Barred hamlet. $1, Jewelfish. $1.20, Bluehead wrasse. $1.50, Queen angelfish. $1.75, Queen triggerfish.
No. 2129, $1.65: a, Jack-knife fish. b, Cuban hogfish. c, Sergeant major. d, Neon goby. e, Jawfish. f, Flamefish.
No. 2130, $1.65: a, Rock beauty. b, Yellowtail snapper. c, Creole wrasse. d, Slender filefish. e, Squirrel fish. f, Fairy basslet.
No. 2131, $6, Black-capped gramma. No. 2132, $6, Porkfish.

1998, Feb. 19
2123-2128   A347   Set of 6   4.25 4.25
Sheets of 6, #a-f
2129-2130   A347   Set of 2   13.00 13.00
Souvenir Sheets
2131-2132   A347   Set of 2   10.00 10.00

Cedar Hall Moravian Church, 175th Anniv.
A348

Designs: 20c, First church, manse, 1822-40. 45c, Cedar Hall School, 1840. 75c, Hugh A. King, former minister. 90c, Present structure. $1.20, Water tank, 1822. $2, Former manse demolished, 1978.
$6, Present structure, diff.

1998, Mar. 16   Litho.   Perf. 14
2133-2138   A348   Set of 6   4.00 4.00
Souvenir Sheet
2139   A348 $6 multicolored   4.75 4.75
No. 2139 contains one 50x37mm stamp.

Lighthouses — A349

Lighthouse, location: 45c, Trinity, Europa Point, Gibraltar, vert. 65c, Tierra Del Fuego, Argentina. 75c, Point Loma, California, US. 90c, Groenpoint, South Africa, vert. $1, Youghal, County Cork, Ireland, vert. $1.20, Launceston, Tasmania, Australia, vert. $1.65, Point Abino, Ontario, Canada. $1.75, Great Inagua, Bahamas.
$6, Capa Hatteras, North Carolina, US.

1998, Apr. 20
2140-2147   A349   Set of 8   8.00 8.00
Souvenir Sheet
2148   A349 $6 multi, vert.   7.75 7.75

Winnie the Pooh
A350

No. 2149, $1: a, Pooh, Tigger in January. b, Pooh, Piglet in February. c, Piglet in March. d, Tigger, Pooh, Piglet in April. e, Kanga, Roo in May. f, Pooh, Owl in June.
No. 2150, $1,: a, Pooh, Eeyore, Tigger, Piglet in July. b, Pooh, Piglet in August. c, Christopher Robin in September. d, Eeyore in October. e, Pooh, Rabbit in November. f, Pooh, Piglet in December.
No. 2151, $6, Pooh, Rabbit holding blanket, Spring. No. 2152, $6, Pooh holding hand to mouth, Summer. No. 2153, $6, Pooh holding rake, Fall. No. 2154, $6, Eeyore, Pooh, Winter.

1998, May 11   Litho.   Perf. 13½x14
Sheets of 6, #a-f
2149-2150   A350   Set of 2   13.50 13.50
Souvenir Sheet
2151-2154   A350   Set of 4   19.00 19.00

Thomas Oliver Robinson Memorial High School, Cent.
A351

Designs: 20c, $6, Nellie Robinson (1880-1972), founder, vert. 45c, School picture, 1985. 65c, Former building, 1930-49. 75c, Students with present headmistress, Natalie Hurst. 90c, Ina Loving (1908-96), educator, vert. $1.20, Present building, 1950.

1998, July 23   Litho.   Perf. 14
2155-2160   A351   Set of 6   4.00 4.00
Souvenir Sheet
2161   A351 $6 multicolored   4.00 4.00
No. 2161 is a continuous design.

Intl. Year of the Ocean
A352

No. 2162 — Marine life, "20,000 Leagues Under the Sea": a, Spotted eagle ray. b, Manta ray. c, Hawksbill turtle. d, Jellyfish. e, Queen angelfish. f, Octopus. g, Emperor angelfish. h, Regal angelfish. i, Porkfish. j, Raccoon butterfly fish. k, Atlantic barracuda. l, Sea horse. m, Nautilus. n, Trumpet fish. o, White tip shark. p, Spanish galleon. q, Black tip shark. r, Longnosed butterfly fish. s, Green moray eel. t, Captain Nemo. u, Treasure chest. v, Hammerhead shark. w, Divers. x, Lion fish. y, Clown fish.
No. 2163 — Wildlife and birds: a, Maroon tailed conure. b, Cocoi heron. c, Common tern. d, Rainbow lorikeet. e, Saddleback butterfly fish. f, Goatfish, cat shark. g, Blue shark, stingray. h, Majestic snapper. i, Nassau grouper. j, Black-cap gramma, blue tang. k, Stingrays. l, Stingrays, giant starfish.
No. 2164, $6, Fiddler ray. No. 2165, $6, Humpback whale.

1998, Aug. 17
2162   A352 40c Sheet of 25, #a.-
              y.   8.25 8.25
2163   A352 75c Sheet of 12, #a.-l. 7.75 7.75
Souvenir Sheets
2164-2165   A352   Set of 2   9.75 9.75

Ships
A353

No. 2166, each $1.75: a, Savannah. b, Viking ship. c, Greek warship.
No. 2167, each $1.75: a, Clipper. b, Dhow. c, Fishing cat.
No. 2168, $6, Dory, vert. No. 2169, $6, Baltimore clipper. No. 2170, $6, English warship, 13th cent.

1998, Aug. 18   Perf. 14x14½
Sheets of 3, #a-c
2166-2167   A353   Set of 2   7.25 7.25
Souvenir Sheets
Perf. 14
2168-2170   A353 $6 Set of 3 15.00 15.00

CARICOM, 25th Anniv. — A354

1998, Aug. 20   Litho.   Perf. 13½
2171   A354 $1 multicolored   1.40 1.40

Antique Automobiles — A355

No. 2172 $1.65: a, 1911 Torpedo. b, 1913 Mercedes 22. c, 1920 Rover. d, 1956 Mercedes Benz. e, 1934 Packard V12. f, 1924 Opel.
No. 2173, $1.65 — Fords: a, 1896. b, 1903 Model A. c, 1928 Model T. d, 1922 Model T. e, 1929 Blackhawk. f, 1934 Sedan.
No. 2174, $6, 1908 Ford. No. 2175, $6, 1929 Ford.

1998, Sept. 1   Perf. 14
Sheets of 6, #a-f
2172-2173   A355   Set of 2   15.00 15.00
Souvenir Sheets
2174-2175   A355   Set of 2   9.00 9.00
Nos. 2174-2175 each contain one 60x40mm stamp.

Aircraft
A356

No. 2176, $1.65: a, NASA Space Shuttle. b, Saab Grippen. c, Eurofighter EF2000. d, Sukhoi SU 27. e, Northrop B-2. f, Lockheed F-117 Nighthawk.
No. 2177, $1.65: a, Lockheed-Boeing General Dynamics Yf-22. b, Dassault-Breguet Rafale BO 1. c, MiG 29. d, Dassault-Breguet Mirage 2000D. e, Rockwell B-1B Lancer. f, McDonnell-Douglas C-17A.
No. 2178, $6, Sukhoi SU 35. No. 2179, $6, F-18 Hornet.

1998, Sept. 21   Sheets of 6, #a-f
2176-2177   A356   Set of 2   14.50 14.50
Souvenir Sheets
2178-2179   A356   Set of 2   10.50 10.50

Inventors and Inventions — A357

No. 2180 $1: a, Rudolf Diesel (1858-1913). b, Internal combustion, diesel engines. c, Zeppelin war balloon, Intrepid. d, Ferdinand von Zeppelin (1838-1917). e, Wilhelm Conrad Röntgen (1845-1923). f, X-ray machine. g, Saturn rocket. h, Wernher von Braun (1912-77).
No. 2181, $1: a, Carl Benz (1844-1929). b, Internal combustion engine, automobile. c, Atomic bomb. d, Albert Einstein. e, Leopold Godowsky, Jr. (1901-83) and Leopold Damrosch Mannes (1899-1964). f, Kodachrome film. g, First turbo jet airplane. h, Hans Pabst von Ohain (1911-98).
No. 2182, $6, Hans Geiger (1882-1945), inventor of the Geiger counter. No. 2183, $6, William Shockley (1910-89), developer of transistors.

1998, Nov. 10   Litho.   Perf. 14
Sheets of 8, #a-h
2180-2181   A357   Set of 2   16.50 16.50
Souvenir Sheets
2182-2183   A357   Set of 2   10.50 10.50
Nos. 2180b-2180c, 2180f-2180g, 2181b-2181c, 2181f-2181g are 53x38mm.

Diana, Princess of Wales (1961-97) — A358

Designs: a, Peach bar with country name on left side. b, Peach bar with country name on right side.

1998, Nov. 18
2184 A358 $1.20 Pair, #a.-b.   1.10 1.10
No. 2184 was printed in sheets containing 3 pairs.

Gandhi — A359

Portraits: 90c, Up close, later years. $1, Seated with hands clasped. $1.20, Up close, early years. $1.65, Primary school, Rajkot, age 7. $6, With stick, walking with boy (in margin).

1998, Nov. 18
2185-2188 A359   Set of 4   6.00 6.00
Souvenir Sheet
2189 A359 $6 multicolored   5.00 5.00

Picasso — A360

Paintings: $1.20, Figures on the Seashore, 1931, horiz. $1.65, Three Figures Under a Tree, 1907. $1.75, Two Women Running on the Beach, 1922, horiz.
$6, Bullfight, 1900, horiz.

1998, Nov. 18
2190-2192 A360   Set of 3   3.00 3.00
Souvenir Sheet
2193 A360 $6 multicolored   5.00 5.00

1998 World Scouting Jamboree, Chile A361

90c, Handshake. $1, Scouts hiking. $1.20, Sign.
$6, Lord Baden-Powell.

1998, Oct. 8   Litho.   Perf. 14
2194-2196 A361   Set of 3   2.25 2.25
Souvenir Sheet
2197 A361 $6 multicolored   4.50 4.50

Organization of American States, 50th Anniv. A362

1998, Nov. 18   Perf. 13½
2198 A362 $1 multicolored   .80 .80

Enzo Ferrari (1898-1988), Automobile Manufacturer — A363

No. 2199, each $1.75: a, Top view of Dino 246 GT-GTS. b, Front view of Dino 246 GT-GTS. c, 1977 365 GT4 BB.
$6, Dino 246 GT GTS.

1998, Nov. 18   Perf. 14
2199 A363   Sheet of 3, #a.-c.   8.00 8.00
Souvenir Sheet
2200 A363 $6 multicolored   8.00 8.00
No. 2200 contains one 92x35mm stamp.

Royal Air Force, 80th Anniv. A364

No. 2201, each $1.75: a, McDonnell Douglas Phantom FGR1. b, Sepecat Jaguar GR1A. c, Panavia Tornado F3. d, McDonnell Douglas Phantom FGR2.
No. 2202, $6, Eurofighter 2000, Hurricane. No. 2203, $6, Hawk, biplane.

1998, Nov. 18
2201 A364   Sheet of 4, #a.-d.   6.25 6.25
Souvenir Sheets
2202-2203 A364   Set of 2   11.00 11.00

Sea Birds A365

Designs: 15c, Brown pelican. 25c, Dunlin. 45c, Atlantic puffin. 90c, Pied cormorant.
No. 2208: a, King eider. b, Inca tern. c, Dovekie. d, Ross's bull. e, Brown noddy. f, Marbled murrelet. g, Northern gannet. h, Razorbill. i, Long-tailed jaeger. j, Black guillemot. k, Whimbrel. l, Oystercatcher.
No. 2209, $6, Rhynchops niger. No. 2210, $6, Diomedea exulans.

1998, Nov. 24
2204-2207 A365   Set of 4   2.00 2.00
2208 A365 75c Sheet of 12, #a.-l. 8.50 8.50
Souvenir Sheets
2209-2210 A365   Set of 2   11.00 11.00

Christmas A366

Dogs with Christmas decorations: 15c, Border collie. 25c, Dalmatian. 65c, Weimaraner.

75c, Scottish terrier. 90c, Long-haired dachshund. $1.20, Golden retriever. $2, Pekingese.
No. 2218, $6, Dalmatian, diff. No. 2219, $6, Jack Russell terrier.

1998, Dec. 10
2211-2217 A366   Set of 7   7.00 7.00
Souvenir Sheet
2218-2219 A366   Set of 2   9.25 9.25

Disney Characters in Water Sports A367

No. 2220, $1 — Water skiing: a, Goofy, maroon skis. b, Mickey. c, Goofy, Mickey. d, Donald. e, Goofy, blue skis. f, Minnie.
No. 2221, $1 — Surfing: a, Goofy running with board. b, Mickey. c, Donald holding board. d, Donald, riding board. e, Minnie. f, Goofy in water.
No. 2221G, Sailing & sailboarding: h, Mickey wearing cap. i, Mickey, Goofy, counterbalancing boat. j, Goofy sailboarding. k, Mickey, seagull overhead. l, Goofy puffing at sail. m, Mickey sailboarding.
No. 2222, Mickey. No. 2223, Minnie. No. 2224, Goofy. No. 2225, Donald.

1999, Jan. 11   Litho.   Perf. 13½x14
Sheets of 6, #a-f
2220-2221 A367   Set of 2   11.00 11.00
2221G A367 $1 Sheet of 6,
#h.-m.   5.50 5.50
Souvenir Sheets
2222-2225 A367   Set of 4   18.50 18.50
Mickey Mouse, 70th anniv.

Hell's Gate Steel Orchestra, 50th Anniv. A368

Designs: 20c, Nelson's Dockyard, 1996. 60c, Holiday Inn, Rochester, New York, 1992. 75c, World's Fair, 1964, Eustace Henry (AKA Manning). $1.20, Alston Henry playing double tenor.
No. 2231, $4, Like #2229, vert. No. 2232, $4, The early years, vert.

1999, Feb. 1   Litho.   Perf. 14
2226-2230 A368   Set of 5   3.25 3.25
Souvenir Sheets
2231-2232 A368   Set of 2   6.75 6.75

Flowers A369

Designs, vert: 60c, Tulip. 75c, Fuschia. $1.20, Calla lily. $1.65, Sweet pea.
No. 2237: a, Morning glory. b, Geranium. c, Blue hibiscus. d, Marigolds. e, Sunflower. f, Impatiens. g, Petunia. h, Pansy. i, Saucer magnolia.
No. 2238: a, Primrose. b, Bleeding heart. c, Pink dogwood. d, Peony. e, Rose. f, Hellebores. g, Lily. h, Violet. i, Cherry blossoms.
No. 2239, $6, Lily, vert. No. 2240, $6, Zinnias, vert.

1999, Apr. 19   Litho.   Perf. 14
2233-2236 A369   Set of 4   3.00 3.00
2237 A369 90c Sheet of 9, #a.-i. 6.25 6.25
2238 A369 $1 Sheet of 9, #a.-i. 7.25 7.25
Souvenir Sheets
2239-2240 A369   Set of 2   9.25 9.25

Elle Macpherson, Model — A370

Various portraits, each $1.20.

1999, Apr. 26   Perf. 13½
2241 A370   Sheet of 8, #a.-h.   8.50 8.50
Australia '99 World Stamp Expo.

John Glenn's Space Flight — A371

Space Exploration — A372

No. 2242 — John Glenn, 1962, each $1.75: a, Climbing into Mercury Capsule. b, Formal portrait. c, Having helmet adjusted. d, Entering pressure chamber.
No. 2243, $1.65: a, Luna 2. b, Mariner 2. c, Giotto space probe. d, Rosat. e, Intl. Ultraviolet Explorer. f, Ulysses Space Probe.
No. 2244, $1.65: a, Mariner 10. b, Luna 9. c, Advanced X-ray Astrophysics Facility. d, Magellan Spacecraft. e, Pioneer-Venus 2. f, Infra-red Astronomy Satellite.
No. 2245, $6, Salyut 1, horiz. No. 2246, $6, MIR, horiz.

1999, May 6   Litho.   Perf. 14
2242 A371   Sheet of 4, #a.-d.   6.50 6.50
Sheets of 6, #a-f
2243-2244 A372   Set of 2   15.00 15.00
Souvenir Sheets
2245-2246 A372   Set of 2   9.00 9.00
Nos. 2245-2246 are incorrectly inscribed.

Prehistoric Animals A373

Designs: 65c, Brachiosaurus. 75c, Oviraptor, vert. $1, Homotherium. $1.20, Macrauchenia, vert.
No. 2251, each $1.65: a, Leptictidium. b, Ictitherium. c, Plesictis. d, Hemicyon. e, Diacodexis. f, Stylinodon. g, Kanuites. h, Chriacus. i, Argyrolagus.
No. 2252, each $1.65: a, Struthiomimus. b, Corythosaurus. c, Dsungaripterus. d, Compognathus. e, Prosaurolophus. f, Montanoceratops. g, Stegosaurus. h, Deinonychus. i, Ouranosaurus.
No. 2253, each $6, Pteranodon. No. 2254, $6, Eurhinodelphus.

1999, May 26
2247-2250 A373 Set of 4   3.50   3.50
Sheets of 9, #a-i
2251-2252 A373 A373   22.00   22.00
Souvenir Sheets
2253-2254 A373 Set of 2   9.00   9.00
Illustrations on Nos. 2247-2248 are switched.

IBRA'99, World Stamp Exhibition, Nuremberg — A374

Exhibition emblem, Leipzig-Dresden Railway ad: No. 2255, $1, Caroline Islands #19. No. 2257, $1.65, Caroline Islands #4.
Emblem, Gölsdorf 4-4-0 and: No. 2256, $1.20, Caroline Islands #16. No. 2258, $1.90, Caroline Islands #8, #10.
$6, Registered label on cover.

1999, June 24   Litho.   Perf. 14
2255-2258 A374 Set of 4   5.00   5.00
Souvenir Sheet
2259 A374 $6 multicolored   4.75   4.75

Paintings by Hokusai (1760-1849) — A375

No. 2260, $1.65 — Details or entire paintings: a, Asakusa Honganji. b, Dawn at Isawa in Kai Province. c, Samurai with Bow and Arrow (bows level). d, Samurai with Bow and Arrow (bows at different angles). e, Kajikazawa in Kai Province. f, A Great Wave.
No. 2261, $1.65: a, People on the Balcony of the Sazaido. b, Nakahara in Sagami Province. c, Defensive Positions (2 men). d, Defensive Positions (3 men). e, Mount Fuji in Clear Weather. f, Nihonbashi in Edo.
No. 2262, $6, Gotenyama At Shinagawa on Tokaido Highway, vert. No. 2263, $6, A Netsuke Workshop, vert.

1999, June 24   Sheets of 6, #a-f
2260-2261 A375 Set of 2   15.00   15.00
Souvenir Sheets
2262-2263 A375 Set of 2   9.25   9.25

Johann Wolfgang von Goethe (1749-1832), Poet — A376

No. 2264, each $1.75: a, Three archangels in "Faust." b, Portraits of Goethe and Friedrich von Schiller (1759-1805). c, Faust reclining in landscape with spirits.
$6, Profile portrait of Goethe.

1999, June 24   Litho.   Perf. 14
2264 A376 Sheet of 3, #a.-c.   4.50   4.50
Souvenir Sheet
2265 A376 $6 multicolored   4.50   4.50

Souvenir Sheets

Philexfrance '99, World Philatelic Exhibition — A377

Locomotives: No. 2266, Crampton 1855-69. No. 2267, 232-U1 4-Cylinder Compound 4-6-4, 1949.

1999, June 24   Perf. 13¾
2266 A377 $6 multicolored   5.00   5.00
2267 A377 $6 multicolored   5.00   5.00

Wedding of Prince Edward and Sophie Rhys-Jones — A378

No. 2268: a, Sophie. b, Sophie, Edward. c, Edward.
$6, Horse and carriage, couple.

1999, June 24   Perf. 13½
2268 A378 $3 Sheet of 3, #a.-c.   6.75   6.75
Souvenir Sheet
2269 A378 $6 multicolored   5.00   5.00

A379

Various white kittens: 35c, 45c, 60c, 75c, 90c, $1.
No. 2276, $1.65: a, One holding paw on another. b, Black & white. c, White kitten, black kitten. d, One with yarn. e, Two in basket. f, One looking up.
No. 2277, $1.65: a, One playing with red yarn. b, Two long-haired. c, Yellow tabby. d, One with mouse. e, Yellow tabby on pillow. f, Black & gray tabby.
No. 2278, $6, Tabby cat carrying kitten. No. 2279, $6, Yellow kitten in tree.

1999, May 25   Litho.   Perf. 14½x14
2270-2275 A379 Set of 6   3.00   3.00
Sheets of 6
2276-2277 A379 Set of 2   15.00   15.00
Souvenir Sheets
2278-2279 A379 Set of 2   9.25   9.25
Australia '99, World Stamp Expo (Nos. 2276-2279).

A380

UN Rights of the Child Convention, 10th Anniv. — No. 2280: a, Three children. b, Adult hand taking child's hand, silhouette of mother holding infant. c, UN Building, member flags, dove.
$6, Dove.

1999, June 22   Perf. 14
2280 A380 $3 Sheet of 3, #a.-c.   6.75   6.75
Souvenir Sheet
2281 A380 $6 multicolored   5.00   5.00

Boats — A381

Designs: 25c, Missa Ferdie. 45c, Sailboats. 60c, Jolly Roger Pirate Ship. 90c, $4, Freewinds. $1.20, Monarch of the Seas.

1999, June 24   Litho.   Perf. 13x11
2282-2286 A381 Set of 5   3.25   3.25
2286a   Souvenir sheet, #2282-2286   3.75   3.75
Souvenir Sheet
Perf. 13¾
2287 A381 $4 multicolored   3.75   3.75
No. 2287 contains one 51x38mm stamp.

A382

Butterflies: 65c, Fiery jewel. 75c, Hewitson's blue hairstreak. $1.20, Scarce bamboo page, horiz. $1.65, Paris peacock, horiz.
No. 2292, horiz.: a, California dog face. b, Small copper. c, Zebra swallowtail. d, White M hairstreak. e, Old world swallowtail. f, Buckeye. g, Apollo. h, Sonoran blue. i, Purple emperor.
No. 2293, $6, Monarch. No. 2294, $6, Cairns birdwing, horiz.

1999, Aug. 16   Perf. 14
2288-2291 A382 Set of 4   3.75   3.75
2292 A382 $1 Sheet of 9, #a.-i.   8.50   8.50
Souvenir Sheets
2293-2294 A382 Set of 2   11.00   11.00

Christmas A383

15c, Madonna and child in a Wreath of Flowers by Peter Paul Rubens. 25c, Shroud of Christ Held by Two Angels, by Albrecht Dürer. 45c, Madonna and Child Enthroned Between Two Saints, by Raphael. 60c, Holy Family with the Lamb, by Raphael. $2, The Transfiguration, by Raphael. $4, Three Putti Holding a Coat of Arms, by Dürer.
$6, The Coronation of the Holy St. Catherine, by Rubens.

1999, Nov. 22   Litho.   Perf. 13¾
2295-2300 A383 Set of 6   6.50   6.50
Souvenir Sheet
2301 A383 $6 multicolored   5.50   5.50

Famous Elderly People A384

Designs: a, Katharine Hepburn. b, Martha Graham. c, Eubie Blake. d, Agatha Christie. e, Eudora Welty. f, Helen Hayes. g, Vladimir Horowitz. h, Katharine Graham. i, Pablo Casals. j, Pete Seeger. k, Andres Segovia. l, Frank Lloyd Wright.

2000, Jan. 18   Litho.   Perf. 14
2302 A384 90c Sheet of 12, #a-l   8.00   8.00

Charlie Chaplin A385

Designs: a, "Modern Times," street scene. b, "The Gold Rush," with other actor. c, Unidentified film. d, "Modern Times," on gears. e, "The Gold Rush," arms akimbo. f, "The Gold Rush," with cane.

2000, Jan. 18   Perf. 13¾
2303 A385 $1.65 Sheet of 6, #a-f   7.25   7.25

Sir Cliff Richard, Rock Musician A386

2000, Jan. 18   Perf. 13¼
2304 A386 $1.65 multi   1.25   1.25
Issued in sheets of 6.

Birds
A387

Designs: 75c, Streamertail. 90c, Yellow-bellied sapsucker. $1.20, Rufous-tailed jacamar. $2, Spectacled owl.
No. 2309, $1.20: a, Ground dove. b, Wood stork. c, Saffron finch. d, Green-backed heron. e, Lovely cotinga. f, St. Vincent parrot. g, Cuban grassquit. h, Red-winged blackbird.
No. 2310, $1.20: a, Scarlet macaw. b, Yellow-fronted amazon. c, Queen-of-Bavaria. d, Nanday conure. e, Jamaican tody. f, Smooth-billed ani. g, Puerto Rican woodpecker. h, Ruby-throated hummingbird.
No. 2311, $6, Vermilion flycatcher. No. 2312, $6, Red-capped manakin, vert.

2000, Apr. 17   Litho.   Perf. 14
2305-2308 A387   Set of 4   4.00   4.00
Sheets of 8, #a-h
Perf. 13¾x14
2309-2310 A387   Set of 2   15.00 15.00
Souvenir Sheets
Perf. 13¾
2311-2312 A387   Set of 2   9.25   9.25
The Stamp Show 2000, London (Nos. 2309-2312). Size of stamps: Nos. 2309-2310, 48x31mm; No. 2311, 50x38mm; No. 2312, 38x50mm.

Paintings of Anthony Van Dyck — A388

No. 2313, $1.20: a, Arthur Goodwin. b, Sir Thomas Wharton. c, Mary Villers (as Venus), Daughter of the Duke of Buckingham. d, Christina Bruce, Countess of Devonshire. e, James Hamilton, 3rd Marquis and 1st Duke of Hamilton. f, Henry Danvers, Earl of Danby.
No. 2314, $1.20: a, Charles I in Robes of State. b, Henrietta Maria. c, Queen Henrietta Maria with Her Dwarf Sir Jeffrey Hudson. d, Charles I in Armor. e, Henrietta Maria in Profile, facing right. f, Queen Henrietta Maria.
No. 2315, $1.20: a, Marie de Raet, Wife of Philippe le Roy. b, Jacomo de Cachiopin. c, Princess Henrietta of Lorraine Attended by a Page. d, Portrait of a Man. e, Portrait of a Woman. f, Philippe le Roy, Seigneur de Ravels.
No. 2316, $5, Charles I on Horseback with Monsieur de St. Antoine. No. 2317, $5, Le Roi a La Chasse (Charles I hunting). No. 2318, $5, Charles I in Three Positions. No. 2319, $5, Charles I and Queen Henrietta.
No. 2320, $6, Portrait of Two Young English Gentlemen, Sons of the Duke of Lenox. No. 2321, $6, George, Lord Digby, and William, Lord Russell.
Illustration reduced.

2000, May 15   Perf. 13¾
Sheets of 6, #a-f
2313-2315 A388   Set of 3   15.00 15.00
Souvenir Sheets
2316-2319 A388   Set of 4   15.50 15.50
2320-2321 A388   Set of 2   9.25   9.25

Butterflies — A389

No. 2322, $1.65: a, Orange theope. b, Sloane's urania. c, Gold-drop helicopis. d, Papilio velovis. e, Graphium androcles. f, Cramer's mesene.
No. 2323, $1.65, horiz.: a, Euploea miniszeki. b, Doris. c, Evenus coronata. d, Anchisiades swallowtail. e, White-spotted tadpole. f, Morpho patroclus.
No. 2324, $1.65, horiz.: a, Mesosemia loruhama. b, Bia actorion. c, Ghost brimstone. d, Blue tharops. e, Catasticta manco. f, White-talled page.
No. 2325, $6, Reakirt's blue. No. 2326, $6, Graphium encelades, horiz. No. 2327, $6, Graphium milon, horiz.
Illustration reduced.

2000, May 29   Perf. 14
Sheets of 6, #a-f
2322-2324 A389   Set of 3   22.50 22.50
Souvenir Sheets
2325-2327 A389   Set of 3   14.00 14.00

Prince William, 18th Birthday — A390

Prince William — No. 2328: a, With checked shirt, waving. b, In jacket and white shirt. c, With arms clasped. d, In striped shirt, waving.
$6, With Prince Harry, Princess Diana and unidentified man.

2000, June 21   Perf. 14
2328 A390 $1.65 Sheet of 4, #a-d   4.75   4.75
Souvenir Sheet
Perf. 13¾
2329 A390 $6 multi   4.25   4.25

100th Test Cricket Match at Lord's Ground — A391

90c, Richie Richardson. $5, Viv Richard. $6, Lord's Ground, horiz.

2000, June 26   Perf. 14
2330-2331 A391   Set of 2   4.50   4.50
Souvenir Sheet
2332 A391 $6 multi   4.50   4.50

Souvenir Sheet

2000 Summer Olympics, Sydney — A392

Designs: a, Cyclist. b, Diver. c, Italian flag, Flaminio Stadium, Rome. d, Ancient Greek javelin thrower.

2000, June 26
2333 A392 $2 Sheet of 4, #a-d   6.00   6.00

First Zeppelin Flight, Cent. — A393

No. 2334: a, LZ-1. b, LZ-2. c, LZ-3. $6, LZ-7.

2000, June 26   Perf. 13½
2334 A393 $3 Sheet of 3, #a-c   6.75   6.75
Souvenir Sheet
Perf. 14¼
2335 A393 $6 multi   4.25   4.25
No. 2334 contains three 45x27mm stamps.

Cats — A394

No. 2336: a, Long-haired blue & white. b, Snow shoe. c, Persian. d, Chocolate lynx point. e, Brown & white sphynx. f, White tortoiseshell.
$6, Lavender tortie.

2000, May 29   Litho.   Perf. 14
2336 A394 $1.65 Sheet of 6, #a-f 7.50   7.50
Souvenir Sheet
2337 A394 $6 multi   4.50   4.50

Souvenir Sheet

Public Railways, 175th Anniv. — A395

No. 2338: a, Locomotion No. 1, George Stephenson. b, John Bull.

2000, June 26
2338 A395 $3 Sheet of 2, #a-b   4.50   4.50
The Stamp Show 2000, London.

Souvenir Sheet

Johann Sebastian Bach (1685-1750) — A396

2000, June 26
2339 A396 $6 multi   4.25   4.25

Berlin Film Festival, 50th Anniv. — A397

No. 2340: a, Une Femme Est Une Femme. b, Carmen Jones. c, Die Ratten. d, Die Vier im Jeep. e, Lilies of the Field. f, Invitation to the Dance.
$6, Sense and Sensibility.

2000, June 26
2340 A397 $1.65 Sheet of 6, #a-f 7.25   7.25
Souvenir Sheet
2341 A397 $6 multi   4.50   4.50

Flowers — A398

Designs: 45c, Epidendrum pseudepidndrum. 65c, Odontoglossum cervantesii. 75c, Cattleya dowiana. 90c, Beloperone guttata. $1, Colliandra haematocephala. $1.20, Brassavola nodosa.

No. 2348, $1.65: a, Masdevallia coccinea. b, Paphinia cristata. c, Vanilla planifolia. d, Cattleya percivaliana. e, Lycaste skinneri. f, Cattleya percivaliana.

No. 2349, $1.65: a, Anthurium andreanum. b, Doxantha unguiscati. c, Hibiscus rosasinensis. d, Canna indica. e, Heliconius umilis. f, Strelitzia reginae.

No. 2350, $1.65: a, Pseudocalymna alliaceum. b, Datura candida. c, Ipomoea tuberosa. d, Allamanda cathartica. e, Aspasia epidendroides. f, Maxillaria cucullata.

No. 2351, $6, Strelitzia reginae. No. 2352, $6, Cattleya leopoldii. No. 2353, $6, Rossioglossum grande.

2000, May 29		Litho.	Perf. 14	
2342-2347	A398	Set of 6	3.50	3.50
Sheets of 6, #a-f				
2348-2350	A398	Set of 3	22.50	22.50
Souvenir Sheets				
2351-2353	A398	Set of 3	13.00	13.00

Dogs — A399

Designs: 90c, Boxer. $1, Wire-haired pointer (inscribed Alaskan malamute). $2, Alaskan malamute (inscribed Wire-haired pointer). $4, Saluki.

No. 2358: a, Bearded collie. b, Cardigan Welsh corgi. c, Saluki. d, Basset hound. e, Standard poodle. f, Boston terrier.

$6, Cavalier King Charles Spaniel.

2000, May 29				
2354-2357	A399	Set of 4	5.50	5.50
2358	A399	$1.65 Sheet of 6, #a-f	7.00	7.00
Souvenir Sheet				
2359	A399	$6 multi	4.50	4.50

Space Achievements — A400

No. 2360, $1.65: a, Sputnik 1. b, Explorer 1. c, Mars Express. d, Luna 1. e, Ranger 7. f, Mariner 4.

No. 2361, $1.65: a, Mariner 10. b, Soho. c, Mariner 2. d, Giotto. e, Exosat. f, Pioneer.

No. 2362, $6, Hubble Space Telescope. No. 2363, $6, Vostok 1.

2000, June 26		Sheets of 6, #a-f		
2360-2361	A400	Set of 2	14.00	14.00
Souvenir Sheets				
2362-2363	A400	Set of 2	9.00	9.00
World Stamp Expo 2000, Anaheim.				

Apollo-Soyuz Mission, 25th Anniv. — A401

No. 2364: a, Alexei Leonov. b, Soyuz 19. c, Valeri Kubasov.

$6, Leonov and Thomas Stafford.

2000, June 26				
2364	A401	$3 Sheet of 3, #a-c	6.50	6.50
Souvenir Sheet				
2365	A401	$6 multi	4.25	4.25

Souvenir Sheet

Albert Einstein (1879-1955) — A402

2000, June 26			Perf. 14¼	
2366	A402	$6 multi	4.25	4.25

Girls' Brigade A403

Designs: 20c, Outreach program to Sunshine Home for Girls. 60c, Ullida Rawlins Gill, Intl. vice-president, vert. 75c, Officers and girls. 90c, Raising the flag, vert. $1.20, Members with 8th Antigua Company flag.

$5, Emblem, vert.

2000, July 13			Perf. 14	
2367-2371	A403	Set of 5	2.75	2.75
Souvenir Sheet				
2372	A403	$5 multi	3.75	3.75

A404

Queen Mother, 100th Birthday — A405

No. 2373: a, As child. b, In 1940. c, With Princess Anne, 1951. d, In Canada, 1989.

$6, Inspecting the troops. $20, In gardens.

Litho., Margin Embossed				
2000, Aug. 4			Perf. 14	
2373	A404	$2 Sheet of 4, #a-d, + label	6.00	6.00
Souvenir Sheet				
Perf. 13¾				
2374	A404	$6 multi	4.50	4.50
Without Gum				
Litho. & Embossed				
Die Cut 8¾x9				
2375	A405	$20 gold & multi		

No. 2374 contains one 38x51mm stamp. See Nos. 2536-2537.

Popes — A406

No. 2376, $1.65: a, Alexander VI, 1492-1503, hands clasped. b, Benedict XIII, 1724-30. c, Boniface IX, 1389-1404. d, Alexander VI, no hands. e, Clement VIII, 1592-1605. f, Clement VI, 1342-52.

No. 2377, $1.65: a, John Paul II, 1978-present. b, Benedict XV, 1914-22. c, John XXIII, 1958-63. d, Pius XI, 1922-39. e, Pius XII, 1939-58. f, Paul VI, 1963-78.

No. 2378, $6, Pius II, 1458-1464. No. 2379, $6, Pius VII, 1800-23.

2000, Aug. 21		Litho.	Perf. 13¾	
Sheets of 6, #a-f				
2376-2377	A406	Set of 2	15.00	15.00
Souvenir Sheets				
2378-2379	A406	Set of 2	9.25	9.25

Monarchs — A407

No. 2380, $1.65: a, Donaldbane of Scotland, 1093-97. b, Duncan I of Scotland, 1034-40. c, Duncan II of Scotland, 1094. d, Macbeth of Scotland, 1040-57. e, Malcolm III of Scotland, 1057-93. f, Edgar of Scotland, 1097-1107.

No. 2381, $1.65: a, Charles I of Great Britain, 1625-49. b, Charles II of Great Britain, 1660-85. c, Charles Edward Stuart, the "Young Pretender," 1720-1788. d, James II of Great Britain, 1685-89. e, James II of Scotland, 1437-60. f, James III of Scotland, 1460-88.

No. 2382, $6, Robert I of Scotland, 1306-29. No. 2383, $6, Anne of Great Britain, 1702-14. Illustration reduced.

2000, Aug. 21				
Sheets of 6, #a-f				
2380-2381	A407	Set of 2	15.00	15.00
Souvenir Sheets				
2382-2383	A407	Set of 2	9.25	9.25

Millennium (#2385) — A408

No. 2384 — Chinese paintings: a, Admonitions of the Instructress to the Court Ladies, attributed to Ku K'ai-chih. b, Ink drawing on silk, 3rd cent. B.C. c, Ink and color drawing on silk, 2nd cent. B.C. d, Scholars of the Northern Qi Collating Texts (detail), attributed to Yang Zihua. e, Spring Outing (detail), attributed to Zhan Ziqian. f, Portrait of the Emperors (detail), attributed to Yen Liben. g, Sailing Boats and a Riverside Mansion, attributed to Li Sixun. h, Two Horses and a Groom (detail), by Han Kan. i, King's Portrait (detail), attributed to Wu Daozi. j, Court Ladies Wearing Flowered Headdresses (detail), attributed to Zhou Fang. k, Wintry Groves and Layered Banks, by Dong Yuan. l, Mount Kuanglu, by Jing Hao. m, Pheasant and Small Birds by a Jujube Shrub, by Huang Jucai. n, Deer Among Red Maples, by anonymous painter. o, Wintry Groves and Layered Banks, diff., by Dong Yuan. p, Literary Gathering, by Han Huang (60x40mm). q, Sketches of Birds and Insects (detail), by Huang Quan.

Perf. 12¾x12½				
2000, Aug. 21			Litho.	
2384	A408	25c Sheet of 17, #a-q, + label	5.00	5.00

Highlights of 1250-1300: a, Expansion of the Inquisition. b, Chartres Cathedral. c, Sculptures in Naumburg Cathedral. d, 1st English Parliament. e, The Madonna in Majesty (Maestà), by Cimabue. f, Marco Polo. g

Divine wind. h, Death of St. Thomas Aquinas. i, Arezzo Cathedral. j, Margaret, Queen of Scotland. k, Jewish exodus from England. l, Fall of Acre to Muslims. m, Moses de León writes much of The Zohar. n, German Civil War. o, Death of Kublai Khan. p, Dante writes La Vita Nuova (60x40mm). q, Chao Meng-fu paints Autumn Colors on the Quiao and Hua Mountains.

2000, Aug. 21
2385 A408 60c Sheet of 17, #a-q
+ label   9.00 9.00

Battle of Britain, 60th Anniv. — A409

No. 2386, $1.20: a, Bristol Blenheim. b, Winston Churchill. c, Bristol Blenheim and barrage balloon. d, Heinkel. e, Spitfire. f, German rescue vessel. g, Messerschmitt 109. h, RAF air and sea rescue launch.
No. 2387, $1.20: a, German lookout. b, Children being evacuated. c, Youngsters evacuated from hospitals. d, Hurricane. e, Rescue workers. f, British political cartoon. g, King George VI and Queen Elizabeth inspect wreckage. h, Barrage balloon over Tower Bridge.
No. 2388, $6, Spitfires. No. 2389, $6, Junkers 87B.

2000, Oct. 16   Litho.   Perf. 14
Sheets of 8, #a-h
2386-2387 A409 Set of 2   14.50 14.50
Souvenir Sheets
2388-2389 A409 Set of 2   9.25 9.25

Rainforest Fauna — A410

Designs: 75c, Agouti. 90c, Capybara. $1.20, Basilisk lizard. $2, Heliconid butterfly.
No. 2394, $1.65: a, Green violet-ear hummingbird. b, Harpy eagle. c, Three-toed sloth. d, White uakari monkey. e, Anteater. f, Coati.
No. 2395, $1.75: a, Red-eyed tree frog. b, Black spider monkey. c, Emerald toucanet. d, Kinkajou. e, Spectacled bear. f, Tapir.
No. 2396, $6, Keel-billed toucan, horiz. No. 2397, $6, Scarlet macaw, horiz.

2000, Sept. 25   Litho.   Perf. 14
2390-2393 A410 Set of 4   3.75 3.75
Sheets of 6, #a-f
2394-2395 A410 Set of 2   15.00 15.00
Souvenir Sheets
2396-2397 A410 Set of 2   9.25 9.25

Submarines — A411

Designs: 65c, Sea Cliff. 75c, Beaver Mark IV. 90c, Reef Ranger. $1, Cubmarine. $1.20, Alvin. $3, Argus.
No. 2404, $2: a, Revenge. b, Walrus. c, Los Angeles. d, Daphne. e, USS Ohio. f, USS Skipjack.
No. 2405, $6, Trieste. No. 2406, $6, German Type 209.

2000, Oct. 2
2398-2403 A411 Set of 6   5.50 5.50
2404 A411 $2 Sheet of 6, #a-f   8.75 8.75
Souvenir Sheets
2405-2406 A411 Set of 2   9.00 9.00

Paintings from the Prado — A412

No. 2407, $1.65: a, Three men. b, Man's head. c, Three women. d, Man on white horse. e, Man on brown horse. f, Man leading horse. a-c from Family Portrait, by Adriaen Thomasz Key. d-f from The Devotion of Rudolf I, by Peter Paul Rubens and Jan Wildens.
No. 2408, $1.65: a, Seated man. b, Man with sash. c, Group of men. d, Laureated figure. e, Men working at anvil. f, Two workers. a-c from The Defense of Cadiz Against the English by Francisco de Zurbaran. d-f from Vulcan's Forge, by Diego Velázquez.
No. 2409, $1.65: a, Mandolin player. b, Woman with fan. c, Two men. d, Bald man. e, Two Magi. f, Jesus, Mary and Joseph. a-c from The Concert, by Vicente Palmaroli y Gonzalez. d-f from The Adoration of the Magi, by Juan Bautista Maino
No. 2410, $6, The Seller of Fans, by José del Castillo. No. 2411, $6, Portrati of a Family in a Garden, by Jan van Kessel, the Younger. No. 2412, $6, The Deliverance of St. Peter, by José de Ribera, horiz.
Illustration reduced.

2000, Oct. 6   Perf. 12x12¼, 12¼x12
Sheets of 6, #a-f
2407-2409 A412 Set of 3   20.00 20.00
Souvenir Sheets
2410-2412 A412 Set of 3   13.00 13.00
España 2000 Intl. Philatelic Exhibition.

Christmas — A413

Designs (background): 25c, No. 2417a, Angels, full body (blue). 45c, No. 2417b, Angel's heads (orange). 90c, No. 2417c, Angel's heads (blue). $5, No. 2417d, Angels, full body (yellow).

2000, Dec. 4   Perf. 14
2413-2416 A413 Set of 4   4.50 4.50
2417 A413 $1.75 Sheet of 4, #a-d   5.25 5.25
Souvenir Sheet
2418 A413 $6 Jesus   4.50 4.50

Rijksmuseum, Amsterdam, Bicent. (in 2000) — A414

No. 2419, $1: a, Dr. Ephraim Bueno, by Rembrandt. b, Woman Writing a Letter, by Frans van Mieris, the Elder. c, Mary Magdalene, by Jan van Scorel. d, Portrait of a Woman (inscribed Anna Coddle), by Maarten van Heemskerck. e, Cleopatra's Banquet, by Gerard Lairesse. f, Titus van Rijn in Friar's Habit, by Rembrandt.
No. 2420, $1.20: a, Saskia van Uylenburgh, by Rembrandt. b, In the Month of July, by Paul Joseph Constantin Gabriel. c, Maria Trip, by Rembrandt. d, Still Life with Flowers, by Jan van Huysum. e, Hesje van Cleyburgh, by Rembrandt. f, Girl in a White Kimono, by George Hendrik Breitner.

No. 2421, $1.65: a, Man and woman at spinning wheel, by Pieter Pietersz. b, Self-portrait, by Rembrandt. c, Jeremiah Lamenting the Destruction of Jerusalem, by Rembrandt. d, The Jewish Bride, by Rembrandt. e, Tobit and Anna with a Kid, by Rembrandt. f, The Prophetess Anna, by Rembrandt.
No. 2422, $6, Doubting Thomas, by Hendrick ter Brugghen. No. 2423, $6, Still Life with Cheeses, by Floris van Dijck. No. 2424, $6, Isaac Blessing Jacob, by Govert Flinck.

2001, Jan. 15   Litho.   Perf. 13¾
Sheets of 6, #a-f
2419-2421 A414 Set of 3   17.00 17.00
Souvenir Sheets
2422-2424 A414 Set of 3   13.50 13.50

Pokémon — A415

No. 2425: a, Starmie. b, Misty. c, Brock. d, Geodude. e, Krabby. f, Ash.

2001, Feb. 13
2425 A415 $1.75 Sheet of 6, #a-f 7.25 7.25
Souvenir Sheet
2426 A415 $6 Charizard   4.25 4.25

Mushrooms A416

Designs: 25c, Blue-toothed entoloma. 90c, Common morel. $1, Red cage fungus. $1.75, Fawn shield-cap.
No. 2431, $1.65: a, Lilac bonnet. b, Silky volvar. c, Poplar field cap. d, St. George's mushroom. e, Red-stemmed tough shank. f, Fly agaric.
No. 2432, $1.65: a, Copper trumpet. b, Meadow mushroom. c, Green-gilled parasol. d, Panther. e, Death cap. f, King bolete.
No. 2433, $6, Yellow parasol. No. 2434, Mutagen milk cap.

2001, Mar. 26   Perf. 13¾x13¼
2427-2430 A416 Set of 4   3.00 3.00
Sheets of 6, #a-f
2431-2432 A416 Set of 2   15.00 15.00
Souvenir Sheets
2433-2434 A416 Set of 2   9.25 9.25
Hong Kong 2001 Stamp Exhibition (2431-2434).

Population and Housing Census — A417

Map of Antigua with various graphs. Denominations: 15c, 25c, 65c, 90c.

2001, Apr. 2   Perf. 13¾
2435-2438 A417 Set of 4   1.50 1.50
Souvenir Sheet
2439 A417 $6 Map, emblem   4.50 4.50

Phila Nippon '01, Japan — A418

Designs: 45c Two women facing right, from Yuna (Bath-house Women). 60c, Woman facing left, from Yuna. 65c, Two women, from Yuna. 75c, Man with stringed instrument at top, from Hikone Screen. $1, Woman with stringed instrument at bottom, from Hikone Screen. $1.20, Two people, from Hikone Screen.
No. 2446 — Namban Screen, by Naizen Kano, each $1.65: a, Ship's stern. b, Ship's bow. c, Man with closed umbrella. d, Man with open umbrella.
No. 2447 — Merry Making Under the Cherry Blossoms, by Naganobu Kano, each $1.65: a, Steps. b, Tree. c, Four people near building. d, Four people, mountains. e, Three people. f, One person.
No. 2448, $6, Visiting a Shrine on a Rainy Night, by Harunobu Suzuki. No. 2449, $6, Courtesan on a Veranda Upstairs, by Kokan Shiba. No. 2450, $6, Daruma, by Tsujo Kano.

2001, May 28   Litho.   Perf. 14¼x14
2440-2445 A418 Set of 6   3.50 3.50
2446 A418 Sheet of 4, #a-d   5.00 5.00
2447 A418 Sheet of 6, #a-f   7.50 7.50
Souvenir Sheets
Perf. 13¾
2448-2450 A418 Set of 3   12.50 12.50
Nos. 2448-2450 each contain one 38x51mm stamp.
No. 2449 is incorrectly inscribed. It actually depicts "Courtesan on a Veranda Upstairs," by Kokan.

Orchids A419

Designs: 45c, Hintleya burtii. 75c, Neomoovea irrovata. 90c, Comparettia speciosa. $1, Cypripedium crapeanum.
No. 2455, $1.20, vert.: a, Trichoceuos muralis. b, Dracula rampira. c, Psychopsis papilio. d, Lycaste clenningiana. e, Telipogon nevuosus. f, Masclecallia ayahbacana.
No. 2456, $1.65, vert.: a, Rhyncholaelia glanca. b, Oncidium barbatum. c, Phaius tankervillege. d, Ghies brechtiana. e, Angraecum leonis. f, Cychnoches loddigesti.
No. 2457, $1.65, vert.: a, Cattleya dowiana. b, Dendrobium cruentum. c, Bulbophyllum lobbi. d, Chysis laevis. e, Ancistrochilus rothschildicanus. f, Angraecum sororium.
No. 2458, $6, Trichopilia fragrans, vert. No. 2459, $6, Symphalossum sanguinem, vert.

2001, June 11   Perf. 14
2451-2454 A419 Set of 4   2.40 2.40
Sheets of 6, #a-f
2455-2457 A419 Set of 3   19.00 19.00
Souvenir Sheets
2458-2459 A419 Set of 2   9.00 9.00

Souvenir Sheets

I Love Lucy — A420

Designs: No. 2460, $6, Fred and Ricky. No. 2461, $6, Lucy and Ethel. No. 2462, $6, Lucy and fireplace. No. 2463, $6, Lucy and open door.

2001, Mar. 5	**Litho.**		**Perf. 13¾**
2460-2463 A420	Set of 4	18.00	18.00

See Nos. 2522-2525.

Marine Life and Birds A421

Designs: 25c, Yellowtail damselfish. 45c, Indigo hamlet. 65c, Great white shark. No. 2467, 90c, Bottlenose dolphin. No. 2468, 90c, Palette surgeonfish. $1, Octopus.

No. 2470, $1.20: a, Common dolphin. b, Franklin's gull. c, Rock beauty. d, Bicolor angelfish. e, Beaugregory. f, Banded butterflyfish.

No. 2471, $1.20: a, Common tern. b, Flying fish. c, Queen angelfish. d, Blue-striped grunt. e, Porkfish. f, Blue tang.

No. 2472, $1.65: a, Dugong. b, White-tailed tropicbird. c, Bull shark and Spanish grunt. d, Manta ray. e, Green turtle. f, Spanish grunt.

No. 2473, $1.65: a, Red-footed booby. b, Bottlenose dolphin. c, Hawksbill turtle. d, Monk seal. e, Bull shark and coral. f, Lemon shark.

No. 2474, $5, Sailfish. No. 2475, $5, Beaugregory and brown pelican, vert. No. 2476, $6, Hawksbill turtle. No. 2477, $6, Queen triggerfish.

2001, June 11			**Perf. 14**
2464-2469 A421	Set of 6	3.25	3.25
Sheets of 6, #a-f			
2470-2473 A421	Set of 4	24.00	24.00
Souvenir Sheets			
2474-2477 A421	Set of 4	16.00	16.00

Ship Freewinds — A422

Designs: 30c, Maiden voyage anniversary in Antigua. 45c, In St. Barthelemy. 75c, In Caribbean at sunset. 90c, In Bonaire. $1.50, In Bequia.

No. 2483, $4, With lights on during eclipse. No. 2484, $4, In Curacao.

2001, June 15			
2478-2482 A422	Set of 5	3.00	3.00
Souvenir Sheets			
2483-2484 A422	Set of 2	6.00	6.00

Toulouse-Lautrec Paintings — A423

No. 2485: a, Monsieur Georges-Henri Manuel Standing. b, Monsieur Louis Pascal. c, Roman Coolus. d, Monsieur Fourcade. $5, Dancing at the Moulin de la Galette.

2001, July 3			**Perf. 13¾**
2485 A423	$2 Sheet of 4, #a-d	6.00	6.00
Souvenir Sheet			
2486 A423	$5 multi	3.75	3.75

Giuseppe Verdi (1813-1901), Opera Composer — A424

No. 2487: a, Verdi in hat. b, Character and score from Don Carlos. c, Conductor and score for Aida. d, Musicians and score for Rigoletto.

2001, July 3			**Perf. 14**
2487 A424	$2 Sheet of 4, #a-d	6.00	6.00
Souvenir Sheet			
2488 A424	$5 Verdi, score	3.75	3.75

Marlene Dietrich — A425

No. 2489: a, With cigarette. b, On sofa. c, Color photograph. d, With piano.

2001, July 3			**Perf. 13¾**
2489 A425	$2 Sheet of 4, #a-d	6.00	6.00

Queen Victoria (1819-1901) — A426

No. 2490: a, Blue dress. b, Red hat. c, Crown. d, Crown and blue sash.

2001, July 3			**Perf. 14**
2490 A426	$2 Sheet of 4, #a-d	6.00	6.00
Souvenir Sheet			
2491 A426	$5 As old woman	3.75	3.75

Queen Elizabeth II, 75th Birthday — A427

No. 2492: a, At birth, 1926. b, In 1938. c, In 1939. d, At coronation, 1953. e, In 1956. f, In 1985.

2001, July 3			
2492 A427	$1 Sheet of 6, #a-f	3.75	3.75
Souvenir Sheet			
2493 A427	$6 In 1940	4.50	4.50

Photomosaic of Queen Elizabeth II — A428

2001, July 3	**Litho.**		**Perf. 14**
2494 A428	$1 multi	.75	.75

Queen Elizabeth II, 75th birthday. Issued in sheets of 8.

Monet Paintings — A429

No. 2495, horiz.: a, Water Lilies. b, Rose Portals, Giverny. c, The Water Lily Pond, Harmony in Green. d, The Artist's Garden, Irises. $5, Jerusalem Artichokes.

2001, July 3			**Perf. 13¾**
2495 A429	$2 Sheet of 4, #a-d	6.00	6.00
Souvenir Sheet			
2496 A429	$5 multi	3.75	3.75

Endangered Animals — A430

Designs: 25c, Collared peccary. 30c, Baird's tapir. 45c, Agouti. 75c, Bananaquit. 90c, Six-banded armadillo. $1, Roseate spoonbill.

No. 2503, each $1.80: a, Mouse opossum. b, Magnificent black frigatebird. c, Northern jacana. d, Painted bunting. e, Haitian solenodon. f, St. Lucia iguana.

No. 2504, each $2.50: a, West Indian iguana. b, Scarlet macaw. c, Cotton-topped tamarin. d, Kinkajou.

No. 2505, $6, Ocelot, vert. No. 2506, $6, King vulture, vert.

2001, Sept. 10			**Perf. 14**
2497-2502 A430	Set of 6	2.50	2.50
2503 A430	Sheet of 6, #a-f	8.00	8.00
2504 A430	Sheet of 4, #a-d	7.00	7.00
Souvenir Sheets			
2505-2506 A430	Set of 2	9.00	9.00

Rudolph Valentino (1895-1926), Actor — A431

No. 2507, $1: a, Blood and Sand. b, Eyes of Youth. c, All Night. d, Last known photo of Valentino. e, Camille. f, Cobra.

No. 2508, $1: a, The Son of the Sheik. b, The Young Rajah. c, The Eagle. d, The Sheik. e, A Sainted Devil. f, Monsieur Beaucaire.

No. 2509, $6, The Four Horsemen of the Apocalypse. No. 2510, $6, Valentino with Natasha Rambova.

2001, Oct. 2			**Perf. 13¾**
Sheets of 6, #a-f			
2507-2508 A431	Set of 2	9.00	9.00
Souvenir Sheets			
2509-2510 A431	Set of 2	9.00	9.00

Scenes From Shirley Temple Movies — A432

No. 2511, $1.65 — Scenes from Baby, Take a Bow, with Temple: a, In polka-dot dress. b, With man on steps. c, With man holding gun. d, With woman.

No. 2512, $1.80, horiz. — Scenes from The Little Princess, with Temple: a, With man. b, Washing floor. c, With woman and child. d, With old woman.

No. 2513, $1.50 — Scenes from The Little Princess, with Temple: a, With woman. b, In pink dress. c, Holding doll. d, On throne. e, With man. f, With birthday cake.

No. 2514, $1.65, horiz. — Scenes from Baby, Take a Bow, with Temple: a, With woman and five children. b, With arms around man. c, Being tucked in bed. d, With man. e, Standing with man and woman. f, Looking in cradle.

No. 2515, $6, In polka-dot dress, from Baby, Take a Bow. No. 2516, With soldiers, from The Little Princess.

2001, Oct. 2   Sheets of 4, #a-d
2511-2512 A432   Set of 2   10.50 10.50
Sheets of 6, #a-f
2513-2514 A432   Set of 2   14.00 14.00
Souvenir Sheets
2515-2516 A432   Set of 2   8.00   8.00

Nobel Prizes, Cent. — A433

No. 2517, $1.50 — Chemistry laureates: a, Melvin Calvin, 1961. b, Linus C. Pauling, 1954. c, Vincent du Vigneaud, 1955. d, Richard Synge, 1952. e, Archer Martin, 1952. f, Alfred Werner, 1913.
No. 2518, $1.50 — Chemistry laureates: a, Robert F. Curl, Jr., 1996. b, Alan J. Heeger, 2000. c, Michael Smith, 1993. d, Sidney Altman, 1989. e, Elias James Corey, 1990. f, William Francis Giauque, 1949.
No. 2519, $6, Ernest Rutherford, Chemistry, 1908. No. 2520, $6, International Red Cross, Peace, 1944. No. 2521, $6, Ernst Otto Fischer, Chemistry, 1973.

2001, Nov. 29   Perf. 14
Sheets of 6, #a-f
2517-2518 A433   Set of 2   13.50 13.50
Souvenir Sheets
2519-2521 A433   Set of 3   13.50 13.50

I Love Lucy Type of 2001

Designs: No. 2522, $6, Fred at desk. No. 2523, $6, Lucy and Fred. No. 2524, $6, Lucy, closed door. No. 2525, $6, Fred and Ricky at desk, horiz.

2001   Perf. 13¾
2522-2525 A420   Set of 4   18.00 18.00

Christmas — A434

Paintings: 25c, Madonna and Child with Angels, by Filippo Lippi. 45c, Madonna of Corneto Tarquinia, by Lippi. 50c, Madonna and Child, by Domenico Ghirlandaio. 75c, Madonna and Child, by Lippi. $4, Madonna del Ceppo, by Lippi.
$6, Madonna Enthroned with Angels and Saints, by Lippi.

2001, Dec. 4   Litho.   Perf. 14
2526-2530 A434   Set of 5   4.50   4.50
Souvenir Sheet
2531 A434 $6 multi   4.50   4.50

2002 World Cup Soccer Championships, Japan and Korea — A435

No. 2532, $1.50: a, Scene from final game, 1950. b, Ferenc Puskas, 1954. c, Raymond Kopa, 1958. d, Mauro, 1962. e, Gordon Banks, 1966. f, Pelé, 1970.
No. 2533, $1.50: a, Daniel Passarella, 1978. b, Karl-Heinz Rummenigge, 1982. c, World Cup trophy, 1986. d, Diego Maradona, 1990. e, Roger Milla, 1994. f, Zinedine Zidane, 1998.
No. 2534, $6, Head from Jules Rimet Cup, 1930. No. 2535, $6, Head and globe from World Cup trophy, 2002.

2001, Dec. 17   Perf. 13¾x14¼
Sheets of 6, #a-f
2532-2533 A435   Set of 2   12.00 12.00
Souvenir Sheets
Perf. 14¼
2534-2535 A435   Set of 2   8.00   8.00

**Queen Mother Type of 2000
Redrawn**

No. 2536, each $2: a, As child. b, In 1940. c, With Princess Anne, 1951. d, In Canada, 1989.
$6, Inspecting the troops.

2001, Dec.   Perf. 14
Yellow Orange Frames
2536 A404 Sheet of 4, #a-d, + label   6.00   6.00
Souvenir Sheet
Perf. 13¾
2537 A404 $6 multi   4.50   4.50

Queen Mother's 101st birthday. No. 2537 contains one 38x51mm stamp with a darker appearance than that found on No. 2374. Sheet margins of Nos. 2536-2537 lack embossing and gold arms found on Nos. 2373-2374.

US Civil War — A436

No. 2538: a, Battle of Nashville. b, Battle of Atlanta. c, Battle of Spotsylvania. d, Battle of the Wilderness. e, Battle of Chickamauga Creek. f, Battle of Gettysburg. g, Battle of Chancellorsville. h, Battle of Fredericksburg. i, Battle of Antietam. j, Second Battle of Bull Run. k, Battle of Five Forks. l, Seven Days' Battle. m, Battle of Bull Run. n, Battle of Shiloh. o, Battle of Seven Pines. p, Battle of Fort Sumter. q, Battle of Chattanooga. r, Surrender at Appomattox.
No. 2539, vert.: a, Gen. Ulysses S. Grant. b, Pres. Abraham Lincoln. c, Confederate Pres. Jefferson Davis. d, Gen. Robert E. Lee. e, Gen. George A. Custer. f, Adm. Andrew Hull Foote. g, General Thomas "Stonewall" Jackson. h, Gen. J.E.B. Stuart. i, Gen. George G. Meade. j, Gen. Philip H. Sheridan. k, Gen. James Longstreet. l, Gen. John S. Mosby.
No. 2540, $6, Monitor. No. 2541, $6, Merrimack.

2002, Jan. 28   Perf. 14¾
2538 A436 45c Sheet of 18, #a-r   10.00 10.00
2539 A436 50c Sheet of 12, #a-l   8.00   8.00
Souvenir Sheets
Perf. 14½x14¾ (#2540), 13¾
2540-2541 A436   Set of 2   11.00 11.00
No. 2541 contains one 50x38mm stamp.

GOLDEN JUBILEE - 6th February, 2002
50th Anniversary of Her Majesty Queen Elizabeth II's Accession

Reign of Queen Elizabeth II, 50th Anniv. — A437

No. 2542: a, Striped dress. b, Green patterned dress. c, Orange patterned dress. d, White jacket.
$6, Queen with Princess Margaret.

2002, Feb. 6   Perf. 14¼
2542 A437 $2 Sheet of 4, #a-d   7.00   7.00
Souvenir Sheet
2543 A437 $6 multi   4.50   4.50

United We Stand — A438

2002, Feb. 11   Perf. 13½x13¼
2544 A438 $2 multi   1.50   1.50
Printed in sheets of 4.

Cricket Player Sir Vivian Richards, 50th Birthday — A439

Designs: 25c, Raising bat. 30c, Receiving gift. 50c, With arms raised. 75c, At bat. $1.50, Wearing sash, with woman. $1.80, Standing next to photograph of himself.
No. 2551, $6, Holding sword. No. 2552, $6, With Antigua color guard.

2002, Mar. 7   Perf. 13½x13¼
2545-2550 A439   Set of 6   4.00   4.00
Souvenir Sheets
2551-2552 A439   Set of 2   9.00   9.00

Flora and Fauna A440

Designs: 50c, Thick-billed parrot. 75c, Lesser long-nosed bat. $1.50, Montserrat oriole. $1.80, Miss Perkin's blue butterfly.
No. 2557, 90c: a, Quetzals. b, Two-toed sloth. c, Lovely cotinga. d, Giant hairstrak butterfly. e, Magenta-throated woodstar. f, Bull's-eye silk moth. g, Golden toads. h, Collared peccaries. i, Tamandua anteater.
No. 2558, $1: a, St. Lucia parrot. b, Cuban kite. c, West Indian whistling duck. d, Poey's sulphur butterfly. e, Scarlet ibis. f, Black-capped petrel. g, St. Lucia whiptail. h, Cuban

Solenodon. i, False androgeus swallowtail butterfly.
No. 2559, $6, Margay. No. 2560, $6, Olive Ridley turtle.

2002, Apr. 8   Perf. 14
2553-2556 A440   Set of 4   3.50   3.50
Sheets of 9, #a-i
2557-2558 A440   Set of 2   14.00 14.00
Souvenir Sheets
2559-2560 A440   Set of 2   9.00   9.00

Antigua Community Players, 50th Anniv. — A441

Various photos: 20c, 25c, 30c, 75c, 90c, $1.50, $1.80.
No. 2568, $4, Former Pres. Edie Hill-Thibou, vert. No. 2569, $4, Acting Pres. and Music Director Yvonne Maginley, vert.

Perf. 13½x13¾
2002, June 11   Litho.
2561-2567 A441   Set of 7   4.25   4.25
Souvenir Sheets
Perf. 14
2568-2569 A441   Set of 2   6.00   6.00

Endangered Animals — A442

No. 2570, each $1.50: a, Red-billed tropicbird. b, Brown pelican. c, Magnificent frigatebird. d, Ground lizard. e, West Indian whistling duck. f, Antiguan racer snake. g, Spiny lobster. h, Hawksbill turtle. i, Queen conch.

2002, July 12   Perf. 14
2570 A442 Sheet of 9, #a-i   12.00 12.00

2002 Winter Olympics, Salt Lake City — A443

Designs: No. 2571, $2, Cross-country skiing. No. 2572, $2, Pairs figure skating.

2002, July 15   Perf. 13½x13¼
2571-2572 A443   Set of 2   3.50   3.50
2572a   Souvenir sheet, #2571-2572   3.50   3.50

First Solo Transatlantic Flight, 75th
Anniv. — A444

No. 2573, each $2.50: a, Charles Lindbergh
and The Spirit of St. Louis. b, Arrival at Le
Bourget Airport, Paris. c, Lindbergh receiving
hero's welcome, New York.
$6, Lindbergh in airplane.

2002, July 15   **Perf. 13¼x13½**
2573 A444 Sheet of 3, #a-c   5.75 5.75
Souvenir Sheet
2574 A444 $6 multi   4.50 4.50

Intl. Year of Mountains — A445

No. 2575: a, Mt. Fuji. b, Machu Picchu. c,
Matterhorn.

2002, July 15   **Perf. 13½x13¼**
2575 A445 $2 Sheet of 3, #a-c 4.50 4.50

Amerigo Vespucci (1454-1512),
Explorer — A446

No. 2576, horiz., each $2.50: a, Vespucci
with gray head covering. b, Vespucci with red
head covering. c, Hands and map.
$6, Vespucci and compass.

Perf. 13¼x13½, 13½x13¼
2002, July 15
2576 A446 Sheet of 3, #a-c   6.00 6.00
Souvenir Sheet
2577 A446 $6 multi   4.50 4.50

Princess Diana (1961-97) — A447

No. 2578: a, Wearing seven-strand pearl
necklace. b, Wearing tiara and white dress. c,
Wearing hat. d, Wearing earrings and black
dress. e, Wearing tiara, no dress seen. f,
Wearing earrings, no dress seen.
$6, Wearing white dress.

2002, July 29   **Perf. 14**
2578 A447 $1.80 Sheet of 6, #a-f 7.50 7.50
Souvenir Sheet
2579 A447 $6 multi   4.50 4.50

Presidents John F. Kennedy and
Ronald Reagan — A448

No. 2580, $1.50, horiz.: a, John, Robert and
Edward Kennedy. b, Kennedy with Danny
Kaye. c, Kennedy addressing nation. d, With
wife, Jacqueline. e, Shaking hands with young
Bill Clinton. f, Family members at funeral.
No. 2581, $1.50, horiz.: a, Reagan with wife,
Nancy, and Pope John Paul II. b, As George
Gipp in movie *Knute Rockne, All American*. c,
With Gen. Matthew Ridgeway at Bitburg Cem-
etery. d, With Vice-president George H. W.
Bush and Mikhail Gorbachev. e, With Presi-
dents Ford, Carter, and Nixon. f, On horse-
back, with Queen Elizabeth II.
No. 2582, $6, Kennedy and flag. No. 2583,
$6, Reagan.

2002, July 29   **Litho.**
Sheets of 6, #a-f
2580-2581 A448 Set of 2   13.50 13.50
Souvenir Sheets
2582-2583 A448 Set of 2   9.00 9.00

Elvis Presley
(1935-77)
A449

2002, Aug. 20   **Perf. 13¾**
2584 A449 $1 multi   1.25 1.25
Printed in sheets of 9.

Teddy Bears, Cent. — A450

No. 2585: a, Cheerleader bear. b, Figure
skater bear. c, Ballet dancer bear. d, Aerobics
instructor bear.

2002, Aug. 26
2585 A450 $2 Sheet of 4, #a-d 7.00 7.00

Pokémon — A451

No. 2586: a, Croconau. b, Mantine. c, Ferali-
gatr. d, Quilfish. e, Remoraid. f, Quagsire.
$6, Chinchou.

2002, Aug. 26
2586 A451 $1.50 Sheet of 6, #a-f 6.75 6.75
Souvenir Sheet
2587 A451 $6 multi   4.50 4.50

Lee Strasberg
(1901-82), Movie
Actor and
Director — A452

2002, Sept. 16   **Perf. 14**
2588 A452 $1 multi   .75   .75
Printed in sheets of 9.

Charlie Chaplin (1889-1977),
Actor — A453

No. 2589: a, Wearing bowler hat, facing forward. b, Wearing suit and vest. c, Wearing top
hat. d, Wearing bowler hat, profile. e, Wearing
bow tie and suit. f, With hand at chin.
$6, Wearing bowler hat, diff.

2002, Sept. 16
2589 A453 $1.80 Sheet of 6, #a-f 8.25 8.25
Souvenir Sheet
2590 A453 $6 multi   4.50 4.50

Marlene Dietrich (1901-92),
Actress — A454

No. 2591: a, With hands at side of face. b,
Wearing top hat. c, Faciing forward. d, With
hand on chin. e, Wearing black hat. f, Wearing
gloves.
$6, Facing forward, diff.

2002, Sept. 16
2591 A454 $1.50 Sheet of 6, #a-f 6.75 6.75
Souvenir Sheet
2592 A454 $6 multi   4.50 4.50

Bob Hope — A455

No. 2593: a, Wearing red cap. b, Wearing
hat with strap. c, Wearing top hat. d, Wearing
black cap. e, Wearing camouflage. f, Wearing
white cap.

2002, Sept. 16
2593 A455 $1.50 Sheet of 6, #a-f 7.50 7.50

Ferrari
Race Cars
A456

Designs: 20c, 1957 801. 25c, 1959 256 F1.
30c, 1960 246P F1. 90c, 1966 246 F1. $1,
1971 312 B2. $1.50, 1969 312 F1. $2, 1997
F310B. $4, 2002 F2002.

2002, Oct. 14			Litho.	
2594-2601	A456	Set of 8	7.75	7.75

Independence, 21st Anniv. — A457

Designs: 25c, Flag. 30c, Arms, vert. $1.50,
Mt. St. John's Hospital nearing completion.
$1.80, Parliament Building.
No. 2606, $6, Prime Minister Lester B. Bird,
vert. No. 2607, $6, Sir Vere C. Bird, vert.

2002, Oct. 31			Perf. 14	
2602-2605	A457	Set of 4	3.50	3.50
		Souvenir Sheets		
2606-2607	A457	Set of 2	9.00	9.00

Nos. 2606-2607 each contain one
38x50mm stamp.

Second Round of World Cup Soccer
Championships — A458

No. 2608, $1.65: a, Pyo Lee. b, Ji Sung
Park. c, Jung Hwan Ahn. d, Filippo Inzaghi. e,
Paolo Maldini. f, Damiano Tommasi.
No. 2609, $1.65: a, Juan Valeron. b, Iker
Casillas. c, Fernando Hierro. d, Gary Kelly. e,
Damien Duff. f, Matt Holland.
No. 2610, $3: a, South Korean coach Guus
Hiddink. b, Chul Sang Yoo.
No. 2611, $3: a, Francesco Totti. b, Italy
coach Giovanni Trapattoni.
No. 2612, $3: a, Spain coach Jose Antonio
Camacho. b, Carlos Gamarra.
No. 2613, $3: a, Robbie Keane. b, Ireland
coach Mick McCarthy.

2002, Nov. 4			Perf. 13½x13¼	
		Sheets of 6, #a-f		
2608-2609	A458	Set of 2	15.00	15.00
		Souvenir Sheets, #a-b		
2610-2613	A458	Set of 4	18.00	18.00

Christmas
A459

Designs: 25c, Coronation of the Virgin, by
Domenico Ghirlandaio. 45c, Adoration of the
Magi (detail), by Ghirlandaio. 75c, Annunciation (detail), by Simone Martini, vert. 90c, Adoration of the Magi (detail, diff.) by Ghirlandaio.
$5, Madonna and Child, by Giovanni Bellini.
$6, Madonna and Child, by Martini.

2002, Nov. 18			Perf. 14	
2614-2618	A459	Set of 5	5.50	5.50
		Souvenir Sheet		
2619	A459	$6 multi	4.50	4.50

Worldwide
Fund for
Nature
(WWF)
A460

Antiguan racer snake: a, Head. b, Snake
with head near tail. c, Snake and dried leaves.
d, Snake on rocks.

2002, Nov. 25				
2620		Strip of 4	3.75	3.75
a.-d.	A460	$1 Any single	.90	.90

Printed in sheets of 4 strips.

Flora & Fauna — A461

No. 2621, $1.50: a, Magnificent frigatebird.
b, Sooty tern. c, Bananaquit. d, Yellow-
crowned night heron. e, Greater flamingo. f,
Belted kingfisher.
No. 2622, $1.50: a, Killer whale. b, Sperm
whale. c, Minke whale. d, Blainville's beaked
whale. e, Blue whale. f, Cuvier's beaked
whale.
No. 2623, $1.80: a, Hieroglyphic moth. b,
Hypocrita dejanira. c, Snowy eupseudosoma
moth. d, Composia credula. e, Giant silkworm
moth. f, Diva moth.
No. 2624, $1.80: a, Epidendrum fragrans. b,
Dombeya. c, Yellow poui. d, Milky wave plant.
e, Cinderella plant. f, Coral orchid.
No. 2625, $5, Snowy egret. No. 2626, $5,
Rothschildia orizaba. No. 2627, $6, Humpback
whale. No. 2628, $6, Ionopsis utricularoides.

2002, Nov. 25			Litho.	
		Sheets of 6, #a-f		
2621-2624	A461	Set of 4	32.50	32.50
		Souvenir Sheets		
2625-2628	A461	Set of 4	19.00	19.00

Souvenir Sheet

Pan-American Health Organization,
Cent. — A462

No. 2629: a, Dr. Margaret O'Garro. b, Nurse
Ineta Wallace. c, Public Health Worker Vincent
Edwards.

2002, Dec. 2				
2629	A462	$1.50 Sheet of 3, #a-c	3.50	3.50

Souvenir Sheets

Science Fiction — A463

No. 2630, $6, Writings of Nostradamus. No.
2631, $6, *2001: A Space Odyssey*, by Arthur
C. Clarke. No. 2632, $6, Are We Alone?

2002, Dec. 12			Perf. 13¾	
2630-2632	A463	Set of 3	13.50	13.50

A464

20th World Scout Jamboree,
Thailand — A465

No. 2633, horiz.: a, Lord Robert Baden-
Powell. b, Ernest Thompson Seton, first Chief
Scout. c, First black troop.
No. 2634: a, Brownie with broad neckerchief
"X." b, Brownie with narrow neckerchief "X." c,
Brownie with incomplete neckerchief "X."
No. 2635, Seton. No. 2636, Scout salute.

2002, Dec. 12		Litho.	Perf. 14	
2633	A464	$3 Sheet of 3, #a-c	7.00	7.00
2634	A465	$3 Sheet of 3, #a-c	7.00	7.00
		Souvenir Sheet		
2635	A464	$6 multi	4.50	4.50
2636	A465	$6 multi	4.50	4.50

Ram, by Liu
Jiyou — A466

2003, Feb. 10			Perf. 13¾	
2637	A466	$1.80 multi	1.40	1.40

New Year 2003 (Year of the Ram). Issued in
sheets of 4.

A467

Coronation of Queen Elizabeth II, 50th
Anniv. — A468

No. 2638, each $3: a, In uniform. b, With tan
jacket. c, With white dress and hat.
$6, With white dress.

2003		Litho.	Perf. 14	
2638	A467	Sheet of 3, #a-c	6.75	6.75
		Souvenir Sheet		
2639	A467	$6 multi	4.50	4.50
		Miniature Sheet		
		Litho. & Embossed		
		Perf. 13¼x13		
2640	A468	$20 gold & multi	17.50	17.50

Issued: Nos. 2638-2639, 5/14; No. 2640,
2/10.

Paintings of
Lucas
Cranach the
Elder (1472-
1553)
A469

Designs: 75c, Lucretia. 90c, Venus and
Cupid. $1, Judith with the Head of Holofernes,
c. 1530. $1.50, Portrait of a Young Lady.
No. 2645: a, Portrait of the Wife of a Jurist.
b, Portrait of a Jurist. c, Johannes Cuspinian.
d, Portrait of Anna Cuspinian.

$6, Judith with the Head of Holofernes, c. 1532.

2003, Apr. 30   Litho.   Perf. 14¼
2641-2644 A469 Set of 4   3.25 3.25
2645 A469 $2 Sheet of 4, #a-d   6.00 6.00
Souvenir Sheet
2646 A469 $6 multi   4.50 4.50

Paintings of Yoshitoshi Taiso (1839-92) A470

Designs: 25c, A High Class Maid Training in a Samurai Household. 50c, A Castle-Toppler Known as "Keisei": A Beautiful Woman Able to Seduce a Ruler So That He Forgets the Affairs of the State. $1, Stylish Young Geisha Battling a Snowstorm on Her Way to Work. $5, A Lady in Distress Being Treated With Moxa.

No. 2651: a, A Lady of the Imperial Court Wearing Four Layers of Robes. b, Young Mother Adoring Her Infant Son. c, Lady-in-waiting Looking Amused Over a Veranda in the Household of a Great Lord. d, A High-ranking Courtesan Known as "Oiran" Waiting For a Private Assignation.

$6, A Girl Teasing Her Cat.

2003, Apr. 30
2647-2650 A470 Set of 4   5.00 5.00
2651 A470 $2 Sheet of 4, #a-d   6.00 6.00
Souvenir Sheet
2652 A470 $6 multi   4.50 4.50

Paintings of Raoul Dufy (1877-1953) — A471

Designs: 90c, Boats at Martigues. $1, Harvesting. $1.80, Sailboats in the Port of Le Havre. $5, The Big Bather, vert.

No. 2657: a, The Beach and the Pier at Trouville. b, Port With Sailing Ships. c, Black Cargo. d, Nice, the Bay of Anges.

No. 2658, $6, The Interior With an Open Window. No. 2659, $6, Vence.

2003, Apr. 30
2653-2656 A471 Set of 4   6.50 6.50
2657 A471 $2 Sheet of 4, #a-d   6.00 6.00
Size: 96x76mm
Imperf
2658-2659 A471 Set of 2   9.00 9.00

Prince William, 21st Birthday — A472

No. 2660: a, With yellow and black shirt. b, With polo helmet. c, With blue shirt.
$6, In suit.

2003, May 14   Perf. 14
2660 A472 $3 Sheet of 3, #a-c   7.00 7.00
Souvenir Sheet
2661 A472 $6 multi   4.50 4.50

Salvation Army in Antigua, Cent. — A473

Designs: 30c, Emblem, Tamarind tree, Parham, vert. 90c, Salvation Army Pre-school, vert. $1, Meals on Wheels. $1.50, St. John's Citadel Band. $1.80, Salvation Army Citadel. $6, Tamarind tree, Parham, vert.

2003, May 19   Perf. 14¼
2662-2666 A473 Set of 5   4.25 4.25
Souvenir Sheet
2667 A473 $6 multi   4.50 4.50

Antigua & Barbuda Scouts Association, 90th Anniv. — A474

Designs: 30c, First Anglican Scout troop, 1931. $1, National Scout Camp, 2002. $1.50, Woodbadge Training Course, 2000, horiz. $1.80, Men visiting National Scout Camp, 1986, horiz.

No. 2672: a, Edris George. b, Theodore George. c, Edris James.
$6, Scout with semaphore flags.

2003, June 9   Perf. 14
2668-2671 A474 Set of 4   3.75 3.75
2672 A474 90c Sheet of 3, #a-c   2.25 2.25
Souvenir Sheet
2673 A474 $6 multi   4.75 4.75

Tour de France Bicycle Race, Cent. — A475

No. 2674, $2: a, Cesar Garin, 1903. b, Henri Cornet, 1904. c, Louis Trousselier, 1905. d, René Pottier, 1906.

No. 2675, $2: a, Lucien Petit-Breton, 1907. b, Petit-Breton, 1908. c, François Faber, 1909. d, Octave Lapize, 1910.

No. 2676, $2: a, Gustave Garrigou, 1911. b, Odile Defraye, 1912. c, Philippe Thys, 1913. d, Thys, 1914.

No. 2677, $6, Pierre Giffard. No. 2678, $6, Henri Desgrange. No. 2679, $6, Comte de Dion.

2003, June 9   Perf. 13¼
Sheets of 4, #a-d
2674-2676 A475 Set of 3   18.00 18.00
Souvenir Sheets
2677-2679 A475 Set of 3   13.50 13.50

Caribbean Community, 30th Anniv. — A476

2003, July 4   Perf. 14
2680 A476 $1 multi   .80 .80

Intl. Year of Fresh Water — A477

No. 2681, horiz.: a, Chutes de Carbet and rocks. b, Chutes de Carbet and foliage at left and right. c, Rocks at base of Chutes de Carbet.
$6, Ocho Rios Waterfall.

2003, July 14   Perf. 13¼
2681 A477 $2 Sheet of 3, #a-c   5.25 5.25
Souvenir Sheet
2682 A477 $6 multi   5.00 5.00

General Motors Automobiles — A478

No. 2683, $2 — Cadillacs: a, 1955 Eldorado convertible. b, 1937 Series 60. c, 1959 Eldorado. d, 2002 Eldorado.

No. 2684, $2 — Chevrolet Corvettes: a, 1954 convertible. b, 1964 Sting Ray. c, 1964 Sting Ray convertible. d, 1998 convertible.

No. 2685, $6, 1953 Cadillac Eldorado. No. 2686, $6, 1956 Corvette convertible.

2003, July 14   Perf. 13¼x13½
Sheets of 4, #a-d
2683-2684 A478 Set of 2   12.00 12.00
Souvenir Sheets
2685-2686 A478 Set of 2   9.00 9.00
Cadillac, cent.; Corvette, 50th anniv.

History of Aviation — A479

No. 2687, $2: a, First Wright Brothers flight, 1903. b, First free flight in helicopter by Paul Cornu, 1907. c, First landing on ship, by E. B. Ely. d, Curtiss A-1, first hydroplane, 1911.

No. 2688, $2: a, Bell X-5, 1951. b, Convair XFY-1, 1954. c, North American X-15, 1959. d, Alexei Leonov, first man to walk in space, 1965.

No. 2689, $2: a, Concorde, 1969. b, Martin X-24, 1969. c, Apollo-Soyuz space mission, 1975. d, Mars probe Viking, 1976.

No. 2690, $6, Boeing Model 200 Monomail, 1930. No. 2691, $6, Breaking of sound barrier by Bell X-1, 1947. No. 2692, $6, Grumman X-29, 1984.

2003, July 28   Perf. 14
Sheets of 4, #a-d
2687-2689 A479 Set of 3   20.00 20.00
Souvenir Sheets
2690-2692 A479 Set of 3   13.50 13.50

Bird Type of 1995
Designs: $5, Montezuma oropendola. $10, Green jay.

2003, Aug. 11   Litho.   Perf. 15x14
2693 A296 $5 multi   3.75 3.75
2694 A296 $10 multi   7.50 7.50

Circus Performers — A480

No. 2695, $1.80 — Clowns: a, Apes. b, Mo Lite. c, Gigi. d, "Buttons" McBride.
No. 2696, $1.80 — Performers: a, Chun Group. b, Casselly Sisters. c, Oliver Groszer. d, Keith Nelson.

2003, Sept. 1   Perf. 14
Sheets of 4, #a-d
2695-2696 A480 Set of 2   11.00 11.00

Christmas A481

Designs: 25c, Madonna and Child, by Bartolomeo Vivarini. 30c, Holy Family, by Pompeo Girolamo Batoni. 45c, Madonna and Child, by Benozzo Gozzoli. 50c, Madonna and Child (Calci Parish Church), by Gozzoli. 75c, Madonna and Child Giving Blessings, by Gozzoli. 90c, Madonna and Child, by Master of the Female Half-figures. $2.50, Benois Madonna, by Leonardo da Vinci.

$6, The Virgin and Child with Angels, by Rosso Fiorentino.

2003, Nov. 10   Litho.   Perf. 14¼
2697-2703 A481 Set of 7   4.25 4.25
Souvenir Sheet
2704 A481 $6 multi   4.50 4.50

Orchids — A482

No. 2705, $2.50, vert.: a, Psychopsis papilio. b, Amesiella philippinensis. c, Maclellanara Pagan Dove Song. d, Phalaenopsis Little Hal.

No. 2706, $2.50: a, Daeliocattleya Amber Glow. b, Hygrochilus parishii. c, Dendrobium crystallinum. d, Disa hybrid.

$5, Cattleya deckeri.

2003, Dec. 8   *Perf. 13½*
Sheets of 4, #a-d
2705-2706 A482   Set of 2   17.50 17.50
Souvenir Sheet
2707 A482 $5 multi   5.00 5.00

Birds — A483

No. 2708, $2.50, vert.: a, Blue and gold macaw. b, Green-winged macaw. c, Greennaped lorikeet. d, Lesser sulfur-crested cockatoo.

No. 2709, $2.50: a, Severe macaw. b, Blueheaded parrot. c, Budgerigar. d, Sun conure.

$5, Bald ibis.

2003, Dec. 8   **Sheets of 4, #a-d**
2708-2709 A483   Set of 2   19.50 19.50
Souvenir Sheet
2710 A483 $5 multi   5.00 5.00

Butterflies — A484

No. 2711, $2: a, Esmerelda. b, Tiger pierid. c, Blue night. d, Charaxes nobilis.

No. 2712, $2.50: a, Orange-barred sulphur. b, Scarce bamboo page. c, Charaxes latona. d, Hewitson's blue hairstreak.

$5, Diaethia meridionalis.

2003, Dec. 8   **Sheets of 4, #a-d**
2711-2712 A484   Set of 2   17.50 17.50
Souvenir Sheet
2713 A484 $5 multi   5.00 5.00

Sharks — A485

No. 2714: a, Bull. b, Gray reef. c, Black tip. d, Leopard.

$5, Great white.

2003, Dec. 8
2714 A485 $2 Sheet of 4, #a-d   7.50 7.50
Souvenir Sheet
2715 A485 $5 multi   4.50 4.50

New Year 2004 (Year of the Monkey) — A486

No. 2716, each $1.50: a, Monkey with black face and white chest. b, Monkey with brown face and white chest. c, Monkey with black, gray and yellow face. d, Red brown monkey on branch.

2004, Jan. 19   *Perf. 14*
2716 A486   Sheet of 4, #a-d   5.00 5.00

Arthur and Friends — A487

No. 2717, each $1.50: a, Binky. b, Buster. c, Francine. d, D.W. e, Sue Ellen. f, Muffy.

No. 2718, each $1.80: a, Binky. b, Muffy. c, Francine. d, Buster.

No. 2719, each $2.50: a, Arthur hitting baseball. b, Sue Ellen. c, Binky. d, Arthur with foot on home plate.

2004, Feb. 16   *Perf. 13¼*
2717 A487   Sheet of 6, #a-f   6.75 6.75
Sheets of 4, #a-d
2718 2719 A487   Set of 2   13.00 13.00

Paintings by Ren Xiong (1820-57) — A488

No. 2720, each $1.50: a, Purple hills. b, Cliffside waves. c, Hills at left, trees, Chinese text at right. d, House and tree.

No. 2721, each $1.50: a, Rocky pinnacles. b, Rocks at left and right. c, Hills, trees and bridge, Chinese text at top right. d, Waterfall at right, Chinese text at top left. e, Waterfalls, Chinese text at top left. f, Rocks and flowers, Chinese text at top left.

No. 2722, each $1.50: a, Bird on flowering tree. b, Bird in tree.

2004, Feb. 16
2720 A488   Sheet of 4, #a-d   4.50 4.50
2721 A488   Sheet of 6, #a-f   6.75 6.75
2722 A488   Sheet of 2, #a-b   4.00 4.00

Paintings by Pablo Picasso — A489

No. 2723: a, Woman with a Flower. b, Marie-Thérèse Seated. c, The Red Armchair (Marie-Thérèse) Seated. d, The Dream (Marie-Thérèse) Seated.

$5, Bust of a Girl (Marie-Thérèse).

2004, Mar. 8   *Perf. 14¼*
2723 A489 $2 Sheet of 4, #a-d   6.50 6.50
Imperf
2724 A489 $5 shown   4.00 4.00
No. 2723 contains four 38x50mm stamps.

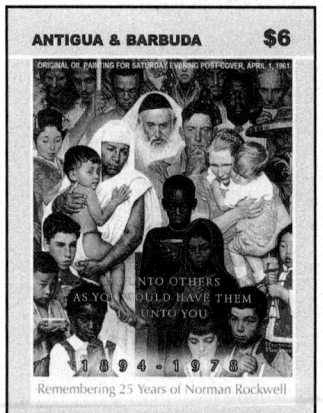

Paintings by Norman Rockwell — A490

No. 2725: a, Freedom of Speech. b, Freedom to Worship. c, Freedom from Want. d, Freedom from Fear.

$5, Painting for cover of Apr. 1, 1961 Saturday Evening Post.

2004, Mar. 8
2725 A490 $2 Sheet of 4, #a-d   6.00 6.00
Imperf
2726 A490 $6 shown   4.50 4.50
No. 2725 contains four 38x50mm stamps.

Paintings by Paul Gauguin (1848-1903) — A491

Designs: 25c, Vaite Goupil, vert. 30c, Autoportrait prés de Golgotha, vert. 75c, Le Moulin David à Pont-Aver. $2.50, Moisson en Bretagne, vert.

$4, Cavaliers sur la Plage.

2004, Mar. 8   Litho.   *Perf. 14¼*
2727-2730 A491   Set of 4   3.00 3.00
Imperf
Size: 77x63mm
2731 A491 $4 multi   4.75 4.75

Paintings by Joan Miró (1893-1983) — A492

Designs: 75c, The Smile of Flaming Wings. 90c, The Bird's Song in the Dew of the Moon. $1, Dancer II, vert. $4, Painting, 1954, vert.

No. 2736, $2 — Painting Based on a Collage, description in: a, LL. b, LR. c, UL. d, UR.

$5, Bather. $6, Flame in Space and Nude Woman, vert.

2004, Mar. 8   Litho.   *Perf. 14¼*
2732-2735 A492   Set of 4   5.50 5.50
2736 A492 $2 Sheet of 4, #a-d   6.50 6.50
Imperf
Size: 102x83mm
2737 A492 $5 multi   4.00 4.00
Size: 83x102mm
2738 A492 $6 multi   5.00 5.00

Wedding of Prince Felipe de Borbón of Spain and Letizia Ortiz A493

Designs: 30c, Couple. 50c, Couple, diff. 75c, Letizia. 90c, Prince Felipe. $1, Couple, diff. No. 2744, $5, Couple, diff.

No. 2745: a, Spanish royal family. b, Flags and Prince Felipe in uniform. c, Prince Felipe, his grandfather, Juan de Borbón y Battenberg, and his father, King Juan Carlos. d, Letizia, Prince Felipe, King Juan Carlos and Queen Sophia, horiz. e, Similar to 75c. f, Similar to 90c.

No. 2746, $5, Couple, diff. No. 2747, $5, Similar to #2745a. No. 2748, $5, Similar to #2745c. No. 2749, $6, Letizia, map of Europe. No. 2750, $6, Similar to #2745b. No. 2751, $6, Similar to #2745d, horiz.

2004, May 21   *Perf. 13¼*
2739-2744 A493   Set of 6   6.50 6.50
2745 A493 $1.80 Sheet of 6, #a-f   8.50 8.50
Souvenir Sheets
2746-2751 A493   Set of 6   25.00 25.00

Election of Pope John Paul II, 25th Anniv. (in 2003) — A494

No. 2752: a, Pope with Mother Teresa. b, Pope in the Holy Land. c, Pope meeting with Pres. George W. Bush. d, Pope waving, dark background. e, Pope waving, light background.

2004, June 17   *Perf. 14*
2752 A494 $1.80 Sheet of 5, #a-e   7.25 7.25
Inscription of "2000" on No. 2752a is incorrect.

United Nations
International Year of Peace

Intl. Year of Peace — A495

No. 2753 Dove and: a, Intl. Year of Peace emblem. b, Earth. c, UN emblem.

2004, June 17
2753 A495 $3 Sheet of 3, #a-c 6.75 6.75

2004 Summer Olympics, Athens A496

Designs: $1, Poster for 1964 Tokyo Olympics. $1.65, Commemorative medal for 1964 Tokyo Olympics. $1.80, Fencing, horiz. $2, Wrestlers, horiz.

2004, June 17   *Perf. 14¼*
2754-2757 A496 Set of 4 5.00 5.00

EuroCup 04

European Soccer Championships, Portugal — A497

No. 2758: a, Milan Galic. b, Slava Metreveli. c, Igor Netto. d, Parc des Princes. $6, 1960 USSR team.

2004, June 17   *Perf. 14*
2758 A497 $2 Sheet of 4, #a-d 7.50 7.50
    Souvenir Sheet
       Perf. 14¼
2759 A497 $6 multi 5.00 5.00
No. 2758 contains four 28x42mm stamps.

Locomotives, Signals and Stations — A498

No. 2760, $1: a, Evening Star. b, Indian Railways XC Pacific. c, German Kreigslokomotive. d, Bulleid Light Pacific. e, G. W. R. copper cap chimney. f, Tallylyn Railway. g, Preservation volunteers. h, N. E. R. Y7 0-4-0T. h, Breda 0-4-0 WT, locomotive shed, Asmara, Eritrea.
No. 2761, $1, vert.: a, King Class 4-6-0. b, Argentinian 11B Class 2-8-0. c, Baldwin Mikado. d, Round trackside signal with red horizontal band. e, Wooden box with button signal. f, Signal house, signals with red and yellow arms. g, Signal house, signal with two red arms. h, Window of signal house. i, Signal lights.

No. 2762, $1, vert.: a, 2-4-0T on Douglas to Port Erin line, Isle of Man. b, South African Railways 4-8-2S. c, China Railways SY Class 2-8-2. d, St. Pancras Station. e, Ulverston Station, f, Bolton Station. g, Liverpool St. Station. h, Cannon St. Station. i, Malvern Station.
No. 2763, $5, Settle-Carlisle line. No. 2764, $6, Douro Valley Railway. No. 2765, $6, Train over Lake Egridir, Turkey.

2004, June 17   *Perf. 14*
    Sheets of 9, #a-i
2760-2762 A498 Set of 3 21.00 21.00
    Souvenir Sheets
2763-2765 A498 Set of 3 14.00 14.00

D-Day, 60th Anniv. A499

Designs: 30c, Derrick Tysoe. 45c, Lt. Gen. Walter Bedell Smith. $1.50, Les Perry. $3, Maj. Gen. Percy Hobart.
No. 2770, $2: a, Tiger II tank. b, Standartenfuhrer Kurt Meyer. c, Canadian infantry. d, British infantry.
No. 2771, $2: a, Hamilcar disgorges Tetrarch tank. b, Horsa glider unloads cargo. c, Beachheads established. d, Liberation begins.
No. 2772, $6, Sherman tank. No. 2773, $6, Mulberry Harbor.

2004, July 26   *Perf. 14¼*
    Stamp + Label (#2766-2769)
2766-2769 A499 Set of 4 4.00 4.00
    Sheets of 4, #a-d
2770-2771 A499 Set of 2 12.00 12.00
    Souvenir Sheets
2772-2773 A499 Set of 2 9.00 9.00

    Miniature Sheet

Queen Juliana of the Netherlands (1909-2004) — A500

No. 2774 — Netherlands flag and: a, Juliana. b, Juliana and Prince Bernhard. c, Juliana and Princess Beatrix. d, Juliana and Princess Irene. e, Juliana and Princess Margriet. f, Juliana and Princess Christina.

2004, June 17   Litho.   *Perf. 13¼*
2774 A500 $2 Sheet of 6, #a-f 9.00 9.00

    Miniature Sheet

National Basketball Association Players — A501

No. 2775: a, Mike Bibby, Sacramento Kings. b, Jim Jackson, Houston Rockets. c, Tracy McGrady, Houston Rockets. d, Chris Webber, Sacramento Kings. e, Peja Stojakovic, Sacramento Kings. f, Yao Ming, Houston Rockets.

2004, Nov. 8   *Perf. 12*
2775 A501 $1.50 Sheet of 6, #a-f 6.75 6.75

FIFA (Fédération Internationale de Football Association), Cent. — A502

No. 2776: a, Zinedine Zidane. b, Roberto Baggio. c, Franz Beckenbauer. d, Ossie Ardiles.
$6, Jimmy Greaves.

2004, Nov. 8   *Perf. 12¾x12½*
2776 A502 $2 Sheet of 4, #a-d 6.00 6.00
    Souvenir Sheet
2777 A502 $6 multi 4.50 4.50

    Miniature Sheet

John Denver (1943-97), Singer — A503

No. 2778, each $1.50: a, At microphone. b, Tuning guitar. c, With arm extended. d, Facing left, playing guitar.

2004, Nov. 22   *Perf. 14*
2778 A503 Sheet of 4, #a-d 4.50 4.50

    Miniature Sheet

George Herman "Babe" Ruth (1895-1948), Baseball Player — A504

No. 2779, each $1.80: a, Wearing blue cap. b, Wearing crown. c, Wearing pinstriped cap. d, Holding bat.

2004, Nov. 22
2779 A504 Sheet of 4, #a-d 5.50 5.50

The Family Circus, Comic Strip by Bil and Jeff Keane — A505

No. 2780, $2: a, "Billy attackled me too hard," purple panel. b, "His ears came from where his eyes are." c, "Tennessee!" d, "One candy or one bowl?"
No. 2781, $2: a, "If you had wider shoulders, Daddy, you could be a two-seater." b, "Billy attackled me too hard," red panel. c, "Who teepeed the mummies?" d, "Looking out there makes me realize it's indeed the little things that count."
No. 2782, $2: a, "Someday I might travel to another planet, but I'm not sure why." b, "Adam and Eve were lucky. They didn't have any history to learn." c, "My backpack is too full. Will somebody help me stand up?" d, "I tripped because one foot tried to hug the other foot."
No. 2783, $2: a, "If you don't put enough stamps on it the mailman will only take it part way." b, "Gee, Grandma, you have a lot of thoughts on your wall." c, "Shall I play for you pa-rum-pa-pum-pummm. . .?" d, "You have to do that when you're married."
No. 2784, $2: a, Billy. b, Jeffy. c, PJ. d, Dolly.

     Perf. 13¼, 14¼(#2784)
2004, Nov. 22   **Sheets of 4, #a-d**
2780-2784 A505 Set of 5 30.00 30.00

World AIDS Day A506

2004, Dec. 1   *Perf. 14*
2785 A506 $2 multi 1.75 1.75

Christmas A507

Designs: 20c, Madonna in Floral Wreath, by Jan Breughel the Elder and Peter Paul Rubens. 25c, Madonna and Child, by Jan Gossaert. 30c, Santa Claus on skis. 45c, Santa Claus with raised arms. 50c, Santa Claus, reindeer on roof. $1, Floral Wreath with Virgin and Child, by Daniel Seghers. $1.80, Madonna and Child, by Andrea Mantegna.
$6, Madonna in a Floral Wreath, by Seghers.

2004, Dec. 13   *Perf. 12¼x12*
2786-2792 A507 Set of 7 3.50 3.50
    Souvenir Sheet
2793 A507 $6 multi 5.00 5.00

Dogs — A508

Designs: 30c, American pit bull terrier. 90c, Maltese. $1.50, Rottweiler. $3, Australian terrier.
$6, German shepherd, horiz.

2005, May 23 Litho. Perf. 12¾
2794-2797 A508 Set of 4 8.00 8.00
Souvenir Sheet
2798 A508 $6 multi 6.25 6.25

Cats — A509

Designs: 75c, Golden Persian. $1, Calico shorthair. $1.50, Siamese. $3, Tabby Persian. $5, Turkish.

2005, May 23
2799-2802 A509 Set of 4 6.00 6.00
Souvenir Sheet
2803 A509 $5 multi 5.00 5.00

Insects — A510

No. 2804, horiz.: a, Figure-of-eight butterfly. b, Honeybee. c, Migratory grasshopper. d, Hercules beetle.
$5, Cramer's Mesene butterfly.

2005, May 23
2804 A510 $2 Sheet of 4, #a-d 7.75 7.75
Souvenir Sheet
2805 A510 $5 multi 4.50 4.50

Marine Life — A511

No. 2806: a, Yellowtail damselfish. b, French angelfish. c, Horseshoe crab. d, Emerald mithrax crab.
$6, Spanish hogfish.

2005, May 23
2806 A511 $2 Sheet of 4, #a-d 7.25 7.25
Souvenir Sheet
2807 A511 $6 multi 5.75 5.75

Prehistoric Animals — A512

No. 2808, $2: a, Mammuthus imperator. b, Brontops. c, Hyracotherium. d, Propaleotherium.
No. 2809, $2.50: a, Ceratosaur. b, Coelurosaurs. c, Ornitholestes. d, Baryonyx.
No. 2810, $3: a, Plateosaurus. b, Yangchuanosaurus. c, Ceolophysis. d, Lystrosaurus.
No. 2811, $4, Triceratops. No. 2812, $5, Stegoasurus, vert. No. 2813, $6, Coelodonta.

2005, May 23
Sheets of 4, #a-d
2808-2810 A512 Set of 3 28.00 28.00
Souvenir Sheets
2811-2813 A512 Set of 3 13.00 13.00

Miniature Sheet

Pres. Ronald Reagan (1911-2004) — A513

No. 2814 — Background colors: a, Gray blue. b, Gray brown. c, Pink. d, White. e, Gray green. f, Buff.

2005, June 15 Perf. 14
2814 A513 $1.50 Sheet of 6, #a-f 7.50 7.50

New Year 2005 (Year of the Rooster) A514

Mother Hen and Her Brood, by Wang Ning: $1, Detail. $4, Entire painting.

2005, June 15 Perf. 14¼
2815 A514 $1 multi .75 .75
Souvenir Sheet
2816 A514 $4 multi 4.00 4.00
No. 2815 printed in sheets of 4.

Friedrich von Schiller (1759-1805), Writer — A515

No. 2817: a, Bust of Schiller, by C. L. Richter, Central Park, New York. b, Actors in "Kabale und Liebe." c, Schiller's birthplace, Marbach, Germany.
$6, Sculpture of Schiller, by Ernst Rau, Lincoln Park, Chicago.

2005, June 15 Perf. 14
2817 A515 $3 Sheet of 3, #a-c 6.75 6.75
Souvenir Sheet
2818 A515 $6 multi 5.25 5.25

Jules Verne (1828-1905), Writer — A516

No. 2819, vert. — Movie posters for Verne works: a, Monster Island, 1961. b, Journey to the Center of the Earth, 1961. c, From the Earth to the Moon, 1956. d, Sea Devils, 1961.
$5, Michael Strogoff, 1956.

2005, June 15
2819 A516 $2 Sheet of 4, #a-d 6.00 6.00
Souvenir Sheet
2820 A516 $5 multi 3.75 3.75
No. 2819 contains four 28x42mm stamps.

World Cup Soccer Championships, 75th Anniv. — A517

No. 2821, each $1.50 — Uruguayan flag, first place medal and: a, 1930 Uruguay team. b, Hector Castro scoring goal against Argentina. c, Crowd in Estadio Centenario. d, Hector Castro.
$6, Uruguay team celebrating 1930 victory.

2005, June 15 Perf. 14¼
2821 A517 Sheet of 4, #a-d 8.00 8.00
Souvenir Sheet
2822 A517 $6 multi 4.50 4.50

End of World War II, 60th Anniv. — A518

No. 2823, $1.50: a, Soldiers in Red Square, Moscow, May 9, 1945. b, Gen. Bernard Law Montgomery. c, Marshal Georgi K. Zhukov. d, Gen. Omar N. Bradley.
No. 2824, $2, horiz.: a, Winston Churchill, Franklin D. Roosevelt and Joseph Stalin at Yalta Summit. b, Raising of US flag on Mount Suribachi. c, Gen. Douglas MacArthur signing Japanese surrender documents. d, Japanese officials at surrender ceremony.

2005, June 15 Perf. 14
Sheets of 4, #a-d
2823-2824 A518 Set of 2 10.50 10.50

Battle of Trafalgar, Bicent. — A519

Various ships in battle: 90c, $1, $1.50, $1.80.
$6, The Victory firing during the Battle of Trafalgar.

2005, June 15 Perf. 14¼
2825-2828 A519 Set of 4 6.75 6.75
Souvenir Sheet
2829 A519 $6 multi 7.75 7.75

National Basketball Association Players — A520

Designs: No. 2830, 75c, Ray Allen, Seattle Supersonics. No. 2831, 75c, Lucious Harris, Cleveland Cavaliers. No. 2832, 75c, Dwight Howard, Orlando Magic. No. 2833, 75c, Antonio McDyess, Detroit Pistons. No. 2834, 75c, Emeka Okafor, Charlotte Bobcats.

2005 Perf. 14
2830-2834 A520 Set of 5 3.00 3.00

Pope John Paul II (1920-2005) and Meir Lau, Chief Rabbi of Israel — A521

2005, Oct. 10 Perf. 13½x13¼
2835 A521 $3 multi 4.25 4.25
Printed in sheets of 6.

Albert Einstein (1879-1955),
Physicist — A522

No. 2836 — Photograph of Einstein in: a,
Brown. b, Olive green. c, Black.

2005, Oct. 10 Litho. Perf. 13¼x13½
2836 A522 $3 Sheet of 3, #a-c   6.75 6.75

Hans Christian Andersen (1805-75),
Author — A523

No. 2837: a, Portrait of Andersen. b, Statue
of Andersen, Central Park, New York City. c,
Andersen's gravesite.
$6, Andersen seated.

2005, Oct. 10 Perf. 13½x13¼
2837 A523 $3 Sheet of 3, #a-c   6.75 6.75
Souvenir Sheet
2838 A523 $6 multi   5.25 5.25

Rotary International, Cent. — A524

No. 2839, vert.: a, Italy #1372. b, Paul Harris
Medallion. c, Paul P. Harris, first Rotary
President.
$6, Children.

2005, Oct. 10 Perf. 13½x13¼
2839 A524 $3 Sheet of 3, #a-c   7.25 7.25
Souvenir Sheet
Perf. 13¼x13½
2840 A524 $6 multi   6.00 6.00

Pope Benedict
XVI — A525

2005, Nov. 21 Perf. 13½x13¼
2841 A525 $2 multi   1.75 1.75

Christmas — A526

Churches: 25c, Gilbert's Memorial Methodist Church. No. 2843, 30c, People's Church,
Barbuda. No. 2844, 30c, Tyrell's Roman Catholic Church. 45c, St. Barnabas Anglican
Church. 50c, St. Peter's Anglican Church. No.
2847, 75c, Spring Gardens Moravian Church.
No. 2848, 75c, St. Steven's Anglican Church.
No. 2849, 90c, Holy Family Catholic Cathedral. No. 2850, 90c, Pilgrim Holiness Church,
vert. $1, Ebenezer Methodist Church.
No. 2852, $5, St. John's Cathedral. No.
2853, $5, Worship service, Spring Gardens
Moravian Church, vert.

2005, Dec. 19 Perf. 12¾
2842-2851 A526 Set of 10   6.75 6.75
Souvenir Sheets
2852-2853 A526 Set of 2   8.00 8.00

Elvis Presley (1935-77) — A527

Serpentine Die Cut 8¾x9
2005 Litho. & Embossed
2854 A527 $20 gold & multi   16.00 16.00

National
Parks
A528

Designs: No. 2855, 20c, Joiner's Loft, Nelson's Dockyard Natl. Park. No. 2856, 20c, Pay
Office, Nelson's Dockyard Natl. Park, vert. No.
2857, 30c, Admiral's House Museum, Nel-
son's Dockyard Natl. Park. No. 2858, 30c,
Bakery, Nelson's Dockyard Natl. Park. No.
2859, 75c, Devil's Bridge Natl. Park. No. 2860,
75c, View from Shirley Heights Lookout, Nel-
son's Dockyard Natl. Park. No. 2861, 90c,
Green Castle Hill Natl. Park. No. 2862, 90c,
Fort Berkeley, Nelson's Dockyard Natl. Park.
No. 2863, $1.50, Pigeon Point Beach, Nel-
son's Dockyard Natl. Park. No. 2864, $1.50,
Half Moon Bay Natl. Park. $1.80, Cannon at
Ft. Berkeley.
No. 2866, $5, Codrington Lagoon Natl.
Park. No. 2867, $5, Museum, Nelson's Dock-
yard Natl. Park, vert.

2006, Jan. 9 Perf. 14
2855-2865 A528 Set of 11   7.00 7.00
Souvenir Sheets
2866-2867 A528 Set of 2   9.50 9.50

National Parks of the United
States — A529

No. 2868: a, Yellowstone. b, Olympic. c,
Glacier. d, Grand Canyon. e, Yosemite. f,
Great Smoky Mountains.
$6, Mount Rainier.

2006, Jan. 6 Perf. 14¼
2868 A529 $1.50 Sheet of 6, #a-f 7.50 7.50
Souvenir Sheet
Perf. 14
2869 A529 $6 multi   4.75 4.75
No. 2868 contains six 50x38mm stamps.

Moravian Church
Antigua
Conference, 250th
Anniv. — A530

Designs: 30c, Bishop John Ephraim Knight.
$1, John Andrew Buckley. $1.50, Old Spring
Gardens Moravian Church, horiz.
No. 2873, $5, Sandbox tree. No. 2874, $5,
Westerby Memorial. No. 2875, $5, Spring Gar-
dens Teachers College, horiz.

2006, Apr. 3 Perf. 12¾
2870-2872 A530 Set of 3   2.25 2.25
Souvenir Sheets
2873-2875 A530 Set of 3   13.00 13.00

Marilyn Monroe
(1926-62),
Actress — A531

2006, Apr. 10 Perf. 13¼
2876 A531 $3 multi   2.25 2.25
Printed in sheets of 4.

Queen Elizabeth II, 80th
Birthday — A532

No. 2877: a, As young woman (black and
white photo). b, Wearing pearl necklace. c,
Wearing white blouse. d, Wearing crown.
$6, Wearing crown, diff.

2006, Apr. 10
2877 A532 $2 Sheet of 4, #a-d 6.50 6.50
Souvenir Sheet
2878 A532 $6 multi   4.75 4.75

2006 Winter Olympics, Turin — A533

Designs: No. 2879, 75c, Austria #715. No.
2880, 75c, Poster for 1972 Sapporo Winter
Olympics, vert. No. 2881, 90c, Austria #714.
No. 2882, 90c, Japan #1103, vert. $2, Austria
#717. $3, Poster for 1964 Innsbruck Winter
Olympics, vert.

2006, May 11 Litho. Perf. 14¼
2879-2884 A533 Set of 6   7.00 7.00

Miniature Sheets

A534

Washington 2006 World Philatelic
Exhibition — A535

No. 2885: a, Framed circular portrait of Benjamin Franklin wearing red jacket with fur collar. b, Framed circular portrait of Franklin
seated. c, Framed circular portrait of Franklin
wearing gray jacket.
No. 2886: a, Unframed portrait of Franklin
wearing jacket with fur collar. b, US #1. c,
Unframed portrait of Franklin wearing black
coat. d, Framed oval portrait like #2885a
(73x87mm).

2006, May 29 Perf. 11½
2885 A534 $3 Sheet of 3, #a-c 7.50 7.50
Perf. 11½, Imperf. (#2886d)
2886 A535 $3 Sheet of 4, #a-d 9.50 9.50

Miniature Sheet

Wolfgang Amadeus Mozart (1756-91),
Composer — A536

No. 2887: a, Mozart's viola. b, Mozart at age
11. c, Young Mozart. d, Mozart in Verona,
1770.

2006, July 3 Perf. 12¾
2887 A536 $3 Sheet of 4, #a-d 11.00 11.00

Miniature Sheet

Posters of Elvis Presley
Movies — A537

No. 2888: a, Charro! b, Follow That Dream. c, G.I. Blues. d, Blue Hawaii.

2006, July 12   *Perf. 13¼*
2888   A537 $3 Sheet of 4, #a-d   10.00 10.00

Antigua and Barbuda Girl Guides, 75th Anniv. — A538

Designs: 25c, Leaders after garbage collection race, 2002. 30c, Girl Guides color party, horiz. 45c, Uniformed and non-uniformed members. 50c, Girl Guides marching band, horiz. $1, Leeward Islands leaders training camp, 1946.

No. 2894, $5, Assistant Commissioner Lisa Simon. a, $5, Girl Guides gathering at Fort James, 1935, horiz. No. 2896, $5, Enrollment ceremony, 2006, horiz.

2006, July 17   *Perf. 12¾*
2889-2893   A538   Set of 5   2.75 2.75
Souvenir Sheets
2894-2896   A538   Set of 3   12.50 12.50

Leeward Islands Air Transport, 50th Anniv. A539

Designs: 30c, HS-748 Hawker Siddely Avro. No. 2898, 50c, BN2 Islanders. No. 2899, 50c, BN2 Norman Islander. No. 2900, 50c, Beechcraft Twin Bonanza, vert. $1.50, BAC 111, HS-748. $2.50, DH8-300 de Havilland.

$5, Sir Frank Delisle, LIAT founder, and Beechcraft Twin Bonanza, vert.

2006, Oct. 2   Litho.   *Perf. 14¼*
2897-2902   A539   Set of 6   6.25 6.25
Souvenir Sheet
2903   A539 $5 multi   5.25 5.25

Independence, 25th Anniv. — A540

Designs: 30c, Pineapple. $1, Flag. $1.50, Coat of arms.

No. 2907: a, One magnificent frigatebird. b, Two fallow deer. c, One fallow deer. d, Two magnificent frigatebirds.

$5, New Parliament Building, vert.

2006, Oct. 30   *Perf. 12¾*
2904-2906   A540   Set of 3   2.50 2.50
2907   A540   25c Sheet of 4, #a-d   1.50 1.50
Souvenir Sheet
2908   A540 $5 multi   5.50 5.50

No. 2908 contains one 38x50mm stamp.

Civil Rights Leaders — A541

No. 2909, $2: a, Dalai Lama. b, Pres. Abraham Lincoln. c, Susan B. Anthony. d, Harriet Tubman.

No. 2910, $2: a, Mahatma Gandhi. b, Nelson Mandela. c, Rosa Parks.

$5, Dr. Martin Luther King, Jr.

2006, Nov. 20   Perf. 12, 12½ (#2910)
2909   Horiz. strip of 4   8.00 8.00
a.-d.   A541 $2 Any single   1.75 1.75

2910   A541 $2 Sheet of 3, #a-c   5.00 5.00
Souvenir Sheet
2911   A541 $5 multi   5.50 5.50

Rembrandt (1606-69), Painter A542

Designs: 50c, Landscape with the Baptism of the Eunuch. 75c, Landscape with a Coach. $1, River Landscape with Ruins. $2, Landscape with a Castle.

No. 2916, $2: a, The Holy Family (Joseph at table). b, The Good Samaritan Arriving at the Inn. c, Rebecca Taking Leave of Her Family. d, The Holy Family (Madonna and Child).

No. 2917, $2 — Samson Posting the Riddle to the Wedding Guests: a, Woman with beads in hair. b, Three men. c, Two men. d, Woman holding glass.

No. 2918, $5, Self-portrait. No. 2919, $5, Rembrandt's Mother.

2006, Dec. 20   *Perf. 12¼x12*
2912-2915   A542   Set of 4   5.00 5.00
Sheets of 4, #a-d
2916-2917   A542   Set of 2   13.50 13.50
Imperf
Size: 70x100mm
2918-2919   A542   Set of 2   9.00 9.00

Betty Boop — A543

No. 2920, vert. — Background color: a, Yellow. b, Green. c, Red violet. d, Orange. e, Blue green. f, Purple.

No. 2921: a, Text, "Betty Boop" and stars. b, Betty Boop and cat.

2006, Dec. 20   *Perf. 14¼*
2920   A543 $1.50 Sheet of 6, #a-f   7.50 7.50
Souvenir Sheet
2921   A543 $3 Sheet of 2   5.00 5.00

Space Achievements — A544

No. 2922: a, JSC Shuttle mission simulator. b, STS-1 prime crew in classroom. c, STS-1 Columbia on launch pad. d, Launch of Columbia. e, Columbia landing at Edwards Air Force Base. f, Columbia on runway.

No. 2923, $3: a, Molniya 8K78M launch vehicle. b, Luna 9 flight apparatus. c, Moon

---

images transmitted by Luna 9. d, Luna 9 capsule.

No. 2924, $3: a, Apollo crew boards transfer van. b, Handshake after Apollo-Soyuz linkup. c, Display of Apollo-Soyuz plaque. d, Recovery of Apollo command module.

No. 2925, $6, Artist's conception of NASA spaceship to orbit Moon. No. 2926, $6, Calipso Satellite. No. 2927, $6, Space Station Mir.

2006   *Perf. 12¾*
2922   A544 $2 Sheet of 6, #a-f   10.00 10.00
Sheets of 4, #a-d
2923-2924   A544   Set of 2   21.00 21.00
Souvenir Sheets
2925-2927   A544   Set of 3   16.00 16.00

Christmas — A545

Ornaments: 30c, Ball. 90c, Star. $1, Bell. $1.50, Christmas tree.

No. 2932: a, Ball. b, Star. c, Bell. d, Christmas tree.

$6, Santa Claus at beach.

2006   *Perf. 13½*
2928-2931   A545   Set of 4   3.00 3.00
2932   A545 $2 Sheet of 4, #a-d   6.75 6.75
Souvenir Sheet
2933   A545 $6 multi   6.00 6.00

Scouting, Cent. — A546

Scout emblem at: $4, UL. 90, LR.

2007, Jan. 18   *Perf. 13½*
2934   A546 $4 multi   4.00 4.00
Souvenir Sheet
2935   A546 $6 multi   6.00 6.00

No. 2934 was printed in sheets of 3.

Christopher Columbus (1451-1506), Explorer — A547

Designs: 75c, Map of North and South America, Columbus on bended knee. 90c, Portrait of Columbus. $2, Portrait, diff. $3, Portrait, diff.

$6, Columbus and ships.

2007, Jan. 18   *Perf. 13¼*
2936-2939   A547   Set of 4   7.00 7.00
Souvenir Sheet
2940   A547 $6 multi   6.00 6.00

Pres. John F. Kennedy (1917-63) — A548

No. 2941, $3: a, Wearing naval ensign dress uniform. b, With crew. c, On PT-109. d, Wearing light jacket in South Pacific.

No. 2942, $3: a, Campaigning on crutches. b, Wearing t-shirt. c, With John F. Fitzgerald and Joseph P. Kennedy. d, Celebrating victory with sister.

Sheets of 4, #a-d
2007, Jan. 18   Litho.
2941-2942   A548   Set of 2   22.00 22.00

Mushrooms — A549

No. 2943: a, Cantharellus cibarius. b, Auricularia auricula-judae. c, Mycena acicula. d, Peziza vesiculosa.

$6, Pleurotus djamor.

2007, Apr. 2   Litho.   *Perf. 14¼*
2943   A549 $2 Sheet of 4, #a-d   9.00 9.00
Souvenir Sheet
2944   A549 $6 multi   6.50 6.50

Butterflies — A550

Designs: 75c, Figure-of-eight. 90c, Tiger pierid. $1, Purple mort bleu. $4, Mosaic.

No. 2949: a, Small lacewing. b, Clorinde. c, Common morpho. d, White peacock.

$5, Grecian shoemaker.

2007, Apr. 2
2945-2948   A550   Set of 4   8.00 8.00
2949   A550 $2 Sheet of 4, #a-d   7.00 7.00
Souvenir Sheet
2950   A550 $5 multi   6.50 6.50

Flowers — A551

Designs: 75c, Allamanda. 90c, Bidens sulphurea. $1, Alstromeria caryophyflacea. $4, Bougainvillea.

No. 2955, $2, horiz.: a, Canna limbata. b, Gazania rigens. c, Gloriosa rothschildiana. d, Hibiscus sinensis.

No. 2956, $3, horiz.: a, Oncidium flexuosum. b, Paphiopedilum pinocchio. c, Cattleyopsis lindenii. d, Cattleyopsis cubensis.

No. 2957, $6, Caesalpinia pulcherrima. No. 2958, $6, Osmoglossum pulchellum.

2007, Apr. 2
2951-2954	A551	Set of 4	8.00	8.00
Sheets of 4, #a-d				
2955-2956	A551	Set of 2	20.00	20.00
Souvenir Sheets				
2957-2958	A551	Set of 2	12.00	12.00

Cricket Players — A552

Designs: 25c, Kenneth Benjamin. 30c, Anderson Roberts. 90c, Ridley Jacobs. $1, Curtly Ambrose. $1.50, Richard Richardson. $5, Sir Vivian Richards.

2007, Apr. 5   *Perf. 12¾*
2959-2963	A552	Set of 5	3.75	3.75
Souvenir Sheet				
2964	A552	$5 multi	6.00	6.00

Wedding of Queen Elizabeth II and Prince Philip, 60th Anniv. A553

No. 2965: a, Couple. b, Wedding sandals. $6, Couple, vert.

2007, May 1   *Perf. 14*
2965	A553	$1.50 Pair, #a-b	3.00	3.00
Souvenir Sheet				
2966	A553	$6 multi	6.00	6.00

No. 2965 was printed in sheets containing three of each stamp.

Painted Fans by Qi Baishi (1864-1957) — A554

No. 2967, horiz.: a, Camellias and butterfly. b, Two Shrimp and Arrowhead Leaves. c, Gourd and Ladybug. d, Bird. e, Landscape. f, Five Shrimp.
No. 2968: a, Chrysanthemums. b, Maple Leaves.
$6, Wisteria.

2007, May 1   *Perf. 14¼*
| 2967 | A554 | $1.50 Sheet of 6, | | |
| | | #a-f | 7.50 | 7.50 |

2968	A554	$3 Sheet of 2,		
		#a-b	6.00	6.00
Souvenir Sheet				
2969	A554	$6 multi	6.00	6.00
Miniature Sheet				

Ferrari Automobiles — A555

No. 2970: a, 1969 365 GTS4. b, 2005 Superamerica. c, 1990 F1 90. d, 1976 400 Automatic. e, 1954 250 GT Coupe. f, 1960 156 F2. g, 1972 312 P h, 1956 D 50.

2007, June 4   *Perf. 13¼*
| 2970 | A555 | $1.40 Sheet of 8, | | |
| | | #a-h | 10.00 | 10.00 |

Concorde — A556

No. 2971, $1.50 — Concorde O1: a, On ground, red frame. b, In air, green frame. c, On ground, blue violet frame. d, In air, red frame. e, On ground, green frame. f, In air, blue violet frame.
No. 2972, $1.50 — Concorde in flight and: a, Millennium Wheel, green denomination. b, Sydney Opera House, black denomination. c, Millennium Wheel, red violet denomination. d, Sydney Opera House, red orange denomination. e, Millennium Wheel, black denomination. f, Sydney Opera House, blue denomination.

2007, June 20   *Perf. 12¾*
| **Sheets of 6, #a-f** | | | | |
| 2971-2972 | A556 | Set of 2 | 17.50 | 17.50 |

First Helicopter Flight, Cent. — A557

No. 2973, horiz.: a, NH 90. b, BO 105, black denomination at LR. c, NH 90. d, AS-61 over water. e, BO 105, black denomination at LL. f, AS-61 from below.
$6, UH-1 Iroquois.

2007, June 20   *Perf. 12¾*
2973	A557	$1.50 Sheet of 6, #a-f	9.25	9.25
Souvenir Sheet				
2974	A557	$6 multi	6.75	6.75

Pope Benedict XVI — A558

2007, July 30   *Perf. 13¾*
| 2975 | A558 | $1.40 multi | 1.50 | 1.50 |

Printed in sheets of 8.

Miniature Sheet

Elvis Presley (1935-77) — A559

No. 2967 — Presley: a, Wearing black jacket. b, Facing left, wearing striped shirt, brown background. c, Wearing jacket and holding guitar. d, Facing forward, wearing striped shirt, brown background. e, Wearing red shirt. f, Holding guitar, purple background.

2007, July 30   *Perf. 13¼*
| 2976 | A559 | $1.50 Sheet of 6, | | |
| | | #a-f | 11.00 | 11.00 |

Princess Diana (1961-97) — A560

No. 2977 — Princess Diana wearing: a, Beige suit. b, Lilac dress. c, Purple jacket with black-edged collar. d, Hat.
$6, White robe.

2007, July 30
2977	A560	$2 Sheet of 4, #a-d	7.50	7.50
Souvenir Sheet				
2978	A560	$6 multi	5.75	5.75

Flora — A561

Designs: 15c, Bird of paradise. 20c, Seaside mahoe. 30c, Hibiscus. 50c, Agave. 70c, Barringtonia tree. 75c, Coconut tree. 90c, Mesquite tree, horiz. $1, Tamarind tree. $1.50, Black willow flowers, horiz. $1.80, Baobab tree, horiz. $2, Petrea volubilis. $2.50, Opuntia cochenillifera, horiz. $5, Locust fruit, horiz. $10, Barbuda black warri. $20, Castor oil plant.

Perf. 12½x13¼, 13¼x12½
2007, Oct. 1   Litho.
2979	A561	15c multi	.25	.25
2980	A561	20c multi	.25	.25
2981	A561	30c multi	.30	.25
2982	A561	50c multi	.45	.40
2983	A561	70c multi	.70	.55
2984	A561	75c multi	.75	.60
2985	A561	90c multi	.90	.70
2986	A561	$1 multi	1.00	.75
2987	A561	$1.50 multi	1.40	1.10
2988	A561	$1.80 multi	1.75	1.40
2989	A561	$2 multi	2.25	1.50
2990	A561	$2.50 multi	2.75	1.90
2991	A561	$5 multi	5.00	3.75
2992	A561	$10 multi	8.00	7.50
2993	A561	$20 multi	19.00	15.00
Nos. 2979-2993 (15)			44.75	35.90

Miniature Sheet

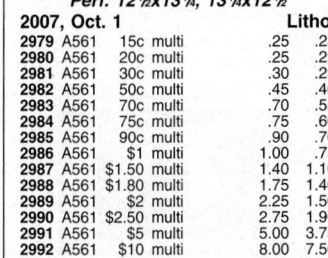

Intl. Holocaust Remembrance Day — A562

No. 2994 — United Nations delegates, each $1.40: a, John W. Ashe, Antigua & Barbuda. b, Alfred Capelle, Marshall Islands. c, Masao Nakayama, Micronesia. d, Gilles Noghes, Monaco. e, Baatar Choisuren, Mongolia. f, Filipe Chidumo, Mozambique. g, Marlene Moses, Nauru. h, Franciscus Majoor, Netherlands.

2007, Oct. 25   *Perf. 13¼*
| 2994 | A562 | Sheet of 8, #a-h | 10.00 | 10.00 |

Christmas A563

Designs: 30c, Stylized map of Antigua & Barbuda, sailboat, candy canes. 90c, Dancers, sailboat, decorated palm tree. $1, Decorated cake. $1.50, Woman in costume.

2007, Nov. 5   *Perf. 14¾x14*
| 2995-2998 | A563 | Set of 4 | 2.75 | 2.75 |

Hospice and Palliative Care A564

Emblem of Hospice Antigua & Barbuda and: No. 2999, 30c, Clock. No. 3000, 30c, Hands.

2007, Dec. 27   *Perf. 13¼*
| 2999-3000 | A564 | Set of 2 | .85 | .85 |

National Heroes — A565

Designs: No. 3001, 90c, King Court (1691-1736), slave rebellion leader. No. 3002, 90c, Dame Georgianna E. (Nellie) Robinson (1880-1972), educator. $1, Sir Vivian Richards, cricket player. $1.50, Sir Vere Cornwall Bird, Sr. (1909-99), first Prime Minister.

2008, Mar. 7 Litho. Perf. 12¾
3001-3004 A565 Set of 4 4.00 4.00

World Glaucoma Day — A566

Designs: 30c, Person applying glaucoma eyedrops. 50c, Normal and glaucomatous optic nerves. $1, Braille writing.

2008, Mar. 7 Perf. 13¼
3005-3007 A566 Set of 3 2.25 2.25

32nd America's Cup Yacht Races, Off Valencia, Spain — A567

No. 3008 — Various yachts with text "32nd America's Cup" in: a, $1.20, Yellow. b, $1.80, White. c, $3, Blue. d, $5, Orange.

2008, Mar. 25 Perf. 12½
3008 A567 Block of 4, #a-d 8.25 8.25

Miniature Sheet

2000 Summer Olympics, Beijing — A568

No. 3009, each $1.40: a, Pierre de Coubertin. b, Poster for 1896 Athens Olympic Games. c, Spiridon Louis, 1896 marathon gold medalist. d, Paul Masson, 1896 cycling gold medalist.

2008, Mar. 25 Perf. 12¾
3009 A568 Sheet of 4, #a-d 4.25 4.25

2008 World Stamp Championship, Israel — A569

2008, May 14 Imperf.
3010 A569 $6 multi 4.75 4.75

Visit of Pope Benedict XVI to United States A570

2008, June 18 Perf. 13¼
3011 A570 $2 multi 1.75 1.75
Printed in sheets of 4.

Miniature Sheet

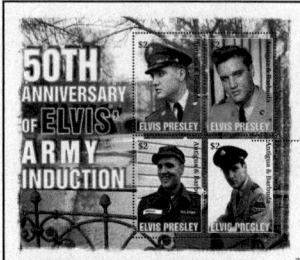

Army Induction of Elvis Presley, 50th Anniv. — A571

No. 3012 — Presley wearing: a, Dress uniform and cap. b, Dress uniform, no cap. c, Army fatigues and cap. d, Dress uniform with shoulder insignia and cap.

2008, June 18
3012 A571 $2 Sheet of 4, #a-d 6.50 6.50

Space Achievements — A572

No. 3013, $1.50, vert. — Vanguard I: a, Against black background, with five rods showing. b, Against white and green background. c, Against black background, with six rods showing.
No. 3014, $1.50: a, Explorer III and equipment, vert. b, Explorer III and Earth, vert. c, Diagram of Van Allen radiation belts.
No. 3015, $2, vert. — Vanguard I and: a, Black background. b, Multicolored background.
No. 3016, $2, vert. — Explorer III and: a, Red and green background. b, Black background.
No. 3017, $6, Vanguard I. No. 3018, $6, Explorer III.

2008, July 29 Perf. 13¼
Horiz. Strips of 3, #a-c
3013-3014 A572 Set of 2 9.00 9.00
Pairs, #a-b
3015-3016 A572 Set of 2 8.00 8.00
Souvenir Sheets
3017-3018 A572 Set of 2 12.00 12.00
Nos. 3013-3014 were each printed in sheets containing two strips. Nos. 3015-3016 were each printed in sheets containing two pairs.

Miniature Sheets

Muhammad Ali, Boxer — A573

No. 3019 — Ali with words or letters in background: a, "ws" at UR. b, "learned" above denomination. c, "is so ugly" at UR. d, "should donate" at UR. e, "greates" at UR. f, "hat" at UR.
No. 3020 — Ali, each $2: a, Hitting punching bag. b, Wearing robe. c, With bare shoulders. d, Wearing protective headgear.

2008, Sept. 29 Perf. 11½
3019 A573 $1.50 Sheet of 6, #a-f 7.50 7.50
Perf. 13¼
3020 A573 Sheet of 4, #a-d 6.50 6.50
No. 3020 contains four 37x50mm stamps.

Star Trek — A574

No. 3021: a, Capt. James Kirk and Mr. Spock. b, Chief Engineer Scott, Dr. Leonard McCoy, Kirk and Spock. c, Lt. Uhura, Spock. d, Actors on planetary city set. e, Uhura. f, Scott.
No. 3022: a, McCoy. b, Spock. c, Kirk. d, Hikaru Sulu.

2008, Sept. 29 Perf. 11½
3021 A574 $1.50 Sheet of 6, #a-f 8.00 8.00
Perf. 13¼
3022 A574 $2 Sheet of 4, #a-d 7.50 7.50
No. 3022 contains four 50x37mm stamps.

Miniature Sheet

Pres. John F. Kennedy (1917-63) — A575

No. 3023 — Kennedy: a, Looking right. b, Looking forward, curtains in background. c, Looking forward, smiling with teeth showing. d, Looking right with hand at chin.

2008, Dec. 18 Perf. 13¼
3023 A575 $2 Sheet of 4, #a-d 6.75 6.75

Miniature Sheet

Marilyn Monroe (1926-62), Actress — A576

No. 3024 — Monroe wearing: a, Orange sweater, with arm raised. b, Orange sweater, arms at side. c, Pink sweater. d, Purple sweater.

2008, Dec. 18
3024 A576 $2 Sheet of 4, #a-d 8.50 8.50

Christmas A577

Stained-glass windows: 30c, Holy Family. 90c, Infant Jesus in manger. $1, Madonna and Child, vert. $1.50, Sts. Elizabeth and John the Baptist, vert.

2009, Jan. 2 Perf. 14¾x14, 14x14¾
3025-3028 A577 Set of 4 3.00 3.00

Miniature Sheet

China 2009 World Stamp Exhibition — A578

No. 3029: a, Baseball. b, Beach volleyball. c, Artistic gymnastics. d, Judo.

2009, Jan. 5 Perf. 11¼x11½
3029 A578 $1.40 Sheet of 4, #a-d 4.50 4.50

Miniature Sheet

Pres. Abraham Lincoln (1809-65) — A579

No. 3030: a, Lincoln's first inaugural address, 1861. b, Lincoln, flag. c, Lincoln's second inaugural address, 1865. d, Lincoln at right, crowd at second inaugural.

2009, Jan. 5 Perf. 11½x11¼
3030 A579 $2 Sheet of 4, #a-d 7.25 7.25

Inauguration of US Pres. Barack Obama — A580

Pres. Obama facing: $2.75, Right. $10, Left.

2009, Jan. 20   **Perf. 12¼x11¾**
3031 A580 $2.75 multi   2.75 .275
Souvenir Sheet
Perf. 13¼x13½
3032 A580 $10 multi   7.75 7.75
No. 3031 was printed in sheets of 4. No. 3032 contains one 37x51mm stamp.

New Year 2009 (Year of the Ox) A581

2009, Jan. 26   **Perf. 11½x12**
3033 A581 $1 multi   1.25 1.25
Printed in sheets of 4.

A582

A583

2009, Apr. 10   **Perf. 13½x13¼**
3034 A582 $1 multi   1.10 1.10
Souvenir Sheet
Perf. 13
3035 A583 $5 multi   4.75 4.75
No. 3034 was printed in sheets of 8.

Miniature Sheet

Elvis Presley (1935-77) — A584

No. 3036 — Presley wearing: a, Hat. b, Suit with handkerchief in pocket. c, Black shirt and pants. d, Pink, white and black windbreaker. e, Blue shirt and lei. f, Suit without handkerchief.

2009, Apr. 14   **Perf. 14x14¼**
3036 A584 $1.50 Sheet of 6, #a-f 7.75 7.75

Miniature Sheets

A585

China 2009 World Stamp Exhibition — A586

No. 3037 — Landmarks in China: a, Bell Tower, Xian. b, St. Sophia Church, Harbin. c, Great Hall of the People, Chongqing. d, Fenghua Bridge, Tianjin.
No. 3038 — First emperor of China: a, Qin Shi Huang (259-210 B.C.). b, Horses of Terracotta Army. c, Soldiers of Terracotta Army. d, Excavated Terracotta Army.

2009, June 29   **Litho.**   **Perf. 12**
3037 A585 $1.40 Sheet of 4, #a-d   5.50 5.50
Perf. 12½x12¾
3038 A586 $1.40 Sheet of 4, #a-d   5.50 5.50

A587

2009, July 9   **Perf. 14x15**
3039 A587 $4 multi   3.50 3.50

Miniature Sheets

Dogs — A588

No. 3040, $2.50 — Labrador retrievers: a, Puppy in canoe. b, Two puppies at window. c, Two puppies with stick. d, Puppy in bucket.
No. 3041, $2.50 — Dachshunds: a, Dog and carrying case. b, Dog and flowers. c, Two dogs in flower box. d, Dog near flower pot.

2009, Aug. 13   **Perf. 12**
Sheets of 4, #a-d
3040-3041 A588   Set of 2   21.00 21.00

A589

Michael Jackson (1958-2009), Singer — A590

No. 3042 — Jackson: a, Holding microphone, wearing black coat with gold trim. b, Wearing black coat with gold trim, not holding microphone. c, Wearing red and black shirt. d, Wearing jacket with eagle and shield.
No. 3043 — Jackson: a, Wearing black pants, white above red orange frame at top of stamp. b, Wearing pants with buckles along leg, white above red orange frame at top of stamp. c, As "b," with black above red orange frame. d, As "a," with black above red orange frame.
$6, Jackson singing.

2009   **Litho.**   **Perf. 11¼x11½**
3042 A589 $2.50 Sheet of 4, #a-d   9.50 9.50
Perf. 12x11½
3043 A590 $2.50 Sheet of 4, #a-d   9.50 9.50
Souvenir Sheet
Perf. 13¼
3044 A590 $6 multi   4.75 4.75
Issued: Nos. 3042-3043, 9/30; No. 3044, 12/3. No. 3044 contains one 37x50mm stamp.

Meeting of US Pres. Barack Obama and Pope Benedict XVI — A591

No. 3045, vert.: a, Pres. Obama. b, Pope Benedict XVI. c, Michelle Obama.
$6, Pope Benedict XVI and Pres. Obama.

2009, Nov. 4   **Perf. 11¼x11½**
3045 A591 $2.75 Sheet of 3, #a-c   7.50 7.50
Souvenir Sheet
Perf. 11½x12
3046 A591 $6 multi   5.75 5.75

Chinese Aviation, Cent. — A592

No. 3047 — Aerobatic team: a, Six airplanes with blue, white and red contrails. b, Six airplanes flying right in double triangle formation. c, Six airplanes flying left in diagonal line formation. d, Five airplanes.
$6, J-7GB.

2009, Nov. 12   **Perf. 14**
3047 A592 $2 Sheet of 4, #a-d   6.75 6.75
Souvenir Sheet
Perf. 14¼
3048 A592 $6 multi   5.00 5.00
Aeropex 2009 Intl. Philatelic Exhibition, Biejing. No. 3048 contains one 50x37mm stamp.

First Man on the Moon, 40th Anniv. — A593

No. 3049: a, Apollo 11 patch, US flag on Moon. b, Lunar Module on Moon. c, Passive seismic experiment package. d, Apollo 11 on launch pad.
$6, Apollo 11 Command and Service Modules.

2009, Nov. 13   **Perf. 12¾x12½**
3049 A593 $2.50 Sheet of 4, #a-d   9.50 9.50
Souvenir Sheet
Perf. 12¾x13
3050 A593 $6 multi   5.50 5.50
Intl. Year of Astronomy.

Souvenir Sheets

A594

A595

A596

Elvis Presley (1935-77) — A597

2009, Nov. 26   **Perf. 13¼**
3051 A594 $6 multi   5.50 5.50
3052 A595 $6 multi   5.50 5.50
3053 A596 $6 multi   5.50 5.50
3054 A597 $6 multi   5.50 5.50
    Nos. 3051-3054 (4)   22.00 22.00

Worldwide Fund for Nature
(WWF) — A598

No. 3055 — Caribbean coots: a, Pair in water. b, Pair taking off. c, Pair and chick. d, Adult and chick.

2009, Dec. 3   **Perf. 13¼**
3055   Strip of 4   7.50 7.50
  a.-d. A598 $2.65 Any single   1.75 1.75
  e. Miniature sheet, 2 each
    #3055a-3055d   20.00 20.00

Christmas
A599

Christmas light displays: 90c, Candles. $1, Palm tree and reindeer. $1.80, Bells. $3, Nativity scene, horiz.

2009, Dec. 3   **Perf. 14x14¾, 14¾x14**
3056-3059 A599   Set of 4   5.00 5.00

Sir Vere Cornwall Bird, Sr. (1909-99), First Chief Minister, Premier and Prime Minister — A600

Bird: 30c, In chair. 75c, With blue, white and red stripes in background. 90c, Wearing red hat. $1.50, With building in background.
No. 3064: a, Like 75c. b, Like 30c. c, Like 90c. d, Like $1.50.
$6, Bird, map of Antigua with flag.

2009, Dec. 8   **Perf. 11¼x11½**
3060-3063 A600   Set of 4   3.00 3.00
3064 A600 $2.50 Sheet of 4, #a-
    d   8.00 8.00
    Souvenir Sheet
    Perf. 12x11½
3065 A600 $6 multi   5.00 5.00

Birds
A601

Designs: $1.20, Glossy ibis. $1.80, Green-winged teal. No. 3068, $3, California clapper rail. $5, Cattle egret, vert.
No. 3070: a, Green heron. b, Common ground dove. c, White-tailed hawk. d, Black-faced grassquit.
No. 3071, $3: a, Bananaquit. b, Osprey.

   Perf. 11½x11¼, 11¼x11½
2009, Dec. 8
3066-3069 A601   Set of 4   7.75 7.75
    Perf. 11½x12
3070 A601 $2.50 Sheet of 4, #a-
    d   9.00 9.00
    Souvenir Sheet
3071 A601 $3 Sheet of 2, #a-
    b   5.50 5.50

Souvenir Sheet

New Year 2010 (Year of the Tiger) — A602

No. 3072 — Chinese bronze tigers of: a, Western Han Dynasty. b, Shang Dynasty.

2010, Jan. 4   **Perf. 11½x12**
3072 A602 $5 Sheet of 2, #a-b   7.75 7.75

Ferrari Automobiles and Their Parts — A603

No. 3073, $1.25: a, Engine of 1960 246 P F1. b, 1960 246 P F1.
No. 3074, $1.25: a, Engine of 1964 158 F1. b, 1964 158 F1.
No. 3075, $1.25: a, Interior of 1966 365P Speciale. b, 1966 365P Speciale.
No. 3076, $1.25: a, Air foil and rear wheel of 1968 312 F1-68. b, 1968 312 F1-68.

2010, Feb. 22   **Perf. 12**
    Vert. Pairs, #a-b
3073-3076 A603   Set of 4   8.25 8.25
   Nos. 3073-3076 exist imperf. Value, set of pairs $25.

Whales and Dolphins
A604

Designs: $1.20, Risso's dolphin. $1.80, Common dolphin. $3, Humpback whale. $5, Sperm whale.
No. 3081: a, Shortsnout dolphin. b, Spotted dolphin. c, Cuvier's beaked whale. d, Shortfin pilot whale. e, Gulf Stream beaked whale. f, Rough-toothed dolphin.

2010, Feb. 23   **Litho.**
3077-3080 A604   Set of 4   10.00 10.00
3081 A604 $2 Sheet of 6, #a-f 11.00 11.00

Miniature Sheets

A605

A606

Princess Diana (1961-97) — A607

No. 3082 — Diana wearing: a, White dress. b, Pink dress. c, Lilac suit. d, White dress, holding flowers.
No. 3083 — Diana wearing tiara and: a, White dress, two earrings visible. b, Red dress, earring with black stone. c, Red dress, pearl earring. d, White dress with high collar.
No. 3084 — Diana wearing: a, Lei. b, Lilac dress. c, Blue and white dress and hat. d, Red orange hat and dress.

2010   **Litho.**   **Perf. 12x11½**
3082 A605 $2 Sheet of 4,
    #a-d   6.50 6.50
3083 A606 $2.75 Sheet of 4,
    #a-d   8.25 8.25
3084 A607 $2.75 Sheet of 4,
    #a-d   8.25 8.25
   Nos. 3082-3084 (3) 23.00 23.00
   Issued: No. 3082, 2/23; Nos. 3083-3084, 5/10.

Butterflies
A608

Designs: $1.20, Common buckeye. $1.80, Red postman. $3, Red admiral. $5, Zebra longwing.
No. 3089: a, Orange sulfur. b, Blue morpho. c, Queen butterfly. d, Zebra swallowtail. e, Malachite. f, Gatekeeper butterfly.

2010, Apr. 14   **Perf. 14**
3085-3088 A608   Set of 4   10.00 10.00
    Perf. 14¾x14
3089 A608 $2 Sheet of 6, #a-f 10.50 10.50
   No. 3089 contains six 40x30mm stamps.

Sharks
A609

Designs: $1.20, Nurse shark. $1.80, Caribbean reef shark. $3, Tiger shark. $5, Whale shark.
No. 3094: a, Caribbean sharpnose shark. b, Blacktip shark. c, Oceanic whitetip shark. d, Bull shark.

2010, Apr. 14   **Perf. 14**
3090-3093 A609   Set of 4   10.50 10.50
    Perf. 14¾x14
3094 A609 $2.75 Sheet of 4,
    #a-d   10.00 10.00
   No. 3094 contains four 40x30mm stamps.

Pope John Paul II (1920-2005) — A610

2010, May 10   **Perf. 11¼x11½**
3095 A610 $2.75 multi   2.10 2.10
   Printed in sheets of 4, with each stamp having slight differences in background.

Boy Scouts of America, Cent. — A611

No. 3096, $2.50: a, Scout at lectern. b, Scouts canoeing.
No. 3097, $2.50: a, Statue of Liberty giving Scout salute. b, Scouts using map and compass.

2010, May 10   **Pairs, #a-b**   **Perf. 13¼**
3096-3097   A611   Set of 2   7.50 7.50

Nos. 3096 and 3097 each were printed in sheets containing two pairs.

Girl Guides, Cent. — A612

No. 3098: a, Rainbows. b, Brownies. c, Guides. d, Senior Section.
$6, Girl Guides, diff.

2010, May 10   **Perf. 11½x12**
3098   A612 $2.75 Sheet of 4, #a-d   8.50 8.50

Souvenir Sheet
Perf. 11½
3099   A612 $6 multi   4.75 4.75

Miniature Sheet

Expo 2010, Shanghai — A613

No. 3100: a, Dancers, Shanghai Intl. Culture and Art Festival. b, China National Grand Theater, Beijing. c, Rice terraces, Guangxi Province, China. d, Dance performance, Beijing.

2010, May 10   **Perf. 11½**
3100   A613 $1.50 Sheet of 4, #a-d   4.50 4.50

Miniature Sheet

Mother Teresa (1910-97), Humanitarian — A614

No. 3101 — Mother Teresa and: a, Princess Diana. b, Queen Elizabeth II. c, Pres. Ronald Reagan. d, Pope John Paul II.

2010, May 10   **Perf. 11½x12**
3101   A614 $2.50 Sheet of 4, #a-d   7.50 7.50

Miniature Sheet

Pres. John F. Kennedy (1917-63) — A615

No. 3102: a, Sitting in limousine. b, Standing. c, Sitting in rocking chair. d, Behind microphones.

2010, May 10   **Perf. 11¼x11½**
3102   A615 $2.75 Sheet of 4, #a-d   8.25 8.25

Miniature Sheet

Awarding of Nobel Peace Prize to Pres. Barack Obama — A616

No. 3103 — Pres. Obama: a, Holding diploma and medal, blue curtain in background. b, At lectern, with hand closed. c, At lectern, with hand open. d, Holding diploma and medal.

2010, May 10   **Perf. 12x11½**
3103   A616 $2.75 Sheet of 4, #a-d   8.25 8.25

Miniature Sheets

A617

Pres. Abraham Lincoln (1809-65) — A618

Various photographs of Lincoln.

2010, May 10   **Perf. 11¼x11½**
3104   A617 $2.75 Sheet of 4, #a-d   8.25 8.25
3105   A618 $2.75 Sheet of 4, #a-d   8.25 8.25

Miniature Sheets

A619

Elvis Presley (1935-77) — A620

No. 3106: a, Wearing rhinestone-studded jacket, microphone in front of mouth. b, Wearing black open-neck shirt. c, Two portraits. d, Wearing white jacket with lapels and pockets with dark trim.
No. 3107: a, Presley holding guitar, parts of "E" and "L" in background. b, Presley holding guitar, parts of "L" and "V" in background. c, Presley holding guitar, parts of "V" and "7" in background. d, Three portraits.

2010, May 10   **Perf. 13¼**
3106   A619 $2.75 Sheet of 4, #a-d   8.25 8.25
3107   A620 $2.75 Sheet of 4, #a-d   8.25 8.25

Miniature Sheet

Chinese Zodiac Animals — A621

No. 3108: a, Rat. b, Ox. c, Tiger. d, Rabbit. e, Dragon. f, Snake. g, Horse. h, Goat. i, Monkey. j, Cock. k, Dog. l, Pig.

2010, Jan. 4   **Litho.**   **Perf. 12¼**
3108   A621   60c Sheet of 12, #a-l   5.50 5.50

Miniature Sheet

The Three Stooges — A622

No. 3109: a, Moe and Larry with cowboy hats, Curly with pick. b, Moe, Larry and Curly in painter's coveralls. c, Moe and Larry in surgical garb examining Curly. d, Moe and Larry squeezing Curly's neck in giant nutcracker.

2010, Sept. 27   **Litho.**   **Perf. 11½x12**
3109   A622 $2.50 Sheet of 4, #a-d   7.50 7.50

2010 World Cup Soccer Championships, South Africa — A623

No. 3110: a, Maximiliano Pereira. b, John Heitinga. c, Edinson Cavani. d, Mark Van Bommel. e, Martin Caceres. f, Giovanni van Bronckhorst.
No. 3111, $3.50: a, Netherlands Coach Bert van Marwijk. b, Netherlands flag on soccer ball.
No. 3112, $3.50: a, Uruguay Coach Oscar Tabarez. b, Uruguay flag on soccer ball.

2010, Oct. 18   **Perf. 12**
3110   A623 $1.50 Sheet of 6, #a-f   7.75 7.75

Souvenir Sheets of 2, #a-b
3111-3112   A623   Set of 2   11.00 11.00

Henri Dunant (1828-1910), Founder of Red Cross — A624

No. 3113 — Red Cross, scenes from Battle of Solferino and portrait of Dunant in: a, Blue green. b, Brown. c, Lilac. d, Blue gray.
$6, Red Cross, Battle of Solferino, Dunant in lilac.

2010, Dec. 20
3113   A624 $2.50 Sheet of 4, #a-d   8.00 8.00

Souvenir Sheet
3114   A624 $6 multi   4.75 4.75

Cats — A625

No. 3115: a, California spangled cat. b, Siamese cat. c, British shorthair cat. d, Norwegian forest cat. e, Egyptian Mau cat. f, American curl longhair cat.
$6, Manx cat.

2010, Dec. 20
3115 A625 $2.50 Sheet of 6,
#a-f   13.00 13.00
Souvenir Sheet
3116 A625 $6 multi   5.00 5.00
No. 3115 contains six 30x40mm stamps.

A626

Pope Benedict XVI — A627

No. 3118 — Pope Benedict XVI and: a, Buff area below "G" in "Antigua," brown area below "U" in "Antigua." b, Red brown area below "IG" of "Antigua," buff area below first "A" in "Antigua." c, Dark brown areas below "ANTIG" of "Antigua." d, Buff areas below first and second "A" of "Antigua."

2010, Dec. 20   Litho.   Perf. 12
3117 A626 $2.75 multi   2.10 2.10
3118 A627 $2.75 Sheet of 4,
#a-d   8.50 8.50
No. 3117 issued in sheets of 4.

Souvenir Sheet

New Year 2011 (Year of the Rabbit) — A628

No. 3119: a, Rabbit. b, Chinese character for "rabbit."

2011, Jan. 3
3119 A628 $4 Sheet of 2, #a-b   6.00 6.00

Pandas — A629

No. 3120: a, Panda with mouth open. b, Head of panda. c, Panda eating, large leaf partially covering head. d, Panda eating, diff. $5, Panda, diff.

2011, Jan. 3
3120 A629 $2 Sheet of 4, #a-d   7.00 7.00
Souvenir Sheet
3121 A629 $5 multi   4.25 4.25
Beijing 2010 Intl. Philatelic Exhibition.

Christmas
2010 — A630

Designs: 30c, Casini Madonna, by Tommaso Masaccio. 75c, Madonna of the Stars, by Tintoretto. 90c, Wall mosaic, Basilica of Sant'Apollinaire Nuovo, Ravenna, Italy. $1.50, The Annunciation, by Fra Angelico.

2011, Jan. 17   Perf. 12¾x12½
3122-3125 A630   Set of 4   2.60 2.60

Engagement of Prince William and Catherine Middleton — A631

Design: No. 3126, Couple.
No. 3127: a, Prince William. b, Middleton.
No. 3128, $6, Prince William wearing striped shirt and necktie, vert. No. 3129, $6, Prince William wearing white shirt and bow tie, vert.

2011, Feb. 14   Perf. 13 Syncopated
3126 A631 $2.50 multi   1.90 1.90
3127 A631 $2.50 Horiz. pair,
#a-b   3.75 3.75
Souvenir Sheets
3128-3129 A631   Set of 2   9.00 9.00
No. 3126 printed in sheets of 4. No. 3127 printed in sheets of 2 pairs.

Miniature Sheets

A632

Mohandas K. Gandhi (1869-1948), Indian Nationalist — A633

No. 3130 — Gandhi and: a, Qutub Minar Tower, Delhi. b, Asoka pillar. c, Hyderabad Mosque. d, Taj Mahal.
No. 3131 — Crowd and: a, Profile of Gandhi, robe visible. b, Gandhi looking forward. c, Profile of Gandhi, robe not visible. d, Gandhi looking right.

2011, Mar. 1   Perf. 12
3130 A632 $2.75 Sheet of 4,
#a-d   8.25 8.25
3131 A633 $2.75 Sheet of 4,
#a-d   8.25 8.25
2011 Indipex Intl. Philatelic Exhibition, New Delhi

Beatification of Pope John Paul II — A634

No. 3132 — Pope John Paul II: a, Holding crucifix. b, Wearing red stole.
$6, Head of Pope John Paul II.

2011, Apr. 4   Perf. 13 Syncopated
3132 A634 $2 Pair, #a-b   3.00 3.00
Souvenir Sheet
Perf. 12
3133 A634 $6 multi   4.50 4.50

Miniature Sheets

United States Civil War, 150th Anniv. — A635

No. 3134, $2.50 — Eagle, shield, flags, Generals Henry R. Jackson and Joseph J. Reynolds of Battle of Greenbrier River, Oct. 3, 1861, and: a, Battle map by A. T. McRae, Quitman Guards. b, Skirmish along the Greenbrier river. c, Union forces assembling near Greenbrier River. d, Battle scene.
No. 3135, $2.50 — Eagle, shield, flags, Confederate Secretary of the navy Stephen Mallory, Union Lt. Commander Alexander Murray of Battle of Cockle Creek, Oct. 5, 1861, and: a, Warships of the Atlantic Blockading Squadron. b, Flotilla of Union warships. c, Confederate privateers near Delaware Bay. d, USS Minnesota.
No. 3136, $2.50 — Eagle, shield, flags, Confederate Brigadier General Richard H. Anderson, Union Colonel Harvey Brown of Battle of Santa Rosa Island, Oct. 9, 1861, and: a, Fort Pickens. b, Drawing of Fight at Santa Rosa Island, by John Volck. c, Boats cutting off confederate dispatch galley. d, Col. Brown commanding 3rd U.S. Infantry.

Sheets of 4, #a-d
2011, Apr. 4   Perf. 12
3134-3136 A635   Set of 3   22.50 22.50

Mushrooms — A636

No. 3137: a, Tylopilus potamogeton. b, Amanita campinaranae. c, Cantharellus altratus. d, Tylopilus orsonianus. e, Boletellus ananas. f, Amanita craseoderma.

No. 3138: a, Amanita cyanopus. b, Phyllobolites miniatus. c, Chroogomphus jamaicensis. d, Coltricia cf. montagnei.
No. 3139, $6, Austroboletus rostrupii. No. 3140, $6, Austroboletus festivus.

2011, May 9   Litho.
3137 A636 $2 Sheet of 6,
#a-f   10.00 10.00
3138 A636 $2.50 Sheet of 4,
#a-d   7.50 7.50
Souvenir Sheets
3139-3140 A636   Set of 2   9.00 9.00

1997 Visit of Princess Diana To Barbuda — A637

Designs: No. 3141, $10, Princess Diana, her sons, family friend and airplane. No. 3142, $10, Princess Diana.
$50, Princess Diana, horiz.

2011, July 12   Perf. 12
3141-3142 A637   Set of 2   17.00 17.00
Souvenir Sheet
3143 A637 $50 multi   37.50 37.50
Nos. 3141-3142 each were issued in sheets of 5.

Wedding of Prince William and Catherine Middleton — A638

No. 3144, $2.50 — a, Prince William wearing cap. b, Middleton, name at left in one line. c, Couple.
No. 3145, $2.50 — a, Prince William waving. b, Middleton, name at top in two lines. c, Couple kissing.
$6, Couple, diff.

2011, Aug. 15   Perf. 13x13¼
3144 A638   Sheet of 4, #3144a-
3144b, 2 #3144c   7.50 7.50
3145 A638   Sheet of 4, #3145a-
3145b, 2 #3145c   7.50 7.50
Souvenir Sheet
Perf. 12
3146 A638 $6 multi   4.50 4.50

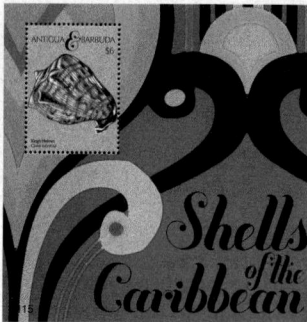

Shells — A639

No. 3147: a, Bleeding tooth nerite. b, Pen shell. c, Banded tulip shell. d, Chank shell. e, Flame helmet. f, Atlantic partridge tun.
No. 3148: a, Pink conch. b, Sunrise tellin. c, Flamingo tongue. d, Queen's helmet.
No. 3149, $6, King's helmet. No. 3150, $6, Triton's trumpet, horiz.

Perf. 13¼x13, 13x13¼

2011, Aug. 15
3147	A639	$2 Sheet of 6,		
		#a-f	9.00	9.00
3148	A639	$2.75 Sheet of 4,		
		#a-d	8.25	8.25

Souvenir Sheets
3149-3150	A639	Set of 2	9.00	9.00

Pres. John F. Kennedy (1917-63) — A640

No. 3151, vert. — Pres. Kennedy: a, Inspecting Mercury capsule, Feb. 22, 1962. b, On Cape Canaveral tour, Nov. 16, 1963. c, At Saturn rocket briefing, Nov. 16, 1963. d, At Cape Canaveral, pointing, Nov. 16, 1963.
$6, Kennedy and flag.

2011, Sept. 9   Perf. 12
3151	A640	$2.75 Sheet of 4,		
		#a-d	8.25	8.25

Souvenir Sheet
Perf. 12¾
3152	A640	$6 multi	4.50	4.50

No. 3151 contains four 30x40mm stamps.

Pres. Barack Obama, 50th Birthday — A641

No. 3153 — Pres. Obama: a, Looking right, wearing dark tie and flag lapel pin. b, Wearing light patterned tie, standing in front of microphone. c, Wearing dark patterned tie, standing in front of microphones. d, Looking left.
$6, Pres. Obama, diff.

2011, Sept. 9   Perf. 13 Syncopated
3153	A641	$2.75 Sheet of 4,		
		#a-d	8.25	8.25

Souvenir Sheet
3154	A641	$6 multi	5.00	5.00

Princess Diana (1961-97) — A642

No. 3155 — Princess Diana: a, Seated on sofa. b, Wearing beige and white dress. c, Wearing white dress. d, With Prince Charles.
$6, Princess Diana, horiz.

2011, Sept. 9   Perf. 12
3155	A642	$2.75 Sheet of 4,		
		#a-d	8.25	8.25

Souvenir Sheet
Perf. 12¾
3156	A642	$6 multi	4.50	4.50

No. 3156 contains one 51x38mm stamp.

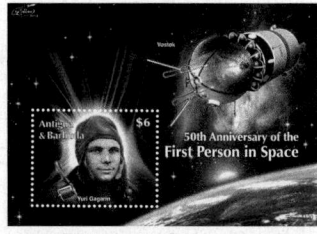

First Man in Space, 50th Anniv. — A643

No. 3157, $2.75: a, Liftoff of Vostok 1. b, Russian tracking ship named after Yuri Gagarin. c, Vostok 1 mission emblem. d, Alan Shepard, first American astronaut.
No. 3158, $2.75: a, Map of Gagarin's flightpath. b, Vostok 8K72K rocket. c, Gagarin, first cosmonaut. d, Virgil "Gus" Grissom, American astronaut, and rocket.
No. 3159, $6, Gagarin, diff. No. 3160, $6, Vostok spacecraft and Earth.

Sheets of 4, #a-d
2011, Sept. 9   Perf. 12
3157-3158	A643	Set of 2	16.50	16.50

Souvenir Sheets
3159-3160	A643	Set of 2	9.00	9.00

ELVIS PRESLEY®

A644

A645

A646

Elvis Presley (1935-77) — A647

No. 3161 — Presley: a, With building in background. b, On train steps. c, On motorcycle.
No. 3162 — Presley wearing: a, Army dress uniform. b, Dress uniform, standing next to railing. c, Battle fatigues. d, Battle fatigues, reading letter.
No. 3163 — Presley wearing: a, Glasses and red shirt. b, Suit, facing right. c, Sequined suit, facing forward. d, Suit, facing left.
No. 3164 — Presley: a, On stage. b, Wearing sweater.

2011, Sept. 9   Perf. 13 Syncopated
3161	A644	$2 Sheet of 3,		
		#a-c	4.50	4.50
3162	A645	$2.75 Sheet of 4,		
		#a-d	8.25	8.25
3163	A646	$2.75 Sheet of 4,		
		#a-d	8.25	8.25
	Nos. 3161-3163 (3)		21.00	21.00

Souvenir Sheet
3164	A647	$3 Sheet of 2,		
		#a-b	4.50	4.50

Miniature Sheets

A648

Visit of Pope Benedict XVI to Germany — A649

No. 3165 — Pope Benedict XVI: a, With church spires behind head. b, With arm extended, crucifix visible, hand in front of church steeple. c, With mountain behind head, chuch steeple and building with flowers at right.
No. 3166 — Pope Benedict XVI: a, Facing right, church with red roof at right. b, With arm extended, no crucifix visible, chuch at right.c, With Brandenburg Gate at left.

2011, Aug. 3   Litho.   Perf. 12
3165	A648	$3 Sheet of 3, #a-c	6.75	6.75
3166	A649	$3 Sheet of 3, #a-c	6.75	6.75

Fish — A650

No. 3167, $3.50: a, Queen angelfish. b, Ocean surgeonfish. c, Rock beauty. d, Gray angelfish.
No. 3168, $3.50: a, Foureye butterflyfish. b, French grunt. c, French angelfish. d, Spotfin butterflyfish.
No. 3169, $9, Great barracuda (80x30mm). No. 3170, $9, Banded butterflyfish (40x40mm).

Sheets of 4, #a-d
2011, Sept. 30   Perf. 12
3167-3168	A650	Set of 2	21.00	21.00

Souvenir Sheets
3169-3170	A650	Set of 2	13.50	13.50

Hu Jintao, President of People's Republic of China — A651

Pres. Hu and flag of People's Republic of China: $3, At lower left. $6, In background.

2011, Oct. 24
3171	A651	$3 multi	2.25	2.25

Souvenir Sheet
3172	A651	$6 multi	4.50	4.50

China 2011 Intl. Philatelic Exhibition, Wuxi (No. 3172).

Christmas A652

Paintings: 30c, Madonna and Child with Angels, by Giottino. 75c, The Annunciation and Two Saints, by Simone Martini. $1.50, Paradise, by Giusto de' Menabuoi. $3, Madonna, by Vitale da Bologna.

2011, Nov. 15   Perf. 14
3173-3176	A652	Set of 4	4.25	4.25

Miniature Sheet

Chinese Zodiac Animals — A653

No. 3177: a, Rat. b, Ox. c, Tiger. d, Rabbit. e, Dragon. f, Snake. g, Horse. h, Sheep. i, Monkey. j, Rooster. k, Dog. l, Boar.

Litho. With Foil Application
2011, Nov. 15   Perf. 13 Syncopated
3177	A653	65c Sheet of 12, #a-l	5.75	5.75

Pres. Abraham Lincoln (1809-65) — A654

No. 3178: a, Lincoln without beard. b, Campaign poster for Lincoln and Hannibal Hamlin. c, Eyes and nose of Lincoln. d, Linoln with beard.
$6, Lincoln, vert.

2011, Dec. 19   Litho.   Perf. 12
3178 A654 $2.75 Sheet of 4,
#a-d   8.25   8.25
Souvenir Sheet
3179 A654 $6 multi   4.50   4.50
No. 3179 contains one 30x50mm stamp.

Sinking of the Titanic, Cent. — A655

No. 3180 — Titanic passengers: a, Joseph Bruce Ismay (1862-1937), chairman of White Star Line. b, William Stead (1849-1912), journalist. c, Benjamin Guggenheim (1865-1912), businessman. d, Thomas Andrews (1873-1912), naval architect of Titanic.
$9, Titanic, horiz.

2012, Jan. 25
3180 A655 $3.50 Sheet of 4,
#a-d   10.50 10.50
Souvenir Sheet
3181 A655 $9 multi   6.75   6.75
No. 3181 contains one 50x30mm stamp.

Reign of Queen Elizabeth II, 60th Anniv. — A656

No. 3182 — Queen Elizabeth II as young girl: a, At piano. b, Color photograph, looking left. c, In meadow, looking right. d, Near house and flowers.
$9, Queen Elizabeth II and flowers, vert.

2012, Mar. 26
3182 A656 $3.50 Sheet of 4,
#a-d   10.50 10.50
Souvenir Sheet
3183 A656 $9 multi   6.75   6.75

First Wedding Anniversary of the Duke and Duchess of Cambridge — A657

No. 3184 — Duke and Duchess, rose and background color of: a Dark red violet. b, Red. c, Rose. d, Pink.

No. 3185: a, Rose and Duke of Cambridge. b, Rose and Duchess of Cambridge.

2012, May 3   Perf. 13 Syncopated
3184 A657 $3.50 Sheet of 4,
#a-d   10.50 10.50
Souvenir Sheet
3185 A657 $4.50 Sheet of 2,
#a-b   6.75   6.75
Miniature Sheet

2012 Summer Olympics, London — A658

No. 3186: a, Rhythmic gymnastics. b, Hurdles. c, Judo. d, Three runners.

2012, June 18   Perf. 12
3186 A658 $2.20 Sheet of 4, #a-d   6.50   6.50

Charles Dickens (1812-70), Writer — A659

No. 3187: a, Illustration from Great Expectations. b, Illustration from Oliver Twist. c, Sketch of Dickens. d, Photograph of Dickens. e, Illustration from David Copperfield. f, Illustration from A Christmas Carol.
$9, Illustration from A Tale of Two Cities, horiz.

2012, July 30   Perf. 14
3187 A659 $2.75 Sheet of 6,
#a-f   12.50 12.50
Souvenir Sheet
Perf. 12
3188 A659 $9 multi   6.75   6.75

Princess Diana (1961-97) — A660

No. 3189 — Princess Diana wearing: a, White gown, denomination at UL. b, White jacket, denomination at UL. c, Red dress. d, White dress and necklace, denomination at UR.
$9, Princess Diana and school children.

2012, July 30   Perf. 14
3189 A660 $3.50 Sheet of 4,
#a-d   10.50 10.50
Souvenir Sheet
3190 A660 $9 multi   6.75   6.75

Miniature Sheet

Seahorses — A661

Various seahorses.

2012, Sept. 24   Perf. 14
3191 A661 $3 Sheet of 5, #a-e 11.50 11.50

War of 1812 — A662

No. 3192: a, HMS Shannon Leading Her Prize The American Frigate Chesapeake into Halifax Harbor, by Louis Haghe. b, Action Between USS Constitution and HMS Guerriere, by Michele F. Corne. c, Portrait of Pres. James Madison, by John Vanderlyn. d, Portrait of Pres. Andrew Jackson, by Ralph E. W. Earl. e, The U.S. Capitol After Burning by the British, by George Munger. f, Battle of Lake Erie, by William H. Powerll.
$9, A View of the Bombardment of Fort McHenry, Near Baltimore, by John Bower.

2012, Nov. 12   Perf. 12
3192 A662 $2.75 Sheet of 6,
#a-f   12.50 12.50
Souvenir Sheet
3193 A662 $9 multi   6.75   6.75

Christmas
A663

Paintings: 30c, Adoration of the Child, by Antonio da Correggio. 75c, Madonna and Child with Two Angels, by Fra Filippo Lippi. $1.50, Virgin and Child, by Peter Paul Rubens. $2, Madonna and Child, by Parmigianino. $3, The Grand Duke's Madonna, by Raphael. $3.25, Adoration of the Magi, by Sandro Botticelli.

2012, Nov. 19   Perf. 12¾
3194-3199 A663   Set of 6   8.00   8.00

Miniature Sheet

Marine Life — A664

No. 3200: a, Copperband butterflyfish. b, Butterfly fish. c, Moon jellyfish, tentacles at bottom. d, Moon jellyfish, tentacles at top. e, Masked butterflyfish. f, Head of Green sea turtle. g, Rear of Green sea turtle, Ocellaris clownfish. h, Forbes sea star. i, Fan coral, red coral at left. j, Fan coral at left. k, Ocellaris clownfish and sea anemone. l, Sea anemone.

2012, Dec. 3   Perf. 13 Syncopated
3200 A664 $1.25 Sheet of 12,
#a-l   11.50 11.50

Stingrays and Skates — A665

No. 3201: a, Dipturus batis. b, Dipturus oxyrhynchus without long appendages near tail. c, Dipturus oxyrhynchus with long appendages near tail. d, Raja microocellata.
$9, Leucoraja naevus, vert.

2012, Dec. 3   Perf. 13¾
3201 A665 $3 Sheet of 4, #a-d   9.00   9.00
Souvenir Sheet
Perf. 12¾
3202 A665 $9 multi   6.75   6.75
No. 3202 contains one 38x51mm stamp.

Turtles — A666

No. 3203: a, Chelonia mydas. b, Trachemys decorata. c, Dermochelys coriacea. d, Chelonoidis carbonaria.
$9, Chelus fimbriatus.

2012, Dec. 3   Perf. 14
3203 A666 $3.50 Sheet of 4,
#a-d   10.50 10.50
Souvenir Sheet
Perf. 12
3204 A666 $9 multi   6.75   6.75

RAPHAEL

Paintings by Raphael — A667

No. 3205: a, Andrea Navagero. b, La Muta. c, Self-portrait. d, La Fornarina. $9, Portrait of a Cardinal.

2013, Feb. 20 **Perf. 12½**
3205 A667 $3.25 Sheet of 4, #a-
d 9.75 9.75
Souvenir Sheet
3206 A667 $9 multi 6.75 6.75

Souvenir Sheets

Elvis Presley (1935-77) — A668

Presley: No. 3207, $9, Standing in front of sign depicting him playing guitar, purple frame. No. 3208, $9, Wearing suit and tie, black frame. No. 3209, $9, Holding microphone, red frame. No. 3210, $9, With guitar on back, looking at music stand, red frame. No. 3211, $9, With Pres. Richard M. Nixon, gray frame.

2013, Feb. 20
3207-3211 A668 Set of 5 34.00 34.00

Coronation of Queen Elizabeth II, 60th Anniv. — A669

No. 3212 — Queen Elizabeth II: a, As young woman in field. b, As young woman at piano. c, With Prince Philip. d, Behind microphone. e, Wearing tiara. f, Boarding airplane. $9, Queen Eliazbeth II wearing hat, vert.

2013, May 13 **Litho.** **Perf. 13¾**
3212 A669 $2.50 Sheet of 6,
#a-f 11.50 11.50
Souvenir Sheet
Perf. 12½
3213 A669 $9 multi 6.75 6.75
No. 3213 contains one 38x51mm stamp.

CONSTELLATIONS

Constellations — A670

No. 3214: a, Ursa Major. b, Ursa Minor. c, Sagittarius. d, Orion. e, Gemini. f, Cassiopeia. $9, Canis Major, vert.

2013, May 13 **Litho.** **Perf. 13¾**
3214 A670 $2.50 Sheet of 6,
#a-f 11.50 11.50
Souvenir Sheet
Perf. 12½
3215 A670 $9 multi 6.75 6.75
No. 3215 contains one 38x51mm stamp.

THE ELECTION OF
HIS HOLINESS POPE FRANCIS

Election of Pope Francis — A671

No. 3216 — Pope Francis: a, Waving, orange background. b, Behind microphone, cardinal in background. c, Waving, behind lectern and microphone. d, Facing right, waving, cardinals in background. $9, Pope Francis waving, diff.

Perf. 13¼x12½
2013, June 19 **Litho.**
3216 A671 $3.25 Sheet of 4, #a-
d 9.75 9.75
Souvenir Sheet
Perf. 13½
3217 A671 $9 multi 6.75 6.75
No. 3217 contains one 38x51mm stamp.

Dolphins of the Caribbean

Dolphins — A672

No. 3218: a, Bottlenose dolphins. b, Spotted dolphins. c, Striped dolphins. d, Fraser's dolphins. $9, Pygmy killer whale.

Perf. 12½x13¼
2013, June 19 **Litho.**
3218 A672 $3.25 Sheet of 4, #a-
d 9.75 9.75
Souvenir Sheet
Perf. 12½x12
3219 A672 $9 multi 6.75 6.75

Mythological Beings of Asia — A673

No. 3220: a, Rakshasa. b, Indra. c, Vayu.

$9, Garuda.

2013, Oct. 28 **Litho.** **Perf. 12½**
3220 A673 $3.75 Sheet of 3, #a-
c 8.50 8.50
Souvenir Sheet
3221 A673 $9 multi 6.75 6.75
Thailand 2013 World Stamp Exhibition, Bangkok.

Tourist Attractions in China — A674

No. 3222: a, Dazu Rock Carvings. b, Terracotta warriors. c, Seventeen-arch bridge at Summer Palace. d, Temple of Heaven.
No. 3223: a, Forbidden City. b, Potala Palace.

2013, Oct. 28 **Litho.** **Perf. 14**
3222 A674 $3.25 Sheet of 4, #a-
d 9.75 9.75
Souvenir Sheet
3223 A674 $4.75 Sheet of 2, #a-
b 7.00 7.00
2013 China International Collection Expo, Beijing.

Dogs — A675

No. 3224: a, Chow chow. b, Japanese chin. c, Poodle. d, French bulldog. $9, Toy spaniel.

2013, Oct. 28 **Litho.** **Perf. 14**
3224 A675 $3.25 Sheet of 4, #a-
d 9.75 9.75
Souvenir Sheet
Perf. 12
3225 A675 $9 multi 6.75 6.75

Birth of Prince George of Cambridge — A676

No. 3226 — Duke and Duchess of Cambridge with Prince George: a, Duke holding Prince. b, Duchess holding Prince, Duke waving. c, Duke holding Prince, head of prince visible. d, Duchess holding Prince, shoulder of Duke visible. $9, Duke and Duchess of Cambridge with Prince George, diff.

2013, Oct. 28 **Litho.** **Perf. 13¾**
3226 A676 $3.25 Sheet of 4, #a-
d 9.75 9.75
Souvenir Sheet
3227 A676 $9 multi 6.75 6.75

ANIMALS OF SOUTH AMERICA

Animals of South America — A677

No. 3228: a, Black howler. b, South American tapir. c, Spectacled bear, d, Maned wolf. $9, Toco toucan.

2013, Nov. 18 **Litho.** **Perf. 12½x12**
3228 A677 $3.25 Sheet of 4, #a-
d 9.75 9.75
Souvenir Sheet
3229 A677 $9 multi 6.75 6.75
2013 Brasiliana World Stamp Exhibition, Rio de Janeiro.

Christmas
A678

Paintings: 30c, Holy Family, by Alessandro Buonvicino. 75c, Christ Blessing, by Girolamo Romani (Il Romanino). 90c, Madonna, by Correggio. $1.50, The Adoration of the Shepherds, by Girolamo Savoldo. $3, Madonna and Child, by Giovanni da Pordenone.

2013, Dec. 2 **Litho.** **Perf. 12½**
3230-3234 A678 Set of 5 4.75 4.75

New Year 2014 (Year of the Horse) — A679

No. 3235 — Various paintings of horses, by Liu Jiyu (1918-83), with: a, Artist's name at UL, "Year of the Horse" in red at LL. b, Artist's name at LL, "Year of the Horse" in red at UR. c, Artist's name at LL, no "Year of the Horse" inscription. d, Artist's name at UL, "Year of the Horse" in tan at LL.
No. 3236, horiz. — Various paintings of horses, by Liu Jiyu, with "Year of the Horse" at: a, LR. b, LL.

2013, Dec. 2　　Litho.　　Perf. 14
3235 A679 $3.25 Sheet of 4, #a-
　　　　　d　　　　　　9.75　9.75

Souvenir Sheet
Perf. 12
3236 A679 $3.50 Sheet of 2, #a-
　　　　　b　　　　　　5.25　5.25

A680

A681

Nelson Mandela (1918-2013),
President of South Africa — A682

No. 3237 — Mandela: a, Behind
microphone. b, Wearing blue shirt with circular
designs. c, Sitting in chair. d, With cap lifted. e,
Wearing black shirt. f, Wearing sunglasses.

No. 3238 — Mandela: a, Wearing black-
and-white patterned shirt, with red ribbon near
collar. b, Wearing black-and-white patterned
shirt, no red ribbon. c, Wearing white shirt and
jacket with leopard-skin pattern. d, Waving. e,
Wearing black, white and red patterned shirt,
with red ribbon near collar. f, Wearing tasseled
cap.

$9, Mandela with people in background.
$13.50, Mandela, diff.

2013, Dec. 15　　Litho.　　Perf. 13¾
3237 A680 $2.50 Sheet of 6,
　　　　　#a-f　　　　11.00　11.00
3238 A681 $2.50 Sheet of 6,
　　　　　#a-f　　　　11.00　11.00

Souvenir Sheets
3239 A681　$9 multi　　6.75　6.75

Litho.; Margin Embossed With Foil
Application
Imperf
3240 A682 $13.50 multi　　10.00　10.00

Characters From *Downton Abbey*
Television Series — A683

No. 3241: a, Mrs. Hughes. b, Miss O'Brein.
c, Thomas Barrow. d, William Mason.
$9, Mrs. Patmore and Daisy, horiz.

2014, Mar. 24　　Litho.　　Perf. 14
3241 A683 $3.25 Sheet of 4, #a-
　　　　　d　　　　　9.75　9.75

Souvenir Sheet
3242 A683　$9 multi　　6.75　6.75

Parrots — A684

No. 3243, $4.75: a, Eclectus parrot. b, Blue-
and-yellow macaw. c, Black-capped lory. d,
Sun parakeet.
No. 3244, $4.75: a, Blue-and-yellow macaw,
leg near beak. b, Lilac-crowned Amazon. c,
Saint Vincent Amazon. d, Indian ring-necked
parakeet.
No. 3245, $9.50: a, Scarlet macaw. b, Yel-
low-headed Amazon.
No. 3246, $9.50: a, Rainbow lorikeet. b,
Hyacinth macaw.

2014, June 23　　Litho.　　Perf. 14
Sheets of 4, #a-d
3243-3244 A684　Set of 2　28.00　28.00
Souvenir Sheets of 2, #a-b
3245-3246 A684　Set of 2　28.00　28.00

A685

A686

A687

Aloe Vera — A688

No. 3247: a, Plant in pot. b, Plant (no pot
and plus signs). c, Close-up of plant.
No. 3248: a, Plant and roots. b, Plant diago-
nally. c, Close-up of plant, diff.
No. 3249: a, Plant (no plus signs). b, Plant
and plus signs.
No. 3250: a, Plant (no plus signs). diff. b,
Plant cut into pieces and plus signs.

2014, June 23　　Litho.　　Perf. 13¾
3247 A685 $4.75 Sheet of 4,
　　　　　#3247a-
　　　　　3247b, 2
　　　　　#3247c　14.00　14.00
3248 A686 $4.75 Sheet of 4,
　　　　　#3248a-
　　　　　3248b, 2
　　　　　#3248c　14.00　14.00

Souvenir Sheets
3249 A687 $9.50 Sheet of 2,
　　　　　#a-b　　14.00　14.00
3250 A688 $9.50 Sheet of 2,
　　　　　#a-b　　14.00　14.00

Christmas
A689

Paintings by Raphael: $2.25, Holy Family
Below the Oak. $3.50, Madonna with the Blue
Diadem. No. 3253, $5, Incoronazione della
Vergine, detta Pala Oddi. No. 3254, $5,
Aldobrandini Madonna.

2014, Dec. 29　　Litho.　　Perf. 14¼
3251-3254 A689　Set of 4　12.00　12.00

New Year 2015 (Year of the
Ram) — A690

No. 3255 — Ram with: a, Orange horns (at
right). b, Red horns (at left). c, Green horns (at
left). d, Olive horns at right.
$10, Ram with red horns at right.

2015, Jan. 2　　Litho.　　Perf. 14
3255 A690 $3.25 Sheet of 4,
　　　　　#a-d　　9.75　9.75
Souvenir Sheet
Perf.
3256 A690　$10 multi　　7.50　7.50
No. 3256 contains one 38mm diameter
stamp.

Rare Stamps — A691

No. 3257: a, Canada #3. b, Livingston, Alabama #51X1. c, Belgium #123B.
$10, Canada #387a, horiz.

2015, Jan. 2　　Litho.　　Perf. 13¼x12½
3257 A691 $3.50 Sheet of 3, #a-
　　　　　c　　7.75　7.75

Souvenir Sheet
Perf. 12½x13¼
3258 A691　$10 multi　　7.50　7.50

Hummingbirds — A692

No. 3259, $3.25: a, Broad-tailed humming-
bird, flower at LL. b, Broad-billed hummingbird, beak at right. c, Rufous-tailed hummingbird. d, Allen's hummingbird in flight.
No. 3260, $3.25: a, Allen's hummingbird on
perch. b, Broad-tailed hummingbird, flower at
UR. c, Broad-billed hummingbird, beak and
flower at left. d, Ruby-throated hummingbird.
No. 3261, $5: a, Ruby-throated humming-
bird on branch. b, Buff-bellied hummingbird.
No. 3262, $5: a, Anna's hummingbird. b,
Calliope hummingbird.

Perf. 14, 12 (#3262)
2015, Jan. 2　　　　　Litho.
Sheets of 4, #a-d
3259-3260 A692　Set of 2　19.50　19.50
Souvenir Sheets of 2, #a-b
3261-3262 A692　Set of 2　15.00　15.00

Macaws — A693

No. 3263, $3.25: a, Red-shouldered macaw. b, Hyacinth macaw. c, Blue-and-yellow macaw. d, Military macaw.
No. 3264, $3.25, vert.: a, Blue-headed macaw. b, Blue-throated macaw. c, Catalina macaw. d, Miligold macaw.
No. 3265, $5, vert.: a, Harlequin macaw. b, Scarlet macaw.
No. 3266, $5, vert.: a, Great green macaw. b, Green-winged macaw.

Perf. 14, 12 (#3264)
2015, Jan. 2   Litho.
Sheets of 4, #a-d
3263-3264 A693   Set of 2   19.50 19.50
Souvenir Sheets of 2, #a-b
3265-3266 A693   Set of 2   15.00 15.00

Ducks and Geese — A694

No. 3267, $3.25: a, Hartlaub's ducks. b, Wood ducks. c, Common shelducks. d, Mallards.
No. 3268, $3.25: a, Ruddy shelducks. b, White-backed duck and eggs in nest. c, Knob-billed ducks. d, Fulvous whistling ducks.
No. 3269, $5: a, Egyptian geese. b, Chiloé wigeons.
No. 3270, $5: a, White-face whistling ducks. b, Red-billed teals.

2015, Jan. 2   Litho.   Perf. 14
Sheets of 4, #a-d
3267-3268 A694   Set of 2   19.50 19.50
Souvenir Sheets of 2, #a-b
3269-3270 A694   Set of 2   15.00 15.00

Corals — A695

No. 3271, $3.25: a, Purple wide-mesh sea fans. b, Orange wide-mesh sea fan. c, Brain coral with green spots. d, Brain coral with red spots.
No. 3272, $3.25: a, Solitary disk coral. b, Antler coral. c, Common mushroom coral. d, Common lettuce coral.
No. 3273: a, Elkhorn coral. b, Orage cup coral.
$10, Great star coral, vert.

2015, Jan. 2   Litho.   Perf. 14
Sheets of 4, #a-d
3271-3272 A695   Set of 2   19.50 19.50
3273   A695 $5 Sheet of 2, #a-b   7.50 7.50
Souvenir Sheet
Perf. 12½
3274   A695 $10 multi   7.50 7.50
No. 3274 contains oner 38x51mm stamp.

Prince George of Cambridge — A696

No. 3275 — Prince George in hands of: a, Duchess of Cambridge. b, Duke of Cambridge.
No. 3276, $9.50, Prince George, black panel at bottom. No. 3277, $9.50, Prince George, Duchess of Cambridge, red panel at bottom.

Perf. 13 Syncopated
2015, Jan. 2   Litho.
3275   A696 $3.25 Pair, #a-b   5.00 5.00
Souvenir Sheets
3276-3277 A696   Set of 2   14.00 14.00
No. 3275 was printed in sheets containing three pairs.

Julie Mango Tree — A697

2015, Jan. 16   Litho.   Perf. 13¾
3278   A697   25c multi   .25 .25

Pink Desert Roses — A698

2015, Feb. 24   Litho.   Perf. 14
3279   A698 $2.20 multi   1.75 1.75
Souvenir Sheet
Perf. 12
3280   A698 $10 Pink desert roses, diff.   7.50 7.50
No. 3279 was printed in sheets of 8 + central label.

Valentina Tereshkova, First Woman in Space — A699

No. 3281: a, Space capsule and Earth, conical section of capsule at left. b, Space capsule and Earth, conical section of capsule at bottom. c, Tereshkova. d, Rocket lift-off.
$10, Capsule, diff.

2015, Mar. 24   Litho.   Perf. 14
3281   A699 $3.25 Sheet of 4, #a-d   9.75 9.75
Souvenir Sheet
Perf. 12¾
3282   A699 $10 multi   7.50 7.50
No. 3282 contains one 51x38mm stamp.

International Year of Light — A700

No. 3283: a, Solar eclipse. b, Rainbow. c, Aurora Borealis. d, Sunset.
$10, Sunlight.

2015, Mar. 24   Litho.   Perf. 12¾
3283   A700 $3.25 Sheet of 4, #a-d   9.75 9.75
Souvenir Sheet
Perf.
3284   A700 $10 multi   7.50 7.50
No. 3284 contains one 38mm diameter stamp.

Paintings by Vincent van Gogh (1853-90) — A701

No. 3285: a, Cafén Terrace at Night, 1888. b, Self-portrait, 1889. c, Vincent's Bedroom in Arles, 1888. d, Starry Night, 1889. e, Vase with 12 Sunflowers, 1888. f, Interior of a Restaurant, 1887.
$10, Postman Joseph Roulin, 1888.

2015, Mar. 24   Litho.   Perf. 12¾
3285   A701 $3.15 Sheet of 6, #a-f   14.00 14.00
Souvenir Sheet
3286   A701 $10 multi   7.50 7.50

A702

Horses in Art — A703

No. 3287 — Various unattributed paintings depicting: a, Roundup of wild horses. b, Rider on horse, woman tending to two horses. c, Brown horse facing left. d, White horse and attendant facing left. e, Horse and colt. f, White horse facing right.
No. 3288 — Various unattributed paintings depicting: a, Horses and jockeys at race track.
b, Horses and riders at seashore. c, Horse and jockey with race track grandstand in background. d, Horse and fence.
No. 3289, $10, Black horse with clipped tail facing left. No. 3290, $10, Rider on galloping horse beside running dogs.

2015, Mar. 24   Litho.   Perf. 12¾
3287   A702 $3.15 Sheet of 6, #a-f   14.00 14.00
3288   A703 $3.25 Sheet of 4, #a-d   9.75 9.75
Souvenir Sheets
3289-3290 A703   Set of 2   15.00 15.00

Landscapes A704

Designs: 30c, White sand beach, Barbuda. 75c, Aerial view of St. John's, Antigua. 90c, English Harbor, Antigua. $1, Pink sand beach, Barbuda. $1.50, Green Island.

2015, Apr. 20   Litho.   Perf. 13¼x12½
3291-3295 A704   Set of 5   3.50 3.50

Flag of Antigua and Barbuda — A705

Coat of Arms of Antigua and Barbuda — A706

2015, Apr. 20   Litho.   Perf. 13¼x12½
3296   A705 $50 multi   37.50 37.50
3297   A706 $100 multi   75.00 75.00

Queen Elizabeth II, Longest-Reigning British Monarch — A707

No. 3298 — Queen Elizabeth II: a, As young woman. b, Wearing tiara. c, Wearing hat. d, Wearing blue dress. e, Wearing green dress. f, Wearing pink jacket.
No. 3299 — Queen Elizabeth II: a, As child. b, As older woman wearing white hat.

2015, July 8   Litho.   Perf. 14
3298   A707 $3.15 Sheet of 6, #a-f   14.00 14.00
Souvenir Sheet
Perf. 12
3299   A707 $5 Sheet of 2, #a-b   7.50 7.50

Souvenir Sheets

Elvis Presley (1935-77) — A708

Various photographs of Presley with panel at bottom of stamp in: No. 3300, $10, Dull green. No. 3301, $10, Purple. No. 3302, $10, Orange. No. 3303, $10, Salmon.

2015, Aug. 31   Litho.   Perf. 14
3300-3303 A708 Set of 4   30.00 30.00

Battle of Waterloo, 200th Anniv. — A709

No. 3304: a, King William II of the Netherlands. b, Portrait of the Duke of Wellington. c, Emperor Napoleon in His Study at the Tuileries. d, Gebhard Lebrecht von Blücher.
$10, The Battle of Waterloo, horiz.

2015, Dec. 1   Litho.   Perf. 12x12½
3304 A709 $3.25 Sheet of 4, #a-d   9.75 9.75
Souvenir Sheet
Perf. 13½
3305 A709 $10 multi   7.50 7.50
No. 3305 contains one 51x38mm stamp.

Christmas A710

Paintings by Sandro Botticelli: 90c, The Virgin Adoring the Sleeping Christ Child. $2.25, Madonna and Child with St. John the Baptist. $3.50, Madonna and Child. $5, Madonna and Child with an Angel.

2015, Nov. 3   Litho.   Perf. 12½
3306-3309 A710 Set of 4   8.75 8.75

Gemstones — A711

No. 3310: a, Diamond. b, Sapphire. c, Aquamarine. d, Topaz. e, Turquoise. f, Emerald.
$10, Opal.

2015, Dec. 28   Litho.   Perf. 13¾
3310 A711 $3.15 Sheet of 6, #a-f   14.00 14.00
Souvenir Sheet
3311 A711 $10 multi   7.50 7.50

World War I Events of 1915 — A712

No. 3312: a, Zeppelins. b, Sinking of British steamer Andex. c, Diagrams of torpedoed RMS Lusitania. d, Fokker airplane. e, Serbian refugees. f, Evacuation of Gallipoli.
$10, Soldier wearing gas mask.

2015, Dec. 28   Litho.   Perf. 12
3312 A712 $3.15 Sheet of 6, #a-f   14.00 14.00
Souvenir Sheet
3313 A712 $10 multi   7.50 7.50

New Horizons Space Probe — A713

No. 3314: a, New Horizons above Earth, Jan. 19, 2006. b, New Horizons near Asteroid 2002 JF 56, June 12, 2006. c, Voyager 2 flying by Neptune, Summer, 1989. d, New Horizons crossing Neptune orbit, Aug. 25, 2014.
$10, Rocket launch.

2015, Dec. 28   Litho.   Perf. 14
3314 A713 $3.25 Sheet of 4, #a-d   9.75 9.75
Souvenir Sheet
3315 A713 $10 multi   7.50 7.50

Miniature Sheet

New Year 2016 (Year of the Monkey) — A714

No. 3316 — Stone figurines: a, Monkey holding ball. b, Monkey on pedestal. c, Two monkeys. d, Monkey in tree.

2016, Jan. 28   Litho.   Perf. 14
3316 A714 $2 Sheet of 4, #a-d   6.00 6.00

Visit of Pope Francis to New York City — A715

No. 3317 — Pope Francis in front of: a, Flags, teeth visible. b, United Nations Building and flags, waving. c, As "a," waving hand. d, As "b," no hands visible. e, As "a," teeth not visible. f, As "b," waving with hand raised above head.
$10, Pope Francis waving, flags.

2016, Jan. 28   Litho.   Perf. 14
3317 A715 $3.15 Sheet of 6, #a-f   14.00 14.00
Souvenir Sheet
Perf. 12
3318 A715 $10 multi   7.50 7.50

Paintings — A716

No. 3319, $3.50 — Details of *Consequences of War*, by Peter Paul Rubens: a, Left portion. b, Center portion. c, Right portion.
No. 3320, $3.50: a, *The Death of General Wolfe*, by Benjamin West. b, *Lady with an Ermine*, by Leonardo da Vinci. c, *An Old Man and His Grandson*, by Domenico Ghirlandaio.
No. 3321, $10, The Tempest, by Giorgione. No. 3322, $10, The Virgin and Child with St. Anne, by Leonardo.

2016, Feb. 2   Litho.   Perf. 12½
Sheets of 3, #a-c
3319-3320 A716 Set of 2   15.50 15.50

Size: 100x100mm
Imperf
3321-3322 A716 Set of 2   15.00 15.00

Klingons From *Star Trek* — A717

No. 3323: a, Klingon holding tangled Christmas lights. b, Three Klingons caroling. c, Klingon snowman. d, Klingon as Santa Claus. e, Klingon family and Christmas stocking. f, Two Klingon holding mugs.
$10, Klingon as Santa Claus, vert.

2016, Feb. 15   Litho.   Perf. 12½
3323 A717 $3.15 Sheet of 6, #a-f   14.00 14.00
Souvenir Sheet
Perf. 11¼x11½
3324 A717 $10 multi   7.50 7.50
No. 3324 contains one 30x50mm stamp.

Mushrooms — A718

No. 3325: a, Weeping bolete. b, Saffron milk cap. c, Black trumpet. d, Parasol mushroom. e, Green-cracking russula. f, Common puffball.
No. 3326, vert.: a, Red-capped scaber stalk. b, Porcino. c, Fly agaric. d, Psilocybe cubensis.
$10, Chanterelle, vert.

2016, May 11   Litho.   Perf. 14
3325 A718 $3.15 Sheet of 6, #a-f   14.00 14.00
3326 A718 $3.25 Sheet of 4, #a-d   9.75 9.75
Souvenir Sheet
Perf. 12
3327 A718 $10 multi   7.50 7.50

Marine Mammals — A719

No. 3328: a, Sperm whale. b, Dugong. c, Spinner dolphins. d, Harbor porpoise. e, Humpback whale. f, West Indian manatee.
No. 3329: a, California sea lion. b, Polar bear. c, Northern fur seal. d, Harp seal.
$10, Walruses, horiz.

2016, May 25   Litho.   Perf. 13¾
3328 A719 $3.15 Sheet of 6, #a-f   14.00 14.00
3329 A719 $3.25 Sheet of 4, #a-d   9.75 9.75
Souvenir Sheet
Perf. 14
3330 A719 $10 multi   7.50 7.50
No. 3330 contains one 40x30mm stamp.

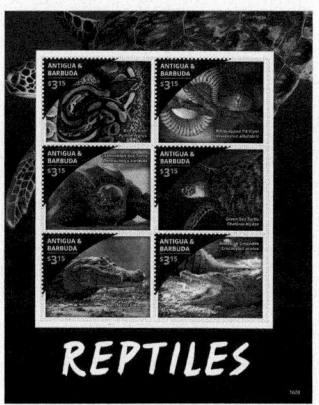

Reptiles — A720

No. 3331: a, Ball python. b, White-lipped pit viper. c, Leatherback sea turtle. d, Green sea turtle. e, Spectacled caiman. f, American crocodile.
No. 3332: a, Carolina anole. b, Dwarf yellow-headed gecko. c, Little striped whiptail. d, Giant girdled lizard.
$10, Panther chameleon.

2016, May 25   Litho.   Perf. 14
3331 A720 $3.15 Sheet of 6,
             #a-f   14.00 14.00
Perf. 12
3332 A720 $3.25 Sheet of 4,
             #a-d   9.75 9.75
Souvenir Sheet
3333 A720 $10 multi   7.50 7.50

Jimi Hendrix (1942-70), Rock Musician — A721

No. 3334 — Various photographs of Hendrix, as shown.
$10, Hendrix, diff.

2016, May 25   Litho.   Perf. 14
3334 A721 $3.15 Sheet of 6,
             #a-f   14.00 14.00
Souvenir Sheet
Perf. 12
3335 A721 $10 multi   7.50 7.50
No. 3335 contains one 30x50mm stamp.

A722

A723

A724

Atlantic Goliath Grouper — A725

2016, June 8   Litho.   Perf. 12
3336   Strip of 4   9.75 9.75
  a. A722 $3.25 multi   2.40 2.40
  b. A723 $3.25 multi   2.40 2.40
  c. A724 $3.25 multi   2.40 2.40
  d. A725 $3.25 multi   2.40 2.40
  e. Miniature sheet of 8, 2 each
      #3336a-3336d   19.50 19.50
Worldwide Fund for Nature (WWF).

William Shakespeare (1564-1616), Writer — A726

No. 3337 — Various scenes from *Hamlet*. a, Hamlet and Claudius. b, Hamlet holding sword. c, Hamlet and Ophelia. d, Hamlet holding skull.
$10, Shakespeare.

2016, July 22   Litho.   Perf. 14
3337 A726 $3.25 Sheet of 4,
             #a-d   9.75 9.75
Souvenir Sheet
Perf. 13¾
3338 A726 $10 multi   7.50 7.50
No. 3338 contains one 35x35mm stamp.

Sergei Korolev (1907-66), Rocket Engineer — A727

No. 3339: a, Statue depicting Korolev, Moscow. b, Luna 3 and Moon. c, Sputnik 1. d, Vostok 1.
$14, Soyuz TMA-ISS rocket launch.

2016, July 29   Litho.   Perf. 14
3339 A727 $4 Sheet of 4,
             #a-d   12.00 12.00
Souvenir Sheet
Perf. 12
3340 A727 $14 multi   10.50 10.50

Queen Elizabeth II, 90th Birthday — A728

No. 3341: a, Queen Elizabeth II wearing pink jacket and hat. b, Royal coat of arms. c, Queen Elizabeth II wearing blue jacket and hat. d, Queen's royal cypher.
No. 3342, vert.: a, Queen's flag. b, Queen Elizabeth II wearing white and apple green hat.

2016, July 29   Litho.   Perf. 13¾
3341 A728 $4 Sheet of 4, #a-
             d   12.00 12.00
Souvenir Sheet
Perf. 12½
3342 A728 $7 Sheet of 2, #a-
             b   10.50 10.50
No. 3342 contains two 38x51mm stamps.

Souvenir Sheets

Elvis Presley (1935-77) — A729

Inscriptions: No. 3343, $14, First top-billed film. No. 3344, $14, Last Ed Sullivan appearance. No. 3345, $14, Graceland welcomes Scatter. No. 3346, $14, Performs at Messick High School, horiz.

Perf. 13¼x13, 13x13¼
2016, Aug. 16   Litho.
3343-3346 A729 Set of 4   42.00 42.00

Statue of Liberty, 130th Anniv. — A730

No. 3347 — Various depictions of the Statue of Liberty, as shown.
$14, Statue of Liberty, diff.

2016, Aug. 29   Litho.   Perf. 14
3347 A730 $3.15 Sheet of 6,
             #a-f   14.00 14.00
Souvenir Sheet
Perf.
3348 A730 $14 multi   10.50 10.50
No. 3348 contains one 33x44mm oval stamp.

Characters From *Star Trek* Television Series — A731

No. 3349: a, Captain Kirk. b, Spock. c, Uhura. d, Chekov. e, McCoy. f, Scotty.
No. 3350, $7, horiz.: a, Captain Kirk, diff. b, Mirror Captain Kirk.
No. 3351, $7, horiz.: a, Spock, diff. b, Mirror Spock.

2017, Jan. 9   Litho.   Perf. 14
3349 A731 $3 Sheet of 6, #a-f 13.50 13.50
Souvenir Sheets of 2, #a-b
Perf. 12½
3350-3351 A731 Set of 2   21.00 21.00
Nos. 3350-3351 each contain two 51x38mm stamps.

Christmas — A732

Designs: No. 3352, $5.50, Christmas tree. No. 3353, $5.50, Snowflake. No. 3354, $10, Reindeer. No. 3355, $10, Angel.

2017, Jan. 23   Litho.   Perf. 12½
3352-3355 A732 Set of 4   23.00 23.00

A733

A734

New Year 2017 (Year of the Rooster) — A735

No. 3357: a, Two roosters, pale mauve background. b, One rooster, brown background. c, One rooster, head pointing left,

white background. d, One rooster, head pointing right, white background with flowers.
No. 3358 — Rooster facing: a, Right. b, Left. c, Right, streak of color at LL. b, Left, streak of color at LR.

2017, Jan. 23   Litho.   Perf. 12
3356 A733 $5.50 multi   4.25   4.25
Miniature Sheets
Perf. 12½
3357 A734 $5.50 Sheet of 4,
            #a-d   16.50 16.50
3358 A735 $5.50 Sheet of 4,
            #a-d   16.50 16.50

No. 3356 comes in sheets of 4.

A736

A737

Monkey King — A738

No. 3359 — Various scenes from *The Monkey King*, as shown.

2017, Mar. 15   Litho.   Perf. 12½
3359 A736 $5.50 Sheet of 4,
            #a-d   16.50 16.50
Souvenir Sheets
3360 A737 $10 multi   7.50   7.50
Perf. 14
3361 A738 $10 multi   7.50   7.50

Zeppelins — A739

No. 3362: a, Spotlight on Zeppelin. b, Zeppelins and airplanes. c, Zeppelin crash in ocean, ship in background. d, Zeppelin on fire.
No. 3363: a, Z2. b, LZ 127.

2017, Apr. 5   Litho.   Perf. 14
3362 A739 $5.50 Sheet of 4,
            #a-d   16.50 16.50
Souvenir Sheet
Perf. 12
3363 A739 $7.50 Sheet of 2,
            #a-b   11.00 11.00

Count Ferdinand von Zeppelin (1838-1917). No. 3363 contains two 50x30mm stamps.

Miniature Sheet

Acheivements of Pres. John F. Kennedy (1917-63) — A740

No. 3364: a, Kennedy signing copy of *Why England Slept*, 1940 (35x70mm). b, Kennedy at his inauguration, 1961 (70x35mm). c, Kennedy wearing naval uniform (35x70mm). d, Kennedy as child wearing police uniform (35x35mm). e, Kennedy graduating from Harvard, 1940 (35x35mm).

2017, June 3   Litho.   Perf. 13¾
3364 A740 $3.50 Sheet of 5,
            #a-e   13.00 13.00

First Man in Space, 55th Anniv. (in 2016) — A741

No. 3365: a, Vostok mission patch. b, Yuri Gagarin in military uniform. c, Gagarin in space suit. d, Vostok 1 capsule. e, Vostok mission patch with "CCCP." f, Coin depicting Gagarin.
No. 3366: a, Nose of Vostok 1 at lift-off. b, Vostok 1 engines and exhaust at lift-off.

2017, June 3   Litho.   Perf. 14
3365 A741 $3 Sheet of 6, #a-f 13.50 13.50
Souvenir Sheet
Perf. 13¼
3366 A741 $8 Sheet of 2, #a-b 12.00 12.00

No. 3366 contains two 35x35mm stamps.

Miniature Sheets

A742

Elvis Presley (1935-77) — A743

No. 3367 — Presley wearing: a, Suit and tie. b, Shirt and tie. c, Black and blue shirt d, Jacket and striped shirt.
No. 3368 — Presley: a, Wearing striped jacket. b, Holding guitar. c, Wearing striped shirt, color photograph. d, Wearing sweater. e, Wearing shirt and tie. f, Wearing ribbed shirt, black-and-white photograph.

2017, July 25   Litho.   Perf. 14
3367 A742 $3.50 Sheet of 4,
            #a-d   10.50 10.50
3368 A743 $3.50 Sheet of 6,
            #a-f   15.50 15.50

Princess Diana (1961-97) — A744

No. 3369 — Princess Diana wearing: a, White dress covering shoulders. b, Tiara and necklace. c, Black dress, hand touching face. d, White dress not covering shoulders. e, Tiara and gown. f, Collared jacket.
No. 3370 — Princess Diana wearing: a, Black and white hat. b, Pink hat.

2017, July 25   Litho.   Perf. 12
3369 A744 $3.50 Sheet of 6,
            #a-f   15.50 15.50
Souvenir Sheet
3370 A744 $3.50 Sheet of 2,
            #a-b   5.25   5.25

Paintings by Edgar Degas (1834-1917) — A745

No. 3371: a, At the Cafe des Ambassadeurs. b, Young Woman with Ibis. c, The Orchestra at the Opera. d, Visit to a Museum.
No. 3372: a, The Green Dancer. b, Ballet Dancers on the Stage. c, Ballet Class.

2017, July 25   Litho.   Perf. 14
3371 A745 $5.50 Sheet of 4,
            #a-d   16.50 16.50
Souvenir Sheet
3372 A745 $5 Sheet of 3,
            #a-c   11.00 11.00

Piping Plovers — A746

No. 3373 — Plover: a, Facing left, beak open. b, In flight. c, Walking left, beak closed. $10, Head of plover, vert.

2017, July 25   Litho.   Perf. 14
3373 A746 $5 Sheet of 3   11.00 11.00
Souvenir Sheet
3374 A746 $10 multi   7.50   7.50

Horses — A747

No. 3375: a, Two Icelandic horses running left. b, New Forest pony. c, Camargue horse. d, Hutsul horse. e, Two Icelandic horses standing. f, Orlov trotter.
No. 3376: a, Morgan horse. b, Arabian horse. c, Lippizan horse.

2017, July 28   Litho.   Perf. 12½x13¼
3375 A747 $4 Sheet of 6,
            #a-f   18.00 18.00
Souvenir Sheet
3376 A747 $7.50 Sheet of 3,
            #a-c   17.00 17.00

A748

Fallow Deer — A749

No. 3377: a, Buck looking over shoulder. b, Profile of Buck. c, Doe in green foilage. d, Doe in field.
No. 3378: a, Fawn. b, Doe in grass by tree. c, Buck profile in tall grass.

2017, Aug. 1   Litho.   Perf. 14
3377 A748 $7.50 Sheet of 4,
            #a-d   22.50 22.50
Souvenir Sheet
3378 A749 $7 Sheet of 3,
            #a-c   15.50 15.50

Macaws — A750

No. 3379: a, Blue-and-yellow macaw facing right. b, Scarlet macaw facing right, on branch. c, Blue-and-yellow macaw facing left. d, Scarlet macaw facing left on branch. e, Head of Blue-and-yellow macaw. f, Scarlet macaw faing right, diff.
No. 3380: a, Military macaw. b, Scarlet macaw in flight. c, Blue-and-yellow macaw in flight.

2017, Aug. 1   Litho.   Perf. 14
3379 A750 $4 Sheet of 6, #a-f 18.00 18.00
Souvenir Sheet
3380 A750 $7 Sheet of 3, #a-c 15.50 15.50

Miniature Sheets

A751

Hawksbill Turtles — A752

Various photographs of Hawksbill turtles, as shown.

2017, Aug. 1   Litho.   Perf. 14
3381 A751 $7 Sheet of 4, #a-d   21.00 21.00
3382 A752 $7 Sheet of 4, #a-d   21.00 21.00

Miniature Sheets

Fruits and Vegetables — A753

No. 3383: a, Apple bananas. b, Malay apples. c, Sapodillas. d, Eggplants.
No. 3384: a, Papayas. b, Cacao pods. c, Spanish limes. d, Avocados.

2017, Aug. 1   Litho.   Perf. 14
3383 A753 $7 Sheet of 4, #a-d   21.00 21.00

Perf. 13¾
3384 A753 $7 Sheet of 4, #a-d   21.00 21.00
No. 3384 contains four 35x35mm stamps.

Jellyfish — A754

No. 3385: a, Pacific sea nettle (40x60mm). b, Moon jellyfish (40x30mm). c, Black sea nettle, blue background (40x30mm). d, Sea nettle jellyfish (40x30mm). e, Black sea nettle, black lilac background (40x30mm).
No. 3386, vert.: a, Blue bubbler (30x40mm). b, Brown jellyfish (30x40mm). c, Lion's mane jellyfish (30x40mm).
No. 3387, vert.: a, Barrel jellyfish (30x40mm). b, Spotted jellyfish (30x40mm).

2017, Aug. 1   Perf. 14
3385 A754 $5 Sheet of 5,
                    #a-e   18.50 18.50
3386 A754 $7 Sheet of 3,
                    #a-c   15.50 15.50
Souvenir Sheet
3387 A754 $7.50 Sheet of 2,
                    #a-b   11.00 11.00

Animals — A755

No. 3388: a, Prehensile-tailed porcupine. b, San Clemente Island fox. c, Jaguarundi. d, Grevy's zebra.
$15, Snowy owl.

2017, Aug. 14   Litho.   Perf. 12½
3388 A755 $6 Sheet of 4, #a-
                    d   18.00 18.00
Souvenir Sheet
3389 A755 $15 multi   11.00 11.00

Miniature Sheets

Paintings by Norman Rockwell (1894-1978) — A756

No. 3390: a, $4, Boy in Dining Car (30x40mm). b, $4, Breaking Home Ties (30x40mm). c, $4, Homecoming Marine (30x40mm). d, $4, Retribution (30x40mm). e, $10, Triple Self-portrait (60x80mm).
No. 3391: a, $4, Russian Schoolroom (30x40mm). b, $4, Southern Justice (Murder in Mississippi) (30x40mm). c, $4, The Circus Barker (30x40mm). d, $4, The Love Song (30x40mm). e, $10, Little Boy Writing a Letter (60x80mm).
No. 3392: a, $4, The Problem We All Live With (30x40mm). b, $4, The Scoutmaster (30x40mm). c, $4, They Remembered Me (30x40mm). d, $4, We, Too, Have a Job to Do (30x40mm). e, $10, The Runaway (60x 80mm).

2017, Aug. 22   Litho.   Perf. 14
Sheets of 5, #a-e
3390-3392 A756 Set of 3   57.50 57.50

Miniature Sheet

Seadragons — A757

No. 3393: a, Weedy seadragon facing left. b, Weedy seadragon facing right. c, Weedy seadragon facing right, diff. d, Leafy seadragon.

2017, Aug. 22   Litho.   Perf. 14
3393 A757 $7 Sheet of 4, #a-d   21.00 21.00

Seahorses — A758

No. 3394: a, Thorny seahorse. b, Thorny seahorse and coral. c, Yellow seahorse.

2017, Aug. 22   Litho.   Perf. 12
3394 A758 $7 Sheet of 3, #a-c   15.50 15.50

Horses — A759

No. 3395: a, Icelandic horses walking to left. b, New Forest pony. c, Camargue horse. d, Hutsul horse. e, Icelandic horses standing. f, Orlov trotter.
No. 3396: a, Morgan horse. b, Arabian horse. c, Lipizzan horse.

Perf. 12½x13¼
2017, Sept. 26   Litho.
3395 A759 $4 Sheet of 6,
                    #a-f   18.00 18.00
Souvenir Sheet
3396 A759 $7.50 Sheet of 3,
                    #a-c   17.00 17.00

Miniature Sheet

New Year 2018 (Year of the Dog) — A760

No. 3397: a, Rottweiler at left. b, English bulldog at right. c, English bulldog at left. d, Rottweiler at right.

2017, Nov. 7   Litho.   Perf. 14
3397 A760 $7 Sheet of 4, #a-d   21.00 21.00

Muhammad Ali (1942-2016), Boxer — A761

No. 3398 — Ali with: a, One hand visible, punching bag at right. b, Both hands visible, punching bag at left. c, Both hands visible, punching bag at right.
$12, Ali, fist by chin.

2018, Jan. 23   Litho.   Perf. 13¼x12½
3398 A761 $7 Sheet of 3, #a-
                    c   15.50 15.50

Souvenir Sheet
Perf. 13¼
3399 A761 $12 multi   9.00 9.00
No. 3399 contains one 38x51mm stamp.

Miniature Sheet

Marine Mammals — A762

No. 3400: a, $2, Killer whale. b, $3, Humpback whale. c, $4, Sperm whale. d, $5, False killer whales. e, $6, Spinner dolphins. f, $7, Bottlenose dolphin.

2018, May 8   Litho.   Perf. 14
3400 A762   Sheet of 6, #a-f   20.00 20.00

Solar System — A763

No. 3401: $7: a, Mercury. b, Venus. c, Earth. d, Mars.
No. 3402: a, $6, Jupiter. b, $6, Neptune. c, $8, Saturn. d, $8, Uranus.
$12, Sun.

2018, May 9   Litho.   Perf.
Sheets of 4, #a-d
3401-3402 A763 Set of 2   42.00 42.00
Souvenir Sheet
3403 A763 $12 multi   9.00 9.00

Caribbean Reef Octopus — A764

No. 3404 — Various photographs of octopus: a, $6. b, $7. c, $8. d, $9.
$10, Octopus, diff.

2018, May 29   Litho.   Perf. 14
3404 A764   Sheet of 4, #a-d   22.50 22.50
Souvenir Sheet
Perf. 12½
3405 A764 $10 multi   7.50 7.50
No. 3405 contains one 51x38mm stamp.

Coronation of Queen Elizabeth II, 65th
Anniv. — A765

No. 3406: a, $3, Coronation pen
(35x35mm). b, $3, Coronation glove
(35x35mm). c, $5, Diamond diadem
(35x35mm). d, $6, Imperial State Crown
(35x35mm). e, $6, Coronation gown and Robe
of State (35x70mm).
No. 3407: a, Gold State Coach (40x30mm).
b, Queen Elizabeth II and Prince Philip
(40x30mm).

2018, May 29		**Litho.**	**Perf. 13¾**	
3406	A765	Sheet of 5, #a-e	17.00	17.00

Souvenir Sheet
Perf. 14

3407	A765	$6.50 Sheet of 2, #a-b	9.75	9.75

Miniature Sheet

Visit to Vatican City of Pres. Donald
Trump — A766

No. 3408 — Pope Francis and: a, $4, Pres.
Trump, shaking hands (40x30mm). b, $4,
Melania Trump (40x30mm). c, $4, Ivanka
Trump (40x30mm). d, $4, Pres Trump, stand-
ing (40x30mm). e, $6, Trump family and Jared
Kushner (80x30mm).
$10, Trump family and Kushner.

2018, July 25		**Litho.**	**Perf. 14**	
3408	A766	Sheet of 5, #a-e	16.50	16.50

Souvenir Sheet
Perf. 14

3409	A766	$10 multi	7.50	7.50

No. 3409 contains one 40x30mm stamp.

Miniature Sheet

Scalloped Hammerhead
Sharks — A767

No. 3410 — Various photographs of sharks:
a, $4. b, $5. c, $6. d, $7.

2018, July 25		**Litho.**	**Perf. 12**	
3410	A767	Sheet of 4, #a-d	16.50	16.50

Corals and Sponges — A768

No. 3411: a, $1, Elkhorn coral. b, $2, Azure
vase sponge. c, $3, Giant barrel sponge. d,
$4, Branching fire coral. e, $5, Staghorn coral.
f, $6, Branching vase sponge.
$10, Pillar coral, vert.

2018, July 25		**Litho.**	**Perf. 14**	
3411	A768	Sheet of 6, #a-f	15.50	15.50

Souvenir Sheet
Perf. 12½

3412	A768	$10 multi	7.50	7.50

No. 3412 contains one 38x51mm stamp.

Flowers — A769

No. 3413: a, $2, Desert rose. b, $3, White
frangipani. c, $4, Heliconia. d, $5, Red hibiscus. e, $6, Bougainvillea. f, $7, White
oleander.
$12, Dagger log, vert.

2018, July 25		**Litho.**	**Perf. 14**	
3413	A769	Sheet of 6, #a-f	20.00	20.00

Souvenir Sheet
Perf. 12

3414	A769	$12 multi	9.00	9.00

No. 3414 contains one 30x50mm stamp.

Engagement of Prince Harry and
Meghan Markle — A770

No. 3415: a, Couple, Prince Harry waving.
b, Hands of couple. c, Couple, Prince Harry
touching suit button.
$10, Couple, horiz.

2018, Aug. 22		**Litho.**	**Perf. 14**	
3415	A770	$5.50 Sheet of 3, #a-c	12.50	12.50

Souvenir Sheet
Perf. 12½

3416	A770	$10 multi	7.50	7.50

No. 3416 contains one 51x38mm stamp.

Muhammad Ali (1942-2016),
Boxer — A771

No. 3417 — Ali boxing against: a, George
Foreman, 1974. b, Joe Frazier, 1975. c, Earnie
Shavers, 1977. d, Leon Spinks, 1978.
$10, Ali with arms raised, horiz.

2018, Aug. 22		**Litho.**	**Perf. 14**	
3417	A771	$6 Sheet of 4, #a-d	18.00	18.00

Souvenir Sheet

3418	A771	$10 multi	7.50	7.50

Air Mail Centenary — A772

No. 3419: a, Charles Lindbergh in plane
cockpit. b, 1929 Antigua air mail postmark. c,
Antigua stamps on air mail cover. d, Linbergh
and the Spirit of St. Louis.
$10, Sikorsky S-38A.

2018, Aug. 22		**Litho.**	**Perf. 14**	
3419	A772	$5.50 Sheet of 4, #a-d	16.50	16.50

Souvenir Sheet
Perf. 12½

3420	A772	$10 multi	7.50	7.50

No. 3420 contains one 51x38mm stamp.

Miniature Sheet

Birth of Prince Louis of
Cambridge — A773

No. 3421: a, Duke and Duchess of Cambridge with Prince Louis. b, Princess Charlotte
of Cambridge. c, Prince George of Cambridge. d, Prince Louis of Cambridge in arms
of his mother.

2018, Aug. 28		**Litho.**	**Perf. 13¾**	
3421	A773	$5.50 Sheet of 4, #a-d	16.50	16.50

Wedding of Prince Harry and Meghan
Markle — A774

No. 3422: a, Groom, lamp in background. b,
Bride, lamp in background. c, Groom, tile floor
in background. d, Bride, tile floor in
background.
$10, Bride and groom on steps, horiz.

2018, Aug. 28		**Litho.**	**Perf. 12**	
3422	A774	$5 Sheet of 4, #a-	15.00	15.00

Souvenir Sheet
Perf. 12½

3423	A774	$10 multi	7.50	7.50

No. 3423 contains one 102x38mm stamp.

Magnificent Frigatebirds — A775

No. 3424 — Frigatebird: a, $5, On perch. b,
$5, In flight. c, $6, Facing left. b, $6, Facing
right.
$10, Two birds.

2018, Oct. 1		**Litho.**	**Perf. 14**	
3424	A775	Sheet of 4, #a-d	16.50	16.50

Souvenir Sheet

3425	A775	$10 multi	7.50	7.50

No. 3425 contains one 80x30mm stamp.

Bees — A776

No. 3426: a, $2, Metallic green bee (40x30mm). b, $3, Buff-tailed bumblebee (40x30mm). c, $4, Leafcutter bee (40x30mm). d, $5, Eastern carpenter bee (40x30mm). e, $6, Buff-tailed bumblebee, diff. (40x60mm). $10, Honeybee, vert.

2018, Oct. 1	Litho.	Perf. 14	
3426 A776	Sheet of 5, #a-e	15.00	15.00

Souvenir Sheet
Perf. 12½

3427 A776	$10 multi	7.50	7.50

No. 3427 contains one 38x51mm stamp.

Miniature Sheets

United States Presidents — A777

No. 3428: a, 1c, George Washington. b, 2c, John Adams. c, 3c, Thomas Jefferson. d, 4c, James Madison. e, 5c, James Monroe. f, 6c, John Quincy Adams. g, 7c, Andrew Jackson. h, 8c, Martin Van Buren. i, 9c, William Henry Harrison. j, 10c, John Tyler. k, 11c, James Knox Polk. l, $5, Seal of the President of the United States.

No. 3429: a, 12c, Zachary Taylor. b, 13c, Millard Fillmore. c, 14c, Franklin Pierce. d, 15c, James Buchanan. e, 16c, Abraham Lincoln. f, 17c, Andrew Johnson. g, 18c, Ulysses S. Grant. h, 19c, Rutherford B. Hayes. i, 20c, James Garfield. j, 21c, Chester A. Arthur. k, 22c, Grover Cleveland. l, $4, White House.

No. 3430: a, 23c, Benjamin Harrison. b, 24c, Grover Cleveland. c, 25c, William McKinley. d, 26c, Theodore Roosevelt. e, 27c, William Howard Taft. f, 28c, Woodrow Wilson. g, 29c, Warren G. Harding. h, 30c, Calvin Coolidge. i, 31c, Herbert Hoover. j, 32c, Franklin D. Roosevelt. k, 33c, Harry S. Truman. l, $3, U.S. Capitol.

No. 3431: a, 34c, Dwight D. Eisenhower. b, 35c, John F. Kennedy. c, 36c, Lyndon B. Johnson. d, 37c, Richard M. Nixon. e, 38c, Gerald R. Ford. f, 39c, Jimmy Carter. g, 40c, Ronald Reagan. h, 41c, George H. W. Bush. i, 42c, Bill Clinton. j, 43c, George W. Bush. k, 44c, Barack Obama. l, 45c, Donald Trump.

2018, Nov. 1	Litho.	Perf. 13¾	
3428 A777	Sheet of 12, #a-l	4.25	4.25
3429 A777	Sheet of 12, #a-l	4.50	4.50
3430 A777	Sheet of 12, #a-l	4.50	4.50
3431 A777	Sheet of 12, #a-l	3.50	3.50
Nos. 3428-3431 (4)		16.75	16.75

A778

New Year 2019 (Year of the Pig) — A779

No. 3432: a, Red pig. b, Black pig.

2018, Nov. 1	Litho.	Perf. 14	
3432 A778	$3 Pair, #a-b	4.50	4.50

Souvenir Sheet
Perf. 13¾

3433 A779	$6 multi	4.50	4.50

No. 3432 was printed in sheets containing two pairs.

Miniature Sheet

Flowers — A780

No. 3434: a, $2, Lobster claw plant. b, $3, Easter lily. c, $4, Flamingo flower. d, $5, Red frangipani. e, $6, False bird of paradise. f, $7, Flaming torch.

2018, Nov. 1	Litho.	Perf. 14	
3434 A780	Sheet of 6, #a-f	20.00	20.00

First Man on the Moon, 50th Anniv. (in 2019) — A781

No. 3435 — Apollo 11 astronauts: a, Edwin "Buzz" Aldrin, Jr. b, Neil Armstrong. c, Michael Collins. $10, Footprint on Moon.

2018, Nov. 1	Litho.	Perf. 12	
3435 A781	$6 Sheet of 3, #a-c	13.50	13.50

Souvenir Sheet
Perf. 12½

3436 A781	$10 multi	7.50	7.50

No. 3436 contains one 38x51mm stamp.

Classic Stamps — A782

Most expensive variety of the illustrated stamp: No. 3437, $6, United States #7X1. No. 3438, $6, United States #11X6. No. 3439, $6, United States #1. No. 3440, $6, United States #2. No. 3441, $6, United States #5. No. 3442, $6, United States #85E. No. 3443, $6, United States #85F. No. 3444, $6, United States #120b. No. 3445, $6, United States #121b. No. 3446, $6, United States #181. No. 3447, $6, United States #292. No. 3448, $6, United States #294a. No. 3449, $6, United States #295a. No. 3450, $6, United States #C3a. No. 3451, $6, United States #C15. No. 3452, $6, Confederate States #36X1. No. 3453, $6, Confederate States #51X1. No. 3454, $6, Confederate States #62X6. No. 3455, $6, Confederate States #86X5. No. 3456, $6, Canal Zone #157a. No. 3457, $6, Hawaii #3. No. 3458, $6, Argentina #10. No. 3459, $6, Australian States - New South Wales #2s. No. 3460, $6, Australian States - Queensland #3. No. 3461, $6, Australian States - Tasmania #8. No. 3462, $6, Australian States - Western Australia #3a. No. 3463, $6, Austria #226a. No. 3464, $6, Barbados #21c. No. 3465, $6, Belgium #1. No. 3466, $6, Belgium #123B. No. 3467, $6, Bermuda #X1. No. 3468, $6, Bermuda #1b. No. 3469, $6, Brazil #1c. No. 3470, $6, British Central Africa #31. No. 3471, $6, British Central Africa #71. No. 3472, $6, British Central Africa #72. No. 3473, $6, British Guiana #1. No. 3474, $6, British Guiana #7. No. 3475, $6, British Guiana #13. No. 3476, $6, Canadian Provinces - New Brunswick #5. No. 3477, $6, Canadian Provinces - Newfoundland #9. No. 3478, $6, Canadian Provinces - Newfoundland #C1. No. 3479, $6, Canadian Provinces - Nova Scotia #6b. No. 3480, $6, Canada #1. No. 3481, $6, Canada #2. No. 3482, $6, Canada #3. No. 3483, $6, Canada #387a, No. 3484, $6, Cape of Good Hope #7b. No. 3485, $6, Ceylon #5. No. 3486, $6, Ceylon #7a. No. 3487, $6, Ceylon #218. No. 3488, $6, China #83. No. 3489, $6, Denmark #1. No. 3490, $6, Dominica #14. No. 3491, $6, Falkland Islands #151a. No. 3492, $6, Finland #2a. No. 3493, $6, France #9a. No. 3494, $6, France #19a. No. 3495, $6, German States - Bavaria #1b. No. 3496, $6, German States - Brunswick #9f. No. 3497, $6, German States - Lubeck #1. No. 3498, $6, German States - Saxony #1a. No. 3499, $6, Gibraltar #30a. No. 3500, $6, Gold Coast #24. No. 3501, $6, Great Britain #1c. No. 3502, $6, Great Britain #2c. No. 3503, $6, Great Britain #92. No. 3504, $6, Honduras #178. No. 3505, $6, Hong Kong #1a. No. 3506, $6, India #A3. No. 3507, $6, India #6c. No. 3508, $6, Italian States - Tuscany #23. No. 3509, $6, Italian States - Two Sicilies #8. No. 3510, $6, Jamaica #83a. No. 3511, $6, Kenya, Uganda and Tanzania #41D. No. 3512, $6, Malta #65. No. 3513, $6, Mauritius #2. No. 3514, $6, Mauritius #15. No. 3515, $6, Mexico #C74. No. 3516, $6, Nevis #13. No. 3517, $6, New Zealand #123a. No. 3518, $6, Niger Coast Protectorate #34. No. 3519, $6, Northern Nigeria #18A. No. 3520, $6, Norway #1. No. 3521, $6, Peru #1. No. 3522, $6, Reunion #1. No. 3523, $6, Romania #4. No. 3524, $6, Rhodesia #118c. No. 3525, $6, St. Helena #1. No. 3526, $6, Sierra Leone #63A. No. 3527, $6, Spain #8a. No. 3528, $6, Sweden #2. No. 3529, $6, Switzerland #1L1. No. 3530, $6, Switzerland #2L1. No. 3531, $6, Switzerland #3L1a. No. 3532, $6, Switzerland #4. No. 3533, $6, Switzerland #5. No. 3534, $6, Transvaal #3a. No. 3535, $6, Trinidad "Lady McLeod" stamp. No. 3536, $6, Uruguay #5d.

Die Cut Perf. 9x9½, 10¾ (#3449, 3482, 3512, 3515)

2018, Nov. 1		Embossed	
	On Gold-Faced Paper		
3437-3536 A782	Set of 100	450.00	450.00

Christmas 2018 — A783

Designs: 90c, Ornaments on Christmas tree. $2.25, Decorated Christmas tree. $3.50, Candles. $5, Christmas stocking and gifts near fireplace.

2019, Jan. 8	Litho.	Perf. 12¾	
3537-3540 A783	Set of 4	8.75	8.75

A784

Designs: 10c, Team running. 30c, Team holding banner. 90c, Team on boat. $1.50, Team holding oars. $100, Team holding flares. $10, Team holding flares, diff.

2019, Mar. 20	Litho.	Perf. 14	
3541-3545 A784	Set of 5	76.00	76.00
3543a	Souvenir sheet of 6, 2 each #3541-3543	2.00	2.00

Souvenir Sheet
Perf. 12

3546 A784	$10 multi	7.50	7.50

Team Antigua Island Girls, 13th place finishers in Talisker Whisky Atlantic Challenge.

Team Antigua Island Girls rowed from the Canary Islands to Antigua in 47 days, 8 hours and 25 minutes. No. 3546 contains one 50x30mm stamp.

Miniature Sheet

Mohandas K. Gandhi (1869-1948), Indian Nationalist Leader — A785

No. 3547 — Various photographs of Gandhi on 1930 Salt March with "Mahatma Gandhi": a, $4, At UL, in black, reading up (40x30mm). b, $4, At UL, in white, reading horizontally (40x30mm). c, $4, At UR, in black, reading down (Gandhi holding walking stick, 40x30mm). d, $4, At UR, in black, reading down (Gandhi's walking stick not visible, 40x30mm). e, $5, Gandhi bending down to touch salt (40x60mm).

2019, June 11	Litho.	Perf. 14	
3547 A785	Sheet of 5, #a-e	15.50	15.50

Souvenir Sheet

Elvis Presley (1935-77) — A786

Inscriptions: $11, "I can sing this song all day." $12, "Started a revolution, ended up a king," horiz. $13, "It Happened at the World's Fair." $14, Elvis's iconic sunglasses.

2019, June 11	Litho.	Perf. 14	
3548-3551 A786	Set of 4	37.00	37.00

Miniature Sheet

Roses — A787

No. 3552 — a, $3, Pink roses and butterfly. b, $3, White roses and pink buds. c, $4, Yellow roses. d, $4, Pale yellow roses. e, $5, White roses and butterflies. f, $5, Pink roses.

2019, June 1   Litho.   Perf. 14
3552 A787   Sheet of 6, #a-f   18.00 18.00

2019 China World Stamp Exhibition, Wuhan — A788

No. 3553 — Sights in Cherry Blossom Park, Wuhan: a, $4, Cherry blossoms, pagoda. b, $5, Lanterns and cherry blossoms. c, $6, Cherry blossoms. d, $7, Pagoda, cherry trees, lake.
$14, Pagoda, cherry trees, vert.

2019, June 1   Litho.   Perf. 14
3553 A788   Sheet of 4, #a-d   16.50 16.50
Souvenir Sheet
3554 A788 $14 multi   10.50 10.50

Pres. Franklin D. Roosevelt (1882-1945) — A789

No. 3555 — Roosevelt: a, At 1933 Presidential inauguration. b, Working on stamp collection, 1936. c, With wife, Eleanor, 1939. d, Making radio address, 1939. e, Signing declaration of war, 1941. f, With Winston Churchill, 1941.
$14, Official Presidential portrait, by Frank O. Salisbury, vert.

2019, June 1   Litho.   Perf. 14
3555 A789 $4 Sheet of 6, #a-f   18.00 18.00
Souvenir Sheet
Perf. 12½
3556 A789 $14 multi   10.50 10.50
No. 3556 contains one 38x51mm stamp.

Miniature Sheet

Beans — A790

No. 3557 — a, $3, Vanilla bean and orchid. b, $3, Bowl of vanilla ice cream. c, $4, Cocoa bean. d, $4, Chocolate bar. e, $5, Coffee beans. f, $5, Cup of coffee.

2019, June 11   Litho.   Perf. 14
3557 A790   Sheet of 6, #a-f   18.00 18.00

Sea Birds — A791

No. 3558 — a, $1, Brown pelican. b, $2, White-tailed tropicbird. c, $3, Cory's shearwater. d, $4, Brown boobies. e, $5, Red-footed booby. f, $6, Masked boobies.
No. 3559 — a, $7.50, Magnificent frigatebird chick. b, $8.50, Male Magnificent frigatebird.

2019, June 11   Litho.   Perf. 14
3558 A791   Sheet of 6, #a-f   15.50 15.50
Souvenir Sheet
Perf. 12½
3559 A791   Sheet of 2, #a-b   12.00 12.00
No. 3559 contains two 51x38mm stamps.

Beaches — A792

No. 3560 — a, $2, Darkwood Beach, Antigua. b, $3, Ffryes Beach, Antigua. c, $4, Galley Bay Beach, Antigua. d, $5, Pink Sand Beach, Barbuda. e, $6, Turners Beach, Antigua. f, $7, Valley Church Beach, Antigua.
No. 3561 — a, $8, Galleon Beach, Antigua. b, $9, Princess Diana Beach, Barbuda.

2019, June 11   Litho.   Perf. 14
3560 A792   Sheet of 6, #a-f   20.00 20.00
Souvenir Sheet
3561 A792   Sheet of 2, #a-b   12.50 12.50

Miniature Sheet

Leonard Bernstein (1918-90), Conductor — A793

No. 3562 — Bernstein: a, Wearing jacket and bow tie. b, Standing near microphone stand. c, Wearing white shirt, conducting. d, Wearing black shirt, conducting.

2019, June 17   Litho.   Perf. 14
3562 A793 $5.50 Sheet of 4, #a-d   16.50 16.50

Miniature Sheet

American Crocodiles — A794

No. 3563 — Various photographs of crocodiles with denominations of: a, $4. b, $5.50. c, $6. d, $6.50.

2020, Jan. 15   Litho.   Perf. 13¾
3563 A794   Sheet of 4, #a-d   16.50 16.50

Terracotta Soldiers, People's Republic of China — A795

No. 3564: a, $3, Armored figure. b, $5, General. c, $6, Officer.
$10, Head of statue.

2020, Jan. 15   Litho.   Perf. 12
3564 A795   Sheet of 3, #a-c   10.50 10.50
Souvenir Sheet
3565 A795 $10 multi   7.50 7.50

Flamingos — A796

No. 3566 — Various photographs of Phoenicopterus ruber with denominations of: a, $2. b, $3. c, $4. d, $5.
$14, Phoenicopterus ruber feeding chick, vert.

2020, May 20   Litho.   Perf. 13¾
3566 A796   Sheet of 4, #a-d   10.50 10.50
Souvenir Sheet
Perf. 12
3567 A796 $14 multi   10.50 10.50
No. 3567 contains one 30x50mm stamp.

Turkey Vultures — A797

No. 3568 — Cathartes aura: a, $1, In flight. b, $1, Landing. c, $1.50, Standing in tall grass. d, $2, Head.
$14, Cathartes aura on roof, vert.

2020, May 20   Litho.   Perf. 12
3568 A797   Sheet of 4, #a-d   4.25 4.25
Souvenir Sheet
3569 A797 $14 multi   10.50 10.50

Sheep — A798

No. 3570 — Various photographs of heads of Merino sheep with denominations of: a, $3. b, $4. c, $5.
$14, Blackface sheep.

2020, May 20   Litho.   Perf. 13¾
3570 A798   Sheet of 3, #a-c   9.00 9.00
Souvenir Sheet
3571 A798 $14 multi   10.50 10.50

Mallard Ducks — A799

No. 3572 — Mallard duck: a, $4, Facing right. b, $5, Facing right, diff. c, $6, In flight. d, $7, Facing left.
$14, Mallard duck in flight, diff.

2020, May 20   Litho.   Perf. 14
3572 A799   Sheet of 4, #a-d   16.50 16.50
Souvenir Sheet
Perf. 12½
3573 A799 $14 multi   10.50 10.50
No. 3573 contains one 51x38mm stamp.

Spotted Cleaner Shrimp — A800

No. 3574 — Various depictions of spotted cleaner shrimp: a, $4. b, $5. c, $6. d, $7. $14, Spotted cleaner shrimp, vert.

2020, May 20	Litho.	**Perf. 14**	
3574	A800	Sheet of 4, #a-d	16.50 16.50

Souvenir Sheet
Perf. 12½

| 3575 | A800 | $14 multi | 10.50 10.50 |

No. 3575 contains one 38x51mm stamp.

Seashells — A801

No. 3576 — Various unnamed seashells with frame color of: a, $3, Light blue. b, $3, Red brown. c, $4, Lilac. d, $4, Yellow brown. e, $5, Yellow brown. f, $5, Blue green. $14, Conch shell, dark blue frame.

2020, May 20	Litho.	**Perf. 13¾**	
3576	A801	Sheet of 6, #a-f	18.00 18.00

Souvenir Sheet

| 3577 | A801 | $14 multi | 10.50 10.50 |

WAR TAX STAMPS

No. 31 and Type A3 Overprinted in Black or Red

1916-18		**Wmk. 3**	**Perf. 14**	
MR1	A3	½p green	4.75	3.75
MR2	A3	½p green (R) ('17)	1.60	3.50
MR3	A3	1½p orange ('18)	1.75	1.75
		Nos. MR1-MR3 (3)	8.10	9.00

ARGENTINA

ár-jən-'tē-nə

LOCATION — In South America
GOVT. — Republic
AREA — 1,084,120 sq. mi.
POP. — 36,737,664 (est. 1999)

CAPITAL — Buenos Aires
100 Centavos = 1 Peso (1858, 1992)
100 Centavos = 1 Austral (1985)

Catalogue values for unused stamps in this country are for Never Hinged items, beginning with Scott 587 in the regular postage section, Scott B12 in the semipostal section, Scott C59 in the airpost section, Scott CB1 in the airpost semi-postal section and Scott O79 in the officials section.

Watermarks

Wmk. 84 — Italic RA

Wmk. 85 — Small Sun, 4½mm

Wmk. 86 — Large Sun, 6mm

Wmk. 87 — Honeycomb

Wmk. 88 — Multiple Suns

Wmk. 89 — Large Sun

In this watermark the face of the sun is 7mm in diameter, the rays are heavier than in the large sun watermark of 1896-1911 and the watermarks are placed close together, so that parts of several frequently appear on one stamp. This paper was intended to be used for fiscal stamps and is usually referred to as "fiscal sun paper."

Wmk. 90 — RA in Sun

In 1928 watermark 90 was slightly modified, making the diameter of the Sun 9mm instead of 10mm. Several types of this watermark exist.

Wmk. 205 — AP in Oval

The letters "AP" are the initials of "AHORRO POSTAL." This paper was formerly used exclusively for Postal Savings stamps.

Wmk. 287 — Double Circle and Letters in Sheet

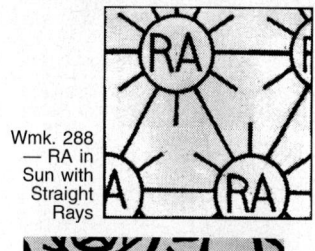

Wmk. 288 — RA in Sun with Straight Rays

Wmk. 365 — Argentine Arms, "Casa de Moneda de la Nacion" & "RA" Multiple

Values for Unused

Unused values for Nos. 5-17 are for examples without gum. Examples with original gum command higher prices. Unused values of Nos. 1-4B and stamps after No. 17 are for examples with original gum as defined in the catalogue introduction.

Argentine Confederation

Symbolical of the Argentine Confederation — A1

1858, May 1	**Unwmk.** Litho.	**Imperf.**	
1	A1	5c red	1.50	40.00
a.		Colon after "5"	1.75	32.50
b.		Colon after "V"	1.75	32.50
2	A1	10c green	2.50	90.00
f.		Diagonal half used as 5c on cover		1,000.
3	A1	15c blue	18.00	250.00
c.		Horiz. third used as 5c on cover		10,000.
		Nos. 1-3 (3)	22.00	380.00

There are nine varieties of Nos. 1, 2 and 3. Counterfeits and forged cancellations of Nos. 1-3 are plentiful.

Symbolical of the Argentine Confederation — A2

1860, Jan.

4	A2	5c red	3.25	100.00
4A	A2	10c green	7.00	—
4B	A2	15c blue	30.00	—
		Nos. 4-4B (3)	40.25	

Nos. 4A and 4B were never placed in use. Some compostitions of Nos. 4-4B contain 8 different types across the sheet. Other settings exist with minor variations. Counterfeits and forged cancellations of Nos. 4-4B are plentiful.

Argentine Republic

Seal of the Republic — A3

Broad "C" in "CENTAVOS," Accent on "U" of "REPUBLICA"

1862, Jan. 11				
5	A3	5c rose	49.00	37.50
6	A3	10c green	175.00	80.00
7	A3	15c blue	350.00	225.00
a.		Without accent on "U"	8,000.	5,000.
b.		Tete beche pair	150,000.	120,000.
d.		15c ultramarine	500.00	350.00
e.		Diagonal third used as 5c on cover		12,000.

No. 6g is printed on white wove paper.
Only one used example of No. 7b is known. It has faults. Two unused examples are known. One is sound with origional gum, the other is in a block, without gum, and has tiny faults. No. 7u is known only used in Mendoza.

Broad "C" in "CENTAVOS," No Accent on "U"

1863				
7C	A3	5c rose	20.00	21.00
i.		5c rose lilac	200.00	250.00
7F	A3	10c yellow green	1,000.	250.00

Narrow "C" in "CENTAVOS," No Accent on "U"

1864				
7H	A3	5c rose red	225.00	32.50

The so-called reprints of 10c and 15c are counterfeits. They have narrow "C" and straight lines in shield. Nos. 7C and 7H have been extensively counterfeited.

Rivadavia Issue

Bernardino Rivadavia
A4   A5

Rivadavia — A6

1864-67	Engr.	**Wmk. 84**	**Imperf.**	
		Clear Impressions		
8	A4	5c brown rose	2,500.	250.
a.		5c brick red ('67)	2,500.	250.
9	A5	10c green	3,000.	1,750.

10	A6	15c blue	13,500. 6,500.

Perf. 11½
Dull to Worn Impressions

11	A4	5c brown rose ('65)	40.00	15.00
11B	A4	5c lake	100.00	22.00
12	A5	10c green	150.00	70.00
a.		Diagonal half used as 5c on cover		2,000.
b.		Vert. half used as 5c on cover		3,000.
c.		Horiz. pair, imperf. vert.		5,000.
13	A6	15c blue	450.00	150.00

1867-72		Unwmk.	*Imperf.*	
14	A4	5c carmine ('72)	350.	100.
15	A4	5c rose, thin white paper	350.	100.
15A	A5	10c green, medium white paper	3,000.	3,200.
16	A6	15c blue, medium white paper	3,000.	2,700.

Nos. 15A-16 issued without gum.

1867			*Perf. 11½*	
17	A4	5c carmine	1,000.	200.00

Rivadavia A7   Manuel Belgrano A8

Jose de San Martin — A9

Groundwork of Horizontal Lines

1867-68			*Perf. 12*	
18	A7	5c vermilion	225.00	17.50
18A	A8	10c green	50.00	7.50
b.		Diag. half used as 5c on cover		2,500.
19	A9	15c blue	100.00	22.50

Groundwork of Crossed Lines

20	A7	5c vermilion	15.00	1.25
21	A9	15c blue	120.00	16.00

See Nos. 27, 33-34, 39 and types A19, A33, A34, A37. For surcharges and overprints see Nos. 30-32, 41-42, 47-51, O6-O7, O26.

Gen. Antonio G. Balcarce A10   Mariano Moreno A11

Carlos Maria de Alvear A12   Gervasio Antonio Posadas A13

Cornelio Saavedra — A14

1873				
22	A10	1c purple	6.00	2.25
a.		1c gray violet	10.00	2.25
23	A11	4c brown	6.00	.75
a.		4c red brown	15.00	2.00
24	A12	30c orange	140.00	25.00
a.		Vert. pair, imperf horiz.		4,000.
25	A13	60c black	160.00	5.00
26	A14	90c blue	60.00	3.00
		Nos. 22-26 (5)	372.00	36.00

For overprints see Nos. O5, O12-O14, O19-O21, O25, O29.
Four examples of No. 24a are known. Three examples of No. 26 are known on cover.

1873			Laid Paper	
27	A8	10c green	325.00	32.50

Nos.18, 18A Surcharged in Black

Nos. 30-31   No. 32

1877, Feb.			Wove Paper	
30	A7	1c on 5c vermilion	75.00	25.00
a.		Inverted surcharge	1,000.	300.00
31	A7	2c on 5c vermilion	125.00	75.00
a.		Inverted surcharge	1,200.	750.00
32	A8	8c on 10c green	160.00	40.00
b.		Inverted surcharge	2,500.	1,000.
		Nos. 30-32 (3)	360.00	140.00

Varieties also exist with double and triple surcharges, surcharge on reverse, 8c on No. 27, all made clandestinely from the original cliches of the surcharges.
Forgeries of these surcharges include the inverted and double varieties.

1876-77			*Rouletted*	
33	A7	5c vermilion	200.00	85.00
34	A7	8c lake ('77)	35.00	.65

Belgrano A17   Dalmacio Vélez Sarsfield A18

San Martín — A19

1878			*Rouletted*	
35	A17	16c green	12.00	1.10
36	A18	20c blue	20.00	2.25
37	A19	24c blue	30.00	3.50
		Nos. 35-37 (3)	62.00	6.85

See No. 56. For overprints see Nos. O9-O10, O15-O17, O22, O28.

Vicente Lopez — A20   Alvear — A21

1877-80			*Perf. 12*	
38	A20	2c yellow green	5.00	.75
39	A7	8c lake ('80)	4.50	.75
a.		8c brown lake	52.50	.75
40	A21	25c lake ('78)	30.00	6.00
		Nos. 38-40 (3)	39.50	7.50

No. 38 measures 19.9 mm x 25.3 mm. No. 38a measaures 19.8 mm x 25.3 mm.
For overprints see Nos. O4, O11, O18, O24.

No. 18 Surcharged in Black

Large "P"   Small "P"

1882

41	A7	½c on 5c ver	2.75	2.75
a.		Double surcharge	100.00	100.00
b.		Inverted surcharge	50.00	50.00
c.		"PROVISORIO" omitted	110.00	110.00
d.		Fraction omitted	100.00	
e.		"PROVISOBIO"	50.00	50.00
f.		Pair, one without surcharge	250.00	
g.		Small "P" in "PROVISORIO"	2.75	2.75
h.		As "a," small "P" in "PROVISORIO"	75.00	75.00
i.		As "b," small "P" in "PROVISORIO"	75.00	75.00
j.		As "d," small "P" in "PROVISORIO"	30.00	30.00

Perforated across Middle of Stamp

42	A7	½c on 5c ver	6.00	6.00
a.		"PROVISORIQ"	50.00	50.00
b.		Large "P" in "PROVISORIO"	40.00	30.00

A23

1882		Typo.	*Perf. 12½*	
43	A23	½c brown	2.25	1.50
a.		Imperf., pair	100.00	80.00
44	A23	1c red	15.00	6.00
45	A23	12c ultra	90.00	14.00

Perf. 14¼

44A	A23	1c red	3.50	1.50
45A	A23	12c ultra	65.00	12.00

Engr.

46	A23	12c grnsh blue	225.00	16.00
		Nos. 43-46 (6)	400.75	51.00

See type A29. For overprints see Nos. O2, O8, O23, O27.

No. 21 Surcharged in Red

a   b

c

1884		Engr.	*Perf. 12*	
47	A9 (a)	½c on 15c blue	3.00	2.00
a.		Groundwork of horiz. lines	150.00	90.00
b.		Inverted surcharge	35.00	25.00
48	A9 (b)	1c on 15c blue	22.50	16.50
a.		Groundwork of horiz. lines	13.00	11.50
b.		Inverted surcharge	100.00	62.50
c.		Double surcharge	50.00	40.00
d.		Triple surcharge	400.00	

Nos. 20-21 Surcharged in Black

49	A7 (a)	½c on 5c ver	5.00	4.50
a.		Inverted surcharge	200.00	150.00
b.		Date omitted	200.00	—
c.		Pair, one without surcharge	500.00	
d.		Double surcharge	550.00	
50	A9 (a)	½c on 15c blue	15.00	12.00
a.		Groundwork of horiz. lines	50.00	35.00
b.		Inverted surcharge	90.00	70.00
c.		Pair, one without surcharge	400.00	
51	A7 (c)	4c on 5c ver	12.00	9.00
a.		Inverted surcharge	35.00	28.00
b.		Double surcharge	700.00	350.00
c.		Pair, one without surcharge but with "4" in manuscript	750.00	650.00
d.		Pair, one without surcharge	400.00	
		Nos. 47-51 (5)	57.50	44.00

A29

1884-85		Engr.	*Perf. 12*	
52	A29	½c red brown	1.50	.65
a.		Horiz. pair, imperf. vert.		1,200.
53	A29	1c rose red	7.00	.65
a.		Horiz. pair, imperf. vert.	300.00	250.00
54	A29	12c deep blue	35.00	1.50
a.		12c grnsh blue ('85)	50.00	1.50
b.		Horiz. pair, imperf vert.	300.00	250.00
		Nos. 52-54 (3)	43.50	2.80

For overprints see Nos. O1, O3, O9.

San Martin Type of 1878

1887			Engr.	
56	A19	24c blue	20.00	1.40

Justo Jose de Urquiza — A30   Lopez — A31

Miguel Juarez Celman — A32   Rivadavia (Large head) — A33

Rivadavia (Small head) A34   Domingo F. Sarmiento A35

Nicolas Avellaneda — A36

San Martin — A37   Julio A. Roca — A37a

Belgrano — A37b   Manuel Dorrego — A38

Moreno — A39   Bartolome Mitre — A40

CINCO CENTAVOS.
A33 — Shows collar on left side only.
A34 — Shows collar on both sides. Lozenges in background larger and clearer than in A33.

1888-90		Litho.	*Perf. 11½*	
57	A30	½c blue	1.75	.75
b.		Vert. pair, imperf. horiz.	200.00	200.00
c.		Horiz. pair, imperf. vert.	200.00	200.00

58	A31	2c yel grn	20.00	10.00
b.	Vert. pair, imperf. horiz.		130.00	
c.	Horiz. pair, imperf. vert.		250.00	
59	A32	3c blue green	3.50	1.50
b.	Horiz. pair, imperf. vert.		60.00	
c.	Horiz. pair, imperf. btwn.		130.00	
d.	Vert. pair, imperf. btwn.		25.00	25.00
60	A33	5c carmine	18.00	.75
b.	Vert. pair, imperf. horiz.		175.00	
61	A34	5c carmine	26.00	2.25
b.	Vert. pair, imperf. btwn.		200.00	
c.	Vert. pair, imperf. horiz.			400.00
62	A35	6c red	50.00	20.00
b.	Vert. pair, imperf. btwn.		150.00	
c.	Perf. 12		100.00	50.00
63	A36	10c brown	26.00	1.50
64	A37	15c orange	27.50	2.25
d.	Vert. pair, imperf. btwn.			600.00
64A	A37a	20c green	25.00	1.50
64B	A37b	25c purple	45.00	4.00
65	A38	30c brown	40.00	4.00
b.	30c reddish chocolate brown		400.00	80.00
c.	Horiz. pair, imperf. btwn.		700.00	500.00
66	A39	40c slate, perf. 12	150.00	3.00
a.	Perf. 11½		300.00	4.00
b.	Horiz. pair, imperf. btwn. (#66)			800.00
67	A40	50c blue	350.00	20.00
		Nos. 57-67 (13)	782.75	71.50

In this issue there are several varieties of each value, the difference between them being in the relative position of the head to the frame.

Imperf., Pairs

57a	A30	½c	85.00	67.50
58a	A31	2c	100.00	
59a	A32	3c	45.00	27.50
61a	A34	5c		100.00
62a	A35	6c	150.00	150.00
63a	A36	10c	55.00	
64c	A37	15c		200.00
65a	A38	30c	325.00	225.00

Urquiza A41

Velez Sarsfield A42

Miguel Juarez Celman A43

Rivadavia (Large head) A44

Sarmiento A45

Juan Bautista Alberdi A46

1888-89		**Engr.**	**Perf. 11½, 11½x12**	
68	A41	½c ultra	.75	.45
a.	Vert. pair, imperf. horiz.			—
b.	Imperf., pair		30.00	
69	A42	1c brown	1.50	.75
a.	Vert. pair, imperf. horiz.		65.00	
b.	Vert. pair, imperf. btwn.			—
c.	Imperf., pair		30.00	
d.	Horiz. pair, imperf. btwn.		100.00	
70	A43	3c blue green	6.00	1.75
71	A44	5c rose	4.50	.75
a.	Imperf., pair		50.00	—
72	A45	6c blue black	3.00	.90
b.	Perf. 11½x12		15.00	4.50
73	A46	12c blue	8.75	3.75
a.	Imperf., pair		45.00	
b.	bluish paper		9.50	3.75
c.	Perf. 11½		14.00	3.00
		Nos. 68-73 (6)	24.50	8.35

Nos. 69-70 exist with papermakers' watermarks.

See No. 77, types A50, A61. For surcharges see Nos. 83-84.

Jose Maria Paz — A48

Santiago Derqui — A49

Rivadavia (Small head) A50

Avellaneda A51

Moreno A53

Mitre A54

Gervasio Antonio de Posadas — A55

1890		**Engr.**	**Perf. 11½**	
75	A48	¼c green	.65	.45
76	A49	2c violet	1.50	.75
a.	2c purple		2.00	.75
b.	2c slate		2.00	.75
c.	Horiz. pair, imperf. btwn.		30.00	25.00
d.	Imperf., pair		37.50	
e.	Perf. 11½x12		9.00	.75
77	A50	5c carmine	3.50	.45
a.	Imperf., pair		70.00	32.50
b.	Perf. 11½x12		10.00	1.25
c.	Vert. pair, imperf. btwn.		75.00	60.00
d.	Horiz. pair, imperf. btwn.		75.00	60.00
78	A51	10c brown	4.50	.75
b.	Imperf., pair		150.00	
c.	Vert. pair, imperf. btwn.		225.00	
80	A53	40c olive green	8.00	1.50
a.	Imperf., pair		55.00	
b.	Horiz. pair, imperf. btwn.			250.00
81	A54	50c orange	9.00	1.50
a.	Imperf., pair		80.00	
b.	Perf. 11½x12		40.00	3.00
82	A55	60c black	20.00	4.50
a.	Imperf., pair			—
b.	Vert. pair, imperf. btwn.		125.00	100.00
		Nos. 75-82 (7)	47.15	9.90

Type A50 differs from type A44 in having the head smaller, the letters of "Cinco Centavos" not as tall, and the curved ornaments at sides close to the first and last letters of "Republica Argentina."

Lithographed Surcharge on No. 73 in Black or Red

1890			**Perf. 11½x12**	
83	A46	¼c on 12c blue	.75	.75
a.	Perf. 11½		50.00	40.00
b.	Double surcharge		75.00	47.50
c.	Inverted surcharge		100.00	
84	A46	¼c on 12c blue (R)	.75	.75
a.	Double surcharge		55.00	50.00
b.	Perf. 11½		8.00	6.00

Surcharge is different on Nos. 83 and 84. Nos. 83-84 exist as pairs, one without surcharge. These were privately produced.

Rivadavia A57

Jose de San Martin A58

Gregorio Araoz de Lamadrid A59

Admiral Guillermo Brown A60

1891		**Engr.**	**Perf. 11½**	
85	A57	8c carmine rose	1.50	.65
a.	Imperf., pair		130.00	
86	A58	1p deep blue	50.00	12.00
87	A59	5p ultra	325.00	45.00
88	A60	20p green	500.00	100.00
		Nos. 85-88 (4)	876.50	157.65

A 10p brown and a 50p red were prepared but not issued. Values: 10p $1,500 for fine, 50p $1,200 with rough or somewhat damaged perfs.

Velez Sarsfield — A61

1890			**Perf. 11½**	
89	A61	1c brown	1.25	.65
	Horiz. pair, imperf. btwn.			550.00

Type A61 is a re-engraving of A42. The figure "1" in each upper corner has a short horizontal serif instead of a long one pointing downward. In type A61 the first and last letters of "Correos y Telegrafos" are closer to the curved ornaments below than in type A42. Background is of horizontal lines (crosshatching on No. 69).

"Santa Maria," "Nina" and "Pinta" — A62

1892, Oct. 12		**Wmk. 85**	**Perf. 11½**	
90	A62	2c light blue	8.50	3.00
a.	Double impression		225.00	
91	A62	5c dark blue	9.50	4.00

Discovery of America, 400th anniv. Counterfeits of Nos. 90-91 are litho.

Rivadavia A63

Belgrano A64

San Martin — A65

1892-95		**Wmk. 85**	**Perf. 11½**	
92	A63	½c dull blue	1.00	.35
a.	½c bright ultra		80.00	40.00
93	A63	1c brown	.65	.50
94	A63	2c green	1.00	.35
95	A63	3c org ('95)	1.75	.35
96	A63	5c carmine	1.75	.35
b.	5c green (error)		700.00	700.00
98	A64	10c car rose	13.50	.60
99	A64	12c dp bl ('93)	10.00	.60
100	A64	16c gray	16.50	.65
101	A64	24c gray brown	16.50	.65
102	A64	50c blue green	27.50	.75
103	A65	1p lake ('93)	12.00	1.00
a.	1p red brown		20.00	5.00
104	A65	2p dark green	27.50	3.50
105	A65	5p dark blue	37.50	3.50
		Nos. 92-105 (13)	167.15	13.15

Perf. 12

92E	A63	½c dull blue	6.00	1.00
93E	A63	1c brown	10.00	2.00
94E	A63	2c green	10.00	4.00

95E	A63	3c org ('95)	30.00	5.00
96E	A63	5c carmine	35.00	1.00
98E	A64	10c car rose	21.00	3.50
99E	A64	12c dp bl ('93)	40.00	4.00
100E	A64	16c gray	40.00	4.00
101E	A64	24c gray brown	30.00	17.00
102E	A64	50c blue green	30.00	6.00
104E	A65	2p dark green	125.00	40.00
		Nos. 92E-104E (11)	377.00	86.50

Perf. 11½x12

92F	A63	½c dull blue	18.00	10.00
93F	A63	1c brown	15.00	8.00
94F	A63	2c green	40.00	15.00
95F	A63	3c org ('95)	55.00	22.50
96F	A63	5c carmine	20.00	4.00
98F	A64	10c car rose	30.00	7.50
99F	A64	12c dp bl ('93)	60.00	27.50
100F	A64	16c gray	60.00	27.50
102F	A64	50c blue green	60.00	10.00
103F	A64	1p red brown	60.00	10.00
104F	A65	2p dark green	175.00	75.00
		Nos. 92F-104F (11)	593.00	217.00

The high values of this and succeeding issues are frequently punched with the word "INUTILIZADO," parts of the letters showing on each stamp. These punched stamps sell for only a small fraction of the catalogue values.

Examples of No. 95 in yellow shades are changelings.

Reprints of No. 96b have white gum. The original stamp has yellowish gum. Value $125.

Imperf., Pairs

92b	A63	½c	60.00
93a	A63	1c	60.00
94a	A63	2c	30.00
96a	A63	5c	30.00
98a	A64	10c	60.00
99a	A64	12c	60.00
100a	A64	24c	60.00
102a	A64	50c	60.00
103b	A65	1p	60.00
105a	A65	5p	150.00

Nos. 102a, 103b and 105a exist only without gum; the other imperfs are found with or without gum, and values are the same for either condition.

Vertical Pairs, Imperf. Between

92c	A63	½c	125.00
93b	A63	1c	100.00
94b	A63	2c	50.00
95a	A63	3c	250.00
96c	A63	5c	45.00 —
98b	A64	10c	100.00
99b	A64	12c	100.00

Horizontal Pairs, Imperf. Between

93c	A63	1c	110.00	
94c	A63	2c	55.00	
96d	A63	5c	55.00	45.00
98c	A64	10c	110.00	

1896-97		**Wmk. 86**	**Perf. 11½**	
106	A63	½c slate	.65	.30
a.	½c gray blue		.65	.30
b.	½c indigo		.65	.30
107	A63	1c brown	.65	.30
108	A63	2c yellow green	.65	.30
109	A63	3c orange	.65	.30
110	A63	5c carmine	.65	.30
a.	Imperf., pair		100.00	
111	A64	10c carmine rose	10.00	.30
112	A64	12c deep blue	5.00	.30
a.	Imperf., pair			—
113	A64	16c gray	13.50	.90
114	A64	24c gray brown	13.50	1.25
a.	Imperf., pair			—
115	A64	30c orange ('97)	13.50	.70
116	A64	50c blue green	13.50	.70
117	A64	80c dull violet	20.00	.90
118	A65	1p lake	30.00	1.60
119	A65	1p20c black ('97)	13.50	3.50
120	A65	2p dark green	20.00	10.00
121	A65	5p dark blue	135.00	13.50
		Nos. 106-121 (16)	290.75	35.15

Perf. 12

106E	A63	½c slate	2.00	1.00
a.	½c gray blue		10.00	4.00
b.	½c indigo		10.00	4.00
107E	A63	1c brown	1.75	1.00
108E	A63	2c yellow green	2.50	1.00
109E	A63	3c orange	45.00	2.00
110E	A63	5c carmine	3.50	1.00
111E	A64	10c car rose	15.00	1.00
112E	A64	12c deep blue	11.00	2.00
113E	A64	16c gray	35.00	5.50
114E	A64	24c gray brown	52.50	11.00
115E	A64	30c orange ('97)	52.50	2.50
116E	A64	50c blue green	65.00	.80
117E	A64	80c dull violet	65.00	22.50
118E	A65	1p lake	65.00	3.50
119E	A65	1p20c black ('97)	65.00	22.50
121E	A65	5p dark blue	800.00	20.00
		Nos. 106E-121E (15)	1,281.	97.30

Perf. 11½x12

106F	A63	½c slate	20.00	11.00
107F	A63	1c brown	30.00	25.00
108F	A63	2c yellow green	20.00	11.00
109F	A63	3c orange	13.00	8.00
110F	A63	5c carmine	26.00	4.50
111F	A64	10c car rose	45.00	18.00
112F	A64	12c deep blue	47.50	15.00
113F	A64	16c gray	60.00	20.00
115F	A64	30c org ('97)	—	75.00

116F	A64	50c blue green	—	75.00
117F	A64	80c dull violet	—	75.00
119F	A65	1p20c black ('97)	100.00	60.00
		Nos. 106F-119F (12)	361.50	397.50

Vertical Pairs, Imperf. Between

106c	A63	½c	200.00	
107a	A63	1c	125.00	
108a	A63	2c	125.00	
109a	A63	3c	200.00	
110b	A63	5c	125.00	125.00
112b	A64	12c	125.00	100.00

Horizontal Pairs, Imperf. Between

107b	A63	1c	125.00	
108b	A63	2c	125.00	
110c	A63	5c	125.00	80.00
111a	A64	10c	125.00	
112c	A64	12c	125.00	

Allegory, Liberty Seated
A66   A67

1899-1903   **Perf. 11½**

122	A66	½c yel brn	.40	.30
123	A66	1c green	.60	.30
124	A66	2c slate	.60	.30
125	A66	3c org ('01)	.80	.50
126	A66	4c yel ('03)	1.40	.60
127	A66	5c car rose	.60	.30
128	A66	6c blk ('03)	.90	.60
129	A66	10c dk grn	1.40	.40
130	A66	12c dull blue	.95	.60
131	A66	12c ol grn ('01)	.95	.60
132	A66	15c sea grn ('01)	2.50	.60
132B	A66	15c dl blue ('01)	2.50	.60
133	A66	16c orange	8.00	8.00
134	A66	20c claret	1.90	.30
135	A66	24c violet	4.00	1.00
136	A66	30c rose	7.25	.60
137	A66	30c ver ('01)	4.00	.50
a.		30c scarlet	47.50	3.00
138	A66	50c brt blue	4.50	.50
139	A67	1p bl & blk	15.00	1.25
a.		Center inverted	2,000.	1,000.
140	A67	5p org & blk	57.50	11.00
a.		Punch cancellation		3.00
a.		Center inverted	2,750.	2,500.
141	A67	10p grn & blk	70.00	18.00
a.		Punch cancellation		3.00
a.		Center inverted	5,000.	
		Punch cancellation		675.00
142	A67	20p red & blk	200.00	35.00
		Punch cancellation		3.00
a.		Center invtd. (punch cancel)		4,000.
		Nos. 122-142 (22)	385.75	81.85

Nos. 139-142 used are valued with violet oval or black boxed parcel cancels. Examples with letter cancels are worth ⅓rd more.

Perf. 12

122E	A66	½c yellow brown	1.50	1.20
123E	A66	1c green	2.00	.60
124E	A66	2c slate	1.50	.60
125E	A66	3c orange ('01)	3.50	1.75
126E	A66	4c yellow ('03)	10.00	3.50
127E	A66	5c carmine rose	5.25	.60
128E	A66	6c black ('03)	8.50	1.75
129E	A66	10c dark green	8.50	1.75
130E	A66	12c dull blue	8.50	2.00
131E	A66	12c ol grn ('01)	8.50	2.00
132E	A66	15c sea grn ('01)	17.00	1.75
133E	A66	16c orange	10.00	9.50
134E	A66	20c claret	12.00	9.50
135E	A66	24c violet	11.00	8.50
136E	A66	30c rose	28.00	3.50
137E	A66	30c ver ('01)	60.00	4.00
a.		30c scarlet	47.50	3.00
138E	A66	50c brt blue	27.50	3.50
139E	A67	1p bl & blk	500.00	160.00
		Nos. 122E-139E (18)	723.25	216.25

Perf. 11½x12

122F	A66	½c yellow brown	25.00	15.00
		Never hinged	37.50	
		On cover, single franking		20.00
123F	A66	1c green	25.00	15.00
		Never hinged	37.50	
		On cover		1.00
124F	A66	2c slate	12.00	3.00
		Never hinged	18.00	
		On cover		1.00
125F	A66	3c orange ('01)	47.50	18.00
		Never hinged	72.50	
		On cover		1.50
127F	A66	5c carmine rose	12.00	6.00
		Never hinged	18.00	
		On cover		1.00
128F	A66	6c black ('03)	32.50	20.00
		Never hinged	47.50	
		On cover		2.00
129F	A66	10c dark green	30.00	6.50
		Never hinged	45.00	
		On cover		1.50
130F	A66	12c dull blue	50.00	15.00
		Never hinged	75.00	
		On cover		2.00

131F	A66	12c ol grn ('01)	50.00	10.00
		Never hinged	75.00	
		On cover		2.00
132F	A66	15c sea grn ('01)	50.00	8.00
		Never hinged	75.00	
		On cover		2.50
134F	A66	20c claret	60.00	12.00
		Never hinged	90.00	
		On cover		1.00
135F	A66	24c violet	50.00	10.00
		Never hinged	75.00	
		On cover		5.00
136F	A66	30c rose	120.00	20.00
		Never hinged	175.00	
		On cover		5.00
137F	A66	30c ver ('01)	140.00	25.00
		Never hinged	210.00	
		On cover		5.00
138F	A66	50c brt blue	120.00	20.00
		Never hinged	175.00	
		On cover		10.00
		Nos. 122F-138F (15)	824.00	203.50

Imperf., Pairs

122a	A66	½c	35.00
123a	A66	1c	50.00
124a	A66	2c	17.50
125a	A66	3c	325.00
127a	A66	5c	17.50
128a	A66	6c	60.00
129a	A66	10c	50.00
132a	A66	15c	50.00

Vertical Pairs, Imperf. Between

122b	A66	½c	10.00	9.50
123b	A66	1c	10.00	9.50
124b	A66	2c	5.00	4.50
125b	A66	3c	325.00	200.00
126a	A66	4c	400.00	275.00
127b	A66	5c	4.50	3.50
128b	A66	6c	13.50	10.00
129b	A66	10c	85.00	
132b	A66	15c	15.00	10.00

Horizontal Pairs, Imperf. Between

122c	A66	½c	30.00	19.00
123c	A66	1c	47.50	27.50
124c	A66	2c	10.00	9.00
125c	A66	3c	325.00	200.00
126b	A66	4c	400.00	
127c	A66	5c	10.00	5.00
128c	A66	6c	17.00	10.00
129c	A66	10c	17.00	10.00
132d	A66	15c	40.00	23.00
138a	A66	50c	165.00	

River Port of Rosario
A68

1902, Oct. 26   **Perf. 11½, 11½x12**

143	A68	5c deep blue	4.75	2.00
a.		Imperf., pair	95.00	
b.		Vert. pair, imperf. btwn.	60.00	
c.		Horiz. pair, imperf. btwn.	90.00	

Completion of port facilities at Rosario.

San Martin
A69   A70

1908-09   **Typo.**   **Perf. 13½x12½**

144	A69	½c violet	.50	.30
145	A69	1c brnsh buff	.50	.30
146	A69	2c chocolate	.60	.30
147	A69	3c green	.65	.40
148	A69	4c redsh violet	1.25	.40
149	A69	5c carmine	.60	.30
150	A69	6c olive bister	.75	.40
151	A69	10c gray green	1.75	.30
152	A69	12c yellow buff	1.00	.60
153	A69	12c dk blue ('09)	1.75	.30
155	A69	20c ultra	1.25	.30
156	A69	24c red brown	3.50	.60
157	A69	30c dull rose	6.00	.60
158	A69	50c black	6.00	.50
159	A70	1p sl bl & pink	18.00	12.50
		Nos. 144-159 (15)	44.10	8.10

The 1c blue was not issued. Value $500.
Wmk. 86 appears on ½, 1, 6, 20, 24 and 50c. Other values have similar wmk. with wavy rays.
Stamps lacking wmk. are from outer rows printed on sheet margin.

Perf. 13½

146A	A69	2c chocolate	1.20	.25
147A	A69	3c green	2.00	1.00
148A	A69	4c redsh violet	1.30	.50
149A	A69	5c carmine	1.00	.30
151A	A69	10c gray green	6.25	2.25
152A	A69	12c yellow buff	1.20	.70
153A	A69	12c dk blue ('09)	4.25	1.00
154A	A69	15c apple green	.60	.50
156A	A69	24c red brown	4.75	1.30
157A	A69	30c dull rose	9.50	1.30
159A	A70	1p sl bl & pink	20.00	1.30

Pyramid of May — A71

Nicolas Rodriguez Pena and Hipolito Vieytes — A72

Meeting at Pena's Home — A73

Designs: 3c, Miguel de Azcuenaga (1754-1833) and Father Manuel M. Alberti (1763-1811). 4c, Viceroy's house and Fort Buenos Aires. 5c, Cornelio Saavedra (1759-1829). 10c, Antonio Luis Beruti (1772-1842) and French distributing badges. 12c, Congress building. 20c, Juan Jose Castelli (1764-1812) and Domingo Matheu (1765-1831). 24c, First council. 30c, Manuel Belgrano (1770-1820) and Juan Larrea (1782-1847). 50c, First meeting of republican government, May 25, 1810. 1p, Mariano Moreno (1778-1811) and Juan Jose Paso (1758-1833). 5p, Oath of the Junta. 10p, Centenary Monument. 20p, Jose Francisco de San Martin (1778-1850).

Inscribed "1810 1910"
Various Frames

1910, May 1   **Engr.**   **Perf. 11½**

160	A71	½c bl & gray bl	.30	.25
161	A72	1c bl grn & blk	.30	.30
b.		Horiz. pair, imperf. between	65.00	
162	A73	2c olive & gray	.25	.30
163	A72	3c green	.70	.40
164	A73	4c dk blue & grn	.70	.40
165	A71	5c carmine	.40	.25
166	A73	10c yel brn & blk	1.10	.50
167	A73	12c brt blue	1.10	.50
168	A72	20c gray brn & blk	3.25	.60
169	A73	24c org brn & bl	1.75	1.25
170	A72	30c lilac & blk	1.75	1.00
171	A71	50c car & blk	4.50	1.25
172	A72	1p brt blue	9.50	3.25
173	A73	5p orange & vio	72.50	35.00
		Punch cancel		5.00
174	A71	10p orange & blk	90.00	62.50
		Punch cancel		10.00
175	A71	20p dp blue & ind	150.00	100.00
		Punch cancel		15.00
		Nos. 160-175 (16)	338.10	207.75

Centenary of the republic.

Center Inverted

160a	A71	½c	1,000.
161a	A72	1c	1,000.
162a	A73	2c	800.00
164a	A73	4c	650.00
167a	A73	12c	1,000.
171a	A71	50c	1,000.
173a	A73	5p	750.00

Domingo F. Sarmiento — A87

1911, May 15   **Typo.**   **Perf. 13½**

176	A87	5c gray brn & blk	.80	.40

Domingo Faustino Sarmiento (1811-88), pres. of Argentina, 1868-74.

Agriculture — A88

Size: 19x25mm

Wmk. 86, without Face

1911   **Engr.**   **Perf. 12**

177	A88	5c vermilion	.40	.25
178	A88	12c deep blue	5.00	.50

Size: 18x23mm

Wmk. 86, with Face

1911   **Typo.**   **Perf. 13½x12½**

179	A88	½c violet	.50	.30
180	A88	1c brown ocher	.30	.30
181	A88	2c chocolate	.30	.25
a.		Perf. 13½	15.00	4.00
b.		Imperf., pair	40.00	
182	A88	3c green	.50	.50
183	A88	4c brown violet	.50	.30
184	A88	10c gray green	.50	.30
185	A88	20c ultra	4.00	.95
186	A88	24c red brown	6.00	3.75
187	A88	30c claret	3.00	.50
188	A88	50c black	6.00	.80
		Nos. 179-188 (10)	21.60	7.95

The 5c dull red is a proof. In this issue Wmk. 86 comes: straight rays (4c, 20c, 24c) and wavy rays (2c). All other values exist with both forms.

Wmk. 87 (Horiz. or Vert.)

1912-14   **Perf. 13½x12½**

189	A88	½c violet	.30	.30
190	A88	1c ocher	.30	.30
191	A88	2c chocolate	.50	.30
192	A88	3c green	.50	.50
193	A88	4c brown violet	.50	.60
194	A88	5c red	.40	.30
195	A88	10c deep green	1.75	.30
196	A88	12c deep blue	.60	.30
197	A88	20c ultra	3.00	.50
198	A88	24c red brown	6.00	2.00
199	A88	30c claret	5.00	7.00
200	A88	50c black	9.00	.90
		Nos. 189-200 (12)	27.85	13.30

See Nos. 208-212. For overprints see Nos. OD1-OD8, OD47-OD54, OD102-OD108, OD146-OD152, OD183-OD190, OD235-OD241, OD281-OD284, OD318-OD323.

Perf. 13½

189a	A88	½c	1.00	.30
190a	A88	1c	1.00	.30
191a	A88	2c	1.00	.30
192a	A88	3c	150.00	30.00
193a	A88	4c	2.50	1.25
194a	A88	5c	.90	.30
196a	A88	12c	3.50	1.50
197a	A88	20c	9.00	.90
		Nos. 189a-197a (8)	168.90	34.85

A89

1912-13   **Perf. 13½**

201	A89	1p dull bl & rose	10.00	1.10
		Punch cancel		.30
202	A89	5p slate & ol grn	19.00	7.00
		Punch cancel		1.00
203	A89	10p violet & blue	75.00	17.50
		Punch cancel		1.40
204	A89	20p dp blue & claret	210.00	80.00
		Punch cancel		2.00
		Nos. 201-204 (4)	314.00	105.60

1915   **Unwmk.**   **Perf. 13½x12½**

208	A88	1c ocher	.50	.30
209	A88	2c chocolate	.90	.30
212	A88	5c red	.50	.30
		Nos. 208-212 (3)	1.90	.90

Only these denominations were printed on paper without watermark.
Other stamps of the series are known unwatermarked but they are from the outer rows of sheets the other parts of which are watermarked.

Francisco Narciso de Laprida
A90   Declaration of Independence
A91

A92   A92a
Jose de San Martin
Perf. 13½, 13½x12½

1916, July 9   Litho.   **Wmk. 87**
215	A90	½c violet	.60	.30
216	A90	1c buff	.50	.30

Perf. 13½x12½
217	A90	2c chocolate	.60	.30
218	A90	3c green	.60	.60
219	A90	4c red violet	.60	.60

Perf. 13½
220	A91	5c red	.50	.30
a.		Imperf., pair	40.00	
221	A91	10c gray green	1.50	.30
222	A92	12c blue	.90	.35
223	A92	20c ultra	.70	.70
224	A92	24c red brown	2.75	1.40
225	A92	30c claret	2.75	1.60
226	A92	50c gray black	6.75	1.60
227	A92a	1p slate bl & red	10.00	10.00
		Punch cancel		.50
a.		Imperf., pair	325.00	
228	A92a	5p black & gray grn	100.00	80.00
		Punch cancel		15.00
229	A92a	10p violet & blue	150.00	135.00
		Punch cancel		9.00
230	A92a	20p dull blue & cl	150.00	100.00
		Punch cancel		7.00
a.		Imperf., pair	650.00	
		Nos. 215-230 (16)	428.75	333.35

Cent. of Argentina's declaration of independence of Spain, July 9, 1816.
The watermark is either vert. or horiz. on Nos. 215-220, 222; only vert. on No. 221, and only horiz. on Nos. 223-230.
For overprints see Nos. OD9, OD55-OD56, OD109, OD153, OD191-OD192, OD285, OD324.

A93   A94

A94a

1917   *Perf. 13½*
231	A93	½c violet	.60	.60
a.		Imperf. pair	70.00	
232	A93	1c buff	.60	.30
a.		Imperf., pair	70.00	
233	A93	2c brown	.60	.30
a.		Imperf., pair	70.00	
234	A93	3c lt green	1.00	.30
a.		imperf. pair	70.00	
235	A93	4c red violet	1.50	.60
a.		Imperf., pair	70.00	
236	A93	5c red	1.25	.50
		Never hinged	1.90	
a.		Imperf., pair	15.00	
237	A93	10c gray green	4.00	.50
a.		Imperf., pair	70.00	
		Nos. 231-237 (7)	9.55	3.10

Perf. 13½x12½
231B	A93	½c violet	.30	.30
232B	A93	1c buff	.40	.40
233B	A93	2c brown	.40	.40
234B	A93	3c lt green	1.00	.30
235B	A93	4c red violet	2.00	.50
236B	A93	5c red	.30	.30
237B	A93	10c gray green	3.00	.25
		Nos. 231B-237B (7)	7.40	2.45

Perf. 13½
238	A94	12c blue	1.00	.25
239	A94	20c ultra	2.50	.30
240	A94	24c red brown	6.00	3.00
241	A94	30c claret	6.00	1.50
242	A94	50c gray black	6.00	.60
243	A94a	1p slate bl & red	6.00	.60
244	A94a	5p blk & gray grn	19.00	3.00
		Punch cancel		1.50
245	A94a	10p violet & blue	47.50	12.00
		Punch cancel		1.50

246	A94a	20p dull blue & cl	90.00	50.00
		Punch cancel		1.00
a.		Center inverted	1,500.	1,500.
		Nos. 231-246 (16)	193.55	74.35

The watermark is either vert. or horiz. on Nos. 231-236, 238 and 231B-236B, 238B; only vert. on No. 237 and 237B, and only horiz. on Nos. 239-246.
All known examples of No. 246a are off-center to the right.

Juan Gregorio Pujol — A95

1918, June 15   Litho.   *Perf. 13½*
247	A95	5c bister & gray	.60	.30

Cent. of the birth of Juan G. Pujol (1817-61), lawyer and legislator.

1918-19   Unwmk.   *Perf. 13½*
248	A93	½c violet	.30	.25
249	A93	1c buff	.30	.25
a.		Imperf., pair	35.00	
250	A93	2c brown	.30	.25
251	A93	3c lt green	.50	.25
252	A93	4c red violet	.50	.25
253	A93	5c red	.80	.25
254	A93	10c gray green	.80	.25
255	A94	12c blue	1.25	.25
256	A94	20c ultra	2.00	.25
257	A94	24c red brown	2.40	.25
258	A94	30c claret	3.00	.30
259	A94	50c gray black	8.00	1.00
		Nos. 248-259 (12)	20.15	3.80

Perf. 13½x12½
248B	A93	½c violet	.70	.25
249B	A93	1c buff	.70	.25
250B	A93	2c brown	.70	.25
251B	A93	3c lt green	.90	.25
252B	A93	4c red violet	.90	.25
253B	A93	5c red	.60	.25
254B	A93	10c gray green	2.00	.25
		Nos. 248B-254B (7)	6.50	1.75

The stamps of this issue sometimes show letters of papermakers' watermarks.
There were two printings, in 1918 and 1923, using different ink and paper.

1920   **Wmk. 88**
264	A93	½c violet	.50	.25
265	A93	1c buff	.50	.25
266	A93	2c brown	.50	.25
267	A93	3c green	2.00	1.00
268	A93	4c red violet	2.50	1.50
269	A93	5c red	.50	.25
270	A93	10c gray green	6.00	.30

Perf. 13½
264A	A93	½c violet	.80	.30
265A	A93	1c buff	.80	.30
266A	A93	2c brown	1.00	.30
267A	A93	3c green	2.00	1.00
269A	A93	5c red	4.00	.30
270A	A93	10c gray green	55.00	15.00
271	A94	12c blue	3.00	.30
272	A94	20c ultra	4.25	.40
274	A94	30c claret	15.00	3.00
275	A94	50c gray black	10.00	3.00
		Nos. 264-275 (17)	108.35	27.70

See Nos. 292-300, 304-307A, 310-314, 318, 322.
For overprints see Nos. OD10-OD20, OD57-OD71, OD74, OD110-OD121, OD154-OD159, OD161-OD162, OD193-OD207, OD209-OD211, OD242-OD252, OD254-OD255, OD286-OD290, OD325-OD328, OD330.

Belgrano's Mausoleum A96   Creation of Argentine Flag A97

Gen. Manuel Belgrano — A98

1920, June 18
280	A96	2c red	1.00	.30
a.		Perf. 13½x12½	3.00	1.00
281	A97	5c rose & blue	1.00	.30
282	A98	12c green & blue	2.00	1.00
		Nos. 280-282 (3)	4.00	1.60

Belgrano (1770-1820), Argentine general, patriot and diplomat.

Gen. Justo Jose de Urquiza — A99

1920, Nov. 11
283	A99	5c gray blue	.60	.30

Gen. Justo Jose de Urquiza (1801-70), pres. of Argentina, 1854-60. See No. 303.

Bartolome Mitre — A100

1921, June 26   Unwmk.
284	A100	2c violet brown	.50	.30
285	A100	5c light blue	.50	.30

Bartolome Mitre (1821-1906), pres. of Argentina, 1862-65.

Allegory, Pan-America — A101

1921, Aug. 25   *Perf. 13½*
286	A101	3c violet	1.50	.30
287	A101	5c blue	2.00	.30
288	A101	10c vio brown	3.00	.50
289	A101	12c rose	3.50	1.00
		Nos. 286-289 (4)	10.00	2.10

Inscribed "Buenos Aires-Agosto de 1921" A102   Inscribed "Republica Argentina" A103

1921, Oct.   *Perf. 13½x12½*
290	A102	5c rose	.60	.30
291	A103	5c rose	3.00	.40

Perf. 13½
290A	A102	5c rose	2.50	.40
291A	A103	5c rose	7.00	.60

1st Pan-American Postal Cong., Buenos Aires, Aug., 1921.
See Nos. 308-309, 319. For overprints see Nos. OD72, OD160, OD208, OD253, OD329.

1920   **Wmk. 89**   *Perf. 13½x12½*
292	A93	½c violet	1.60	.80
293	A93	1c buff	4.50	1.50
294	A93	2c brown	4.00	.50
297	A93	5c red	5.00	.35
298	A93	10c gray green	5.00	.35

Perf. 13½
294A	A93	2c brown	7.00	1.50
297A	A93	5c red	52.50	9.00
298A	A93	10c gray green	40.00	2.00
299	A93	12c blue	6,000.	200.00
300	A94	20c ultra	12.00	1.50

1920   **Wmk. 89**
303	A99	5c gray blue	500.00	400.00

1922-23   **Wmk. 90**   *Perf. 13½*
304	A93	½c violet	.60	.25
305	A93	1c buff	1.00	.30
306	A93	2c brown	1.00	.30
307	A93	3c green	.60	.40
307A	A93	4c red violet	1.50	1.00
308	A102	5c rose	10.00	3.00
309	A103	5c red	5.00	.80
310	A93	10c gray green	9.00	1.00
311	A94	12c blue	1.00	.40
312	A94	20c ultra	2.00	.50
313	A94	24c red brown	20.00	10.00
314	A94	30c claret	10.00	1.00

Perf. 13½x12½
304B	A93	½c violet	.50	.30
305B	A93	1c buff	.50	.30
306B	A93	2c brown	.50	.30
307B	A93	3c green	1.00	.80
307C	A93	4c red violet	22.50	10.00
308B	A102	5c rose	6.00	1.00
309B	A103	5c red	.60	.30
310B	A93	10c gray green	2.25	.25
		Nos. 304-310B (20)	95.55	32.20

Paper with Gray Overprint RA in Sun

1922-23   Unwmk.   *Perf. 13½*
318	A93	2c brown	4.00	1.00
319	A103	5c red	10.00	1.00
322	A94	20c ultra	35.00	2.00

Perf. 13½x12½
318A	A93	2c brown	4.00	1.00
319A	A103	5c red	3.50	.60

A104   San Martín — A105

With Period after Value
Perf. 13½x12½

1923, May   Litho.   **Wmk. 90**
323	A104	½c red violet	.50	.30
324	A104	1c buff	.80	.30
325	A104	2c dark brown	.60	.30
326	A104	3c lt green	.80	.40
327	A104	4c red brown	.80	.40
328	A104	5c red	.80	.30
329	A104	10c dull green	7.00	.30
330	A104	12c deep blue	.70	.30
331	A104	20c ultra	2.00	.30
332	A104	24c lt brown	5.00	3.00
333	A104	30c claret	16.00	.80
334	A104	50c black	62.00	7.00

Perf. 13½
323A	A104	½c red violet	.80	.30
324A	A104	1c buff	1.50	.30
325A	A104	2c dark brown	41.00	.30
326A	A104	3c lt green	3.00	1.00
327A	A104	4c red brown	3.00	1.00
328A	A104	5c red	3.00	.30
329A	A104	10c dull green	10.00	1.00
330A	A104	12c deep blue	12.50	3.00
331A	A104	20c ultra	11.00	.70
332A	A104	24c lt brown	20.00	5.00
333A	A104	30c claret	20.00	3.00
334A	A104	50c black	8.00	1.00

Without Period after Value
Perf. 13½
Wmk. 87
335	A105	1p blue & red	10.00	.80
336	A105	5p gray lil & grn	30.00	6.00
		Punch cancel		1.00
337	A105	10p clar & blue	90.00	15.00
				2.00
338	A105	20p sl & brn lake	120.00	45.00
		Punch cancel		1.00
a.		Center inverted		
		Nos. 323-338 (28)	480.80	97.40

Nos. 335-338 and 353-356 canceled with round or oval killers in purple (revenue cancellations) sell for one-fifth to one-half as much as postally used copies.
For overprints see Nos. 399-404.

Design of 1923
Without Period after Value
Perf. 13½x12½

1923-24 **Litho.** **Wmk. 90**

340	A104	½c red violet	.50	.30
341	A104	1c buff	.50	.30
342	A104	2c dk brown	.50	.30
343	A104	3c green	.60	.30
a.		Imperf., pair	60.00	
344	A104	4c red brown	.80	.30
345	A104	5c red	.50	.30
346	A104	10c dull green	.50	.30
347	A104	12c deep blue	.80	.30
348	A104	20c ultra	1.00	.30
349	A104	24c lt brown	4.00	1.25
350	A104	25c purple	2.00	.40
351	A104	30c claret	4.00	.40
352	A104	50c black	6.00	.40

Perf. 13½

340B	A104	½c red violet	180.00	60.00
345B	A104	5c red	75.00	30.00
346B	A104	10c dull green	75.00	30.00
349B	A104	24c lt brown	150.00	50.00
353	A105	1p blue & red	6.00	.70
354	A105	5p dk vio & grn	35.00	2.00
355	A105	10p claret & blue	75.00	8.00
356	A105	20p slate & lake	120.00	15.00
		Nos. 340-356 (21)	737.70	200.85

1931-33 **Typo.**

343b	A104	3c	3.00	.50
345a	A104	5c	4.50	.50
346a	A104	10c	7.50	.50
347a	A104	12c	15.00	3.50
348a	A104	20c	55.00	3.50
350a	A104	25c	40.00	2.00
351a	A104	30c	25.00	1.50
		Nos. 343b-351a (7)	150.00	12.00

The typographed stamps were issued only in coils and have a rough impression with heavy shading about the eyes and nose. Nos. 343 and 346 are known without watermark. Nos. 341-345, 347-349, 351a may be found in pairs, one with period.

See note after No. 338. See Nos. 362-368. For overprints see Nos. OD21-OD33, OD75-OD87, OD122-OD133, OD163-OD175, OD212-OD226, OD256-OD268, OD291-OD304, OD331-OD345.

Rivadavia — A106

1926, Feb. 8 *Perf. 13½*

357	A106	5c rose	.60	.30

Presidency of Bernardino Rivadavia, cent.

Rivadavia
A108

San Martin
A109

General Post Office, 1926 — A110

General Post Office, 1826 — A111

1926, July 1 *Perf. 13½x12½*

358	A108	3c gray green	.50	.30
359	A109	5c red	.50	.30

Perf. 13½

360	A110	12c deep blue	1.25	.40
361	A111	25c chocolate	3.25	.80
a.		"1326" for "1826"	15.00	10.00
		Nos. 358-361 (4)	5.50	1.80

Centenary of the Post Office.
For overprints see Nos. OD34, OD88, OD134, OD227-OD228, OD269, OD305, OD346.

Type of 1923-31 Issue
Without Period after Value

1927 **Wmk. 205** *Perf. 13½x12½*

362	A104	½c red violet	.60	.50
a.		Pelure paper	2.75	2.50
363	A104	1c buff	.60	.50
364	A104	2c dark brown	.60	.30
a.		Pelure paper	1.00	.70
365	A104	5c red	.80	.30
a.		Period after value	15.00	9.00
b.		Pelure paper	1.00	.70
366	A104	10c dull green	5.00	3.00
367	A104	20c ultra	50.00	10.00

Perf. 13½

368	A105	1p blue & red	40.00	7.00
		Nos. 362-368 (7)	97.60	16.60

Arms of Argentina and Brazil
A112

Wmk. RA in Sun (90)

1928, Aug. 27 *Perf. 12½x13*

369	A112	5c rose red	1.50	.40
370	A112	12c deep blue	2.50	.70

Cent. of peace between the Empire of Brazil and the United Provinces of the Rio de la Plata.

Allegory, Discovery of the New World — A113

"Spain" and "Argentina" — A114

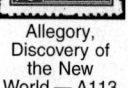

"America" Offering Laurels to Columbus A115

1929, Oct. 12 **Litho.** *Perf. 13½*

371	A113	2c lilac brown	2.00	.40
372	A114	5c light red	2.00	.40
373	A115	12c dull blue	6.00	1.00
		Nos. 371-373 (3)	10.00	1.80

Discovery of America by Columbus, 437th anniv.

Spirit of Victory Attending Insurgents — A116

March of the Victorious Insurgents A117

Perf. 13½x12½ (A116), 12½x13 (A117)

1930

374	A116	½c violet gray	1.00	.50
375	A116	1c myrtle green	1.00	.50
376	A117	2c dull violet	1.00	.50
377	A116	3c green	1.00	.50
378	A116	4c violet	1.00	.70
379	A116	5c rose red	1.00	.30
380	A116	10c gray black	1.00	.70
381	A117	12c dull blue	1.75	.80
382	A117	20c ocher	2.00	1.00
383	A117	24c red brown	6.50	2.50
384	A117	25c green	7.50	2.50
385	A117	30c deep violet	9.50	3.50
386	A117	50c black	13.00	6.25
387	A117	1p sl bl & red	25.00	10.00
388	A117	2p black & org	37.50	14.00
389	A117	5p dull grn & blk	100.00	32.50
390	A117	10p dp red brn & dull blue	140.00	47.50
391	A117	20p yel grn & dl bl	260.00	125.00
392	A117	50p dk grn & vio	900.00	800.00
		Nos. 374-390 (17)	349.75	124.25

Revolution of 1930.
Nos. 387-392 with oval (parcel post) cancellation sell for less.
For overprint see No. 405.

1931 *Perf. 12½x13*

393	A117	½c red violet	1.00	.50
394	A117	1c gray black	1.50	1.00
395	A117	3c green	1.50	.70
396	A117	4c red brown	1.00	.50
397	A117	5c red	.80	.50
a.		Plane omitted, top left corner	10.00	8.00
398	A117	10c dull green	1.90	.80
		Nos. 393-398 (6)	7.70	4.00

Revolution of 1930.

Stamps of 1924-25 Overprinted in Red or Green

1931, Sept. 6 *Perf. 13½, 13½x12½*

399	A104	3c green	.50	.50
400	A104	10c dull green	.70	.70
401	A104	30c claret (G)	5.00	3.25
402	A104	50c black	5.00	3.25

Overprinted in Blue

403	A105	1p blue & red	6.00	3.25
404	A105	5p dk violet & grn	60.00	22.50

No. 388 Overprinted in Blue

Perf. 12½x13

405	A117	2p black & orange	12.00	8.00
		Nos. 399-405 (7)	89.20	41.45

1st anniv. of the Revolution of 1930.
See Nos. C30-C34.

Refrigeration Compressor — A118

Perf. 13½x12½

1932, Aug. 29 **Litho.**

406	A118	3c green	1.25	.50
407	A118	10c scarlet	2.25	.40
408	A118	12c gray blue	7.50	1.10
		Nos. 406-408 (3)	11.00	2.00

6th Intl. Refrigeration Congress.

Port of La Plata
A119

Pres. Julio A. Roca — A120

Municipal Palace
A121

Cathedral of La Plata — A122

Dardo Rocha
A123

Perf. 13½x13, 13x13½ (10c)

1933, Jan.

409	A119	3c green & dk brn	.50	.30
410	A120	10c orange & dk vio	.70	.30
411	A121	15c dk bl & dp bl	2.50	1.50
412	A122	20c violet & yel brn	2.25	1.00
413	A123	30c dk grn & vio brn	14.00	7.00
		Nos. 409-413 (5)	19.95	10.10

50th anniv. of the founding of the city of La Plata, Nov. 19th, 1882.

Christ of the Andes — A124

Buenos Aires Cathedral
A125

1934, Oct. 1 *Perf. 13x13½, 13½x13*

414	A124	10c rose & brown	1.00	.30
415	A125	15c dark blue	3.00	.60

32nd Intl. Eucharistic Cong., Oct. 10-14.

"Liberty" with Arms of Brazil and Argentina
A126

Symbolical of "Peace" and "Friendship"
A127

1935, May 15 *Perf. 13x13½*

416	A126	10c red	1.00	.30
417	A127	15c blue	2.00	.60

Visit of Pres. Getulio Vargas of Brazil.

Belgrano
A128

Sarmiento
A129

Urquiza — A130

Louis Braille — A131

San Martin — A132

Brown — A133

Moreno A134 / Alberdi A135

Nicolas Avellaneda A136

Rivadavia A137

Mitre A138

Bull (Cattle Breeding) A139

Martin Güemes A140

Agriculture A141

Merino Sheep (Wool) A142

Sugar Cane A143

Oil Well (Petroleum) — A144

Map of South America
A145   A146

Fruit — A147

Iguacu Falls (Scenic Wonders) A148

Grapes (Vineyards) A149

Cotton — A150

Two types of A140:
Type I — Inscribed Juan Martin Guemes.
Type II — Inscribed Martin Güemes.

Perf. 13, 13½x13, 13x13½

1935-51   Litho.   Wmk. 90

418	A128	½c red violet	.30	.25
419	A129	1c buff	.30	.25
a.		Typo.	2.00	.25
420	A130	2c dark brown	.50	.25
421	A131	2½c black ('39)	.40	.25
422	A132	3c green	.60	.25
423	A132	3c lt gray ('39)	.60	.25
424	A134	3c lt gray ('46)	.50	.25
425	A133	4c lt gray	.60	.25
426	A133	4c sage grn ('39)	.50	.25
427	A134	5c yel brn, typo.	.80	.25
a.		Tete beche pair, typo.	20.00	10.00
b.		Booklet pane of 8, typo.		
c.		Booklet pane of 4, typo.		
d.		Litho.	5.00	.50
428	A135	6c olive green	.50	.25
429	A136	8c orange ('39)	.50	.25
430	A137	10c car, perf. 13½ (typo.)	4.00	.25
a.		Perf. 13½x13	3.00	.25
431	A137	10c brown ('42)	.40	.25
432	A138	12c brown	1.00	.25
433	A138	12c red ('39)	.40	.25
434	A139	15c slate bl ('36)	1.50	.25
435	A139	15c pale ultra ('39)	3.00	.25
436	A140	15c lt gray bl (II) ('42)	50.00	3.00
437	A140	20c lt ultra (I)	1.00	.25
438	A140	20c lt ultra (II) ('36)	1.00	.25
439	A140	20c bl gray (II) ('39)	3.00	.25
439A	A139	20c dk bl & pale bl, ('42) 22x33mm	1.00	.25
440	A139	20c blue ('51)	1.00	.25
a.		Typo.	.30	.25

441	A141	25c car & pink ('36)	1.25	.25
442	A142	30c org brn & yel brown ('36)	1.00	.25
443	A143	40c dk vio ('36)	1.00	.25
444	A144	50c red & org ('36)	1.00	.25
445	A145	1p brn blk & lt bl ('36)	25.00	1.00
446	A146	1p brn blk & lt bl ('37)	16.00	.30
a.		Chalky paper	100.00	2.00
447	A147	2p brn lake & dk ultra ('36)	2.50	.25
448	A148	5p ind & ol grn ('36)	4.00	.25
449	A149	10p brn lake & blk	15.00	1.25
450	A150	20p bl grn & brn ('36)	25.00	3.00
		Nos. 418-450 (34)	165.15	15.80

See Nos. 485-500, 523-540, 659, 668. For overprints see Nos. O37-O41, O43-O51, O53-O56, O58-O78, O108, O112, OD35-OD46, OD89-OD101, OD135-OD145, OD176-OD182C, OD229-OD234F, OD270-OD280, OD306-OD317, OD347-OD357.
No. 439A exists with attached label showing medallion. Value $42.50 unused, $22.50 used.

Souvenir Sheet

A151

Without Period after Value

1935, Oct. 17   Litho.   Imperf.

452	A151	Sheet of 4	75.00	35.00
a.		10c dull green	16.50	7.50

Phil. Exhib. at Buenos Aires, Oct. 17-24, 1935. The stamps were on sale during the 8 days of the exhibition only. Sheets measure 83x101mm.

Plaque — A152

1936, Dec. 1   Perf. 13x13½

453	A152	10c red	.80	.40

Inter-American Conference for Peace.

Domingo Faustino Sarmiento — A153

1938, Sept. 5

454	A153	3c sage green	.50	.50
455	A153	5c red	.50	.50
456	A153	15c deep blue	2.25	.70
457	A153	50c orange	4.25	1.00
		Nos. 454-457 (4)	7.50	2.70

50th anniv. of the death of Domingo Faustino Sarmiento, pres., educator and author.

"Presidente Sarmiento" — A154

1939, Mar. 16

458	A154	5c greenish blue	.80	.30

Final voyage of the training ship "Presidente Sarmiento."

Allegory of the UPU — A155

Coat of Arms — A157

Post Office, Buenos Aires — A156

Iguacu Falls — A158

Bonete Hill, Nahuel Huapi Park — A159

Allegory of Modern Communications A160

Argentina, Land of Promise A161

Lake Frias, Nahuel Huapi Park — A162

Perf. 13x13½, 13½x13

1939, Apr. 1   Photo.

459	A155	5c rose carmine	1.00	.25
460	A156	15c grnsh black	1.00	.40
461	A157	20c brt blue	1.00	.25
462	A158	25c dp blue grn	2.00	.40
463	A159	50c brown	3.00	1.00
464	A160	1p brown violet	6.50	2.75
465	A161	2p magenta	27.50	17.50
466	A162	5p purple	62.50	52.50
		Nos. 459-466 (8)	104.50	75.05

Universal Postal Union, 11th Congress.

Souvenir Sheets

A163

A164

1939, May 12   Wmk. 90   Imperf.

467	A163	Sheet of 4	15.00	7.50
a.		5c rose carmine (A155)	2.00	1.50
b.		20c bright blue (A157)	2.00	1.50
c.		25c deep blue green (A158)	2.00	1.50
d.		50c brown (A159)	2.00	1.50
468	A164	Sheet of 4	15.00	7.50

Issued in four forms:

a.	Unsevered horizontal pair of sheets, type A163 at left, A164 at right	30.00	16.00
b.	Unsevered vertical pair of sheets, type A163 at top, A164 at bottom	30.00	15.00
c.	Unsevered block of 4 sheets, type A163 at left, A164 at right	65.00	50.00
d.	Unsevered block of 4 sheets, type A163 at top, A164 at bottom	65.00	50.00

11th Cong. of the UPU and the Argentina Intl. Phil. Exposition (C.Y.T.R.A.).
No. 468 contains Nos. 467a-467d.

Family and New House A165

Perf. 13½x13

1939, Oct. 2   Litho.   Wmk. 90

469	A165 5c bluish green		.50	.25

1st Pan-American Housing Congress.

Bird Carrying Record A166 | Head of Liberty and Arms of Argentina A167

Record and Winged Letter A168

Perf. 13x13½, 13½x13 (#472)

1939, Dec. 11   Photo.

470	A166 1.18p indigo		14.00	10.00
471	A167 1.32p bright blue		14.00	10.00
472	A168 1.50p dark brown		52.50	35.00
	Nos. 470-472 (3)		80.50	55.00

These stamps were issued for the recording and mailing of flexible phonograph records.

Map of the Americas — A169

1940, Apr. 14   Perf. 13x13½

473	A169 15c ultramarine		1.00	.25

50th anniv. of the Pan American Union.

Souvenir Sheet

Reproductions of Early Argentine Stamps — A170

Wmk. RA in Sun (90)

1940, May 25   Litho.   Imperf.

474	A170	Sheet of 5	25.00	10.00
a.		5c dark blue (Corrientes A2)	2.50	1.75
b.		5c red (Argentina A1)	2.50	1.75
c.		5c dark blue (Cordoba #1)	2.50	1.75
d.		5c red (Argentina A3)	2.50	1.75
e.		10c dark blue (Buenos Aires A1)	2.50	1.75

100th anniv. of the first postage stamp.

General Domingo French and Colonel Antonio Beruti A171

1941, Feb. 20   Perf. 13½x13

475	A171 5c dk gray blue & lt blue		.60	.25

Issued in honor of General French and Colonel Beruti, patriots.

Marco M. de Avellaneda — A172

1941, Oct. 3   Perf. 13x13½

476	A172 5c dull slate blue		.60	.25

Avellaneda, (1814-41), army leader and martyr.

Statue of Gen. Julio Roca — A173

1941, Oct. 19   Photo.   Wmk. 90

477	A173 5c dark olive green		.50	.25

Dedication of a monument to Lt. Gen. Julio Argentino Roca (1843-1914).

Carlos Pellegrini and Bank of the Nation A174

1941, Oct. 26   Perf. 13½x13

478	A174 5c brown carmine		.60	.25

Founding of the Bank of the Nation, 50th anniv.

Gen. Juan Lavalle — A175

1941, Dec. 5   Perf. 13x13½

479	A175 5c bright blue		.60	.25

Gen. Juan Galo de Lavalle (1797-1841).

National Postal Savings Bank A176

1942, Apr. 5   Litho.   Perf. 13½x13

480	A176 1c pale olive		.60	.25

Jose Manuel Estrada — A177

1942, July 13   Perf. 13x13½

481	A177 5c brown violet		.60	.25

Jose Estrada (1842-1894), writer and diplomat.
Exists imperf. Value, pair $45.
No. 481 exists with label, showing medallion, attached. Value, pair $11.

Types of 1935-51

Perf. 13, 13x13½, 13½x13

1942-50		Litho.	Wmk. 288
485	A128 ½c brown violet	10.00	2.00
486	A129 1c buff ('50)	.40	.30
487	A130 2c dk brown ('50)	.40	.25
488	A132 3c lt gray	16.00	1.25
489	A134 3c lt gray ('49)	.30	.25
490	A137 10c red brn ('49)	2.50	.25
491	A138 12c red	.50	.25
492	A140 15c lt gray blue (II)	1.00	.25
493	A139 20c dk sl bl & pale bl	4.50	.30
494	A141 25c dull rose ('49)	1.00	.25
495	A142 30c org brn ('49)	1.50	.25
496	A143 40c violet ('49)	10.00	1.00
497	A144 50c red & org ('49)	10.00	.50
498	A146 1p brn blk & lt bl	10.00	.40
499	A147 2p brn lake & bl ('49)	22.50	3.00

500	A148 5p ind & ol grn ('49)	65.00	4.00
	Nos. 485-500 (16)	155.60	14.50

No. 493 measures 22x33mm.

Post Office, Buenos Aires — A178

Inscribed: "Correos y Telegrafos."

1942, Oct. 5   Litho.   Perf. 13

503	A178 35c lt ultra		10.00	.25

See Nos. 541-543.

Proposed Columbus Lighthouse A179

1942, Oct. 12   Wmk. 288

504	A179 15c dull blue		10.00	.50

Wmk. 90

505	A179 15c dull blue		70.00	8.00

450th anniv. of the discovery of America by Columbus.

Jose C. Paz — A180

1942, Dec. 15   Wmk. 288

506	A180 5c dark gray		.50	.25

Cent. of the birth of Jose C. Paz, stateman and founder of the newspaper La Prensa.

Books and Argentine Flag — A181

1943, Apr. 1   Litho.   Perf. 13

507	A181 5c dull blue		.50	.25

1st Book Fair of Argentina.

Arms of Argentina Inscribed "Honesty, Justice, Duty" — A182

1943-50   Wmk. 288   Perf. 13
Size: 20x26mm

508	A182 5c red ('50)		6.00	.25

Wmk. 90

509	A182 5c red		.60	.25
a.	5c dull red, unsurfaced paper		8.00	.25
510	A182 15c green		.60	.25

Perf. 13½x13
Size: 22x33mm

511	A182 20c dark blue		.95	.25
	Nos. 508-511 (4)		8.15	1.00

Change of political organization, 6/4/43.

Independence House, Tucuman — A183

1943-51 **Wmk. 90** **Perf. 13**
512 A183 5c blue green 1.00 .25
Wmk. 288
513 A183 5c blue green ('51) .50 .25
Restoration of Independence House.

Liberty Head and Savings Bank — A184

1943, Oct. 25 **Wmk. 90**
514 A184 5c violet brown .50 .25
Wmk. 288
515 A184 5c violet brown 60.00 8.00
1st conference of National Postal Savings.

Port of Buenos Aires in 1800 — A185

1943, Dec. 11 **Wmk. 90**
516 A185 5c gray black .50 .25
Day of Exports.

Warship, Merchant Ship and Sailboat — A186

1944, Jan. 31 **Perf. 13**
517 A186 5c blue .60 .25
Issued to commemorate Sea Week.

Arms of Argentine Republic — A187

1944, June 4
518 A187 5c dull blue .60 .35
1st anniv. of the change of political organization in Argentina.

St. Gabriel A188   Cross at Palermo A189

1944, Oct. 11
519 A188 3c yellow green .70 .25
520 A189 5c deep rose .80 .25
Fourth national Eucharistic Congress.

Allegory of Savings — A190

1944, Oct. 24
521 A190 5c gray .50 .25
20th anniv. of the National Savings Bank.

Reservists A191

1944, Dec. 1
522 A191 5c blue .50 .25
Day of the Reservists.

Types of 1935-51
Perf. 13x13½, 13½x13
1945-47 **Litho.** **Unwmk.**
523 A128 ½c brown vio ('46) .25 .25
524 A129 1c yellow brown .25 .25
525 A130 2c sepia .25 .25
526 A132 3c lt gray (San Martin) 2.50 .25
527 A134 3c lt gray (Moreno) ('46) .25 .25
528 A135 6c olive grn ('47) .50 .35
529 A137 10c brown ('46) 2.00 .30
530 A140 15c lt gray bl (II) 1.25 .25
531 A139 20c dk sl bl & pale bl 3.00 .25
532 A141 25c dull rose 2.50 .25
533 A142 30c orange brown 1.00 .25
534 A143 40c violet 2.00 .35
535 A144 50c red & orange 3.00 .25
536 A146 1p brn blk & lt bl 4.50 .25
537 A147 2p brown lake & bl 35.00 1.00
538 A148 5p ind & ol grn ('46) 60.00 4.00
539 A149 10p dp cl & int blk 17.50 2.50
540 A150 20p bl grn & brn ('46) 15.00 2.50
Nos. 523-540 (18) 150.75 13.75
No. 531 measures 22x33mm.

Post Office Type Inscribed

1945 **Unwmk.** **Perf. 13x13½**
541 A178 35c lt ultra 2.50 .25
Wmk. 90
542 A178 35c lt ultra 1.60 .25
Wmk. 288
543 A178 35c lt ultra .50 .25
Nos. 541-543 (3) 4.60 .75
Nos. 541 and 543 exist imperf. Value, each, pair $10.

Bernardino Rivadavia
A192   A193

Mausoleum of Rivadavia A194

Perf. 13½x13
1945, Sept. 1 **Litho.** **Unwmk.**
544 A192 3c blue green .40 .25
545 A193 5c rose .40 .25
546 A194 20c blue .50 .25
Nos. 544-546 (3) 1.30 .75
Cent. of the death of Bernardino Rivadavia, Argentina's first president.
No. 546 exists imperf. Value, pair $20.
No. 546 exists with mute label attached. Value, pair, $4.50.

San Martin — A195

1945-46 **Wmk. 90** **Typo. or Litho.**
547 A195 5c carmine .30 .25
a. Litho. ('46) .25 .25
Wmk. 288
548 A195 5c carmine, litho. 125.00 30.00
Unwmk.
549 A195 5c carmine ('46) 1.50 .25
a. Litho. ('46) .30 .25
Nos. 547 and 547a exist imperf. Values, pairs: No. 547, $17.50; No. 547a, $10.
For overprints see Nos. O42, O57.

Monument to Army of the Andes, Mendoza — A196

1946, Jan. 14 **Litho.** **Perf. 13½x13**
550 A196 5c violet brown .40 .25
Issued to honor the Unknown Soldier of the War for Independence.

Franklin D. Roosevelt — A197

1946, Apr. 12
551 A197 5c dark blue .30 .25

A198

Liberty Administering Presidential Oath.

1946, June 4 **Perf. 13x13½**
552 A198 5c blue .30 .25
Inauguration of Pres. Juan D. Perón, 6/4/46.

Argentina Receiving Popular Acclaim A199

1946, Oct. 17 **Perf. 13½x13**
553 A199 5c rose violet .80 .30
554 A199 10c blue green 1.25 .40
555 A199 15c dark blue 1.75 .60

556 A199 50c red brown 2.25 .50
557 A199 1p carmine rose 3.00 1.20
Nos. 553-557 (5) 9.05 3.00
First anniversary of the political organization change of Oct. 17, 1945.

Coin Bank and World Map — A200

1946, Oct. 31 **Unwmk.**
558 A200 30c dk rose car & pink .60 .30
Universal Day of Savings, October 31, 1946.

Argentine Industry — A201

1946, Dec. 6 **Perf. 13x13½**
559 A201 5c violet brown .50 .25
Day of Argentine Industry, Dec. 6.

International Bridge Connecting Argentina and Brazil A202

1947, May 21 **Litho.** **Perf. 13½x13**
560 A202 5c green .40 .25
Opening of the Argentina-Brazil International Bridge, May 21, 1947.

Map of Argentine Antarctic Claims — A203

1947-49 **Unwmk.** **Perf. 13x13½**
561 A203 5c violet & lilac 1.00 .25
562 A203 20c dk car rose & rose 2.00 .25
Wmk. 90
563 A203 20c dk car rose & rose 4.00 .30
Wmk. 288
564 A203 20c dk car rose & rose ('49) 7.00 .50
Nos. 561-564 (4) 14.00 1.30
1st Argentine Antarctic mail, 43rd anniv. Nos. 561 and 563 exist imperf. Values, pairs: No. 561, $13.50; No. 563, $27.50.

Justice — A204

1947, June 4 **Unwmk.**
565 A204 5c brn vio & pale yel .30 .25
1st anniversary of the Peron government.

Icarus Falling A205

1947, Sept. 25   *Perf. 13½x13*
566 A205 15c red violet   .40 .25

Aviation Week.

Training Ship Presidente Sarmiento — A206

1947, Oct. 5   *Perf. 13x13½*
567 A206 5c blue   .50 .25

50th anniv. of the launching of the Argentine training frigate "Presidente Sarmiento."

Cervantes and Characters from Don Quixote A207

1947, Oct. 12   *Photo.*   *Perf. 13½x13*   **Wmk. 90**
568 A207 5c olive green   .40 .25

400th anniv. of the birth of Miguel de Cervantes Saavedra, playwright and poet. Exists imperf. Value, pair $10.

Gen. Jose de San Martin A208

1947-49   *Unwmk.*   *Perf. 13½x13*   **Litho.**
569 A208 5c dull green   .40 .25
Wmk. 288
570 A208 5c dull green ('49)   .40 .25

Transfer of the remains of Gen. Jose de San Martin's parents.
Nos. 569 and 570 exist imperf. Value for pair, each $10.

School Children — A209

1947-49   *Unwmk.*   *Perf. 13x13½*
571 A209 5c green   .30 .25
Wmk. 90
574 A209 20c brown   .50 .25
Wmk. 288
575 A209 5c green ('49)   .50 .25
   Nos. 571-575 (3)   1.30 .75

Argentine School Crusade for World Peace.
Nos. 571 and 574 exist imperf. Value for pair, each $10.

Statue of Araucanian Indian — A210

1948, May 21   **Wmk. 90**
576 A210 25c yellow brown   .30 .25

American Indian Day, Apr. 19.
No. 576 exists imperf. Value, pair $10.

Cap of Liberty — A211

1948, July 16
577 A211 5c ultra   .30 .25

Revolution of June 4, 1943, 5th anniv.

Manual Stop Signal — A212

1948, July 22
578 A212 5c chocolate & yellow   .30 .25

Traffic Safety Day, June 10.
No. 578 exists imperf. Value, pair $10.

Post Horn and Oak Leaves — A213

1948, July 22   **Unwmk.**
579 A213 5c lilac rose   .40 .25

200th anniversary of the establishment of regular postal service on the Plata River.
No. 579 exists imperf. Value, pair $10.

Argentine Farmers — A214

   Perf. 13x13½
1948, Sept. 20   **Wmk. 288**
580 A214 10c red brown   .30 .25

Agriculture Day, Sept. 8, 1948.

Liberty and Symbols of Progress — A215

   Perf. 13x13½
1948, Nov. 23   *Photo.*   **Wmk. 287**
581 A215 25c red brown   .50 .25

3rd anniversary of President Juan D. Peron's return to power, October 17, 1945.
No. 581 exists imperf. Value, pair $10.

Souvenir Sheets

A216

15c, Mail coach. 45c, Buenos Aires in 18th cent. 55c, 1st train, 1857. 85c, Sailing ship, 1767.

1948, Dec. 21   *Unwmk.*   *Imperf.*
582 A216 Sheet of 4   12.00 5.00
  a.   15c dark green   1.00 .75
  b.   45c orange brown   1.00 .75
  c.   55c lilac brown   1.00 .75
  d.   85c ultramarine   1.00 .75

A217

Designs: 85c, Domingo de Basavilibaso (1709-75). 1.05p, Postrider. 1.20p, Sailing ship, 1798. 1.90p, Courier in the Andes, 1772.

583 A217 Sheet of 4   32.50 20.00
  a.   85c brown   4.75 3.25
  b.   1.05p dark green   4.75 3.25
  c.   1.20p dark blue   4.75 3.25
  d.   1.90p red brown   4.75 3.25

200th anniversary of the establishment of regular postal service on the Plata River.

Winged Wheel — A218

   Perf. 13½x13
1949, Mar. 1   **Wmk. 288**
584 A218 10c blue   .50 .25

Railroad nationalization, 1st anniv.

Liberty A219

1949, June 20   *Engr.*   **Wmk. 90**
585 A219 1p red & red violet   1.25 .30

Ratification of the Constitution of 1949.

Allegory of the UPU A220

1949, Nov. 19
586 A220 25c dk grn & yel grn   .40 .25

75th anniv. of the UPU.

> **Catalogue values for unused stamps in this section, from this point to the end of the section, are for Never Hinged items.**

Gen. Jose de San Martin — A221

San Martin at Boulogne sur Mer — A222

Mausoleum of San Martin — A223

20c, 50c, 75c, Different portraits of San Martin. 1p, House where San Martin died.

Engr., Photo. (25c, 1p, 2p)
1950, Aug. 17   *Wmk. 90*   *Perf. 13½*
587 A221 10c indigo & dk pur   .45 .25
588 A221 20c red brn & dk brn   .45 .25
589 A222 25c brown   .45 .30
590 A221 50c dk green & ind   .75 .30
591 A221 75c choc & dk grn   1.10 .30
  a.   Souv. sheet of 4, #587, 588,
     590, 591, imperf.   5.00 3.00
592 A222 1p dark green   2.50 .40
593 A223 2p dp red lilac   3.00 .50
   Nos. 587-593 (7)   8.70 2.30

Death cent. of General Jose de San Martin.

Map Showing Antarctic Claims — A224

1951, May 21   Litho.   Perf. 13x13½
594 A224 1p choc & lt blue   1.10   .25
For overprint see No. O52.
No. 594 exists imperf. Value, pair $25.

Pegasus and Train A225

Communications Symbols — A226

Design: 25c, Ship and dolphin.

1951, Oct. 17   Photo.   Perf. 13½
595 A225 5c dark brown   1.50   .25
596 A225 25c Prus green   3.00   .30
597 A226 40c rose brown   3.50   .30
  Nos. 595-597 (3)   8.00   .85

Close of Argentine Five Year Plan.

Woman Voter and "Argentina" A227

1951, Dec. 14   Perf. 13½x13
598 A227 10c brown violet   .60   .25
Granting of women's suffrage.

Eva Peron
A228   A229

Litho. or Engraved (#605)
1952, Aug. 26   Wmk. 90   Perf. 13
599 A228 1c orange brown   .35   .25
600 A228 5c gray   .35   .25
601 A228 10c rose lilac   .35   .25
602 A228 20c rose pink   .35   .25
603 A228 25c dull green   .40   .25
604 A228 40c dull violet   .50   .25
605 A228 45c deep blue   .50   .25
606 A228 50c dull brown   .75   .25

Photo.
607 A229 1p dark brown   1.00   .30
608 A229 1.50p deep green   4.00   .30
609 A229 2p brt carmine   1.00   .30
610 A229 3p indigo   1.60   .30
  Nos. 599-610 (12)   11.15 3.20

For overprints see Nos. O79-O85.

Nos. 599, 601-604 and 606 exist imperf. Value for set of 6 pairs, $235.

Inscribed: "Eva Peron"
1952-53   Perf. 13x13½
611 A229 1p dark brown   1.00   .35
612 A229 1.50p deep green   2.00   .35
613 A229 2p brt car ('53)   2.00   .40
614 A229 3p indigo   4.00   .90

Engr.
Perf. 13½x13
Size: 30x40mm
615 A229 5p red brown   5.00   2.00
616 A229 10p red   8.00   4.00
617 A229 20p green   17.50   8.50
618 A228 50p ultra   40.00   20.00
  Nos. 611-618 (8)   79.50   36.50

For overprints see Nos. O86-O93.

Indian Funeral Urn — A230

1953, Aug. 28   Photo.   Perf. 13x13½
619 A230 50c blue green   .60   .25
Founding of Santiago del Estero, 400th anniv.

Rescue Ship "Uruguay" — A231

1953, Oct. 8   Perf. 13½
620 A231 50c ultra   1.25   .50
50th anniv. of the rescue of the Antarctic expedition of Otto C. Nordenskjold.

Planting Argentine Flag in the Antarctic A232

1954, Jan. 20   Engr.   Perf. 13½x13
621 A232 1.45p blue   1.40   .50
50th anniv. of Argentina's 1st antarctic p.o. and the establishing of the La Hoy radio p.o. in the South Orkneys.

Wired Communications A233

Television A234

Perf. 13x13½, 13½x13
1954, Apr.   Photo.   Wmk. 90
622 A233 1.50p shown   .50   .30
623 A233 3p Radio   2.00   .30
624 A234 5p shown   3.00   .40
  Nos. 622-624 (3)   5.50 1.00
Intl. Plenipotentiary Conf. of Telecommunications, Buenos Aires, 1952.

Pediment, Buenos Aires Stock Exchange A235

1954, July 13   Perf. 13½x13
625 A235 1p dark green   .75   .25
Cent. of the establishment of the Buenos Aires Stock Exchange.

Eva Peron — A236

1954   Wmk. 90
626 A236 3p dp car rose   3.00   .50
Wmk. 288
627 A236 3p dp car rose   250.00 50.00
2nd anniv. of the death of Eva Peron.

Jose de San Martin — A237

Wheat — A238

Industry — A238a

Eva Peron Foundation Building A239

Cliffs of Humahuaca — A240

Gen. Jose de San Martin — A241

Designs: 50c, Buenos Aires harbor. 1p, Cattle ranch (Ganaderia). 3p, Nihuil Dam. 5p, Iguacu Falls, vert. 20p, Mt. Fitz Roy, vert.

Engraved (#632, 638-642),
Photogravure (#634-637)
Perf. 13½, 13x13½ (80c), 13½x13 (#639, 641-642)
1954-59   Wmk. 90
628 A237 20c brt red, typo.   .25   .25
629 A237 20c red, litho. ('55)   1.00   .25
630 A237 40c red, litho. ('56)   .40   .25
631 A237 40c brt red, typo. ('55)   .40   .25
632 A239 50c blue ('56)   .40   .25
633 A239 50c bl, litho. ('59)   .30   .25
634 A238 80c brown   .40   .25
635 A239 1p brown ('58)   .40   .25
636 A238a 1.50p ultra ('58)   .40   .25
637 A239 2p dk rose lake   .50   .25
638 A239 3p violet brn ('56)   .50   .25
639 A240 5p gray grn ('55)   8.00   .25
  a. Perf. 13½   10.00
640 A240 10p yel grn ('55)   8.00   .25
641 A240 20p dull vio ('55)   11.00   1.00
  a. Perf. 13½   14.00   1.50
642 A241 50p ultra & ind ('55)   12.00   1.50
  a. Perf. 13½   15.00   1.50
  Nos. 628-642 (15)   43.95   5.25

See Nos. 699-700. For similar designs inscribed "Republica Argentina" see Nos. 823-827, 890, 935, 937, 940, 990, 995, 1039, 1044, 1048.
For overprints see Nos. O94-O106, O142, O153-O157.

Allegory A242

1954, Aug. 26   Typo.   Perf. 13½
643 A242 1.50p slate black   .80   .25
Cent. of the establishment of the Buenos Aires Grain Exchange.

Clasped Hands and Congress Medal — A243

1955, Mar. 21   Photo.   Perf. 13½x13
644 A243 3p red brown   1.50   .30
Issued to publicize the National Productivity and Social Welfare Congress.

Allegory of
Aviation — A244

1955, June 18   Wmk. 90   Perf. 13½
645 A244 1.50p olive gray   1.00 .25
Commercial aviation in Argentina, 25th anniv.

Argentina Breaking
Chains — A245

1955, Oct. 16   Litho.
647 A245 1.50p olive green   .70 .25
Liberation Revolution of Sept. 16, 1955.

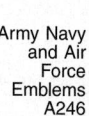

Army Navy
and Air
Force
Emblems
A246

Perf. 13½x13
1955, Dec. 31   Photo.   Wmk. 90
648 A246 3p blue   .75 .25
"Brotherhood of the Armed Forces."

Justo Jose de
Urquiza — A247

1956, Feb. 3   Perf. 13½
649 A247 1.50p dk grn, lt grn   .70 .25
Battle of Caseros, 104th anniversary.
No. 649 exists imperf. Value, pair $30.

Coin and
Die — A248

1956, July 28   Engr.   Perf. 13½x13
650 A248 2p multicolored   .40 .25
75th anniversary of the Argentine Mint.

1856 Stamp of
Corrientes
A249

Juan G.
Pujol — A250

Design: 2.40p, Stamp of 1860-78.

1956, Aug. 21
651 A249   40c dk grn & blue   .30 .25
652 A249   2.40p brn & lil rose   .40 .25
Photo.
653 A250   4.40p brt blue   .90 .30
a.   Souv. sheet, #651-653, imperf. 9.00 6.00
      Nos. 651-653 (3)   1.60 .80
Centenary of Argentine postage stamps.
No. 653a for the Argentine stamp cent. and
Philatelic Exhib. for the Cent. of Corrientes
Stamps, Oct. 12-21. The 4.40p is photo., the
other two stamps and border litho. Colors of
40c and 2.40p differ slightly from engraved
stamps.

Felling Trees,
La Pampa
A251

Maté Herb and
Gourd,
Misiones — A252

1p, Cotton plant and harvest, Chaco.

1956, Sept. 1   Perf. 13½
654 A251   50c ultra   .80 .25
655 A251   1p magenta   .80 .25
656 A252   1.50p green   .80 .25
       Nos. 654-656 (3)   2.40 .75
Elevation of the territories of La Pampa,
Chaco and Misiones to provinces.

"Liberty" — A253

Perf. 13½
1956, Sept. 15   Wmk. 90   Photo.
657 A253 2.40p lilac rose   .75 .25
1st anniv. of the Revolution of Liberation.

Florentino
Ameghino — A254

1956, Nov. 30
658 A254 2.40p brown   .60 .25
Issued to honor Florentino Ameghino (1854-
1911), anthropologist.
For overprint see No. O110.

Adm. Brown Type of 1935-51
Two types:
I. Bust touches upper frame line of name
panel at bottom.
II. White line separates bust from frame line.
Size: 19½-20½x26-27mm
1956   Litho.   Perf. 13
659 A133 20c dull purple (I)   .25 .25
a.   Type II   .25 .25
b.   Size 19½x25¼mm (I)   .50 .25
For overprint see No. O108.

Benjamin
Franklin
A255

1956, Dec. 22   Photo.   Perf. 13½
660 A255 40c intense blue   .65 .25
250th anniv. of the birth of Benjamin
Franklin.

Frigate
"Hercules"
A256

Guillermo Brown
A257

1957, Mar. 2
661 A256   40c brt blue   .25 .25
662 A257   2.40p gray black   .40 .25
       Nos. 661-662,C63-C65 (5)   1.50 1.25
Admiral Guillermo (William) Brown (1777-
1857), founder of the Argentine navy.

Roque Saenz Pena
(1851-1914)
A258

1957, Apr. 1
663 A258 4.40p grnsh gray   .65 .25
Roque Saenz Pena, pres. 1910-14.
For overprint see No. O111.

Church of Santo
Domingo,
1807 — A259

1957, July 6   Wmk. 90
664 A259 40c brt blue green   .30 .25
150th anniv. of the defense of Buenos Aires.

"La Portena"
A260

1957, Aug. 31   Wmk. 90   Perf. 13½
665 A260 40c pale brown   .75 .25
Centenary of Argentine railroads.

Esteban
Echeverria — A261

1957, Sept. 2   Perf. 13x13½
666 A261 2p claret   .30 .25
Esteban Echeverria (1805-1851), poet.
For overprint see No. O109.

"Liberty" — A262

1957, Sept. 28   Perf. 13½
667 A262 40c carmine rose   .40 .25
Constitutional reform convention.

Portrait Type of 1935-51
1957, Oct. 28   Litho.   Perf. 13½
Size: 16½x22mm
668 A128 5c Jose Hernandez   .25 .25
For overprint see No. O112.

Oil Derrick
and Hands
Holding
Oil — A263

Perf. 13½
1957, Dec. 21   Wmk. 90   Photo.
669 A263 40c bright blue   .65 .25
50th anniv. of the national oil industry.
No. 669 exists imperf. Value, pair $30.

Museum, La Plata — A264

1958, Jan. 11
670 A264 40c dark gray   .30 .25
  City of La Plata, 75th anniversary.

A265   A266

40c, Locomotive & arms of Argentina & Bolivia. 1p, Map of Argentine-Bolivian boundary & plane.

1958, Apr. 19   Wmk. 90   Perf. 13½
671 A265 40c slate & dp car   .55 .25
672 A266 1p dark brown   .55 .25
  Argentine-Bolivian friendship. No. 671 for the opening of the Jacuiba-Santa Cruz railroad; No. 672, the exchange of presidential visits.

Symbols of the Republic A267

1958, Apr. 30   Photo. & Engr.
673 A267 40c multicolored   .40 .25
674 A267 1p multicolored   .50 .25
675 A267 2p multicolored   .85 .25
   Nos. 673-675 (3)   1.75 .75
  Transmission of Presidential power.

Flag Monument — A268

1958, June 21   Litho.   Wmk. 90
676 A268 40c blue & violet bl   .30 .25
  1st anniv. of the Flag Monument of Rosario. Exists imperf. Value, pair $40.

Map of Antarctica — A269

1958, July 12   Perf. 13½
677 A269 40c car rose & blk   .70 .40
  International Geophysical Year, 1957-58. Exists imperf. Value, pair $80.

Stamp of Cordoba and Mail Coach A270

1958, Oct. 18
678 A270 40c pale blue & slate   .30 .25
   Nos. 678,C72-C73 (3)   .80 .75
  Centenary of Cordoba postage stamps.

"Slave" by Michelangelo and UN Emblem — A271

Engraved and Lithographed
1959, Mar. 14   Wmk. 90   Perf. 13½
679 A271 40c violet brn & gray .30 .25
  10th anniv. (in 1958) of the signing of the Universal Declaration of Human Rights. No UN Emblem (error) Value, $200.
  Exists imperf. Value, pair $50.

Orchids and Globe — A272

1959, May 23   Photo.   Perf. 13½
680 A272 1p dull claret   .30 .25
  1st International Horticulture Exposition. Exists imperf. Value, pair $50.

Pope Pius XII — A273

1959, June 20   Engr.   Perf. 13½
681 A273 1p yellow & black .40 .25
  Pope Pius XII, 1876-1958.
  Exists imperf. Value, pair $50.

William Harvey — A274

1p, Claude Bernard. 1.50p, Ivan P. Pavlov.

1959, Aug. 8   Litho.   Wmk. 90
682 A274 50c green   .25 .25
683 A274 1p dark red   .25 .25
684 A274 1.50p brown   .30 .25
   Nos. 682-684 (3) .80 .75
  21st Intl. Cong. of Physiological Sciences, Buenos Aires.

Type of 1958 and

Domestic Horse — A275   Jose de San Martin — A276

Tierra del Fuego A277

Inca Bridge, Mendoza — A278

Ski Jumper A279

Mar del Plata A280

Designs: 10c, Cayman. 20c, Llama. 50c, Puma. No. 690, Sunflower. 3p, Zapata Slope, Catamarca. 12p, 23p, 25p, Red Quebracho tree. 20p, Nahuel Huapi Lake. 22p, "Industry" (cogwheel and factory).
Two overall paper sizes for 1p, 5p:
  I — 27x37½mm or 37½x27mm.
  II — 27x39mm or 39x27mm.

Perf. 13x13½

			Wmk.	90
1959-70		**Litho.**		
685	A275	10c slate green	.35	.25
686	A275	20c dl red brn ('61)	.35	.25
687	A275	50c bister ('60)	.35	.25
688	A275	50c bis, typo. ('60)	.35	.25
689	A275	1p rose red	.35	.25

Perf. 13½

690	A278	1p brn, photo., I ('61)	.25	.25
a.		Paper II ('69)	1.00	.25
690B	A278	1p brown, I	1.00	.50
691	A276	2p rose red ('61)	.40	.25
692	A276	2p red, typo. (19½ x 26mm) ('61)	.50	.25
a.		Redrawn (19½ x 25mm)	4.00	.25
693	A277	3p dk bl, photo. ('60)	.25	.25
694	A276	4p red, typo ('62)	1.00	.25
694A	A276	4p red ('62)	.60	.25
695	A277	5p gray brn, photo., I	.30	.25
e.		5p dark brown, paper II ('70)	9.00	4.00
695A	A276	8p ver ('65)	2.00	.25
695B	A276	8p red, typo. ('65)	.30	.25
695C	A276	10p ver ('66)	.60	.25
695D	A276	10p red, typo. ('66)	.60	.25

Photo.

696	A278	10p lt red brn ('60)	.50	.25
697	A278	12p dk brn vio ('62)	1.00	.25
697A	A278	12p dk brn, litho. ('64)	12.00	.30
698	A278	20p Prus grn ('60)	3.00	.25
698A	A276	20p red, typo. ('67)	.30	.25

699	A238a	22p ultra ('62)	2.00	.25
700	A238a	22p ultra, litho. ('62)	25.00	.30
701	A278	23p green ('65)	5.00	.25
702	A278	25p dp vio ('66)	2.00	.25
703	A278	25p pur, litho. ('66)	6.00	.25
704	A279	100p blue ('61)	8.00	.25
705	A280	300p dp vio ('62)	5.00	.25
		Nos. 685-705 (29)	79.35	7.60

Imperf and imperf between examples of some numbers exist.
  See Nos. 882-887, 889, 892, 923-925, 928-930, 938, 987-989, 991.
  For overprints and surcharges see Nos. 1076, C82-C83, O113-O118, O122-O124, O126-O141, O143-O145, O163.
  The 300p remained on sale as a 3p stamp after the 1970 currency exchange.

Symbolic Sailboat — A281

1959, Oct. 3   Litho.   Perf. 13½
706 A281 1p blk, red & bl .30 .25
  Red Cross sanitary education campaign.

Child Playing with Doll — A282

1959, Oct. 17
707 A282 1p red & blk   .30 .25
  Issued for Mother's Day, 1959.

Buenos Aires 1p Stamp of 1859 — A283

1959, Nov. 21   Wmk. 90   Perf. 13½
708 A283 1p gray & dk bl .30 .25
  Issued for the Day of Philately.

Bartolomé Mitre and Justo José de Urquiza — A284

1959, Dec. 12   Photo.   Perf. 13½
709 A284 1p purple   .30 .25
  Treaty of San Jose de Flores, centenary. Exists imperf. Value, pair $40.

WRY Emblem — A285

1960, Apr. 7   Litho.   Wmk. 90
710 A285 1p bister & car .35 .25
711 A285 4.20p apple grn & dp claret .35 .25
  World Refugee Year, July 1, 1959-June 30, 1960. See No. B25.

Abraham
Lincoln — A286

1960, Apr. 14   Photo.   Perf. 13½
712 A286 5p ultra   .45 .25
  Sesquicentennial (in 1959) of the birth of
Abraham Lincoln.
  Exists imperf. Value, pair $70.

Cornelio
Saavedra
and Cabildo,
Buenos
Aires — A287

  "Cabildo" and: 2p, Juan José Paso. 4.20p,
Manuel Alberti and Miguel Azcuénaga.
10.70p, Juan Larrea and Domingo Matheu.

Perf. 13½
1960, May 28   Wmk. 90   Photo.
713 A287   1p rose lilac   .25 .25
714 A287   2p bluish grn   .25 .25
715 A287   4.20p gray & grn   .30 .25
716 A287   10.70p gray & ultra .45 .25
  Nos. 713-716,C75-C76 (6)   1.85 1.50

  150th anniversary of the May Revolution.
Souvenir sheets are Nos. C75a and C76a.

Luis Maria
Drago — A288

1960, July 8
717 A288 4.20p brown   .30 .25
  Centenary of the birth of Dr. Luis Maria
Drago, statesman and jurist.
  Exists imperf. Value, pair $40.

Juan Bautista
Alberdi — A289

1960, Sept. 10   Wmk. 90   Perf. 13½
718 A289 1p green   .30 .25
  150th anniversary of the birth of Juan Bautista Alberdi, statesman and philosopher.
  Exists imperf. Value, pair $40.

Map of Argentina
and Antarctic
Sector — A290

1960, Sept. 24   Litho.   Perf. 13½
719 A290 5p violet   .75 .25
  National census of 1960.
  Exists imperf. Value, pair $70.

Caravel and
Emblem
A291

1960, Oct. 1   Photo.
720 A291 1p dk olive grn   .40 .25
721 A291 5p brown   .65 .25
  Nos. 720-721,C78-C79 (4)   2.25 1.10
  8th Congress of the Postal Union of the
Americas and Spain.

Virgin of Luján,
Patroness of
Argentina — A292

1960, Nov. 12   Wmk. 90   Perf. 13½
722 A292 1p dark blue   .60 .25
  First Inter-American Marian Congress.
  Exists imperf. Value, pair $30.

Argentine Boy
Scout
Emblem — A293

1961, Jan. 17   Litho.
723 A293 1p car rose & blk   .30 .25
  International Patrol Encampment of the Boy
Scouts, Buenos Aires.
  Exists imperf. Value, pair $70.

"Shipment of Cereals," by Quinquela
Martin — A294

1961, Feb. 11   Photo.   Perf. 13½
724 A294 1p red brown   .30 .25
  Export drive: "To export is to advance."
  Exists imperf. Value, pair $40.

Naval Battle of San
Nicolás — A295

1961, Mar. 2   Perf. 13½
725 A295 2p gray   .30 .25
  Naval battle of San Nicolas, 150th anniv.
  Exists imperf. Value, pair $67.50.

Mariano
Moreno by
Juan de Dios
Rivera
A296

1961, Mar. 25   Perf. 13½
726 A296 2p blue   .30 .25
  Mariano Moreno (1778-1811), writer, politician, member of the 1810 Junta.
  Exists imperf. Value, pair $40.

Emperor Trajan
Statue — A297

1961, Apr. 11
727 A297 2p slate green   .30 .25
  Visit of Pres. Giovanni Gronchi of Italy to
Argentina, April 1961.
  Exists imperf. Value, pair $40.

Rabindranath
Tagore — A298

1961, May 13   Photo.   Perf. 13½
728 A298 2p purple, grysh   .95 .25
  Centenary of the birth of Rabindranath
Tagore, Indian poet.

San Martin
Statue,
Madrid
A299

1961, May 24   Wmk. 90
729 A299 1p olive gray   .30 .25
  Unveiling of a statue of General José de
San Martin in Madrid.
  Exists imperf. Value, pair $40.

Manuel
Belgrano
A300

1961, June 17   Perf. 13½
730 A300 2p violet blue   .60 .25
  Erection of a monument by Hector Rocha,
to General Manuel Belgrano in Buenos Aires.
  Exists imperf. Value, pair $40.

Explorers,
Sledge and
Dog Team
A301

1961, Aug. 19   Photo.   Wmk. 90
731 A301 2p black   .85 .30
  10th anniversary of the General San Martin
Base, Argentine Antarctic.
  Exists imperf. Value, pair $75.

Spanish
Conquistador and
Sword — A302

1961, Aug. 19   Litho.
732 A302 2p red & blk   .75 .25
  First city of Jujuy, 400th anniversary.
  Exists imperf. Value, pair $40.

Sarmiento Statue by
Rodin, Buenos
Aires — A303

1961, Sept. 9   Photo.
733 A303 2p violet   .30 .25
  Domingo Faustino Sarmiento (1811-88),
political leader and writer.
  Exists imperf. Value, pair $40.

Symbol of
World Town
Planning
A304

1961, Nov. 25   Litho.   Perf. 13½
734 A304 2p ultra & yel   .30 .25
  World Town Planning Day, Nov. 8.

Manuel Belgrano
Statue, Buenos
Aires — A305

1962, Feb. 24   Photo.
735 A305 2p Prus blue   .30 .25
  150th anniversary of the Argentine flag.
  Exists imperf. Value, pair $40.

Grenadier, Flag and
Regimental
Emblem — A306

1962, Mar. 31   Wmk. 90   Perf. 13½
736 A306 2p carmine rose   .60 .25
  150th anniversary of the San Martin Grenadier Guards regiment.
  Exists imperf. Value, pair $40.

Mosquito and
Malaria
Eradication
Emblem
A307

1962, Apr. 7   Litho.
737 A307 2p vermilion & blk   .35 .25
  WHO drive to eradicate malaria.

Church of the Virgin of Lujàn — A308

1962, May 12   *Perf. 13½*
738 A308 2p org brn & blk   .30   .25

75th anniversary of the pontifical coronation of the Virgin of Lujan.

Bust of Juan Jufrè — A309

1962, June 23   **Photo.**
739 A309 2p Prus blue   .30   .25

Founding of San Juan, 4th cent.
Exists imperf. Value, pair $40.

"Soaring into Space" — A310

1962, Aug. 18   Litho.   Perf. 13½
740 A310 2p maroon, blk & bl   .30   .25

Argentine Air Force, 50th anniversary.
Exists imperf. Value, pair $40.

Juan Vucetich — A311

1962, Oct. 6   Photo.   Wmk. 90
741 A311 2p green   .30   .25

Juan Vucetich (1864-1925), inventor of the Argentine system of fingerprinting.
Exists imperf. Value, pair $40.

Domingo F. Sarmiento — A312

Design: 4p, Jose Hernandez.

1962-66   Photo.   Perf. 13½
742   A312 2p deep green   .50   .25
      Litho.
742A   A312 2p lt green ('64)   .50   .25
      Photo.
742B   A312 4p dull red ('65)   .50   .25
      Photo.
742C   A312 4p rose red ('66)   1.25   .25
      Nos. 742-742C (4)   2.75   1.00

No. 742A exists imperf. Value, pair $40.
See No. 817-819. For overprints see Nos.
O119-O121, O125, O149.

February 20th Monument, Salta — A313

1963, Feb. 23   Photo.   Wmk. 90
743 A313 2p dark green   .60   .25

150th anniversary of the Battle of Salta, War of Independence.
Exists imperf. Value, pair $40.

Gear Wheels A314

1963, Mar. 16   Litho.   Perf. 13½
744 A314 4p gray, blk & brt rose   .60   .25

Argentine Industrial Union, 75th anniv.
Exists imperf. Value, pair $40.

National College, Buenos Aires — A315

1963, Mar. 16   Wmk. 90
745 A315 4p dull org & blk   .65   .25

National College of Buenos Aires, cent.
Exists imperf. Value, pair $40.

Child Draining Cup — A316

1963, Apr. 6
746 A316 4p multicolored   .30   .25

FAO "Freedom from Hunger" campaign.
Exists imperf. Value, pair $40.

Frigate "La Argentina," 1817, by Emilio Biggeri A317

1963, May 18   Photo.
747 A317 4p bluish green   .90   .25

Issued for Navy Day, May 17.
Exists imperf. Value, pair $40.

Seat of 1813 Assembly and Official Seal — A318

1963, July 13   Litho.   Perf. 13½
748 A318 4p lt blue & blk   .60   .25

150th anniversary of the 1813 Assembly.
Exists imperf. Value, pair $40.

Battle of San Lorenzo, 1813 A319

1963, Aug. 24
749 A319 4p grn & blk, *grnsh*   .60   .25

Sesquicentennial of the Battle of San Lorenzo.

Queen Nefertari Offering Papyrus Flowers, Abu Simbel A320

1963, Sept. 14   Perf. 13½
750 A320 4p ocher, blk & bl grn   .60   .25

Campaign to save the historic monuments in Nubia.
Exists imperf. Value, pair $40.

Government House, Buenos Aires — A321

1963, Oct. 12   Wmk. 90   Perf. 13½
751 A321 5p rose & brown   .60   .25

Inauguration of President Arturo Illia.
Exists imperf. Value, pair $40.

"Science" — A322

1963, Oct. 16   Litho.
752 A322 4p org brn, bl & blk   .65   .25

10th Latin-American Neurosurgery Congress.
Exists imperf. Value, pair $40.

Francisco de las Carreras, Supreme Court Justice — A323

1963, Nov. 23   Photo.   Perf. 13½
753 A323 5p bluish green   .30   .25

Centenary of judicial power.
Exists imperf. Value, pair $40.

Blackboards A324

1963, Nov. 23   Litho.
754 A324 5p red, blk & bl   .30   .25

Issued to publicize "Teachers for America" through the Alliance for Progress program.

Exists imperf. Value, pair $40.

Kemal Atatürk — A325

1963, Dec. 28   Photo.   Perf. 13½
755 A325 12p dark gray   .60   .25

25th anniversary of the death of Kemal Atatürk, president of Turkey.
Exists imperf. Value, pair $40.

"Payador" by Juan Carlos Castagnino — A326

1964, Jan. 25   Litho.
756 A326 4p ultra, blk & lt bl   .60   .25

Fourth National Folklore Festival.
Exists imperf. Value, pair $40.

Maps of South Georgia, South Orkney and South Sandwich Islands A327

4p, Map of Argentina & Antarctic claims, vert.

1964, Feb. 22   Wmk. 90   Perf. 13½
          Size: 33x22mm
757 A327 2p lt & dk bl & bister   1.40   .30
          Size: 30x40mm
758 A327 4p lt & dk bl & ol grn   2.10   .30
      Nos. 757-758,C92 (3)   6.25   1.35

Argentina's claim to Antarctic territories, 60th anniv.
Exist imperf. Value, set of 3 pairs, $150.

Jorge Newbery in Cockpit A328

1964, Feb. 23   Photo.
759 A328 4p deep green   .65   .25

Newbery, aviator, 50th death anniv.
Exists imperf. Value, pair $40.

John F. Kennedy A329

1964, Apr. 14   Engr.   Wmk. 90
760 A329 4p claret & dk bl   .50   .25

President John F. Kennedy (1917-63).
Exists imperf. Value, pair $100.

José Brochero by José Cuello — A330

1964, May 9   Photo.   *Perf. 13½*
761 A330 4p light sepia   .60   .25
  50th anniversary of the death of Father Jose Gabriel Brochero.
  Exists imperf. Value, pair $50.

Soldier of Patricios Regiment A331

1964, May 29   Litho.   Wmk. 90
762 A331 4p blk, ultra & red   .75   .25
  Issued for Army Day. Later Army Day stamps, inscribed "Republica Argentina," are of type A340a.
  Exists imperf. Value, pair $40.

Pope John XXIII — A332

1964, June 27   Engr.
763 A332 4p orange & blk   .30   .25
  Issued in memory of Pope John XXIII.
  Exists imperf. Value, pair $50.

University of Cordoba Arms — A333

1964, Aug. 22   Litho.   Wmk. 90
764 A333 4p blk, ultra & yel   .30   .25
  350th anniv. of the University of Cordoba.

Pigeons and UN Building, NYC — A334

1964, Oct. 24   *Perf. 13½*
765 A334 4p dk blue & lt blue   .35   .25
  Issued for United Nations Day.
  Exists imperf. Value, pair $40.

Joaquin V. Gonzalez — A335

1964, Nov. 14   Photo.
766 A335 4p dk rose carmine   .60   .25
  Centenary (in 1963) of the birth of Joaquin V. Gonzalez, writer.
  Exists imperf. Value, pair $40.

Julio Argentino Roca — A336

1964, Dec. 12   *Perf. 13½*
767 A336 4p violet blue   .30   .25
  General Julio A. Roca, (1843-1914), president of Argentina, (1880-86, 1898-1904).
  Exists imperf. Value, pair $40.

Market at Montserrat Square, by Carlos Morel — A337

1964, Dec. 19   Photo.
768 A337 4p sepia   .35   .25
  19th century Argentine painter Carlos Morel.
  Exists imperf. Value, pair $40.

General Belgrano Base, Antarctica A338

4p, Icebreaker General San Martin.

1965   *Perf. 13½*
769 A338 2p dull purple   .60   .25
770 A338 4p ultra   1.20   .25
  Issued to publicize the natl. territory of Tierra del Fuego, Antarctic and South Atlantic Isles.
  Issue dates: 4p, Feb. 27; 2p, June 5.
  No. 769 exists imperf. Value, pair $5.

Girl with Piggy Bank — A339

1965, Apr. 3   Litho.
771 A339 4p red org & blk   .30   .25
  National Postal Savings Bank, 50th anniv.
  Exists imperf. Value, pair $40.

Sun and Globe A340

1965, May 29
772 A340 4p blk, org & dl bl   .60   .30
  Nos. 772,C98-C99 (3)   2.55   1.15
  International Quiet Sun Year, 1964-65.
  Exists imperf. Value, pair $40.

Hussar of Pueyrredon Regiment — A340a

1965, June 5   Wmk. 90   *Perf. 13½*
773 A340a 8p dp ultra, blk & red   .75   .25
  Issued for Army Day. See Nos. 796, 838, 857, 893, 944, 958, 974, 1145.
  Exists imperf. Value, pair $50.

Ricardo Rojas (1882-1957) A341

  Portraits: No. 775, Ricardo Guiraldes (1886-1927). No. 776, Enrique Larreta (1873-1961). No. 777, Leopoldo Lugones (1874-1938). No. 778, Roberto J. Payro (1867-1928).

1965, June 26   Photo.
774 A341 8p brown   .35   .25
775 A341 8p brown   .35   .30
776 A341 8p brown   .35   .25
777 A041 0p brown   .05   .£5
778 A341 8p brown   .35   .25
  Nos. 774-778 (5)   1.75   1.30
  Issued to honor Argentine writers. Printed se-tenant in sheets of 100 (10x10); 2 horizontal rows of each design with Guiraldes in top rows and Rojas in bottom rows.
  Nos. imperf. Value, strip of 5, $250.

Hipolito Yrigoyen A342

1965, July 3   Litho.
779 A342 8p pink & black   .30   .25
  Hipolito Yrigoyen (1852-1933), president of Argentina 1916-22, 1928-30.

Children Looking Through Window A343

1965, July 24   Photo.
780 A343 8p salmon & blk   .60   .25
  International Seminar on Mental Health.
  Exists imperf. Value, pair $40.

Child's Funerary Urn and 16th Century Map A344

1965, Aug. 7   Litho.
781 A344 8p lt grn, dk red, brn & ocher   .35   .25
  City of San Miguel de Tucuman, 400th anniv.
  Exists imperf. Value, pair $40.

Cardinal Cagliero — A345

1965, Aug. 21   Photo.
782 A345 8p violet   .30   .25
  Juan Cardinal Cagliero (1839-1926), missionary to Argentina and Bishop of Magida.
  Exists imperf. Value, pair $40.

Dante Alighieri — A346

1965, Sept. 16   Wmk. 90   *Perf. 13½*
783 A346 8p light ultra   .60   .25
  Dante Alighieri (1265-1321), Italian poet.
  Exists imperf. Value, pair $40.

Clipper "Mimosa" and Map of Patagonia A347

1965, Sept. 25   Litho.
784 A347 8p red & black   .35   .25
  Centenary of Welsh colonization of Chubut, and the founding of the city of Rawson. Exists imperf. Value, pair $40.

A348

  Design: Map of Buenos Aires, cock and compass Emblem of federal police.

1965, Oct. 30   Photo.   *Perf. 13½*
785 A348 8p carmine rose   .35   .25
  Issued for Federal Police Day. Exists imperf. Value, pair $40.

Child's Drawing of Children A349

1965, Nov. 6   Litho.   Wmk. 90
786 A349 8p lt yel grn & blk   .35   .25
  Public education law, 81st anniversary.
  Exists imperf. Value, pair $40.

Church of St. Francis, Catamarca — A350

1965, Dec. 8
787 A350 8p org yel & red brn .30 .25
Brother Mamerto de la Asuncion Esquiu, preacher, teacher and official of 1885 Provincial Constitutional Convention.

Ruben Dario — A351

Litho. and Photo.
1965, Dec. 22 **Perf. 13½**
788 A351 15p bl vio, *gray* .30 .25
Ruben Dario (pen name of Felix Ruben Garcia Sarmiento, 1867-1916), Nicaraguan poet, newspaper correspondent and diplomat. Exists imperf. Value, pair $40.

"The Orange Seller" A352

Pueyrredon Paintings: No. 790, "Stop at the Grocery Store." No. 791, "Landscape at San Fernando" (sailboats). No. 792, "Bathing Horses at River Plata."

1966, Jan. 29 **Photo.** **Perf. 13½**
789 A352 8p bluish green .70 .50
790 A352 8p bluish green .70 .50
791 A352 8p bluish green .70 .50
792 A352 8p bluish green .70 .50
  a. Block of 4, #789-792 + 2 labels 3.50 3.50
Prilidiano Pueyrredon (1823-1870), painter.

Sun Yat-sen, Flags of Argentina and China — A353

1966, Mar. 12 **Wmk. 90** **Perf. 13½**
793 A353 8p dk red brown .70 .30
Dr. Sun Yat-sen (1866-1925), founder of the Republic of China. Exists imperf. Value, pair $100.

Souvenir Sheet

Rivadavia Issue of 1864 — A354

Wmk. 90
1966, Apr. 20 **Litho.** *Imperf.*
794 A354 Sheet of 3 1.10 1.10
  a. 4p gray & red brown .25 .25
  b. 5p gray & green .25 .25
  c. 8p gray & dark blue .25 .25
2nd Rio de la Plata Stamp Show, Buenos Aires, Mar. 16-24. Exists with flags omitted (error). Value, $150.

People of Various Races and WHO Emblem A355

1966, Apr. 23 **Perf. 13½**
795 A355 8p brown & black .30 .25
Opening of the WHO Headquarters, Geneva. Exists imperf. Value, pair $40.

Soldier Type of 1965

Army Day: 8p, Cavalryman, Guemes Infernal Regiment.

1966, May 28 **Litho.**
796 A340a 8p multicolored .75 .30
Exists imperf. Value, pair $40.

Coat of Arms — A356

Arms: a, National. b, Buenos Aires. c, La Rioja. d, Catamarca. e, Cordoba. f, Corrientes. g, Chaco. h, Chubut. i, Entre Rios. j, Formosa. k, Jujuy. l, La Pampa. m, Federal Capital. n, Mendoza. o, Misiones. p, Neuquen. q, Salta. r, San Juan. s, San Luis. t, Santa Cruz. u, Santa Fe. v, Santiago del Estero. w, Tucuman. x, map of Rio Negro. y, Map of Tierra del Fuego, Antarctica, South Atlantic Islands.

1966, July 30 **Wmk. 90** **Perf. 13½**
797 A356 Sheet of 25 35.00
  a.-y. A356 10p black & multi 1.00 1.00
150th anniv. of Argentina's Declaration of Independence. Exists imperf. Value, sheet $2,000.

Three Crosses, Caritas Emblem A357

1966, Sept. 10 **Litho.** **Perf. 13½**
798 A357 10p ol grn, blk & lt bl .30 .25
Caritas, charity organization.

Hilario Ascasubi (1807-75) — A358

Portraits: No. 800, Estanislao del Campo (1834-80). No. 801, Miguel Cane (1851-1905). No. 802, Lucio V. Lopez (1848-94). No. 803, Rafael Obligado (1851-1920). No. 804, Luis Agote (1868-1954), M.D. No. 805, Juan B. Ambrosetti (1865-1917), naturalist and archaeologist. No. 806, Miguel Lillo (1862-1931), botanist and chemist. No. 807, Francisco P. Moreno (1852-1919), naturalist and paleontologist. No. 808, Francisco J. Muñiz (1795-1871), physician.

1966 **Photo.** **Wmk. 90**
799 A358 10p dk blue green .40 .30
800 A358 10p dk blue green .40 .30
801 A358 10p dk blue green .40 .30
802 A358 10p dk blue green .40 .30
803 A358 10p dk blue green .40 .30
804 A358 10p deep violet .40 .30
805 A358 10p deep violet .40 .30
806 A358 10p deep violet .40 .30
807 A358 10p deep violet .40 .30
808 A358 10p deep violet .40 .30
  Nos. 799-808 (10) 4.00 3.00
Nos. 799-803 issued Sept. 17 to honor Argentine writers. Printed se-tenant in sheets of 100 (10x10); 2 horizontal rows of each portrait. Nos. 804-808 issued Oct. 22 to honor Argentine scientists; 2 horizontal rows of each portrait. Scientists set has value at upper left, frame line with rounded corners.

Anchor A359

1966, Oct. 8 **Litho.**
809 A359 4p multicolored .30 .25
Argentine merchant marine. Exists imperf. Value, pair $40.

Flags and Map of the Americas A360

1966, Oct. 29 **Perf. 13½**
810 A360 10p gray & multi .30 .25
7th Conference of American Armies.

Argentine National Bank — A361

1966, Nov. 5 **Photo.**
811 A361 10p brt blue green .30 .25
75th anniv. of the Argentine National Bank. Exists imperf. Value, pair $40.

La Salle Monument and College, Buenos Aires — A362

1966, Nov. 26 **Litho.** **Perf. 13½**
812 A362 10p brown org & blk .30 .25
75th anniv. of the Colegio de la Salle, Buenos Aires, and to honor Saint Jean Baptiste de la Salle (1651-1719), educator. Exists imperf. Value, pair $125.

Map of Argentine Antarctica and Expedition Route — A363

1966, Dec. 10 **Wmk. 90**
813 A363 10p multicolored .75 .35
1965 Argentine Antarctic expedition, which planted the Argentine flag on the South Pole. Exists imperf. Value, pair $70.
See No. 851.

Juan Martin de Pueyrredon — A364

1966, Dec. 17 **Photo.** **Perf. 13½**
814 A364 10p dull red brn .30 .25
Issued to honor Juan Martin de Pueyrredon (1777-1850), Governor of Cordoba and of the United Provinces of the River Plata.

Gen. Juan de Las Heras — A365

1966, Dec. 17 **Engr.**
815 A365 10p black .30 .25
Issued to honor Gen. Juan Gregorio de Las Heras (1780-1866), Peruvian field marshal and aide-de-camp to San Martin.

Inscribed "Republica Argentina" Types of 1955-61 and

Jose Hernandez — A366

Trout Leaping in National Park — A366a

Designs: 50p, Gen. Jose de San Martin. 90p, Guillermo Brown. 500p, Red deer in forest.

Two overall paper sizes for 6p, 50p (No. 827) and 90p:
  I — 27x37½mm
  II — 27x39mm

Perf. 13½
1965-68 **Wmk. 90** **Photo.**
817 A366 6p rose red, litho, I ('67) 1.50 .25
818 A366 6p rose red ('67), II 5.50 .25

819	A366	6p brn, 15x22mm ('68)	.30	.25
823	A238a	43p dk car rose	7.00	.25
824	A238a	45p brn ('66)	3.50	.25
825	A238a	45p brn, litho ('67)	8.00	.25
826	A241	50p dk bl, 29x40mm	8.50	.40
827	A241	50p dk bl, 22x31½mm, I ('67)	4.50	.25
a.		Paper II	2.25	.25
828	A366	90p ol bis, I ('67)	3.00	.25
a.		Paper II	14.00	3.75

Engr.

829	A495	500p yellow grn ('66)	2.50	.30
829A	A366a	1,000p vio bl ('68)	8.00	.25
		Nos. 817-829A (11)	52.30	2.95

The 500p and 1,000p remained on sale as 5p and 10p stamps after the 1970 currency exchange.

See Nos. 888, 891, 939, 992, 1031, 1045-1047. For surcharge and overprints see Nos. 1077, O153-O158, O162.

Pre-Columbian Pottery — A367

1967, Feb. 18   Litho.   Perf. 13½
830 A367 10p multicolored   .35 .25
20th anniv. of UNESCO. Exists imperf. Value, pair $40.

"The Meal" by Fernando Fader — A368

1967, Feb. 25   Photo.   Wmk. 90
831 A368 10p red brown   .35 .25
Issued in memory of the Argentine painter Fernando Fader (1882-1935). Exists imperf. Value, pair $40.

Col. Juana Azurduy de Padilla (1781-1862), Soldier — A369

Famous Argentine Women: No. 833, Juana Manuela Gorriti, writer. No. 834, Cecilia Grierson (1858-1934), physician. No. 835, Juana Paula Manso (1819-75), writer and educator. No. 836, Alfonsina Storni (1892-1938), writer and educator.

1967, May 13   Photo.   Perf. 13½

832	A369	6p dark brown	.40	.25
833	A369	6p dark brown	.40	.25
834	A369	6p dark brown	.40	.25
835	A369	6p dark brown	.40	.25
836	A369	6p dark brown	.40	.25
		Nos. 832-836 (5)	2.00	1.25

Printed se-tenant in sheets of 100 (10x10); 2 horizontal rows of each portrait.

Schooner "Invencible," 1811 — A370

1967, May 20   Litho.
837 A370 20p multicolored   1.00 .35
Issued for Navy Day. Exists imperf. Value, pair $50.

Soldier Type of 1965

Army Day: 20p, Highlander (Arribeños Corps).

1967, May 27
838 A340a 20p multicolored   .65 .30
Exists imperf. Value, pair $50.

Souvenir Sheet

Manuel Belgrano and José Artigas — A371

1967, June 22   Imperf.

839	A371	Sheet of 2	.85	.55
a.		6p gray & brown	.25	.25
b.		22p brown & gray	.25	.25

Third Rio de la Plata Stamp Show, Montevideo, Uruguay, June 18-25.

Peace Dove and Valise — A372

1967, Aug. 5   Litho.   Perf. 13½
840 A372 20p multicolored   .35 .25
Issued for International Tourist Year 1967.

PADELAI Emblem — A373

1967, Aug. 12   Litho.
841 A373 20p multicolored   .30 .25
75th anniv. of the Children's Welfare Association (Patronato de la Infancia-PADELAI).

Stagecoach and Modern City — A374

1967, Sept. 23   Wmk. 90   Perf. 13½
842 A374 20p rose, yel & blk   .30 .25
Centenary of Villa Maria, Cordoba.

San Martin by Ibarra — A375

"Battle of Chacabuco" by P. Subercaseaux — A376

1967, Sept. 30   Litho.
843 A375 20p blk brn & pale yel   .50 .25

Engr.
844 A376 40p blue black   .80 .30
Battle of Chacabuco, 150th anniversary.

Exhibition Rooms — A377

1967, Oct. 11   Photo.
845 A377 20p blue gray   .30 .25
Government House Museum, 10th anniv.

Pedro L. Zanni, Fokker and 1924 Flight Route A378

1967, Oct. 21   Litho.   Perf. 13½
846 A378 20p multicolored   .35 .25
Issued for Aviation Week and to commemorate the 1924 flight of the Fokker seaplane "Province of Buenos Aires" from Amsterdam, Netherlands, to Osaka, Japan.

Training Ship General Brown, by Emilio Biggeri A379

1967, Oct. 28   Wmk. 90
847 A379 20p multicolored   1.00 .35
Issued to honor the Military Naval School.

Ovidio Lagos and Front Page — A380

1967, Nov. 11   Photo.
848 A380 20p sepia   .30 .25
Centenary of La Capital, Rosario newspaper. Imperf pair $40.

St. Barbara A381

1967, Dec. 2   Perf. 13½
849 A381 20p rose red   .35 .25
St. Barbara, patron saint of artillerymen.

Portrait of his Wife, by Eduardo Sivori — A382

1968, Jan. 27   Photo.   Perf. 13½
850 A382 20p blue green   .35 .25
Eduardo Sivori (1847-1918), painter.

Antarctic Type of 1966 and

Admiral Brown Scientific Station A383

Planes over Map of Antarctica — A384

6p, Map showing radio-postal stations 1966-67.

1968, Feb. 17   Litho.   Wmk. 90
851 A363 6p multicolored   .50   .25
852 A383 20p multicolored   .70   .25
853 A384 40p multicolored   1.20   .50
   Nos. 851-853 (3)   2.40 1.00

Issued to publicize Argentine research projects in Argentine Antarctica.

The Annunciation, by Leonardo da Vinci — A385

1968, Mar. 23   Photo.   Perf. 13½
854 A385 20p lilac rose   .30   .25

Issued for the Day of the Army Communications System and its patron saint, Gabriel. Exists imperf. Value, pair $40.

Man in Wheelchair and Factory — A386

1968, Mar. 23   Litho.
855 A386 20p green & black   .30   .25

Day of Rehabilitation of the Handicapped.

Children and WHO Emblem — A387

1968, May 11   Wmk. 90   Perf. 13½
856 A387 20p dk vio bl & ver   .30   .25

20th anniv. of WHO.

Soldier Type of 1965

Army Day: 20p, Uniform of First Artillery Regiment "General Iriarte."

1968, June 8   Litho.
857 A340a 20p multicolored   .75   .30

Frigate "Libertad," Painting by Emilio Biggeri — A388

1968, June 15   Wmk. 90
858 A388 20p multicolored   1.20   .30

Issued for Navy Day. Exists imperf. Value, pair $40.

Guillermo Rawson and Old Hospital A389

1968, July 20   Photo.   Perf. 13½
859 A389 6p olive bister   .35   .25

Cent. of Rawson Hospital, Buenos Aires.

Student Directing Traffic for Schoolmates A390

1968, Aug. 10   Litho.   Perf. 13½
860 A390 20p lt bl, blk, buff & car   .55   .25

Traffic safety and education.

O'Higgins Joining San Martin at Battle of Maipu, by P. Subercaseaux — A391

1968, Aug. 15   Engr.
861 A391 40p bluish black   .65   .30

Sesquicentennial of the Battle of Maipu.

Osvaldo Magnasco (1864-1920), Lawyer, Professor of Law and Minister of Justice — A392

1968, Sept. 7   Photo.   Perf. 13½
862 A392 20p brown   .40   .25

Grandmother's Birthday, by Patricia Lynch — A393

The Sea, by Edgardo Gomez — A394

1968, Sept. 21   Litho.
863 A393 20p multicolored   .30   .25
864 A394 20p multicolored   .30   .25

The designs were chosen in a competition among kindergarten and elementary school children.

Mar del Plata at Night A395

1968, Oct. 19   Litho.   Perf. 13½
865 A395 20p black, ocher & bl   .30   .25
   Nos. 865,C113-C114 (3)   2.30 1.05

4th Plenary Assembly of the Intl. Telegraph and Telephone Consultative Committee, Mar del Plata, Sept. 23-Oct. 25.

Frontier Gendarme A396

Patrol Boat A397

1968, Oct. 26
866 A396 20p multicolored   .30   .25
867 A397 20p blue, vio bl & blk   .30   .25

No. 866 honors the Gendarmery; No. 867 the Coast Guard.

Aaron de Anchorena and Pampero Balloon A398

1968, Nov. 2   Photo.
868 A398 20p blue & multi   .30   .25

22nd Aeronautics and Space Week.

St. Martin of Tours, by Alfredo Guido — A399

1968, Nov. 9   Litho.
869 A399 20p lilac & dk brn   .30   .25

St. Martin of Tours, patron saint of Buenos Aires.

Municipal Bank Emblem A400

1968, Nov. 16
870 A400 20p multicolored   .30   .25

Buenos Aires Municipal Bank, 90th anniv.

Anniversary Emblem A401

1968, Dec. 14   Wmk. 90   Perf. 13½
871 A401 20p car rose & dk grn   .30   .25

ALPI (Fight Against Polio Assoc.), 25th anniv.

Shovel and State Coal Fields Emblem — A402

Pouring Ladle and Army Manufacturing Emblem — A403

1968, Dec. 21   Litho.
872 A402 20p orange, bl & blk   .30   .25
873 A403 20p dl vio, dl yel & blk .30   .25

Issued to publicize the National Coal and Steel industry at the Rio Turbio coal fields and the Zapla blast furnaces.

Woman Potter, by Ramon Gomez Cornet — A404

1968, Dec. 21   Photo.   Perf. 13½
874 A404 20p carmine rose   .50   .40

Centenary of the Witcomb Gallery.

View of Buenos Aires and Rio de la Plata by Ulrico Schmidl A405

1969, Feb. 8   Litho.   Wmk. 90
875 A405 20p yellow, blk & ver   .50   .35

Ulrico Schmidl (c. 1462-1554) who wrote "Journey to the Rio de la Plata and Paraguay."

Types of 1955-67

Designs: 50c, Puma. 1p, Sunflower. 3p, Zapata Slope, Catamarca. 5p, Tierra del Fuego. 6p, José Hernandez. 10p, Inca Bridge, Mendoza. 50p, José de San Martin. 90p, Guillermo Brown. 100p, Ski jumper.

Photo.; Litho. (50c, 3p, 10p)
1969-70   Wmk. 365   Perf. 13½
882 A275 50c bister ('70)   1.00   .60
883 A277 5p brown   1.40   .90
884 A279 100p blue   26.00 8.00
Unwmk.
885 A278 1p brown ('70)   .40   .25
886 A277 3p dk blue ('70)   .65   .25
  a.   Wmk. 90   10.00 3.00
887 A277 5p brown ('70)   .75   .25
888 A366 6p red brn,
           15x22mm
           ('70)   .90   .25
889 A278 10p dull red ('70)   .50   .25
  a.   Wmk. 90   475.00 60.00
890 A241 50p dk bl,
           22x31½mm
           ('70)   1.25   .25
891 A366 90p ol brn,
           22x32mm
           ('70)   3.50   .50
892 A279 100p blue ('70)   11.00 1.00
   Nos. 882-892 (11)   47.35 12.50

For surcharges see Nos. 1076-1077.

Soldier Type of 1965

Army Day: 20p, Sapper (gastador) of Buenos Aires Province, 1856.

Wmk. 365
1969, May 31   Litho.   Perf. 13½
893 A340a 20p multicolored   .85   .35

Frigate Hercules, by Emilio Biggeri — A406

1969, May 31
894 A406 20p multicolored   1.50   .30

Issued for Navy Day.

"All Men are Equal" — A407

1969, June 28   **Wmk. 90**
895 A407 20p black & ocher   .30 .25
   International Human Rights Year.

ILO Emblem — A408

1969, June 28   **Litho.**   **Wmk. 365**
896 A408 20p lt green & multi   .30 .25
   50th anniv. of the ILO. Exists imperf. Value, pair $100.

Pedro N. Arata (1849-1922), Chemist — A409

   Portraits: No. 898, Miguel Fernandez (1883-1950), zoologist. No. 899, Angel P. Gallardo (1867-1934), biologist. No. 900, Cristobal M. Hicken (1875-1933), botanist. No. 901, Eduardo Ladislao Holmberg, M.D. (1852-1937), natural scientist.

1969, Aug. 9   **Wmk. 365**   **Perf. 13½**
897 A409 6p Arata   .45 .30
898 A409 6p Fernandez   .45 .30
899 A409 6p Gallardo   .45 .30
900 A409 6p Hicken   .45 .00
901 A409 6p Holmberg   .45 .30
     Nos. 897-901 (5)   2.25 1.50
   Argentine scientists. See No. 778 note.

Radar Antenna, Balcarce Station and Satellite — A410

1969, Aug. 23   **Wmk. 99**
902 A410 20p yellow & blk   .30 .25
   Communications by satellite through Intl. Telecommunications Satellite Consortium (INTELSAT). Exists imperf. Value, pair $40. See No. C115.

Nieuport 28, Flight Route and Map of Buenos Aires Province A411

1969, Sept. 13   **Litho.**   **Wmk. 90**
903 A411 20p multicolored   .30 .25
   50th anniv. of the first Argentine airmail service from El Palomar to Mar del Plata, flown Feb. 23-24, 1919, by Capt. Pedro L. Zanni.

Military College Gate and Emblem A412

1969, Oct. 4   **Wmk. 365**   **Perf. 13½**
904 A412 20p multicolored   .30 .25
   Cent. of the National Military College, El Palomar (Greater Buenos Aires).

Gen. Angel Pacheco — A413

1969, Nov. 8   **Photo.**   **Wmk. 365**
905 A413 20p deep green   .30 .25
   Gen. Angel Pacheco (1795-1869).

La Farola, Logotype of La Prensa — A414

   Design: No. 907, Bartolomé Mitre & La Nacion logotype.

1969, Nov. 8   **Litho.**   **Perf. 13½**
906 A414 20p orange, yel & blk   .70 .30
907 A414 20p brt green & blk   .70 .30
   Cent. of newspapers La Prensa and La Nacion.

Julian Aguirre — A415

   Musicians: No. 909, Felipe Boero. No. 910, Constantino Gaito. No. 911, Carlos Lopez Buchardo. No. 912, Alberto Williams.

Wmk. 365
1969, Dec. 6   **Photo.**   **Perf. 13½**
908 A415 6p Aguirre   .65 .30
909 A415 6p Boero   .65 .30
910 A415 6p Gaito   .65 .30
911 A415 6p Buchardo   .65 .30
912 A415 6p Williams   .65 .30
     Nos. 908-912 (5)   3.25 1.50
   Argentine musicians. See No. 778 note.

Lt. Benjamin Matienzo and Nieuport Plane — A416

1969, Dec. 13   **Litho.**
913 A416 20p multicolored   .50 .35
   23rd Aeronautics and Space Week.

High Power Lines and Map A417

   Design: 20p, Map of Santa Fe Province and schematic view of tunnel.

1969, Dec. 13
914 A417 6p multicolored   .50 .25
915 A417 20p multicolored   1.00 .25
   Completion of development projects: 6p for the hydroelectric dams on the Limay and Neuquen Rivers, the 20p the tunnel under Rio Grande from Sante Fe to Parana. Set exists imperf.©

Lions Emblem A418

1969, Dec. 20   **Wmk. 365**   **Perf. 13½**
916 A418 20p black, emer & org   .70 .25
   Argentine Lions Intl. Club, 50th anniv.

Madonna and Child, by Raul Soldi — A419

1969, Dec. 27   **Litho.**
917 A419 20p multicolored   .65 .30
   Christmas 1969.

Manuel Belgrano, by Jean Gericault A420

The Creation of the Flag, Bas-relief by Jose Fioravanti — A421

Perf. 13½
1970, July 4   **Unwmk.**   **Photo.**
918 A420 20c deep brown   .40 .25

   Litho.   **Perf. 12½**
919 A421 50c bister, blk & bl   .75 .50
   Gen. Manuel Belgrano (1770-1820), Argentine patriot.

San Jose Palace A422

1970, Aug. 9   **Litho.**   **Perf. 13½**
920 A422 20c yellow grn & multi   .30 .25
   Gen. Justo Jose de Urquiza (1801-70), pres. of Argentina, 1854-60.

Schooner "Juliet" — A423

1970, Aug. 8   **Unwmk.**
921 A423 20c multicolored   1.10 .40
   Issued for Navy Day.

Receiver of 1920 and Waves A424

1970, Aug. 29
922 A424 20c lt blue & multi   .45 .30
   50th anniv. of Argentine broadcasting.

Types of 1955-67 Inscribed "Republica Argentina" and

Belgrano A425   Lujan Basilica A426

   Designs: 1c, Sunflower. 3c, Zapata Slope, Catamarca. 5c, Tierra del Fuego. 8c, No. 931, Belgrano. 10c, Inca Bridge, Mendoza. 25c, 50c, 70c, Jose de San Martin. 65c, 90c, 1.20p, San Martin. 1p, Ski jumper. 1.15p, 1.80p, Adm. Brown.

1970-73   **Photo.**   **Unwmk.**   **Perf. 13½**
923 A278 1c dk green ('71)   .25 .25
924 A277 3c car rose ('71)   .25 .25
925 A277 5c blue ('71)   .25 .25
926 A425 6c deep blue   .25 .25
927 A425 8c green ('72)   .25 .25
928 A278 10c dull red ('71)   .30 .25
929 A278 10c brn, litho. ('71)   .60 .25
930 A278 10c org brn ('72)   .25 .25
931 A425 10c brown ('73)   .25 .25
932 A426 18c yel & dk brn, litho ('73)   .25 .25
933 A425 25c brown ('71)   .35 .25
934 A425 50c scarlet ('72)   .90 .25
935 A241 65c brn, 22x31½mm, paper II ('71)   .85 .25
936 A425 70c dk blue ('73)   .25 .25
937 A241 90c emer, 22x31½mm ('72)   2.25 .25

938 A279 1p brn,
22½x29½mm
('71) 4.00 .25
939 A366 1.15p dk bl,
22½x32mm
('71) .85 .25
940 A241 1.20p org,
22x31½mm
('73) .90 .25
941 A366 1.80p brown ('73) .30 .25
Nos. 923-941 (19) 13.55 4.75

The imprint "Casa de Moneda de la Nacion" (in capitals) appears on 3c, 5c, Nos. 928-929; 65c, 90c, 1p, 1.20p.

On type A425 only the 6c is inscribed "Ley 18.188" below denomination.

Fluorescent paper was used in printing the 25c, 50c, and 70c. The 3c, 5c, 8c, No. 931 and 65c were issued on both ordinary and fluorescent paper.

See Nos. 987-996, 1032-1038, 1042-1043, 1089-1107. For overprint and surcharge see Nos. 1010, 1078.

Soldier Type of 1965

Galloping messenger of Field Army, 1879.

1970, Oct. 17 Litho. *Perf. 13½*
944 A340a 20c multicolored .85 .30

Dome of Cathedral of Cordoba A430

1970, Nov. 7 Unwmk.
945 A430 50c gray & blk .80 .25

Bishopric of Tucuman, 400th anniv. See No. C131.

People Around UN Emblem A431

1970, Nov. 7
946 A431 20c tan & multi .30 .25

25th anniversary of the United Nations.

State Mint and Medal A432

1970, Nov. 28 Unwmk. *Perf. 13½*
947 A432 20c gold, grn & blk .30 .25

Inauguration of the State Mint Building, 25th anniversary.

St. John Bosco and Dean Funes College A433

1970, Dec. 19 Litho.
948 A433 20c olive & blk .30 .25

Honoring the work of the Salesian Order in Patagonia.

Nativity, by Horacio Gramajo Gutierrez — A434

1970, Dec. 19
949 A434 20c multicolored .55 .35

Christmas 1970.

Argentine Flag, Map of Argentine Antarctica A435

1971, Feb. 20 Litho. *Perf. 13½*
950 A435 20c multicolored 1.25 .25

Argentine South Pole Expedition, 5th anniv.

Phosphorescent Sorting Code and Albert Einstein — A436

1971, Apr. 30 Unwmk. *Perf. 13½*
951 A436 25c multicolored .45 .30

Electronics in postal development.

Symbolic Road Crossing A437

1971, May 29 Litho.
952 A437 25c blue & blk .25 .25

Inter-American Regional Meeting of the Intl. Federation of Roads, Buenos Aires, 3/28-31.

Elias Alippi — A438

Actors: No. 954, Juan Aurelio Casacuberta. No. 955, Angelina Pagano. No. 956, Roberto Casaux. No. 957, Florencio Parravicini. See No. 778 note.

1971, May 29 Litho.
953 A438 15c Alippi .30 .25
954 A438 15c Casacuberta .30 .25
955 A438 15c Pagano .30 .30
956 A438 15c Casaux .30 .25
957 A438 15c Parravicini .30 .25
Nos. 953-957 (5) 1.50 1.30

Soldier Type of 1965

Army Day, May 29: Artilleryman, 1826.

1971, July 3 Unwmk. *Perf. 13½*
958 A340a 25c multicolored 1.25 .25

Bilander "Carmen," by Emilio Biggeri — A439

1971, July 3
959 A439 25c multicolored 1.25 .25

Navy Day

Peruvian Order of the Sun A440

1971, Aug. 28
960 A440 31c multicolored .60 .25

Sesquicentennial of Peru's independence.

Güemes in Battle, by Lorenzo Gigli A441

Design: No. 962, Death of Güemes, by Antonio Alice.

1971, Aug. 28 Size: 39x29mm
961 A441 25c multicolored .50 .25
Size: 84x29mm
962 A441 25c multicolored .50 .25

Sesquicentennial of the death of Martin Miguel de Güemes, leader in Gaucho War, Governor and Captain General of Salta Province.

Stylized Tulip — A442

1971, Sept. 18
963 A442 25c tan & multi .35 .25

3rd Intl. and 8th Natl. Horticultural Exhib.

Father Antonio Saenz, by Juan Gut — A443

1971, Sept. 18
964 A433 25c gray & multi .35 .25

Sesquicentennial of University of Buenos Aires, and to honor Father Antonio Saenz, first Chancellor and Rector.

Fabricaciones Militares Emblem — A444

1971, Oct. 16 Unwmk. *Perf. 13½*
965 A444 25c brn, gold, bl & blk .25 .25

30th anniv. of military armament works.

Cars and Trucks A445

Design: 65c, Tree converted into paper.

1971, Oct. 16
966 A445 25c dull bl & multi .50 .25
967 A445 65c green & multi 1.25 .30
Nos. 966-967,C134 (3) 2.55 .85

Nationalized industries.

Luis C. Candelaria and his Plane, 1918 — A446

1971, Nov. 27
968 A446 25c multicolored .35 .25

25th Aeronautics and Space Week.

Observatory and Nebula of Magellan — A447

1971, Nov. 27
969 A447 25c multicolored .65 .25

Cordoba Astronomical Observatory, cent.

Christ in Majesty A448

1971, Dec. 18 Litho.
970 A448 25c blk & multi .30 .25

Christmas 1971. Design is from a tapestry by Horacio Butler in Basilica of St. Francis, Buenos Aires.

Mother and
Child, by J. C.
Castagnino
A449

1972, May 6　　Unwmk.　　Perf. 13½
971　A449　25c fawn & black　　　.40　.25
　25th anniv. (in 1971) of UNICEF.

Mailman's Bag — A450

1972, Sept. 2　　Litho.　　Perf. 13½
972　A450　25c lemon & multi　　.30　.25
　Bicentenary of appointment of first Argentine mailman.

Adm. Brown Station, Map of
Antarctica — A451

1972, Sept. 2
973　A451　25c blue & multi　　　.65　.30
　10th anniv. (in 1971) of Antarctic Treaty.

Soldier Type of 1965

Army Day: 25c, Sergeant, Negro and
Mulatto Corps, 1806-1807.

1972, Sept. 23
974　A340a　25c multicolored　　.65　.35

Brigantine "Santisima
Trinidad" — A452

1972, Sept. 23
975　A452　25c multicolored　　　.90　.35
　Navy Day. See No. 1006.

Oil
Pump — A453

1972, Sept. 30　　Litho.　　Perf. 13½
976　A453　45c multicolored　　　.75　.25
　50th anniv. of the organ. of the state oil
fields (Yacimientos Petroliferos Fiscales).

Sounding
Balloon — A454

1972, Sept. 30
977　A454　25c multicolored　　　.25　.25
　Cent. of Natl. Meteorological Service.

Trees and Globe — A455

1972, Oct. 14　　　　Perf. 13x13½
978　A455　25c bl, blk & lt bl　　.60　.25
　7th World Forestry Congress, Buenos Aires,
Oct. 4-18.

Arms of Naval School, Frigate
"Presidente Sarmiento" — A456

1972, Oct. 14
979　A456　25c gold & multi　　　.70　.25
　Centenary of Military Naval School.

Early Balloon
and Plane,
Antonio de
Marchi — A457

1972, Nov. 4　　　　　Perf. 13½
980　A457　25c multicolored　　　.45　.30
　Aeronautics and Space Week, and in honor
of Baron Antonio de Marchi (1875-1934), aviation pioneer.

Bartolomé
Mitre — A458

1972, Nov. 4　　　　　　Engr.
981　A458　25c dark blue　　　.45　.30
　Pres. Bartolome Mitre (1821-1906), writer,
historian, soldier.

Flower and
Heart — A459

1972, Dec. 2　　Litho.　　Perf. 13½
982　A459　90c lt bl, ultra & blk　.50　.30
　"Your heart is your health," World Health
Day.

"Martin Fierro,"
by Juan C.
Castagnino
A460

"Spirit of the
Gaucho," by
Vicente
Forte — A461

1972, Dec. 2　　Litho.　　Perf. 13½
983　A460　50c multicolored　　　.30　.25
984　A461　90c multicolored　　　.45　.30
　Intl. Book Year 1972, and cent. of publication of the poem, Martin Fierro, by Jose Hernandez (1834-86).

Iguacu Falls and Tourist Year
Emblem — A462

1972, Dec. 16　　　　Perf. 13x13½
985　A462　45c multicolored　　　.30　.25
　Tourism Year of the Americas.

King, Wood
Carving, 18th
Century
A463

1972, Dec. 16　　　　　Perf. 13½
986　A463　50c multicolored　　　.45　.25
　Christmas 1972.

Types of 1955-73 Inscribed
"Republica Argentina" and

Moon Valley,
San Juan
Province —
A463a

Designs: 1c, Sunflower. 5c, Tierra del
Fuego. 10c, Inca Bridge, Mendoza. 50c, Lujan
Basilica. 65c, 22.50p, San Martin. 1p, Ski
jumper. 1.15p, 4.50p, Guillermo Brown. 1.80p,
Manuel Belgrano.

Litho.; Photo. (1c, 65c, 1p)
Perf. 13½, 12½ (1.80p)

1972-75			Wmk. 365	
987	A278	1c dk green	.25	.25
988	A277	5c dark blue	.25	.25
989	A278	10c bister brn	.30	.25
989A	A426	50c dull pur ('75)	.25	.25
990	A241	65c gray brown	3.25	.25
991	A279	1p brown	4.00	.25
992	A366	1.15p dk gray bl	1.50	.45
993	A425	1.80p blue ('75)	.30	.25
994	A366	4.50p green ('75)	.45	.25
995	A241	22.50p vio bl ('75)	1.50	.30
996	A463a	50p multi ('75)	1.40	.25
	Nos. 987-996 (11)		13.45	3.00

Paper size of 1c is 27½x39mm; others of
1972, 37x27, 27x37mm.
Size of 22.50p, 50p: 26½x38½mm.
See Nos. 1050, 1108.

Cock (Symbolic
of
Police) — A464

1973, Feb. 3　　Litho.　　Unwmk.
997　A464　50c lt green & multi　.30　.25
　Sesqui. of Federal Police of Argentina.

First Coin of Bank
of Buenos
Aires — A465

1973, Feb. 3　　　　　Perf. 13½
998　A465　50c purple, yel & brn　.25　.25
　Sesquicentennial of the Bank of Buenos
Aires Province.

DC-3 Planes Over Antarctica — A466

1973, Apr. 28　　Litho.　　Perf. 13½
999　A466　50c lt blue & multi　　1.40　.50
　10th anniversary of Argentina's first flight to
the South Pole.

Rivadavia's Chair, Argentine Arms and Colors — A467

1973, May 19   Litho.   Perf. 13½
1000 A467 50c multicolored   .25   .25
Inauguration of Pres. Hector J. Campora, May 25, 1973.

San Martin, by Gil de Castro — A468

San Martin and Bolivar A469

1973, July 7   Litho.   Perf. 13½
1001 A468 50c lt green & multi   .35   .25
1002 A469 50c yellow & multi   .35   .25
Gen. San Martin's farewell to the people of Peru and his meeting with Simon Bolivar at Guayaquil July 26-27, 1822.

Eva Peron A470

1973, July 26   Litho.   Perf. 13½
1003 A470 70c black, org & bl   .30   .25
Maria Eva Duarte de Peron (1919-1952), political leader.

House of Viceroy Sobremonte, by Hortensia de Virgilion — A471

1973, July 28   Perf. 13x13½
1004 A471 50c blue & multi   .35   .25
400th anniversary of the city of Cordoba.

Woman, by Lino Spilimbergo A472

1973, Aug. 28   Litho.   Perf. 13½
1005 A472 70c multicolored   .70   .25
Philatelists' Day. See Nos. B60-B61.

Ship Type of 1972
Navy Day: 70c, Frigate "La Argentina."

1973, Oct. 27   Litho.   Perf. 13½
1006 A452 70c multicolored   .55   .25

New and Old Telephones — A473

1973, Oct. 27
1007 A473 70c brt blue & multi   .35   .25
Natl. telecommunications system, 25th anniv.

Plume Made of Flags of Participants A474

1973, Nov. 3   Perf. 13½
1008 A474 70c yellow bis & multi   .30   .25
12th Cong. of Latin Notaries, Buenos Aires.

No. 940 Overprinted

1973, Nov. 30   Photo.
1010 A241 1.20p orange   .85   .30
Assumption of presidency by Juan Peron, Oct. 12.

Virgin and Child, Window, La Plata Cathedral A476

Christmas: 1.20p, Nativity, by Bruno Venier, b. 1914.

1973, Dec. 15   Litho.   Perf. 13½
1011 A476   70c gray & multi   .35   .25
1012 A476 1.20p black & multi   .65   .35

The Lama, by Juan Battle Planas — A477

Paintings: 50c, Houses in Boca District, by Eugenio Daneri, horiz. 90c, The Blue Grotto, by Emilio Pettoruti, horiz.

1974, Feb. 9   Litho.   Perf. 13½
1013 A477 50c multicolored   .45   .25
1014 A477 70c multicolored   .45   .25
1015 A477 90c multicolored   .45   .30
Nos. 1013-1015,B64 (4)   1.70 1.05
Argentine painters.

Mar del Plata A478

1974, Feb. 9
1016 A478 70c multicolored   .35   .25
Centenary of Mar del Plata.

Weather Symbols — A479

1974, Mar. 23   Litho.   Perf. 13½
1017 A479 1.20p multicolored   .30   .25
Cent. of intl. meteorological cooperation.

Justo Santa Maria de Oro — A480

1974, Mar. 23
1018 A480 70c multicolored   .30   .25
Bicentenary of the birth of Brother Justo Santa Maria de Oro (1772-1836), theologian, patriot, first Argentine bishop.

Belisario Roldan (1873-1922), Writer — A481

1974, June 29   Photo.   Unwmk.
1019 A481 70c bl & brn   .30   .25

Poster with Names of OAS Members — A482

1974, June 29   Litho.
1020 A482 1.38p multicolored   .30   .25
Organization of American States, 25th anniv.

ENCOTEL Emblem — A483

1974, Aug. 10   Litho.   Perf. 13
1021 A483 1.20p blue, gold & blk   .45   .25
ENCOTEL, Natl. Post and Telegraph Press.

Flags of Argentina, Bolivia, Brazil, Paraguay, Uruguay A484

1974, Aug. 16   Perf. 13½
1022 A484 1.38p multicolored   .30   .25
6th Meeting of Foreign Ministers of Rio de la Plata Basin Countries.

El Chocon Hydroelectric Complex, Limay River — A485

Somisa Steel Mill, San Nicolas A486

Gen. Belgrano Bridge, Chaco-Corrientes — A487

Perf. 13½, 13x13½ (4.50p)
1974, Sept. 14
1023 A485 70c multicolored   .35   .25
1024 A486 1.20p multicolored   .60   .30
1025 A487 4.50p multicolored   1.75   .45
Nos. 1023-1025 (3)   2.70 1.00
Development projects.

Brigantine Belgrano, by Emilio Biggeri — A488

1974, Oct. 26   Litho.   *Perf. 13½*
1026 A488 1.20p multicolored   1.00   .30
Departure into exile in Chile of General San Martin, Sept. 22, 1822.

Alberto R. Mascias and Bleriot Plane — A489

1974, Oct. 26   Unwmk.
1027 A489 1.20p multicolored   .55   .25
  a.   Wmk 365
Air Force Day, Aug. 10, and to honor Alberto Roque Garcias (1878-1951), aviation pioneer.

Hussar, 1812, by Eleodoro Marenco A490

1974, Oct. 20
1028 A490 1.20p multicolored   .55   .25
Army Day.

Post Horn and Flags A491

1974, Nov. 23   Unwmk.   *Perf. 13½*
1029 A491 2.65p multicolored   .75   .25
  a.   Wmk 365   45.00 22.50
Centenary of Universal Postal Union.

Franciscan Monastery — A492

1974, Nov. 23   Litho.
1030 A492 1.20p multicolored   .35   .25
400th anniversary, city of Santa Fe.

Trout Type of 1968

1974   Engr.   Unwmk.
1031 A366a 1000p vio bl   1.40   .25
Due to a shortage of 10p stamps a quantity of this 1,000p was released for use as 10p.

Types of 1954-73 Inscribed "Republica Argentina" and

Red Deer in Forest — A495

Congress Building — A497

Designs: 30c, 60c, 1.80p, Manuel Belgrano. 50c, Lujan Basilica. 1.20p, 2p, 6p, San Martin (16x22½mm). 2.70p, 7.50p, 22.50p, San Martin (22x31½mm). 4.50p, 13.50p, Guillermo Brown. 10p, Leaping trout.

1974-76 Unwmk. Photo.   *Perf. 13½*
1032	A425	30c brown vio	.30	.25
1033	A426	50c blk & brn red	.30	.25
1034	A426	50c bister & bl	.25	.25
1035	A425	60c ocher	.30	.25
1036	A425	1.20p red	.30	.25
1037	A425	1.80p deep blue	.30	.25
1038	A425	2p dark purple	.40	.30
1039	A241	2.70p dk bl, 22x31½mm	.30	.25
1040	A366	4.50p green	1.50	
1041	A495	5p yel green	.40	.25
1042	A425	6p red orange	.30	.25
1043	A425	6p emerald	.30	.25
1044	A241	7.50p grn, 22x31½mm	.90	.25
1045	A366a	10p violet blue	2.00	.25
1046	A366	13.50p scar, 16x22½mm	.45	.25
1047	A366	13.50p scar, 22x31½mm	.90	.35
1048	A241	22.50p dp bl, 22x31½mm	.90	.45
1049	A497	30p yel & dk red brn	3.50	.25
1050	A463a	50p multicolored	1.40	.25
		Nos. 1032-1050 (19)	15.00	5.10

Issued: 10p, 5/74; 30c, 1.20p, 2.70p, 5/15/74; 5p, 11/20/74; 30p, 12/10/74; 2p, 3/1/75; 60c, 7.50p, 4/30/75; 4.50p, 7/21/75; 1.80p, Nos. 1042, 1047, 22.50p, 8/14/75; No. 1046, 10/10/75; No. 1034, 10/30/75; No. 1043, 11/6/75; 50p, 2/76.

Fluorescent paper was used in printing No. 1036, 2p, Nos. 1044 and 1047. The 30p was issued on both ordinary and fluorescent paper.

See No. 829. For type of A495 overprinted see No. 1144.

Miniature Sheet

A498

1974, Dec. 7   Litho.   *Perf. 13½*
1052 A498 Sheet of 6   3.00   3.00
  a. 1p Mariano Necochea   .35   .25
  b. 1.20p Jose de San Martin   .35   .25
  c. 1.70p Manuel Isidoro Suarez .35   .25
  d. 1.90p Juan Pascual Pringles .35   .25
  e. 2.70p Latin American flags .35   .25
  f. 4.50p Jose Felix Bogado   .35   .25
Sesqui. of Battles of Junin and Ayacucho.

Dove, by Vito Campanella — A499

St. Anne, by Raul Soldi — A500

1974, Dec. 21   Litho.   *Perf. 13½*
1053 A499 1.20p multicolored   .65   .25
1054 A500 2.65p multicolored   .65   .30
Christmas 1974.

Boy Looking at Stamp — A501

1974, Dec. 21
1055 A501 1.70p black & yel   .35   .25
World Youth Philately Year.

Space Monsters, by Raquel Forner — A502

Argentine modern art: 4.50p, Dream, by Emilio Centurion.

1975, Feb. 22   Litho.   *Perf. 13½*
1056 A502 2.70p multi   .85   .25
1057 A502 4.50p multi   1.60 .35

Indian Woman and Cathedral, Catamarca — A503

Tourist Publicity: No. 1059, Carved chancel and street scene. No. 1060, Logging operations and monastery yard. No. 1061, Painted pottery and power station. No. 1062, Farm cart and colonial mansion. No. 1063, Perito Moreno glacier and spinning mill. No. 1064, Lake Lapataia and scientific surveyor. No. 1065, Los Alerces National Park and oil derrick.

1975   Litho.   *Perf. 13½*
Unwmk., Wmk 365 (6p)
1058	A503	1.20p shown	.30	.25
1059	A503	1.20p Jujuy	.30	.25
1060	A503	1.20p Salta	.30	.25
1061	A503	1.20p Santiago del Estero	.30	.25
1062	A503	1.20p Tucuman	.30	.25
1063	A503	6p Santa Cruz	.55	.25

1064	A503	6p Tierra del Fuego	.55	.25
1065	A503	6p Chubut	.55	.25
		Nos. 1058-1065 (8)	3.15	2.00

Issue dates: 1.20p, Mar. 8; 6p, Dec. 20.

"We Have Been Inoculated" A504

1975, Apr. 26   Unwmk.   *Perf. 13½*
1066 A504 2p multi   .45   .25
Children's inoculation campaign (child's painting).

Hugo A. Acuña and South Orkney Station — A505

Designs: No. 1068, Francisco P. Moreno and Lake Nahuel Huapi. No. 1069, Lt. Col. Luis Piedra Buena and cutter, Luisito. No. 1070, Ensign José M. Sobral and Snow Hill House. No. 1071, Capt. Carlos M. Moyano and Cerro del Toro (mountain).

1975, June 28   Litho.   *Perf. 13*
1067	A505	2p grnsh bl & multi	.30	.25
1068	A505	2p yel grn & multi	.30	.25
1069	A505	2p lt vio & multi	.30	.25
1070	A505	2p gray bl & multi	.30	.25
1071	A505	2p pale grn & multi	.30	.25
		Nos. 1067-1071 (5)	1.50	1.25

Pioneers of Antarctica.

Frigate "25 de Mayo" A506

1975, Sept. 27   Unwmk.   *Perf. 13½*
1072 A506 6p multi   .85   .25
Navy Day 1975.

Eduardo Bradley and Balloon A507

1975, Sept. 27   Wmk. 365
1073 A507 6p multi   .45   .25
Air Force Day.

Declaration of Independence, by Juan M. Blanes — A508

1975, Oct. 25
1074 A508 6p multi .70 .25
Sesquicentennial of Uruguay's declaration of independence.

Flame A509

1975, Oct. 17 Unwmk.
1075 A509 6p gray & multi .35 .25
Loyalty Day, 30th anniversary of Pres. Peron's accession to power.

No. 886 Surcharged

No. 891 Surcharged

No. 932 Surcharged

1975 Lithographed, Photogravure
1076 A277 6c on 3p .25 .25
a. On #886a 50.00
1077 A366 30c on 90p .30 .25
1078 A426 5p on 18c .35 .25
Nos. 1076-1078 (3) .90 .75
Issued: 6c, 10/30; 30c, 11/20; 5p, 10/24.

A510

Design: International Bridge, flags of Argentina & Uruguay.

1975, Oct. 25 Litho. Wmk. 365
1081 A510 6p multi .35 .25

Post Horn, Surcharged A511

1975, Nov. 8
1082 A511 10p on 20c multi .50 .25
Introduction of postal code. Not issued without surcharge.

Nurse Holding Infant A512

1975, Dec. 13 Litho. Perf. 13½
1083 A512 6p multi .70 .25
Children's Hospital, centenary.

Nativity, Nueva Pompeya Church — A513

1975, Dec. 13 Litho. Unwmk.
1084 A513 6p multicolored .45 .25
Christmas 1975.

Types of 1970-75 and

Church of St. Francis, Salta — A515

Designs: 3p, No. 1099, 60p, 90p, Manuel Belgrano. 12p, 15p, 20p, 30p, No. 1100, 100p, 110p, 120p, 130p, San Martin. 15p, 70p, Guillermo Brown. 300p, Moon Valley (lower inscriptions italic). 500p, Adm. Brown Station, Antarctica.

1976-78 Photo. Unwmk. Perf. 13½
1089 A425 3p slate .30 .25
1090 A425 12p rose red .25 .25

Perf. 12½x13
Litho. Wmk. 365
1091 A425 12p rose red .35 .25
1092 A425 12p emerald .35 .25

Perf. 13½
Photo. Unwmk.
1093 A425 12p emer ('77) .35 .25
1094 A425 15p rose red .30 .25
1095 A425 15p vio bl ('77) .35 .25
1097 A425 20p rose red ('77) .35 .25
1098 A425 30p rose red ('77) .35 .25
1099 A425 40p dp grn 1.00 .25
1100 A425 40p rose red ('77) .35 .25
1101 A425 60p dk bl ('77) 1.50 .25
1102 A425 70p dk bl ('77) 1.50 .30
1103 A425 90p emer ('77) .75 .25
1104 A425 100p red 1.00 .25
1105 A425 110p rose red ('78) .35 .25
1106 A425 120p rose red ('78) .35 .25
1107 A425 130p rose red ('78) .50 .25

Litho.
1108 A463a 300p multi 3.00 .30
a. Wmk 365 17.50 5.00
1109 A515 500p multi ('77) 5.00 .30
a. Wmk 365 120.00 14.00
1110 A515 1000p multi ('77) 4.00 8.00
Nos. 1089-1110 (21) 22.25 13.15

Fluorescent paper was used in printing both 12p rose red, 15p rose red, 20p, 30p, 40p rose red, 100p, 110p, 120p, 130p.
No. 1099 and the 300p were issued on both ordinary and fluorescent paper.
Nos. 1108 and 1109 exist imperf. Values, pairs: No. 1108 $250; No. 1109 $120.
See Nos. B73-B74.

A516

1976 Photo. Unwmk. Perf. 13½
1112 A516 12c gray & blk .25 .25
1113 A516 50c gray & grn .25 .25
1114 A516 1p red & blk .25 .25
1115 A516 4p bl & blk .25 .25
1116 A516 5p org & blk .30 .25
1117 A516 6p dp brn & blk .25 .25
1118 A516 10p gray & vio bl .50 .25
1119 A516 27p lt grn & blk .35 .25
1120 A516 30p lt bl & blk 1.75 .25
1121 A516 45p yel & blk 1.00 .25
1122 A516 50p dl grn & blk 1.00 .25
1123 A516 100p brt grn & red 1.00 .25

Perf. 13x12½
1976 Litho. Wmk. 365
1124 A516 5p org & blk .30 .25
1125 A516 27p lt grn & blk .75 .25
1126 A516 45p yel & blk 1.00 .25
Nos. 1112-1126 (15) 9.25 3.75
The 1p, 6p, 10p, 50p and No. 1116 were issued on both ordinary and fluorescent paper.

Jet and Airlines Emblem — A517

Perf. 13x13½
1976, Apr. 24 Litho. Unwmk.
1130 A517 30p bl, lt bl & dk bl 1.10 .25
Argentine Airlines, 25th anniversary.

Frigate Heroina & Map of Falkland Islands — A518

1976, Apr. 26
1131 A518 6p multi 3.00 .40
Argentina's claim to Falkland Islands.

Louis Braille — A519

Wmk. 365
1976, May 22 Engr. Perf. 13½
1132 A519 19.70 deep blue .30 .25
Sesquicentennial of the invention of the Braille system of writing for the blind by Louis Braille (1809-1852).

Private, 7th Infantry Regiment A520

1976, May 29 Litho. Unwmk.
1133 A520 12p multi .45 .25
Army Day.

Schooner Rio de la Plata, by Emilio Biggeri — A521

1976, June 19
1134 A521 12p multi .45 .25
Navy Day.

Dr. Bernardo Houssay — A522

Argentine Nobel Prize Winners: 10p, Bernardo Houssay, medicine and physiology, 1947. 15p, Luis F. Leloir, chemistry, 1970. 20p, Carlos Saavedra Lamas, peace, 1936.

1976, Aug. 14 Litho. Perf. 13½
1135 A522 10p org & blk .30 .25
1136 A522 15p yel & blk .30 .25
1137 A522 20p ocher & blk .30 .25
Nos. 1135-1137 (3) .90 .75

Rio de la Plata International Bridge — A523

1976, Sept. 18 Litho. Perf. 13½
1138 A523 12p multi .70 .25
Inauguration of International Bridge connecting Puerto Unzue, Argentina, and Fray Bentos, Uruguay.

Pipelines & Cooling Tower, Gen. Mosconi Plant A524

1976, Nov. 20 Litho. Perf. 13½
1139 A524 28p multi .45 .25

Pablo Teodoro Fels & Bleriot Monoplane, 1910 — A525

1976, Nov. 20
1140 A525 15p multi .35 .25
Air Force Day.

Nativity
A526

1976, Dec. 18   Litho.   Perf. 13½
1141 A526 20p multi   .65 .30

Christmas. Painting by Edith Chiapetto.

Water Conference
Emblem — A527

1977, Mar. 19   Litho.   Perf. 13½
1142 A527 70p multi   .65 .25

UN Water Conf., Mar del Plata, Mar. 14-25.

Dalmacio Velez Sarsfield — A528

1977, Mar. 19   Engr.
1143 A528 50p blk & red brn   .70 .30

Dalmacio Velez Sarsfield (1800-1875), author of Argentine civil code.

Red Deer Type
of 1974
Surcharged

1977, July 30   Photo.   Perf. 13½
1144 A495 100p on 5p brn   1.40 .30

Sesquicentennial of Uruguayan postal service. Not issued without surcharge.

Soldier, 16th
Lancers
A529

1977, July 30
1145 A529 30p multi   .85 .25

Army Day.

Schooner Sarandi, by Emilio
Biggeri — A530

1977, July 30
1146 A530 30p multi   .85 .25

Navy Day.

Soccer Games'
Emblem
A531

70p, Argentina '78 emblem, flags & soccer field.

1977, May 14
1147 A531 30p multi   .45 .25
1148 A531 70p multi   .75 .25

11th World Cup Soccer Championship, Argentina, June 1-25, 1978.

The
Visit, by
Horacio
Butler
A532

Consecration,
by Miguel P.
Caride — A533

1977, Mar. 26   Litho.
1149 A532 50p multi   .50 .25
1150 A533 70p multi   .75 .30

Argentine artists.

Sierra de la Ventana — A534

Views: No. 1152, Civic Center, Santa Rosa. No. 1153, Skiers, San Martin de los Andes. No. 1154, Boat on Lake Fonck, Rio Negro.

1977, Oct. 8   Litho.   Perf. 13x13½
1151 A534 30p multi   .35 .25
1152 A534 30p multi   .35 .25
1153 A534 30p multi   .35 .25
1154 A534 30p multi   .35 .25
     Nos. 1151-1154 (4)   1.40 1.00

Guillermo
Brown, by R.
del
Villar — A535

1977, Oct. 8   Perf. 13½
1155 A535 30p multi   .35 .25

Adm. Guillermo Brown (1777-1857), leader in fight for independence, bicentenary of birth.

Jet
A536

Double-decker, 1926 — A537

1977   Litho.   Perf. 13½
1156 A536 30p multi   .25 .25
1157 A537 40p multi   .30 .25

50th anniversary of military plane production (30p); Air Force Day (40p).
Issue dates: 30p, Dec. 3; 40p, Nov. 26.

Adoration of
the
Kings — A538

1977, Dec. 17
1158 A538 100p multi   .90 .25

Christmas 1977.

Historic City Hall,
Buenos
Aires — A539

Chapel of
Rio Grande
Museum,
Tierra del
Fuego
A540

5p, 20p, La Plata Museum. 10p, Independence Hall, Tucuman. 40p, City Hall, Salta. No. 1165, City Hall, Buenos Aires. 100p, Columbus Theater, Buenos Aires. 200p, flag Monument, Rosario. 280p, 300p, Chapel of Rio Grande Museum, Tierra del Fuego. 480p, 520p, 800, Ruins of Jesuit Mission Church of San Ignacio, Misiones. 500p, Candonga Chapel, Cordoba. 1000p, G.P.O., Buenos Aires. 2000p, Civic Center, Bariloche, Rio Negro.

Three types of 10p: I. Nine vertical window bars; small imprint "E. MILIAVACA Dib." II. Nine bars; large imprint "E. MILIAVACA DIB." III. Redrawn; 5 bars; large imprint.

1977-81   Photo.   Unwmk.   Perf. 13½
Size: 32x21mm, 21x32mm
1159 A540 5p gray & blk   .25 .25
1160 A540 10p lt ultra &
            blk, I   .25 .25
 a.   Type II   .30 .25
1161 A540 10p lt bl & blk,
            III   .25 .25
1162 A540 20p citron &
            blk, litho.   .25 .25
1163 A539 40p gray bl &
            blk   .30 .25
1164 A539 50p yel & blk   .35 .25
1165 A540 50p citron & blk   .50 .25
1166 A540 100p org & blk,
            litho.   .30 .25
 a.   Wmk. 365   100.00 18.00
1167 A540 100p red org &
            blk   .30 .25
1168 A540 100p turq & blk   .25 .25
1169 A539 200p lt bl & blk   .50 .25
1170 A540 280p rose & blk   6.50 .80
1171 A540 300p lemon &
            blk   .80 .25
1172 A540 480p org & blk   1.00 .25
1173 A540 500p yel grn &
            blk   .35 .25
1174 A540 520p org & blk   .70 .30
1175 A540 800p rose lil &
            blk   1.25 .30
1176 A540 1000p lem bis &
            blk   1.00 .40
1177 A540 1000p gold & blk,
            40x29mm   1.75 .25
1178 A540 2000p multi   .80 .40
     Nos. 1159-1178 (20)   17.65 5.95

Nos. 1161, 1163, 1165, 1167, 1169, 1171, 1173, 1176, 1177 were issued on both ordinary and fluorescent paper. No. 1174 was issued only on fluorescent paper. All others were issued only on ordinary paper.
Issued: No. 1164, 5/30/77; 280p, 12/15/77; No. 1160, 3/14/78; 480p, 5/22/78; 5p, 7/25/78; 20p, 500p, 9/8/78; No. 1166, 9/20/78; No. 1177, 9/28/78; 520p, 9/30/78; 300p, 10/5/78; 40p, 12/1/78; No. 1161, 1979; No. 1165, 1/8/79; 800p, 3/20/79; No. 1167, 4/25/79; 200p, 6/23/79; No. 1176, 12/15/79; 2000p, 6/25/80; No. 1168, 5/26/81.
For overprints see Nos. 1253, 1315.

Soccer
Games'
Emblem
A544

1978, Feb. 10   Photo.   Perf. 13½
1179 A544 200p yel grn & bl   .85 .30
 a.   Wmk 365   100.00 75.00

11th World Cup Soccer Championship, Argentina, June 1-25.

View of El Rio, Rosario — A545

Designs (Argentina '78 Emblem and): 100p, Rio Tercero Dam, Cordoba. 150p, Cordillera Mountains, Mendoza. 200p, City Center, Mar del Plata. 300p, View of Buenos Aires.

1978, May 6   Litho.   Perf. 13½
1180 A545 50p multi   .30 .25
1181 A545 100p multi   .30 .25
1182 A545 150p multi   .50 .25
1183 A545 200p multi   .50 .25
1184 A545 300p multi   .90 .30
     Nos. 1180-1184 (5)   2.50 1.30

Sites of 11th World Cup Soccer Championship, June 1-25.

Children — A546

1978, May 20
1185 A546 100p multi .35 .25
50th anniversary of Children's Institute.

Labor Day, by
B. Quinquela
Martin — A547

Design: No. 1187, Woman's torso, sculpture by Orlando Pierri.

1978, May 20 **Perf. 13½**
1186 A547 100p multi .50 .25
1187 A547 100p multi .50 .25

Argentina, Hungary, France, Italy and
Emblem — A548

Stadium — A549

Teams and Argentina '78 Emblem: 200p, Poland, Fed. Rep. of Germany, Tunisia, Mexico. 300p, Austria, Spain, Sweden, Brazil. 400p, Netherlands, Iran, Peru, Scotland.

1978 **Litho.** **Perf. 13**
1188 A548 100p multi .30 .25
1189 A548 200p multi .70 .25
1190 A548 300p multi 1.00 .30
1191 A548 400p multi 1.25 .30
Nos. 1188-1191 (4) 3.25 1.10

Souvenir Sheet
Lithographed and Engraved
Perf. 13½
1192 A549 700p buff & blk 2.75 2.75

11th World Cup Soccer Championship, Argentina, June 1-25. Issued: Nos. 1188-1191, 6/6; No. 1192, 6/3.

Stadium Type of 1978 Inscribed in
Red

Lithographed and Engraved
1978, Sept. 2 **Perf. 13½**
1193 A549 1000p buff, blk & red 4.25 4.25
Argentina's victory in 1978 Soccer Championship. No. 1193 has margin similar to No.

1192 with Rimet Cup emblem and text added in red.

Young Tree Nourished by Old Trunk,
UN Emblem — A550

1978 Sept. 2 **Litho.**
1194 A550 100p multi .35 .25
Technical Cooperation among Developing Countries Conf., Buenos Aires, Sept. 1978.

Emblems of Buenos Aires &
Bank — A551

1978, Sept. 16
1195 A551 100p multi .35 .25
Bank of City of Buenos Aires, centenary.

General Savio & Steel
Production — A552

1978, Sept. 16
1196 A552 100p multi .35 .25
Gen. Manuel N. Savio (1892-1948), general manager of military heavy industry.

San
Martin — A553

1978, Oct. **Engr.**
1197 A553 2000p grnsh blk 4.00 .30

1979 **Wmk. 365**
1198 A553 2000p grnsh blk 5.50 1.00
Gen Jose de San Martin (1778-1850), soldier and statesman. See No. 1292.

Globe &
Argentine
Flag — A554

1978, Oct. 7 **Litho.** **Perf. 13½**
1199 A554 200p multi .80 .25
12th Intl. Cancer Cong., Buenos Aires, Oct. 5-11.

Chessboard,
Queen &
Pawn — A555

1978, Oct. 7
1200 A555 200p multi 4.25 .65
23rd National Chess Olympics, Buenos Aires, Oct. 25-Nov. 12.

Correct
Positioning
of Stamps
A557

50p, Use correct postal code number.

1978 **Photo.** **Perf. 13½**
1201 A557 20p ultra .25 .25
1203 A557 50p carmine .25 .25
No. 1201 issued on both ordinary and fluorescent paper.

A558 A559

1978-82 **Photo.** **Perf. 13½**
1204 A558 150p bl & ultra .35 .25
1205 A558 180p bl & ultra .35 .25
1206 A558 200p bl & ultra .50 .25
1207 A559 240p ol bis & bl ('79) .35 .25
1208 A559 260p blk & lt bl ('79) .35 .25
1209 A559 290p brn & lt bl ('79) .45 .25
1210 A559 310p mag & bl ('79) .45 .25
1211 A559 350p ver & bl ('79) .55 .25
1212 A559 450p ultra & bl .50 .25
1213 A559 600p grn & bl ('80) 1.10 .25
1214 A559 700p blk & bl ('80) .65 .25
1215 A559 800p red & bl ('81) .45 .25
1216 A559 1100p gray & bl ('81) .90 .25
1217 A559 1500p blk & bl ('81) .50 .25
1218 A559 1700p grn & bl ('82) .50 .25
Nos. 1204-1218 (15) 7.95 3.75

No. 1204 issued on fluorescent and ordinary paper. No. 1206 issued only on fluorescent paper.
For overprint see No. 1338.

Balsa
"24"
A561

Ships: 200p, Tug Legador. 300p, River Parana tug No. 34. 400p, Passenger ship Ciudad de Parana.

1978, Nov. 4 **Litho.** **Perf. 13½**
1220 A561 100p multi .30 .25
1221 A561 200p multi .50 .25
1222 A561 300p multi .70 .25
a. Pair, #1221-1222 1.50
1223 A561 400p multi .95 .50
a. Pair, #1220, 1223 1.50
Nos. 1220-1223 (4) 2.45 1.25

20th anniversary of national river fleet. Issued on fluorescent paper.

View
and
Arms of
Bahia
Blanca
A562

1978, Nov. 25 **Litho.** **Perf. 13½**
1224 A562 20p multi .50 .25
Sesquicentennial of Bahia Blanca.

"Spain," (Queen Isabella and
Columbus) by Arturo Dresco — A563

1978, Nov. 25
1225 A563 300p multi 2.75 .35
Visit of King Juan Carlos and Queen Sofia of Spain to Argentina, Nov. 26.

Virgin and
Child, San
Isidro
Cathedral
A564

1978, Dec. 16
1226 A564 200p gold & multi .65 .25
Christmas 1978.

Slope at Chacabuco, by Pedro
Subercaseaux — A565

Painting: 1000p, The Embrace of Maipu (San Martin and O'Higgins), by Pedro Subercaseaux, vert.

1978, Dec. 16 **Litho.** **Perf. 13½**
1227 A565 500p multi 2.00 .35
1228 A565 1000p multi 3.50 .35
José de San Martin, 200th birth anniversary.

Adolfo
Alsina
A566

Design: No. 1230, Mariano Moreno.

1979, Jan. 20
1229 A566 200p lt bl & blk .50 .25
1230 A566 200p yel red & blk .50 .25

Adolfo Alsina (1828-1877), political leader, vice-president; Mariano Moreno (1778-1811), lawyer, educator, political leader.

Argentina No. 37 and UPU
Emblem — A567

1979, Jan. 20
1231 A567 200p multi　　　　　.50　.25
Centenary of Argentina's UPU membership.

Still-life,
by
Carcova
A568

Painting: 300p, The Laundresses, by Faustino Brughetti.

1979, Mar. 3
1232 A568 200p multi　　　　　.45　.25
1233 A568 300p multi　　　　　.85　.30
Ernesto de la Carcova (1866-1927) and Faustino Brughetti (1877-1956), Argentine painters.

Balcarce Earth
Station — A569

1979, Mar. 3
1234 A569 200p multicolored　　　.65　.25
Third Inter-American Telecommunications Conference, Buenos Aires, March 5-9.

Stamp
Collecting — A570

1979
1235 A570 30p multicolored　　　　.25　.25
Printed on ordinary and fluorescent paper.

European
Olive — A571

1979, June 2　　Litho.　　Perf. 13½
1236 A571 100p shown　　　　.65　.35
1237 A571 200p Tea　　　　　.65　.35
1238 A571 300p Sorghum　　　1.25　.45
1239 A571 400p Common flax　1.25　.55
　　Nos. 1236-1239 (4)　　　3.80 1.70

Laurel and
Regimental
Emblem
A572

1979, June 9
1240 A572 200p gold & multi　　.45　.25
Founding of Subteniente Berdina Village in memory of Sub-lieutenant Rodolfo Hernan Berdina, killed by terrorists in 1975.

"75" and Automobile Club
Emblem — A573

1979, June 9
1241 A573 200p gold & multi　　.35　.25
Argentine Automobile Club, 75th anniv.

Exchange Building and
Emblem — A574

1979, June 9
1242 A574 200p bl, blk & gold　　.35　.25
Grain Exchange, 125th anniversary.

Cavalry Officer,
1817 — A575

1979, July 7　　Litho.　　Perf. 13½
1243 A575 200p multi　　　　1.00　.30
Army Day.

Corvette Uruguay and Navy
Emblem — A576

Design: No. 1245, Hydrographic service ship & emblem.

1979　　　　　　　　**Perf. 13**
1244 A576 250p multi　　　　1.00　.35
1245 A576 250p multi　　　　1.00　.35
Navy Day; Cent. of Naval Hydrographic Service. Issued: No. 1244, July 28; No. 1245, July 7.

Tree and
Man — A577

1979, July 28　　　　　Perf. 13½
1246 A577 250p multi　　　　.60　.25
Protection of the Environment Day, June 5.

"Spad" Flying over Andes, and Vicente
Almandos Almonacid — A578

1979, Aug. 4
1247 A578 250p multi　　　　.75　.25
Air Force Day.

Gen. Julio A. Roca Occupying Rio
Negro, by Juan M. Blanes — A579

1979, Aug. 4
1248 A579 250p multi　　　　.75　.25
Conquest of Rio Negro Desert, centenary.

Rowland
Hill — A580

1979, Sept. 29　　Litho.　　Perf. 13½
1249 A580 300p gray red & blk　.65　.25
Sir Rowland Hill (1795-1879), originator of penny postage.

Viedma
Navarez
Monument
A581

1979, Sept. 29
1250 A581 300p multi　　　　.85　.25
Viedma and Carmen de Patagones towns, bicentenary.

Pope Paul
VI — A582

Design: No. 1252, Pope John Paul I.

1979, Oct. 27　　Engr.　　Perf. 13½
1251 A582 500p black　　　1.00　.30
1252 A582 500p sepia　　　1.00　.30

No. 1169
Overprinted in Red

1979, Nov. 10　　Photo.　　Perf. 13½
1253 A539 200p lt blue & blk　.65　.25
Rosario Philatelic Society, 75th anniversary.

A583

1979, Nov. 10　　　　　　Litho.
1254 A583 300p multi　　　　.75　.30
Frontier resettlement.

A584

1979, Dec. 1　　Litho.　　Perf. 13½
1255 A584 300p multi　　　　.75　.30
Military Geographic Institute centenary.

Christmas 1979 — A585

1979, Dec. 1
1256 A585 300p multi　　　　.65　.25

General Mosconi Birth
Centenary — A586

1979, Dec. 15   **Engr.**   *Perf. 13½*
1257 A586 1000p blk & bl   1.50   .50

Rotary
Emblem
and
Globe
A587

1979, Dec. 29   **Litho.**
1258 A587 300p multi   1.75   .35
Rotary International, 75th anniversary.

Child and IYC
Emblem
A588

Family, by Pablo Menicucci — A589

1979, Dec. 29
1259 A588 500p lt bl & sepia   .75   .35
1260 A589 1000p multi   1.50   .25
International Year of the Child.

Microphone, Waves, ITU
Emblem — A590

1980, Mar. 22   **Litho.**   *Perf. 13x13½*
1261 A590 500p multi   1.40   .25
Regional Administrative Conference on
Broadcasting by Hectometric Waves for Area
2, Buenos Aires, Mar. 10-29.

Guillermo
Brown — A591

1980   **Engr.**   *Perf. 13½*
1262 A591 5000p black   5.00   .25
See No. 1372.

Argentine Red Cross
Centenary — A592

1980, Apr. 19   **Litho.**   *Perf. 13½*
1263 A592 500p multi   .55   .25

OAS Emblem
A593

1980, Apr. 19
1264 A593 500p multi   .55   .25
Day of the Americas, Apr. 14.

Dish Antennae, Balcarce — A594

No. 1266, Hydroelectric Station, Salto
Grande. No. 1267, Bridge, Zarate-Brazo
Largo.

1980, Apr. 26   **Litho. & Engr.**
1265 A594 300p shown   .45   .25
1266 A594 300p multicolored   .45   .25
1267 A594 300p multicolored   .45   .25
   Nos. 1265-1267 (3)   1.35   .75

Capt. Hipolito Bouchard, Frigate
"Argentina" — A595

1980, May 31   **Litho.**   *Perf. 13x13½*
1268 A595 500p multicolored   .85   .30
Navy Day.

"Villarino," San Martin, by Theodore
Gericault — A596

1980, May 31
1269 A596 500p multicolored   .85   .30
Return of the remains of Gen. Jose de San
Martin to Argentina, centenary.

Buenos Aires Gazette, 1810,
Signature — A597

1980, June 7   *Perf. 13½*
1270 A597 500p multicolored   .55   .25
Journalism Day.

Miniature Sheet

Coaches in Victoria Square — A598

1980 June 14
1271 A598   Sheet of 14   17.50   17.50
a.-n.   500p any single   .75   .50
Buenos Aires, 400th anniv. No. 1271 shows
ceramic mural of Victoria Square by Rodolfo
Franco in continuous design. See No. 1285.

Gen. Pedro
Aramburu
A599

1980, July 12   **Litho.**   *Perf. 13½*
1272 A599 500p yel & blk   .65   .25
Gen. Pedro Eugenio Aramburu (1903-
1970), provisional president, 1955.

Army
Day
A600

1980, July 12
1273 A600 500p multicolored   .85   .30

Gen. Juan Gregorio de Las Heras
(1780-1866), Hero of 1817 War of
Independence — A601

Grandees of Argentina Bicentenary: No.
1275, Rivadavia. No. 1276, Brig. Gen Jose
Matias Zapiola (1780-1874), naval commander and statesman.

1980, Aug. 2   **Litho.**   *Perf. 13½*
1274 A601 500p tan & blk   .55   .25
1275 A601 500p multicolored   .55   .25
1276 A601 500p lt lilac & blk   .55   .25
   Nos. 1274-1276 (3)   1.65   .75

Avro "Gosport" Biplane, Maj. Francisco
de Artega — A602

1980, Aug. 16   *Perf. 13*
1277 A602 500p multicolored   .60   .25
Air Force Day. Arteaga (1882-1930) was first
director of Military Aircraft Factory where Avro
"Gosport" was built (1927).

University of La Plata, 75th
Anniversary — A603

1980, Aug. 16   *Perf. 13½*
1278 A603 500p multi   .55   .25

Souvenir Sheets

A604

A605

No. 1279: a, King penguin. b, Bearded pen-
guin. c, Adelie penguins. d, Papua penguins.
e, Sea elephants. f, Puerto Soledad, 1829. g,
Puerto Soledad harbor, 1829. h, Fur seals. i,
Giant petrels. j, Blue-eyed cororants. k,
Stormy petrels. l, Antarctic doves.
No. 1280: Letters a-e and h-l are the same
as No. 1279. f, South Orkneys Argentine
Base, towers and buildings. g, South Orkneys
Argentine Base, buildings and mountains.

1980, Sept. 27   **Litho.**   *Perf. 13½*
1279 A604 Sheet of 12   20.00   20.00
a.-l.   500p, any single   .75   .60
1280 A605 Sheet of 12   20.00   20.00
f.-g.   500p, any single   .75   .60
75th anniv. of Argentina's presence in the
South Orkneys and 150th anniv. of political
and military command in the Falkland Islands.
Nos. 1279-1280 each contain 12 stamps (4x3)
with landscape designs in center of sheets.
Silhouettes of Argentine exploration ships in
margins. No. 1280 contains Nos. 1279a-
1279e, 1279h-1279m, 1280a-1280b.

Anti-smoking Campaign A608

1980, Oct. 11
1282 A608 700p multi   .90   .25

National Census — A609

1980, Sept.
1283 A609 500p blk & bl   1.10   .25

Madonna and Child (Congress Emblem) — A610

1980, Oct. 1   Litho.
1284 A610 700p multi   .85   .25

National Marian Cong., Mendoza, Oct. 8-12

Mural Type of 1980
Miniature Sheet
1980, Oct. 25
1285   Sheet of 14   17.50 17.50
  a.-n. A598 500p, any single   .65   .50

Buenos Aires, 400th anniv./Buenos Aires '80 Stamp Exhib., Oct. 24-Nov. 2. No. 1285 shows ceramic mural Arte bajo la Ciudad by Alfredo Guido in continuous design.

Technical Military Academy, 50th Anniversary A611

1980, Nov. 1
1286 A611 700p multi   .75   .25

Amateur Radio Operation A612

1980, Nov. 1
1287 A612 700p multi   .75   .25

Medal — A613

Lujan Cathedral Floor Plan — A614

1980, Nov. 29   Litho.   Perf. 13½
1288 A613 700p multi   .75   .30
1289 A614 700p olive & brn   .75   .30

Christmas 1980. 150th anniv. of apparition of Holy Virgin to St. Catherine Laboure, Paris (No. 1288), 350th anniv. of apparition at Lujan.

150th Death Anniversary of Simon Bolivar — A615

1980, Dec. 13
1290 A615 700p multi   .75   .25

Soccer Gold Cup Championship, Montevideo, 1980 — A616

1981, Jan. 3   Litho.
1291 A616 1000p multi   1.10   .25

San Martin Type of 1978
1981, Jan. 20   Engr.   Perf. 13½
1292 A553 10,000p dark blue   7.50   .25

Landscape in Lujan, by Marcos Tiglio — A617

Paintings: No. 1304, Expansion of Light along a Straight Line, by Miguel Angel Vidal, vert.

1981, Apr. 11   Litho.
1303 A617 1000p multi   .90   .35
1304 A617 1000p multi   .90   .35

Intl. Sports Medicine Congress, June 7-12 — A618

1981, June 6   Litho.   Perf. 13½
1305 A618 1000p bl & dk brn   .75   .25

Esperanza Base, Antarctica — A619

Cargo Plane, Map of Vice-Commodore Marambio Island — A620

Perf. 13½, 13x13½ (No. 1308)
1981, June 13
1306 A619 1000p shown   1.40   .45
1307 A619 2000p Almirante Irizar   2.50   .50
1308 A620 2000p shown   2.40   .80
  Nos. 1306-1308 (3)   6.30   1.75

Antarctic Treaty 20th anniv.

Antique Pistols (Military Club Centenary) — A621

1981, June 27   Perf. 13½
1309 A621 1000p Club building   .80   .25
1310 A621 2000p shown   .80   .25

Gen. Juan A. Alvarez de Arenales (1770-1831) A622

Famous Men: No. 1312, Felix G. Frias (1816-1881), writer. No. 1313, Jose E. Uriburu (1831-1914), statesman.

1981, Aug. 8   Litho.   Perf. 13½
1311 A622 1000p multi   .70   .25
1312 A622 1000p multi   .70   .25
1313 A622 1000p multi   .70   .25
  Nos. 1311-1313 (3)   2.10   .75

Naval Observatory Centenary — A623

1981, Aug. 15   Litho.   Perf. 13x13½
1314 A623 1000p multi   1.00   .30

No. 1176 Overprinted in Red

1981, Aug. 15   Photo.   Perf. 13½
1315 A540 1000p lem & blk   1.75   .35

50th anniv. of Bahia Blanca Philatelic and Numismatic Society.

St. Cayetano, Stained-glass Window, Buenos Aires — A624

1981, Sept. 5   Litho.   Perf. 13½
1316 A624 1000p multi   .70   .25

St. Cayetano, founder of Teatino Order, 500th birth anniv.

Pablo Castaibert (1883-1909) and his Monoplane (Air Force Day) — A625

1981, Sept. 5   Perf. 13x13½
1317 A625 1000p multi   1.10   .30

Intl. Year of the Disabled A626

1981, Sept. 10   Perf. 13½
1318 A626 1000p multi   .75   .25

22nd Latin-American Steelmakers' Congress, Buenos Aires, Sept. 21-23 — A627

1981, Sept. 19
1319 A627 1000p multi   .60   .25

Army Regiment No. 1 (Patricios),
175th Anniv. — A628

1981, Oct. 10   Litho.   Perf. 13½
1320   1500p Natl. arms   .45   .25
1321   1500p shown   .45   .25
  a.   A628 Pair, #1320-1321   1.10   1.10

A629

San Martin as artillery Captain in Battle of
Bailen, 1808.

1981, Oct. 5
1322   Sheet of 8 + 4 labels   4.75   4.75
  a.   A629 1000p multi   .35   .30
  b.   A629 1500p multi   .50   .35

Espamer '81 Intl. Stamp Exhib. (Americas,
Spain, Portugal), Buenos Aires, Nov. 13-22.
No. 1322 contains 2 each se-tenant pairs
with label between.

A630

1981, Oct. 5
1323   A630 1000p multi   6.75   .40

Anti-indiscriminate whaling.

Espamer '81
Emblem and
Ship
A631

1981
1324   A631 1300p multi   1.00   .40

No. 1324
Overprinted
in Blue

1981, Nov. 7   Photo.   Perf. 13½
1325   A631 1300p multi   1.50   .25

Postal Administration philatelic training
course.

Soccer Players
A632

Designs: Soccer players.

1981, Nov. 13   Litho.
1326   Sheet of 4 + 2 labels   8.00   8.00
  a.   A632 2000p multi   1.50   1.25
  b.   A632 3000p multi   1.75   1.50
  c.   A632 5000p multi   2.00   1.75
  d.   A632 15,000p multi   2.25   2.00

Espamer '81.

"Peso" Coin Centenary — A633

2000p, Patacon, 1881. 3000p, Argentine
Oro, 1881.

1981, Nov. 21
1327   A633 2000p multicolored   .55   .25
1328   A633 3000p multicolored   .55   .25

Christmas
1981 — A634

1981, Dec. 12
1329   A634 1500p multi   2.40   .50

Traffic
Safety
A635

1000p, Observe traffic lights, vert. 2000p,
Drive carefully, vert. 3000p, Cross at white
lines. 4000p, Don't shine headlights.

1981, Dec. 19   Litho.
1330   A635 1000p multicolored   1.50   .40
1331   A635 2000p multicolored   .80   .50
1332   A635 3000p multicolored   1.25   .45
1333   A635 4000p multicolored   1.25   .65
         Nos. 1330-1333 (4)   4.80   2.00

Francisco Luis
Bernardez,
Ciuda
Laura — A636

Writers and title pages from their works:
2000p, Lucio V. Mansilla, Excursion a los
indios ranqueles. 3000p, Conrado Nale Roxlo,
El Grillo. 4000p, Victoria Ocampo, Sur.

1982, Mar. 20   Litho.
1334   A636 1000p shown   1.50   .40
1335   A636 2000p multi   .80   .40
1336   A636 3000p multi   .80   .50
1337   A636 4000p multi   1.50   .40
         Nos. 1334-1337 (4)   4.60   1.60

No. 1218 Overprinted

1982, Apr. 17   Photo.   Perf. 13½
1338   A559 1700p green & blue   .70   .25

Argentina's claim on Falkland Islands.

Robert
Koch — A637

1982, Apr. 17   Litho.   Wmk. 365
1339   A637 2000p multi   1.10   .25

TB bacillus centenary and 25th Intl. Tuberculosis Conference.

American
Airforces
Commanders'
22nd
Conf. — A638

1982, Apr. 17
1340   A638 2000p multi   1.25   .30

Stone Carving, City Founder's
Signature (Don Hernando de
Lerma) — A639

1982, Apr. 17
1341   A639 2000p multi   1.50   .30

Souvenir Sheet
1342   A639 5000p multi   3.00   3.00

City of Salta, 400th anniv. No. 1342 contains one 43x30mm stamp.

Naval Center Centenary — A640

1982, Apr. 24   Perf. 13x13½
1343   A640 2000p multi   .80   .30

Chorisia
Speciosa — A641

200p, Zinnia peruviana. 300p, Ipomoea
purpurea. 400p, Tillandsia aeranthos. 800p,
Oncidium bifolium. 1000p, Erythrina crista-
galli. 2000p, Jacaranda mimosi-folia. 3000p,
Bauhinia candicans. 5000p, Tecoma stans.
10,000p, Tabebuia ipe. 20,000p, Passiflora
coerulea. 30,000p, Aristolochia littoralis.
50,000p, Oxalis enneaphylla.

1982   Unwmk.   Photo.   Perf. 13½
1344   A641   200p multi   .30   .25
1345   A641   300p multi   .30   .25
1346   A641   400p multi   .25   .25
1347   A641   500p shown   .25   .25
1348   A641   800p multi   .25   .25
1349   A641   1000p multi   .30   .25
1350   A641   2000p multi   .30   .25
1351   A641   3000p multi   .65   .25
1352   A641   5000p multi   .60   .25
1353   A641 10,000p multi   1.00   .25
1354   A641 20,000p multi   1.25   .35
1355   A641 30,000p multi   1.75   .40
1356   A641 50,000p multi   3.50   .65
         Nos. 1344-1356 (13)   10.70   3.90

Nos. 1344-1346, 1348-1350 issued on fluorescent paper. Nos. 1353-1356 issued on ordinary paper. Others issued on both fluorescent
and ordinary paper.

Issued: 500p, 2000p, 5000p, 10,000p, 5/22;
200p, 300p, 1000p, 20,000p, 9/25; 400p,
800p, 30,000p, 50,000p, 12/4; 3000p, 12/18.
See Nos. 1429-1443A, 1515-1527, 1683-
1691. For overprint see No. 1382.

10th Death Anniv. of Gen. Juan C.
Sanchez — A641a

1982, May 29   Litho.   Wmk. 365
1364   A641a 5000p grn & blk   .90   .25

Luis Vernet, First Commander —
A641b

1982, June 12
1365   A641b 5000p org & blk   1.75   .55
Size: 83x28mm
1366   A641b 5000p Map   1.00   .40
  a.   Pair, Nos. 1365-1366   2.75   2.00

153rd Anniv. of Malvinas Political and Military Command District.
Compare with No. 1411.

Visit of Pope
John Paul II —
A641c

1982, June 12
1367   A641c 5000p multi   2.00   .55

Organ Grinder, by Aldo Severi (b. 1928) — A641d

3000p, Still Life, by Santiago Cogorno (b. 1915).

1982, July 3 **Wmk. 365**
1368 A641d 2000p shown .80 .35
1369 A641d 3000p multi .80 .35

Guillermo Brown Type of 1980 and

Jose de San Martin — A641e

Litho. and Engr.
1982 **Unwmk.** **Perf. 13½**
1372 A591 30,000p blk & bl 3.75 .70
1376 A641e 50,000p sepia & car 7.50 1.00
Issue dates: 30,000p, June; 50,000p, July.

Scouting Year — A641f

Wmk. 365
1982, Aug. 7 **Litho.** **Perf. 13½**
1380 A641f 5000p multi 2.40 .40

Alconafta Fuel Campaign — A641g

1982, Aug. 7 **Wmk. 365**
1381 A641g 2000p multi .85 .25

No. 1352 Overprinted

1982, Aug. 7 **Photo.** **Unwmk.**
1382 A641 5000p multi 2.40 1.00

Rio III Central Nuclear Power Plant, Cordoba A642

Wmk. 365
1982, Sept. 4 **Litho.** **Perf. 13½**
1383 A642 2000p shown .45 .25
1384 A642 2000p Control room .45 .25

Namibia Day — A643

1982, Sept. 4
1385 A643 5000p Map .95 .25

Formosa Cathedral — A644

Churches and Cathedrals of the Northeast: 2000p, Our Lady of Itati, Corrientes, vert. 3000p, Resistencia Cathedral, Chaco, vert. 10,000p, St. Ignatius Church ruins, Misiones.

1982, Sept. 18 **Litho. & Engr.**
1386 A644 2000p dk grn & blk .55 .55
1387 A644 3000p dk brn & brn .55 .55
1388 A644 5000p dk bl & brn 1.00 .55
1389 A644 10,000p dp org & blk 1.50 .55
Nos. 1386-1389 (4) 3.60 2.20

Tension Sideral, by Mario Alberto Agatiello A645

Sculpture (Espamer '81 and Juvenex '82 Exhibitions): 3000p, Sugerencia II, by Eduardo Mac Entyre. 5000p, Storm, by Carlos Silva.

1982, Oct. 2 **Litho.** **Perf. 13½**
1390 A645 2000p multi 2.00 .40
1391 A645 3000p multi 2.00 .40
1392 A645 5000p multi 2.00 .45
Nos. 1390-1392 (3) 6.00 1.25

Santa Fe Bridge A646

1982, Oct. 16 **Litho. & Engr.**
1393 A646 2000p bl & blk 1.00 .25
2nd Southern Cross Games, Santa Fe and Rosario, Nov. 26-Dec. 5.

10th World Men's Volleyball Championship — A647

1982, Oct. 16 **Litho.** **Wmk. 365**
1394 A647 2000p multi .35 .25
1395 A647 5000p multi .50 .25

Los Andes Newspaper Centenary — A648

Design: Army of the Andes Monument, Hill of Glory, Mendoza.

1982, Oct. 30
1396 A648 5000p multi .60 .30

A649

1982, Oct. 30 **Wmk. 365**
1397 A649 5000p Signs .65 .25
50th Anniv. of Natl. Roads, Administration.

A650

A650a

La Plata City Cent., each 2500p: No. 1400: a, Cathedral, diff. b, Head, top. c, Observatory. d, City Hall, diff. e, Head, bottom. f, University.

1982, Nov. 20 **Litho.**
1398 A650 5000p Cathedral .85 .25
1399 A650 5000p City Hall .85 .25
1400 A650a Sheet of 6 2.50 2.50
a.-f. 2500p Any single .35 .25

Well, Natl. Hydrocarbon Congress Emblem — A651

1982, Nov. 20
1401 A651 5000p multi 1.20 .25
Oil Discovery, Comodoro Rivadavia, 75th anniv.

Jockey Club of Buenos Aires Centenary A652

Design: No. 1403, Carlos Pellegrini, first president.

1982, Dec. 4 **Litho.**
1402 A652 5000p Emblem 1.00 .25
1403 A652 5000p multi 1.00 .25

Christmas A653

3000p, St. Vincent de Paul. 5000p, St. Francis of Assisi.

1982, Dec. 18 **Perf. 13½**
1404 A653 3000p multi 2.00 .40

Size: 29x38mm
1405 A653 5000p multi 1.40 .25

Pedro B. Palacios (1854-1917), Writer — A654

Writers: 2000p, Leopoldo Marechal (1900-1970). 3000p, Delfina Bunge de Galvez (1881-1952). 4000p, Manuel Galvez (1882-1962). 5000p, Evaristo Carriego (1883-1912).

1983, Mar. 26 **Litho.** **Perf. 13**
1406 A654 1000p multi .50 .3
1407 A654 2000p multi .50 .3
1408 A654 3000p multi .50 .3
1409 A654 4000p multi .50 .3
1410 A654 5000p multi .50 .3
a. Strip of 5, #1406-1410 2.60 2.6

Recovery of the Malvinas (Falkland Islands) — A655

20,000p, Map, flag.

1983, Apr. 9   Litho.   Perf. 13½
1411 A655 20,000p multi   1.75 .60
    Compare No. 1411 with No. 1366.

Telecommunications Systems — A656

No. 1412, SITRAM, No. 1413, ARPAC network.

1983, Apr. 16   Wmk. 365
1412 A656 5000p multi   1.25 .65
1413 A656 5000p multi   1.25 .65

Naval League Emblem A657

1983, May 14   Litho.   Perf. 13½
1414 A657 5000p multi   .65 .25
Navy Day and 50th anniv. of Naval League.

Allegory, by Victor Rebuffo A658

1983, May 14
1415 A658 5000p multi   .65 .30
    Natl. Arts Fund, 25th Anniv.

75th Anniv. of Colon Opera House, Buenos Aires — A659

1983, May 28   Wmk. 365
1416 A659 5000p Main hall   .75 .40
1417 A659 10000p Stage   1.00 .40

Protected Species — A660

1p, Chrysocyon brachyurus. 1.50p, Ozotocerus bezoarticus. 2p, Myrmecophaga tridactyla. 2.50p, Leo onca.

1983, July 2   Litho.   Perf. 13½
1418 A660   1p multicolored   1.00 .40
1419 A660 1.50p multicolored   1.50 .40
1420 A660   2p multicolored   1.60 .40
1421 A660 2.50p multicolored   1.90 .40
    Nos. 1418-1421 (4)   6.00 1.60

City of Catamarca, 300th Anniv. — A661

Foundation of the City of Catamarca, by Luis Varela Lezana (1900-1982).

1983, July 16   Litho.   Perf. 13½
1422 A661 1p multi   .50 .40

Mamerto Esquiu (1826-1883) A662

1983, July 16
1423 A662 1p multi   .50 .40

Bolivar, by Herrera Toro — A663

Bolivar, Engraving by Kepper — A664

Perf. 13 (A663), 13½ (A664)
1983   Unwmk.
1424 A663   1p multi   .45 .35
1425 A664   2p blk & maroon   .65 .40
1426 A664 10p San Martin   3.50 .80
    Nos. 1424-1426 (3)   4.60 1.20
Issue dates: 1p, 2p, July 23. 10p, Aug. 20.
See Nos. 1457-1462B.

Gen. Toribio de Luzuriaga (1782-1842) A665

1983, Aug. 20   Litho.   Perf. 13½
1427 A665 1p multi   .60 .40

50th Anniv. of San Martin National Institute A666

1983, Aug. 20   Engr.   Unwmk.
1428 A666 2p sepia   .60 .40

Flower Type of 1982 in New Currency

1983-85			Photo.	Perf. 13½
1429	A641	5c like #1347	.50	.25
1430	A641	10c like #1349	.25	.25
1431	A641	20c like #1350	.25	.25
1432	A641	30c like #1351	.40	.25
1433	A641	40c Eichhornia crassipes	.25	.25
1434	A641	50c like #1352	.25	.25
1435	A641	1p like #1353	.30	.25
1435A	A641	1.80p Mutisia retusa	.30	.25
1436	A641	2p like #1354	.35	.25
1437	A641	3p like #1355	.40	.25
1438	A641	5p like #1356	.40	.25
1439	A641	10p Alstroemeria aurantiaca	1.10	.80
1440	A641	20p like #1345	.40	.25
1441	A641	30p Embothrium coccineum	2.00	.25
1442	A641	50p like #1346	.60	.40
1443	A641	100p like #1348	1.75	.25
1443A	A641	300p Cassia carnaval	2.00	.50
		Nos. 1429-1443A (17)	11.50	5.20

Issued: 20p, 8/27/84; 50p, 10/19/84; 100p, 12/84; 300p, 6/15/85.
Nos. 1429, 1433, 1435A issued on fluorescent paper. Nos. 1443, 1443A issued on ordinary paper. Others issued on both ordinary and fluorescent paper.
No. 1440 has denomination at UL.
For overprint and surcharge see Nos. 1489, 1530.

Intl. Rotary South American Regional Conference, Buenos Aires, Sept. 25-28 — A667

1983, Sept. 24   Litho.
1444 A667 1p multi   .65 .25

9th Pan American Games, Caracas, Aug. 13-28 — A668

1983, Sept. 24
1445 A668 1p Track   .45 .25
1446 A668 2p Emblem   .60 .25

World Communications Year — A669

1983, Oct. 8   Perf. 13½
1447 A669 2p multi   .60 .25

Squash Peddler by Antonio Berni (1905-1981) A670

2p, Figure in Yellow by Luis Seoane (1910-79).

1983, Oct. 15   Perf. 13½
1448 A670 1p multi   .50 .25
1449 A670 2p multi   .60 .25

World Communications Year — A671

Designs: 1p, Wagon, 18th cent. 2p, Post chaise, 19th cent. 4p, Steam locomotive, 1857. 5p, Tramway, 1910.

1983, Nov. 19   Litho.   Perf. 13½
1450 A671 1p multi   .60 .35
1451 A671 2p multi   .60 .35
1452 A671 4p multi   .85 .35
1453 A671 5p multi   .85 .35
    Nos. 1450-1453 (4)   2.90 1.40

World Communications Year — A672

2p, General Post Office.

1983, Nov. 26 Litho. Perf. 12½x12
1454 A672 2p multicolored   .40 .30

Return to Elected Government A673

1983, Dec. 10   Photo.   Perf. 13½
1455 A673 2p Coin, 1813   .65 .25

Eudyptes Crestatus A674

Designs: b, Diomedea exulans. c, Diomedea melanophris. d, Eudyptes chrysolophus. e, Luis Piedra Buena. f, Carlos Maria Moyano. g, Luis Py. h, Augusto Lasserre. i, Phoebetria palpebrata. j, Hydrurga leptonyx. k, Lobodon carcinophagus. l, Leptonychotes weddelli.

1983, Dec. 10   **Litho.**
1456   Sheet of 12   12.50   12.50
   a.-l. A674 2p any single   .40   .25

Southern pioneers and fauna. Margin depicts various airplanes and emblems.

Bolivar Type of 1983

Famous men: 10p, Angel J. Carranza (1834-99), historian. No. 1458, 500p, Guillermo Brown. No. 1459, Estanislao del Campo (1834-80), poet. 30p, Jose Hernandez (1834-86), author. 40p, Vicente Lopez y Planes (1784-1856), poet and patriot. 50p, San Martin. 200p, Belgrano.

1983-85   **Litho. & Engr.**   **Perf. 13½**
1457	A664	10p pale bl & dk bl	.50	.40
1458	A664	20p dk bl & blk	.50	.40
1459	A664	20p dl brn ol & ol blk	.50	.40
1460	A664	30p pale bl & bluish blk	.60	.40
1461	A664	40p lt bl grn & blk	1.00	.40
1462	A664	50p Prus grn & choc	2.40	1.50
1462A	A664	200p int bl & blk	2.10	1.00
1462B	A664	500p brn & int bl	2.00	.50
		Nos. 1457-1462B (8)	9.60	5.00

Issued: No. 1458, 10/6; 10p, No. 1459, 30p, 40p, 3/23/85; 50p, 4/23/85; 200p, 11/2/85; 500p, 5/2/85.

Christmas 1983 — A675

Nativity Scenes: 2p, Tapestry, by Silke. 3p, Stained-glass window, San Carlos de Bariloche's Wayn Church, vert.

1983, Dec. 17   **Litho.**   **Perf. 13½**
1463	A675	2p multi	.45	.25
1464	A675	3p multi	.90	.30

Centenary of El Dia Newspaper A676

4p, Masthead, printing roll.

1984, Mar. 24   **Litho.**
1465	A676	4p multicolored	.45	.25

Alejandro Carbo Teachers' College Centenary — A677

1984, June 2   **Litho.**   **Perf. 13½**
1466	A677	10p Building	.45	.30

1984 Olympics A678

Designs: No. 1468, Weightlifting, discus, shot put. No. 1469, Javelin, fencing. No. 1470, Bicycling, swimming.

1984, July 28   **Litho.**   **Perf. 13½**
1467	A678	5p shown	.30	.25
1468	A678	5p multicolored	.30	.25
1469	A678	10p multicolored	.50	.30
1470	A678	10p multicolored	.50	.30
		Nos. 1467-1470 (4)	1.60	1.10

Rosario Stock Exchange Centenary A679

1984, Aug. 11
1471	A679	10p multicolored	.50	.30

Wheat A680

1984, Aug. 11
1472	A680	10p shown	.60	.30
1473	A680	10p Corn	.60	.30
1474	A680	10p Sunflower	.60	.30
		Nos. 1472-1474 (3)	1.80	.90

18th FAO Regional Conference for Latin America and Caribbean (No. 1472); 3rd Natl. Corn Congress (No. 1473); World Food Day (No. 1474).

Wildlife Protection — A681

No. 1475, Hippocamelus bisulcus. No. 1476, Vicugna vicugna. No. 1477, Aburria jacutinga. No. 1478, Mergus octosetaceus. No. 1479, Podiceps gallardoi.

1984, Sept. 22   **Litho.**   **Perf. 13½**
1475	A681	20p multicolored	1.00	.30
1476	A681	20p multicolored	1.00	.30
1477	A681	20p multicolored	1.00	.30
1478	A681	20p multicolored	1.00	.30
1479	A681	20p multicolored	1.00	.30
		Nos. 1475-1479 (5)	5.00	1.50

First Latin American Theater Festival, Cordoba, Oct. — A682

1984, Oct. 13   **Litho.**   **Perf. 13½**
1480	A682	20p Mask	.40	.30

Intl. Eucharistic Congress, 50th Anniv. — A683

Apostles' Communion, by Fra Angelico.

1984, Oct. 13
1481	A683	20p multicolored	.45	.30

Glaciares Natl. Park (UNESCO World Heritage List) — A684

1984, Nov. 17   **Litho.**
1482	A684	20p Sea	.70	.25
1483	A684	30p Glacier	1.10	.25

City of Puerto Deseado Centenary — A685

No. 1485, Ushuaia centenary.

1984, Nov. 17   **Perf. 13½**
1484	A685	20p shown	.70	.30
1485	A685	20p multicolored	.70	.30

Childrens' Paintings, Christmas 1984 — A686

1984, Dec. 1   **Litho.**   **Perf. 13½**
1486	A686	20p Diego Aguero	.60	.30
1487	A686	30p Leandro Ruiz	.75	.30
1488	A686	50p Maria Castillo, vert.	.80	.30
		Nos. 1486-1488 (3)	2.15	.90

No. 1439 Overprinted

1984, Dec. 1   **Photo.**   **Perf. 13½**
1489	A641	10p multicolored	.45	.45

Buenos Aires Philatelic Center, 50th anniv.

Vista Del Jardin Zoologico, by Fermin Eguia — A687

Paintings: No. 1491, El Congreso Iluminado, by Francisco Travieso. No. 1492, Galpones (La Boca), by Marcos Borio.

1984, Dec. 15   **Perf. 13½**
1490	A687	20p multi	.50	.30
1491	A687	20p multi, vert.	.50	.30
1492	A687	20p multi, vert.	.50	.30
		Nos. 1490-1492 (3)	1.50	.90

Gen. Martin Miguel de Guemes (1785-1821) — A688

1985, Mar. 23   **Litho.**   **Perf. 13½**
1493	A688	30p multicolored	.30	.30

ARGENTINA '85 Exhibition — A689

First airmail service from: 20p, Buenos Aires to Montevideo, 1917. 40p, Cordoba to Villa Dolores, 1925. 60p, Bahia Blanca to Comodoro Rivadavia, 1929. 80p, Argentina to Germany, 1934. 100p, naval service to the Antarctic, 1952.

1985, Apr. 27
1494	A689	20p Bleriot Gnome	.25	.25
1495	A689	40p Junker F-13L	.40	.25
1496	A689	60p Latte 25	.60	.25
1497	A689	80p L.Z. 127 Graf Zeppelin	.75	.40
1498	A689	100p Consolidated PBY Catalina	1.00	.45
		Nos. 1494-1498 (5)	3.00	1.60

Central Bank, 50th Anniv. A690

80p, Bank Building, Buenos Aires.

1985, June 1
1499	A690	80p multicolored	.70	.25

Jose A. Ferreyra (1889-1943), Director of Munequitas Portenas — A691

Famous directors and their films: No. 1501, Leopoldo Torre Nilsson (1924-1978), scene from Martin Fierro.

1985, June 1
1500	A691	100p shown	.75	.35
1501	A691	100p multi	.75	.35

Carlos Gardel (1890-1935), Entertainer A692

Paintings: No. 1502, Gardel playing the guitar on stage, by Carlos Alonso (b. 1929). No. 1503, Gardel in a wide-brimmed hat, by Hermenegildo Sabat (b. 1933). No. 1504, Portrait of Gardel in an ornamental frame, by Aldo Severi (b. 1928) and Martiniano Arce (b. 1939).

1985, June 15
1502	A692	200p multi	1.50	.45
1503	A692	200p multi	1.50	.45
1504	A692	200p multi	1.50	.45
	Nos. 1502-1504 (3)		4.50	1.35

The Arrival, by Pedro Figari A693

A Halt on the Plains, by Prilidiano Pueyrredon — A693a

Oil paintings (details): 30c, The Wagon Square, by C. B. de Quiros.

1985, July 6   Litho.   Perf. 13½
1505	A693	20c multi	1.00	.40
1506	A693	30c multi	1.40	.40

Souvenir Sheet
Perf. 12
1507	A693a	Sheet of 2	3.75	3.75
a.		20c Pilgrims, vert.	.40	.40
b.		30c Wagon	.45	.45

ARGENTINA '85. No. 1507 contains one 30x40mm and one 40x30mm stamp. See No. 1542.

Buenos Aires to Montevideo, 1917 Teodoro Fels Flight — A694

Historic flight covers: No. 1509, Villa Dolores to Cordoba, 1925. No. 1510, Buenos Aires to France, 1929 St. Exupery flight. No. 1511, Buenos Aires to Bremerhaven, 1934

Graf Zeppelin flight. No. 1512, 1st Antarctic flight, 1952.

1985, July 13   Perf. 12x12½
1508	A694	10c emer & multi	.45	.25
1509	A694	10c ultra & multi	.45	.25
1510	A694	10c lt choc & multi	.45	.25
1511	A694	10c chnt & multi	.45	.25
1512	A694	10c ap grn & multi	.45	.25
	Nos. 1508-1512 (5)		2.25	1.25

ARGENTINA '85.

Illuminated Fruit, by Fortunato Lacamera (1887-1951) — A695

Paintings: 20c, Woman with Bird, by Juan del Prete, vert.

1985, Sept. 7   Perf. 13½
1513	A695	20c multi	.90	.40
1514	A695	30c multi	1.00	.40

Flower Types of 1982-85

Designs: 1a, Begonia micranthera var. hieronymi. 5a, Gymnocalycium bruchii.

1985-88   Photo.   Perf. 13½
1515	A641	½c like #1356	.50	.25
1516	A641	1c like #1439	.30	.25
1517	A641	2c like #1345	.30	.25
1518	A641	3c like #1441	.30	.25
1519	A641	5c like #1346	.30	.25
1520	A641	10c like #1348	.50	.25
1521	A641	20c like #1347	.40	.25
1522	A641	30c like #1443A	.80	.30
1523	A641	50c like #1344	1.10	.30
1524	A641	1a multi	1.50	.35
1525	A641	2a like #1351	.60	.25
1526	A641	5a multi	3.50	2.50

Size: 15x23mm
1527	A641	8½c like #1349	.30	.25
	Nos. 1515-1527 (13)		10.40	5.70

Issued: ½c, 1c, 12/16; 2c, 8½c, 30c, 9/18; 3c, 5c, 10c, 50c, 1a, 9/7; 20c, 10/17; 5a, 3/21/87; 2a, 12/5/88.

No. 1435 Surcharged
1986, Nov. 4   Photo.   Perf. 13½
1530	A641	10c on 1p No. 1435	1.00	.50

Folk Musical Instruments A699

1985, Sept. 14   Litho.   Perf. 13½
1531	A699	20c Frame drum	.60	.40
1532	A699	20c Long flute	.60	.40
1533	A699	20c Jew's harp	.60	.40
1534	A699	20c Pan flutes	.60	.40
1535	A699	20c Musical bow	.60	.40
	Nos. 1531-1535 (5)		3.00	2.00

Skaters A701

Deception, by J. H. Rivoira — A702

Juan Bautista Alberdi (1810-1884), Historian, Politician A700

Famous men: 20c, Nicolas Avellaneda (1836-1885), President in 1874. 30c, Fr. Luis Beltran (1784-1827), military and naval engineer. 40c, Ricardo Levene (1885-1959), historian, author.

1985, Oct. 5
1536	A700	10c multi	.25	.25
1537	A700	20c multi	.45	.25
1538	A700	30c multi	.65	.40
1539	A700	40c multi	1.20	.45
	Nos. 1536-1539 (4)		2.55	1.35

Type of 1985 and

1985, Oct. 19   Litho.   Perf. 13½
1540	A701	20c multi	.60	.40
1541	A702	30c multi	.65	.40

Size: 147x75mm
Imperf
1542	A693a	1a multi	3.50	3.50

IYY. No. 1542 is inscribed in silver with the UN 40th anniversary and IYY emblems.

Provincial Views — A703

Designs: No. 1543, Rock Window, Buenos Aires. No. 1544, Forclaz Windmill, Entre Rios. No. 1545, Lake Potrero de los Funes, San Luis. No. 1546, Mission church, north-east province. No. 1547, Penguin colony, Punta Tombo, Chubut. No. 1548, Water Mirrors, Cordoba.

1985, Nov. 23   Perf. 13½
1543	A703	10c multi	.45	.25
1544	A703	10c multi	.45	.25
1545	A703	10c multi	.45	.25
1546	A703	10c multi	.45	.25
1547	A703	10c multi	.45	.25
1548	A703	10c multi	.45	.25
	Nos. 1543-1548 (6)		2.70	1.50

Christmas 1985 — A704

Designs: 10c, Birth of Our Lord, by Carlos Cortes. 20c, Christmas, by Hector Viola.

1985, Dec. 7
1549	A704	10c multi	.40	.25
1550	A704	20c multi	.85	.50

Natl. Campaign for the Prevention of Blindness — A705

1985, Dec. 7
1551	A705	10c multi	.40	.25

Rio Gallegos City, Cent. — A716

1985, Dec. 21   Litho.   Perf. 13½
1552	A716	10c Church	1.50	.40

Natl. Grape Harvest Festival, 50th Anniv. A717

1986, Mar. 15
1553	A717	10c multi	.45	.30

Exists with Wmk. 365, Value $20.

Historical Architecture in Buenos Aires — A718

Designs: No. 1554, Valentin Alsina House, Italian Period, 1860-70. No. 1555, House on Cerrito Street, French influence, 1880-1900. No. 1556, House on the Avenida de Mayo y Santiago del Estero, Art Nouveau, 1900-10. No. 1557, Customs Building, academic architecture, 1900-15. No. 1558, Isaac Fernandez Blanco Museum, house of architect Martin Noel, natl. restoration, 1910-30. Nos. 1554-1556 vert.

1986, Apr. 19
1554	A718	20c multi	.60	.40
1555	A718	20c multi	.60	.40
1556	A718	20c multi	.60	.40
1557	A718	20c multi	.60	.40
1558	A718	20c multi	.60	.40
	Nos. 1554-1558 (5)		3.00	2.00

Antarctic Bases, Pioneers and Fauna — A719

Designs: a, Base, Jubany. b, Arctocephalus gazella. c, Otaria byronia. d, Gen. Belgrano Base. e, Daption capensis. f, Diomedia melanophris. g, Apterodytes patagonica. h, Macronectes giganteus. i, Hugo Alberto Acuna (1885-1953). j, Spheniscus magellanicus. k, Gallinago gallinage. l, Capt. Agustin del Castillo (1855-89).

1986, May 31
1559   Sheet of 12   17.50 17.50
a.-l.   A719 10c any single   .90   .85

Famous
People — A720

Designs: No. 1560, Dr. Alicia Moreau de
Justo, human rights activist. No. 1561, Dr.
Emilio Ravignani (1886-1954), historian. No.
1562, Indira Gandhi.

1986, July 5   Litho.   Perf. 13½
1560 A720 10c multi   .45   .40
1561 A720 10c multi   .45   .40
1562 A720 30c multi   1.40   .75
     Nos. 1560-1562 (3)   2.30 1.55

Statuary,
Buenos
Aires — A721

20c, Fountain of the Nereids, by Dolores
Lola Mora (1866-1936). 30c, Lamenting at
Work, by Rogelio Yrurtia (1879-1950), horiz.

1986, July 5
1563 A721 20c multi   .90   .30
1564 A721 30c multi   .90   .30

Famous
Men — A722

Designs: No. 1565, Francisco N. Laprida
(1786-1829), politician. No. 1566, Estanislao
Lopez (1786-1838), brigadier general. No.
1567, Francisco Ramirez (1786-1821),
general.

1986, Aug. 9   Litho.   Perf. 13
1565 A722 20c dl yel, brn & blk   .50   .40
1566 A722 20c dl yel, brn & blk   .50   .40
1567 A722 20c dl yel, brn & blk   .50   .40
     Nos. 1565-1567 (3)   1.50 1.20

Fr. Ceferino
Namuncura
(1886-1905)
A723

1986, Aug. 30   Perf. 13½
1568 A723 20c multi   .60   .40

Miniature Sheets

Natl. Team Victory, 1986 World Cup
Soccer Championships,
Mexico — A724

Designs: No. 1569a-1569d, Team. Nos.
1569e-1569h, Shot on goal. Nos. 1570a-
1570d, Action close-up. Nos. 1570e-1570h,
Diego Maradona holding soccer cup.

1986, Nov. 8   Litho.   Perf. 13½
1569 A724 Sheet of 8   12.50 12.50
a.-h.   75c any single   1.25   1.25
1570 A724 Sheet of 8   12.50 12.50
a.-h.   75c any single   1.25   1.25

San Francisco (Cordoba),
Cent. — A725

20c, Municipal Building.

1986, Nov. 8
1571 A725 20c multicolored   .50   .35

Trelew City (Chubut), Cent. — A726

20c, Old railroad station, 1865.

1986, Nov. 22   Litho.   Perf. 13½
1572 A726 20c multicolored   .50   .35

Mutualism Day — A727

1986, Nov. 22
1573 A727 20c multicolored   .75   .40

Christmas — A728

Designs: 20c, Naif retable, by Aniko Szabo
(b. 1945). 30c, Everyone's Tree, by Franca
Delacqua (b. 1947).

1986, Dec. 13   Litho.   Perf. 13½
1574 A728 20c multicolored   1.00   .45
1575 A728 30c multicolored   1.10   .45

Santa Rosa de
Lima, 400th
Birth
Anniv. — A729

1986, Dec. 13
1576 A729 50c multicolored   1.90   .75

Rio Cuarto
Municipal
Building
A730

No. 1578, Court Building, Cordoba.

1986, Dec. 20
1577 A730 20c shown   .90   .30
1578 A730 20c multicolored   .90   .30
     Rio Cuarto City, bicent. Court Building, Cor-
doba, 50th anniv.

Antarctic
Treaty, 25th
Anniv. — A731

1987, Mar. 7   Litho.   Perf. 13½
1579 A731 20c Marine biologist   1.00   .45
1580 A731 30c Ornithologist   1.25   .45
Souvenir Sheet
Perf. 12
1581   Sheet of 2   5.50 5.50
a.   A731 20c like No. 1579   2.00 1.50
b.   A731 30c like No. 1580   3.00 2.00
     No. 1581 contains 2 stamps, size:
40x50mm. Exist imperf. Value $500.

Natl. Mortgage Bank, Cent. — A732

1987, Mar. 21   Perf. 13½
1582 A732 20c multicolored   .80   .40

Natl. Cooperative Associations
Movement — A733

1987, Mar. 21
1583 A733 20c multicolored   .80   .40

Second State
Visit of Pope
John
Paul II — A734

Engr., Litho. (No. 1585)
1987, Apr. 4   Perf. 13½
1584 A734 20c shown   .40   .25
1585 A734 80c Papal blessing   1.50   .70
Souvenir Sheet
Perf. 12
1586 A734 1a like 20c   3.50 2.50
     No. 1586 contains one 40x50mm stamp.

Intl.
Peace
Year
A735

30c, Pigeon, abstract sculpture by Victor
Kaniuka.

1987, Apr. 11   Litho.
1587 A735 20c multicolored   .70   .30
1588 A735 30c multicolored   .70   .30

Low Handicap
World Polo
Championships
A736

Polo Players, painting by Alejandro Moy.

1987, Apr. 11
1589 A736 20c multicolored   .90   .25

Miniature Sheet

ICOM '86 — A737

Designs: a, Emblem. b, Family crest,
National History Museum, Buenos Aires. c, St.
Bartholomew, Enrique Larreta Museum of
Spanish Art, Buenos Aires. d, Zoomorphic
club, Patagonian Museum, San Carlos de
Bariloche. e, Supplication, anthropomorphic
sculpture, Natural Sciences Museum, La
Plata. f, Wrought iron lattice from the house of

J. Urquiza, president of the Confederation of Argentina, Entre Rios History Museum, Parana. g, St. Joseph, 18th cent. wood figurine, Northern History Museum, Salta. h, Funerary urn, Provincial Archaeological Museum, Santiago del Estero.

1987, May 30
1590 A737 Sheet of 8   3.75 3.75
  a.-h. 25c any single   .45 .45
Intl. Council of Museums, 14th general conf.

Natl. College of Monserrat, Cordoba, 300th Anniv. — A738

1987, July 4   *Imperf.*
1591 A738 1a multicolored   1.50 1.50
Monserrat '87 Philatelic Exposition.

Fight Drug Abuse A739

The Proportions of Man, by da Vinci.

1987, Aug. 15   *Perf. 13½*
1592 A739 30c multicolored   1.10 .30

Famous Men A740

Portraits and quotations: 20c, Jorge Luis Borges (1899-1986), writer. 30c, Armando Discepolo (1887-1971), playwright. 50c, Carlos A. Pueyrredon (1887-1962), professor, Legion of Honor laureate.

1987, Aug. 15
1593 A740 20c multicolored   .50 .45
1594 A740 30c multicolored   .50 .45
1595 A740 50c multicolored   .50 .45
     Nos. 1593-1595 (3)   1.50 1.35

Pillar Boxes
A741   A742

1987   *Photo.*   *Perf. 13½*
1596 A741 (30c) yel, blk & dark
           red   .90 .30
     Booklet with 10 stamps   9.00
1597 A742 (33c) lt blue grn, blk
           & yel   .90 .35
     Complete booklet, 10 #1597 9.00
Issue dates: (30c), June 8; (33c), July 13.

The Sower, by Julio Vanzo A743

1987, Sept. 12
1598 A743 30c multicolored   .75 .30
Argentine Agrarian Federation, 75th anniv.

10th Pan American Games, Indianapolis, Aug. 7-25 — A744

1987, Sept. 26
1599 A744 20c Basketball   .45 .25
1600 A744 30c Rowing   .50 .25
1601 A744 50c Yachting   .50 .25
     Nos. 1599-1601 (3)   1.45 .75

Children Playing Doctor, WHO Emblem A745

1987, Oct. 7
1602 A745 30c multi   .50 .30
Vaccinate every child campaign.

Heroes of the Revolution A746

Signing of the San Nicolas Accord, 1852, by Rafael del Villar A747

Independence anniversaries and historic events: No. 1603, Maj.-Col. Ignacio Alvarez Thomas (1787-1857). No. 1604, Col. Manuel Crispulo Bernabe Dorrego (1787-1829). No. 1606, 18th cent. Spanish map of the Falkland Isls., administered by Jacinto de Altolaguirre.

1987, Oct. 17
1603 A746 25c shown   .50 .25
1604 A746 25c multi   .50 .25
1605 A747 50c shown   1.00 .35
1606 A747 50c multi   1.00 .35
     Nos. 1603-1606 (4)   3.00 1.20
Museum established in the House of the San Nicholas Accord, 50th anniv. (No. 1605); Jacinto de Altolaguirre (1754-1787), governor the Malvinas Isls. for the King of Spain (No. 1606).

Celedonio Galvan Moreno, 1st Director — A748

1987, Nov. 21
1607 A748 50c multicolored   .80 .45
Postas Argentinas magazine, 50th anniv.

LRA National Radio, Buenos Aires, 50th Anniv. — A749

1987, Nov. 21
1608 A749 50c multicolored   .80 .45

Natl. Philatelic Society, Cent. A750

1987, Nov. 21
1609 A750 1a Jose Marco del
           Pont   1.60 .50

Christmas A751

Tapestries: 50c, *Navidad*, by Alisia Frega. 1a, *Vitral*, by Silvina Trigos.

1987, Dec. 5
1610 A751 50c multicolored   .60 .30
1611 A751 1a multicolored   1.25 .45

Natl. Parks — A752

1987, Dec. 19   *Perf. 13x13½*
1612 A752 50c Baritu   1.50 .35
1613 A752 50c Nahuel Huapi   1.50 .35
1614 A752 50c Rio Pilcomayo   1.50 .35
1615 A752 50c Tierra del Fuego 1.50 .35
1616 A752 50c Iguacu   1.50 .35
     Nos. 1612-1616 (5)   7.50 1.75
See Nos. 1647-1651, 1715-1719, 1742-1746.

Landscapes in Buenos Aires Painted by Jose Cannella — A753

No. 1617, Caminito. No. 1618, Viejo Almacen.

1988-89   *Litho.*   *Perf. 13½*
1617 A753 5a multi   2.40 1.25
1618 A753 10a multi   4.75 2.50
1618A A753 10a like No.
           1618   1.25 .60
1618B A753 50a like No.
           1617   1.25 .60
   c. Wmk 365   125.00 20.00
     Nos. 1617-1618B (4)   9.65 4.95
No. 1618 inscribed "Viejo Almacen"; No. 1618A inscribed "El Viejo Almacen."
Issue dates: 5a, No. 1618, 3/15; No. 1618A, 10/20; 50a, 5/30/89.
For overprint see No. 1635.

Minstrel in a Tavern, by Carlos Morel A754

Paintings: No. 1620, Interior of Curuzu, by Candido Lopez.

1988, Mar. 19   *Litho.*   *Perf. 13½*
1619 A754 1a shown   1.00 .35
1620 A754 1a multicolored   1.00 .35
See Nos. 1640-1641.

Argentine-Brazilian Economic Cooperation and Integration Program for Mutual Growth — A755

1988, Mar. 19
1621 A755 1a multicolored   .65 .35

Cities of Alta Gracia and Corrientes, 400th Annivs. — A756

No. 1622, Alta Gracia Church. No. 1623, Chapel of St. Anne, Corrientes.

1988, Apr. 9   *Litho.*   *Perf. 13½*
1622 A756 1a multicolored   1.00 .45
1623 A756 1a multicolored   1.00 .45

Labor Day — A757

Grain Carriers, a tile mosaic by Alfredo Guido, Line D of Nueve de Julio station, Buenos Aires subway: a, (UL). b, (UR). c, (LL). d, (LR).

1988, May 21
1624	A757	Block of 4	4.00	4.00
a.-d.		50c any single	.55	.55

1988 Summer Olympics, Seoul — A758

1988, July 16 Litho. Perf. 13½
1625	A758	1a Running	.50	.30
1626	A758	2a Soccer	1.10	.30
1627	A758	3a Field hockey	1.60	.50
1628	A758	4a Tennis	2.00	.65
		Nos. 1625-1628 (4)	5.20	1.75

Mendoza Bank, Cent. — A759

Natl. Gendarmerie, Cent. — A760

1988, Aug. 13
1629	A759	2a multicolored	1.20	.50
1630	A760	2a multicolored	1.20	.50

Sarmiento and Cathedral School to the North, Buenos Aires — A761

1988, Sept. 10 Litho. Perf. 13½
1631	A761	3a multicolored	1.25	.35

Domingo Faustino Sarmiento (1811-1888), educator, politician.

St. Cayetano, Patron of Workers A762

El Amor, by Antonio Berni, Pacific Gallery, Buenos Aires — A763

3a, Our Lady of Carmen, Cuyo.

1988, Sept. 10 Litho.
1632	A762	2a multicolored	.55	.45
1633	A762	3a multicolored	.85	.85

Souvenir Sheet
Perf. 12
1634	A763	5a multicolored	2.75	2.75

Liniers Philatelic Circle and the Argentine Western Philatelic Institution (IFADO), 50th anniv.
No. 1634 contains one 40x30mm stamp.

No. 1617 Ovptd.

1988, Oct. 29 Litho. Perf. 13½
1635	A753	5a multicolored	6.75	2.00

21st Congress of the Intl. Urology Soc.

Tourism — A763a

3a, Purmamarca, Jujuy. 20a, Ushuaia.

1988, Nov. 1 Litho. Perf. 13½
1635A	A763a	3a multi	.70	.30

Size: 28½x38mm
1635B	A763a	20a multi	4.50	2.00

Buenos Aires Subway, 75th Anniv. A764

5a, Train, c. 1913.

1988, Dec. 17 Litho. Perf. 13½
1636	A764	5a multicolored	1.40	.60

Christmas A765

Frescoes in Ucrania Cathedral, Buenos Aires: No. 1637, Virgin Patron. No. 1638, Virgin of Tenderness.

1988, Dec. 17
1637	A765	5a multicolored	2.25	.60
1638	A765	5a multicolored	2.25	.60

St. John Bosco (1815-1888), Educator, and Church in Ushuaia — A766

1989, Apr. 8 Litho. Perf. 13½
1639	A766	5a multicolored	.90	.25

Dated 1988.

Art Type of 1988

Paintings: No. 1640, Blancos, by Fernando Fader (1882-1935). No. 1641, Rincon de los Areneros, by Justo Lynch (1870-1953).

1989, Apr. 8
1640	A754	5a multicolored	1.75	.30
1641	A754	5a multicolored	1.75	.30

Holy Week A767

Sculpture and churches: No. 1642, The Crown of Thorns, Calvary of Tandil, and Church of Our Lady Carmelite, Tandil. No. 1643, Jesus the Nazarene and Metropolitan Cathedral, Buenos Aires. No. 1644, Jesus Encounters His Mother (scene of the crucifixion), La Quebrada Village, San Luis. No. 1645, Our Lady of Sorrow and Church of Humahuaca, Jujuy.

1989, Apr. 22 Litho. Perf. 13½
1642	A767	2a multicolored	.30	.25
1643	A767	2a multicolored	.30	.25
1644	A767	3a multicolored	.40	.25
1645	A767	3a multicolored	.40	.25
a.		Block of 4 + 2 labels	1.50	1.25
		Nos. 1642-1645 (4)	1.40	1.00

Printed in sheets of 16+4 labels containing blocks of 4 of each design. Labels picture Jesus's arrival in Jerusalem (Palm Sunday).

Prevent Alcoholism — A768

1989, Apr. 22
1646	A768	5a multicolored	.75	.30

Natl. Park Type of 1987
1989, May 6 Perf. 13x13½
1647	A752	5a Lihue Calel	1.25	.30
1648	A752	5a El Palmar	1.25	.30
1649	A752	5a Calilegua	1.25	.30
1650	A752	5a Chaco	1.25	.30
1651	A752	5a Los Glaciares	1.25	.30
		Nos. 1647-1651 (5)	6.25	1.50

Admission of Argentina to the ITU, Cent. — A769

1989, May 6 Perf. 13½
1652	A769	10a multicolored	1.75	.30

World Model Aircraft Championships — A770

No. 1653, F1A glider. No. 1654, F1B rubber band motor. No. 1655, F1C gas motor.

1989, May 27 Litho. Perf. 13½
1653	A770	5a multi	.60	.25
1654	A770	5a multi	.60	.25
1655	A770	10a multi	1.10	.30
		Nos. 1653-1655 (3)	2.30	.80

French Revolution, Bicent. — A771

Designs: 10a, "All men are born free and equal." 15a, French flag and La Marianne, by Gandon. 25a, Liberty Guiding the People, by Delacroix.

1989, July 1 Litho. Perf. 13½
1656	A771	10a shown	.60	.30
1657	A771	15a multicolored	.60	.30

Souvenir Sheet
Perf. 12
1658	A771	25a multicolored	1.50	1.50

No. 1658 contains one 40x30mm stamp.

The Republic, a Bronze Bust in the Congreso de la Nacion, Buenos Aires — A772

1989, Aug. 12 Litho. Perf. 13½
1659	A772	300a on 50a multi	1.75	.50

Peaceful transition of power (presidential office). Not issued without surcharge.

Immigration to Argentina — A773

150a, S.S. Weser, 1889. 200a, Immigrant hotel, 1889.

1989, Aug. 19   Perf. 13½
1660 A773 150a multi   1.75   .50
1661 A773 200a multi   1.75   .60

Souvenir Sheet
Perf. 12
1662   Sheet of 2   2.75   2.75
  a.   A773 150a like No. 1660   1.25   1.25
  b.   A773 200a like No. 1661   1.25   1.25

No. 1662 contains 40x30mm stamps.

Famous Men A774

Designs: No. 1663, Fr. Guillermo Furlong (1889-1974), historian, and title page of *The Jesuits*. No. 1664, Dr. Gregorio Alvarez (1889-1986), physician, and title page of *Canto a Chos Malal*. 200a, Brig.-Gen. Enrique Martinez (1789-1870) and lithograph *La Batalla de Maipu*, by Teodoro Gericault.

1989, Oct. 7   Litho.   Perf. 13½
1663 A774 100a multicolored   .55   .35
1664 A774 150a multicolored   .55   .35
1665 A774 200a multicolored   .55   .35
   Nos. 1663-1665 (3)   1.65   1.05

America Issue — A775

Emblem of the Postal Union of the Americas and Spain (PUAS) and pre-Columbian art from Catamarca Province: 200a, Wooden mask from Atajo, Loma Morada. 300a, Urn of the Santa Maria Culture (Phase 3) from Punta de Balastro, Santa Maria Department.

1989, Oct. 14
1666 A775 200a multicolored   1.25   .50
1667 A775 300a multicolored   1.90   .60

Federal Police Week — A776

Children's drawings: No. 1668, Diego Molinari, age 13. No. 1669, Carlos Alberto Sarago, age 8. No. 1670, Roxana Andrea Osuna, age 7. No. 1671, Pablo Javier Quaglia, age 9.

1989, Oct. 28   Litho.   Perf. 13½
1668 A776 100a multi   .65   .25
1669 A776 100a multi   .65   .25
1670 A776 150a multi   1.10   .35
1671 A776 150a multi   1.10   .35
   Nos. 1668-1671 (4)   3.50   1.20

Battle of Vuelta de Obligado, 1845 — A777

1989, Dec. 2   Litho.   Perf. 13x13½
1672 A777 300a multicolored   1.50   .30

Paintings — A778

Cristo de los Cerros, Sculpture by Chipo Cespedes A779

No. 1673, Gato Frias. No. 1674, Maria Carballido.

1989, Dec. 2   Perf. 13½
1673 A778 200a multi   1.10   .30
1674 A778 200a multi   1.10   .30
1675 A779 300a shown   1.10   .30
   Nos. 1673-1675 (3)   3.30   .90

Christmas.

Buenos Aires Port, Cent. — A780

1990, Mar. 3   Litho.   Perf. 13½
1676 A780   Strip of 4   15.00   15.00
  a.-d.   200a any single   1.50   .75

Aconcagua Intl. Fair, Mendoza — A781

Design: Aconcagua mountain, Los Horcones Lagoon and fair emblem.

1990, Mar. 3
1677 A781   Pair, #a.-b.   2.00   1.25

Natl. Savings and Insurance Fund, 75th Anniv. — A782

1990, May 5   Litho.   Perf. 13½
1678 A782 1000a multicolored   .60   .30

Miniature Sheet

1990 World Cup Soccer Championships, Italy — A783

Designs: a, Athlete's torso (striped jersey). b, Athlete's torso (solid jersey). c, Players' feet, soccer ball. d, Player (knee to waist).

1990, May 5
1679 A783   Sheet of 4   7.00   7.00
  a.-d.   2500a multicolored   1.75   1.25

Carlos Pellegrini, Commercial High School Founder, Cent. — A784

1990, June 2   Litho.   Perf. 13½
1680 A784 2000a multicolored   1.50   .60

Youth Against Drugs A785

1990, June 2
1681 A785 2000a multicolored   1.50   .60

Intl. Literacy Year A786

1990, July 14   Litho.   Perf. 13½
1682 A786 2000a multicolored   1.50   .60

Flower Type of 1982 in New Currency
1989-90   Photo.   Perf. 13½
1683 A641   10a like #1433   .35   .25
1684 A641   20a like #1440   .30   .25
1685 A641   50a like #1354   .35   .25
1686 A641   100a like #1439   .45   .25
1687 A641   300a like #1345   1.50   .50
1688 A641   500a like #1441   2.50   .75
1689 A641   500a like #1355   .75   .35
1690 A641   5000a like #1349   3.75   .35
1691 A641   10,000a like #1350   6.00   3.25
   Nos. 1683-1691 (9)   15.95   6.20

Issued: 20a, 100a, 300a, 8/1/89; 10a, 8/24/89; 50a, 8/30/89; 1000, 3/8/90; 5000a, 4/6/90; 10,000a, 7/2/90.

World Basketball Championships A787

1990, Aug. 11   Litho.   Perf. 13½
1703 A787 2000a multicolored   2.00   1.50

Souvenir Sheet
Perf. 12
1704 A787 5000a Jump ball   6.50   6.00

Postal Union of the Americas and Spain, 14th Congress — A788

No. 1705, Arms, seal. No. 1706, Sailing ships. No. 1707, Modern freighter. No. 1708, Van, cargo plane.

1990, Sept. 15   Litho.   Perf. 13½
1705 A788 3000a multi   1.75   .75
1706 A788 3000a multi   1.75   .75
1707 A788 3000a multi   1.75   .75
1708 A788 3000a multi   1.75   .75
   Nos. 1705-1708 (4)   7.00   3.00

America Issue A789

No. 1709, Iguacu Falls, hamelia erecta. No. 1710, Puerto Deseado, elephant seal.

1990, Oct. 13
1709 A789 3000a multicolored   2.50   1.25
1710 A789 3000a multicolored   2.50   1.25

Natl. Park Type of 1987
1990, Oct. 27   Perf. 13x13½
1715 A752 3000a Lanin   2.00   .90
1716 A752 3000a Laguna Blanca   2.00   .90
1717 A752 3000a Perito Moreno   2.00   .90
1718 A752 3000a Puelo   2.00   .90
1719 A752 3000a El Rey   2.00   .90
   Nos. 1715-1719 (5)   10.00   4.50

Stamp Day A790

1990, Oct. 27   Perf. 13½
1720 A790 3000a multicolored   1.50   .55

Salvation Army, Cent. — A793

Designs: No. 1722, Natl. University of the Littoral, Santa Fe, cent.

1990, Dec. 1   Litho.   Perf. 13½

1721	A793	3000a multicolored	1.75	.90
1722	A793	3000a multicolored	1.75	.90
a.		Pair, #1721-1722 + label	7.50	6.50

Miniature Sheets

Christmas — A794

Stained glass windows: No. 1723, The Immaculate Conception. No. 1724, The Nativity. No. 1725, Presentation of Jesus at the Temple.

1990, Dec. 1   Perf. 13½x13
Sheets of 4

1723	A794	3000a #a.-d.	7.50	7.50
1724	A794	3000a #a.-d.	7.50	7.50
1725	A794	3000a #a.-d.	7.50	7.50

Landscapes — A795

Paintings: No. 1726, Los Sauces, by Atilio Malinverno. No. 1727, Paisaje, by Pío Collivadino, vert.

1991, May 4   Litho.   Perf. 13½

1726	A795	4000a multicolored	1.50	.90
1727	A795	4000a multicolored	1.50	.90

Return of Remains of Juan Manuel de Rosas (1793-1877) A796

1991, June 1   Litho.   Perf. 13½

1728	A796	4000a multicolored	1.25	.75

Swiss Confederation, 700th Anniv. — A797

1991, Aug. 3   Litho.   Perf. 13½

1729	A797	4000a multicolored	1.25	.75

Miniature Sheet

Cartoons — A798

Designs: a, Hernan, the Corsair by Jose Luis Salinas. b, Don Fulgencio by Lino Palacio. c, Medical Rules of Salerno by Oscar Esteban Conti. d, Buenos Aires Undershirt by Alejandro del Prado. e, Girls! by Jose A.G. Divito. f, Langostino by Eduardo Carlos Ferro. g, Mafalda by Joaquin Salvador Lavoro. h, Mort Cinder by Alberto Breccia.

1991, Aug. 3

1730	A798	4000a Sheet of 8,		
		#a.-h.	19.00	19.00

City of La Rioja, 400th Anniv. — A799

1991, Sept. 14   Litho.   Perf. 13½

1731	A799	4000a multicolored	1.25	.75

First Balloon Flight over the Andes, 75th Anniv. — A800

1991, Sept. 14

1732	A800	4000a multicolored	1.25	.75

America Issue A801

Designs: No. 1733, Magellan's caravel, Our Lady of Victory. No. 1734, Ships of Juan Diaz de Solis.

1991, Nov. 9   Litho.   Perf. 13½

1733	A801	4000a multicolored	1.75	.75
1734	A801	4000a multicolored	1.75	.75

Anniversaries — A802

Designs: a, Johann Heinrich Pestalozzi, Swiss pedagogue and educational reformer, whose Argentine school, the Colegio Pestalozzi, was associated with the anti-fascist newspaper Argentinisches Tageblatt. b, Leandro N. Alem, founder of Radical People's Party. c, Man with rifle, emblem of Argentine Federal Shooting Club. d, Dr. Nicasio Etcheparreborda, emblem of College of Odontology. e, Dalmiro Huergo, emblem of Graduate School of Economics.

1991, Nov. 30

1735	A802	4000a Strip of 5,		
		#a.-e.	8.00	8.00

Christmas — A803

Stained glass windows from Our Lady of Lourdes Basilica, Buenos Aires: Nos. 1736a-1736b, Top and bottom portions of Virgin of the Valley, Catamarca. Nos. 1736c-1736d, Top and bottom portions of Virgin of the Rosary of the Miracle, Cordoba.

1991, Nov. 30

1736	A803	4000a Block of 4,		
		#a.-d.	6.00	6.00
a.		Sheet of 16, 4 ea #a-d, + 4 labels	26.00	26.00

The four labels of No. 1736a form a nativity scene across the middle of the sheet.

Famous Men — A804

Designs: a, Gen. Juan de Lavalle (1797-1841), Peruvian medal of honor. b, Brig. Gen. Jose Maria del Rosario Ciriaco Paz (1791-1854), medal. c, Marco Manuel de Avellaneda (1813-1841), lawyer. d, Guillermo Enrique Hudson (1841-1922), author.

1991, Dec. 14   Litho.   Perf. 13½

1737	A804	4000a Block of 4, #a.-d.	5.75	5.75

Birds — A805

No. 1738, Pterocnemia pennata. No. 1739, Morphnus guianensis. No. 1740, Ara chloroptera.

1991, Dec. 28

1738	A805	4000a multicolored	1.60	1.00
1739	A805	4000a multicolored	1.60	1.00
1740	A805	4000a multicolored	1.60	1.00
		Nos. 1738-1740 (3)	4.80	3.00

Miniature Sheet

Arbrafex '92, Argentina-Brazil Philatelic Exhibition — A806

Traditional costumes: a, Gaucho, woman. b, Gaucho, horse. c, Gaucho in store. d, Gaucho holding lariat.

1992, Mar. 14   Litho.   Perf. 13½

1741	A806	38c Sheet of 4, #a.-d.	7.00	7.00

Natl. Park Type of 1987

No. 1742, Alerces. No. 1743, Formosa Nature Reserve. No. 1744, Petrified Forest. No. 1745, Arrayanes. No. 1746, Laguna de los Pozuelos.

1992, Apr. 4   Litho.   Perf. 13x13½

1742	A752	38c multicolored	1.50	.50
1743	A752	38c multicolored	1.50	.50
1744	A752	38c multicolored	1.50	.70
1745	A752	38c multicolored	1.50	.50
1746	A752	38c multicolored	1.50	.50
		Nos. 1742-1746 (5)	7.50	2.70

Mushrooms — A807

10c, Psilocybe cubensis. 25c, Coprinus atramentarius. 50c, Suillus granulatus. 51c, Morchella esculenta. 61c, Amanita muscaria. 68c, Coprinus comatus. 1.77p, Stropharia oeruginosa.

1992-94   Photo.   Perf. 13½

1748	A807	10c multi	1.00	.30
1749	A807	25c multi	1.10	.30
a.		Wmk. 365	30.00	4.00
1750	A807	38c like #1748	1.10	.30
1751	A807	48c like #1749	1.40	.60
1752	A807	50c multi	2.25	.30
1753	A807	51c multi	1.40	.60
1754	A807	61c multi	1.75	.75
1755	A807	68c multi	2.75	.50
1756	A807	1p like #1754	4.50	.80
1757	A807	1.25p like #1752	4.50	.50
1758	A807	1.77p multi	7.00	2.75
1759	A807	2p like #1753	9.25	2.25
		Nos. 1748-1759 (12)	38.00	9.95

No. 1758 not issued without overprint "Centro Filatelico de Neuquen y Rio Negro 50th Aniversario."

Issued: 38c, 4/4/92; 48c, 51c, 61c, 8/1/92; 1.77p, 11/7/92; 25c, 50c, 8/17/93; 1p, 2p, 8/26/93; 10c, 1/11/94; 68c, 1.25p, 10/10/92; No. 1749a, 1997.

See design A838.

Falkland Islands War, 10th Anniv. A808

No. 1767, Pucara 1A-58. No. 1768, Cruiser Gen. Belgrano. No. 1769, Soldier and truck.

1992, May 2 Litho. Perf. 13½
1767 A808 38c multicolored 1.60 .80
1768 A808 38c multicolored 1.60 .80
1769 A808 38c multicolored 1.60 .80
Nos. 1767-1769 (3) 4.80 2.40

Miniature Sheet

Preserve the Environment — A809

a, Deer. b, Geese. c, Butterflies. d, Whale.

1992, June 6 Litho. Perf. 12
1770 A809 38c Sheet of 4, #a.-d. 8.00 8.00

Paintings by Florencio Molina Campos — A810

No. 1771, A La Sombra. No. 1772, Tileforo Areco, vert.

1992, June 6 Perf. 13½
1771 A810 38c multicolored 1.50 .90
1772 A810 38c multicolored 1.50 .90

Famous Men A811

Designs: No. 1773, Gen. Lucio N. Mansilla (1792-1871). No. 1774, Jose Manuel Estrada (1842-1894), writer. No. 1775, Brig. Gen. Jose I. Garmendia (1842-1915).

1992, July 4 Litho. Perf. 13½
1773 A811 38c multicolored 1.00 .70
1774 A811 38c multicolored 1.00 .70
1775 A811 38c multicolored 1.00 .70
Nos. 1773-1775 (3) 3.00 2.10

Fight Against Drugs — A812

1992, Aug. 1 Perf. 13½x13
1776 A812 38c multicolored 1.40 .70

Col. Jose M. Calaza, 140th Birth Anniv. A813

1992, Sept. 5 Litho. Perf. 13½
1777 A813 38c multicolored 1.25 .70

Discovery of America, 500th Anniv. — A814

Designs: a, Columbus, castle, ship. b, Native drawings, Columbus.

1992, Oct. 10 Litho. Perf. 13½
1778 A814 38c Pair, #a.-b. 4.00 4.00

Argentine Film Posters A815

No. 1779, Dios Se Lo Pague, 1948. No. 1780, Las Aguas Bajan Turbias, 1952. No. 1781, Un Guapo Del 900, 1960. No. 1782, La Tregua, 1974. No. 1783, La Historia Oficial, 1984.

1992, Nov. 7 Litho. Perf. 13½
1779 A815 38c multicolored 1.50 .50
1780 A815 38c multicolored 1.50 .50
1781 A815 38c multicolored 1.50 .50
1782 A815 38c multicolored 1.50 .50
1783 A815 38c multicolored 1.50 .50
Nos. 1779-1783 (5) 7.50 2.50

Christmas A816

1992, Nov. 28
1784 A816 38c multicolored 1.25 .60

Miniature Sheet

Iberoprenfil '92 — A817

Lighthouses: a, Punta Mogotes. b, Rio Negro. c, San Antonio. d, Cabo Blanco.

1992, Dec. 5
1785 A817 38c Sheet of 4, #a.-d. 16.00 12.00

A818

Fight Against AIDS — A819

1992, Dec. 12 Litho. Perf. 13½
1786 A818 10c multicolored 2.50 .30
1787 A819 26c multicolored 5.00 .30

Intl. Space Year A820

1992, Dec. 19
1788 A820 38c multicolored 1.25 .50

Souvenir Sheet

Miraculous Lord Crucifix, 400th Anniv. of Arrival in America — A821

1992, Dec. 26 Perf. 12
1789 A821 76c multicolored 4.50 4.50

Jujuy City, 400th Anniv. — A822

1993, Apr. 24 Litho. Perf. 13½
1790 A822 38c multicolored 1.25 .60

Argentina Soccer Assoc., Cent. — A823

1993, Mar. 27
1791 A823 38c multicolored 1.25 .60

Souvenir Sheet

Intl. Philatelic Exhibitions — A824

Designs: a, 38c, City Hall, Poznan, Poland. b, 48c, Statue of Christ the Redeemer, Rio de Janeiro, Brazil. c, 76c, Royal Palace, Bangkok, Thailand.

1993, May 8 Litho. Perf. 12
1792 A824 Sheet of 3, #a.-c. 5.00 5.00

Polska '93 (No. 1792a), Brasiliana '93 (No. 1792b), Bangkok '92 (No. 1792c).

Luis C. Candelaria's Flight Over Andes Mountains, 75th Anniv. — A825

1993, June 26 Litho. Perf. 13x13½
1793 A825 38c multicolored 1.50 .60

Order of San Martin, 50th Anniv. — A826

National History Academy, Cent. — A827

1993, May 29 Perf. 13½
1794 A826 38c multicolored 1.50 .60
1795 A827 38c multicolored 1.50 .60

Armed Forces Memorial Day — A828

No. 1796, Natl. Gendarmerie. No. 1797, Coast Guard.

1993, June 12
1796	A828	38c multicolored	1.50	.60
1797	A828	38c multicolored	1.50	.60

Paintings — A829

Designs: No. 1798, Old House, by Norberto Russo. No. 1799, Pa'las Casas, by Adriana Zaefferer.

1993, Aug. 14　Litho.　Perf. 13½
1798	A829	38c multicolored	1.50	.60
1799	A829	38c multicolored	1.50	.60

Pato — A830

1993, Aug. 28　Litho.　Perf. 12
1800	A830	1p multicolored	3.25	1.25

Nut-Bearing Trees — A831

Designs: No. 1801, Enterolobium contortisiliquum. No. 1802, Prosopis alba. No. 1803, Magnolia grandiflora. No. 1804, Erythrina falcata.

1993, Sept. 25　Litho.　Perf. 13x13½
1801	A831	75c multicolored	2.50	1.00
1802	A831	75c multicolored	2.50	1.00
1803	A831	1.50p multicolored	5.00	2.00
1804	A831	1.50p multicolored	5.00	2.00
		Nos. 1801-1804 (4)	15.00	6.00

America Issue A832

Whales: 50c, Eubalaena australis. 75c, Cephalorhynchus commersonii.

1993, Oct. 9　　Perf. 13½
1805	A832	50c multicolored	1.75	.80
1806	A832	75c multicolored	2.75	1.25

Miniature Sheet

Christmas, New Year — A833

Denomination at: a, UL. b, UR. c, LL. d, LR.

1993, Dec. 4　Litho.　Perf. 13½
1807	A833	75c Sheet of 4, #a.-d.	9.00	8.00

Cave of the Hands, Santa Cruz — A834

1993, Dec. 18
1808	A834	1p multicolored	3.00	1.25

New Emblem, Argentine Postal Service — A835

1994, Jan. 8　　Perf. 11½
1809	A835	75c multicolored	4.50	1.25

See Nos. 1883A-1884.

A836

Players from: 25c, Germany, 1990. 50c, Brazil, 1970. 75c, 1.50p, Argentina, 1986. 1p, Italy, 1982.

1994, June 11　Litho.　Perf. 13½
1810	A836	25c multicolored	.75	.45
1811	A836	50c multicolored	1.50	.90
1812	A836	75c multicolored	2.25	1.40
1813	A836	1p multicolored	3.50	2.00
		Nos. 1810-1813 (4)	8.00	4.75

Souvenir Sheet
Perf. 12
1814	A836	1.50p multicolored	5.00	5.00

No. 1814 contains one 40x50mm stamp with continuous design.

1994 World Cup Soccer Championships, US — A837

Drawings of championships by: No. 1815, Julian Lisenberg. No. 1816, Matias Taylor, vert. No. 1817, Torcuato S. Gonzalez Agote, vert. No. 1818, Maria Paula Palma.

1994, July 23　　Perf. 13½
1815	A837	75c multicolored	3.00	1.00
1816	A837	75c multicolored	3.00	1.00
1817	A837	75c multicolored	3.00	1.00
1818	A837	75c multicolored	3.00	1.00
		Nos. 1815-1818 (4)	12.00	4.00

Issued in sheet containing a block of 4 of each stamp + 4 labels.

A838

Molothrus Badius — A838a

1994-95　Litho.　Perf. 13½
1819	A838	10c like #1748	.25	.25
1820	A838	25c like #1749	.60	.35
1823	A838	50c like #1752	1.25	.60
1828	A838	1p like #1754	2.50	1.25
1832	A838	2p like #1753	5.00	2.50
1835	A838a	9.40p multicolored	25.00	25.00
		Nos. 1819-1835 (6)	34.60	29.95

See designs A807, A849.
Issued: 10c, 25c, 50c, 1p, 2p, 6/14/94; 9.40p, 4/12/95.

Wildlife of Falkland Islands A839

Designs: 25c, Melanodera melanodera. 50c, Pygoscelis papua. 75c, Tachyeres brachypterus. 1p, Mirounga leonina.

1994, Aug 6
1839	A839	25c multicolored	.90	.55
1840	A839	50c multicolored	1.40	.75
1841	A839	75c multicolored	2.75	1.50
1842	A839	1p multicolored	4.00	2.00
		Nos. 1839-1842 (4)	9.05	4.80

City of San Luis, 400th Anniv. — A840

1994, Aug. 20
1843	A840	75c multicolored	3.75	1.50

Province of Tierra del Fuego, Antarctica and South Atlantic Islands A841

1994, Aug. 20
1844	A841	75c multicolored	3.00	1.50

Argentine Inventors — A842

Designs: No. 1845, Ladislao Jose Biro (1899-1985), ball point pen. No. 1846, Raul Pateras de Pescara (1890-1966), helicopter. No. 1847, Quirino Cristiani (1896-1984), animated drawings. No. 1848, Enrique Finochietto (1881-1948), surgical instruments.

1994, Oct. 1
1045	A842	75c multicolored	2.10	2.10
1846	A842	75c multicolored	2.10	2.10
1847	A842	75c multicolored	2.10	2.10
1848	A842	75c multicolored	2.10	2.10
a.		Block of 4, #1845-1848	8.50	8.50

Issued in sheets containing 4 No. 1848a + 4 labels.

UNICEF Christmas A843

75c, Bell, red ornament, star.

1994, Nov. 26　Litho.　Perf. 11½
1849	A843	50c shown	1.50	1.00
1850	A843	75c multicolored	2.25	1.50

Take Care of Our Planet A844

Children's paintings: No. 1851, Boy, girl holding earth, vert. No. 1852, Children outdoors, vert. No. 1853, World as house. No. 1854, People around "world" table.

1994, Dec. 3　　Perf. 13½
1851	A844	25c multicolored	.75	.50
1852	A844	25c multicolored	.75	.50
1853	A844	50c multicolored	1.25	.80
1854	A844	50c multicolored	1.25	.80
		Nos. 1851-1854 (4)	4.00	2.60

Christmas — A845

1994, Dec. 10
1855	A845	50c Annunciation	1.50	1.00
1856	A845	75c Madonna & Child	2.25	1.00

Nos. 1855-1856 each issued in sheets of 20 + 5 labels.

12th Pan American Games, Mar del Plata — A846

1995			Litho.		Perf. 13½
1857	A846	75c	Running	2.25	.65
1858	A846	75c	Cycling	2.25	.65
1859	A846	75c	Diving	2.25	.65
1860	A846	1.25p	Gymnastics, vert.	3.50	.75
1861	A846	1.25p	Soccer, vert.	3.50	.75
		Nos. 1857-1861 (5)		13.75	3.45

Issued: No. 1857, 2/18; others, 3/11.

Natl. Constitution — A847

Design: 75c, Natl. Congress Dome, woman from statue The Republic Triumphant.

1995, Apr. 8				
1862	A847	75c	multicolored	2.25	.70

21st Intl. Book Fair — A848

1995, Apr. 8				
1863	A848	75c	multicolored	2.25	.70

Birds A849

5p, Carduelis magellanica. 10p, Zonotrichia capensis.

1995			Litho.		Perf. 13½
1876	A849	5p	multicolored	15.00	15.00
1880	A849	10p	multicolored	30.00	30.00

Issued: 5p, 10p, 5/23/95.

A850

1995, Mar. 25			Litho.	Die Cut
Self-Adhesive				
1883A	A850	25c	multicolored	11.00	1.00
1884	A850	75c	multicolored	3.00	1.00
a.		Booklet pane, 2 #1883A, 6 #1884		42.00	
		Complete booklet, #1884a		55.00	
b.		Booklet pane, 4 #1883A, 12 #1884		82.50	
		Complete booklet, #1884b		95.00	

See Nos. 1921A-1921B.

Argentine Engineers' Center, Cent. — A851

1995, June 3				Perf. 13½
1885	A851	75c	multicolored	2.25	.60

Jose Marti (1853-95) — A852

No. 1887, Antonio Jose de Sucre (1795-1830).

1995, Aug. 12			Litho.		Perf. 13½
1886	A852	1p	multicolored	3.00	.75
1887	A852	1p	multicolored	3.00	.75

Fauna — A853

Type I

Type II

25c Penguin:
Type I — Penguin 16mm tall, with top of penguin's head barely above blue background circle and eyes below the outer limit of the circle.
Type II — Penguin 17mm tall, with top of penguin's head well above blue background circle and eyes even with the outer limit of the circle.

1995, Sept. 1			Litho.		Perf. 13½
1888	A853	5c	Ostrich	.30	.25
1889	A853	25c	Penguin, type I	.80	.35
1889A	A853	25c	Penguin, type II	—	—
1890	A853	50c	Toucan	1.50	.35
1891	A853	75c	Condor	2.10	.35
1892	A853	1p	Owl	4.25	.35
1893	A853	2p	Bigua	6.25	.35
1894	A853	2.75p	Tero	10.50	.35

Booklet Stamps
Perf. 13½ on 2 or 3 Sides

1895	A853	25c	Alligator	.80	.40
1896	A853	50c	Fox	1.50	.70
1897	A853	75c	Anteater	2.25	1.00
1898	A853	75c	Deer	2.25	1.00
1899	A853	75c	Whale	2.25	1.00
a.		Booklet pane, 1 each Nos. 1889, 1890, 1891, 1895-1899		13.50	13.50
		Complete booklet, #1899a		14.50	
		Nos. 1888-1899 (12)		34.75	6.45

See Nos. 1958, 2004-2004A.

Native Heritage — A854

a, Cave drawings, shifting sands. b, Stone mask. c, Anthropomorphous vessel. d, Woven textile.

1995, Sept. 9				
1900	A854	75c	Block of 4, #a.-d.	9.00	9.00

Sunflower, Postal Service Emblem — A855

1995, Oct. 7				
1901	A855	75c	multicolored	8.00	1.00

Juan D. Peron (1895-1974) — A856

1995, Oct. 7				
1902	A856	75c	lt ol bis & dk bl	2.00	.60

Miniature Sheet

Anniversaries — A857

Annivs: a, UN, 50th. b, ICAO, 50th (in 1994). c, FAO, 50th. d, ILO, 75th (in 1994).

1995, Oct. 14				Perf. 12
1903	A857	75c	Sheet of 4, #a.-d.	9.00	9.00

Christmas and New Year — A858

Designs: Nos. 1904, 1908, Christmas tree, presents. No. 1905, "1996." No. 1906, Champagne glasses. No. 1907, Present.

1995, Nov. 25			Litho.		Perf. 13½
1904	A858	75c	multicolored	2.00	.45

Booklet Stamps
Perf. 13½ on 1 or 2 Sides

1905	A858	75c	multicolored	2.50	.75
1906	A858	75c	multicolored	2.50	.75
1907	A858	75c	multicolored	2.50	.75
1908	A858	75c	multicolored	2.50	.75
a.		Booklet pane, #1905-1908 + label		10.00	
		Complete booklet, #1908a		20.00	
		Nos. 1904-1908 (5)		12.00	3.45

No. 1908a is a continuous design. Ribbon extends from edge to edge on No. 1908 and stops at edge of package on No. 1905.

Miniature Sheet

Motion Pictures, Cent. — A859

Black and white film clips, director: a, The Battleship Potemkin, Sergei Eisenstein (Soviet Union). b, Casablanca, Michael Curtiz (US). c, Bicycle Thief, Vittorio De Sica (Italy). d, Limelights, Charles Chaplin (England). e, The 400 Blows, Francois Truffaut (France). f, Chronicle of the Lonely Child, Leonardo Favio (Argentina).

1995, Dec. 2				Perf. 13½
1909	A859	75c	Sheet of 6, #a.-f.	25.00	25.00

The Sky — A860

1995, Dec. 16			Perf. 13½ on 3 Sides
Booklet Stamps			
1910	A860	25c	Dirigible	.70	.35
1911	A860	25c	Kite	.70	.35
1912	A860	25c	Hot air balloon	.70	.35
1913	A860	50c	Balloons	1.50	.35
1914	A860	50c	Paper airplane	1.50	.35
1915	A860	75c	Airplane	2.25	.35
1916	A860	75c	Helicopter	2.25	.35
1917	A860	75c	Parachute	2.25	.35
a.		Booklet pane, #1910-1917 + label		13.00	
		Complete booklet, No. 1917a		25.00	

Nos. 1910-1917 do not appear in Scott number order in No. 1917a, which has a continuous design.

America Issue A861

Postal vehicles from Postal &Telegraph Museum: No. 1918, Horse & carriage. No. 1919, Truck.

1995, Dec. 16   **Perf. 13½**
1918 A861 75c multicolored   2.50 .75
1919 A861 75c multicolored   2.50 .75

Olympic Games, Cent. A862

1996, Mar. 30   Litho.   Perf. 13½
1920 A862 75c Running   2.50 .75
1921 A862 1p Discus   3.00 .90

Type of 1995
Self-Adhesive
Coil Stamps
Country Name and Denomination in Blue

1996   Litho.   Die Cut
1921A A850 25c multi   7.00 2.00
1921B A850 75c multi   13.00 3.00

Physicians A863

Designs: a, Francisco J. Muniz (1795-1871). b, Ricardo Gutierrez (1838-96). c, Ignacio Pirovano (1844-95). d, Esteban L. Maradona (1895-1995).

1996, Apr. 20   Litho.   Perf. 12
1922 A863 50c Sheet of 4   6.00 6.00
a.-d.   Any single   1.00 1.00

Jerusalem, 3000th Anniv. — A864

7th cent. mosaic maps of city, denomination at: No. 1923, LL. No. 1924, LR.

1996, May 18   Litho.   Perf. 13½
1923 A864 75c multicolored   1.50 .75
1924 A864 75c multicolored   1.50 .75
a.   Pair, #1923-1924   6.00 4.00

No. 1924a is a continuous design and was issued in sheets of 8 + 4 labels.

Endangered Fauna — A865

1996, June 15   Litho.   Perf. 13½
1925 A865 75c Capybara   2.00 .75
1926 A865 75c Guanaco   2.00 .75
a.   Pair, #1925-1926   5.00 5.00

America Issue.

Summer Olympic Games A866

Designs: 75c, Torch bearer, Buenos Aires, candidate for 2004 Games. 1p, Men's eight with coxswain, Atlanta, 1996.

1996, July 6
1927 A866 75c multicolored   2.00 .70
1928 A866 1p multicolored   2.50 .90

National Parks — A867

Wildlife, national park: No. 1929, Mountain turkey, Diamante. No. 1930, Parrot, San Antonio Nature Reserve. No. 1931, Deer, Otamendi Natl. Reserve. No. 1932, Rabbit, El Leoncito Nature Reserve.

1996, Aug. 24   Litho.   Perf. 13x13½
1929 A867 75c multicolored   2.25 .70
1930 A867 75c multicolored   2.25 .70
1931 A867 75c multicolored   2.25 .70
1932 A867 75c multicolored   2.25 .70
Nos. 1929-1932 (4)   9.00 2.80

Central Post Office, Buenos Aires — A868

1996, Oct. 5   Litho.   Die Cut
Self-Adhesive
Size: 25x35mm
1933 A868 75c multicolored   8.50 1.00

Vignette of No. 1933 is broken by circular and rectangular die cut areas to guard against reuse.
See Nos. 1983-1984.

Carousel Figures — A869

Designs: No. 1934, Hand-carved decorative ornaments. No. 1935, Child on carousel horse. No. 1936, Carousel. No. 1937, Heads of horses. No. 1938, Child in airplane. No. 1939, Carousel pig. No. 1940, Boy in car.

1996, Oct. 5   Perf. 13½ Horiz.
Booklet Stamps
1934 A869 25c multicolored   .50 .30
1935 A869 25c multicolored   .50 .30
1936 A869 25c multicolored   .50 .30
1937 A869 50c multicolored   1.00 .60
1938 A869 50c multicolored   1.00 .60
1939 A869 50c multicolored   1.00 .60
1940 A869 75c multicolored   1.50 .70
a.   Booklet pane, #1934-1940   7.00
    Complete booklet, #1940a   9.00

Sequence of stamps in No. 1940a: No. 1940, 1934, 1937, 1935, 1938, 1936, 1939.

Port Belgrano Naval Base, Cent. — A870

Designs: 25c, LST "San Antonio." 50c, Corvette *Rosales.* 75c, Destroyer *Hercules.* 1p, Aircraft carrier, "25th of May."

1996-97   Litho.   Perf. 13½
1941 A870 25c multicolored   1.25 .50
1942 A870 50c multicolored   1.25 .50
1943 A870 75c multicolored   2.50 .75
1944 A870 1p multicolored   3.00 1.00
Nos. 1941-1944 (4)   8.00 2.75

Issued: 25c, 1p, 10/5/96; 50c, 75c, 2/1/97.

Christmas — A871

Tapestries: 75c, Nativity, by Gladys Angelica Rinaldi, vert. 1p, Candles, by Norma Bonet de Maekawa.

1996, Nov. 30   Litho.   Perf. 13½
1945 A871 75c multicolored   1.75 .75
1946 A871 1p multicolored   2.50 1.00

Exploration of Antarctica — A872

Designs: 75c, Melchior Base. 1.25p, Icebreaker ARA Alte. Irizar.

1996, Nov. 30
1947 A872 75c multicolored   2.00 .75
1948 A872 1.25p multicolored   3.00 1.25

National Gallery, Cent. A873

Paintings of women by: 75c, Paul Gauguin, vert. No. 1950, Edouard Manet, vert. No. 1951, Amedeo Modigliani, vert. 1.25p, Pablo Picasso.

1996, Dec. 14
1949 A873   75c multicolored   2.00 .70
1950 A873   1p multicolored   2.75 1.00
1951 A873   1p multicolored   2.75 1.00
1952 A873 1.25p multicolored   4.50 1.25
Nos. 1949-1952 (4)   12.00 3.95

Mining Industry — A874

1997, Feb. 1   Litho.   Perf. 13½
1953 A874   75c Granite   1.75 .75
1954 A874 1.25p Borax   3.25 1.10

Traditional Costumes — A875

1997, Feb. 22   Litho.   Perf. 13½
1955 A875 75c multicolored   2.50 .75
America issue.

Repatriation of the Curved Sword of Gen. San Martin, Cent. — A876

1997, Mar. 15   Litho.   Perf. 13½
1956 A876 75c multicolored   2.25 .60

29th Youth Rugby World Championships — A877

1997, Mar. 22
1957 A877 75c multicolored   2.25 .75

Fauna Type of 1995
1997, Feb. 22   Litho.   Perf. 13½
1958 A853 10c Reddish sandpiper   1.40 .25

Buenos Aires-Rio de Janeiro Regatta, 50th Anniv. — A879

1997, Apr. 5   Litho.   Perf. 13½
1960 A879 75c Fortuna II   2.25 .75

Natl. History Museum, Cent. — A880

1997, May 17
1961 A880 75c multicolored   2.25 .75

La Plata Natl. University, Cent. — A881

1997, May 17
1962 A881 75c multicolored   2.25   .75

Lighthouses A882

a, Cabo Virgenes. b, Isla Pingüino. c, San Juan de Salvamento. d, Punta Delgada.

1997, May 31
1963 A882 75c Sheet of 4,
      #a.-d.   10.00 8.00

Ramón J. Cárcano (1860-1946), Developer of Postal and Telegraph System A883

1997, May 31
1964 A883 75c multicolored   2.25   .75

Buenos Aires, Candidate for 2004 Summer Olympics — A884

1997, June 21
1965 A884 75c multicolored   2.25   .50

First Electric Tram in Buenos Aires, Cent. A885

Designs: a, Lacroze Suburban Service Tram Co, 1912. b, Lacroze Urban Service Tram Co., 1907. c, Anglo Argentina Tram Co., 1930. d, Buenos Aires City Transportation Corp., 1942. e, Military Manufacture Tram, 1956. f, South Electric Tram, 1908.

1997, July 12   **Sheet of 6**
1966 A885 75c #a.-f. + 2 la-
          bels   12.50 12.50

Monument to Joaquín V. González (1863-1923), La Rioja — A886

1997, Aug. 9
1967 A886 75c multicolored   2.25   .75

Musicians and Composers A887

Paintings: No. 1968, Alberto Ginastera (1916-83), by Carlos Nine. No. 1969, Astor Piazzolla (1921-92), by Carlos Alonso. No. 1970, Aníbal Troilo (1914-75), by Hermenegildo Sabat. No. 1971, Atahualpa Yupanqui (b. 1908), by Luis Scafati.

1997, Aug. 9
1968 A887 75c multicolored   2.10   .70
1969 A887 75c multicolored   2.10   .70
1970 A887 75c multicolored   2.10   .70
1971 A887 75c multicolored   2.10   .70
     Nos. 1968-1971 (4)   8.40 2.80

Argentine Authors — A888

Designs: No. 1972, Jorge Luis Borges (1899-1986), maze. No. 1973, Julio Cortázar (1914-84), hop scotch game.

1997, Aug. 30   **Litho.**   **Perf. 13**
1972 A888 1p multicolored   2.60 1.00
1973 A888 1p multicolored   2.60 1.00

Women's Political Rights Law, 50th Anniv. A889

1997, Sept. 6   **Litho.**   **Perf. 13½**
1974 A889 75c Eva Perón   2.50 1.00

Mercosur (Common Market of Latin America) A890

1997, Sept. 27 **Litho.**   **Perf. 13½**
1975 A890 75c multicolored   2.25   .60
    See Bolivia No. 1019, Brazil No. 2646, Paraguay No. 2564, Uruguay No. 1681.

Launching of Frigate President Sarmiento, Cent. — A891

Designs: No. 1976, Painting of ship by Hugo Leban.
    No. 1977: a, Ship. b, Ship's figurehead, vert.

1997, Oct. 4
1976 A891 75c multicolored   2.50   .75
      Souvenir Sheet
        Perf. 12
1977 A891 75c Sheet of 2, #a.-b. 5.00 4.00
    No. 1977 contains one 40x30mm stamp and one 30x40mm stamp.

Ernesto "Che" Guevara (1928-67) A892

1997, Oct. 18
1978 A892 75c multicolored   5.00   .75

Ecology on Stamps — A893

Children's drawings: No. 1979, Animal, by J. Chiapparo, vert. No. 1980, Vicuna, by L.L. Portal, vert. No. 1981, Seal, by A. Lloren. No. 1982, Bird in flight, by J. Saccone.

1997, Nov. 8   **Litho.**   **Perf. 13½**
1979 A893 50c multicolored   1.50   .50
1980 A893 50c multicolored   1.50   .50
1981 A893 75c multicolored   2.00   .75
1982 A893 75c multicolored   2.00   .75
     Nos. 1979-1982 (4)   7.00 2.50

Central Post Office, Buenos Aires, Type of 1996

1997, July 24 **Litho.**   **Die Cut**
      Self-Adhesive
      Size: 23x35mm
1983 A868 25c multicolored   12.00   .75
1984 A868 75c multicolored   5.00   .75
  a. Bklt. pane, 2 #1983, 6 #1984 55.00
      Complete booklet, #1984a   60.00
    Nos. 1983-1984 are broken at both the top and bottom of each stamp by three lines of wavy die cutting.

Christmas — A893a

Nativity scene tapestries by: Nos. 1984B, 1984G, Mary José. No. 1984C, Elena Aguilar. No. 1984D, Silvia Pettachi. No. 1984E, Ana Escobar. No. 1984F, Alejandra Martinez. No. 1984H, Nidia Martinez.

1997, Nov. 22 **Litho.**   **Perf. 13½**
1984B A893a 75c multicolored   2.25   .75
      Booklet Stamps
      Self-Adhesive
      Size: 44x27mm
        Die Cut
1984C A893a 25c multicolored   .75   .50
1984D A893a 25c multicolored   1.00   .50
1984E A893a 50c multicolored   1.50   .75
1984F A893a 50c multicolored   1.50   .75
1984G A893a 75c multicolored   2.00   .75
1984H A893a 75c multicolored   2.00   .75
   i. Booklet pane, #1984C-
       1984H   10.00
    Nos. 1984C-1984H are broken at upper right by three die cut chevrons. By its nature, No. 1984Hi is a complete booklet.

Mother Teresa (1910-97) — A893b

1997, Dec. 27
1984J A893b 75c multicolored   2.25   .75

Dr. Bernardo A. Houssay (1887-1971), 1947 Nobel Prize Winner in Medicine — A894

1998, Jan. 31 **Litho.**   **Perf. 13½**
1985 A894 75c multicolored   2.25   .60

First Ascension of Mount Aconcagua, Cent. — A895

1998, Feb. 14   **Perf. 12**
1986 A895 1.25p multicolored   3.50 1.10

Founding of San Martin de los Andes, Cent. — A896

1998, Mar. 14   Litho.   Perf. 13½
1987   A896   75c multicolored   2.25   .75

Regimental Quarters of Gen. San Martin's Mounted Grenadiers A897

Designs: a, Statue. b, Large jar with painting of San Martin. c, Regimental seal. d, Regimental quarters.

1998, Mar. 21   Litho.   Perf. 13½
1988   A897   75c Block of 4, #a.-d.   8.00   6.00

Protection of the Ozone — A898

1998, Mar. 28   Litho.   Perf. 13½
1989   A898   75c multicolored   2.25   .75

America Issue — A899

Letter carriers: No. 1990, Wearing white uniform. No. 1991, Carrying letter bag with shoulder strap.

1998, Apr. 4
1990   A899   75c multicolored   2.50   .75
1991   A899   75c multicolored   2.50   .75

Characters from Stories by Maria Elena Walsh — A900

Designs: No. 1992, El Reino Del Reves. No. 1993, Zoo Loco. No. 1994, Dailan Kifki. No. 1995, Manuelita.

1998, Apr. 17   Litho.   Die Cut
Booklet Stamps
Self-Adhesive
1992   A900   75c multicolored   3.75   3.00
1993   A900   75c multicolored   3.75   3.00
1994   A900   75c multicolored   3.75   3.00
1995   A900   75c multicolored   3.75   3.00
   a.   Complete booklet, #1992-
        1995   20.00

Historic Chapels A901

Designs: No. 1996, San Pedro de Fiambalá, Catamarca. No. 1997, Huacalera, Jujuy. No. 1998, Santo Domingo, La Rioja. No. 1999, Tumbaya, Jujuy.

1998, Apr. 25   Litho.   Perf. 13x13½
1996   A901   75c multicolored   2.00   .75
1997   A901   75c multicolored   2.00   .75
1998   A901   75c multicolored   2.00   .75
1999   A901   75c multicolored   2.00   .75
       Nos. 1996-1999 (4)   8.00   3.00

White Helmets, A Commitment to Humanity — A902

1998, May 23   Litho.   Perf. 13½
2000   A902   1p multicolored   2.75   1.00

Beginning with No. 2001, many Argentine stamps are inscribed "Correo Oficial," but these are not Official stamps (i.e., for government use only). The addition of "Correo Oficial" distinguishes these stamps, which are products of the Argentine Postal Service, from other stamps from a private post, OCA, which are also inscribed "Republica Argentina."

1998 World Cup Soccer Championships, France — A903

Stylized players representing: a, Argentina. b, Croatia. c, Jamaica. d, Japan.

1998, May 30
2001   A903   75c Block of 4, #a.-d.   7.50   7.50

Journalist's Day — A904

1998, June 20
2002   A904   75c multicolored   2.25   .75

Creation of Argentine Postal System, 250th Anniv. — A905

a, Corrientes design A2, peso coin. b, Building, post box.

1998, June 27
2003   A905   75c Pair, #a.-b.   4.50   3.25

Fauna Type of 1995
1998   Litho.   Die Cut
Self-Adhesive (#2004)
2004   A853   60c Picaflor   1.75   .50
Perf. 13½
2004A   A853   3.25p Tero   10.00   .50

No. 2004 is broken at bottom right by 3 or 5 lines of wavy die cutting.
   Issued: 60c, 12/12; 3.25p, 7/22.

Ruins, Mission St. Ignacio A906

1998, July 25   Litho.   Perf. 13½
2005   A906   75c multicolored   2.25   .75
       Mercosur.

Cattle A907

1998, Aug. 1
2006   A907   25c Brahman   .65   .50
2007   A907   25c Aberdeen-Angus   .65   .50
2008   A907   50c Hereford   1.25   .50
2009   A907   50c Criolla   1.25   .50
2010   A907   75c Holland-Argentina 1.75   1.00
2011   A907   75c Shorthorn   1.75   1.00
       Nos. 2006-2011 (6)   7.30   4.00

Deception Island Base, Antarctica, 50th Anniv. — A908

1998, Aug. 15   Litho.   Perf. 14½
2012   A908   75c multicolored   2.40   1.00

State of Israel, 50th Anniv. A909

1998, Sept. 5   Litho.   Perf. 13½
2013   A909   75c multicolored   2.25   .75

Argentina-Japan Friendship Treaty, Cent. — A910

1998, Oct. 3
2014   A910   75c multicolored   2.25   .75

Post Office Building, Buenos Aires, 70th Anniv. A911

Designs: No. 2015, Building, clock, tile. No. 2016, Column ornamentation, tile, bench.

1998, Oct. 3
2015   A911   75c multicolored   1.75   .75
2016   A911   75c multicolored   1.75   .75
   a.   Pair, #2015-2016   4.25   4.25

Cartoons — A912

Designs: a, Patoruzu, by Quinterno. b, Matias, by Sendra. c, Clemente, by Caloi. d, El Eternauta, by Oesterheld and López. e, Loco Chavez, by Trillo and Altuna. f, Inodoro Pereyra, by Fontanarrosa. g, Tia Vicenta, by Landrú. h, Gaturro, by Nik.

1998, Oct. 17   Litho.   Perf. 13¾x13¼
2017   A912   75c Sheet of 8,
              #a.-h.   22.00 22.00

Dr. Pedro de Elizalde's Children's Hospital, 220th Anniv. — A913

1998, Oct. 24   Litho.   Perf. 13½
2025   A913   75c multicolored   2.25   .75

Raoul Wallenberg (1912-47), Humanitarian — A914

1998, Nov. 21
2026   A914   75c multicolored   2.25   .75

Espamer '98 — A915

25c, Spanish flags, arms. 75c, 18th cent. schooner. 75c+75c, Brigantine, gray sails. 1.25p+1.25p, Brigantine, white sails.

1998, Nov. 21 *Die Cut*
Booklet Stamps
Self-Adhesive

2027	A915	25c multicolored	1.10	.75
2028	A915	75c multicolored	3.50	2.00
2029	A915	75c +75c multi	6.75	4.00
2030	A915	1.25p +1.25p multi	11.00	3.25
a.	Booklet pane, #2027-2030		21.00	

Nos. 2027-2030 are broken at top right of each stamp by four lines of wavy die cutting. No. 2030a is a complete booklet.

Organization of American States, 50th Anniv. — A916

1998, Nov. 28 *Perf. 13½*
2031 A916 75c multicolored 2.25 .75

Dinosaurs of Argentina — A917

Designs: a, Eoraptor. b, Gasparinisaura. c, Giganotosaurus. d, Patagosaurus.

1998, Nov. 28
2032 A917 75c Sheet of 4, #a.-d. 10.00 9.00

Christmas A918

1998, Dec. 5
2033 A918 75c multicolored 2.25 .75

Newspaper El Liberal, Cent. A919

1998, Dec. 5
2034 A919 75c Juan A. Figueroa 2.25 .75

La Nueva Provincia, Daily Newspaper, Cent. A920

1998, Dec. 12
2035 A920 75c Enrique Julio 2.25 .75

Universal Declaration of Human Rights, 50th Anniv. — A921

1998, Dec. 12
2036 A921 75c multicolored 2.25 .75

Holocaust Memorial, Cathedral of Buenos Aires — A922

1998, Dec. 12
2037 A922 75c multicolored 2.25 1.00

Southern Cross — A923

Inscriptions: 8.75p, Sur postal express. 17.50p, Sur postal 24.

1999-2000 *Litho.* *Die Cut*
Self-Adhesive

2038	A923	8.75p bl & silver	21.50	15.00
2039	A923	17.50p bl & gold	45.00	30.00

Issued: 8.75p, 7/1/99; 17.50p, 3/2/00. Nos. 2038-2039 are broken at right by five wavy lines of die cutting.

National Fund for the Arts, 40th Anniv. A925

1999, Mar. 6 *Litho.* *Perf. 13½*
2042 A925 75c multicolored 1.75 .75

Intl. Year of the Ocean (in 1998) A926

1999, Mar. 6
2043 A926 50c Penguin, vert. 1.50 1.00
2044 A926 75c Dolphins 1.60 1.00

Postmen — A927

Designs: 25c, Early postman, city scene. 50c, Early postman, people on bicycles, factory. 75c, Modern postman, city buildings.

1998-2001 *Litho.* *Die Cut*
Self-Adhesive

2045	A927	25c multicolored	60.00	.75
2046	A927	75c multicolored	30.00	.50
a.	Strip of 4, 1 #2045, 3 #2046		150.00	

Booklet Stamps
Serpentine Die Cut 6

2047	A927	25c multicolored	40.00	1.00
2048	A927	75c multicolored	15.00	1.00
a.	Bklt. pane, 2 #2047, 6 #2048		175.00	
	Complete booklet, #2048a		180.00	

Serpentine Die Cut 11

2048B	A927	25c multi	2.00	.25
2048C	A927	75c multi	6.00	.50
d.	Booklet pane, 2 #2048B, 6 #2048C		45.00	
	Complete booklet, 2 #2048Cd		90.00	
	Complete booklet, 4 #2048Cd		180.00	

Size: 21x27mm
Die Cut

2049	A927	25c multicolored	3.50	.50
2050	A927	50c multicolored	3.50	1.00
2051	A927	75c multicolored	3.50	1.75
a.	Bklt. pane, 2 ea #2049-2051		21.00	
	Complete booklet, #2051a		30.00	

Nos. 2045-2048C are broken at lower right by five lines of wavy die cutting. Nos. 2049-2051 are broken in center by five wavy lines of die cutting. Nos. 2045-2046 have darker vignettes than Nos. 2047-2048.
Issued: Nos. 2045-2048, 12/9/98. Nos. 2049-2051, 2/2/99. Nos. 2048B-2048C, Feb. 2001.

25th Book Fair A928

Designs: a, Book. b, Obelisk, readers.

1999, Apr. 17 Litho. Perf. 13¾x13½
2052 A928 75c Pair, a.-b. 3.50 3.50

Argentine Rugby Union, Cent. — A929

75c, Player, balls. 1.50p, Old, modern players.

1999, Apr. 24 Litho. Perf. 13¾x13½
2054 A929 75c multicolored 1.75 1.00
Souvenir Sheet
2055 A929 1.50p multi + 3 labels 3.50 3.50

Cafes of Buenos Aires — A930

Designs: a, Mug, Giralda Dairy. b, Two glasses, Homero Manzi Cafe. c, Hat hanging on rack, Ideal Sweet Shop. d, Cup and saucer, Tortoni Cafe.

Serpentine Die Cut
1999, Apr. 30 *Litho.*
Self-Adhesive

2056		Booklet pane of 4	9.50	8.00
a.	A930 25c multicolored		.60	.50
b.-c.	A930 75c multi, each		1.75	1.00
d.	A930 1.25p multicolored		3.00	1.25
	Complete booklet, #2056		12.00	

Argentine Olympic Committee, 75th Anniv. — A931

1999, May 15 *Perf. 14x13¼*
2057 A931 75c Pierre de Coubertin 1.75 .70

Enrico Caruso (1873-1921), Opera Singer — A932

Designs: a, Portrait of Caruso. b, Singer, various musical instruments. c, Outside of Colon Theatre, Buenos Aires. d, Scene from opera, "El Matrero."

1999, May 15 *Perf. 13½*
2058 A932 75c Sheet of 4, #a.-d. 9.00 9.00

Famous Women A933

Designs: a, Rosario Vera Penaloza (1873-1950), educator. b, Julieta Lanteri (1862-1932), physician.

1999, June 5 *Perf. 14x13¼*
2059 A933 75c Pair, #a.-b. 3.50 2.00

Souvenir Sheets

Paintings from Natl. Museum of Art, Buenos Aires — A934

No. 2060: a, Anarchy of Year 20, by Luis Felipe Noé. b, Retrato de L.E.S., by Carlos Alonso.
No. 2061: a, Typical Orchestra, by Antonio Berni. b, Untitled, (Woman seated), by Aída Carballo.

1999, June 5 *Perf. 14*
Sheets of 2

2060 A934 75c #a.-b. 5.00 3.25
2061 A934 75c #a.-b. 5.00 3.25

No. 2060b is 40x40mm, No. 2061a, 70x50mm, No. 2061b, 40x50mm.

Carrier Pigeon A935

1999, June 12　**Perf. 13¾x13½**
2062　A935　75c multicolored　2.25　.75

Maps — A936

1999, June 12　**Die Cut**
Self-Adhesive
2063　A936　35c Local highway　1.00　.50
2064　A936　40c City street　1.10　.50
2065　A936　50c Regional highway　1.40　.50
　　　Nos. 2063-2065 (3)　3.50　1.50

Nos. 2063-2065 are broken at lower left by five wavy lines of die cutting.

Dogs A937

Designs: a, 25c, Boxer. b, 25c, English sheepdog. c, 50c, Collie. d, 50c, St. Bernard. e, 75c, German shepherd. f, 75c, Siberian husky.

1999, July 24　**Litho.**　**Perf. 13½**
2066　A937　Sheet of 6, #a.-f.　10.50　10.50

Natl. Telecommunications Day — A938

1999, July 24　**Perf. 13½x13¾**
2067　A938　75c multicolored　1.75　.75

Justo José de Urquiza School, Concepcion del Uruguay, 150th Anniv. — A939

1999, Aug. 7　**Perf. 13¾x13½**
2068　A939　75c multicolored　1.75　.75

Otto Krause Technical School, Buenos Aires, Cent. — A940

1999, Aug. 7　**Perf. 13½x13¾**
2069　A940　75c multicolored　1.75　.75

Bethlehem 2000 Project — A941

1999, Aug. 21　**Perf. 13½**
2070　A941　75c multicolored　1.75　.75

America Issue, A New Millennium Without Arms — A942

No. 2072, Tree of hands, vert.

Perf. 13½x13¾, 13¾x13½
1999, Aug. 21
2071　A942　75c shown　2.00　.75
2072　A942　75c multicolored　2.00　.75

National Parks — A943

Parks and animals: No. 2073, Mburucuyá, coypu. No. 2074, Quebrada de Los Condoritos, condor. No. 2075, San Guillermo, vicuna. No. 2076, Sierra de las Quijadas, puma. No. 2077, Talampaya, gray fox.

1999, Sept. 25　**Litho.**　**Perf. 14x13½**
2073　A943　50c multicolored　1.40　.60
2074　A943　50c multicolored　1.40　.60
2075　A943　50c multicolored　1.40　.60
2076　A943　75c multicolored　2.00　.75
2077　A943　75c multicolored　2.00　.75
　　　Nos. 2073-2077 (5)　8.20　3.30

For surcharge, see Nos. 2853A-2854.

Inter-American Development Bank, 40th Anniv. — A944

1999, Oct. 9　**Litho.**　**Perf. 13½x13¾**
2078　A944　75c multi　1.75　1.00

UPU, 125th Anniv. A945

1999, Oct. 9　**Perf. 13¾x13½**
2079　A945　1.50p multi　3.50　1.50

Trees — A946

a, Nothofagus pumilio. b, Prosopis caldenia. c, Schinopsis balansae. d, Cordia trichotoma.

1999, Oct. 16　**Perf. 13½x13¾**
2080　A946　75c Strip of 4, #a-d　7.25　7.25

Sinking of A.R.A. Fournier, 50th Anniv. A947

1999, Oct. 16　**Perf. 13¾x13½**
2081　A947　75c multi　1.75　.75

Aviation Anniversaries — A948

Designs: No. 2082, Late 25 airplane. No. 2083, Parachutists.

1999, Oct. 30　**Perf. 13¾x13½**
2082　A948　75c multi　1.75　.75
2083　A948　75c multi　1.75　.75

First Argentine airmail flight, 70th anniv. (No. 2082), Hundred consecutive jumps by Argentine Parachute Club, 50th anniv.

Souvenir Sheets

Millennium — A949

No. 2084: a, 75c, Head of soccer player. b, 50c, Machine as soccer player.
No. 2085: a, 50c, Cane, vert. b, 75c, Head of Jorge Luis Borges (1899-1986), writer.
No. 2086: a, 50c, Accordion player on bed, vert. b, 75c, Stylized tango dancers.

1999, Oct. 30　**Perf. 14**
2084　A949　Sheet of 2, #a.-b.　3.25　3.25
2085　A949　Sheet of 2, #a.-b.　3.25　3.25
2086　A949　Sheet of 2, #a.-b.　3.25　3.25

Size of 75c stamps: 40x40mm.

Argentine Soccer Teams — A950

Designs: No. 2087, Banner and flags of River Plate team. No. 2088, Banner of Boca Juniors team, balloons.
River Plate team (red and white team colors) — No. 2089: a, Stadium, emblem, soccer balls. b, Team on field. c, Fans. d, Emblem. e, Trophy. f, Banner in stadium. g, Player, ball.
Boca Juniors team (blue and yellow team colors) — No. 2090: a, Two players, ball. b, Emblem. c, Four players celebrating. d, Fans, balloons. e, Banner in stadium. f, Blurred shot of players in action. g, Blurred shot of players, diff.

1999　**Perf. 13½x13¼**
2087　A950　75c multi　1.60　.50
2088　A950　75c multi　1.60　.50
Self-Adhesive
Die Cut
2089　Pane of 7　37.50
　a.　A950 25c multi　2.50　2.00
　b.-c.　A950 50c any single　2.50　2.00
　d.-f.　A950 75c any single　5.50　5.50
　g.　A950 1.50p multi　11.00　10.00
2090　Pane of 7　37.50
　a.　A950 25c multi　2.50　2.00
　b.-c.　A950 50c any single　3.50　2.00
　d.-f.　A950 75c any single　5.50　5.00
　g.　A950 1.50p multi　11.00　10.00

Issued: Nos. 2087-2088, 11/13; Nos. 2089-2090, 11/15.
Sizes: Nos. 2089a-2089f, 2090a-2090f, 37x27mm; No. 2089g, 2090g, 37x37mm.

Canonization of Brother Héctor Valdivielso Sáez — A951

1999, Nov. 20　**Perf. 13¼x13½**
2091　A951　75c multi　1.75　.75

Manuel Belgrano National Naval School, Bicent. A952

1999, Nov. 27
2092　A952　75c multi　1.75　.75

Souvenir Sheet

Launch of Corvette Uruguay, 125th Anniv. — A953

1999, Nov. 27　**Litho.**　**Perf. 14**
2093　A953　1.50p multi　6.50　6.50

Christmas
A955

No. 2094, Figurines of Holy Family.
No. 2095: a, Magus. b, Bell. c, Two Magi, camels. d, Leaf. e, Angel with star. f, Nativity scene. g, Star. h, Ornaments.

1999, Dec. 4 **Perf. 13¾x13½**
2094 A954 75c multi 1.25 .60

Perf. 14
2095 Sheet of 8 10.00 10.00
a.-b A955 25c any single .75 .50
c.-d A955 50c any single 1.25 1.00
e.-h A955 75c any single 1.50 1.25

Sizes: Nos. 2095a, 2095b, 2095g, 2095h, 30x30mm.

Viticulture — A956

Designs: a, 25c, Grape on vine. b, 50c, Bottoms of wine bottles. c, 50c, Cork and corkscrew. d, 25c, Glass of wine, wine bottle.

2000, Feb. 26 **Litho.** **Perf. 13¼**
2096 A956 Block of 4, #a-d 8.50 8.50

World Mathematics Year — A957

2000, Mar. 18 **Perf. 13¾x13½**
2097 A957 75c multi 1.50 1.50

Birds
A958

a, Leptotila verrauxi. b, Columba picazuro. c, Columbina picni. d, Zenaida auriculata.

2000, Mar. 18 **Die Cut**
Self-Adhesive
2098 Booklet of 4 10.00
a.-d. A958 75c any single 2.50 1.50

Souvenir Sheet

Bangkok 2000 Stamp
Exhibition — A959

Designs: a, 25c, Vanda coerulea. b, 75c, Erythrina crista-galli.

2000, Mar. 25 **Perf. 14**
2099 A959 Sheet of 2, #a-b 3.50 3.50

Miniature Sheet

Libraries — A960

Designs: a, 25c, National Public Library Protection Commission. b, 50c, Jujuy Public Library. c, 75c, Argentine Library for the Blind. d, 1p, Argentine National Library.

Litho., Litho. & Embossed (#2100c)
2000, Apr. 15 **Perf. 13½**
2100 A960 Sheet of 4, #a-d 6.75 6.75

Gen. Luis Maria Campos Military School, Cent. A961

2000, Apr. 29 **Perf. 13¾x13½**
2101 A961 75c multi 1.75 1.75

Discovery of Brazil, 500th
Anniv. — A962

a, 75c, Pedro Cabral, 1558 map of Brazil coastline. b, 25c, Compass rose and ship.

2000, Apr. 29
2102 A962 Pair, #a-b 3.50 3.50

Souvenir Sheet

The Stamp Show 2000,
London — A963

Designs: a, 25c, Great Britain #1 and design A1, La Porteña, 1st locomotive in Argentina. b, 75c, Argentina No. 7, mail box.

2000, May 20 **Perf. 14**
2103 A963 Sheet of 2, #a-b 3.00 3.00

91st Intl. Convention of Rotary International, Buenos Aires — A964

2000, June 3 Litho. **Perf. 13½x13¾**
2104 A964 75c multi 1.75 1.75

Stampin' the Future — A965

Children's Stamp Design Contest Winners: 25c, Rocío Casado. 50c, Carolina Cáceres, vert. 75c, Valeria A. Pizarro. 1p, Cristina Ayala Castro, vert.

Perf. 13½x13¼, 13¼x13½
2000, June 24
2105-2108 A965 Set of 4 6.00 6.00

America
Issue
A966

AIDS Prevention: No. 2109, Handshake. No. 2110, Heart and hands.

2000, July 8 **Perf. 13¾x13½**
2109-2110 A966 75c Set of 2 4.00 4.00

Antoine de Saint-Exupéry (1900-44),
Pilot, Writer — A967

Designs: Nos. 2111, 2115, Potez 25. Nos. 2112, 2116, Late 28. No. 2113, Saint-Exupéry. No. 2114, Henri Guillaumet, Vicente A. Almonacid and Jean Mermoz. No. 2117, Map of southern Argentina, tail of Late 25 plane. 1p, Nose of Late 25 plane, cover from 1st airmail flight to Trelew.

2000, July 29 **Perf. 13½**
2111 A967 25c multi .50 .40
2112 A967 50c multi 1.10 .80

Booklet Stamps
Perf. 14
Size: 30x30mm
2113 A967 25c multi 2.25 .50
2114 A967 50c multi 3.25 1.10

Size: 60x20mm
2115 A967 25c multi 2.25 .50
2116 A967 50c multi 3.25 1.10
a. Booklet pane, #2113-2116 12.00
Size: 40x30mm
2117 A967 50c multi 3.25 1.10
2118 A967 1p multi 4.75 1.75
a. Booklet pane, #2117-2118 8.75
Booklet, #2116a, 2118a 22.50
Nos. 2111-2118 (8) 20.60 7.25

Argentine airmail service, 73rd anniv., Aerofila 2000 Philatelic Exhibition, Buenos Aires (No. 2118a).

President Arturo U. Illia (1900-82) A968

2000, Aug. 5 **Perf. 13½x13¼**
2119 A968 75c multi 1.75 1.75

José de San Martín (1778-1850) A969

2000, Aug. 26 **Perf. 13½**
2120 A969 75c multi 1.75 1.75

Dalmacio Vélez Sarsfield (1800-75),
Writer of Civil Code — A970

Perf. 13½x13¼
2000, Sept. 23 **Litho.**
2121 A970 75c multi 1.75 1.75

2000 Summer Olympic,
Sydney — A971

No. 2122: a, Windsurfing. b, Field hockey. c, Volleyball. d, Pole vault.

2000, Sept. 23 **Perf. 13½**
2122 A971 75c Block of 4, #a-d 7.50 7.50

Horses
A972

No. 2123: a, Argentine Petiso. b, Argentine Carriage Horse. c, Peruvian. d, Criolla. e, Argentine Saddle Horse. f, Argentine Polo.

No. 2124: a, Horse-drawn mail coach. b, Horse's head.

2000, Oct. 7		Perf. 13¾x13½	
2123	Sheet of 6 + 2 labels	7.00	7.00
a.-b.	A972 25c Any single	.85	.85
c.-d.	A972 50c Any single	1.00	1.00
e.-f.	A972 75c Any single	1.60	1.60

Souvenir Sheet
Perf. 14

2124	Sheet of 2	3.50	3.50
a.	A972 25c multi	1.25	1.25
b.	A972 25c mutli	1.75	1.75

España 2000 Intl. Philatelic Exhibition.

Archaeological Artifacts — A973

Designs: 10c, Ceremonial hatchet, Santa Maria culture. 25c, Musical pipes. 50c, Loom, Mapuche culture. 60c, Poncho. 75c, Funerary mask, Tafi culture. 1p, Basket, Mbayá Indians. 2p, Drum, Mapuche culture. 3.25p, Ceremonial mask, Chané culture. 5p, Funerary urn, Belén culture. 9.40p, Rhea-feather costume.

Perf. 13½x13¾ Syncopated

2000			Litho.
2125	A973	10c multi	.25	.25
2126	A973	25c multi	.60	.50
2127	A973	50c multi	1.00	.80
2128	A973	60c multi	1.25	1.00
2129	A973	75c multi	1.60	1.25
2130	A973	1p multi	2.10	1.75
2131	A973	2p multi	4.25	3.00
2132	A973	3.25p multi	8.00	5.50
2133	A973	5p multi	10.50	7.00
2134	A973	9.40p multi	20.00	9.50
	Nos. 2125-2134 (10)	49.55	30.55

Issued: 10c, 60c, 11/16; 25c, 50c, 75c, 9.40p, 10/26; 1p, 2p, 9/13; 3.25p, 5p, 8/30.

See Nos. 2495, 2670-2672. For surcharges, see Nos. 2841, 2849.

Natl. Atomic Energy Commission, 50th Anniv. A974

2000, Nov. 11	Litho.	Perf. 13½	
2135	A974 75c multi	1.75	1.75

Fileteado Art Style and the Tango — A975

No. 2136: a, Left side of Fileteado design. b, Right side of Fileteado design. c, Musicians. d, Tango dancers.

2000, Nov. 11		Perf. 13¾x13½	
2136	A975 75c Block of 4, #a-d	10.00	10.00

Organ Donation Campaign A976

2000, Nov. 25		Perf. 13½	
2137	A976 75c multi	1.75	1.75

Christmas A977

2000, Nov. 25			
2138	A977 75c multi	1.75	1.00

Medicinal Plants — A978

Designs: No. 2139, 75c, Mirabilis jalapa. No. 2140, 75c, Senna corymbosa. No. 2141, 75c, Eugenia uniflora. No. 2142, 75c, Commelina erecta.

2000, Nov. 25			
2139-2142	A978	Set of 4	6.50	6.50

Pre-Columbian Art — A979

Various artifacts. Background colors: a, Bright orange. b, Red orange. c, Green. d, Red violet.

2000, Dec. 9			
2143	A979 75c Block of 4, #a-d	7.50	7.50

A979a

2001, Feb. 6	Litho.	Self-Adhesive		
Background Color				
2143E	A979a	10c blue grn	.65	.25
2143F	A979a	25c brt green	1.75	.55
2143G	A979a	60c orange	3.50	1.40
2143H	A979a	75c red	5.25	1.60
2143I	A979a	1p blue	6.75	2.10
2143J	A979a	3p red brn	21.00	6.50
2143K	A979a	3.25p yel green	22.50	7.00
2143L	A979a	5.50p rose	40.00	12.00
	Nos. 2143E-2143L (8)	101.40	31.40

Nos. 2143E-2143L are broken at right by five die cut wavy lines. Sold at Unidad Postal outlets. See Nos. 2217-2224A.

Miniature Sheet

Cenozoic Mammals — A980

No. 2144: a, Megaterio (Megatherium americanum). b, Gliptodonte (Doedicurus clavicaudatus). c, Macrauquenia (Macrauchenia patachonica). d, Toxodonte (Toxodon platensis).

2001, Mar. 10		Perf. 13¾x13½	
2144	A980 75c Sheet of 4, #a-d	10.00	10.00

Antarctic Bases, 50th Anniv. — A981

Map and: No. 2145, 75c, Cormorant, Base Brown. No. 2146, 75c, Skua, Base San Martín.

Perf. 13¾x13½			
2001, Mar. 24			Litho.
2145-2146	A981	Set of 2	4.00	4.00

Apiculture — A982

No. 2147: a, Bee on flower. b, Bees on honeycomb. c, Bees, apiarist, and hives. d, Honey, pollen.

2001, Apr. 7		Perf. 13½x13¼	
2147	Block of 4	12.00	12.00
a.-d.	A982 75c Any single	2.10	2.10

Souvenir Sheet

Argentine Antarctic Institute, 50th Anniv. — A983

No. 2148: a, Scientist with fossils. b, Scientist with mapping equipment.

2001, Apr. 21		Perf. 14	
2148	A983 75c Sheet of 2, #a-b	8.00	8.00

Spain to Argentina Flight of Plus Ultra Seaplane, 75th Anniv. — A984

2001, Apr. 28		Perf. 13¾x13½	
2149	A984 75c multi	1.75	1.75

Art in Silver — A985

No. 2150: a, Bridle (Freno). b, Stirrups (Estribos). c, Spurs (Espuelas). d, Gaucho's ornament (Rastra).

2001, May 19	Litho.	Perf. 13¾x13½	
2150	A985 75c Block of 4, #a-d	10.00	10.00

World Youth Soccer Championships — A986

Designs: No. 2151, 75c, Player kicking ball. No. 2152, 75c, Goalie catching ball.

2001, June 16			
2151-2152	A986	Set of 2	3.25	3.25

Souvenir Sheet

Belgica 2001 Intl. Stamp Exhibition, Brussels — A987

No. 2153: a, 25c, Washerwoman by the Banks of the Belgrano, by Prilidiano Pueyrredón. b, 75c, The Hay Harvest, by Pieter Breughel, the Elder.

2001, June 16		Perf. 14	
2153	A987	Sheet of 2, #a-b	3.50	3.50

2001 Census — A988

Perf. 13½x13¾ Syncopated
2001, July 14
2154 A988 75c multi   1.75 1.75

SAC-C
Satellite,
Birds and
Flowers
A989

2001, July 14   **Perf. 13¾x13½**
2155 A989 75c multi   1.75 1.75
Environmental protection.

Bandoneón
Recital — 1990,
by Aldo
Severi — A990

2001, July 28   **Perf. 13½x13¾**
2156 A990 75c multi   1.75 1.75
The tango in art.

Souvenir Sheet

Phila Nippon '01, Japan — A991

No. 2157: a, Tango dancers, musical score.
b, Kabuki dancer.

2001, July 28   **Perf. 14**
2157 A991 75c Sheet of 2, #a-b   5.00 5.00
Exists imperf. Value, pair $200.

Miniature Sheet

Wild Cats — A992

No. 2158: a, 25c, Puma. b, 25c, Jaguar. c,
50c, Jaguarundi and young. d, 50c, Ocelot. e,
75c, Mountain cat. f, 75c, Huiña.

2001, July 28   **Perf. 13¾x13½**
2158 A992   Sheet of 6, #a-f,
       +2 labels   10.00 10.00

Enrique Santos
Discépolo
(1901-51),
Tango
Lyricist — A993

2001, Aug. 4   **Perf. 13½x13¾**
2159 A993 75c multi   2.25 2.25

America Issue — UNESCO World
Heritage — A994

No. 2160 — Buildings and artifacts from
Jesuit Block and Estancias of Cordoba: a,
Denomination at UL. b, Denomination at UR.

2001, Aug. 11   **Perf. 13¾x13½**
2160 A994 75c Horiz. pair, #a-b   6.00 6.00

Prevention of
Breast
Cancer — A995

2001, Sept. 1   **Perf. 13½x13¾**
2161 A995 75c multi   1.75 1.75

World Championship Race Cars of
Juan Manuel Fangio — A996

No. 2162 — Cars and track layouts: a, Alfa
Romeo 159 Alfetta, Barcleona, 1951. b, Mercedes-Benz W196, Reims, France, 1954. c,
Lancia-Ferrari D50, Monte Carlo, Monaco,
1956. d, Maserati 250F, Nürburgring, Germany, 1957.

2001, Oct. 6   **Perf. 13¾x13½**
2162 A996 75c Block of 4, #a-d   9.00 9.00

Politicians — A997

Designs: No. 2163, 75c, Roque Sáenz Peña
(1851-1914). No. 2164, 75c, Justo José de
Urquiza (1801-70).

2001, Oct. 20
2163-2164 A997   Set of 2   3.50 3.50

Bulnesia
Sarmientoi
A998

2001, Oct. 20 Litho.   **Perf. 13½x13¾**
2165 A998 75c multi   1.75 1.75

Souvenir Sheet

Hafnia 01 Philatelic Exhibition,
Copenhagen — A999

No. 2166: a, 25c, Argentine post rider, 18th
cent. b, 75c, European post rider, 17th cent.

2001, Oct. 27   **Litho.**   **Perf. 14**
2166 A999   Sheet of 2, #a-b   3.50 3.50

Items in
Argentine
Museums
A1000

Designs: No. 2167, 75c, Ammonite, skele-
ton of Carnotaurus sastrei, from Argentine
Naural Science Museum. No. 2168, 75c, Let-
ter from Buenos Aires, stagecoach "La
Pobladora," from Enrique Udaondo Graphic
Museum Complex. No. 2169, 75c, Icons from
Averias culture, funerary urn from Las Merce-
des culture, from Emilio and Duncan Wagner
Museum of Anthropological and Natural Sci-
ences, vert. No. 2170, 75c, Crucifix of Juan
Martin de Pueyrredon, and detail, from Pueyr-
redon Museum, vert.

Perf. 13¾x13½, 13½x13¾
2001, Nov. 10   **Litho.**
2167-2170 A1000   Set of 4   7.50 7.50

Aviators
and Their
Airplanes
A1001

Designs: No. 2171, 75c, Carola Lorenzini
(1899-1941) and Focke Wulf 44-J. No. 2172,
75c, Jean Mermoz (1901-36) and "Arc-en-
Ciel."

2001, Nov. 24   **Perf. 13¾x13½**
2171-2172 A1001   Set of 2   3.50 3.50
No. 2171 exists imperf. Value, pair $150.

Christmas
A1002

2001, Nov. 24   **Perf. 13½x13¾**
2173 A1002 75c multi   1.75 1.25

Dances
A1003

No. 2174: a, Flamenco. b, Waltz. c, Zamba.
d, Tango.

Perf. 13¾x13½
2001, Nov. 29   **Litho.**
2174   Booklet pane of 4   6.50 —
a.-d.   A1003 75c Any single   1.60 1.60
     Booklet, #2174   8.50

Dancers'
Day
A1004

2001, Dec. 1 Litho.   **Perf. 13¾x13½**
2175 A1004 75c multi   2.00 2.00

Argentine Television, 50th
Anniv. — A1005

No. 2176: a, Television, camera,
microphone, test pattern. b, Televisions and
videotape reels. c, Television, astronaut and
satellite dish. d, Televisions, cables and VCR
remote control.

2001, Dec. 1   **Perf. 13¾x13½**
2176 A1005 75c Block of 4, #a-d 7.00 7.00

Argentina
in the
Antarctic
A1006

Designs: No. 2177, 75c, Esperanza Base,
50th anniv. No. 2178, 75c, First air and sea
courier service, 50th anniv.

2002, Mar. 9
2177-2178 A1006   Set of 2   3.25 3.25

America
Issue —
Education
A1007

No. 2179: a, School and Argentine flag. b, Children playing hop scotch.

2002, Mar. 23
2179 A1007 75c Vert. pair, #a-b　　3.50 3.50

Falkland
Islands
Birds
A1008

Designs: No. 2180, 50c, Charadrius falklandicus. No. 2181, 50c, Larus scoresbii. No. 2182, 75c, Chloephaga rubidiceps, vert. No. 2183, 75c, Aptenodytes patagonicus, vert.

Perf. 13¾x13½, 13½x13¾
2002, Apr. 13　　　　　　　　Litho.
2180-2183 A1008　Set of 4　　6.00 6.00

2002 World Cup Soccer
Championships, Japan and
Korea — A1009

No. 2184: a, Flags, soccer ball and field (38mm diameter). b, Soccer players, years of Argentinian championships.

2002, Apr. 27　Litho.　Perf. 12¾
2184 A1009 75c Horiz. pair, #a-b 3.25 3.25

See Brazil No. 2840, France No. 2891, Germany No. 2163, Italy No. 2526, Uruguay No. 1946.

Anniversaries — A1010

No. 2185, 25c: a, Rosario riverfront, Ship on Paraná River, arms. b, Rosario riverfront, National Flag Monument.
No. 2186, 50c: a, Mt. Fitzroy, Nahuel Huapi Natl. Park. b, Dr. Francisco P. Moreno.
No. 2187, 75c: a, Flower, aerial view of San Carlos de Bariloche. b, Church and town map.

2002, May 11　Litho.　Perf. 13½x13¾
Horiz. Pairs, #a-b
2185-2187 A1010　Set of 3　　6.00 6.00

Pan-American
Health
Organization,
Cent. — A1011

2002, June 1
2188 A1011 75c multi　　　　1.50 1.50

Doctors — A1012

No. 2189: a, Cosme Mariano Argerich (1758-1820), founder of Military Health Service. b, José María Ramos Mejía (1849-1914), psychiatric educator. c, Salvador Mazza (1886-1946), Chagas' disease specialist. d, Carlos Arturo Gianantonio (1926-95), pediatrician.

Perf. 13¾x13½
2002, June 15　　　　　　　Litho.
2189 A1012 50c Block of 4, #a-d 4.00 4.00

Landscapes — A1013

No. 2190: a, Seven-colored Mountain, Jujuy Province. b, Iguaçu Falls, Misiones Province. c, Talampaya Natl. Park, La Rioja Province. d, Mt. Aconcagua, Mendoza Province. e, Rose Garden, Buenos Aires. f, San Jorge Lighthouse, Chubut. g, Perito Moreno Glacier, Santa Cruz Province. h, Lapataia Bay, Tierra del Fuego Province.

2002, July 29　　　　Perf. 14x13½
2190　　Block of 8　　12.00 12.00
　a.-h.　A1013 75c Any single　　1.50 1.50

For surcharge, see No. 2847.

Eva Perón
(1919-52)
A1014

No. 2191: a, Official portrait. b, Embossed profile. c, At microphone. d, Painting by Nicolas García Uriburu.

Litho., Litho & Embossed (#2191b)
2002, July 27　　　Perf. 13½x13¾
2191　　Horiz. strip of 4　　6.00 6.00
　a.-d.　A1014 75c Any single　1.25 1.25

Worldwide Fund for Nature
(WWF) — A1015

No. 2192: a, Ozotoceros bezoarticus. b, Vicugna vicugna. c, Pudu puda. d, Catagonus wagneri.

2002, July 27　Litho.　Perf. 13¾x13½
2192 A1015 $1 Block of 4, #a-d　6.75 6.75

Souvenir Sheet

Philakorea 2002 World Stamp
Exhibition, Seoul — A1016

No. 2193: a, Argentine soccer player (blue and white shirt). b, Korean soccer player (red shirt).

2002, Aug. 10　　　　　Perf. 14
2193 A1016 1.50p Sheet of 2,
　　　　　#a-b　　　　　6.00 6.00

Sports — A1016a

10c, Cycling. 25c, Tennis. 50c, Auto racing. 75c, Parachuting. 1p, Horse racing. 2p, Golf. 5p, Sailing.

Perf. 13½x13¾ Syncopated
2002, Sept. 6　　　　　　　　Litho.
2193C　A1016a 10c multi　　2.25　.35
2193D　A1016a 25c multi　　2.25　.35
2193E　A1016a 50c multi　　2.25　.40
2193F　A1016a 75c multi　　4.00　.75
2193G　A1016a 1p multi　　4.00 1.05
2193H　A1016a 2p multi　　6.75 2.10
2193I　A1016a 5p multi　　9.75 5.25
　Nos. 2193C-2193I (7)　31.25 10.25

Nos. 2193C-2193I were sold only to customers who met certain mailing requirements but could be used on mail by anyone without restrictions.

Valdés Peninsula Tourism — A1017

Whale breaching: a, Head. b, Tail.

2002, Sept. 14　　　Perf. 13½x13¾
2194 A1017 75c Horiz. pair, #a-b 3.50 3.50

Insects
A1018

Designs: 25c, Edessa meditabunda. 50c, Elaechlora viridis. 75c, Chrysodina aurata. 1p, Steirastoma breve.

2002, Sept. 21　　　Perf. 13¾x13½
2195-2198 A1018　Set of 4　　5.25 5.25

Men's Volleyball
World
Championships
A1019

Various players with background colors of: No. 2199, 75c, Blue green (shown). No. 2200, 75c, Light blue. No. 2201, 75c, Bright yellow green. No. 2202, 75c, Pale orange.

Perf. 13½x13¾
2002, Sept. 28　　　　　　Litho.
2199-2202 A1019　Set of 4　　6.25 6.25

On Nos. 2199-2202 portions of the design were applied by a thermographic process producing a shiny, raised effect.

Argentine Highway Association, 50th
Anniv. — A1020

2002, Oct. 5　　　　Perf. 13¾x13½
2203 A1020 75c multi　　　1.60 1.60

Argentine Personalities — A1021

Designs: No. 2204, 75c, Roberto Arlt (1900-42), novelist. No. 2205, 75c, Beatriz Guido (1924-88), writer. No. 2206, 75c, Niní Marshall (1903-96), actress. No. 2207, 75c, Luis Sandrini (1905-80), actor.

2002, Oct. 19
2204-2207 A1021　Set of 4　　6.00 6.00

Immigrant
Agricultural
Colonies
A1022

Flags of France, Switzerland, Spain and Italy and: a, Hotel for immigrants, mother and son, stamped passport. b, Two immigrants and ship. c, Two immigrants, Provisory Hotel for immigrants, French immigrant instruction book. d, Farmer plowing field, family of immigrants.

2002, Oct. 19 Litho. Perf. 13½x13¾
2208   Horiz. strip of 4   6.00 6.00
a.-d. A1022 75c Any single   1.50 1.50

Argentine Federation of Philatelic
Entities, 50th Anniv. — A1023

Designs: No. 2209, 75c, Stamped cover,
stagecoach, EXFICEC '56 exhibition cancel,
Head of Ceres from Corrientes issue. No.
2210, 75c, ESPAMER '98 Cancel, postman,
ship and map, coat of arms.

2002, Nov. 2   Perf. 13¾x13½
2209-2210 A1023   Set of 2   2.75 2.75

Christmas — A1024

2002, Nov. 16
2211 A1024 75c multi   1.50 .50

Folk Musicians
A1025

Designs: No. 2212, 75c, Gustavo "Cuchi"
Leguizamón (1917-2000). No. 2213, 75c,
Armando Tejada Gómez (1929-92). No. 2214,
75c, Carlos Vega (1898-1966). No. 2215, 75c,
Andrés Chazarreta (1876-1960).

2002, Dec. 7   Perf. 13½x13¾
2212-2215 A1025   Set of 4   6.00 6.00

Puppets
A1026

No. 2216: a, Marionette of woman. b, King
and fish hand puppets. c, Rod puppet of man.
d, Shadow theater.

2002, Dec. 7   Perf. 13¾x13½
2216   Booklet pane of 4   8.00 8.00
a.-d.   A1026 75c Any single   2.00 2.00
     Booklet, #2216   9.25

Unidad Postal Type of 2001
Perf. 13¾x13½ Syncopated
2002   Litho.
Size: 35x24mm (10p, 35x25mm)
Background Color

2217	A979a	10c blue green	.30	.25
2218	A979a	25c brt green	.60	.40
2219	A979a	50c tan	1.15	.55
2220	A979a	75c red	1.75	.85
2221	A979a	1p blue	2.60	1.20
2222	A979a	2p gray	5.25	1.75
2223	A979a	3p brown	6.25	2.00
2224	A979a	5p olive bister	10.00	2.60
2224A	A979a	10p yellow	20.00	3.50
	Nos. 2217-2224A (9)		47.90	13.10

Issue dates: Nos. 2217-2224, 6/02; 10p,
8/16/02.
Nos. 2217-2224A were sold only at Unidad
Postal outlets.
For surcharge, see No. 2843.

Communal Vegetable
Gardens — A1027

Designs: No. 2225, 75c, Cabbage. No.
2226, 75c, Corn, vert.

Perf. 13¾x13½, 13½x13¾
2003, Mar. 8
2225-2226 A1027   Set of 2   2.50 2.50

Native Handicrafts — A1028

Designs: No. 2227, 75c, Sieve, by Mbyá
people, fork and spoon by Wichi people. No.
2228, 75c, Woven waistband of Pilagal'ek
people, Bag by Nam Qom people.

2003, Mar. 8   Perf. 13¾x13½
2227-2228 A1028   Set of 2   2.75 2.75

National Parks — A1029

Animals and parks: No. 2229, 50c, Lama
guanicoe, Los Cardones National Park. No.
2230, 50c, Piaya cayana, Colonia Benítez Natural Reserve. No. 2231, 50c, Mazama
gouazoupira, Copo National Park. No. 2232,
75c, Tinamotis pentlandii, Campo de los
Alisos National Park. No. 2233, 75c, Spheniscus magellanicus, Monte León, planned
National Park.

2003, Mar. 22   Perf. 14x13½
2229-2233 A1029   Set of 5   5.50 5.50

Paintings
A1030

Designs: No. 2234, 25c, Composición con
Trapo Rejilla, by Kenneth Kemble. No. 2235,
25c, Pintura, by Roberto Aizenberg, vert. 50c,
Pantalla, by Rómulo Macció, vert. No 2237,
75c, La Giaconda, by Guillermo Roux. No.
2238, 75c, Hacerse Humo, by Antonio Seguí.
1p, San P., by Xul Solar (with attached label).

Perf. 13¾x13½, 13½x13¾
2003, Apr. 12
2234-2239 A1030   Set of 6   8.00 8.00

Nos. 2234-2238 were each printed in sheets
of 4; No. 2239 was printed in sheets of 2 + 2
labels.

Argentina, Champions of 2002 Intl.
Sporting Events — A1031

Designs: No. 2240, 75c, Women's field
hockey. No. 2241, 75c, Soccer for blind
players.

Litho., Litho. & Embossed (#2241)
2003, May 3   Perf. 13¾x13½
2240-2241 A1031   Set of 2   3.00 3.00

Comic Strips — A1032

No. 2242: a, 25c, Mago Fafa, by Alberto
Bróccoli. b, 25c, Astronaut, by Crist (Cristóbal
Reinoso). c, 50c, Hijitus, by Manuel García
Ferré. d, 50c, Savarese, by Domingo Man-
drafina and Robin Wood. e, 75c, Sónoman, by
Oswal (Oswaldo Walter Viola). f, 75c, El Tipito,
by Daniel Paz and Rudy (Marcelo E. Rudaeff).
g, 75c, La Vaca Aurora, by Domingo Mirco
Repetto. h, 75c, Diógenes y el Linyera, by
Tabaré (Gómez Laborde), Jorge Guinzberg
and Carlos Abrevaya.

2003, May 17 Litho.   Perf. 13½x13¾
2242 A1032   Sheet of 8, #a-h   9.50 9.50

Silver Tableware — A1033

No. 2243: a, Soup bowl with lid (sopera). b,
Kettle and burner, maté kettle and drinking
tube. c, Chocolate pot and jar with handle. d,
Sugar bowl (azucarera).

2003, May 24   Perf. 13¾x13½
2243 A1033 75c Block of 4, #a-d   5.75 5.75

Food — A1034

Designs: Nos. 2244a, 2245a, Empanadas
(red denomination). Nos. 2244b, 2245b, Locro
(orange denomination) Nos. 2244c, 2246a,
Parrillada (green denomination) Nos. 2244d,
2246b, Pastelitos (blue denomination).

2003, June 7   Perf. 13¾x13½
2244 A1034 75c Vert strip of 4,
    #a-d, + 4 la-
    bels   6.00 6.00

Booklet Panes
Perf. 14
2245 A1034 75c Pane of 2,
    #a-b, + 2 la-
    bels   11.00 11.00
2246 A1034 75c Pane of 2,
    #a-b, + 2 la-
    bels   11.00 11.00
    Complete booklet, #2245-
    2246   25.00

Size of stamps in booklet panes: 40x30mm.

Miniature Sheet

Children's Games — A1035

No. 2247: a, El Elástico. b, La escondida
(hide and seek). c, La mancha (tag). d, Martín
Pescador.

2003, July 12   Perf. 13¾x13½
2247 A1035 50c Sheet of 4, #a-d 6.50 6.50

Landscapes — A1036

No. 2248: a, Mbiguá Marsh, Formosa Province. b, Dead Man's Salt Flats, Catamarca
Province. c, Quilmes Ruins, Tucumán Province. d, Iberá Marshes, Corrientes Province. e,
Ischigualasto Provincial Park, San Juan Province. f, Mar del Plata, Buenos Aires Province.
g, Caleu Caleu Department, La Pampa Province. h, Lanín National Park, Nequén
Province.

2003, July 19   Perf. 14x13¾
2248 A1036 75c Block of 8,
    #a-h   12.00 12.00

For surcharge, see No. 2845.

Opening of Nuestra Señora del
Rosario Bridge and Roadway,
Rosario-Victoria — A1037

No. 2249: a, 25c, Bridge, map of roadway.
b, 75c, Bridge and cross-section.

Perf. 13½x13¾
2003, Aug. 23   Litho.
2249 A1037   Horiz. pair, #a-b 5.00 5.00

Argentine
History
A1038

Designs: No. 2250, 75c, Dr. Vicente Fidel López (1815-1903), Education minister, headquarters of Province of Buenos Aires Bank. No. 2251, 75c, First page of constitution, medal and signature of Juan Bautista Alberdi. No. 2252, 75c, Emblem and squadron of General San Martín Mounted Grenadiers Regiment. No. 2253, 75c, Presidential sash and staff, Casa Rosada. No. 2254, 75c, Arms of Río Negro Province, vert.

Perf. 13¾x13½, 13½x13¾

2003, Sept. 6
2250-2254 A1038 Set of 5 ... 7.00 7.00

Constitution, 150th anniv. (No. 2251), Revival of General San Martín Mounted Grenadiers Regiment, cent. (No. 2252), Presidential inauguration (No. 2253).

Souvenir Sheet

Bangkok 2003 World Philatelic Exhibition — A1039

No. 2255: a, Quebrada de Humahuacha black demon mask, Argentine flag. b, Phi Ta Khon Festival mask, Thailand flag.

Litho. with Foil Application
2003, Oct. 4 **Perf. 14**
2255 A1039 75c Sheet of 2, #a-b 3.50 3.50

America Issue — Flora and Fauna A1040

Designs: No. 2256, 75c, Nothofagus pumilio. No. 2257, 75c, Vultur gryphus.

2003, Oct. 11 Litho. Perf. 13¾x13½
2256-2257 A1040 Set of 2 3.25 3.25

Jubany Base, Antarctica, 50th Anniv. — A1041

2003, Oct. 18
2258 A1041 75c multi 1.60 1.60

Rescue of Swedish Scientific Expedition by A. R. A. Uruguay, Cent. — A1042

Designs: No. 2259, Welcome, (ship and penguins) by Eduardo De Martino.
No. 2260: a, A. R. A. Uruguay. b, A. R. A. Uruguay and Lt. Julián Irízar.

2003, Oct. 18 Perf. 13¾x13½
2259 A1042 75c multi 1.60 1.60

Souvenir Sheet
Perf. 14
2260 A1042 75c Sheet of 2, #a-b 4.00 4.00
No. 2260 contains two 40x30mm stamps.

Agricultural and Industrial Products — A1043

Designs: No. 2261, 75c, Cattle. No. 2262, 75c, Soybeans. No. 2263, 75c, Aluminum. No. 2264, 75c, Teradi 800 cobalt therapy machine.

2003, Oct. 18 Perf. 13¾x13½
2261-2264 A1043 Set of 4 6.00 6.00

Christmas A1044

Designs: No. 2265, 75c, Purmamarca clay creche figures. No. 2266, 75c, Gaucho Birth, carved wood creche figures by Eloy López.

2003, Nov. 8 Perf. 13½x13¾
2265-2266 A1044 Set of 2 3.00 1.50

20th Century Architecture A1045

Designs: No. 2267, 75c, Barolo Palace, Buenos Aires, by Mario Palanti, 1923. No. 2268, 75c, Tucumán Province Bank Building, San Miguel de Tucumán, by Alejandro Virasoro, 1928. No. 2269, 75c, Córdoba Province Savings Bank Building, Córdoba, by Jaime Roca, 1929. No. 2270, 75c, Minetti Palace, Rosario, by Juan B. Durand, Leopoldo Schwarz and José Gerbino, 1930.

2003, Nov. 8
2267-2270 A1045 Set of 4 5.50 5.50

Orcadas Base, Antarctica, Cent. — A1046

Designs: No. 2271, Helicopter, Orcadas Base.
No. 2272: a, #127 with 1904 South Orcadas cancel, vert. b, Meteorological observatory and weather vane.

2004, Feb. 21 Perf. 13¾x13½
2271 A1046 75c multi 2.00 2.00

Souvenir Sheet
Perf. 14
2272 A1046 75c Sheet of 2, #a-b 5.00 5.00
No. 2272 contains one 30x40mm and one 40x30mm stamp.

Quebrada de Humahuaca UNESCO World Heritage Site — A1047

No. 2273 — View of Rio Grande Valley and: a, Decorated llama, rock painting, person in front of door. b, Santa Rosa de Lima Church, costumed carnival participants.

2004, Mar. 27 Perf. 13½x13¾
2273 A1047 75c Horiz. pair, #a-b 3.50 3.50

America Issue — Forest Conservation — A1048

No. 2274 — Forest and timeline charting hectares of forest with years: a, 1914, 1956. b, 1989, 2004.

2004, Mar. 27
2274 A1048 75c Horiz. pair, #a-b 4.00 4.00
No. 2274b has large hole in center of stamp.

La Voz del Interior Newspaper, Cent. — A1049

2004, Apr. 17 Perf. 13¾x13½
2275 A1049 75c multi 1.75 1.75
For surcharge, see No. 2846.

Landscapes — A1050

No. 2276: a, Molinos, Salta Province. b, Pampa del Indio Provincial Park, Chaco Province. c, Rio Hondo Dam, Santiago del Estera Province. d, Bridge, Santa Fe de la Vera Cruz, Santa Fe Province. e, San Roque Lake, Córdoba Province. f, El Palmar National Park, Entre Rios Province. g, Potrero de los Funes, San Luis Province. h, Mt. Tronador, Río Negro Province.

2004, Apr. 17 Perf. 14x13½
2276 A1050 75c Block of 8, #a-h 15.00 15.00

FIFA (Fédération Internationale de Football Association), Cent. — A1051

Paintings of soccer players by Rubén Ramonda: No. 2277, 75c, The Tunnel (blue background). No. 2278, 75c, El Picado (orange background).

2004, May 22 Litho. Perf. 13¾x13½
2277-2278 A1051 Set of 2 3.50 3.50

Souvenir Sheet

España 2004 World Philatelic Exhibition — A1052

No. 2279: a, Return of the Fishing Fleet, by Joaquín Sorolla y Bastida. b, A Stop in the Pampas, by Angel Della Valle, vert.

2004, May 22 Perf. 14
2279 A1052 75c Sheet of 2, #a-b 5.00 5.00

Naval Hydrographic Service, 125th Anniv. — A1053

No. 2280 — Nautical chart and: a, Binnacle. b, Sextant. c, Cabo Vírgenes Lighthouse. d, Oceanographic ship Puerto Deseado.

2004, June 5 Perf. 13¾x13½
2280 A1053 75c Block of 4, #a-d 7.00 7.00
Printed in sheets of four blocks separated by a central column of labels.

Souvenir Sheet

Circus — A1054

No. 2281: a, Trained dogs. b, Clown on stilts, trapeze artist. c, Clown juggling on unicycle. d, Bareback rider.

2004, June 12
2281 A1054 50c Sheet of 4, #a-d 7.00 7.00

Characters From Comic Strip "Patoruzito," by Dante Quinterno — A1055

No. 2282: a, 25c, Isidorito. b, 25c, Upita. c, 50c, Patoruzito. d, 50c, Malén. e, 75c, Pamperito. f, 75c, Chacha.
No. 2283: a, Patoruzito (20x60mm). b, Pamperito (20x60mm). c, Isidorito (30x30mm)
No. 2284: a, Malén (30x40mm). b, Upita (30x40mm). c, Chacha (30x40mm)

2004, July 10 Litho. Perf. 13½x13¾
2282 A1055   Sheet of 6 + 2 labels   7.50 7.50
Booklet Panes
Perf. 14
2283   Booklet pane of 3 + label   11.50 11.50
a.-c.   A1055 75c Any single   3.50   3.50
2284   Booklet pane of 3 + label   11.50 11.50
a.-c.   A1055 75c Any single   3.50   3.50
         Complete booklet, #2283-2284   25.00

Fish of the Falkland Islands Area A1056

Designs: No. 2285, 75c, Salilota australis. No. 2286, 75c, Patagonotothen ramsayi. No. 2287, 75c, Dissostichus eleginoides. No. 2288, 75c, Bathyraja griseocauda.

2004, July 17 Litho. Perf. 13¾x13½
2285-2288 A1056   Set of 4   7.00 7.00

Assistance Dogs — A1057

Designs: No. 2289, 75c, Rescue dog. No. 2290, 75c, Seeing-eye dog, vert.

Perf. 13¾x13½, 13½x13¼
2004, July 17
2289-2290 A1057   Set of 2   3.75 3.75

2004 Summer Olympics, Athens — A1058

No. 2291: a, Cycling. b, Judo. c, Swimming. d, Tennis.

2004, Aug. 7   Perf. 13¾x13½
2291 A1058 75c Block of 4, #a-d 7.00 7.00

Legends A1059

Designs: No. 2292, 75c, El Pehuén. No. 2293, 75c, La Yacumama. No. 2294, 75c, La Pachamama. No. 2295, 75c, La Difunta Correa.

2004, Aug. 21
2292-2295 A1059   Set of 4   7.00 7.00

Souvenir Sheet

World Stamp Championship 2004, Singapore — A1060

No. 2296: a, Mangifera indica. b, Syagrus romanzoffiana.

2004, Aug. 21   Perf. 14
2296 A1060 75c Sheet of 2, #a-b 3.50 3.50

Centenaries — A1061

Designs: No. 2297, 75c, Agronomy and Veterinary Science Institute for Higher Learning, Buenos Aires. No. 2298, 75c, City of Neuquén. No. 2299, 75c, Philatelic Association of Rosario.

2004, Sept. 11   Perf. 13¾x13½
2297-2299 A1061   Set of 3   5.00 5.00

Prevention of Uterine Cancer A1062

2004, Sept. 18   Perf. 13½x13¾
2300 A1062 75c multi   1.75 1.75

Preservation of Water Resources — A1063

No. 2301: a, Hourglass with clean water. b, Hourglass with polluted water.

2004, Sept. 18   Perf. 13¾x13½
2301 A1063 75c Vert. tete beche pair, #a-b   3.25 3.25

Landmarks in Argentina — A1063a

Designs: 25c, Ruins of San Ignacio Miní, Misiones Province. 50c, Iruya. 1p, Buenos Aires. 2p, Aconcagua Provincial Park. 3p, Valdes Peninsula. 5p, Mina Clavero. 10p, Ushuaia.

Perf. 13¾x13½ Syncopated
2004, Sept. 24   Litho.
2301C A1063a 25c multi   .35   .35
2301D A1063a 50c multi   .50   .50
2301E A1063a 1p multi   1.00 1.00
2301F A1063a 2p multi   2.00 2.00
2301G A1063a 3p multi   3.00 3.00
2301H A1063a 5p multi   5.00 5.00
 j.   With label   3.50 3.50
2301I A1063a 10p multi   9.50 9.50
 Nos. 2301D-2301I (6)   21.00 21.00

Issued: No. 2301Hj, 5/11/10.
See Nos. 2357, 2586-2587, 2678-2679.

The Nativity A1064

Virgin Mary — A1065

2004, Oct. 16 Litho. Perf. 13½x13¾
2302 A1064 75c multi   1.25   .65
2303 A1065 75c multi   1.25   .65
Christmas, Stained glass windows, St. Felicitas Church, Buenos Aires.

Numismatics — A1066

No. 2304 — Halves of 1813 silver 1 real coin and 1813 gold 8 escudos coin: a, Obverse (sun). b, Reverse (coat of arms).

2004, Oct. 23
2304 A1066 75c Horiz. pair, #a-b 2.75 2.75

Andrés Bello and Front Page of Spanish Grammar for Americans — A1067

2004, Nov. 6   Perf. 13¾x13½
2305 A1067 75c multi   1.50 1.50
Third Intl. Spanish Language Congress, Rosario.

Buenos Aires Commodities Exchange, 150th Anniv. — A1068

2004, Nov. 6
2306 A1068 75c multi   1.50 1.50

Medicinal Plants A1069

Designs: No. 2307, 75c, Aloysia citriodora. No. 2308, 75c, Minthostachys mollis. No. 2309, 75c, Lippia turbinata. No. 2310, 75c, Tagetes minuta.

2004, Nov. 20   Perf. 13½x13¾
2307-2310 A1069   Set of 4   7.00 7.00

12th Pan-American Scout Jamboree — A1070

2005, Jan. 15   Perf. 13¾x13½
2311 A1070 75c multi   1.10 1.10

Argentina — Thailand Diplomatic Relations, 50th Anniv. A1071

Designs: No. 2312, 75c, Tango dancers, Argentina. No. 2313, 75c, Tom-tom dancers, Thailand.

2005, Feb. 5   Perf. 13½x13¾
2312-2313 A1071   Set of 2   3.00 3.00

Paintings by
Antonio Berni
(1905-81)
A1072

Designs: No. 2314, Woman with a Red
Sweater.
No. 2315 — Details from Manifestation: a,
75c, Bearded man, man looking up
(40x50mm). b, 75c, Child, two men with hats
in foreground, horiz. (50x40mm).

2005, Mar. 12   Perf. 13½x13¾
2314 A1072 75c shown   1.10 1.10
Souvenir Sheet
Perf. 14
2315 A1072   Sheet of 2, #a-b   2.75 2.75

Rotary International, Cent. — A1073

2005, Mar. 19   Perf. 13¾x13½
2316 A1073 75c multi   1.00 1.00

Writers
A1074

Designs: No. 2317, 75c, Silvina Ocampo
(1903-93). No. 2318, 75c, Ezequiel Martínez
Estrada (1895-1964).

2005, Mar. 19   Perf. 13½x13¾
2317-2318 A1074   Set of 2   3.75 3.75

Argentine Motor Vehicles — A1075

Designs: No. 2319, 75c, Graciela sedan.
No. 2320, 75c, Justicialista Sport. No. 2321,
75c, Rastrojero Diesel truck. No. 2322, 75c,
Siam Di Tella 1500. No. 2323, 75c, Torino 380
W.

2005, Apr. 9 Litho. Perf. 13¾x13½
2319-2323 A1075   Set of 5   7.00 7.00
A portion of the design of each stamp is
coated with a glossy varnish.

Intl.
Year of
Physics
A1076

Designs: No. 2324, 75c, José Antonio Balseiro, founder of Balseiro Institute, nuclear

reactor. No. 2325, 75c, Albert Einstein, front
page of Einstein's theory of relativity.

2005, Apr. 23 Litho. Perf. 13¾x13½
2324-2325 A1076   Set of 2   3.00 3.00
Balseiro Institute, 50th anniv.

Pope John
Paul II (1920-
2005)
A1077

Designs: No. 2326, Pope waving.
No. 2327: a, Pope with crucifix, Papal arms.
b, Pope and crowd.

2005, Apr. 23   Perf. 13½x13¾
2326 A1077 75c shown   2.50 2.50
Souvenir Sheet
Perf. 14
2327 A1077 75c Sheet of 2, #a-b 4.75 4.75
No. 2327 contains two 40x50mm stamps.

General
Workers
Confederation,
75th Anniv.
A1078

La Capital
Newspaper,
Mar del Plata,
Cent. — A1079

Sunday Blue
Law No. 4661,
Cent. — A1080

2005, May 21 Litho. Perf. 13½x13¾
2328 A1078 75c multi   .90   .90
2329 A1079 75c multi   .90   .90
2330 A1080 75c multi   .90   .90
    Nos. 2328-2330 (3)   2.70 2.70

César Milstein (1927-2002), 1984
Nobel Laureate in Physiology or
Medicine — A1081

2005, June 4   Perf. 13¾x13½
2331 A1081 75c multi   1.40 1.40

Volunteer
Firefighters
A1082

Designs: No. 2332, 75c, Orestes Liberti
(1860-1936), first commander of volunteer
firefighter brigade, horse-drawn fire engine.
No. 2333, 75c, Fire fighters in action, fire
truck.

2005, June 4   Perf. 13½x13¾
2332-2333 A1082   Set of 2   2.50 2.50

Argentine Red Cross, 125th
Anniv. — A1083

2005, June 11   Perf. 13¾x13½
2334 A1083 75c multi   1.10 1.10

Juan Filloy (1894-2000),
Writer — A1084

2005, July 16
2335 A1084 75c multi   1.00 1.00

Miniature Sheet

Cats — A1085

No. 2336: a, 25c, Birman. b, 25c, Siamese.
c, 50c, Oriental. d, 50c, Persian. e, 75c, Abyssinian. f, 75c, European.

2005, July 16
2336 A1085   Sheet of 6, #a-f, +
                2 labels   6.00 6.00

Wine Regions — A1086

Glass of wine, map, vineyard in: No. 2337,
75c, Salta Province, Torrontés grapes. No.
2338, 75c, Mendoza Province, Malbec grapes.
No. 2339, 75c, San Juan Province, Syrah
grapes. No. 2340, 75c, Río Negro Province,
Merlot grapes.

2005, July 16   Perf. 14x13½
2337-2340 A1086   Set of 4   5.25 5.25
For surcharges, see Nos. 2855-2857.

Historic
Houses
of
Worship
A1087

Designs: No. 2341, 75c, Our Lady of the
Rosary of Candonga Chapel, Sierra Chicas.
No. 2342, 75c, Al Ahmad Mosque, Buenos
Aires. No. 2343, 75c, Temple of the Israelite
Congregation, Buenos Aires. No. 2344, 75c,
Vision of the Middle Buddhist Temple, Buenos
Aires.

2005, Aug. 6   Perf. 13¾x13½
2341-2344 A1087   Set of 4   4.75 4.75

Local
Grocery
Stores
A1088

Designs: No. 2345, 75c, Pulpería de Cacho
di Catarina, Mercedes. No. 2346, 75c,
Pulpería El Torito, Baradero. No. 2347, 75c,
Pulpería Perucho, General Lavalle. No. 2348,
75c, Pulpería Impini, Larroque.

2005, Sept. 10
2345-2348 A1088   Set of 4   4.75 4.75

Antarctic
Science
A1089

Designs: No. 2349, Iceberg, Antarctic Treaty
emblem
No. 2350: a, Major General Hernán Pujato
and members of First Argentine Polar Expedition air crew. b, Divers, raft, iceberg.

2005, Sept. 24   Perf. 13¾x13½
2349 A1089 75c multi   1.60 1.60
Souvenir Sheet
Perf. 14
2350 A1089 75c Sheet of 2, #a-b 4.00 4.00
No. 2350 contains two 40x30mm stamps.

Colón Theater Companies, 80th
Anniv. — A1090

No. 2351: a, Dancer Julio Bocca, ballet
dancers, Colón Theater building. b, Orchestra,
choir, opera singers.

2005, Sept. 24   Perf. 13½x13¾
2351 A1090 75c Horiz. pair, #a-b 2.00 2.00

Alternative
Energy
Sources
A1091

Designs: 75c, Solar power. 4p, Wind power.

2005, Oct. 15
2352-2353 A1091   Set of 2   5.50 5.50

Christmas
A1092

Details from altarpiece by Elena Storni: No. 2354, Madonna and Child.
No. 2355: a, The Annunciation, Mary and Elizabeth. b, Nativity. c, Magi. d, Presentation of Jesus in the Temple.

2005, Oct. 15   **Perf. 13½x13¾**
2354 A1092 75c shown   1.00   .50

Souvenir Sheet
Perf. 14
2355 A1092 75c Sheet of 4, #a-d 4.00 4.00

No. 2355 contains four 40x40mm stamps.

Fourth Summit of the Americas, Mar
del Plata — A1093

2005, Oct. 29 Litho. Perf. 13¾x13½
2356 A1093 75c multi   1.25 1.25

Landmarks Type of 2004
Design: Perito Moreno Glacier

Perf. 13¾x13½ Syncopated
2005, Nov. 18
2357 A1063a 4p multi   3.75 3.75

Immigrants to Argentina — A1095

Designs: No. 2358, 75c, German immigrants in Cañada de Gómez, bandoneon. No. 2359, 75c, Slovakian immigrants in Buenos Aires, weather indicator. No. 2360, 75c, Welsh immigrants, Chubut Central Railway train, railway lantern. No. 2361, 75c, Jewish settlers, Moisés Ville, wheat.

2005, Nov. 19   **Perf. 13¾x13½**
2358-2361 A1095   Set of 4   3.75 3.75

Boxers
A1096

Designs: No. 2362, 75c, Lius Angel Firpo (1894-1960). No. 2363, 75c, Nicolino Locche (1939-2005).

2005, Dec. 17   **Perf. 13½x13¾**
2362-2363 A1096   Set of 2   2.00 2.00

Argentine Design — A1097

Designs: No. 2364, 75c, Image and sound design. No. 2365, 75c, Clothes and textile design, vert. No. 2366, 75c, Industrial design, vert. No. 2367, 75c, Graphic design.

Perf. 13¾x13½, 13½x13¾
2005, Dec. 17
2364-2367 A1097   Set of 4   4.00 4.00

Pres. Bartolomé Mitre (1821-
1906) — A1098

2006, Jan. 21   **Perf. 13¾x13½**
2368 A1098 75c multi   1.00 1.00

Esquel,
Cent.
A1099

2006, Feb. 18
2369 A1099 75c multi   1.00 1.00

Wine Producing Regions — A1100

No. 2370: a, Merlot grapes and wine, Alto Valle, Río Negro (70x30mm). b, Wine flowing from vat (50x30mm).
No. 2371: a, Wine barrels (50x30mm). b, Torrontés grapes and wine, Cafayate, Salta (70x30mm).
No. 2372: a, Grape harvesters (50x30mm). b, Syrah grapes and wine, Valle del Zonda, San Juan (70x30mm).
No. 2373: a, Malbec grapes and wine, Valle del Tupungato, Mendoza (70x30mm). b, Wine in glass and bottle (50x30mm).

2006, Mar. 3   Litho.   Perf. 14
2370 A1100	Booklet pane of 2	4.00	4.00
a.	50c multi	.40	.40
b.	3.50p multi	3.00	3.00
	Complete booklet, #2370	4.50	
2371 A1100	Booklet pane of 2	4.00	4.00
a.	75c multi	.65	.65
b.	3.25p multi	2.75	2.75
	Complete booklet, #2371	4.50	
2372 A1100	Booklet pane of 2	4.00	4.00
a.	1p multi	.90	.90
b.	3p multi	2.75	2.75
	Complete booklet, #2372	4.50	
2373 A1100	Booklet pane of 2	5.00	5.00
a.	1.25p multi	1.50	1.50
b.	2.75p multi	3.25	3.25
	Complete booklet, #2373	5.50	
Nos. 2370-2373 (4)		17.00	

Dr. Ramón Carrillo (1906-56),
Neurologist — A1101

Perf. 13¾x13½
2006, Mar. 11   Litho.
2374 A1101 75c multi   1.00 1.00

Musical
Instruments
A1102

Designs: 75c, Charango. 3.50p, Drum.

2006, Mar. 11   Perf. 13½x13¾
2375-2376 A1102   Set of 2   4.75 4.75

Miniature Sheet

Lighthouses — A1103

No. 2377: a, Primero de Mayo. b, Año Nuevo. c, El Rincón. d, Recalada a Bahía Blanca.

2006, Mar. 18
2377 A1103 75c Sheet of 4, #a-d 4.25 4.25

Souvenir Sheet

Start of Military Dictatorship, 30th
Anniv. — A1104

No. 2378: a, Man, left side of Navy Mechanics School. b, Flower, right side of Navy Mechanics School.

2006, Mar. 25   Perf. 14
2378 A1104 75c Sheet of 2, #a-b 2.75 2.75

Silver Religious Objects — A1105

No. 2379: a, Crown. b, Candelabra. c, Chalice. d, Viaticum.

2006, Apr. 8   Perf. 13¾x13½
2379 A1105 75c Block of 4, #a-d 3.50 3.50

Auto
Racing
A1106

Races and winning automobiles: No. 2380, 75c, Rally Nacional A8, Toyota Corolla WRC. No. 2381, 75c, Turismo Carretera, Ford Falcon. No. 2382, 75c, Turismo Competición 2000, Ford Focus. No. 2383, 75c, Class 3 Turismo Nacional, Ford Escort.

2006, May 6
2380-2383 A1106   Set of 4   4.00 4.00

Miniature Sheet

Dogs — A1107

No. 2384: a, 25c, Springer spaniel. b, 25c, Yorkshire terrier. c, 50c, Argentino dog. d, 50c, Miniature schnauzer. e, 75c, Poodle. f, 75c, Chow chow.

2006, May 20
2384 A1107   Sheet of 6 #a-f, +
           2 labels   5.50 5.50

A1108

2006 World Cup Soccer
Championships — A1109

No. 2386: a, Serbia & Montenegro player. b, Argentina player, blue and white background. No. 2387: a, Ivory Coast player. b, Netherlands player.

2006, May 20 Litho. Perf. 13¾x13½
2385 A1108 4p shown   4.75 4.75
Booklet Panes
Perf. 14¼
2386   Pane of 2   3.25 3.25
a.-b.   A1109 1p Either single   1.45 1.45
2387   Pane of 2   3.25 3.25
a.-b.   A1109 1p Either single   1.45 1.45
         Complete booklet, #2386-2387   7.25
Souvenir Sheet
2388 A1109 1.50p shown   3.50 3.50

World No Tobacco Day — A1110

2006, May 27 Litho. Perf. 14x13½
2389 A1110 75c multi   1.00 1.00

Intl. Year of Deserts and
Desertification — A1111

Designs: No. 2390, 75c, Lizard and plant. No. 2391, 75c, Impression of lizard in sand, dead plant.

Perf. 13¾x13½
2006, June 10   Litho.
2390-2391 A1111 Set of 2   2.00 2.00

Famous
Men — A1112

Designs: No. 2392, 75c, Tato Bores (1927-96), television actor. No. 2393, 75c, Rodolfo Walsh (1927-77), kidnapped journalist.

2006, June 10   Perf. 13½x13¾
2392-2393 A1112 Set of 2   2.00 2.00

Winter Sports — A1113

No. 2394: a, Alpine skiing. b, Snowboarding. c, Cross-country skiing. d, Biathlon.

2006, June 17   Perf. 13¾x13½
2394 A1113 75c Block of 4, #a-d 4.00 4.00

Tango
Dancing
A1114

Designs: 75c, Musician. 4p, Dancers.

2006, June 24
2395-2396 A1114 Set of 2   5.00 5.00
See France Nos. 3224-3225.

Patoruzito Riding Pamperito — A1115

2006, July 8
2397 A1115 75c multi   1.00 1.00

Endangered Animals — A1116

Designs: No. 2398, 75c, Eubalaena australis. No. 2399, 75c, Hippocamelus bisulcus. No. 2400, 75c, Hippocamelus antisensis. No. 2401, 75c, Panthera onca.

2006, July 8   Perf. 14x13¾
2398-2401 A1116 Set of 4   5.50 5.50
For surcharges, see Nos. 2850-2853.

30th Mercosur
Common
Market Council
and Summit of
Presidents,
Córdoba
A1117

2006, July 22   Perf. 13¾x13½
2402 A1117 3.50p multi   3.75 3.75

Souvenir Sheet

First British Invasion of Buenos Aires
and Reconquest, Bicent. — A1118

2006, July 22   Perf. 14
2403 A1118 1.50p multi   2.25 2.25

Energy Conservation — A1119

Winning designs in children's art contest: No. 2404, 75c, Light bulb, house and electrical cord, by Florencia Tovi. No. 2405, 75c, Plant in sunlight, unplugged lamp, by Camila Suárez.

2006, July 22   Perf. 13¾x13½
2404-2405 A1119 Set of 2   2.00 2.00

First Postage Stamps of Corrientes,
150th Anniv. — A1120

Designs: 75c, August 21, 1856 Corrientes cancel. 1.50p, Corrientes #1.

Litho. & Embossed
2006, Aug. 19   Perf. 13¾x13½
2406 A1120 75c multi   1.10 1.10
Souvenir Sheet
Litho.
Perf. 14
2407 A1120 1.50p multi   2.25 2.25
No. 2407 contains one 40x40mm stamp.

Interjurisdictional Committee on the
Colorado River, 50th Anniv. — A1121

Perf. 13½x13¾
2006, Aug. 26   Litho.
2408 A1121 75c multi   1.25 1.25

Patricios
Infantry Corps,
Bicent.
A1122

2006, Sept. 9
2409 A1122 75c multi   1.10 1.10

Grapes, Wines and
Vineyards — A1123

Designs: No. 2410, 75c, Syrah grapes and wine, Catamarca vineyards. No. 2411, 75c, Torrontés Riojano grapes and wine, La Rioja

---

vineyards. No. 2412, 75c, Pinot Noir grapes and wine, Neuquén vineyards.

2006, Sept. 16   Perf. 14x13½
2410-2412 A1123   Set of 3   2.75 2.75
For surcharges, see Nos. 2840, 2842, 2844.

Col.
Ramón
L.
Falcón
Federal
Police
Cadet
School,
Cent.
A1124

2006, Oct. 14 Litho. Perf. 13¾x13½
2413 A1124 75c multi   1.00 1.00

Border Bridges — A1125

Designs: No. 2414, 75c, Pres. Tancredo Neves Intl. Bridge. No. 2415, 75c, San Roque González de Santa Cruz Intl. Bridge.

2006, Oct. 14   Perf. 14x13¾
2414-2415 A1125   Set of 2   2.00 2.00
For surcharges, see Nos. 2858-2859.

Christmas
A1126

Paintings by Alfredo Guttero: No. 2416, 75c, Madonna and Dove. No. 2417, 75c, The Annunciation, horiz.

Perf. 13½x13¾, 13¾x13½
2006, Oct. 21
2416-2417 A1126   Set of 2   1.25 .60

Natl. Institute of Agricultural and Cattle
Ranching Technology, 50th
Anniv. — A1127

Perf. 13¾x13½
2006, Nov. 11   Litho.
2418 A1127 75c multi   1.00 1.00

Rock
Musicians
A1128

Designs: No. 2419, 75c, Tanguito (1945-72). No. 2420, 75c, Luca Prodan (1953-87). No.

2421, 75c, Miguel Abuelo (1946-88). No. 2422, 75c, Pappo (1950-2005).

2006, Nov. 18   *Perf. 13½x13¾*
2419-2422   A1128   Set of 4   4.00   4.00

Caciques
A1129

Designs: No. 2423, 75c, Valentín Sayhueque (1823-1903), Huilliche cacique. No. 2424, 75c, Casimiro Biguá, Tehuelche cacique.

2006, Dec. 2
2423-2424   A1129   Set of 2   2.00   2.00

Frigate Hercules, Detail From *Battle of Martín García Island,* by Emilio Biggeri — A1130

2007, Mar. 10   *Perf. 13¾x13½*
2425   A1130   75c multi   1.00   1.00

Adm. Guillermo Brown (1777-1857).

Wine-Growing Regions — A1131

No. 2426: a, Hand picking bunch of grapes. b, Vineyard, grapes, bottle of Pinot Noir, Neuquén Region (60x30mm).
No. 2427: a, Harvester cutting grapes from vine. b, Vineyard, grapes, bottle of Torrontés Riojano, La Rioja Region (60x30mm).
No. 2428: a, Harvester inspecting grapes on vine. b, Vineyard, grapes, bottle of Syrah, Catamarca Region (60x30mm).

2007, Mar. 10   **Litho.**   **Perf. 14**
2426   Booklet pane of 2   5.50   5.50
  a.   A1131 75c multi   1.05   1.05
  b.   A1131 3.25p multi   4.25   4.25
    Complete booklet, #2426   5.75
2427   Booklet pane of 2   5.50   5.50
  a.   A1131 75c multi   1.05   1.05
  b.   A1131 3.25p multi   4.25   4.25
    Complete booklet, #2427   5.75
2428   Booklet pane of 2   5.50   5.50
  a.   A1131 75c multi   1.05   1.05
  b.   A1131 3.25p multi   4.25   4.25
    Complete booklet, #2428   5.75

Complete booklets include a plastic wine bottle spout.

Falkland Islands War, 25th Anniv. A1132

Map of the Falkland Islands and: No. 2429, 75c, Argentina No. C90 in changed colors with Islas Malvinas cancel. No. 2430, 75c, IAI Dagger fighters. No. 2431, 75c, Battle cruiser ARA General Belgrano. No. 2432, 75c, Decorated war veteran. No. 2433, 75c, War decoration, vert.

Perf. 13¾x13½, 13½x13¾
2007, Mar. 31   **Litho.**
2429-2433   A1132   Set of 5   4.75   4.75

Postal and Telecommunications Workers Federation, 50th Anniv. — A1133

2007, Apr. 14   *Perf. 13¾x13½*
2434   A1133   75c multi   .90   .90

Map of Antarctica, Icebreaker Almirante Irízar — A1134

No. 2436 — Antarctic fauna: a, Phalacrocorax atriceps. b, Leptonychotes weddellii. c, Sterna vittata, denomination at UR. d, Sterna vittata, denomination at UL. e, Pygoscelis adeliae. f, Chionis alba. g, Pygoscelis papua, denomination at UR. h, Pygoscelis papua, denomination at UL.

2007, Apr. 21
2435   A1134   4p shown   3.75   3.75
2436   Sheet of 8   5.00   5.00
  a.-h.   A1134 75c Any single   .40   .40

Miniature Sheet

Toys — A1135

No. 2437: a, Rocking horse. b, Tea set. c, Toy train and stations. d, Toy soldiers.

2007, May 5   **Litho.**   *Perf. 13¾x13½*
2437   A1135   Sheet of 4   4.00   4.00
  a.-d.   75c Any single   .45   .45

Museums — A1136

Designs: 75c, Latin American Art Museum, Buenos Aires. 3.25p, High Mountain Archaeological Museum, Salta.

2007, May 5
2438-2439   A1136   Set of 2   4.50   4.50

Road Safety Year — A1137

2007, May 19   **Litho.**   *Perf. 13½x13¾*
2440   A1137   75c red & silver   .90   .90

Souvenir Sheet

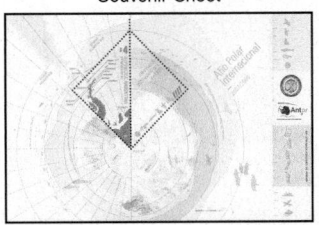

Intl. Polar Year — A1138

2007, June 2   *Perf. 14*
2441   A1138   4p multi + label   4.50   4.50

Defense of Buenos Aires From British Attack, Bicent. A1139

Perf. 13¾x13½
2007, June 23   **Litho.**
2442   A1139   75c multi   .80   .80

Pierre Auger Observatory A1140

2007, July 14   **Litho.**   *Perf. 13½x13¾*
2443   A1140   75c multi   .80   .80

St. Joseph Calasanctius (1557-1648) A1141

2007, July 14
2444   A1141   1p multi   1.00   1.00

Souvenir Sheet

Campo del Cielo Meteorite — A1142

2007, July 28   *Perf. 14*
2445   A1142   6p multi   10.00   10.00

No. 2445 was sold with, but unattached to, a booklet cover, and 3-D glasses.

Homero Manzi (1907-51), Political Leader, Tango Lyricist A1143

Perf. 13½x13¾
2007, Aug. 11   **Litho.**
2446   A1143   1p multi   .90   .90

Tourism Along Route 40 — A1144

No. 2447: a, Road to San Carlos de Bariloche (30x30mm). b, El Acay Pass (40x30mm). c, Road to Perito Moreno (70x30mm). d, La Trochita locomotive (40x30mm). e, Lanin Volcano (40x30mm). f, Rio Grande (50x30mm). g, Animals on road, San José Jachal (40x30mm). h, Cuesta de Miranda (50x30mm) i, Nuestra Senora del Tránsito Chapel (30x30mm). j, Quilmes Ruins (30x30mm). k, Road to Oratorio (40x30mm).

2007, Aug. 25   **Litho.**   *Perf. 14*
2447   Sheet of 11   11.00   11.00
  a.-b.   A1144 50c Either single   .50   .50
  c.-k.   A1144 1p Any single   1.00   1.00

Souvenir Sheet

Diplomatic Relations Between Argentina and Germany, 150th Anniv. — A1145

2007, Sept. 8
2448   A1145   4p multi   4.25   4.25

Prevention of Carbon Monoxide Accidents — A1146

Children's art by: No. 2449, 1p, Julieta Saavedra Barragán. No. 2450, 1p, Leandro Ventancour. No. 2451, 1p, Efraín Osvaldo

Rost, vert. No. 2452, 1p, Camila M. Alvarez Petrone, vert.

Perf. 13¾x13½, 13½x13¾
2007, Sept. 8
2449-2452　A1146　Set of 4　　4.00　4.00

San Lorenzo de Almagro Athletic Club, Cent. — A1147

2007, Sept. 22　　　**Perf. 13½x13¾**
2453　A1147　1p multi　　　　.90　.90

Beatification of Ceferino Namuncurá (1886-1905) — A1148

2007, Oct. 13　Litho.　Perf. 13¾x13½
2454　A1148　1p multi　　　　.90　.90

Contemporary Art — A1149

Designs: No. 2455, 1p, Corrientes Esquina Uruguay, photograph by Horacio Coppola. No. 2456, 1p, 0611, painting by Pablo Siquier. No. 2457, 1p, Diálogo, digital photograph by Liliana Porter, vert. No. 2458, 1p, Imaginando el Estupor, mosaic by Marta Minujin, vert.

Perf. 13¾x13½, 13½x13¾
2007, Oct. 27
2455-2458　A1149　Set of 4　　4.25　4.25
Nos. 2455-2458 each were printed in sheets of 4.

Christmas A1150

Designs: 25c, Adoration of the Magi. 1p, Holy Family.

2007, Nov. 10　　　**Perf. 13½x14**
2459-2460　A1150　Set of 2　　1.75　1.25

First Balloon Crossing of Río de la Plata, Cent. A1151

Perf. 13¾x13½
2007, Nov. 24　　　　　　Litho.
2461　A1151　1p multi　　　　1.10　1.10

Discovery of Oil and Gas in Argentina, Cent. — A1152

2007, Nov. 24
2462　A1152　1p multi　　　　1.10　1.10

2007 Presidential Inauguration A1153

2007, Dec. 15　　　**Perf. 13½x13¾**
2463　A1153　1p multi　　　　.90　.90

Festivals A1154

Designs: No. 2464, 1p, National Chamamé Festival, Corrientes Province. No. 2465, 1p, National Poncho Festival, Catamarca Province. No. 2466, 1p, National Festival of Dressage and Folklore, Jesús María, Cordoba Province. No. 2467, 1p, National Snow Festival, San Carlos de Bariloche, Río Negro Province.

2007, Dec. 15
2464-2467　A1154　Set of 4　　4.25　4.25

2008 Summer Olympics, Beijing A1155

Designs: No. 2468, 50c, Mountain biking. No. 2469, 50c, Taekwondo. 1p, Basketball. 4p, Pole vault.

Perf. 13½x13¾
2008, Mar. 29　　　　　　Litho.
2468-2471　A1155　Set of 4　　5.00　5.00

Natl. Scientific and Technical Research Council, 50th Anniv. — A1156

Designs: No. 2472, 1p, Bone tissue bridges with 45S5 bioactive glass particles. No. 2473, 1p, Pollen grain of Polygonum sp. No. 2474, 1p, Remnants of Supernova W44. No. 2475, 1p, Cave paintings, Epuyén River Valley. No. 2476, 1p, Gas heater device.

2008, Apr. 12　　　**Perf. 13¾x13½**
2472-2476　A1156　Set of 5　　4.00　4.00

Association of Argentine Private Radio Stations, 50th Anniv. — A1157

2008, Apr. 26
2477　A1157　1p multi　　　　.80　.80

Pres. Arturo Frondizi (1908-95), Oil Pumps — A1158

2008, Apr. 26
2478　A1158　1p multi　　　　1.00　1.00

Birds — A1159

Male and female: 1p, Sturnella loyca. 4p, Xanthopsar flavus.

2008, Apr. 26　　　**Perf. 13½x13¾**
2479-2480　A1159　Set of 2　　4.75　4.75

Argentine Aero Club, Cent. — A1160

2008, May 10　　　**Perf. 14x13½**
2481　A1160　1p multi　　　　.90　.90

Colón Theater, Buenos Aires, Cent. — A1161

2008, May 24
2482　A1161　1p multi　　　　.90　.90

Aimé Bonpland (1773-1858), Founder of Corrientes Natural Sciences Museum — A1162

2008, May 24　　　**Perf. 13¾x13½**
2483　A1162　1p multi　　　　.80　.80

Dr. Marcos Sastre (1808-87), Textbook Writer, and Text from Reading Book, Anagnosia — A1163

Perf. 13¾x13½
2008, June 21　　　　　　Litho.
2484　A1163　1p multi　　　　.80　.80

Luciano-Honorato Valette (1880-1957), Antarctic Naturalist — A1164

Disappearance of Rescue Ship ARA Guaraní, 50th Anniv. — A1165

2008, June 28
2485　A1164　1p multi　　　　.75　.75
2486　A1165　1p multi　　　　.75　.75

Characters From "The Mail Song," by Maria Elena Walsh A1166

Character From "Big Brother," by Silvia Schujer A1167

Characters From "Letters to Santa Claus," by Luis María Pescetti — A1168

Character From "Mammarachos por Carta," by Ricardo Mariño — A1169

Perf. 13½x13¾, 13¾x13½
2008, July 26

2487	A1166	1p multi	.90	.90
2488	A1167	1p multi	.90	.90
2489	A1168	1p multi	.90	.90
2490	A1169	1p multi	.90	.90
	Nos. 2487-2490 (4)		3.60	3.60

Children's songs and literature.

Scenes From "The Mail Song," by María Elena Walsh — A1170

Scenes From "Mamarrachos por Carta," by Ricardo Mariño — A1171

Characters From "Letters to Santa Claus," by Luis María Pescetti — A1172

Characters From "Big Brother," by Silvia Schujer — A1173

No. 2491: a, Bird holding Argentina #2216b in beak. b, Mailbox. c, Paper airplane, letters. d, Post office, letters. e, Smokestacks behind open envelope with letter. f, Philatelic office, Argentina #2236, #2239 and its adjacent label.

No. 2492: a, Postman holding letter. b, Postman and woman reading letter. c, Bird reading letter. d, Man with pipe. e, Birds on mail box. f, Monkey with banana.

No. 2493: a, Child writing letter to Santa Claus. b, Santa Claus reading letter from child.

No. 2494: a, Girl at table playing card game (40x50mm). b, Boy and mother, horiz. (70x40mm).

2008, July 26 Litho. Perf. 13½x13¾
Booklet Stamps

2491	A1170	Block of 6	5.25	5.25
a.-f.		1p Any single	.85	.85
g.		Booklet pane, 2 #2491	10.50	10.50

2492	A1171	Block of 6	5.25	5.25
a.-f.		1p Any single	.85	.85
g.		Booklet pane, 2 #2492	10.50	10.50

Perf. 14¼

2493	A1172	Booklet pane of 2	7.00	7.00
a.-b.		4p Either single	3.50	3.50

Perf. 14

2494	A1173	Booklet pane of 2	7.00	7.00
a.-b.		4p Either single	3.50	3.50
		Complete booklet, #2491g, 2492g, 2493, 2494	35.00	

Complete booklet is a spiral-bound book containing the four booklet panes, postal cards, text pages and pieces for a children's card game.

Archaeological Artifacts Type of 2000

Design: Jar, Yocavil culture.

Perf. 13½x13¾ Syncopated
2008, Aug. 2

2495	A973	10p multi	6.75	6.75

Souvenir Sheet

Olympex 2008 World Stamp Exhibition, Beijing — A1174

Litho. With Foil Application
2008, Aug. 2   **Perf. 14**

2496	A1174	4p multi	3.00	3.00

Immigrants to Argentina — A1175

Designs: No. 2497, 1p, Cherry blossoms, koi, immigrants from Japan. No. 2498, 1p, Metal decorative plates and immigrants from Lebanon. No. 2499, 1p, Tiles, guitar and immigrants from Portugal. No. 2500, 1p, Wooden decorative box, embroidered silk, Ugaritic alphabet and immigrants from Syria.

Perf. 13¾x13½
2008, Sept. 20   **Litho.**

2497-2500	A1175	Set of 4	2.60	2.60

Souvenir Sheets

National Flower Festival — A1176

Designs: No. 2501, 5p, Gerbera daisy, gardenia and rose (shown). No. 2502, 5p, Carnation, gold-banded lily and delphinium.

2008, Sept. 27   **Perf. 14**

2501-2502	A1176	Set of 2	7.25	7.25

Nos. 2501-2502 are impregnated with a floral scent.

Souvenir Sheets

Sports Personalities — A1177

Designs: No. 2503, 5p, Hand of Manu Ginobili, basketball and hoop. No. 2504, 5p, Rugby football kicked by Hugo Porta, goal posts, silhouettes of rugby player kicking ball. No. 2505, 5p, Silhouette of golfer putting, foot of Roberto De Vicenzo, vert. No. 2506, 5p, Juan Manuel Fangio in race car, vert.

2008, Oct. 11   **Perf. 14**

2503-2506	A1177	Set of 4	16.00	16.00

See Nos. 2541-2544, 2632-2635.

Science Teaching Year — A1178

2008, Oct. 25   **Perf. 13¾x13½**

2507	A1178	1p multi	1.00	1.00

Flowers A1179

Designs: No. 2508, 1p, Ceiba chodatii. No. 2509, 1p, Nelumbo nucifera.

2008, Oct. 25

2508-2509	A1179	Set of 2	2.50	2.50

See Viet Nam Nos. 3343-3344.

Souvenir Sheet

First Stamps of Argentina, Buenos Aires and Cordoba,150th Anniv. — A1180

No. 2510: a, Cordoba No. 2 (30x30mm). b, Buenos Aires No. 4 (40x30mm). c, Argentina No. 3 (30x40mm).

2008, Nov. 1   *Perf. 14*
2510 A1180 1p Sheet of 3, #a-c   4.00 4.00

Christmas
A1181

2008, Nov. 15   *Perf. 13½x13¾*
2511 A1181 1p multi   .80 .60

Dances
A1182

Designs: No. 2512, 1p, Malambo sureño dancer, Argentina. No. 2513, 1p, Hoy-nazan dancers, Armenia.

2008, Nov. 22   *Litho.*
2512-2513 A1182 Set of 2   1.75 1.75
     See Armenia Nos. 790-791.

El Cronista Comercial Newspaper, Cent. — A1183

2008, Dec. 13   *Perf. 13¾x13½*
2514 A1183 1p multi   .80 .80

School of Forestry, 50th Anniv. A1184

2008, Dec. 13   *Perf. 13½x3¾*
2515 A1184 1p multi   .80 .80

Festivals A1185

Designs: No. 2516, 1p, Chaya Festival, La Rioja Province. No. 2517, 1p, Natl. Grape Harvest Festival, Mendoza Province. No. 2518, 1p, Natl. Cherry Festival, Los Antiguos, Santa

Cruz Province. No. 2519, 1p, Natl. Sea Festival, Mar del Plata, Buenos Aires Province.

2009, Feb. 14   *Perf. 13½x13¾*
2516-2519 A1185 Set of 4   3.25 3.25

Souvenir Sheet

Preservation of Polar Regions and Glaciers — A1186

No. 2520: a, Retreat of Piedras Blancas Glacier. b, Retreat of Argentine Antarctic Territory ice.

2009, Mar. 7   *Perf. 14*
2520 A1186 5p Sheet of 2, #a-b   7.00 7.00

Bishop Colombres Memorial Experimental Agribusiness, Cent. — A1187

2009, Mar. 21   *Perf. 13¾x13½*
2521 A1187 1p multi   .80 .80

Souvenir Sheet

New Year 2009 (Year of the Ox) — A1188

Litho. & Embossed, Margin With Foil Application
2009, Apr. 4   *Perf. 14*
2522 A1188 5p multi   4.25 4.25
     China 2009 World Stamp Exhibition, Luoyang.

Holy Cross Exaltation Parish, Puerto Santa Cruz, Cent. — A1189

2009, Apr. 18 Litho. *Perf. 13½x13¾*
2523 A1189 1p multi   .80 .80

Argentine Exports — A1190

Designs: 1p, Wine. 5p, Agricultural machines.

2009, Apr. 18   *Perf. 13¾x13½*
2524-2525 A1190 Set of 2   4.00 4.00

Endangered Species A1191

Designs: No. 2526, 1p, Harpyhaliaetus coronatus. No. 2527, 1p, Chelonoidis chilensls, horlz.

Perf. 13½x13¾, 13¾x13½
2009, Apr. 18
2526-2527 A1191 Set of 2   2.00 2.00

Pres. Raúl Ricardo Alfonsín (1927-2009) A1192

2009, May 9   *Perf. 13½x13¾*
2528 A1192 1p multi   .80 .80

Children of the Holy Virgin of the Garden Congregation in Argentina, 150th Anniv. A1193

2009, May 23
2529 A1193 1p multi   .80 .80

Raúl Scalabrini Ortiz (1898-1959), Writer — A1194

2009, May 23
2530 A1194 1p multi   .80 .80

Political and Military Command of the Malvinas (Falkland Islands), 180th Anniv. A1195

Paintings: 1p, Luis Vernet, governor of the Malvinas, by Luisa Vernet Lavalle Lloveras. 5p, Ship and houses near cliff, by Vernet, map of Malvinas.

2009, June 13   *Perf. 13½x13¾*
2531 A1195 1p multi   .85 .85
              Souvenir Sheet
                  Perf. 14
2532 A1195 5p multi   3.75 3.75
     No. 2532 contains one 70x30mm stamp.

Water — A1196

No. 2533: a, Droplets. b, Drops, clouds and hand, vert.

2009, June 27   *Perf. 14*
2533   Sheet of 2, unscratched 7.00 7.00
   a. A1196 5p multi   3.50 3.50
   b. A1196 5p multi, unscratched 3.50 3.50
   c. As "b," scratched   3.50
   No. 2533b and sheet margin have scratch-off panels.

Flora and Fauna A1197

Designs: No. 2534, 1p, Polybetes pythagoricus. No. 2535, 1p, Passiflora caerulea.

2009, July 25   *Perf. 13¾x13½*
2534-2535 A1197 Set of 2   1.60 1.60

Amusement Park Rides — A1198

No. 2536: a, Bumper cars. b, Roller coaster. c, Ferris wheel. d, Ghost train.

2009, Aug. 1
2536   Horiz. strip of 4 +
           flanking label   2.75 2.75
   a.-d. A1198 1p Any single   .65 .65

Miniature Sheet

Sheep — A1199

No. 2537: a, Merino ram. b, Romney Marsh yearling. c, Corriedale ewe and lamb. d, Hampshire Down ewe and lamb. e, Lincoln ewe. f, Frisian ewe.

2009, Aug. 22
2537 A1199 1p Sheet of 6, #a-f,
+ 2 labels   4.50 4.50

Soil Erosion — A1200

No. 2538 — Erosion by: a, Water. b, Wind.

2009, Sept. 12   *Perf. 14x13½*
2538   Horiz. pair   1.60 1.60
a.-b.   A1200 1p Either single   .80 .80

A1201

America Issue, Education For
All — A1202

Perf. 13¾x13½
2009, Sept. 12   Litho.
2539 A1201 1p multi   .75 .75
2540 A1202 1p multi   .75 .75

Sports Personalities Type of 2008

Designs: No. 2541, 5p, Delfo Cabrera running in 1948 Summer Olympics, vert. No. 2542, 5p, Tennis ball and shorts of Guillermo Vilas (38mm diameter). No. 2543, 10p, Field hockey players, stick of Luciana Aymar, vert. No. 2544, 10p, Cyclists chasing Juan Curuchet, vert.

Perf. 14, Perf. (No. 2542)
2009, Sept. 26   Litho.
2541-2544 A1177   Set of 4   18.00 18.00
The tennis ball on No 2542 is covered with flocking.

National
Technological
University, 50th
Anniv.
A1203

2009, Oct. 17   *Perf. 13½x13¾*
2545 A1203 1p multi   .80 .80

Souvenir Sheets

A1204

Italia 2009 Intl. Philatelic Exhibition,
Rome — A1205

No. 2546: a, La Scala Theater, Milan. b, Colon Theater, Buenos Aires.
No. 2547: a, Froilán González racing in Ferrari 375 (85x30mm rhomboid) b, Ferrari F60 race car (60x20mm).

2009, Oct. 24   Litho.   *Perf. 14*
2546 A1204 6p Sheet of 2, #a-b   7.00 7.00
2547 A1205 6p Sheet of 2, #a-b   7.00 7.00

Intl. Year of Astronomy — A1206

Designs: 1p, Telescope, National University of Córdoba Astronomical Observatory.
10p, Galileo Galilei (1564-1642), diagram of solar system orbits.

2009, Oct. 24   Litho.   *Perf. 13¾x13½*
2548 A1206 1p multi   .80 .80

Souvenir Sheet
Perf. 14
2549 A1206 10p multi   7.25 7.25
No. 2549 contains one 80x20mm stamp.

Children's Art — A1207

Winning art in "I Can Slow TB Down" children's stamp design contest: No. 2550, 1p, Boxing gloves hitting "TB," by Alberto Penayo Pardo. No. 2551, 1p, Lungs with bandage, by Candela Alemany Fiandrino. No. 2552, 1p, Boy coughing, doctor holding sign, by Rocío Cabrera, vert. No. 2553, 1p, Hands holding lungs, by Juliana Benzo, vert.

Perf. 13¾x13½, 13½x13¾
2009, Nov. 14   Litho.
2550-2553 A1207   Set of 4   3.25 3.25

Christmas
A1208

2009, Nov. 21   *Perf. 13½x14*
2554 A1208 1p multi   .80 .45

Historic Buildings — A1209

No. 2555, 1p — San Martín Mansion, 1910: a, Exterior. b, Interior.
No. 2556, 1p — Ortiz Basualdo Mansion, 1918: a, Exterior. b, Interior.
No. 2557, 1p — Fernandez-Anchorena Mansion, 1909: a, Exterior. b, Interior.
No. 2558, 1p — Duhau Mansion, 1934: a, Exterior. b, Interior.

Perf. 13¾x13½
2009, Dec. 12   Litho.
Horiz. Pairs, #a-b
2555-2558 A1209   Set of 4   6.00 6.00
Nos. 2555-2558 each were printed in sheets containing 8 pairs and 4 labels.

Festivals
A1210

Designs: No. 2559, 1.50p, National Apple Festival, General Roca, Río Negro Province. No. 2560, 1.50p, National Sun Festival, San Juan, San Juan Province. No. 2561, 1.50p, National Students Festival, San Salvador de Jujuy, Jujuy Province. No. 2562, 1.50p, National Tradition Festival, San Antonio de Areco, Buenos Aires Province.

2010, Feb. 20   *Perf. 13½x13¾*
2559-2562 A1210   Set of 4   4.25 4.25

South
American Sails
2010 Regatta
A1211

Designs: 1.50p, Argentine Navy frigate Libertad.
No. 2564: a, Chilean Navy schooner Esmerelda. b, Libertad, diff.

Perf. 13¾x13½ Syncopated
2010, Feb. 20
2563 A1211 1.50p multi   1.00 1.00
Souvenir Sheet
Perf. 14
2564 A1211   6p Sheet of 2,
#a-b, + 12 labels   7.75 7.75
No. 2564 contains two 40x50mm stamps.

May Revolution,
Bicent. — A1212

Perf. 13½x13¾ Syncopated
2010, Mar. 6
2565 A1212 1.50p multi   .90 .90

National
Symbols
A1213

Designs: No. 2566, 1.50p, Coat of arms. No. 2567, 1.50p, Flag, horiz.

Perf. 13½x13¾, 13¾x13½
2010, Mar. 27
2566-2567 A1213   Set of 2   1.75 1.75

A Culture of Peace — A1214

No. 2568: a, Dove. b, Map of South America.

2010, Apr. 24   Litho.   *Perf. 13½x13¾*
2568 A1214 1.50p Horiz. pair,
#a-b   1.75 1.75

Buenos Aires City Symphony,
Cent. — A1215

2010, Apr. 24   *Perf. 14x13½*
2569 A1215 1.50p multi   1.00 1.00

Argentine
Army, Bicent.
A1216

2010, May 8   *Perf. 13½x13¾*
2570 A1216 1.50p multi   1.00 1.00

Argentine Naval Command, Bicent. — A1217

2010, May 29   **Perf. 13¾x13½**
2571 A1217 1.50p multi   1.00 1.00

Bicentenary Mural — A1218

No. 2572: a, Cabildo, Buenos Aires (30x50mm). b, General Manuel Belgrano, flag of Argentina on pole, Casa de Tucumán, San Miguel de Tucumán (30x50mm). c, Gen. José de San Martín on horseback, raising sword (40x80mm). d, National Constitution (30x50mm). e, Ships unloading immigrants (30x50mm). f, Sword battle, people voting, "1910," horiz. (70x30mm). g, National Congress, Blind Justice (30x50mm). h, Trolley, film set, bridge, horiz. (40x30mm). i, Palm tree, crowd, banners, men with feet in fountain, baby with umbilical cord (30x60mm). j, Military with guns, cardinal, man smoking cigar, eyes, "the disappeared" in pit (30x40mm). k, Mothers of the Plaza de Mayo holding pictures of the disappeared, May Pyramid statue (40x60mm). l, Motorcyclist, men with briefcases holding cellular phones, man on computer, airplanes (40x60mm).

2010, May 29   **Litho.**   **Perf. 14**
2572   Sheet of 12   13.00 13.00
  a.-l. A1218 1.50p Any single   1.00 1.00

Gazeta de Buenos-Ayres, Bicent. A1219

2010, June 5   **Litho.**   **Perf. 13½x13¾**
2573 A1219 1.50p multi   1.00 1.00

A1220

2010 World Cup Soccer Championships, South Africa — A1221

2010 World Cup emblem and stylized player from: No. 2574, 1.50p, Nigeria. No. 2575,

1.50p, Greece, vert. 5p, South Korea. 7p, Argentina, vert.
No. 2578, 5p, Argentina player sliding to kick ball. No. 2579, 5p, Argentina player heading ball into net. No. 2580, 5p, Argentina player making scissor kick. No. 2581, 5p, Goalie making save, vert.

Perf. 13¾x13½, 13½x13¾
2010, June 5
2574-2577 A1220   Set of 4   9.50 5.00
Souvenir Sheets
Perf. 14
2578-2581 A1221   Set of 4   12.50 12.50
Nos. 2578-2579 each contain one 70x40mm stamp, No. 2580 contains one 60x40mm stamp, and No. 2581 contains one 40x60mm stamp.

World Junior Rugby Championships, Argentina — A1222

2010, June 19   **Perf. 13¾x13½**
2582 A1222 1.50p multi   1.00 1.00

Souvenir Sheet

First Government Junta, Bicent. — A1223

2010, July 24   **Perf. 14**
2583 A1223 5p multi   3.00 3.00

Miniature Sheet

Toys and Games — A1224

No. 2584: a, Sulky-cycle (sulky-ciclo). b, Cup and ball (balero). c, Top (trompo). d, Hoop (aro). e, Doll (muñeca).

Perf. 13½x13¾ Syncopated
2010, July 24   **Litho.**
2584 A1224 2p Sheet of 5, #a-e,
              + 15 labels   6.50 6.50
The stamps and labels of No. 2584 are puzzle pieces that when separated and rearranged form a picture.

Jorge Luis Borges (1899-1986), Writer A1225

Perf. 13¾x13½ Syncopated
2010, Aug. 14   **Litho.**
2585 A1225 7p multi   4.25 4.25
2010 Frankfurt Book Fair. See Germany No. 2585.

Landmarks Type of 2004

Designs: 1.50p, Parana River, Corrientes. 6p, Les Eclaireurs Lighthouse, Tierra del Fuego.

Perf. 13¾x13½ Syncopated
2010   **Litho.**
2586 A1063a 1.50p multi + label 1.50 1.50
2587 A1063a 6p multi   6.50 6.50
Issued: 1.50p, 5/11; 6p, 2/12.

Mountain Lakes — A1226

Flags of Romania and Argentina and: 1.50p, Lake Ballea, Romania. 7p, Lake Nahuel Huapi, Argentina.

2010, Aug. 14   **Perf. 13¾x13½**
2588-2589 A1226   Set of 2   5.00 5.00
See Romania Nos. 5201-5202.

Women's Field Hockey World Cup Championships, Rosario — A1227

2010, Aug. 28
2590 A1227 1.50p multi   1.00 1.00

Games A1228

Designs: No. 2591, 1.50p, Truco (card game). No. 2592, 1.50p, Bocce.

2010, Aug. 28   **Perf. 13½x13¾**
2591-2592 A1228   Set of 2   1.90 1.90

2010 Census A1229

Perf. 13¾x13½ Syncopated
2010, Sept. 18
2593 A1229 1.50p multi   1.00 1.00

Juan Bautista Alberdi (1810-84), Lawyer and Diplomat A1230

2010, Sept. 18   **Perf. 13½x13¾**
2594 A1230 1.50p multi   1.00 1.00

National Library, Bicent. A1231

Perf. 13¾x13½
2010, Sept. 18   **Litho.**
2595 A1231 1.50p multi   1.00 1.00

Souvenir Sheet

Weather Stations in Austria and Argentina — A1232

No. 2596 — Weather station in: a, Stadtpark, Vienna. b, Buenos Aires Botanical Garden.

2010, Oct. 16   **Perf. 14**
2596 A1232 5p Sheet of 2, #a-b 6.25 6.25
See Austria No. 2283.

The Child of Bethlehem, by Aldo Severi — A1233

2010, Nov. 13   **Perf. 13¾x13½**
2597 A1233 1.50p multi   1.00 .50
Christmas.

Federal Electric Power Council, 50th Anniv. A1234

2010, Nov. 27   **Perf. 13½x13¾**
2598 A1234 1.50p multi   1.00 1.00

Souvenir Sheets

Lighthouses — A1235

Portuguese Ceramic Tile — A1236

No. 2599: a, Querandí Lighthouse, Argentina. b, Santa Marta Lighthouse, Portugal.

2010, Sept. 25   **Perf. 14**
2599 A1235   5p Sheet of 2, #a-b   6.00   6.00
2600 A1236   10p multi   6.00   6.00

Portugal 2010 Intl. Philatelic Exhibition, Lisbon. Portions of the designs of Nos. 2599a-2599b were applied by a thermographic process producing a shiny, raised effect.

World Post Day — A1237

2010, Oct. 9   Litho.   Perf. 13½x13¾
2601 A1237   1.50p multi   .90   .90

A Song to Work, Sculpture by Rogelio Yrurtia — A1238

2010, Oct. 16   Perf. 14x13½
2602 A1238   1.50p multi   .90   .90

Dakar Rally in Argentina — A1239

No. 2603 — Photographs of 2009 and 2010 Rallies: a, Starting line of Rally, Buenos Aires (60x40mm). b, Motorcycle No. 107 (50x50mm). c, Car No. 300 on dirt road (60x40mm). d, Truck No. 502 on dirt road, (50x50mm). e, Vehicles on dirt road (50x50mm). f, Quad No. 251 (40x80mm). g, Quad No. 277 (40x80mm).

No. 2604: a, Car No. 375 on dirt road (60x50mm). b, Two quad riders in sand near hill (60x40mm). c, Car No. 377 in air (60x40mm). d, Motorcycle No. 1 (40x50mm).

e, Tree near Laguna del Pescado (40x50mm). f, White clouds over mountain near Tucumán (40x50mm). g, Road and bridge near Jujuy (40x50mm). h, Truck No. 500 in water (70x50mm).

2010, Dec. 11   Perf. 14
2603   Booklet pane of 7   12.00   12.00
a.-e.   A1239 1.50p Any single   .90   .90
f.   A1239 5p multi   3.00   3.00
g.   A1239 7p multi   4.25   4.25
2604   Booklet pane of 8   12.50   12.50
a.-g.   A1239 1.50p Any single   .90   .90
h.   A1239 10p multi   6.00   6.00
    Complete booklet, #2603-
    2604 + post card   25.00

Intl. Year of Forests A1240

2011, Mar. 19   Perf. 13½x13¾
2605 A1240   2p multi   1.00   1.00

Postal Union of the Americas, Spain and Portugal (UPAEP), Cent. — A1241

2011, Mar. 19   Perf. 13¾x13½
2606 A1241   8p multi   4.00   4.00

Buenos Aires, 2010 World Book Capital — A1242

No. 2607 — Stylized buildings spelling: a, "Buenos Aires Capital." b, "Mundial del Libro 2011."

2011, Apr. 16   Perf. 14x13½
2607   Horiz. pair   2.25   2.25
a.-b.   A1242 2p Either single   1.10   1.10

A1243

Antarctic Treaty, 50th Anniv. — A1244

Designs: 2p, Iceberg and Antarctic Treaty emblem.
No. 2609: a, Pygoscelis papua. b, Scientist and equipment.

2011, Apr. 16   Perf. 13¾x13½
2608 A1243   2p multi   1.00   1.00

Souvenir Sheet
Perf. 14
2609 A1244   8p Sheet of 2, #a-b   8.00   8.00
34th Antarctic Treaty Consultative Meeting, Buenos Aires.

Mariano Moreno (1778-1811), Politician — A1245

2011, May 21   Perf. 13¾x13½
2610 A1245   2p multi   1.00   1.00

World Blood Donor Day — A1246

Perf. 13¾x13½ Syncopated
2011, May 21
2611 A1246   5p multi   2.50   2.50

Year of Decent Labor, Health and Safety for Workers A1247

2011, June 4   Perf. 13¾x13½
2612 A1247   2p multi   1.00   1.00

Pres. Domingo Faustino Sarmiento (1811-88) A1248

2011, June 25   Perf. 13½x13¾
2613 A1248   2.50p multi   1.25   1.25

May Pyramid, Buenos Aires, Bicent. — A1249

2011, June 25   Perf. 13½x14
2614 A1249   2.50p multi   1.25   1.25

America Cup Soccer Tournament — A1250

No. 2615 — Players from Group A teams: a, Argentina and Bolivia. b, Colombia and Costa Rica.
No. 2616 — Players from Group B teams: a, Venezuela and Brazil. b, Paraguay and Ecuador.
No. 2617 — Players from Group C teams: a, Peru and Uruguay. b, Mexico and Chile.

2011, June 25   Perf. 14
2615   Wheel with 2 sheets   8.00   8.00
a.-b.   A1250 5p Either sheet   4.00   4.00
2616   Wheel with 2 sheets   8.00   8.00
a.-b.   A1250 5p Either sheet   4.00   4.00
2617   Wheel with 2 sheets   8.00   8.00
a.-b.   A1250 5p Either sheet   4.00   4.00
    Nos. 2615-2617 (3)   24.00   24.00

Nos. 2615a-2615b, 2616a-2616b and 2617a-2617b are attached to wheels with a metal grommet at the center of the wheels.

Launch of SAC-D/Aquarius Satellite — A1251

2011, July 23   Litho.   Perf. 13¾x13½
2618 A1251   2.50p multi   1.25   1.25

Mailboxes — A1252

Designs: No. 2619, 2.50p, Corneta type mailbox, cancel. No. 2620, 2.50p, Pillar box, handwritten letter, vert.

Perf. 13¾x13½, 13½x13¾
2011, Aug. 20
2619-2620 A1252   Set of 2   2.75   2.75

Festivals A1253

Designs: No. 2621, 2.50p, National Beer Festival, Villa General Belgrano. No. 2622, 2.50p, National Horse Festival, San Cristóbal. No. 2623, 2.50p, Foreign Communities Fair, Comodoro Rivadavia. No. 2624, 2.50p, National Tea Festival, Campo Viera.

2011, Sept. 10   Perf. 13½x13¾
2621-2624 A1253   Set of 4   6.00   6.00

Orchids
A1254

Designs: No. 2625, 2.50p, Zygopetalum maxillare. No. 2626, 2.50p, Sacoila lanceolata, vert.

Perf. 13¾x13½, 13½x13¾
2011, Sept. 24
2625-2626 A1254 Set of 2 5.00 5.00

Train on the Clouds — A1255

No. 2627: a, Train cars, bridge (yellow orange panel). b, Locomotive, bridge (blue panel). c, Train on curved bridge (orange panel). d, Train on curved bridge, diff. (red panel).

2011, Sept. 24 **Perf. 14**
2627 Sheet of 4 15.00 15.00
a.-d. A1255 5p Any single 3.75 3.75

Argentine Pediatric Society,
Cent. — A1256

2011, Oct. 22 **Perf. 13¾x13½**
2628 A1256 2.50p multi 1.25 1.25

Miniature Sheet

Pig Breeds — A1257

No. 2629: a, Landrace. b, Hampshire. c, Pietrain. d, Duroc Jersey. e, Spotted Poland. f, Yorkshire.

2011, Oct. 29 **Litho.**
2629 A1257 2.50p Sheet of 6,
#a-f, + 2 la-
bels 8.75 8.75

Christmas
A1258

Litho. With Glitter Affixed
2011, Oct. 29 Perf. 13¾ Syncopated
2630 A1258 2.50p multi 1.25 .60

Souvenir Sheet

Pres. Néstor Carlos Kirchner (1950-
2010), and Casa Rosada — A1259

2011, Nov. 26 **Litho.** **Perf. 14**
2631 A1259 5p multi 2.75 2.75

Sports Personalities Type of 2008
Souvenir Sheets

Designs: No. 2632, 10p, Horse and mallet of Adolfo Cambiaso, polo player, vert. No. 2633, 10p, Chessboard and Miguel Najdorf (1910-97), chess player, vert. (50x60mm). No. 2634, 10p, Sailboard of Carlos Espinola, sailboarder, vert. (50x60mm). No. 2635, 10p, Roller skates of Nora Vega, roller skater (60x40mm).

2011, Nov. 12
2632-2635 A1177 Set of 4 22.50 22.50

Rights of the
Child — A1260

Winning art in children's stamp design contest by: No. 2636, 2.50p, Nicolás Agustín Bernachea (blue panels). No. 2637, 2.50p, Sofía Panagópulo (pink panels). No. 2638, 2.50p, Ezequiel Catalano Segesso (yellow green panels). No. 2639, 2.50p, Laura Florencia Martinessi (orange panels).

2011, Nov. 26 **Perf. 13½x13¾**
2636-2639 A1260 Set of 4 5.50 5.50

Souvenir Sheet

Creation of Argentine Flag and Pledge
of Allegiance, Bicent. — A1261

2012, Mar. 3 **Litho.** **Perf. 14**
2640 A1261 5p multi 2.25 2.25

First Argentine Flight Landing at South
Pole, 50th Anniv. — A1262

2012, Mar. 3 **Litho.** **Perf. 13¾x13½**
2641 A1262 2.50p multi 1.25 1.25

Monument to Gen. Manuel Belgrano,
Buenos Aires, and Argentine
Flag — A1263

2012, Mar. 31 **Perf. 14x13¾**
2642 A1263 2.50p multi 1.25 1.25

Argentine Claims of Sovereignty Over
British South Atlantic Islands — A1264

Argentine flag and map of: No. 2643, 2.50p, Falkland Islands (Isla Gran Malvina and Isla Soledad). No. 2644, 2.50p, South Georgia (Isla San Pedro). No. 2645, 2.50p, South Sandwich Islands (Islas Traverse, Islas Candelaria, Isla Saunders, Isla Jorge, Isla Blanca and Grupo Tule del Sur), vert. (28x67mm).

Perf. 13¾x13½, 13¾x14 (#2645)
2012, Mar. 31
2643-2645 A1264 Set of 3 4.00 4.00

Presidential
Staff and
Argentine
Flag — A1265

2012, Apr. 14 **Perf. 13½x13¾**
2646 A1265 2.50p multi 1.25 1.25
Presidential mandate of Cristina Fernández Kirchner for 2011-15.

Monument to Gen. José de San
Martín, First Deed of Río Gallegos
Town Council — A1266

2012, Apr. 14 **Perf. 14x13¾**
2647 A1266 2.50p multi 1.25 1.25
Río Gallegos Town Council, cent.

Alernative Energies — A1267

Designs: 2.50p, Biogas, biomass and biocombustibles. 9.50p, Solar, wind and hydroelectric energy.

2012, Apr. 28 Litho. Perf. 14x13½
2648-2649 A1267 Set of 2 6.50 6.50

Argentine
Natural History
Museum,
Bicent.
A1268

Museum emblem and: No. 2650, 2.50p, Skeleton of Dahlia the Elephant. No. 2651, 2.50p, Skull of Bonatitan reigi (dinosaur). No. 2652, 2.50p, Agrias narcissus butterflies, horiz. No. 2653, 2.50p, Display in Hall of Birds, horiz.

Perf. 13½x13¾, 13¾x13½
2012, Apr. 28
2650-2653 A1268 Set of 4 5.50 5.50

Intl. Year of Cooperatives — A1269

2012, June 16 **Perf. 13¾x13½**
2654 A1269 2.50p multi 1.40 1.40

Passage of
Sáenz Peña
Universal Male
Suffrage Law,
Cent. — A1270

2012, June 16 **Perf. 13½x13¾**
2655 A1270 2.50p multi 1.40 1.40

Paintings of Historical Events of
1812 — A1271

Painting of: No. 2656, 2.50p, Jujuy Exodus,
by unknown artist. No. 2657, 2.50p, Battle of
Tucuman, by Tomas del Villar.

2012, June 16   **Perf. 13¾x13½**
2656-2657 A1271   Set of 2   3.50 3.50

Argentine School of Military Aviation,
Cent. — A1272

2012, July 21   **Perf. 14x13½**
2658 A1272 2.75p multi   1.50 1.50

Operation Southern Cross for Naval
Assistance in Antarctica — A1273

2012, July 21   **Perf. 13¾x13½**
2659 A1273 5p multi   2.25 2.25

Souvenir Sheet

Eva Perón (1919-52) — A1274

2012, Sept. 1   **Perf. 14**
2660 A1274 10p multi   5.25 5.25

Alzheimer's
Disease
Awareness
A1275

2012, Sept. 15   **Perf. 13½x13¾**
2661 A1275 3p multi   1.75 1.75

Festivals
A1276

Designs: No. 2662, 3p, National Artisans
Festival, Colón. No. 2663, 3p, Maní National
Festival, Hernando. No. 2664, 3p, National
Orange Festival, Bella Vista. No. 2665, 3p,
National Calf Festival and Branding Day,
Ayacucho.

2012, Sept. 25
2662-2665 A1276   Set of 4   6.00 6.00

General San Martín Mounted
Grenadiers Regiment, 200th
Anniv. — A1277

2012, Oct. 13   **Perf. 13¾x13½**
2666 A1277 3p multi   1.25 1.25

Christmas
A1278

2012, Nov. 17   **Perf. 13½x13¾**
2667 A1278 3p multi   1.25 .60

Miniature Sheet

Bats — A1279

No. 2668: a, Sturnira lillium in flight. b,
Sturnira lillium hanging and close-up of head.
c, Histiotus laephotis. d, Histiotus montanus.
e, Chrotopterus auritus in flight. f, Head of
Chrotopterus auritus. g, Head of Noctilio
leporinus. h, Noctilio leporinus in flight.

2012, Dec. 22   **Perf. 13¾x13½**
2668 A1279 3p Sheet of 8, #a-
h   12.00 12.00

Battle of Salta, 200th Anniv. — A1280

2013, Feb. 23   **Perf. 14x13½**
2669 A1280 3.50p multi   1.40 1.40

**Archaeological Artifacts Type of
2000**

Designs: 30p, Ceremonial hatchet, Tehuelche culture. 40p, Basket with handle,
Selk'nam culture. 50p, Basket with handle and
lid, Wichi culture.

Perf. 13½x13¾ Syncopated
2013, Mar. 1
2670 A973 30p multi   15.00 15.00
2671 A973 40p multi   20.00 20.00
2672 A973 50p multi   25.00 25.00
   Nos. 2670-2672 (3)   60.00 60.00

General
Constituent
Assembly of
1813, 200th
Anniv.
A1281

2013, Mar. 9   **Perf. 13½x13¾**
2673 A1281 3.50p multi   2.00 2.00

Festivals
A1282

Designs: No. 2674, 3.50p, National Folklore
Festival, Cosquín. No. 2675, 3.50p, National
Trout Festival, Junín de los Andes. No. 2676,
3.50p, National Lemon Festival, Tafí Viejo,
vert. No. 2677, 3.50p, National Petroleum Festival, Comodoro Rivadavia, vert.

Perf. 13¾x13½, 13½x13¾
2013, Mar. 23
2674-2677 A1282   Set of 4   6.50 6.50

Landmarks Type of 2004
Designs: 3.50p, Cancha de Bochas,
Ischigualasto National Park. 30p, Hill of Seven
Colors, Jujuy.

Perf. 13¾x13½ Syncopated
2013, Mar.
2678 A1063a 3.50p multi   1.75 1.75
2679 A1063a 30p multi   15.00 15.00

Souvenir Sheet

Partido de Esteban Echeverría Area of
Buenos Aires, Cent. — A1283

No. 2680: a, Door on building built in 1789.
b, Plaza and flags, horiz.

2013, Apr. 13   **Litho.**   **Perf. 14**
2680 A1283   Sheet of 2   4.25 4.25
   a.-b.   5p Either single   2.10 2.10

National University of Córdoba, 400th
Anniv. — A1284

2013, Apr. 27   **Perf. 14x13½**
2681 A1284 3.50p multi   1.50 1.50

Election
of Pope
Francis
A1285

No. 2682 — Arms of Pope Francis and: a,
Pope Francis, flags of Vatican City, Italy and
Argentina. b, Pope Francis in profile, flags of
Vatican City and Argentina. c, Pope Francis
waving, flags of Vatican City and Argentina. d,
Pope Francis holding cross, flags of Vatican
City and Argentina.

2013, May 2   **Perf. 13¾x13½**
2682   Vert. strip of 4   13.50 13.50
   a.-b.   A1285 3.50p Either single   1.50 1.50
   c.   A1285 10p multi   4.25 4.25
   d.   A1285 14p multi   6.00 6.00
   See Italy No. 3179, Vatican City Nos. 1523-
1526.

African Union,
50th Anniv.
A1286

2013, June 1   **Litho.**   **Perf. 13½x13¾**
2683 A1286 4p multi   1.50 1.50

Villa
Carlos
Paz,
Cent.
A1287

2013, July 27   **Litho.**   **Perf. 13¾x13½**
2684 A1287 4p multi   1.50 1.50

Souvenir Sheet

125th Session of the International
Olympic Committee, Buenos
Aires — A1288

No. 2685: a, Runners, Pierre de Coubertin
(1863-1937), founder of Intl. Olympic Committee (60x30mm). b, Gymnast, flag of Argentina,
Floralis Generica, sculpture by Eduardo Catalano (60x40mm).

2013, Sept. 14   **Litho.**   **Perf. 14**
2685 A1288 5p Sheet of 2, #a-b   4.00 4.00

Birds
A1289

Designs: No. 2686, 4p, Furnarius rufus. No.
2687, 4p, Podiceps gallardoi. No. 2688, 4p,
Campephilus magellanicus, vert. No. 2689,
4p, Gubernatrix cristata, vert.

Perf. 13¾x13½, 13½x13¾
2013, Oct. 19   **Litho.**
2686-2689 A1289   Set of 4   6.50 6.50

A1290

A1291

A1292

Winning
Designs in
"Right to
Identity"
Children's Art
Contest
A1293

2013, Oct. 22 Litho. Perf. 13¾x13½
2690 A1290 4p multi   1.40 1.40
2691 A1291 4p multi   1.40 1.40

Perf. 13½x13¾
2692 A1292 4p multi   1.40 1.40
2693 A1293 4p multi   1.40 1.40
Nos. 2690-2693 (4)   5.60 5.60

Sergeant Juan
Bautista Cabral
(c. 1789-1813),
Hero in Battle
of San Lorenzo
A1294

San Martín Regiment of Mounted
Grenadiers in Battle of San
Lorenzo — A1295

2013, Nov. 9 Litho. Perf. 13½x13¾
2694 A1294 4p multi   1.40 1.40

Perf. 14x13½
2695 A1295 4p multi   1.40 1.40
Battle of San Lorenzo, 200th anniv.

Campaign Against
Discrimination — A1296

No. 2696 — Stylized people with joined
hands and background color of: a, 4p, White.
b, 13p, Black.

2013, Nov. 9 Litho. Perf. 13½x13¾
2696 A1296   Horiz. pair, #a-b   5.75 5.75
America Issue.

History of the
Argentine Post
Office — A1297

No. 2697: a, Queen Juana of Castile, coat of
arms, postal runner, map of Peru (opening of
first post office in Lima, Peru, (1514)
(30x30mm). b, Manuel Belgrano, Mariano
Moreno, Cabildo, Buenos Aires (Post Office of
the May Revolution, 1810) (30x40mm). c,
President Juan Perón, and his wife, Eva (creation of Post Office and Telecommunications
Secretariat, 1949) (30x40mm). d, Mail box,
postal workers, flag of Argentina (renationalization of Postal Service, 10th anniv., 2013)
(30x40mm). e, Pres. Nelson Kirchner, people
with flags, mail boxes (renationalization of
Postal Service, 2003) (63mm diameter).

**Litho., Litho. With Foil Application
(10p)**
2013, Nov. 19   Perf. 14
2697   Miniature sheet of 5   9.75 9.75
a.-d.   A1297 5p Any single   1.60 1.60
e.   A1297 10p multi   3.25 3.25

Souvenir Sheet

Brasiliana 2013 Intl. Philatelic
Exhibition, Rio de Janeiro — A1298

No. 2698: a, 4p, Dolichandra unguis-cati. b,
13p, Alouatta guariba, vert.

2013, Nov. 23   Litho.   Perf. 14
2698 A1298   Sheet of 2, #a-b   5.50 5.50

Argentine
National
Anthem, 200th
Anniv.
A1299

Perf. 13½x13¾
2013, Nov. 30   Litho.
2699 A1299 4p multi   1.25 1.25

Christmas
A1300

Perf. 13½x13¾
2013, Nov. 30   Litho.
2700 A1300 4p multi   1.25 .60

New Laws, Policies,
and Regulations
Affecting Argentina
Society — A1301

Designs; 25c, New national idenification
cards (resolution 1800/09). 50c, Marriage

equality (law 26,618). 1p, Soccer balls (free
television broadcasts of local soccer games).
2p, Airplane, oil well, envelope and mail box
(nationalization of industries). 5p, Flasks and
chemical symbols (law 26,421 establishing
program to support Network of Argentinian
Researchers and Scientists Abroad). 10p,
Family, hands, roof (establishment of
Pro.Cre.Ar. loan program). 30p, End of Impu-
nity laws and reopening of criminal trials of
Argentina's military dictatorship (law 25,779).
40p, Mandatory open primary elections with
obligatory voting. 50p, Open digital television.

Perf. 13½x13¾ Syncopated
2014, Jan. 20   Litho.
2701 A1301 25c multi   .25 .25
2702 A1301 50c multi   .25 .25
2703 A1301 1p multi   .25 .25
2704 A1301 2p multi   .40 .30
2705 A1301 5p multi   1.00 .50
2706 A1301 10p multi   2.00 1.00
2707 A1301 30p multi   6.00 3.00
2708 A1301 40p multi   8.00 4.00
2709 A1301 50p multi   10.00 4.75
Nos. 2701-2709 (9)   28.15 14.30

New Laws, Policies
and Regulations
Affecting Argentina
Society — A1302

Designs: 25c, Nationalization of pension
funds (law 26,425). 50c, Argentina Connected
national telecommunications plan. 1p, Argen-
tina-Bolivia pipeline integration. 2p, Latin
American integration (Union of South American Nations). 3p, Creation of universities. 4p,
Law regulating audiovisual communication
services (law 26,522). 5p, Argentina Works
Program. 6p, National Assisted Fertilization
Act (law 26,862). 10p, National child allowance
decrees (Decree 1602/09). 30p, Suffrage for
16-year-olds (law 26,774). 50p, Restructuring
of national debt.

Perf. 13½x13¾ Syncopated
2014   Litho.
2710 A1302 25c multi   .25 .25
2711 A1302 50c multi   .25 .25
2712 A1302 1p multi   .25 .25
2713 A1302 2p multi   .50 .30
2714 A1302 3p multi   .75 .40
2715 A1302 4p multi   1.00 .50
2716 A1302 5p multi   1.25 .60
2717 A1302 6p multi   1.50 .75
2718 A1302 10p multi   2.50 1.25
2719 A1302 30p multi   7.50 3.75
2719A A1302 50p multi   12.00 12.00
Nos. 2710-2719A (11)   27.75 20.30
Issued: No. 2710-2719, 1/20; 50p, 8/25.

Jorge A. Newbery (1875-1914), Pilot,
Airplane and Hot Air Balloon — A1303

2014, Mar. 5 Litho. Perf. 13¾x13½
2720 A1303 4.50p multi   1.25 1.25

Hugo Chávez (1954-2013), President
of Venezuela — A1304

Chávez: No. 2721, 10p, Waving, wearing
presidential sash. No. 2722, 10p, Holding map
of South America.

2014, Mar. 5 Litho. Perf. 13¾x13½
2721-2722 A1304   Set of 2   5.25 5.25
America Issue.

Argentine Presence in the Antarctic,
110th Anniv. — A1305

No. 2724 — Latin American Antarctic
Progam Administrators emblem and: a, Scien-
tific researcher and penguin (30x60mm). b,
Plesiosaurs (60x30mm).

Perf. 13¾x13½
2014, Mar. 25   Litho.
2723 A1305 4.50p shown   1.25 1.25

Souvenir Sheet
Perf. 14
2724   Sheet of 2   3.00 3.00
a.-b.   A1305 6p Either single   1.50 1.50
25th reunion of Latin American Antarctic
Program Administrators, Buenos Aires (No.
2724).

Flora and
Fauna of
Iguazu Falls
Area
A1306

No. 2725: a, Doxocopa linda mileta
(40x40mm). b, Billbergia zebrina (30x40mm).
c, Iguazu Falls and Toco toucan (70x40mm).
d, Iguazu Falls (90x30mm)

Litho. & Silk-Screened
2014, Apr. 14   Perf. 14
2725   Miniature sheet of 4   9.00 9.00
a.-b.   A1306 8p Either single   2.00 2.00
c.-d.   A1306 10p Either single   2.50 2.50

Souvenir Sheet

Renationalization of YPF Energy
Company — A1307

2014, May 5   Litho.   Perf. 14
2726 A1307 16p multi   4.00 4.00

Battle of Montevideo, 200th
Anniv. — A1308

2014, May 19 Litho. Perf. 14x13½
2727 A1308 4.50p multi   1.10 1.10

National University of Tucuman, Cent. — A1309

2014, May 26 Litho. *Perf. 14x13½*
2728 A1309 4.50p multi   1.10 1.10

2014 World Cup Soccer Championships, Brazil — A1310

No. 2729 — Shirts and schedules of Group F teams: a, Argentina. b, Bosnia & Herzegovina. c, Iran. d, Nigeria.

2014, May 12 Litho. *Perf. 13½x13¾*
2729   Horiz. strip of 4   28.00 28.00
a.-d. A1310 10p Any single   7.00 7.00
No. 2729 was quickly withdrawn from sale.

Myths and Legends A1311

Designs: No. 2733, 10p, La Flor del Ceibo (the Ceibo flower). No. 2734, 10p, El Viento Zonda (the Zonda wind).

Perf. 13½x13¾
2014, June 30   Litho.
2733-2734 A1311 Set of 2   5.00 5.00
America Issue.

El Enterriano, by Eleodoro Ergasto Marenco (1914-96) A1312

2014, July 14 Litho. *Perf. 13½x13¾*
2735 A1312 5p multi   1.25 1.25

Commercial Aircraft — A1313

Designs: No. 2736, 5p, Comet IV. No. 2737, 5p, Boeing 747-200. No. 2738, 5p, Boeing 737-800NG. No. 2739, 5p, Airbus 340-300.

2014, July 21 Litho. *Perf. 14x13½*
2736-2739 A1313 Set of 4   5.00 5.00

Souvenir Sheet

Control of Aerolíneas Argentinas by Argentine Government, 6th Anniv. — A1314

Litho. & Silk-Screened
2014, July 21   *Perf. 14*
2740 A1314 20p multi   5.00 5.00

Souvenir Sheet

PhilaKorea 2014 Intl. Philatelic Exhibition, Seoul — A1315

No. 2741: a, Bird in flight (29mm diameter). b, Three birds (38mm diameter)

Litho. & Silk-Screened With Foil Application
2014, Aug. 11   *Perf.*
2741 A1315 15p Sheet of 2, #a-b 7.25 7.25

Luis Alberto Spinetta (1950-2012), Rock Musician A1316

Perf. 13½x13¾
2014, Sept. 22   Litho.
2742 A1316 10p multi   2.40 2.40

Monument to the Army of the Andes, Cent. — A1317

Perf. 13½x13¾
2014, Sept. 25   Litho.
2743 A1317 5p multi   1.25 1.25

Festivals A1318

Designs: No. 2744, 5p, Cuevas de las Manos Festival, Perito Moreno. No. 2745, 5p, National Mate Festival, Paraná. No. 2746, 5p, 70th National Agriculture Festival, Esperanza. No. 2747, 5p, National Steam Train Festival, El Maitén.

Perf. 13½x13¾
2014, Sept. 29   Litho.
2744-2747 A1318 Set of 4   4.75 4.75

Souvenir Sheet

1813 Coins of the United Provinces of the River Plate — A1319

No. 2748: a, Gold 8-escudo and silver 8-real coins. b, Silver coins, horiz.

2014, Oct. 14   Litho.   *Perf. 14*
2748 A1319 6p Sheet of 2, #a-b 3.00 3.00

Julio Cortázar (1914-84), Writer — A1320

Prize-winning art in Cortázar stamp design contest by: No. 2749, 5p, Gastón Martino. No. 2750, 5p, José Rivadulla. No. 2751, 5p, Lucía Valentina Piuzzi, vert. No. 2752, 5p, Ana Gauna, vert.

Perf. 13¾x13½, 13½x13¾
2014, Oct. 20   Litho.
2749-2752 A1320 Set of 4   4.75 4.75

Non-Direct Blood Transfusions by Dr. Luis Agote, Cent. — A1321

2014, Nov. 10 Litho. *Perf. 14x13½*
2753 A1321 5p multi   1.25 1.25

Nativity, by Raúl Soldi (1905-94) A1322

Perf. 13½x13¾
2014, Nov. 21   Litho.
2754 A1322 10p multi   2.40 2.40
Christmas. See Vatican City No. 1581.

Movie Stars — A1323

Designs: No. 2755, 5p, Tita Merello (1904-2002), actress. No. 2756, 5p, Alfredo Alcón (1930-2014), actor.

Perf. 13½x13¾
2014, Nov. 25   Litho.
2755-2756 A1323 Set of 2   2.40 2.40
Mar del Plata Intl. Film Festival, 60th anniv.

Nelson Mandela (1918-2013), President of South Africa — A1324

Perf. 13¾x13½
2014, Dec. 15   Litho.
2757 A1324 10p multi   2.40 2.40

Antarctopelta Oliveroi — A1325

First Argentine Expedition to the South Pole, 50th Anniv. — A1326

No. 2759: a, 11p, Map and Col. Jorge Edgard Leal, expedition leader. b, 14p, Expedition members saluting flag of Argentina.

2015, Mar. 9 Litho. *Perf. 13¾x13½*
2758 A1325 6p multi   1.40 1.40
Souvenir Sheet
Perf. 14
2759 A1326 Sheet of 2, #a-b   5.75 5.75
Argentine exploration and science projects in Antarctica.

Festivals
A1327

Designs: No. 2760, 6p, National Festival of the Longest Night, Ushuaia. No. 2761, 6p, National Drum Festival, Frías. No. 2762, 6p, National Chocolate Festival, Bariloche. No. 2763, 6p, National Cotton Festival, Presidéncia Roque Sáenz Peña.

2015, Apr. 27 Litho. Perf. 13½x13¾
2760-2763 A1327 Set of 4　　　5.50 5.50

Miniature Sheet

Trees — A1328

No. 2764: a, Handroanthus impetiginosus. b, Araucaria araucana. c, Salix humboldtiana. d, Cercidium praecox.

2015, Apr. 27 Litho. Perf. 13½x13¾
2764 A1328 6p Sheet of 4, #a-d　5.50 5.50

Souvenir Sheet

Exterior of Néstor Kirchner Cultural Center, Buenos Aires — A1329

2015, May 26 Litho. Perf. 14
2765 A1329 20p multi + 6 labels　4.50 4.50

Free Peoples Congress, 200th Anniv. A1330

Perf. 13½x13¾
2015, June 29 Litho.
2766 A1330 10p multi　　2.25 2.25

A1331

No. 2767: a, Dr. René G. Favaloro (1923-2000), cardiac surgeon. b, Heart with bypass pioneered by Dr. Favaloro.

2015, July 13 Litho. Perf. 13½x13¾
2767 A1331 10p Horiz. pair, #a-b 4.50 4.50

International Telecommunication Union, 150th Anniv. — A1332

2015, Aug. 21 Litho. Perf. 14x13½
2768 A1332 10p multi　　2.25 2.25

United Nations, 70th Anniv. A1333

Perf. 13¾x13½
2015, Aug. 31 Litho.
2769 A1333 10p multi　　2.25 2.25

Souvenir Sheet

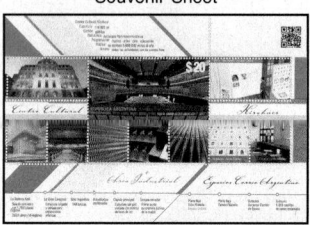

Interior of Nestor Kirchner Cultural Center, Buenos Aires — A1334

2015, Sept. 14 Litho. Perf. 14
2770 A1334 20p multi + 9 labels　4.25 4.25

Miniature Sheet

Birds — A1335

No. 2771: a, Ramphastos dicolorus. b, Ramphastos toco. c, Pteroglossus bailloni. d, Selenidera maculirostris.

Perf. 13¾x13½
2015, Sept. 22 Litho.
2771 A1335 7p Sheet of 4, #a-d 6.00 6.00

Miniature Sheet

Mammals — A1336

No. 2772: a, Lama pacos. b, Lama guanicoe. c, Vicugna vicugna. d, Lama glama.

Perf. 13¾x13½
2015, Sept. 22　　　Litho.
2772 A1336 7p Sheet of 4, #a-d　6.00 6.00

A1337

A1338

A1339

A1340

Gustavo Cerati (1959-2014), Rock Musician — A1341

2015, Oct. 9 Litho. Perf. 13¾x13½
2773 A1337 7p multi　　　　1.50 1.50
2774　　　Horiz. strip of 4　8.50 8.50
　a.　A1338 10p multi　　　2.10 2.10
　b.　A1339 10p multi　　　2.10 2.10
　c.　A1340 10p multi　　　2.10 2.10
　d.　A1341 10p multi　　　2.10 2.10

Souvenir Sheet

Ciudad Evita — A1342

No. 2775: a, Man and house. b, Apartment complex.

Litho. (Sheet Margin Litho. & Embossed)
2015, Oct. 13　　　Perf. 14
2775 A1342 25p Sheet of 2, #a-b　10.50 10.50

Christmas A1343

2015, Nov. 2 Litho. Perf. 13½x13¾
2776 A1343 10p multi　　　2.10 2.10

Souvenir Sheet

Pres. Juan D. Perón (1895-1974) — A1344

2015, Nov. 17 Litho. Perf. 14
2777 A1344 29p multi　　　6.00 6.00

2015 Inauguration of Pres. Mauricio Macri — A1345

2016, May 9 Litho. Perf. 13½x14
2778 A1345 8p multi　　　1.25 1.25

Campaign Against Human
Trafficking — A1346

No. 2779 — Inscription starting with: a, "Yo
le digo. . ." b, "Explotación. . ."

2016, May 23 Litho. Perf. 13½x13¾
2779 A1346 8p Horiz. pair, #a-b 2.50 2.50
America Issue.

Argentine Naval Aviation,
Cent. — A1347

2016, June 6 Litho. Perf. 14x13½
2780 A1347 10p multi 1.40 1.40

Rubén Darío (1867-1916),
Poet — A1348

Perf. 13¾x13½
2016, June 10 Litho.
2781 A1348 20p multi 2.75 2.75

Independence, 200th
Anniv. — A1349

Perf. 13½x13¾ Syncopated
2016, June 27 Litho.
2782 A1349 10p multi 1.40 1.40

Open Cabildo of Buenos Aires of May
25, 1810 — A1350

Battle of
Tucumán
and
Members of
the Second
Triumvirate,
1812
A1351

Argentine Declaration of
Independence, 200th Anniv. — A1352

2016, July 7 Litho. Perf. 14
2783 Sheet of 3 5.50 5.50
a. A1350 10p multi 1.75 1.75
b. A1351 10p multi 1.75 1.75
c. A1352 10p multi 1.75 1.75
Road to Argentine Independence.

A1353

Coats of
Arms — A1354

No. 2784 — Arms of: a, Argentina. b, Corrientes Province. c, Chaco Province. d, Formosa Province. e, Misiones Province. f, Catamarca Province. g, Jujuy Province. h, La Rioja Province. i, Salta Province. j, Santiago del Estero Province. k, Tucumán Province. l, Mendoza Province. m, San Juan Province. n, San Luis Province. o, Autonomous City of Buenos Aires. p, Buenos Aires Province. q, Córdoba Province. r, Entre Ríos Province. s, La Pampa Province. t, Santa Fe Province. u, Chubut Province. v, Neuquén Province. w, Río Negro Province. x, Santa Cruz Province. y, Tierra del Fuego, Antarctica and Southern Atlantic Islands Province.

2016, July 7 Litho. Perf. 14
2784 Sheet of 25 35.00 35.00
a. A1353 10p multi 1.40 1.40
b.-y. A1354 10p Any single 1.40 1.40
z. Booklet pane of 25, #2784a-
2784y — —
Complete booklet, #2784z —

Souvenir Sheet

July 9, 1816, Bas-relief by Lola
Mora — A1355

No. 2785: a, Deputies at Congress of Tucumán, facing right. b, Three deputies, facing left, behind table.

2016, July 7 Litho. Perf. 14
2785 A1355 10p Sheet of 2, #a-
b, + label 2.75 2.75

Fruits — A1356

Designs: 1p, Prunus persica. 2p, Malus domestica. 5p, Citrus limon. 8p, Prunus salicina. 10p, Prunus avium. 30p, Vitis vinifera. 35p, Vaccinum spp. 40p, Pyrus communis. 50p, Citrus sinensis. 100p, Citrullus lanatus.

Perf. 13½x13¾ Syncopated
2016-19 Litho.
2786 A1356 1p multi .25 .25
2787 A1356 2p multi .25 .25
2788 A1356 5p multi .70 .70
2789 A1356 8p multi 1.10 1.10
2790 A1356 10p multi 1.40 1.40
2791 A1356 30p multi 4.00 4.00
2791A A1356 35p sil & multi 1.75 1.75
2792 A1356 40p multi 5.50 5.50
2793 A1356 50p multi 6.75 6.75
2794 A1356 100p multi 13.50 13.50
Nos. 2786-2794 (10) 35.20 35.20
Issued: 1p, 2p, 5p, 7/22; 8p, 10p, 30p, 100p, 8/4; 40p, 50p, 7/26; 35p, 2019.

Vegetables — A1357

Designs: 1p, Daucus carota. 2p, Cynara cardunculus. 3p, Zea mays. 4p, Lycopersicum esculentum. 5p, Asparagus officinalis. 8p, Solanum melongena. 10p, Solanum tuberosum. 30p, Capsicum annuum. 35p, Brassica oleracea var. Itálica. 50p, Cucurbita maxima. 100p, Allium cepa.

Perf. 13½x13¾ Syncopated
2016-19 Litho.
2795 A1357 1p multi .25 .25
2796 A1357 2p multi .25 .25
2797 A1357 3p multi .40 .40
2798 A1357 4p multi .55 .55
2799 A1357 5p multi .70 .70
2800 A1357 8p multi 1.10 1.10
2801 A1357 10p multi 1.40 1.40
2802 A1357 30p multi 4.00 4.00
2802A A1357 35p sil & multi 1.75 1.75
2803 A1357 50p multi 6.75 6.75
2804 A1357 100p multi 13.50 13.50
Nos. 2795-2804 (11) 30.65 30.65
Issued: 1p, 4p, 8p, 50p, 100p, 8/4; 2p, 3p, 7/22; 5p, 10p, 30p, 7/26; 35p, 2019.

Miniature Sheet

International Year of Pulses — A1358

No. 2805: a, Pisum sativum. b, Cicer arietinum. c, Lens culinaris. d, Phaseolus vulgaris.

Perf. 13¾x13½
2016, Aug. 16 Litho.
2805 A1358 10p Sheet of 4, #a-d 5.50 5.50

Miniature Sheet

Aves Argentina, Cent. — A1359

No. 2806: a, Heliomaster furcifer. b, Hylocharis chrysura. c, Sappho sparganura. d, Chlorostilbon lucidus.

Perf. 13¾x13½
2016, Sept. 19 Litho.
2806 A1359 11p Sheet of 4, #a-d 5.75 5.75

Souvenir Sheet

Signing of the Protocol to the Antarctic
Treaty on Environmental Protection,
25th Anniv. — A1360

No. 2807: a, Base Decepción. b, Base Primavera.

2016, Oct. 4 Litho. Perf. 14
2807 A1360 11p Sheet of 2, #a-b 3.00 3.00

Canonization of St. José Gabriel del
Rosario Brochero (1840-
1914) — A1361

2016, Oct. 17 Litho. Perf. 14x13½
2808 A1361 11p gold & multi 1.50 1.50

Russian Tea
and Tea
Service
A1362

Argentinian
Mate and Mate
Service
A1363

Perf. 13½x13¾
2016, Nov. 14 Litho.
2809 A1362 11p gold & multi 1.40 1.40
2810 A1363 11p gold & multi 1.40 1.40
See Russia No. 7784.

Sloop Nuestra Señora del Carmen, Flags of Greece and Argentina A1364

2016, Dec. 5 Litho. Perf. 13½x13¾
2811 A1364 11p multi 1.40 1.40

Remembrance of Greek soldiers who fought for independence for Argentina.

Christmas — A1365

No. 2812 — Angels, by Norah Borges: a, Angel facing right. b, Angel facing left.

Perf. 13½x13¾
2016, Dec. 13 Litho.
2812 A1365 11p Horiz. pair, #a-b 2.75 2.75

Winning Designs in Children's "Healthy Feelings and Values" Art Contest A1366

Art by: No. 2813, 11p, Guadalupe Sotelo. No. 2814, 11p, Victoria Figueroa Fernández. No. 2815, 11p, Morena Gianella Oliva, horiz.

Perf. 13½x13¾, 13¾x13½
2016, Dec. 19 Litho.
2813-2815 A1366 Set of 3 4.25 4.25

Butterflies — A1367

Designs: 11p, Strymon eurytulus. 55p, Morpho epistrophus argentinus.

2017, Jan. 23 Litho. Perf. 13¾x13½
2816-2817 A1367 Set of 2 8.50 8.50

José Luis Cabezas (1961-97), Murdered Photojournalist — A1368

2017, May 9 Litho. Perf. 13¾x13½
2818 A1368 13p multi 1.60 1.60

Pedro Bonifacio Palacios (1854-1917), Poet — A1369

2017, May 15 Litho. Perf. 13¾x13½
2819 A1369 13p multi 1.60 1.60

Marist Brothers, 200th Anniv. — A1370

2017, May 22 Litho. Perf. 14x13½
2820 A1370 13p multi 1.60 1.60

Battle of Humahuaca, 200th Anniv. — A1371

Perf. 13½x13¾
2017, June 26 Litho.
2821 A1371 16p multi 2.00 2.00

Roberto Fontanarrosa (1944-2007), Cartoonist A1372

A1373

Cartoons by Fontanarrosa — A1374

No. 2823: a, Front and profile views of Boogie (70x40mm). b, Dog with Inodoro Pereyra holding flowers (40x60mm). c, Inodoro Pereyra talking with Eulogia (60x60mm). d, Dog of Inodoro Pereyra speaking (40x60mm). e, Boogie holding binoculars (50x40mm).

No. 2824: a, Man holding ball talking to soccer player (80x60mm). b, Man with pens in shirt pocket talking (50x80mm). c, Creator of Frankenstein monster talking to another man (80x60mm).

2017, July 31 Litho. Perf. 13½x13¾
2822 A1372 16p multi 2.25 2.25
Booklet Stamps
Perf. 14
2823 A1373 Booklet pane of 5 13.50 —
a.-d.   16p Any single 2.25 2.25
e.   32p black & silver 4.25 4.25
2824 A1374 Booklet pane of 3 14.00 —
a.-b.   16p Either single 2.25 2.25
c.   68p black & silver 9.25 9.25
      Complete booklet 30.00

Complete booklet contains Nos. 2823, 2824 and No. 2822 in a stamp mount and four post cards. It sold for 250p.

First Air Mail Flight from Buenos Aires to Montevideo, Uruguay, Cent. — A1375

2017, Oct. 2 Litho. Perf. 14x13½
2825 A1375 32p multi 3.75 3.75

Souvenir Sheet

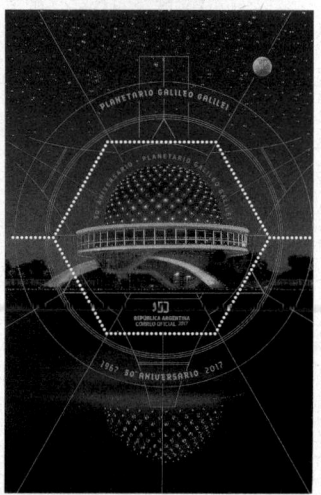

Galileo Galilei Planetarium, Buenos Aires, 50th Anniv. — A1376

Litho. & Silk-Screened
2017, Oct. 31 Perf. 14
2826 A1376 53p multi 6.00 6.00

Argentina Men's Tennis Team, Winners of 2016 Davis Cup — A1377

Designs: 32p, Davis Cup. 53p, Davis Cup held by player's hands, horiz.

2017, Nov. 6 Litho. Perf. 13½x13¾
2827 A1377 32p multi 3.75 3.75
Souvenir Sheet
Perf. 14
2828 A1377 53p multi 6.25 6.25

No. 2828 contains one 40x30mm stamp.

Sandro (Roberto Sánchez-Ocampo) (1945-2010), Singer — A1378

No. 2830: a, Hands of Sandro and guitar (70x40mm). b, Head of Sandro (40x50mm).

Perf. 13¾x13½
2017, Nov. 21 Litho.
2829 A1378 32p multi 3.75 3.75
Souvenir Sheet
Litho. & Silk-Screened
Perf. 14
2830 A1378 Sheet of 2 10.00 10.00
a.   32p multi 3.75 3.75
b.   53p multi 6.25 6.25

Pres. Hipólito Yrigoyen (1852-1933) A1379

Perf. 13½x13¾
2017, Dec. 11 Litho.
2831 A1379 16p multi 1.75 1.75

A1380

A1381

Cartoons by Quino — A1382

No. 2833: a, Girl mailing letter (40x60mm). b, Girl walking (30x50mm).

2017, Dec. 11 Litho. Perf. 14x13½
2832 A1380 32p multi 3.50 3.50
Booklet Stamps
2833 A1381 Booklet pane of 2 9.25 —
a.   32p black & gold 3.50 3.50
b.   53p black & gold 5.25 5.25
2834 A1382 85p Booklet pane of 1 9.25 —
      Complete booklet, #2833-2834 18.50

Christmas.

Souvenir Sheet

Crossing of the Andes of San Martín's Army, 200th Anniv. — A1383

2017, Dec. 26   Litho.   Perf. 14
2835   A1383   53p multi   5.75   5.75

Souvenir Sheet

Renewable Energy — A1384

No. 2836: a, Solar-powered building, biofuel plant, bicycle and automobile at fuel pump. b, Dam and wind generators.

2018, Jan. 15   Litho.   Perf. 14
2836   A1384   16p Sheet of 2, #a-b   3.25   3.25

Souvenir Sheet

Astor Piazzolla (1921-92), Tango Composer — A1385

No. 2837: a, 45p, Piazzolla's hand on bandoneon keys. b, 75p, Piazzolla playing bandoneon.

2018, May 8   Litho.   Perf. 14
2837   A1385   Sheet of 2, #a-b   9.75   9.75

Souvenir Sheet

Map of Continental Shelf Off Argentina and Antarctica — A1386

2018, Sept. 10   Litho.   Perf. 14
2838   A1386   120p sil & multi   6.00   6.00

National Gendarmerie, 80th Anniv. — A1387

Perf. 13½x13¾
2018, Dec. 12   Litho.
2839   A1387   50p multi   2.75   2.75

Nos. 2125, 2190, 2217, 2248, 2275 and 2410-2412 Surcharged in Silver and Black

Methods and Perfs. As Before

2018
2840	A1123	2p on 75c #2411	.35	.35
2841	A973	5p on 10c #2125	.90	.90
2842	A1123	10p on 75c #2410	1.75	1.75
2843	A979a	25p on 10c #2217	4.25	4.25
2844	A1123	40p on 75c #2412	7.00	7.00

Blocks of 8
2845	A1036	25p on 75c #2248	34.00	34.00
a.-h.		Any single	4.25	4.25
2846	A1050	50p on 75c #2276	70.00	70.00
a.-h.		Any single	8.75	8.75
2847	A1013	100p on 75c #2190	140.00	140.00
a.-h.		Any single	17.50	17.50
		Nos. 2840-2847 (8)	258.25	258.25

Placement of surcharge varies.

Nos. 2076-2077, 2129, 2232, 2337, 2339, 2340, 2398-2401, and 2414-2415 Surcharged in Silver and Black With Added "UP" Inscription

Methods and Perfs. As Before

2018
2848	A1029	1p on 75c #2232	.25	.25
2849	A973	2p on 75c #2129	.35	.35
2850	A1116	10p on 75c #2398	1.75	1.75
2851	A1116	10p on 75c #2399	1.75	1.75
2852	A1116	10p on 75c #2400	1.75	1.75
2853	A1116	10p on 75c #2401	1.75	1.75
2853A	A943	30p on 75c #2076	5.75	5.75
2854	A943	30p on 75c #2077	5.25	5.25
2855	A1086	30p on 75c #2337	5.25	5.25
2856	A1086	30p on 75c #2339	5.25	5.25
2857	A1086	30p on 75c #2340	5.25	5.25
2858	A1125	100p on 75c #2414	17.50	17.50
2859	A1125	100p on 75c #2415	17.50	17.50
		Nos. 2848-2859 (13)	69.35	69.35

Placement of surcharge varies.

A1388

Landmarks and Wildlife of Tierra del Fuego, Antarctica and South Atlantic Islands — A1389

Designs: No. 2860, Les Eclaireurs Lighthouse. No. 2861, Pygoscelis papua. No. 2862, Brown Base. No. 2863, Hydrurga leptonyx.

2019, Jan. 28   Litho.   Perf. 13¾x13½
2860   A1388   170p multi   9.25   9.25
2861   A1388   180p multi   9.75   9.75

Inscribed "UP" at Lower Left
2862   A1389   170p multi   9.25   9.25
2863   A1389   180p multi   9.75   9.75
    Nos. 2860-2863 (4)   38.00   38.00

Eighth International Congress of the Spanish Language, Córdoba, Argentina — A1390

No. 2864: a, 35p, Spanish language books making "ñ." b, 145p, Jorge Luis Borges (1899-1986), writer.

Perf. 13½x13¾
2019, Mar. 25   Litho.
2864   A1390   Horiz. pair, #a-b   8.50   8.50

Souvenir Sheet

Icebreaker A.R.A. Almirante Irízar — A1391

No. 2865: a, 40p, Icebreaker and raft (40x30mm). b, 160p, Icebreaker (40x50mm).

Litho. & Silk-Screened
2019, Apr. 29   Perf. 13¾
2865   A1391   Sheet of 2, #a-b   9.00   9.00

Souvenir Sheet

Marambio Base, Antarctica, 50th Anniv. — A1392

No. 2866: a, 40p, Construction of Marambio Base in 1969, DHC-2 Beaver, Fokker F-27. b, 160p, Hercules C-130 and DHC-6 Twin Otter over Marambio Base.

Litho. & Silk-Screened
2019, Apr. 29   Perf. 14
2866   A1392   Sheet of 2, #a-b   9.00   9.00

Diplomatic Relations Between Argentina and Israel, 70th Anniv. A1393

2019, May 27   Litho.   Perf. 13½x13¾
2867   A1393   100p gold & multi   4.50   4.50

New Year 2019 (Year of the Pig) — A1394

Litho. & Embossed
2019, May 27   Perf.
2868   A1394   200p gold & multi   9.00   9.00

A1395

National Parks A1396

Designs: No. 2869, Calilegua National Park. No. 2870, Los Cardones National Park. No. 2871, Río Pilcomayo National Park.No. 2872, El Palmar National Park. No. 2873, Ciervo de los Pantanos National Park. No. 2874, Talampaya National Park. No. 2875, Quebrada del Condorito National Park. No. 2876, Tierra del Fuego National Park. No. 2877, Iguazú National Park. No. 2878, Patagonia National Park. No. 2879, Nahuel Huapi National Park. No. 2880, Perito Moreno National Park.
No. 2881, Campos del Tuyú National Park. No. 2882, Aconquija National Park. No. 2883, El Impenetrable National Park. No. 2884, Sierra de las Quijadas National Park. No. 2885, El Rey National Park. No. 2886, El Leoncito National Park. No. 2887, Pra-Delta National Park. No. 2888, Los Glaciares National Park. No. 2889, Lanín National Park. No. 2889A, Monte León National Park. No. 2889B, Los Alerces National Park.

Perf. 13¾x13½ Syncopated
2019, June 7   Litho.
2869	A1395	1p multi	.25	.25
2870	A1395	2p multi	.25	.25
2871	A1395	5p multi	.25	.25
2872	A1395	10p multi	.50	.50
2873	A1395	20p multi	.95	.95
2874	A1395	30p multi	1.40	1.40
2875	A1395	40p multi	1.90	1.90
2876	A1395	50p multi	2.40	2.40

2877	A1395	100p multi	4.75	4.75
2878	A1395	200p multi	9.50	9.50
2879	A1395	300p multi	14.00	14.00
2880	A1395	400p multi	19.00	19.00

Nos. 2869-2880 (12) 55.15 55.15

Inscribed "UP" at Lower Left

2881	A1396	1p multi	.25	.25
2882	A1396	2p multi	.25	.25
2883	A1396	5p multi	.25	.25
2884	A1396	10p multi	.50	.50
2885	A1396	20p multi	.95	.95
2886	A1396	40p multi	1.90	1.90
2887	A1396	50p multi	2.40	2.40
2888	A1396	100p multi	4.75	4.75
2889	A1396	200p multi	9.50	9.50
2889A	A1396	300p multi	14.00	14.00
2889B	A1396	400p multi	19.00	19.00

Nos. 2881-2889B (11) 53.75 53.75

Buses A1397

Designs: No. 2890, 50p, Chevrolet bus used on Line 45, 1942. No. 2891, 50p, Mercedes-Benz 312 bus used on Line 159, 1961.

2019, July 29 Litho. *Perf. 13¾x13½*
2890-2891 A1397 Set of 2 4.50 4.50

A1398

Carlos Gardel (1890-1935), Tango Singer — A1399

Perf. 13½x13¾
2019, Aug. 27 Litho.
2892 A1398 100p gold & multi 3.50 3.50

Souvenir Sheet
Perf. 14
2893 A1399 225p gold & multi 7.75 7.75

Angel Villoldo (1861-1919), Tango Musician — A1400

Street Lamp and Tango Dancers A1401

Tango Score and Don Filatango, Mascot of 2019 International Philatelic Exhibition, Buenos Aires — A1402

Statue of Carlos Gardel (1890-1935), Tango Singer — A1403

Sign From Boedo Neighborhood, Buenos Aires — A1404

Perf. 13¾x13½
2019, Aug. 28 Litho.
2894		Booklet pane of 5	8.75	—
a.	A1400	50p gold & multi	1.75	1.75
b.	A1401	50p gold & multi	1.75	1.75
c.	A1402	50p gold & multi	1.75	1.75
d.	A1403	50p gold & multi	1.75	1.75
e.	A1404	50p gold & multi	1.75	1.75
		Complete booklet, #2894	8.75	

Tango seritage of Barracas, Caminito, San Telmo, Downtown and Boedo neighborhoods of Buenos Aires.

Mohandas K. Gandhi (1869-1948), Indian Nationalist Leader — A1405

Perf. 13¾x13½
2019, Sept. 30 Litho.
2895 A1405 235p multi 8.25 8.25

Souvenir Sheet

Solo 1925-28 Buenos Aires-Washington D.C. Journey of A. F. Tschiffely (1895-1954) With Horses Mancha and Gato — A1406

2019, Oct. 7 Litho. *Perf. 13¾x14*
2896 A1406 180p multi 6.00 6.00

Southern Fuegian Railway (Train at the End of the World), Ushuaia A1407

Various trains: 195p, 225p, 235p.

2019, Oct. 15 Litho. *Perf. 13¾x13½*
2897-2899 A1407 Set of 3 22.00 22.00

Estudiantes de la Plata Soccer Team, Winners of 1968 Intercontinental Cup — A1408

2019, Nov. 11 Litho. *Perf. 13½x14*
2900 A1408 125p multi 4.25 4.25

Souvenir Sheet

Mercado de Abasto, Buenos Aires, Designed by Viktor Sulcic (1895-1973) — A1409

2019, Nov. 25 Litho. *Perf. 14*
2901 A1409 270p multi 9.00 9.00

Joint Issue between Argentina and Slovenia. See Slovenia No. 1365.

Loss of ARA San Juan Submarine, 2nd Anniv. — A1410

2019, Nov. 15 Litho. *Perf. 14x13½*
2902 A1410 35p multi 1.25 1.25

La Nacion Newspaper, 150th Anniv. — A1411

2019, Dec. 4 Litho. *Perf. 14x13½*
2903 A1411 80p multi 2.75 2.75

Christmas — A1412

2019, Dec. 9 Litho. *Perf. 13¾x13½*
2904 A1412 80p multi 2.75 2.75

A gritty substance covers parts of the vignette of No. 2904. Values are for stamps with surrounding selvage.

SEMI-POSTAL STAMPS

Samuel F. B. Morse — SP1   Globe — SP2

Landing of Columbus — SP5

Designs: 10c+5c, Alexander Graham Bell. 25c+15c, Rowland Hill.

Wmk. RA in Sun (90)
1944, Jan. 5 Litho. *Perf. 13*
B1	SP1	3c +2c lt vio & sl bl	1.00	1.50
B2	SP2	5c +5c dl red & sl bl	.80	.50
B3	SP1	10c +5c org & slate bl	1.50	.50
B4	SP1	25c +15c red brn & sl bl	2.25	1.10
B5	SP5	1p +50c lt grn & sl bl	9.50	10.00

Nos. B1-B5 (5) 15.05 13.60

The surtax was for the Postal Employees Benefit Association.

Map of Argentina — SP6

1944, Feb. 17 Wmk. 90 *Perf. 13*
B6	SP6	5c +10c ol yel & slate	1.10	.50
B7	SP6	5c +50c vio brn & slate	5.00	1.50
B8	SP6	5c +1p dl org & slate	13.50	7.00
B9	SP6	5c +20p dp bl & slate	30.00	30.00

Nos. B6-B9 (4) 49.60 39.00

The surtax was for the victims of the San Juan earthquake.

Souvenir Sheets

National Anthem and Flag — SP7

1944, July 17 *Imperf.*
B10 SP7 5c +1p vio brn & lt
    bl   9.00 5.00
B11 SP7 5c +50p bl blk & lt
    bl   425.00 275.00

Surtax for the needy in the provinces of La Rioja and Catamarca.

> **Catalogue values for unused stamps in this section, from this point to the end of the section, are for Never Hinged items.**

Stamp Designing SP8

1950, Aug. 26   **Photo.**   *Perf. 13½*
B12 SP8 10c +10c violet   .25   .25
    Nos. B12,CB1-CB5 (6) 20.95 15.40

Argentine Intl. Philatelic Exhibition, 1950.

Poliomyelitis Victim — SP9

1956, Apr. 14   *Perf. 13½x13*
B13 SP9 20c +30c slate   .30   .25

The surtax was for the poliomyelitis fund. Head in design is from Correggio's "Antiope," Louvre.

Stamp of 1858 and Mail Coach on Raft — SP10

Designs: 2.40p+1.20p, Album, magnifying glass and stamp of 1858. 4.40p+2.20p, Government seat of Confederation, Parana.

1958, Mar. 29   **Litho.**   *Perf. 13½*
B14 SP10 40c +20c brt grn &
    dl pur   .50   .50
B15 SP10 2.40p +1.20p ol gray &
    bl   .50   .50

B16 SP10 4.40p +2.20p lt bl & dp
    claret   .50   .50
    Nos. B14-B16,CB8-CB12 (8) 6.20 5.50

Surtax for Intl. Centennial Philatelic Exhibition, Paraná, Entre Rios, Apr. 19-27. Nos. B14-B16 exist imperf. Value, set of pairs, $200.

View of Flooded Land — SP11

1958, Oct. 4   **Photo.**   *Perf. 13½*
B17 SP11 40c +20c brown   .25   .25
    Nos. B17,CB13-CB14 (3) 1.55 1.30

The surtax was for flood victims in the Buenos Aires district. Exists imperf. Value, pair $37.50.

Child Receiving Blood — SP12

1958, Dec. 20   **Litho.**   **Wmk. 90**
B18 SP12 1p +50c blk & rose red .75   .25

The surtax went to the Anti-Leukemia Foundation. Exists imperf. Value, pair $25.

Runner SP13

Designs: 50c+20c, Basketball players, vert. 1p+50c, Boxers, vert.

1959, Sept. 5   *Perf. 13½*
B19 SP13 20c +10c emer &
    blk   .25   .25
B20 SP13 50c +20c yel &
    blk   .25   .25
  a.   Torch missing   200.00 200.00
B21 SP13 1p +50c mar &
    blk   .25   .25
  a.   Torch missing   150.00 150.00
    Nos. B19-B21,CB15-CB16 (5) 1.75 1.50

3rd Pan American Games, Chicago, Aug. 27-Sept. 7, 1959.
See Nos. CB15-CB16.

Condor — SP14

Fork-tailed Flycatchers — SP14a

Magellanic Woodpecker — SP14b

1960, Feb. 6
B22 SP14 20c +10c dk bl   .40   .25
B23 SP14a 50c +20c dp vio bl   .40   .25
B24 SP14b 1p +50c brn & buff .40   .25
    Nos. B22-B24,CB17-CB18 (5) 2.15 1.35

The surtax was for child welfare work.
See Nos. B30, CB17-CB18, CB29.

Souvenir Sheet

Uprooted Oak Emblem — SP15

1960, Apr. 7   **Wmk. 90**   *Imperf.*
B25 SP15 Sheet of 2   1.40 1.40
  a.   1p + 50c bister & carmine .50   .50
  b.   4.20p + 2.10p app grn & dp clar .50   .50

WRY, July 1, 1959-June 30, 1960.
The surtax was for aid to refugees.

Jacaranda — SP16

Flowers: 1p+1p, Passionflower. 3p+3p, Orchid. 5p+5p, Tabebuia.

1960, Dec. 3   **Photo.**   *Perf. 13½*
B26 SP16 50c +50c deep blue   .25   .25
B27 SP16 1p +1p bluish grn   .25   .25
B28 SP16 3p +3p henna brn   .55   .35
B29 SP16 5p +5p dark brn   .95   .60
    Nos. B26-B29 (4)   2.00 1.45

"TEMEX 61" (Intl. Thematic Exposition). For overprints see Nos. B31-B34.

Type of 1960

Bird: 4.20p+2.10p, Blue-eyed shag.

1961, Feb. 25   **Wmk. 90**   *Perf. 13½*
B30 SP14 4.20p +2.10p chest
    brn   .65   .35

Surtax for child welfare work. See No. CB29.

Nos. B26-B29 Ovptd. in Black, Brown, Blue or Red

1961, Apr. 15
B31 SP16 50c +50c deep blue   .35   .25
B32 SP16 1p +1p bluish grn
    (Brn)   .35   .25
B33 SP16 3p +3p hen brn (Bl)   .65   .25
B34 SP16 5p +5p dk brn (R)   .95   .40
    Nos. B31-B34 (4)   2.30 1.15

Day of the Americas, Apr. 14.

Cathedral, Cordoba SP17

Stamp of 1862 — SP18

Design: 10p+10p, Cathedral, Buenos Aires.

1961, Oct. 21   **Wmk. 90**   **Photo.**
B35 SP17 2p +2p rose claret   .25   .25
B36 SP18 3p +3p green   .30   .25
B37 SP17 10p +10p brt blue   .70   .60
  a.   Souvenir sheet of 3   2.50 1.50
    Nos. B35-B37 (3)   1.25 1.10

1962 International Stamp Exhibition.
No. B37a contains three imperf. stamps similar to Nos. B35-B37 in dark blue.

Flight into Egypt, by Ana Maria Moncalvo — SP19

1961, Dec. 16   **Litho.**
B38 SP19 2p +1p lilac & blk brn .25   .25
B39 SP19 10p +5p lt & dp clar   .40   .25

The surtax was for child welfare.

Mimus Saturninus Modulator SP20

Design: 12p+6p, Zonotrichia capensis hypoleuca.

1962, Dec. 29   *Perf. 13½*
B40 SP20 4p +2p bis, brn & bl
    grn   1.10 .65
B41 SP20 12p +6p gray, yel, grn
    & brn   1.75 1.25

The surtax was for child welfare. See Nos. B44, B47, B48-B50, CB32, CB35-CB36.

Soccer — SP21

No. B43, Horsemanship.

1963, May 18   *Perf. 13½*
B42 SP21 4p +2p multi   .25   .25
B43 SP21 12p +6p multi   .45   .35
  a.   Dark carmine (jacket) omitted 15.00
    Nos. B42-B43,CB31 (3)   1.30 1.10

4th Pan American Games, Sao Paulo.
See No. CB31.

Bird Type of 1962

4p +2p, Pyrocephalus rubineus rubineus.

1963, Dec. 21   **Litho.**
B44 SP20 4p +2p multi   .60   .30

The surtax was for child welfare. See No. CB32.

Fencers — SP22

4p+2p, National Stadium, Tokyo, horiz.

1964, July 18 Wmk. 90 Perf. 13½
B45 SP22 4p +2p red, ocher & brn .25 .25
B46 SP22 12p +6p bl grn & blk .35 .25
Nos. B45-B46,CB33 (3) 1.50 1.20

18th Olympic Games, Tokyo, Oct. 10-25, 1964. See No. CB33.

Bird Type of 1962

4p +2p, Cardinal paroaria coronata.

1964, Dec. 23 Litho.
B47 SP20 4p +2p multi .90 .30

The surtax was for child welfare. See No. CB35.

SP22a

Designs: 8p+4p, Belonopterus cayennensis lampronotus. 10p+5p, Amblyramphus holosericeus, horiz. 20p+10p, Chloroceryle amazona.

1966-67 Perf. 13½
B48 SP22a 8p +4p blk, ol, brt grn & red .80 .35
B49 SP22a 10p +5p blk, bl, org & grn .80 .55
B50 SP22a 20p +10p blk, yel, bl & pink .40 .35
Nos. B48-B50,CB36,CB38-CB39 (6) 5.00 3.50

The surtax was for child welfare.
Issue dates: 8p+4p, Mar. 26, 1966. 10p+5p, Jan. 14, 1967. 20p+10p, Dec. 23, 1967.

Grandmother's Birthday, by Patricia Lynch; Lions Emblem — SP23

Perf. 12½x13½
1968, Dec. 14 Litho. Wmk. 90
B51 SP23 40p + 20p multi .45 .40

1st Lions Intl. Benevolent Phil. Exhib. Surtax for the Children's Hospital Benevolent Fund.

White-faced Tree Duck — SP24

1969, Sept. 20 Wmk. 365 Perf. 13½
B52 SP24 20p + 10p multi .50 .35

Surtax for child welfare. See No. CB40.

Slender-tailed Woodstar (Hummingbird) SP25

1970, May 9 Wmk. 365 Perf. 13½
B53 SP25 20c + 10c multi .45 .40

The surtax was for child welfare. See Nos. CB41, B56-B59, B62-B63.

Dolphinfish — SP26

1971, Feb. 20 Unwmk. Perf. 12½
Size: 75x15mm
B54 SP26 20c + 10c multi .50 .45

Surtax for child welfare. See No. CB42.

Children with Stamps, by Mariette Lydis — SP27

1971, Dec. 18 Litho. Perf. 13½
B55 SP27 1p + 50p multi .50 .30

2nd Lions Intl. Solidarity Stamp Exhib.

Bird Type of 1970

Birds: 25c+10c, Saffron finch. 65c+30c, Rufous-bellied thrush, horiz.

1972, May 6 Unwmk. Perf. 13½
B56 SP25 25c + 10c multi .30 .25
B57 SP25 65c + 30c multi .45 .30

Surtax was for child welfare.

Bird Type of 1970

Birds: 50c+25c, Southern screamer (chaja). 90c+45c, Saffron-cowled blackbird, horiz.

1973, Apr. 28
B58 SP25 50c + 25c multi .55 .30
B59 SP25 90c + 45c multi .75 .55

Surtax was for child welfare.

Painting Type of Regular Issue

Designs: 15c+15c, Still Life, by Alfredo Guttero, horiz. 90c+90c, Nude, by Miguel C. Victorica, horiz.

1973, Aug. 28 Litho. Perf. 13½
B60 A472 15c + 15c multi .35 .25
B61 A472 90c + 90c multi 1.10 .75

Bird Type of 1970

Birds: 70c+30c, Blue seed-eater. 1.20p+60c, Hooded siskin.

1974, May 11 Litho. Perf. 13½
B62 SP25 70c + 30c multi .60 .35
B63 SP25 1.20p + 60c multi 1.00 .50

Surtax was for child welfare.

Painting Type of 1974

Design: 70c+30c, The Lama, by Juan Batlle Planas.

1974, May 11 Litho. Perf. 13½
B64 A477 70c + 30c multi .35 .25

PRENFIL-74 UPU, Intl. Exhib. of Phil. Periodicals, Buenos Aires, Oct. 1-12.

Plushcrested Jay — SP28

Designs: 13p+6.50p, Golden-collared macaw. 20p+10p, Begonia. 40p+20p, Teasel.

1976, June 12 Litho. Perf. 13½
B65 SP28 7p + 3.50p multi .60 .30
B66 SP28 13p + 6.50p multi .70 .35
B67 SP28 20p + 10p multi .80 .40
B68 SP28 40p + 20p multi 1.10 .60
Nos. B65-B68 (4) 3.20 1.65

Argentine philately.

Telegraph, Communications Satellite — SP29

Designs: 20p+10p, Old and new mail trucks. 60p+30p, Old, new packet boats. 70p+35p, Biplane and jet.

1977, July 16 Litho. Perf. 13½
B69 SP29 10p + 5p multi .30 .25
B70 SP29 20p + 10p multi .60 .60
B71 SP29 60p + 30p multi 1.25 .85
B72 SP29 70p + 35p multi 1.40 .90
Nos. B69-B72 (4) 3.55 2.60

Surtax was for Argentine philately.
No. B70 exists with wmk. 365.

Church of St. Francis Type, 1977

Inscribed "EXPOSICION ARGENTINA '77"

1977, Aug. 27
B73 A515 160p + 80p multi 2.50 2.00

Surtax was for Argentina '77 Philatelic Exhibition. Issued in sheets of 4. Value $12

No. B73 Overprinted with Soccer Cup Emblem

1978, Feb. 4 Litho. Perf. 13½
B74 A515 160p + 80p multi 4.50 4.25
  a. Souvenir sheet of 4 22.50 20.00

11th World Cup Soccer Championship, Argentina, June 1-25.

Spinus Magellanicus SP30

Birds: No. B76, Variable seedeater. No. B77, Yellow thrush. No. B78, Pyrocephalus rubineus. No. B79, Great kiskadee.

1978, Aug. 5 Litho. Perf. 13½
B75 SP30 50p + 50p multi 1.60 1.00
B76 SP30 100p + 100p multi 1.60 1.00
B77 SP30 150p + 150p multi 2.50 1.50
B78 SP30 200p + 200p multi 2.50 1.75
B79 SP30 500p + 500p multi 4.50 3.50
Nos. B75-B79 (5) 12.70 8.75

ARGENTINA '78, Inter-American Philatelic Exhibition, Buenos Aires, Oct. 27-Nov. 5. Nos. B75-B79 issued in sheets of 4 with marginal inscriptions commemorating Exhibition and 1978 Soccer Championship. Value, set $62.50.

Caravel "Magdalena," 16th Century — SP31

Sailing Ships: 500+500p, 3 master "Rio de la Plata," 17th cent. 600+600p, Corvette "Descubierta," 18th cent. 1500+1500p, Naval Academy yacht "A.R.A. Fortuna," 1979.

1979, Sept. 8 Litho. Perf. 13½
B80 SP31 400p +400p multi 3.50 2.25
B81 SP31 500p +500p multi 4.25 2.50
B82 SP31 600p +600p multi 6.00 3.25
B83 SP31 1500p +1500p multi 14.00 8.00
Nos. B80-B83 (4) 27.75 16.00

Buenos Aires '80, Intl. Philatelic Exhibition, 10/24-11/2/80. Issued in sheets of 4. Value, set $125.

Purmamarca Church SP32

Churches: 200p + 100p, Molinos. 300p + 150p, Animana. 400p + 200p, San Jose de Lules.

1979, Nov. 3 Litho. Perf. 13½
B84 SP32 100p + 50p multi .30 .25
B85 SP32 200p + 100p multi .45 .30
B86 SP32 300p + 150p multi .65 .30
B87 SP32 400p + 200p multi .90 .50
Nos. B84-B87 (4) 2.30 1.30

Buenos Aires No. 3, Exhibition and Society Emblems — SP33

Argentine Stamps: 750p+750p, type A580. 1000p+1000p, No. 91. 2000p+2000p, type A588.

1979, Dec. 15 Litho. Perf. 13½
B88 SP33 250p + 250p 1.50 1.25
B89 SP33 750p + 750p 2.75 2.25
B90 SP33 1000p + 1000p 8.00 6.00
B91 SP33 2000p + 2000p 6.75 6.00
Nos. B88-B91 (4) 19.00 15.50

PRENFIL '80, Intl. Philatelic Literature and Publications Exhib., Buenos Aires, Nov. 7-16, 1980.

Minuet,
by
Carlos
E.
Pellegrini
SP34

Paintings: 700p+350p, Media Cana, by Carlos Morel. 800p+400p, Cielito, by Pellegrini. 1000p+500p, El Gato, by Juan Leon Palliere.

1981, July 11   Litho.   Perf. 13½

B92	SP34	500p + 250p multi	.80	.45
B93	SP34	700p + 350p multi	1.20	.80
B94	SP34	800p + 400p multi	1.25	1.00
B95	SP34	1000p + 500p multi	1.60	1.40
		Nos. B92-B95 (4)	4.85	3.65

Espamer '81 Intl. Stamp Exhib. (Americas, Spain, Portugal), Buenos Aires, Nov. 13-22.

Canal, by Beatrix Bongliani (b. 1933) — SP35

Tapestries: 1000p+500p, Shadows, by Silvia Sieburger, vert. 2000p+1000p, Interpretation of a Rectangle, by Silke R. de Haupt, vert. 4000p+2000p, Tilcara, by Tana Sachs.

1982, July 31   Litho.   Perf. 13½

B96	SP35	1000p + 500p multi	.40	.40
B97	SP35	2000p + 1000p multi	.50	.50
B98	SP35	3000p + 1500p multi	.60	.60
B99	SP35	4000p + 2000p multi	.70	.70
		Nos. B96-B99 (4)	2.20	2.20

Boy Playing Marbles SP36

No. B101, Jumping rope. No. B102, Hopscotch. No. B103, Flying kites. No. B104, Spinning top.

1983, July 2   Litho.   Perf. 13½

B100	SP36	20c + 10c shown	.30	.30
B101	SP36	30c + 15c multi	.35	.30
B102	SP36	50c + 25c multi	.70	.60
B103	SP36	1p + 50c multi	.90	.70
B104	SP36	2p + 1p multi	1.25	1.00
		Nos. B100-B104 (5)	3.50	2.90

Surtax was for natl. philatelic associations. See Nos. B106-B110.

Compass, 15th Cent. — SP37

ARGENTINA '85 Intl. Stamp Show: b, Arms of Spain, Argentina. c, Columbus' arms. d-f, Columbus' arrival at San Salvador Island. Nos. B105d-B105f in continuous design; ships shown on singles range in size, left to right, from small to large. Surtax was for exhibition.

1984, Apr. 28   Litho.   Perf. 13½

B105		Block of 6	4.00	4.00
a.-f.	SP37	5p + 2.50p, any single	.60	.40

Children's Game Type of 1983

No. B106, Blind Man's Buff. No. B107, The Loop. No. B108, Leap Frog. No. B109, Rolling the loop. No. B110, Ball Mold.

1984, July 7   Litho.   Perf. 13½

B106	SP36	2p + 1p multi	.35	.25
B107	SP36	3p + 1.50p multi	.35	.30
B108	SP36	4p + 2p multi	.50	.40
B109	SP36	5p + 2.50p multi	.50	.40
B110	SP36	6p + 3p multi	.70	.60
		Nos. B106-B110 (5)	2.40	1.95

Butterflies — SP38

No. B111, Rothschildia jacobaeae. No. B112, Heliconius erato phyllis. No. B113, Precis evarete hilaris. No. B114, Cyanopepla pretiosa. No. B115, Papilio androgeus.

1985, Nov. 9   Litho.   Perf. 13½

B111	SP38	5c + 2c multi	.90	.30
B112	SP38	10c + 5c multi	.90	.60
B113	SP38	20c + 10c multi	1.25	.75
B114	SP38	25c + 13c multi	1.90	1.50
B115	SP38	40c + 20c multi	2.50	2.25
		Nos. B111-B115 (5)	7.45	5.40

Children's Drawings — SP39

No. B116, N. Pastor, vert. No. B117, T. Valleistein. No. B118, J.M. Flores, vert. No. B119, M.E. Pezzuto. No. B120, E. Diehl.

1986, Aug. 30   Litho.

B116	SP39	5c + 2c multi	.25	.25
B117	SP39	10c + 5c multi	.35	.35
B118	SP39	20c + 10c multi	.60	.60
B119	SP39	25c + 13c multi	.85	.85
B120	SP39	40c + 20c multi	1.25	1.25
		Nos. B116-B120 (5)	3.30	3.30

Surtax for natl. philatelic associations.

Miniature Sheets

Fresh-water Fish — SP40

No. B121: a, Metynnis maculatus. b, Cynolebias nigripinnis. c, Leporinus solarii. d, Aphyocharax rathbuni. e, Corydoras aeneus. f, Thoracocharax securis. g, Cynolebias melanotaenia. h, Cichlasoma facetum.

No. B122: a, Tetragonopterus argenteus. b, Hemigrammus caudovittatus. c, Astyanax bimaculatus. d, Gymnocorymbus ternetzi. e, Hoplias malabaricus. f, Aphyocharax rubripinnis. g, Apistogramma agassizi. h, Pyrrhulina rachoviana.

1987, June 27

B121	SP40	Sheet of 8	3.00	3.00
a.-h.		10c +5c, any single	.25	.25
B122	SP40	Sheet of 8	7.00	7.00
a.-h.		20c +10c, any single	.45	.35

PRENFIL '88, Intl. Philatelic Literature and Media Exhibition, Buenos Aires, Nov. 25-Dec. 2 — SP41

Locomotives and railroad car: No. B123, Yatay locomotive, 1888. No. B124, FCCA electric passenger car, 1914. No. B125, B-15 locomotive, 1942. No. B126, GT-22 No. 200 locomotive, 1988.

1988, June 4   Litho.   Perf. 13½

B123	SP41	1a +50c multi	1.25	.60
B124	SP41	1a +50c multi	1.25	.60
B125	SP41	1a +50c multi	1.25	.60
B126	SP41	1a +50c multi	1.25	.60
		Nos. B123-B126 (4)	5.00	2.40

Nos. B123-B125 each issued in sheets of 4. Value, set $16.

Horses
SP42

Paintings: No. B127, *The Waiting*, by Gustavo Solari. No. B128, *Mare and Foal*, by E. Castro. No. B129, *Saint Isidor*, by Castro. No. B130, *At Lagoon's Edge*, by F. Romero Carranza. No. B131, *Under the Tail*, by Castro.

1988, Oct. 29   Litho.   Perf. 13½

B127	SP42	2a +1a multi	1.75	.60
B128	SP42	2a +1a multi	1.75	.60
B129	SP42	2a +1a multi	1.75	.60
B130	SP42	2a +1a multi	1.75	.60
B131	SP42	2a +1a multi	1.75	.60
		Nos. B127-B131 (5)	8.75	3.00

PRENFIL '88 — SP43

Covers of philatelic magazines: No. B132, *Cronaca Filatelica*, Italy. No. B133, *CO-FI*, Brazil. No. B134, *References de la Poste*, France. No. B135, *Postas Argentinas*.

1988, Nov. 26   Litho.   Perf. 13½

B132	SP43	1a +1a multi	1.00	.40
B133	SP43	1a +1a multi	1.00	.40
B134	SP43	1a +1a multi	1.00	.40
B135	SP43	2a +1a multi	1.00	.40
		Nos. B132-B135 (4)	4.00	1.60

Nos. B132-B135 printed in sheets of 4. Value, set $14.

Souvenir Sheet

ARBRAPEX '88 — SP44

Designs: No. B136a, *Candel Delivery at San Ignacio*, by Leonie Matthis, Cornelio Saavedra Museum, Buenos Aires. No. B136b, *Immaculate Conception*, a statue in the Isaac Fernandez Blanco Museum, Buenos Aires.

1988, Nov. 26   Perf. 12

B136	SP44	Sheet of 2	3.00	3.00
a.		2a +2a multi	1.00	.75
b.		3a +3a multi	1.75	1.25

Fish
SP45

Designs: No. B137, Diplomystes viedmensis. No. B138, Haplochiton taeniatus. No. B139, Percichthys trucha. No. B140, Galaxias platei. No. B141, Salmo fario.

1989, June 24   Litho.   Perf. 13½

B137	SP45	10a +5a multi	.90	.40
B138	SP45	10a +5a multi	.90	.40
B139	SP45	10a +5a multi	.90	.40
B140	SP45	10a +5a multi	.90	.40
B141	SP45	10a +5a multi	.90	.40
		Nos. B137-B141 (5)	4.50	2.00

Nos. B137-B141 printed in sheets of 4. Value, set $15.

Discovery of America 500th Anniv. (in 1992) and ESPAMER '90 — SP46

Documents and chronicles: No. B142, Columbus's coat of arms, *Book of Privileges* title page. No. B143, Illustration from *New Chronicle and Good Government*, by Guaman Poma de Ayala. No. B144, Illustration from *Discovery and Conquest of Peru*, by Pedro de Cieza de Leon. No. B145, Illustration from *Travel to the River Plate*, by Ulrico Schmidl.

1989, Sept. 16   Litho.   Perf. 13½
Yellow, Rose Violet & Black

B142	SP46	100a +50a	2.00	.85
B143	SP46	150a +50a	2.00	.85
B144	SP46	200a +100a	2.00	.85
B145	SP46	250a +100a	2.00	.85
		Nos. B142-B145 (4)	8.00	3.40

Nos. B142-B145 printed in sheets of 4. Value, set $17.

Insects
SP47

Designs: No. B146, *Podisus nigrispinus*. No. B147, *Adalia bipunctata*. No. B148, *Nabis punctipennis*. No. B149, *Hippodamia convergens*. No. B150, *Calleida suturalis*.

1990, June 30   Litho.   Perf. 13½

B146	SP47	1000a +500a multi	1.15	.95
B147	SP47	1000a +500a multi	1.15	.95
B148	SP47	1000a +500a multi	1.15	.95
B149	SP47	1000a +500a multi	1.15	.95
B150	SP47	1000a +500a multi	1.15	.95
		Nos. B146-B150 (5)	5.75	4.75

Nos. B146-B150 printed in sheets of 4. Value, set $24.

Souvenir Sheet

First Natl. Exposition of Aerophilately — SP48

a, Lieut. Marcos A. Zar, Macchi seaplane. b, Capt. Antonio Parodi, Ansaldo SVA biplane.

1990, July 14 **Litho.** **Perf. 12**
B151 SP48 Sheet of 2   9.50 6.50
  a.   2000a +2000a multi   3.00 2.50
  b.   3000a +3000a multi   3.00 2.50

Souvenir Sheet

1992 Summer Olympics, Barcelona — SP49

Designs: a, Shot put. b, High jump. c, Hurdles. d, Pole vault.

1990, Dec. 15 **Litho.** **Perf. 13½**
B152 SP49 Sheet of 4   11.00 11.00
  a.-d.   2000a +2000a multi   2.50 2.50

Espamer '91 Philatelic Exhibition.
See No. B155.

Souvenir Sheet

Discovery of America, 500th Anniv. (in 1992) — SP50

Voyage of Alesandro Malaspina, 1789-1794: a, Sailing ship. b, Malaspina. c, Indian, hut. d, Indian, horse, artist drawing.

1990, Oct. 13 **Litho.** **Perf. 13½**
B153 SP50 Sheet of 4   11.00 11.00
  a.-d.   2000a +1000a, any single   2.00 2.00

Espamer '91, Buenos Aires.

Souvenir Sheet

Race Cars and Drivers — SP51

Designs: a, Juan Manuel Fangio. b, Juan Manuel Bordeu. c, Carlos Alberto Reutemann. d, Oscar and Juan Galvez.

1991 **Litho.** **Perf. 13½**
B154 SP51 Sheet of 4   6.50 6.50
  a.-d.   2500a +2500a, any single   1.40 1.25

Espamer '91.

1992 Summer Olympics Type of 1990
Souvenir Sheet

Women's gymnastics routines: a, Floor exercise. b, Uneven parallel bars. c, Balance beam. d, Rhythmic gymnastics.

1991, June 29 **Litho.** **Perf. 13½**
B155 SP49 Sheet of 4   6.50 6.50
  a.-d.   2500a +2500a, any single   1.40 1.25

Espamer '91.

Iberoprenfil '92   SP52

Designs: No. B156, Castor missile. No. B157, Satellite LUSAT 1.

1991, Dec. 28 **Litho.** **Perf. 13½**
B156 SP52 4000a +4000a multi   3.00 3.00
B157 SP52 4000a +4000a multi   3.00 3.00

Dinosaurs SP53

No. B158, Carnotaurus. No. B159, Amargasaurus.

1992, May 2 **Litho.** **Perf. 13½**
B158 SP53 38c +38c multi   1.75 1.75
B159 SP53 38c +38c multi   1.75 1.75
  a.   Pair, #B158-B159   4.50 4.50

Iberoprenfil '92, Buenos Aires — SP54

Paintings by Raul Soldi (b. 1905): No. B160, The Fiesta. No. B161, Church of St. Anne of Glew.

1992, Sept. 5 **Litho.** **Perf. 13½**
B160 SP54 76c +76c multi   3.75 3.00
B161 SP54 76c +76c multi   3.75 3.00

Parafil '92 — SP55

1992, Nov. 21 **Litho.** **Perf. 13½**
B162 SP55 76c +76c multi   3.75 3.00

2nd Argentine-Paraguayan Philatelic Exhibition, Buenos Aires.

Souvenir Sheet

Birds — SP56

a, Egretta thula. b, Amblyramphus holosericeus. c, Paroaria coronata. d, Chloroceryle amazona.

1993, July 17 **Litho.** **Perf. 13½**
B163 SP56 38c +38c Sheet of 4   8.00 8.00

Souvenir Sheet

Latin American Air Post Philatelic Exhibition — SP57

Designs: a, 25c+25c, Antoine de Saint-Exupery (1940-44), pilot, author. b, 75c+75c, "The Little Prince," vert.

1995, June 3 **Litho.** **Perf. 12**
B164 SP57 Sheet of 2, #a.-b.   7.00 7.00

For overprint see No. B180.

Souvenir Sheet

Exploration of Antarctica — SP58

75c+25c, Transport ship ARA Bahia Aguirre. 1.25p+75c, Argentine Air Force Hercules C-130.

1995, July 8
B165 SP58 Sheet of 2, #a.-b.   9.00 9.00

Aerofila '96 SP59

Historic airplanes, pilots: No. B166, "Plus ultra," Ramón Franco Bahamonde (1896-1938). No. B167, 14 Bis, Alberto Santos-Dumont (1873-1932). No. B168, Spirit of St. Louis, Charles A. Lindbergh (1902-1974). No. B169, Buenos Aires, Eduardo A. Olivero (1896-1966).

1996, July 13 **Litho.** **Perf. 13½**
B166 SP59 25c +25c multi   1.50 1.20
B167 SP59 25c +25c multi   1.50 1.20
B168 SP59 50c +50c multi   3.00 2.40
B169 SP59 50c +50c multi   3.00 2.40
  Nos. B166-B169 (4)   9.00 7.20

Ceramic Murals from Buenos Aires Subway SP60

1996, Sept. 21 **Litho.** **Perf. 13½**
B170 SP60 1p +50c Dragon   3.75 3.75
B171 SP60 1.50p +1p Bird   5.50 5.50

MEVIFIL '97, 1st Intl. Exhibition of Audio-Visual and Philatelic Information Media — SP61

Designs: No. B172, France Type A1. No. B173, Spain Type A3. No. B174, Argentina Type A4. No. B175, Buenos Aires Type A1.

1997, May 10 **Litho.** **Perf. 13½**
B172 SP61 50c +50c multi   2.25 2.25
B173 SP61 50c +50c multi   2.25 2.25
B174 SP61 50c +50c multi   2.25 2.25
B175 SP61 50c +50c multi   2.25 2.25
  a.   Block of 4, #B172-B175   10.00 10.00

Issued in sheets of 16 stamps + 4 labels.

Trains — SP62

Designs: No. B176, Las Nubes (Train to the Clouds), Salta. No. B177, Historical train, Buenos Aires. No. B178, Old Patagonian Express, Rio Negro-Chubut. No. B179, Southern Fueguino Railway, Tierra Del Fuego.

1997, Sept. 6 **Litho.** **Perf. 13**
B176 SP62 50c +50c multi   3.75 3.25
B177 SP62 50c +50c multi   3.75 3.25
B178 SP62 50c +50c multi   3.75 3.25
B179 SP62 50c +50c multi   3.75 3.25
  Nos. B176-B179 (4)   15.00 13.00

No. B164 Overprinted in Red Violet

1997, Sept. 27 **Litho.** **Perf. 12**
B180 SP57 Sheet of 2   7.50 7.50

Cartography — SP63

Maps of the Buenos Aires area from: 25c+25c, 1546. No. B182, 17th century. No. B183, 1910. 75c+75c, 1999.

Perf. 13¾x13½

1999, Nov. 20			**Litho.**	
B181	SP63	25c + 25c multi	1.00	1.00
B182	SP63	50c + 50c multi	2.00	2.00
B183	SP63	50c + 50c multi	2.00	2.00
B184	SP63	75c + 75c multi	3.00	3.00
a.	Block of 4, #B181-B184		13.00	13.00

Methods of Transportation — SP64

No. B185: a, Bicycle. b, Graf Zeppelin. c, Train. d, Trolley.

2000, Oct. 21		**Litho.**	**Perf. 14x13½**	
B185		Block of 4	11.00	11.00
a.	SP64 25c +25c multi		1.20	1.20
b.-c.	SP64 50c +50c Any single		2.40	2.40
d.	SP64 75c +75c multi		3.50	3.50

Cetaceans — SP65

No. B186: a, Burmeister's porpoise (Mariposa espinosa). b, River Plate dolphin. c, Minke whale. d, Humpback whale (Yubarta).

2001, Sept. 15		**Litho.**	**Perf. 14x13½**	
B186		Block of 4	15.00	15.00
a.	SP65 25c +25c multi		1.10	1.10
b.-c.	SP65 50c +50c Any single		2.25	2.25
d.	SP65 75c +75c multi		3.25	3.25

Reptiles — SP66

No. B187: a, Boa constrictor occidentalis. b, Caiman yacare. c, Tupinambis merianae. d, Chelonoidis carbonaria.

2002, Aug. 24		**Litho.**	**Perf. 14x13½**	
B187		Block of 4	9.00	9.00
a.	SP66 25c +25c multi		.80	.80
b.-c.	SP66 50c +50c Either single		1.35	1.35
d.	SP66 75c +75c multi		2.25	2.25

Bicycles — SP67

No. B188: a, Velocipede, 1855, Cycling Club champions, 1902. b, Velocipede, 1867, postman with delivery tricycle. c, Coventry Eagle touring bicycle, 1949, cyclists in park. d, Racing bicycle, 1960s, Palermo Velodrome, 1902.

2003, Aug. 9		**Litho.**	**Perf. 14x13¾**	
B188		Block of 4	5.50	5.50
a.	SP67 25c+25c multi		.70	.70
b.-c.	SP67 50c+50c Either single		1.20	1.20
d.	SP67 75c+75c multi		1.75	1.75

Ships — SP68

No. B189: a, A. R. A. Villarino. b, A. R. A. Pampa. c, A. R. A. Bahia Thetis. d, A. R. A. Cabo de Hornos.

2004, Aug. 21	**Litho.**	**Perf. 14x13½**		
B189		Block of 4	5.25	5.25
a.	SP68 25c +25c multi		.55	.55
b.-c.	SP68 50c +50c either single		.85	.85
d.	SP68 75c +75c multi		1.40	1.40

Merchant Ships — SP69

No. B190: a, Río de la Plata. b, Libertad. c, Campo Durán. d, Isla Soledad.

2005, Sept. 24	**Litho.**	**Perf. 14x13½**		
B190		Block of 4	5.25	5.25
a.	SP69 25c +25c multi		.55	.55
b.-c.	SP69 50c +50c either single		.85	.85
d.	SP69 75c +75c multi		1.40	1.40

River Boats — SP70

No. B191: a, Ciudad de Buenos Aires. b, Lambaré. c, Madrid. d, Rawson.

2006, Aug. 19	**Litho.**	**Perf. 14x13½**		
B191		Block of 4	5.25	5.25
a.	SP70 25c +25c multi		.55	.55
b.-c.	SP70 50c +50c either single		.85	.85
d.	SP70 75c +75c multi		1.40	1.40

Scouting, Cent. — SP71

No. B192: a, Scouts at campfire. b, Scout saluting near tent. c, Scout saluting, Scout with patrol flag. d, Scouts pulling rope.

2007, July 28		**Litho.**	**Perf. 13½x14**	
B192		Horiz. strip of 4	4.50	4.50
a.	SP71 25c +25c multi		.40	.40
b.	SP71 50c +50c multi		.80	.80
c.	SP71 75c +75c multi		1.10	1.10
d.	SP71 1p +1p multi		1.40	1.40

Shells — SP72

Designs: 25c+25c, Calliostoma militaris. 50c+50c, Epitonium fabrizioi. 75c+75c, Odontocymbiola magellanica. 1p+1p, Trophon geversianus.

Perf. 13½x13¾

2008, Aug. 23			**Litho.**	
B193-B196	SP72	Set of 4	4.00	4.00

Astronomical Observatories — SP73

Designs: No. B197, 50c+50c, Radio telescope, Argentine Institute of Radioastronomy. No. B198, 50c+50c, Telescope, La Plata Astronomical Observatory. No. B199, 1p+1p, El Lioncito Astronomical Complex. No. B200, 1p+1p, Telescope, Félix Aguilar Astronomical Observatory.

2009, Aug. 22	**Litho.**	**Perf. 14x13½**		
B197-B200	SP73	Set of 4	4.50	4.50

Girl Guides and Girl Scouts, Cent. — SP74

Designs: No. B201, 75c+75c, Girl Scout salute. No. B202, 75c+75c, Hands of five Girl Scouts joined. No. B203, 1p+1p, Hands of Girl Scouts joined, campfire. No. B204, 1p+1p, Hand on shoulder of Girl Scout.

2010, Aug. 21	**Litho.**	**Perf. 13½x14**		
B201-B204	SP74	Set of 4	4.25	4.25

Minerals SP75

Designs: No. B205, 1.25p+1.25p, Rhodochrosite (rodocrisita). No. B206, 1.25p+1.25p, Sulphur (azufre). No. B207, 1.25p+1.25p, Pyrite (pirita). No. B208, 1.25p+1.25p, Quartz (cuarzo).

2011, Aug. 20		**Perf. 13¾x13½**		
B205-B208	SP75	Set of 4	5.75	5.75

Minerals Type of 2011

Designs: No. B209, 1.50p+1.50p, Agate (agata). No. B210, 1.50p+1.50p, Amethyst (amatista). No. B211, 1.50p+1.50p, Fluorite (fluorita). No. B212, 1.50p+1.50p, Malachite (malaquita).

2012, Aug. 25				
B209-B212	SP75	Set of 4	6.00	6.00

Extreme Sports — SP76

Designs: No. B213, 2p+2p, Skiing. No. B214, 2p+2p, Skateboarding. No. B215, 2p+2p, BMX cycling. No. B216, 2p+2p, Surfing.

2013, Dec. 21	**Litho.**	**Perf. 14x13½**		
B213-B216	SP76	Set of 4	5.00	5.00

Volcanoes — SP77

Designs: No. B217, 5p+5p, Payú Liso. No. B218, 5p+5p, Llullaillaco. No. B219, 5p+5p, Lanín. No. B220, 5p+5p, Maipo.

Perf. 13¾x13½

2014, Aug. 19			**Litho.**	
B217-B220	SP77	Set of 4	9.50	9.50

Clocks and Sundials SP78

Designs: No. B221, 7p+7p, Los Colosos de Siemens Clock, Buenos Aires. No. B222, 7p+7p, Palacio Fuentes Clock Tower, Rosario. No. B223, 7p+7p, Jesuit Estate Sundial, Alta Gracia. No. B224, 7p+7p, Miroglio Brothers Clock, Buenos Aires.

2015, Dec. 4	**Litho.**	**Perf. 13½x13¾**		
B221-B224	SP78	Set of 4	11.50	11.50

Railroad Mail Cars — SP79

No. B225: a, Mail car with open door. b, Diagram of interior of mail car. c, Postal workers in mail car and on ground transfering mail. d, Mail car with closed doors.

2016, Aug. 22	**Litho.**	**Perf. 14x13½**		
B225	SP79	10p+10p Block of 4, #a-d	11.00	11.00

Ponchos SP80

Designs: No. B226, 16p+16p, 60-stripe poncho, Litoral region. No. B227, 16p+16p, Cayupán poncho, La Pampa Province. No. B228, 16p+16p, Andino poncho, Catamarca Province. No. B229, 16p+16p, Pilagá poncho, Chaco Province.

Perf. 13½x13¾

2017, Aug. 23			**Litho.**	
B226-B229	SP80	Set of 4	15.00	15.00

Map of Corrientes Province, Mesenger on Horseback, Postman, and Truck — SP81

Post Office Palace, Buenos Aires, and Tile — SP82

2018, Dec. 26   Litho.   Perf. 14x13½
B230 SP81 30p+15p sil & multi   2.40 2.40
B231 SP82 30p+15p sil & multi   2.40 2.40

Mail delivery in Corrientes area, 270th anniv., and Post Office Palace, 90th anniv.

Tango — SP83

Designs: No. B232, 50p+25p, Tango dancers. No. B233, 50p+25p, Bandoneon player.

Perf. 13½x13¾
2019, Aug. 26   Litho.
B232-B233 SP83   Set of 2   5.25 5.25

AIR POST STAMPS

Airplane Circles the Globe — AP1

Eagle — AP2

Wings Cross the Sea — AP3

Condor on Mountain Crag — AP4

Perforations of Nos. C1-C37 vary from clean-cut to rough and uneven, with many skipped perfs.

Perf. 13x13½, 13½x13
1928, Mar. 1   Litho.   Wmk. 90
C1 AP1   5c lt red   1.50   .60
C2 AP1   10c Prus blue   2.50   1.10
C3 AP2   15c lt brown   2.50   1.00
C4 AP1   18c lilac gray   4.00   3.00
  a.   18c brown lilac   4.50   3.00
  b.   Double impression   375.00
C5 AP2   20c ultra   3.00   1.00
C6 AP2   24c deep blue   5.00   3.00
C7 AP3   25c brt violet   5.00   1.60
C8 AP3   30c rose red   6.00   1.25
C9 AP4   35c rose   5.00   1.10
C10 AP1   36c bister brn   3.00   1.60
C11 AP4   50c gray black   5.00   .75
C12 AP2   54c chocolate   5.00   2.25
C13 AP2   72c yellow grn   6.00   2.25
  a.   Double impression   350.00
C14 AP3   90c dk brown   11.00   2.00
C15 AP3   1p slate bl & red   13.00   .90
C16 AP3 1.08p rose & dk bl   18.00   5.00
C17 AP4 1.26p dull vio & grn 25.00 10.00

C18 AP4 1.80p blue & lil rose   25.00 10.00
C19 AP4 3.60p gray & blue   50.00 22.00
    Nos. C1-C19 (19)   195.50 70.40

The watermark on No. C4a is larger than on the other stamps of this set, measuring 10mm across Sun.

Zeppelin First Flight

Air Post Stamps of 1928 Overprinted in Blue

1930, May
C20 AP2   20c ultra   10.00   5.00
  a.   Inverted overprint   500.00
C21 AP4   50c gray black   20.00 10.00
  a.   Inverted overprint   500.00
C22 AP3   1p slate bl &
              red   25.00 12.50
  a.   Inverted overprint   850.00
C23 AP4 1.80p blue & lil
              rose   70.00 30.00
C24 AP4 3.60p gray & blue   200.00 90.00
    Nos. C20-C24 (5)   325.00 147.50

Overprinted in Green
C25 AP2   20c ultra   13.00   8.00
C26 AP4   50c gray black   15.00 10.00
C27 AP3   90c dark brown   13.00   8.00
C28 AP3   1p slate bl &
              red   25.00 15.00
C29 AP4 1.80p blue & lil
              rose   700.00 500.00
  a.   Thick paper   1,000.
    Nos. C25-C29 (5)   766.00 541.00

Air Post Stamps of 1928 Overprinted in Red or Blue

On AP1-AP2

On AP3-AP4

1931
C30 AP1   18c lilac gray   2.00   1.50
C31 AP2   72c yellow green   14.00 10.50
C32 AP3   90c dark brown   14.00 10.50
C33 AP4 1.80p bl & lil rose
              (Bl)   30.00 22.50
C34 AP4 3.60p gray & blue   57.50 40.00
    Nos. C30-C34 (5)   117.50 85.00

1st anniv. of the Revolution of 1930.

Zeppelin Issue
Nos. C1, C4, C4a, C14 Overprinted in Blue or Red

On AP1

On AP3

1932, Aug. 4
C35 AP1   5c lt red (Bl)   3.00   2.00
C36 AP1   18c lilac gray (R)   12.50   9.00
  a.   18c brown lilac (R)   100.00 60.00
C37 AP3   90c dark brown (R)   32.50 26.00
    Nos. C35-C37 (3)   48.00 37.00

Plane and Letter — AP5

Mercury — AP6

Plane in Flight — AP7

Perf. 13½x13, 13x13½
1940, Oct. 23   Photo.   Wmk. 90
C38 AP5   30c deep orange   12.00   .40
C39 AP6   50c dark brown   12.00   .40
C40 AP7   1p carmine   5.00   .25
C41 AP7 1.25p deep green   2.00   .25
C42 AP5 2.50p bright blue   4.00   .60
    Nos. C38-C42 (5)   35.00   1.90

Plane and Letter — AP8

Mercury and Plane — AP9

Perf. 13½x13, 13x13½
1942, Oct. 6   Litho.   Wmk. 90
C43 AP8   30c orange   .25   .25
C44 AP9   50c dull brn & buff   .40   .25

No. C43 exists imperf. Value, pair $20.
See Nos. C49-C52, C57, C61.

Plane over Iguaçu Falls — AP10

Plane over the Andes — AP11

Perf. 13½x13
1946, June 10   Unwmk.
C45 AP10 15c dull red brn   .25   .25
C46 AP11 25c gray green   .25   .25

See Nos. C53-C54.

Allegory of Flight AP12

Astrolabe — AP13

Perf. 13½x13, 13x13½
1946, Sept. 25   Litho.   Unwmk.
Surface-Tinted Paper
C47 AP12 15c sl grn, pale grn   .55   .25
C48 AP13 60c vio brn, ocher   .55   .35

Types of 1942
1946-48   Unwmk.   Perf. 13½x13
C49 AP8   30c orange   1.40   .25
C50 AP9   50c dull brn & buff   2.50   .25
C51 AP8   1p carmine ('47)   1.25   .25
C52 AP8 2.50p brt blue ('48)   5.50   .75
    Nos. C49-C52 (4)   10.65   1.50

No. C51 exists imperf. Value, pair $30.

Types of 1946
1948   Wmk. 90
C53 AP10 15c dull red brn   .25   .25
C54 AP11 25c gray green   .25   .25

Atlas (National Museum, Naples) — AP14

Map of Argentine Republic, Globe and Caliper — AP15

Perf. 13½x13, 13x13½
1948-49   Photo.   Wmk. 288
C55 AP14 45c dk brown ('49)   .40   .25
C56 AP15 70c dark green   .70   .40

4th Pan-American Reunion of Cartographers, Buenos Aires, Oct.-Nov., 1948.

Mercury Type of 1942
1949   Litho.   Perf. 13x13½
C57 AP9   50c dull brn & buff   .40   .25

Marksmanship Trophy — AP16

1949, Nov. 4   Photo.
C58 AP16 75c brown   .75   .25

World Rifle Championship, 1949.

Catalogue values for unused stamps in this section, from this point to the end of the section, are for Never Hinged items.

Douglas
DC-3
and
Condor
AP17

Perf. 13x13½
1951, June 20 **Wmk. 90**
C59 AP17 20c dk olive grn .50 .25
10th anniversary of the State air lines.

Douglas DC-6
and
Condor — AP18

1951, Oct. 17 **Perf. 13½**
C60 AP18 20c blue .50 .25
End of Argentine 5-year Plan.

Plane-Letter Type of 1942
1951 **Litho.** **Perf. 13½x13**
C61 AP8 1p carmine .40 .25
No. C61 exists imperf. Value, pair $20.

Jesus by
Leonardo da
Vinci (detail,
"Virgin of the
Rocks")
AP19

Perf. 13½x13
1956, Sept. 29 **Photo.** **Wmk. 90**
C62 AP19 1p dull purple .80 .25
Issued to express the gratitude of the children of Argentina to the people of the world for their help against poliomyelitis.

Battle of
Montevideo
AP20

Leonardo
Rosales and
Tomas
Espora
AP21

Guillermo
Brown — AP22

1957, Mar. 2 **Perf. 13½**
C63 AP20 60c blue gray .25 .25
C64 AP21 1p brt pink .30 .25
C65 AP22 2p brown .30 .25
  Nos. C63-C65 (3) .85 .75
Cent. of the death of Admiral Guillermo Brown, founder of the Argentine navy.

Map of Americas &
Arms of Buenos
Aires — AP23

1957, Aug. 16
C66 AP23 2p rose violet .50 .25
Issued to publicize the Inter-American Economic Conference in Buenos Aires.

Modern
locomotive
AP24

1957, Aug. 31 **Wmk. 90** **Perf. 13½**
C67 AP24 60c gray .45 .25
Centenary of Argentine railroads.

AP25

No. C68, Globe, Flag,Compass Rose. No. C69, Key.

1957, Sept. 14
C68 AP25 1p multi .25 .25
C69 AP25 2p multi .30 .25
1957 International Congress for Tourism.

Birds
Carrying
Letters
AP26

1957, Nov. 6
C70 AP26 1p bright blue .35 .25
Issued for Letter Writing Week, Oct. 6-12.

Early Plane
AP27

1958, May 31 **Perf. 13½**
C71 AP27 2p maroon .25 .25
50th anniv. of the Argentine Aviation Club.

Stamp Anniv. Type
Designs: 80c, Stamp of Buenos Aires and view of the Plaza de la Aduana. 1p, Stamp of 1858 and "The Post of Santa Fe."

1958 **Litho.** **Perf. 13½**
C72 A270 80c pale bis & sl bl .25 .25
C73 A270 1p red org & dk bl .25 .25
Cent. of the 1st postage stamps of Buenos Aires & the Argentine Confederation.
Issue dates: 80c, Oct. 18; 1p, Aug. 23.

Comet
Jet over
World
Map
AP29

1959, May 16 **Perf. 13½**
C74 AP29 5p black & olive .40 .25
Inauguration of jet flights by Argentine Airlines.

Type of Regular Issue, 1960
"Cabildo" and: 1.80p, Mariano Moreno. 5p, Manuel Belgrano and Juan Jose Castelli.

Perf. 13½
1960, May 28 **Wmk. 90** **Photo.**
C75 A287 1.80p red brown .25 .25
  a. Souvenir sheet of 3 1.40 .95
C76 A287 5p buff & purple .35 .25
  a. Souvenir sheet of 3 2.00 1.50
Souvenir sheets are imperf. No. C75a contains one No. C75 and 1p and 2p resembling Nos. 713-714; stamps in reddish brown. No. C76a contains one No. C76 and 4.20p and 10.70p resembling Nos. 715-716; stamps are in green.

Symbolic of New
Provinces — AP30

1960, July 8 **Litho.**
C77 AP30 1.80p dk car & blue .30 .25
Elevation of the territories of Chubut, Formosa, Neuquen, Rio Negro and Santa Cruz to provinces.

Type of Regular Issue, 1960
1960, Oct. 1 **Photo.** **Perf. 13½**
C78 A291 1.80p rose lilac .50 .25
C79 A291 10.70p brt grnsh blue .70 .35

UNESCO
Emblem
AP31

1962, July 14 **Litho.**
C80 AP31 13p ocher & brown .40 .25
15th anniv. of UNESCO.

Mail Coach
AP32

1962, Oct. 6 **Wmk. 90** **Perf. 13½**
C81 AP32 5.60p gray brn & blk .75 .25
Mailman's Day, Sept. 14, 1962.

No. 695 and
Type of 1959
Surcharged
in Green

1962, Oct. 31 **Photo.**
C82 A277 5.60p on 5p brown .30 .25
C83 A277 18p on 5p brn, *grnsh* 1.00 .25

UPAE
Emblem — AP33

1962, Nov. 24 **Photo.** **Perf. 13½**
C84 AP33 5.60p dark blue .40 .25
50th anniv. of the founding of the Postal Union of the Americas and Spain, UPAE.

Skylark — AP34

Design: 11p, Super Albatros.

1963, Feb. 9 **Litho.**
C85 AP34 5.60p blue & black .25 .25
C86 AP34 11p blue, blk & red .40 .25
9th World Gliding Championships.

Symbolic
Plane
AP35

1963-65 **Wmk. 90** **Perf. 13½**
C87 AP35 5.60p dk pur, car & brt grn .55 .25
C88 AP35 7p black & bis ('64) .75 .25
C88A AP35 7p black & bis ('65) 8.00 1.00
C89 AP35 11p blk, dk pur & grn .80 .25
C90 AP35 18p dk pur, red & vio bl 1.75 .35
C91 AP35 21p brown, red & gray 2.40 .40
  Nos. C87-C91 (6) 14.25 2.50
"Argentina" reads down on No. C88, up on No. C88A. See Nos. C101-C104, C108-C111, C123-C126, C135-C141. For overprint and surcharges see Nos. C96, C146-C150.

Type of Regular Issue, 1964
Map of Falkland Islands (Islas Malvinas).

1964, Feb. 22 **Perf. 13½**
Size: 33x22mm
C92 A327 18p lt & dk bl & ol grn 2.75 .75

UPU
Monument,
Bern, and UN
Emblem
AP36

1964, May 23 **Engr.** **Perf. 13½**
C93 AP36 18p red & dk brown .60 .25
15th UPU Cong., Vienna, Austria, 5-6/64.

Discovery of America, Florentine Woodcut AP37

1964, Oct. 10   **Litho.**
C94 AP37 13p tan & black   .90   .35
Day of the Race, Columbus Day.

Lt. Matienzo Base, Antarctica AP38

1965, Feb. 27   **Photo.**   *Perf. 13½*
C95 AP38 11p salmon pink   .50   .25
Issued to publicize the national territory of Tierra del Fuego, Antarctic and South Atlantic Isles.

No. C88A Overprinted in Silver

1965, Mar. 17   **Litho.**
C96 AP35 7p black & bister   .30   .25
1st Rio de la Plata Stamp Show, sponsored jointly by the Argentine and Uruguayan Philatelic Associations, Montevideo, Mar. 19-28.

ITU Emblem — AP39

1965, May 11   **Wmk. 90**   *Perf. 13½*
C97 AP39 18p slate, blk & red   .40   .25
Centenary of the ITU.

Ascending Rocket — AP40

Design: 50p, Earth with trajectories and magnetic field, horiz.

1965, May 29   **Photo.**   *Perf. 13½*
C98 AP40 18p red org   .70   .30
C99 AP40 50p ultra   1.25   .55
6th Symposium on Space Research, held in Buenos Aires, and to honor the Natl. Commission of Space Research.

Type of 1963-65 Inscribed "Republica Argentina"

1965, Oct. 13   **Litho.**   **Wmk. 90**
C101 AP35   12p dk car rose & brn   1.40   .25
C102 AP35   15p vio blue & dk red   1.50   .50
C103 AP35   27.50p dk bl grn & gray   2.50   1.00
C104 AP35   30.50p dk brown & dk bl   3.00   1.50
   Nos. C101-C104 (4)   8.40   3.25

Argentine Antarctica Map and Centaur Rocket AP41

1966, Feb. 19   *Perf. 13½*
C105 AP41 27.50p bl, blk & dp org   1.10   .85
Launchings of sounding balloons and of a Gamma Centaur rocket in Antarctica during February, 1965.

Sea Gull and Southern Cross AP42

1966, May 14   *Perf. 13½*
C106 AP42 12p Prus blue, blk & red   .40   .25
50th anniv. of the Naval Aviation School.

Blériot Plane Flown by Fels, 1917 — AP43

1967, Sept. 2   **Litho.**   *Perf. 13½*
C107 AP43 26p olive, bl & blk   .30   .25
Flight by Theodore Fels from Buenos Aires to Montevideo, Sept. 2, 1917, allegedly the 1st intl. airmail flight.

Type of 1963-65 Inscribed "Republica Argentina" Reading Down

1967, Dec. 20   *Perf. 13½*
C108 AP35 26p brown   .60   .25
C109 AP35 40p violet   5.25   .30
C110 AP35 68p blue green   3.50   .45
C111 AP35 78p ultra   1.50   .60
   Nos. C108-C111 (4)   10.85   1.60

Vito Dumas and Ketch "Legh II" AP44

1968, July 27   **Litho.**   **Wmk. 90**
C112 AP44 68p bl, blk, red & vio bl   .65   .40
Issued to commemorate Vito Dumas's one-man voyage around the world in 1943.

Type of Regular Issue and Assembly Emblem — AP45

40p, Globe and map of South America.

1968, Oct. 19   **Litho.**   *Perf. 13½*
C113 A395 40p brt pink, lt bl & blk   .75   .30
C114 AP45 68p bl, lt bl, gold & blk   1.25   .50
4th Plenary Assembly of the Intl. Telegraph and Telephone Consultative Committee, Mar del Plata, Sept. 23-Oct. 25.

Radar Antenna, Balcarce Station AP46

     Perf. 13½
1969, Aug. 23   **Wmk. 90**   **Photo.**
C115 AP46 40p blue gray   .70   .25
Communications by satellite through Intl. Telecommunications Consortium (INTELSAT).

Atucha Nuclear Center AP47

1969, Dec. 13   **Litho.**   **Wmk. 365**
C116 AP47 26p blue & multi   2.00   .80
Completion of Atucha Nuclear Center.

Type of 1963-65 Inscribed "Republica Argentina" Reading Down

1969-71   *Perf. 13½*
C123 AP35 40p violet   5.75   .40
C124 AP35 68p dk blue grn ('70)   2.10   .60
     Unwmk.
C125 AP35 26p yellow brn ('71)   .35   .25
C126 AP35 40p violet ('71)   3.00   .40
   Nos. C123-C126 (4)   11.20   1.65

Old Fire Engine and Fire Brigade Emblem AP48

1970, Aug. 8   **Litho.**   **Unwmk.**
C128 AP48 40c green & multi   1.50   .30
Centenary of the Fire Brigade.

Education Year Emblem AP49

1970, Aug. 29   *Perf. 13½*
C129 AP49 68c blue & blk   .80   .30
Issued for International Education Year.

Fleet Leaving Valparaiso, by Antonio Abel — AP50

1970, Oct. 17   **Litho.**   *Perf. 13½*
C130 AP50 26c multicolored   1.00   .35
150th anniv. of the departure for Peru of the liberation fleet from Valparaiso, Chile.

Sumampa Chapel — AP51

1970, Nov. 7   **Photo.**
C131 AP51 40c multicolored   1.00   .40
Bishopric of Tucuman, 400th anniversary.

Buenos Aires Planetarium — AP52

1970, Nov. 28   **Litho.**   *Perf. 13½*
C132 AP52 40c multicolored   .75   .25

Jorge Newbery and Morane Saulnier Plane AP53

1970, Dec. 19
C133 AP53 26c bl, blk, yel & grn   .45   .25
24th Aeronautics and Space Week.

Industries Type of Regular Issue
Design: 31c, Refinery.

1971, Oct. 16   **Litho.**   *Perf. 13½*
C134 A445 31c red, blk & yel   .80   .30

Type of 1963-65 Inscribed "Republica Argentina" Reading Down

1971-74   **Unwmk.**
C135 AP35 45c brown   3.50   .25
C136 AP35 68c red   .50   .25
C137 AP35 70c vio blue ('73)   2.75   .50
C138 AP35 90c emerald ('73)   2.75   .50

C139 AP35 1.70p blue ('74) .60 .25
C140 AP35 1.95p emerald ('74) .60 .25
C141 AP35 2.65p dp claret ('74) .60 .25
Nos. C135-C141 (7) 11.30 2.25

Fluorescent paper was used for Nos. C135-C136, C138-C141. The 70c was issued on both papers. Value, 70c on fluorescent paper $5.50

Don Quixote, Drawing by Ignacio Zuloaga AP54

1975, Apr. 26   Photo.   Perf. 13½
C145 AP54 2.75p yellow, blk & red .60 .35

Day of the Race and for Espana 75 Intl. Philatelic Exhibition, Madrid, Apr. 4-13.

No. C87 Surcharged

1975, Sept. 15   Litho.   Wmk. 90
C146 AP35 9.20p on 5.60p .90 .25
C147 AP35 19.70p on 5.60p 1.25 .45
C148 AP35 100p on 5.60p 5.50 2.25
Nos. C146-C148 (3) 7.65 2.95

No. C87 Surcharged

1975, Oct. 15
C149 AP35 9.20p on 5.60p .90 .30
C150 AP35 19.70p on 5.60p 1.50 .60

Argentine State Airline, 50th Anniv. — AP55

No. C151, Junkers JU52-3M. No. C152, Grumman SA-16. No. C153, Fokker F-27. No. C154, Fokker F-28.

1990, Sept. 15   Litho.   Perf. 13½
C151 AP55 2500a multi 1.60 .90
C152 AP55 2500a multi 1.60 .90
C153 AP55 2500a multi 1.60 .90
C154 AP55 2500a multi 1.60 .90
Nos. C151-C154 (4) 6.40 3.60

AIR POST SEMI-POSTAL STAMPS

Catalogue values for unused stamps in this section are for Never Hinged items.

Philatelic Exhibition Type

Designs: No. CB1, Stamp engraving. No. CB2, Proofing stamp die. No. CB3, Sheet of stamps. No. CB4, The letter. No. CB5, Gen. San Martin.

Perf. 13½
1950, Aug. 26   Wmk. 90   Photo.
CB1 SP8 45c + 45c vio bl .35 .25
CB2 SP8 70c + 70c dk brn .60 .40
  a. Souv. sheet of 3, #B12, CB1, CB2, imperf. 5.00 3.00
CB3 SP8 1p + 1p cerise 1.25 1.25
CB4 SP8 2.50p + 2.50p ol gray 8.50 6.00
CB5 SP8 5p + 5p dull grn 10.00 7.25
Nos. CB1-CB5 (5) 20.70 15.15

Argentine Intl. Philatelic Exhib., 1950.

Pieta by Michelangelo SPAP2

1951, Dec. 22   Perf. 13½x13
CB6 SPAP2 2.45p +7.55p grnsh blk 22.50 14.00

Surtax as for the Eva Peron Foundation.

Flower and Child's Head SPAP3

1958, Mar. 15   Perf. 13½
CB7 SPAP3 1p +50c deep claret .30 .30

Surtax for National Council for Children.

Stamp of 1858 — SPAP4

1958, Mar. 29   Litho.   Wmk. 90
CB8 SPAP4 1p + 50c gray ol & bl .45 .35
CB9 SPAP4 2p + 1p rose lilac & vio .55 .45
CB10 SPAP4 3p + 1.50p green & brown .60 .55
CB11 SPAP4 5p + 2.50p gray ol & car rose 1.10 .90
CB12 SPAP4 10p + 5p gray ol & brn 2.00 1.75
Nos. CB8-CB12 (5) 4.70 4.00

The surtax was for the Intl. Centennial Philatelic Exhibition, Buenos Aires, Apr. 19-27.

Type of Semi-Postal Issue, 1958

Designs: 1p+50c, Flooded area. 5p+2.50p, House and truck under water.

1958, Oct. 4   Photo.   Perf. 13½
CB13 SP11 1p + 50c dull purple .30 .25
CB14 SP11 5p + 2.50p grnsh blue 1.00 .80

The surtax was for victims of a flood in the Buenos Aires district.

Type of Semi-Postal Issue

1959, Sept. 5   Litho.   Perf. 13½
CB15 SP13 2p + 1p Rowing .40 .25
  a. Torch missing 170.00 170.00
CB16 SP13 3p + 1.50p Woman diver .60 .50
  a. Torch missing 170.00 170.00

Bird Type of Semi-Postal Issue

2p+1p, Rufous tinamou. 3p+1.50p, Rhea.

1960, Feb. 6   Perf. 13½
CB17 SP14 2p + 1p rose car & sal .45 .25
CB18 SP14 3p + 1.50p slate green .50 .35

The surtax was for child welfare work. See No. CB29.

Buenos Aires Market Place, 1810 SPAP5

6p+3p, Oxcart water carrier. 10.70p+5.30p, Settlers landing. 20p+10p, The Fort.

1960, Aug. 20   Photo.   Wmk. 90
CB19 SPAP5 2 + 1p rose brown .25 .25
CB20 SPAP5 6 + 3p gray .35 .25
CB21 SPAP5 10.70 + 5.30p blue .60 .50
CB22 SPAP5 20 + 10p bluish grn 1.00 .85
Nos. CB19-CB22 (4) 2.20 1.85

Inter-American Philatelic Exhibition EFIMAYO 1960, Buenos Aires, Oct. 12-24, held to for the sesquicentennial of the May Revolution of 1810.
No. CB22 exists imperf. Value, pair $40.
For overprints see Nos. CB25-CB28.

Seibo, National Flower — SPAP6

#CB24, Copihue, Chile's national flower.

1960, Sept. 10   Perf. 13½
CB23 SPAP6 6 + 3p lilac rose .50 .30
CB24 SPAP6 10.70 + 5.30p ver .70 .40

The surtax was for earthquake victims in Chile. Nos. CB23-CB24 exist imperf. Value, each pair $40.

Nos. CB19-CB22 Overprinted

1960, Oct. 8
CB25 SPAP5 2 + 1p rose brown .25 .25
CB26 SPAP5 6 + 3p gray .30 .30
CB27 SPAP5 10.70 + 5.30p blue .50 .40
CB28 SPAP5 20 + 10p bluish green 1.00 .75
Nos. CB25-CB28 (4) 2.05 1.70

United Nations Day, Oct. 24, 1960.

Type of Semi-Postal Issue, 1960

Design: Emperor penguins.

1961, Feb. 25   Photo.   Wmk. 90
CB29 SP14 1.80p + 90c gray .40 .25

The surtax was for child welfare work. Exists imperf. Value, pair $50.

Stamp of 1862 — SPAP7

1962, May 19   Litho.
CB30 SPAP7 6.50p + 6.50p Prus bl & grnsh bl .70 .65

Opening of the "Argentina 62" Philatelic Exhibition, Buenos Aires, May 19-29. Exists imperf. Value, pair $40.

Type of Semi-Postal Issue, 1963

1963, May 18   Wmk. 90   Perf. 13½
CB31 SP21 11p + 5p Bicycling .60 .50

Exists imperf. Value, pair $40.

Type of Semi-Postal Issue, 1962

Design: Pitangus sulphuratus bolivianus.

1963, Dec. 21   Perf. 13½
CB32 SP20 11p + 5p multi 1.10 .60

The surtax was for child welfare.

Type of Semi-Postal Issue, 1964

1964, July 18   Litho.
CB33 SP22 11p + 5p Sailboat .90 .70

Exists imperf. Value, pair $50.

Crutch, Olympic Torch and Rings — SPAP8

1964, Sept. 19   Litho.   Perf. 13½
CB34 SPAP8 18p + 9p bluish grn, blk, red & yel .60 .60

13th "Olympic" games for the handicapped, Tokyo, 1964. Exists imperf. Value, pair $50.

Bird Type of Semi-Postal Issue, 1962

Design: Iridoprocne leucopyga.

1964, Dec. 23   Litho.   Wmk. 90
CB35 SP20 18p + 9p multi 1.10 .85

The surtax was for child welfare.

Furnarius Rufus Rufus — SP22a

1966, Mar. 26   Perf. 13½
CB36 SP22a 27.50p + 12.50p bl, ocher, yel & grn 1.10 .85

The surtax was for child welfare.

Coat of Arms — SPAP9

1966, June 25   Litho.   Perf. 13½
CB37 SPAP9 10p + 10p multi 1.75 1.40

ARGENTINA '66 Philatelic Exhibition held in connection with the sesquicentennial celebration of the Declaration of Independence, Buenos Aires, July 16-23. The surtax was for the Exhibition. Issued in sheets of 4.

Designs: 15p+7p, Thraupis bonariensis. 26p+13p, Ramphastos toco.

1967 Litho. Wmk. 90
CB38 SP22a 15p + 7p blk, bl, grn & yel 1.40 1.00
CB39 SP22a 26p + 13p blk, org, yel & bl .50 .40
The surtax was for child welfare.
Issued: 15p+7p, Jan. 14; 26p+13p, Dec. 23.

Bird Type of Semi-Postal Issue, 1969
Design: Ceophloeus lineatus.
1969, Sept. 20 Wmk. 365 Perf. 13½
CB40 SP24 26p + 13p multi .75 .40
The surtax was for child welfare.

Bird Type of Semi-Postal Issue, 1970
Design: Phoenicopterus ruber chilensis.
1970, May 9 Litho. Wmk. 365
CB41 SP25 40c + 20c multi .75 .40
The surtax was for child welfare.

Fish Type of Semi-Postal Issue, 1971
Design: Odostethes platensis.
1971, Feb. 20 Unwmk. Perf. 12½
Size: 75x15mm
CB42 SP26 40c + 20c multl .50 .40
The surtax was for child welfare.

OFFICIAL STAMPS

Regular Issues Overprinted in Black — a

1884-87 Unwmk. Perf. 12, 14
O1 A29 ½c brown 40.00 25.00
O2 A23 1c red 15.00 10.00
  b. Perf. 12 100.00 80.00
O3 A29 1c red 1.00 .50
  b. Double overprint 100.00 100.00
O4 A20 2c green 1.00 .50
  b. Double overprint 120.00 120.00
O5 A11 4c brown 1.00 .50
O6 A7 8c lake 1.00 1.00
O7 A8 10c green 100.00 50.00
O8 A23 12c ultra (#45) 10.00 5.00
  a. Perf. 14 1,000. 250.00
O9 A29 12c grnsh blue 1.50 1.00
O10 A19 24c blue 2.00 1.50
O11 A21 25c lake 40.00 30.00
O12 A12 30c orange 80.00 70.00
O13 A13 60c black 50.00 40.00
O14 A14 90c blue 40.00 30.00
  b. Double overprint 120.00 120.00
Nos. O1-O14 (14) 382.50 265.00

Inverted Overprint
O1a A29 ½c 30.00 20.00
O2a A23 1c Perf. 14 100.00 80.00
  c. Perf. 12 75.00 —
O3a A29 1c 2.50 1.00
O4a A20 2c 120.00 100.00
O5a A11 4c 60.00 50.00
O6a A7 8c (Inverted overprint on reverse) 500.00 —
O8b A23 12c Perf. 12 20.00 —
O9a A29 12c 300.00 250.00
O10a A19 24c 2.00 2.00
O13a A13 60c 150.00 120.00
O14a A14 90c 120.00 120.00

1884 Rouletted
O15 A17 16c green 3.00 2.00
  a. Double overprint 25.00 —
  b. Inverted overprint 300.00
O16 A18 20c blue 15.00 12.00
  a. Inverted overprint 120.00 80.00
O17 A19 24c blue 2.50 1.50
  a. Inverted overprint 6.00 5.00
  b. Double ovpt., one inverted 250.00 —
Nos. O15-O17 (3) 20.50 15.50

Overprinted Diagonally in Red
1885 Perf. 12
O18 A20 2c green 5.00 4.00
  a. Inverted overprint 100.00

O19 A11 4c brown 3.00 2.00
  a. Inverted overprint 100.00
  b. Double overprint 100.00 100.00
O20 A13 60c black 50.00 40.00
O21 A14 90c blue 450.00 275.00

1885 Rouletted
O22 A19 24c blue 40.00 20.00
On all of these stamps, the overprint is found reading both upwards and downwards. Counterfeits exist of No. O21 overprint and others.

Regular Issues Handstamped Horizontally in Black — b

1884 Perf. 12, 14
O23 A23 1c red 100.00 50.00
  a. Perf. 12 400.00 300.00
O24 A20 2c green, diagonal overprint 60.00 40.00
  a. Horizontal overprint 450.00 300.00
O25 A11 4c brown 25.00 20.00
O26 A7 8c lake 25.00 20.00
O27 A23 12c ultra 60.00 50.00

Overprinted Diagonally
O28 A19 24c bl, rouletted 50.00 35.00
O29 A13 60c black 30.00 15.00
Counterfeit overprints exist.

Liberty Head — O1

Perf. 11½, 12 and Compound
1901, Dec. 1 Engr.
O31 O1 1c gray .50 .25
  b. Vert. pair, imperf. horiz. 80.00
  c. Horiz. pair, imperf. vert. 100.00
O32 O1 2c orange brown .50 .25
O33 O1 5c red .50 .25
  b. Vert. pair, imperf. horiz. 100.00
O34 O1 10c dark green 1.00 .25
O35 O1 30c dark blue 8.00 3.00
O36 O1 50c orange 4.00 2.00
Nos. O31-O36 (6) 14.50 6.00

Imperf, Pairs
O31a O1 1c 80.00
O32a O1 2c 80.00
O33a O1 5c 100.00
O34a O1 10c 80.00
O35a O1 30c 100.00
O36a O1 50c 150.00

Regular Stamps of 1935-51 Overprinted in Black — c

Perf. 13x13½, 13½x13, 13
1938-54 Wmk. RA in Sun (90)
O37 A129 1c buff ('40) .50 .25
O38 A130 2c dk brn ('40) .50 .25
O39 A132 3c grn ('39) 1.25 .50
O40 A132 3c lt gray ('39) .50 .25
O41 A134 5c yel brn .50 .25
O42 A195 5c car ('53) .50 .25
O43 A137 10c carmine .60 .25
O44 A137 10c brn ('39) 1.00 .25
O45 A140 15c lt gray bl, type II ('47) .60 .25
O46 A139 15c slate blue .50 .25
O47 A139 15c pale ultra ('39) .60 .25
O48 A139 20c blue ('53) 1.25 .50
O49 A141 25c carmine .50 .25
  a. Overprint 11mm 1.00 .25
O49B A143 40c dk violet 2.50 .80
O50 A144 50c red & org .50 .25
  a. Overprint 11mm .50 .25
O51 A146 1p brn blk & lt bl ('40) .60 .25
  a. Overprint 11mm 9.00 .50
O52 A224 1p choc & lt bl ('51) 2.00 .30
  a. Overprint 11mm 1.50 .25
O53 A147 2p brn lake & dk ultra (ovpt. 11mm) ('54) 2.00 .50
Nos. O37-O53 (18) 16.90 5.85

Overprinted in Black on Stamps and Types of 1945-47
Perf. 13x13½, 13½x13
1945-46 Unwmk.
O54 A130 2c sepia 6.00 5.00
O55 A134 3c lt gray 4.00 4.00
O56 A134 5c yel brn .60 .25
O57 A195 5c dp car .50 .25
O58 A137 10c brown 1.00 .25
  a. Double overprint
O59 A140 15c lt gray bl, type II .70 .25
O61 A141 25c dull rose .50 .25
O62 A144 50c red & org 1.00 .25
O63 A146 1p brn blk & lt bl 1.00 .25
O64 A147 2p brn lake & bl .60 .25
O65 A148 5p ind & ol grn .80 .25
O66 A149 10p dp cl & int blk 1.25 .50
O67 A150 20p bl grn & brn 2.50 2.00
Nos. O54-O67 (13) 20.45 13.75

Overprinted in Black on Stamps and Types of 1942-50
Perf. 13, 13x13½
1944-51 Wmk. 288
O73 A132 3c lt gray 6.00 2.00
O74 A134 5c yellow brown 2.00 .50
O75 A137 10c red brown .60 .25
O76 A140 15c lt gray bl, type II 1.00 .25
O77 A144 50c red & org (overprint 11 mm) 8.00 2.00
O78 A146 1p brn blk & lt bl (overprint 11mm) 10.00 5.00
Nos. O73-O78 (6) 27.60 10.00

> **Catalogue values for unused stamps in this section, from this point to the end of the section, are for Never Hinged items.**

Nos. 600-606 Overprinted in Black — d

1953 Wmk. 90 Perf. 13
O79 A228 5c gray .50 .25
O80 A228 10c rose lilac .50 .25
O81 A228 20c rose pink .50 .25
O82 A228 25c dull green .50 .25
O83 A228 40c dull violet .50 .25
O84 A228 45c deep blue .60 .25
O85 A228 50c dull brown .50 .25

Nos. 611-617 Overprinted in Blue — e

Perf. 13x13½, 13½x13
O86 A229 1p dk brown .50 .25
O87 A229 1.50p dp green .60 .25
O88 A229 2p brt carmine .60 .25
O89 A229 3p indigo .60 .35

Size: 30x40mm
O90 A229 5p red brown 1.25 .80
O91 A228 10p red 10.00 7.00
O92 A229 20p green 100.00 90.00
Nos. O79-O92 (14) 117.15 100.65

No. 612 Overprinted in Blue — f
O93 A229 1.50p dp grn 3.00 1.50

Regular Issues of 1954-59 Variously Overprinted in Black or Blue

g

h

Perf. 13½, 13x13½, 13½x13
1955-61 Litho. Wmk. 90
O94 A237(c) 20c red (#629) .50 .25
O95 A237(d) 20c red (#629) .50 .25
O96 A237(d) 40c red, ovpt. 15mm (#630) .50 .25

Engr.
O97 A239(g) 50c bl (#632) .50 .25

Photo.
O98 A239(h) 1p brn (#635) .50 .25
O99 A239(e) 1p brn (Bl, #635) .50 .25
O100 A239(e) 1p brn (Bk, #635) .50 .25

Engr.
O101 A239(h) 3p vio brn (#638) .50 .25
O102 A240(h) 5p gray grn (#639) 1.00 .40
O103 A240(e) 10p yel grn (#640) 1.50 .50
O104 A240(f) 20p dl vio (#641) 3.00 2.00
O105 A240(h) 20p dl vio (#641) 1.50 .80
  a. Perf 13½ (#641a) 2.00 1.00
O106 A241(e) 50p ultra & ind (#642) 3.00 1.50
Nos. O94-O106 (13) 14.00 7.20

The overprints on Nos. O99-O100 & O103-O104 are horizontal; that on No. O106 is vertical. On No. O106 overprint measures 23mm.
Issued: No. O102, 1957; Nos. O97, O101, O103, O105, 1958; Nos. O98-O99, O104, 1959; No. O100, 1960; No. O106, 1961.

No. 659 Overprinted Type "d"
1957 Wmk. 90 Litho. Perf. 13
O108 A133 20c dl pur (ovpt. 15mm) .50 .25

Nos. 666, 658 and 663 Variously Overprinted
1957 Photo. Perf. 13x13½, 13½
O109 A261(g) 2p claret .50 .25
O110 A254(e) 2.40p brown .50 .30
O111 A258(c) 4.40p grnsh gray .50 .25
Nos. O109-O111 (3) 1.50 .80

Nos. 668, 685-687, 690-691, 693-705, 742, 742C and Types of 1959-65 Overprinted in Black, Blue or Red Types "e," "g," or

i

j

k

m

n

Lithographed; Photogravure

1960-68		**Perf. 13x13½, 13½**		
O112	A128(g)	5c buff (vert. ovpt.)	.50	.25
O113	A275(j)	10c sl grn	.50	.30
O114	A275(j)	20c dl red brn	1.00	.80
O115	A275(i)	50c bister	.50	.25
O116	A278(k)	1p brn	.60	.30
O117	A278(j)	1p brn, photo. (vert. ovpt.)	2.00	.25
O117A	A278(j)	1p brn, litho., (down)	10.00	2.00
O118	A276(j)	2p rose red	.50	.25
O119	A312(m)	2p dp grn	1.00	.25
O120	A312(j)	2p brt grn (up)	2.00	.30
O121	A312(j)	2p grn litho. (down)	2.00	1.00
O122	A277(e)	3p dk bl (horiz.)	.50	.25
O123	A277(j)	3p dk blue	30.00	10.00
O124	A276(j)	4p red, litho.	.50	.25
O125	A312(j)	4p rose red, litho. (down)	1.00	.25
O126	A277(e)	5p brn (Bl) (horiz.)	.80	.30
O127	A277(e)	5p brn (Bk) (horiz.)	.60	.25
O128	A277(j)	5p sepia	1.00	.25
O130	A276(j)	8p red	.50	.25
O131	A278(i)	10p lt red brn	.60	.25
O132	A276(j)	10p vermilion	1.00	.25
O133	A278(j)	10p brn car (up)	4.00	1.00
O133A	A278(j)	10p brn car (down)	90.00	30.00
O134	A278(m)	12p dk brn vio (horiz.)	.50	.25
O135	A278(k)	20p Prus grn	.60	.30
O136	A278(j)	20p Prus grn (up)	.60	.25
O137	A276(j)	20p red, litho.	.60	.30
O138	A276(m)	20p red, litho. (horiz.)	.80	.30
O139	A278(j)	23p grn (vert. ovpt.)	1.50	.50

O140	A278(j)	25p dp vio, photo. (R) (up)	2.50	.80
O141	A278(j)	25p pur, litho. (R) (down)	2.50	1.00
O142	A241(n)	50p dk blue	6.00	3.00
O143	A279(m)	100p bl (horiz. ovpt.)	4.00	2.00
O144	A279(m)	100p blue (up)	4.00	1.00
O145	A280(m)	300p dp violet (horiz.)	12.00	8.00
		Nos. O112-O133,O134-O145 (34)	96.70	36.95

The "m" overprint measures 15½mm on 2p; 14½mm on 12p, 100p and 300p; 13mm on 20p.

Issued: Nos. O122, O127, O135, 1961; Nos. O112-O114, O116, O118, 1962; No. O124, 1963; Nos. O119, O134, O143, 1964; Nos. O117, O125, O130, O139, O144, 1965; Nos. O120, O128, O132-O133, O136, O140, O142, O145, 1966; Nos. O121, O129, O137-O138, O141, 1967; No. O117A, 1968.

Nos. 699, 823-825, 827-829, and Type of 1962 Overprinted in Black or Red Types "j," "m," or "o"

o

Inscribed: "Republica Argentina"

Litho., Photo., Engr.

1964-67		**Wmk. 90**	**Perf. 13½**	
O149	A312(j)	6p rose red (down)	2.00	1.00
O153	A238a(m)	22p ultra	1.25	.50
O154	A238a(j)	43p dk car rose (down)	3.00	1.00
O155	A238a(j)	45p brn, photo. (up)	3.00	1.00
O156	A238a(j)	45p brn, litho. (up)	10.00	8.00
O157	A241(j)	50p dk bl (up) (R)	8.00	1.50
O158	A366(j)	90p ol bis (up)	10.00	8.00
O162	A495(o)	500p yel grn	25.00	20.00
		Nos. O149-O162 (8)	62.25	41.00

Issued: No. O153, 1964; No. O155, 1966; Nos. O149, O156-O162, 1967.

Type of 1959-67 Ovptd. Type "j"

1969	**Litho.**	**Wmk. 365**	**Perf. 13½**	
O163	A276	20p vermilion	1.00	.80

Beginning with No. 2001, many Argentine stamps are inscribed "Correo Official," but are not official stamps.

OFFICIAL DEPARTMENT STAMPS

Regular Issues of 1911-38 Overprinted in Black Ministry of Agriculture

No. OD1

1913		**Type I**	**Perf. 13½x12½**	
OD1	A88	2c choc (#181)	.50	.50
OD2	A88	1c ocher (#190)	.50	.50
OD3	A88	2c choc (#191)	.50	.50
OD4	A88	5c red (#194)	1.00	.50
a.		Perf. 13½ (#194a)	3.00	1.00
OD5	A88	12c dp bl (#196)	10.00	.50
a.		Perf. 13½ (#196a)	3.00	.50
		Nos. OD2-OD5 (4)	12.50	2.00

1915

No. OD9

OD6	A88	1c ocher (#208)	1.50	.50
OD7	A88	2c chocolate (#209)	1.00	.50
OD8	A88	5c red (#212)	2.00	.50
		Nos. OD6-OD8 (3)	4.50	1.50

1916			**Perf. 13½**	
OD9	A91	5c red (#220)	.50	.50

No. OD11   No. OD15

1918

OD10	A94	12c blue (#238)	3.00	.50
OD11	A93	1c buff (#249)	.50	.50
OD12	A93	2c brown (#250)	.50	.50
OD13	A93	5c red (#253)	.50	.50
OD14	A94	12c blue (#255)	.50	.50
OD15	A94	20c ultra (#256)	.50	.50
		Nos. OD10-OD15 (6)	5.50	3.00

1920		**Perf. 13½, 13½x12½ (OD16)**		
OD16	A93	1c buff (#265)	2.00	.50
OD17	A93	2c brown (#266A)	8.00	1.00
OD18	A93	5c red (#269A)	.70	.50
a.		Perf. 13½x12½ (#269)	1.40	.30
		Nos. OD16-OD18 (3)	10.70	2.00

1922			**Perf. 13½**	
OD19	A94	12c blue (#311)	4.00	.75
OD20	A94	20c ultra (#312)	75.00	

No. OD23

1923		**Perf. 13½x12½**		
OD21	A104	1c buff (#324)	2.00	.50
a.		Perf. 13½ (#324A)	10.00	10.00
OD22	A104	2c dk brn (#325)	.50	.50
OD23	A104	5c red (#328)	.50	.50
a.		Perf. 13½ (#328A)	2.00	.50
OD24	A104	12c deep blue (#330)	.80	.50
OD25	A104	20c ultra (#331)	.80	.50
a.		Perf. 13½ (#331A)	12.00	8.00
		Nos. OD21-OD25 (5)	4.60	2.50

1924

OD26	A104	1c buff (#341)	.50	.50
a.		Inverted ovpt.	20.00	15.00
OD27	A104	2c dk brn (#342)	.50	.50
OD29	A104	5c red (#345)	.50	.50
OD30	A104	10c dl grn (#346)	1.00	.50
OD31	A104	12c dp bl (#347)	.50	.50
OD32	A104	20c dp bl (#348)	.50	.50
a.		Inverted ovpt.	80.00	60.00
		Nos. OD26-OD32 (6)	3.50	3.00

No. OD34

1926				
OD34	A110	12c deep blue (#360)	.50	.50

No. OD28B

Type II

1931-36		**Perf. 13x13½, 13½x13**		
OD27B	A104	2c dk brn (#342)	10.00	6.00
OD28B	A104	3c green (#343)	.50	.50
OD29B	A104	5c red (#345)	.50	.50
OD30B	A104	10c dl grn (#346)	.50	.50
c.		Typo (coil) (#346a)	1.00	.50
OD32B	A104	20c ultra (#348)	1.00	.50
c.		Typo (coil) (#348a)	1.00	.25
OD33B	A104	30c claret (#351)	.50	.25
c.		Typo (coil) (#351a)	1.00	.50

No. OD46

1936-38			**Litho.**	
OD35	A129	1c buff (#419)	.50	.50
OD36	A130	2c dk brn (#420)	.50	.50
OD37	A132	3c green (#422)	1.00	.50
OD38	A134	5c yel brn (#427)	1.00	.50
OD40	A139	15c lt gray bl (#436)	5.00	1.00
OD41	A140	20c lt ultra (#437)	6.00	.50
OD42	A140	20c lt ultra (#438)	.80	.50
OD43	A141	25c car & pink (#441), perf. 13x13½	.50	.50
OD44	A142	30c org brn & yel brown (#442)	.50	.50
OD45	A145	1p brn blk & Lt bl (#445)	10.00	4.00
OD46	A146	1p brn blk & lt bl (#446)	3.00	.50
		Nos. OD35-OD46 (11)	28.80	9.50

		Typo.	**Perf. 13½**	
OD38A	A134	5c yel brn (#427)	1.00	.50
OD39A	A137	10c carmine (#430)	1.00	.50
b.		Perf. 13½x13 (#430a)	1.00	.50

Ministry of War

No. OD47

1913		**Type I**	**Perf. 13½x12½**	
OD47	A88	2c choc (#181)	.80	.50
OD48	A88	1c ocher (#190)	.50	.50
OD49	A88	2c choc (#191)	8.00	.50
a.		Perf. 13½ (#191a)	20.00	20.00
OD50	A88	5c red (#194)	1.00	.50
a.		Inverted ovpt.	50.00	—
OD51	A88	12c dp bl (#196)	.50	.50
a.		Perf. 13½ (#196a)	10.00	6.00
		Nos. OD48-OD51 (4)	10.00	2.00

1915

OD52	A88	1c ocher (#208)	60.00	12.00
OD53	A88	2c chocolate (#209)	4.00	.50
OD54	A88	5c red (#212)	8.00	.50
		Nos. OD52-OD54 (3)	72.00	13.00

1916			**Perf. 13½**	
OD55	A91	5c red (#220)	3.00	1.00
OD56	A92	12c blue (#222)	6.00	1.00

1918

OD57	A93	1c buff (#232)	2.00	.50
a.		Perf. 13½x12½ (#232B)	10.00	6.00
OD58	A93	2c brown (#233)	24.00	1.50
a.		Perf. 13½x12½ (#233B)	3.00	.50
OD59	A93	5c red (#236B) (Perf. 13½x12½)	1.50	.50
OD60	A94	12c blue (#238)	4.00	1.50
		Nos. OD57-OD60 (4)	31.50	4.00

1918

OD61	A93	1c buff (#249)	3.00	1.00
a.		Perf. 13½x12½ (#249B)	6.00	5.00
OD62	A93	2c brown (#250)	.50	.50
a.		Perf. 13½x12½ (#250B)	1.00	.50
OD63	A93	5c red (#253)	2.00	1.00
a.		Perf. 13½x12½ (#253B)	.50	.50
OD64	A94	12c blue (#255)	1.50	.50
OD65	A94	20c ultra (#256)	8.00	1.25
		Nos. OD61-OD65 (5)	15.00	4.25

1920

OD66	A93	2c brown (#266A)	12.00	6.00
a.		Perf. 13½x12½ (#266)	1.00	.50
OD67	A93	5c red (#269A)	10.00	6.00
a.		Perf. 13½x12½ (#269)	10.00	.50
OD68	A94	12c blue (#271)	2.00	.30
		Nos. OD66-OD68 (3)	24.00	12.30

1921

OD69	A94	12c blue (#299)	18.00	2.00

No. OD72

1922

OD70	A93	1c buff (#305)	5.00	.60
OD71	A93	2c brown		
		(13½x12½)		
		(#306B)	10.00	2.00
OD72	A103	5c red (#309)	5.00	1.00
OD73	A94	20c ultra (#312)	5.00	1.00
		Nos. OD70-OD73 (4)	22.00	4.10

Perf. 13½x12½

OD74	A93	2c brown (#318A)	10.00	2.00

1923   **Perf. 13½x12½**

OD75	A104	1c buff (#324)	1.50	.50
a.		Inverted ovpt.	20.00	18.00
b.		Perf. 13½ (#324A)	45.00	24.00
OD76	A104	2c dk brn (#325)	.50	.50
a.		Perf. 13½ (#325A)	2.00	.50
OD77	A104	5c red (#328)	1.00	.50
a.		Inverted ovpt.	20.00	18.00
b.		Perf. 13½ (#328A)	4.00	4.00
OD78	A104	12c dp bl (#330)	2.00	.50
OD79	A104	20c ultra (#331)	6.00	.50
a.		Perf. 13½ (#331A)	6.00	1.00
b.		As "a.," inverted ovpt.	20.00	18.00
		Nos. OD75-OD79 (5)	11.00	2.50

1924

OD80	A104	1c buff (#341)	10.00	3.00
OD81	A104	2c dk brn (#342)	1.00	.50
OD82	A104	3c green (#343)	2.00	.50
OD83	A104	5c red (#345)	.50	.50
OD84	A104	10c dl grn (#346)	6.00	.50
OD85	A104	20c ultra (#348)	.50	.50
OD86	A104	30c claret (#351)	10.00	1.00
OD87	A105	1p blue & red (#353)	10.00	2.00
		Nos. OD80-OD87 (8)	40.00	8.50

No. OD88

1926

OD88	A109	5c red (#359)	3.00	.50

No. OD82B

Type II

1931-36   **Perf. 13½x12½, 13 (OD87B)**

OD82B	A104	3c green (#343)	6.00	1.00
OD83B	A104	5c red (#345)	1.25	.50
c.		Inverted ovpt.	—	60.00
OD84B	A104	10c dl grn (#346)	1.00	.50
c.		Typo (coil) (346a)	5.00	1.00
OD85B	A104	20c ultra (#348)	1.00	.50
c.		Typo (coil) (#348a)	5.00	.50
OD86B	A104	30c claret (#351)	1.50	.50
c.		Typo (coil) (#351a)	2.00	.50
OD87B	A105	1p blue & red (#353)	10.00	2.00
		Nos. OD82B-OD87B (6)	20.75	5.00

No. OD90

1936-38   **Litho.**

OD89	A129	1c buff (#419)	.50	.50
OD90	A130	2c dk brn (#420)	.50	.50
OD91	A132	3c green (#422)	1.00	.50
OD92	A134	5c yel brn (#427)	.50	.50
OD93	A137	10c car (#430)	.50	.50
OD94	A139	15c slate bl (#434)	1.60	.50
OD95	A140	20c lt ultra (#437)	14.00	.50
OD96	A140	20c lt ultra (#438)	1.00	.50
OD97	A141	25c car & pink (#441)	.50	.50
OD98	A142	30c org brn & yel brown (#442)	.50	.50
OD99	A144	50c red & org (#444)	1.50	.50

OD100	A145	1p brn blk & lt bl (#445)	4.00	2.00
OD101	A146	1p brn blk & lt bl (#446)	2.00	1.00
		Nos. OD89-OD101 (13)	28.10	8.50

Typo.   **Perf. 13½**

OD92B	A134	5c yel brn (#427)	.50	.50
c.		Inverted ovpt.	20.00	15.00
OD93B	A137	10c car (#430)	.50	.50
c.		Inverted ovpt.	50.00	35.00
d.		Perf. 13½x13 (#430a)	2.00	1.00

Ministry of Finance

No. OD102

1913   **Type I**   **Perf. 13½x12½**

OD102	A88	2c choc (#181)	.50	.50
OD103	A88	1c ocher (#190)	.50	.50
OD104	A88	2c choc (#191)	.50	.50
OD105	A88	5c red (#194)	.50	.50
OD106	A88	12c dp bl (#196)	.50	.50
a.		Perf. 13½ (#196a)	180.00	35.00
		Nos. OD103-OD106 (4)	2.00	2.00

1915

OD107	A88	2c choc (#209)	.50	.50
OD108	A88	5c red (#212)	.50	.50

1916   **Perf. 13½**

OD109	A91	5c red (#220)	.70	.60

1917

OD110	A93	2c brown (#233)	.50	.50
OD111	A93	5c red (#236)	8.00	1.00
OD112	A94	12c blue (#238)	.50	.50
		Nos. OD110-OD112 (3)	9.00	2.00

1918

OD113	A93	2c brown (#250)		100.00
OD114	A93	5c red (#253)	.70	.50
a.		Perf. 13½x12½ (#253B)	4.00	.50
OD115	A94	12c blue (#255)	.70	.50
OD116	A94	20c ultra (#256)	2.00	1.00
		Nos. OD113-OD116 (4)	3.40	102.00

1920

OD117	A93	1c buff (#265)	6.00	3.00
OD118	A93	2c brown (#266)	9.00	5.00
OD119	A93	5c #269	20.00	12.00
a.		Perf. 13½ (#269A)	3.00	1.00
OD120	A94	12c blue (#271) (perf. 13½)	3.00	1.00
		Nos. OD117-OD120 (4)	38.00	21.00

1922

OD121	A94	20c ultra (#312)	60.00	15.00

1923   **Perf. 13½x12½, 13½**

OD122	A104	1c buff (#324)	20.00	10.00
a.		Perf. 13½ (#324A)	10.00	6.00
OD123	A104	2c dk brn (#325)	.50	.50
a.		Perf. 13½ (#325A)	—	12.00
OD124	A104	5c red (#328)	.50	.50
a.		Inverted ovpt.	—	35.00
b.		Perf. 13½ (#328A)	2.00	1.00
OD125	A104	12c dp bl (#330)	.70	.50
a.		Perf. 13½ (#330A)	5.00	1.00
OD126	A104	20c ultra (#331)	.50	.50
a.		Perf. 13½ (#331A)	10.00	4.00
		Nos. OD122-OD126 (5)	22.20	12.00

1924   **Perf. 13½x12½**

OD127	A104	2c dk brn (#342)	250.00	250.00
OD128	A104	5c red (#345)	2.00	.50
OD130	A104	12c dp bl (#347)	80.00	35.00
OD131	A104	20c ultra (#348)	.50	.50
		Nos. OD127-OD131 (4)	332.50	286.00

1926

OD134	A110	12c dp bl (#360)	60.00	25.00

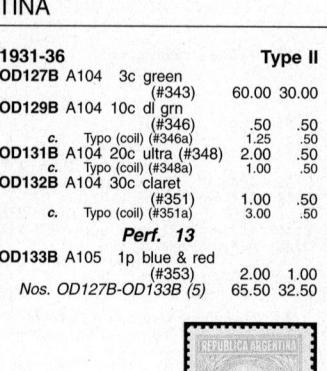

No. OD129B   No. OD133B

1931-36   **Type II**

OD127B	A104	3c green (#343)	60.00	30.00
OD129B	A104	10c dl grn (#346)	.50	.50
c.		Typo (coil) (#346a)	1.25	.50
OD131B	A104	20c ultra (#348)	2.00	.50
c.		Typo (coil) (#348a)	1.00	.50
OD132B	A104	30c claret (#351)	1.00	1.00
c.		Typo (coil) (#351a)	3.00	.50

Perf. 13

OD133B	A105	1p blue & red (#353)	2.00	1.00
		Nos. OD127B-OD133B (5)	65.50	32.50

No. OD135

1936-38   **Litho.**   **Perf. 13½x13**

OD135	A129	1c buff (#419)	.50	.50
OD136	A130	2c dk brn (#420)	.50	.50
OD137	A132	3c green (#422)	1.50	1.00
OD138	A134	5c yel brn (Perf. 13½) (#427d)	.50	.50
OD139	A137	10c car (#430)	.50	.50
OD140	A139	15c slate blue (#434) ('36)	6.00	1.60
a.		Inverted ovpt.	—	80.00
OD141	A140	20c lt ultra (#437)	5.00	1.00
OD142	A140	20c lt ultra (#438)	.50	.50
OD143	A142	30c org brn & yel brown (#442)	.50	.50
OD144	A145	1p brn blk & lt bl (#445)	10.00	3.00
OD145	A146	1p brn blk & lt bl (#446)	1.20	.80
		Nos. OD135-OD145 (11)	26.70	9.90

Typo.   **Perf. 13½**

OD138A	A134	5c yel brn (#427)	.50	.50
b.		Inverted ovpt.	50.00	50.00
OD139A	A137	10c car (#430)	2.00	.50
b.		Perf. 13½x13 (#430a)	40.00	1.00

Ministry of the Interior

No. OD147

1913   **Type I**   **Perf. 13½x12½**

OD146	A88	2c choc (#181)	2.00	.50
OD147	A88	1c ocher (#190)	.50	.50
OD148	A88	2c choc (#191)	5.00	2.00
OD149	A88	5c red (#194)	3.00	.50
OD150	A88	12c dp bl (#196)	2.50	.50
a.		Perf. 13½ (#196a)	10.00	3.00
		Nos. OD146-OD150 (5)	13.00	4.00

1915

OD151	A88	2c chocolate (#209)	4.00	1.20
OD152	A88	5c red (#212)	4.00	1.20

1916   **Perf. 13½**

OD153	A91	5c red (#220)	4.00	1.60

1918

OD154	A93	5c red (#236B)	10.00	1.00
OD155	A93	2c brown (#250)	.50	.50
OD156	A93	5c red (#253)	.70	.50
a.		Perf. 13½x12½ (#253B)	2.00	.50
		Nos. OD154-OD156 (3)	11.20	2.00

1920

OD157	A93	1c buff (13½x12½) (#265)	10.00	3.00
OD158	A93	5c red (#269)	10.00	2.00

1922   **Perf. 13½**

OD160	A103	5c red (#309)	20.00	8.00
OD161	A94	12c blue (#311)	5.00	1.00
OD162	A94	20c ultra (#312)	2.00	.50
		Nos. OD160-OD162 (3)	27.00	9.50

1923   **Perf. 13½x12½**

OD163	A104	1c buff (#324)	6.00	1.00
a.		Perf. 13½ (#324A)	4.00	2.00

OD164	A104	2c dark brown (#325)	.50	.50
a.		Perf. 13½ (#325A)	50.00	30.00
OD165	A104	5c red (#328)	1.20	.50
a.		Perf. 13½ (#328A)	10.00	1.00
OD166	A104	12c deep blue (#330)	12.00	4.00
a.		Perf. 13½ (#330A)	45.00	20.00
OD167	A104	20c ultra (#331)	20.00	2.00
a.		Perf. 13½ (#331A)	20.00	10.00
		Nos. OD163-OD167 (5)	39.70	8.00

1924

OD168	A104	1c buff (#341)	.50	.50
OD169	A104	2c dk brn (#342)	1.00	.50
OD170	A104	3c green (#343)	8.00	2.00
OD171	A104	5c red (#345)	1.00	.50
OD173	A104	12c dp bl (#347)	1.00	.50
OD174	A104	20c ultra (#348)	20.00	8.00
		Nos. OD168-OD174 (6)	31.50	12.00

No. OD172B

Type II

1931-36   **Perf. 13½x12½**

OD170B	A104	3c green (#343)	2.00	2.00
OD171B	A104	5c red (#345)	.75	.50
OD172B	A104	10c dull green (#346)	1.00	.50
c.		Typo (coil) (#346a)	.50	.50
OD174B	A104	20c ultra (#348)	2.00	1.00
c.		Typo (coil) (#348a)	2.00	1.00
OD175B	A104	30c claret (#351)	6.00	1.00
c.		Typo (coil) (#351a)	16.00	5.00
		Nos. OD170B-OD175B (5)	11.75	5.00

No. OD182A

1936-38   **Litho.**   **Perf. 13½x13**

OD176	A129	1c buff (#419)	.50	.50
OD177	A130	2c dk brn (#420)	.50	.50
OD178	A132	3c green (#422)	1.00	.50
OD178A	A134	5c yel brn (#427d)	.50	.50
OD180	A139	15c slate bl (#434) ('36)	1.40	.50
OD181	A140	20c lt ultra (#437)	6.00	1.00
OD182	A140	20c lt ultra (#438)	1.00	.50
OD182A	A142	30c org brn & yel brown (#442)	.50	.50
OD182B	A145	1p brn blk & lt blue (#445)	10.00	6.00
OD182C	A146	1p brn blk & lt bl (#446) ('37)	1.25	1.00
		Nos. OD176-OD182C (10)	22.65	11.00

Typo.   **Perf. 13½**

OD178D	A134	5c yel brn (#427)	1.25	.50
e.		Inverted ovpt.		75.00
OD179D	A137	10c car (#430)	1.60	.50
e.		Perf. 13½x13 (#430a)	1.25	.75

Ministry of Justice and Instruction

No. OD184

1913   **Type I**   **Perf. 13½x12½**

OD183	A88	2c choc (#181)	6.00	2.00
OD184	A88	1c ocher (#190)	8.00	1.00
OD185	A88	2c choc (#191)	6.00	1.00
a.		Perf. 13½ (#191a)	—	30.00
OD186	A88	5c red (#194)	2.00	.50
OD187	A88	12c dp bl (#196)	3.00	.50
		Nos. OD184-OD187 (4)	19.00	3.00

1915
OD188 A88 1c ocher (#208) 2.00 1.00
OD189 A88 2c chocolate (#209) 2.00 .50
OD190 A88 5c red (#212) 6.00 .80
Nos. OD188-OD190 (3) 10.00 2.30

1916 Perf. 13½
OD191 A91 5c red (#220) 3.00 .50
OD192 A92 12c blue (#222) 4.00 1.60

1918
OD193 A93 1c buff (#232) 3.00 1.00
  a. Perf. 13½x12½ (#232) 2.00 1.00
OD194 A93 2c brown (#233) 8.00 8.00
  a. Perf. 13½x12½ (#233B) 4.00 1.00
OD195 A93 5c red (#236) 20.00 2.00
  a. Perf. 13½x12½ (#236B) 10.00 1.00
OD196 A94 12c blue (#238) 90.00 20.00
Nos. OD193-OD196 (4) 121.00 31.00

OD197 A93 1c buff (#249) .60 .50
  a. Perf. 13½x12½ (#249B) 200.00 14.00
OD198 A93 2c brown (#250) .50 .50
  a. Perf. 13½x12½ (#250B) 1.00 .50
OD199 A93 5c red (#253) .50 .50
  a. Perf. 13½x12½ (#253B) 1.00 .50
OD200 A94 12c blue (#255) .50 .50
OD201 A94 20c ultra (#256) 2.00 1.00
Nos. OD197-OD201 (5) 4.10 3.00

1920 Perf. 13½x12½
OD202 A93 1c buff (#265) 1.50 1.00
OD203 A93 2c brown (#266) 1.00 .50
OD204 A93 5c red (#269) 1.00 .50
  a. Perf. 13½ (#269A) 16.00 8.00
OD205 A94 12c blue (perf. 13½) (#271) 2.00 1.00
Nos. OD202-OD205 (4) 5.50 3.00

1922 Perf. 13½
OD206 A93 1c buff (#305) 6.00 2.00
  a. (#305B) 1.50 .50
OD207 A93 2c brown, (perf. 13½x12½) (#306B) 8.00 2.00
OD208 A103 5c red (#309) 1.50 .50
  a. Perf. 13½x12½ (#309B) 1.00 .50
OD209 A94 12c blue (#311) 50.00 16.00
OD210 A94 20c ultra (#312) 8.00 1.25
Nos. OD206-OD210 (5) 73.50 21.75

1922 Perf. 13½x12½
OD211 A93 2c brown (#318A) 7.00 2.00

1923
OD212 A104 1c buff (#324) 1.25 .50
  a. Perf. 13½ (#324A) 2.50 1.00
OD213 A104 2c dk brn (#325) 1.00 .50
  a. Perf. 13½ (#325A) 2.00 1.00
  b. As "a," inverted ovpt. 25.00 20.00
OD214 A104 5c red (#328) 1.00 .50
  a. Perf. 13½ (#328A) 2.00 1.00
OD215 A104 12c dp bl (#330) .50 .50
OD216 A104 20c ultra (#331) 1.00 .50
  a. Perf. 13½ (#331A) 2.00 1.00
Nos. OD212-OD216 (5) 4.25 2.50

1924
OD218 A104 1c buff (#341) .50 .50
OD219 A104 2c dk brn (#342) .50 .50
OD220 A104 3c green (#343) .60 .50
OD221 A104 5c red (#345) 2.00 2.00
OD222 A104 10c dl grn (#346) 5.00 2.00
OD223 A104 12c dp bl (#347) .50 .50
OD224 A104 20c ultra (#348) .50 .50
Nos. OD218-OD224 (7) 9.60 6.50

1926
OD227 A109 5c red (#359) .75 .50
  a. Inverted ovpt. 35.00 30.00
OD228 A110 12c dp bl (#360) 1.00 .50

No. OD217B

Type II
1931-36 Perf. 13½x12½, 13
OD217B A104 ½c red vio (#340) 10.00 6.00
OD218B A104 1c buff (#341) 1.00 .50
OD220B A104 3c green (#343) .50 .50
  c. Typo (coil) (#343b) .50 .50
OD221B A104 5c red (#345) 2.00 2.00
OD222B A104 10c dl grn (#346) .80 .50
  c. Typo (coil) (#346a) 1.00 1.00
OD223B A104 12c dp bl (#347) 6.00 .60
OD224B A104 20c ultra (#348) .50 .50
  c. Typo (coil) (#348a) .50 .50
OD225B A104 30c claret (#351) .50 .50
  c. Typo (coil) (#351a) 2.50 1.00

OD226B A105 1p blue & red (Perf. 13½) (#353) 2.00 1.25
Nos. OD217B-OD226B (9) 23.30 12.85

No. OD229

1936-38 Perf. 13½x13
OD229 A129 1c buff (#419) .50 .50
OD230 A130 2c dk brn (#420) .50 .50
OD231 A132 3c green (#422) .50 .50
OD232 A134 5c yel brn (#427d) .50 .50
OD234 A139 15c slate bl (#434) 2.00 1.00
OD234A A140 20c lt ultra (#437) .50 .50
OD234B A140 20c lt ultra (#438) .60 .50
OD234C A141 25c car & pink (#441) .50 .50
OD234D A142 30c org brn & yel brn (#442) 1.00 .50
OD234E A145 1p brn blk &l lt bl (#445) 6.00 3.00
OD234F A146 1p brn blk &l lt bl (#446) 6.00 2.00
Nos. OD229-OD234F (11) 18.60 10.00

Typo. Perf. 13½
OD232A A134 5c yel brn (#427) .50 .50
OD233 A137 10c car (#430) .50 .50
  a. Perf. 13½x13 (#430a) .50 .50

Ministry of Marine

No. OD236

1913 Type I Perf. 13½x12½
OD235 A88 2c choc (#181) 1.25 .50
  a. Perf. 13½ (#181a) 150.00 75.00
OD236 A88 1c ocher (#190) .50 .50
OD237 A88 2c choc (#191) 24.00 .50
OD238 A88 5c red (#194) 3.00 .50
  a. Perf. 13½ (#194a) 80.00 16.00
OD239 A88 12c dp bl (#196) .60 .50
Nos. OD236-OD239 (4) 28.10 2.00

1915
OD240 A88 2c chocolate (#209) 6.00 .50
OD241 A88 5c red (#212) 6.00 .50

1918
OD242 A93 1c buff (#232) .70 .50
OD243 A93 2c brown (#233) .70 .50
OD244 A93 5c red (#236) 1.40 .50
  a. Perf. 13½ (#236B) 4.00 1.00
Nos. OD242-OD244 (3) 2.80 1.50

1920 Perf. 13½
OD245 A93 1c buff (#249) .50 .50
OD246 A93 2c brown (#250) .70 .50
  a. Perf. 13½x12½ (#250) 6.00 2.00
OD247 A93 5c red (#253) 7.00 .50
  a. Perf. 13½x12½ (#253B) .60 .50
OD248 A94 12c blue (#255) 2.50 .60
OD249 A94 20c ultra (#256) 16.00 3.00
Nos. OD245-OD249 (5) 26.70 5.10

1920
OD250 A93 1c buff (#265A) (perf. 13½x12½) .50 .50
OD251 A93 2c brown (#266A) .70 .50
  a. Perf. 13½x12½ (#266) .80 .50
OD252 A93 5c red (#269A) .80 .50
Nos. OD250-OD252 (3) 2.00 1.50

1922
OD253 A103 5c red (#309) 10.00 2.00
  a. Perf. 13½x12½ (#309B) 3.00 .60
OD254 A94 12c blue (#311) 60.00 20.00
OD255 A94 20c ultra (#312) 90.00 16.00
Nos. OD253-OD255 (3) 160.00 38.00

1923 Perf. 13½x12½
OD256 A104 1c buff (#324) .50 .50
  a. Perf. 13½ (#324A) 150.00 60.00

OD257 A104 2c dk brn (#325) 2.00 .50
  a. Inverted overprint — 75.00
  b. Perf. 13½ (#325A) 24.00 2.00
OD258 A104 5c red (#328) 5.00 .50
  a. Inverted overprint — 75.00
  b. Perf. 13½ (#328A) 30.00 5.00
  c. As "b," inverted overprint — 75.00
OD259 A104 12c deep blue (#330) 2.50 .50
  a. Perf. 13½ (#330A) 36.00 4.00
OD260 A104 20c ultra (#331) 3.00 .50
  a. Perf. 13½ (#331A) 16.00 2.00
Nos. OD256-OD260 (5) 13.00 2.50

1924
OD261 A104 1c buff (#341) 10.00 2.50
OD262 A104 2c dk brn (#342) .50 .50
OD264 A104 5c red (#345) .50 .50
OD266 A104 20c ultra (#348) 16.00 .50
Nos. OD261-OD266 (4) 27.00 4.50

1926
OD269 A109 5c red (#359) .50 .25

No. OD264B

Type II
1931-36 Perf. 13½x12½, 13
OD263B A104 3c grn (#343) 20.00 1.60
OD264B A104 5c red (#345) 3.00 .50
OD265B A104 10c dl grn (#346) 10.00 2.00
  c. Typo (coil) (#346a) 2.00 .50
OD266B A104 20c ultra (#348) 20.00 2.00
  c. Typo (coil) (#348a) 10.00 1.00
OD267B A104 30c claret (#351) 8.00 1.60
OD268B A105 1p blue & red (Perf. 13½) (#353) 120.00 60.00

No. OD270

1936-38 Perf. 13½x13
OD270 A129 1c buff (#419) 1.00 .50
OD271 A130 2c dk brn (#420) .50 .50
OD272 A132 3c green (#422) 1.00 1.00
OD273 A134 5c yel brn (#427d) .50 .50
OD275 A139 15c slate bl (#434) ('36) 2.50 .60
OD276 A140 20c lt ultra (#437) 4.00 1.00
OD277 A140 20c lt ultra (#438) 2.00 .50
OD278 A142 30c org brn & yel brn (#442) ('36) 1.50 .50
OD279 A145 1p brn blk & lt bl (#445) ('36) 24.00 16.00
OD280 A146 1p brn blk & lt bl (#446) ('37) 16.00 4.00
Nos. OD270-OD280 (10) 53.00 25.10

Typo. Perf. 13½
OD273A A134 5c yel brn (#427) 1.00 .60
  b. Inverted overprint 25.00 25.00
OD274A A137 10c car (#430) 4.00 .50
  b. Perf. 13½x13 (#430a) 1.50 .75

Ministry of Public Works

No. OD281

1913 Type I Perf. 13½x12½
OD281 A88 2c choc (#181) 4.00 .50
  a. Perf. 13½ (#181a) 25.00 4.00
OD282 A88 1c ocher (#190) 2.00 .50
OD283 A88 5c red (#194) 3.00 .50

OD284 A88 12c dp bl (#196) 20.00 8.00
  a. Perf. 13½ (#196a) 15.00 6.00
Nos. OD282-OD284 (3) 25.00 9.00

1916 Perf. 13½
OD285 A91 5c red (#220) 70.00 20.00

1918 Perf. 13½x12½
OD286 A93 2c brown (#233) 30.00 20.00
OD287 A93 5c red (#236) 18.00 9.00

1920 Perf. 13½
OD288 A93 2c brown (#266) 35.00 8.00
OD289 A93 5c red (#269) 20.00 2.00
OD290 A94 12c blue (#271) 50.00 20.00
Nos. OD288-OD290 (3) 105.00 30.00

1923 Perf. 13½x12½
OD291 A104 1c buff (#324) .60 .50
  a. Perf. 13½ (#324A) 40.00 15.00
OD292 A104 2c dk brn (#325) .50 .50
  a. Perf. 13½ (#325A) 2.00 2.00
OD293 A104 5c red (#328) 4.00 1.00
  a. Perf. 13½ (#328A) 6.00 2.00
OD294 A104 12c dp bl (#330) 4.00 2.00
  a. Perf. 13½ (#330A) 4.00 1.00
OD295 A104 20c ultra #331 4.00 .60
  a. Perf. 13½ (#331A) 16.00 1.25
Nos. OD291-OD295 (5) 13.10 4.60

1924
OD296 A104 1c buff (#341) .50 .50
OD297 A104 2c dk brn (#342) .50 .50
OD299 A104 5c red (#345) .50 .50
OD301 A104 12c dp bl (#347) 60.00 20.00
OD302 A104 20c ultra (#348) .50 .50
Nos. OD296-OD302 (5) 62.00 22.00

1926
OD305 A109 5c red (#359) .60 .25

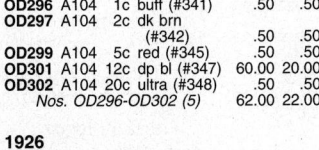
No. OD299B

Type II
1931-36 Perf. 13½x12½, 13
OD298B A104 3c grn (#343) .50 .50
  c. Typo (coil) (#343b) — 40.00
OD299B A104 5c red (#345) .60 .50
OD300B A104 10c dl grn (#346) .60 .50
  c. Typo (coil) (#346a) 4.00 .50
OD301B A104 20c ultra typo (coil) (#348b) 50.00 10.00
OD303B A104 30c claret (#351) 1.80 .50
OD304B A105 1p blue & red (13½) (#353) 200.00 —
Nos. OD298B-OD304B (6) 253.50 12.00

No. OD307

1936-38 Perf. 13½x13
OD306 A129 1c buff (#419) .50 .50
OD307 A130 2c dk brn (#420) .60 .50
OD308 A132 3c green (#422) 2.00 .50
OD309 A134 5c yel brn (#427d) 1.00 .50
OD311 A139 15c slate bl (#434) 3.00 1.00
OD312 A140 20c lt ultra (#437) 6.00 .50
OD313 A140 20c lt ultra (#438) 1.00 .50
OD314 A142 30c org brn & yel brn (#442) ('36) .60 .50
OD315 A144 50c red & org (#444) ('36) 5.00 5.00
OD316 A145 1p brn blk & lt bl (#445) ('36) 10.00 6.00
OD317 A146 1p brn blk & lt bl (#446) ('37) 2.00 1.00
Nos. OD306-OD317 (11) 31.70 16.50

Typo. Perf. 13½
OD309A A134 5c yel brn (#427) 1.25 .50
  b. Inverted overprint — 75.00
OD310 A137 10c car (#430) 4.00 .50
  a. Perf. 13½x13 (#430a) 2.00 .50

Ministry of Foreign Affairs and Religion

No. OD318

1913   **Type I**   *Perf. 13½x12½*
OD318	A88	2c choc (#181)	90.00	20.00
OD319	A88	1c ocher (#190)	.50	.50
OD320	A88	2c choc (#191)	.50	.50
OD321	A88	5c red (#194)	3.00	1.00
OD322	A88	12c dp bl (#196)	1.25	.50
a.		Perf. 13½ (#196a)	100.00	40.00
		Nos. OD319-OD322 (4)	5.25	2.50

1915
OD323	A88	5c red (#212)	3.00	1.75

1916   *Perf. 13½*
OD324	A91	5c red (#220)	2.50	.50

1918
OD325	A94	20c ultra (#256)	20.00	8.00

1922
OD326	A93	1c buff, perf. 13½x12½ (#265)	3.00	1.00
OD327	A93	5c red (#269)	1.25	.60

1922-23   *Perf. 13½x12½*
OD328	A93	2c brn (#306)	80.00	30.00
OD329	A103	5c red (#309B)	100.00	

    Perf. 13½
OD330	A93	12c blue (#311)	100.00	
OD330A	A94	20c ultra (#312)	100.00	

1923   *Perf. 13½x12½*
OD331	A104	1c buff (#324)	.80	.50
a.		Perf. 13½ (#324A)	25.00	10.00
OD332	A104	2c dk brn (#325)	1.00	.60
a.		Perf. 13½ (#325A)	25.00	16.00
OD333	A104	5c red (#328)	.50	.50
a.		Perf. 13½ (#328A)	6.00	2.00
OD334	A104	12c dp bl (#330)	.50	.50
a.		Perf. 13½ (#330A)	5.00	2.00
OD335	A104	20c ultra (#331)	.50	.50
		Nos. OD331-OD335 (5)	3.30	2.60

No. OD344

1924
OD337	A104	1c buff (#341)	.60	.50
OD338	A104	2c dk brn (#342)	.50	.50
OD339	A104	3c green (#343)	.50	.50
OD340	A104	5c red (#345)	.50	.50
OD341	A104	10c dl grn (#346)	8.00	1.00
OD342	A104	12c dp bl (#347)	.60	.50
OD343	A104	20c ultra (#348)	.60	.50
OD344	A104	30c claret (#351)	4.00	2.00
		Nos. OD337-OD344 (8)	15.30	6.00

1926
OD346	A110	12c dp bl (#360)	.50	.60

Type II
1931-36   *Perf. 13½x12½, 13½*
OD336B	A104	½c red vio (#340)	10.00	5.00
OD341B	A104	10c dl grn (#346)	.60	.60
OD343B	A104	20c ultra (typo, coil) (#348a)	.60	.60
OD344B	A104	30c claret (typo, coil) (#351a)	.60	.60
OD345B	A105	1p blue & red, perf. 13½ (#353)	1.50	1.00
		Nos. OD336B-OD345B (5)	13.30	7.80

No. OD347

1935-37   **Typo.**   *Perf. 13x13½*
OD347	A129	1c buff (#419)	.50	.50
OD348	A130	2c dk brn (#420)	.50	.50
OD349	A132	3c green (#422)	.50	.50
OD350	A134	5c yel brn (#427d)	.50	.50
OD352	A139	15c slate bl (#434)	.70	.50
OD353	A140	20c lt ultra (#437)	1.00	.50
OD354	A140	20c lt ultra (#438)	.50	.50
OD355	A142	30c org brn & yel brn (#442)	.50	.50
OD356	A145	1p brn blk & lt bl (#445)	20.00	10.00
OD357	A146	1p brn blk & lt bl (#446)	1.50	1.00
		Nos. OD347-OD357 (10)	26.20	15.00

    Typo.   *Perf. 13½*
OD350B	A134	5c yel brn (#427)	.60	.50
OD351B	A137	10c car (#430)	.50	.50
c.		Perf. 13½x13 (#430a)	4.00	.50

PARCEL POST STAMPS

PP1

Postal Service Headquarters, Buenos Aires — PP2

2001   **Litho.**   *Serpentine Die Cut 11*
Self-Adhesive
Q1	PP1	1p red & black	20.00	20.00

    Die Cut
Q1A	PP1	1p red & black	40.00	20.00
Q2	PP2	7p blue & black	27.50	20.00
Q3	PP2	11p brown & black	40.00	30.00
		Nos. Q1-Q3 (3)	87.50	70.00

Nos. Q1-Q3 were sold only at Unidas Postal outlets. No. Q3 is inscribed "Caja Envio 2."

Stamps of Type PP2 lacking "U.P." in denominations of 7p, 11p, 16p, and 23p were issued in 1999, but were applied by postal workers to packages brought to post offices by customers with large mailings (Grandes Clientes). These stamps were not to be sold to any customers purchasing them. Value, unused $160.

The same sale and use restrictions applied to four other non-denominated stamps for use by "Grandes Clientes," which are inscribed "Caja Normalizada," have blue, brown-violet, gray-green, and ocher frames, and were issued in 1995. Value, set unused $550.

Nos. Q2 and Q3, though inscribed "Grandes Clientes," apparently were available for purchase by any customers, at Unidas Postal outlets.

BUENOS AIRES

The central point of the Argentine struggle for independence. At intervals Buenos Aires maintained an independent government but after 1862 became a province of the Argentine Republic.

8 Reales = 1 Peso

Values of Buenos Aires Nos. 1-8 vary according to condition. Quotations are for fine examples. Very fine to superb specimens sell at much higher prices, and inferior or poor stamps sell at reduced values, depending on the condition of the individual specimen.

Nos. 1-8 are normally found without gum, and the values below are for such items. Examples with original gum sell for higher prices.

Steamship — A1

1858   **Unwmk.**   **Typo.**   *Imperf.*
1	A1	1 (in) pesos lt brn	500.00	300.
a.		Double impression		700.
2	A1	2 (dos) pesos blue	300.00	150.
b.		Diag. half used as 1p on cover		7,500.
3	A1	3 (tres) pesos grn	1,500.	950.
a.		3p dark green	2,000.	1,500.
4	A1	4 (cuatro) pesos ver	5,000.	4,500.
a.		Half used as 2p on cover		25,000.
b.		4p chestnut brown (error)	30,000.	40,000.
5	A1	5 (cinco) pesos org	5,000.	3,000.
a		5p ocher	5,000.	3,000.
b.		5p olive yellow	5,000.	3,000.

Issued: Nos. 2-5, Apr. 29; No. 1, Oct. 26.

1858, Oct. 26
6	A1	4 (cuatro) reales brown	350.00	300.
a.		4r gray brown	400.00	300.
b.		4r chestnut	350.00	300.

1859, Jan. 1
7	A1	1 (in) pesos blue	200.	100.
a.		1p indigo	300.	150.
b.		Impression on reverse of stamp in blue	28,500.	
c.		Double impression	2,800.	700.
d.		Vert. tête-bêche pair	675,000.	
e.		Horiz. tête-bêche pair	—	
f.		Half used as 4r on cover		7,500.
8	A1	1 (to) pesos blue	600.	325.

No. 7e is valued with faults.

Nos. 1, 2, 3 and 7 have been reprinted on very thick, hand-made paper. The same four stamps and No. 8 have been reprinted on thin, hard, white wove paper.

Counterfeits of Nos. 1-8 are plentiful.

Liberty Head — A2

1859, Sept. 3
9	A2	4r green, *bluish*	400.00	275.00
10	A2	1p blue, fine impression	40.00	30.00
d.		Double impression	600.00	400.00
e.		Partial double impression	325.00	175.00
11	A2	2p vermilion, fine impression	500.00	300.00
a.		2p red, blurred impression	375.00	125.00
b.		Vert. half used as 1p on cover		4,000.

Both fine and blurred impressions of these stamps may be found. They have generally been called Paris and Local prints, respectively, but the opinion now obtains that the differences are due to the impression and that they do not represent separate issues. Values are for fine impressions. Rough or blurred impressions sell for less.

Many shades exist of Nos. 1-11.

1862, Oct. 4
12	A2	1p rose	350.00	150.00
13	A2	2p blue	350.00	90.00

All three values have been reprinted in black, brownish black, blue and red brown on thin hard white paper. The 4r has also been reprinted in green on bluish paper.

Values are for fine impressions. Rough or blurred impressions sell for less.

No. 13 exists with papermaker's wmk.

CORDOBA

A province in the central part of the Argentine Republic.

100 Centavos = 1 Peso

Arms of Cordoba — A1

Unwmk.
1858, Oct. 28   **Litho.**   *Imperf.*
Laid Paper
1	A1	5c blue	150.
2	A1	10c black	3,000.

Cordoba stamps were printed on laid paper, but stamps from edges of the sheets sometimes do not show any laid lines and appear to be on wove paper. Counterfeits are plentiful.

CORRIENTES

The northeast province of the Argentine Republic.

1 Real M(oneda) C(orriente) = 12½ Centavos M.C. = 50 Centavos
100 Centavos Fuertes = 1 Peso Fuerte

Nos. 1-2 were issued without gum. Nos. 3-8 were issued both with and without gum (values the same).

Ceres — A1

Unwmk.
1856, Aug. 21   **Typo.**   *Imperf.*
1	A1	1r black, *blue*	100.00	40.00

No. 1 used is valued with pen cancellation.

Pen Stroke Through "Un Real"
1860, Feb. 8
2	A1	(3c) black, *blue*	600.00	120.00

No. 2 used is valued with pen cancellation.

Ceres — A2

1860-80
3	A2	(3c) black, *blue*	9.50	30.00
4	A2	(2c) blk, yel grn ('64)	50.00	100.00
a.		(2c) black, *blue green*	92.50	150.00
5	A2	(2c) blk, yel ('67)	7.50	19.00
6	A2	(3c) blk, dk bl ('71)	3.00	19.00
7	A2	(3c) blk, rose red ('76)	150.00	70.00
a.		(3c) black, lil rose ('75)	200.00	100.00
8	A2	(3c) blk, dk rose ('79)	8.00	35.00
a.		(3c) black, red vio ('77)	75.00	50.00
		Nos. 3-8 (6)	228.00	273.00

Pen canceled examples of Nos. 3-8 that do not indicate the town of origin sell for much less.

Printed from settings of 8 varieties, 3 or 4 impressions constituting a sheet. Some impressions were printed inverted and tete beche pairs may be cut from adjacent impressions.

From Jan. 1 to Feb. 24, 1864, No. 4 was used as a 5 centavos stamp but examples so used can only be distinguished when they bear dated cancellations.

The reprints show numerous spots and small defects which are not found on the originals. They are printed on gray blue, dull blue, gray green, dull orange and light magenta papers.

ARMENIA

är-'mē-nē-ə

LOCATION — South of Russia bounded by Georgia, Azerbaijan, Iran and Turkey
GOVT. — Republic
AREA — 11,490 sq. mi.
POP. — 3,409,234 (est. 1999)
CAPITAL — Yerevan

With Azerbaijan and Georgia, Armenia made up the Transcaucasian Federation of Soviet Republics.

Stamps of Armenia were replaced in 1923 by those of Transcaucasian Federated Republics.

With the breakup of the Soviet Union on Dec. 26, 1991, Armenia and ten former Soviet republics established the Commonwealth of Independent States.

100 Kopecks = 1 Ruble
100 Luma = 1 Dram (1993)

Catalogue values for unused stamps in this country are for Never Hinged items, beginning with Scott 430 in the regular postage section.

Counterfeits abound of all Armenian stamps through Scott 390, both of the basic stamps and of overprinted and surcharged stamps.

Watermark

Wmk. 171 — Diamonds

Perforations
Perforations are the same as the basic Russian stamps.

National Republic
Russian Stamps of 1902-19
Handstamped

At least thirteen types exist of both framed and unframed overprints ("a" and "c"). The device is the Armenian "H," initial of Hayasdan (Armenia). Inverted and double overprints are found.

Surcharged

Type I — Without periods (two types).
Type II — Periods after 1st "K" and "60."

Black Surcharge

1919		**Unwmk.**	**Perf. 14x14½**	
1	A14	60k on 1k orange (II)	2.00	5.00
a.		Imperf. (I)	2.00	5.00
b.		Imperf. (II)	2.00	3.00

Violet Surcharge

2	A14	60k on 1k orange (II)	5.00	5.00

Handstamped in Violet
a

6	A15	4k carmine	5.00	7.00
7	A14	5k claret, imperf.	5.00	7.00
a.		Perf.	10.00	10.00
9	A14	10k on 7k lt blue	10.00	15.00
10	A11	15k red brn & bl	5.00	7.00
11	A8	20k blue & car	5.00	7.00

13	A11	35k red brn & grn	5.00	7.00
14	A8	50k violet & green	5.00	7.00
15	A14	60k on 1k orange (II)	5.00	7.00
a.		Imperf. (I)	10.00	10.00
b.		Imperf. (II)	15.00	15.00
18	A13	5r dk bl, grn & pale bl	20.00	25.00
a.		Imperf.	20.00	30.00
19	A12	7r dk green & pink	35.00	40.00
20	A13	10r scar, yel & gray	35.00	40.00

Handstamped in Black

31	A14	2k green, imperf.	4.00	4.00
a.		Perf.	10.00	10.00
32	A14	3k red, imperf.	3.00	3.00
a.		Perf.	10.00	10.00
33	A15	4k carmine	10.00	10.00
a.		Imperf.	15.00	15.00
34	A14	5k claret	1.10	1.10
a.		Imperf.	10.00	10.00
36	A15	10k dark blue	2.00	2.00
37	A14	10k on 7k lt blue	1.50	4.50
38	A11	15k red brn & bl	4.00	7.50
a.		Imperf.	8.00	15.00
39	A8	20k blue & car	2.00	5.00
40	A11	25k green & gray vio	2.00	5.00
41	A11	35k red brn & grn	2.00	4.00
42	A8	50k violet & green	3.00	5.00
43	A14	60k on 1k orange (II)	3.00	5.00
43A	A11	70k brown & org	3.00	3.00
b.		Imperf.	2.00	4.00
44	A9	1r pale brn, dk brn & org	3.00	5.00
a.		Imperf.	8.00	8.00
45	A12	3½r mar & lt grn, imperf.	3.00	5.00
a.		Perf.	10.00	10.00
46	A13	5r dk bl, grn & pale bl	8.00	10.00
a.		Imperf.	12.00	15.00
47	A12	7r dk green & pink	6.50	6.50
48	A13	10r scar, yel & gray	30.00	50.00

Handstamped in Violet
c

Wove Paper

			Unwmk.	**Perf.**
62	A14	2k green, imperf.	12.00	12.00
a.		Perf.	15.00	15.00
63	A14	3k red, imperf.	2.50	2.50
a.		Perf.	15.00	15.00
64	A15	4k carmine	10.00	10.00
65	A14	5k claret	5.00	5.00
a.		Perf.	15.00	15.00
67	A15	10k dark blue	5.00	10.00
68	A14	10k on 7k bl	3.50	3.50
69	A11	15k red brn & bl	5.00	10.00
70	A8	20k blue & car	3.00	6.00
71	A11	25k grn & gray vio	25.00	15.00
72	A11	35k red brn & grn	15.00	20.00
73	A8	50k violet & grn	5.00	10.00
74	A14	60k on 1k org (II)	10.00	12.00
a.		Imperf. (I)	10.00	12.00
b.		Imperf. (II)	10.00	12.00
75	A9	1r pale brn, dk brn & org	12.50	12.50
a.		Imperf.	10.00	12.00
76	A12	3½r mar & lt grn, imperf.	6.00	6.00
a.		Perf.	10.00	10.00
77	A13	5r dk bl, grn & pale bl, imperf.	12.50	12.50
a.		Perf.	8.00	8.00
78	A12	7r dk green & pink	30.00	30.00
79	A13	10r scar, yel & gray	50.00	50.00

Imperf

85	A11	70k brown & org	25.00	25.00

Handstamped in Black

Perf.

90	A14	1k orange	10.00	10.00
a.		Imperf.	10.00	10.00
91	A14	2k green, imperf.	1.25	3.00
a.		Perf.	8.00	10.00
92	A14	3k red, imperf.	8.00	12.00
a.		Perf.	1.50	2.00
93	A15	4k carmine	3.00	3.00
94	A14	5k claret	1.00	2.00
a.		Imperf.	2.00	5.00
95	A14	7k light blue	5.00	8.00
96	A15	10k dark blue	10.00	10.00
97	A14	10k on 7k lt bl	1.25	5.00
98	A11	15k red brn & bl	2.00	5.00
99	A8	20k blue & car	5.00	7.00
100	A11	25k grn & gray vio	2.00	5.00
101	A11	35k red brn & grn	3.00	5.00
102	A8	50k violet & grn	2.00	5.00
102A	A14	60k on 1k org, imperf. (I)	20.00	30.00
b.		Imperf. (I)	4.00	6.00
c.		Perf. (II)	8.00	10.00
103	A9	1r pale brn, dk brn & org	2.00	5.00
a.		Imperf.	2.00	5.00

104	A12	3½r maroon & lt grn	5.00	8.00
a.		Imperf.	5.00	8.00
105	A13	5r dk bl, grn & pale bl	7.00	9.00
a.		Imperf.	8.00	12.00
106	A12	7r dk green & pink	15.00	20.00
107	A13	10r scar, yel & gray	25.00	50.00

Imperf

113	A11	70k brown & org	2.50	4.00

Handstamped in Violet or Black

Violet Surcharge, Type f

1920				**Perf.**
120	A14	3r on 3k red, imperf.	10.00	15.00
a.		Perf.	10.00	15.00
121	A14	5r on 3k red	10.00	10.00
122	A15	5r on 4k car	10.00	12.00
123	A14	5r on 5k claret, imperf.	5.00	12.00
a.		Perf.	12.00	20.00
124	A15	5r on 10k dk blue	20.00	30.00
125	A14	5r on 10k on 7k lt bl	20.00	30.00
126	A8	5r on 20k bl & car	10.00	15.00

Imperf

127	A14	5r on 2k green	12.00	12.00
128	A11	5r on 35k red brn & grn	12.00	12.00

Black Surcharge, Type f or Type g (#130)

Perf.

130	A14	1r on 1k orange	10.00	12.00
			15.00	15.00
131	A14	3r on 3k red	8.00	8.00
a.		Imperf.	2.00	5.00
132	A15	3r on 4k carmine	25.00	25.00
133	A14	5r on 2k grn, imperf.	2.50	3.00
a.		Perf.	5.00	5.00
134	A14	5r on 3k red	12.00	12.00
a.		Imperf.	5.00	5.00
135	A15	5r on 4k carmine	4.00	10.00
a.		Imperf.	10.00	10.00
136	A14	5r on 5k claret	3.50	4.00
a.		Imperf.	1.50	2.00
137	A14	5r on 7k lt blue	3.00	4.00
138	A15	5r on 10k dk blue	2.00	4.00
139	A14	5r on 10k on 7k lt bl	2.00	5.00
140	A11	5r on 14k bl & rose	2.50	2.50
141	A11	5r on 15k red brn & blue	1.00	3.00
a.		Imperf.	3.00	6.00
142	A8	5r on 20k bl & car	1.00	3.00
143	A11	5r on 20k on 14k bl & rose	75.00	100.00
144	A11	5r on 25k grn & gray vio	10.00	15.00

Black Surcharge, Type g or Type f (#148A, 151)

145	A14	10r on 1k org, imperf.	1.10	1.10
a.		Perf.	125.00	125.00
146	A14	10r on 3k red	175.00	175.00
147	A14	10r on 5k claret	18.00	18.00
a.		Imperf.	15.00	
148	A8	10r on 20k bl & car	15.00	15.00
148A	A11	10r on 25k grn & gray vio	10.00	10.00
149	A11	10r on 25k grn & gray vio	5.00	6.00
a.		Imperf.	10.00	20.00
150	A11	10r on 35k red brn & grn	1.50	1.50
151	A8	10r on 50k brn vio & grn	50.00	50.00
152	A8	10r on 50k brn vio & grn	2.00	3.00
152A	A11	10r on 70k brn & org, imperf.	5.00	5.00
b.		Imperf.	5.00	5.00
152C	A8	25r on 20k bl & car	8.00	10.00
153	A11	25r on 25k grn & gray vio	5.00	5.00
154	A11	25r on 35k red brn & grn	20.00	25.00
a.		Imperf.	4.00	4.00

155	A8	25r on 50k vio & grn	5.00	8.00
a.		Imperf.	6.00	8.00
156	A11	25r on 70k brn & org	8.00	8.00
a.		Imperf.	5.00	5.00
157	A9	50r on 1r pale brn, dk brn & org, imperf.	2.00	2.00
a.		Perf.	20.00	25.00
158	A13	50r on 5r dk bl, grn & lt bl	45.00	45.00
a.		Imperf.	50.00	50.00
159	A12	100r on 3½r mar & lt grn	15.00	18.00
a.		Imperf.	10.00	10.00
160	A13	100r on 5r dk bl, grn & pale bl	15.00	20.00
a.		Imperf.	25.00	35.00
161	A12	100r on 7r dk grn & pink	10.00	15.00
a.		Imperf.	42.00	42.00
162	A13	100r on 10r scar, yel & gray	15.00	20.00

Wmk. Wavy Lines (168)
Perf. 11½
Vertically Laid Paper

163	A12	100r on 3½r blk & gray	150.00	150.00
164	A12	100r on 7r blk & yel	150.00	150.00

No. 168

1920		**Unwmk.**		**Imperf.**
		Wove Paper		
166	A14 (g)	1r on 60k on 1k org (I)	12.00	14.50
168	A14 (f)	5r on 1k orange	12.00	12.00
173	A11 (f)	5r on 35k red brn & grn	15.00	15.00
177	A11 (g)	50r on 70k brn & org	6.00	10.00
179	A12 (g)	50r on 3½r mar & lt grn	20.00	20.00
181	A9 (g)	100r on 1r pale brn, dk brn & org	25.00	25.00

Romanov Issues
Surcharged Types g or f (#185-187, 190) on Stamps of 1913

No. 187	No. 187C

1920				**Perf. 13½**
184	A16	1r on 1k brn org	200.00	200.00
185	A18	3r on 3k rose red	75.00	75.00
186	A19	5r on 4k dull red	10.00	10.00
187	A22	5r on 14k blue grn	40.00	40.00
187A	A19	10r on 4k dull red	40.00	
187B	A26	10r on 35k gray vio & dk grn	100.00	
187C	A19	25r on 4k dull red	100.00	100.00
188	A26	25r on 35k gray vio & dk grn	100.00	100.00
189	A28	25r on 70k yel grn & brn	100.00	100.00
190	A31	50r on 3r dk vio	—	—
190A	A16	100r on 1k brn org	125.00	125.00
190B	A17	100r on 2k green	125.00	125.00
191	A30	100r on 2r brown	125.00	125.00
192	A31	100r on 3r dk vio	100.00	10.00

On Stamps of 1915, Type g

Thin Cardboard Inscriptions on Back
Perf. 12

193	A21	100r on 10k blue	20.00
194	A23	100r on 15k brn	20.00
195	A24	100r on 20k ol grn	18.00

On Stamps of 1916, Type f

Perf. 13½

196	A20	5r on 10k on 7k brown	8.00	8.00
197	A22	5r on 20k on 14k bl grn	25.00	35.00

Surcharged Types f or g (#204-205A, 207-207C, 210-211) over Type c

Type c in Violet
Perf.

200	A15	5r on 4k car	50.00	55.00
201	A15	5r on 10k dk bl	50.00	50.00
202	A11	5r on 15k red brn & bl	50.00	50.00
203	A8	5r on 20k blue & car	50.00	50.00
204	A11	10r on 25k grn & gray vio	50.00	50.00
205	A11	10r on 35k red brn & grn	55.00	55.00
205A	A8	10r on 50k brn vio & grn	—	—
206	A8	25r on 50k brn vio & grn	150.00	150.00
207	A9	50r on 1r pale brn, dk brn & org, imperf.	50.00	50.00
a.		Perf.	50.00	50.00
207B	A12	100r on 3½r mar & lt grn	100.00	100.00
207C	A12	100r on 7r dk grn & pink	100.00	100.00

Imperf

208	A14	5r on 2k green	50.00	50.00
209	A14	5r on 5k claret	50.00	50.00
210	A11	25r on 70k brn & org	75.00	75.00
211	A13	100r on 5r dk bl, grn & pale bl	100.00	110.00

Surcharged Types g or f (212-213, 215, 219-219A, 221-222) over Type c

Type c in Black
Perf.

212	A14	5r on 7k lt bl	150.00	150.00
213	A14	5r on 10k on 7k lt bl	75.00	75.00
214	A11	5r on 15k red brn & bl	50.00	60.00
215	A8	5r on 20k blue & car	50.00	50.00
215A	A11	10r on 5r on 25k grn & gray vio	50.00	50.00
216	A11	10r on 35k red brn & grn	50.00	60.00
217	A8	10r on 50k brn vio & grn	50.00	50.00
217A	A9	50r on 1r pale brn, dk brn & org	50.00	75.00
b.		Imperf.	40.00	50.00
217C	A12	100r on 3½r mar & lt grn	35.00	40.00
218	A13	100r on 5r dk bl, grn & pale bl	35.00	40.00
a.		Imperf.	35.00	45.00
219	A12	100r on 7r dk grn & pink	50.00	50.00
219A	A13	100r on 10r scar, yel & gray	45.00	55.00

Imperf

220	A14	1r on 60k on 1k org (I)	50.00	50.00
221	A14	5r on 2k green	20.00	20.00
222	A14	5r on 5k claret	50.00	50.00

223	A11	10r on 70k brn & org	50.00	50.00
224	A11	25r on 70k brn & org	50.00	50.00

Surcharged Types g or f (#233) over Type a

Type a in Violet
Imperf

231	A9	50r on 1r pale brn, dk brn & org	150.00	175.00
232	A13	100r on 5r dk bl, grn & pale bl	150.00	160.00

Type a in Black
Perf.

233	A8	5r on 20k blue & car	45.00	45.00
233A	A11	10r on 25k grn & gray vio	35.00	35.00
234	A11	10r on 35k red brn & grn	185.00	185.00
235	A12	100r on 3½r mar & lt grn	—	—
a.		Imperf.	—	—

Imperf

237	A14	5r on 2k green	150.00	150.00
237A	A11	10r on 70k brn & org	—	—

Surcharged Type a and New Value

Type a in Violet
Perf.

£00	A11	10r on 15k red brn & blue	30.00	30.00

Type a in Black

239	A8	5r on 20k blue & car		
239A	A8	10r on 20k blue & car	20.00	20.00
239B	A8	10r on 50k brn red & grn	30.00	40.00

Imperf

240	A12	100r on 3½r mar & lt grn	50.00	60.00

Surcharged Type c and New Value

Type c in Black

1920				Perf.
241	A15	5r on 4k red	—	—
242	A11	5r on 15k red brn & bl	—	—
243	A8	10r on 20k blue & car	50.00	50.00
243A	A11	10r on 25k grn & gray vio	50.00	50.00
244	A11	10r on 35k red brn & grn	50.00	50.00
a.		With additional srch. "5r"	100.00	100.00
245	A12	100r on 3½r mar & lt grn	—	—

No. 248

Imperf

247	A14	3r on 3k red	32.50	32.50
248	A14	5r on 2k green	30.00	30.00
249	A9	50r on 1r pale brn, dk brn & org	35.00	35.00

Type c in Violet

249A	A14	5r on 2k green	—	—

Russia AR1-AR3 Surcharged

A1   A2   A3

Perf. 14½x15
Wmk. 171

250	A1	60k on 1k red & buff	75.00	75.00
251	A2	1r on 1k red & buff	75.00	75.00
252	A3	5r on 5k green & buff	75.00	75.00
253	A3	5r on 10k brn & buff	75.00	75.00

Russian Semi-Postal Stamps of 1914-18 Srchd. with Armenian Monogram & New Values

On Stamps of 1914
Unwmk.   Perf.

255	SP5	25r on 1k red brn & dk grn, straw	75.00	75.00
256	SP5	25r on 3k mar & gray grn, pink	75.00	75.00
257	SP5	50r on 7 dk brn & dk grn, buff	125.00	150.00
258	SP5	100r on 1k red brn & dk grn, straw	100.00	100.00
259	SP5	100r on 3k mar & gray grn, pink	100.00	100.00
260	SP5	100r on 7k dk brn, buff	100.00	100.00

No. 261

On Stamps of 1915-19

261	SP5	25r on 1k org brn & gray	125.00	125.00
262	SP5	25r on 3k car & gray	90.00	90.00
263	SP5	50r on 10k dk bl & brn	50.00	50.00
264	SP5	100r on 1k org brn & gray	100.00	100.00
265	SP5	100r on 10k dk bl & brn	125.00	125.00

These surcharged semi-postal stamps were used for ordinary postage.

A set of 10 stamps in the above designs was prepared in 1920, but not issued for postal use, though some were used fiscally. Value of set, $30. Reprints abound.

Soviet Socialist Republic

Hammer and Sickle — A7

Mythological Monster — A8

Symbols of Soviet Republics on Designs from old Armenian Manuscripts A9

Ruined City of Ani — A10

Mythological Monster — A11

Armenian Soldier — A12

Mythological Monster A13

Soviet Symbols, Armenian Designs — A14

Mt. Alagöz and Plain of Shirak A15

Fisherman on River Aras — A16

Post Office in Erevan and Mt. Ararat A17

Ruin in City of Ani — A18

Street in Erevan — A19

Lake Sevan and Sevan Monastery — A20

Mythological Subject from old Armenian Monument — A21

Mt. Ararat — A22

1921		Unwmk.	Perf. 11½	
278	A7	1r gray green	1.00	
279	A8	2r slate gray	1.00	
280	A9	3r carmine	1.00	
281	A10	5r dark brown	1.00	
282	A11	25r gray	1.00	5.00
283	A12	50r red	1.00	
284	A13	100r orange	1.00	
285	A14	250r dark blue	1.00	
286	A15	500r brown vio	1.00	
287	A16	1,000r sea green	1.00	

288	A17	2,000r bister	1.00	
289	A18	5,000r dark brown	1.00	
290	A19	10,000r dull red	1.00	
291	A20	15,000r slate blue	75.00	
292	A21	20,000r lake	2.00	
293	A22	25,000r gray blue	6.00	
294	A22	25,000r brown olive	10.00	
		Nos. 278-294 (17)	106.00	

Imperf.

278a	A7	1r	12.00	
279a	A8	2r	1.00	
280a	A9	3r	1.00	
281a	A10	5r	1.00	
282a	A11	25r	1.00	5.00
283a	A12	50r	45.00	
284a	A13	100r	1.00	
285a	A14	250r	1.00	
286a	A15	500r	1.00	
287a	A16	1,000r	1.00	
288a	A17	2,000r	1.00	
289a	A18	5,000r	1.00	
290a	A19	10,000r	1.00	
291a	A20	15,000r	90.00	
292a	A21	20,000r	2.00	
293a	A22	25,000r	5.00	
294a	A22	25,000r	5.00	
		Nos. 278a-294a (17)	170.00	5.00

Except the 25r, Nos. 278-294 were not regularly issued and used. Most examples of Nos. 278-294a on the market are forgeries. Values are for genuine stamps.
For surcharges see Nos. 347-390.

Russian Stamps of 1909-17 Surcharged

Lozenges of Varnish on Face

1921, Aug.   Wove Paper   Perf. 13½

295	A9	5,000r on 1r	25.00
296	A12	5,000r on 3½r	25.00
297	A13	5,000r on 5r	25.00
298	A12	5,000r on 7r	25.00
299	A13	5,000r on 10r	25.00
		Nos. 295-299 (5)	125.00

Nos. 295-299 were not officially issued. Counterfeits abound.

A23

Mt. Ararat & Soviet Star — A24

Soviet Symbols — A25

Crane — A26

Peasant — A27

Harpy — A28

Peasant Sowing — A29

Soviet Symbols — A30

Forging — A31

Plowing A32

1922			Perf. 11½	
300	A23	50r green & red	.85	
301	A24	300r slate bl & buff	1.00	
302	A25	400r blue & pink	1.00	
303	A26	500r vio & pale lil	1.00	
304	A27	1,000r dull bl & pale bl	1.00	
305	A28	2,000r black & gray	1.25	
306	A29	3,000r black & grn	1.25	
307	A30	4,000r black & lt brn	1.25	
308	A31	5,000r blk & dull red	1.25	
309	A32	10,000r black & pale rose	1.25	
a.		Tête-bêche pair	100.00	
		Nos. 300-309 (10)	11.10	

Nos. 300-309 were not issued without surcharge.
Stamps of types A23 to A32, printed in other colors than Nos. 300 to 309, are essays.

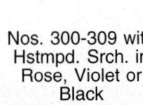

Nos. 300-309 with Hstmpd. Srch. in Rose, Violet or Black

1922				
310		10,000 on 50r (R)	90.00	90.00
311		10,000 on 50r (V)	100.00	60.00
312		10,000 on 50r	25.00	35.00
313		15,000 on 300r (R)	120.00	120.00
314		15,000 on 300r (V)	100.00	90.00
315		15,000 on 300r	25.00	35.00
316		25,000 on 400r (V)	75.00	60.00
317		25,000 on 400r	25.00	35.00
318		30,000 on 500r (R)	120.00	120.00
319		30,000 on 500r (V)	50.00	60.00
320		30,000 on 500r	25.00	35.00
321		50,000 on 1,000r (R)	250.00	250.00
322		50,000 on 1,000r (V)	200.00	200.00
323		50,000 on 1,000r	25.00	25.00
324		75,000 on 3,000r	25.00	35.00
325		100,000 on 2,000r (R)	250.00	275.00
326		100,000 on 2,000r (V)	100.00	60.00
327		100,000 on 2,000r	25.00	25.00
328		200,000 on 4,000r (V)	35.00	35.00
329		200,000 on 4,000r	20.00	20.00
330		300,000 on 5,000r (V)	50.00	60.00
331		300,000 on 5,000r	20.00	20.00
332		500,000 on 10,000r (V)	100.00	100.00
333		500,000 on 10,000r	12.00	12.00
		Nos. 310-333 (24)	1,867.	1,857.

Forgeries exist.

Goose — A33

Armenian Woman at Well — A35

Armenian Village Scene A34

Mt. Ararat A36

Mt. Ararat A37

New Values in Gold Kopecks, Handstamped Surcharge in Black

1922			Imperf.	
334	A33	1(k) on 250r rose	25.00	35.00
335	A33	1(k) on 250r gray	25.00	35.00
336	A34	2(k) on 500r rose	25.00	35.00
337	A34	3(k) on 500r gray	25.00	35.00
338	A35	4(k) on 1,000r rose	25.00	35.00
339	A35	4(k) on 1,000r gray	25.00	35.00
340	A36	5(k) on 2,000r gray	25.00	35.00
341	A36	10(k) on 2,000r rose	25.00	35.00
342	A37	15(k) on 5,000r rose	47.50	52.50
343	A37	20(k) on 5,000r gray	25.00	35.00
		Nos. 334-343 (10)	272.50	367.50

Nos. 334-343 were issued for postal tax purposes.
Nos. 334-343 exist without surcharge but are not known to have been issued in that condition. Counterfeits exist of both sets.

Regular Issue of 1921 Handstamped with New Values in Black or Red Short, Thick Numerals

1922			Imperf.	
347	A8	2(k) on 2r (R)	125.00	200.00
350	A11	4(k) on 25r (R)	125.00	125.00
353	A13	10(k) on 100r (R)	24.00	24.00
354	A14	15(k) on 250r	5.00	5.00
355	A15	20(k) on 500r	18.00	18.00
a.		With "k" written in red	12.00	12.00
357	A22	50(k) on 25,000r bl (R)	500.00	500.00
358	A22	50(k) on 25,000r brn ol (R)	150.00	150.00
359	A22	50(k) on 25,000r brn ol	—	—
		Nos. 347-358 (7)	947.00	1,022.

Perf. 11½

360	A7	1(k) on 1r, imperf.	75.00	75.00
a.		Perf.	50.00	50.00
361	A7	1(k) on 1r (R)	45.00	45.00
a.		Imperf.	45.00	75.00
362	A8	2(k) on 2r, imperf.	47.50	60.00
a.		Perf.	50.00	50.00
363	A15	2(k) on 500r	100.00	150.00
a.		Imperf.	100.00	100.00
364	A15	2(k) on 500r (R)	200.00	200.00
365	A11	4(k) on 25r, imperf.	30.00	30.00
a.		Perf.	50.00	50.00
366	A12	5(k) on 50r, imperf.	24.00	36.00
a.		Perf.	100.00	100.00
367	A13	10(k) on 100r	24.00	25.00
a.		Perf.	50.00	50.00
368	A21	35(k) on 20,000r, imperf.	75.00	100.00
a.		With "k" written in violet	150.00	125.00
b.		Perf.	90.00	100.00
c.		As "a," perf.	90.00	100.00
d.		With "kop" written in violet, imperf.		
		Nos. 360-368 (9)	620.50	721.00

Manuscript Surcharge in Red
Perf. 11½

371	A14	1k on 250r dk bl	100.00	60.00

Handstamped in Black or Red
Tall, Thin Numerals

No. 381

Imperf

377	A11	4(k) on 25r (R)	125.00	125.00
379	A13	10(k) on 100r	90.00	100.00
380	A15	20(k) on 500r	7.25	7.25
381	A22	50k on 25,000r bl	25.00	90.00
a.		Surcharged "50" only	60.00	60.00
382	A22	50k on 25,000r bl (R)	14.50	14.50
382A	A22	50k on 25,000r brn ol	29.00	29.00
382B	A22	50k on 25,000r brn ol (R)	750.00	750.00
		Nos. 377-382A (6)	290.75	365.75

On Nos. 381, 382 and 382A the letter "k" forms part of the surcharge.

Perf. 11½

383	A7	1(k) on 1r (R)	40.00	40.00
a.		Imperf.	100.00	
384	A14	1(k) on 250r	100.00	100.00
385	A15	2(k) on 500r	150.00	150.00
a.		Imperf.	150.00	150.00
386	A15	2(k) on 500r (R)	24.00	24.00
387	A9	3(k) on 3r	40.00	50.00
a.		Imperf.	40.00	50.00
388	A21	3(k) on 20,000r, imperf.	150.00	150.00
a.		Perf.	150.00	150.00
389	A11	4(k) on 25r	100.00	100.00
a.		Imperf.	120.00	120.00
390	A12	5(k) on 50r, imperf.	45.00	50.00
a.		Perf.	50.00	75.00
		Nos. 383-390 (8)	649.00	664.00

> Catalogue values for unused stamps in this section, from this point to the end of the section, are for Never Hinged items.

Mt. Ararat — A45

a, 20k. b, 2r. c, 5r.

1992, May 28   Litho.   Perf. 14

430	A45	Strip of 3, #a.-c.	3.50	3.50

Souvenir Sheet

431	A45	7r Eagle & Mt. Ararat	45.00	45.00

AT & T Communications System in Armenia — A45a

1992, July 1   Litho.   Perf. 13x13½

431A	A45a	50k multicolored	4.50	4.50

A46

1992 Summer Olympics, Barcelona: a, 40k, Ancient Greek wrestlers. b, 3.60r, Boxing. c, 5r, Weight lifting. d, 12r, Gymnastics.

1992, July 25   Litho.   Perf. 14

432	A46	Strip of 4, #a.-d.	3.50	3.50

A47

20k, Natl. flag. 1r, Goddess Waroubini, Orgov radio telescope. 2r, Yerevan Airport. No. 436, Goddess Anahit. No. 437, Runic message, 7th cent B.C. 5r, UPU emblem. 20r, Silver cup.

1992-93   Litho.   Perf. 14½, 15x14½

433	A47	20k multicolored	.30	.30
434	A47	1r gray green	.30	.30
435	A47	2r blue	.40	.40
436	A47	3r brown	.60	.60
437	A47	3r bronze	.30	.30
438	A47	5r brown black	.90	.90
439	A47	20r gray	.70	.70
		Nos. 433-439 (7)	3.50	3.50

No. 435 is airmail. See Nos. 464-471, 521-524.

Issued: No. 436, 20k, 2r, 5r, 8/25/92; others, 5/12/93.

Religious Artifacts — A50

David of Sassoun, by Hakop Kojoian
A50a

40k, Marker. 80k, Gospel page. 3.60r, Bas-relief, 13th cent. 5r, Icon of the Madonna.

1993, May 23   Litho.   Perf. 14

448	A50	40k multicolored	.25	.25
449	A50	80k multicolored	.30	.30
450	A50	3.60r multicolored	.90	.90
451	A50	5r multicolored	1.75	1.75
		Nos. 448-451 (4)	3.20	3.20

Souvenir Sheet
Perf. 14x13½

451A	A50a	12r multicolored	8.00	8.00

Scenic Views — A51

Designs: 40k, Garni Canyon, vert. 80k, Shaki Waterfall, Zangezur, vert. 3.60r, Arpa River Canyon, vert. 5r, Lake Sevan. 12r, Mount Aragats.

1993, May 24   Perf. 14

452	A51	40k multicolored	.25	.25
453	A51	80k multicolored	.25	.25
454	A51	3.60r multicolored	.50	.50
455	A51	5r multicolored	.70	.70
456	A51	12r multicolored	1.75	1.75
		Nos. 452-456 (5)	3.45	3.45

Yerevan '93 — A52

1993, May 25   Perf. 14½

457	A52	10r multicolored	.85	.85
a.		Min. sheet of 6 + 2 labels	5.50	5.50

For surcharges see Nos. 485-486.

Souvenir Sheet

Noah's Descent from Mt. Ararat, by Hovhannes Aivazovsky — A52a

1993, Aug. 4   Litho.   Perf. 14½

458	A52a	7r multicolored	4.50	4.50

Religious Relics, Echmiadzin — A53

Designs: 3r, Wooden panel, descent from cross, 9th cent. 5r, Gilded silver reliquary for Holy Cross of Khotakerats. 12r, Cross depicting right hand of St. Karapet, 14th cent. 30r, Reliquary for arm of St. Thaddeus the Apostle, 17th cent. 50r, Gilded silver vessel for consecrated ointment, 1815.

1994, Aug. 4   Litho.   Perf. 14x14½

459	A53	3d multicolored	.25	.25
460	A53	5d multicolored	.25	.25
461	A53	12d multicolored	.65	.65
462	A53	30d multicolored	1.25	1.25
463	A53	50d multicolored	2.00	2.00
		Nos. 459-463 (5)	4.40	4.40

Artifacts and Landmarks Type of 1993

Gods of Van (Urartu): 10 l, Shivini, god of the sun. 50 l, Tayshaba, god of elements. 10d, Khaldi, supreme god. 25d, Natl. arms.

1994, Aug. 4   Perf. 14½

464	A47	10 l black & brown	.25	.25
465	A47	50 l black & red brown	.25	.25
469	A47	10d black & gray	.85	.85
471	A47	25d red & bister	2.00	2.00
		Nos. 464-471 (4)	3.35	3.35

A54

1994, Dec. 31   Litho.   Perf. 14½x14

479	A54	16d No. 1a	.40	.40

First Armenian postage stamp, 75th anniv.

Early Printing Press — A54a

1994, Dec. 30   Litho.   Perf. 14x14½

480	A54a	30d multicolored	.60	.60

First Armenian periodical, 200th anniv.

Natl. Arms, Stadium — A54h

1994, Dec. 30   Litho.   Perf. 14x14½

481	A54b	30d multicolored	.65	.65

Natl. Olympic Committee.

Olympic Rings — A54c

1994, Dec. 30   Litho.   Perf. 14x14½

482	A54c	40d multicolored	1.00	1.00

Intl. Olympic Committee, Cent.

A54d

1994, Dec. 31   Litho.   Perf. 14x14½

483	A54d	50d multi + label	1.00	1.00

Ervand Otian (1869-1926)

A54e

1994, Dec. 31   Litho.   Perf. 14½x14
484 A54e 50d multi + label   1.00 1.00
Levon Shant (1869-1951).

No. 457 Surcharged in Blue or Red Brown

a   b

1994, Sept. 10   Litho.   Perf. 14
485 A52(a) 40d on 10r (Bl)   5.50 5.50
486 A52(b) 40d on 10r (RB)   5.50 5.50
Yerevan '94.

A55

Christianity in Armenia: 60d, Cross, 10th-11th cent. No. 488, Kings Abgar & Trdat, 1836. No. 489, St. Bartholomew, St. Thaddeus. 80d, St. Gregory, the Illuminator. 90d, Baptism of the Armenian people, 1892. 400d, Plan of Echmiadzin, c. 1660, engr. by Jakob Peeters.

1995, Apr. 3   Litho.   Perf. 14x15
487 A55 60d multicolored   .65   .65
488 A55 70d multicolored   .65   .65
489 A55 70d multicolored   .65   .65
490 A55 80d multicolored   1.00 1.00
491 A55 90d multicolored   1.10 1.10
    Nos. 487-491 (5)   4.05 4.05
Souvenir Sheet
492 A55 400d multicolored   5.50 5.50
Nos. 488-489 are 45x44mm.

A56

1995, Apr. 3
493 A56 150d gray & black   1.50 1.50
Vazgen I (1908-94), Catholikos of All Armenians.

Armenia Fund
A57

1995, Apr. 27   Perf. 15x14
494 A57 90d multicolored   .90   .90

UN, 50th Anniv.
A58

1995, Apr. 28
495 A58 90d multicolored   .90   .90

Cultural Artifacts — A59

Designs: 30d, Black polished pottery, 14th-13th cent. B.C. 60d, Silver cup, 5th cent. B.C. 130d, Gohar carpet, 1700 A.D.

1995, Apr. 27   Perf. 15x14
496 A59 30d multicolored   .35   .35
497 A59 60d multicolored   .65   .65
498 A59 130d multicolored   1.50 1.50
    Nos. 496-498 (3)   2.50 2.50

Birds — A60

1995, Apr. 27   Perf. 14
499 A60 40d Milvus milvus   .65   .65
500 A60 60d Aquila chrysaetos   .95   .95

End of World War II, 50th Anniv.
A61

Designs: No. 501, P. Kitsook, 408th Armenian Rifle Division. No. 502, A. Sargissin, N. Safarian, 89th Taman Armenian Triple Order-Bearer Division. No. 503, B. Chernikov, N. Tavartkeladze, V. Penkovsky, 76th Armenian Alpine Rifle Red Banner (51st Guards) Division. No. 504, S. Zakian, H. Babayan, I. Lyudnikov, 390th Armenian Rifle Division. No. 505, A. Vasillian, M. Dobrovolsky, Y. Grechany, G. Sorokin, 409th Armenian Rifle Division.
No. 506, vert.: a, Marshal Hovhannes Baghramian. b, Adm. Hovhannes Issakov. c, Marshal Hamazasp Babajanian. d, Marshal Sergey Khoudyakov.
No. 507: Return of the Hero, by Mariam Aslamazian.

1995, Sept. 30   Litho.   Perf. 15x14
501 A61 60d multicolored   .60   .60
502 A61 60d multicolored   .60   .60
503 A61 60d multicolored   .60   .60
504 A61 60d multicolored   .60   .60
505 A61 60d multicolored   .60   .60
    Nos. 501-505 (5)   3.00 3.00
Miniature Sheet
Perf. 15x14½
506 A61 60d Sheet of 4, #a.-d.   3.25 3.25
Souvenir Sheet
Perf. 15x14
507 A61 300d multicolored   4.00 4.00

Authors
A62

Designs: No. 508, Ghevond Alishan (1820-1901). No. 509, Gregor Artsruni (1845-92), vert. No. 510, Franz Werfel (1890-1945), vert.

1995, Oct. 5   Litho.   Perf. 15x14
508 A62 90d blue & black   .85   .85
509 A62 90d cream, blk, gold   .85   .85
510 A62 90d blue & maroon   .85   .85
    Nos. 508-510 (3)   2.55 2.55
Nos. 508-510 issued with se-tenant label.

A64

Prehistoric artifacts: 40d, Four-wheeled carriages, 15th cent. BC. 60d, Bronze model of geocentric solar system, 11-10th cent. BC, vert. 90d, Tombstone, Red Tufa, 7-6th cent. BC, vert.

1995, Dec. 5   Perf. 14½x15, 15x14½
512 A64 40d multicolored   .40   .40
513 A64 60d multicolored   .60   .60
514 A64 90d multicolored   .80   .80
    Nos. 512-514 (3)   1.80 1.80

A65

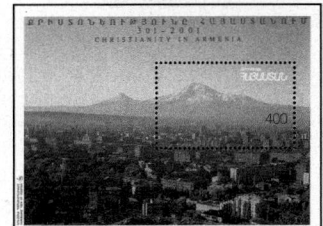

Christianity in Armenia — A66

Views of Yerevan: 60d, Brandy distillery, wine cellars. 80d, Abovian Street. 90d, Sports and concert complex. 100d, Baghramian Avenue. 120d, Republic Square.
400d, Panoramic photograph of Yerevan.

1995, Dec. 5   Perf. 15x14
515 A65 60d salmon & black   .50   .50
516 A65 80d pale org & blk   .60   .60
517 A65 90d buff & black   .70   .70
Size: 61x24mm
518 A65 100d pale yel bis & blk   .80   .80
519 A65 120d dull org & blk   1.00 1.00
    Nos. 515-519 (5)   3.60 3.60
Souvenir Sheet
520 A66 400d multicolored   4.25 4.25

No. 464 Surcharged in Green, Red, Blue Violet, or Red Brown

1996, Mar. 30   Litho.   Perf. 14½
521 A47 40d on 10l (G)   1.75 1.75
522 A47 100d on 10l (R)   3.50 3.50
523 A47 150d on 10l (BV)   5.00 5.00
524 A47 200d on 10l (RB)   7.00 7.00
    Nos. 521-524 (4)   17.25 17.25

Alexsandre Griboyedov (1795-1829), Writer — A67

1996, Apr. 24   Litho.   Perf. 14x14½
525 A67 90d multi + label   .90   .90

Khrimian Hayrik (1820-1907), Catholicos of All Armenians — A68

1996, Apr. 30   Perf. 14½x14
526 A68 90d brown & blue   .90   .90
No. 526 is printed se-tenant with label.

Admiral Lazar Serbryakov (1795-1862) — A69

1996, Apr. 30
527 A69 90d multi + label   .90   .90

Armenian Red Cross, 75th Anniv. — A70

1996, May 4   Perf. 14x14½
528 A70 60d multicolored   .60   .60

Motion Pictures, Cent.
A71

1996, May 4   Perf. 14½x14
529 A71 60d multicolored   .60   .60
No. 529 exists imperf. Value $45.

Endangered Fauna — A72

1996, May 3   Perf. 14
530 A72 40d Carpa aegagrus   .70   .70
531 A72 60d Panthera pardus   1.10 1.10

1996 Summer Olympics, Atlanta — A73

Designs: a, 40d, Cyclist. b, 60d, Athletic event. c, 90d, Wrestling.

1996, July 25
532 A73 Strip of 3, #a.-c.   1.90 1.90

Modern Olympic Games, Cent. — A74

1996, July 25   **Perf. 14x14½**
533 A74 60d multicolored   .60 .60

Fridtjof Nansen (1861-1930), Arctic Explorer — A75

1996, May 20 Litho. Perf. 14x14½
534 A75 90d multicolored   1.00 1.00

32nd Chess Olympiad, Yerevan — A76

Designs: No. 535, Petrosian-Botvinnik, World Championship match, Moscow, 1963. No. 536, Kasparov-Karpov, World Championship Match, Leningrad, 1986. No. 537, G. Kasparian, first prize winner, Contest of the Shakhmati v SSSR magazine, 1939. No. 538, 32nd Chess Olympiad, Yerevan.

1996, Sept. 15 Litho. Perf. 14
535 A76 40d multicolored   .70 .70
536 A76 40d multicolored   .70 .55
537 A76 40d multicolored   .70 .70
538 A76 40d multicolored   .70 .70
   a. Booklet pane, #535-538   3.00
     Complete booklet, 2 #538a   7.50
     Nos. 535-538 (4)   2.80 2.65

No. 538a issued 9/24.
Nos. 535-538 also exist imperf. Value $30.

Tigran Petrosian, World Chess Champion, Chess House, Yerevan — A77

1996, Sept. 20   **Perf. 14x15**
539 A77 90d multicolored   .75 .75

No. 539 also exists imperf. Value $20.

Capra Aegagrus A78

World Wildlife Fund: 70d, Two running. 100d, One standing. 130d, One holding head down. 350d, Two facing forward.

1996, Oct. 20 Litho. Perf. 14½x14
540 A78 70d multicolored   .60 .60
541 A78 100d multicolored   .70 .70
542 A78 130d multicolored   1.00 1.00
543 A78 350d multicolored   2.50 2.50
   a. Block of 4, #540-543   5.00 5.00
   b. Booklet pane, 2 #543a   10.00 10.00
     Complete booklet, #543b   12.00 12.00

Issued in sheets of 16 stamps.

Christianity in Armenia, 1700th Anniv. — A79

Armenian churches: No. 544, St. Catherine Church, St. Petersburg, 1780. No. 545, Church of the Holy Mother, Kishinev, 1803. No. 546, Church of the Holy Mother, Samarkand, 1903. No. 547, Armenian Church, Lvov, 1370. No. 548, St. Hripsime Church, Yalta, 1913.
500d, Church of St. Gevorg of Etchmiadzin, Tbilisi, 1805.

1997, Mar. 19 Litho. Perf. 14x15
544 A79 100d multicolored   1.00 1.00
545 A79 100d multicolored   1.00 1.00
546 A79 100d multicolored   1.00 1.00
547 A79 100d multicolored   1.00 1.00
548 A79 100d multicolored   1.00 1.00
     Nos. 544-548 (5)   5.00 5.00

Souvenir Sheet
549 A79 500d multicolored   4.00 4.00

First Armenian Printing Press, Etchmiadzin, 225th Anniv. — A80

1997, Mar. 26 Litho. Perf. 15x14
550 A80 70d multicolored   1.00 1.00

Armenian Entertainers — A81

Designs: No. 551, Folk singer, Jivani (1846-1909). No. 552, Arno Babajanian (1921-83), composer, vert.

1997, Mar. 26   **Perf. 15x14, 14x15**
551 A81 90d multicolored   .60 .60
552 A81 90d multicolored   .60 .60

Paintings from Natl. Gallery of Armenia A82

Designs: No. 553, "One of my Dreams," by Eghishe Tadevossian. No. 554, "Countryside," by Gevorg Bashinjaghian. No. 555, "Portrait of Natalia Tehumian," by Hakob Hovnatanian. No. 556, "Salomé," by Vardges Sureniants.

1997, May 28 Litho. Perf. 15x14
553 A82 150d multi   1.00 1.00
554 A82 150d multi   1.00 1.00
555 A82 150d multi, vert.   1.00 1.00
556 A82 150d multi, vert.   1.00 1.00
     Nos. 553-556 (4)   4.00 4.00

See Nos. 573-575.

Rouben Mamulian (1897-1987), Motion Picture Director — A83

1997, Oct. 8 Litho. Perf. 15x14
557 A83 150d multicolored   1.00 1.00

Moscow '97, World Philatelic Exhibition — A84

170d, St. Basil's Cathedral.

1997, Oct. 17   **Perf. 14x15**
558 A84 170d multicolored   1.25 1.25

Eghishe Charents (1897-1937), Poet — A85

1997, Oct. 19   **Perf. 15x14**
559 A85 150d multicolored   1.00 1.00

A86

Europa (Stories and Legends): 170d, Hayk, the Progenitor of the Armenians. 250d, Vahagn, the Dragon Slayer.

1997, Oct. 18   **Perf. 14x15**
560 A86 170d multicolored   3.00 3.00
561 A86 250d multicolored   4.00 4.00

A87

40d, Iris lycotis. 170d, Iris elegantissima.

1997, Dec. 19 Litho. Perf. 14
562 A87 40d multicolored   .30 .30
563 A87 170d multicolored   1.20 1.20

Religious Buildings — A88

Designs: No. 564, San Lazzaro, the Mekhitarian Congregation, Venice. No. 565, St. Gregory the Illuminator Cathedral, Anthelias. No. 566, St. Khach Armenian Church, Rostov upon Don. No. 567, St. James Monastery, Jerusalem. No. 568, Nercissian School, Tbilisi.

500d, Lazarian Seminary, Moscow.

1997, Dec. 22   **Perf. 15x14, 14x15**
564 A88 100d multi, horiz.   .70 .70
565 A88 100d multi   .70 .70
566 A88 100d multi   .70 .70
567 A88 100d multi, horiz.   .70 .70
    Size: 60x21mm
568 A88 100d multi, horiz.   .70 .70
     Nos. 564-568 (5)   3.50 3.50

Souvenir Sheet
569 A88 500d multicolored   3.00 3.00

Christianity in Armenia, 1700th anniv. (in 2001).

Christmas — A89

1997, Dec. 26   **Perf. 14x15**
570 A89 40d multicolored   .50 .50

Diana, Princess of Wales (1961-97) A90

1998, Apr. 8 Litho. Perf. 15x14
571 A90 250d multicolored   2.00 2.00

No. 571 was issued in sheets of 5 + label.

Karabakh Movement, 10th Anniv. — A91

1000, Feb. 20 Litho. Perf. 10½x14
572 A91 250d multicolored   2.75 2.75

Paintings from Natl. Gallery of Armenia Type of 1997

Designs: No. 573, "Tartar Women's Dance," by Alexander Bazhbeouk-Melikian. No. 574, "Family. Generations," by Yervand Kochar. No. 575, "Spring in Our Yard," by Haroutiun Kalents.

1998, Feb. 21   **Perf. 15x14, 14x15**
573 A82 150d multi   1.50 1.50
574 A82 150d multi, vert.   1.50 1.50
575 A82 150d multi, vert.   1.50 1.50
     Nos. 573-575 (3)   4.50 4.50

1998 World Cup Soccer Championships, France — A92

1998, June 10 Litho. Perf. 14x15
576 A92 250d multicolored   2.25 2.25

No. 576 was issued in sheets of 10 and sheets of 8 + 2 labels. Value, sheet of 8 + 2 labels $20. Same, imperf $125.

National Holidays and Festivals A93

Europa: 170d, Couple jumping over fire, Trndez. 250d, Girls taking part in traditional ceremony, Ascension Day.

1998, June 24   Litho.   *Perf. 15x14*
577 A93 170d multicolored   1.50 1.50
578 A93 250d multicolored   2.50 2.50

Butterflies — A94

1998, June 26   *Perf. 14*
579 A94 170d Papilio alexanor   1.00 1.00
580 A94 250d Rethera komarovi   1.50 1.50

National Costumes — A95

1998, July 16   Litho.   *Perf. 14x13½*
581 A95 170d Ayrarat   1.25 1.25
582 A95 250d Vaspurakan   1.75 1.75

See Nos. 591-592.

Christianity in Armenia, 1700th Anniv. (in 2001) — A96

Churches: a, St. Forty Children's, 1958, Milan. b, St. Sargis, London, 1923. c, St. Vardan Cathedral, 1968, New York. d, St. Hovannes Cathedral, 1902, Paris. e, St. Gregory the Illuminator Cathedral, 1938, Buenos Aires.

1998, Sept. 25   Litho.   *Perf. 11½*
583 A96 100d Sheet of 5, #a.-e.   3.00 3.00

Memorial to Armenian Earthquake Victims A97

1998, Sept. 26   *Perf. 15x14*
584 A97 250d multicolored   2.25 2.25

No. 584 was issued in sheets of 10 and sheets of 8 + 2 labels. Value, sheet of 8 + 2 labels $35.

Minerals A98

1998, Oct. 23
585 A98 170d Pyrite   1.25 1.25
586 A98 250d Agate   1.75 1.75

See Nos. 616-617.

Valery Bryusov (1873-1924), Writer — A99

1998, Dec. 1   *Perf. 14x15*
587 A99 90d multicolored   .75   .75

Souvenir Sheet

Sergei Parajanov, Film Director, 75th Birth Anniv. — A100

1999, Apr. 19   Litho.   *Perf. 14x13¾*
588 A100 500d multicolored   4.00 4.00
  a.   IBRA 99 emblem in margin   4.50 4.50

State Reserves A101

1999, Apr. 22   *Perf. 14¾x14¼*
589 A101 170d Khosrov   1.50 1.50
590 A101 250d Kilijan   2.50 2.50

Europa.

National Costumes Type of 1998

1999, Apr. 20   Litho.   *Perf. 14x13½*
591 A95 170d Karin   1.25 1.25
592 A95 250d Zangezour   2.00 2.00

Council of Europe, 50th Anniv. — A102

1999, June 12
593 A102 170d multicolored   4.50 4.50

Cilician Ships A103

1999, Aug. 12   Litho.   *Perf. 14¾x14*
Sail Colors
594 A103 170d orange & blue   1.25 1.25
595 A103 250d red & white   2.00 2.00

With PhilexFrance 99 Emblem at LR
596 A103 250d red & white   2.25 2.25
     Nos. 594-596 (3)   5.50 5.50

Domesticated Animals — A104

1999, Aug. 19   *Perf. 13¼x13¾*
597 A104 170d Armenian gampr dog   1.25 1.25
598 A104 250d Van cat   2.00 2.00

With China 1999 World Philatelic Exhibition Emblem at LR
599 A104 250d Van cat   2.50 2.50
     Nos. 597-599 (3)   5.75 5.75

Souvenir Sheet

First Pan-Armenian Games — A105

1999, Aug. 28   *Perf. 14¾x14*
600 A105 250d multicolored   3.00 3.00

Souvenir Sheet

Christianity in Armenia, 1700th Anniv. (in 2001) — A106

Churches: a, St. Gregory the Illuminator, Cairo. b, St. Gregory the Illuminator, Singapore. c, St. Khach, Suceava, Romania. d, St. Savior, Worcester, Mass. e, Church of the Holy Mother, Madras, India.

1999, Aug.   Litho.   *Perf. 13¼x13¾*
601 A106 70d Sheet of 5, #a.-e. + label   7.50 7.50

UPU, 125th Anniv. A107

1999, Oct.   *Perf. 14¾x14¼*
602 A107 270d multicolored   2.25 2.25

Politicians Assassinated Oct. 27, 1999 — A108

Designs: No. 603, Parliament Speaker Karen Demirchyan, Parliament building. No. 604, Prime Minister Vazgen Sargsyan, troops. 540d, Demirchyan, Sargsyan, Yuri Bakhshyan, Ruben Miroyan, Henrik Abrahamyan, Armenak Armenakyan, Leonard Petrossyan and Mikael Kotanyan.

Perf. 14¾x14¼
2000, Feb. 21   Litho.
603 A108 250d multi   2.50 2.00
604 A108 250d multi   2.50 2.00
  a.   Sheet, 5 each #603-604 65.00 65.00

Imperf
Size: 60x44mm
605 A108 540d multi   5.00 5.00

Fish — A109

Designs: 50d, Salmo ischchan. 270d, Barbus goktschaicus.

2000, May 23   Litho.   *Perf. 13¼x13¾*
606 A109 50d multi   1.00 1.00
607 A109 270d multi   2.00 2.00

Fairy Tales A110

70d, The Liar Hunter. 130d, The King and the Peddler.

2000, May 25   *Perf. 14¾x14¼*
608 A110 70d multicolored   .65   .65
609 A110 130d multicolored   1.25 1.25

Europa, 2000
Common Design Type

2000, June 19   *Perf. 14¼x14¾*
610 CD17 40d multi   .75   .75
611 CD17 500d multi   4.00 4.00

Christianity as State Religion, 1700th Anniv. — A111

No. 612: a, St. Gayane Church, Vagharshapat. b, Etchmiadzin Cathedral, Vagharshapat. c, Church of the Holy Mother, Khor Virap. d, St. Shoghakat Church, Vagharshapat. e, St. Hripsime Church, Vagharshapat.

2000, July 10   Litho.   *Perf. 13¼x13¾*
612 A111 70d Sheet of 5, #a-e, + label   4.00 4.00

2000 Summer Olympics, Sydney — A112

Designs: 10d, Basketball. 30d, Tennis. 500d, Weight lifting.

2000, July 11   *Perf. 13½x13¾*
613-615 A112 Set of 3   5.00 5.00

Mineral Type of 1998

Designs: 170d, Quartz. 250d, Molybdenite.

2000, Sept. 4   *Perf. 14¾x14*
616-617 A98 Set of 2   3.25 3.25

A113

2000, Sept. 11   *Perf. 14x14¾*
618 A113 270d multi   2.00 2.00

Nerses Shnorhali (1100-73), poet and musician.

Christmas — A114

2000, Sept. 15
619 A114 170d multi   1.40 1.40

Avetik Issahakian (1875-1957),
Poet — A115

2000, Sept. 17   **Perf. 14¾x14**
620 A115 130d multi   .90 .90

Musical Instruments
A116

Designs: 170d, Dhol. 250d, Duduk.

2000, Dec. 22   Litho.   Perf. 14x13¼
621-622 A116 Set of 2   3.50 3.50

Famous
Armenians — A117

No. 623: a, Viktor Hambartsoumian (1908-96), cosmologist. b, Abraham Alikhanov (1904-70), physicist. c, Andranik Iossifian (1905-93), engineer. d, Sargis Saltikov (1905-83), metallurgist. e, Samuel Kochariants (1909-87), nuclear weapons scientist. f, Atrem Mikoyan (1905-70), aircraft designer. g, Norayr Sissakian (1907-66), biologist. h, Ivan Knunyants (1906-90), chemist. i, Nikoghayos Yenikolopian (1924-93), chemist.

No. 624: a, Nikoghayos Adonts (1871-1942), historian. b, Manouk Abeghian (1865-1944), grammarian. c, Hovhannes Toumanian (1869-1923), poet. d, Hrachya Ajarian (1876-1953), linguist. e, Gevorg Emin (1918-98), writer. f, Yervand Lalayan (1864-1931), anthropologist. g, Daniel Varoujan (1884-1915), poet. h, Paruyr Sevak (1924-71), writer. i, William Saroyan (1908-81), writer.

No. 625: a, Hamo Beknazarian (1892-1965), actor. b, Alexandre Tamanian (1878-1936), architect. c, Vahram Papazian (1888-1968), actor. d, Vassil Tahirov (1859-1938), viticulturist. e, Leonid Yengibarov (1935-72), mime. f, Haykanoush Danielian (1893-1958), singer. g, Sergo Hambartsoumian (1910-83) "Strongest man on Earth". h, Hrant Shahinian (1923-96), gymnast. i, Toros Toramanian (1864-1934), architectural historian.

No. 626: a, Komitas (1869-1935), composer. b, Aram Khachatourian (1903-78), composer. c, Martiros Sarian (1880-1972), artist. d, Avet Terterian (1929-94), composer. e, Alexandre Spendiarian (1871-1928), composer. f, Arshile Gorky (1904-48), artist. g, Minas Avetissian (1928-75), artist. h, Levon Orbeli (1882-1958), physiologist. i, Hripsimeh Simonian (1916-98), artist.

2000, Dec. 23   **Perf. 14¾x14¼**
623   Booklet pane of 9   8.75 8.75
  a.-i. A117 110d Any single   .90 .90
624   Booklet pane of 9   8.75 8.75
  a.-i. A117 110d Any single   .90 .90
625   Booklet pane of 9   8.75 8.75
  a.-i. A117 110d Any single   .90 .90
626   Booklet pane of 9   8.75 8.75
  a.-i. A117 110d Any single   .90 .90
         Booklet, #623-626   45.00

Battle of Avarayr, 1550th
Anniv. — A118

No. 627: a, 170d, St. Vardan Mamikonian (388-451). b, 270d, Battle of Avarayr, 451.

2001, June 7   Litho.   Perf. 14x14¾
627 A118   Sheet of 2, #a-b   4.50 4.50

Record of Lamentations, by St. Grigor
Narekatzi, 1000th Anniv. — A119

2001, June 8   Litho.   Perf. 14¾x14
628 A119 25d multi   2.00 2.00

Europa
A120

Designs: 50d, Lake Sevan. 500d, Spandarian Reservoir.

2001, June 9
629-630 A120   Set of 2   5.75 5.75

Armenian
Admission
to Council
of Europe
A121

2001, June 11
631 A121 240d multi   2.25 2.25

Worldwide Fund for Nature
(WWF) — A122

Sciurus persicus: a, 40d, On branch. b, 50d, Eating. c, 80d, Close-up. d, 120d, Digging.

Perf. 13¼x13¾
2001, Aug. 25   **Litho.**
632 A122   Block of 4, #a-d   4.00 4.00

Second Pan-Armenian Games — A123

2001, Aug. 18   Litho.   Perf. 14¾x14
633 A123 300d multi   4.00 4.00

Christianity in Armenia, 1700th
Anniv. — A124

Views of St. Gregory the Illuminator Cathedral, Yerevan: a, 50d, Front. b, 205d, Side (45x30mm). c, 240d, Side, diff. (45x30mm).

Perf. 13¾x13¼, 13¼x13¾
2001, Aug. 27
634 A124   Sheet of 3, #a-c, +
           6 labels   7.00 7.00
  d.   As No. 634, with brown in-
       scriptions in margins   65.00 65.00

Marginal inscriptions on No. 634d read "INTERNATIONAL / PHILATELIC EXHIBITION / ARMENIA '01/ 10-16 September, 2001, Yerevan," in English, Armenian, Russian and French. Souvenir sheet can be formed into a box which shows cathedral from various angles.

Ivan Lazarev (1735-1801) and Institute
of Eastern Languages,
Moscow — A125

2001, Sept. 26   Litho.   Perf. 14¾x14
635 A125 300d multi   8.00 8.00

       See Russia No. 6665.

Native
Costumes — A126

Man and woman from: 50d, Javakhch. 250r, Artzakh.

2001, Sept. 27   **Perf. 14x13½**
636-637 A126   Set of 2   3.00 3.00

6th World Wushu
Championships
A127

2001, Oct. 3   **Perf. 13¼x13¾**
638 A127 180d black   2.75 2.75

Year of Dialogue
Among
Civilizations — A128

2001, Oct. 9   **Perf. 14x14¾**
639 A128 275d multi   6.00 6.00

Commonwealth of
Independent States,
10th Anniv. — A129

2001, Nov. 29
640 A129 205d multi   2.25 2.25

European
Year of
Languages
A130

2001, Dec. 21   **Perf. 14¾x14**
641 A130 350d multi   5.00 5.00

Independence, 10th Anniv. — A131

2001, Dec. 22
642 A131 300d multi   2.75 2.75

Transportation
A132

Designs: 180d, Cart. 205d, Phaeton.

2001, Dec. 24   **Perf. 13½x14**
643-644 A132   Set of 2   3.75 3.75

Medicinal
Plants — A133

Designs: 85d, Hypericum perforatum. 205d, Thymus serpyllum.

2001, Dec. 25   **Perf. 13¼x13¾**
645-646 A133   Set of 2   3.50 3.50

Eagle — A134

2002, Mar. 28   Litho.   *Perf. 14¾x14*
647 A134 10d brown .60 .60
648 A134 25d green .75 .75
649 A134 50d dk blue 1.00 1.00
Nos. 647-649 (3) 2.35 2.35
See Nos. 674-676.

Industries
A135

Designs: 120d, Calendar belt, 2nd cent. B.C., copper smelter. 350d, Containers, 7th cent. B.C., hops, barley, beer kettles.

2002, Apr. 26
650-651 A135 Set of 2 6.50 6.50

National Gallery
Artworks — A136

Designs: No. 652, 200d, Lily, by Edgar Chahine. No. 653, 200d, Salomé, sculpture by Hakob Gurjian.

2002, Apr. 29   *Perf. 14x14¾*
652-653 A136 Set of 2 3.50 3.50

2002 World Cup Soccer
Championships, Japan and
Korea — A137

2002, May 2   *Perf. 14¾x14*
654 A137 350d multi 2.75 2.75

Souvenir Sheet

Hovsep Pushman (1877-1906),
Artist — A138

2002, May 9
655 A138 650d multi 5.00 5.00

Hovhannes Tevossian (1902-58),
Engineer — A139

2002, May 14
656 A139 350d multi 2.75 2.75

Europa — A140

Designs: 70d, Magician's hat. 500d, Clown.

2002, July 30   Litho.   *Perf. 14x14¾*
657-658 A140 Set of 2 4.00 4.00

Artemy
Aivazian,
Composer,
Cent. of
Birth
A141

2002, July 31   *Perf. 14¾x14*
659 A141 600d multi 4.75 4.75

Souvenir Sheet

Cathedral of Ani, 1000th Anniv. (in
2001) — A142

**   *Perf. 13¼x13¾***
2002, Sept. 24   Litho.
660 A142 550d multi 4.50 4.50

Intl. Year of
Mountains
A143

2002-03   *Perf. 14¾x14*
661 A143 350d multi 3.00 3.00
661a Booklet pane of 3 9.00 9.00
Issued: No. 661, 9/26/02. No. 661a, 2003.

Reptiles — A144

Designs: 170d, Lacerta armeniaca. 220d, Vipera raddei.

2002-03   *Perf. 13¼x13¾*
662-663 A144 Set of 2 3.50 3.50
663a Booklet pane, 2 each #662-663 7.00 7.00
Issued: Nos. 662-663, 9/27/02. No. 663a, 2003.

Women for
Peace
A145

2002, Dec. 20   Litho.   *Perf. 14¾x14*
664 A145 220d multi 2.00 2.00

Alexandrapol — Yeravan Railway,
Cent. — A146

2002, Dec. 21
665 A146 350d multi 3.00 3.00

Flowers — A147

Designs: 150d, Galanthus artjuschenkoae. 200d, Merendera mirzoevae.

2002, Dec. 23   *Perf. 13¼x13¾*
666-667 A147 Set of 2 3.00 3.00
667a Booklet pane, 2 each #666-667 6.00 —
Complete booklet, #661a, 663a, 667a 22.00
Issued: No. 667a, 2003.

Space
Research
A148

Designs: 120d, Cosmic ray research. 220d, Orion 1 and Orion 2 space observatories.

2002, Dec. 24   *Perf. 14¾x14*
668-669 A148 Set of 2 3.00 3.00

Europa — A149

Poster art: 170d, Handle With Care!, by Artak Bagdassaryan. 250d, Armenia, Our Home, by Karen Koyojan.

**   *Perf. 13½x13¼***
2003, June 24   Litho.
670-671 A149 Set of 2 3.50 3.50
671a Booklet pane, 4 each #670-671 14.00 14.00
No. 671a was sold with booklet cover, but was unattached to it.

Aram Khatchaturian
(1903-78),
Composer — A150

**   *Perf. 13½x13¼***
2003, June 25   Litho.
672 A150 350d multi 3.00 3.00

Larus Armenicus
A151

2003, June 26   *Perf. 12½*
673 A151 220d multi 1.60 1.60

Eagle Type of 2002
**   *Perf. 13¼x13½***
2003, Sept. 23   Litho.
674 A134 70d red .70 .70
675 A134 300d dk blue 2.50 2.50
676 A134 500d bister brn 5.00 5.00
Nos. 674-676 (3) 8.20 8.20

Souvenir Sheet

Transport Corridor Europe —
Caucausus — Asia (TRACECA), 10th
Anniv. — A152

2003, Oct. 9   *Perf. 13*
677 A152 480d multi 6.50 6.50

First
Armenian
Postal
Dispatch,
175th
Anniv.
A153

2003, Nov. 24   *Perf. 13¼x13½*
678 A153 70d multi .75 .75

Introduction of Dram Currency, 10th
Anniv. — A154

2003, Nov. 25
679 A154 170d multi 1.50 1.50

A155

2003, Nov. 25   *Perf. 13½x13¼*
680 A155 350d multi 3.25 3.25
Siamanto (1878-1915), poet.

A156

2003, Nov. 27
681 A156 200d multi   2.00 2.00
Vahan Tekeyan (1878-1945), poet.

Neurophysiology — A157

2003, Nov. 28   **Perf. 13¼x13½**
682 A157 120d multi   1.25 1.25

Souvenir Sheet

Third Pan-Armenian Games,
Yerevan — A158

2003, Nov. 28
683 A158 350d multi   4.00 4.00

Souvenir Sheet

The Baptism, Miniature From Gospel
of Ejmiatsin — A159

2003, Nov. 28   **Perf. 13½x13¼**
684 A159 550d multi   6.50 6.50

A160

Paintings in Museum of Russian Art: 200d,
Still Life, by Alexander Shevchenko. 220d, In a
Restaurant, by Konstantin Roudakov.

2004, Sept. 6   Litho.   Perf. 13½x13¼
685-686 A160   Set of 2   4.00 4.00

A161

2004, Sept. 9
687 A161 350d multi   3.50 3.50
FIFA (Fédération Internationale de Football
Association), Cent.

Grapes — A162

Grape color: 170d, Yellow. 220d, Purple.

2004, Sept. 8   **Perf. 12½**
688-689 A162   Set of 2   4.00 4.00

Souvenir Sheet

Armenian Settlement of New Julfa,
400th Anniv. — A163

2004, Sept. 9   **Perf. 13**
690 A163 590d multi   6.00 6.00

Animated
Films
A164

Designs: 70d, Cat and Dog, 1937. 120d,
Foxbook, 1975.

2004, Sept. 10   **Perf. 13¼x13½**
691-692 A164   Set of 2   2.00 2.00

Aramayis Yerzinkyan
(1879-1931),
Statesman — A165

2004, Sept. 11   **Perf. 13½x13¼**
693 A165 220d multi   2.50 2.50

Karabakh
Horse — A166

2005, Feb. 14   Litho.   Perf. 12½
694 A166 350d multi   3.50 3.50
Dated 2004.

2004 Summer
Olympics,
Athens — A167

Hand: 70d, With Olympic Rings. 170d, As
runner. 350d, As pistol.

2005, Feb. 14
695-697 A167   Set of 3   10.00 10.00
Dated 2004.

Intl. Day Against
Desertification
A168

2005, Feb. 21   **Perf. 13½x13¼**
698 A168 360d multi   3.25 3.25
Dated 2004.

Heart,
Molecule
and
Chemistry
Apparatus
A169

2005, Feb. 22
699 A169 220d multi   2.25 2.25
Dated 2004.

Michael Nalbandian (1829-66),
Writer — A170

2005, Feb. 23
700 A170 220d multi   2.25 2.25
Dated 2004.

Mouratsan (1854-1908),
Writer — A171

2005, Feb. 24
701 A171 350d multi   3.50 3.50
Dated 2004.

Tigran
Petrosian
(1929-84),
Chess
Champion
A172

2005, Feb. 25
702 A172 220d multi   3.00 3.00

Europa
A173   A174
2005, Mar. 16   **Perf. 13½x13¼**
703 A173 70d multi   1.50 1.50
704 A174 350d multi   2.50 2.50
Dated 2004.

Souvenir Sheet

Goshavank Monastery — A175

2005, Mar. 17   **Perf. 12½**
705 A175 480d multi   5.00 5.00
Dated 2004.

Armen Tigranian (1879-1950),
Composer — A176

2005, Mar. 18   **Perf. 13¼x13½**
706 A176 220d multi   2.25 2.25
Dated 2004.

A177

2005, Apr. 21   **Perf. 13½x13¼**
707 A177 350d multi   3.25 3.25
Armenian genocide, 90th anniv.

A178

2005, Apr. 29
708 A178 350d multi 4.00 4.00

End of World War II, 60th anniv.
No. 708 was issued in sheets of 10 and sheets of 8 + 2 labels. Value, sheet of 8 + 2 labels $425.

Anushavan Arzumanian (1904-65), Educator — A179

2005, May 2 ***Perf. 13¼x13½***
709 A179 220d multi 2.00 2.00

Dated 2004.

Paintings by Martiros Sarian (1880-1972)
A180 A181

2005, May 10 ***Perf. 13½x13¼***
710 A180 170d Self-portrait 1.50 1.50
711 A181 200d Mount Aragats 1.75 1.75

Mother's Day A182

2005, Oct. 4 Litho. ***Perf. 13¼x13½***
712 A182 350d multi 3.25 3.25

A183

Europa: 70d, Bread. 350d, Porridge.

2005, Oct. 4 ***Perf. 13½x13¼***
713-714 A183 Set of 2 4.00 4.00
714a Booklet pane, 4 each #713-714 16.00 —

No. 714a was sold with booklet cover, but unattached to it.

A184

2005, Oct. 5
715 A184 70d multi .75 .75

Armenian alphabet, 1600th anniv.

A185

2005, Oct. 5
716 A185 70d multi .75 .75

Vardan Ajemian (1905-77), theater director.

A186

2005, Oct. 5
717 A186 170d multi 1.75 1.75

Anania Shirakatsi (605-85), scientist.

Mher Mkrtchian (1930-93), Actor — A187

2005, Oct. 6 ***Perf. 13¼x13½***
718 A187 120d multi 1.10 1.10

Artem Mikoyan (1905-70), Aircraft Designer, and MiG Fighters — A188

2005, Oct. 6
719 A188 350d multi 3.25 3.25

Rugs — A189

Rugs from: 60d, 19th cent. 350d, 1904. 480d, 18th cent.

2005, Oct. 6 ***Perf. 13½x13¼***
720-721 A189 Set of 2 3.50 3.50

Souvenir Sheet

722 A189 480d multi 4.50 4.50

No. 722 contains one 28x42mm stamp.

Armenia Year in Russia — A190

2006, Jan. 22 Litho. ***Perf. 11¼***
723 A190 350d multi 4.50 4.50

See Russia No. 6938.

Alexander Melik-Pashaev (1905-64), Conductor — A191

2006, Mar. 27 ***Perf. 13¼x13½***
724 A191 70d multi .90 .90

Dated 2005.

St. Mary's Russian Orthodox Cathedral, Yerevan — A192

2006, Mar. 27
725 A192 170d multi 2.00 2.00

Dated 2005.

Vakhtang Ananyan (1805-80), Writer — A193

2006, Mar. 27
726 A193 170d multi 2.00 2.00

Dated 2005.

Raphael Patkanian (1830-92), Writer — A194

2006, Mar. 27 ***Perf. 13½x13¼***
727 A194 220d multi 2.25 2.25

Dated 2005.

2006 Winter Olympics, Turin — A195

Mountains and: 120d, 2006 Winter Olympics emblem. 170d, Emblem, map of Italy on snowboard.

2006, Mar. 27 ***Perf. 12½x12¾***
728-729 A195 Set of 2 3.25 3.25
729a Miniature sheet, 5 each #728-729 *30.00 30.00*

Dated 2005.

Spiridon Melikian (1880-1933), Musician — A196

2006, Mar. 28 ***Perf. 13½x13¼***
730 A196 350d multi 3.50 3.50

Dated 2005.

Souvenir Sheet

Miniature Art Depicting Nativity and Adoration of the Magi — A197

2006, Mar. 28 ***Perf. 13¼x13½***
731 A197 480d multi 5.50 5.50

Dated 2005.

Native Costumes — A198

Costumes from: 170d, Sassoun. 200d, Shatakhk.

2006, Mar. 28 ***Perf. 13½x13¼***
732-733 A198 Set of 2 3.50 3.50

Dated 2005.

Insects — A199

Designs: 170d, Porphyrophora hamelii. 350d, Procerus scabrosus fallettianus.

2006, Mar. 28   **Perf. 12¾x12½**
734-735   A199   Set of 2   5.00 5.00
Dated 2005.

Europa Stamps, 50th Anniv. — A200

Designs: Nos. 736, 740a, 70d, Orange panel and "C." Nos. 737, 740b, 70d, Blue panel and "E." Nos. 738, 740c, 70d, Red panel and "P." Nos. 739, 740d, 70d, Green panel and "T."

2006, Mar. 28   **Perf. 12¾x12½**
Stamps With "Europa 1956-2006" Inscription
736-739   A200   Set of 4   3.50 3.50
Souvenir Sheet
Stamps Without "Europa 1956-2006" Inscription
740   A200   70d Sheet of 4, #a-d   4.00 4.00
Dated 2005.

Souvenir Sheet

Independence, 15th Anniv. — A201

2006, Sept. 10   **Litho.**   **Perf. 13¾**
741   A201   480d multi   5.00 5.00

World Peace — A202

2006, Oct. 16   **Perf. 13½x13¼**
742   A202   50d multi   .50 .50

Souvenir Sheet

Gospel of Haghpat to Jerusalem — A203

2006, Oct. 16
743   A203   220d multi   2.50 2.50

2006 World Cup Soccer Championships, Germany — A204

2006, Oct. 17   **Perf. 13¼x13½**
744   A204   350d multi   3.75 3.75

Europa A205

Designs: 200d, Gears and clock hands. 350d, Keys.

2006, Oct. 17
745-746   A205   Set of 2   4.50 4.50

Sergei Merkyurov (1881-1952), Sculptor — A206

2006, Oct. 18
747   A206   230d multi   2.25 2.25

Souvenir Sheet

Armenian General Benevolent Union, Cent. — A207

No. 748: a, Boghos Nubar (1851-1930). b, Signed document. c, Alex Manoogian (1901-96).

2006, Oct. 18   **Perf. 13½x13¼**
748   A207   120d Sheet of 3, #a-c   3.75 3.75

On Nov. 30, 2006, the Armenian Postal Service was sold to a Dutch-owned firm, HayPost CJSC, affiliated with the Netherlands Postal Corporation. The items illustrated below were released in early 2007 by the stamp producer for the Armenian Postal Service prior to this sale, but as of December 2007, were never put on sale at any HayPost CJSC post office and were not valid for postage. HayPost CJSC acquired the remaining stock of these items from the producer and is negotiating with the Armenian government to place these items on sale and make the items valid for postage. All valid postage stamps from 2007, starting with No. 749 below are inscribed "Post." The items illustrated below do not have this inscription.

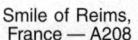

Smile of Reims, France — A208

Nativity, 15th Cent. Miniature, Armenia — A209

2007, May 22   Litho.   Perf. 13¼x13
749 A208 70d multi   1.50 1.50
750 A209 350d multi   7.50 7.50

See France Nos. 3335-3336.

Apricot — A210

2007, July 6   Perf. 13¼x13¾
751 A210 350d multi   4.00 4.00

King Tigran the Great (c. 140-55 B.C.) — A211

2007, July 19   Perf. 14¾x14
Background Color
752 A211 50d red   .60 .60
753 A211 60d olive green   .75 .75
754 A211 70d green   .90 .90
755 A211 120d blue   1.50 1.50
    Nos. 752-755 (4)   3.75 3.75
See Nos. 780-783. Compare with types A240, A256, A271-A272.

Europa A212

2007, Sept. 12
756 A212 350d multi   4.00 4.00
    Scouting, cent.

Gusan Sheram (1857-1938), Composer — A213

2007, Sept. 13   Perf. 14x14¾
757 A213 280d multi   3.00 3.00

Margar Sedrakyan (1907-73), Cognac Producer A214

2007, Sept. 14   Perf. 14¾x14
758 A214 170d multi   2.00 2.00

Souvenir Sheet

Genocide Memorial, Tsitsernakaberd — A215

2007, Oct. 9   Perf. 14x14¾
759 A215 480d multi   3.50 3.50

Children's Art A216

2007, Oct. 24   Perf. 14¾x14
760 A216 35d multi   .55 .55

Rural Landscape, by Gevorg
Bashinjaghyan (1857-1925) — A217

Kazbek, by Bashinjaghyan — A218

2007, Oct. 24   **Litho.**
761 A217 160d multi   1.50 1.50
762 A218 220d multi   2.25 2.25

Souvenir Sheet

Fourth Pan-Armenian Games,
Yerevan — A219

2007, Oct. 25   **Perf. 14x14¾**
763 A219 360d multi   3.50 3.50

Jean Garzou (1907-2000),
Painter — A220

Seda, by
Garzou — A221

2007, Oct. 25   **Perf. 14¾x14**
764 A220 180d multi   1.75 1.75
765 A221 220d multi   2.25 2.25

Norayr
Sisakyan
(1907-66),
Biochemist
A222

2007, Oct. 26   **Perf. 14¾x14**
766 A222 120d multi   1.25 .90

Kamancha — A223

2007, Oct. 27   **Perf. 14x14¾**
767 A223 110d multi   1.10 .90

Birds — A224

Designs: 120d, Pelecanus crispus. 200d,
Aegypius monachus.

2007, Oct. 27   **Perf. 13¼x13¾**
768-769 A224   Set of 2   4.00 3.00

Matenadaran Ancient Book
Depository — A225

2007, Oct. 29   **Perf. 14¾x14**
770 A225 200d multi   2.00 2.00

Bagrat Nalbandyan (1902-90),
Communications Administrator — A226

2007, Oct. 29   **Litho.**
771 A226 230d multi   2.25 1.75

N. Baghdasaryan
(1907-88),
Photojournalist
A227

2007, Oct. 31   **Perf. 14¾x14**
772 A227 200d multi   2.00 1.75

Intl. Solar
Year
A228

2007, Nov. 7   **Perf. 14¾x14**
773 A228 170d multi   1.75 1.25

Busts of
Goddesses — A229

Designs: 70d, Greek Goddess Aphrodite.
350d, Armenian Goddess Anahit.

2007, Dec. 14   **Litho.**   **Perf. 14x113½**
774-775 A229 Set of 2   5.00 5.00

See Greece Nos. 2328-2329.

2008 Summer
Olympics,
Beijing — A230

Perf. 13¼x13¾
2008, June 11   **Litho.**
776 A230 350d multi   3.50 3.50

Wood
Carving — A231

2008, June 17   **Perf. 14x14¾**
777 A231 120d multi   1.25 1.25

Europa
A232

2008, June 18   **Perf. 14¾x14**
778 A232 350d multi   3.50 3.50

Alexander
Shirvanzade (1858-
1935),
Writer — A233

2008, June 19   **Perf. 14x14¾**
779 A233 280d multi   2.50 2.50

King Tigran the Great Type of 2007
2008, June 20   **Perf. 14¾x14**
Background Color
780 A211   10d bright blue   .25 .25
781 A211   20d orange brn   .30 .25
782 A211   50d rose lilac   .60 .40
783 A211   1100d purple   9.00 9.00
     Nos. 780-783 (4)   10.15 9.90

Flowers — A234

Designs: 120d, Anemone fasciculata. 280d,
Scabiosa caucasica.

2008, Oct. 9   **Litho.**   **Perf. 13¼x14**
784-785 A234   Set of 2   4.00 4.00

Yerevan State University of
Architecture and Construction, 75th
Anniv. — A235

2008, Oct. 28   **Perf. 14¾x14**
786 A235 220d multi   2.25 2.25

William Saroyan
(1908-81),
Writer — A236

2008, Oct. 29   **Perf. 14x14¾**
787 A236 350d multi   3.50 3.50

Victor Hambardzumyan (1908-96),
Astrophysicist — A237

2008, Oct. 20   **Perf. 14¾x14**
788 A237 120d multi   1.25 1.25

Famous Men — A238

No. 789: a, Peyo Yavorov (1878-1914), Bul-
garian poet. b, Andranik Ozanian (1865-1927),
Armenian general who participated in Balkan
Wars.

2008, Nov. 10   **Perf. 13**
789   Horiz. pair   4.00 4.00
a.   A238 70d multi   .60 .60
b.   A238 350d multi   3.40 3.40

See Bulgaria No. 4492.

Dances — A239

Designs: 70d, Malambo sureño dancer,
Argentina. 350d, Hoy-nazan dancers,
Armenia.

2009, Apr. 4   **Perf. 12½x12¾**
790-791 A239   Set of 2   3.75 3.75

See Argentina Nos. 2512-2513.

King Tigran the Great
(c. 140-55 B.C.) — A240

2009, Apr. 8   **Perf. 13¼**
Granite Paper
Background Color

792	A240	10d olive green	.25	.25
793	A240	25d yel bister	.25	.25
794	A240	50d cerise	.45	.45
795	A240	70d brown	.65	.65
796	A240	120d purple	1.10	1.10
797	A240	220d dark blue	2.10	2.10
798	A240	280d dk bl violet	2.60	2.60
799	A240	350d plum	3.25	3.25
	Nos. 792-799 (8)		10.65	10.65

Numerals are in a different font than on Type A211. Compare with types A256, A271-A272.

Van, Ancient Armenian Capital A241

2009, Apr. 29   **Perf. 14¾x14**
800 A241 220d multi   1.75 1.75

Europa — A242

2009, July 1   **Perf. 13¼x13¾**
801 A242 350d multi   2.75 2.75

Intl. Year of Astronomy.

38th Chess Olympiad, Dresden, Germany A243

Designs: 70d, Chess board, Armenian players holding flag. 280d, Chess pieces, Armenian flag.

2009, July 29   **Perf. 13¾x13¼**
802-803	A243	Set of 2	3.50	3.50
803a		Miniature sheet of 10, 5 each #802-803	25.00	25.00

European Court of Human Rights, 50th Anniv. A244

Perf. 12¾x13¼
2009, Nov. 13   **Litho.**
804 A244 70d multi   15.00 15.00

Council of Europe, 60th Anniv. — A245

2009, Nov. 13   **Perf. 13¼x12¾**
805 A245 280d multi   15.00 15.00

Louis Braille (1809-52), Educator of the Blind A246

2009, Nov. 24   **Litho.**   **Perf. 14¾x14**
806 A246 110d multi   1.10 1.10

No. 806 was issued in sheets of 10 and sheets of 8 + 2 labels. Value, sheet of 8 + 2 labels $12.

Daniel Varuzhan (1884-1915), Poet — A247

2009, Dec. 8   **Perf. 13¼x12¾**
807 A247 230d multi   2.00 2.00

Souvenir Sheet

Davit of Sasun Monument, Yerevan, 50th Anniv. — A248

2009, Dec. 11   **Perf. 14**
808 A248 360d multi   3.00 3.00

Souvenir Sheet

Olympic Champions — A249

No. 809: a, 70d, Hrant Shahinyan, gymnastics, 1952. b, 120d, Igor Novikov, pentathlon, 1956, 1964. c, 160d, Albert Azaryan, gymnastics, 1956, 1960.

2009, Dec. 11   **Litho.**
809 A249 Sheet of 3, #a-c   3.25 3.25

Khachatur Abovyan (1809-48), Writer A250

2009, Dec. 15   **Perf. 12¾x13¼**
810 A250 170d multi   1.50 1.50

Animals — A251

Designs: 120d, Lutra lutra meridionalis. 160d, Ursus arctos syriacus.

2009, Dec. 16   **Perf. 14**
811-812	A251	Set of 2	2.25	2.25
812a		Miniature sheet of 10, 5 each #811-812	12.00	12.00

Paintings in the National Gallery — A252

Designs: No. 813, 200d, Autumn. A Corner in Yerevan, by Sedrak Arakelyan. No. 814, 200d, Panna Paskevich, by Georgi Yakulov.

Perf. 13¼x12¾
2009, Dec. 16   **Litho.**
813-814 A252 Set of 2   3.75 3.75

Vagharshapat Churches on UNESCO World Heritage List — A253

No. 815: a, Zvarnots Church. b, St. Hripsime Church. c, Mother See of Holy Etchmiadzin Church. d, St. Gayane Church.

2009, Dec. 18   **Perf. 14**
815 A253 70d Sheet of 4, #a-d   6.00 6.00

Christmas A254

Madonna and Child with: 280d, Country name in white. 650d, Country name in black.

Perf. 13½x13¾
2009, Dec. 18   **Litho.**
816 A254 280d multi   2.50 2.50

No. 816 was issued in sheets of 9 and sheets of 6 + 3 labels.

Souvenir Sheet
Perf. 14
817 A254 650d multi   5.75 5.75

No. 817 contains one 30x60mm stamp.

New Year 2010 — A255

Litho. with Flocking
2009, Dec. 18   **Perf. 14**
818 A255 120d multi   7.50 7.50

King Tigran the Great (c. 140-55 B.C.) — A256

2010, Jan. 29   **Litho.**   **Perf. 13x13¼**
Background Color

819	A256	10d cerise	.25	.25
820	A256	25d dark blue	.25	.25
821	A256	50d yel bister	.50	.50
822	A256	70d vermilion	.65	.65
823	A256	100d brown	.85	.85
824	A256	120d maroon	1.00	1.00
825	A256	200d gray	1.75	1.75
826	A256	220d purple	2.00	2.00
827	A256	280d red brown	2.50	2.50
828	A256	650d yel green	6.00	6.00
	Nos. 819-828 (10)		15.75	15.75

Self-Adhesive
Serpentine Die Cut 11¼

829	A256	10d cerise	.25	.25
830	A256	25d dark blue	.25	.25
831	A256	50d yel bister	.40	.40
832	A256	70d vermilion	.55	.55
833	A256	100d brown	.75	.75
834	A256	120d maroon	.90	.90
835	A256	200d gray	1.50	1.50
836	A256	220d purple	1.75	1.75
837	A256	280d red brown	2.10	2.10
838	A256	650d yel green	5.00	5.00
	Nos. 829-838 (10)		13.45	13.45

Type A256 has no lettering below king's neck. The country name is smaller than that found on types A211 and A240. Compare with types A271-A272.

Henrik Kasparyan (1910-95), Chess Player — A257

2010, Feb. 27   **Perf. 14**
839 A257 870d multi   8.00 8.00

Victory in World War II, 65th Anniv. — A258

2010, May 6   **Perf. 13¼x12¾**
840 A258 350d multi   2.75 2.75

Cemetery for Russian Officers, Gyumri — A259

2010, Aug. 20   **Litho.**   **Perf. 13¼x13**
Background Color
841 A259 350d light blue   2.75 2.75

Souvenir Sheet
842 A259 650d maroon   5.75 5.75

Mt. Ararat A260

Flag of Armenia — A261

2010, Sept. 21   *Perf. 12½x13*
843 A260 350d multi   2.75 2.75
    Perf. 13¼
844 A261 650d multi   5.00 5.00
    Independence Day.

Yerevan and Mt. Ararat — A262

Armenian Pavilion at Expo 2010, Shanghai — A263

2010, Sept. 22   *Perf. 14*
845 A262 280d multi   2.25 2.25
    Perf. 12½x13
846 A263 280d multi   2.25 2.25
    Expo 2010, Shanghai.

Europa — A264

2010, Oct. 8   *Perf. 13¼*
847 A264 350d multi   2.50 2.50

2010 Youth Olympics, Singapore A265

2010, Nov. 26   *Perf. 12½x13*
848 A265 870d multi   6.50 6.50

2010 World Cup Soccer Championships, South Africa — A266

2010, Nov. 26   Litho.
849 A266 1100d multi   8.50 8.50

Souvenir Sheet

Olympic Champions — A267

No. 850: a, Vladimir Yengibaryan, boxing gold medalist, 1956. b, Faina Melnik, discus gold medalist, 1972. c, Yuri Vardanyan, weight lifting gold medalist, 1980.

2010, Nov. 26   *Perf. 13¼*
850 A267 160d Sheet of 3, #a-c   3.75 3.75

Souvenir Sheet

2010 Winter Olympics, Vancouver — A268

No. 851 — Skiers and 2010 Winter Olympics emblem at: a, 350d, Upper left. b, 500d, Center. c, 500d, Upper right.

2010, Nov. 26
851 A268   Sheet of 3, #a-c   11.00 11.00

Arakel Babakhanyan (1860-1932), Historian — A269

2010, Dec. 27   *Perf. 12½x13*
852 A269 220d multi   1.75 1.75

Raffi (Hakob Melik Hakobyan) (1835-88), Writer — A270

2010, Dec. 27   *Perf. 13x12½*
853 A270 220d multi   1.75 1.75

King Tigran the Great (c. 140-55 B.C.)
A271   A272

2011, Feb. 1   Litho.   *Perf. 13¼*
    Granite Paper
    Background Color
854 A271   10d dark blue   .25 .25
855 A272   35d gray brn   .30 .30
856 A272   50d green   .35 .35
857 A272   70d blue green   .55 .55
858 A272   120d org brown   .90 .90
859 A272   160d maroon   1.25 1.25
860 A272   220d dark red   1.75 1.75
861 A272   280d purple   2.10 2.10
862 A272   350d bister   2.75 2.75
863 A272   1100d dk brown   8.50 8.50
    Nos. 854-863 (10)   18.70 18.70

Nos. 854-863 lack the word "Post." Compare with Types A211, A240 and A256.

Ruben Sevak (1885-1915), Writer — A273

2011, Feb. 2   *Perf. 13¼*
864 A273 280d multi   2.00 2.00
    Dated 2010.

A274

2011, Feb. 2   *Perf. 13¼*
865 A274 280d multi   2.00 2.00
    Vahan Teryan (1885-1920), writer. Dated 2010.

A275

Paintings in National Gallery: No. 866, 450d, Portrait of Actress Khmara, by Haroutyun Kalents. No. 867, 450d, Catholicos Mkrtich Khrimyan, by Vardghes Sourenyants.

2011, Feb. 2   *Perf. 13x12½*
866-867 A275   Set of 2   6.50 6.50
    Dated 2010.

Souvenir Sheet

Pepo, First Armenian Film With Sound, 75th Anniv. (in 2010) — A276

No. 868: a, 170d, Actors Avet Avetisyan and Davit Malyan. b, 200d, Actor Hrachya Nercissyan. c, 500d, Actress Tatiana Makhmuryan.

2011, Feb. 2   *Perf. 13¼*
868 A276   Sheet of 3, #a-c   6.50 6.50
    Dated 2010.

Leonid Yenigbarov (1935-72), Circus Clown — A277

2011, Feb. 2   Litho.   *Perf. 13x12½*
869 A277 220d multi   1.60 1.60

Flora — A278

Designs: No. 870, 280d, Fritillaria armena. No. 871, 280d, Sambucus tigranii.

2011, Feb. 2   *Perf. 13¼*
870-871 A278   Set of 2   4.00 4.00

Souvenir Sheet

Easter — A279

2011, Apr. 15   Litho.   *Perf. 12½x13*
872 A279 1100d multi   7.50 7.50

Andranik Iossifian (1905-93), Designer of Meteorological Satellites — A280

First Man in Space, 50th Anniv. A281

2011, Apr. 18   *Perf. 13x12½*
873 A280 200d multi   1.50 1.50
    Perf. 12½x13
874 A281 350d multi   2.50 2.50

Capitals of Belarus and Armenia — A282

No. 875 — Buildings and arms of: a, Minsk, Belarus. b, Yerevan, Armenia.

2011, June 1   Litho.   *Perf. 13*
875 A282 200d Horiz. pair, #a-b   3.00 3.00
    See Belarus No. 771.

Souvenir Sheet

Communications Regional
Commonwealth, 20th Anniv. — A283

2011, June 1
876 A283 200d multi   1.50 1.50

Writers — A284

Designs: 120d, Hovhannes Tumanian
(1869-1923). 230d, Valery Bryusov (1873-1924).

2011, June 1   **Perf. 12¾**
877-878 A284   Set of 2   3.00 3.00
878a   Vert. pair, #877-878   3.00 3.00

Nos. 877-878 each were printed in sheets of
9 + label. No. 878a was printed in sheets containing five pairs.
See Russia Nos. 7273-7274.

Souvenir Sheet

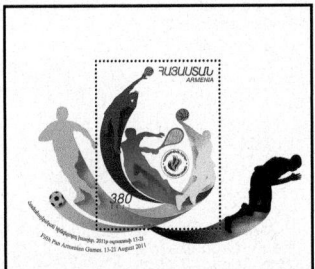

Fifth Pan-Armenian Games — A285

2011, Aug. 20
879 A285 380d multi   3.00 3.00

Birds — A286

Designs: 230d, Luscinia svecica. 330d,
Parus major.

2011, Sept. 5   **Perf. 13¼**
880 A286 230d multi   1.75 1.75
881 A286 330d multi   2.75 2.75
  a.   Horiz. pair, #880-881   4.50 4.50

Independence of
Nagorno Karabakh
From Azerbaijan,
20th
Anniv. — A287

2011, Sept. 13   **Perf. 13x13¼**
882 A287 330d multi   2.50 2.50

Independence of
Armenia, 20th
Anniv. — A288

2011, Sept. 13
883 A288 380d multi   3.00 3.00

A289

Design: Fridtjof Nansen (1861-1930), Polar
Explorer, Diplomat Assisting in Alleviating
Armenian Refugee Crisis.

2011, Nov. 9   **Perf. 13½**
884 A289 350d olive bister   2.75 2.75

Commonwealth of
Independent States,
20th Anniv. — A290

2011, Dec. 1   **Perf. 13x12½**
885 A290 280d multi   2.10 2.10

Souvenir Sheet

Joint United Nations Program on
AIDS — A291

No. 886 — AIDS ribbons: a, 200d. b, 280d.

2011, Dec. 1   **Perf. 13¼**
886 A291   Sheet of 2, #a-b   3.75 3.75

2011 Junior Eurovision Song Contest,
Yerevan — A292

2011, Dec. 3   **Perf. 13¼x13**
887 A292 230d multi   1.75 1.75
  a.   Souvenir sheet of 4   7.00 7.00

No. 887 was printed in sheets of 8.

Europa
A293

Photographs of forest in Dilijan Reserve with
denominations at: No. 888, 350d, LL. No. 889,
350d, LR.

2011, Dec. 14   **Perf. 12½x13**
888-889 A293   Set of 2   5.00 5.00

Intl. Year of Forests.

Grigor Zohrap
(1861-1915),
Lawyer and
Writer — A294

2011, Dec. 23   **Perf. 13¼x13**
890 A294 170d multi   1.25 1.25

Children — A295

No. 891: a, 100d, Girl holding grapes and
bird, flag of Armenia. b, 120d, Boy holding
wheat stalks, flag of Nagorno Karabakh.

2011, Dec. 27   **Litho.**
891 A295   Horiz. pair, #a-b   1.75 1.75

Youth philately. No. 891 was printed in
sheets containing two pairs.

Souvenir Sheet

UNESCO World Heritage
Sites — A296

No. 892: a, 230d, Sanahin Monastery. b,
330d, Haghpat Monastery.

2011, Dec. 27   **Perf. 13¼x13**
892 A296   Sheet of 2, #a-b   5.00 5.00

Christmas and New Year's
Day — A297

2011, Dec. 27   **Perf. 13¼**
893 A297 220d multi   1.75 1.75

Armenian Army,
20th
Anniv. — A298

Army coat of arms and: 200d, Soldiers,
tank, military vehicle, airplanes. 280d, Armenian flag.

2012, Feb. 9   **Perf. 13¼x13**
894-895 A298   Set of 2   3.75 3.75

Admission
to United
Nations,
20th Anniv,
A299

2012, Mar. 23   Litho.   **Perf. 13x13¼**
896 A299 350d multi   2.60 2.60

Souvenir Sheet

Yerevan, World Book Capital — A300

2012, Apr. 22
897 A300 560d multi   5.00 5.00

Garegin Nzhdeh
(1886-1955),
Statesman
A301

2012, May 3   **Perf. 13¼**
898 A301 200d multi   1.60 1.60

Misak Metsarents
(1886-1908),
Poet — A302

2012, May 3   **Perf. 13¼x13**
899 A302 280d black   2.10 2.10

Armenian
Alphabet — A303

First seven letters of Armenian alphabet in capital and lower-case.

2012, May 14   **Perf. 13x13¼**
Color of Panel at Left
900 A303 10d dull rose .25 .25
901 A303 25d yel green .25 .25
902 A303 50d gray blue .45 .45
903 A303 70d dull blue .50 .50
904 A303 100d greenish gray .75 .75
905 A303 120d dull blue .95 .95
906 A303 280d lilac rose 2.10 2.10
Nos. 900-906 (7) 5.25 5.25

See Nos. 940-946, 983-989, 1066-1072, 1100-1104, 1110-1113, 1140-1142.

Khachkars — A304

Khachkar: 200d, By Master Poghos, Goshavank, 1291. 280d, Arinj, 13th cent.

2012, June 14   **Perf. 13¼**
907-908 A304 Set of 2 3.50 3.50

Souvenir Sheet

Armenian Olympic Gold
Medalists — A305

No. 909: a, Eduard Azaryan. b, Levon Julfalakyan. c, Hoksen Mirzoyan.

2012, June 15
909 A305 160d Sheet of 3, #a-c 3.50 3.50

Souvenir Sheet

Mesrop Mashtots (361-440),
Monk — A306

2012, June 19   **Perf. 14½x14¼**
910 A306 560d multi 3.75 3.75

Hagigadar Monastery — A307

2012, Aug. 11   **Perf. 13¼**
911 A307 380d multi 2.75 2.75
a. Souvenir sheet of 2 + 2 labels 5.50 5.50
See Romania No. 5383.

Armenian Membership in Organization
for Security and Cooperation in
Europe, 20th Anniv. — A308

2012, Sept. 7   **Perf. 13x13¼**
912 A308 330d multi 2.25 2.25

Ancient Artashat, Capital of Kingdom
of Armenia, 185 B.C.-120 A.D.
A309

2012, Oct. 30
913 A309 220d multi 1.60 1.60

Mount Ararat and Alexander Misnikyan
(1886-1925), Bolshevik
Leader — A310

2012, Oct. 30
914 A310 230d multi 1.50 1.50

Samvel Kocharyants (1909-93),
Nuclear Physicist — A311

2012, Nov. 30   **Perf. 14x13½**
915 A311 350d multi 2.50 2.50

2012 Summer
Olympics,
London — A312

2012, Nov. 30   **Perf. 13¼**
916 Horiz. strip of 3 4.50 4.50
a. A312 170d Boxing 1.25 1.25
b. A312 200d Weight lifting 1.40 1.40
c. A312 230d Wrestling 1.75 1.75

Miniature Sheet

Armenian Olympic Gold
Medalists — A313

No. 917: a, Hrachya Petikyan, shooting, 1992. b, Israyel Militosyan, weight lifting, 1992. c, Mnatsakan Iskandaryan, boxing, 1992. d, Armen Nazaryan, boxing, 1996.

2012, Nov. 30
917 A313 120d Sheet of 4, #a-d 3.50 3.50

Perch Proshyan
(1837-1907),
Writer — A314

2012, Dec. 4   **Litho.**
918 A314 170d multi 1.25 1.25

Lusine Zakaryan (1937-92), Opera Singer A315

2012, Dec. 4   **Perf. 13x13¼**
919 A315 220d multi 1.50 1.50

Religious Treasures of
Etchmiadzin — A316

No. 920: a, 200d, Reliquary of Geghard, 1687. b, 220d, Cross with relic, 1746. c, 450d, Reliquary, Argadsz, St. Nshan, 13th cent.

2012, Dec. 4   **Perf. 13¼x13**
920 A316 Horiz. strip of 3, #a-c 6.50 6.50

Ashot Hovhannisyan (1887-1977), First
Secretary of Armenian Communist
Party — A317

2012, Dec. 5   **Perf. 13x13¼**
921 A317 170d black 1.75 1.75

A318

2012, Dec. 5   **Perf. 13¼x13**
922 A318 280d multi 2.00 2.00
Hovsep Orbeli (1887-1961), President of Armenian Academy of Arts and Sciences.

A319

2012, Dec. 5
923 A319 280d multi 2.00 2.00
Hayk Bzhishkyants (1887-1937), military leader.

Tigran Tchoukhadjian
(1837-98),
Composer — A320

2012, Dec. 6   **Litho.**
924 A320 330d multi 2.50 2.50

Hayastan All-Armenian Fund, 20th
Anniv. — A321

2012, Dec. 12   **Perf. 13x13¼**
925 A321 380d multi 3.00 3.00

Collective Security
Treaty Organization,
20th Anniv. — A322

2012, Dec. 17   **Perf. 13¼x13**
926 A322 230d multi 1.75 1.75

Tadevos Minasyants (1912-82),
Minister of Communications — A323

2012, Dec. 27   **Perf. 13x13¼**
927 A323 170d multi 1.25 1.25

Tatev Monastery — A324

2012, Dec. 27   **Litho.**
928 A324 350d multi 2.50 2.50
a. Sheet of 4 + 2 labels 10.00 10.00
Europa.

Paintings in National Gallery of Armenia — A325

Designs: 220d, Dacha, by Marc Chagall. 280d, Self-portrait, by Rudolf Khachatryan.

2012, Dec. 27 **Perf. 13¼x13**
929-930 A325 Set of 2 3.50 3.50

Souvenir Sheet

Sayat-Nova (1712-95), Musician — A326

2012, Dec. 27
931 A326 560d multi 4.25 4.25

Children's Art — A327

Designs: 100d, Trees. 120d, Soccer player.

2012, Dec. 28 **Perf. 13¾**
932-933 A327 Set of 2 1.60 1.60

Mammals A328

Designs: 230d, Allactaga elater. 330d, Ovis orientalis gmelinii.

2012, Dec. 28 **Perf. 12½**
934 A328 230d multi 1.50 1.50
935 A328 330d multi 2.25 2.25
a. Horiz. pair, #934-935 4.00 4.00

Christmas and New Year's Day A329

2012, Dec. 28 **Perf. 13x13¼**
936 A329 220d multi 1.60 1.60

St. Sargis's Day — A330

2013, Jan. 29 **Perf. 13¼x13**
937 A330 280d multi 1.90 1.90

Souvenir Sheet

Churches — A331

No. 938: a, 160d, Holy Trinity Church, Yerevan. b, 200d, Church of Holy Archangels, St. Etchmiadzin. c, 200d, Church of St. Hakob of Msbin, Gyumri.

2013, Apr. 4 **Perf. 13¼**
938 A331 Sheet of 3, #a-c 4.00 4.00

Brandy Production in Armenia A332

2013, June 18 **Perf. 13x13¼**
939 A332 300d multi 1.90 1.90

No. 939 was printed in sheets of 8 + 2 labels.

Armenian Alphabet Type of 2012

Second group of seven letters of Armenian alphabet in capital and lower-case.

2013, July 30 **Perf. 13x13¼**
Color of Panel at Left
940 A303 10d olive bister .25 .25
941 A303 35d salmon rose .25 .25
942 A303 50d green .40 .40
943 A303 60d blue .45 .45
944 A303 70d rose .55 .55
945 A303 100d greenish blue .75 .75
946 A303 120d gray blue .95 .95
Nos. 940-946 (7) 3.60 3.60

Europa A333

2013, Aug. 15 **Litho.**
947 A333 350d multi 2.75 2.75
a. Souvenir sheet of 4 11.00 11.00

Johannes Lepsius (1858-1926), Documenter of Armenian Genocide — A334

James Bryce (1838-1922), Documenter of Armenian Genocide — A335

2013, Aug. 16 **Perf. 13x13¼**
948 A334 280d multi 2.00 2.00
Perf. 13¼x13
949 A335 330d multi 2.50 2.50
Armenian Genocide, cent. (in 2015).

Souvenir Sheet

Church of St. Grigor, Kecharis Monastery, Tsakhkadsor — A336

2013, Aug. 24 **Litho.** **Perf. 13¼x13**
950 A336 480d multi 4.00 4.00

Souvenir Sheet

Aurora Mardiganian (1901-94), Writer of Memoir "Ravished Armenia" — A337

Perf. 14¼x14½
2013, Sept. 24 **Litho.**
951 A337 480d multi 4.00 4.00

Souvenir Sheet

Diplomatic Relations Between Armenia and Belarus, 20th Anniv. — A338

2013, Oct. 24 **Litho.** **Perf. 13**
952 A338 650d multi 5.00 5.00
See Belarus No. 879.

Anton Kochinyan (1913-90), Politician A339

2013, Oct. 25 **Litho.** **Perf. 13x13¼**
953 A339 230d multi 1.75 1.75

A340

Chess — A341

No. 954: a, 200d, Chess pieces and board, stylized globe. b, 280d, Chessboard with rook in background.

No. 955 — Half of trophy, globe, chess pieces and chess board with: a, 200d, Black squares. b, 280d, White squares.

2013, Nov. 6 **Litho.** **Perf. 13¼**
954 A340 Horiz. pair, #a-b 4.00 4.00
c. Souvenir sheet of 4, 2 each #954a-954b 8.00 8.00
d. Souvenir sheet of 8, 4 each #954a-954b, + 8 labels 17.00 17.00
955 A341 Horiz. pair, #a-b 4.00 4.00
c. Souvenir sheet of 4, 2 each #955a-955b 8.00 8.00
d. Souvenir sheet of 8, 4 each #955a-955b, + 8 labels 17.00 17.00

Armenia as World Chess Team Champion (No. 954); Armenia as 3-time Chess Olympiad champion (No. 955).

Souvenir Sheet

Church of St. Hovhannes, Gandzasar Monastery — A342

2013, Nov. 8 **Litho.** **Perf. 14¼x14½**
956 A342 560d multi 4.50 4.50

Gyumri, Cultural Capital of Commonwealth of Independent States — A343

2013, Nov. 11 **Litho.** **Perf. 13x13¼**
957 A343 560d multi + 2 flanking labels 4.50 4.50

Award of the President of Armenia — A344

No. 958 — Medal depicting: a, 180d, Eagle. b, 220d, Coat of arms.

2013, Nov. 15 **Litho.** **Perf. 13¼x13**
958 A344 Horiz. pair, #a-b 3.25 3.25

Ancient Capitals of Armenia A345

Designs: 160d, Armavir. 170d, Yervandashat.

2013, Nov. 19 **Litho.** **Perf. 13x13¼**
959-960 A345 Set of 2 2.50 2.50

Beniamin Markarian (1913-85), Astrophysicist — A346

2013, Nov. 21 **Litho.** **Perf. 13x13¼**
961 A346 170d multi 1.25 1.25

Armenian Chairmanship of Council of Europe in 2013 — A347

2013, Nov. 25   Litho.   Perf. 13¼x13
962 A347 380d multi   3.00 3.00

Paintings — A348

Designs: 230d, Family, by Ara Bekarian. 330d, Portrait of the Painter's Mother, by Stepan Aghajanian.

2013, Nov. 25   Litho.   Perf. 13¼x13
963-964 A348 Set of 2   4.50 4.50

Mushrooms A349

Designs: 230d, Macrolepiota rhacodes. 330d, Boletus edulis.

2013, Nov. 25   Litho.   Perf. 12½
965 A349 230d multi   1.75 1.75
966 A349 330d multi   2.75 2.75
  a.   Horiz. pair, #965-966   4.50 4.50

Nos. 965-966 each were printed in sheets of 8 + 2 labels. No. 966a was printed in a sheet containing 5 pairs.

Hakop Kojoian (1883-1959), Painter — A350

Armenian Herald, by Kojoian — A351

2013, Nov. 27   Litho.   Perf. 13¼x13
967 A350 240d multi   1.75 1.75
968 A351 240d multi   1.75 1.75
  a.   Horiz. pair, #967-968   3.50 3.50

Nos. 967-968 each were printed in sheets of 8. No. 968a was printed in sheets containing 4 pairs.

Dram Currency, 20th Anniv. A352

2013, Nov. 29   Litho.   Perf. 13x13¼
969 A352 380d multi   4.00 4.00

Souvenir Sheet

2014 Winter Olympics, Sochi, Russia — A353

No. 970: a, 350d, Cross-country skiing. b, 1100d, Alpine skiing.

2013, Dec. 2   Litho.   Perf. 13¼
970 A353 Sheet of 2, #a-b   10.00 10.00

Lord Byron (1788-1824), Poet and Compiler of Armenian-English Dictionary — A354

2013, Dec. 5   Litho.   Perf. 12½
971 A354 350d multi   2.75 2.75

Telephones in Armenia, Cent. A355

2013, Dec. 10   Litho.   Perf. 13x13¼
972 A355 170d multi   1.40 1.40

Vahran Papazian (1888-1968), Actor — A356

2013, Dec. 16   Litho.   Perf. 13x13¼
973 A356 230d multi   1.75 1.75

Chess A357

Designs: 100d, Chess pieces and boards. 120d; Chess pieces and board.

2013, Dec. 16   Litho.   Perf. 13x13¼
974-975 A357 Set of 2   1.75 1.75

Souvenir Sheet

Civil Aviation in Armenia, 80th Anniv. — A358

2013, Dec. 16   Litho.   Perf. 13¾
976 A358 500d multi   3.50 3.50

New Year 2014 A359

2013, Dec. 16   Litho.   Perf. 13x13¼
977 A359 220d multi   1.75 1.75

Wine Production in Armenia — A360

2013, Dec. 28   Litho.   Perf. 13x13¼
978 A360 330d multi + label   2.50 2.50

No. 978 was printed in sheets of 4 + 4 labels. Two different labels were made available on separate sheets.

Armenian Kingdom of Cilicia A361

Designs: 120d, King Levon III, ruler from 1270-89. 240d, Queen Keran, wife of King Levon III.

2013, Dec. 28   Litho.   Perf. 13x13¼
979-980 A361 Set of 2   2.75 2.75
  980a   Horiz. pair, #979-980   2.75 2.75

Nos. 979-980 each were printed in sheets of 10. No. 980a was printed in sheets containing two pairs.

Souvenir Sheet

Artsakh Movement (Campaign to Transfer Jurisdiction of Nagorno-Karabakh to Armenia), 25th Anniv. — A362

2013, Dec. 28   Litho.   Perf. 13x13¼
981 A362 400d multi   3.00 3.00

Souvenir Sheet

Archaeological Items Found in Areni-1 Cave — A363

No. 982: a, 160d, Matting, c. 3500 B.C. b, 220d, Shoe, c. 3500 B.C.

2013, Dec. 28   Litho.   Perf. 13¼x13
982 A363 Sheet of 2, #a-b   3.00 3.00

Armenian Alphabet Type of 2012

Third group of seven letters of Armenian alphabet in capital and lower-case.

2014, May 8   Litho.   Perf. 13x13¼
Color of Panel at Left
983 A303 70d dull bl green   .60   .60
984 A303 120d rose lilac   1.00   1.00
985 A303 170d lilac   1.40   1.40
986 A303 220d gray green   1.75   1.75
987 A303 230d green blue   1.90   1.90

---

988 A303 280d blue   2.25   2.25
989 A303 380d rose   3.25   3.25
        Nos. 983-989 (7)   12.15 12.15

Intelligence Officers — A364

No. 990: a, Yakov Davtian (1888-1938). b, Ivan Agayants (1911-68). c, Haik Ovakimian (1898-1967). d, Ashot Akopian (1915-81). 350d, Gevork Vartanian (1924-2012).

2014, May 20   Litho.   Perf. 13x13¼
990 A364 230d Sheet of 4, #a-d 6.50 6.50
Souvenir Sheet
Perf. 13¼x13½
991 A364 350d multi   2.50 2.50

No. 991 contains one 45x28mm stamp.

Europa A365

Musical instruments: No. 992, 350d, Pku. No. 993, 350d, Zurna.

2014, May 23   Litho.   Perf. 13x13¼
992-993 A365 Set of 2   5.00 5.00

2014 World Cup Soccer Championships, Brazil — A366

2014, June 27   Litho.   Perf. 13x13¼
994 A366 380d multi   2.75 2.75

Armenian Kingdom of Cilicia A367

Map and: No. 995, 240d, Ruins, Ayas. No. 996, 240d, Anamur Fortress. No. 997, 240d, Korikos Fortress.

2014, July 4   Litho.   Perf. 13x13¼
995-997 A367 Set of 3   5.00 5.00
  997a   Souvenir sheet of 6, 2
             each #995-997   10.00 10.00

John Kirakossian (1929-85), Historian A368

2014, July 29   Litho.   Perf. 13x13¼
998 A368 330d multi   2.50 2.50

Armenian Genocide Monuments
A369

Monument in: No. 999, 280d, Boston, Massachusetts. No. 1000, 280d, Montevideo, Uruguay, horiz. 380d, Paris, France.

Perf. 13¼x13, 13x13¼
2014, July 29 **Litho.**
999-1001 A369 Set of 3 7.00 7.00

Souvenir Sheet

Danish Mothers of Armenian Orphans — A370

No. 1002 — Medal and: a, Karen Jeppe (1875-1935). b, Maria Jacobsen (1882-1960).

2014, July 29 **Litho.** **Perf. 13¼x13**
1002 A370 200d Sheet of 2, #a-b 3.00 3.00

Famous Men
A371

Building and: No. 1003, 280d, Toros Toramanian (1864-1934), architect. No. 1004, 280d, Nikolay Marr (1864-1934), archaeologist, linguist and architect.

2014, Aug. 13 **Litho.** **Perf. 13x13¼**
1003-1004 A371 Set of 2 4.00 4.00

Hounan Avetissian (1914-43), Military Hero — A372

2014, Aug. 15 **Litho.** **Perf. 13¼x13**
1005 A372 170d multi 1.25 1.25

Ancient Capitals of Armenia
A373

Designs: No. 1006, 240d, Dvin. No. 1007, 240d, Tigranakert.

2014, Aug. 21 **Litho.** **Perf. 13x13¼**
1006-1007 A373 Set of 2 3.50 3.50

Hamo Sahian (1914-93), Poet
A374

Stepan Zorian (1889-1967), Writer — A375

2014, Sept. 5 **Litho.** **Perf. 13x13¼**
1008 A374 220d multi 1.50 1.50
1009 A375 230d multi 1.75 1.75

Flora and Fauna — A376

Designs: 230d, Dianthus gabrielianae. 330d, Upupa epops.

2014, Sept. 23 **Litho.** **Perf. 12¾**
1010-1011 A376 Set of 2 4.00 4.00

Souvenir Sheet

Voskan Yerevantsi (1614-74), Book Publisher — A377

Perf. 13¼x13½
2014, Sept. 26 **Litho.**
1012 A377 650d multi 5.00 5.00

Souvenir Sheet

World War I, Cent. — A378

2014, Sept. 29 **Litho.** **Perf. 13¼x13**
1013 A378 480d multi 3.50 3.50

Cross Stones (Khachkars)
A379

Designs: No. 1014, 240d, Holy Redeemer khachkar, Urtz, 1279. No. 1015, 240d, Mastara khachkar, 13th cent.

2014, Dec. 12 **Litho.** **Perf. 13¼**
1014-1015 A379 Set of 2 3.50 3.50

Souvenir Sheet

Holy Transfiguration Cathedral, Moscow — A380

2014, Dec. 12 **Litho.** **Perf. 13¼x13**
1016 A380 870d multi 6.00 6.00

Skier — A381

2014, Dec. 15 **Litho.** **Perf. 13¼**
1017 A381 350d multi 2.75 2.75

Dzitoghtyans House Museum, Gyumri — A383

No. 1019: a, Building exterior. b, Dining room.

2014, Dec. 30 **Litho.** **Perf. 13x13¼**
1019 A383 280d Horiz. pair, #a-b 4.00 4.00

Shushi
A384

2014, Dec. 30 **Litho.** **Perf. 13x13¼**
1020 A384 240d multi 1.75 1.75

Traditional Costumes — A385

Designs: 120d, Man and woman from Yerevan. 230d, Man, woman and child from Gyumri.

2014, Dec. 30 **Litho.** **Perf. 13¼x13**
1021-1022 A385 Set of 2 2.75 2.75

A386

A387

Children's Art — A388

2014, Dec. 30 **Litho.** **Perf. 13x13¼**
1023 A386 100d multi .75 .75

Perf. 13¼x13
1024 A387 100d multi .75 .75
1025 A388 100d multi .75 .75
Nos. 1023-1025 (3) 2.25 2.25

Forget-me-not
A389

2015, Jan. 29 **Litho.** **Perf. 13¼x13**
Background Color
1026 A389 70d white .45 .45
1027 A389 120d pale yellow .80 .80
1028 A389 240d pale peach 1.50 1.50
1029 A389 280d pale green 1.75 1.75
1030 A389 330d light blue 2.25 2.25
1031 A389 350d dull mauve 2.40 2.40
a. Souvenir sheet of 1 2.40 2.40
1032 A389 870d pale red vio 5.75 5.75
a. Souvenir sheet of 1 5.75 5.75
b. Sheet of 14, 2 each #1026-
1032 + central label 30.00 30.00
Nos. 1026-1032 (7) 14.90 14.90

Armenian Genocide, cent. Nos. 1026-1032 were each printed in sheets of 14 + central label. See Nos. 1048-1050.

Paintings by Panos Terlemezian (1865-1941) — A390

No. 1033: a, 230d, Self-portrait. b, 330d, Mount Sipan from Ktuts Island.

2015, Mar. 3 **Litho.** **Perf. 13x13¼**
1033 A390 Horiz. pair, #a-b 3.75 3.75

Melkonian Orphanage, Nicosia, Cyprus — A391

2015, Apr. 2 **Litho.** **Perf. 14½x14¼**
1034 A391 350d multi 2.40 2.40
See Cyprus No. 1232.

Anatole France (1844-1924),
Writer — A392

2015, Apr. 23   Litho.   Perf. 13x13¼
1035 A392 300d multi   2.25 2.25

Henry
Morgenthau, Sr.
(1856-1946), U.S.
Ambassador to
the Ottoman
Empire — A393

2015, Apr. 23   Litho.   Perf. 13¼x13
1036 A393 300d multi   2.25 2.25

Souvenir Sheet

American Committee for Relief in the
Near East, Cent. — A394

2015, May 6   Litho.   Perf. 13
1037 A394 480d multi   3.75 3.75

Victory in
World War
II, 70th
Anniv.
A395

2015, May 8   Litho.   Perf. 13x13¼
1038 A395 230d multi   1.75 1.75

Eurasian
Economic
Union — A396

2015, May 12   Litho.   Perf. 13¼x13
1039 A396 560d multi   4.25 4.25

Missak
Manouchian
(1906-44),
Poet — A397

2015, May 26   Litho.   Perf. 13¼x13
1040 A397 170d multi   1.40 1.40

Souvenir Sheet

Sixth Pan-Armenian Games — A398

2015, Aug. 5   Litho.   Perf. 13½x13¼
1041 A398 380d multi   3.25 3.25

Armenian Olympic
Committee, 25th
Anniv. — A399

2015, Sept. 29   Litho.   Perf. 13¼
1042 A399 230d multi   1.90 1.90

Souvenir Sheet

Blessing of the Holy Chrism — A400

2015, Sept. 29   Litho.   Perf. 13¼x13
1043 A400 480d multi   3.75 3.75

Constitutional Court, 20th
Anniv. — A401

2015, Oct. 8   Litho.   Perf. 13x13¼
1044 A401 330d multi   2.40 2.40

Lazarev
Institute,
Moscow,
200th
Anniv.
A402

2015, Oct. 23   Litho.   Perf. 13x13¼
1045 A402 380d multi   3.00 3.00

Resistance to the Armenian
Genocide — A403

No. 1046: a, 200d, Resistance in Van, Turkey. b, 280d, Resistance at Mount Musa.

2015, Oct. 29   Litho.   Perf. 13x13¼
1046 A403 Horiz. pair, #a-b   3.75 3.75

Armenian Genocide Museum and
Institute, Yerevan — A404

No. 1047: a, 230d, Museum exterior and
displays. b, 280d, Museum interior.

2015, Nov. 21   Litho.   Perf. 13x13¼
1047 A404 Horiz. pair, #a-b   4.25 4.25

Forget-me-not Type of 2015
2015, Dec. 24   Litho.   Perf. 13¼x13
Background Color

1048 A389 40d yellow   .35   .35
1049 A389 50d light blue   .40   .40
1050 A389 60d pink   .50   .50
      Nos. 1048-1050 (3)   1.25 1.25

Nos. 1048-1050 were each printed in sheets
of 14 + central label.

A405

Children's
Art — A406

2015, Dec. 24   Litho.   Perf. 13x13¼
1051 A405 70d multi   .70   .70
1052 A406 70d multi   .70   .70

Top — A407

2015, Dec. 28   Litho.   Perf. 13¼
1053 A407 350d multi   3.50 3.50

Europa.

Flora and
Fauna — A408

Designs: 220d, Lynx lynx dinniki. 280d,
Sorbus hajastana.

2015, Dec. 28   Litho.   Perf. 12⅝
1054-1055 A408 Set of 2   3.75 3.75

Vladimir
Vysotsky
(1938-80),
Singer
A409

2015, Dec. 30   Litho.   Perf. 13x13¼
1056 A409 350d multi   2.75 2.75

Armenian State
Philharmonia,
Yerevan — A410

2015, Dec. 30   Litho.   Perf. 13¼x13
1057 A410 380d multi   3.00 3.00

Souvenir Sheet

Operation Nemesis — A411

2015, Dec. 30   Litho.   Perf. 13¼x13
1058 A411 360d multi   2.75 2.75

Operation Nemesis was a series of assassi-
nations of people responsible for the Armenian
Genocide.

Souvenir Sheets

A412

Medals and Orders for Fund-raising for
Genocide Survivors — A413

No. 1059 — Order inscribed: a, Armenia. b,
Servia, Syria, Armenia.
No. 1060 — Medal depicting: a, Two-
headed bird. b, Cross.

2015, Dec. 30 **Litho.** **Perf. 13¼**
1059 A412 280d Sheet of 2, #a-b 4.25 4.25
Perf.
1060 A413 280d Sheet of 2, #a-b 4.25 4.25

Souvenir Sheet

2016 Posteurop Plenary Assembly, Yerevan — A414

2016, Apr. 20 **Litho.** **Perf. 13¼**
1061 A414 870d multi 6.50 6.50

Souvenir Sheet

2016 World Stamp Show, New York — A415

2016, May 29 **Litho.** **Perf.**
1062 A415 650d multi 5.00 5.00

Souvenir Sheet

2016 Summer Olympics, Rio de Janeiro — A416

2016, May 29 **Litho.** **Perf. 13¼**
1063 A416 650d multi 5.00 5.00

Visit to Armenia of Pope Francis — A417

No. 1064: a, 170d, Pope Francis and Yerevan. b, 230d, Pope Francis, cupola of St. Peter's Basilica. c, 380d, Pope Francis, statue of St. Gregory the Illuminator. d, 480d, Pope Francis, Etchmiadzin Cathedral.
870d, Pope Francis, St. Peter's Basilica, Etchmiadzin Cathedral, horiz.

2016, June 24 **Litho.** **Perf. 13¼**
1064 A417 Sheet of 4, #a-d, + label 12.00 12.00
Souvenir Sheet
Perf. 13¾x14
1065 A417 870d multi 6.50 6.50
No. 1065 contains one 45x33mm stamp.

Armenian Alphabet Type of 2012
Fourth group of seven letters of Armenian alphabet in capital and lower-case.

2016, July 7 **Litho.** **Perf. 13x13¼**
Color of Panel at Left
1066 A303 70d salmon pink .50 .50
1067 A303 120d apple green .90 .90
1068 A303 170d red lilac 1.25 1.25
1069 A303 230d bister 1.75 1.75
1070 A303 280d olive 2.10 2.10
1071 A303 330d lt red brown 2.50 2.50
1072 A303 380d gray blue 3.00 3.00
Nos. 1066-1072 (7) 12.00 12.00

2016 European Soccer Championships, France — A418

2016, July 15 **Litho.** **Perf. 13x13¼**
1073 A418 500d multi 3.75 3.75

A419

Independence, 25th Anniv. — A420

2016, Sept. 21 **Litho.** **Perf. 13x13¼**
1074 A419 200d multi 1.50 1.50
Perf. 13¼x13
1075 A420 300d multi 2.25 2.25

Tatevik Sazandarian (1916-99), Opera Singer — A421

2016, Oct. 4 **Litho.** **Perf. 13¼x13**
1076 A421 230d multi 1.75 1.75

Arshak Fetvadjian (1866-1947), Painter — A422

No. 1077: a, 170d, Fetvadjian. b, 230d, Woman Playing the Mandolin, by Fetvadjian.

2016, Oct. 7 **Litho.** **Perf. 13¼x13**
1077 A422 Pair, #a-b 3.00 3.00

Srbuhi Tyusab (1841-1901), Writer — A423

2016, Oct. 20 **Litho.** **Perf. 13x13¼**
1078 A423 230d multi 1.75 1.75

Souvenir Sheet

First Bible Printed in Armenian, 350th Anniv. — A424

2016, Nov. 13 **Litho.** **Perf. 13¼x13**
1079 A424 560d multi 4.25 4.25

Sergey Paradjanov Museum, Yerevan — A425

2016, Nov. 18 **Litho.** **Perf. 13¼**
1080 Horiz. pair 5.50 5.50
a. A425 300d Museum exterior 2.50 2.50
b. A425 380d Museum interior 3.00 3.00

Telbats Koubati — A426

2016, Nov. 28 **Litho.** **Perf. 13¼x13**
1081 A426 170d multi 1.40 1.40

Europa — A427

No. 1082: a, Dead and living trees. b, City, bicyclist, wind generators.

2016, Dec. 1 **Litho.** **Perf. 13x13¼**
1082 A427 350d Pair, #a-b 5.25 5.25
Think Green Issue.

Souvenir Sheet

Argentine Boca Juniors Soccer Team, 1977, 2000 and 2003 Intercontinental Soccer Cup Champions — A428

2016, Dec. 12 **Litho.** **Perf. 14**
1083 A428 500d multi 3.75 3.75

Ancient Capitals of Armenia A429

Designs: 230d, Bagara, 2nd cent. B.C. 330d, Vagharshapat, 2nd cent. A.D.

2016, Dec. 15 **Litho.** **Perf. 13x13¼**
1084-1085 A429 Set of 2 4.25 4.25

Armenia on Ancient Maps A430

Designs: 300d, Babylonian map of the world, 6th cent. B.C. 330d, Map of Ptolemy's Greater Armenia, 2nd cent. A.D.

2016, Dec. 15 **Litho.** **Perf. 13x13¼**
1086-1087 A430 Set of 2 5.00 5.00

Commonwealth of Independent States, 25th Anniv. — A431

2016, Dec. 21 **Litho.** **Perf. 13¼x13**
1088 A431 380d multi 3.00 3.00

Stylized Animals — A432

Designs: No. 1089, 100d, Armenian gull. No. 1090, 100d, Van cat. No. 1091, 100d, Armenian mouflon.

2016, Dec. 26 **Litho.** **Perf. 13¼x13**
1089-1091 A432 Set of 3 2.25 2.25
Children's Philately.

Birds — A433

Designs: 230d, Neophron percnopterus. 280d, Falco tinnunculus.

2016, Dec. 29　Litho.　Perf. 12½
1092-1093 A433　Set of 2　4.00 4.00

Flowers — A434

Designs: 230d, Tulipa sylvestris. 330d, Orchis tridentata.

2016, Dec. 29　Litho.　Perf. 12½
1094-1095 A434　Set of 2　4.50 4.50

Anna Hedwig Büll (1887-1981), Missionary Who Rescued Orphans From Armenian Genocide — A435

2016, Dec. 30　Litho.　Perf. 13¼x13
1096 A435 280d multi　2.10 2.10

Armenian Army, 25th Anniv. A436

No. 1097 — Emblem and: a, Soldiers, tanks, trucks and flag. b, Soldiers and flags.

2017, Jan. 27　Litho.　Perf. 13x13¼
1097 A436 280d Pair, #a-b　4.25 4.25

No. 1097 was printed in sheets containing two pairs.

Alexander Mantashian (1842-1911), Industrialist and Philanthropist — A437

2017, Mar. 3　Litho.　Perf. 14
1098 A437 380d multi　3.25 3.25

Souvenir Sheet

Artur Aleksanyan, 2016 Olympic Greco-Roman Wrestling Gold Medalist — A438

2017, May 30　Litho.　Perf.
1099 A438 480d multi　4.00 4.00

Armenian Alphabet Type of 2012
29th-32nd letters of Armenian alphabet in capital and lower-case.

2017, June 2　Litho.　Perf. 13x13¼
Color of Panel at Left
1100 A303　10d gray blue　.25 .25
1101 A303　50d olive green　.40 .40
1102 A303　70d dull rose　.55 .55
1103 A303　100d dull purple　.80 .80
　Nos. 1100-1103 (4)　2.00 2.00

First Postage Stamps of Republic of Armenia, 25th Anniv. — A439

2017, June 15　Litho.　Perf. 12½
1104 A439 100d multi　.90 .90

Amberd Castle — A440

2017, July 10　Litho.　Perf. 14
1105 A440 350d multi　3.00 3.00

Europa.

Hamo Beknazarian (1891-1965), Film Director and Actor — A441

2017, July 13　Litho.　Perf. 14
1106 A441 170d multi　1.50 1.50

Paintings by Gabriel Gyurjian (1892-1987) A442

Designs: 170d, Nork. 230d, Dsegh. Sunrise, and Gyurjian.

2017, July 20　Litho.　Perf. 13x13¼
1107-1108 A442　Set of 2　3.25 3.25

Helix Nebula A443

2017, July 27　Litho.　Perf. 13x13¼
1109 A443 280d multi　2.25 2.25

Regional Astronomical Center. No. 1109 was printed in sheets of 8 + central label.

Armenian Alphabet Type of 2012
Last group of four letters of Armenian alphabet in capital and lower-case.

2017, Aug. 23　Litho.　Perf. 13x13¼
Color of Panel at Left
1110 A303　230d brn rose　1.90 1.90
1111 A303　280d gray lilac　2.40 2.40
1112 A303　330d yellow brown　2.75 2.75
1113 A303　380d dl blue grn　3.25 3.25
　Nos. 1110-1113 (4)　10.30 10.30

Independence, 25th Anniv. — A444

No. 1114: a, 200d, National colors of flags and Government House. b, 300d, Nation colors of flag & new building for various governmental ministries.

2017, Oct. 9　Litho.　Perf. 13x13¼
1114 A444　Horiz. pair, #a-b　4.25 4.25

Mekhitarist Congregation on St. Lazarus Island, 300th Anniv. — A445

2017, Oct. 23　Litho.　Perf. 13x13¼
1115 A445 230d multi　1.90 1.90

Souvenir Sheet

Houses of Worship — A446

No. 1116: a, 300d, Blue Mosque, Yerevan. b, 350d, Holy Savior Cathedral, Isfahan, Iran.

2017, Oct. 25　Litho.　Perf. 13¾x14
1116 A446　Sheet of 2, #a-b　5.50 5.50

Joint issue between Armenia and Iran. See Iran No. 3178.

Miniature Sheet

Paintings by Ivan Aivazovsky (1817-1900) — A447

No. 1117: a, 170d, Self-portrait, 1874 (29x35mm). b, 220d, Noah's Descent from Mt. Ararat, 1889 (43x25mm). c, 230d, Bayron's Visit to the Mekhitarists on the Island of St. Lazarus, 1899 (43x25mm). d, 380d, Seascape. Mediterranean Seashore, 1892 (43x25mm). e, 450d, The Ninth Wave, 1850 (43x25mm).

Perf. 14x13¾ (170d), 14
2017, Nov. 7　　　　　　Litho.
1117 A447　Sheet of 5, #a-e　12.00 12.00

Souvenir Sheet

Diplomatic Relations Between Armenia and Russia, 25th Anniv. — A448

No. 1118 — Coat of arms of: a, Armenia ("25" at LL). b, Russia ("25" at LR).

2017, Nov. 21　Litho.　Perf. 13½
1118 A448 280d Sheet of 2, #a-b 4.75 4.75

Flag of Armenia and Emblem of Collective Security Treaty Organization — A449

2017, Nov. 30　Litho.　Perf. 13x13¼
1119 A449 230d multi　1.90 1.90

Collective Security Treaty, 25th anniv., Collective Security Treaty Organization, 15th anniv.

Sergey Aganov (1917-96), Soviet Marshal — A450

2017, Dec. 17　Litho.　Perf. 13¼x13
1120 A450 160d multi　1.40 1.40

Ruins of Shirakavan, Capital of Armenia, 890-929 A451

Map of Kars, Capital of Armenia, 929-61 A452

2017, Dec. 12　Litho.　Perf. 13x13¼
1121 A451 160d multi　1.40 1.40
1122 A452 160d multi　1.40 1.40

Kirk Kerkorian (1917-2015), Businessman and Philanthropist A453

2017, Dec. 14　Litho.　Perf. 13¼x13
1123 A453 380d multi　3.25 3.25

Kutahya Ceramics, 19th Cent. A454

2017, Dec. 18　Litho.　Perf. 13x13¼
1124 A454 170d multi　1.50 1.50

Holy Martyrs of the Armenian Genocide — A455

2017, Dec. 18   Litho.   Perf. 13½
1125 A455 450d multi   3.75 3.75
No. 1125 was printed in sheets of 8 + 4 labels.

Yuri Oganessian, Nuclear Physicist Source of Name of Element 118, Oganesson — A456

2017, Dec. 28   Litho.   Perf. 14
1126 A456 70d multi   .70 .70

Ghazanchetsots Cathedral, Shushi — A457

2017, Dec. 28   Litho.   Perf. 13x13¼
1127 A457 230d multi   1.90 1.90
Liberation of Shushi, 25th anniv.

Kevork V (1847-1930), Catholicos of Armenian Apostolic Church — A458

2017, Dec. 28   Litho.   Perf. 13¼x13
1128 A458 280d multi   2.40 2.40

Dinosaurs A459

Designs: 230d, Pterosaur. 280d, Tyrannosaurus.

2017, Dec. 28   Litho.   Perf. 13x13¼
1129-1130 A459   Set of 2   4.50 4.50

Christmas — A460

2017, Dec. 28   Litho.   Perf. 13¼x13
1131 A460 220d multi   1.90 1.90
When you turn stamp upside down you see a Christmas tree.

Flora and Fauna — A461

Designs: 230d, Ixiolirion montanum. 330d, Mustela nivalis.

2017, Dec. 29   Litho.   Perf. 12½
1132-1133 A461   Set of 2   4.75 4.75

Souvenir Sheet

Dragon Stones — A462

No. 1134: a, 160d, 360-centimeter tall dragon stone. b, 220d, 375-centimeter tall dragon stone.

2017, Dec. 29   Litho.   Perf. 14
1134 A462   Sheet of 2, #a-b   3.25 3.25

Souvenir Sheet

World Cup and Flag of Brazil — A463

2017, Dec. 29   Litho.   Perf. 13½
1135 A463 480d multi   4.00 4.00
Brazil, five-time World Cup Champion.

Souvenir Sheet

Intercontinental Cup and A. C. Milan Soccer Players — A464

2017, Dec. 29   Litho.   Perf. 14
1136 A464 500d multi   4.25 4.25
A. C. Milan, three-time Intercontinental Cup Champion.

Souvenir Sheet

St. Grigor Narekatsi (951-1003), Poet — A465

2017, Dec. 29   Litho.   Perf. 13x13¼
1137 A465 870d multi   7.50 7.50

Souvenir Sheet

Lavash Bread — A466

2017, Dec. 29   Litho.   Perf. 13½
1138 A466 1100d multi   9.25 9.25

Babken Nersisian (1917-86), Actor — A467

2018, Apr. 4   Litho.   Perf. 14
1139 A467 170d multi   1.50 1.50

Armenian Alphabet Type of 2012
33rd-35th letters in the Armenian alphabet.

2018, Apr. 5   Litho.   Perf. 13x13¼
Color of Panel at Left
1140 A303 70d ochre   .60 .60
1141 A303 230d gray green   2.00 2.00
1142 A303 330d gray olive   2.75 2.75
  Nos. 1140-1142 (3)   5.35 5.35

2018 Winter Olympics, Pyeongchang, South Korea — A468

2018, June 6   Litho.   Perf. 13½
1143 A468 380d multi   3.25 3.25

Office of the Prosecutor, Cent. — A469

2018, July 1   Litho.   Perf. 13¾x14
1144 A469 330d multi   2.75 2.75

2018 World Cup Soccer Championships, Russia — A470

2018, July 25   Litho.   Perf. 13x13¼
1145 A470 450d multi   4.00 4.00

Armenian General Athletic Union Scouts, Cent. — A471

2018, July 26   Litho.   Perf. 14
1146 A471 330d multi   2.75 2.75

Goris, Cultural Capital of the Commonwealth of Independent States — A472

2018, July 27   Litho.   Perf. 13½
1147 A472 330d multi   2.75 2.75

Dances — A473

No. 1148: a, Hov Arek dancers, Armenia. b, Manipuri dancers, India.

2018, Aug. 29   Litho.   Perf. 13x13¼
1148 A473 280d Horiz. pair, #a-b 4.75 4.75
See India Nos. 3053-3054.

Armenian Security Bodies, Cent. A474

2018, Sept. 24   Litho.   Perf. 13x13¼
1149 A474 170d multi   1.50 1.50

Natural Bridge, Tsakkar A475

2018, Oct. 2   Litho.   Perf. 13x13¼
1150 A475 350d multi   3.00 3.00
Europa.

Souvenir Sheet

First Republic of Armenia,
Cent. — A476

2018, Oct. 4   Litho.   Perf. 13¼
1151 A476 480d multi   4.25 4.25

Souvenir Sheet

17th Francophone Summit,
Yerevan — A477

2018, Oct. 8   Litho.   Perf. 14
1152 A477 870d multi   7.50 7.50

Souvenir Sheet

Charles Aznavour (1924-2018),
Singer — A478

2018, Oct. 11   Litho.   Perf. 13½
1153 A478 870d multi   7.50 7.50

National
Police,
Cent.
A479

2018, Oct. 31   Litho.   Perf. 13x13¼
1154 A479 120d multi   1.10 1.10

Paintings by
Hovhannes
Zardaryan
(1918-92)
A480

Designs: 170d, Spring. 230d, Winter Landscape, and Zardaryan.

2018, Nov. 6   Litho.   Perf. 13x13¼
1155-1156 A480   Set of 2   3.50 3.50

Shikahogh Reserve — A481

2018, Nov. 8   Litho.   Perf. 14
1157 A481 230d multi   1.90 1.90

A482

2018, Nov. 22   Litho.   Perf. 13x13¼
1158 A482 100d multi   .85 .85
Jamanak, Armenian Language Daily Newspaper of Istanbul, Turkey, 110th anniv.

Dram Currency, 25th Anniv. — A483

2018, Nov. 22   Litho.   Perf. 13¾
1159 A483 230d multi   1.90 1.90
Values are for stamps with surrounding selvage.

Miniature Sheet

Yerevan, 2800th Anniv. — A484

No. 1160: a, 220d, Erebuni Fortress excavations. b, 230d, Buildings on Amiryan Street, 1920. c, 350d, Yerevan Railroad Station. d, 650d, Alexander Spendidaryan National Academic Theater of Opera and Ballet.

2018, Nov. 29   Litho.   Perf. 13¼
1160 A484 Sheet of 4, #a-d   12.00 12.00

State Award for Global Contribution in
Information Technology
Sphere — A485

No. 1161: a, 160d, Medal. b, 170d, Trophy.

2018, Nov. 30   Litho.   Perf. 13¼x13
1161 A485   Horiz. pair, #a-b   2.75 2.75

Spitak
Earthquake,
30th Anniv.
A486

2018, Dec. 7   Litho.   Perf. 13x13¼
1162 A486 230d multi   1.90 1.90

George VI (1868-
1954), Catholicos
of All Armenians
A487

2018, Dec. 10   Litho.   Perf. 13¼x13
1163 A487 230d multi   1.90 1.90

Prehistoric
Animals
A488

Designs: 220d, Argentinosaurus. 280d, Tapejara.

2018, Dec. 14   Litho.   Perf. 13x13¼
1164-1165 A488   Set of 2   4.25 4.25

Flora and
Fauna — A489

Designs: 230d, Punica granatum. 330d, Capoeta capoeta sevangi.

2018, Dec. 19   Litho.   Perf. 12½
1166-1167 A489   Set of 2   4.75 4.75

Armenpress
(Armenian
News
Service),
Cent.
A490

2018, Dec. 21   Litho.   Perf. 13x13¼
1168 A490 120d multi   1.10 1.10

Hakob Paronian
(1843-91) — A491

2018, Dec. 28   Litho.   Perf. 13¼x13
1169 A491 230d multi   1.90 1.90

ErAZ
762 — A492

2018, Dec. 28   Litho.   Perf. 13x13¼
1170 A492 380d multi   3.25 3.25

Anahit — A493

Found
Dream — A494

2018, Dec. 28   Litho.   Perf. 13¼x13
1171 A493 100d multi   .85 .85
Perf. 12½
1172 A494 230d multi   1.90 1.90
Armenian animated films.

Intercontinental Soccer Cup and
Nacional Soccer Players of
Uruguay — A495

2018, Dec. 28   Litho.   Perf. 14
1173 A495 500d multi   4.25 4.25

Saint Hripsime Cathedral,
Vagharshapat, 1400th Anniv. — A496

2018, Dec. 28   Litho.   Perf. 13½
1174 A496 870d multi   7.50 7.50

Christmas and
New
Year — A497

2018, Dec. 28   Litho.   Perf. 12½
1175 A497 220d multi   1.90 1.90

New Year
2019 (Year
of the Pig)
A498

2018, Dec. 28   Litho.   Perf. 13x13¼
1176 A498 330d multi   2.75 2.75

Silva Kaputikyan (1919-2006), Poet — A499

2019, Jan. 22 Litho. Perf. 13¼x13
1177 A499 120d multi   1.10 1.10

8th Century B.C. Seals of the Kingdom of Ararat — A500

Various seals.

2019, Feb. 6 Litho. Perf. 13x13¼
1178 A500 70d multi   .60 .60
1179 A500 120d multi   1.00 1.00
1180 A500 230d multi   1.90 1.90
1181 A500 330d multi   2.75 2.75
    Nos. 1178-1181 (4)   6.25 6.25

Souvenir Sheet

Hovhannes Toumanian (1869-1923), Poet — A501

2019, Feb. 18 Litho. Perf. 13
1182 A501 1100d multi   9.25 9.25

Calouste Sarkis Gulbenkian (1869-1955), Businessman and Philanthropist — A502

No. 1183 — Gulbenkian and: a, 230d, Jeweled peacock. b, 330d, Ceramic bowl, 18th cent.

2019, Mar. 26 Litho. Perf. 13x13¼
1183 A502 Horiz. pair, #a-b   4.75 4.75

Joint Issue between Armenia & Portugal. See Portugal Nos. 4109-4110.

Mammuthus Trogontherii A503

2019, Mar. 27 Litho. Perf. 13x13¼
1184 A503 230d multi   1.90 1.90

Firefighters and Fire Truck A504

2019, May 6 Litho. Perf. 13x13¼
1185 A504 330d multi   2.75 2.75

Historic Capitals of Armenia A505

Designs: 160d, Map of Ani, 10th cent. capital, Ani Cathedral and bowl. 170d, Aerial view and map of Yerevan, 20th cent. capital, and bowl.

2019, May 16 Litho. Perf. 13x13¼
1186-1187 A505 Set of 2   2.75 2.75

Hirundo Rustica — A506

2019, May 21 Litho. Perf. 13¼x13
1188 A506 350d multi   3.00 3.00

Europa.

Mohandas K. Gandhi (1869-1948), Indian Nationalist Leader — A507

2019, May 23 Litho. Perf. 13¼x13
1189 A507 650d multi   5.50 5.50

Henrikh Mkhitaryan, Captain of Armenian National Soccer Team — A508

2019, June 4 Litho. Perf. 13½x12¾
1190 A508 450d multi   4.00 4.00

Yerevan State University, Cent. A509

2019, June 27 Litho. Perf. 13x13¼
1191 A509 220d multi   1.90 1.90

Emblem of Eurasian Economic Union and Flags of Members as Puzzle Pieces A510

2019, Aug. 9 Litho. Perf. 13½
1192 A510 330d multi   2.75 2.75

Souvenir Sheet

7th Pan-Armenian Games — A511

2019, Aug. 20 Litho. Perf. 13¼
1193 A511 870d multi   7.50 7.50

Etchmiadzin Cathedral, Vagharshapat — A512

2019, Sept. 18 Litho. Perf. 13x13¼
1194 A512 220d multi   1.00 1.00

Aram Khachaturian (1903-78), Composer — A513

2019, Sept. 27 Litho. Perf. 13x13¼
1195 A513 380d multi   1.75 1.75

Gevorg Emin (1919-98), Writer — A514

2019, Sept. 30 Litho. Perf. 13¼x13
1196 A514 120d multi   .55 .55

History Museum of Armenia A515

2019, Sept. 30 Litho. Perf. 13x13¼
1197 A515 220d multi   1.00 1.00

Souvenir Sheet

2019 World Congress on Information Technology, Yerevan — A516

2019, Oct. 7 Litho. Perf. 13¼
1198 A516 650d multi   3.00 3.00

First Armenian Postage Stamps, Cent. A517

2019, Nov. 11 Litho. Perf. 13x13¼
1199 A517 230d multi   1.10 1.10

Fauna — A518

Designs: 230d, Alcedo atthis. 330d, Panthera pardus ciscaucasica.

2019, Nov. 12 Litho. Perf. 12½
1200-1201 A518 Set of 2   2.50 2.50

A519   A520
Chalcedony   Jet Seal
Seal

2019, Nov. 27 Litho. Perf. 13x13¼
1202 A519 10d multi   .25 .25
1203 A520 50d multi   .30 .30

Souvenir Sheet

Komitas (1869-1935), Priest and Composer — A521

2019, Dec. 1 Litho. Perf. 13¼x13
1204 A521 1100d multi   5.00 5.00

Hrachya Hovhannissian (1919-97), Poet — A522

2019, Dec. 11   Litho.   Perf. 13¼
1205 A522 120d multi   .55 .55

Admiral Ivan Isakov (1894-1967) A523

2019, Dec. 24   Litho.   Perf. 13¼x13
1206 A523 120d multi   .75 .75

Daredevils of Sassoun Cartoon Character A524

2019, Dec. 24   Litho.   Perf. 13x13¼
1207 A524 120d multi   .75 .75

Souvenir Sheet

Peñarol Soccer Team, Winners of 1961, 1966 and 1982 Intercontinental Cup — A525

2019, Dec. 24   Litho.   Perf. 14
1208 A525 500d multi   3.25 3.25

Airplane and Mount Ararat — A526

2019, Dec. 26   Litho.   Perf. 14
1209 A526 220d multi   1.40 1.40

New Year 2020 (Year of the Rat) — A528

2019, Dec. 26   Litho.   Perf. 13¼x13
1211 A528 230d multi   1.40 1.40

7th Century B.C. Bronze Van Kingdom Throne Decoration — A529

2020, May 26   Litho.   Perf. 13x13¼
Background Color
1212 A529 10d orange   .25 .25
1213 A529 50d greenish blue   .25 .25
1214 A529 70d rose pink   .30 .30
1215 A529 100d yellow green   .45 .45
1216 A529 120d light blue   .55 .55
1217 A529 230d vermilion   1.10 1.10
1218 A529 330d plum   1.50 1.50
    Nos. 1212-1218 (7)   4.40 4.40

Prehistoric Animals A530

Designs: 230d, Basilosaurus. 280d, Diplodocus.

2020, June 16   Litho.   Perf. 13x13¼
1219-1220 A530   Set of 2   2.25 2.25

Bullet-riddled Wall With Armenian Inscription — A531

2020, June 26   Litho.   Perf. 13x13¼
1221 A531 280d multi   1.25 1.25
    End of World War II, 75th anniv.

Horse-drawn Mail Wagon in Gyumri — A532

2020, July 3   Litho.   Perf. 13x13¼
1222 A532 350d multi   1.50 1.50
    Europa.

Souvenir Sheet

Napoleon Bonaparte (1769-1821), Emperor of France — A533

2020, July 10   Litho.   Perf. 13¼x13
1223 A533 650d multi   3.00 3.00

Paintings by Jean Jansem (1920-2013) A534

Designs: 280d, Self-portrait. 330d, Man, Woman and Child.

2020, July 20   Litho.   Perf. 13¼x13
1224-1225 A534   Set of 2   2.75 2.75

Souvenir Sheet

Henri Verneuil (1920-2002), Film Director — A535

2020, Sept. 1   Litho.   Perf.
1226 A535 1100d multi   4.75 4.75

Sergo Hambardzumyan (1910-83), Weight Lifter — A536

2020, Sept. 9   Litho.   Perf. 13¼x13
1227 A536 120d multi   .55 .55

Alexander Harutyunyan (1920-2012), Composer A537

2020, Sept. 11   Litho.   Perf. 13¼
1228 A537 220d multi   .95 .95

Church of St. Gregory the Illuminator, Singapore A538

2020, Sept. 17   Litho.   Perf. 13x13¼
1229 A538 120d multi   .55 .55

SEMI-POSTAL STAMPS

International Children's Day — SP1

2008, June 1   Litho.   Perf. 14¾x14
B1 SP1 70d +30d multi   1.00 1.00
    Surtax (on sheet margin) was for UNICEF.

Marguerite Barankitse, Burundian Humanitarian Awarded 2016 Aurora Prize — SP2

2017, May 26   Litho.   Perf. 12¾x13¼
B2 SP2 350d +150d multi + label   4.00 4.00
    No. B2 was printed in sheets of 3 + 3 labels. The label is on either side of the stamp.

SP3

Insurance Foundation for Servicemen — SP4

No. B4 — Emblem of Insurance Foundation for Servicemen and: a, 350d, Soldier writing. b, 1100d, Soldier in watch tower.

2017, Sept. 18   Litho.   Perf. 13x13¼
B3 SP3 350d +150d multi + label   4.25 4.25
Souvenir Sheet
B4 SP4 Sheet of 2, #a-b   90.00 90.00
    No. B4 was sold with a 10,000d surtax.

Dr. Tom Catena, Recipient of 2017 Aurora Prize — SP5

2018, June 4   Litho.   Perf. 14
B5 SP5 350d +150d multi + label   4.25 4.25

Kyaw Hla Aung, Recipient of 2018 Aurora Prize — SP6

2019, Oct. 16   Litho.   Perf. 14
B6 SP6 350d +150d multi + label   3.25 3.25

AIR POST STAMPS

AP1

Design: 90d, Artiom Katsian (1886-1943), world record holding pilot on range and altitude in 1909.

1995, Dec. 5   Litho.   Perf. 14x15
C1 AP1 90d multicolored   .75 .75

AP2

1996, Apr. 30   Litho.   Perf. 14x14½
C2 AP2 90d multicolored   .90 .90
Nelson Stepanian (1913-44), WWII fighter ace.

ARUBA

ə-'rü-bə

LOCATION — West Indies, north of Venezuela
AREA — 78 sq. mi.
POP. — 67,014
CAPITAL — Oranjestad

On Jan. 1, 1986 Aruba, formerly part of Netherlands Antilles, achieved a separate status within the Kingdom of the Netherlands.

100 Cents = 1 Gulden

| Catalogue values for all unused stamps in this country are for Never Hinged items. |

| Used values are for CTO or stamps removed from first day covers. Postally used examples sell for more. |

Traditional House — A1

Perf. 14x13
1986-87   Litho.   Unwmk.
1   A1   5c shown   .40   .25
2   A1   15c King William III
          Tower   .90   .40
3   A1   20c Loading crane   .65   .30
4   A1   25c Lighthouse   1.20   .40
5   A1   30c Snake   .80   .65
6   A1   35c Owl   1.20   .65
7   A1   45c Shell   1.00   .65
8   A1   55c Frog   1.20   .65
9   A1   60c Water skier   1.20   .80
10 A1   65c Net fishing   1.15 1.00
11 A1   75c Music box   1.50 1.10
12 A1   85c Pre-Columbian
          bisque pot   1.50   .80
13 A1   90c Bulb cactus   1.60 1.10
14 A1 100c Grain   1.60 1.10
15 A1 150c Watapana tree   2.40 1.60
16 A1 250c Aloe plant   3.25 3.25
        Nos. 1-16 (16)   21.55 14.70

Issued: 5c, 30c, 60c, 150c, 1/1; 15c, 35c, 65c, 250c, 2/5; 20c, 45c, 75c, 100c, 4/7/87; 25c, 55c, 85c, 90c, 7/17/87.

Independence A2

25c, Map. 45c, Coat of arms, vert. 55c, Natl. anthem, vert. 100c, Flag.

1986, Jan. 1   Perf. 14x13, 13x14
18 A2   25c multicolored   1.75   .60
19 A2   45c multicolored   1.75 1.15
20 A2   55c multicolored   1.75 1.75
21 A2 100c multicolored   2.25 2.25
        Nos. 18-21 (4)   7.50 5.75

Intl. Peace Year — A3

1986, Aug. 29   Litho.   Perf. 14x13
22 A3   60c shown   2.00 1.25
23 A3 100c Barbed wire   3.50 2.00

Princess Juliana and Prince Bernhard, 50th Wedding Anniv. — A4

1987, Jan. 7   Photo.   Perf. 13x14
24 A4 135c multicolored   3.50 2.75

State Visit of Queen Beatrix and Prince Claus of the Netherlands A5

60c, Prince William-Alexander.

1987, Feb. 16   Litho.   Perf. 14x13
25 A5   55c shown   1.75 1.20
26 A5   60c multicolored   1.75 1.20

Tourism — A6

1987, June 5   Litho.
27 A6   60c Beach and sea   1.75 1.50
28 A6 100c Rock and cacti   2.50 2.00

Aloe Vera Plant — A7

1988, Jan. 27   Litho.   Perf. 13x14
29 A7   45c Field   1.90 1.00
30 A7   60c Plant   2.00 1.25
31 A7 100c Harvest   2.40 1.50
        Nos. 29-31 (3)   6.30 3.75

Coins — A8

1988, Mar. 16   Litho.   Perf. 13x14
32 A8   25c 25-cent   1.40   .50
33 A8   55c 50-cent   1.75 1.00
34 A8   65c 5 and 10-cent   2.10 1.35
35 A8 150c 1-florin   3.25 2.40
        Nos. 32-35 (4)   8.50 5.25

Love Issue — A9

135c, Seashells, coastal scenery.

1988, May 4
36 A9   70c shown   1.75 1.00
37 A9 135c multicolored   2.25 2.00

A10

1988, Aug. 24
38 A10   35c shown   1.50   .90
39 A10 100c Emblems   2.50 1.60

Aruba, the 162nd member of the Intl. Olympic Committee (35c), 1988 Summer Olympics, Seoul (100c).

Carnival A11

1989, Jan. 5   Perf. 14x13
40 A11   45c Two children   2.00 1.00
41 A11   60c Girl   2.00 1.00
42 A11 100c Entertainer   2.50 1.50
        Nos. 40-42 (3)   6.50 3.50

Maripampun, Omphalophalmum Rubrum — A12

1989, Mar. 16   Litho.   Perf. 14x13
43 A12   35c Leaves   1.50   .75
44 A12   55c Pods   1.50 1.00
45 A12 200c Blossom   4.00 3.00
        Nos. 43-45 (3)   7.00 4.75

New Year 1990 — A13

Dande band members playing instruments or singing: 25c, Violin, tambor, cuatro, marimba. 70c, Lead singer, guitar. 150c, Accordion, urri, guitar.

1989, Nov. 16   Litho.   Perf. 13x14
46 A13   25c multicolored   1.00   .50
47 A13   70c multicolored   1.40 1.00
48 A13 150c multicolored   2.60 2.00
        Nos. 46-48 (3)   5.00 3.50

UPU — A14

1989, June 8   Litho.   Perf. 13x14
49 A14 250c multicolored   6.00 3.75

Crotalus durissus unicolor A15

1989, Aug. 24   Perf. 14x13
50 A15   45c shown   1.50   .75
51 A15   55c multi, diff.   1.75 1.00
52 A15   60c multi, diff.   1.75 1.00
        Nos. 50-52 (3)   5.00 2.75

Snake species in danger of extinction.

Man Living in Harmony with Nature — A16

1990, Feb. 7   Perf. 13x14, 14x13
53 A16   45c The land   1.50 1.00
54 A16   55c shown   1.75 1.00
55 A16 100c The sea   3.00 2.00
        Nos. 53-55 (3)   6.25 4.00

Environmental protection. Nos. 53, 55 horiz.

Marine Life — A17

Designs: 60c, Giant caribbean anemone, Pederson's cleaning shrimp. 70c, Queen angelfish, red and orange coral. 100c, Banded coral shrimp, fire sponge, yellow boring sponge.

1990, Apr. 4   Litho.   Perf. 14x13
56 A17   60c multicolored   1.60 1.00
57 A17   70c multicolored   2.10 1.50
58 A17 100c multicolored   3.00 2.50
        Nos. 56-58 (3)   6.70 5.00

A18

200c, Character trademark.

1990, May 30   Litho.   Perf. 13x14
59 A18   35c multicolored   1.50 1.00
60 A18 200c multicolored   4.50 3.25

World Cup Soccer Championships, Italy.

A19

1990, Sept. 12
61 A19   45c Tools   1.40 1.00
62 A19   60c Stone figure   1.60 1.00
63 A19 100c Jar   2.75 1.50
        Nos. 61-63 (3)   5.75 3.50

Archeological discoveries.

Landscapes A20

1991, Jan. 31   Litho.   Perf. 14x13
64 A20   55c Seashore   1.25 1.00
65 A20   65c Desert   1.50 1.30
66 A20 100c Cactus, ocean view 2.25 2.00
        Nos. 64-66 (3)   5.00 4.30

Working Women — A21

Designs: 35c, Taking care of others. 70c, Housewife. 100c, Women in society.

1991, Mar. 28   Litho.   *Perf. 13x14*
67	A21	35c multicolored	1.00 .50
68	A21	70c multicolored	1.50 1.25
69	A21	100c multicolored	2.00 1.75
		Nos. 67-69 (3)	4.50 3.50

Style of inscriptions varies.

Medicinal Plants — A22

65c, Ocimum sanctum. 75c, Jatropha gossypifolia. 95c, Croton flavens.

1991, May 29
70	A22	65c multicolored	1.50 1.00
71	A22	75c multicolored	1.75 1.25
72	A22	95c multicolored	2.00 1.50
		Nos. 70-72 (3)	5.25 3.75

A23

Aruban Handicrafts: 35c, Fish net, wood float, wooden needle. 250c, Straw hat, hat block.

1991, July 31   Litho.   *Perf. 13x14*
73	A23	35c lt bl, dk bl & blk	1.00 .75
74	A23	250c pink, lil rose & blk	4.25 3.50

A24

35c, Toucan. 70c, People shaking hands. 100c, Windmill.

1991, Nov. 29   Litho.   *Perf. 13x14*
75	A24	35c multicolored	1.00 1.00
76	A24	70c multicolored	1.50 1.00
77	A24	100c multicolored	2.50 2.00
		Nos. 75-77 (3)	5.00 4.00

Welcome to Aruba.

Aruba Postal Service, Cent. — A25

60c, Government decree, 1892, vert. 75c, First post office. 80c, Current post office.

Perf. 13x14, 14x13
1992, Jan. 31   Litho.
78	A25	60c multicolored	1.25 1.00
79	A25	75c multicolored	1.50 1.00
80	A25	80c multicolored	2.00 1.50
		Nos. 78-80 (3)	4.75 3.50

Equality Day — A26

No. 81, People of five races. No. 82, Woman, man, scales.

1992, Mar. 25   Litho.   *Perf. 14x13*
81	A26	100c multicolored	2.00 1.50
82	A26	100c multicolored	2.00 1.50

Discovery of America, 500th Anniv. — A27

1992, July 30   Litho.   *Perf. 13x14*
83	A27	30c Columbus	1.50 .50
84	A27	40c Sailing ship	1.50 .75
85	A27	50c Natives, map	1.50 1.00
		Nos. 83-85 (3)	4.50 2.25

Natural Bridges in Aruba — A28

Designs: 70c, Seroe Colorado Bridge, south coast. 80c, Natural Bridge, north coast.

1992, Nov. 30   Litho.   *Perf. 14x13*
86	A28	70c multicolored	1.50 1.00
87	A28	80c multicolored	1.75 1.00

Express Mail Service — A29

1993, Jan. 29   Litho.   *Perf. 13x14*
88	A29	200c multicolored	4.50 3.25

A30

Various rock formations found in Districts of Ayo and Casibari.

1993, Mar. 31   Litho.   *Perf. 13x14*
89	A30	50c multicolored	1.00 1.00
90	A30	60c multicolored	1.25 1.00
91	A30	100c multicolored	2.00 1.75
		Nos. 89-91 (3)	4.25 3.75

Folklore — A31

40c, String instruments, drum. 70c, Traditional music & games. 80c, Dera Gai song lyrics.

1993, May 28   Litho.   *Perf. 13x14*
92	A31	40c multicolored	1.20 1.00
93	A31	70c multicolored	1.30 1.00
94	A31	80c multicolored	1.50 1.50
		Nos. 92-94 (3)	4.00 3.50

Sailing Sports — A32

1993, July 30   Litho.   *Perf. 13x14*
95	A32	50c Sailboating	1.15 1.00
96	A32	65c Land sailing	1.35 1.00
97	A32	75c Wind surfing	1.50 1.25
		Nos. 95-97 (3)	4.00 3.25

Iguana Iguana — A33

Perf. 14x13, 13x14
1993, Sept. 1   Litho.
98	A33	35c Young	1.50 1.00
99	A33	60c Almost grown	1.65 1.25
100	A33	100c Mature, vert.	2.25 2.00
		Nos. 98-100 (3)	5.40 4.25

Burrowing Owl — A34

5c, Two adults. 10c, Two adults, young. 35c, Adult with prey, vert. 40c, Adult, vert.

Perf. 14x13, 13x14
1994, Jan. 28   Litho.
101	A34	5c multicolored	1.75 .50
102	A34	10c multicolored	1.75 .75
103	A34	35c multicolored	2.25 1.00
104	A34	40c multicolored	2.25 1.50
		Nos. 101-104 (4)	8.00 3.75

World Wildlife Fund.

A35

Intl. Olympic Committee, Cent.: 90c, Baron Pierre de Coubertin (1863-1937), founder of modern Olympics.

1994, Mar. 29   Litho.   *Perf. 13x14*
105	A35	50c multicolored	1.25 1.00
106	A35	90c multicolored	1.75 1.40

A36

150c, Mascot, soccer ball.

1994, July 7   Litho.   *Perf. 13x14*
107	A36	65c shown	1.50 1.25
108	A36	150c multicolored	3.00 2.50

1994 World Cup Soccer Championships, US.

Wild Fruit — A37

Designs: 40c, Malpighia punicifolia. 70c, Cordia sebestena. 85c, Pithecellobium unguis-cati. 150c, Coccoloba uvifera.

1994, Sept. 28   Litho.   *Perf. 13x14*
109	A37	40c multicolored	1.10 1.00
110	A37	70c multicolored	1.50 1.00
111	A37	85c multicolored	1.90 1.50
112	A37	150c multicolored	3.25 2.50
		Nos. 109-112 (4)	7.75 6.00

Architectural Landmarks A38

Designs: 35c, Government building, 1888. 60c, Ecury residence, 1929, vert. 100c, Protestant Church, 1846, vert.

1995, Jan. 27   Litho.   *Perf. 14x13*
113	A38	35c multicolored	.90 .80

Perf. 13x14
114	A38	60c multicolored	1.50 1.00
115	A38	100c multicolored	2.10 1.90
		Nos. 113-115 (3)	4.50 3.70

UN, 50th Anniv. — A39

Designs: 30c, Flags, sea, UN emblem, dove, text from UN charter. 200c, World with flags, doves, UN emblem.

1995, Mar. 29   Litho.   *Perf. 13x14*
116	A39	30c multicolored	1.25 .75
117	A39	200c multicolored	3.75 3.25

Interpaso Horses — A40

Designs: 25c, 10-time champion Casanova II, ribbons, horiz. 75c, Paso Fino, horiz. 80c, Horse doing figure 8. 90c, Girl on horse.

1995, May 26   *Perf. 14x13, 13x14*
118	A40	25c multicolored	.90 .50
119	A40	75c multicolored	1.60 1.25
120	A40	80c multicolored	1.60 1.50
121	A40	90c multicolored	1.90 1.50
		Nos. 118-121 (4)	6.00 4.75

Vegetables — A41

25c, Vigna sinensis. 50c, Cucumis anguria. 70c, Hibiscus esculentus. 85c, Cucurbita moschata.

1995, July 28   Litho.   Perf. 13x14
122 A41 25c multicolored .85 .50
123 A41 50c multicolored 1.40 1.00
124 A41 70c multicolored 1.50 1.25
125 A41 85c multicolored 1.75 1.50
   Nos. 122-125 (4) 5.50 4.25

Turtles — A42

1995, Sept. 27   Litho.   Perf. 14x13
126 A42 15c Hawksbill 1.75 .55
127 A42 50c Green 2.25 1.00
128 A42 95c Loggerhead 2.40 1.50
129 A42 100c Leatherback 2.75 1.50
   Nos. 126-129 (4) 9.15 4.55

Separate Status, 10th Anniv. — A43

Statesmen and politicians: No. 130, Jan Hendrik Albert Eman (1887-1957). No. 131, Juan Enrique Irausquin (1904-62). No. 132, Cornelis Albert Eman (1916-67). No. 133, Gilberto Francois Croes (1938-86).

1996, Jan. 1   Litho.   Perf. 13x14
130 A43 100c multicolored 1.90 1.50
131 A43 100c multicolored 1.90 1.50
132 A43 100c multicolored 1.90 1.50
133 A43 100c multicolored 1.90 1.50
   Nos. 130-133 (4) 7.60 6.00

The 1986 date on No. 133 is in error.

America Issue — A44

National dresswear: 65c, Woman wearing long, full dress, apron, vert. 70c, Man wearing hat, bow tie, white shirt, black pants, vert. 100c, Couple dancing.

Perf. 13x14, 14x13
1996, Mar. 25   Litho.
134 A44 65c multicolored 2.25 1.00
135 A44 70c multicolored 2.25 1.00
136 A44 100c multicolored 3.00 1.50
   Nos. 134-136 (3) 7.50 3.50

1996 Summer Olympic Games, Atlanta — A45

1996, May 28   Litho.   Perf. 14x13
137 A45 85c Runners 2.00 1.25
138 A45 130c Cyclist 2.50 2.25

A46

Famous Women: No. 139, Livia (Mimi) Ecury (1920-91), nurse. No. 140, Lolita Euson (1914-94), poet. No. 141, Laura Wernet-Paskel (1911-62), teacher.

1996, Sept. 27   Litho.   Perf. 13x14
139 A46 60c multicolored 1.50 1.50
140 A46 60c multicolored 1.50 1.50
141 A46 60c multicolored 1.50 1.50
   Nos. 139-141 (3) 4.50 4.50

A47

Year of Papiamento 1997: 50c, Sign promoting use of Papiamento language, children playing on beach, people in water, boat. 140c, "Papiamento," sunrise.

1997, Jan. 23   Litho.   Perf. 13x14
142 A47 50c multicolored 1.00 1.00
143 A47 140c multicolored 2.50 2.50

Mailman on Bicycle, 1936-57 A48

America issue: 70c, Mailman handing mail to woman, jeep, 1957-88. 80c, Mailman on motor scooter placing mail in mailbox, 1995.

1997, Mar. 27   Litho.   Perf. 14x13
144 A48 60c multicolored 2.75 1.50
145 A48 70c multicolored 2.75 1.50
146 A48 80c multicolored 2.75 1.50
   Nos. 144-146 (3) 8.25 4.50

Aruban Architectrue A49

30c, Decorated cunucu house. 65c, Steps with "popchi's." 100c, Arends's Building, vert.

1997, May 22   Litho.   Perf. 14x13
147 A49 30c multicolored .90 .75
148 A49 65c multicolored 1.75 1.25

Perf. 13x14
149 A49 100c multicolored 2.00 1.75
   Nos. 147-149 (3) 4.65 3.75

Marine Life — A50

Designs: a, Marlin jumping out of water, lighthouse. b, Dolphin jumping out of water, trees, plants on beach. c, Iguana on rock, beach. d, Dolphin, fish. e, Two dolphins, fish. f, Fish, turtles, owl on beach. g, Various fish among coral. h, Diver, shipwreck, fish, coral. i, Various fish.

1997, May 29   Litho.   Perf. 12½x13
150 A50 90c Sheet of 9, #a.-i. 27.50 27.50
   PACIFIC 97.

Cruise Tourism A51

Designs: 35c, Ship at pier, tourists walking toward ship. 50c, Ship with gangway lowered, tourists. 150c, Ship out to sea, small boat.

1997, July 24   Litho.   Perf. 14x13
151 A51 35c multicolored 1.25 .85
152 A51 50c multicolored 1.50 1.10
153 A51 150c multicolored 3.00 2.50
   Nos. 151-153 (3) 5.75 4.45

Aruban Wild Flowers A52

50c, Erythrina velutina. 60c, Cordia dentata. 70c, Tabebuia billbergii. 130c, Guaiacum officinale.

1997, Sept. 25
154 A52 50c multicolored 1.50 1.00
155 A52 60c multicolored 1.75 1.25
156 A52 70c multicolored 2.00 1.25
157 A52 130c multicolored 2.75 2.00
   Nos. 154-157 (4) 8.00 5.50

Fort Zoutman, Bicent. — A53

1998, Jan. 13   Litho.   Perf. 14x13
158 A53 30c sepia & multi 1.00 .75
159 A53 250c gray & multi 4.25 3.75

Total Solar Eclipse, 1998 — A54

100c, Map, track of eclipse.

1998, Feb. 26   Litho.   Perf. 13x14
160 A54 85c shown 2.25 1.50
161 A54 100c multicolored 2.75 1.60

Native Birds — A55

50c, Mimus gilvus. 60c, Falco sparverius. 70c, Icterus icterus. 150c, Coereba flaveola.

Perf. 14x13, 13x14
1998, July 10   Litho.
162 A55 50c multi 1.80 1.00
163 A55 60c multi, vert. 2.00 1.25
164 A55 70c multi, vert. 2.25 1.25
165 A55 150c multi 3.25 2.75
   Nos. 162-165 (4) 9.30 6.25

World Stamp 1998 — A56

1998, Sept. 8   Litho.   Perf. 14x13
166 A56 225c multicolored 5.50 4.25

Endangered Animals A57

Equus asinus: 40c, Two standing on hill. 65c, Three standing, rocks, cacti, tree. 100c, Adult, foal standing among rocks, cacti.

1999, June 21   Litho.   Perf. 14x13
167 A57 40c multicolored 1.40 .75
168 A57 65c multicolored 1.60 1.25
169 A57 100c multicolored 2.40 2.00
   Nos. 167-169 (3) 5.40 4.00

Cacti — A58

Designs: 50c, Opuntia wentiana. 60c, Lemaireocereus griseus. 70c, Cephalocereus lanuginosus. 75c, Cephalocereus lanuginosus (in bloom).

1999, Mar. 31   Litho.   Perf. 14x13
170 A58 50c multicolored 1.50 1.00
171 A58 60c multicolored 1.75 1.25
172 A58 70c multicolored 1.75 1.25
173 A58 75c multicolored 2.00 1.50
   Nos. 170-173 (4) 7.00 5.00

Dogs — A59

Various dogs, background: 40c, Trees. 60c, Cactus, aloe plant, rocks. 80c, Tree, sea. 165c, Sky, clouds.

1999, May 31   Litho.   Perf. 13x14
174 A59 40c multicolored 1.50 1.00
175 A59 60c multicolored 1.75 1.25
176 A59 80c multicolored 2.00 1.50
177 A59 165c multicolored 3.25 2.75
   Nos. 174-177 (4) 8.50 6.50

Discovery of Aruba, 500th Anniv. — A60

1999, Aug. 9   Litho.   Perf. 14x13
178 A60 150c shown 2.75 2.25
179 A60 175c Abstract paintings 3.25 2.75
   a. Souvenir sheet, #178-179 7.00 6.00

Natl. Library, 50th Anniv. — A61

1999, Aug. 20
180 A61 70c shown 1.50 1.50
181 A61 100c Original building 2.25 2.00

Christmas — A62

Coil Stamps
Die Cut Perf. 13x13½
1999, Dec. 1   Self-Adhesive   Litho.
182 A62 40c Magi on shore 1.80 1.00
183 A62 70c Magi in desert 2.25 1.25
184 A62 100c Holy Family 2.75 1.75
   Nos. 182-184 (3) 6.80 4.00

Tourist Attractions A62a

Reptiles
A63

Tourist Attractions: 25c, Guadirikiri Cave. 55c, Cactus landscape. 85c, Hooiberg. 500c, Conchi. Reptiles: 40c, Norops lineatus. 60c, Iguana iguana, vert. 75c, Leptodeira annulata, vert. 150c, Cnemidophorus murinus.

2000	Litho.		Perf. 14x13, 13x14	
185	A62a	25c multi	1.00	.50
186	A63	40c multi	1.25	.75
187	A62a	55c multi	1.40	1.00
188	A63	60c multi	1.40	1.25
189	A63	75c multi	1.60	1.25
190	A62a	85c multi	1.75	1.50
191	A63	150c multi	3.25	2.25
192	A62a	500c multi	8.50	7.25
	Nos. 185-192 (8)		20.15	15.75

Issued: 40c, 60c, 75c, 150c, 1/31; 25c, 55c, 85c, 500c, 6/5.
See Nos. 197-204.

America Issue, Campaign Against AIDS — A64

175c, Ribbon on globe, vert.

	Perf. 14x13, 13x14			
2000, Mar. 2			Litho.	
193	A64	75c Flags	2.00	2.00
194	A64	175c multicolored	4.00	4.00

Organization Anniversaries A65

Designs: 150c, Aruba Bank N.V., 75th anniv. 165c, Alto Vista Church, 250th anniv.

2000, Apr. 20			Litho.	Perf. 14x13
195	A65	150c multi	3.00	2.50
196	A65	165c multi	3.25	2.75

Type of 2000

Animals: 5c, Cat. 15c, Shells. 30c, Tortoise. 35c, Mud house, vert. 50c, Rabbit. 100c, Balashi gold smelter, vert. 200c, Parakeet. 250c, Rock crystals.

	Perf. 14x13, 13x14 (#200, 202)			
2001			Litho.	
197	A63	5c multi	1.10	.50
198	A62a	15c multi	.50	.40
199	A63	30c multi	1.75	1.00
200	A62a	35c multi	1.00	.95
201	A63	50c multi	1.75	1.00
202	A62a	100c multi	2.50	2.10
203	A63	200c multi	4.50	4.00
204	A62a	250c multi	5.25	4.75
	Nos. 197-204 (8)		18.35	14.70

Issued: 5c, 30c, 50c, 200c, 1/31. 15c, 35c, 100c, 250c, 8/6.

Mascaruba, 40th Anniv. — A66

Actors on stage and audience in: 60c: Background. 150c, Foreground.

2001, Mar. 26		Litho.	Perf. 14x13
205-206	A66	Set of 2	4.50 4.00

Classic Motor Vehicles A67

Designs: 25c, 1930 Ford Crown Victoria Leatherback. 40c, 1933 Citroen Commerciale. 70c, 1948 Plymouth pickup truck. 75c, 1959 Ford Edsel.

2001, May 31			
207-210	A67	Set of 4	8.00 5.75

Year of Dialogue Among Civilizations A68

2001, Oct. 9		Litho.	Perf. 14x13
211	A68	175c multi	4.00 3.25

Airport Views — A69

Designs: 30c, Dakota Airport, 1950. 75c, Queen Beatrix Airport, 1972. 175c, Queen Beatrix Airport, 2000.

2002, Jan. 31		Litho.	Perf. 14x13
212-214	A69	Set of 3	6.25 5.00

Royal Wedding A70

Prince Willem-Alexander, Maxima Zorreguieta and: 60c, Royal palace, golden coach. 300c, Bourse of Berlage, New Church.

2002, Feb. 2			
215-216	A70	Set of 2	6.50 6.25

Water and Energy Company, 70th Anniv. — A71

Designs: 60c, Faucet and water drop, vert. 85c, Pipeline. 165c, Meter and meter-reading equipment, vert.

	Perf. 13x14, 14x13		
2002, June 3			Litho.
217-219	A71	Set of 3	6.50 6.25

America Issue — Youth, Education and Literacy A72

Designs: 25c, Hand writing letters with quill pen. 100c, Child looking over wall of letters.

2002, July 15		Litho.	Perf. 14x12¾
220-221	A72	Set of 2	3.75 2.75

Aruba in World War II — A73

Designs: 60c, Attack on Lago Oil Refinery by German U-boat U-156. 75c, Torpedoing of ships by U-156. 150c, Statue of "Boy" Ecury, Aruban resistance fighter, Aruban militiaman, vert.

	Perf. 14x13, 13x14		
2002, Sept. 9			Litho.
222-224	A73	Set of 3	8.00 5.50

Mud Houses A74

Various houses with frame color of: 40c, Yellow green. 60c, Blue green. 75c, Red.

2003, Jan. 31		Litho.	Perf. 14x13
225-227	A74	Set of 3	3.75 3.00

De Trupialen Performing Organization, 50th Anniv. — A75

Designs: 30c, Trupialen Boys' Choir. 50c, Play handbills. 100c, Emblems.

2003, Mar. 31		Litho.	Perf. 14x13
228-230	A75	Set of 3	3.75 3.00

Orchids A76

Designs: 75c, Schomburgkia humboldtii. 500c, Brassavola nodosa.

2003, May 30		Litho.	Perf. 14x13
231-232	A76	Set of 2	11.00 11.00

Butterflies A77

Designs: 40c, Orange-barred sulphur. 75c, Monarch. 85c, Hairstreak. 175c, Gulf fritillary.

2003, July 31			
233-236	A77	Set of 4	8.75 7.00

Endangered Animals — A78

Turtles: 25c, Eretmochelys imbricata, vert. 60c, Dermochelys coriacea. 75c, Chelonia mydas, vert. 150c, Caretta caretta.

	Perf. 13x14, 14x13		
2003, Sept. 30			Litho.
237-240	A78	Set of 4	7.50 6.00

Birds — A80

Designs: 70c, Sterna sandvicensis. 75c, Pelecanus occidentalis. 80c, Fregata magnificens. 90c, Larus atricilla.

2004, Mar. 31			Perf. 13x14
244-247	A80	Set of 4	7.00 5.00

Fish — A81

Designs: 40c, Parrotfish. 60c, Queen angelfish. 75c, Squirrelfish. 100c, Smallmouth grunt.

2004, May 31		Litho.	Perf. 14x13
248-251	A81	Set of 4	6.50 5.00

Christmas and New Year's Day — A82

Designs: 50c, Children, Christmas tree, gifts. 85c, Choir, stained glass window, candle, gifts. 125c, Fireworks display.

2004, Dec. 1		Litho.	Perf. 13x14
252-254	A82	Set of 3	4.00 4.00

Kingdom Statutes, 50th Anniv. — A83

Designs: 160c, Collage of Netherlands Antilles islands. 165c, Kingdom Statute Monument.

2004, Dec. 15			Perf. 14x13
255-256	A83	Set of 2	4.50 4.50

Greetings A84

Designs: 60c, Sun, flower (Thank you). 75c, Cacti and rabbits (Love). 135c, Fish (Get well soon). 215c, Balloons and flag (Congratulations).

2005, Jan. 31		Litho.	Perf. 14x13
257-260	A84	Set of 4	7.25 7.25

Drag Racing — A85

Drag racers: 60c, One car going airborne. 85c, One car with chute deployed. 185c, Cars at start line.

2005, Mar. 16			
261-263	A85	Set of 3	5.50 5.00

Carnival, 50th Anniv. — A79

Designs: 60c, Masks. 75c, Carnival Queen, vert. 150c, Aruba flag, Carnival participants.

	Perf. 14x13, 13x14		
2004, Jan. 30			Litho.
241-243	A79	Set of 3	4.50 4.50

Souvenir Sheet

Reign of Queen Beatrix, 25th
Anniv. — A86

No. 264: a, 30c, At coronation, 1980. b, 60c, Making speech, 1991. c, 75c, With Nelson Mandela, 1999. d, 105c, Visiting Aruba and the Netherlands Antilles, 1999. e, 215c, Speaking before European Parliament, 2004.

2005, Apr. 30 Litho.   Perf. 13¼x13¾
264 A86   Sheet of 5, #a-e   7.50 7.50

Sunsets — A87

Designs: 60c, Birds and cacti. 100c, Palm tree. 205c, Pelicans and pilings.

2005, May 31   Perf. 13x14
265-267 A87   Set of 3   5.75 5.75

Birds of
Prey — A88

Designs: 60c, Falco sparverius. 75c, Athene cunicularia. 135c, Pandion haliaetus. 200c, Polyborus plancus.

2005, July 29 Litho.   Perf. 14x13
268-271 A88   Set of 4   8.75 8.75
271a   Souvenir sheet, #268-271   8.75 8.75

A89

Corals: 60c, Staghorn coral. 75c, Blade fire coral. 100c, Deepwater sea fan. 215c, Smooth brain coral.

2005, Sept. 30 Litho.   Perf. 13x14
272-275 A89   Set of 4   7.00 7.00

A90

Children and philately: 75c, Girl, stamps. 85c, Boy with magnifying glass and stamp album. 125c, Boy with tongs and stock book.

2005, Oct. 31
276-278 A90   Set of 3   4.75 4.75

Paintings
A91

Designs: 60c, House at Savaneta, by Jean Georges Pandellis. 75c, Haf di Rei, by Mateo Hayde. 185c, Landscape, by Julie Q. Oduber.

2006, Feb. 6 Litho.   Perf. 14x13
279-281 A91   Set of 3   5.50 5.50

Aruba YMCA, 50th
Anniv. — A92

Designs: 75c, YMCA emblem. 205c, Children in playground, horiz.

Perf. 13x14, 14x13
2006, Apr. 3   Litho.
282-283 A92   Set of 2   4.50 4.50

Souvenir Sheet

Washington 2006 World Philatelic
Exhibition — A93

No. 284 — Exhibition emblem and: a, Natural Bridge, head of iguana, tree and cactus. b, Cacti, tail of iguana, sailboat, vert.

2006, May 27 Litho.   Perf. 12¾
284 A93   500c Sheet of 2, #a-b 13.50 13.50

2006 World Cup Soccer
Championships, Germany — A94

Designs: 75c, Children's drawing of goalie. 215c, Goalie's gloves and ball.

2006, June 5 Litho.   Perf. 14x13
285-286 A94   Set of 2   4.50 4.50

Hi-Winds
Windsurfing
Regatta, 20th
Anniv. — A95

Designs: 60c, Hotel, windsurfers, kitesurfer, and fishing boats. 100c, Kitesurfers, windsurfer and flag in water. 125c, Windsurfers.

2006, July 3 Litho.   Perf. 14x13
287-289 A95   Set of 3   4.00 4.00

Fire
Prevention
A96

Designs: 60c, Fire prevention, safety and extinguishing strategies. 100c, Firemen at house fire. 205c, Fire trucks.

2006, Sept. 29 Litho.   Perf. 14x13
290-292 A96   Set of 3   5.75 5.75

Arikok
National
Park — A97

Designs: 75c, Cas di Torto, goat and garden, Cunucu Arikok. 100c, View of Miralamar, vert. 200c, Dunes of Boca Prins.

2006, Oct. 31 Litho.   Perf. 14x13
293-295 A97   Set of 3   5.25 5.25

Souvenir Sheet

New Year 2007 (Year of the
Pig) — A98

No. 296: a, 205c, Pig. b, 215c, Dragon, vert.

2007, Feb. 15 Litho.   Perf. 12¾
296 A98   Sheet of 2, #a-b   6.50 6.50

Casa Cuna
Children's
Home
Foundation,
50th
Anniv. — A99

Designs: 50c, Original Casa Cuna building, Luciana Maria Koolman. 125c, Children in hands. 150c, New Casa Cuna building.

2007, Apr. 4   Perf. 14x13
297-299 A99   Set of 3   4.50 4.50

Museums in
Oranjestad
A100

Designs: 70c, Museum of Antiquities. 85c, Numismatic Museum. 100c, Archaeological Museum. 135c, Historical Museum.

2007, July 2 Litho.   Perf. 14x13
300-303 A100   Set of 4   5.00 5.00

Souvenir Sheet

Wrecks and Reefs — A101

No. 304: a, 200c, Pipeline system of wrecked oil tanker Pedernalis. b, 300c, Convair 400 airplane near Sonesta Island. c, 500c, Sea turtle, wreck of freighter Jane. d, 500c, Fish, wreck of freighter Antilla.

2007, Sept. 3 Litho.   Perf. 14x13
304 A101   Sheet of 4, #a-d   17.00 17.00

Christmas
and New
Year's
Day — A102

Designs: 70c, Infant and mother. 100c, Girl with toys and gift box. 150c, Boy at New Year's celebration.

2007, Oct. 17
305-307 A102   Set of 3   4.00 4.00

Heineken
Aruba
Catamaran
Regatta
A103

Designs: 40c, Catamarans on beach. 80c, Catamarans racing near race buoy. 125c, Competitor leaning off side of catamaran. 130c, Row of catamarans in race.

2007, Nov. 8
308-311 A103   Set of 4   4.75 4.75

Alto Vista
Church —
A103a

2007-09 Litho.   Perf. 14x13
Frame Color

311A	A103a	5c pink	1.00	1.00
311B	A103a	10c blue	1.00	1.00
311C	A103a	25c lt bl grn	1.00	1.00
311D	A103a	50c yel green	1.00	1.00
311E	A103a	85c green	1.00	1.00
311F	A103a	90c lt grnsh bl	1.00	1.00
311G	A103a	100c salmon	1.00	1.00
311H	A103a	125c violet	1.50	1.50
311I	A103a	130c lt blue	1.50	1.50
311J	A103a	135c beige	1.50	1.50
311K	A103a	140c violet	1.50	1.50
311L	A103a	200c dull org	2.00	2.00
311M	A103a	215c gray	2.50	2.50
311N	A103a	220c gray	2.50	2.50

Nos. 311A-311N (14)   17.45 17.45

Issued: 5c, 50c, 85c, 100c, 200c, 7/30/07; 135c, 9/3/08; 90c, 130c, 140c, 220c, 3/9/09. Others, 2007.

Most sets between Nos. 312-465 were printed in sheets containing two sets separated by a row of pictorial tabs. Sets with these tabs command a small premium.

Queen Beatrix, 70th
Birthday — A104

Queen Beatrix: 75c, As one-year old with Dutch dignitaries. 125c, With Prince Claus and newborn Crown Prince Willem Alexander. 250c, In royal robes on day of accession to throne. 300c, With family of Crown Prince Willem Alexander.

2008, Jan. 31   Perf. 13x14
312-315 A104   Set of 4   9.00 9.00

Aruban
Cultural
Year — A105

Designs: 80c, Carnival participants. 130c, Organ grinders. 205c, Dera Gai celebration. 275c, Dande musicians visiting home.

2008, Mar. 18   **Litho.**   **Perf. 14x13**
316-319 A105   Set of 4   7.50 7.50

2008 Summer Olympics, Beijing A106

Designs: 50c, Running. 75c, Synchronized swimming. 100c, Men's rings, vert. 125c, Judo.

2008, Apr. 1   **Perf. 14x13, 13x14**
320-323 A106   Set of 4   4.75 4.75

Athene Cunicularia Arubensis — A107

Aruban burrowing owl: 100c, Entire bird. 150c, Two birds, horiz. 350c, Head of bird.

Perf. 13x14, 14x13
2008, June 2   **Litho.**
324-326 A107   Set of 3   7.50 7.50

Harley-Davidson Motorcycles — A108

Designs: 175c, FRX Super Glide Big Boy. 225c, Knucklehead. 305c, Roadking.

2008, July 4   **Litho.**   **Perf. 14x13**
327-329 A108   Set of 3   8.00 8.00

Aruban Culture A109

Designs: No. 330, Poem by Federico Oduber. No. 331, 240c, Watapana Magazine covers, vert. No. 332, Henry Habibe and poem by Habibe, vert.

2008, July 8   **Litho.**   **Perf. 13¾**
330 A109 240c multi   6.75 6.75
331 A109 240c multi   6.75 6.75
332 A109 240c multi   6.75 6.75
  a. Souvenir sheet of 5, #330-
       332, Netherlands #1311,
       Netherlands Antilles #1187,
       + etiquette   23.00 23.00
     Nos. 330-332 (3)   20.25 20.25

No. 332a sold for 10g. No. 330 also was available on Netherlands Nos. 1313a and 1313b and Netherlands Antilles No. 1189a.

Flowers — A110

No. 333: a, 100c, Calatropis procera. b, 215c, Passiflora foetida.

No. 334: a, 185c, Thespesia populnea. b, 200c, Cryptostegia grandiflora.

2008, Aug. 8   **Litho.**   **Perf. 13½**
333 A110   Pair, #a-b   3.50 3.50
334 A110   Pair, #a-b   4.50 4.50

Drawings by Rembrandt (1606-69) — A111

Designs: 350c, Self-portrait, 1652. 425c, Self-portrait, 1630. 500c, Beggars at door, 1648.

2008, Sept. 30   **Litho.**   **Perf. 13x14**
335-337 A111   Set of 3   14.00 14.00

Aruba in the Past — A112

Designs: 100c, Carting of potable water. 200c, Clay houses. 215c, Processing of aloe resin.

2008, Nov. 3   **Litho.**   **Perf. 14x13**
338-340 A112   Set of 3   5.75 5.75

Louis Braille (1809-52), Educator of the Blind — A113

Designs: 200c, Braille. 215c, Walking stick for the blind.

2009, Jan. 5   **Litho.**   **Perf. 13x14**
341-342 A113   Set of 2   5.50 5.50

Miniature Sheet

Carnival, 55th Anniv. — A114

No. 343: a, 75c, Miss Carnival on float. b, 100c, Clown on float. c, 175c, Float with "55" and champagne bottle. d, 225c, Carnival dancers.

2009, Feb. 6   **Litho.**   **Perf. 13¼x13¾**
343 A114   Sheet of 4, #a-d   8.50 8.50

Caves A115

Designs: 175c, Tunnel of Love Cave. 200c, Fountain Cave. 225c, Guadirikiri Cave.

2009, Apr. 1   **Perf. 14x13**
344-346 A115   Set of 3   6.75 6.75

Souvenir Sheet

Global Warming — A116

No. 347: a, 200c, Hurricane over map of Caribbean. b, 250c, Map of polar regions, mountains, parched earth. c, 250c, Pollution from industry and vehicles. d, 300c, Fluorescent light bulb, recycling symbols, windmill.

2009, June 2
347 A116   Sheet of 4, #a-d   12.00 12.00

Souvenir Sheet

Architecture — A117

No. 348: a, 175c, California Lighthouse. b, 250c, Plaza Daniel Leo, horiz. c, 275c, Henriquez Building, horiz. d, 325c, Ecury Complex main building.

2009, July 3   **Perf. 12¾**
348 A117   Sheet of 4, #a-d   11.50 11.50

National Library, 60th Anniv. — A118

Book reader: 185c, Girl. 300c, Woman.

2009, Aug. 20   **Litho.**   **Perf. 13x14**
349-350 A118   Set of 2   5.75 5.75
350a   Vert. pair, #349-350   5.75 5.75

Dolphins A119

Designs: 125c, Stenella frontalis. 200c, Steno bredanensis. 300c, Two Stenella frontalis. 325c, Group of Steno bredanensis at surface.

2009, Sept. 30   **Perf. 14x13**
351-354 A119   Set of 4   14.00 14.00

Christmas A120

Designs: 75c Madonna and Child. 120c, Angel and stars. 125c, Hands, globe, stars, "2009." 210c, Shepherds and sheep.

2009, Oct. 19
355-358 A120   Set of 4   6.00 6.00

Miniature Sheet

Personalized Stamps — A120a

No. 358A: b, Church. c, House. d, Boat. e, Lizard and flower. f, Lighthouse. g, Tree.

2009, Dec. 18   **Litho.**   **Perf. 13¼x14**
358A A120a (295c) Sheet of 6,
                 #b-g   22.00 22.00

No. 358A sold for 1770c or $20 in U.S. currency. Stamps could be personalized. Butterfly images shown are generic.

Recycling A121

Various works of art from recycled materials: 90c, Island landscape. 180c, Post office, tree, and animal. 325c, Fish.

2010, Jan. 22   **Litho.**   **Perf. 13¼**
359-361 A121   Set of 3   6.75 6.75

Historic Airplanes — A122

No. 362: a, 250c, Seaplane. b, 500c, Seaplane and lighthouse.

2010, Mar. 26   **Perf. 13¼x13**
362 A122   Horiz. pair, #a-b   8.50 8.50

Scouting in Aruba, 10th Anniv. — A123

No. 363: a, 85c, Scouts observing nature. b, 95c, Scouts building fire. c, 135c, Scout near tent. d, 180c, Scouts playing drums.

2010, Apr. 1   **Litho.**
363 A123   Block of 4, #a-d   6.50 6.50

End of World War II, 65th Anniv. A124

No. 364: a, 140c, Large cannon. b, 200c, Beached torpedo. 275c, Equipment and ramp.

2010, May 4 **Litho.** **Perf. 13¼x13**
364 A124 Vert. strip of 3, #a-c 7.50 7.50

Parrots — A125

No. 365 — Various parrots: a, 85c. b, 90c. c, 180c.

2010, June 2 **Perf. 13x13¼**
365 A125 Horiz. strip of 3, #a-c 5.00 5.00

Paintings by Vincent Van Gogh — A126

No. 366: a, 200c, Self-portrait with Gray Felt Hat. b, 250c, Still Life: Vase with Fifteen Sunflowers. c, 305c, Starry Night. d, 500c, Wheat Field with Crows.

2010, July 29 **Perf. 13¼x13**
366 A126 Block of 4, #a-d 15.00 15.00

Rum Shops A127

No. 367: a, 100c, Essoville Rum Shop. b, 200c, Aruba Rum Shop. c, 255c, Caribbean Store.

2010, Sept. 13
367 A127 Vert. strip of 3, #a-c 7.50 7.50

Flowers — A128

No. 368: a, Caesalpinia pulcherrima. b, Dipladenia sanderi. c, Hibiscus. d, Adenium obesum. e, Bougainvillea. f, Ixora. g, Eichhornia crassipes. h, Passiflora caerulea. i, Allamanda cathartica. j, Nerium oleander.

2010, Sept. 29 **Perf. 14**
368 A128 Block of 10 23.00 23.00
a.-j. A128 200c Any single 2.25 2.25

Houses of Worship — A129

No. 369: a, 85c, Synagogue. b, 90c, Church. c, 135c, Church, diff. d, 240c, Church interior.

2010, Oct. 28 **Perf. 13x13¼**
369 A129 Block of 4, #a-d 6.75 6.75

Birds — A130

No. 370: a, Falco sparverius. b, Icterus icterus. c, Mimus gilvus. d, Egretta alba. e, Aratinga pertinax. f, Pelecanus occidentalis. g, Athene cunicularia arubensis. h, Coerba flaveola. i, Polyborus plancus. j, Colibri thalassinus.

2010, Nov. 17 **Litho.** **Perf. 14**
370 A130 Block of 10 23.00 23.00
a.-j. A130 200c Any single 2.25 2.25

Briareus Caribbean Reef Octopus — A131

No. 371 — Various depictions of octopus: a, 100c. b, 175c. c, 255c. d, 300c.

2010, Nov. 30 **Perf. 13¼x13**
371 A131 Block of 4, #a-d 10.00 10.00

Butterflies — A132

No. 372: a, Zuleika. b, Blue morpho. c, Monarch. d, White peacock. e, Sulphur. f, Zebra. g, Malachite. h, Owl. i, Postman. j, Gulf fritillary.

2010, Dec. 22 **Perf. 14**
372 Block of 10 23.00 23.00
a.-j. A132 200c Any single 2.25 2.25

Separate Political Status, 25th Anniv. — A133

No. 373 — Curved lines and: a, 200c, Star. b, 300c, "Status Aparte." c, 300c, F. B. Tromp, first governor of Aruba, and J. H. A. Eman, first prime minister of Aruba, country name in white at UL. d, 400c, A. J. Booi, first president of Parliament, and G. F. Croes, political party leader, country name in red at LR.

2011, Jan. 1
373 A133 Block of 4, #a-d 14.00 14.00

Flowers A134

No. 374: a, Catharanthus roseus. b, Echinopsis lageniformis. c, Allamanda cathartica. d, Cordia sebestena. e, Ipomoea pes-caprae. f, Hibiscus rosa-sinensis. g, Cassia fistula. h, Bougainvillea glabra. i, Delonix regia. j, Nerium oleander.

2011, Feb. 16 **Perf. 14**
374 Block of 10 19.00 19.00
a.-j. A134 160c Any single 1.90 1.90

America Issue — A135

No. 375 — Hands with flags of: a, 200c, Portugal, United States, Cuba and Brazil. b, 250c, Honduras, Canada, Colombia and Chile. c, 350c, United States, Brazil, Aruba and Panama. d, 400c, Suriname, Colombia, Chile and Spain.
No. 376: a, Like No. 375a. b, Like No. 375b. c, Like No. 375c. d, Like No. 375d.

2011, Mar. 23
375 Vert. strip of 4 13.50 13.50
a. A135 200c multi 2.25 2.25
b. A135 250c multi 2.75 2.75
c. A135 350c multi 4.00 4.00
d. A135 400c multi 4.50 4.50

Miniature Sheet
376 A135 300c Sheet of 4, #a-d 13.50 13.50

Postal Union of the Americas, Spain and Portugal (UPAEP), cent.

Bank Notes — A136

No. 377: a, 1964 Indonesia 25 sen note. b, 1986 Bhutan 2 ngultrum note. c, 1949 Philippines 50 centavo note. d, 1987 Sudan 25 piastre note. e, 1976 Mozambique 100 escudo note. f, 1993 Haiti 25 gourde note. g, 1917 Göttingen 25 pfennig note. h, 1997 Turkey 250,000 lira note. i, 1977 Solomon Islands 10 dollar note. j, 1915 Lille 25 centime note. k, 1985 Egypt 25 piastre note. l, 1976 Albania 100 lek note.

2011, Apr. 4
377 A136 Block of 12 24.00 24.00
a.-l. 167c Any single 2.00 2.00

Maastricht Paper Money Fair.

Peonies — A137

No. 378 — Color of flowers: a, Dark red. b, Yellow. c, White. d, Pink.
350c, Pink peony.

2011, May 11 **Litho.** **Perf. 14**
378 A137 110c Sheet of 4, #a-d 5.50 5.50

Souvenir Sheet
379 A137 350c multi 4.25 4.25

Fish — A138

No. 380: a, Holacanthus ciliaris. b, Chaetodon capistratus. c, Sparisoma viride. d, Pomacanthus paru. e, Balistes vetula. f, Lactophrys triqueter. g, Holocentrus rufus. h, Chaetodon striatus. i, Diodon holocanthus. j, Equetus punctatus.

2011, June 15
380 Block of 10 14.00 14.00
a.-j. A138 120c Any single 1.40 1.40

Chess — A139

No. 381 — Positions of chess pieces at end of 1956 match between Donald Byrne and winner Bobby Fischer: a, White queen on tan square. b, Black king on tan square. c, White knight on tan square. d, Black bishop on tan square. e, White pawn on tan square. f, Black bishop on green square. g, Black knight on tan square. h, Black rook on green square. i, White pawn on green square. j, White king on tan square. k, Black pawn on green square.

2011, July 22

381	Sheet of 15, #a-j, 5 #k + 49 labels	32.50	32.50
a.-k.	A139 180c Any single	2.10	2.10

Mail Boxes of the World — A140

No. 382: a, Dark red rectangular pillar box. b, Orange red Estonian Post mail box. c, Yellow mail box. d, Blue USPS mail box. e, Yellow mail box inscribed "Postbriefkasten." f, Blue mail box with Cyrillic letters. g, Green pillar box with Chinese inscriptions. h, Red mail box inscribed "Brieven Drukwerken." i, Green mail box with two legs. j, Red hexagonal British pillar box.

2011, Aug. 19

382	Block of 10	17.50	17.50
a.-j.	A140 150c Any single	1.75	1.75

Paintings by Jan Vermeer (1632-75) — A141

No. 383: a, Girl with a Red Hat (red frame). b, The Milkmaid (blue frame). c, The Lacemaker (brown frame). d, Girl with a Pearl Earring (red frame).

2011, Sept. 21   Litho.   *Perf. 14*

383	Vert. strip of 4	11.50	11.50
a.	A141 200c multi	2.25	2.25
b.-c.	A141 250c Either single	2.75	2.75
d.	A141 300c multi	3.50	3.50

Ships — A142

No. 384 — Various tall ships with panel color of: a, 200c, Blue violet. b, 225c, Maroon, horiz. c, 250c, Blue violet, horiz. d, 250c, Maroon, horiz. e, 275c, Maroon, horiz. f, 300c, Blue violet.

2011, Oct. 25

384	A142 Block of 6, #a-f	17.50	17.50

Butterflies A143

Designs: No. 385, 160c, Diaethria neglecta. No. 386, 160c, Lycaena cupreus lapidicola. No. 387, 160c, Pyrrhogyra edocla. No. 388, 160c, Anartia amathea amathea. No. 389, 160c, Anglais urticae. No. 390, 160c, Morpho aega. No. 391, 160c, Junonia coenia coenia (red violet background). No. 392, 160c, Junonia coenia coenia (dark purple background). No. 393, 160c, Dione juno juno. No. 394, 160c, Lycaena heteronea austin.

2011, Dec. 1

385-394	A143 Set of 10	18.50	18.50

Nos. 385-394 were printed in sheets containing two of each stamp + a central label.

Birds — A144

No. 395: a, Pithecophaga jeffreyi. b, Harpia harpyja. c, Morphnus guaianensis. d, Caracara plancus. e, Lophaetus occipitalis. f, Stephanoaetus coronatus. g, Haliaeetus leucocephalus. h, Vultur gryphus. i, Aquila chrysaetos. j, Falco sparverius.

2012, Jan. 19

395	Block of 10	17.50	17.50
a.-j.	A144 150c Any single	1.75	1.75

Aruban Goats — A145

No. 396: a, Three goats on rocks. b, Two goats on rocks, horiz. c, Goat, horiz. d, Goat and cactus.

2012, Feb. 21

396	Strip of 4	11.00	11.00
a.	A145 175c multi	2.00	2.00
b.	A145 225c multi	2.50	2.50
c.	A145 275c multi	3.00	3.00
d.	A145 300c multi	3.50	3.50

2012 Summer Olympics, London — A146

No. 397: a, Torch. b, Swimmer, horiz. c, Hurdler, horiz. d, "Olympia."

2012, Apr. 27

397	A146 500c Block of 4, #a-d	22.50	22.50
e.	Souvenir sheet of 4, #397a-397d	22.50	22.50

Whales A147

No. 398: a, Delphinapterus leucas. b, Kogia breviceps. c, Balaena mysticetus. d, Orcinus orca. e, Physeter macrocephalus. f, Balaenoptera musculus. g, Globicephala macrorhynchus. h, Mesoplodon europaeus. i, Balaenoptera edeni. j, Megaptera novaeangliae.

2012, May 15

398	Block of 10	14.00	14.00
a.-j.	A147 120c Any single	1.40	1.40

Women's Dresses — A148

No. 399: a, 175c, Woman. b, 200c, Woman with Aruban flag. c, 200c, Two women dancing. d, 250c, Two women, diff.

2012, June 21

399	A148 Block of 4, #a-d	9.25	9.25

2012 Rembrandt Regatta — A149

No. 400 — Various sailboats: a, 150c, Horiz. b, 150c, Vert. c, 175c, Horiz. d, 175c, Vert. e, 200c, Horiz. f, 200c, Vert.

2012, Aug. 7

400	A149 Block of 6, #a-f	12.00	12.00

A150

A151

A152

A153

A154

A155

A156

Cats — A157

2012, Sept. 20

401	A150	110c multi	1.25	1.25
402	A151	110c multi	1.25	1.25
403	A152	110c multi	1.25	1.25
404	A153	110c multi	1.25	1.25
405	A154	110c multi	1.25	1.25
406	A155	110c multi	1.25	1.25
407	A156	110c multi	1.25	1.25
408	A157	110c multi	1.25	1.25
	Nos. 401-408 (8)		10.00	10.00

Nos. 401-408 were printed in sheets containing two of each stamp and two labels.

Christmas and New Year's Day — A158

No. 409: a, 75c, Ornaments and tree. b, 120c, Gifts and Nativity manger. c, 125c, Candles. d, 210c, Fireworks and champagne flutes.

2012, Oct. 18

409	A158 Block of 4, #a-d	6.00	6.00

A159

A160

A161

A162

A163

A164

A165

A166

A167

Underwater
Exploration
A168

2012, Nov. 15

410	Block of 10	11.00	11.00
a.	A159 100c multi	1.10	1.10
b.	A160 100c multi	1.10	1.10
c.	A161 100c multi	1.10	1.10
d.	A162 100c multi	1.10	1.10
e.	A163 100c multi	1.10	1.10
f.	A164 100c multi	1.10	1.10
g.	A165 100c multi	1.10	1.10
h.	A166 100c multi	1.10	1.10
i.	A167 100c multi	1.10	1.10
j.	A168 100c multi	1.10	1.10

Orchids — A169

No. 411: a, Laelia xanthina. b, Dendrobium. c, Dendrobium convolutum. d, Brassavola nodosa. e, Rossioglossum grande. f, Cattleya aclandiae. g, Cattleya. h, Epidendrum cinnabarinum. i, Phragmipedium cardinale. j, Phragmipedium. k, Phalaenopsis. l, Cattleya gaskelliana.

2012, Dec. 20

411	A169 200c Block of 12, #a-l	27.00	27.00

Butterflies — A170

Designs: No. 412, 150c, Graphium sarpedon. No. 413, 150c, Danaus plexippus. No. 414, 150c, Danis danis. No. 415, 150c, Pseudacraea boisduvali. No. 416, 150c, Morpho peleides. No. 417, 150c, Scoptes alphaeus. No. 418, 150c, Jumonia oritya. No. 419, 150c, Palla ussheri. No. 420, 150c, Eryphanis polyxena. No. 421, 150c, Diaethria clymena. No. 422, 150c, Colias eurytheme. No. 423, 150c, Anthocharis cardamis.

2013, Jan. 16

412-423	A170 Set of 12	20.00	20.00

Nos. 412-423 were printed in sheets of 24 containing two of each stamp + a central label.

Wedding Dresses — A171

No. 424: a, Brown and green dress. b, Blue gray strapless dress. c, Brown dress with white veil. d, Lilac dress with sash. e, White dress with black ribbon. f, Red dress with gray collar.

2013, Feb. 28

424	A171 200c Block of 6, #a-f	13.50	13.50

Aruban Bank
Notes — A172

No. 425: a, 10-florin banknote. b, 25-florin banknote. c, 50-florin banknote. d, 100-florin banknote. e, 500-florin banknote.

2013, Apr. 5

425	Horiz. strip of 5	11.50	11.50
a.-e.	A172 200c Any single	2.25	2.25

Printed in sheets containing two tete-beche strips.

A173

A174

A175

A176

Cruise
Ships — A177

2013, May 16

426	Horiz. strip of 5	14.00	14.00
a.	A173 250c multi	2.75	2.75
b.	A174 250c multi	2.75	2.75
c.	A175 250c multi	2.75	2.75
d.	A176 250c multi	2.75	2.75
e.	A177 250c multi	2.75	2.75

No. 426 was printed in sheets containing two tete-beche strips.

A178

Paintings by Frans Hals (c. 1582-1666) — A179

Designs: Nos. 427a, 428a, Jester with a Lute. Nos. 427b, 428b, Singing Boy with a Flute.

2013, June 17

427	A178 500c Horiz. pair, #a-b	11.50	11.50

Souvenir Sheet

428	A179 500c Sheet of 2, #a-b	11.50	11.50

Birds — A180

No. 429: a, Coereba flaveola. b, Aratinga pertinax arubensis. c, Anas bahamensis. d, Zonotrichia capensis. e, Colinus cristatus. f, Columbigallina passerina. g, Egretta thula. h, Icterus icterus. i, Mimus gilvus. j, Pelecanus occidentalis. k, Sterna eurygnatha. l, Athene cunicularia.

2013, Aug. 1

429	A180 167c Block of 12, #a-l	22.50	22.50

Flowers — A181

No. 430: a, Passiflora. b, Canna. c, Bougainvillea. d, Aramyllis. e, Hibiscus. f, Ipomoea. g, Strelitzia. h, Lillium. i, Allamanda. j, Lantana.

2013, Sept. 5 Litho. Perf. 14

430	Block of 10	22.50	22.50
a.-j.	A181 200c Any single	2.25	2.25

Printed in sheets containing two blocks that are tete-beche in relationship to each other.

Shells — A182

No. 431: a, 200c, Tonna maculosa. b, 200c, Nerita versicolor. c, 250c, Tellina radiata. d, 275c, Cymatium caribbaeum. e, 275c, Oliva caribaeensis. f, 300c, Voluta musica.

2013, Oct. 4 Litho. Perf. 14

431	A182 Block of 6, #a-f	17.00	17.00

Nature
Photography
A183

No. 432: a, Blenchi, by Eddie Thodé. b, Dos Playa, by Lara Kuiperi. c, Iris, by r. Kock. d, Barancanan di Ayo, by Stan Kuiperi. e, Respeta nos Naturalesa, by Joost Howard. f, Un Tesoro, by Bruce Harms. g, Serenidad, by Melissa Sweerts. h, Cactus Landscape, by Lara Kuiperi. i, Palo di Bonchi, by J. Dania. j, Tres Burico, by Lara Kuiperi.

2013, Nov. 12 Litho. Perf. 14

432	Block of 10	14,00	14.00
a.-j.	A183 120c Any single	1.40	1.40

Wildlife
A184

No. 433: a, Agalychnis calidryas. b, Panthera onca with spotted fur. c, Ara macao. d, Ranitomega benedicta. e, Saimiri sciureus. f, Panthera onca with black fur. g, Ramphastos sulfuratus. h, Saguinus imperator.

2013, Dec. 16 Litho. Perf. 14

433	Block of 8	16.00	16.00
a.-h.	A184 175c Any single	2.00	2.00

Paintings by
Salvador Dalí
(1904-89) — A185

No. 435: a, St. James of Compostela, 1957. b, Flores Surrealistas (Gala-Narciso), 1938. c, The Hallucinogenic Toreador, 1968-70. d, The Persistence of Memory, 1931, horiz. e, The Swallow's Tail, 1983, horiz. f, Elephants, 1948, horiz.

2014, Jan. 17 Litho. Perf. 14

434	Block of 6	18.00	18.00
a.-f.	A185 258c Any single	3.00	3.00

Aruban Carnaval, 60th Anniv. — A186

No. 435: a, 300c, Woman with crown, vert. b, 300c, Woman with mask and feathered headdress, horiz. c, 325c, Woman with headdress, horiz. d, 325c, Woman with headdress and feathers, vert.

2014, Feb. 13   Litho.   Perf. 14
435   A186   Block of 4, #a-d   14.00 14.00

Automobiles A187

No. 436: a, Ford Thunderbird convertible. b, MG Midget convertible. c, Dodge Challenger. d, Ford Crown Victoria. e, Ford Mustang convertible. f, Chevrolet Corvette Sting Ray.

2014, Mar. 14   Litho.   Perf. 14
436   Block of 6   15.00 15.00
a.-f.   A187 225c Any single   2.50   2.50

Birds of Paradise — A188

No. 437: a, Paradisaea rudolphi. b, Lophorina superba, green background. c, Seleucidis melanoleuca. d, Paradisaea apoda. e, Paradisaea minor. f, Lophorina superba, yellow background. g, Ptiloris victoriae. h, Cicinnurus regius. i, Cicinnurus respublica. j, Parotia carolae.

2014, Apr. 24   Litho.   Perf. 14
437   Block of 10   27.50 27.50
a.-j.   A188 250c Any single   2.75   2.75

2014 World Cup Soccer Championships, Brazil — A189

No. 438 — World Cup trophy and: a, Player's foot approaching soccer ball. b, Two players attempting to head ball. c, Player making a diving kick. d, Player dribbling ball. e, Penalty kick. f, Soccer field.

2014, May 29   Litho.   Perf. 14
438   A189 400c Block of 6, #a-f   27.00 27.00

Astronomy — A190

No. 439: a, 350c, Twin planets in circle. b, 350c, Ringed planet. c, 375c, Venus. d, 375c, Star and planets.

2014, June 19   Litho.   Perf. 14
439   A190   Block of 4, #a-d   16.50 16.50

Miniature Sheets

Attacus Atlas — A191

Papilio Cresphontes — A192

No. 440: a, Latin name of moth, "2014," part of wing. b, Head of moth. c, Tip of upper wing. d, Large country name, tip of wing. e, Abdomen of moth, bottom of wing. f, Bottom of wing.
No. 441: a, "2014," "cresphontes," part of wing. b, Parts of wings. c, Edge of top wing. d, Large country name, "Papilio," head of butterfly. e, Abdomen of butterfly. f, Bottom of wing.

2014, Aug. 21   Litho.   Perf. 14
440   A191 200c Sheet of 6, #a-f   13.50 13.50
441   A192 200c Sheet of 6, #a-f   13.50 13.50

Fruit — A193

No. 442: a, Citrullus lanatus. b, Carica papaya. c, Mangifera indica. d, Annona muricata. e, Musa acuminata. f, Cucumis melo. g, Anacardium occidentale. h, Punica granatum.

2014, Sept. 26   Litho.   Perf. 14
442   A193 175c Block of 8, #a-h   16.00 16.00

Christmas A194

No. 443 — Ribbon with bow and: a, Bells. b, Gifts, candles, ornaments. c, Stars. d, Ornaments.

2014, Oct. 23   Litho.   Perf. 14
443   Vert. strip of 4   6.50   6.50
a.   A194 85c multi   .95   .95
b.   A194 130c multi   1.50   1.50
c.   A194 135c multi   1.50   1.50
d.   A194 220c multi   2.50   2.50

Fishing Boats — A195

No. 444: a, 250c, Six boats. b, 275c, Laly. c, 300c, Pikudito and other boats. d, 325c, Phasha and another boat.

2014, Nov. 19   Litho.   Perf. 14
444   A195   Block of 4, #a-d   13.00 13.00

Dutch Royalty — A196

Designs: No. 445, 300c, King Willem-Alexander. No. 446, 300c, Queen Máxima. No. 447, 300c, King Willem-Alexander and Queen Máxima. No. 448, 300c, King Willem-Alexander, Queen Máxima, Queen Beatrix, Princess Catharina-Amalia, Princess Alexia and Princess Ariane. No. 449, 300c, King Willem-Alexander, Queen Máxima, Princess Catharina-Amalia, Princess Alexia and Princess Ariane waving.

2015, Jan. 30   Litho.   Perf. 14
445-449   A196   Set of 5   17.00 17.00
Nos. 445-449 were printed in sheets of 10 containing two of each stamp + 2 labels.

Blue Flowers — A197

Designs: No. 450, 200c, Sisyrinchium angustifolium. No. 451, 200c, Lupinus lepidus. No. 452, 200c, Linum lewisii. No. 453, 200c, Amsonia tabernaemontana. No. 454, 200c, Ipomoea learii. No. 455, 200c, Guaiacum officinale. No. 456, 200c, Gentianopsis crinita. No. 457, 200c, Gentiana andrewsii. No. 458, 200c, Campanulastrum americanum. No. 459, 200c, Campanula rotundifolia.

2015, Feb. 26   Litho.   Perf. 14
450-459   A197   Set of 10   22.50 22.50
Nos. 450-459 were printed in sheets of 20 containing two of each stamp + a central label.

UNICEF — A198

No. 460: a, 225c, Child holding finger of adult. b, 250c, Child's hand on adult's hand. c, 325c, Adult hand holding child's hand. d, 350c, Adult's hands holding child's feet.

2015, Mar. 25   Litho.   Perf. 14
460   A198   Block of 4, #a-d   13.00 13.00

Paintings by Sandro Botticelli (c. 1445-1510) — A199

Paintings or Details: No. 461, The Birth of Venus (De geboorte van Venus). No. 462, The Madonna of the Book (Madonna del Libro). No. 463, Allegorical Portrait of a Woman, Possibly Simonetta Vespucci (Simonetta Vespucci als Maria Lactans). No. 464, The Annunciation (De Blijde Boodschap). No. 465, Madonna of the Magnificat (Madonna del Magnificat).

2015, Mar. 27   Litho.   Perf. 14
461   A199 275c multi   3.25   3.25
462   A199 275c multi   3.25   3.25
463   A199 275c multi   3.25   3.25
464   A199 275c multi   3.25   3.25
465   A199 275c multi   3.25   3.25
a.   Block of 5, #461-465, + label   16.50 16.50
Nos. 461-465 (5)   16.25 16.25
Nos. 461-465 were printed in sheets of 10 containing two of each stamp + 2 labels.

Butterflies — A200

No. 466: a, Colias hyale. b, Carcharodus lavatherae. c, Anthocharis cardamines. d, Carcharodus flocciferus. e, Colias palaeno. f, Euchloe ausonia. g, Gonepteryx cleopatra. h, Heteropterus morpheus. i, Ochlodes venatus. j, Pyrgus fritillarius.

2015, June 30   Litho.   Perf. 14
466   A200 220c Block of 10, #a-j   24.50 24.50

Cave Art — A201

No. 467: a, 350c, Black spirals in circle. b, 350c, Anthromorphic figure with curved arms and legs. c, 375c, Circles connected by lines. d, 375c, Oval with curved lines and dots.

2015, July 31   Litho.   Perf. 14
467   A201   Block of 4, #a-d   16.50 16.50

Struthio Camelus — A202

No. 468: a, Juvenile facing right, both feet on ground. b, Chick facing right, one foot raised. c, Adult facing left, bending with neck curved. d, Adult facing left with head up. e, Two chicks. f, Head of chick. g, Head of adult. h, Adult facing right. i, Head of adult near chick. j, Adult and juvenile.

2015, Aug. 28   Litho.   Perf. 14
468   A202   225c Block of 10,
              #a-j   25.00 25.00

Beaches — A203

No. 469 — Various beaches: a, 275c. b, 300c. c, 325c. d, 350c.

2015, Sept. 23   Litho.   Perf. 14
469   A203   Block of 4, #a-d   14.00 14.00

Historic Buildings — A204

No. 470: a, Old Hotel Colombia (red and white building with damaged wall). b, Quinta del Carmen. c, Eloy Arends Building (City Hall) (green and white building). d, Henriquez

House (yellow building with red roof and stairway to second floor). e, Wild Family House (red and white building adjacent to parking lot). f, Former Aruba Bank Building (yellow building with red roof, cactus at right). g, Willem III Tower, Fort Zoutman (red and white tower), vert. h, San Nicolas Watertower (brown and yellow tower), vert.

2015, Oct. 16   Litho.   Perf. 14
470   A204   175c Block of 8, #a-h   16.00 16.00

Tourist Attractions — A205

No. 471: a, Alto Vista Chapel. b, Cruise liner. c, Bushiribana Gold Mill ruins. d, California Lighthouse. e, Double-decker streetcar. f, Rock formations

2015, Nov. 13   Litho.   Perf. 14
471   A205   250c Block of 6, #a-f   17.00 17.00

Fish — A206

Designs: 90c, Black beauty. 130c, Bluehead wrasse. 205c, Longfin damselfish. 220c, Blue Caribbean tang. 320c, Blackbar soldierfish.

Perf. 13¼x12¾
2016, Feb. 29   Litho.
472-476   A206   Set of 5   11.00 11.00

National Symbols — A207

Aruban: No. 477, 500c, Coat of arms. No. 478, 500c, Flag. No. 479, 500c, National anthem.

Perf. 12¾x13¼
2016, Mar. 16   Litho.
477-479   A207   Set of 3   17.00 17.00
479a   Souvenir sheet of 3,
                  #477-479   17.00 17.00

Burrowing Owls — A208

Designs: 140c, Two owls. 200c, One owl. 320c, Three owls. 65c, Owl in flight.

Perf. 13¼x12¾
2016, Mar. 31   Litho.
480-483   A208   Set of 4   15.00 15.00

Butterflies — A209

Designs: 85c, Graphium weiskei. 90c, Papilio glaucus. 100c, Jacoona amrita. 130c, Agrias claudina. 135c, Eunica eurota. 220c, Papilio palinurus. 320c, Arginnis paphia. 420c, Aglais io.

2016, Apr. 29   Litho.   Perf. 12¾x13¼
484-491   A209   Set of 8   17.00 17.00

Medicinal Plants — A210

Designs: 100c, Aloe vera. 130c, Moringa olifera. 220c, Jatropha gossypiifolia. 250c, Lippia alba. 320c, Croton flavens.

2016, May 31   Litho.   Perf. 12¾x13¼
492-496   A210   Set of 5   11.50 11.50

2016 Summer Olympics, Rio de Janeiro A211

Designs: 100c, Synchronized swimming. 130c, Swimming. 220c, Sailing. 500c, Abstract design.

Perf. 13¼x12¾
2016, June 30   Litho.
497-500   A211   Set of 4   11.00 11.00

Vegetables — A212

Designs: 90c, Phaseolus vulgaris. 130c, Capsicum annuum. 205c, Cucumis savitus. 220c, Solanum melongena. 320c, Hibiscus esculentus.

2016, July 29   Litho.   Perf. 12¾x13¼
501-505   A212   Set of 5   11.00 11.00

Birds — A213

Designs: 50c, Tricolored herons. 85c, Snowy egrets. 90c, Roseate spoonbills. 100c, Blue-winged teals. 130c, Scarlet ibises. 220c, Black skimmers. 250c, Ruby-topaz hummingbird. 325c, Whistling heron.

Perf. 13¼x12¾
2016, Aug. 31   Litho.
506-513   A213   Set of 8   14.00 14.00

Insects A214

Designs: 50c, Odonata anisoptera. 90c, Blattaria periplaneta. 100c, Formicidae solenopsis. 130c, Tettigonia viridissima. 200c, Apis mellifera. 220c, Musca domestica. 275c, Vespula vulgaris. 320c, Psaltoda moerens.

Perf. 13¼x12¾
2016, Sept. 30   Litho.
514-521   A214   Set of 8   15.50 15.50

Musical Instruments A215

G clef and: 100c, Bongo drums. 140c, Güiro (raspa). 205c, Accordion. 220c, Marimba. 500c, Steelpan drum.

2016, Oct. 31   Litho.   Perf. 13¼x12¾
522-526   A215   Set of 5   13.00 13.00

Antiques A216

Designs: 90c, Sewing machine, coffee mill, oil lamp, sadiron. 130c, Sewing machine. 205c, Sadiron. 250c, Phonograph. 325c, Coffee mill and sadiron.

Perf. 13¼x12¾
2016, Nov. 30   Litho.
527-531   A216   Set of 5   11.50 11.50

Souvenir Sheet

New Year 2017 (Year of the Rooster) — A217

No. 532: a, 200c, Rooster. b, 420c, Dragon.

2017, Feb. 28   Litho.   Perf. 14x13¼
532   A217   Sheet of 2, #a-b   7.00 7.00

Miniature Sheet

Underwater Panorama — A218

No. 533: a, 90c, Diver, rays, fish, coral. b, 130c, Sea turtles, fish, tube worm. c, 220c, Fish, coral, starfish. d, 650c, Fish and seaweed.

Perf. 13¾x12¾
2017, Mar. 31   Litho.
533   A218   Sheet of 4, #a-d   12.50 12.50

Houses A219

Various houses: 85c, 90c, 100c, 130c, 140c, 200c, 220c, 320c.

2017, Apr. 28   Litho.   Perf. 13¼x12¾
534-541   A219   Set of 8   14.50 14.50

Sports
A220

Designs: 50c, Cycling. 85c, Baseball. 90c, Cross-country biking. 100c, Basketball. 130c, Soccer. 220c, Go-karting. 305c, Skateboarding. 390c, Tennis.

2017, May 31 Litho. Perf. 13¼x12¾
542-549 A220 Set of 8   15.50 15.50

Birds — A221

Designs: 85c, Black-crowned night heron. 90c, Purple gallinule. 100c, Saffron finch. 130c, Yellow oriole. 200c, Amazon kingfisher. 220c, American flamingo. 250c, Least bittern. 305c, Yellow-billed cuckoo.

Perf. 12¾x13¼
2017, June 30   Litho.
550-557 A221 Set of 8   15.50 15.50

Postal Services in Aruba, 125th Anniv. A222

Designs: 90c, Post office, man with wheelbarrow. 130c, Post office. 320c, Mailman on bicycle making delivery. 390c, Motorcyclist and Central Post Office.

2017, July 31 Litho. Perf. 13¼x12¾
558-561 A222 Set of 4   10.50 10.50

Communication Devices — A223

Designs: 90c, Radio. 130c, Television, horiz. 220c, Telegraph, horiz. 305c, Typewriter, horiz. 420c, Telephone, horiz.

Perf. 12¾x13¼, 13¼x12¾
2017, Aug. 31   Litho.
562-566 A223 Set of 5   13.00 13.00

Tourist Attractions A224

Designs: 65c, Anchor and donkey, Seroe Colorado. 90c, Lizard, Hooiberg. 100c, Ayo rock formation. 130c, Windsurfer near shipwreck. 200c, California Lighthouse. 220c, Fisherman and fishing boat. 300c, Fisherman casting net. 320c, Arikok National Park.

Perf. 13¼x12¾
2017, Sept. 29   Litho.
567-574 A224 Set of 8   16.00 16.00

Flowers — A225

Designs: 50c, Plumeria rubra. 90c, Erythrania velutina. 130c, Opuntia wentiana, horiz. 135c, Passiflora foetidal, horiz. 200c, Antigonon leptopus, horiz. 220c, Ixora coccinea, horiz. 305c, Calotropis procera. 320c, Acacia tortuosa.

Perf. 12¾x13¼, 13¼x12¾
2017, Oct. 31   Litho.
575-582 A225 Set of 8   16.50 16.50

Christmas — A226

Designs: 90c, Christmas ornaments and palm trees. 130c, Stocking cap on lighthouse. 220c, Candles, poinsettias, heart. 320c, Christmas gifts and beach umbrella.

Perf. 12¾x13¼
2017, Nov. 30   Litho.
583-586 A226 Set of 4   8.50 8.50

A227

A228

A229

Personalized Stamps A230

2018, Apr. 24 Litho. Perf. 13¼x14
587 A227 130c multi   1.50 1.50
588 A228 130c multi   1.50 1.50
589 A229 130c multi   1.50 1.50
590 A230 130c multi   1.50 1.50
      Nos. 587-590 (4)   6.00 6.00

Vignette portions of Nos. 587-590 could be personalized. The vignettes shown for types A227-A230 are generic images.

2018 World Cup Soccer Championships, Russia — A231

Designs: 130c, Two soccer players. 220c, Goalie making save.

2018, June 15 Litho. Perf. 13¼x13
591-592 A231 Set of 2   4.00 4.00

Greetings A232

Designs: 85c, Birthday cake (Happy Birthday). 90c, Hands holding apple (Get Well), vert. 100c, Heart and hands (Valentine), vert. 130c, Orchid (Condolences). 230c, Flowers and hands (Thank You), vert. 650c, Hand and champagne bottle (Congratulations), vert.

Perf. 13¼x12¾, 12¾x13¼
2018, July 31   Litho.
593-598 A232 Set of 6   14.50 14.50

Aspects of Aruban Culture A233

Designs: 90c, Dancers (Celebrations). 130c, Aloe hanging from doorway (Traditions). 220c, Woman in dress (Folklorico Dress). 420c, Fish on plate (Typical food).

Perf. 13¼x12¾
2018, Aug. 31   Litho.
599-602 A233 Set of 4   9.75 9.75

Water Sports A234

Designs: 90c, Windsurfing. 130c, Surfing. 135c, Kitesurfing. 200c, Kayaking. 220c, Bodyboarding. 320c, Parasailing.

Perf. 13¼x12¾
2018, Sept. 28   Litho.
603-608 A234 Set of 6   12.50 12.50

Pets — A235

Designs: 90c, Cats. 100c, Dog. 130c, Rabbit. 135c, Fish. 220c, Turtle. 500c, Parrots.

2018, Oct. 31 Litho. Perf. 13¼x12¾
609-614 A235 Set of 6   13.00 13.00

Sustainable Energy A236

Designs: 90c, Wind generators. 100c, Electric car. 130c, Solar panel, vert. 220c, Electric tram, vert. 320c, Bicycle.

Perf. 13¼x12¾, 12¾x13¼
2018, Nov. 30   Litho.
615-619 A236 Set of 5   9.75 9.75

65th Aruba Carnaval A237

Designs: 90c, Musicians and dancers. 130c, Singer in uniform, vert. 220c, Dancer, vert. 420c, Three dancers.

Perf. 13¼x12¾, 12¾x13¼
2019, Mar. 1   Litho.
620-623 A237 Set of 4   9.75 9.75

Children at Play — A238

Designs: 90c, Girl jumping rope, girls in sack race. 100c, Girls with hula hoops, boy playing hop scotch. 130c, Boys rolling hoops and tires. 320c, Boys with top and yo-yo.

2019, Apr. 28 Litho. Perf. 12¾x13¼
624-627 A238 Set of 4   7.25 7.25

Sports Stars — A239

Designs: No. 628, 220c, Sarah-Quita Offringa, windsurfer. No. 629, 220c, Xander Bogaerts, baseball player. No. 630, 220c, Shanayah Howell, bicycle motocross. No. 631, 220c, Chiara Petrocchi, taekwondo.

Perf. 13¼x12¾
2019, June 28   Litho.
628-631 A239 Set of 4   10.00 10.00
631a   Souvenir sheet of 4,
            #628-631   10.00 10.00

Medicinal Plants A240

Designs: 90c, Origanum vulgare. 130c, Mentha spicata, vert. 220c, Senna alexandrina, vert. 500c, Cymbopogon.

Perf. 13¼x12¾, 12¾x13¼
2019, Aug. 30   Litho.
632-635 A240 Set of 4   10.50 10.50

SEMI-POSTAL STAMPS

Surtax for child welfare organizations unless otherwise stated.

Solidarity SP1

1986, May 7   Litho.   Perf. 14x13
B1 SP1 30c + 10c shown   1.75 1.00
B2 SP1 35c + 15c Three ropes   1.75 1.00
B3 SP1 60c + 25c One rope   2.50 1.50
      Nos. B1-B3 (3)   6.00 3.50

Surtax for social and cultural projects.

Child Welfare
SP2

No. B4, Boy, caterpillar. No. B5, Boy, cocoon. No. B6, Girl, butterfly.

1986, Oct. 29   Litho.   Perf. 14x13

B4	SP2	45c + 20c multi	2.75	1.00
B5	SP2	70c + 25c multi	2.75	1.75
B6	SP2	100c + 40c multi	3.50	2.25
		Nos. B4-B6 (3)	9.00	5.00

Christmas
(Child Welfare)
SP3

No. B7, Boy on beach. No. B8, Drawing Christmas tree. No. B9, Child, creche figures.

1987, Oct. 27   Litho.   Perf. 14x13

B7	SP3	25c +10c multi	1.50	.75
B8	SP3	45c +20c multi	2.00	1.00
B9	SP3	70c +30c multi	2.75	1.50
		Nos. B7-B9 (3)	6.25	3.25

Solidarity
SP4

YMCA emblem in various geometric designs.

1988, Aug. 3   Litho.   Perf. 14x13

B10	SP4	45c +20c shown	2.00	1.00
B11	SP4	60c +25c multi, diff.	2.00	1.50
B12	SP4	100c +50c multi, diff.	2.50	2.00
		Nos. B10-B12 (3)	6.50	4.50

11th YMCA world council.
Surtax for social and cultural projects.

Children's Toys (Child Welfare) — SP5

1988, Oct. 26   Perf. 13x14

B13	SP5	45c +20c Jacks	2.25	1.00
B14	SP5	70c +30c Top	2.25	1.50
B15	SP5	100c +50c Kite	3.00	2.00
		Nos. B13-B15 (3)	7.50	4.50

Child Welfare
SP6

No. B16, Baby spoon. No. B17, Chasing a ball. No. B18, Adult & child holding hands.

1989, Oct. 26   Perf. 14x13

B16	SP6	45c +20c multi	2.00	1.00
B17	SP6	60c +30c multi	2.25	1.25
B18	SP6	100c +50c multi	3.00	2.00
		Nos. B16-B18 (3)	7.25	4.25

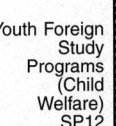

Solidarity
SP7

No. B20, Family, house.

1990, July 25

B19	SP7	55c +25c shown	2.00	1.50
B20	SP7	100c +50c multi	3.50	2.50

Surtax for social and cultural projects.

Child Welfare — SP8

Christmas song: No. B21, Wind surfboards. No. B23, Kites, lizard.

1990, Oct. 24   Litho.   Perf. 13x14

B21	SP8	45c +20c multi	1.50	1.00
B22	SP8	60c +30c shown	2.00	1.25
B23	SP8	100c +50c multi	3.00	2.25
		Nos. B21-B23 (3)	6.50	4.50

Child Welfare — SP9

Literacy: 45c+25c, Discovery of reading. 60c+35c, Pointing to letter. 100c+50c, Child reading.

1991, Oct. 25   Litho.   Perf. 13x14

B24	SP9	45c +25c multi	1.50	1.25
B25	SP9	60c +35c multi	2.00	1.40
B26	SP9	100c +50c multi	3.00	2.25
		Nos. B24-B26 (3)	6.50	4.90

Solidarity
SP10

55c+30c, Girl scouts, flag & emblem. 100c+50c, Hand holding cancer fund emblem, people.

1992, May 27   Litho.   Perf. 14x13

B27	SP10	55c +30c multi	2.00	1.50
B28	SP10	100c +50c multi	3.50	2.25

Surtax for social and cultural projects.

Postal Services of Aruba, Cent. (Child Welfare) SP11

Designs: 50c+30c, Heart. 70c+35c, Airplane, letters. 100c+55c, Pigeon with letter in beak, vert.

1992, Oct. 30   Litho.   Perf. 14x13

B29	SP11	50c +30c multi	1.90	1.25
B30	SP11	70c +35c multi	2.10	1.40

Perf. 13x14

B31	SP11	100c +50c multi	3.00	2.25
		Nos. B29-B31 (3)	7.00	4.90

Youth Foreign Study Programs (Child Welfare) SP12

Abstract designs of: 50c+30c, Landscapes. 75c+40c, Young man, scenes of other countries, vert. 100c+50c, Integrating cultures.

1993, Oct. 27   Perf. 14x13, 13x14

B32	SP12	50c +30c multi	1.50	1.25
B33	SP12	75c +40c multi	2.00	1.90
B34	SP12	100c +50c multi	2.50	2.25
		Nos. B32-B34 (3)	6.00	5.40

Solidarity
SP13

Intl. Year of the Family: 50c+35c, Family seated, reading, studying. 100c+50c, Family playing in front of house.

1994, May 30   Litho.   Perf. 14x13

B35	SP13	50c +35c multi	1.50	1.25
B36	SP13	100c +50c multi	2.75	2.50

Surtax for social and cultural projects.

Child Welfare
SP14

Designs: 50c+30c, Children on anchor with umbrella. 80c+35c, Children inside Sun. 100c+50c, Child riding owl.

1994, Oct. 27   Litho.   Perf. 14x13

B37	SP14	50c +30c multi	2.00	1.50
B38	SP14	80c +35c multi	2.40	2.00
B39	SP14	100c +50c multi	2.50	2.50
		Nos. B37-B39 (3)	6.90	6.00

Child Welfare — SP15

Children's drawings: 50c+25c, Children with balloons, house. 70c+35c, Three people with picnic basket on sunny day. 100c+50c, People gardening on sunny day.

1995, Oct. 26   Litho.   Perf. 13x14

B40	SP15	50c +25c multi	1.75	1.25
B41	SP15	70c +35c multi	2.25	1.75
B42	SP15	100c +50c multi	3.00	2.50
		Nos. B40-B42 (3)	7.00	5.50

Solidarity — SP16

El Sol Naciente Lodge, 75th Anniv.: 60c+30c, Masonic emblems. 100c+ 50c, Columns, terrestrial and celestial globes.

1996, July 26   Litho.   Perf. 13x14

B43	SP16	60c +30c multi	2.50	1.50
B44	SP16	100c +50c multi	3.50	2.50

Surtax for social and cultural projects (Solidarity)

Child Welfare
SP17

Cartoons: 50c+25c, Mother, baby rabbit waiting at school bus stop. 70c+35c, Mother, baby owl, outside school. 100c+50c, Children flying kite.

1996, Oct. 24   Litho.   Perf. 14x13

B45	SP17	50c +25c multi	1.75	1.25
B46	SP17	70c +35c multi	2.25	1.75
B47	SP17	100c +50c multi	2.50	2.40
		Nos. B45-B47 (3)	6.50	5.40

Child Welfare
SP18

Designs: 50c+25c, Girl sitting among aloe plants. 70c+35c, Boy, butterfly, cactus, vert. 100c+50c, Girl swimming under water, fish, coral.

Perf. 14x13, 13x14

1997, Oct. 23   Litho.

B48	SP18	50c +25c multi	1.50	1.25
B49	SP18	70c +35c multi	2.50	2.00
B50	SP18	100c +50c multi	2.50	2.50
		Nos. B48-B50 (3)	6.50	5.75

Solidarity
SP19

Service Organizations: 60c+30c, Globe, emblem of Lions Intl., wheelchair balanced on map of Aruba. 100c+50c, Child reading book, emblem of Rotary Intl., woman in rocking chair.

1998, May 29   Litho.   Perf. 14x13

B51	SP19	60c +30c multi	2.50	1.50
B52	SP19	100c +50c multi	3.50	2.75

Surtax for social and cultural projects.

Child Welfare — SP20

50c+25c, Girl performing traditional ribbon dance. 80c+40c, Boy playing a cuarta. 100c+50c, Two boys playing basketball.

1998, Oct. 22   Litho.   Perf. 13x14

B53	SP20	50c +25c multi	1.75	1.50
B54	SP20	80c +40c multi	2.50	2.25
B55	SP20	100c +50c multi	3.00	2.50
		Nos. B53-B55 (3)	7.25	6.00

Child Welfare
SP21

Designs: 60c+30c, Child on beach with man with fishing net. 80c+40c, Adult reading to children. 100c+50c, Mother, child, vert.

Perf. 14x13, 13x14

1999, Oct. 21   Litho.

B56	SP21	60c +30c multi	1.75	1.50
B57	SP21	80c +40c multi	2.50	2.00
B58	SP21	100c +50c multi	3.00	2.50
		Nos. B56-B58 (3)	7.25	6.00

Solidarity
SP22

75c+35c, Children on playground equipment. 100c+50c, Children playing in sand.

2000, Aug. 28   Litho.   Perf. 14x13

B59-B60	SP22	Set of 2	5.75	4.25

Child Welfare
SP23

Children's art: 60c+30c, House with solar collectors. 80c+40c, House, girl, garbage can. 100c+50c, Flying automobiles.

2000, Oct. 26
B61-B63   SP23   Set of 3   8.00 6.00

Child
Welfare — SP24

Intl. Volunteers Year: 40c+20c, Children at crosswalk. 60c+30c, Boys walking dog. 100c+50c, Children depositing trash in can at beach.

2001, Oct. 31   Litho.   Perf. 13x14
B64-B66   SP24   Set of 3   7.00 5.75

Child
Welfare — SP25

Designs: 40c+20c, Boy, iguana and goat. 60c+30c, Girl, hawksbill turtle, red crab, horiz. 100c+50c, Boy, pelicans, parakeet, conch shell.

2002, Oct. 31 *Perf. 13x14, 14x13*
                    Litho.
B67-B69   SP25   Set of 3   7.00 5.75

Child Welfare
SP26

Children playing: 40c+20c, Baseball. 60c+30c, Volleyball. 100c+50c, Soccer.

2003, Oct. 31   Litho.   Perf. 14x13
B70-B72   SP26   Set of 3   6.00 6.00

Children's
Welfare — SP27

Children playing: 60c+30c, Maracas. 85c+40c, Steel drum. 100c+50c, Tambourine, wiri.

2004, Oct. 29   Litho.   Perf. 13x14
B73-B75   SP27   Set of 3   5.50 5.00

ASCENSION

ə-'sen͵t͵-shən

LOCATION — An island in the South Atlantic Ocean, 900 miles from Liberia
GOVT. — A part of the British Crown Colony of St. Helena
AREA — 34 sq. mi.
POP. — 1,117 (1993)

In 1922 Ascension was placed under the administration of the Colonial Office

and annexed to the British Crown Colony of St. Helena. The only post office is at Georgetown.

> 12 Pence = 1 Shilling
> 20 Shillings = 1 Pound
> 100 Pence = 1 Pound (1971)

> **Catalogue values for unused stamps in this country are for Never Hinged items, beginning with Scott 50.**

Stamps and Types
of St. Helena,
1912-22
Overprinted in
Black or Red

1922   Wmk. 4   Perf. 14
1	A9	½p green & blk	8.00	29.00
2	A10	1p green	8.00	29.00
3	A10	1½p rose red	21.00	60.00
4	A9	2p gray & blk	21.00	16.00
5	A9	3p ultra	16.00	29.00
6	A10	8p dl vio & blk	34.00	62.50
7	A10	2sh ultra & blk, *blue*	120.00	150.00
8	A10	3sh vio & blk	175.00	200.00

Wmk. 3
9	A9	1sh blk, *gray grn* (R)	35.00	60.00
		Nos. 1-9 (9)	438.00	635.50
		Set, never hinged	675.00	

Seal of
Colony — A3

1924-33   Typo.   Wmk. 4   Perf. 14
Chalky Paper
10	A3	½p black & gray	6.75	19.00
11	A3	1p green & blk	7.00	17.00
12	A3	1½p rose red	10.00	50.00
13	A3	2p bluish gray & gray	25.00	13.00
14	A3	3p ultra	10.00	19.00
15	A3	4p blk & gray, *yel*	60.00	100.00
16	A3	5p ol & lil ('27)	24.00	29.00
17	A3	6p rose lil & gray	62.50	125.00
18	A3	8p violet & gray	21.00	52.50
19	A3	1sh brown & gray	25.00	62.50
20	A3	2sh ultra & gray, *blue*	75.00	115.00
21	A3	3sh blk & gray, *blue*	110.00	110.00
		Nos. 10-21 (12)	436.25	712.00
		Set, never hinged	675.00	

View of Georgetown — A4

Map of
Ascension — A5

Sooty Tern
Breeding
Colony
A9

Designs: 1½p, Pier at Georgetown. 3p, Long Beach. 5p, Three Sisters. 5sh, Green Mountain.

1934, July 2   Engr.
23	A4	½p violet & blk	1.10	1.00
24	A5	1p lt grn & blk	2.25	1.60
25	A4	1½p red & black	2.25	2.75
26	A5	2p org & black	2.25	3.00
27	A4	3p ultra & blk	2.75	1.90
28	A4	5p blue & black	2.75	4.00
29	A5	8p dk brn & blk	5.25	6.75
30	A9	1sh car & blk	22.50	12.00
31	A5	2sh6p violet & blk	57.50	50.00
32	A4	5sh brown & blk	62.50	70.00
		Nos. 23-32 (10)	161.10	153.00
		Set, never hinged	240.00	

Common Design Types pictured following the introduction.

Silver Jubilee Issue
Common Design Type
1935, May 6   Perf. 11x12
33	CD301	1½p car & dk blue	3.50	15.00
34	CD301	2p blk & ultra	10.00	37.50
35	CD301	5p ind & grn	22.50	32.50
36	CD301	1sh brn vio & indigo	22.50	42.50
		Nos. 33-36 (4)	58.50	127.50
		Set, never hinged	100.00	

25th anniv. of the reign of King George V.

Coronation Issue
Common Design Type
1937, May 19   Perf. 13½x14
37	CD302	1p deep green	.75	1.50
38	CD302	2p deep orange	1.00	.65
39	CD302	3p bright ultra	1.00	.60
		Nos. 37-39 (3)	2.75	2.75
		Set, never hinged	3.50	

Georgetown — A11

Designs: No. 41, 41A, 2p, 4p, Green Mountain. No. 41D, 6p, 10sh, Three Sisters. 1½p, 2sh6p, Pier at Georgetown. 3p, 5sh, Long Beach.

Perf. 13, 13¼ (#41, 44, 46), 14 (#43C)
1938-53   Center in Black
40	A11	½p violet ('44)	.80	4.00
		Never hinged	1.50	
a.		Perf. 13½	4.00	4.00
		Never hinged	8.00	
41	A11	1p green	30.00	13.50
		Never hinged	45.00	
41A	A11	1p org yel ('42)	.25	.60
		Never hinged	.45	
b.		Perf. 14 ('49)	.40	16.00
		Never hinged	.70	
c.		Perf. 13½	8.00	9.00
		Never hinged	14.50	
41D	A11	1p green ('49)	.35	1.50
		Never hinged	.60	
42	A11	1½p red ('44)	.65	.80
		Never hinged	1.00	
a.		Perf. 14 ('49)	1.90	13.50
		Never hinged	3.75	
b.		Perf. 13½	5.75	1.40
		Never hinged	9.00	
42C	A11	1½p lilac rose ('53)	.30	6.50
		Never hinged	.55	
d.		Perf. 14 ('49)	1.35	1.10
		Never hinged	2.25	
e.		1½p carmine, perf 14	6.50	6.50
		Never hinged	12.00	
43	A11	2p orange ('44)	.50	.40
		Never hinged	.80	
a.		Perf. 14 ('49)	2.25	37.50
		Never hinged	3.50	
b.		Perf. 13½	5.75	1.00
		Never hinged	9.50	
43C	A11	2p red ('49)	.90	1.90
		Never hinged	1.50	
44	A11	3p ultra	65.00	30.00
		Never hinged	110.00	
44A	A11	3p black ('44)	.35	1.00
		Never hinged	.70	
c.		Perf. 13½ ('40)	13.50	4.00
		Never hinged	21.00	
44B	A11	4p ultra ('44)	3.00	3.00
		Never hinged	5.25	
d.		Perf. 13½	10.00	3.75
		Never hinged	17.50	
45	A11	6p gray blue	7.25	2.50
		Never hinged	13.00	
a.		Perf. 13 ('44)	7.50	7.50
		Never hinged	12.50	
46	A11	1sh dk brn ('44)	3.50	2.00
		Never hinged	5.00	
a.		Perf. 13½	13.00	3.00
		Never hinged	22.50	
47	A11	2sh6p car ('44)	20.00	37.50
		Never hinged	30.00	
a.		Perf. 13½	30.00	12.00
		Never hinged	47.50	

b.		Frame printed doubly, one albino	3,750.	5,000.
		Never hinged	5,250.	
48	A11	5sh yel brn ('44)	25.00	45.00
		Never hinged	40.00	
a.		Perf. 13½	62.50	12.00
		Never hinged	100.00	
49	A11	10sh red vio ('44)	45.00	62.50
		Never hinged	62.50	
a.		Perf. 13½	65.00	50.00
		Never hinged	120.00	
b.		10sh brt aniline red pur, perf 13	65.00	50.00
		Never hinged	125.00	
		Nos. 40-49 (16)	202.85	212.70
		Set, never hinged	315.00	

> **Catalogue values for unused stamps in this section, from this point to the end of the section, are for Never Hinged items.**

Peace Issue
Common Design Type
Perf. 13½x14
1946, Oct. 21   Engr.   Wmk. 4
50	CD303	2p deep orange	.40	1.00
51	CD303	4p deep blue	.40	1.00

Silver Wedding Issue
Common Design Types
1948, Oct. 20   Photo.   Perf. 14x14½
52	CD304	3p black	.55	.45

Engraved; Name Typographed
Perf. 11½x11
53	CD305	10sh red violet	55.00	50.00

> The stamps formerly listed as Nos. 54-56 have been merged into the rest of the George VI definitive series as Nos. 41//43C.

UPU Issue
Common Design Types
Engr.; Name Typo. on Nos. 58, 59
1949, Oct. 10   Perf. 13½, 11x11½
57	CD306	3p rose carmine	1.25	2.00
58	CD307	4p indigo	4.25	1.50
59	CD308	6p olive	1.60	3.50
60	CD309	1sh slate	4.00	2.00
		Nos. 57-60 (4)	11.10	9.00

Coronation Issue
Common Design Type
1953, June 2   Engr.   Perf. 13½x13
61	CD312	3p gray & black	1.25	2.75

Reservoir
A16

Designs: 1p, Map of Ascension. 1½p, Georgetown. 2p, Map showing Ascension between South America and Africa and cable lines. 2½p, Mountain road. 3p, Yellow-billed tropic bird. 4p, Longfinned tuna. 6p, Waves. 7p, Young green turtles. 1sh, Land crab. 2sh6p, Sooty tern (wideawake). 5sh, Perfect Crater. 10sh, View from Northwest.

1956, Nov. 19   Wmk. 4   Perf. 13
Center in Black
62	A16	½p brown	.25	.50
63	A16	1p lilac rose	2.75	2.50
64	A16	1½p orange	.85	1.10
65	A16	2p carmine	3.00	3.25
66	A16	2½p org brown	1.50	3.25
67	A16	3p blue	3.75	1.10
68	A16	4p turq blue	1.25	1.75
69	A16	6p dark blue	1.25	2.50
70	A16	7p olive	2.50	1.75
71	A16	1sh scarlet	1.60	1.60
72	A16	2sh6p brown violet	30.00	9.00
73	A16	5sh bright green	40.00	19.00
74	A16	10sh purple	55.00	40.00
		Nos. 62-74 (13)	143.20	87.30

Brown
Booby — A17

Birds: 1½p, Black tern. 2p, Fairy tern. 3p, Red-billed tropic bird in flight. 4½p, Brown noddy. 6p, Sooty tern. 7p, Frigate bird. 10p, Blue-faced booby. 1sh, Yellow-billed tropic bird. 1sh6p, Red-billed tropic bird. 2sh6p, Madeiran storm petrel. 5sh, Red-footed booby (brown phase). 10sh, Frigate birds. £1, Red-footed booby (white phase).

Perf. 14x14½

			Wmk. 314	
1963, May 23		**Photo.**		
75	A17	1p multicolored	1.15	.30
76	A17	1½p multicolored	1.75	1.00
b.		Blue omitted	130.00	
77	A17	2p multicolored	1.40	.30
78	A17	3p multicolored	1.50	.30
79	A17	4½p multicolored	1.50	.30
80	A17	6p multicolored	1.40	.30
81	A17	7p multicolored	1.40	.30
82	A17	10p multicolored	1.40	.30
83	A17	1sh multicolored	1.40	.30
84	A17	1sh6p multicolored	4.50	2.25
		Complete booklet, 4 each #75, 76, 77, 78, 80 and 84, in blocks of 4	90.00	
85	A17	2sh6p multicolored	8.00	12.00
86	A17	5sh multicolored	8.00	12.00
87	A17	10sh multicolored	14.50	14.00
88	A17	£1 multicolored	22.00	16.00
		Nos. 75-88 (14)	69.90	59.65

Freedom from Hunger Issue
Common Design Type

			Wmk. 314	
1963, June 4				
89	CD314	1sh6p car rose	1.00	.50

Red Cross Centenary Issue
Common Design Type

			Perf. 13	
1963, Sept. 2		**Litho.**		
90	CD315	3p black & red	2.50	1.10
91	CD315	1sh6p ultra & red	4.25	2.25

ITU Issue
Common Design Type

			Perf. 11x11½	
1965, May 17		**Litho.**	**Wmk. 314**	
92	CD317	3p mag & violet	.50	.40
93	CD317	6p grnsh bl & brn org	1.40	.90

Intl. Cooperation Year Issue
Common Design Type

				Perf. 14½
1965, Oct. 25		**Wmk. 314**		
94	CD318	1p bl grn & claret	.40	.50
95	CD318	6p lt vio & green	.90	.90

Churchill Memorial Issue
Common Design Type

				Perf. 14
1966, Jan. 24		**Photo.**		
Design in Black, Gold and Carmine Rose				
96	CD319	1p bright blue	.50	.50
97	CD319	3p green	1.75	.90
98	CD319	6p brown	2.25	1.50
99	CD319	1sh6p violet	5.50	3.50
		Nos. 96-99 (4)	10.00	6.40

World Cup Soccer Issue
Common Design Type

			Perf. 14	
1966, July 1		**Litho.**		
100	CD321	3p multicolored	1.00	.75
101	CD321	6p multicolored	1.50	1.25

WHO Headquarters Issue
Common Design Type

			Perf. 14	
1966, Sept. 20		**Litho.**		
102	CD322	3p multicolored	2.10	1.10
103	CD322	1sh6p multicolored	4.50	2.25

Apollo Satellite Station, Ascension — A18

			Wmk. 314	
1966, Nov. 7		**Photo.**	**Perf. 14**	
104	A18	4p purple & black	.25	.25
105	A18	8p blue grn & blk	.25	.25
106	A18	1sh3p brn ol & blk	.25	.25
107	A18	2sh6p brt grnsh blue & black	.25	.25
		Nos. 104-107 (4)	1.00	1.00

Opening of the Apollo communications satellite-earth station, part of the US Apollo program.

UNESCO Anniversary Issue
Common Design Type

			Perf. 14	
1967, Jan. 3		**Litho.**		
108	CD323	3p "Education"	2.50	1.40
109	CD323	6p "Science"	3.50	1.90
110	CD323	1sh6p "Culture"	5.00	2.50
		Nos. 108-110 (3)	11.00	5.80

BBC Emblem A19

Photo.; Gold Impressed

			Wmk. 314	Perf. 14½
1967, Dec. 1				
111	A19	1p ultra & gold	.25	.25
112	A19	3p dk green & gold	.25	.25
113	A19	6p brt purple & gold	.25	.25
114	A19	1sh6p brt red & gold	.25	.25
		Nos. 111-114 (4)	1.00	1.00

Opening of the British Broadcasting Company's South Atlantic Relay Station on Ascension Island.

Human Rights Flame and Chain — A20

			Perf. 14½x14	
1968, July 8		**Litho.**	**Wmk. 314**	
115	A20	6p org, car & blk	.25	.25
116	A20	1sh6p gray, mag & blk	.30	.30
117	A20	2sh6p brt grn, plum & blk	.30	.30
		Nos. 115-117 (3)	.85	.85

International Human Rights Year.

Blackfish A21

Fish: No. 119, Sailfish. 6p, Oldwife. 8p, Leather jackets. 1sh9p, Yellowtails. 1sh9p, Tuna. 2sh3p, Mako sharks. 2sh11p, Rock hind (jack).

			Perf. 13x12½	
1968-69		**Wmk. 314**	**Litho.**	
118	A21	4p brt grnsh bl & blk	.30	.25
119	A21	4p red & multi	.35	.35
120	A21	6p yel olive & multi	.40	.40
121	A21	8p brt rose lil & multi	.60	.45
122	A21	1sh6p brown & multi	1.50	2.00
123	A21	1sh9p emer & multi	1.00	.95
124	A21	2sh3p ocher & multi	1.50	1.25
125	A21	2sh11p dp org & multi	3.00	2.75
		Nos. 118-125 (8)	8.65	8.40

Issue dates: No. 119, 6p, 1sh6p, 2sh11p, Mar. 3, 1969; others, Oct. 23, 1968.
See Nos. 130-133.

Arms of R.N.S. Rattlesnake A22

Coats of Arms of Royal Naval Ships: 9p, Weston. 1sh9p, Undaunted. 2sh3p, Eagle.

			Perf. 14x14½	
1969, Oct. 1		**Photo.**	**Wmk. 314**	
126	A22	4p multicolored	.65	.50
127	A22	9p multicolored	.75	.60
128	A22	1sh9p multicolored	1.25	.75

129	A22	2sh3p multicolored	1.40	.85
a.		Min. sheet of 4, #126-129	8.50	8.50
		Nos. 126-129 (4)	4.05	2.70

See Nos. 134-137, 152-159, 166-169.

Fish Type of 1968

Deep-sea fish: 4p, Wahoo. 9p, Coalfish. 1sh9p, Dolphinfishes. 2sh3p, Soldierfish.

			Perf. 14	
1970, Apr. 6		**Litho.**		
130	A21	4p bluish grn & multi	4.00	2.75
131	A21	9p org & multi	3.00	2.75
132	A21	1sh9p ultra & multi	5.00	3.50
133	A21	2sh3p gray & multi	5.00	3.50
		Nos. 130-133 (4)	17.00	12.50

Naval Arms Type of 1969

4p, Penelope. 9p, Carlisle. 1sh6p, Amphion. 2sh6p, Magpie.

			Perf. 12½x12	
1970, Sept. 7		**Photo.**	**Wmk. 314**	
134	A22	4p ultra, gold & blk	1.25	.30
135	A22	9p lt bl, blk, gold & red	1.50	.55
136	A22	1sh6p grnsh bl, gold & blk	1.60	1.50
137	A22	2sh6p lt grnsh bl, gold & blk	2.25	2.10
a.		Miniature sheet of 4, #134-137	12.00	14.00
		Nos. 134-137 (4)	6.60	4.45

Decimal Currency Issue

Tycho Brahe's Observatory, Quadrant and Supernova, 1572 — A23

Man into Space: ½p, Chinese rocket, 1232, vert. 1p, Medieval Arab astronomers, vert. 2p, Galileo, his telescope and drawing of moon, 1609. 2½p, Isaac Newton, telescope and apple. 3½p, Harrison's chronometer and ship, 1735. 4½p, First American manned orbital flight (Project Mercury, 1962, vert.). 5p, Reflector of Palomar telescope and ring nebula in Lyra, Messier 57. 7½p, Jodrell Bank telescope. 10p, Mariner 7, 1969, and telescopic view of Mars. 12½p, Sputnik 2 and dog Laika, 1957. 25p, Astronaut walking in space, 1965 (Gemini 4; vert.). 50p, US astronauts and moon landing module, 1969. £1, Future space research station.

			Perf. 14½	
1971, Feb. 15		**Litho.**		
138	A23	½p multicolored	.25	.25
139	A23	1p multicolored	.25	.25
140	A23	1½p multicolored	.30	.30
141	A23	2p multicolored	.35	.35
142	A23	2½p multicolored	1.10	.90
143	A23	3½p multicolored	2.25	.90
		Complete booklet, 4 each #138-143	30.00	
144	A23	4½p multicolored	1.50	.95
145	A23	5p multicolored	1.25	.90
146	A23	7½p multicolored	3.50	2.00
147	A23	10p multicolored	3.50	3.25
148	A23	12½p multicolored	4.50	3.50
149	A23	25p multicolored	5.50	3.25
150	A23	50p multicolored	4.50	3.75
151	A23	£1 multicolored	4.50	4.50
		Nos. 138-151 (14)	33.25	25.05

For overprints see Nos. 189-191.
Booklet also exists with a date of 5/71 on the back cover. Value, $45.

Arms of H.M.S. Phoenix — A24

Coats of Arms of Royal Naval Ships: 4p, Milford. 9p, Pelican. 15p, Oberon.

			Perf. 13½x13	
1971, Nov. 15		**Photo.**		
152	A24	2p gold & multi	1.00	.25
153	A24	4p gold & multi	1.10	.45
154	A24	9p gold & multi	1.50	1.10
155	A24	15p gold & multi	1.60	2.25
a.		Souvenir sheet of 4, #152-155	7.50	10.00
		Nos. 152-155 (4)	5.20	4.05

Naval Arms Type of 1969

1½p, Lowestoft. 3p, Auckland. 6p, Nigeria. 17½p, Bermuda.

			Perf. 14x14½	
1972, May 22		**Litho.**		
156	A22	1½p gold & blk	.85	.65
157	A22	3p grnsh bl, gold & blk	.95	.70
158	A22	6p grn, gold, blk & bl	1.00	1.00
159	A22	17½p lil, gold, blk & red	1.50	2.25
a.		Miniature sheet of 4, #156-159	4.25	6.50
		Nos. 156-159 (4)	4.30	4.60

Course of Quest — A25

Designs: 4p, Shackleton and "Quest", horiz. 7½p, Shackleton's cabin and Quest in pack ice, horiz. 11p, Shackleton statue, London, and memorial cairn, South Georgia.

			Perf. 14	
1972, Aug. 2				
160	A25	2½p multicolored	.55	.50
161	A25	4p multicolored	.60	.65
162	A25	7½p multicolored	.60	.70
163	A25	11p multicolored	.75	.90
a.		Souvenir sheet of 4, #160-163	3.00	5.00
		Nos. 160-163 (4)	2.50	2.75

Sir Ernest Henry Shackleton (1874-1922), explorer of Antarctica.

Silver Wedding Issue, 1972
Common Design Type

Design: Queen Elizabeth II, Prince Philip, land crab and shark.

			Perf. 14x14½	
1972, Nov. 20		**Photo.**		
164	CD324	2p violet & multi	.25	.25
165	CD324	16p car rose & multi	.45	.45

Naval Arms Type of 1969

2p, Birmingham. 4p, Cardiff. 9p, Penzance. 13p, Rochester.

			Wmk. 314	
1973, May 28		**Litho.**		
166	A22	2p blue & multi	2.25	1.40
167	A22	4p yel grn & multi	2.75	1.40
168	A22	9p lt blue & multi	3.25	1.60
169	A22	13p violet & multi	3.75	1.60
a.		Min. sheet of 4, #166-169	24.00	15.00
		Nos. 166-169 (4)	12.00	6.00

Turtles — A26

			Perf. 13½	
1973, Aug. 28				
170	A26	4p Green	2.50	1.10
171	A26	9p Loggerhead	3.25	2.25
172	A26	12p Hawksbill	4.50	3.50
		Nos. 170-172 (3)	10.25	6.85

Light Infanty Marine Sergeant, 1900 — A27

Uniforms (Royal Marines): 6p, Private, 1816. 12p, Officer, Light Infantry, 1880. 20p, Color Sergeant, Artillery, 1910.

1973, Oct. 31   **Perf. 14½**
173 A27   2p multicolored   1.75   1.50
174 A27   6p lt green & multi   2.75   1.90
175 A27 12p lt blue & multi   3.00   2.75
176 A27 20p lt lilac & multi   3.50   3.00
   Nos. 173-176 (4)   11.00   9.15

Departure of the Royal Marines from Ascension, 50th anniv.

Princess Anne's Wedding Issue
Common Design Type
1973, Nov. 14   **Perf. 14**
177 CD325   2p ocher & multi   .25   .25
178 CD325 18p multicolored   .35   .35

Letter and UPU Emblem A29

UPU Cent.: 9p, Emblem and Mercury.

Wmk. 314
1974, Mar. 27   Litho.   Perf. 14½
179 A29   2p multicolored   .25   .25
180 A29   9p vio blue & multi   .40   .40

Young Churchill and Blenheim Palace A30

25p, Churchill and UN Headquarters, NYC.

1974, Nov. 30   Litho.   Unwmk.
181 A30   5p slate grn & multi   .25   .25
182 A30 25p purple & multi   .70   .70
  a. Souvenir sheet of 2, #181-182   1.75   2.50

Sir Winston Churchill (1874-1965).

Skylab over Photograph of Ascension Taken by Skylab 3 — A31

Skylab Space Station: 18p, Command module and photo of Ascension from Skylab 4.

1975, Mar. 20   Wmk. 314   Perf. 14½
183 A31   2p multicolored   .25   .25
184 A31 18p multicolored   .70   .70

US Air Force C-141A Starlifter — A32

Aircraft: 5p, Royal Air Force C-130 Hercules. 9p, Vickers VC-10. 24p, U.S. Air Force C-5A Galaxy.

Perf. 13½x14
1975, June 19   Litho.   Wmk. 314
185 A32   2p multicolored   1.00   .60
186 A32   5p multicolored   1.50   .75
187 A32   9p multicolored   1.50   1.50
188 A32 24p multicolored   2.50   2.50
  a. Souvenir sheet of 4, #185-188 17.00 17.50
   Nos. 185-188 (4)   6.50   5.35

Wideawake Airfield, Ascension Island.

Nos. 144, 148-149 Overprinted

1975, Aug. 18   Litho.   Perf. 14½
189 A23   4½p multicolored   .25   .25
190 A23 12½p multicolored   .35   .35
191 A23   25p multicolored   .50   .50
   Nos. 189-191 (3)   1.10   1.10

Apollo Soyuz space test project. (Russo-American cooperation), launching July 15; link-up, July 17.

HMS Peruvian and Zenobia Arriving Oct. 22, 1815 A33

Designs: 5p, Water Supply, Dampiers Drip. 9p, First Landing, Oct. 1815. 15p, The Garden on Green Mountain. All designs after paintings by Isobel McManus.

1975, Oct. 22   Wmk. 373   Perf. 14½
192 A33   2p lt blue & multi   .25   .25
193 A33   5p lt blue & multi   .25   .25
194 A33   9p red & multi   .35   .35
195 A33 15p red & multi   .65   .65
   Nos. 192-195 (4)   1.50   1.50

British occupation, 160th anniv.

Canaries A34

2p, Fairy tern, vert. 3p, Waxbills. 4p, Black noddy. 5p, Brown noddy. 6p, Common mynah. 7p, Madeira storm petrels. 8p, Sooty terns. 9p, White booby. 10p, Red-footed booby. 15p, Red-throated francolin. 18p, Brown booby. 25p, Red-billed bo'sun bird. 50p, Yellow-billed bo'sun bird. £1, Ascension frigatebird. £2, Boatswain Island Bird Sanctuary and birds.

Perf. 14x14½, 14½x14
1976, Apr. 26   Litho.   Wmk. 373
Size: 35x27mm, 27x35mm
196 A34   1p multi   .50   1.75
197 A34   2p multi   .55   1.75
198 A34   3p multi   .55   1.75
199 A34   4p multi, vert.   .60   1.75
200 A34   5p multi   .75   1.75
201 A34   6p multi   .75   1.75
202 A34   7p multi, vert.   .75   1.75
203 A34   8p multi   .75   1.75
204 A34   9p multi, vert.   .75   1.75
205 A34 10p multi   .75   1.75
206 A34 15p multi, vert. 1.50   1.75
207 A34 18p multi, vert. 1.50   1.75
208 A34 25p multi   1.60   1.75
209 A34 50p multi   2.25   2.75
210 A34 £1 multi, vert.   2.75   3.25

Perf. 13½
Size: 46x33mm
211 A34 £2 multicolored   5.50   5.00
   Nos. 196-211 (16)   21.80 33.75

Great Britain Type A1 with Ascension Cancel — A35

9p, Ascension No. 1, vert. 25p, Freighter Southampton Castle.

1976, May 4   Perf. 13½x14, 14x13½
212 A35   5p lt brn, car & blk   .25   .25
213 A35   9p gray grn, grn & blk   .25   .25
214 A35 25p blue & multi   .50   .50
   Nos. 212-214 (3)   1.00   1.00

Festival of Stamps 1976. See Tristan da Cunha No. 208a for souvenir sheet that contains one each of Ascension No. 214, St. Helena No. 297, and Tristan da Cunha No. 208.

US Base A36

Designs: 9p, NASA Station, Devil's Ashpit. 25p, Viking satellite landing on Mars.

Wmk. 373
1976, July 4   Litho.   Perf. 13½
215 A36   8p black & multi   .30   .30
216 A36   9p black & multi   .40   .40
217 A36 25p black & multi   .80 1.00
   Nos. 215-217 (3)   1.50   1.70

American Bicentennial. No. 215 also for the 20th anniv. of Bahamas Long Range Proving Ground (extension) Agreement.

Queen in Coronation Coach — A37

Designs: 8p, Prince Philip on Ascension Island, 1957, vert. 12p, Queen leaving Buckingham Palace in coronation coach.

Perf. 14x13½, 13½x14
1977, Feb. 7   Litho.   Wmk. 373
218 A37   8p multicolored   .25   .25
219 A37 12p multicolored   .25   .25
220 A37 25p multicolored   .30   .40
   Nos. 218-220 (3)   .80   .90

Reign of Queen Elizabeth II, 25th anniv.

Water Pipe in Tunnel — A38

5p, Breakneck Valley wells. 12p, Break tank in pipe line, horiz. 25p, Dam & reservoir, horiz.

1977, June 27   Litho.   Perf. 14½
221 A38   3p multicolored   .25   .25
222 A38   5p multicolored   .25   .25
223 A38 12p multicolored   .30   .30
224 A38 25p multicolored   .50   .60
   Nos. 221-224 (4)   1.30   1.40

Water supplies constructed by Royal Marines, 1832 and 1881.

Mars Bay Site, 1877 A39

Designs: 8p, Mars Bay and instrument sites. 12p, Prof. and Mrs. Gill before their tent. 25p, Map of Ascension.

Perf. 13½x14
1977, Oct. 3   Litho.   Wmk. 373
225 A39   3p multicolored   .25   .25
226 A39   8p multicolored   .25   .25
227 A39 12p multicolored   .30   .40
228 A39 25p multicolored   .60   .70
   Nos. 225-228 (4)   1.40   1.60

Centenary of visit of Prof. David Gill (1843-1914), astronomer, to Ascension.

Elizabeth II Coronation Anniversary Issue
Souvenir Sheet
Common Design Types
Unwmk.
1978, May 21   Litho.   Perf. 15
229   Sheet of 6   2.00   2.00
  a. CD326 25p Lion of England   .30   .30
  b. CD327 25p Elizabeth II   .30   .30
  c. CD328 25p Green turtle   .30   .30

No. 229 contains 2 se-tenant strips of Nos. 229a-229c, separated by horizontal gutter with commemorative and descriptive inscriptions and showing central part of coronation procession with coach.

East Crater (Broken Tooth) — A40

Volcanoes: 5p, Hollands Crater (Hollow Tooth). 12p, Bears Back. 15p, Green Mountain. 25p, Two Boats village.

1978, Sept. 4   Litho.   Perf. 14½
230 A40   3p multicolored   .25   .25
231 A40   8p multicolored   .25   .25
232 A40 12p multicolored   .30   .30
233 A40 15p multicolored   .40   .40
234 A40 25p multicolored   .65   .65
  a. Souvenir sheet, 2 each #230-234 3.00   4.75
  b. Strip of 5, #230-234   2.00   2.00

No. 234b shows panoramic view of volcanic terrain.

Resolution A41

Capt. Cook's voyages: 8p, Cook's chronometer. 12p, Green turtle. 25p, Cook after Flaxman/Wedgwood medallion.

Litho.; Litho. & Embossed. (25p)
1979, Jan. 8   Perf. 11
235 A41   3p multicolored   .25   .25
236 A41   8p multicolored   .30   .30
237 A41 12p multicolored   .55   .55
238 A41 25p multicolored   .75   .85
   Nos. 235-238 (4)   1.85   1.95

St. Mary's Church, Georgetown — A42

Designs: 12p, Old map of Ascension Island. 50p, Ascension, by Rembrandt.

Wmk. 373
1979, May 24   Litho.   Perf. 14½
239 A42   8p multicolored   .25   .25
240 A42 12p multicolored   .25   .25
241 A42 50p multicolored   .40   .50
   Nos. 239-241 (3)   .90   1.00

Ascension Day.

Landing Cable at Comfortless
Cove — A43

Eastern Telegraph Co., 80th anniv.: 8p,
Cable Ship Anglia. 12p, Map showing cables
across the Atlantic, vert. 15p, Cable-laying
ship. 25p, Cable and earth station.

1979, Sept. 15

242	A43	3p rose car & black	.25	.25
243	A43	8p dk yel grn & black	.25	.25
244	A43	12p yel bister & black	.30	.30
245	A43	15p violet & black	.40	.40
246	A43	25p deep org & black	.50	.50
		Nos. 242-246 (5)	1.70	1.70

Ascension
No.
45 — A44

1979, Dec. 17   Wmk. 373   Perf. 14

247	A44	3p shown	.25	.25
248	A44	8p No. 73	.25	.25
249	A44	12p No. 14, vert.	.25	.25
250	A44	50p Hill portrait, vert.	.45	.65
		Nos. 247-250 (4)	1.20	1.40

Sir Rowland Hill (1795-1879), originator of
penny postage.

Anogramma
Ascensionis
A45

6p, Xiphopteris ascensionense. 8p,
Sporobolus caespitosus. 12p, Sporobolus
durus, vert. 18p, Dryopteris ascensionis, vert.
24p, Marattia purpurascens, vert.

1980, Feb. 18   Litho.   Perf. 14½

251	A45	3p shown	.25	.25
252	A45	6p multicolored	.25	.25
253	A45	8p multicolored	.25	.25
254	A45	12p multicolored	.25	.25
255	A45	18p multicolored	.25	.40
256	A45	24p multicolored	.30	.55
		Nos. 251-256 (6)	1.55	1.95

17th Century
Bottle Post,
London 1980
Emblem
A46

12p, 36-gun frigate, 19th century. 15p,
"Garth Castle," 1863. 50p, "St. Helena," Lockheed C141.

1980, May 1   Wmk. 373   Perf. 14

257	A46	8p shown	.25	.25
258	A46	12p multicolored	.30	.30
259	A46	15p multicolored	.35	.35
260	A46	50p multicolored	.75	.75
a.		Souvenir sheet of 4, #257-260	1.75	2.25
		Nos. 257-260 (4)	1.65	1.65

London 1980 Intl. Stamp Exhib., May 6-14.

Queen Mother Elizabeth Birthday
Common Design Type

1980, Aug. 11   Litho.   Perf. 14

261	CD330	15p multicolored	.40	.40

Lubbock's
Yellowtail
A47

10p, Resplendent angelfish. 25p, Hedgehog
butterflyfish. 40p, Marmalade razorfish.

1980, Sept. 15   Litho.   Perf. 13½x14

262	A47	3p shown	.40	.40
263	A47	10p multicolored	.50	.50
264	A47	25p multicolored	1.00	.90
265	A47	40p multicolored	1.25	1.50
		Nos. 262-265 (4)	3.15	3.30

Tortoisen,
by
Thomas
Maxon
A48

Map of
South
Atlantic
Ridge and
Continental
Drift — A49

15p, Wideawake Fair, by Linton Palmer,
1866.

1980, Nov. 17   Perf. 13½, 14 (60p)

266	A48	10p multicolored	.25	.40
267	A48	15p multicolored	.30	.45
268	A49	60p multicolored	.90	1.25
		Nos. 266-268 (3)	1.45	2.10

Royal Geographical Soc., 50th anniv.

Green Mountain Farm, 1881 — A50

Designs: 15p, Two Boats, 1881. 20p, Green
Mountain and Two Boats farms, 1981. 30p,
Green Mountain Farm, 1981.

1981, Feb. 15   Litho.   Perf. 14

269	A50	12p multicolored	.25	.25
270	A50	15p multicolored	.30	.30
271	A50	20p multicolored	.30	.35
272	A50	30p multicolored	.40	.50
		Nos. 269-272 (4)	1.25	1.40

Cable and
Wireless
Earth
Station
A51

1981, Apr. 27   Litho.   Perf. 14

273		Sheet of 10	4.00	4.00
a.	A51	15p multicolored	.40	.40

Flight of Columbia space shuttle. Gutter
contains story of Ascension and space shuttle;
margin shows craft and dish antenna.

Poinsettia — A52

2p, Clustererd wax flower. 3p, Kolanchoe,
vert. 4p, Yellow pops. 5p, Camel's foot
creeper. 8p, White oleander. 10p, Ascension
lily, vert. 12p, Coral plant, vert. 15p, Yellow
allamanda. 20p, Ascension euphorbia. 30p,
Flame of the forest, vert. 40p, Bougainvillea.
50p, Solanum. £1, Ladies petticoat. £2, Red
hibiscus.

1981, May 11   Wmk. 373   Perf. 13½

274	A52	1p shown	.90	1.10
275	A52	2p multicolored	.70	1.10
276	A52	3p multicolored	.70	1.10
277	A52	4p multicolored	.90	1.10
278	A52	5p multicolored	.90	1.10
279	A52	8p multicolored	.90	1.10
280	A52	10p multicolored	.65	.95
281	A52	12p multicolored	1.75	1.10
282	A52	15p multicolored	.75	.95
		Complete booklet, 4 ea. #275, 276, 280 and 282, in blocks of 4	15.00	
283	A52	20p multicolored	1.10	.95
284	A52	30p multicolored	1.35	1.60
285	A52	40p multicolored	1.35	3.00

Size: 42x53mm

286	A52	50p multicolored	1.40	3.25
287	A52	£1 multicolored	2.10	4.00
288	A52	£2 multicolored	3.25	6.00
		Nos. 274-288 (15)	18.70	28.40

1982, Aug. 27   Inscribed "1982"

275a	A52	2p Clustererd wax flower	.60	1.25
276a	A52	3p Kolanchoe, vert.	.60	1.25
280a	A52	10p Ascension lily, vert.	.55	.75
282a	A52	15p Yellow allamanda	.60	.75
283a	A52	20p Ascention euphorbia	1.10	.75
287a	A52	£1 Ladies petticoat	1.75	2.75
		Nos. 275a-287a (6)	5.20	7.50

For overprints see Nos. 321-322.

Linschoten's Map of Ascension,
1599. — A53

Maxwell's
Map of
Ascension,
1793 — A54

Old maps of Ascension: 12p, Maxwell,
1793, diff. 15p, Eckberg & Chapman, 1811.
40p, Campbell, 1819.

1981, May 22   Perf. 14½

289	A53	Sheet of 4	.60	.60
a.-d.		5p any single	.25	.25
290	A54	10p shown	.25	.25
291	A54	12p multicolored	.30	.30
292	A54	15p multicolored	.35	.35
293	A54	40p multicolored	.65	.65
		Nos. 289-293 (5)	2.15	2.15

Royal Wedding Issue
Common Design Type

1981, July 22   Wmk. 373   Perf. 14

294	CD331	10p Bouquet	.25	.25
295	CD331	15p Charles	.25	.25
296	CD331	50p Couple	.50	.50
		Nos. 294-296 (3)	1.00	1.00

Nos. 294-296 each se-tenant with label.

Man Shining
Cannon — A55

1981, Sept. 14   Litho.   Perf. 14

297	A55	5p shown	.25	.25
298	A55	10p Mountain climbing	.25	.25
299	A55	15p First aid treatment	.25	.25
300	A55	40p Duke of Edinburgh	.35	.35
		Nos. 297-300 (4)	1.10	1.10

Duke of Edinburgh's Awards, 25th anniv.

Scouting
Year
A56

10p, Parallel rope walking. 15p, 1st Ascension scout flag. 25p, Radio operators. 40p,
Baden-Powell.

1982, Feb. 22   Litho.   Perf. 14

301	A56	10p multicolored	.25	.35
302	A56	15p multicolored	.35	.50
303	A56	25p multicolored	.50	.65
304	A56	40p multicolored	.65	.95
a.		Souvenir sheet of 4	1.60	2.25
		Nos. 301-304 (4)	1.75	2.45

No. 304a contains stamps in designs of
Nos. 301-304 (30x30mm, perf. 14½, diamond-
shape).

Sesquicentennial of Charles Darwin's
Visit — A57

1982, Apr. 19

305	A57	10p Portrait	.30	.40
306	A57	12p Pistols	.35	.50
307	A57	15p Rock crab	.45	.55
308	A57	40p Beagle	.85	.95
		Nos. 305-308 (4)	1.95	2.40

40th Anniv. of Wideawake
Airfield — A58

5p, Fairey Swordfish. 10p, North American
B25C Mitchell. 15p, Boeing EC-135N Aria.
50p, Lockheed Hercules.

1982, June 15   Litho.   Perf. 14

309	A58	5p multicolored	.85	.85
310	A58	10p multicolored	1.00	1.00
		Complete booklet, 4 ea. #309 and 310, in blocks of 4	7.75	
311	A58	15p multicolored	1.25	1.25
312	A58	50p multicolored	2.00	2.00
		Nos. 309-312 (4)	5.10	5.10

The cover of the booklet containing Nos.
309 and 310 exists with both brown and blue
inscriptions. Same value.

Princess Diana Issue
Common Design Type
Perf. 14½x14

1982, July 1   Wmk. 373

313	CD333	12p Arms	.55	.55
314	CD333	15p Diana	.55	.55
315	CD333	25p Wedding	.90	.90
316	CD333	50p Portrait	1.50	1.50
		Nos. 313-316 (4)	3.50	3.50

Christmas and 50th Anniv. of BBC
Overseas Broadcasting — A59

Anniv. Emblem and: 5p, Bush House
(London headquarters). 10p, Atlantic relay station. 25p, Lord Reith, first director general.
40p, King George V delivering Christmas
address, 1932.

1982, Dec. 20   Litho.   Perf. 14

317	A59	5p multicolored	.25	.25
318	A59	10p multicolored	.25	.25
319	A59	25p multicolored	.60	.60
320	A59	40p multicolored	.90	.90
		Nos. 317-320 (4)	2.00	2.00

Nos. 282a-283a Overprinted

1982   Litho.   Perf. 13½
321 A52 15p multicolored   .30   .30
322 A52 20p multicolored   .40   .40

12th Commonwealth Games, Brisbane, Australia, Sept. 30-Oct. 9.

A60

7p, Marasmius echinosphaerus. 12p, Chlorophyllum molybdites. 15p, Leucocoprinus cepaestipes. 20p, Lycoperdon marginatum. 50p, Marasmiellus distantifolius.

1983, Mar. 1   Perf. 14
323 A60 7p multicolored   .60   .30
324 A60 12p multicolored   .90   .50
325 A60 15p multicolored   1.00 .60
326 A60 20p multicolored   1.25 .70
327 A60 50p multicolored   1.60 1.75
        Nos. 323-327 (5)   5.35 3.85

View of Georgetown A61

15p, Farm, Green Mountain. 20p, Boatswain Bird Island. 60p, Telemetry Hill.

1983, May 12   Litho.   Perf. 14
328 A61 12p shown   .25   .25
329 A61 15p multicolored   .25   .25
330 A61 20p multicolored   .35   .35
331 A61 60p multicolored   .80   .80
        Nos. 328-331 (4)   1.65 1.65

See Nos. 359-362.

Manned Flight Bicentenary — A62

Military Aircraft: 12p, Wessex Five helicopter. 15p, Vulcan B2. 20p, Nimrod MR2P. 60p, Victor K2.

1983, Aug. 1   Wmk. 373   Perf. 14
332 A62 12p multicolored   .75   .75
333 A62 15p multicolored   .85   .85
334 A62 20p multicolored   .80   .80
335 A62 60p multicolored   1.40 1.40
        Nos. 332-335 (4)   3.80 3.80

Introduced Species A63

1983, Sept.   Litho.   Wmk. 373
336 A63 12p Iguanid   .40   .40
337 A63 15p Rabbit   .50   .50
338 A63 20p Cat   .60   .60
339 A63 60p Donkey   1.25 1.25
        Nos. 336-339 (4)   2.75 2.75

Tellina Antonii Philippi A64

12p, Nodipecten nodosus. 15p, Cypraea lurida oceanica. 20p, Nerita ascensionis gmelin. 50p, Micromelo undatus.

1983, Nov. 28   Litho.   Perf. 14½
340 A64 7p shown   .25   .25
341 A64 12p multicolored   .30   .30
342 A64 15p multicolored   .40   .40
343 A64 20p multicolored   .50   .50
344 A64 50p multicolored   1.10 1.10
        Nos. 340-344 (5)   2.55 2.55

St. Helena Colony, 150th Anniv. — A65

Designs: First issue inscribed Ascension instead of overprinted.

1984, Jan. 10   Litho.   Perf. 14
345 A65 12p No. 3   .25   .40
346 A65 15p No. 4   .35   .45
347 A65 20p No. 6   .45   .55
348 A65 60p No. 9   1.00 1.25
        Nos. 345-348 (4)   2.05 2.65

Souvenir Sheet

Visit of Prince Andrew — A66

1984, Apr. 10   Perf. 14½x14
349 A66 Sheet of 2   1.50 1.50
  a.   12p Andrew   .25   .25
  b.   70p In naval uniform   1.10 1.10

Lloyd's List Issue
Common Design Type

12p, Naval semaphore. 15p, "Southampton Castle". 20p, Pier Head. 70p, Dane.

1984, May 28
351 CD335 12p multicolored   .45   .25
352 CD335 15p multicolored   .55   .35
353 CD335 20p multicolored   .65   .45
354 CD335 70p multicolored   1.25 1.50
        Nos. 351-354 (4)   2.90 2.55

1984 Coins and Wildlife A67

12p, One penny, yellowfin tuna. 15p, Two pence, donkeys. 20p, Fifty pence, green turtle. 70p, One pound, sooty terns.

1984, June   Perf. 14
355 A67 12p multicolored   .70   .70
356 A67 15p multicolored   .90   .90
357 A67 20p multicolored   .90   .90
358 A67 70p multicolored   1.50 2.00
        Nos. 355-358 (4)   4.00 4.50

View Type of 1983

12p, Devil's Riding School. 15p, St. Mary's Church. 20p, Two Boats Village. 70p, Ascension Island.

1984, Oct.   Litho.   Wmk. 373
359 A61 12p multicolored   .25   .25
360 A61 15p multicolored   .30   .30
361 A61 20p multicolored   .45   .45
362 A61 70p multicolored   1.25 1.25
        Nos. 359-362 (4)   2.25 2.25

Trees — A68

7p, Bermuda cypress. 12p, Norfolk Island pine. 15p, Screwpine. 20p, Eucalyptus. 65p, Spore tree.

1985, Mar. 8   Litho.   Perf. 14½x14
363 A68 7p multicolored   .55   .45
364 A68 12p multicolored   .60   .50
365 A68 15p multicolored   .70   .65
366 A68 20p multicolored   .75   .75
367 A68 65p multicolored   1.90 1.90
        Nos. 363-367 (5)   4.50 4.25

Military Firearms A69

Large guns and insignia: 12p, Thirty-two pounder small bore muzzle loader, c. 1820; Royal Marines hat plate, c. 1816. 15p, Seven-inch rifled muzzle loader, c. 1866; royal cipher. 20p, Seven-pounder rifled muzzle loader, c. 1877; Royal Artillery badge. 70p, HMS Hood 5.5-inch gun; ship crest.

1985, July 21   Wmk. 373   Perf. 14½
368 A69 12p multicolored   .55   .55
369 A69 15p multicolored   .80   .80
370 A69 20p multicolored   .80   .80
371 A69 70p multicolored   2.00 2.50
        Nos. 368-371 (4)   4.15 4.65

Queen Mother 85th Birthday
Common Design Type

12p, With Duke of York, Balmoral, 1924. 15p, With Princes Andrew and Edward. 20p, At Ascot. 70p, Christening of Prince Henry, Windsor Castle. 75p, Leaving the QEII, 1968.

Perf. 14½x14
1985, June 7   Wmk. 384
372 CD336 12p multicolored   .50   .50
373 CD336 15p multicolored   .50   .50
374 CD336 20p multicolored   .65   .65
375 CD336 70p multicolored   1.50 1.50
        Nos. 372-375 (4)   3.15 3.15

Souvenir Sheet
376 CD336 75p multicolored   1.50 1.50

Intl. Youth Year, Girl Guides 75th Anniv. — A70

12p, Guides' banner. 15p, First aid. 20p, Camping. 70p, Lady Baden-Powell.

1985, Oct. 4   Wmk. 373
377 A70 12p multicolored   .60   .60
378 A70 15p multicolored   .65   .55
379 A70 20p multicolored   .75   .65
380 A70 70p multicolored   2.00 2.50
        Nos. 377-380 (4)   4.00 4.30

Wildflowers — A71

12p, Clerodendrum fragrans. 15p, Shell ginger. 20p, Cape daisy. 70p, Ginger lily.

Wmk. 384
1985, Dec. 6   Litho.   Perf. 14
381 A71 12p multicolored   .60   .60
382 A71 15p multicolored   .70   .70
383 A71 20p multicolored   .80   .80
384 A71 70p multicolored   1.60 2.25
        Nos. 381-384 (4)   3.70 4.35

Halley's Comet — A72

Designs: 12p, Newton's reflector telescope. 15p, Edmond Halley, Old Greenwich Observatory. 20p, Short's Gregorian telescope, comet, 1759. 70p, ICE space probe, Ascension satellite tracking station.

1986, Mar. 7
385 A72 12p multicolored   .60   .75
386 A72 15p multicolored   .70   .85
387 A72 20p multicolored   .75   .85
388 A72 70p multicolored   2.00 2.75
        Nos. 385-388 (4)   4.05 5.20

Queen Elizabeth II 60th Birthday
Common Design Type

Designs: 7p, Infant photograph, 1926. 15p, 1st worldwide Christmas broadcast, 1952. 20p, Garter Ceremony, Windsor Castle, 1983. 35p, Royal Tour, New Zealand, 1981. £1, Visiting Crown Agents' offices, 1983.

1986, Apr. 21   Perf. 14x14½
389 CD337 7p scarlet, blk & sil   .25   .25
390 CD337 15p ultra, blk & sil   .35   .35
391 CD337 20p green & multi   .45   .45
392 CD337 35p violet & multi   .50   .50
393 CD337 £1 rose vio & multi   1.25 1.75
        Nos. 389-393 (5)   2.80 3.30

For overprints see Nos. 431-435.

AMERIPEX '86 — A73

1986, May 22   Perf. 14½
394 A73 12p No. 183   .35   .50
395 A73 15p No. 260   .50   .60
396 A73 20p No. 215   .65   .75
397 A73 70p No. 310   1.35 2.00
        Nos. 394-397 (4)   2.85 3.85

Souvenir Sheet
398 A73 75p Statue of Liberty, New York Harbor   3.50 3.50

Statue of Liberty, cent.

Royal Wedding Issue, 1986
Common Design Type

Designs: 15p, Couple kissing. 35p, Andrew in navy uniform, helicopter.

Wmk. 384
1986, July 23   Litho.   Perf. 14
399 CD338 15p multicolored   .50   .50
400 CD338 35p multicolored   1.10 1.10

Ships
A74

1p, Ganymede, c. 1811. 2p, Kangaroo, c. 1811. 4p, Trinculo, c. 1811. 5p, Daring, c. 1811. 9p, Thais, c. 1811. 10p, Pheasant, 1819. 15p, Myrmidon, 1819. 18p, Atholl, 1825. 20p, Medina, 1830. 25p, Saracen, 1840. 30p, Hydra, c. 1845. 50p, Sealark, 1840. 70p, Rattlesnake, 1868. £1, Penelope, 1889. £2, Monarch, 1897.

1986, Oct. 14   Wmk. 384   Perf. 14½

401	A74	1p multicolored	.90	1.25
402	A74	2p multicolored	1.00	1.25
403	A74	4p multicolored	1.00	1.25
404	A74	5p multicolored	1.00	1.25
405	A74	9p multicolored	1.10	1.25
406	A74	10p multicolored	1.10	1.25
407	A74	15p multicolored	1.25	1.75
408	A74	18p multicolored	1.25	1.75
409	A74	20p multicolored	1.25	1.75
410	A74	25p multicolored	1.25	2.00
411	A74	30p multicolored	1.25	2.00
412	A74	50p multicolored	1.75	2.75
413	A74	70p multicolored	2.50	3.25
414	A74	£1 multicolored	3.50	4.25
415	A74	£2 multicolored	6.50	8.00
		Nos. 401-415 (15)	26.60	35.00

For surcharges see Nos. 502-504.

Edible Bush Fruits
A75

1987, Jan. 29   Perf. 14

416	A75	12p Cape gooseberry	.90	.90
417	A75	15p Prickly pear	1.00	1.00
418	A75	20p Guava	1.10	1.10
419	A75	70p Loquat	2.00	2.50
		Nos. 416-419 (4)	5.00	5.50

1st American Manned Orbital Space Flight, 25th Anniv. — A76

15p, Ignition. 18p, Lift-off. 25p, Reentry. £1, Splashdown.
70p, Friendship 7 capsule.

1987, Mar. 30

420	A76	15p multicolored	.85	.85
421	A76	18p multicolored	.95	.95
422	A76	25p multicolored	1.25	1.25
423	A76	£1 multicolored	3.50	3.50
		Nos. 420-423 (4)	6.55	6.55

Souvenir Sheet

424	A76	70p multicolored	2.50	2.50

Military Uniforms, 1815-20 — A77

Designs: a, Captains in full dress, 1st landing on Ascension. b, Surgeon and sailors at campsite. c, Seaman returning from Dampier's Drip with water supply. d, Midshipman at lookout post. e, Commander and surveyor.

1987, June 29

425		Strip of 5	4.00	4.00
a.-e.		A77 25p multicolored	.70	.70

See Nos. 458, 482, 507.

Butterflies
A78

1987, Aug. 10   Perf. 14½

426	A78	15p Painted lady	1.10	1.10
427	A78	18p Monarch	1.10	1.10
428	A78	25p Diadem	1.50	1.50
429	A78	£1 Long-tailed blue	4.00	4.00
		Nos. 426-429 (4)	7.70	7.70

See Nos. 436-439, 459-462.

Birds — A79

Designs: a, Ascension frigatebirds (males). b, Brown booby, frigatebird, white boobies. c, Frigatebird, white booby. d, Ascension frigatebirds (females). e, Adult frigatebird feeding young.

1987, Oct. 8   Wmk. 373   Perf. 14

430		Strip of 5	11.00	11.00
a.-e.		A79 25p any single	2.00	2.00

No. 430 has continuous design.
See No. 453.

Nos. 389-393 Ovptd. "40TH WEDDING ANNIVERSARY" in Silver

Perf. 14x14½

1987, Dec. 9   Wmk. 384

431	CD337	7p scar, blk & sil	.25	.25
432	CD337	15p ultra, blk & sil	.30	.30
433	CD337	20p green & multi	.50	.50
434	CD337	35p violet & multi	.75	.75
435	CD337	£1 rose vio & multi	1.50	1.50
		Nos. 431-435 (5)	3.30	3.30

40th wedding anniv. of Queen Elizabeth II and Prince Philip.

Insects Type of 1987

15p, Field cricket. 18p, Bush cricket. 25p, Ladybug. £1, Burnished brass moth.

1988, Jan. 18   Perf. 14½

436	A78	15p multicolored	.80	.80
437	A78	18p multicolored	.90	.90
438	A78	25p multicolored	1.25	1.25
439	A78	£1 multicolored	4.25	4.25
		Nos. 436-439 (4)	7.20	7.20

Capt. William Bate (d. 1838), 1st Garrison Commander and Colonial Founder of Ascension
A80

Designs: 9p, Bate's Memorial, St. Mary's Church. 15p, Commodore's Cottage, Cross Hill. 18p, North East or Bate's Cottage, 1833. 25p, Landmarks on map. 70p, Bate and 3 soldiers.

1988, Apr. 14   Litho.   Perf. 14

440	A80	9p multicolored	.30	.30
441	A80	15p multicolored	.50	.50
442	A80	18p multicolored	.60	.60
443	A80	25p multicolored	.85	.85
444	A80	70p multicolored	2.00	2.00
		Nos. 440-444 (5)	4.25	4.25

Australia Bicentennial Emblem and Ships Named HMS Resolution — A81

9p, 3-Masted squarerigger, 1667. 18p, 3-Masted squarerigger, 1772. 25p, Navy cruiser, 1892. 65p, Battleship, 1916.

1988, June 23   Litho.   Perf. 14

445	A81	9p multicolored	1.25	.50
446	A81	18p multicolored	1.75	.80
447	A81	25p multicolored	2.00	1.00
448	A81	65p multicolored	3.00	2.00
		Nos. 445-448 (4)	8.00	4.30

Australia bicentennial.

Nos. 445-448 Overprinted

Wmk. 384

1988, July 30   Litho.   Perf. 14

449	A81	9p multicolored	.75	.55
450	A81	18p multicolored	1.25	.90
451	A81	25p multicolored	1.25	.95
452	A81	65p multicolored	2.50	2.50
		Nos. 449-452 (4)	5.75	4.90

SYDPEX '88, July 30-Aug. 7.

Bird Type of 1987

Behaviors of the wideawake tern, Sterna fuscata: a, Two adults, flock overhead. b, Nesting (two birds). c, Nesting (three birds). d, Adult and young. e, Tern flapping its wings.

1988, Aug. 15   Perf. 14

453		Strip of 5	10.00	10.00
a.-e.		A79 25p any single	1.90	1.90

No. 453 has continuous design.

Lloyds of London, 300th Anniv.
Common Design Type

8p, Lloyd's Coffee House, Tower Street, 1688. 18p, Cable ship Alert, horiz. 25p, Satellite recovery in space, horiz. 65p, Ship Good Hope Castle on fire off Ascension, 1973.

Wmk. 373

1988, Oct. 17   Litho.   Perf. 14

454	CD341	8p multicolored	.40	.40
455	CD341	18p multicolored	.85	.85
456	CD341	25p multicolored	1.25	1.25
457	CD341	65p multicolored	2.50	2.50
		Nos. 454-457 (4)	5.00	5.00

Military Uniforms Type of 1987

Uniforms of the Royal Marines: a, Marines arrive in Ascension (marines), 1821. b, Semaphore station (officer, marine), 1829. c, Octagonal tank (sergeant), 1831. d, Water pipe tunnel (officers), 1833. e, Constructing barracks (officer), 1834.

1988, Nov. 21

458		Strip of 5	8.50	8.50
a.-e.		A77 25p multicolored	1.50	1.50

Insect Type of 1987
Wmk. 384

1989, Jan. 16   Litho.   Perf. 14½

459	A78	15p Plume moth	1.25	.80
460	A78	18p Green bottle	1.25	.90
461	A78	25p Weevil	1.00	.90
462	A78	£1 Paper wasp	5.00	3.25
		Nos. 459-462 (4)	8.50	5.85

Land Crabs, Gecarcinus Lagostoma — A82

1989, Apr. 17

463	A82	15p multicolored	.75	.75
464	A82	18p multi, diff.	.80	.80
465	A82	25p multi, diff.	1.25	1.25
466	A82	£1 multi, diff.	4.00	4.00
		Nos. 463-466 (4)	6.80	6.80

Background designs continuous

467	A82	15p multicolored	.55	.55
467A	A82	18p multi, diff.	.75	.75
467B	A82	25p multi, diff.	.95	.95
467C	A82	£1 multi, diff.	4.00	4.00
d.		Souvenir sheet of 4, #467-467C	7.50	7.50

Moon Landing, 20th Anniv.
Common Design Type

Apollo 7: 15p, Tracking Station, Ascension Is. 18p, Launch, Cape Kennedy. 25p, Mission emblem. 70p, Expended Saturn IVB stage. £1, Lunar landing profile for the Apollo 11 mission.

1989, July 20   Perf. 14x13½
Size of Nos. 469-470: 29x29mm

468	CD342	15p multicolored	.90	.65
469	CD342	18p multicolored	1.00	.75
470	CD342	25p multicolored	1.25	.95
471	CD342	70p multicolored	2.25	2.25
		Nos. 468-471 (4)	5.40	4.60

Souvenir Sheet

472	CD342	£1 multicolored	4.00	4.00

Souvenir Sheet

A83

1989, July 7   Perf. 14x13½

473	A83	75p Emblems, No. 60	4.25	4.25

Miniature Sheet

World Stamp Expo '89, Washington, DC, and PHILEXFRANCE '89, Paris — A84

The Statue of Liberty and scenes from the centenary celebrations, 1986: a, Operation Sail. b, Face. c, Upper body. d, Three crown points. e, Ships in harbor, view of lower Manhattan. f, Ship in port, New York City.

1989, Aug. 21   Wmk. 373

474	A84	Sheet of 6	5.00	5.00
a.-f.		15p any single	.70	.70

Devil's Ashpit Tracking Station A85

1989, Sept. 30   Wmk. 384   Perf. 14
475   Sheet, 5 each #a.-b.   10.50 10.50
a.   A85 18p shown   .70   .70
b.   A85 25p US space shuttle launch   1.10   1.10

Termination of NASA tracking operations, begun in 1965, at the station.

Shells and Mollusks A86

Designs: 8p, Strombus latus. 18p, Tonna galea. 25p, Harpa doris. £1, Charonia variegata.

Wmk. 384
1989, Nov. 6   Litho.   Perf. 14
476   A86   8p multicolored   .70   .45
477   A86   18p multicolored   1.25   .65
478   A86   25p multicolored   1.75   .90
479   A86   £1 multicolored   4.25 3.50
  Nos. 476-479 (4)   7.95 5.50

Donkeys — A87

Perf. 14 on 3 Sides
1989, Nov. 17   Litho.   Wmk. 384
Booklet Stamps
480   A87   18p shown   1.50 1.60
a.   Booklet pane of 6   9.50
481   A87   25p Green turtle   2.00 1.60
a.   Booklet pane of 4   8.00

No. 480a sold for £1.

Military Type of 1987

Royal Navy equipment, c. 1815-1820: a, Seaman's pistol, hat, cutlass. b, Midshipman's belt buckle, button, sword, hat. c, Surgeon's hat, sword, instrument chest. d, Captain's hat, telescope, sword. e, Admiral's epaulet, megaphone, hat, pocket.

1990, Feb. 12   Litho.   Perf. 14
482   Strip of 5   6.50 6.50
a.-e.   A77 25p any single   1.10 1.10

World Wildlife Fund — A88

Frigate birds (Fregata aquila): 9p, Family group. 10p, Chick. 11p, Male in flight. 15p, Female and immature in flight.

Perf. 14½x14
1990, Mar. 5   Litho.   Wmk. 373
483   A88   9p multicolored   3.50 1.10
484   A88   10p multicolored   3.50 1.25
485   A88   11p multicolored   3.50 1.50
486   A88   15p multicolored   3.50 2.00
  Nos. 483-486 (4)   14.00 5.85

Great Britain Nos. 1-2 A89

Exhibition emblem and: 18p, Early Ascension cancellations. 25p, Unloading mail at

Wideawake Airfield. £1, Main P.O., Royal Mail van.

1990, May 3   Litho.   Perf. 14
487   A89   9p shown   .50   .50
488   A89   18p multicolored   .80   .80
489   A89   25p multicolored   1.10 1.10
490   A89   £1 multicolored   4.00 4.00
  Nos. 487-490 (4)   6.40 6.40

Penny Black 150th anniv., Stamp World London '90.

Queen Mother, 90th Birthday
Common Design Types

25p, Portrait, 1940. £1, King, Queen with soldiers.

1990, Aug. 4   Wmk. 384   Perf. 14x15
491   CD343   25p multi   1.25 1.25

Perf. 14½
492   CD344   £1 multi   3.50 3.50

Garth Castle, 1910 — A90

Designs: 18p, RMS St. Helena, 1982. 25p, Launching new RMS St. Helena, 1989. 70p, Duke of York launching new RMS St. Helena. £1, New RMS St. Helena.

Wmk. 373
1990, Sept. 13   Litho.   Perf. 14½
493   A90   9p multicolored   1.25 1.25
494   A90   18p multicolored   1.60 1.60
495   A90   25p multicolored   2.50 2.50
496   A90   70p multicolored   4.25 4.25
  Nos. 493-496 (4)   9.60 9.60

Souvenir Sheet
497   A90   £1 multicolored   6.75 6.75

See St. Helena Nos. 535-539, Tristan da Cunha Nos. 482-486.

Christmas — A91

Sculpture (8p) and paintings of Madonna and Child by: 8p, Felici. 18p, Unknown artist. 25p, Gebhard. 65p, Gritti.

1990, Oct. 24   Perf. 14
498   A91   8p multicolored   1.00   .80
499   A91   18p multicolored   1.75 1.40
500   A91   25p multicolored   2.50 1.90
501   A91   65p multicolored   4.00 4.00
  Nos. 498-501 (4)   9.25 8.10

Nos. 410, 412 & 414 Ovptd. in Silver "BRITISH FOR 175 YEARS"
1991, Feb. 5   Wmk. 384   Perf. 14½
502   A74   25p on #410   2.75 2.75
503   A74   50p on #412   3.25 3.25
504   A74   £1 on #414   4.50 4.50
  Nos. 502-504 (3)   10.50 10.50

Elizabeth & Philip, Birthdays
Common Design Types

1991, June 18
505   CD345   25p multicolored   1.40 1.60
506   CD346   25p multicolored   1.40 1.60
a.   Pair, #505-506 + label   3.50 3.75

Military Uniforms Type of 1987

Royal Marines Equipment 1821-1844: a, Officer's shako, epaulettes, belt plate, button. b, Officer's cap, sword, epaulettes, belt plate. c, Drum Major's shako with cords, staff. d, Sergeant's shako, chevrons, belt plate, canteen. e, Drummer's drum, sticks, shako.

1991, Aug. 1   Wmk. 373   Perf. 14
507   A77   25p Strip of 5, #a.-e.   9.50 9.50

Atlantic Relay Station, 25th Anniv. A92

15p, BBC Atlantic relay station. 18p, English Bay transmitters. 25p, Satellite receiving station. 70p, Antenna support tower.

1991, Sept. 17   Wmk. 384   Perf. 14½
508   A92   15p multi   1.40 1.40
509   A92   18p multi   1.60 1.60
510   A92   25p multi, vert.   2.00 2.00
511   A92   70p multi, vert.   4.50 4.50
  Nos. 508-511 (4)   9.50 9.50

Christmas A93

Designs: 8p, St. Mary's Church, exterior. 18p, St. Mary's Church, interior. 25p, Grotto of Our Lady of Ascension, exterior. 65p, Grotto of Our Lady of Ascension, interior.

1991, Oct. 1   Perf. 14
512   A93   8p multicolored   .85   .70
513   A93   18p multicolored   1.50 1.25
514   A93   25p multicolored   2.00 1.50
515   A93   65p multicolored   3.75 4.50
  Nos. 512-515 (4)   8.10 7.95

Fish A94

1p, Blackfish. 2p, Five finger. 4p, Resplendent angelfish. 5p, Silver fish. 9p, Gurnard. 10p, Blue dad. 15p, Cunning fish. 18p, Grouper. 20p, Moray eel. 25p, Hardback soldierfish. 30p, Blue marlin. 50p, Wahoo. 70p, Yellowfin tuna. £1, Blue shark. £2.50, Bottlenose dolphin.

Wmk. 373
1991, Dec. 10   Litho.   Perf. 14
516   A94   1p multi   .70   .70
517   A94   2p multi   1.00   .75
518   A94   4p multi   1.10   .95
519   A94   5p multi   1.10   .95
520   A94   9p multi   1.50 1.10
521   A94   10p multi   1.50 1.10
522   A94   15p multi   2.00 1.10
523   A94   18p multi   2.00 1.25
524   A94   20p multi   2.00 1.50
525   A94   25p multi   2.00 1.60
526   A94   30p multi   2.00 1.75
527   A94   50p multi   2.50 2.50
528   A94   70p multi   3.25 3.25
529   A94   £1 multi   3.75 3.75
530   A94   £2.50 multi   7.50 7.50
  Nos. 516-530 (15)   33.90 29.75

Queen Elizabeth II's Accession to the Throne, 40th Anniv.
Common Design Type

Wmk. 373
1992, Feb. 6   Litho.   Perf. 14
531   CD349   9p multicolored   .45   .45
532   CD349   15p multicolored   .75   .75
533   CD349   18p multicolored   .90   .90
534   CD349   25p multicolored   1.25 1.25
535   CD349   70p multicolored   2.75 2.75
  Nos. 531-535 (5)   6.10 6.10

Discovery of America, 500th Anniv. — A95

9p, STV Eye of the Wind. 18p, STV Soren Larsen. 25p, Pinta, Santa Maria, & Nina. 70p, Columbus, Santa Maria.

Wmk. 373
1992, Feb. 18   Litho.   Perf. 14
536   A95   9p multicolored   1.40   .65
537   A95   18p multicolored   2.25   .95
538   A95   25p multicolored   2.75 1.25
539   A95   70p multicolored   5.00 2.75
  Nos. 536-539 (4)   11.40 5.60

World Columbian Stamp Expo '92, Chicago and Genoa '92 Intl. Philatelic Exhibitions.

Wideawake Airfield, 50th Anniv. — A96

15p, Control tower. 18p, Nose hangar. 25p, Construction work. 70p, Laying fuel pipeline.

Wmk. 373
1992, May 5   Litho.   Perf. 14
540   A96   15p multicolored   .95   .95
541   A96   18p multicolored   1.25 1.25
542   A96   25p multicolored   1.50 1.50
543   A96   70p multicolored   3.75 3.75
  Nos. 540-543 (4)   7.45 7.45

Ascension's Participation in Falkland Islands' Liberation, 10th Anniv. — A97

15p, Nimrod Mk.2. 18p, VC10. 25p, Wessex HU Mk.5 helicopter. 65p, Vulcan B2.
No. 548a, 15p + 3p like #544. b, 18p + 4p like #545. c, 25p + 5p like #546. d, 65p + 13p like #547.

Wmk. 373
1992, June 12   Litho.   Perf. 14
544   A97   15p multicolored   1.25 1.10
545   A97   18p multicolored   1.25 1.10
546   A97   25p multicolored   1.90 1.50
547   A97   65p multicolored   3.00 4.25
  Nos. 544-547 (4)   7.40 7.95

Souvenir Sheet
548   A97   Sheet of 4, #a.-d.   8.00 8.00

Surtax for Soldiers,' Sailors,' and Airmen's Families Association.

Christmas A98

Children's drawings: 8p, Snowman, rocks, candle. 18p, Underwater Santa, Christmas tree. 25p, Hello, bells. 65p, Nativity Scene, angel.

Wmk. 384
1992, Oct. 13   Litho.   Perf. 14
549   A98   8p multicolored   1.10   .90
550   A98   18p multicolored   1.60 1.25
551   A98   25p multicolored   1.90 1.50
552   A98   65p multicolored   3.50 3.50
  Nos. 549-552 (4)   8.10 7.15

Yellow Canary — A99

15p, Singing male. 18p, Adult male, female. 25p, Young calling for food. 70p, Mixed flock.

Wmk. 373

1993, Jan. 12	Litho.	Perf. 14½
553 A99 15p multicolored	1.25	1.25
554 A99 18p multicolored	1.40	1.40
555 A99 25p multicolored	1.75	1.75
556 A99 70p multicolored	4.00	4.00
Nos. 553-556 (4)	8.40	8.40

Royal Air Force, 75th Anniv.
Common Design Type

Designs: 20p, Sopwith Snipe. No. 558, Supermarine Southampton. 30p, Avro Anson. 70p, Vickers Wellington 1C.
No. 561a, Westland Lysander. b, Gloster Meteor. c, DeHavilland Comet. d, British Aerospace Nimrod.

Wmk. 373

1993, Apr. 1	Litho.	Perf. 14
557 CD350 20p multicolored	2.00	1.50
558 CD350 25p multicolored	2.00	1.50
559 CD350 30p multicolored	2.10	1.60
560 CD350 70p multicolored	3.75	4.25
Nos. 557-560 (4)	9.85	8.85

Souvenir Sheet

561 CD350 25p Sheet of 4, #a.-d.	5.75	5.75

South Atlantic Cable Company, 25th Anniv. A100

Designs: 20p, Map showing cable route. 25p, Cable ship laying cable. 30p, Map of Ascension. 70p, Cable ship off Ascension.

Perf. 14x14½		
1993, June 8	Litho.	Wmk. 384
562 A100 20p multicolored	1.10	1.10
563 A100 25p multicolored	1.35	1.35
564 A100 30p multicolored	1.50	1.50
565 A100 70p multicolored	3.50	3.50
Nos. 562-565 (4)	7.45	7.45

Flowers A101

Perf. 14x14½		
1993, Aug. 3	Litho.	Wmk. 384
566 A101 20p Lantana camara	1.50	.75
567 A101 25p Moonflower	1.75	.97
568 A101 30p Hibiscus	1.75	1.10
569 A101 70p Frangipani	4.00	3.50
Nos. 566-569 (4)	9.00	6.32

Christmas A102

Designs: 12p, Child mailing Christmas card. 20p, Mail loaded onto Tristar. 25p, Plane in flight. 30p, Mail unloaded at Wideawake Airfield. 65p, Child reading card, Georgetown.

Perf. 14½x14		
1993, Oct. 19	Litho.	Wmk. 373
570 A102 12p multicolored	.75	.40
571 A102 20p multicolored	1.25	.45
572 A102 25p multicolored	1.40	.50
573 A102 30p multicolored	2.25	2.25
574 A102 65p multicolored	2.75	2.75
a. Souvenir sheet of 5, #570-574	11.00	11.00
Nos. 570-574 (5)	6.35	6.35

Stamps from No. 574a show a continuous design, while Nos. 570-574 have white borders on sides.

Prehistoric Aquatic Reptiles — A103

12p, Ichthyosaurus. 20p, Metriorhynchus. 25p, Mosasaurus. 30p, Elasmosaurus. 65p, Plesiosaurus.

1994, Jan. 25	Wmk. 373	Perf. 14
575 A103 12p multi	1.00	1.00
576 A103 20p multi	1.25	1.25
577 A103 25p multi	1.50	1.50
578 A103 30p multi	1.50	1.50
579 A103 65p multi	2.75	2.75
Nos. 575-579 (5)	8.00	8.00

Ovptd. with Hong Kong '94 Emblem
1994, Feb. 18

580 A103 12p on #575	1.00	1.00
581 A103 20p on #576	1.60	1.60
582 A103 25p on #577	1.60	1.60
583 A103 30p on #578	1.75	1.75
584 A103 65p on #579	3.00	3.00
Nos. 580-584 (5)	8.95	8.95

Green Turtle A104

20p, Four on beach. 25p, Crawling in sand. No. 587, Crawling from sea. 30p, Swimming.
No. 589a, Side view, crawling from sea. b, Digging nest. c, Hatchlings heading to sea. d, Digging nest, diff.

1994, Mar. 22		
585 A104 20p multicolored	2.25	2.25
586 A104 25p multicolored	2.75	2.75
587 A104 30p multicolored	2.75	2.75
588 A104 65p multicolored	4.25	5.50
Nos. 585-588 (4)	12.00	13.25

Souvenir Sheet

589 A104 30p Sheet of 4, #a.-d.	13.50	13.50

Civilian Ships A105

Ships serving during Falkland Islands War, 1982: 20p, Tug Yorkshireman. 25p, Minesweeper support ship RMS St. Helena. 30p, Oil tanker British ESK. 65p, Cruise liner Uganda, hospital ship.

1994, June 14		
590 A105 20p multicolored	2.50	2.50
591 A105 25p multicolored	2.75	2.75
592 A105 30p multicolored	2.75	2.75
593 A105 65p multicolored	5.00	5.00
Nos. 590-593 (4)	13.00	13.00

Sooty Tern A106

1994, Aug. 16		
594 A106 20p Chick	1.40	1.40
595 A106 25p Juvenile	1.50	1.50
596 A106 30p Brooding adult	1.75	1.75
597 A106 65p Displaying male	2.75	2.75
Nos. 594-597 (4)	7.40	7.40

Souvenir Sheet

598 A106 £1 Dread	6.50	6.50

Christmas A107

Donkeys: 12p, Mare with foal. 20p, Young adult. 25p, Foal. 30p, Adult, egrets. 65p, Adult.

1994, Oct. 11		Perf. 14x14½
599 A107 12p multicolored	1.25	1.00
600 A107 20p multicolored	1.75	1.40
601 A107 25p multicolored	1.75	1.40
602 A107 30p multicolored	1.90	1.50
603 A107 65p multicolored	3.50	4.50
Nos. 599-603 (5)	10.15	9.80

Flowers A108

20p, Leonurus japonicus. 25p, Periwinkle. 30p, Four o'clock. 65p, Blood flower.

1995, Jan. 10		Perf. 14
604 A108 20p multi, vert.	2.00	2.00
605 A108 25p multi	2.00	2.00
606 A108 30p multi, vert.	2.75	2.75
607 A108 65p multi	3.75	3.75
Nos. 604-607 (4)	10.50	10.50

Island Scenes, c. 1895 A109

Designs: 12p, Horse-drawn wagon, Two Boats, Green Mountain. 20p, Island stewards' store. 25p, Royal Navy headquarters, barracks. 30p, Police office. 65p, Pier head.

1995, Mar. 7	Wmk. 384	Perf. 14½
608 A109 12p sepia	.70	.70
609 A109 20p sepia	1.00	1.00
610 A109 25p sepia	1.40	1.40
611 A109 30p sepia	2.50	2.50
612 A109 65p sepia	2.75	2.75
Nos. 608-612 (5)	8.35	8.35

End of World War II, 50th Anniv.
Common Design Types

Designs: 20p, 5.5-inch guns taken from HMS Hood, 1941. 25p, Fairey Swordfish, first aircraft to land at Ascension. 30p, HMS Dorsetshire patrolling South Atlantic. 65p, HMS Devonshire patrolling South Atlantic.
£1, Reverse of War Medal, 1939-45.

1995, May 8	Wmk. 373	Perf. 14
613 CD351 20p multicolored	2.25	2.25
614 CD351 25p multicolored	2.50	2.50
615 CD351 30p multicolored	3.00	3.00
616 CD351 65p multicolored	5.00	5.00
Nos. 613-616 (4)	12.75	12.75

Souvenir Sheet

617 CD352 £1 multicolored	8.75	8.75
Nos. 613-617 (5)	21.50	21.50

Butterflies — A110

20p, Long-tailed blue. 25p, Painted lady. 30p, Diadem. 65p, African monarch. £1, Red admiral.

1995, Sept. 1		Wmk. 384
618 A110 20p multi	1.90	1.90
619 A110 25p multi	2.25	2.25
620 A110 30p multi	2.25	2.25
621 A110 65p multi	3.50	3.50
Nos. 618-621 (4)	9.90	9.90

Souvenir Sheet

622 A110 £1 multi	8.50	8.50

Singapore '95 (No. 622).

Christmas A111

Designs based on children's drawings: 12p, Santa on boat. 20p, Santa on wall. 25p, Santa in chimney. 30p, Santa on dolphin. 65p, South Atlantic run.

1995, Oct. 10		Wmk. 373
623 A111 12p multicolored	1.25	1.25
624 A111 20p multicolored	1.60	1.60
625 A111 25p multicolored	1.75	1.75
626 A111 30p multicolored	2.00	2.00
627 A111 65p multicolored	3.50	3.50
Nos. 623-627 (5)	10.10	10.10

Mollusks A112

12p, Cypraea lurida. 25p, Cypraea spurca. 30p, Harpa doris. 65p, Umbraculum umbraculum.

	Wmk. 384	
1996, Jan. 10	Litho.	Perf. 14
628 A112 12p multicolored	2.50	2.50
629 A112 25p multicolored	3.00	3.00
630 A112 30p multicolored	3.25	3.25
631 A112 65p multicolored	4.00	4.00
a. Strip of 4, #628-631	14.00	14.00

Queen Elizabeth II, 70th Birthday
Common Design Type

Various portraits of Queen, scenes of Ascension:
20p, St. Marys Church. 25p, The Residency. 30p, Roman Catholic Grotto. 65p, The Exiles Club.

	Wmk. 384	
1996, Apr. 22	Litho.	Perf. 13½
632 CD354 20p multicolored	.80	.80
633 CD354 25p multicolored	.90	.90
634 CD354 30p multicolored	1.10	1.10
635 CD354 65p multicolored	2.50	2.50
Nos. 632-635 (4)	5.30	5.30

CAPEX '96 A113

Island transport: 20p, US Army Jeep. 25p, 1924 Citroen 7.5HP two seater. 30p, 1930 Austin Ten-four Tourer. 65p, Series 1 Land Rover.

	Wmk. 384	
1996, June 8	Litho.	Perf. 14
636 A113 20p multicolored	1.25	1.25
637 A113 25p multicolored	1.40	1.40
638 A113 30p multicolored	1.50	1.50
639 A113 65p multicolored	2.75	2.75
Nos. 636-639 (4)	6.90	6.90

Birds and Their Young — A114

1p, Madeiran storm petrel. 2p, Red-billed tropicbird. 4p, Indian mynah. 5p, House sparrow. 7p, Common waxbill. 10p, White tern. 12p, Francolin. 15p, Brown noddy. 20p, Yellow canary. 25p, Black noddy. 30p, Red-footed booby. 40p, Yellow-billed tropicbird. 65p, Brown booby. £1, Masked booby. £2, Sooty tern. £3, Ascension frigate bird.

Wmk. 373

1996, Aug. 12	**Litho.**			***Perf. 13***
640 A114	1p multicolored		.25	1.00
641 A114	1p multicolored		.25	1.00
642 A114	4p multicolored		.25	1.00
643 A114	5p multicolored		.25	1.00
644 A114	7p multicolored		.25	1.00
645 A114	10p multicolored		.35	1.25
646 A114	10p multicolored		.40	1.50
647 A114	15p multicolored		.50	1.50
648 A114	20p multicolored		.75	1.50
649 A114	25p multicolored		.90	1.50
650 A114	30p multicolored		1.10	1.50
651 A114	40p multicolored		1.50	2.00
652 A114	65p multicolored		2.50	3.25
a.	Sheet of 1, perf. 14		4.50	4.50
653 A114	£1 multicolored		4.00	4.75
a.	Souvenir sheet of 1		4.50	4.50
654 A114	£2 multicolored		8.25	9.00
655 A114	£3 multicolored		10.00	12.00
Nos. 640-655 (16)			31.50	44.75

No. 652a for Hong Kong '97. Issued 2/3/97.
No. 653a for return of Hong Kong to China. Issued 7/1/97.

BBC Atlantic Relay Station, 30th Anniv. A115

Various views of relay station: 20p, 25p, Towers. 30p, Towers, buildings. 65p, Satellite dish, towers, beach.

1996, Sept. 9	**Wmk. 384**			***Perf. 14***
656 A115	20p multicolored		.85	.85
657 A115	25p multicolored		1.00	1.00
658 A115	30p multicolored		1.10	1.10
659 A115	65p multicolored		2.50	2.50
Nos. 656-659 (4)			5.45	5.45

Christmas A116

Santa Claus: 12p, On satellite dish. 20p, Playing golf. 25p, By beach. 30p, On RAF Tristar. 65p, Aboard RMS St. Helena.

	Perf. 14x14½			
1996, Sept. 23	**Litho.**		**Wmk. 373**	
660 A116	12p multicolored		.50	.50
661 A116	20p multicolored		.90	.90
662 A116	25p multicolored		.90	.90
663 A116	30p multicolored		1.10	1.10
664 A116	65p multicolored		2.50	2.50
Nos. 660-664 (5)			5.90	5.90

UNICEF, 50th anniv.

A117

20p, Date palm. 25p, Mauritius hemp. 30p, Norfolk Island pine. 65p, Dwarf palm.

Wmk. 373

1997, Jan. 7	**Litho.**			***Perf. 14½***
665 A117	20p multi		.80	.80
666 A117	25p multi		1.00	1.00
667 A117	30p multi		1.15	1.15
668 A117	65p multi		2.25	2.25
Nos. 665-668 (4)			5.20	5.20

Hong Kong '97.

A118

Flag, ship or aircraft: 12p, Great Britain Red Ensign, tanker Maserk Ascension. 25p, RAF Ensign, Tristar. 30p, NASA emblem, Space Shuttle Atlantis. 65p, Royal Navy White Ensign, HMS Northumberland.

Wmk. 373

1997, Apr. 1	**Litho.**			***Perf. 14½***
669 A118	12p multicolored		1.10	1.10
670 A118	25p multicolored		1.60	1.60
671 A118	30p multicolored		1.75	1.75
672 A118	65p multicolored		3.25	3.25
Nos. 669-672 (4)			7.70	7.70

Herbs — A119

Designs: a, Solanum sodomaeum. b, Ageratum conyzoides. c, Leonurus sibricus. d, Cerastium vulgatum. e, Commelina diffusa.

	Perf. 14x14½			
1997, June 7	**Litho.**		**Wmk. 373**	
673 A119	30p Strip of 5, #a.-e.		8.50	8.50

A120

Queen Elizabeth II and Prince Philip, 50th Wedding Anniv.: No. 674, Queen Elizabeth II. No. 675, Prince Elizabeth II. No. 675, Prince Philip playing polo. No. 676, Queen petting horse. No. 677, Prince Philip. No. 678, Prince Philip, Queen Elizabeth II. No. 679, Prince Harry, Prince William riding horses.
£1.50, Queen Elizabeth, Prince Philip riding in open carriage.

1997, July 10	**Wmk. 384**			
				Perf. 13½
674 A120	20p multicolored		1.50	1.50
675 A120	20p multicolored		1.50	1.50
a.	Pair, #674-675		3.75	3.75
676 A120	25p multicolored		1.60	1.60
677 A120	25p multicolored		1.60	1.60
a.	Pair, #676-677		4.00	4.00
678 A120	30p multicolored		1.75	1.75
679 A120	30p multicolored		1.75	1.75
a.	Pair, #678-679		4.25	4.25
Nos. 674-679 (6)			9.70	9.70

Souvenir Sheet

680 A120	£1.50 multicolored		7.75	7.75

Birds — A121

Booklet Stamps

1997, Sept. 1	***Perf. 14 on 3 Sides***		**Wmk. 373**	
681 A121	15p like #644		2.75	2.75
682 A121	35p like #648		3.50	3.50
a.	Booklet pane, 2 ea #681-682		12.50	
	Complete booklet, #682a		12.50	

Game Fish — A122

12p, Black marlin. 20p, Atlantic sailfish. 25p, Swordfish. 30p, Wahoo. £1, Yellowfin tuna.

	Perf. 14x14½			
1997, Sept. 3	**Litho.**		**Wmk. 373**	
683 A122	12p multi		.90	.90
684 A122	20p multi		1.40	1.40
685 A122	25p multi		1.50	1.50
686 A122	30p multi		1.60	1.60
687 A122	£1 multi		4.25	4.25
Nos. 683-687 (5)			9.65	9.65

A123

St. Mary's Church (Christmas): 15p, Interior view. 35p, Stained glass window, Madonna and Child. 40p, Stained glass window, Falklands, 1982. 50p, Stained glass window.

Wmk. 384

1997, Oct. 1	**Litho.**			***Perf. 14***
688 A123	15p multicolored		.90	.90
689 A123	35p multicolored		1.75	1.75
690 A123	40p multicolored		1.90	1.90
691 A123	50p multicolored		2.25	2.25
Nos. 688-691 (4)			6.80	6.80

A124

Insects: 15p, Cactoblastis cactorum. 35p, Teleonemia scrupulosa. 40p, Neltumius arizonensis. 50p, Algarobius prosopis.

Wmk. 373

1998, Feb. 10	**Litho.**			***Perf. 14***
692 A124	15p multicolored		1.60	1.60
693 A124	20p multicolored		2.10	2.10
694 A124	40p multicolored		2.75	2.75
695 A124	50p multicolored		2.75	2.75
Nos. 692-695 (4)			9.20	9.20

Diana, Princess of Wales (1961-97)
Common Design Type

a, In polka-dotted dress. b, In yellow blouse. c, With longer hair style. d, Holding flowers.

	Perf. 14½x14			
1998, Mar. 31	**Litho.**		**Wmk. 373**	
696 CD355	35p Sheet of 4, #a.-d.		5.25	5.25

No. 696 sold for £1.40 + 20p, with surtax from international sales being donated to the Princess Diana Memorial Fund and surtax from national sales being donated to designated local charity.

Royal Air Force, 80th Anniv.
Common Design Type of 1993
Re-inscribed

15p, Fairey Fawn. 35p, Vickers Vernon. 40p, Supermarine Spitfire F-22. 50p, Bristol Britannia C2.
No. 701: a, Blackburn Kangaroo. b, SE5a. c, Curtiss Kittyhawk III. d, Boeing Fortress II (B-17).

Wmk. 384

1998, Apr. 1	**Litho.**			***Perf. 14***
697 CD350	35p multicolored		1.00	1.00
698 CD350	35p multicolored		2.10	2.10
699 CD350	40p multicolored		2.25	2.25
700 CD350	50p multicolored		2.75	2.75
Nos. 697-700 (4)			8.10	8.10

Souvenir Sheet

701 CD350	50p Sheet of 4, #a.-d.		8.00	8.00

Birds — A125

Wmk. 373

1998, June 15	**Litho.**			***Perf. 14***
702 A125	15p Swallow		1.25	1.25
703 A125	25p House martin		1.75	1.75
704 A125	35p Cattle egret		2.10	2.10
705 A125	40p Swift		2.10	2.10
706 A125	50p Allen's gallinule		2.25	2.25
Nos. 702-706 (5)			9.45	9.45

Island Sports — A126

Wmk. 373

1998, Aug. 17	**Litho.**			***Perf. 14***
707 A126	15p Cricket		2.50	2.00
708 A126	35p Golf		3.25	2.50
709 A126	40p Soccer		2.50	2.50
710 A126	50p Trapshooting		2.50	2.50
Nos. 707-710 (4)			10.75	9.50

Christmas A127

Designs: 15p, Children's nativity play. 35p, Santa arriving on Ascension. 40p, Santa arriving at a party. 50p, Carol singers.

Wmk. 373

1998, Oct. 1	**Litho.**			***Perf. 14***
711 A127	15p multicolored		1.10	1.10
712 A127	35p multicolored		1.90	1.90
713 A127	40p multicolored		2.10	2.10
714 A127	50p multicolored		2.10	2.10
Nos. 711-714 (4)			7.20	7.20

World War II Aircraft A128

15p, Curtiss C-46 Commando. 35p, Douglas C-47 Dakota. 40p, Douglas C-54 Skymaster. 50p, Consolidated Liberator Mk.V. £1.50, Consolidated Liberator LB-30.

Wmk. 373

1999, Jan. 20	**Litho.**			***Perf. 14***
715 A128	15p multicolored		1.25	1.25
716 A128	35p multicolored		2.00	2.00
717 A128	40p multicolored		2.25	2.25
718 A128	50p multicolored		2.25	2.25
Nos. 715-718 (4)			7.75	7.75

Souvenir Sheet

719 A128	£1.50 multicolored		11.00	11.00

Winston Churchill, 125th birth anniv.

Australia '99, World Stamp Expo A129

Union Castle Mail Ships: 15p, SS Glengorm Castle. 35p, SS Gloucester Castle. 40p, SS Durham Castle. 50p, SS Garth Castle. £1, HMS Endeavour.

1999, Mar. 5 Litho. Wmk. 373
Perf. 14½x14

720	A129	15p multicolored	1.25	1.25
721	A129	35p multicolored	2.25	2.25
722	A129	40p multicolored	2.40	2.40
723	A129	50p multicolored	2.40	2.40
		Nos. 720-723 (4)	8.30	8.30

Souvenir Sheet
724	A129	£1 multicolored	6.75	6.75

World Wildlife Fund — A130

Fairy tern: No. 725, Two on branch. No. 726, One on branch. No. 727, Adult feeding chick. No. 728, Two in flight.

Wmk. 384
1999, Apr. 27 Litho. Perf. 14½

725	A130	10p multicolored	.50	.45
726	A130	10p multicolored	.50	.45
727	A130	10p multicolored	.50	.45
728	A130	10p multicolored	.50	.45
a.		Sheet of 16, 4 each #725-728	10.00	10.00
		Nos. 725-728 (4)	2.00	1.80

Wedding of Prince Edward and Sophie Rhys-Jones
Common Design Type
Perf. 13¾x14
1999, June 19 Litho. Wmk. 384

729	CD356	50p Separate por- traits	1.50	1.50
730	CD356	£1 Couple	3.00	3.00

1st Manned Moon Landing, 30th Anniv.
Common Design Type

Designs: 15p, Command and service modules. 35p, Moon from Apollo 11. 40p, Devil's Ashpit Tracking Station. 50p, Lunar module lifts off moon. £1.50, Looking at earth from moon.

Perf. 14x13¾
1999, July 20 Litho. Wmk. 384

731	CD357	15p multicolored	1.25	1.25
732	CD357	35p multicolored	1.60	1.60
733	CD357	40p multicolored	1.60	1.60
734	CD357	50p multicolored	1.60	1.60
		Nos. 731-734 (4)	6.05	6.05

Souvenir Sheet
Perf. 14
735	CD357	£1.50 multicolored	6.75	6.75

No. 735 contains one 40mm circular stamp.

Queen Mother's Century
Common Design Type

Queen Mother: 15p, With King George VI, Winston Churchill. 35p, With Prince Charles. 40p, At Clarence House, 88th birthday. 50p, With drummers at Clarence House. £1.50, With Titanic.

Wmk. 384
1999, Aug. 20 Litho. Perf. 13½

736	CD358	15p multicolored	1.25	1.25
737	CD358	35p multicolored	1.75	1.75
738	CD358	40p multicolored	2.00	2.00
739	CD358	50p multicolored	2.50	2.50
		Nos. 736-739 (4)	7.50	7.50

Souvenir Sheet
740	CD358	£1.50 black	8.00	8.00

Christmas A131

Wmk. 384
1999, Oct. 6 Litho. Perf. 13¾

741	A131	15p 3 children	1.10	1.10
742	A131	35p 2 children, hats	2.10	2.10
743	A131	40p 2 children, bed	2.10	2.10
744	A131	50p 4 children	2.10	2.10
		Nos. 741-744 (4)	7.40	7.40

Cable and Wireless, Cent. A132

Perf. 13¼x13¾
1999, Dec. 13 Litho. Wmk. 373

745	A132	15p CS Anglia	1.75	1.75
746	A132	35p CS Cambria	2.50	2.50
747	A132	40p Map	2.50	2.50
748	A132	50p CS Colonia	2.75	2.75
		Nos. 745-748 (4)	9.50	9.50

Souvenir Sheet
749	A132	£1.50 CS Seine	8.00	8.00

Turtle Project — A133

15p, Young turtles. 35p, Turtle, trail at left. 40p, Turtle with tracking device on beach. 50p, Turtle with tracking device heading to sea.
No. 754: a, Turtle head, rock. b, Like 15p. c, Turtle on beach, sea. d, Turtle in surf.

2000, Mar. 8 Litho. Perf. 13¾

750	A133	15p multi	1.10	1.10
751	A133	35p multi	1.90	1.90
752	A133	40p multi	1.90	1.90
753	A133	50p multi	2.10	2.10
		Nos. 750-753 (4)	7.00	7.00

Souvenir Sheet
Perf. 14
754	A133	25p Sheet of 4, #a-d	7.50	7.50
e.		With Stamp Show 2000 emblem in margin	7.50	7.50

No. 754 contains four 40x26mm stamps.
No. 754e issued 5/8.

Prince William, 18th Birthday
Common Design Type

William: 10p, As baby laying on stomach and stuffed animal. 15p, As toddler, vert. 35p, Wearing suit and wearing cap, vert. 40p, Holding flowers, and in parka. 50p, In suit and in checked shirt.

Perf. 13¾x14¼, 14¼x13¾
2000, June 21 Litho. Wmk. 373
Stamps With White Border

755	CD359	15p multi	1.00	1.00
756	CD359	35p multi	1.50	1.50
757	CD359	40p multi	2.25	2.25
758	CD359	50p multi	2.75	2.75
		Nos. 755-758 (4)	7.50	7.50

Souvenir Sheet
Stamps Without White Border
Perf. 14¼
759		Sheet of 5	8.00	8.00
a.	CD359	10p multi	.50	.50
b.	CD359	35p multi	.75	.75
c.	CD359	15p multi	1.50	1.50
d.	CD359	40p multi	1.75	1.75
e.	CD359	50p multi	2.25	2.25

Forts A134

Designs: 15p, 1815 fortifications. 35p, Fort Thornton, 1817. 40p, Fort Hayes, 1860. 50p, Fort Bedford, 1940.

Wmk. 373
2000, Aug. 14 Litho. Perf. 14
760-763	A134	Set of 4	9.00	9.00

Christmas — A135

Carols: 15p, I Saw Three Ships. 25p, Silent Night. 40p, Away in a Manger. 90p, Hark, the Herald Angels Sing.

2000, Oct. 16 Wmk. 384
764-767	A135	Set of 4	12.50	12.50

Souvenir Sheet

New Year 2001 (Year of the Snake) — A136

Turtles: a, 25p, Green. b, 40p, Loggerhead.

Wmk. 373
2001, Feb. 1 Litho. Perf. 14½
768	A136	Sheet of 2, #a-b	5.00	5.00

Hong Kong 2001 Stamp Exhibition.

Sinking of the Roebuck, Tercentenary A137

Designs: 15p, Capt. William Dampier. 35p, Drawing of the Roebuck, horiz. 40p, Cave dwelling at Dampier's Drip, horiz. 50p, Map.

2001, Feb. 25 Litho. Perf. 14
769-772	A137	Set of 4	11.00	11.00

Discovery of Ascension Island, 500th Anniv. — A138

Designs: 15p, Alfonso de Albuquerque. 35p, Portuguese caravel. 40p, Cantino map. 50p, Rear admiral Sir George Cockburn.

Perf. 14¾x14¼
2001, Mar. 25 Litho. Wmk. 384
773-776	A138	Set of 4	10.50	10.50

The Age of Victoria A139

Designs: 15p, Great Britain Type A1 with Ascension cancel, vert. 25p, Parade, 1901. 35p, HMS Phoebe. 40p, The Red Lion, 1863. 50p, Queen Victoria, vert. 65p, Sir Joseph Dalton Hooker, botanist, vert. £1.50, Queen Victoria's Funeral.

Wmk. 373
2001, May 24 Litho. Perf. 14
777-782	A139	Set of 6	11.50	11.50

Souvenir Sheet
783	A139	£1.50 multi	9.00	9.00

Souvenir Sheet

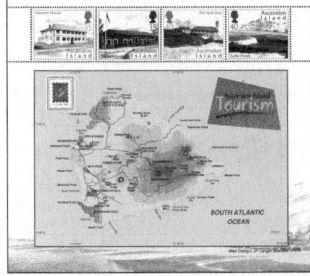

Belgica 2001 Intl. Stamp Exhibition, Brussels — A140

Ascension tourist sites: a, 35p, Islander Hostel. b, 35p, The Residency. c, 40p, The Red Lion. d, 40p, Turtle Ponds.

Wmk. 373
2001, June 9 Litho. Perf. 14¼
784	A140	Sheet of 4, #a-d	10.50	10.50

Birdlife International World Bird Festival — A141

Ascension frigate bird: 15p, On rock with wings outstretched. 35p, Chick, with mouth open. 40p, Pair in flight, horiz. 50p, Close-up of bird, horiz.

Perf. 13¾x14¼, 14¼x13¾
2001, Oct. 1 Litho. Wmk. 373
785-788	A141	Set of 4	7.75	7.75

Souvenir Sheet
789		Sheet, #785-788, 789a, perf. 14¼	8.00	8.00
a.	A141	10p Two birds on rock	1.15	1.15

Reign Of Queen Elizabeth II, 50th Anniv. Issue
Common Design Type

Designs: Nos. 790, 794a, 15p, Princess Elizabeth with dog. Nos. 791, 794b, 35p, In 1978. Nos. 792, 794c, 40p, In 1946. Nos. 793, 794d, 50p, In 1998. No. 794e, 60p, 1955 portrait by Annigoni (38x50mm).

Perf. 14¼x14½, 13¾ (#794e)
2002, Feb. 6 Litho. Wmk. 373
With Gold Frames

790	CD360	15p multicolored	1.10	1.10
791	CD360	35p multicolored	1.25	1.25
792	CD360	40p multicolored	1.75	1.75
793	CD360	50p multicolored	2.00	2.00
		Nos. 790-793 (4)	6.10	6.10

Souvenir Sheet
Without Gold Frames
794	CD360	Sheet of 5, #a-e	8.00	8.00

Falkland Islands War, 20th Anniv. A142

Designs: 15p, Troops landing at English Bay. 35p, Weapons testing at Ascension. 40p, HMS Hermes and helicopter. 50p, Vulcan bomber at Wideawake Airfield.

Wmk. 373
2002, June 14 Litho. Perf. 14
795-798	A142	Set of 4	6.00	6.00

Queen Mother Elizabeth (1900-2002)
Common Design Type

Designs: 35p, Wearing flowered bonnet (sepia photograph). 40p, Wearing pink hat.

No. 801: a, 50p, Wearing hat (sepia photograph). b, £1, Wearing blue hat.

Wmk. 373
2002, Aug. 5   Litho.   Perf. 14¼
With Purple Frames
799 CD361 35p multicolored   1.10 1.10
800 CD361 40p multicolored   1.75 1.75
Souvenir Sheet
Without Purple Frames
Perf. 14½x14¼
801 CD361   Sheet of 2, #a-b   6.00 6.00

Flowers and Local Scenes A143

Designs: 10p, Vinca, Travellers palm. 15p, Mexican poppy, Broken Tooth. 20p, Ascension lily, St. Mary's Church. 25p, Goatweed, Boatswain Bird Island. 30p, Mauritius hemp, Cannon. 35p, Frangipani, Guest House. 40p, Ascension spurge, Wideawake tern. 50p, Lovechaste, Pier head. 65p, Yellowboy, Sisters Peak. 90p, Persian lilac, Two Boats School. £2, Wild currant, Green turtle. £5, Coral tree, Wideawake Airfield.

Wmk. 373
2002, Aug. 28   Litho.   Perf. 14
802 A143 10p multi   .35   .45
803 A143 15p multi   .60   .70
804 A143 20p multi   .80   .95
805 A143 25p multi   1.00   1.10
806 A143 30p multi   1.25   1.25
807 A143 35p multi   1.50   1.80
808 A143 40p multi   1.60   1.90
809 A143 50p multi   2.00   2.40
810 A143 65p multi   2.75   3.25
811 A143 90p multi   3.50   4.00
812 A143 £2 multi   7.00   8.00
813 A143 £5 multi   18.00   35.00
Nos. 802-813 (12)   40.35 60.80

Christmas — A144

Paintings: 15p, Ecce Ancilla Dominii, by Dante Gabriel Rossetti. 25p, The Holy Family and a Shepherd, by Titian, horiz. 35p, Christ Carrying the Cross, by Ambrogio Bergognone. 75p, Sketch for "The Ascension," by Benjamin West.

Perf. 14x14¼, 14¼x14
2002, Oct. 9   Litho.   Wmk. 373
814-817 A144   Set of 4   6.50 6.50

Ariane Downrange Tracking Station — A145

Designs: 35p, Ariane 4 on launchpad, vert. 40p, Map of downrange tracking stations. 65p, Automated Transfer vehicle in space. 90p, Ariane 5 launch, vert.

2003, Jan. 13   Litho.   Perf. 14½
818-821 A145   Set of 4   9.50 9.50
821a   Souvenir sheet, #818-821   9.50 9.50

Head of Queen Elizabeth II
Common Design Type
Wmk. 373
2003, June 2   Litho.   Perf. 13¾
822 CD362 £3 multi   12.50 12.50
Nos. 822 (1)   12.50 12.50

Coronation of Queen Elizabeth II, 50th Anniv.
Common Design Type

Designs: Nos. 823, 825a, 40p, Queen in carriage. Nos. 824, 825b, £1, Queen with crown at coronation.

Perf. 14¼x14½
2003, June 2   Litho.   Wmk. 373
Vignettes Framed, Red Background
823 CD363 40p multicolored   1.75 1.75
824 CD363 £1 multicolored   4.50 4.50
Souvenir Sheet
Vignettes Without Frame, Purple Panel
825 CD363   Sheet of 2, #a-b   6.25 6.25

Prince William, 21st Birthday
Common Design Type
No. 826: a, Color photograph at right. b, Color photograph at left.

Wmk. 373
2003, June 21   Litho.   Perf. 14¼
826   Horiz. pair   7.25 7.25
a.-b.   CD364 75p Either single   3.00 3.00

Powered Flight, Cent. — A146

Designs: 15p, Bleriot XI. 20p, Vickers VC-10. 35p, BAe Harrier FRS Mk 1. 40p, Westland Sea King HAS Mk 4. 50p, Rockwell Space Shuttle. 90p, General Dynamics F-16. £1.50, Fairey Swordfish Mk II.

Wmk. 373
2003, Aug. 12   Litho.   Perf. 14
Stamp + Label
827-832 A146   Set of 6   11.00 11.00
Souvenir Sheet
833   A146 £1.50 multi   8.00 8.00

Democracy, 1st Anniv., and Christmas — A147

Dove and: 15p, Casting ballot. 25p, Island council session. 40p, Higher education. £1, Government headquarters.

Wmk. 373
2003, Nov. 1   Litho.   Perf. 14
834-837 A147   Set of 4   7.00 7.00

Birdlife International A148

Masked booby: 15p, Adult and chick. 35p, Two adults, vert. 40p, Adult in flight, vert. 50p, Adult with neck and wings extended. 90p, Adult.

Perf. 14¼x13¾, 13¾x14¼
2004, Feb. 6   Litho.   Wmk. 373
838-842 A148   Set of 5   10.00 10.00
842a   Souvenir sheet, #838-842, perf. 14¼   10.00 10.00

Royal Horticultural Society, Bicent. — A149

Flora: 15p, Bougainvillea glabra (red flowers). 35p, Bougainvillea glabra (red violet flowers). 40p, Bougainvillea glabra (white flowers). 90p, Bougainvillea spectabilis. £1.50, Pteris adscensionis.

Wmk. 373
2004, May 25   Litho.   Perf. 14
843-846 A149   Set of 4   8.00 8.00
Souvenir Sheet
847 A149 £1.50 multi   7.00 7.00

Fish A150

Designs: 15p, Blue marlin underwater. 35p, Swordfish. 40p, Sailfish. 90p, White marlin. £1.50, Blue marlin breaching surface.

Wmk. 373
2004, July 26   Litho.   Perf. 13¾
848-851 A150   Set of 4   8.50 8.50
Souvenir Sheet
852 A150 £1.50 multi   7.25 7.25

The Moon — A151

Designs: 15p, Lunar eclipse from Hummock Point. 25p, Lunar eclipse from Sister's Peak. 35p, Lunar eclipse from Daly's Craggs. £1.25, Moon and birds from Mars Bay.

Wmk. 373
2004, Oct. 28   Litho.   Perf. 13½
853-856 A151   Set of 4   8.50 8.50
856a   Souvenir sheet of 1   6.00 6.00

Merchant Ships A152

Designs: 15p, MV Ascension. 35p, RMS St. Helena. 40p, RMS Caronia. £1.25, MV Maersk Gannet.

2004, Nov. 26   Perf. 13¼
857-860 A152   Set of 4   9.50 9.50

Battle of Trafalgar, Bicent. — A153

Designs: 15p, British carronade on sliding carriage. 25p, Royal Marine drummer boy, 1805, vert. 35p, HMS Britannia, vert. 40p, Horatio Nelson, by Jean Frances Rigaud. 50p, HMS Neptune and Santissima Trinidad. 90p, HMS Victory.
No. 867, vert.: a, Horatio Nelson, by Lemuel Francis Abbott. b, HMS Ajax.

Wmk. 373, Unwmkd. (#866)
2005, Apr. 29   Litho.   Perf. 13½
861-866 A153   Set of 6   9.50 9.50
Souvenir Sheet
867 A153 £1 Sheet of 2, #a-b   8.25 8.25

No. 866 has particles of wood from the HMS Victory embedded in the areas covered by a thermographic process that produces a shiny, raised effect.

Birdlife International A154

Birds: 15p, Fairy tern. 35p, White-tailed tropicbird. 40p, Brown booby. 50p, Brown noddy. £1.25, Red-billed tropicbird.

Wmk. 373
2005, May 27   Litho.   Perf. 13¾
868-872 A154   Set of 5   10.00 10.00
872a   Souvenir sheet, #868-872   10.00 10.00

Tuna Fish A155

Designs: 35p, Three yellowfin tunas. 40p, Skipjack tunas. 50p, Albacore tunas. £1.25, Bigeye tunas. £1.50, Yellowfin tuna jumping.

Wmk. 373
2005, July 22   Litho.   Perf. 13¾
873-876 A155   Set of 4   9.00 9.00
Souvenir Sheet
877 A155 £1.50 multi   6.50 6.50

Pope John Paul II (1920-2005) A156

Wmk. 373
2005, Aug. 18   Litho.   Perf. 14
878 A156 40p multi   2.00 2.00

Battle of Trafalgar, Bicent. — A157

Designs: 40p, HMS Victory. 65p, Ships in battle, horiz. 90p, Admiral Horatio Nelson.

Perf. 13¼
2005, Oct. 21   Litho.   Unwmk.
879-881 A157   Set of 3   9.50 9.50

Christmas — A158

Stories by Hans Christian Andersen (1805-75): 15p, The Little Fir Tree. 25p, The Mailcoach Passengers. 35p, The Little Match Girl. £1.25, The Snow Man.

2005, Oct. 3   Wmk. 373   Perf. 14
882-885 A158   Set of 4   8.50 8.50

Fish
A159

Designs: 20p, Black jack. 35p, Almaco jack. 50p, Horse-eye jack. £1, Rainbow runner. £1.50, Longfin crevalle jack.

Wmk. 373
2006, Jan. 24   Litho.   Perf. 13¾
886-889 A159   Set of 4   9.00 9.00
Souvenir Sheet
890 A159   £1.50 multi   6.25 6.25

Queen Elizabeth II, 80th Birthday
A160

"80" and Queen: 20p, As child. 40p, Wearing tiara. 50p, Wearing tiara, diff. £1.30, Wearing hat.
No. 895: a, Wearing tiara, diff. b, Without head covering.

Wmk. 373
2006, Apr. 21   Litho.   Perf. 14¼
891-894 A160   Set of 4   10.00 10.00
Souvenir Sheet
895 A160   £1 Sheet of 2, #a-b   8.75 8.75

Anniversaries — A161

No. 896, 20p: a, HMS Beagle. b, Charles Darwin.
No. 897, 35p: a, SS Great Britain. b, Isambard Kingdom Brunel.
No. 898, 40p: a, Niña. b, Christopher Columbus.
No. 899, 50p: a, Map with lines of magnetic variation of the compass. b, Edmond Halley.

Perf. 13x13¼
2006, July 24   Litho.   Wmk. 373
Horiz. Pairs, #a-b
896-899 A161   Set of 4   13.00 13.00

Darwin's voyage on the Beagle, 175th anniv., birth of Brunel, 200th anniv., death of Columbus, 500th anniv., birth of Halley, 350th anniv.

Greetings
A162

Designs: 15p, Long Beach (Greetings from Ascension). 25p, Sunset over lava flow (Merry Christmas). 35p, Dewpond (Seasons Greetings). £1.25, Boatswain Bird Island (Happy New Year).

Wmk. 373
2006, Oct. 30   Litho.   Perf. 14¼
900-903 A162   Set of 4   9.00 9.00

Worldwide Fund for Nature (WWF)
A163

Resplendent angelfish: 35p, Three fish. 40p, Seven fish. 50p, Three fish, diff. £1.25, Four fish.

2007, Mar. 23   Litho.   Unwmk.
904-907 A163   Set of 4   9.00 9.00
907a   Sheet, 4 each #904-907   35.00 35.00

Falkland Islands War, 25th Anniv.
A164

Designs: Nos. 908, 913a, 35p, Handley Page Victor K Mk 2 tanker plane. Nos. 909, 912b, 40p, HMS Dumbarton Castle and Chinook helicopter. Nos. 910, 912c, 50p, HMS Fearless, landing craft and helicopters. Nos. 911, 913d, £1.25, Vulcan XM607 leaving Wideawake Airfield.
No. 912: a, 35p, RFA Tidespring refueling HMS Antrim. d, £1.25, Atlantic Conveyor and Harrier jet.
No. 913: b, 40p, Vickers VC 10 transport plane. c, 50p, Nimrod MR2 maritime reconnaisance plane.

2007, May 25   Perf. 13¼x13
Stamps With White Frames
908-911 A164   Set of 4   11.50 11.50
Stamps Without White Frames
912 A164   Sheet of 4, #a-d   12.00 12.00
913 A164   Sheet of 4, #a-d   12.00 12.00

Scouting, Cent.
A165

Lord Robert Baden-Powell blowing kudu horn and: 35p, Fleur-de-lis of scouts. 40p, Scouts rescuing turtle. 50p, Scouts on gun of HMS Hood. £1.25, Scouts on Land Rover.

2007, July 9   Perf. 14
914-917 A165   Set of 4   12.00 12.00

Mother Teresa (1910-97) and Princess Diana (1961-97) — A166

2007, Aug. 31
918 A166 50p multi   2.25 2.25

Wedding of Queen Elizabeth II and Prince Philip, 60th Anniv. — A167

No. 919: a, 35p, Couple in 1947. b, 90p, Wedding program. c, £1.25, Couple in 2006.

2007, Nov. 20   Litho.   Perf. 14¼
919 A167   Horiz. strip of 3,
              #a-c   10.50 10.50

British Ornithological Union Expedition, 50th Anniv. — A168

No. 920, 15p: a, British Ornithological Union base. b, Drawing of extinct rail.
No. 921, 25p: a, Scientist recording sounds of Wideawake tern. b, Wideawake terns.
No. 922, 40p: a, Boatswainbird Island outpost. b, Masked booby.
No. 923, 50p: a, Scientist pushing dinghy in surf. b, Red-footed booby.

2007, Dec. 10   Perf. 14¼
Horiz. Pairs, #a-b
920-923 A168   Set of 4   12.00 12.00

Oviparous Creatures — A169

Creature and eggs: 15p, Long-tailed blue butterfly. 20p, Ladybird beetle. 25p, Spiny lobster. 30p, Desert locust. 35p, Green turtle. 40p, Land crab. 50p, Red-footed booby. 65p, Coconut palm gecko. 90p, Common waxbill. £1, Yellowtail damselfish. £2.50, Madeiran storm petrel. £5, Red-necked francolin.

2008, Feb. 5   Litho.   Perf. 14¼
924 A169   15p multi   .55   .55
925 A169   20p multi   .75   .75
926 A169   25p multi   .90   .90
927 A169   30p multi   1.15   1.15
928 A169   35p multi   1.25   1.25
929 A169   40p multi   1.40   1.40
930 A169   50p multi   1.75   1.75
931 A169   65p multi   2.40   2.40
932 A169   90p multi   3.50   3.50
933 A169   £1 multi   3.75   3.75
934 A169   £2.50 multi   9.00   9.00
935 A169   £5 multi   18.00 18.00
        Nos. 924-935 (12) 44.40 44.40

Sharks
A170

Designs: 35p, Bluntnose sixgill shark. 40p, Scalloped hammerhead shark. 50p, Shortfin mako shark. £1.25, Whale shark. £1.50, Bigeye thresher shark.

2008, Mar. 14   Litho.   Perf. 14
936-939 A170   Set of 4   11.00 10.00
939a   Sheet of 16, 4 each
        #936-939   50.00 50.00
Souvenir Sheet
940 A170   £1.50 multi   6.25 6.25

National Aeronautical and Space Administration, 50th Anniv. — A171

Designs: No. 941, 35p, Bell X-1E airplane. No. 942, 35p, Apollo 11 Moon walk. 40p, Apollo 17 Lunar Rover. 50p, Space Shuttle Columbia. 65p, Hubble Space Telescope. 90p, International Space Station.

2008, May 23   Litho.   Perf. 14
941-946 A171   Set of 6   12.00 12.00

Royal Air Force, 90th Anniv.
A172

Airplanes: 15p, Sopwith 7F.1 Snipe. 35p, Vickers Wellington Mk 1C. 40p, Supermarine Spitfire Mk IX. 50p, Gloster Meteor F. IV. 65p, BAe Hawk. 90p, Typhoon F-2 Eurofighter.

Unwmk.
2008, June 20   Litho.   Perf. 14
947-952 A172   Set of 6   14.00 14.00

Botanists and Flowers — A173

Designs: 35p, Valerius Cordus (1515-44), and Cordia sebestena. 40p, Nehemiah Grew (1641-1712), and Grewia occidentalis. 50p, Charles Plumier (1646-1704), and Plumeria rubra. £2, Carl Peter Thunberg (1743-1828), and Thunbergia grandiflora.

2008, Aug. 28   Litho.   Perf. 14
953-956 A173   Set of 4   13.50 13.50

Christmas — A174

Santa Claus: 15p, Holding microphone. 25p, With reindeer in surf. 50p, On inflatable lounger in water. £2, Piloting flying sleigh.

2008, Nov. 22
957-960 A174   Set of 4   11.00 11.00

Longest-Reigning British Monarchs — A175

Designs: 35p, King Henry III and Tower of London. 40p, King James I and Stirling Castle. 50p, King George III and Windsor Castle. 65p, Queen Victoria and Osborne House. £1.25, Queen Elizabeth II and Buckingham Palace.

2008, Dec. 15
961-965 A175   Set of 5   11.00 11.00

Marine Mammals — A176

Designs: 35p, Bottlenose dolphins. 40p, Pantropical spotted dolphins. 50p, Sperm whale. £1.25, Gervais' beaked whales. £2, Humpback whale.

2009, Mar. 23   Perf. 14x14¾
966-969 A176   Set of 4   11.50 11.50
969a   Sheet, 4 each #966-969   40.00 40.00
Souvenir Sheet
970 A176   £2 multi   9.00 9.00

Naval Aviation, Cent. — A177

No. 971, 35p: a, Flight Sub-lieutenant Rex Warneford and Victoria Cross. b, Moraine-Saulnier L destroys Zeppelin LZ-37.
No. 972, 35p: a, Squadron Commander Richard Bell Davies and Victoria Cross. b, Nieuport 10 taking off.
No. 973, 40p: a, Lieutenant Commander Eugene Esmonde and Victoria Cross. b, Fairey Swordfish attacking German warships.
No. 974, 50p: a, Lieutenant Robert Hampton Gray and Victoria Cross. b, Corsair bombing Japanese warships.

2009, May 7   *Perf. 14*
Horiz. Pairs, #a-b
971-974 A177   Set of 4   11.50 11.50

Botany
A178

Designs: No. 975, 35p, Raspberry. No. 976, 35p, Blue water lily. 40p, Prickly pear. 50p, Ascension lily. 65p, Yellowboy. 90p, Joseph Dalton Hooker (1817-1911), botanist.

2009, Sept. 7   *Perf. 14*
975-980 A178   Set of 6   11.00 11.00

Turtle Research and
Conservation — A179

No. 981, 15p: a, Early turtle tracking and head of turtle. b, Dr. Archie Carr (1909-87) and map of Ascension.
No. 982, 35p: a, Turtle laying eggs and head of turtle. b, Turtle hatchlings and map of Ascension.
No. 983, 40p: a, Beach raking and head of turtle. b, Population monitoring and map of Ascension.
No. 984, 65p: a, Turtle rescue and head of turtle. b, Turtle rescue and map of Ascension.

2009, Oct. 1   *Perf. 13¾*
Horiz. Pairs, #a-b
981-984 A179   Set of 4   10.00 10.00

Charles Darwin (1809-82),
Naturalist — A180

Darwin and: 35p, Woodpecker finch. 40p, Marine iguanas. 50p, Galapagos tortoise. £2, Galapagos penguins.

2009, Nov. 9   Unwmk.   *Perf. 14*
985-988 A180   Set of 4   12.50 12.50

White-tailed Tropicbird — A181

Designs: 35p, Bird in rock crevice. 40p, Bird on rock. 50p, Juvenile in flight. £1.25, Adult in flight.

2009, Dec. 4   Litho.   *Perf. 14*
989-992 A181   Set of 4   11.50 11.50
992a   Sheet, 4 each #989-992   47.50 47.50

Reef
Fish — A182

Designs: 35p, Hardback soldier. 40p, Grouper. 50p, Five fingers. £1.25, Rock bullseye. £2, Softback soldier.

2010, Mar. 19   *Perf. 13¾*
993-996 A182   Set of 4   11.00 11.00
996a   Sheet, 4 each #993-996   47.50 47.50
Souvenir Sheet
997 A182   £2 multi   8.25 8.25

A183

Girl Guides, Cent. — A184

Designs: 40p, Girl Guides wearing clown noses. 50p, Girl Guides and fish. 90p, Leaders holding cake. £1.25, Girl Guide climbing rock.
No. 1002: a, Olave Baden-Powell (1889-1977). b, Agnes Baden-Powell (1858-1945). c, Lord Robert Baden-Powell (1857-1941).

2010, Apr. 10   *Perf. 14*
998-1001 A183   Set of 4   11.50 11.50
Souvenir Sheet
1002 A184   £1 Sheet of 3, #a-
     c   11.50 11.50

Miniature Sheet

Battle of Britain, 70th Anniv. — A185

No. 1003: a, Supermarine Spitfire R6803. b, Hawker Hurricane V7383. c, Supermarine Spitfire X4036. d, Hawker Hurricane R4175. e, Supermarine Spitfire R6885. f, Hawker Hurricane V6684. g, Supermarine Spitfire K9998. h, Hawker Hurricane R4118.

2010, May 7   *Perf. 14*
1003 A185   50p Sheet of 8 #a-
     h   15.00 15.00
London 2010 Festival of Stamps.

Yellow
Canary — A186

Designs: 15p, Juvenile. 35p, Adult male on branch. 60p, Adult female. 90p, Adult male on ground.

2010, Oct. 11   *Perf. 13¾*
1004-1007 A186   Set of 4   8.25 8.25
1007a   Miniature sheet of 16, 4
    each #1004-1007   36.00 36.00

Christmas — A187

Designs: 15p, Christmas lunch. 40p, Christmas parade. 50p, Christingle. £1.25, Nativity play.

2010, Nov. 17   *Perf. 14*
1008-1011 A187   Set of 4   8.50 8.50

Rediscovery of
the Parsley
Fern — A188

Ascension National Park emblem and: 15p, HMS Erebus and HMS Terror approaching Ascension, 1843. 15p, Parsley fern. 35p, Parsley fern in situ. 40p, Parsley fern seedlings in pots. £1, Parsley fern cultivation at Kew Gardens.

2011, Feb. 10   *Perf. 13¾*
1012-1016 A188   Set of 5   7.00 7.00

Service of Queen Elizabeth II and
Prince Philip — A189

Designs: 15p, Queen Elizabeth II. 25p, Queen and Prince Philip. 35p, Queen and Prince Philip, diff. 40p, Queen and Prince Philip, diff. 60p, Queen and Prince Philip, diff. £1.25, Prince Philip.
£2, Queen and Prince Philip, diff.

2011, Mar. 23   *Perf. 13¼*
1017-1022 A189   Set of 6   9.50 9.50
1022a   Sheet of 6, #1017-1022,
    + 3 labels   9.50 9.50
Souvenir Sheet
1023 A189   £2 multi   6.50 6.50

Royal Air Force Search and Rescue,
70th Anniv. — A190

Emblem and Sea King helicopter: 35p, On airplane's cargo ramp. 40p, Flying near Ascension. 90p, Approaching HMS Dumbarton Castle. £1, Approaching HMS Spartan submarine.
£2.50, Sea King helicopter in flight.

2011, May 19
1024-1027 A190   Set of 4   8.25 8.25
Souvenir Sheet
1028 A190   £2.50 multi   7.75 7.75

Miniature Sheet

Peonies — A191

No. 1029 — Peony color: a, Red. b, Gray lilac. c, Light orange. d, White.

2011, June 22   *Perf. 13¾*
1029 A191   50p Sheet of 4, #a-d   6.25 6.25

Wedding of Prince William and
Catherine Middleton — A192

Couple, with Middleton: 35p, Wearing hat. 90p, Without hat. £1.25, Seated in coach in wedding dress.
£2, Couple standing on wedding day, vert.

2011, July 20   *Perf. 14*
1030-1032 A192   Set of 3   7.75 7.75
Souvenir Sheet
Perf. 14¾x14
1033 A192   £2 multi   6.25 6.25
No. 1033 contains one 29x45mm stamp.

Worldwide Fund for Nature
(WWF) — A193

Phaethon aethereus: Nos. 1034, 1038a, 35p, Bird in rock crevice. Nos. 1035, 1038b, 40p, Two birds in flight. Nos. 1036, 1038c, 50p, Adult and juvenile in rock crevice. Nos. 1037, 1038d, £1.25, Bird in flight.

2011, Aug. 31
Stamps With White Frames
1034-1037 A193 Set of 4   7.50 7.50
Stamps Without White Frames
1038 A193 Strip of 4, #a-d   8.00 8.00

Nos. 1038a-1038d were printed in sheets of 16 stamps containing four strips.

Christmas — A194

Pantomimes: 15p, Mother Goose. 40p, Jack and the Beanstalk. 50p, Aladdin. £1.25, Cinderella.

2011, Nov. 16   **Perf. 14**
1039-1042 A194 Set of 4   6.75 6.75

Reign of Queen Elizabeth II, 60th Anniv. — A195

Photographs of Queen Elizabeth II taken in: 15p, 2011. 25p, 1998. 35p, 1988. 40p, 1975. 60p, 1961. £1.25, 1953. £2, 1977.

2012, Feb. 6   **Perf. 13¼**
1043-1048 A195 Set of 6   9.00 9.00
1048a   Sheet of 6, #1043-1048, + 3 labels   9.00 9.00
Souvenir Sheet
1049 A195 £2 multi   6.00 6.00

Reef Fish
A196

Designs: 35p, Trumpetfish. 40p, Peacock flounder. 90p, Queen triggerfish. £1, Scrawled filefish. £2, Yellow goatfish.

2012, Apr. 15   Litho.   Perf. 13¾
1050-1053 A196 Set of 4   8.00 8.00
1053a   Sheet, 4 each #1050-1053   32.50 32.50
Souvenir Sheet
1054 A196 £2 multi   6.00 6.00

Sinking of the Titanic, Cent. A197

Designs: 20p, The departure. 45p, The boat deck. 50p, The iceberg. £1, The sinking. £2, Abandoning ship.

2012, Aug. 1   **Perf. 14**
1055-1058 A197 Set of 4   6.50 6.50
Souvenir Sheet
1059 A197 £2 multi   6.00 6.00

Shackleton-Rowett Antarctic Expedition, 90th Anniv. — A198

No. 1060, 45p: a, Sir Ernest Shackleton (36x36mm). b, John Quiller Rowett (18x36mm). c, Frank Wild (36x36mm).
No. 1061, 50p: a, Quest leaving London (36x36mm). b, Quest at Ascension (18x36mm). c, Quest in ice (36x36mm).

2012, Sept. 17   **Perf. 13¼**
Horiz. Strips of 3, #a-c
1060-1061 A198 Set of 2   8.50 8.50

Christmas
A199

Scenes from *A Christmas Carol*, by Charles Dickens: 25c, Ebenezer Scrooge passing Christmas carolers. 40p, Ghost visiting Scrooge. 50p, Scrooge carrying Tiny Tim, vert. £1.25, Scrooge watching boy deliver turkey, vert.

2012, Nov. 15   **Perf. 13¼x13½**
1062-1065 A199 Set of 4   7.25 7.25

Miniature Sheet

Wideawake Airfield, 70th Anniv. — A200

No. 1066: a, 45p, Wideawake tern. b, 50p, Douglas DC-3 Dakota. c, £1, Eurofighter Typhoon. d, £1.45, Masked booby.

2012, Dec. 5   **Perf. 13¼**
1066 A200 Sheet of 4, #a-d   13.00 13.00

Aircraft
A201

Designs: 15p, Fairey Swordfish. 20p, North American B-25 Mitchell. 25p, Lockheed C-130K Hercules. 30p, Hawker Siddeley Nimrod MR2. 40p, BAE Sea Harrier FRS1. 45p, Lockheed C-5 Galaxy. 50p, Douglas DC-3 Dakota. 65p, Avro Vulcan. 90p, McDonnell Douglas Phantom F-4. £1, Eurofighter Typhoon. £2.50, Lockheed C-121. £5, Shorts Belfast.

2013, Jan. 15   **Perf. 13¾**
1067 A201   15p multi   .50 .50
1068 A201   20p multi   .65 .65
1069 A201   25p multi   .80 .80
1070 A201   30p multi   .95 .95
1071 A201   40p multi   1.25 1.25
1072 A201   45p multi   1.40 1.40
1073 A201   50p multi   1.60 1.60
1074 A201   65p multi   2.10 2.10
1075 A201   90p multi   3.00 3.00
1076 A201   £1 multi   3.25 3.25
1077 A201   £2.50 multi   8.00 8.00
1078 A201   £5 multi   16.00 16.00
    Nos. 1067-1078 (12)   39.50 39.50

Items Commemorating British Coronations — A202

Coronation of Queen Elizabeth II, 60th Anniv. — A203

Various items commemorating the coronation of: 45p, Queen Victoria. 50p, King Edward VII. 70p, King George V. £1.10, King George VI. £1.25, Queen Elizabeth II.

2013, Feb. 6   **Perf. 14**
1079-1083 A202 Set of 5   12.00 12.00
Souvenir Sheet
Perf. 14¾x14¼
1084 A203 £2 multi   8.00 8.00

British Settlement of Ascension, Bicent. (in 2015) — A204

Imprisonment of Napoleon Bonaparte on Ascension: 45p, Joséphine Bonaparte at Malmaison, by François Pascal Simon. 50p, Bonaparte at the Bridge of Arcole, by Antoine-Jean Gros. 60p, Napoleon and his General Staff, by Jean-Léon Gérôme. £1.45, Napoleon as First Consul, detail of painting by Jean-Baptiste Isabey.

2013, May 21   **Perf. 13¾**
1085-1088 A204 Set of 4   11.00 11.00

Lady Margaret Thatcher (1925-2013), British Prime Minister — A205

Photographs of Thatcher: 45p, Giving "Victory" sign, 1976. 50p, In cockpit of Sea Harrier jet, 1982. 60p, Holding teacup during visit to Ascension, 1992. £1.45, At Order of the Garter ceremony, 1995.

2013, June 14
1089-1092 A205 Set of 4   11.00 11.00

Ascension Frigatebirds — A206

Designs: 20p, Male and female. 45p, Male on egg. 50p, Chick. 60p, Female and chick. £1.10, Juvenile. £1.45, Male in flight.

2013, Aug. 16   **Perf. 13¼x13½**
1093-1098 A206 Set of 6   16.00 16.00

Shallow Marine Surveys Group A207

Marine life: Nos. 1099, 1103a, 45p, Fire worm. Nos. 1100, 1103b, 50p, Black bar soldier fish. Nos. 1101, 1103c, 60p, Endemic white hawk fish. Nos. 1102, 1103d, £1.45, Atlantic blue tang.
No. 1104a, £1, Anemone, vert.

2013, Aug. 29   **Perf. 13¼x13½**
Stamps With White Frames
1099-1102 A207 Set of 4   11.00 11.00
Stamps Without White Frames
1103 A230 Strip of 4, #a-d   11.00 11.00
Souvenir Sheet
Perf. 13½x13¼
1104 A207 Sheet of 3 (see footnote)   11.00 11.00
    a.   A207 £1 multi   3.75 3.75

No. 1104 contains No. 1104a, Falkland Islands No. 1107a and South Georgia and South Sandwich Islands No. 485a. This sheet was sold in Ascension, Falkland Islands and South Georgia and South Sandwich Islands.

Churches
A208

Stained-Glass Windows A209

Designs: 45p, Grotto of Our Lady Catholic Church. 50p, Window depicting Madonna and Child. 60p, St. Mary's Anglican Church. £1, Window depicting St. Michael.

2013, Nov. 18   Litho.   Perf. 13¼
Stamps With White Frames
1105 A208 45p multi   1.50 1.50
1106 A209 50p multi   1.75 1.75
1107 A208 60p multi   2.00 2.00
1108 A209 £1 multi   3.25 3.25
    Nos. 1105-1108 (4)   8.50 8.50
Stamps Without White Frames
1109   Horiz. strip of 4   8.50 8.50
    a.   A208 45p multi   1.50 1.50
    b.   A209 50p multi   1.75 1.75
    c.   A208 60p multi   2.00 2.00
    d.   A209 £1 multi   3.25 3.25

Christmas.

British Settlement of Ascension, Bicent. (in 2015) — A210

The Napoleonic Years: 50p, Engraving of Napoleon Bonaparte after signing of Treaty of Amiens, 1802. 55p, Napoleon I in Coronation Robes, by François Gérard. 60p, Lord Horatio Nelson, by Lemuel Francis Abbott. £1.60, Napoleon at Wagram, by Emile Jean-Horace Vernet.

2014, Apr. 28   Litho.   Perf. 13¾
1110-1113 A210 Set of 4   12.50 12.50

Royal Christenings A211

Photograph from christening of: 50p, Queen Elizabeth II, 1926. 55p, Prince Charles, 1948. 60p, Prince William, 1982. £1.60, Prince George, 2013.

2014, May 21   Litho.   Perf. 13x13¼
1114-1117 A211   Set of 4   12.50 12.50

World War I, Cent. — A212

Various poppies: 50p, 55p, 60p, £1.60.

2014, Aug. 4   Litho.   Perf. 14¾x14
1118-1121 A212   Set of 4   12.50 12.50

Royal Marines, 350th Anniv. — A213

Designs: 20p, Duke of York and Albany's Maritime Regiment of Foot on man-of-war, 1664. 50p, Light Infantry and barracks on Ascension, 19th cent. 55p, Light Infantry at Gallipoli, 1915. 60p, Royal Marines Commandos at Eastney, 1970s. 65p, Royal Marines Band Service Bugler at Deal, 1996. £1, Royal Marines Commandos, 2014.

2014, Oct. 28   Litho.   Perf. 14
1122-1127 A213   Set of 6   12.50 12.50

Rosetta Mission A214

Designs: 35p, Ariane 5 launching Rosetta. 55p, Rosetta spacecraft. 65p, Deploying Philae lander. £1.60, Descent of Philae. £3, Comet 67P/Churyumov-Gerasimenko.

2014, Dec. 30   Litho.   Perf. 14
1128-1131 A214   Set of 4   9.75 9.75
Souvenir Sheet
1132 A214   £3 multi   9.25 9.25

British Settlement of Ascension, Bicent. — A215

The Napoleonic Wars: 55p, Napoleon Bonaparte on the Borodino Heights, by Vasily V. Vereshchagin. 60p, Napoleon at Fontainebleau, by Paul Delaroche. 65p, Arthur Wellesley, 1st Duke of Wellington, by Thomas Lawrence. £1.60, Napoleon dictating his memoirs in exile.

2015, Apr. 27   Litho.   Perf. 13¾
1133-1136 A215   Set of 4   9.50 9.50

Magna Carta, 800th Anniv. A216

Designs: 50p, King John examining Magna Carta. 55p, Ascension Government building. 60p, Magistrate's Court, Ascension. £1.60, Arms of Ascension, King John.

2015, June 15   Litho.   Perf. 13
1137-1140 A216   Set of 4   9.50 9.50

Queen Elizabeth II, Longest-Reigning British Monarch — A217

Queen Elizabeth II and events during her reign: 50p, Publications reporting on her coronation, 1953. 55p, First men on the Moon, 1969. 65p, Avro Vulcan (end of Cold War), 1991. £1.60, The Spirit of Chartwell in Diamond Jubilee celebration, 2012.

2015, Sept. 9   Litho.   Perf. 14
1141-1144 A217   Set of 4   9.00 9.00

British Settlement of Ascension, Bicent. — A218

200th anniversary emblem and: 35p, King George III. 50p, Flag of Ascension. 55p, Coat of arms of Ascension. £1.60, Queen Elizabeth II.

2015, Oct. 22   Litho.   Perf. 14
1145-1148 A218   Set of 4   8.50 8.50

William Dampier (1651-1715), Explorer — A219

Designs: 25p, Dampier. 35p, Dampier's ship, HMS Roebuck. £1, Sinking of HMS Roebuck at Ascension Island, 1701. £1.60, Diver and bell of HMS Roebuck.

2015, Dec. 1   Litho.   Perf. 14
1149-1152 A219   Set of 4   8.75 8.75

Worldwide Fund for Nature (WWF) — A220

Red-footed booby: 20p, Bird on rock. 50p, Adult and chick. 55p, Heads of brown and white morphs. £2, Juvenile.

Perf. 13¼x13½
2016, Feb. 22   Litho.
Stamps With White Frames
1153-1156 A220   Set of 4   8.75 8.75
Stamps Without White Frames
1157   Strip of 4   9.50 9.50
a.   A220 20p multi   .60   .60
b.   A220 50p multi   1.40   1.40
c.   A220 55p multi   1.60   1.60
d.   A220 £2 multi   5.75   5.75

Queen Elizabeth II, 90th Birthday — A221

Photograph of Queen Elizabeth II from: 50p, 1951. 55p, 1973. 65p, 1974. £1.60, 1995. £3, Queen Elizabeth II in 1961.

2016, Apr. 21   Litho.   Perf. 14
1158-1161 A221   Set of 4   8.75 8.75
Souvenir Sheet
1162 A221   £3 multi   8.00 8.00

British Broadcasting Corporation Transmitting Station on Ascension, 50th Anniv. — A222

Designs: 20p, Original control desk. 25p, Klinka Klub and short wave antenna array towers, 1980s. 50p, Atlantic relay station, English Bay. 55p, Current transmitting station. 65p, BBC wind turbines, turtle. £1.60, Current transmitting station main office.

2016, July 3   Litho.   Perf. 13½
1163-1168 A222   Set of 6   9.50 9.50

Scenes from Plays by William Shakespeare (1564-1616) — A223

Designs: 50p, Twelfth Night. 55p, Henry V. 65p, Hamlet. £1.60, Romeo and Juliet.

2016, Aug. 8   Litho.   Perf. 14
1169-1172 A223   Set of 4   7.75 7.75

Fish A224

Designs: 50p, Resplendent angelfish. 55p, White hawkfish. 65p, Ascension wrasse. £1.60, Yellowtail damselfish.

2016, Oct. 17   Litho.   Perf. 13¼x13½
1173-1176 A224   Set of 4   7.25 7.25

Eels — A225

Designs: 20p, Broadbanded moray eel. 35p, Whitespotted moray eel. 50p, Chain moray eel. 55p, Goldtail moray eel. 65p, Brown moray eel. £1.60, Spotted snake eel.

2017, Apr. 12   Litho.   Perf. 13¼
1177-1182 A225   Set of 6   10.00 10.00

70th Wedding Anniversary of Queen Elizabeth II and Prince Philip A226

Photographs of Queen Elizabeth II and Prince Philip from: 50p, 1947. 55p, 1963. 65p, 1982. £1.60, 2006.

2017, Nov. 20   Litho.   Perf. 13x13¼
1183-1186 A226   Set of 4   8.00 8.00

Plankton A227

Designs: 20p, Hyperiid amphipod. 35p, Land crab zoea larva. 50p, Sapphirinid copepod. 55p, Stomatopod shrimp larva. 65p, Gastropod mollusc larva. £1.60, Polychaete worm larva.

2017, Dec. 6   Litho.   Perf. 13¼x13½
1187-1192 A227   Set of 6   10.50 10.50

Johngarthia Lagostoma — A228

Designs: 20p, Female crab with eggs. 35p, Crab in megalops phase. 50p, Juvenile crab. 55p, Crab feeding on moss. 65p, Crab in purple morph stage. £1.60, Crab in yellow morph stage.

2018, Jan. 24   Litho.   Perf. 13½x13¾
1193-1198 A228   Set of 6   11.00 11.00

Royal Air Force, Cent. A229

Designs: 20p, Royal Aircraft Factory SE5a. 35p, Hawker Hurricane. 50p, Avro Vulcan. £2, Tornado.

2018, July 2   Litho.   Perf. 13¼x13½
1199-1202 A229   Set of 4   8.00 8.00

Wedding of Prince Harry and Meghan Markle A230

Designs: 20p, Engagement photograph. 50p, Couple at dance performance. 55p, Couple at altar. £2, Couple in carriage. £3, Couple leaving St. George's Chapel on wedding day, vert.

Perf. 13¼x13½
2018, Aug. 14   Litho.
1203-1206 A230   Set of 4   8.50 8.50
Souvenir Sheet
Perf. 13½x13¼
1207 A230   £3 multi   7.75 7.75

Ships A231

Designs: £1.60, RMS St. Helena I, 1978-90. £2, RMS St. Helena II, 1990-2018.

2018, Oct. 8 Litho. Perf. 13¼x13¾
1208-1209 A231 Set of 2   9.25 9.25

Migratory Turtles — A232

No. 1210, 65p — Hawksbill turtle and map of: a, South America. b, Ascension Island and Africa.
No. 1211, £1 — Green turtle and map of: a, South America. b, Ascension Island and Africa.

2018, Dec. 5 Litho. Perf. 13¼x13½
Horiz. Pairs, #a-b
1210-1211 A232 Set of 2   8.50 8.50

D-Day, 75th Anniv. A233

Designs: 20p, Troops in door of glider. 35p, Third Infantry Division soldiers on French beach. 50p, Commandos coming ashore. £2, HMS Warspite shelling German batteries.

2019, June 6 Litho. Perf. 13¼x13½
1212-1215 A233 Set of 4   7.75 7.75

First Man on the Moon, 50th Anniv. A234

Designs: 35p, Lunar Module in space. 55p, Astronaut on ladder of Lunar Module. £1, Astronaut on Moon. £1.60, Astronaut and United States flag on Moon.

2019, Dec. 6 Litho. Perf. 13¼
1216-1219 A234 Set of 4   9.25 9.25

AIR POST STAMPS

AP1   AP2

AP3   AP4

AP5   AP6

Green Turtles

2015, Feb. 14 Litho. Perf. 13¼
Stamps With White Frames

C1	AP1 (50p) multi	1.40	1.40
a.	Dated "2019"	1.40	1.40
C2	AP2 (50p) multi	1.40	1.40
a.	Dated "2019"	1.40	1.40
C3	AP3 (50p) multi	1.40	1.40
a.	Dated "2019"	1.40	1.40
C4	AP4 (50p) multi	1.40	1.40
a.	Dated "2019"	1.40	1.40
C5	AP5 (50p) multi	1.40	1.40
a.	Dated "2019"	1.40	1.40

C6	AP6 (50p) multi	1.40	1.40
a.	Dated "2019"	1.40	1.40
	Nos. C1-C6 (6)	8.40	8.40

Miniature Sheet
Stamps Without White Frames

C7	Sheet of 6	8.50	8.50
a.	AP1 (50p) multi	1.40	1.40
b.	AP2 (50p) multi	1.40	1.40
c.	AP3 (50p) multi	1.40	1.40
d.	AP4 (50p) multi	1.40	1.40
e.	AP5 (50p) multi	1.40	1.40
f.	AP6 (50p) multi	1.40	1.40
g.	Sheet of 6, #C7h-C7m, dated "2019"	8.50	8.50
h.	As #C7a, dated "2019"	1.40	1.40
i.	As #C7b, dated "2019"	1.40	1.40
j.	As #C7c, dated "2019"	1.40	1.40
k.	As #C7d, dated "2019"	1.40	1.40
l.	As #C7e, dated "2019"	1.40	1.40
m.	As #C7f, dated "2019"	1.40	1.40

Issued: Nos. C1a-C6a, C7g, 12/12/19.

POSTAGE DUE STAMPS

Outline Map of Ascension — D1

1986 Litho. Perf. 15x14

J1	D1	1p beige & brown	.25	.30
J2	D1	2p orange & brown	.25	.30
J3	D1	5p org ver & brn	.25	.30
J4	D1	7p violet & black	.25	.50
J5	D1	10p ultra & black	.45	.75
J6	D1	25p pale green & blk	.90	1.25
		Nos. J1-J6 (6)	2.35	3.40

AUSTRALIAN STATES

NEW SOUTH WALES

'nü sauth 'wā̠ə̣lz

LOCATION — Southeast coast of Australia in the South Pacific Ocean
GOVT. — British Crown Colony
AREA — 309,432 sq. mi.
POP. — 1,500,000 (estimated, 1900)
CAPITAL — Sydney

In 1901 New South Wales united with five other British colonies to form the Commonwealth of Australia. Stamps of Australia are now used.

12 Pence = 1 Shilling
20 Shillings = 1 Pound

Watermarks

Wmk. 12 —
Crown and Single-lined A

Wmk. 13 —
Large Crown and Double-lined A

Wmk. 49 —
Double-lined Numerals Corresponding with the Value

Wmk. 50 —
Single-lined Numeral

Wmk. 51 —
Single-lined Numeral

Wmk. 52 —
Single-lined Numeral

Wmk. 53 —
5/-

Wmk. 54 —
Small Crown and NSW

Wmk. 55 —
Large Crown and NSW

Wmk. 56
— NSW

Wmk. 57 —
5/- NSW in Diamond

Wmk. 58 —
20/- NSW in Circle

Wmk. 70 — V and Crown

Wmk. 199 —
Crown and A in Circle

Values for unused stamps are for examples with original gum as defined in the catalogue introduction except for Nos. 1-20 which are rarely found with gum and are valued without gum. Very fine examples of Nos. 35-100, F3-F5, J1-J10 and O1-O40 will have perforations touching the framelines or design on one or more sides due to the narrow spacing of the stamps on the plates and imperfect perforation methods. Stamps with perfs clear of the design on all four sides are scarce and will command higher prices.

Seal of the Colony — A1

A1 has no clouds. A2 has clouds added to the design, except in pos. 15.

1850 Unwmk. Engr. Imperf.
Yellowish Wove Paper

1	A1	1p red, yelsh wove	16,000.	625.00
a.		1p brownish red	17,250.	650.00
c.		1p carmine	17,250.	650.00
d.		1p crimson lake	17,250.	650.00

Bluish Wove Paper

b.		1p red, bluish wove	15,000.	650.00
1e	A1	1p lake	16,000.	650.00

Seal of the Colony — A2

Re-engraved, with Clouds

1850, Aug. Yellowish Wove Paper

2	A2	1p red, yelsh wove	14,000.	550.00
f.		Hill unshaded	18,500.	850.00
g.		No clouds	18,500.	850.00
h.		No trees	18,500.	850.00
2i	A2	1p vermilion	13,750.	675.00

Bluish Wove Paper

c.	A3	1p carmine red, bluish wove	13,250.	750.00
j.		Hill unshaded	18,000.	750.00
k.		No clouds	18,000.	750.00
l.		No trees	18,000.	750.00
2m	A2	1p brownish lake	13,500.	750.00
2n	A2	1p crimson lake	13,500.	750.00
2o	A2	1p gooseberry red	16,500.	750.00

Laid Paper

b.	A2	1p carmine red, yellowish laid	18,000.	800.00
p.		Hill unshaded	—	1,275.
q.		No clouds	—	1,275.
r.		No trees	—	1,275.
e.		1p carmine red, bluish laid		
2s	A2	1p vermilion, bluish	19,000.	600.00

Printed in panes of 25 (5x5). Twenty-five varieties.
Stamps from early impressions of the plate sell at considerably higher prices.
No. 1 was reproduced by the collotype process in a souvenir sheet distributed at the London International Stamp Exhibition 1950. The paper is white.

Plate I — A3   Plate II — A4

Plate I: Vertically lined background.
Plate I re-touched: Lines above and below "POSTAGE" and "TWO PENCE" deepened. Outlines of circular band around picture also deepened.
Plate II (First re-engraving of Plate I): Horizontally lined background; the bale on the left side is dated and there is a dot in the star in each corner.
Plate II retouched: Dots and dashes added in lower spandrels.

Plate I
1850, Jan. 1 Early Impressions

a.	Early impression	20,000.	625.00
b.	Double line on bale (Pos. 2/7)		1,250.

3c	A3	2p deep blue, *yelsh wove*		18,000.	725.00

Intermediate Impressions

3d	A3	2p gray blue, *yelsh*		12,750.	425.00
3e	A3	2p deep blue, *yelsh*		13,750.	500.00

Late (worn plate) Impressions

3	A3	2p blue, *yelsh wove*		10,500.	225.00
3f	A3	2p blue, *yelsh wove*		10,500.	225.00

Printed in panes of 24 (12x2). Twenty-four varieties.

Plate I, Retouched

4	A3	2p blue, *yelsh wove*		12,750.	360.00
4a	A3	2p gray blue, *yelsh wove*		13,750.	450.00

Twelve varieties.

Plate II

1850, Apr.   **Early Impressions**

	h.	Early impression		16,500.	350.00
	j.	"CREVIT" omitted (Pos. 2/1)		22,500.	1,000.
	k.	Pick & shovel omitted (Pos. 1/10)		22,000.	625.00
	l.	No whip (Pos. 1/4, 1/8, 2/8)		—	525.00
5m	A3	2p bright blue, *bluish wove*		16,500.	350.00
5n	A3	2p indigo blue, *yelsh wove*		16,500.	375.00
5o	A3	2p lilac blue, *yelsh wove*			1,750.

Late (worn plate) Impressions

5	A4	2p blue, *yelsh wove*		10,500.	175.00
	a.	2p blue, *bluish wove*		10,500.	175.00
	b.	2p blue, *grayish wove*		10,500.	175.00
5p	A4	2p prussian blue, *bluish wove*		10,500.	225.00
	c.	"CREVIT" omitted		16,500.	675.00
	d.	Pick and shovel omitted		—	450.00
	e.	No whip		14,750.	365.00

Plate II, Retouched

5F	A4	2p blue, *bluish wove*		11,500.	270.00
	g.	No whip		—	425.00
	i.	"CREVIT" omitted		—	585.00
5q	A4	2p prussian blue, *bluish wove*		11,500.	360.00

Eleven varieties.

Plate III   Plate IV
A5   A6

Plate III (Second re-engraving of Plate I): The bale is not dated and, with the exception of Nos. 7, 10 and 12, it is single-lined. There are no dots in the stars.

Plate IV (Third re-engraving of Plate I): The bale is double-lined and there is a circle in the center of each star.

1850-51   **Wove Paper**

6	A5	2p bl, *grayish wove*		11,500.	270.00
	a.	Fan with 6 segments		14,500.	585.00
	b.	Double-lined bale		—	375.00
	c.	No whip		—	425.00
6d	A5	2p ultramarine		11,500.	270.00
7	A6	2p blue, *bluish wove* ('51)		12,500.	225.00
	b.	2p blue, *grayish wove*		12,500.	250.00
	c.	Fan with 6 segments (Pos. 2/8)		—	375.00
	d.	No clouds (Pos. 2/10)		—	375.00
	e.	Hill not shaded (Pos. 1/12)		—	400.00
	f.	No waves (Pos. 1/9, 2/5)		—	550.00
7g	A6	2p 2p ultramarine		12,500.	270.00
7h	A6	2p 2p prussian blue		12,500.	225.00

Laid Paper

7a	A6	2p ultra, *white laid*		13,500.	275.00
7i	A6	2p prussian blue		14,500.	340.00
	j.	Fan with 6 segments (Pos. 2/8)		—	450.00
	k.	No clouds (Pos. 2/10)		17,500.	450.00
	l.	Hill not shaded (Pos. 1/12)		—	450.00
	m.	No waves (Pos. 1/9, 2/5)		—	400.00
	n.	"PENOE" (Pos. 1/10, 2/12)		—	450.00

Twenty-four varieties.

Plate V — A7

A8

Plate V (Fourth re-engraving of Plate I): There is a pearl in the fan-shaped ornament below the central design.

1850-51   **Wove Paper**

8	A7	2p blue, *grayish wove* ('51)		12,500.	270.00
	b.	Fan with 6 segments (Pos. 2/8)		—	450.00
	c.	Pick and shovel omitted (Pos. 2/5)		—	475.00
8d	A7	2p ultramarine		12,500.	270.00

Laid Paper

	a.	2p ultra, *yellowish laid*		15,500.	450.00
	e.	Fan with 6 segments (Pos. 2/8)		—	650.00
	f.	Pick and shovel omitted (Pos. 2/5)		—	650.00

Yellowish Wove Paper

	a.	3p green, *yellowish wove*		12,500.	350.00
9h	A8	3p emerald green		14,500.	375.00
	e.	No whip		—	550.00
	f.	"SIGIIIUM" for "SIGILLUM" (Pos. 5/3)		—	725.00
9g	A8	3p myrtle green		23,500.	1,500.

Bluish Wove Paper

9	A8	3p green, *bluish wove*		12,500.	325.00
9d	A8	3p emerald green		13,500.	325.00
	i.	No whip (Pos. 4/3, 4/4)		—	450.00
	j.	"SIGIIIUM" for "SIGILLUM" (Pos. 5/3)		—	650.00

Laid Paper

	b.	3p green, *yellowish laid*		17,500.	825.00
	k.	No whip (Pos. 4/3, 4/4)		—	1,000.
	l.	"SIGIIIUM" for "SIGILLUM" (Pos. 5/3)		—	1,200.
	c.	3p green, *bluish laid*		17,500.	825.00
9m	A8	3p bright green, *yellowish laid*		19,000.	900.00

Twenty-four varieties of No. 8, twenty-five of No. 9.

Queen Victoria — A9

TWO PENCE
Plate I — Background of wavy lines.
Plate II — Stars in corners.
Plate III (Plate I re-engraved) — Background of crossed lines.

1851   **Yellowish Wove Paper**

10	A9	1p carmine		4,500.	360.00
	b.	No leaves to right of "SOUTH"		6,000.	900.00
	c.	Two leaves to right of "SOUTH"		6,000.	1,000.
	d.	"WALE"		6,000.	1,000.
11	A9	2p ultra, Plate I		2,250.	135.00

1852   **Bluish Laid Paper**

12	A9	1p orange brown		7,500.	540.00
	a.	1p claret		7,500.	525.00
	b.	As "a," no leaves to right of "SOUTH"			1,125.
	c.	As "a," two leaves to right of "SOUTH"			1,250.
	d.	As "a," "WALE"			1,250.

Queen Victoria — A10

SIX PENCE
Plate I — Background of fine lines.
Plate II (Plate I re-engraved) — Background of coarse lines.

1852-55

Bluish or Grayish Wove Paper

13	A9	1p red		2,250.	180.00
	a.	1p carmine		2,250.	180.00
	b.	1p scarlet		2,250.	225.00
	c.	1p brick red		2,250.	180.00
	d.	As "c," no leaves to right of "SOUTH"		4,500.	375.00
	e.	As "c," two leaves to right of "SOUTH"			500.00
	f.	As "c," "WALE"			500.00
14	A9	2p blue, Plate I		1,700.	42.50
	a.	2p ultramarine		1,800.	42.50
	b.	2p slate		1,750.	42.50
	c.	2p chalky blue		1,750.	42.50
	d.	2p prussian blue		1,250.	42.50

15	A10	2p blue, Plate II ('53)		2,600.	120.00
	a.	"WAEES"		3,000.	525.00
	b.	2p deep ultramarine		2,600.	150.00
	c.	2p prussian blue		2,600.	135.00
	d.	As "c," "WAEES"		—	550.00
16	A9	2p blue, Plate III ('55)		1,450.	85.00
	a.	"WALES" partly covered with wavy lines		5,500.	325.00
	b.	2p blue, *white paper* ('55)		1,450.	85.00
	c.	As "b," "WALES" partly covered with wavy lines		—	300.00
17	A9	3p green		5,500.	190.00
	a.	3p emerald		6,250.	270.00
	b.	As "a," "WACES"		—	725.00
	c.	3p deep green		6,250.	270.00
	d.	3p yellow green		6,250.	250.00
	e.	As "d," "WACES"		—	575.00
	f.	3p blue green, *thick paper*		6,250.	300.00
	g.	As "f," "WACES"			825.00
18	A9	6p brown, Plate I		5,000.	400.00
	a.	"WALLS"		5,750.	1,250.
	b.	6p black brown		5,000.	1,250.
	c.	6p yellow brown		5,750.	325.00
	d.	6p chocolate brown		5,250.	325.00
	e.	6p yellow brown, *white paper*			1,200.
	f.	As "e," "WALLS"			2,700.
19	A9	6p brown, Plate II		5,750.	375.00
	a.	6p bister brown		5,250.	375.00
20	A9	8p yellow ('53)		19,000.	1,000.
	a.	8p orange		20,000.	1,000.
	b.	No leaves to right of "SOUTH"		—	2,250.
	c.	No bow at back of head		—	2,250.
	d.	No lines in spandrel		—	1,350.

The plates of the 1, 2, 3 and 8p each contained 50 varieties and those of the 6p 25 varieties.

The 2p, plate II, 6p, plate II, and 8p have been reprinted on grayish blue wove paper. The reprints of the 2p have the spandrels and background much worn. Most of the reprints of the 6p have no floreate ornaments to the right and left of "South." On all the values the wreath has been retouched.

Type of 1851 and

A11   A12

A13   A14

1854-55   **Wmk. 49**   *Imperf.*

23	A9	1p orange		575.00	52.50
	a.	No leaves to right of "SOUTH"		1,100.	180.00
	b.	Two leaves to right of "SOUTH"		1,450.	200.00
	c.	"WALE"		1,450.	200.00
	d.	1d orange vermilion		525.00	52.50
24	A9	2p blue		475.00	15.00
	a.	2p ultramarine		475.00	17.50
	b.	2p Prussian blue		475.00	17.50
25	A9	3p green		800.00	55.00
	a.	"WACES"		2,150.	225.00
	b.	Watermarked "2"		7,250.	2,000.

Value for No. 25b is for copy with the design cut into.

26	A11	5p green		1,600.	725.00
27	A12	6p sage green		2,000.	42.50
28	A12	6p brown		1,950.	42.50
	a.	Watermarked "8"		4,750.	160.00
29	A12	6p gray		750.00	85.00
	a.	6p greenish gray		1,950.	75.00
	b.	6p bluish gray		1,950.	85.00
	c.	6p deep slate		2,150.	75.00
	d.	As "c," wmk sideways			1,250.
	e.	6p fawn		1,950.	160.00
	f.	As "e," watermarked "8"		4,750.	145.00
	g.	As "f," wmk sideways			540.00
30	A13	8p orange ('55)		25,000.	1,750.
	a.	8p yellow		25,000.	1,575.
31	A14	1sh pale red brown		5,250.	125.00
	a.	1sh red		5,000.	100.00
	b.	1sh rose vermilion		7,750.	100.00
	c.	As "b," watermarked "8"		10,000.	225.00

See Nos. 38-42, 56, 58, 65, 67.
Nos. 38-42 exist with wide margins. Stamps with perforations trimmed are often offered as Nos. 26, 30, and 30a.

A15

1856   *Imperf.*

32	A15	1p red		350.00	27.50
	a.	1p orange red		425.00	27.50
	b.	As "a," printed on both sides		4,250.	2,500.
	c.	Watermarked "2"			9,500.
	d.	1p carmine vermilion		400.00	27.50
33	A15	2p blue		350.00	12.50
	a.	Watermarked "1"			9,500.
	b.	Watermarked "5"		1,250.	95.00
	c.	Watermarked "8"			8,250.
	d.	2p dp turquoise blue		375.00	15.00
	e.	2p ultramarine		350.00	15.00
	f.	2p pale blue		350.00	16.00
34	A15	3p green		2,000.	125.00
	a.	3p yellow green		1,850.	125.00
	b.	Watermarked "2"			5,000.
	c.	3p bluish green ('56)		1,950.	125.00

Nos. 32-34 (3)   2,700.   165.00

The two known examples of No. 33c are in museums. Both are used.

The 1p has been reprinted in orange on paper watermarked Small Crown and NSW, and the 2p in deep blue on paper watermarked single lined "2." These reprints are usually overprinted "SPECIMEN."

See Nos. 34C-37, 54, 63, 90.

1859   *Litho.*

34C	A15	2p light blue		—	925.00
		On cover			4,500.

1860-63   **Engr.**   **Wmk. 49**   *Perf. 13*

35	A15	1p red		175.00	25.00
	a.	1p orange		175.00	25.00
	b.	Perf. 12x13			2,400.
	c.	Perf. 12		310.00	25.00
36	A15	2p blue, perf. 12		275.00	16.00
	a.	Watermarked "1"			4,500.
	b.	Perf. 12x13		3,400.	
	c.	Perf. 12		425.00	
37	A15	3p blue green		110.00	14.00
	a.	3p yellow green		125.00	11.00
	b.	3p deep green		125.00	10.00
	c.	Watermarked "6"		250.00	16.00
	d.	Perf. 12		1,000.	52.50
38	A11	5p dark green		110.00	27.50
	a.	5p yellow green		325.00	85.00
	b.	Perf. 12		475.00	125.00
39	A12	6p brown, perf. 12		875.00	75.00
	a.	6p gray, perf. 12		875.00	65.00
40	A12	6p violet		200.00	8.00
	a.	6p aniline lilac		1,500.	160.00
	b.	Watermarked "5"		850.00	30.00
	c.	Watermarked "12"		800.00	25.00
	e.	Perf. 12		775.00	20.00
	f.	As "b," wmk sideways			1,250.
41	A13	8p yellow		575.00	50.00
	a.	8p orange		600.00	50.00
	b.	As "a," perf. 12		7,750.	1,450.
	c.	8p red orange		575.00	65.00
	d.	As "c," perf. 12		7,750.	1,450.
42	A14	1sh rose		400.00	10.00
	a.	1sh carmine		390.00	10.00
	b.	As "a," perf. 12		400.00	30.00
	c.	1sh crimson lake		400.00	10.00
	d.	1sh brownish red, perf 12		1,750.	75.00
	e.	As "a," pair, imperf. between			—

Nos. 35-42 (8)   2,720.   225.50

1864   **Wmk. 50**   *Perf. 13*

43	A15	1p red		135.00	67.50

A16

1861-80   **Wmk. 53**   *Perf. 13*

44	A16	5sh dull violet		365.00	60.00
	a.	5sh purple		410.00	85.00
	b.	5sh dull violet, perf. 12		2,275.	350.00
	c.	5sh purple, perf. 12		—	90.00
	d.	5sh purple, perf. 10		325.00	90.00
	e.	5sh purple, perf. 12x10		450.00	90.00
	f.	5sh royal purple, perf 13 ('72)		900.00	77.50
	g.	5sh deep rose lilac, perf 13 ('75)		250.00	47.50
	h.	5sh rose lilac, perf 10 ('83)		300.00	60.00
	i.	5sh purple, perf 10x12 ('85)			225.00
	j.	5sh reddish purple, perf 10 ('86)		310.00	67.50
	k.	5sh rose lilac, perf 11 ('88)			150.00

See No. 101. For overprint see No. O11.
Reprints are perf. 10 and overprinted "REPRINT" in black.

A17   A18

1862-65   Typo.   Unwmk.   Perf. 13

45	A17 1p red ('65)	225.00	47.50
a.	Perf. 14	240.00	80.00
b.	1p brick red ('65)	225.00	47.50
46	A18 2p blue	140.00	9.00
a.	Perf. 14	240.00	95.00

1863-64   Wmk. 50   Perf. 13

47	A17 1p red	85.00	11.00
a.	Watermarked "2"	270.00	37.50
b.	1p dark red brown	325.00	50.00
c.	1p brick red	85.00	12.00
d.	1p brick red, shiny surfaced paper ('65)	335.00	175.00
e.	Horiz. pair, imperf between		2,500.
48	A18 2p blue	65.00	3.50
a.	Watermarked "1"	260.00	6.50
b.	2p cobalt blue	65.00	3.50
c.	2p Prussian blue	67.50	4.00

1862   Wmk. 49   Perf. 13

49	A18 2p blue	135.00	40.00
a.	Watermarked "5"	135.00	42.50
b.	Perf. 12x13	675.00	250.00
c.	Perf. 12	240.00	55.00

See Nos. 52-53, 61-62, 70-71.

A19   A20

1867, Sept.   Wmk. 51, 52   Perf. 13

50	A19 4p red brown	125.00	9.00
a.	Imperf.		
b.	4p pale red brown	125.00	9.00
51	A20 10p lilac	55.00	9.00
	Ovptd. "SPECIMEN"	30.00	
a.	Imperf.		
b.	Horiz. pair, imperf between	3,250.	

See Nos. 55, 64, 91, 97, 117, 129.

A21   A22

A23

Typo.; Engr. (3p, 5p, 8p)
1871-84   Wmk. 54   Perf. 13

52	A17 1p red	42.50	3.75
a.	Perf. 10	275.00	40.00
b.	Perf. 13x10	36.00	3.25
c.	Horiz. pair, imperf between		2,900.
d.	1p scarlet, perf. 10	—	190.00
53	A18 2p blue	47.50	2.00
a.	Imperf.		
c.	Horiz. pair, imperf vert.		3,250.
c.	Perf. 10	275.00	27.50
d.	Perf. 13x10	35.00	1.25
e.	Perf. 12x13		
f.	2p Prussian blue, perf. 11x12	275.00	40.00
g.	As "f," perf. 10	145.00	22.50
54	A15 3p green ('74)	75.00	5.00
a.	Perf. 11	180.00	115.00
b.	Perf. 12	—	200.00
c.	Perf. 10x12	160.00	50.00
d.	Perf. 11x12	135.00	42.50
e.	Perf. 10	95.00	12.00
f.	3p bright green, perf. 13x10	110.00	25.00
g.	As "f," perf. 10	130.00	22.50
55	A19 4p red brown ('77)	120.00	17.50
a.	Perf. 10	240.00	60.00
b.	Perf. 13x10	135.00	7.50
c.	Perf. 10x13	175.00	27.50
56	A11 5p dk grn, perf. 10 ('84)	42.50	45.00
a.	Horiz. pair, imperf between		2,250.
b.	Perf. 12	275.00	110.00
c.	Perf. 10x12	125.00	65.00
d.	Perf. 10x13		
e.	12x10	60.00	47.50

57	A21 6p lilac ('72)	105.00	2.50
a.	Horiz. pair, imperf. between	—	3,000.
b.	Perf. 13x10	120.00	2.50
c.	Perf. 10	125.00	2.50
58	A13 8p yellow ('77)	225.00	17.50
a.	Imperf.		
b.	Perf. 10	375.00	25.00
c.	Perf. 13x10	250.00	24.00
59	A22 9p on 10p red brown, perf. 12 (Bk)	25.00	5.50
a.	Double surcharge, blk & bl	400.00	
b.	Perf. 12x10	300.00	225.00
c.	Perf. 10	17.50	12.50
d.	Perf. 12x11	17.50	7.50
e.	Perf. 11x12		
f.	Perf. 12	75.00	15.00
g.	Perf. 10x12	62.50	12.50
h.	Perf. 10x11	75.00	24.00
60	A23 1sh black ('76)	165.00	15.00
a.	Perf. 10	210.00	17.50
c.	Perf. 10	225.00	27.50
d.	Perf. 11		
e.	Vert. pair, imperf between		3,000.
f.	Pair, imperf		2,750.
	Nos. 52-60 (9)	847.50	13.75

The surcharge on No. 59 measures 15mm.
See Nos. 66, 68. For overprints see Nos. O1-O10.

Typo.; Engr. (3p, 5p, 8p)
1882-91   Wmk. 55   Perf. 11x12

61	A17 1p red	11.00	1.50
a.	Perf. 10	25.00	3.00
b.	Perf. 10x13	125.00	9.50
c.	Perf. 10x12	275.00	70.00
d.	Perf. 13		130.00
e.	Perf. 10x11	500.00	130.00
f.	Perf. 11		160.00
g.	Perf. 13	1,000.	475.00
h.	Perf. 13x10	72.50	3.00
i.	Perf. 12x10	—	225.00
j.	Perf. 11x10		
k.	Horiz. pair, imperf between		2,100.
62	A18 2p blue	12.50	1.00
a.	Perf. 10	62.50	1.00
b.	Perf. 13x10	160.00	7.50
c.	Perf. 13	500.00	115.00
d.	Perf. 12x10	425.00	100.00
e.	Perf. 11		100.00
f.	Perf. 12x11	450.00	100.00
g.	Perf. 11x10	500.00	160.00
h.	Perf. 12		250.00
i.	Double impression	—	800.00
63	A15 3p green	6.00	1.00
a.	Imperf., pair	500.00	
b.	Vert. pair, imperf. btwn.		
c.	Horiz. pair, imperf. vert.	750.00	675.00
d.	Double impression		
e.	Perf. 10	35.00	2.50
f.	Perf. 11	10.00	1.00
g.	Perf. 12	15.00	2.50
h.	Perf. 12x11	7.25	1.00
i.	Perf. 10x12	32.50	3.00
m.	Perf. 10x11	40.00	3.25
n.	Perf. 12x10	55.00	4.50
o.	Wmk sideways	65.00	12.50
64	A19 4p red brown	85.00	3.00
a.	Perf. 10	125.00	5.50
b.	Perf. 10x12	225.00	70.00
c.	Perf. 12	325.00	190.00
65	A11 5p dk blue green	11.00	1.25
a.	Imperf., pair	500.00	
b.	Perf. 11	12.00	1.25
c.	Perf. 10	27.50	1.75
d.	Perf. 12	27.50	1.75
e.	Perf. 10x12	175.00	45.00
f.	5p green, perf. 12x11	12.00	1.25
g.	5p green, perf. 11x10	85.00	15.00
h.	5p green, perf. 12x10	90.00	10.00
i.	5p green, perf. 10x11	80.00	12.50
j.	5p green, perf. 11	12.00	1.25
k.	Wmk sideways	25.00	8.00
66	A21 6p lilac, perf. 10	90.00	1.50
a.	Horiz. pair, imperf. between		3,000.
b.	Perf. 10x12	65.00	2.00
c.	Perf. 11x12	135.00	17.50
d.	Perf. 12	135.00	10.00
e.	Perf. 11x10	125.00	2.25
f.	Perf. 11	135.00	7.75
g.	Perf. 10x13		360.00
67	A13 8p yellow, perf. 10	250.00	20.00
a.	Perf. 11	250.00	25.00
b.	Perf. 12	340.00	30.00
c.	Perf. 10x12	310.00	27.50
68	A23 1sh black	145.00	7.50
a.	Perf. 10x13		
b.	Perf. 10	150.00	7.50
c.	Perf. 11	275.00	20.00
d.	Perf. 10x12		290.00
	Nos. 61-68 (8)	610.50	36.75

Nos. 63 and 65 exist with two types of watermark 55 — spacings of 1mm or 2mm between crown and NSW.

See No. 90. For surcharges and overprints see Nos. 92-94, O12-O19.

The 1, 2, 4, 6, 8p and 1sh have been reprinted on paper watermarked Large Crown and NSW. The 1, 2, 4p and 1sh are perforated 11x12, the 6p is perforated 10 and the 8p 11. All are overprinted "REPRINT," the 1sh in red and the others in black.

Perf. 11x12
1886-87   Typo.   Wmk. 56
Bluish Revenue Stamp Paper

70	A17 1p scarlet	22.00	10.00
a.	Perf. 10	60.00	18.00
71	A18 2p dark blue	45.00	8.00
a.	Perf. 10	105.00	24.00
b.	Imperf.		3,250.

For overprint, see No. O20.

A24

Perf. 12 (#73-75), 12x10 (#72, 75A) and Compound
1885-86   "POSTAGE" in Black

72	A24 5sh green & vio	850.00	150.00
a.	Perf. 10	—	
b.	Perf. 13	—	
73	A24 10sh rose & vio	1,750.	275.00
a.	Perf. 10	—	
74	A24 £1 rose & vio	11,500.	4,750.
a.	Perf. 13	—	8,250.

"POSTAGE" in Blue
Bluish Paper

75	A24 10sh rose & vio	325.00	75.00
b.	Perf. 10	1,950.	250.00
c.	Perf. 12x11		

White Paper

75A	A24 £1 rose & vio	9,750.	4,750.

For overprints, see Nos. O21-O23.

The 5sh with black overprint and the £1 with blue overprint have been reprinted on paper watermarked NSW. They are perforated 12x10 and are overprinted "REPRINT" in black.

"POSTAGE" in Blue
1894   White Paper

76	A24 10sh rose & violet, perf 12	350.00	60.00
a.	Double overprint		
b.	10sh mauve & claret, perf 10	625.00	180.00
c.	10sh mauve & violet, perf 11	475.00	100.00
d.	10sh mauve & violet, perf 12x11	350.00	75.00

See No. 108B.

View of Sydney A25   Emu A26

Captain Cook — A27   Victoria and Coat of Arms — A28

Lyrebird A29   Kangaroo A30

1888-89   Wmk. 55   Perf. 11x12

77	A25 1p violet	15.00	1.00
a.	Perf. 12	16.00	.50
b.	Perf. 12x11½	27.50	1.25
78	A26 2p blue	22.00	.50
a.	Imperf., pair	375.00	525.00
b.	Perf. 12	22.00	.50
c.	Perf. 12x11½	22.00	.50
79	A27 4p brown	30.00	5.50
a.	Perf. 12x11½	55.00	8.00
b.	Perf. 12	55.00	5.00
c.	Perf. 11	350.00	115.00
d.	Imperf.		
80	A28 6p carmine rose	37.50	4.50
a.	Perf. 12	40.00	10.50
b.	Perf. 12x11½	50.00	5.00
81	A29 8p red violet	25.00	9.50
a.	Perf. 12	25.00	9.50
b.	Perf. 12x11½	60.00	16.00
82	A30 1sh maroon ('89)	55.00	2.50
a.	Imperf., pair	1,450.	
b.	Perf. 12x11½	57.50	3.00
c.	Perf. 12	65.00	2.50
d.	1sh violet brown, perf 11x12	55.00	3.00

e.	1sh violet brown, perf 12x11½	75.00	5.00
f.	1sh violet brown, perf 12	75.00	2.75
	Nos. 77-82 (6)	184.50	23.50
	Set, ovptd. "SPECIMEN"	210.00	

First British settlement in Australia, cent. For overprints see Nos. O24-O29.

1888   Wmk. 56   Perf. 11x12

83	A25 1p violet	45.00	8.00
84	A26 2p blue	100.00	7.50

See Nos. 104B-106C, 113-115, 118, 125-127, 130.

Map of Australia — A31   Governors Capt. Arthur Phillip (above) and Lord Carrington — A32

1888-89   Wmk. 53   Perf. 10

85	A31 5sh violet ('89)	425.00	60.00
	5sh deep purple	400.00	55.00
86	A32 20sh ultra	750.00	175.00

See Nos. 88, 120. For overprints see Nos. O30-O31.

1890   Wmk. 57   Perf. 10

87	A31 5sh violet	300.00	40.00
a.	Perf. 11	375.00	50.00
b.	Perf. 10x11	400.00	40.00
c.	Perf. 12	450.00	60.00
d.	5sh mauve, perf 10	375.00	40.00
e.	5sh mauve, perf 11	375.00	50.00
f.	Horiz. pair, imperf btwn.		

Perf. 11x12, 12x11
Wmk. 58

88	A32 20sh ultra	400.00	90.00
a.	Perf. 11	450.00	90.00
b.	Perf. 12	475.00	160.00
c.	20sh cobalt blue, perf 10	525.00	170.00
d.	As "c," perf 11	500.00	90.00
	Nos. 87-88, ovptd. "SPECIMEN"	240.00	

For overprints see Nos. O32-O33.

"Australia" — A33

1890, Dec. 22   Wmk. 55   Perf. 11x12

89	A33 2½p ultra	19.00	2.50
a.	Perf. 12	25.00	4.00
b.	Perf. 12x11½	55.00	50.00
	Overprinted "SPECIMEN"	35.00	

For overprint see No. O35.

Type of 1856
1891   Engr.   Wmk. 52   Perf. 10

90	A15 3p green	6.75	50.00
a.	Double impression		
b.	3p light green	16.00	62.50

Type of 1867
1893   Typo.   Perf. 11

91	A20 10p lilac	20.00	11.00
a.	Perf. 10	22.50	13.00
b.	Perf. 11x10 or 10x11	27.50	13.00
c.	Perf. 12x11	160.00	17.00

Types of 1862-84 Surcharged in Black

a   b

1891, Jan. 5   Wmk. 55   Perf. 11x12

92	A17(a) ½p on 1p gray	10.50	7.00
a.	Imperf.		
b.	Surcharge omitted		
c.	Double surcharge	850.00	
93	A21(b) 7½p on 6p brown	6.50	4.00
a.	Perf. 10	5.50	11.00
b.	Perf. 11	5.00	4.00
c.	Perf. 12	15.00	5.00

d.	Perf. 10x12		7.00	7.00

Perf. 12x11½

94	A23(b)	12½p on 1sh red	10.50	8.00
a.		Perf. 11x12	11.50	8.00
b.		Perf. 10	11.50	8.50
c.		Perf. 11	12.25	8.50
d.		Perf. 12	14.00	8.00
		Nos. 92-94 (3)	27.50	19.00
		Nos. 92-94 overprinted		
		"SPECIMEN"		90.00

For overprints see Nos. O34, O36-O37.

Victoria — A37

1892-97   **Perf. 11x12**

95	A37	½p slate ('97)	5.00	.50
a.		Perf. 12x11½	5.00	.65
b.		Perf. 12	5.00	.50
c.		As #95, horiz. pair, imperf between	2,000.	
d.		½p gray, perf. 10	65.00	2.50
e.		As "d," perf. 10x12	90.00	12.50
f.		As "d," perf. 11	100.00	7.25
g.		As "d," perf. 11x12	6.00	.50
		As "g," overprinted "SPECIMEN"		25.00

See Nos. 102, 109, 121. For overprint see No. O38.

Types of 1867-71

1897   **Perf. 11x12**

96	A22	9p on 10p red brn (Bk)	20.00	25.00
a.		9p on 10p org brn (Bk)	20.00	25.00
b.		Surcharge omitted	—	
c.		Double surcharge	325.00	450.00
d.		Perf. 11	12.50	25.00
e.		Perf. 12	13.00	25.00
97	A20	10p violet	35.00	30.00
a.		Perf. 12x11½	12.00	25.00
b.		Perf. 11	27.50	35.00
c.		Perf. 12	24.00	32.50
		Nos. 96-97, overprinted "SPECIMEN"		60.00

The surcharge on No. 96 measures 13½mm.
For overprints see Nos. O39-O40.

Seal A38

Victoria A39

A40

ONE PENNY:
Die I — The first pearl in the crown at the left is merged into the arch, the shading under the fleur-de-lis is indistinct, and the "s" of "WALES" is open.
Die II — The first pearl is circular, the vertical shading under the fleur-de-lis is clear, and the "s" of "WALES" not so open.

2 ½ PENCE:
Die I — There are 12 radiating lines in the star on the Queen's breast.
Die II — There are 16 radiating lines in the star. The eye is nearly full of color.

1897   **Perf. 12**

98	A38	1p rose red, II	5.00	.50
a.		Die I, perf. 11x12	5.00	1.00
b.		Imperf., pair	750.00	
c.		Imperf. horiz., pair	850.00	
d.		Die I, perf. 12x11½	5.00	1.00
e.		Die I, perf. 12	11.00	2.00
f.		Die II, perf. 12x11½	4.00	1.00
g.		Die II, perf. 11x12	5.00	1.00
99	A39	2p deep blue	17.50	1.50
a.		Perf. 11x12	18.00	1.50
b.		Perf. 12x11½	9.00	1.50
100	A40	2½p dp purple, II	42.50	2.50
a.		Die I, perf. 12x11	30.00	2.50
b.		Die I, perf. 11	32.50	4.00
c.		Die I, perf. 11½x12	32.50	2.75
d.		Die II, perf. 11x12	42.50	2.75
e.		Die II, perf. 11½x12	32.50	2.75
		Nos. 98-100 (3)	65.00	4.50
		Nos. 98-100 overprinted "SPECIMEN"		75.00

Sixtieth year of Queen Victoria's reign.
See Nos. 103-104, 110-112, 122-124.

Type of 1861

1897   **Engr.**   **Wmk. 53**   **Perf. 11**

101	A16	5sh red violet	60.00	16.00
a.		Horiz. pair, imperf. btwn.	11,000.	
b.		Perf. 11x12 or 12x11	60.00	24.00
c.		Perf. 12	80.00	45.00

Perf. 12x11½, 11½x12

1899, Oct.   **Typo.**   **Wmk. 55**

HALF PENNY:
Die I — Narrow "H" in "HALF."

102	A37	½p blue green, I	4.00	1.50
a.		Imperf., pair	250.00	350.00
103	A39	2p ultra	5.75	1.00
a.		Imperf., pair	325.00	
104	A40	2½p dk blue, II	9.00	1.75
a.		Imperf., pair	350.00	
104B	A27	4p org brown	18.00	7.50
c.		4p red brown	35.00	17.00
d.		As "c," imperf. pair	600.00	
105	A28	6p emerald	100.00	27.50
a.		Imperf., pair	600.00	
106	A28	6p orange	50.00	5.00
a.		6p yellow	18.00	10.00
		Imperf., pair	600.00	
106C	A29	8p magenta	47.50	6.00
		Nos. 102-106C (7)	234.25	50.25

Lyrebird — A41

1903   **Perf. 12x11½**

107	A41	2sh6p blue green	55.00	22.50
		Overprinted "SPECIMEN"	85.00	

See Nos. 119, 131.

"Australia" — A42

1903   **Wmk. 70**   **Perf. 12½**

108	A42	9p org brn & ultra	20.00	3.50
		Overprinted "SPECIMEN"	50.00	
a.		Perf. 11	5,250.	1,850.

See No. 128.

Type of 1905-06

1904   **Wmk. 56**   **Perf. 12x11**
"POSTAGE" in Blue

108B	A24	10sh brt rose & vio	425.00	90.00
c.		Perf. 11	400.00	75.00
d.		Perf. 14	375.00	85.00
e.		10sh aniline crimson & violet, perf 12	425.00	95.00
f.		As "e," perf 12x11	325.00	55.00
g.		10sh claret & violet, chalky paper, perf 12x11	475.00	95.00

The watermark (NSW) of No. 108B is 20x7mm, with rounded angles in "N" and "W." On No. 75, the watermark is 21x7mm, with sharp angles in the "N" and "W."

HALF PENNY:
Die II — Wide "H" in "HALF."

Perf. 11, 11x12½, 12x11½ and Compound

1905-06   **Wmk. 12**

109	A37	½p blue grn, II	3.00	1.50
a.		½p blue green, I	4.50	1.00
b.		Booklet pane of 12	—	
110	A38	1p car rose, II	2.75	.25
a.		Booklet pane of 6	—	
b.		Booklet pane of 12	—	
111	A39	2p deep ultra	2.25	.40
112	A40	2½p dk blue, II	4.50	3.00
113	A27	4p org brown	10.50	4.50
a.		4p red brown	13.75	5.50
114	A28	6p orange	17.00	3.00
a.		6p yellow	19.00	4.50
b.		Perf. 11	350.00	
115	A29	8p magenta	27.50	8.00
117	A20	10p violet	16.25	6.00
118	A30	1sh vio brown	28.75	1.75
119	A41	2sh6p blue green	80.00	20.00

Wmk. 199

Perf. 12x11 or 11x12

120	A32	20sh ultra	375.00	75.00
a.		Perf. 12	400.00	90.00
b.		Perf. 11	375.00	85.00
		Nos. 109-115,117-120 (11)	567.50	123.40

1906-07   **Wmk. 13**

121	A37	½p green, I	5.00	7.50
122	A38	1p rose, II	27.00	5.00
123	A39	2p ultra	8.50	5.00
124	A40	2½p blue, II	70.00	130.00
125	A27	4p org brown	35.00	35.00
126	A28	6p orange	50.00	50.00
127	A29	8p red violet	32.00	50.00
128	A42	9p yel brn & ultra, perf. 12x12½ ('06)	28.00	2.00
a.		Perf. 11	120.00	75.00
b.		9p org brn & ultra, perf. 12x12½	19.00	2.00
129	A37	10p violet	35.00	60.00
130	A30	1sh vio brown	75.00	12.00
a.		Perf. 11	—	1,700.
131	A41	2sh6p blue green	130.00	130.00
		Nos. 121-131 (11)	495.50	486.50

Portions of some of the sheets on which the above are printed show the watermark "COMMONWEALTH OF AUSTRALIA." Stamps may also be found from portions of the sheet without watermark.

SEMI-POSTAL STAMPS

SP1

Allegory of Charity
SP2

1897, June   **Wmk. 55**   **Perf. 11**

B1	SP1	1p (1sh) grn & brn	50.00	50.00
B2	SP2	2½p (2sh6p) rose, bl & gold	250.00	240.00
		Nos. B1-B2 overprinted "SPECIMEN"	300.00	

Diamond Jubilee of Queen Victoria.
The difference between the postal and face values of these stamps was donated to a fund for a home for consumptives.

REGISTRATION STAMPS

Queen Victoria — R1

Unwmk.

1856, Jan. 1   **Engr.**   **Imperf.**

F1	R1	(6p) orange & blue	1,900.	250.00
F2	R1	(6p) red & blue	2,000.	210.00
a.		Frame printed on back	12,500.	5,250.

1860			**Perf. 12, 13**	
F3	R1	(6p) orange & blue	1,150.	80.00
F4	R1	(6p) red & blue	1,200.	85.00

Nos. F1 to F4 exist also on paper with papermaker's watermark in sheet.

1863			**Wmk. 49**	
F5	R1	(6p) red & blue	375.00	25.00
a.		(6p) red & Prussian blue	375.00	27.50
b.		(6p) red & indigo	475.00	35.00
c.		Double impression of frame	—	850.00

Fifty varieties.

Nos. F1-F2 were reprinted on thin white wove unwatermarked paper and on thick yellowish wove unwatermarked paper; the former are usually overprinted "SPECIMEN."
No. F4 was reprinted on thin white wove unwatermarked paper; perf. 10 and overprinted "REPRINT" in black.

POSTAGE DUE STAMPS

D1

Perf. 10, 11, 11½, 12 and Compound

1891-92   **Typo.**   **Wmk. 55**

J1	D1	½p grn, perf 10	3.60	37.00
a.		Chalky paper		
J2	D1	1p green	35.00	40.00
a.		Perf 12	80.00	40.00
b.		Chalky paper	30.00	4.50
J3	D1	2p green	24.00	4.00
a.		Perf 12x10	80.00	40.00
b.		Chalky paper	27.00	6.50
J4	D1	3p green	65.00	14.00
a.		Chalky paper	90.00	28.00
J5	D1	4p green	60.00	3.75
a.		Chalky paper	60.00	13.00
J6	D1	6p grn, perf 10	60.00	15.00
J7	D1	8p grn, perf 10	125.00	27.00
J8	D1	5sh grn, perf 10	300.00	60.00
a.		Perf 11	750.00	180.00
b.		Perf 11x12	—	375.00

Perf. 12x10

J9	D1	10sh green	550.00	—
a.		Perf. 10	750.00	80.00
J10	D1	20sh green	650.00	—
a.		Perf. 10	850.00	125.00
b.		Perf. 12	1,500.	
		Nos. J1-J10 (10)	1,873.	164.75

Used values for Nos. J8-J10 are for c-t-o stamps.

Nos. J1-J5 exist on both ordinary and chalky paper.
Used values for Nos. J8-J10 are for c-t-o stamps.

OFFICIAL STAMPS

Regular Issues
Overprinted in Black or Red

Perf. 10, 11, 12, 13 and Compound

1879-80   **Wmk. 54**

O1	A17	1p red	55.00	3.00
a.		Perf. 10	225.00	40.00
b.		Perf. 10x13	65.00	5.00
O2	A18	2p blue	55.00	2.75
a.		Perf. 11x12		275.00
b.		Perf. 10	275.00	40.00
O3	A15	3p green (R)	1,000.	375.00
O4	A15	3p green	200.00	32.50
a.		Watermarked "6"	—	600.00
b.		Double overprint	—	925.00
c.		3p yel grn, perf 10	200.00	32.50
d.		3p yel grn, perf 12	250.00	60.00
O5	A19	4p red brown	325.00	10.00
a.		Perf. 10x13	350.00	110.00
O6	A11	5p dark green	27.50	37.50
O7	A21	6p lilac	300.00	9.00
a.		Perf. 10	475.00	52.50
b.		Perf. 13x10	275.00	52.50
O8	A13	8p yellow (R)	1,500.	675.00
O9	A13	8p yellow	—	50.00
a.		Perf. 10	500.00	92.50
O10	A23	1sh black (R)	500.00	25.00
a.		Perf. 10	—	40.00
b.		Perf. 10x13	—	50.00
c.		Perf. 13x10	—	15.00

1880   **Wmk. 53**

O11	A16	5sh lilac, perf. 11	475.00	100.00
a.		Double overprint	4,500.	2,250.
b.		Perf. 10	600.00	125.00
c.		Perf. 12x10	775.00	130.00
d.		Perf. 13	875.00	110.00

Two No. O14 overprint types: Type I, "O" and "S" 7mm apart. Type II, "O" and "S" 5.5mm apart.

1881   **Wmk. 55**

O12	A17	1p red	27.50	2.00
a.		Perf. 10x13		140.00

O13	A18	2p blue	42.50	1.00
a.		Perf. 10x13	275.00	90.00
O14	A15	3p green	15.00	5.50
a.		Double overprint		675.00
b.		Perf. 12	225.00	110.00
c.		Perf. 11		
d.		Type II ovpt	40.00	15.00
e.		As "b," type II ovpt	25.00	15.00
f.		Wmk sideways	350.00	250.00
O15	A19	4p red brown	25.00	8.00
a.		Perf. 10x12	22.50	4.00
b.		Perf. 12	250.00	100.00
O16	A11	5p dark green	275.00	175.00
a.		Perf. 12	125.00	120.00
b.		Perf. 12x10		
c.		Perf. 12x11 ('85)	65.00	16.00
O17	A21	6p lilac	22.00	7.00
a.		Perf. 12		45.00
b.		Perf. 11x12		
c.		Perf. 12x11 ('85)	90.00	20.00
O18	A13	8p yellow	27.50	12.50
a.		Double overprint		
b.		Perf. 12	175.00	45.00
c.		Perf. 11 ('85)	27.50	29.00
d.		Perf. 10x12 or 12x10 ('85)	26.00	11.00
e.		Triple overprint		
O19	A23	1sh black (R)	60.00	15.00
a.		Double overprint		500.00
b.		Perf. 10x13		60.00
c.		Perf. 11x12, comb.	30.00	8.00
		Nos. O12-O19 (8)	494.50	226.00

Beware of other red overprints on watermark 55 stamps.

No. O14 exists with two overprint types: "O" and "S" 7mm and 5.5mm apart. For detailed listings, see the Scott Classic Specialized catalogue.

1881			**Wmk. 56**	
O20	A17	1p red	105.00	9.00
1887-90				
O21	A24	10sh on #75	—	3,500.
O22	A24	£1 on #75A	38,000.	17,500.

No. 75 Overprinted

1889				
O23	A24	10sh rose & vio	5,750.	1,450.
		Overprinted "SPECIMEN"	125.00	
a.		Perf. 10	7,500.	3,750.

Overprinted

1888-89			**Wmk. 55**	
O24	A25	1p violet	6.50	2.00
a.		Overprinted "O" only		
O25	A26	2p blue	5.00	.75
O26	A27	4p red brown	11.00	4.25
O27	A28	6p carmine	10.00	11.00
O28	A29	8p red lilac	27.50	12.00
a.		Perf 12	60.00	17.00
O29	A30	1sh vio brown	42.50	4.75
a.		Double overprint		
b.		1sh purple brown, perf 12	45.00	7.00
c.		1sh maroon, perf 11x12 ('90)	45.00	4.00
d.		1sh maroon, perf 12	45.00	4.50
		Nos. O24-O29 (6)	102.50	34.75
		Wmk. 53		
O30	A31	5sh violet (R)	2,100.	800.00
O31	A32	20sh ultra	20,000.	1,100.
1890			**Wmk. 57**	
O32	A31	5sh violet	400.00	110.00
a.		5sh, dull lilac, perf. 12	850.00	175.00
b.		5sh lilac, perf 10	675.00	175.00
		Wmk. 58		
O33	A32	20sh ultra	21,000.	1,150.
		O32b, O33 ovpted. "SPECIMEN"	325.00	

Centenary of the founding of the Colony (Nos. O24-O33).

1891			**Wmk. 55**	
O34	A17(a)	½p on 1p gray & black	75.00	80.00
a.		Double overprint	2,500.	
O35	A33	2½p ultra	15.00	11.00
O36	A21(b)	7½p on 6p brn & black	55.00	70.00

O37	A23(b)	12½p on 1sh red & black	75.00	115.00
1892				
O38	A37	½p gray, perf 11x12	6.00	20.00
a.		Perf 10	14.00	20.00
b.		Perf 12	13.00	13.00
c.		Perf 12x11½	35.00	18.00
		Overprinted "SPECIMEN"	35.00	
1894			**Wmk. 54**	
O39	A22	9p on 10p red brn	1,250.	1,150.
		Overprinted "SPECIMEN"	85.00	
		Wmk. 52		
O40	A20	10p lilac, perf. 13	425.00	120.00
a.		Perf 11x10 or 10x11	450.00	225.00
b.		Perf 10	450.00	
c.		Double overprint, one albino	475.00	
		Overprinted "SPECIMEN"	75.00	

The official stamps became obsolete on Dec. 31, 1894. In Aug., 1895, sets of 32 varieties of "O.S." stamps, together with some envelopes and postal cards, were placed on sale at the Sydney post office at £2 per set.

These sets contained most of the varieties listed above and a few which are not known in the original issues. An obliteration consisting of the letters G.P.O. or N.S.W. in three concentric ovals was lightly applied to the center of each block of four stamps.

It is understood that the earlier stamps and many of the overprints were reprinted to make up these sets.

QUEENSLAND

'kwēnz-ˌland

LOCATION — Northeastern part of Australia
GOVT. — British Crown Colony
AREA — 670,500 sq. mi.
POP. — 498,129 (1901)
CAPITAL — Brisbane

Originally a part of New South Wales, Queensland was constituted a separate colony in 1859. It was one of the six British Colonies that united in 1901 to form the Commonwealth of Australia.

12 Pence = 1 Shilling
20 Shillings = 1 Pound

MORETON BAY

Until 1860, Queensland, then known as Moreton Bay, utilized the postal service of New South Wales, and stamps of New South Wales were used until November 1, 1860. The New South Wales post offices in Queensland, with their opening dates and assigned canceler numbers, were:

Post Office	Opened
Brisbane	1834 (#95)
Burnett's Inn (became Goodes Inn)	1850 (#108)
Callandoon	1850 (#74)
Condamine	1856 (#151)
Dalby	1854 (#133)
Drayton	1846 (#85)
Gayndah	1850 (#86)
Gladstone	1854 (#131)
Goodes Inn	1858 (#108)
Ipswich	1846 (#87)
Maryborough	1849 (#96)
Rockhampton	1858 (#201)
Surat	1852 (#110)
Taroom	1856 (#152)
Toowoombs	1858 (#214)
Warwick	1848 (#81)

Values for unused stamps are for examples with original gum as defined in the catalogue introduction. Very fine examples of Nos. 4-73, 84-125, 128-140, and F1-F3b will have perforations touching the design on at least one or more sides due to the narrow spacing of the stamps on the plates. Stamps with perfs clear of the design on all four sides are scarce and will command higher prices.

Watermarks

Wmk. 5 — Small Star

Wmk. 6 — Large Star

Wmk. 12 — Crown and Single-lined A

Wmk. 13 — Crown and Double-lined A

Wmk. 65 — "Queensland Postage Stamps" in Sheet in Script Capitals

Wmk. 66

Wmks. 66 & 67 — "Queensland" in Large Single-lined Roman Capitals in the Sheet and Short-pointed Star to Each Stamp (Stars Vary Slightly in Size and Shape)

Wmk. 68 — Crown and Q

Wmk. 69 — Large Crown and Q

There are two varieties of the watermark 68, differing slightly in the position and shape of the crown and the tongue of the "Q."

Wmk. 70 — V and Crown

Queen Victoria — A1

		Wmk. 6		
1860, Nov. 1		**Engr.**		**Imperf.**
1	A1	1p deep rose	6,600.	775.00
2	A1	2p deep blue	18,500.	1,950.
3	A1	6p deep green	10,750.	825.00
		Clean-Cut Perf. 14 to 16		
4	A1	1p deep rose	3,100.	290.00
5	A1	2p deep blue	1,650.	115.00
a.		Horiz. pair, imperf between	—	5,500.
6	A1	6p deep green	1,850.	75.00
		Clean-Cut Perf. 14 to 16		
1860-61			**Wmk. 5**	
6A	A1	2p blue	1,150.	105.00
b.		Horiz. pair, imperf. between		11,000.
6D	A1	3p brown ('61)	875.00	77.50
6E	A1	6p deep green	1,550.	77.50
6F	A1	1sh gray violet	1,750.	115.00
		Regular Perf. 14		
6H	A1	1p rose	475.00	57.50
6I	A1	2p deep blue	1,100.	62.50
		Rough Perf. 14 to 16		
7	A1	1p deep rose	115.00	47.50
8	A1	2p blue	350.00	27.50
a.		Horiz. pair, imperf between		10,250.
9	A1	3p brown ('61)	90.00	30.00
a.		Horiz. pair, imperf. vert.		10,250.
10	A1	6p deep green	675.00	27.50
		6p yellow green	775.00	27.50
11	A1	1sh dull violet	1,350.	90.00
		Thick Yellowish Paper		
		Square Perf. 12½ to 13		
1862-67				**Unwmk.**
12	A1	1p Indian red	525.00	70.00
13	A1	1p orange ('63)	120.00	16.00
a.		Perf. 13, round holes ('67)	125.00	16.00
b.		Horiz. pair, imperf. between		
c.		Imperf., pair	—	2,600.
14	A1	2p deep blue	90.00	9.00
a.		2p pale blue	150.00	25.00
b.		Perf. 13, round holes ('67)	90.00	9.00
c.		Imperf., pair	—	2,500.
f.		Horiz. pair, imperf. between		15,000.
f.		Vert. pair, imperf. between		
15	A1	3p brown ('63)	125.00	42.50
a.		Imperf.		
b.		Perf. 13, round holes ('67)	125.00	42.50
16	A1	6p yellow grn ('63)	190.00	11.00
a.		6p green	300.00	42.50
b.		Perf. 13, round holes ('67)	195.00	13.50
c.		Imperf., pair	—	2,600.
d.		Horiz. pair, imperf. between		16,000.
e.		6p apple green ('63)	190.00	14.00
17	A1	1sh gray ('63)	400.00	22.50
b.		Imperf. horizontally		
c.		Horiz. pair, imperf. between	—	17,000.
d.		Perf. 13, round holes ('67)	400.00	24.00
e.		Vert. pair, imperf between	—	
		White Wove Paper		
1865		**Wmk. 5**	**Rough Perf. 13**	
18	A1	1p orange	125.00	57.50
a.		Horiz. pair, imperf. between	6,250.	
19	A1	2p light blue	125.00	16.00
a.		Vert. pair, imperf. between	8,500.	
b.		Half used as 1p on cover		4,250.
d.		2p deep blue	130.00	17.00
20	A1	6p yellow green	240.00	21.50
a.		6p deep green	290.00	21.50
		Nos. 18-20 (3)	490.00	95.00
1865			**Perf. 12½x13**	
18B	A1	1p orange vermilion	165.00	77.50
19C	A1	2p blue	280.00	77.50

Perf. 13, Round Holes
1866   **Wmk. 65**
21	A1	1p orange vermilion	210.00	42.50
22	A1	2p blue	105.00	16.50
b.		Diagonal half used as 1p on cover		—

1865   **Perf. 12½x13**
21A	A1	1p orange vermilion	290.00	72.50
22C	A1	2p blue	290.00	72.50

1866   **Unwmk. Litho.**   **Perf. 13**
23	A1	4p lilac	525.00	21.50
a.		4p slate	525.00	21.00
		Handstamped "SPECI-MEN"		65.00
24	A1	5sh pink	1,350.	135.00
a.		5sh bright rose	1,450.	175.00
		Handstamped "SPECI-MEN"		80.00
b.		Vert. pair, imperf between		8,750.

Wmk. 66, 67
1868-74   **Engr.**   **Perf. 13**
25	A1	1p orange ('71)	100.00	7.00
26	A1	2p blue	77.50	3.25
a.		2p pale blue	82.50	5.75
b.		2p bright blue	87.50	2.50
c.		2p greenish blue	155.00	2.50
d.		2p dark blue	87.50	2.50
27	A1	3p grnsh brn ('71)	240.00	6.25
a.		3p brown	125.00	5.25
b.		3p olive brown	210.00	6.50
28	A1	6p yel grn ('71)	275.00	7.00
a.		6p deep green	325.00	16.50
b.		6p green	240.00	9.50
30	A1	1sh grnsh gray ('72)	950.00	47.50
31	A1	1sh violet ('74)	425.00	22.50
a.		1sh brownish gray	950.00	47.50

Perf. 12
32	A1	1p orange	525.00	27.50
33	A1	2p blue	1,000.	72.50
34	A1	3p brown	775.00	215.00
a.		3p greenish gray	—	215.00
35	A1	6p deep green	1,850.	47.50
36	A1	1sh violet	900.00	52.50

Perf. 13x12
36A	A1	1p orange	195.00
37	A1	2p blue	1,675.
37A	A1	3p brown	350.00

The reprints are perforated 13 and the colors differ slightly from those of the originals.

1868-75   **Wmk. 68**   **Perf. 13**
38	A1	1p orange	115.00	5.75
a.		Imperf pair	825.00	
39	A1	1p rose ('74)	95.00	15.00
a.		1p deep rose red	170.00	15.00
40	A1	2p blue	85.00	4.50
a.		Vert. pair, imperf between		—
b.		Imperf. pair	600.00	
c.		2p pale blue ('74)	90.00	2.00
41	A1	3p brown ('75)	140.00	15.00
42	A1	6p yel grn ('69)	200.00	6.00
a.		6p apple green	240.00	8.50
b.		6p deep green	210.00	8.50
c.		As "a," imperf pair	725.00	
43	A1	1sh violet ('75)	425.00	67.50
		Nos. 38-43 (6)	1,060.	113.75

1876-78   **Perf. 12**
44	A1	1p orange	77.50	6.00
a.		1p salmon	450.00	
b.		1p pale org vermilion	87.50	6.00
c.		Vert. pair, imperf between		—
45	A1	1p rose	87.50	10.00
a.		1p salmon	125.00	12.50
46	A1	2p blue	75.00	1.75
a.		2p pale blue	135.00	14.00
b.		2p deep blue	75.00	2.00
47	A1	3p brown	125.00	9.00
48	A1	6p yellow green	275.00	4.25
a.		6p apple green	300.00	7.00
b.		6p deep green	275.00	9.50
c.		6p green	210.00	4.00
49	A1	1sh violet	110.00	8.50
m.		Vert. pair, imperf between		—
n.		1sh purple	275.00	5.00
		Nos. 44-49 (6)	750.00	39.50

Nos. 44, 49 exist in vertical pairs, imperf between.

Perf. 13x12
49B	A1	1p orange	145.00
49C	A1	2p blue	1,450. 240.00
49D	A1	4p yellow	625.00
49E	A1	6p deep green	525.00

Perf. 12½x13
49G	A1	1p org ver	575.00
49H	A1	2p deep blue	575.00

The reprints are perforated 12 and are in paler colors than the originals.

1879   **Unwmk.**   **Perf. 12**
50	A1	6p pale emerald	475.00	30.00
a.		Horiz. pair, imperf. vert.	2,250.	

A2

1875-81   **Litho. Wmk. 68**   **Perf. 13**
50B	A1	4p yellow ('75)	2,450.	115.00
a.		Handstamped "SPECI-MEN"		115.00

Perf. 12
51	A1	4p buff ('76)	1,750.	50.00
a.		4p yellow	1,750.	52.50
52	A1	2sh pale blue ('81)	170.00	57.50
		Fiscal cancellation		5.75
a.		2sh deep blue	200.00	57.50
b.		Imperf.		—
c.		2sh blue	165.00	57.50
d.		As "c" horiz. pair, imperf. vert.		9,000.
53	A2	2sh6p lt red ('81)	375.00	75.00
		Fiscal cancellation		5.75
a.		2sh6p bright scarlet	375.00	77.50
54	A1	5sh org brn ('81)	575.00	115.00
		Fiscal cancellation		7.00
a.		5sh fawn	575.00	115.00
55	A1	10sh brown ('81)	975.00	190.00
		Fiscal cancellation		7.00
a.		Imperf., pair	950.00	
b.		10sh bister brown	975.00	190.00
56	A1	20sh rose ('81)	2,600.	275.00
		Fiscal cancellation		7.00
		Nos. 50B-56 (7)	8,895.	877.50

Nos. 53-56, 62-64, 74-83 with pen (revenue) cancellations removed are often offered as unused.

A3

1879-81   **Typo. Wmk. 68**   **Perf. 12**
57	A3	1p rose red	62.50	11.50
a.		1p red orange	67.50	12.00
b.		1p brown orange	87.50	9.00
c.		"QOEENSLAND"	350.00	42.50
d.		Imperf.		—
e.		Vert. pair, imperf. horiz.		750.00
f.		As "a" "QOGENSLAND"	350.00	62.50
g.		As "b" "QOGENSLAND"	650.00	62.50
58	A3	2p gray blue	90.00	3.25
a.		2p deep ultra	95.00	3.00
b.		Imperf.		—
c.		"PENGE"	425.00	47.50
d.		"TW" joined	90.00	1.75
e.		Vert. pair, imperf. horiz.	1,000.	
59	A3	4p orange yellow	475.00	22.50
a.		Imperf.		—
b.		Horiz. pair, imperf. vert.	12,750.	—
60	A3	6p yellow green	200.00	7.00
a.		Imperf.		—
b.		Horiz. pair, imperf. vert.		—
c.		6p deep green	190.00	7.50
61	A3	1sh pale violet ('81)	190.00	17.50
a.		1sh deep violet	200.00	11.50
		Nos. 57-61 (5)	1,018.	61.75

The stamps of type A3 were electrotyped from plates made up of groups of four types, differing in minor details. Two dies were used for the 1p and 2p, giving eight varieties for each of those values.
Nos. 59-60 exist imperf. vertically.
For surcharge see No. 65.

Moiré on Back
1878-79   **Unwmk.**
62	A3	1p brown org ('79)	825.00	115.00
a.		"QOEENSLAND"	1,850.	
63	A3	2p deep ultra ('79)	825.00	57.50
a.		"PENGE"	4,400.	675.00
64	A1	1sh red violet	240.00	105.00
		Nos. 62-64 (3)	1,890.	277.50

No. 57b Surcharged Vertically in Black

1880   **Wmk. 68**
65	A3	½p on 1p brn org	425.00	240.00
a.		"QOEENSLAND"	2,400.	1,250.

On No. 65, the surcharge reads from bottom to top. Stamps with surcharges reading downward are fakes.

A4

1882-83   **Typo.**   **Perf. 12**
66	A4	1p pale red	12.50	1.00
a.		1p rose	12.50	1.00
b.		Imperf. pair		—
c.		1p deep vermilion	12.50	1.00
67	A4	2p gray blue	25.00	1.00
a.		2p deep ultra	25.00	1.00
b.		Horiz. pair, imperf between		—
68	A4	4p yellow ('83)	55.00	3.50
a.		"PENGE"	350.00	47.50
b.		Imperf., single		—
69	A4	6p yellow green	37.50	2.00
70	A4	1sh violet ('83)	57.50	13.50
a.		1sh lilac	30.00	8.00
b.		1sh deep purple	26.00	8.00
c.		1sh pale mauve	13.50	8.00
		Nos. 66-70 (5)	187.50	21.00

There are eight minor varieties of the 1p, twelve of the 2p and four each of the other values. On the 1p there is a period after "PENNY." On all values the lines of shading on the neck extend from side to side.
Compare design A4 with A6, A10, A11, A15, A16.

1883   **Perf. 9½x12**
71	A4	1p rose	170.00	60.00
72	A4	2p gray blue	575.00	80.00
73	A4	1sh pale violet	300.00	75.00
		Nos. 71-73 (3)	1,045.	215.00

Beware of faked perfs.
See Nos. 94, 95, 100.

A5

Wmk. 68 Twice Sideways
1882-85   **Engr.**   **Perf. 12**
Thin Paper
74	A5	2sh ultra	325.00	62.50
75	A5	2sh6p vermilion	140.00	26.00
76	A5	5sh car rose ('85)	140.00	26.50
77	A5	10sh brown	275.00	55.00
78	A5	£1 dk grn ('83)	575.00	130.00
		Nos. 74-78 (5)	1,455.	300.00

The 2sh, 5sh and £1 exist imperf.
There are two varieties of the watermark on Nos. 74-78, as in the 1879-81 issue.
Stamps with revenue cancels sell for $3.25-6.50.

1886   **Wmk. 69**   **Perf. 12**
Thick Paper
79	A5	2sh ultra	350.00	62.50
80	A5	2sh6p vermilion	60.00	26.00
81	A5	5sh car rose	60.00	40.00
82	A5	10sh dark brown	175.00	47.50
83	A5	£1 dark green	350.00	80.00
		Nos. 79-83 (5)	995.00	256.00

High value stamps with cancellations removed are offered as unused.
Stamps with revenue cancels sell for $3.25-6.50.
See Nos. 126-127, 141-144.

A6

Redrawn
1887-89   **Typo. Wmk. 68**   **Perf. 12**
84	A6	1p orange	19.00	1.00
85	A6	2p gray blue	19.00	1.00
a.		2p deep ultra	25.00	1.00
b.		Half used as 1c on cover		—
86	A6	2sh red brown ('89)	85.00	80.00
a.		2sh pale brown	75.00	72.50

Perf. 9½x12
88	A6	2p deep ultra	450.00	85.00
		Nos. 84-88 (4)	573.00	167.00

The 1p has no period after the value.
In the redrawn stamps the shading lines on the neck are not completed at the left, leaving an irregular white line along that side.

Variety "LA" joined exists on Nos. 84-86, 88, 90, 91, 93, 97, 98, 102.
On No. 88 beware of faked perfs.

A7   A8

1890-92   **Perf. 12½, 13**
89	A7	½p green	16.00	2.00
a.		½p pale green	21.00	2.00
b.		½p deep blue green	8.00	2.00
90	A6	1p orange red	9.00	1.00
a.		Imperf, pair	325.00	325.00
b.		Double impression		675.00
91	A6	2p gray blue	10.00	.50
a.		2p pale blue	12.00	1.00
92	A8	2½p rose carmine	18.00	2.50
93	A6	3p brown ('92)	10.00	4.00
94	A4	4p orange	28.50	4.00
a.		"PENGE" for "PENCE"	165.00	32.50
b.		4p orange yellow	32.00	7.50
c.		As "b," "PENGE" for "PENCE"	180.00	45.00
d.		4p yellow	20.00	4.00
e.		As "d," "PENGE" for "PENCE"	120.00	32.50
95	A4	6p green	12.00	2.00
96	A6	2sh red brown	50.00	52.50
a.		2sh pale brown	60.00	57.50
		Nos. 89-96 (8)	153.50	68.50

The ½p and 3p exist imperf.

1895   **Wmk. 69**   **Perf. 12½, 13**
Thick Paper
98	A6	1p orange	5.00	.50
a.		1p reddish vermilion	5.00	.50
99	A6	2p gray blue	7.00	.50

Perf. 12
100	A4	1sh pale violet	47.50	30.00
		Nos. 98-100 (3)	59.50	31.00

A9   A10

Moiré on Back
1895   **Unwmk.**   **Perf. 12½, 13**
101	A9	½p green	11.00	8.00
a.		Without moiré	77.50	
b.		½p deep green	11.00	8.00
102	A6	1p orange	2.50	2.50
a.		"PE" missing	400.00	80.00
b.		1p reddish vermilion	2.50	3.00

Wmk. 68
103	A9	½p green	3.50	2.00
a.		½p deep green	3.50	2.00
b.		Printed on both sides	300.00	
c.		Double impression	2,000.	2,000.
104	A10	1p orange	4.00	.50
a.		1p pale red	9.00	1.00
105	A10	2p gray blue	37.50	.50

Wmk. 69
Thick Paper
106	A9	½p green, perf 12½	3.00	6.50
a.		Perf 13	3.00	6.50
b.		Perf 12	47.50	
c.		1p deep green, perf 12	47.50	

1895-96   **Unwmk.**   **Thin Paper**
Crown and Q Faintly Impressed
107	A9	½p green	2.50	6.50
108	A10	1p orange	3.50	2.50
108A	A6	2p gray blue	14.00	150.00

A11   A12   A13

1895-96   **Wmk. 68**

109	A11	1p red	9.00	.75
110	A12	2½p rose	25.00	5.00
a.		2½p carmine	25.00	5.00
111	A13	5p violet brown	30.00	5.00
111A	A11	6p yellow green		16,000.

Only a few used examples of No. 111A are known, and readable cancels are from 1902. It is suggested that this otherwise unissued design was accidentally included in the plate of No. 120.

 A14   A15

 A16   A17

 A18   A19

TWO PENCE:
Type I — Point of bust does not touch frame.
Type II — First redrawing. The top of the crown, the chignon and the point of the bust touch the frame. The forehead is completely shaded.
Type III — Second redrawing. The top of crown does not touch the frame, though the chignon and the point of the bust do. The forehead and the bridge of the nose are not shaded.

1897-1900   **Perf. 12½, 13**

112	A14	½p deep green	5.50	7.50
a.		Perf. 12		145.00
113	A15	1p red	2.25	.40
a.		Perf. 12	8.50	3.50
114	A16	2p gray blue (I)	9.00	.40
a.		Perf. 12	725.00	7.00
115	A17	2½p rose	17.50	27.50
116	A17	2½p violet, blue	10.00	3.00
117	A15	3p brown	8.50	3.00
118	A15	4p bright yellow	14.00	3.00
119	A18	5p violet brown	9.50	3.00
120	A15	6p yellow green	8.00	3.25
121	A19	1sh lilac	15.00	3.50
a.		1sh light violet	15.00	3.50
122	A19	2sh turq blue	37.50	47.50
		Nos. 112-122 (11)	136.75	102.05

See Nos. 130-140.

1898   **Serrated Roulette 13**

123	A15	1p scarlet	20.00	7.00
a.		Serrated and perf. 13	10.00	6.00
b.		Serrated in black	20.00	13.00
c.		Serrated without color and in black	22.50	26.00
d.		Same as "b," and perf. 13	80.00	90.00
e.		Same as "c," and perf. 13	100.00	100.00

Victoria — A20

1899   **Typo.**   **Perf. 12, 12½, 13**

124	A20	½p blue green	3.50	2.50
a.		½p green, perf 12	120.00	65.00
b.		½p pale green	14.00	4.25

Unwatermarked stamps are proofs.

"Australia" — A21

NINE PENCE:
Type I — "QUEENSLAND" 18x1½mm.

Type II — "QUEENSLAND" 17½x1¼mm.

1903   **Wmk. 70**   **Perf. 12½**

125	A21	9p org brn & ultra, II	60.00	7.50
a.		Type I	45.00	7.50

See No. 128.

Type of 1882
1903-06   **Wmk. 68**   **Perf. 12, 12½-13**
Typographed, Perf. 12½-13 Irreg. ('03)

125B	A5	5sh rose	240.00	57.50
125C	A5	£1 dark green	2,100.	675.00

Lithographed, Perf. 12 ('05-'06)

126	A5	5sh rose	180.00	95.00
127	A5	£1 dark green	575.00	125.00
c.		Perf. 12½-13 Irreg.	1,150.	165.00

1907   **Typo.**   **Wmk. 13**   **Perf. 12½**

128	A21	9p yel brn & ultra, I	24.00	4.50
a.		Type II	80.00	7.00
b.		Perf. 11, type II	5,500.	775.00

1907   **Wmk. 68**   **Perf. 12½, 13**

129	A16	2p ultra, type II	12.00	5.50
129A	A18	5p dark brown	17.50	6.50
b.		5p olive brown	17.50	4.75

1907-09   **Wmk. 12**

130	A20	½p deep green	2.25	4.50
131	A15	1p red	3.50	.30
a.		Imperf., pair	450.00	
132	A16	2p ultra, II	40.00	3.50
133	A16	2p ultra, III	5.50	.30
134	A15	3p pale brown	27.50	2.50
135	A15	4p bright yellow	12.50	4.25
136	A15	4p gray black ('09)	27.50	6.50
137	A18	5p brown	42.50	22.00
a.		5p olive brown	24.00	25.00
138	A15	6p yellow green	22.50	4.00
139	A19	1sh brown	24.00	4.00
140	A19	2sh turquoise bl	40.00	47.50

Wmk. 12 Sideways
Litho.

141	A5	2sh6p org	45.00	45.00
a.		2sh6p dull orange ('10)	85.00	85.00
b.		2sh6p reddish orange ('12)	190.00	210.00
142	A5	5sh rose	90.00	60.00
a.		5sh deep rose ('10)	110.00	85.00
b.		5sh carmine red ('12)	275.00	260.00
143	A5	10sh dark brown	165.00	70.00
a.		10sh sepia ('12)	450.00	300.00
144	A5	£1 blue green	425.00	125.00
a.		£1 dp blue green ('10)	575.00	325.00
b.		£1 yellow green ('12)	1,850.	1,350.
		Nos. 130-144 (15)	972.75	399.35

POSTAL FISCAL STAMPS

Authorized for postal use from Jan. 1, 1880. Authorization withdrawn July 1, 1892.

Used values are for examples with postal cancellations used from Jan. 1, 1880 through June 30, 1892.

Beware of stamps with a pen cancellation removed and a fake postmark added.

Queen Victoria — PF1

1866-74   **Engr.**   **Unwmk.**   **Perf. 13**

AR1	PF1	1p blue	150.00	27.50
AR2	PF1	6p violet	290.00	125.00
AR3	PF1	1sh green	250.00	85.00
AR4	PF1	2sh brown	425.00	210.00
AR5	PF1	2sh 6p red	525.00	170.00
AR6	PF1	5sh yellow	1,350.	425.00
AR7	PF1	6sh violet	2,100.	
AR8	PF1	10sh yel grn	1,650.	575.00
AR9	PF1	20sh rose	3,250.	1,150.

Wmk. 68

AR10	PF1	1p blue	85.00	65.00
AR11	PF1	6p violet	290.00	150.00
AR12	PF1	6p violet	825.00	450.00
AR13	PF1	1sh green	240.00	90.00
AR14	PF1	2sh brown	425.00	170.00
AR15	PF1	5sh yellow	1,400.	375.00
AR16	PF1	10sh yel grn	1,700.	575.00
AR17	PF1	20sh rose	3,250.	1,250.

Queen Victoria — PF2

1872-73   **Wmk. 69**   **Perf. 13**

AR18	PF2	1p lilac	75.00	25.00
AR19	PF2	6p brown	135.00	52.50
AR20	PF2	1sh green	170.00	55.00
AR21	PF2	2sh blue	275.00	75.00
AR22	PF2	2sh 6p ver	450.00	160.00
AR23	PF2	5sh org brn	575.00	240.00
AR24	PF2	10sh brown	1,150.	475.00
AR25	PF2	20sh rose	2,850.	725.00

Perf. 12

AR26	PF2	1p lilac	75.00	25.00
AR27	PF2	6p brown	135.00	50.00
AR28	PF2	2sh blue	275.00	75.00
AR29	PF2	2sh 6p ver	450.00	160.00
AR30	PF2	5sh org brn	575.00	240.00
AR31	PF2	10sh brown	1,150.	475.00
AR32	PF2	20sh rose	3,000.	725.00

Unwmk.
Perf. 13

AR33	PF2	1p lilac	85.00	25.00
AR34	PF2	6p lilac	140.00	52.50
AR35	PF2	6p brown	625.00	160.00
AR36	PF2	1sh green	210.00	52.50
AR37	PF2	2sh blue	350.00	170.00
AR38	PF2	2sh 6p ver	575.00	190.00
AR39	PF2	5sh org brn	775.00	240.00
AR40	PF2	10sh brown	1,375.	475.00
AR41	PF2	20sh rose	2,900.	725.00

Perf. 12

AR42	PF2	1p lilac	85.00	25.00
AR43	PF2	6p lilac	135.00	52.50
AR44	PF2	6p brown	625.00	165.00
AR45	PF2	1sh green	220.00	52.50
AR46	PF2	2sh blue	350.00	170.00
AR47	PF2	2sh 6p ver	575.00	190.00
AR48	PF2	5sh org brn	800.00	240.00
AR49	PF2	10sh brown	1,400.	475.00
AR50	PF2	20sh rose	3,000.	750.00

Queen Victoria — PF3

1878-79   **Engr.**   **Unwmk.**   **Perf. 12**

AR51	PF3	1p violet	100.00	19.50

Wmk. 68

AR52	PF3	1p violet	150.00	75.00

SEMI-POSTAL STAMPS

Queen Victoria, Colors and Bearers — SP1

SP2

Perf. 12, 12½

1900, June 19   **Wmk. 68**

B1	SP1	1p red lilac	160.00	110.00
		On cover		250.00
B2	SP2	2p deep violet	375.00	290.00
		On cover		500.00
		Nos. B1-B2 on one cover		750.00

These stamps were sold at 1sh and 2sh respectively. The difference was applied to a patriotic fund in connection with the Boer War.

REGISTRATION STAMPS

R1

Clean-Cut Perf. 14 to 16

1861   **Wmk. 5**   **Engr.**

F1	R1	(6p) olive yellow	1,250.	100.00
a.		Horiz. pair, imperf. vert.		13,000.

Rough Perf. 14 to 16

F2	R1	(6p) dull yellow	125.00	37.50

1864   **Perf. 12½ to 13**

F3	R1	(6p) golden yellow	190.00	40.00
a.		Imperf.		
b.		Double impression	2,750.	—

The reprints are watermarked with a small truncated star and perforated 12.

SOUTH AUSTRALIA

'sauth o-'strāl-yə

LOCATION — Central part of southern Australia
GOVT. — British Colony
AREA — 380,070 sq. mi.
POP. — 358,346 (1901)
CAPITAL — Adelaide

South Australia was one of the six British colonies that united in 1901 to form the Commonwealth of Australia.

12 Pence = 1 Shilling
20 Shillings = 1 Pound

Values for unused stamps are for examples with original gum as defined in the catalogue introduction.

Very fine examples of Nos. 10-60 and O1-O60 will have perforations slightly cutting into the framelines or design on one or more sides due to the narrow spacing of the stamps on the plates. Stamps with perfs clear on all sides are scarce to rare and will command higher to substantially higher prices.

Watermarks

Wmk. 6 — Star with Long Narrow Points   Wmk. 7 — Star with Short Broad Points

Wmk. 70 — Crown and V   Wmk. 72 — Crown and SA

Wmk. 73 — Crown and SA, Letters Close

Wmk. 74 —
Crown and
Single-lined A

Queen Victoria — A1

1855-56   Engr.   Wmk. 6   *Imperf.*
London Print

1	A1	1p dark green	9,750.	525.
2	A1	2p dull carmine	825.	100.
3	A1	6p deep blue	4,250.	200.
4	A1	1sh violet ('56)	26,500.	

No. 4 was never put in use. Nos. 1 and 3 without watermark are proofs.

1856-59   Local Print

5	A1	1p dp yel grn ('58)	9,750.	625.00
a.		1p yellow green ('58)	8,750.	750.00
6	A1	2p blood red	3,250.	90.00
a.		Printed on both sides		1,400.
b.		2p orange red ('56)	2,400.	92.50
7	A1	2p pale red ('57)	775.	55.00
a.		Printed on both sides		900.00
8	A1	6p slate blue	4,400.	200.00
9	A1	1sh orange ('57)	11,250.	500.00
a.		Printed on both sides		
b.		1sh red orange	—	775.00

1858-59   *Rouletted*

10	A1	1p yel grn ('59)	1,050.	70.00
a.		Horiz. pair, imperf. between	—	—
b.		1p pale yellow green ('59)	1,050.	75.00
11	A1	2p pale red ('59)	375.00	22.50
a.		Printed on both sides		875.00
12	A1	6p slate blue	850.00	70.00
13	A1	1sh orange ('59)	1,900.	55.00
c.		Printed on both sides		2,000.

See Nos. 14-16, 19-20, 25-26, 28-29, 32, 35-36, 41-43, 47, 51-52, 69-70, 73, 113, 118. For overprints see Nos. O1-O2, O5, O7, O9, O11-O13, O17, O20, O27, O30, O32, O39-O40, O42, O52, O76, O85.

A2

A3

Surcharge on #22-24, 34, 49-50

1860-69   *Rouletted*

14	A1	1p dl bl grn	150.00	55.00
a.		1p deep green	575.00	90.00
b.		1p bright green	145.00	55.00
15	A1	1p sage green	165.00	55.00
a.		1p deep yellow green ('69)	300.00	
b.		1p pale sage green ('65)	145.00	
16	A1	2p ver ('62)	165.00	5.50
a.		Horiz. pair, imperf.	4,000.	775.00
b.		Rouletted and perf. all around	2,750.	700.00
c.		2p pale red	275.00	4.25
d.		As "c," printed on both sides	—	575.00
e.		2p bright vermilion ('64)	165.00	5.25
18	A2	4p dull vio ('67)	175.00	45.00
19	A1	6p grnsh bl ('63)	275.00	4.75
20	A1	6p dull blue	350.00	7.50
a.		6p sky blue	275.00	7.75
b.		6p Prussian blue	1,050.	57.50
c.		Horiz. pair, imperf btwn.		3,250.
d.		6p ultramarine	275.00	4.95
e.		Horiz. pair, imperf. btwn. (#20f)	—	2,500.

f.		6p indigo blue	—	75.00
g.		Rouletted and perf. all around (#20f)		575.00
h.		6p violet blue	450.00	8.00
i.		6p violet ultramarine ('68)	425.00	7.00
21	A3	9p gray lilac ('69)	165.00	10.50
a.		Double impression		
b.		Horiz. pair, imperf between		4,500.
c.		Rouletted and perf. all around	2,900.	275.00
22	A3	10p on 9p red org (Bl) ('66)	500.00	50.00
23	A3	10p on 9p yel (Bl) ('67)	750.00	35.00
24	A3	10p on 9p yel (Blk) ('69)	3,750.	90.00
a.		Inverted surcharge		7,500.
c.		Printed on both sides	—	1,250.
d.		Rouletted x perf. 10		
24E	A1	1sh yellow ('61)	1,375.	35.00
f.		Vert. pair, imperf. btwn.	—	6,000.
25	A1	1sh lake brn ('65)	350.00	14.00
a.		Horiz. pair, imperf. btwn.	—	2,500.
26	A1	1sh brown ('63)	425.00	35.00
a.		1sh chestnut ('64)	375.00	12.50
b.		1sh gray brown ('63)	450.00	35.00
27	A2	2sh car ('67)	550.00	37.50
a.		Vert. pair, imperf. btwn.		2,750.

There are six varieties of the surcharge "TEN PENCE" in this and subsequent issues. Nos. 16b, 20g, 21c, 28a, 32c, 33a are rouletted remainders that were later perforated.

See Nos. 31, 33, 46, 48, 53, 63, 68, 72, 74, 112, 113B, 119-120. For surcharges & overprints see Nos. 34, 44-45, 49-50, 59, 67, 71, O4, O6, O8, O10, O16-O19, O18, O21, O26, O28-O29, O31, O33, O36-O38, O41, O41B, O43, O53. Compare with design A6a.

1867-72   *Perf. 11½ to 12½xRoulette*

28	A1	1p blue green	575.00	72.50
a.		Rouletted and perf. all around		775.00
29	A1	1p grayish green ('70)	425.00	32.50
29a	A1	1p bright green	375.00	27.50
b.		1p pale bright green ('67)	400.00	32.50
31	A2	4p dull violet ('68)	3,250.	175.00
a.		4p purple ('69)	—	145.00
32	A1	6p Prus blue	900.00	22.00
a.		6p sky blue	950.00	22.00
b.		Printed on both sides		
c.		Rouletted and perf. all around	—	425.00
d.		6p indigo blue ('69)	1,000.	29.00
e.		As "d," rouletted and perf. all around	—	550.00
33	A3	9p gray lilac ('72)	—	300.00
34	A3	10p on 9p yel (Bl) ('68)	1,500.	40.00
a.		Printed on both sides	—	1,250.
35	A1	1sh chestnut ('68)	475.00	27.50
36	A1	1sh lake brn ('69)	475.00	25.00
a.		Rouletted and perf. all around		

Nos. 44-45 Surcharged

Perf. 10, 11½, 12½ and Compound
1867-74

41	A1	1p yel grn	185.00	25.00
42	A1	1p blue green	190.00	25.00
a.		Printed on both sides		
b.		Horiz. pair, imperf between		1,150.
c.		1p pale bright green ('68)	400.00	75.00
d.		1p gray green ('68)	350.00	75.00
43	A1	2p vermilion		1,500.
44	A2	3p on 4p sky blue (Blk) ('70)	625.00	20.00
a.		3p on 4p ultra, black surcharge	165.00	10.50
b.		Surcharge omitted	45,000.	22,500.
c.		Double surcharge		4,000.
d.		Surcharged on both sides		3,250.
e.		Rouletted	—	1,500.
f.		3p on 4p Prussian blue ('71)		925.00
46	A2	4p dull violet	110.00	9.25
a.		4p dull purple ('68)	120.00	17.50
47	A1	6p Prussian blue	325.00	8.00
a.		6p sky blue	650.00	12.50
b.		Imperf. vert., pair		
c.		Horiz. pair, imperf x perf 11½		2,500.
d.		6p indigo ('69)	350.00	20.00
48	A3	9p red lilac ('72)	120.00	9.00
a.		9p violet	220.00	9.00
b.		9p red violet	220.00	9.50
c.		Printed on both sides		925.00
49	A3	10p on 9p yel (Bl) ('68)	2,200.	55.00
50	A3	10p on 9p yel (Blk) ('69)	450.00	75.00
51	A1	1sh dp brn	185.00	12.50

52	A1	1sh red brown	200.00	12.50
a.		1sh chestnut	220.00	21.00
b.		1sh lake brown ('68)	240.00	20.00
53	A2	2sh carmine	175.00	14.00
a.		Printed on both sides		800.00
b.		Horiz. pair, imperf. vert.		—
c.		2sh pale rose pink ('69)	2,200.	190.00
d.		2sh deep rose pink ('69)	—	125.00
e.		2sh carmine red ('69)	190.00	22.50

Perf. 10

42e	A1	1p brt grn ('71)	300.00	22.50
42f	A1	1p pale br grn ('70)	350.00	22.50
42g	A1	1p gray green ('70)	350.00	25.00
44g	A2	3p on 4p pale ultra (Blk) ('71)	625.00	19.00
44h	A2	3p on 4p ultra (Blk) ('71)	170.00	10.00
44i	A2	3p on 4p Pruss bl (Blk) ('71)	—	1,100.
45	A2	3p on 4p sl bl (Red) ('70)	1,400.	115.00
46b	A2	4p dull lilac ('70)	190.00	12.50
46c	A2	4p dull pur ('71)	190.00	12.50
47e	A1	6p br blue ('71)	375.00	20.00
47f	A1	6p indigo ('71)	525.00	18.50
52c	A1	1sh chest ('71)	350.00	45.00

Perf. 10x11½-12½, 11½-12½x10, or Compound

42h	A1	1p pale br grn ('70)	350.00	24.00
i		Printed on both sides		
42j	A1	1p deep green ('70)	200.00	12.50
42k	A1	1p gray green ('70)	325.00	19.00
44j	A2	3p on 4p ultra (Blk) ('70)	575.00	90.00
46d	A2	4p dull lilac ('70)	—	23.00
46e	A2	4p slate lilac ('70)	200.00	21.00
47g	A1	6p Prus blue ('70)	275.00	9.50
47h	A1	6p br Pruss blue ('70)	300.00	12.00
50a	A3	10p on 9p yel (Blk) ('69)	300.00	57.50
52d	A1	1sh chestnut ('71)	400.00	90.00
53f	A2	2sh carmine ('71)	350.00	70.00
53g	A2	2sh rose pink	—	250.00

See Nos. 67, O14, O28, O36.

A6

A6a

1868   Typo.   Wmk. 72   *Rouletted*

54	A6a	2p orange red	160.00	3.50
a.		Imperf.		
b.		Printed on both sides		775.00
c.		Horiz. pair, imperf. btwn.		1,400.
d.		2p deep brick red	170.00	7.50

1869   *Perf. 11½ to 12½xRoulette*

55	A6a	2p orange red		200.00

1870   *Perf. 10xRoulette*

56	A6a	2p orange red	550.00	42.50

Perf. 10, 11½, 12½ and Compound
1868-75

57	A6	1p bl grn ('75)	110.00	8.50
58	A6a	2p orange red	25.00	1.25
a.		Printed on both sides		450.00
b.		Horiz. pair, imperf. vert.		

Engr.

59	A3	10p on 9p yel (Bl)		1,800.

1869   Typo.   Wmk. 6   *Rouletted*

60	A6a	2p orange red	190.00	25.00
a.		Imperf.		
b.		Printed on both sides		

Perf. 11½ to 12½xRoulette

61	A6a	2p orange red	2,250.	135.00

Perf. 11½ to 12½

61B	A6a	2p orange red	—	1,250.

See Nos. 62, 64-66, 97-98, 105-106, 115-116, 133-134, 145-146. For surcharges & overprints see Nos. 75, O3, O22-O25, O34-O35, O44-O47, O49, O55-O56, O62-O63, O68-O69, O74, O78-O79.

1871   Wmk. 70   Perf. 10

62	A6a	2p orange red	200.00	55.00

Engr.

63	A2	4p dull violet	5,750.	325.00
a.		Printed on both sides		4,750.

Examples of the 4p from edge of sheet sometimes lack watermark.

Perf. 10, 11½, 12½ and Compound
1876-80   Typo.   Wmk. 73

64	A6	1p green	40.00	1.75
65	A6a	2p orange	50.00	.60
66	A6a	2p blood red ('80)	325.00	6.75
		Nos. 64-66 (3)	415.00	9.10

See Nos. 97-98, 105-106, 115-116, 133-134, 145-146.

No. 71

1876-84   Engr.   Wmk. 7

67	A2	3p on 4p ultra	175.00	32.50
a.		3p on 4p deep blue	140.00	22.50
b.		Double surcharge		1,900.
68	A2	4p reddish violet	100.00	6.50
a.		4p dull violet	100.00	8.00
b.		4p slate violet ('79)	175.00	17.50
69	A1	6p deep blue	150.00	5.00
a.		Horiz. pair, imperf. between		
b.		Imperf.		
c.		6p bright blue, perf 10	225.00	19.00
d.		6p Prussian blue, perf 10	200.00	25.00
70	A1	6p pale ultra ('84)	110.00	3.00
71	A3	8p on 9p bister brn	225.00	11.00
a.		8p on 9p yellow brown	200.00	10.50
b.		8p on 9p gray brown ('80)	190.00	10.00
d.		Double surcharge		2,750.
e.		Vert. pair, imperf between	3,250.	
72	A3	9p rose lilac	16.00	5.00
a.		Printed on both sides		675.00
73	A1	1sh red brown	85.00	4.00
a.		1sh brown	90.00	4.00
b.		1sh chocolate	40.00	4.00
c.		As "b," horiz. pair, imperf. btwn.	475.00	
d.		1sh sepia	29.00	5.00
e.		As "d," vert. pair, imperf. btwn.	650.00	
f.		1sh reddish lake brown, perf 10	525.00	
74	A2	2sh carmine	50.00	8.00
a.		Horiz. pair, imperf. vert.		1,950.
b.		Imperf., pair		

For overprint see No. O41.

Surcharged in Black

1882   Wmk. 73   Perf. 10

75	A6	½p on 1p green	15.00	12.50

A9

A10

A11

A12

Perf. 10, 11½, 12½ and Compound
1883-93   Typo.

76	A9	½p chocolate brown	17.50	2.50
a.		½p red brown ('89)	9.50	2.40
b.		½p bister brown	6.00	4.00
78	A10	3p deep green ('93)	24.00	5.50
a.		3p olive green ('90)	26.00	5.50
b.		3p sage green ('86)	26.00	3.25
79	A11	4p violet ('90)	60.00	5.50
a.		4p aniline violet ('93)	52.50	7.50
80	A12	6p pale blue ('87)	65.00	4.00
a.		6p blue ('87)	52.50	4.00
		Nos. 76-80 (4)	166.50	15.25

See Nos. 96, 100-101, 104, 108-109, 111. For surcharges & overprints see Nos. 94-95, 99, O48, O50-O51, O54, O57-O61, O64, O66-O67, O71, O73, O75, O81-O82.

A13

1886-96   *Perf. 10, 11½ to 12½*

81	A13	2sh6p violet	90.00	10.00
		2sh6p bright aniline violet	100.00	10.00
82	A13	5sh rose	110.00	20.00
83	A13	10sh green	275.00	75.00
84	A13	15sh buff	875.00	275.00
85	A13	£1 blue	550.00	190.00
86	A13	£2 red brn	3,750.	550.00
87	A13	50sh rose red	4,500.	700.00
88	A13	£3 ol grn	5,500.	650.00
89	A13	£4 lemon	9,000.	1,450.
90	A13	£5 gray	8,750.	
90A	A13	£5 brn ('96)	5,500.	1,100.
91	A13	£10 bronze	8,500.	1,500.
92	A13	£15 silver	32,500.	2,400.
93	A13	£20 lilac	37,500.	2,750.

Perf. 10

81b	A13	2sh6p violet	135.00	17.50
82a	A13	5sh rose	155.00	20.00
83a	A13	10sh green	300.00	90.00
84a	A13	15sh buff	800.00	400.00
85a	A13	£1 blue	575.00	200.00
86a	A13	£2 red brn	4,000.	575.00
87a	A13	50sh rose red	4,750.	800.00
88a	A13	£3 ol grn	6,000.	750.00
89a	A13	£4 lemon	11,500.	525.00
90b	A13	£5 gray	9,000.	
91a	A13	£10 bronze	9,000.	2,000.
92a	A13	£15 silver	32,500.	
93a	A13	£20 lilac	40,000.	

For overprints see Nos. O83-O84.

#94, 99   #95

Perf. 10, 11½x12½ and Compound

1891   **Brown Surcharge**

94	A11	2½p on 4p green	8.00	3.00
a.		"½" nearer the "2"	27.50	20.00
b.		Pair, imperf. between		3,750.
c.		Fraction bar omitted	125.00	90.00

Carmine Surcharge

95	A12	5p on 6p red brn	20.00	7.00
a.		No period after "D"	190.00	

See No. 99. For overprints see Nos. O48, O57, O59.

Many stamps of the issues of 1855-91 have been reprinted; they are all on paper watermarked Crown and SA, letters wide apart, and are overprinted "REPRINT."

1893   **Typo.**   *Perf. 15*

96	A9	½p brown	12.50	1.60
a.		Horiz. pair, imperf. btwn	400.00	
b.		Pair, perf. 12 btwn; perf. 15 around	350.00	75.00
97	A6	1p green	42.50	1.00
98	A6a	2p orange	25.00	1.00
a.		Vert. pair, imperf. between	1,000.	
99	A11	2½p on 4p green	55.00	3.00
a.		"½" nearer the "2"	135.00	35.00
b.		Fraction bar omitted		
100	A11	4p gray violet	42.50	4.25
101	A12	6p blue	70.00	4.50
		Nos. 96-101 (6)	247.50	15.35

Kangaroo, Palm — A16   Coat of Arms — A17

1894, Mar. 1

102	A16	2½p blue violet	45.00	6.50
103	A17	5p dull violet	45.00	4.00

See Nos. 107, 110, 117, 135-136, 147, 151. For overprints see Nos. O65, O70, O72, O80.

1895-97   *Perf. 13*

104	A9	½p pale brown	5.50	.50
105	A6	1p green	12.50	.45
a.		Vert. pair, imperf. between		
106	A6a	2p orange	16.00	.25
107	A16	2½p blue violet	10.00	2.25
108	A10	3p ol grn ('97)	6.00	3.50
109	A11	4p bright violet	6.50	1.00
110	A17	5p dull violet	11.00	1.75
111	A12	6p blue	11.00	1.60
a.		6p pale blue ('96)	11.00	1.60
		Nos. 104-111 (8)	78.50	11.30

Some authorities regard the so-called redrawn 1p stamps with thicker lettering (said to have been issued in 1897) as impressions from a new or cleaned plate.

Perf. 11½, 12½, Clean-Cut, Compound

1896   **Engr.**   **Wmk. 7**

112	A3	9p lilac rose	16.00	5.75
113	A1	1sh dark brown	27.50	5.00
a.		Horiz. pair, imperf. vert.	475.00	
c.		Vert. pair, imperf. btwn.	650.00	
113B	A2	2sh carmine	42.50	7.25
		Nos. 112-113B (3)	86.00	18.00

Adelaide Post Office — A18

1899   **Typo.**   **Wmk. 73**   *Perf. 13*

114	A18	½p yellow green	8.00	1.50
115	A6	1p carmine	10.00	1.50
a.		1p scarlet	9.00	1.50
116	A6a	2p purple	6.50	.25
117	A16	2½p dark blue	10.00	2.50
		Nos. 114-117 (4)	34.50	5.75

See Nos. 132, 144. For overprint see No. O77.

Perf. 11½, 12½

1901   **Engr.**   **Wmk. 72**

118	A1	1sh dark brown	24.00	17.50
a.		1sh red brown	27.50	37.50
b.		Horiz. pair, imperf. vert.		
119	A2	2sh carmine	27.50	12.50

1902

120	A3	9p magenta	21.00	25.00

A19

The measurements given in parentheses are the length of the value inscription in the bottom panel.

Perf. 11½, 12½ and Compound

1902-03   **Typo.**   **Wmk. 73**

121	A19	3p olive grn	17.50	3.00
a.		3p olive grn (20mm), perf 12	35.00	32.75
b.		Wmk sideways		1,850.
122	A19	4p red org	30.00	4.50
a.		4p red org (17.5-18mm), perf 12	25.00	2.75
123	A19	6p blue grn	12.50	3.00
a.		6p blue grn (15mm), perf 12	27.50	15.00
124	A19	8p ultra (value 19mm long)	9.00	17.50
124A	A19	8p ultra (value 16½mm long) ('03)	12.50	17.50
b.		"EIGNT"	2,400.	3,250.
125	A19	9p claret	15.00	11.00
a.		Vert. pair, imperf. between	2,750.	
b.		Horiz. pair, imperf. between		
c.		9p claret, perf 12	125.00	27.50
126	A19	10p org buff	18.50	19.00
127	A19	1sh brn ('03)	27.50	9.00
a.		Horiz. pair, imperf. btwn.		
b.		Vert. pair, imperf. btwn.	2,750.	
c.		"Postage" and denomination in red brown	1,100.	1,000.
128	A19	2sh6p purple	40.00	15.00
a.		2sh6p pale violet	90.00	50.00

129	A19	5sh rose	135.00	80.00
130	A19	10sh grn ('03)	225.00	100.00
131	A19	£1 blue	500.00	275.00
		Nos. 121-131 (12)	1,043.	554.50

1904   *Perf. 12x11½*

132	A18	½p yellow green	8.50	2.75
133	A6	1p rose	8.75	1.00
134	A6a	2p purple	15.00	1.00
135	A16	2½p dark blue	15.00	4.25
136	A17	5p dull violet	21.00	2.25
		Nos. 132-136 (5)	68.25	11.25

A20

1904-08   *Perf. 12 and 12x11½*

137	A20	6p blue grn	42.50	3.25
a.		Vert. pair, imperf. between	5,000.	
138	A20	8p ultra ('06)	17.50	9.00
139	A20	9p claret	24.00	7.00
139A	A20	10p org buff ('07)	18.00	25.00
b.		Vert. pair, imperf. between	4,250.	
c.		Horiz. pair, imperf. between	3,000.	3,250.
140	A20	1sh brown	32.50	4.25
a.		Vert. pair, imperf between	2,750.	
b.		Horiz. pair, imperf between	3,000.	
141	A20	2sh6p pur ('05)	85.00	42.50
142	A20	5sh scarlet	85.00	52.50
a.		5sh pale rose, Perf 12½, small holes ('10)	125.00	70.00
142B	A20	10sh grn ('08)	225.00	160.00
143	A20	£1 dp blue	240.00	175.00
a.		Perf 12½, small holes ('10)	350.00	200.00
		Nos. 137-143 (9)	769.50	478.50

See Nos. 148-150, 152-157.

1906-12   **Wmk. 74**

144	A18	½p green	16.00	1.40
145	A6	1p carmine	7.00	.25
146	A6a	2p purple	8.00	.30
a.		Horiz. pair, imperf. between	2,500.	
147	A16	2½p dk blue ('11)	11.00	13.50
148	A20	3p ol grn (value 19mm long)	15.50	6.25
a.		Horiz. pair, imperf. between	6,000.	
149	A20	3p ol grn (value 17mm long) ('09)	17.00	11.00
150	A20	4p red org	25.00	9.00
151	A17	5p dl vio ('08)	30.00	6.75
152	A20	6p bl grn ('07)	8.50	9.50
a.		Vert. pair, imperf. between	2,000.	2,750.
153	A20	8p ultra ('09)	13.50	22.50
154	A20	9p claret	22.50	6.00
a.		Vert. pair, imperf. between	2,100.	
b.		Horiz. pair, imperf. between	5,000.	
155	A20	1sh brown	13.00	5.50
a.		Horiz. pair, imperf. between	3,100.	
b.		Vert. pair, imperf. between	3,750.	
156	A20	2sh6p pur ('09)	80.00	32.50
a.		2sh6p pale violet, perf 12 ('10)	80.00	37.50
b.		2sh6p pale violet, perf 12½ ('12)	130.00	120.00
157	A20	5sh lt red ('12)	145.00	145.00
		Nos. 144-157 (14)	412.00	269.45

OFFICIAL STAMPS

For Departments
Regular Issues Overprinted in Red, Black or Blue:

A. (Architect), A. G. (Attorney General), A. O. (Audit Office), B. D. (Barracks Department), B. G. (Botanical Gardens), B. M. (Bench of Magistrates), C. (Customs), C. D. (Convict Department), C. L. (Crown Lands), C. O. (Commissariat Officer), C. S. (Chief Secretary), C. Sgn. (Colonial Surgeon), C. P. (Commissioner of Police), C. T. (Commissioner of Titles), D. B. (Destitute Board), D. R. (Deed

---

Registry), E. (Engineer), E. B. (Education Board), G. P. (Government Printer), G. S. (Government Storekeeper), G. T. (Goolwa Tramway), G. F. (Gold Fields), H. (Hospital), H. A. (House of Assembly), I. A. (Immigration Agent), I. E. (Intestate Estates), I. S. (Inspector of Sheep), L. A. (Lunatic Asylum), L. C. (Legislative Council), L. L. (Legislative Library), L. T. (Land Titles), M. (Military), M. B. (Marine Board), M. R. (Manager of Railways), M. R. G. (Main Roads Gambierton), N. T. (Northern Territory), O. A. (Official Assignee), P. (Police), P. A. (Protector of Aborigines), P. O. (Post Office), P. S. (Private Secretary), P. W. (Public Works), R. B. (Road Board), R. G. (Registrar General of Births, &c.), S. (Sheriff), S. C. (Supreme Court), S.G. (Surveyor General), S. M. (Stipendiary Magistrate), S. T. (Superintendent of Telegraph), T. (Treasurer), T. R. (Titles Registry), V. (Volunteers), V. A. (Valuator), V. N. (Vaccination), W. (Waterworks).

1868-74   **Wmk. 6**   *Rouletted*

O1	A1	1p green	350.00
O2	A1	2p pale red	275.00
O3	A6a	2p vermilion	120.00
O4	A2	4p dull violet	275.00
O5	A1	6p slate blue	275.00
O6	A3	9p gray lilac	500.00
O7	A1	1sh brown	275.00
O8	A2	2sh carmine	275.00

Perf. 11½ to 12½ x Roulette

O9	A1	1p green	275.00
O10	A2	4p dull violet	850.00
O11	A1	6p blue	210.00
O12	A1	1sh brown	200.00

Perf. 10, 11½, 12½ and Compound

O13	A1	1p green	160.00
O14	A2	3p on 4p sl bl (Red)	750.00
O15	A2	3p on 4p sl bl (Blk)	275.00
O16	A2	4p dull violet	200.00
O17	A1	6p deep blue	275.00
O18	A3	9p violet	500.00
O19	A3	10p on 9p yel (Blk)	500.00
O20	A1	1sh brown	140.00 160.00
O21	A2	2sh carmine	100.00

Rouletted
Wmk. 72

O22	A6a	2p orange	120.00

Perf. 11½ x Roulette

O23	A6a	2p orange	160.00
a.		Perf 10 x Roulette	275.00

Perf. 10, 11½, 12½ and Compound

O24	A6a	2p orange	22.50

Wmk. 70
Perf. 10

O25	A6a	2p orange	110.00
O26	A2	4p dull violet	275.00

For General Use

Overprinted in Black   O.S.

Perf. 10, 11½, 12½ and Compound

1874   **Wmk. 6**

O27	A1	1p green	—	500.00
a.		1p dp yel green, perf 11½-12½x10	3,500.	400.00
b.		As "a," printed on both sides		1,275.
O28	A2	3p on 4p ultra	8,750.	3,000.
a.		No period after "S"		4,000.
O29	A2	4p dull violet	95.00	9.50
a.		Inverted overprint		85.00
b.		No period after "S"		
c.		Perf. 11½-12½x10	3,000.	600.00
O30	A1	6p deep blue	240.00	10.00
a.		No period after "S"		110.00
b.		6p Prussian blue, perf 11½-12½x10	175.00	12.00
O31	A3	9p violet	4,250.	1,700.
a.		No period after "S"	4,750.	2,400.
O32	A1	1sh red brown	125.00	10.00
a.		Double overprint		225.00
b.		No period after "S"	400.00	90.00
O33	A2	2sh carmine	275.00	30.00
a.		Double overprint		
b.		No period after "S"		165.00
c.		2sh carmine, perf 11½-12½x10		160.00

1874-75   **Wmk. 72**

O34	A6	1p blue green	240.00	37.50
a.		Inverted overprint		
O35	A6a	2p orange	60.00	7.50

1876-86   **Wmk. 7**

O37	A2	4p dull violet	75.00	6.00
O38	A2	4p reddish vio	75.00	3.00
a.		Double overprint		
b.		Inverted overprint		300.00
c.		Dbl. ovpt., one inverted		

O39	A1 6p dark blue	150.	5.50
a.	Double overprint		190.00
b.	Inverted overprint		
O40	A1 6p ultramarine	150.00	5.50
a.	Double overprint		
b.	Inverted overprint		
O41B	A3 9p violet	9,000.	
O42	A1 1sh red brown	52.50	9.00
a.	Inverted overprint	750.00	275.00
b.	Double overprint		
O43	A2 2sh carmine	300.00	9.00
a.	Double overprint		275.00
b.	Inverted overprint		325.00
c.	No period after "S"		90.00

1880-91   **Wmk. 73**

O44	A6 1p blue green	12.00	1.00
a.	Inverted overprint		40.00
b.	Double overprint	52.50	35.00
c.	Dbl. ovpt., one inverted		750.00
O45	A6 1p yellow green	14.50	1.00
O46	A6a 2p orange	10.00	.80
a.	Inverted overprint		17.50
b.	Double overprint	70.00	32.50
c.	Overprinted sideways		
d.	Dbl. ovpt., one inverted		
e.	Dbl. ovpt., both inverted		95.00
O47	A6a 2p blood red	52.50	8.75
O48	A11 2½p on 4p green	57.50	8.75
a.	"½" nearer the "2"		67.50
b.	Double overprint		
c.	Pair, one without ovpt.		
	Nos. O44-O48 (5)	146.50	20.30

1882-90   **Perf. 10**

O49	A6 ½p on 1p green	57.50	13.50
a.	Inverted overprint		
O50	A11 4p violet	57.50	5.00
O51	A12 6p blue	20.00	1.25
a.	Double overprint		
b.	No period after "S"		
	Nos. O49-O51 (3)	135.00	19.75

Overprinted in Black

Perf. 10, 11½, 12½ and Compound

1891   **Wmk. 7**

O52	A1 1sh red brown	37.50	5.25
a.	No period after "S"		55.00
b.	1sh lake brown, perf 11½-12½	45.00	10.00
O53	A2 2sh carmine	90.00	10.00
a.	Double overprint		
b.	No period after "S"	115.00	

1891-95   **Wmk. 73**

O54	A9 ½p brown	12.50	6.25
a.	No period after "S"	87.50	52.50
O55	A6 1p blue green	17.50	2.00
a.	Double overprint	72.50	30.00
b.	No period after "S"	75.00	17.50
O56	A6a 2p orange	12.00	.50
a.	No period after "S"		45.00
O57	A11 2½p on 4p green	40.00	10.00
a.	"½" nearer the "2"	82.50	30.00
b.	Inverted overprint	145.00	
O58	A11 4p violet	47.50	3.50
a.	Double overprint		
O59	A12 5p on 6p red brn	50.00	14.50
O60	A12 6p blue	18.50	2.50
a.	Double overprint		
b.	No period after "S"		
	Nos. O54-O60 (7)	198.00	39.25

1893   **Perf. 15**

O61	A9 ½p brown	24.00	7.75
O62	A6 1p green	10.00	1.25
O63	A6a 2p orange	10.00	.50
a.	Inverted overprint		16.50
b.	Double overprint		22.50
O64	A11 4p gray violet	57.50	4.50
a.	Double overprint	160.00	32.50
O65	A17 5p dull violet	72.50	10.00
O66	A12 6p blue	24.00	3.00
	Nos. O61-O66 (6)	198.00	27.00

1896   **Perf. 13**

O67	A9 ½p brown	14.50	5.75
a.	Triple overprint	160.00	
O68	A6 1p green	17.50	.60
a.	No period after "S"	52.50	10.00
O69	A6a 2p orange	17.50	.50
a.	No period after "S"	50.00	10.00
O70	A16 2½p blue violet	60.00	6.75
a.	No period after "S"		30.00
O71	A11 4p brt violet	60.00	3.00
a.	Double overprint	125.00	32.50
b.	No period after "S"	125.00	24.00
O72	A17 5p dull violet	62.50	12.00
a.	No period after "S"		
O73	A12 6p blue	27.50	2.00
a.	No period after "S"	90.00	60.00
	Nos. O67-O73 (7)	259.50	30.60

On No. O67a, one overprint is upright, two sideways.

Same Overprint in Dark Blue

1891-95   **Perf. 10**

O74	A6 1p green	200.00	7.50
O75	A12 6p blue		

Black Overprint
Perf. 11½, 12½, Clean-Cut

1897   **Wmk. 7**

O76	A1 1sh brown	35.00	5.50
a.	Double overprint		
b.	No period after "S"		375.00

Overprinted in Black

1900   **Wmk. 73**   **Perf. 13**

O77	A18 ½p yellow green	12.50	5.75
a.	Inverted overprint	110.00	
b.	No period after "S"	62.50	
c.	As "b," inverted overprint	—	
O78	A6 1p carmine rose	11.50	1.60
a.	Inverted overprint	45.00	32.50
b.	Double overprint		475.00
c.	No period after "S"	82.50	22.50
O79	A6a 2p purple	12.50	.80
a.	Inverted ovpt.	40.00	22.00
b.	No period after "S"	77.50	21.00
O80	A16 2½p dark blue	75.00	18.50
a.	Inverted overprint		57.50
b.	No period after "S"	225.00	
O81	A11 4p violet	60.00	4.50
a.	Inverted overprint	165.00	
b.	No period after "S"	200.00	
O82	A12 6p blue	20.00	4.50
a.	No period after "S"	110.00	
	Nos. O77-O82 (6)	191.50	35.65

1901   **Perf. 10**

O83	A13 2sh6p violet	3,500.	2,500.
O84	A13 5sh rose	3,500.	2,500.

On Nos. O77-O82 the letters "O.S." are 11½mm apart; on Nos. O83-O84, 14½mm apart.

Overprinted in Black

1903   **Wmk. 72**   **Perf. 11½, 12½**

O85	A1 1sh red brown		47.50 11.00

TASMANIA

taz-'ma-nē-ə

LOCATION — An island off the south-eastern coast of Australia
GOVT. — British Colony
AREA — 26,215 sq. mi.
POP. — 172,475 (1901)
CAPITAL — Hobart

Tasmania was one of the six British colonies that united in 1901 to form the Commonwealth of Australia. The island was originally named Van Diemen's Land by its discoverer, Abel Tasman, the present name having been adopted in 1853. Stamps of Australia are now used.

12 Pence = 1 Shilling
20 Shillings = 1 Pound

Watermarks

Wmk. 6 — Large Star

Wmk. 139 Double-lined Numeral

Wmk. 49 Double-lined Numeral

Wmk. 50 Single-lined "2"

Wmk. 75 Double-lined Numeral

Wmk. 51 Single-lined "4"

Wmk. 52 — Single-lined "10"

Wmk. 70 — V and Crown

Wmk. 13 — Crown & Double-lined A

Wmk. 76 — TAS   Wmk. 77 — TAS

Wmk. 78 — Multiple TAS

Values for unused stamps are for examples with original gum as defined in the catalogue introduction except for Nos. 1-2b and 10 which are valued without gum as few examples exist with any remaining original gum. Very fine examples of Nos. 17-75a will have perforations touching the design on one or more sides due to the narrow spacing of the stamps on the plates. Stamps with perfs clear of the design on all four sides are scarce and command higher prices.

Queen Victoria
A1   A2

Unwmk.

1853, Nov. 1   **Engr.**   *Imperf*

1	A1 1p blue, fine impression, soft paper	11,500.	1,600
1a	A1 1p blue, blurred impression, hard paper	11,000.	1,350
2	A2 4p red orange	6,250.	550.00
a.	4p yellow orange	5,750.	425.00
	Cut to shape		25.00
b.	4p orange, blurred impression ('55)	5,750.	425.00
	Cut to shape		25.00

Twenty-four varieties of each.
The 4p on vertically laid paper is believed to be a proof. Value, unused, $7,500.

The reprints are made from defaced plates and show marks across the face of each stamp. They are on thin and thick, unwatermarked paper and thin cardboard; only the first are perforated. Nearly all the reprints of Tasmania may be found with and without the overprint "REPRINT."

Nos. 1-47A with pen or revenue cancellations sell for a small fraction of the price of postally used examples. Stamps are found with pen cancellation removed.

Queen Victoria — A3

1855   **Wmk. 6**   **Wove Paper**

4	A3 1p dark carmine	10,500.	1,000.
5	A3 2p green	5,750.	500.00
a.	2p deep green	5,750.	600.00
6	A3 4p deep blue	5,000.	145.00
a.	4p blue	5,000.	145.00

1856-57   **Unwmk.**

7	A3 1p pale red	13,500.	700.00
8	A3 2p emerald ('57)	16,500.	1,000.
9	A3 4p blue ('57)	2,650.	140.00
a.	4p deep blue ('57)	2,650.	140.00
b.	4p pale blue ('57)	—	180.00

1856   **Pelure Paper**

10	A3 1p brown red	8,250.	800.00

1857-69   **Wmk. 49, 75**

11	A3 1p carmine ('67)	375.00	32.50
a.	1p orange red ('65)	375.00	37.50
b.	1p brown red	625.00	42.50
c.	Double impression	650.00	300.00
d.	1p brick red ('63)	450.00	42.50
e.	Wmk. 50 (error) ('69)		
12	A3 2p sage green ('60)	400.00	95.00
a.	2p yellow green	950.00	125.00
b.	2p green		67.50
c.	2p dull emerald green		150.00
d.	As "b," double impression		325.00
13	A3 4p pale blue	425.00	30.00
a.	4p blue	425.00	32.50
b.	Printed on both sides		95.00
c.	4p deep blue		95.00
d.	As "a," double impression		275.00
e.	As "c," double impression		315.00
g.	4p cobalt blue		95.00
	Nos. 11-13 (3)	1,200.	157.50

See Nos. 17-19, 23-25, 29-31, 35-37, 39-41, 45-47A.

A4   A4a

1858-67

14	A4 6p gray lilac ('63)	750.00	95.00
a.	6p red violet ('67)	1,150.	190.00
b.	Double impression ('63)		450.00
c.	6p dull lilac	1,250.	100.00

15	A4	6p blue gray ('65)	1,150.	150.00
16	A4a	1sh vermilion	825.00	90.00
		Nos. 14-16 (3)	2,725.	335.00

No. 15 watermarked large star was not regularly issued.

Issued: No. 14c, 16, 1/58; No. 14, 4/63; No. 15, 2/65; No. 14a, 4/67.

1864   *Rouletted*

17	A3	1p carmine	950.00	325.00
a.		1p brick red	—	500.00
18	A3	2p yellow grn	—	1,250.
19	A3	4p blue	—	475.00
21	A4	6p gray lilac	—	525.00
22	A4a	1sh vermilion	—	1,350.

Values for Nos. 17-22 are for stamps showing rouletting on two or three sides. Examples with full roulettes on all four sides are rare.

1864-69   *Perf. 10*

23	A3	1p brick red	175.00	65.00
a.		1p carmine	145.00	55.00
b.		1p orange red	175.00	55.00
c.		As "b," double impression		
24	A3	2p yellow green	825.00	160.00
a.		2p sage green	850.00	240.00
25	A3	4p blue	400.00	22.50
a.		Double impression		240.00
26	A4	6p lilac	575.00	42.50
a.		6p red lilac	850.00	105.00
27	A4	6p slate blue	775.00	105.00
28	A4a	1sh vermilion	575.00	52.50
		Nos. 23-28 (6)	3,325.	447.50

1864-91   *Perf. 12, 12½*

29	A3	1p carmine	120.00	25.00
a.		1p orange red	160.00	40.00
b.		1p brick red	140.00	62.50
c.		Double impression		3,000.
d.		Wmkd. "2"		325.00
		As "d," pen cancel		325.00
30	A3	2p yellow green	625.00	100.00
a.		2p dark green	475.00	240.00
b.		2p sage green	475.00	240.00
31	A3	4p blue	325.00	26.00
a.		4p deep blue	325.00	—
b.		4p cobalt blue	—	67.50
32	A4	6p red lilac	170.00	47.50
a.		Horiz. pair, imperf between		—
b.		Vert. pair, imperf between		—
c.		6p violet	400.00	32.50
d.		As "c," Vert. pair, imperf between		—
e.		6p purple ('84)	175.00	22.50
f.		Horiz. pair, imperf between	2,200.	—
g.		6p dull claret ('91)	52.50	15.00
34	A4a	1sh vermilion	450.00	75.00
a.		Double impression		200.00
b.		Horiz. pair, imperf between		3,500.

Perf. 10x12

29e	A3	1p carmine	3,250.	
31c	A3	4p blue		2,750.

Perf. 12½

29f	A3	1p carmine	100.00	25.00
29g	A3	1p orange red	160.00	52.50
29h	A3	1p brick red	160.00	52.50
30a	A3	2p yellow green	775.00	180.00
30b	A3	2p sage green	675.00	190.00
31d	A3	4p blue	425.00	57.50
31e	A3	4p bright blue	425.00	60.00
32h	A4	6p purple	850.00	145.00
32i	A4	6p slate violet	575.00	67.50
33	A4	6p slate blue	775.00	110.00
34c	A4a	1sh vermilion	675.00	140.00

Perf. 11½

32j	A4	6p dull lilac	240.00	25.00
32k	A4	6p lilac	225.00	25.00
l.		Pair, imperf between		1,750.
32m	A4	6p dp slate lil ('75)	220.00	25.00
n.		Imperf, pair	—	1,400.
32o	A4	6p brt vio ('78)	240.00	37.50
p.		Double impression		160.00
q.		Horiz. pair, imperf between		3,750.
32r	A4	6p dl reddish lil ('79)	200.00	45.00
34d	A4a	1sh dl ver ('73)	325.00	70.00
e.		Horiz. pair, imperf between		—
34f	A4a	1sh brnsh ver ('73)	300.00	70.00

The reprints are on unwatermarked paper, perforated 11½, and on thin cardboard, imperforate and perforated.

Perf. Pin-perf. 5½ to 9½, 13½ to 14½
1867

35	A3	1p carmine	1,250.	400.00
36	A3	2p yel grn		975.00
37	A3	4p blue		625.00
38	A4	6p gray		650.00
38A	A4	6p red lilac		1,350.
38B	A4a	1sh vermilion		

Pin-perf. 13½ to 14½

35a	A3	1p brick red		800.00
35b	A3	1p dull vermilion		800.00
35c	A3	1p carmine		
36a	A3	2p yel grn		1,350.
37a	A3	4p pale blue		700.00
38Ac	A4	6p gray violet		1,375.
38Bd	A4a	1sh vermilion		

Oblique Roulette 14-15

39	A3	1p carmine		1,200.
a.		1p brick red		1,200.
b.		1p dull vermilion		1,250.
40	A3	2p yel grn		1,600.
41	A3	4p blue		1,250.
42	A4	6p gray		2,000.
43	A4	6p red lilac		—
44	A4a	1sh vermilion		2,500.

Oblique Roulette 10-10½

39c	A3	1p carmine	3,000.	750.00
39d	A3	1p brick red		850.00
40a	A3	2p yellow green		1,250.
41a	A3	4p blue		950.00
43a	A4	6p gray lilac		1,750.

Oblique Roulette Imperf 10-10½

41b	A3	4p blue		950.00

1868   *Serrate Perf. 19*

45	A3	1p carmine	850.00	250.00
46	A3	2p yellow green		850.00
47	A3	4p blue	1,900.	250.00
47A	A3	6p purple	—	1,200.
47B	A3	1sh vermilion		

Queen Victoria — A5

1870-71   *Typo.*   *Wmk. 50*   *Perf. 11½*

48	A5	2p blue green	200.00	10.00
a.		Double impression	5,500.	2,000.
b.		Perf. 12	210.00	11.00
c.		2p green	325.00	20.00
d.		As "c," perf. 12	200.00	11.00
e.		As "d," imperf, pair		

See Nos. 49-75, 98, 108-109.

Wmk. 51   *Perf. 12*

49	A5	1p rose ('71)	150.00	60.00
a.		Imperf., pair	1,300.	1,200.
50	A5	4p blue	1,350.	525.00

Wmk. 52

51	A5	1p rose	130.00	21.00
a.		Imperf. pair	1,350.	1,350.
c.		Perf. 11½	1,350.	
52	A5	10p black	27.50	52.50
a.		Imperf. pair	750.00	
b.		Perf. 11½	52.50	52.50

The reprints are on unwatermarked paper. The 4p has also been reprinted on thin cardboard, imperf and perf.

1871-76   *Wmk. 76*   *Perf. 11½*

53	A5	1p rose	17.00	2.50
a.		Imperf.		
c.		Perf. 12	155.00	29.00
d.		1p carmine	22.50	3.50
e.		1p pink	22.50	3.50
f.		As "d," perf. 12	170.00	30.00
g.		As "e," perf. 12	170.00	14.00
53B	A5	1p ver ('73)	325.00	80.00
54	A5	2p dp grn ('72)	80.00	2.75
a.		2p yellow green	375.00	5.00
b.		2p blue green	57.50	2.75
c.		Imperf. pair		1,750.
d.		2p green, perf. 12	700.00	150.00
e.		Double impression		
55	A5	3p brown	80.00	6.00
a.		3p purple brown	80.00	5.00
b.		As "a," imperf. pair		1,150.
c.		3p brownish purple	70.00	5.00
56	A5	3p red brn ('71)	90.00	5.00
a.		3p indian red	75.00	5.00
b.		Imperf. pair	140.00	
c.		Vert. pair, imperf. horiz.		
d.		Perf. 12	145.00	24.00
e.		3p deep red brown, perf. 12	145.00	24.00
f.		As "e," pair, imperf. between		
57	A5	4p dull yel ('76)	150.00	45.00
a.		Perf. 12	375.00	25.00
b.		4p ocher	90.00	10.00
c.		4p buff	75.00	12.00
58	A5	9p blue	32.50	9.00
a.		Imperf. pair	575.00	
b.		Perf. 12	60.00	52.50
c.		Double impression		3,500.
59	A5	5sh bright violet	325.00	85.00
a.		Imperf.		
b.		Horiz. pair, imperf. vert.		
c.		Perf. 12	500.00	475.00
d.		5sh purple	350.00	85.00
e.		5sh purple, perf. 12	575.00	
		Pen cancel		11.00
		Nos. 53-59 (8)	1,100.	235.25

The reprints are on unwatermarked paper, the 5sh has also been reprinted on thin cardboard; all are perforated.

1878   *Wmk. 77*   *Perf. 14*

60	A5	1p rose	11.00	1.25
61	A5	2p deep green	12.00	1.25
62	A5	8p violet brown	15.00	10.00
		Nos. 60-62 (3)	38.00	12.50

The 8p has been reprinted on thin unwatermarked paper, perforated 11½.

1880-83   *Perf. 12, 11½*

63	A5	3p indian red, perf. 12	10.00	9.00
a.		Imperf. pair	475.00	
b.		Horiz. pair, imperf. between	2,500.	
c.		Perf. 11½	25.00	5.50
64	A5	4p lem, perf. 11½ ('83)	80.00	20.00
a.		4p olive yellow, perf. 11½	160.00	30.00
b.		Printed on both sides	1,600.	
c.		Imperf.		
d.		4p deep yellow, perf. 12	140.00	32.50

Type of 1871
Surcharged in Black

1889   *Perf. 14*

65	A5	½p on 1p carmine	11.00	25.00
a.		"al" sideways in surcharge	2,000.	1,675.

No. 65 has been reprinted on thin cardboard, perforated 12, with the surcharge "Halfpenny" 19mm long.

1889-96   *Perf. 11½*

66	A5	½p red orange	3.25	3.50
a.		½p yellow orange	3.25	3.50
b.		Perf. 12	5.50	7.00
67	A5	1p dull red	15.00	3.50
a.		1p vermilion	11.00	3.00
68	A5	1p car, perf. 12	8.25	3.25
a.		1p pink, perf. 12	42.50	15.00
b.		1p salmon rose, perf. 12	35.00	12.50
c.		Imperf. pair	400.00	375.00

Perf. 12

69	A5	4p bister ('96)	16.00	7.50
70	A5	9p chalky bl ('96)	10.00	3.50
		Nos. 66-70 (5)	52.50	21.25

1891   *Wmk. 76*   *Perf. 11½*

71	A5	½p orange	80.00	50.00
a.		½p brown orange	52.50	45.00
b.		Imperf. pair	325.00	
c.		Perf. 12	70.00	45.00
72	A5	1p salmon rose	25.00	11.00
a.		1p carmine, perf. 12	45.00	42.50
73	A5	4p ol bis, perf. 12	25.00	32.50
		Nos. 71-73 (3)	130.00	93.50

See Nos. 98, 108-109.

Surcharged in Black

1891   *Wmk. 77*   *Perf. 11½*
Surcharge 14mm High

74	A5	2½p on 9p lt blue	17.50	9.25
a.		Dbl. surcharge, one invtd.	850.00	950.00
b.		Imperf. pair		

Perf. 12
Surcharge 15mm High

75	A5	2½p on 9p lt blue	8.50	7.75
a.		Surcharged in blue	10.00	6.50

No. 74 has been reprinted on thin unwatermarked paper, imperforate. There is also a reprint on thin cardboard, in deep ultramarine, with surcharge 16½mm high, and perforated 12.

A8   A9

1892-99   *Typo.*   *Perf. 14*

76	A8	½p orange & vio	4.25	4.25
77	A9	2½p magenta	7.25	7.25
78	A8	5p pale bl & brn	11.50	7.25
79	A8	6p blue vio & blk	15.00	7.25
80	A8	10p red brn & grn ('99)	29.00	21.00
81	A8	1sh rose & green	15.00	7.25
82	A8	2sh6p brown & blue	47.50	35.00
83	A8	5sh brn vio & red	92.50	42.50
84	A8	10sh brt vio & brn	160.00	115.00
85	A8	£1 green & yel	700.00	450.00
		Nos. 76-85 (10)	1,082.	696.75

No. 80 shows the numeral on white tablet.
See Nos. 99, 110-111.

Lake Marion — A10

Mt. Wellington — A11

View of Hobart — A12

Tasman's Arch — A13

Spring River, Port Davey — A14

Russell Falls — A15

Mt. Gould and Lake St. Clair — A16

Dilston Falls — A17

1899-1900   *Engr.*   *Wmk. 78*   *Perf. 14*

86	A10	½p dark green	16.00	12.00
87	A11	1p carmine	10.50	3.00
88	A12	2p violet	25.00	3.50
89	A13	2½p dark blue	35.00	17.50
90	A14	3p dark brown	18.00	9.00
91	A15	4p ocher	42.50	12.00
92	A16	5p ultramarine	47.50	29.00
93	A17	6p lake	45.00	37.50
		Nos. 86-93 (8)	239.50	123.50

See Nos. 94-97, 102-107, 114-117.

Perf. 11, 12½, 11x12½
1902-03   *Litho., Typo.*   *Wmk. 70*

94	A10	½p green	8.00	2.75
95	A11	1p carmine	15.00	2.40
96	A11	1p dull red	22.50	3.00
97	A12	2p violet	14.00	1.40
98	A5	9p blue	15.00	7.25
a.		9p ultramarine	750.00	
b.		9p indigo	240.00	
c.		Perf. 11	15.00	15.00
d.		Perf 12½, wmkd. sideways	40.00	17.00

99	A8	1sh rose & green	32.50	10.50
a.		Perf. 11	75.00	75.00
		Nos. 94-99 (6)	107.00	27.30

Nos. 94, 97 are litho., Nos. 96, 98-99 typo. No. 95 was printed both ways.

No. 78 Surcharged in Black

1904   **Wmk. 77**   *Perf. 14*

100	A8	1½p on 5p blue & brn	2.75	2.75

Perf. 11, 12, 12½ and Compound

1905-08   **Typo.**   **Wmk. 13**

102	A10	½p dull green	4.25	.95
a.		Booklet pane of 12		
103	A11	1p carmine	3.50	.60
a.		Booklet pane of 18		
104	A12	2p violet	18.00	.80
105	A14	3p dark brown	15.00	9.00
106	A15	4p ocher	25.00	7.25
107	A17	6p lake	70.00	12.50
108	A5	8p violet brown	35.00	16.00
109	A5	9p blue	130.00	8.00
110	A8	1sh rose & green	24.00	9.25
111	A8	10sh brt vio & brn	325.00	350.00
a.		Perf. 11	475.00	475.00
		Nos. 102-111 (10)	649.75	414.35

Nos. 104-107 also printed litho.

1911   **Redrawn**

114	A12	2p bright violet	15.00	7.50
a.		Perf. 11	17.00	8.50
b.		Compound perf. 11, 12½	85.00	27.50
c.		Compound perf. 12, 12½	575.00	
115	A15	4p dull yellow	72.50	72.50
a.		Perf. 11	82.50	
116	A17	6p lake	35.00	55.00
a.		Perf. 11	52.50	
b.		Compound perf. 11, 12½	525.00	
		Nos. 114-116 (3)	122.50	135.00

The redrawn 2p measures 33½x25mm instead of 32½x24½mm. There are many slight changes in the clouds and other parts of the design.

The 4p is much lighter, especially the water-fall and trees above it. This appears to be a new or cleaned plate rather than a redrawn one.

In the redrawn 6p there are more colored lines in the waterfall and the river and more white dots in the trees.

No. 114 Surcharged in Red

1912

117	A12	1p on 2p brt vio	2.75	2.75
a.		Perf. 11	3.50	3.50
b.		Compound perf. 12½ 11	240.00	260.00

POSTAL FISCAL STAMPS

Authorized for postal use by Act of November 1, 1882. Authorization withdrawn Nov. 30, 1900.

Used values are for examples with postal cancellations used from Nov. 1, 1882 through Nov. 30, 1900.

Beware of stamps with a pen cancellation removed, often regummed or with a fake postmark added.

PF1   PF2

St. George and the Dragon
PF3   PF4

1863-80   **Engr.**   **Wmk. 139**   *Imperf.*

AR1	PF1	3p green	450.00	200.00
AR2	PF2	2sh 6p car	450.00	180.00
AR3	PF3	5sh green	525.00	250.00
AR4	PF3	5sh brown	900.00	550.00
AR5	PF4	10sh sal ('80)	900.00	575.00
a.		10sh orange	1,200.	550.00

For overprint see No. AR32.

Perf. 10

AR6	PF1	3p green	475.00	300.00
AR7	PF2	2sh 6p car	450.00	
AR8	PF3	5sh brown	650.00	475.00
AR9	PF4	10sh orange	525.00	

Perf. 12

AR10	PF1	3p green	500.00	375.00
AR11	PF2	2sh 6p car	500.00	425.00
AR12	PF3	5sh green	500.00	350.00
AR13	PF3	5sh brown	950.00	
AR14	PF4	10sh orange	600.00	375.00

Perf. 12½

AR15	PF1	3p green	800.00	
AR16	PF2	2sh 6p car	375.00	
AR17	PF3	5sh brown	650.00	
AR18	PF4	10sh orange	575.00	

Perf. 11½

AR19	PF1	3p green		
AR20	PF2	2sh 6p car	750.00	425.00
AR21	PF3	5sh brown	300.00	200.00
AR22	PF4	10sh salmon	350.00	300.00
a.		10sh orange	300.00	140.00

Wmk. 77

Perf. 12

AR23	PF2	2sh 6p car	72.50	52.50

For overprint see No. AR33.

Duck-billed Platypus — PF5

1880   **Engr.**   **Wmk. 77**   *Perf. 14*

AR24	PF5	1p slate	42.50	12.00
AR25	PF5	3p brown	29.00	7.75
AR26	PF5	6p lilac	140.00	21.00
AR27	PF5	1sh rose	200.00	35.00

For overprints see Nos. AR28-AR31.

Nos. AR24-AR27, AR2, AR23, 85 Overprinted "REVENUE"

1900, Nov. 15

AR28	PF5	1p slate	42.50	42.50
AR29	PF5	3p brown	42.50	45.00
AR30	PF5	6p lilac	300.00	140.00
AR31	PF5	1sh rose	500.00	240.00
AR32	PF2	2sh 6p car (#AR2)	675.00	525.00
AR33	PF2	2sh 6p car (#AR23)	450.00	
AR34	PF4	10sh orange	950.00	950.00
AR35	A8	£1 grn & yel (#85)	375.00	350.00

Nos. AR28-AR35 were not supposed to be postally used. Because of imprecise terminology, postal use was tolerated until all postal use of revenues ceased on Nov. 30, 1900. Other denominations and watermarks were overprinted after postal use was no longer allowed.

VICTORIA

vik-ˈtōr-ē-ə

LOCATION — In the extreme southeastern part of Australia
GOVT. — British Colony
AREA — 87,884 sq. mi.
POP. — 1,201,341 (1901)
CAPITAL — Melbourne

Victoria was one of the six former British colonies which united on Jan. 1,

1901, to form the Commonwealth of Australia.

12 Pence = 1 Shilling
20 Shillings = 1 Pound

Unused values for Nos. 1-16 are for stamps without gum as these stamps are seldom found with original gum. Otherwise, unused values are for stamps with original gum as defined in the catalogue introduction.

Very fine examples of all rouletted, perforated and serrate perforated stamps from Nos. 9-109 and F2 will have roulettes, perforations or serrate perforations touching the design. Examples clear on four sides range from scarce to rare and will command higher prices.

Watermarks

Wmk. 6 — Large Star

Wmk. 80

Wmk. 50   Wmk. 80a

Wmk. 81   Wmk. 139

Wmk. 49   Wmk. 75

Wmk. 70 — V and Crown   Wmk. 13 — Crown & Double-lined A

Queen Victoria — A1

A1 TYPES

1p:
Type I — "VICTORIA" very close to top of design, with very thin line of color between "VICTORIA" and frameline.
Type II — Thicker line of color between "VICTORIA" and frameline at top.

2p:
Type I — Border, two sets of nine wavy lines crisscrossing. Background, 22 groups of wavy triple lines below "VICTORIA".
Type II — Border, same. Background, 15 groups of wavy triple lines below "VICTORIA."
Type III — Border, two sets of five wavy lines crisscrossing. Background, same as type II.

3p:
Type I — Orb poorly defined, with white area at right and thicker at left. Central band of orb does not protrude at left.
Type II — Orb clearly defined, with white outlines at left and right. Central band of orb protrudes at left.

1850   **Litho.**   **Unwmk.**   *Imperf.*

1	A1	1p dull red, II	4,000.	225.00
a.		1p dull org ver, II	5,500.	750.00
b.		1p brownish red, II ('51)	1,500.	210.00
c.		1p dull brown, I	19,000.	2,500.
d.		1p orange vermilion, I	30,000.	5,500.
e.		1p orange brown, I		2,100.
2	A1	1p rose, II	3,500.	200.00
a.		1p pink, II	1,750.	190.00
b.		1p reddish brown, II ('51)	5,500.	190.00
3	A1	3p blue, I	6,500.	450.00
a.		3p light blue, I ('52)	2,250.	110.00
b.		3p bright blue, I	7,500.	625.00
4	A1	3p indigo, II	3,000.	100.00
a.		3p pale grnsh blue, II ('52)	3,500.	210.00
		Nos. 1-4 (4)	17,000.	975.00

Nos. 1-4 exist with and without frame line.

5	A1	2p lilac, I	7,500.	550.00
a.		2p brn lilac, I	7,000.	550.00
b.		2p orange brown, I		2,500.
6	A1	2p brn lilac, II	2,500.	250.00
a.		2p gray lilac, II	6,000.	200.00
7	A1	2p brn lilac, III	7,250.	250.00
a.		2p gray lilac, III	11,000.	500.00
b.		Value omitted, III		17,500.
8	A1	2p yel brn, III	3,000.	200.00

Rouletted 7

9	A1	1p vermilion		3,350.
10	A1	3p blue	2,500.	250.00
a.		3p deep blue	2,500.	300.00

Perf. 12

12	A1	3p blue	2,000.	175.00
a.		3p deep blue	2,000.	175.00

Victoria on Throne — A2

1852   **Engr.**   *Imperf.*

14	A2	2p reddish brn	400.00	45.00
a.		2p chestnut		175.00
b.		2p purple brown	575.00	30.00

No. 14 was reprinted on paper with watermark 70, imperf. & perf. 12½, overprinted "REPRINT."

1854   **Litho.**

15	A2	2p gray brown	450.00	45.00
a.		2p purple brown		37.50
16	A2	2p brown lilac	300.00	40.00
a.		2p red lilac		37.50
b.		As "a," "TVO" for "TWO"	10,000.	1,500.

Fifty varieties.

A3   A4

1854-58   **Typo.**

17	A3	6p yellow orange	375.00	32.50
a.		6p dull orange	375.00	32.50
b.		6p reddish brown	725.00	72.50

See Nos. 19-20, 22-24A, 26-28.

Lithographed

18	A4	1sh blue	1,100.	35.00
a.		1sh greenish blue	1,250.	35.00
b.		1sh indigo blue		180.00

See Nos. 21, 25.

Typographed

19	A3	2sh green	3,000.	250.00

1857-58   **Rouletted 7, 9½**
20   A3   6p orange   —   87.50
   a.   6p yellow orange   —   100.00
   b.   6p reddish brown   —   115.00

Lithographed
21   A4   1sh blue   —   160.00
   a.   1sh greenish blue   —   160.00

Typographed
22   A3   2sh green ('58)   7,000.   675.00

Small Serrate Perf. 19
23   A3   6p orange   —   125.00

Large Serpentine Perf. 10½
24   A3   6p orange   —   125.00

Serrate x Serpentine Perf.
24A   A3   6p orange   —   200.00

1859   **Litho.**   **Perf. 12**
25   A4   1sh blue   250.00   25.00
   a.   1sh greenish blue   275.00   27.50
   b.   1sh indigo blue   —   52.50

Typographed
26   A3   2sh green   525.00   70.00

1861   **Wmk. "SIX PENCE" (80)**
27   A3   6p black   300.00   80.00

Wmk. Single-lined "2" (50)
1864   **Perf. 12, 13**
28   A3   2sh blue, *green*   350.00   13.00

A5

Wmk. Large Star (6)
1856, Oct.   **Engr.**   **Imperf.**
29   A5   1p green   250.00   42.50

1858   **Rouletted 5½-6½**
30   A5   6p blue   350.00   28.00
   a.   6p light blue   450.00   45.00

Nos. 29 and 30 have been reprinted on paper watermarked V and Crown. They are imperforate and overprinted "REPRINT."

A6

1857-61   **Typo.**   **Imperf.**
Wove Paper
31   A6   1p yellow green   175.00   25.00
   a.   Printed on both sides   2,750.
   b.   1p deep green   230.00   47.50
32   A6   4p vermilion   450.00   15.00
   a.   Printed on both sides   2,750.
   b.   4p brownish vermilion   425.00   15.00
33   A6   4p rose   375.00   15.00
   a.   4p dull red   260.00   12.00

Rouletted 7 to 9½
34   A6   1p yellow green   625.00   140.00
35   A6   4p rose   —   57.50
   a.   4p vermilion   —   160.00
   b.   4p dull red   —   60.00
35A   A6   4p vermilion   —   575.00

Perf. 12
36   A6   1p yellow green   —   500.00

Unwmk.   **Imperf.**
37   A6   1p blue green   425.00   22.50
   a.   1p emerald green   22.50
38   A6   2p lilac   400.00   21.00
   a.   2p gray lilac   400.00   20.00
39   A6   4p rose   575.00   47.50
   a.   4p rose pink   575.00   42.50
   b.   4p reddish pink   47.50

Examples of No. 39 printed in dull carmine on thin paper are regarded as printer's waste and of little value. They are also found printed on both sides.

Rouletted 7 to 9½
40   A6   1p emerald green   575.00   37.50
   a.   1p pale emerald   525.00   35.00
41   A6   2p lilac   1,150.   725.00
42   A6   4p rose pink   400.00   11.50
   a.   Vert. pair, imperf. btwn.   750.00
   b.   4p reddish pink   20.00
   c.   4p bright rose   400.00   11.50

Perf. 12
43   A6   1p blue green   225.00   20.00
   a.   1p yellow green   325.00   24.00
   b.   Horiz. pair, imperf. btwn.

   c.   As "a," on thin, glazed "Bordeaux" paper   240.00
44   A6   2p lilac   450.00
   a.   2p gray lilac   400.00
45   A6   4p rose   300.00   8.00
   b.   Vert. pair, imperf. btwn.   —

Rouletted 5½-6½
45C   A6   4p dull rose   1,250.

Serrate Rouletted 19
45A   A6   2p lilac   1,100.   600.00

Laid Paper
Imperf
46   A6   4p rose   825.00   35.00

Rouletted 5 to 7
47   A6   2p violet   275.00   10.50
   a.   2p brown lilac   225.00   15.00
   b.   2p dark lilac   300.00   25.00
48   A6   4p rose   250.00   7.25
   a.   4p pale dull red, vertically laid paper   260.00   7.25
   b.   4p pale dull red, horizontally laid paper   1,250.
   c.   4p dull rose red   225.00   6.25

Serrate Rouletted 19
48D   A6   4p rose red   *825.00*

Perf. 12
49   A6   1p green   300.00   25.00
   a.   Laid lines close together   35.00
50   A6   4p rose   200.00   15.00
   a.   Laid lines close together   13.00

Wove Paper
1860   **Wmk. Value in Words (80)**
51   A6   1p pale yellowish green   130.00   10.50
   a.   Wmk. "FOUR PENCE" (error)   9,750.
   b.   1p yellow green   125.00   7.25
52   A6   2p gray lilac   200.00   10.00
   a.   2p brown lilac ('61)   —   52.50
   b.   2p bluish slate ('61)   200.00   9.50
   c.   2p slate gray ('62)   9.50
   d.   2p bluish gray ('63)   230.00   35.00

Wmk. "THREE PENCE" (80)
53   A6   2p bluish gray ('63)   225.00   25.00
   a.   2p gray lilac ('62)   325.00   22.50

Single-lined "2" (50)
54   A6   2p lilac   300.00   18.00
   a.   2p gray lilac   275.00   22.50
   b.   2p brown lilac   225.00   21.00
   c.   As "a," wmkd. single-lined "6"   7,750.
   d.   2p gray violet ('63)   220.00   20.00
   e.   2p slate ('63)   290.00   35.00

A7

1860   **Unwmk.**   **Laid Paper**
56   A7   3p deep blue   625.00   77.50

Wmk. Value in Words (80)
Perf. 11½ to 12
1860-64   **Wove Paper**
57   A7   3p blue ('63)   240.00   12.50
   a.   "TREE" instead of "THREE" in watermark   800.00
   b.   3p pale blue ('61)   240.00   45.00
   c.   3p bright blue ('61)   225.00   12.50
   d.   3p deep blue ('64)   230.00   10.00
58   A7   3p claret   180.00   37.50
   a.   Perf. 13   240.00   47.50
59   A7   4p rose   200.00   7.75
   a.   4p rose pink   12.50
   b.   4p rose red   170.00   7.00
   c.   4p rose carmine   12.50
60   A7   6p orange   5,750.   350.00
61   A7   6p black   250.00   10.50
   a.   6p gray black   275.00   9.25

Wmk. "FIVE SHILLINGS" (80)
62   A7   4p rose   3,000.   30.00

Wmk. Single-lined "4" (80a)
1863   **Imperf.**
63   A7   4p rose   —   175.00

Rouletted
64   A7   4p rose   3,250.   350.00

Perf. 11½ to 12
65   A7   4p rose   180.00   10.50

1863   **Unwmk.**   **Perf. 12**
66   A7   4p rose   625.00   30.00
   a.   4p rose pink, thin glazed "Bordeaux" paper   22.50
   b.   4p rose, thick coarse paper   600.00   22.50

A8   A9

1861-63   **Wmk. 80**   **Perf. 11½ to 12**
67   A8   1p green   140.00   17.00
   a.   1p olive green   16.00
68   A9   6p black   140.00   15.00
   a.   6p gray black   145.00   17.00
   b.   6p jet black   160.00   18.00

Wmk. Double-lined "1" (139)
69   A8   1p green   250.00   18.00
   a.   1p dull green   15.00
   b.   Horiz. pair, imperf between

Wmk. Single-lined Figures (50)
70   A8   1p green   115.00   11.50
   a.   1p apple green   115.00   11.50
   b.   1p olive green   100.00   17.00
71   A9   6p gray black   140.00   11.00
   a.   6p jet black   —   11.50
   b.   6p jet black, perf 13   170.00   11.50
   c.   6p gray black, perf 13   170.00   11.50

The 1p and 6p of 1861-63 are known on paper without watermark but were probably impressions on the margins of watermarked sheets.

A10   A11

A12   A13

Wmk. Single-lined Figures (50, 80a, 81)
1863-67   **Perf. 11½ to 13**
74   A10   1p green   120.00   8.50
   a.   Double impression   1,500.
75   A10   2p gray lilac   120.00   15.00
   a.   2p violet   115.00   11.50
76   A10   4p rose   140.00   5.00
   a.   Double impression   1,500.
77   A11   6p blue   115.00   4.25
78   A10   8p orange   700.00   115.00
79   A12   10p brn, *rose*   200.00   10.50
80   A13   1sh blue, *blue*   200.00   6.50
     Nos. 74-80 (7)   1,595.   164.75

See Nos. 81-82, 84-96, 99-101, 108-112, 115-119, 124-126, 144, 188. Compare type A11 with type A54.

A14

Wmk. Double-lined "1" (139)
81   A10   1p green   125.00   7.00
82   A10   2p gray lilac   325.00   10.50
83   A14   3p lilac   325.00   100.00
84   A11   6p blue   115.00   9.50
     Nos. 81-84 (4)   890.00   127.00

See Nos. 97, 113, 114, 155, 186. Compare type A14 with type A51.

Wmk. Double-lined "2" (49)
85   A11   6p blue   4,250.

Wmk. Single-lined "4" (80a)
86   A10   1p green   200.00   30.00
87   A10   2p gray lilac   250.00   10.50
88   A11   6p blue   2,750.

Wmk. Double-lined "4" (75)
89   A10   1p green   2,500.   160.00
90   A10   2p gray lilac   250.00   8.00
91   A10   4p rose   300.00   9.50
92   A11   6p blue   300.00   35.00

Wmk. Single-lined "6" (50)
93   A10   1p green   325.00   42.50
94   A10   2p gray lilac   350.00   11.50

Wmk. Single-lined "8" (50)
95   A10   1p green   300.00   27.50
96   A10   2p gray lilac   325.00   10.50
97   A14   3p lilac   250.00   57.50
99   A12   10p slate   1,000.   200.00

Wmk. "SIX PENCE" (80)
100   A10   1p green   1,150.   57.50
100A   A10   2p slate gray   *16,000.*
101   A11   6p blue   800.00   42.50
   a.   6p indigo blue   42.50

All values of the 1864-67 series except the 3p and 8p are known on unwatermarked paper. They are probably varieties from watermarked sheets which have been so placed on the printing press that some of the stamps escaped the watermark.

One example of the 2p gray lilac, type A10, is reported to exist with only "PENCE" of watermark 80 showing. Some believe this is part of the "SIX PENCE" watermark.

1870   **Wmk. "THREE PENCE" (80)**
108   A11   6p blue   475.00   17.50

Wmk. "FOUR PENCE" (80)
109   A11   6p blue   800.00   52.50

A15

1867-78   **Wmk. (70)**   **Perf. 11½ to 13**
110   A10   1p green   115.00   5.75
   a.   1p bright olive green   125.00   5.75
111   A10   2p lilac   110.00   5.25
   a.   2p gray lilac   125.00   9.50
112   A10   2p lilac, *lilac*   130.00   14.00
113   A14   3p red lilac   400.00   65.00
114   A14   3p lilac   475.00   72.50
   a.   3p orange   47.50   6.50
   b.   3p yellow   77.50   7.75
     3p org brn, glazed paper ('78)   52.50   17.00
115   A10   4p rose   130.00   11.50
   a.   4p dl rose, glazed paper ('79)   125.00   6.00
   b.   Wmk sideways   200.00
116   A11   6p blue   60.00   4.75
117   A11   6p ultra   72.50   5.00
   a.   6p light blue   130.00   17.50
   b.   6p light Prussian blue ('75)   145.00   4.75
118   A10   8p brn, *rose*   140.00   10.50
   a.   8p choc, *pink* ('78)   160.00   11.50
   b.   Perf. 13x12   460.00
119   A13   1sh bl, *blue*   325.00   17.50
120   A15   5sh bl, *yel*   3,250.   500.00
121   A15   5sh bl & rose   400.00   32.50
   a.   Without blue line under crown   375.00   30.00
   b.   5sh ind bl & car   425.00   42.50
122   A15   5sh ultra & rose   325.00   42.50

See Nos. 126, 144, 188. For surcharge see No. 124.

For additional stamps of type A15, see No. 191. Compare type A15 with type A58.

A16

1870   **Perf. 13**
123   A16   2p lilac   115.00   2.60
   a.   Perf. 12   125.00   3.50

No. 110 Surcharged in Red

1873, July 19   **Perf. 13, 12**
124   A10   ½p on 1p green   100.00   24.00
   a.   Perf. 12   125.00   24.00

No. 79 Surcharged in Blue

1871   **Wmk. Single-lined "10" (81)**
125   A12   9p on 10p brn, *rose*   650.00   25.00
   a.   Double surcharge   2,500.

A19

1873-78   **Typo.**
126 A10 8p brown, *rose* ('78)   175.00   10.50
127 A19 9p brown, *rose*   175.00   27.50

For additional stamps of type A19, see Nos. 128-129, 174-175. Compare type A19 with type A55.

1875   **Wmk. V and Crown (70)**
128 A19 9p brown, *rose*   200.00   27.50

No. 128 Surcharged in Blue

1876
129 A19 8p on 9p brn, *rose*   350.00   32.50

A21

A22

A23

A24

A25

1873-81   **Perf. 13, 12**
130 A21 ½p rose ('74)   24.00   2.00
  a. ½p pink, glazed paper ('80)   24.00   2.00
  b. ½p lil rose ('74)   27.50   2.90
131 A21 ½p rose, *rose* ('78)   70.00   42.50
132 A22 1p grn ('75)   52.50   3.25
  a. 1p yel grn, glazed paper   52.50   3.50
133 A22 1p grn, *gray* ('78)   240.00   110.00
134 A22 1p grn, *yel* ('78)   160.00   30.00
135 A23 2p violet   77.50   1.30
  a. 2p pale mv ('80)   77.50   1.25
  b. 2p pale mv, glazed paper ('79)   77.50   1.60
136 A23 2p vio, *grnsh* ('78)   325.00   40.00
137 A23 2p vio, *buff* ('78)   300.00   40.00
137A A23 2p vio, *lil* ('78)   —   1,200.
138 A24 1sh bl, *bl* ('76)   130.00   6.75
  a. 1sh brt bl, *bl*, glazed paper ('83)   145.00   12.00
139 A25 2sh bl, *grn* ('81)   240.00   35.00
  a. 2sh ultra, *grnsh*, glazed paper ('84)   45.00
  b. Wmk sideways   50.00

See Nos. 140, 156A-158, 184, 189-190. Compare design A21 with design A46, A24 with A56, A25 with A57.

1878   **Double-lined Outer Oval**
140 A23 2p violet   77.50   3.75
  b. Vert. pair, lower stamp imperf horiz.   3,000.

A26

A27

A28

1880-84   **Perf. 12½**
141 A26 1p green ('84)   140.00   22.50
142 A27 2p brown   50.00   1.40
143 A27 2p lilac   37.50   2.25
144 A10 4p car rose   260.00   15.00
  a. 4p lilac rose   125.00   11.50
145 A28 4p car rose ('81)   115.00   10.00
  a. 4p pink ('82)   115.00   9.50
    Nos. 141-145 (5)   602.50   51.15

See Nos. 156, 185, 187. Compare design A26 with design A47, A27 with A49, A28 with A52.

A29

A30

A31

A32

A33   A34

1884-86
146 A29 ½p rose   22.50   2.25
  a. ½p salmon ('85)   26.00   2.40
147 A30 1p green   29.00   2.40
  a. 1p pea green   35.00   3.25
148 A31 2p violet   32.50   1.25
  a. 2p lilac rose   32.50   1.25
149 A00 3p bister   20.00   2.40
  a. 3p ocher   20.00   2.40
150 A32 4p magenta   110.00   6.25
  a. 4p violet (error)   6,000.   1,250.
151 A30 6p bright blue ('85)   125.00   5.00
  a. 6p ultramarine ('85)   85.00   4.75
  b. 6p gray blue ('85)   82.50   4.75
152 A33 8p rose, *rose*   52.50   14.00
153 A34 1sh blue, *yel*   175.00   24.00
154 A33 2sh olive, *grn*   115.00   6.25
    Nos. 146-154 (9)   681.50   63.80

See Nos. 177-178, 192A. Compare designs A31-A32 with designs A37-A38.

Nos. 114, 145, 138-139 Ovptd. Vertically in Blue or Black

1885
155 A14 3p orange (Bl)   115.00   47.50
156 A28 4p car rose (Bl)   105.00   72.50
156A A24 1sh bl, *bl* (Bl)   3,500.
    Revenue cancel   1,250.
157 A24 1sh bl, *bl* (Bk)   175.00   37.50
158 A25 2sh bl, *grn* (Bk)   175.00   35.00
  a. Wmk sideways   100.00   25.00
    Nos. 155-156, 157-158 (4)   570.00   192.50

Reprints of 4p and 1sh have brighter colors than originals. They lack the overprint "REPRINT."

A45

1897
179 A45 1½p yellow green   6.00   6.50

See No. 182. Compare type A45 with type A48.

A35

A36

A37

A38

A39   A40

1886-87   **Perf. 12½**
159 A35 ½p lilac   37.50   9.50
160 A35 ½p rose   17.50   1.40
160A A35 ½p scarlet   7.75   1.40
161 A36 1p green   16.00   2.25
162 A37 2p violet   20.00   .55
  a. 2p red lilac   11.50   .70
  b. Imperf.   1,100.
163 A38 4p red   22.50   2.40
164 A39 6p blue   37.50   3.25
165 A39 6p ultra   32.50   1.10
166 A40 1sh lilac brown   37.50   3.75
    Nos. 159-166 (9)   228.75   25.60

See No. 180.

A41

1889
167 A41 1sh6p blue   260.00   140.00
168 A41 1sh6p orange   35.00   15.00

A42

Southern Cross — A43

Queen Victoria — A44

1890-95   **Perf. 12½**
169 A42 1p org brn   10.00   .75
  a. 1p chocolate brown   12.50   1.10
170 A42 1p yel brn   12.50   .55
171 A42 1p brn org, *pink* ('91)   10.50   4.50
172 A43 2½p brn red, *yel*   19.00   1.75
173 A44 5p choc ('91)   15.00   3.75
174 A19 9p green ('92)   45.00   16.00
175 A19 9p rose red   32.50   6.00
  a. 9p rose ('95)   37.50   11.50
176 A40 1sh deep claret   37.50   2.40
  a. 1sh red brown   32.50   1.40
  b. 1sh maroon   87.50   5.25
177 A33 2sh yel grn   37.50   17.50
178 A33 2sh emerald   35.00   19.00
    Nos. 169-178 (10)   254.50   72.20

In 1891 many stamps of the early issues were reprinted. They are on paper watermarked V and Crown, perforated 12, 12½, and overprinted "REPRINT."
See Nos. 181, 183, 192. Compare type A43 with type A50, A44 with A53.

1899
180 A35 ½p emerald   25.00   5.75
181 A42 1p brt rose   11.50   .55
182 A45 1½p red, *yel*   5.75   3.50
183 A43 2½p dark blue   15.00   15.00
    Nos. 180-183 (4)   57.25   24.80

1901
184 A21 ½p blue green   3.75   3.25
  a. "VICTCRIA"   110.00   62.50
185 A27 2p violet   14.00   3.00
186 A14 3p brown org   22.50   50.00
187 A28 4p bister   42.50   25.00
188 A11 6p emerald   17.50   13.00
189 A24 1sh orange yel   87.50   65.00
190 A25 2sh blue, *rose*   72.50   55.00
191 A15 5sh rose red & bl   90.00   72.50
    Nos. 184-191 (8)   350.25   286.75

1901
192 A42 1p olive green   11.50   7.50
192A A30 3p sage green   40.00   19.00

Nos. 192-192A were available for postal use until June 30, 1901, and thereafter restricted to revenue use.

A46

A47

A48   A49

A50   A51

A52

A53

A54   A55

A56

A57

A58

1901   **Perf. 11, 12½ and Compound**
193 A46 ½p blue green   5.75   1.40
194 A47 1p rose red   4.50   .65
  a. 1p rose   14.00   1.00
  b. Wmk sideways   10.00   5.00
195 A48 1½p red, *yellow*   3.75   1.25
  a. Perf. 11   110.00   110.00
196 A49 2p violet   21.00   1.10
197 A50 2½p blue   15.00   1.10
198 A51 3p brown org   15.00   2.50
  a. Wmk sideways   20.00   8.00
199 A52 4p bister   10.50   1.25
200 A53 5p chocolate   17.50   1.10

201	A54	6p emerald	21.00	2.40
202	A55	9p rose	26.00	4.00
a.		Wmk sideways	30.00	10.00
203	A56	1sh org yel	29.00	5.00
204	A57	2sh blue, *rose*	40.00	5.00
205	A58	5sh rose red & bl	110.00	35.00
a.		5sh carmine & blue	110.00	26.00
		Nos. 193-205 (13)	319.00	61.75

See Nos. 209-229, 232.

King Edward VII
A59   A60

1901-05

206	A59	£1 deep rose	350.00	150.00
a.		Perf. 11 ('05)	475.00	225.00
208	A60	£2 dk blue ('02)	700.00	450.00
a.		Perf. 11 ('05)	2,250.	1,400.

See Nos. 230-231.

1903   **Redrawn**

209	A56	1sh yellow	35.00	5.75
a.		1sh orange	32.50	4.75

No. 209 has the network lighter than No. 203. In the latter the "P" and "E" of "POST-AGE" are in a position more nearly horizontal than on No. 209.

Perf. 11, 12x12½, 12½, 12½x11

1905-10   **Wmk. 13**

218	A46	½p blue green	4.75	.75
219	A47	1p rose red	2.40	.35
a.		1p carmine rose	15.00	3.00
b.		Wmk sideways	10.00	5.00
220	A49	2p violet	9.25	.75
a.		2p purple	10.00	.90
221	A50	2½p blue	5.75	1.00
222	A51	3p brown org	15.00	3.00
a.		3p dull yellow	17.50	3.00
223	A52	4p bister	12.50	1.75
224	A53	5p chocolate	12.50	4.75
225	A54	6p emerald	24.00	2.00
226	A55	9p orange brown	24.00	5.00
a.		9p brown rose	26.00	5.25
227	A55	9p car rose	17.50	3.00
228	A56	1sh yellow ('08)	24.00	4.50
229	A58	5sh orange red & ultra	130.00	26.00
a.		5sh rose red & ultra	140.00	32.50
230	A59	£1 pale red ('07)	450.00	240.00
a.		£1 rose ('10)	350.00	240.00
231	A60	£2 dull blue	1,150.	725.00
		Nos. 218-229 (12)	281.65	52.85

No. 220 Surcharged in Red

1912, July 1

232	A49	1p on 2p violet	1.75	1.25

POSTAL-FISCAL STAMPS

On Jan. 1, 1884, all postage and fiscal stamps were made available for either purpose. Fiscal stamps became invalid after June 30, 1901.

Used values are for examples with postal cancellations used from Jan. 1, 1884 through June 30, 1901.

Beware of stamps with a pen cancellation removed, often regummed or with a fake postmark added.

Stamps inscribed "Stamp Duty" that were issued primarily in postal rates in the normal postage stamp size are listed in the postage section (Nos. 146-178, 180-183, 192-192A). The stamps meeting primarily fiscal stamp rates and in the larger fiscal stamp size, are listed here in the Postal-Fiscal section.

Stamps Inscribed "Stamp Statute"

Victoria — PF1

PF1a (AR3)

PF1b (AR5)   PF1c (AR6)

Coat of Arms — PF2

PF3

Wmk. V and Crown (70)

1870-83   **Typo.**   ***Perf. 13***

AR1	PF1a	1p green	90.00	75.00
		Revenue cancel		7.25
a.		Perf. 12½	140.00	120.00
AR2	PF1	3p lilac	1,150.	600.00
		Revenue cancel		140.00
AR3	PF1a	4p red	1,000.	500.00
		Revenue cancel		125.00
AR4	PF1a	6p blue	125.00	45.00
		Revenue cancel		14.00
a.		Perf. 12	140.00	35.00
		Revenue cancel		10.50
AR5	PF1b	1sh blue, *blue*	140.00	45.00
		Revenue cancel		14.00
a.		Perf. 12	140.00	50.00
		Revenue cancel		17.50
b.		Perf. 12½	140.00	45.00
		Revenue cancel		14.00
c.		Wmk. 50, perf. 13	140.00	32.50
		Revenue cancel		11.50
d.		Wmk. 50, perf. 12	160.00	37.50
		Revenue cancel		13.00
AR6	PF1c	2sh blue, *grn*	225.00	130.00
		Revenue cancel		30.00
a.		Perf. 12	225.00	35.00
		Revenue cancel		35.00
b.		Wmk. 50, perf. 13	300.00	125.00
		Revenue cancel		17.50
c.		Wmk. 50, perf. 12	325.00	125.00
		Revenue cancel		21.00
AR7	PF2	2sh6p org, *yel*	650.00	260.00
		Revenue cancel		72.50
a.		Perf. 12	650.00	260.00
		Revenue cancel		72.50
b.		Perf. 12½	—	300.00
		Revenue cancel		87.50

AR8	PF1a	5sh blue, *yel*	600.00	140.00
		Revenue cancel		72.50
a.		Perf. 12	650.00	—
b.		Perf. 12½	650.00	140.00
		Revenue cancel		72.50
AR9	PF1a	10sh brn, *rose*	1,600.	375.00
		Revenue cancel		90.00
a.		Perf. 12		—
b.		Wmk. 50, perf. 13	1,600.	350.00
		Revenue cancel		75.00
c.		Wmk. 50, perf. 12		
AR10	PF1a	£1 lil, *yel*	1,250.	350.00
		Revenue cancel		90.00
a.		Perf. 12	1,150.	325.00
		Revenue cancel		90.00
b.		Perf. 12½	1,150.	325.00
		Revenue cancel		90.00
AR11	PF3	£5 blk, *grn*	10,000.	1,900.
		Revenue cancel		135.00
a.		Perf. 12		—
b.		Perf. 12½	10,000.	1,900.
		Revenue cancel		150.00

Nos. AR1-AR12 distributed for postal use from Jan. 1, 1884 through Apr. 23, 1884.

No. AR1 Surcharged "½d/HALF"

1879-96

AR12	PF1	½p on 1p grn	120.00	105.00
		Revenue cancel		42.50

Stamps Inscribed "Stamp Duty"

PF4   PF5   PF16   PF17

PF6   PF7   PF18   PF19

PF8   PF9   PF20   PF21

PF10   PF11   PF22

PF12   PF13   PF23

PF24

PF14   PF15   PF25

PF26

PF27

PF28

Wmk. V and Crown (70)

1879-96		**Litho.**		**Perf. 13**	
AR13	PF4	1p green	140.00	45.00	
		Revenue cancel		14.00	
a.		Perf. 12	140.00	45.00	
		Revenue cancel		14.00	
b.		Perf. 12½	—	—	
AR14	PF8	1sh 6p pink	375.00	50.00	
		Revenue cancel		21.00	
a.		Perf. 12	—	65.00	
		Revenue cancel		26.00	
b.		Perf. 12½	—	—	
AR15	PF11	3sh vio, blue	675.00	65.00	
		Revenue cancel		21.00	
a.		Perf. 12	1,000.	100.00	
		Revenue cancel		21.00	
b.		Perf. 12½	—	—	
AR16	PF12	4sh orange	175.00	35.00	
		Revenue cancel		11.00	
a.		Perf. 12	175.00	35.00	
		Revenue cancel		11.00	
b.		Perf. 12½	—	—	
AR17	PF14	6sh green	575.00	70.00	
		Revenue cancel		12.50	
a.		Perf. 12½	—	—	
AR18	PF15	10sh brn, pink	925.00	175.00	
		Revenue cancel		62.50	
a.		Perf. 12	—	—	
b.		Perf. 12½	—	—	
AR19	PF16	15sh lilac	1,750.	325.00	
		Revenue cancel		125.00	
AR20	PF17	£1 orange	800.00	110.00	
		Revenue cancel		25.00	
a.		Perf. 12	800.00	110.00	
AR21	PF18	£1 5sh pink	2,400.	450.00	
		Revenue cancel		125.00	
AR22	PF19	£1 10sh olive	2,750.	275.00	
		Revenue cancel		75.00	
AR23	PF20	35sh lilac	10,000.		
		Revenue cancel		350.00	
AR24	PF21	£2 blue	—	240.00	
		Revenue cancel		37.50	
AR25	PF22	45sh violet	5,000.	425.00	
		Revenue cancel		92.50	
AR26	PF23	£5 rose	9,000.	1,000.	
		Revenue cancel		125.00	
AR27	PF24	£6 blue, pink	—	1,500.	
		Revenue cancel		175.00	
AR28	PF25	£7 vio, blue	—	1,500.	
		Revenue cancel		175.00	
AR29	PF26	£8 scar, yel	—	1,700.	
		Revenue cancel		200.00	
AR30	PF27	£9 grn, grn	—	1,700.	
		Revenue cancel		200.00	
		Typo.			
AR31	PF4	1p green	105.00	45.00	
		Revenue cancel		8.75	
a.		Perf. 12	105.00	45.00	
		Revenue cancel		8.75	
b.		Perf. 12½	—	—	
AR32	PF5	1p brown	40.00	7.75	
		Revenue cancel		1.40	
a.		Perf. 12	40.00	9.25	

		Revenue cancel		1.40	
b.		Perf. 12½	—		
AR33	PF6	6p blue	140.00	22.50	
		Revenue cancel		5.75	
a.		Perf. 12	140.00	37.50	
		Revenue cancel		5.75	
b.		Perf. 12½	—		
AR34	PF7	1sh blue, blue	140.00	11.50	
		Revenue cancel		5.75	
a.		Perf. 12	140.00	14.00	
		Revenue cancel		5.75	
b.		Perf. 12½	140.00	13.00	
		Revenue cancel		5.75	
AR35	PF7	1sh blue, yel, perf 12½	200.00	45.00	
		Revenue cancel		17.50	
AR36	PF8	1sh 6p pink	260.00	50.00	
		Revenue cancel		17.50	
AR37	PF9	2sh blue, grn	325.00	45.00	
		Revenue cancel		13.00	
a.		Perf. 12	—	50.00	
		Revenue cancel		13.00	
b.		Perf. 12½	350.00	52.50	
		Revenue cancel		13.00	
AR38	PF10	2sh 6p org, perf 12½	175.00	37.50	
a.		2sh6p yellow ('85)	115.00	17.50	
b.		2sh6p lemon yellow ('92)	115.00	18.00	
		Revenue cancel		5.75	
AR39	PF11	3sh maroon, bl, perf 12½	700.00	65.00	
		Revenue cancel		14.00	
AR40	PF11	3sh bister	125.00	29.00	
		Revenue cancel		21.00	
AR41	PF12	4sh org, perf 12½	140.00	26.00	
		Revenue cancel		7.25	
AR42	PF13	5sh claret, yel	110.00	11.50	
		Revenue cancel		5.75	
a.		Perf. 12	125.00	22.50	
		Revenue cancel		5.75	
b.		Perf. 12½	100.00	22.50	
		Revenue cancel		5.75	
AR43	PF13	5sh car rose	140.00	35.00	
		Revenue cancel		7.25	
AR44	PF14	6sh green	200.00	85.00	
		Revenue cancel		16.00	
AR45	PF15	10sh brn, pink	—	175.00	
		Revenue cancel		57.50	
a.		Perf. 12	—	—	
b.		Perf. 12½	—	—	
AR46	PF15	10sh green	325.00	65.00	
		Revenue cancel		20.00	
AR47	PF16	15sh brown	1,200.	145.00	
		Revenue cancel		42.50	
AR48	PF17	£1 org, yel, perf 12½	875.00	80.00	
		Revenue cancel		28.00	
a.		Perf. 12	1,100.	95.00	
		Revenue cancel		30.00	
AR49	PF18	£1 5sh pink	2,250.	160.00	
		Revenue cancel		75.00	
AR50	PF19	£1 10sh olive	1,750.	135.00	
		Revenue cancel		50.00	
AR51	PF21	£2 blue	1,350.	125.00	
		Revenue cancel		27.50	
a.		Perf. 12	—	200.00	
		Revenue cancel		27.50	
AR52	PF22	45sh gray lil	5,000.	180.00	
		Revenue cancel		62.50	
AR53	PF23	£5 rose, perf. 12	—	900.00	
		Revenue cancel		105.00	
a.		perf. 12½	—	1,100.	
		Revenue cancel		150.00	
AR54	PF28	£10 lilac	5,500.	210.00	
		Revenue cancel		62.50	
a.		Perf. 12	5,500.	325.00	
		Revenue cancel		62.50	

Nos. AR49-AR52, AR54, used, are valued cto.

PF29

PF30

PF31

Wmk. V and Crown (70)

1879-1900		**Engr.**		**Perf. 12½**	
AR55	PF29	£25 green	75,000.	900.00	
		Revenue cancel		110.00	
a.		Perf. 13		—	
b.		Perf. 12		—	
AR56	PF30	£50 violet	75,000.	975.00	
		Revenue cancel		125.00	
a.		Perf. 13		—	
AR57	PF31	£100 red	147,500.	1,000.	
		Revenue cancel		225.00	
a.		Perf. 13		—	
b.		Perf. 12		225.00	
		Typo.			
AR58	PF29	£25 green	—	325.00	
a.		Lithographed		100.00	
		Revenue cancel			
AR59	PF30	£50 violet	—	500.00	
a.		Lithographed		140.00	
		Revenue cancel			
AR60	PF31	£100 red	—	650.00	
a.		Lithographed		225.00	
		Revenue cancel			

Nos. AR55-AR60, used, are valued cto.

PF32

(continuation)

1887-90				**Typo.**	
AR61	PF32	£5 cl & ultra	4,000.	175.00	
		Revenue cancel		82.50	
AR62	PF32	£6 blue & yel	5,000.	200.00	
		Revenue cancel		90.00	
AR63	PF32	£7 blk & red	5,500.	225.00	
		Revenue cancel		110.00	
AR64	PF32	£8 org & lil	6,000.	250.00	
		Revenue cancel		110.00	
AR65	PF32	£9 red & green	6,500.	275.00	
		Revenue cancel		135.00	

Nos. AR61-AR65, used, are valued cto.

SEMI-POSTAL STAMPS

SP1

Queen Victoria and Figure of Charity SP2

Wmk. V and Crown (70)

1897, Oct.		**Typo.**		**Perf. 12½**	
B1	SP1	1p deep blue	27.50	27.50	
B2	SP2	2½p red brown	140.00	110.00	

These stamps were sold at 1sh and 2sh6p respectively. The premium was given to a charitable institution.

Victoria Cross — SP3

Scout Reporting SP4

1900

B3	SP3	1p brown olive	125.00	75.00
B4	SP4	2p emerald	225.00	225.00

These stamps were sold at 1sh and 2sh respectively. The premium was given to a patriotic fund in connection with the South African War.

REGISTRATION STAMPS

R1

Unwmk.

1854, Dec. 1		**Typo.**		**Imperf.**
F1	R1	1sh rose & blue	2,500.	225.00

1857

				Rouletted 7
F2	R1	1sh rose & blue	8,750.	425.00

LATE FEE STAMP

LF1

Unwmk.

1855, Jan. 1		**Typo.**		**Imperf.**
I1	LF1	6p lilac & green	1,900.	275.00

POSTAGE DUE STAMPS

D1

Wmk. V and Crown (70)

1890		**Typo.**		**Perf. 12½**
J1	D1	½p claret & blue	8.00	7.00
J2	D1	1p claret & blue	11.50	2.60
J3	D1	2p claret & blue	18.00	3.25
J4	D1	4p claret & blue	27.50	4.75
J5	D1	5p claret & blue	26.00	3.50
J6	D1	6p claret & blue	27.50	6.50
J7	D1	10p claret & blue	140.00	90.00
J8	D1	1sh claret & blue	90.00	14.00
J9	D1	2sh claret & blue	200.00	92.50
J10	D1	5sh claret & blue	300.00	140.00
		Nos. J1-J10 (10)	848.50	364.10

1891-94

J11	D1	½p lake & blue	5.50	7.75
J12	D1	1p brn red & blue ('93)	15.00	2.75
J13	D1	2p brn red & blue ('93)	26.00	2.00
J14	D1	4p lake & blue ('94)	22.50	11.50
		Nos. J11-J14 (4)	69.00	24.00

1894-96

J15	D1	½p bl grn & rose	9.50	3.00
J16	D1	1p bl grn & rose	9.00	3.00
J17	D1	2p bl grn & rose	18.00	3.50
J18	D1	4p bl grn & rose	18.00	3.00
J19	D1	5p bl grn & rose	22.50	22.50
J20	D1	6p bl grn & rose	20.00	14.00
J21	D1	10p bl grn & rose	45.00	20.00
J22	D1	1sh bl grn & rose	32.50	6.00
J23	D1	2sh yel grn & rose	115.00	37.50
J24	D1	5sh yel grn & rose	200.00	75.00
		Nos. J15-J24 (10)	489.50	187.50

1897-99

J15a	D1	½p yel grn & pale scar	9.00	1.75
J16a	D1	1p yel grn & pale scar	10.00	1.25
J17a	D1	2p yel grn & pale scar	13.50	1.25
J18a	D1	4p yel grn & pale scar	27.50	2.25
J19a	D1	5p yel grn & pale scar	27.50	7.00
J20a	D1	6p yel grn & pale scar	12.00	4.50
		Nos. J15a-J20a (6)	99.50	18.00

1905-09   Wmk. 13

J25	D1	½p yel grn & rose	10.00	13.00
a.		½p pale green & pink	24.00	22.50
J26	D1	1p yel grn & rose	12.00	4.50
a.		1p pale green & pink	92.50	11.50
J27	D1	2p yel grn & rose	29.00	5.25
J28	D1	4p yel grn & rose	35.00	21.00
		Nos. J25-J28 (4)	86.00	43.75

A 5p with wmk. 13 exists but was not issued.

WESTERN AUSTRALIA

ˈwes-tərn ȯ-ˈstrāl-yə

LOCATION — Western part of Australia, occupying about a third of that continent
GOVT. — British Colony
AREA — 975,920 sq. mi.
POP. — 184,124 (1901)
CAPITAL — Perth

Western Australia was one of the six British colonies that united on January 1, 1901, to form the Commonwealth of Australia.

12 Pence = 1 Shilling
20 Shillings = 1 Pound

Unused values for Nos. 1-10 are for stamps without gum as these stamps are seldom found with original gum. Otherwise, unused values are for stamps with original gum as defined in the catalogue introduction.

Very fine examples of all rouletted and perforated stamps from Nos. 6-34 have roulettes or perforations touching the design. Examples clear on all four sides range from scarce to rare and will command higher prices.

Watermarks

Wmk. 82 — Swan

Wmk. 83 — Crown and W A

Wmk. 70 — V and Crown

Wmk. 13 — Crown & Double-lined A

Wmk. 74 — Crown and Single-lined A

Swan

A1   A2

1854-57   Engr.   Wmk. 82   Imperf.

1	A1	1p black	1,350.	275.

Litho.

2	A2	2p brown, red ('57)	4,000.	800.
a.		2p brown, deep red ('57)	4,250.	1,100.
b.		Printed on both sides	4,250.	950.

See Nos. 4, 6-7, 9, 14-39, 44-52, 54, 59-61. For surcharges see Nos. 41, 55-56.

A3   A4

3	A3	4p blue	450.	275.
a.		Frame inverted		300.000.
		As "a," cut to shape		27.500.
b.		4p slate blue	3,750.	1,350.
4	A2	6p bronze ('57)	6,000.	900.
5	A4	1sh pale brown	550.	400.
a.		1sh dark brown	700.	450.
b.		1sh dark red brown	2,250.	1,000.
c.		1sh pale red brown	26,500.	4,000.

Engraved
Rouletted

6	A1	1p black	3,200.	750.

Lithographed

7	A2	2p brn, red ('57)	9,500.	1,900.
a.		Printed on both sides		2,300.
8	A3	4p blue	—	675.
9	A2	6p bronze ('57)	12,500.	2,000.
10	A4	1sh brown	5,000.	1,000.

The 1p, 2p, 4p and 6p are known with pin-perforation but this is believed to be unofficial. No. 7a is only recorded used and with pin perforations.

1860   Engr.   Imperf.

14	A1	2p vermilion	140.00	130.00
a.		2p pale orange	140.00	130.00
15	A1	4p blue	325.	2,000.
16	A1	6p dull green	2,900.	875.00

Rouletted

17	A1	2p vermilion	800.00	250.00
a.		2p pale orange	650.00	250.00
18	A1	4p deep blue	5,000.	—
19	A1	6p dull green	4,500.	750.00

1861   Clean-Cut Perf. 14 to 16

20	A1	1p rose	700.00	200.00
a.		Imperf.		
21	A1	2p blue	140.00	45.00
a.		Imperf., pair		
b.		Horiz. pair, imperf. vert.		
22	A1	4p vermilion	1,550.	2,400.
a.		Imperf.		
23	A1	6p purple brn	525.00	92.50
a.		Imperf.		

24	A1	1sh green	875.00	140.00
a.		Imperf.		

Rough Perf. 14 to 16

24B	A1	1p rose	300.00	65.00
24C	A1	6p pur brn, bluish	3,500.	525.00
24D	A1	1sh deep green	3,500.	425.00

Perf. 14

25	A1	1p rose	400.00	110.00
25A	A1	2p blue	180.00	72.50
25B	A1	4p vermilion	450.00	300.00

Unwmk.   Perf. 13

26	A1	1p lake	115.00	7.75
28	A1	6p violet	240.00	77.50

1865-79   Wmk. 1   Perf. 12½

29	A1	1p bister	110.00	10.00
30	A1	1p yel ocher	130.00	15.00
31	A1	2p yellow	125.00	4.75
a.		2p lilac (error) ('79)	20,000.	17,500.
b.		2p chrome yellow	160.00	11.00
32	A1	4p carmine	120.00	8.75
a.		Double impression	42,500.	
33	A1	6p violet	160.00	11.50
a.		6p lilac	300.00	11.50
b.		6p red lilac	300.00	11.50
c.		Double impression		27,500.
34	A1	1sh brt grn	200.00	21.00
		Handstamped "SPECIMEN"	175.00	
a.		1sh sage green	525.00	45.00
		Nos. 29-34 (6)	845.00	71.00

An unused example of No. 31a realized the equivalent of U.S. $12,330 at an Australian auction in 2005.
A used example of No. 31a realized the equivalent of U.S. $16,180 at an Australian auction in 2005.
An unused example of No. 32a, with short perforations, realized the equivalent of U.S. $38,530 at an Australian auction in 2005.
A used example of No. 33c realized the equivalent of U.S. $27,740 at an Australian auction in 2005.

1872-78   Perf. 14

35	A1	1p bister	180.00	7.25
36	A1	1p yellow ocher	115.00	5.00
37	A1	2p yellow	115.00	2.40
38	A1	4p carmine	750.00	140.00
39	A1	6p lilac	200.00	6.50
		Nos. 35-39 (5)	1,360.	161.15

A5

1872   Typo.

40	A5	3p red brown	72.50	7.25
a.		3p brown	72.50	8.50
		Handstamped "SPECIMEN"	140.00	

See Nos. 53, 92. For surcharges see Nos. 57, 69-72A.

No. 31 Surcharged in Green

1875   Engr.   Perf. 12½

41	A1	1p on 2p yellow	625.00	80.00
a.		Pair, one without surcharge		
b.		"O" of "ONE" omitted		
c.		Triple surcharge		5,500.

Forged surcharges exist.

1882   Wmk. 2   Perf. 12

44	A1	1p ocher yellow	125.00	8.00
46	A1	2p yellow	160.00	7.75
47	A1	4p carmine	300.00	60.00
48	A1	6p pale violet	575.00	60.00
		Nos. 44-48 (4)	1,160.	135.75

1882   Perf. 14

49	A1	1p ocher yellow	45.00	3.00
50	A1	2p yellow	50.00	4.50
51	A1	4p carmine	180.00	17.50
52	A1	6p pale violet	140.00	5.25
a.		6p violet	140.00	6.50

Handstamped "SPECIMEN"   160.00

Typographed

53	A5	3p red brown	14.00	4.50
a.		3p brown	29.00	4.50
		Nos. 49-53 (5)	429.00	33.25

1883   Engr.   Perf. 12x14

54	A1	1p ocher yellow	4,000.	300.00

Nos. 44 and 49 Surcharged in Red

1884   Perf. 12

55	A1	½p on 1p ocher yel	18.00	32.50

Perf. 14

56	A1	½p on 1p ocher yel	30.00	40.00
a.		Thin fraction bar	97.50	115.00

No. 40 Surcharged in Green

1885   Typo.   Wmk. 1

57	A5	1p on 3p red brown	87.50	26.00
a.		1p on 3p brown	115.00	27.50
b.		"1" with straight top	240.00	75.00
c.		As "a," "1" with straight top	275.00	75.00

A8

Wmk. Crown and C A (2)
1885   Typo.   Perf. 14

58	A8	½p green	7.25	1.25

See No. 89.

1888   Engr.

59	A1	1p rose	35.00	5.75
60	A1	2p slate	90.00	2.75
61	A1	4p red brown	130.00	37.50
		Nos. 59-61 (3)	255.00	46.00

A9

A10

A11

A12

1890-93   Typo.

62	A9	1p carmine rose	35.00	2.00
63	A10	2p slate	37.50	3.00
64	A11	2½p blue	20.00	3.25
65	A12	4p orange brown	14.00	2.75
66	A12	5p bister	15.00	5.00
67	A12	6p violet	21.00	6.50
68	A12	1sh olive green	26.00	7.50
		Nos. 62-68 (7)	168.50	30.00

See Nos. 73-74, 76, 80, 90, 94.

Nos. 40 and 53a Surcharged in Green

1893   Wmk. Crown and C C (1)

69	A5	1p on 3p red brown	16.00	7.75
a.		1p on 3p brown	16.00	7.50
b.		Double surcharge	1,600.	

Wmkd. Crown and C A (2)

70	A5	1p on 3p brown	77.50	10.50

Nos. 40a and 53a
Surcharged in Green

1895   **Wmk. Crown and C C (1)**
71	A5	½p on 3p brown	13.00	35.00
a.	Double surcharge		1,250.	

No. 72 Surcharged in
Green and Red

72	A5	½p on 3p brown	140.00	350.00

Wmk. Crown and C A (2)
72A	A5	½p on 3p brown	100.00	225.00

After the supply of paper watermarked Crown and C C was exhausted, No. 72A was printed. Ostensibly this was to provide samples for Postal Union distribution, but a supply for philatelic demands was also made.

Types of 1890-93 and

A15

1899-1901   **Typo.**   **Wmk. 83**
73	A9	1p carmine rose	7.75	1.75
74	A10	2p yellow	29.00	3.50
75	A15	2½p blue ('01)	14.00	4.75
	Nos. 73-75 (3)		50.75	10.00

A16   A17

A18   A19

A20   A21

A22   Southern Cross — A23

Queen Victoria
A24   A25

Perf. 12½, 12x12½
1902-05   **Wmk. 70**
76	A9	1p car rose	22.00	1.00
a.	1p salmon		—	
b.	Perf. 11		400.00	35.00
c.	Perf. 12½x11		1,200.	675.00
77	A16	2p yellow	22.50	4.75
a.	Perf. 11		400.00	57.50
b.	Perf. 12½x11		1,750.	1,100.
79	A17	4p org brn	29.00	4.00
a.	Perf. 11		1,400.	450.00

80	A12	5p ol bis, perf 12½ ('05)	175.00	115.00
a.	Perf. 11		90.00	100.00
81	A18	8p pale yel grn	30.00	4.75
82	A19	9p orange	50.00	17.50
b.	Perf. 11		175.00	185.00
83	A20	10p red	57.50	13.00
84	A21	2sh org red, yel ('06)	115.00	32.50
a.	Perf. 11		500.00	225.00
b.	2sh orange brown, yel ('11)		77.50	19.00
c.	2sh bright red, yel		130.00	19.00
d.	As "c," perf. 11		350.00	200.00
85	A22	2sh6p dk bl, rose	77.50	14.00
86	A23	5sh blue green	125.00	45.00
87	A24	10sh violet	300.00	130.00
a.	10sh bright purple		725.00	400.00
88	A25	£1 brown org	450.00	225.00
a.	£1 orange		750.00	425.00
	Nos. 76-88 (12)		1,454.	606.50

Perf. 12½, 12x12½
1905-12   **Wmk. 13**
89	A8	½p dp grn ('10)	8.00	9.25
a.	Perf 11		2,750.	
90	A9	1p rose	18.00	1.75
e.	Perf. 11		55.00	21.00
f.	Perf. 12½x11		1,100.	475.00
91	A16	2p yellow	11.50	3.25
a.	Perf. 11		65.00	32.50
b.	Perf. 12½x11		925.00	525.00
92	A5	3p brown	37.50	4.75
a.	Perf. 11		29.00	9.50
b.	Perf. 12½x11		—	1,200.
93	A17	4p orange brn	35.00	12.00
a.	4p bister brown		37.50	13.00
b.	Perf. 11		1,100.	290.00
94	A12	5p olive bis	29.00	15.00
a.	Perf. 11, pale olive bister		52.50	18.00
b.	Perf. 11, olive green		32.50	24.00
95	A18	8p pale yel grn ('12)	32.50	82.50
96	A19	9p orange	45.00	8.75
b.	Perf. 11		200.00	240.00
97	A20	10p red orange	37.50	35.00
98	A23	5s blue green	240.00	180.00
	Nos. 89-98 (10)		494.00	352.25

For surcharge see No. 103.

A26   A27

1906-07   **Wmk. 83**   **Perf. 14**
99	A26	6p bright violet	40.00	3.25
100	A27	1sh olive green	50.00	6.50

1912   **Wmk. 74**   **Perf. 11¼x12**
101	A26	6p bright violet	21.00	19.00
102	A27	1sh gray green	45.00	29.00
a.	Perf. 12½			2,750.

No. 91 Surcharged

1912   **Wmk. 13**   **Perf. 12½**
103	A16	1p on 2p yellow	2.00	2.50
a.	Perf compound 12½x11		750.00	500.00

Stamps of Western Australia were replaced by those of Australia.

POSTAL-FISCAL STAMPS

Postal use of the 1p telegraph stamp was authorized beginning Oct. 25, 1886.

Used values are for examples with postal cancellations.

Beware of stamps with a pen cancellation removed and a fake postmark added.

PF1

1886		**Wmk. 1**	**Perf. 14**	
AR1	PF1	1p bister	65.00	9.25
		Perf. 12½		
AR2	PF1	1p bister	65.00	7.75

Authorized for postal use by the Post and Telegraph Act of Sept. 5, 1893 were the current revenue stamps through the 1sh value.

Beware of stamps with a pen cancellation removed and a fake postmark added.

Because the Act specified current stamps, postally used examples from the provisional issue of of 1881 are not included here.

PF2

1882		**Wmk. 2**	**Perf. 14**	
AR3	PF2	1p purple	26.00	4.00
AR4	PF2	2p purple	260.00	100.00
AR5	PF2	3p purple	90.00	5.75
AR6	PF2	6p purple	105.00	7.75
AR7	PF2	1sh purple	180.00	15.00

The 6p is known postally used but was not authorized.

		Wmk. 83		
AR8	PF2	1p purple	22.50	4.50
AR9	PF2	3p purple	85.00	5.75
AR10	PF2	6p purple	85.00	6.00
AR11	PF2	1sh purple	180.00	22.50

Nos. AR7, AR11 have a rectangular outer frame and a circular frame around the swan. Higher values are known with postal cancels, some postally used, but these were not authorized.

AUSTRALIA

o-ˈstrāl-yə

LOCATION — Oceania, south of Indonesia, bounded on the west by the Indian Ocean
GOVT. — Self-governing dominion of the British Commonwealth
AREA — 2,967,909 sq. mi.
POP. — 17,892,423 (1996)
CAPITAL — Canberra

Australia includes the former British colonies of New South Wales, Victoria, Queensland, South Australia, Western Australia and Tasmania.

12 Pence = 1 Shilling
20 Shillings = 1 Pound
100 Cents = 1 Dollar (1966)

Catalogue values for unused stamps in this country are for Never Hinged items, beginning with Scott 197 in the regular postage section, Scott B1 in the semipostal section, Scott C6 in the air post section, Scott J71 in the postage due section, and all of the Australian Antarctic Territory.

Watermarks

Wmk. 8 — Wide Crown and Wide A

Wmk. 9 — Wide Crown and Narrow A

Wmk. 10 — Narrow Crown and Narrow A

Wmk. 11 — Multiple Crown and A

Wmk. 12 — Crown and Single-lined A   Wmk. 13 — Large Crown and Double-lined A

Wmk. 55 — Large Crown and NSW

Wmk. 203 — Small Crown and A Multiple

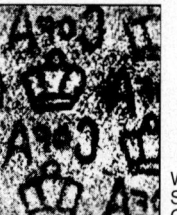

Wmk. 228 — Small Crown and C of A Multiple

Kangaroo and Map — A1

Die I — The inside frameline has a break at left, even with the top of the letters of the denomination.
Die II — The frameline does not show a break (repaired die).
Die III — The left inside frameline shows a break opposite the face of the kangaroo.
Die IV — As Die III, with a break in the top outside frameline above the "ST" of "AUSTRA-LIA." The upper right inside frameline has an incomplete corner.

Dies are only indicated when there are more than one for any denomination.

1913 Typo. Wmk. 8 Perf. 11½, 12

1	A1	½p green	11.50	7.50
		Never hinged	17.00	
2	A1	1p car (I)	17.50	1.75
		Never hinged	24.00	
h.		1p carmine (III)	24.00	2.25
		Never hinged	40.00	
3	A1	2p gray	70.00	10.00
		Never hinged	140.00	
4	A1	2½p dark blue	70.00	25.00
		Never hinged	140.00	
5	A1	3p ol bis, die I	140.00	17.50
		Never hinged	280.00	
a.		Die II	450.00	85.00
		Never hinged	725.00	
6	A1	4p orange	150.00	40.00
		Never hinged	300.00	
7	A1	5p org brn	135.00	50.00
		Never hinged	270.00	
8	A1	6p ultra (II)	125.00	30.00
		Never hinged	250.00	
b.		As #8, (III)	4,650.	1,625.
9	A1	9p purple	140.00	37.50
		Never hinged	280.00	
10	A1	1sh blue green	130.00	22.50
		Never hinged	260.00	
11	A1	2sh brown	300.00	140.00
		Never hinged	575.00	
12	A1	5sh yel & gray	550.00	260.00
		Never hinged	1,100.	
13	A1	10sh pink & gray	1,600.	800.00
		Never hinged	3,500.	
14	A1	£1 ultra & brn	3,250.	2,400.
		Never hinged	6,500.	
15	A1	£2 dp rose & blk	6,000.	3,400.
		Never hinged	12,000.	
		Nos. 1-12 (12)	1,839.	641.75

On No. 4, "2½d" is colorless in solid blue background.
See Nos. 38-59, 96-102, 121-129, 206.

King George V A2

Kookaburra (Kingfisher) A3

1913-14 Unwmk. Engr. Perf. 11

17	A2	1p carmine	5.25	6.50
		Never hinged	8.00	
a.		Vert. pair, imperf. between	2,750.	
b.		Horiz. pair, imperf. between	4,250.	
18	A3	6p lake brown ('14)	100.00	62.50
		Never hinged	160.00	

See No. 95.

A4

ONE PENNY
Die I — Normal die, having outside the oval band with "AUSTRALIA" a white line and a heavy colored line.
Die Ia — As die I with a small white spur below the right serif at foot of the "1" in left tablet.
Die II — A heavy colored line between two white lines back of the emu's neck. A white scratch crossing the vertical shading lines at the lowest point of the bust.

TWO PENCE
Die I — The numeral "2" is thin. The upper curve is 1mm. across and a very thin line connects it with the foot of the figure.
Die II — The "2" is thicker than in die I. The top curve is 1½mm across and a strong white line connects it with the foot of the figure. There are thin vertical lines across the ends of the groups of short horizontal lines at each side of "TWO PENCE."

THREE PENCE
Die I — The ends of the thin horizontal lines in the background run into the solid color of the various parts of the design. The numerals are thin and the letters of "THREE PENCE" are thin and irregular.
Die II — The oval about the portrait, the shields with the numerals, etc., are outlined by thin white lines which separate them from the horizontal background lines. The numerals are thick and the letters of "THREE PENCE" are heavy and regular.

FIVE PENCE
Die I — The top of the flag of the "5" is slightly curved.
Die II — The top of the flag of the "5" is flat. There are thin white vertical lines across the ends of the short horizontal lines at each side of "FIVE PENCE."

1914-24 Typo. Wmk. 9 Perf. 14

19	A4	½p emer ('15)	3.75	1.60
		Never hinged	7.50	
a.		Thin "½" at right	18,000.	9,000.
20	A4	½p org ('23)	4.50	3.50
		Never hinged	7.00	
21	A4	1p red (I)	20.00	1.75
		Never hinged	30.00	
		1p carmine rose (I)	37.50	6.00
		Never hinged	45.00	
b.		1p red (Ia)	500.00	9.00
		Never hinged	1,000.	
c.		1p carmine (II) ('18)	80.00	10.00
		Never hinged	160.00	
d.		1p scar (I), rough paper	22.50	6.00
e.		1p rose red (Ia), rough paper	600.00	22.50
f.		1p brt rose (Ia), rough paper	1,275.	150.00
22	A4	1p vio (I) ('22)	7.00	1.60
		Never hinged	11.50	
		1p red violet	9.50	4.75
		Never hinged	14.00	
23	A4	1p grn (I) ('24)	5.25	2.25
		Never hinged	9.50	
24	A4	1½p choc ('18)	8.50	2.00
		Never hinged	12.50	
a.		1½p red brown	13.00	2.25
		Never hinged	18.00	
b.		1½p black brown	7.25	2.25
		Never hinged	11.50	
25	A4	1½p emer ('23)	6.75	2.50
		Never hinged	12.50	
a.		Rough paper	350.00	145.00
26	A4	1½p scar ('24)	3.75	1.10
		Never hinged	7.00	
27	A4	2p brn org (I) ('20)	16.00	2.75
		Never hinged	30.00	
a.		2p orange (I) ('20)	16.00	2.25
		Never hinged	30.00	
b.		Booklet pane of 6	—	
28	A4	2p red (I) ('22)	16.00	2.75
		Never hinged	30.00	
29	A4	2p red brn (I) ('24)	20.00	11.00
		Never hinged	35.00	
30	A4	3p ultra (I) ('24)	29.00	7.00
		Never hinged	57.50	

31	A4	4p org ('15)	40.00	5.50
		Never hinged	80.00	
a.		4p yellow	125.00	17.00
		Never hinged	300.00	
32	A4	4p violet ('21)	20.00	16.00
		Never hinged	30.00	
33	A4	4p lt ultra ('22)	60.00	12.00
		Never hinged	100.00	
34	A4	4p ol bis ('24)	32.50	12.00
		Never hinged	60.00	
35	A4	4½p violet ('24)	25.00	6.00
		Never hinged	50.00	
36	A4	5p org brn (I) ('15)	42.50	6.50
		Never hinged	85.00	
37	A4	1sh4p lt blue ('20)	100.00	30.00
		Never hinged	180.00	
		Nos. 19-37 (19)	460.50	127.80

See Nos. 60-76, 113-120, 124.

1915 Perf. 11½, 12

38	A1	2p gray	90.00	16.00
		Never hinged	180.00	
39	A1	2½p dark blue	80.00	32.50
		Never hinged	140.00	
40	A1	6p ultra (II)	170.00	25.00
		Never hinged	325.00	
a.		Die III	6,250.	2,500.
41	A1	9p violet	170.00	52.50
		Never hinged	450.00	
42	A1	1sh blue green	160.00	30.00
		Never hinged	360.00	
43	A1	2sh brown	600.00	110.00
		Never hinged	1,500.	
44	A1	5sh yellow & gray	850.00	300.00
		Never hinged	2,250.	
		Nos. 38-44 (7)	2,120.	566.00

1915-24 Wmk. 10

45	A1	2p gray (I)	42.50	7.50
		Never hinged	62.50	
a.		Die II, shiny paper	45.00	17.50
		Never hinged	67.50	
46	A1	2½p dark blue	25.00	10.00
		Never hinged	40.00	
a.		"1" of fraction omitted	47,500.	30,000.
47	A1	3p ol bis (I)	35.00	8.50
		Never hinged	60.00	
a.		Die II	190.00	52.50
		Never hinged	325.00	
b.		3p lt olive (IV)	52.50	13.00
		Never hinged	92.50	
48	A1	6p ultra (II)	100.00	8.75
		Never hinged	190.00	
a.		6p chalky blue (III)	100.00	22.50
		Never hinged	190.00	
c.		6p plum (IV)	100.00	19.00
		Never hinged	180.00	
49	A1	6p yel brn (IV, '23)	25.00	3.75
		Never hinged	45.00	
50	A1	9p violet (IV)	70.00	16.00
		Never hinged	140.00	
a.		9p lilac (II)	60.00	11.00
		Never hinged	120.00	
51	A1	1sh blue grn (II, '16)	55.00	7.00
		Never hinged	110.00	
b.		Die IV	65.00	3.50
52	A1	2sh brn ('16)	240.00	15.00
		Never hinged	500.00	
53	A1	2sh vio brn (II, '24)	70.00	30.00
		Never hinged	160.00	
54	A1	5sh yel & gray ('18)	240.00	100.00
		Never hinged	480.00	
55	A1	10sh brt pink & gray ('17)	650.00	300.00
		Never hinged	1,350.	
56	A1	£1 ultra & brn org ('16)	3,000.	1,750.
		Never hinged	6,500.	
a.		£1 ultra & brn ('16)	3,000.	1,750.
		Never hinged	6,500.	
57	A1	£1 gray (IV, '24)	800.00	350.00
		Never hinged	1,750.	
58	A1	£2 dp rose & blk ('19)	5,500.	3,250.
		Never hinged	12,500.	
59	A1	£2 rose & vio brn ('24)	4,250.	2,500.
		Never hinged	11,000.	
		Nos. 45-54 (10)	902.50	206.50

Perf. 14, 14½, 14½x14

1918-23 Wmk. 11

60	A4	½p emerald	7.25	2.50
		Never hinged	12.50	
a.		Thin "½" at right	100.00	125.00
61	A4	1p rose (I)	26.00	17.00
		Never hinged	45.00	

62	A4	1p dl grn (I) ('24)	13.00	9.25
		Never hinged	24.00	
63	A4	1½p choc ('19)	11.00	2.25
		Never hinged	17.50	
a.		1½p red brown ('19)	11.50	4.00
		Never hinged	23.00	
		Nos. 60-63 (4)	57.25	31.00

1924 Unwmk. Perf. 14

64	A4	1p green (I)	6.50	9.50
		Never hinged	12.50	
65	A4	1½p carmine	22.50	8.00
		Never hinged	45.00	

Perf. 14, 13½x12½

1926-30 Wmk. 203

66	A4	½p orange	3.50	2.00
		Never hinged	7.00	
a.		Perf. 14 ('27)	6.75	7.25
		Never hinged	11.00	
67	A4	1p green (I)	4.25	1.00
		Never hinged	8.00	
a.		1p green (Ia)	50.00	70.00
		Never hinged	75.00	
b.		Perf. 14	4.25	1.75
		Never hinged	8.25	
68	A4	1½p rose red ('27)	4.00	1.75
		Never hinged	8.00	
c.		Perf. 14 ('26)	11.00	2.25
		Never hinged	21.00	
69	A4	1½p red brn ('30)	5.50	5.50
		Never hinged	9.75	
70	A4	2p red brn (II, '28)	14.50	8.00
		Never hinged	29.00	
a.		Perf. 14 (I, '27)	40.00	40.00
		Never hinged	75.00	
71	A4	2p red (II) ('30)	9.00	.90
		Never hinged	20.00	
a.		Tête bêche pair	175,000.	
b.		Unwmkd. (II) ('31)	1,350.	2,400.
72	A4	3p ultra (II) ('29)	30.00	5.00
		Never hinged	52.50	
a.		3p ultra (I)	62.50	20.00
		Never hinged	125.00	
b.		Perf. 14	40.00	10.00
		Never hinged	72.50	
73	A4	4p ol bis ('29)	27.50	3.50
		Never hinged	50.00	
a.		Perf. 14 ('28)	62.50	40.00
		Never hinged	125.00	
74	A4	4½p dk vio ('27)	22.50	5.25
		Never hinged	40.00	
a.		Perf. 13½x12½ ('28)	75.00	29.00
		Never hinged	135.00	
75	A4	5p brn buff (II) ('30)	40.00	7.00
		Never hinged	75.00	
76	A4	1sh4p pale turq bl ('28)	110.00	27.50
		Never hinged	225.00	
a.		Perf. 14 ('27)	125.00	70.00
		Never hinged	275.00	
		Nos. 66-76 (11)	270.75	67.40

For surcharges & overprints see Nos. 106-107, O3-O4.

Parliament House, Canberra A5

Unwmk.

1927, May 9 Engr. Perf. 11

94	A5	1½p brown red	.60	.55
		Never hinged	1.10	
a.		Vert. pair, imperf. btwn.	4,750.	4,250.
b.		Horiz. pair, imperf. btwn.	10,000.	10,000.

Opening of Parliament House at Canberra.

Melbourne Exhibition Issue
Kookaburra Type of 1914
1928, Oct. 29

95	A3 3p deep blue	5.00	7.25
	Never hinged	7.25	
a.	Pane of 4	175.00	225.00
	Never hinged	260.00	

No. 95a was issued at the Melbourne Intl. Phil. Exhib. No marginal inscription. Printed in sheets of 60 stamps (15 panes). No. 95a exists imperf. Value, $300,000.
No. 95 was printed in sheets of 120 and issued Nov. 2 throughout Australia.

Kangaroo-Map Type of 1913
Perf. 11½, 12

1929-30	Wmk. 203		Typo.
96	A1 6p brown	32.50	11.00
	Never hinged	57.50	
97	A1 9p violet	35.00	25.00
	Never hinged	80.00	
98	A1 1sh blue green	45.00	12.50
	Never hinged	90.00	
99	A1 2sh red brown	75.00	17.00
	Never hinged	200.00	
100	A1 5sh yel & gray	240.00	100.00
	Never hinged	500.00	
101	A1 10sh pink & gray	500.00	475.00
	Never hinged	1,000.	
102	A1 £2 dl red & blk ('30)	4,000.00	800.00
	Never hinged	8,000.	
	Nos. 96-102 (7)	4,928.	1,441.

For overprint see No. O5.

Black Swan — A6

Unwmk.
1929, Sept. 28   Engr.   Perf. 11

103	A6 1½p dull red	2.00	2.00
	Never hinged	3.25	

Centenary of Western Australia.

Capt. Charles Sturt — A7

1930, June 2

104	A7 1½p dark red	1.25	1.25
	Never hinged	2.50	
105	A7 3p dark blue	8.00	*10.00*
	Never hinged	11.00	

Capt. Charles Sturt's exploration of the Murray River, cent.

Nos. 68 and 74a surcharged

FIVE PENCE

1930   Wmk. 203   Perf. 13½x12½

106	A4 2p on 1½p rose red	2.50	1.25
	Never hinged	4.00	
107	A4 5p on 4½p dark violet	14.00	*15.00*
	Never hinged	21.00	

"Southern Cross" over Hemispheres A8

Perf. 11, 11½
1931, Mar. 19   Unwmk.

111	A8 2p dull red	2.00	1.25
	Never hinged	3.00	
112	A8 3p blue	7.25	6.25
	Never hinged	12.50	
	Nos. 111-112,C2 (3)	17.25	15.50

Trans-oceanic flights (1928-1930) of Sir Charles Edward Kingsford-Smith (1897-1935). See No. C3 for similar design. For overprints see Nos. CO1, O1-O2.

Types of 1913-23 Issues
Perf. 13½x12½

1931-36	Typo.	Wmk. 228	
113	A4 ½p org ('32)	9.50	6.75
		13.50	
114	A4 1p green (I)	3.00	.40
		5.00	
115	A4 1½p red brn ('36)	8.00	13.50
	Never hinged	12.50	
116	A4 2p red (II)	2.50	.30
	Never hinged	4.50	
117	A4 3p ultra (II) ('32)	22.50	2.00
	Never hinged	45.00	
118	A4 4p ol bis ('33)	22.50	2.00
	Never hinged	45.00	
120	A4 5p brn buff (II) ('32)	22.50	1.00
	Never hinged	35.00	

Perf. 11½, 12; 13½x12½ (1sh4p)

121	A1 6p yel brn ('36)	35.00	*37.50*
	Never hinged	55.00	
122	A1 9p violet ('32)	40.00	3.00
	Never hinged	65.00	
124	A4 1sh4p lt blue ('32)	60.00	9.00
	Never hinged	145.00	
125	A1 2sh red brn ('35)	10.00	2.75
	Never hinged	20.00	
126	A1 5sh yel & gray ('32)	175.00	20.00
	Never hinged	400.00	
127	A1 10sh pink & gray ('32)	400.00	200.00
	Never hinged	1,000.	
128	A1 £1 gray ('35)	700.00	275.00
	Never hinged	1,400.	
129	A1 £2 dl rose & blk ('34)	4,000.00	800.00
	Never hinged	9,250.	
	Nos. 113-129 (15)	5,511.	1,373.

For redrawn 2sh see No. 206. For overprints see Nos. O6-O11.

Sydney Harbor Bridge — A9

Unwmk.
1932, Mar. 14   Engr.   Perf. 11

130	A9 2p red	2.00	*1.60*
	Never hinged	5.00	
131	A9 3p blue	5.00	*4.00*
	Never hinged	10.00	
132	A9 5sh gray green	460.00	275.00
	Never hinged	1,300.	

Wmk. 228
Perf. 10½
Typo.

133	A9 2p red	2.50	2.25
	Never hinged	5.00	

Opening of the Sydney Harbor Bridge on Mar. 19, 1932.
Value for 5sh, used, is for CTO examples.
For overprints see Nos. O12-O13.

Kookaburra — A14

1932, June 1   Perf. 13½x12½

139	A14 6p light brown	15.00	1.25
	Never hinged	27.50	

Male Lyrebird — A16

1932, Feb. 15   Unwmk.   Perf. 11
Size: 21½x25mm

141	A16 1sh dark green	35.00	4.50
	Never hinged	90.00	

See No. 175, 300. For overprint see No. O14.

Yarra Yarra Tribesman, Yarra River and View of Melbourne A17

Wmk. 228
1934, July 2   Engr.   Perf. 10½

142	A17 2p vermilion	3.75	1.75
	Never hinged	6.50	
a.	Perf. 11½	5.00	4.50
	Never hinged	10.00	
143	A17 3p blue	4.50	*4.00*
	Never hinged	10.00	
a.	Perf. 11½	5.00	*5.00*
	Never hinged	9.00	
144	A17 1sh black	52.50	27.50
	Never hinged	110.00	
a.	Perf. 11½	62.50	35.00
	Never hinged	120.00	
	Nos. 142-144 (3)	60.75	33.25

Centenary of Victoria.

Merino Sheep — A18

1934, Nov. 1   Perf. 11½

147	A18 2p copper red	3.00	1.50
	Never hinged	7.00	
a.	Die II	16.00	7.25
	Never hinged	32.00	
148	A18 3p dark blue	12.00	*12.00*
	Never hinged	20.00	
149	A18 9p dark violet	40.00	*35.00*
	Never hinged	75.00	
	Nos. 147-149 (3)	55.00	48.50

Capt. John Macarthur (1767-1834), "father of the New South Wales woolen industry."
Two dies of 2p: I, shading on hill in background uneven from light to dark. II, shading is uniformly dark.

Cenotaph in Whitehall, London — A19

1935, Mar. 18   Perf. 13½x12½

150	A19 2p red	1.50	.50
	Never hinged	3.00	

Perf. 11

151	A19 1sh black	42.50	40.00
	Never hinged	85.00	

Anzacs' landing at Gallipoli, 20th anniv.
The 1sh perf 13½x12½ is a plate proof. Value, unused $2,250, mint never hinged $3,500.

George V on His Charger "Anzac" — A20

1935, May 2   Perf. 11½

152	A20 2p red	2.00	.35
	Never hinged	4.00	
153	A20 3p blue	5.00	*5.00*
	Never hinged	10.00	
154	A20 2sh violet	42.50	*40.00*
	Never hinged	85.00	
	Nos. 152-154 (3)	49.50	45.35

25th anniv. of the reign of King George V.

Amphitrite Joining Cables between Australia and Tasmania A21

1936, Apr. 1

157	A21 2p red	1.00	.60
	Never hinged	2.75	
158	A21 3p dark blue	4.00	3.75
	Never hinged	6.50	

Australia/Tasmania telephone link.

Edward VIII

A unique block of six unissued 2-penny King Edward VIII stamps realized the equivalent of U.S. $387,000 when it was sold at a London auction in 2014. A single stamp was separated from the block and sold at a Melbourne auction in 2015 for the equivalent of U.S. $123,600.

Proclamation Tree and View of Adelaide, 1936 — A22

1936, Aug. 3

159	A22 2p red	1.00	.60
	Never hinged	2.40	
160	A22 3p dark blue	4.00	3.75
	Never hinged	6.50	
161	A22 1sh green	14.00	11.00
	Never hinged	27.50	
	Nos. 159-161 (3)	19.00	15.35

Centenary of South Australia.

Gov. Arthur Phillip at Sydney Cove — A23

1937, Oct. 1   Perf. 13x13½

163	A23 2p red	1.50	.80
	Never hinged	3.00	
164	A23 3p ultra	3.75	3.25
	Never hinged	6.50	
165	A23 9p violet	14.00	12.00
	Never hinged	25.00	
	Nos. 163-165 (3)	19.25	16.05

150th anniversary of New South Wales.

Kangaroo A24

Queen Elizabeth A25

King George VI A26   A27

Koala — A28

Merino Sheep — A29

Kookaburra (Kingfisher) A30

Platypus A31

Queen Elizabeth and King George VI in Coronation Robes
A32   A33

King George VI and Queen Elizabeth A34

Type I   Type II

Two Types of A25 and A26:
Type I — Highlighted background. Lines around letters of Australia Postage and numerals of value.
Type II — Background of heavy diagonal lines without the highlighted effect. No lines around letters and numerals.

Perf. 13½x14, 14x13½

1937-46		**Engr.**		**Wmk. 228**
166	A24	½p org, perf. 15x14 ('42)	.85	.70
		Never hinged	1.90	
a.		Perf. 13½x14 ('38)	1.40	.60
		Never hinged	3.00	
167	A25	1p emerald (I)	1.10	1.00
		Never hinged	2.25	
168	A26	1½p dull red brn (II)	4.00	3.50
		Never hinged	7.00	
a.		Perf. 15x14 ('41)	4.75	5.00
		Never hinged	8.00	
169	A26	2p scarlet (I)	2.00	.80
		Never hinged	2.25	
170	A27	3p ultramarine	37.50	5.00
		Never hinged	65.00	
a.		3p dp ultra, thin paper ('38)	30.00	5.00
		Never hinged	55.00	
171	A28	4p grn, perf. 15x14 ('42)	1.00	.30
		Never hinged	2.00	
a.		Perf. 13½x14 ('38)	3.25	2.50
		Never hinged	9.00	
172	A29	5p pale rose vio, perf. 14x15 ('46)	1.00	.80
		Never hinged	2.00	
a.		Perf. 14x13½ ('38)	3.00	2.50
		Never hinged	4.75	
173	A30	6p vio brn, perf. 15x14 ('42)	1.00	.30
		Never hinged	2.00	
a.		Perf. 13½x14	12.50	2.40
		Never hinged	25.00	
b.		6p chocolate, perf. 15x14	1.40	.55
		Never hinged	2.25	
174	A31	9p sep, perf. 14x15 ('43)	2.00	.45
		Never hinged	3.00	
a.		Perf. 14x13½ ('38)	4.50	2.40
		Never hinged	9.00	
175	A16	1sh gray grn, perf. 15x14 ('41)	1.40	.40
		Never hinged	2.40	
a.		Perf. 13½x14	27.50	3.00
		Never hinged	72.50	
176	A27	1sh4p mag ('38)	1.60	1.60
		Never hinged	3.50	

Perf. 13½

177	A32	5sh dl red brn ('38)	9.75	4.75
		Never hinged	20.00	
178	A33	10sh dl gray vio ('38)	28.00	20.00
		Never hinged	40.00	

179	A34	£1 bl gray ('38)	70.00	42.50
		Never hinged	115.00	
		Nos. 166-179 (14)	161.20	82.10

No. 175 measures 17½x21½mm.
See Nos. 223A, 293, 295, 298, 300. For surch. & overprints see Nos. 190, M1, M4-M5, M7.

1938-42			**Perf. 15x14**	
180	A25	1p emerald (II)	1.00	.70
181	A25	1p dl red brn (II) ('41)	.70	.60
181B	A26	1½p bl grn (II) ('41)	.70	.80
182	A26	2p scarlet (II)	1.00	.30
182B	A26	2p red vio (II) ('41)	.40	.30
183	A27	3p dk ultra ('40)	29.00	3.00
		Never hinged	57.50	
183A	A27	3p dk vio brn ('42)	.40	.30
		Nos. 180-183A (7)	33.20	6.00
		Set, never hinged	72.50	

No. 183 differs from Nos. 170-170a in the shading lines on the king's left eyebrow which go downward, left to right, instead of the reverse. Also, more of the left epaulette shows.
For surcharges & ovpt. see Nos. 188-189, M3.

Coil Perforation

A special perforation was applied to stamps intended for use in coils to make separation easier. It consists of small and large holes (2 small, 10 large, 2 small) on the stamps' narrow side. Some of the stamps so perforated were sold in sheets.
This coil perforation may be found on Nos. 166, 181, 182, 182B, 193, 215, 223A, 231, 257, 315-316, 319, 319a and others.

Nurse, Sailor, Soldier and Aviator — A35

Perf. 13½x13

1940, July 15		**Engr.**		**Wmk. 228**
184	A35	1p green	1.50	1.50
		Never hinged	3.00	
185	A35	2p red	1.60	1.50
		Never hinged	3.25	
186	A35	3p ultra	5.00	7.00
		Never hinged	10.00	
187	A35	6p chocolate	15.00	13.00
		Never hinged	30.00	
		Nos. 184-187 (4)	23.10	23.00

Australia's participation in WWII.

No. 182 Surcharged in Blue

1941, Dec. 10			**Perf. 15x14**	
188	A26	2½p on 2p red	.80	.80
		Never hinged	1.50	

No. 183 Surcharged in Black and Yellow

189	A27	3½p on 3p dk ultra	.90	.90
		Never hinged	1.75	

No. 172a Surcharged in Purple

Perf. 14x13½

190	A29	5½p on 5p pale rose vio	3.25	3.25
		Never hinged	5.25	
		Nos. 188-190 (3)	4.95	4.95

Queen Elizabeth
A36

King George VI
A38   A39

King George VI
A38   A39

George VI and Blue Wrens A40

Emu A41

1942-44		**Engr.**	**Perf. 15x14**	
191	A36	1p brown vio ('43)	.45	.25
192	A37	1½p green	.70	.25
193	A38	2p lt rose vio ('44)	.70	.25
194	A39	2½p red	.70	.30
195	A40	3½p ultramarine	.90	.70
196	A41	5½p indigo	1.25	1.00
		Nos. 191-196 (6)	4.70	2.75
		Set, never hinged	8.00	

See Nos. 224-225. For overprint see No. M2.

> **Catalogue values for unused stamps in this section, from this point to the end of the section, are for Never Hinged items.**

Duke and Duchess of Gloucester A42

1945, Feb. 19		**Engr.**	**Perf. 14½**	
197	A42	2½p brown red	.30	.25
198	A42	3½p bright ultra	.45	.50
199	A42	5½p indigo	.55	.50
		Nos. 197-199 (3)	1.30	1.25

Inauguration of the Duke of Gloucester as Governor General.

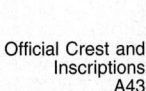

Official Crest and Inscriptions A43

Dove and Australian Flag A44

Angel of Peace; "Motherhood" and "Industry" A45

1946, Feb. 18		**Wmk. 228**	**Perf. 14½**	
200	A43	2½p carmine	.25	.25
201	A44	3½p deep ultra	.65	.50
202	A45	5½p deep yellow green	.70	.50
		Nos. 200-202 (3)	1.60	1.25

End of WWII. See Nos. 1456-1458.

Sir Thomas Mitchell and Map of Queensland A46

1946, Oct. 14				
203	A46	2½p dark carmine	.25	.25
204	A46	3½p deep ultra	.50	.40
205	A46	1sh olive green	.50	.40
		Nos. 203-205 (3)	1.25	1.05

Sir Thomas Mitchell's exploration of central Queensland, cent.

Kangaroo-Map Type of 1913 Redrawn

1945, Dec.		**Typo.**	**Perf. 11½**	
206	A1	2sh dk red brown	5.50	5.50

The R and A of AUSTRALIA are separated at the base and there is a single line between the value tablet and "Two Shillings." On No. 125 the tail of the R touches the A, while two lines appear between value tablet and "Two Shillings." There are many other minor differences in the design.
For overprint see No. M6.

John Shortland A47

Pouring Steel A48

Loading Coal — A49

1947, Sept.		**Engr.**	**Perf. 14½x14**	
207	A47	2½p brown red	.35	.25
		Perf. 14½		
208	A48	3½p deep blue	.65	.65
209	A49	5½p deep green	.65	.40
		Nos. 207-209 (3)	1.65	1.30

150th anniv. of the discovery of the Hunter River estuary, site of Newcastle by Lieut. John Shortland. By error the 2½p shows his father, Capt. John Shortland.

Princess Elizabeth — A50

Perf. 14x14½

1947, Nov. 20			**Wmk. 228**	
210	A50	1p brown violet	.40	.40

See No. 215.

Hereford Bull A51

Crocodile A52

1948, Feb. 16			**Perf. 14½**	
211	A51	1sh3p violet brown	2.50	1.25
212	A52	2sh chocolate	2.50	1.00

See No. 302.

William J. Farrer — A53

Design: No. 214, Ferdinand von Mueller.

1948   *Perf. 14½x14*
213 A53 2½p red   .50   .25
214 A53 2½p dark red   .45   .25

William J. Farrer (1845-1906), wheat researcher, and Ferdinand von Mueller (1825-1896), German-born botanist.
Issue dates: No. 213, July 12. No. 214, Sept. 13.

Elizabeth Type of 1947
1948, Aug.   *Unwmk.*   *Perf. 14x14½*
215 A50 1p brown violet   .40   .25

Scout in Uniform — A55

1948, Nov. 15   *Engr.*   **Wmk. 228**
216 A55 2½p brown red   .45   .25

Pan-Pacific Scout Jamboree, Victoria, Dec. 29, 1948 to Jan. 9, 1949. See No. 249.

Arms of Australia — A56

1949-50   **Wmk. 228**   *Perf. 14x13½*
218 A56 5sh dark red   4.50   1.25
219 A56 10sh red violet   29.00   2.00
220 A56 £1 deep blue   45.00   8.50
221 A56 £2 green ('50)   175.00   26.00
   Nos. 218-221 (4)   253.50   37.75

Henry Hertzberg Lawson (1867-1922), Author and Poet — A57

Perf. 14½x14
1949, June 17   *Unwmk.*
222 A57 2½p rose brown   .50   .25

Outback Mail Carrier and Plane — A58

1949, Oct. 10
223 A58 3½p violet blue   .40   .40

UPU, 75th anniv.

Types of 1938, 1942-44 and

Aborigine — A59

1948-50   *Unwmk.*   *Perf. 14½x14*
223A A24 ½p orange ('49)   .45   .25
224 A37 1½p green ('49)   .35   .45
225 A38 2p lt rose violet   1.00   .55

     Wmk. 228
226 A59 8½p dark brown ('50)   .40   .40
   Nos. 223A-226 (4)   2.20   1.65

Issued: 2p, Dec.; ½p, Sept.; 1½p, 8/29; 8½p, 8/14.
See Nos. 248, 303.

John Forrest — A60

1949, Nov. 28   **Wmk. 228**
227 A60 2½p brown red   .40   .25

Forrest (1847-1918), explorer & statesman.

New South Wales A61   Victoria A62

First stamp designs.

Perf. 14½x14
1950, Sept. 27   *Unwmk.*
228 A61 2½p rose brown   .40   .25
229 A62 2½p rose brown   .40   .25
   a. Pair, #228-229   1.60   1.25

Cent. of Australian adhesive postage stamps. Issued in sheets of 160 stamps containing alternate copies of Nos. 228 and 229.

Elizabeth A63   George VI A64

1950-51   *Engr.*   *Unwmk.*
230 A63 1½p deep green   .80   .75
231 A63 2p yellow grn ('51)   .30   .25
232 A64 2½p violet brn ('51)   .30   .45
233 A64 3p dull green ('51)   .35   .25
   Nos. 230-233 (4)   1.75   1.70

Issued: 1½p, 6/19; 2p, 3/28; 2½p, 5/23; 3p, 11/14.

A65   A66

1950-52   **Wmk. 228**
234 A64 2½p red   .25   .25
235 A64 3p red ('51)   .35   .35
236 A65 3½p red brown ('51)   .35   .25
237 A65 4½p scarlet ('52)   .45   .45
238 A65 6½p choc ('52)   .35   .35
238A A65 6½p blue green ('52)   .45   .25
239 A66 7½p deep blue ('51)   .50   .50
   Nos. 234-239 (7)   2.70   2.40

Issued: 2½p, 4/12; 3p, 2/28; 7½p, 10/31; 3½p, 11/28; 4½p, No. 238, 2/20; No. 238A, 4/9.

A67   Founding of the Commonwealth of Australia, 50th Anniv. — A68

Designs: No. 240, Sir Edmund Barton. No. 241, Sir Henry Parkes, bearded. 5½p, Duke of York opening first Federal Parliament. 1sh6p, Parliament House, Canberra.

Perf. 14½x14
1951, May 1   *Engr.*   *Unwmk.*
240 A67 3p carmine   1.00   .25
241 A67 3p carmine   1.00   .25
   a. Pair, #240, 241   2.00   2.00
242 A68 5½p deep blue   1.20   1.50
243 A68 1sh6p red brown   1.60   1.40
   Nos. 240-243 (4)   4.80   3.40

Edward Hammond Hargraves — A69

Design: No. 245, Charles Joseph Latrobe (1801-1875), first governor of Victoria.

1951, July 2
244 A69 3p rose brown   .80   .25
245 A69 3p rose brown   .80   .25
   a. Pair, #244, 245   2.00   1.60

Discovery of gold in Australia, cent. (No. 244); Establishment of representative government in Victoria, cent. (No. 245). Sheets contain alternate rows of Nos. 244 and 245.

King George VI — A70

1952, Mar. 19   **Wmk. 228**   *Perf. 14½*
247 A70 1sh½p slate blue   2.50   .85

Aborigine Type of 1950 Redrawn
Size: 20½x25mm
248 A59 2sh6p dark brown   5.75   1.25

Portrait as on A59; lettering altered and value repeated at lower left. See No. 303.

Scout Type of 1948
Dated "1952-53"
Perf. 14x14½
1952, Nov. 19   **Wmk. 228**
249 A55 3½p red brown   .45   .25

Pan-Pacific Scout Jamboree, Greystanes, Dec. 30, 1952, to Jan. 9, 1953.

Modern Dairy, Butter Production — A71

Perf. 14½
1953, Feb. 11   *Unwmk.*   *Typo.*
250 A71 3p shown   .90   .40
251 A71 3p Wheat   .90   .40
252 A71 3p Beef   .90   .40
   a. Strip of 3, #250-252   8.00   8.00
253 A71 3½p shown   .90   .40
254 A71 3½p Wheat   .90   .40
255 A71 3½p Beef   .90   .40
   a. Strip of 3, #253-255   7.50   7.50
   Nos. 250-255 (6)   5.40   2.40

Both the 3p and 3½p were printed in panes of 50 stamps: 17 Butter, 17 Wheat and 16 Beef. The stamps were issued to encourage food production.

Queen Elizabeth II — A72

Perf. 14½x14
1953-54   *Unwmk.*   *Engr.*
256 A72 1p purple   .30   .30
256A A72 2½p deep blue ('54)   .45   .30
257 A72 3p dark green   .45   .25
     Wmk. 228
258 A72 3½p dark red   .55   .45
258B A72 6½p orange ('54)   1.50   .75
   Nos. 256-258B (5)   3.25   2.05

Issued: 3½p, 4/21; 3p, 6/17; 1p, 8/19; 2½p, 6½p, 6/23.
See Nos. 292, 296.

Coronation Issue

Queen Elizabeth II A73

1953, May 25   *Unwmk.*
259 A73 3½p rose red   .60   .25
260 A73 7½p violet   1.00   1.00
261 A73 2sh dull green   2.00   1.50
   Nos. 259-261 (3)   3.60   2.75

Boy and Girl with Calf — A74

1953, Sept. 3   *Perf. 14½*
262 A74 3½p dp green & red brn   .50   .25

Official establishment of Young Farmers' Clubs, 25th anniv.

Lieut. Gov. David Collins — A75

Sullivan Cove, Hobart A76

Design: No. 264, Lieut. Gov. William Paterson (facing left).

1953, Sept. 23   *Perf. 14½x14*
263 A75 3½p red brown   .45   .25
264 A75 3½p red brown   .60   .25
   a. Pair, #263-264   1.60   1.60
265 A76 2sh green   4.00   2.50
   Nos. 263-265 (3)   5.05   3.00

Settlement in Tasmania, 150th anniv. Sheets contain alternate rows of Nos. 263 and 264.

Tasmania Stamp of 1853 — A77

1953, Nov. 11   *Perf. 14½*
266 A77 3p red   .40   .40

Tasmania's first postage stamps, cent.

Elizabeth II and Duke of Edinburgh — A78

Elizabeth II — A79

1954, Feb. 2   *Perf. 14½x14, 14x14½*
267 A78 3½p rose red   .35   .25
268 A79 7½p purple   .80   .80
269 A78 2sh green   1.60   1.00
   Nos. 267-269 (3)   2.75   2.05

Visit of Queen Elizabeth II and the Duke of Edinburgh, 1954.

Telegraph Pole and Key — A80

1954, Apr. 7   Engr.   Perf. 14
270 A80 3½p dark red   .45 .25
Inauguration of the telegraph in Australia, cent.

Red Cross and Globe — A81

1954, June 9   Perf. 14½x14
271 A81 3½p deep blue & red   .40 .25
Australian Red Cross Society.

Swan — A82

1954, Aug. 2   Unwmk.   Perf. 14½
274 A82 3½p black   .40 .25
Western Australia's first postage stamp, cent.

Diesel and Early Steam Locomotives A83

1954, Sept. 13   Perf. 14x14½
275 A83 3½p red brown   .45 .25
Centenary of Australian railroads.

Antarctic Flora and Fauna and Map — A84

1954, Nov. 17   Perf. 14
276 A84 3½p black   .40 .25
Australia's interest in the Antarctic continent.

Olympic Circles and Arms of Melbourne — A85

1954, Dec. 1
277 A85 2sh dark blue   5.75 3.25
16th Olympic Games to be held in Melbourne Nov.-Dec. 1956. See No. 286.

Globe, Flags and Rotary Emblem — A86

1955, Feb. 23   Perf. 14x14½
278 A86 3½p carmine   .40 .25
Rotary International, 50th anniv.

Elizabeth II — A87

1955, Mar. 9   Wmk. 228   Perf. 14½
279 A87 1sh½p dk gray blue   3.25 1.00
See No. 301.

Top of US Monument, Canberra — A88

1955, May 4   Unwmk.   Perf. 14x14½
280 A88 3½p deep ultra   .50 .25
Friendship between Australia and the US.

Cobb and Company Mail Coach A89

1955, July 6   Perf. 14½x14
281 A89 3½p dark brown   .50 .25
282 A89 2sh brown   2.25 2.25
Pioneers of Australia's coaching era.

World Map, YMCA Emblem A90

Engr. and Typo.
1955, Aug. 10   Perf. 14
283 A90 3½p Prus green & red   .40 .25
a.   Red omitted   25,000.
Centenary of YMCA.

Florence Nightingale and Modern Nurse — A91

1955, Sept. 21   Engr.   Perf. 14x14½
284 A91 3½p red violet   .40 .25
Centenary of Florence Nightingale's work in the Crimea and of the founding of modern nursing.

Queen Victoria — A92

1955, Oct. 17   Perf. 14½
285 A92 3½p green   .40 .25
South Australia's first postage stamps, cent.

Olympic Type of 1954
1955, Nov. 30   Unwmk.   Perf. 14
286 A85 2sh deep green   3.25 2.40
16th Olympic Games at Melbourne, Nov. 22-Dec. 8, 1956.

Queen Victoria, Queen Elizabeth II and Badges of Victoria, New South Wales and Tasmania A93

1956, Sept. 26   Perf. 14½x14
287 A93 3½p brown carmine   .40 .25
Centenary of responsible government in Victoria, New South Wales and Tasmania.

Melbourne Coat of Arms — A94   Southern Cross, Olympic Torch — A95

Collins Street, Melbourne A96

Design: 2sh, Melbourne across Yarra River.

1956, Oct. 31   Engr.   Perf. 14½, 14
288 A94 4p dark carmine   .50 .25
289 A95 7½p ultramarine   .75 1.00
Photo.
Perf. 14x14½
290 A96 1sh multicolored   .95 .50
Perf. 12x11½
Granite Paper
291 A96 2sh multicolored   1.60 1.25
Nos. 288-291 (4)   3.80 3.00
16th Olympic Games, Melbourne, 11/22-12/8.
A lithographed souvenir sheet incorporating reproductions of Nos. 288-291 in reduced size was of private origin and not postally valid.

Types of 1938-55 and

Queen Elizabeth II — A97

Perf. 14½x14, 14x15, 15x14, 14½
1956-57		Engr.	Unwmk.	
292	A72	3½p dark red	1.40	.55
293	A28	4p green	2.00	.45
294	A97	4p claret ('57)	.45	.25
a.	Booklet pane of 6 ('57)		12.50	
295	A30	6p brown violet	3.50	.55
296	A72	6½p orange	3.50	.25
297	A97	7½p violet ('57)	1.60	.55
298	A31	9p sepia	17.00	2.00
299	A97	10p gray blue ('57)	1.25	.55
300	A16	1sh gray green	7.25	1.10
301	A87	1sh7p redsh brn ('57)	5.25	.70
302	A52	2sh chocolate	14.00	1.10
303	A59	2sh6p brown ('57)	10.50	1.10
	Nos. 292-303 (12)		67.70	9.15

No. 300 measures 17½x21½mm. No. 303 measures 20½x25mm and is the redrawn type of 1952.
Issued: 3½p, 7/2; 2sh, 7/21; No. 293, 6p, 8/18; 6½p, Sept. 9p, 1sh, 12/13; 2sh6p, 1/30; 10p, 3/6; No. 294, 1sh7p, 3/13; 7½p, 11/13.

South Australia Coat of Arms — A99

1957, Apr. 17   Unwmk.   Perf. 14½
304 A99 4p brown red   .40 .25
Centenary of responsible government in South Australia.
No. 304 exists in two types on alternate rows of the sheet. Type I — The scroll just passes through the hyphen between the dates. Type II — The scroll passing through the hyphen between "1857-1957" is longer. Both types are of equal value.

Caduceus and Map of Australia A100

1957, Aug. 21   Perf. 14½x14
305 A100 7p violet blue   .60 .30
Royal Flying Doctor Service of Australia.

Star of Bethlehem and Praying Child A101

1957, Nov. 6   Engr.
306 A101 3½p dull rose   .35 .25
307 A101 4p pale purple   .35 .25
Christmas.

Canberra War Memorial, Sailor and Airman A102

Design: No. 309, As No. 308 with soldier and service woman. Printed in alternate rows in sheet.

1958, Feb. 10   Unwmk.
308 A102 5½p brown carmine   1.60 .70
309 A102 5½p brown carmine   1.60 .70
a.   Pair, #308-309   4.00 3.50

Sir Charles Kingsford-Smith and "Southern Cross" — A103

1958, Aug. 27   Perf. 14x14½
310 A103 8p brt violet blue   1.25 1.00
1st air crossing of the Tasman Sea, 30th anniv. See New Zealand No. 321.

Broken Hill
Mine — A104

1958, Sept. 10   *Perf. 14½x14*
311 A104 4p brown   .40 .25
   Broken Hill mining field, 75th anniv.

Nativity — A105

1958, Nov. 5   *Perf. 14½x15*
312 A105 3½p dark red   .30 .25
313 A105 4p dark purple   .30 .25
     Christmas.

A106   A107

A108   A109

A110

Platypus
A111

Tasmanian
Tiger
A112

Flannel
Flower — A113

Aboriginal
Stockman
Cutting Out a
Steer
A114

Die I

Die II

Designs: 3p, Queen Elizabeth II facing right. 6p, Banded anteater. 8p, Tiger cat. 9p, Kangaroos. 11p, Rabbit bandicoot. 1sh6p, Christmas bells (flower). 2sh3p, Wattle (flower). 2sh5p, Banksia (flower). 3sh, Waratah (flower).

FIVE PENCE
Die I — Four short lines inside "5" at right of ball; six short lines left of ball; full length line above ball is seventh from bottom. Odd numbered horizontal rows in each sheet are in Die I.

Die II — Five short lines inside "5" at right of ball; seven at left; full length line above ball is eighth from bottom. Even numbered horizontal rows in each sheet are in Die II.

Perf. 14½x14, 14x14½, 14½

			Engr.	Unwmk.
1959-64				
314	A106	1p dull violet	.25	.25
315	A107	2p red brn ('62)	.40	.35
316	A108	3p bluish green	.35	.25
317	A108	3½p dark green	.25	.25
318	A109	4p carmine	1.00	.25
a.		Booklet pane of 6	29.00	
319	A110	5p dark blue (I)	1.00	.25
a.		5p dark blue (II)	1.00	.25
b.		Booklet pane of 6 ('60)	17.00	
320	A111	6p chocolate ('60)	1.50	.25
321	A111	8p red brn ('60)	1.50	.25
322	A111	9p brown black	1.90	.75
323	A111	11p dk blue ('61)	1.90	.25
324	A111	1sh slate green	4.50	.70
325	A112	1sh2p dk purple ('62)	1.90	.35
326	A113	1sh6p red, *yel* ('60)	3.00	1.20
327	A113	2sh dark blue	2.00	.25
328	A113	2sh3p green, *yel*	2.25	.25
328A	A113	2sh3p yel grn ('64)	6.00	3.25
329	A113	2sh5p brn, *yel* ('60)	7.50	1.10
330	A113	3sh crimson	3.25	.45
		Wmk. 228		
331	A114	5sh red brown, *cream* ('61)	24.00	2.25
a.		red brown, *white* ('64)	120.00	12.00
		Nos. 314-331 (19)	64.45	12.90

Issued: 1p, 4p, 2/2; 3½p, 3/18; 2sh, 4/8; 3p, 5/20; 3sh, 7/15; 1sh, No. 328, 9/9; 5p, 10/1; 9p, 10/21; 1sh6p, 2/3/60; 2sh5p, 3/16/60; 8p, 5/11/60; 6p, 9/30/60; 11p, 5/3/61; 5sh, 7/26/61; 2p, 1sh2p, 3/21/62; No. 328A, 10/28/64.

Luminescent Printings

Paper with an orange red phosphorescence (surface coating), was used for some printings of the Colombo Plan 1sh, No. 340, the Churchill 5p, No. 389, and several regular postage stamps. These include 2p, 3p, 6p, 8p, 9p, 11p, 1sh2p, 1sh6p and 2sh3p (Nos. 315, 316, 365, 367, 321, 368, 323, 325, 369, 328A).

Stamps printed only on phosphorescent paper include the Monash 5p, Hargrave 5p, ICY 2sh3p and Christmas 5p (Nos. 388, 390-393) and succeeding commemoratives; the 2sh, 2sh6p and 3sh regular birds (Nos. 370, 372, 373); and most of the regular series in decimal currency.

Ink with a phosphorescent content was used in printing most of the 5p red, No. 366, almost all of the 5p red booklets, No. 366a, most of the decimal 4c regular, No. 397, and its booklet pane, No. 397a, and all of No. 398.

Postmaster
Isaac Nichols
Boarding
Vessel to
Receive
Mail — A115

1959, Apr. 22   *Perf. 14½x14*
332 A115 4p dark gray blue   .40 .25
   First post office, Sydney, 150th anniv.

Parliament House,
Brisbane, and
Queensland
Arms — A116

1959, June 5   *Perf. 14x14½*
333 A116 4p dk green & violet   .40 .25
   Cent. of Queensland self-government.

Approach of the
Magi — A117

1959, Nov. 4   *Perf. 15x14½*
334 A117 5p purple   .40 .25
     Christmas.

Girl Guide and Lord Baden-
Powell — A118

1960, Aug. 18   *Perf. 14½x14*
335 A118 5p dark blue   .45 .25
   50th anniversary of the Girl Guides.

The Overlanders
by Sir Daryl
Lindsay — A119

1960, Sept. 21   *Perf. 14½*
336 A119 5p lilac rose   .40 .25
   Exploration of Australia's Northern Territory, cent.
   No. 336 exists in two types. Type I: Top edge of the mane is broken and right ear is not

---

closed. Type II: Mane is smooth and the lines in the ear are closed.

Melbourne Cup
and Archer, 1861
Winner — A120

1960, Oct. 12   *Unwmk.*
337 A120 5p sepia   .40 .25
   Centenary of the Melbourne Cup.

Queen
Victoria — A121

1960 Nov. 2   **Engr.**   *Perf. 14½*
338 A121 5p dark green   .40 .25
   Centenary of the first Queensland stamps.

Open Bible and
Candle — A122

1960, Nov. 9   *Unwmk.*
339 A122 5p maroon   .40 .25
   Christmas; beginning of 350th anniv. year of the publication of the King James translation of the Bible.

Colombo Plan
Emblem — A123

1961, June 30   *Perf. 14x14½*
340 A123 1sh red brown   1.60 .30
   Colombo Plan for the peaceful development of South East Asia countries, 10th anniv.

Dame Nellie Melba,
by Sir Bertram
Mackennal — A124

1961, Sept. 20   *Perf. 14½*
341 A124 5p deep blue   .45 .30
   Dame Nellie Melba, singer, birth cent.

Page from
Book of
Hours, 15th
Century
A125

1961, Nov. 8   *Perf. 14½x14*
342 A125 5p reddish brown   .40 .25
   Christmas; end of the 350th anniv. year of the publication of the King James translation of the Bible.

John McDouall Stuart — A126

1962, July 25   Unwmk.   Perf. 14½
345   A126   5p carmine   .40   .25
First south-north crossing of Australia by John McDouall Stuart, cent.

Nurse and Rev. Flynn's Grave — A127

1962, Sept. 5   Photo.   Perf. 13½
346   A127   5p multicolored   .50   .30
 a.   Red omitted   450.00
Australian Inland Mission founded by Rev. John Flynn, 50th anniv.

Woman and Globe — A128

1962, Sept. 26   Engr.   Perf. 14x14½
347   A128   5p dark green   .40   .25
World Conf. of the Associated Country Women of the World, Melbourne, Oct. 2-12.

Madonna and Child — A129

1962, Oct. 17   Perf. 14½
348   A129   5p deep violet   .40   .25
Christmas.

View of Perth and Kangaroo Paw — A130

Arms of Perth A131

1962, Nov. 1   Photo.   Perf. 14
349   A130   5p multicolored   .75   .25
 a.   Red omitted   5,500.
              Perf. 14½x14
350   A131   2sh3p emer, blk, red
              & ultra   4.00 3.50
British Empire and Commonwealth Games, Perth, Nov. 22-Dec. 1.
Perf 14x14¾ examples of Nos. 349-350 are from a booklet pane issued for the 2006 Commonwealth Games. These stamps were not valid for postage.

Elizabeth II — A132

Elizabeth II and Prince Philip — A133

1963, Feb. 18   Engr.   Perf. 14½
351   A132   5p dark green   .50   .25
352   A133   2sh3 red brown   4.00 3.00
Visit of Elizabeth II and Prince Philip.
Perf 14½x14 lithographed examples of Nos. 351-352 come from the booklet footnoted under No. 2507. These stamps were not valid for postage.

Walter Burley Griffin and Arms of Canberra A134

1963, Mar. 8   Unwmk.   Perf. 14½x14
353   A134   5p dark green   .40   .25
50th anniv. of Canberra; Walter Burley Griffin, American architect, who laid out plan for Canberra.

Red Cross Centenary Emblem — A135

1963, May 8   Photo.   Perf. 13½x13
354   A135   5p dk blue, red & gray   .50   .25
Centenary of the International Red Cross.

Explorers Blaxland, Lawson and Wentworth Looking West from Mt. York — A136

1963, May 28   Engr.   Perf. 14½x14
355   A136   5p dark blue   .40   .25
1st crossing of the Blue Mts., 150th anniv.

Globe, Ship, Plane and Map of Australia A137

1963, Aug. 28   Unwmk.
356   A137   5p red   .40   .25
Importance of exports to Australian economy.

Elizabeth II A138

Black-backed Magpie and Eucalyptus A139

Abel Tasman and Ship — A144

George Bass, Whaleboat — A145

Designs: 6p, Yellow-tailed thornbill, horiz. 1sh6p, Galah on tree stump. 2sh, Golden whistler. 2sh5p, Blue wren and bracken fern. 2sh6p, Scarlet robin, horiz. 3sh, Straw-necked ibis. 5sh, William Dampier and "Roebuck" sailing ship. 7sh6p, Capt. James Cook. 10sh, Matthew Flinders and three-master "Investigator." £2, Admiral Philip Parker King.

              Perf. 15x14
1963-65   Unwmk.   Engr.
365   A138   5p green   .90   .25
 a.   Booklet pane of 6 ('64)   35.00
 b.   Pair, imperf. btwn.   2.75 2.00
366   A138   5p red   .90   .25
 a.   Booklet pane of 6   45.00
              Photo.
              Perf. 13½
367   A139   6p multi   1.10   .35
 a.   Vert. pair, imperf. btwn.
368   A139   9p multi   2.00 1.75
369   A139   1sh6p multi   1.75 1.40
370   A139   2sh multi   2.25   .55
371   A139   2sh5p multi   5.75 3.25
372   A139   2sh6p multi   4.75 3.00
 a.   Red omitted   12,000.12,000.
373   A139   3sh multi   3.25 2.00
              Engr.
         Perf. 14½x14, 14½x15
374   A144   4sh violet
              blue   3.75   .95
              Wmk. 228
375   A145   5sh red
              brown   5.25 2.50
376   A144   7sh6p olive
              green   18.00 13.00
377   A144   10sh deep
              claret   32.50 8.00
378   A145   £1 purple   65.00 30.00
379   A145   £2 brn blk   97.50 80.00
         Nos. 365-379 (15)   244.65 147.25
No. 365a was printed in sheets of 288 which were sold intact by the Philatelic Bureau. These sheets can be broken to obtain pairs and blocks which are imperf. between (see No. 365b).
Issued: No. 365, 4sh, 10/9/63; 10sh, £1, 2/26/64; 9p, 1sh6p, 2sh5p, 3/11/64; 6p, 8/19/64; 7sh6p, £2, 8/26/64; 5sh, 11/25/64; 2sh, 2sh6p, 3sh, 4/21/65; No. 366, 6/30/65.
See Nos. 400-401, 406-417, 1727-1728.

Star of Bethlehem — A146

1963, Oct. 25   Unwmk.   Perf. 14½
380   A146   5p blue   .40   .25
Christmas.

Cable Around World and Under Sea — A147

1963, Dec. 3   Photo.   Perf. 13½
381   A147   2sh3p gray, ver, blk
              & blue   4.50 3.50
Opening of the Commonwealth Pacific (telephone) cable service (COMPAC).
See New Zealand No. 364.

Bleriot 60 Plane, 1914 — A148

1964, July 1   Engr.   Perf. 14½x14
382   A148   5p olive green   .50   .25
383   A148   2sh3p red   3.25 3.25
50th anniv. of the first air mail flight in Australia; Maurice Guillaux, aviator.

Child Looking at Nativity Scene — A149

1964, Oct. 21   Photo.   Perf. 13½
384   A149   5p bl, blk, red &
              buff   .40   .25
 a.   Red omitted   6,250. 2,750.
 b.   Black omitted   2,750.
 c.   Buff omitted   3,500.
Christmas.
No. 384a used is valued on cover. The red ink can be removed from No. 384 by bleaching.

"Simpson and His Donkey" by Wallace Anderson — A150

1965, Apr. 14   Engr.   Perf. 14x14½
385   A150   5p olive bister   .50   .25
386   A150   8p dark blue   .90   .80
387   A150   2sh3p rose claret   2.80 3.00
         Nos. 385-387 (3)   4.20 4.05
50th anniv. of the landing of the Australian and New Zealand Army Corps (ANZAC) at Gallipoli, Turkey, Apr. 25, 1915. Private John Simpson Kirkpatrick saved the lives of many wounded soldiers. The statue erected in his honor stands in front of Melbourne's Shrine of Remembrance.

Radio Mast and Satellite Orbiting Earth — A151

1965, May 10   Photo.   Perf. 13½
388   A151   5p multicolored   .65   .25
 a.   Gray omitted   5,000. 5,000.
ITU, cent.

Winston Churchill — A152

1965, May 24
389   A152   5p lt bl, pale gray,
              dk gray & blk   .40   .25
 a.   Pale gray omitted (white
          face)   5,500.
 b.   Dark gray ("Australia") omit-
          ted   7,500.
Sir Winston Spencer Churchill (1874-1965), statesman and WWII leader.
Two examples of No. 389b recorded, one damaged. Value is for sound example.
See New Zealand No. 371.

John Monash and
Transmission
Tower — A153

1965, June 23   Photo.   Perf. 13½
390 A153 5p red, yel, blk & lt brn   .40   .25
Birth cent. of General Sir John Monash (1865-1931), soldier, Vice-Chancellor of University of Melbourne and chairman of the Victoria state electricity commission.

Lawrence
Hargrave and
Sketch for
1902
Seaplane
A154

1965, Aug. 4   Unwmk.   Perf. 13½
391 A154 5p multicolored   .40   .25
a.   Purple (5d) omitted   600.00   600.00
50th anniv. of the death of Lawrence Hargrave (1850-1915), aviation pioneer.

ICY
Emblem — A155

1965, Sept. 1   Photo.   Perf. 13½
392 A155 2sh3p lt blue & green   3.25 3.00
International Cooperation Year.

Nativity — A156

1965, Oct. 20   Unwmk.   Perf. 13½
393 A156 5p multicolored   .40   .25
a.   Gold omitted   5,500.
b.   Ultramarine omitted   1,000.
c.   Brown omitted (white faces)   5,000.
Christmas.

Types of 1963-65 and

Elizabeth
II — A157

Humbug
Fish — A158

Designs: No. 400, Yellow-tailed thornbill, horiz. 6c, blue-faced honeyeater, horiz. 8c, Coral fish. 9c, Hermit crab. 10c Anemone fish. 13c, Red-necked avocet. 15c, Galah on tree stump. 20c, Golden whistler. 24c Azure kingfisher, horiz. 25c, Scarlet robin, horiz. 30c Straw-necked ibis. 40c Abel Tasman and ship. 50c, William Dampier and "Roebuck" sailing ship. 75c, Capt. James Cook. $1, Matthew Flinders and three-master "Investigator." $2, George Bass and whaleboat. $4, Admiral Philip Parker King.

Perf. 14½x14 (A157); 13½ (A158, A139)
Engr. (A157), Photo. (A158, A139)
1966-71
394 A157 1c red brown   .45   .25
395 A157 2c olive green   .75   .25
396 A157 3c Prus green   .75   .25
397 A157 4c red   .30   .25
a.   Booklet pane of 5 + label   35.00
398 A157 5c on 4c red ('67)   .40   .25
a.   Booklet pane of 5 + label ('67)   7.00
399 A157 5c dk blue ('67)   .75   .25
a.   Booklet pane of 5 + label   12.50

---

400 A139 5c lt grn, blk, brn & yel   .55   .25
a.   Brown omitted   3,500.   —
401 A139 6c gray, blk, lem & bl   .80   .35
b.   Blue omitted   2,500.
401A A157 6c orange ('70)   .50   .25
402 A158 7c brn, ver, blk & gray   1.25
402A A157 7c dp rose lilac ('71)   .75   .40
403 A158 8c multicolored   1.25   .40
404 A158 9c multicolored   1.25   .35
405 A158 10c lt brn, blk, org & bl   1.25   .25
a.   Orange omitted   4,250.
b.   Blue omitted   3,000.   2,000.
406 A139 13c lt bl grn, blk, gray & red   2.25   .40
a.   Red omitted   2,250.
b.   Gray omitted   2,100.
407 A139 15c lt grn, blk, gray & rose   2.25   .90
a.   Rose omitted   4,500.
b.   Gray omitted   2,750.   750.00
408 A139 20c pink, blk, yel & gray   5.25   .30
a.   Yellow omitted   2,900.
b.   Gray omitted   750.00
409 A139 24c tan, blk, vio bl & org   1.10   1.10
410 A139 25c gray, grn, blk & red   4.00   .55
a.   Red omitted   5,750.
411 A139 30c lt grn, buff, blk & red   16.00   .85
a.   Red omitted   3,000.

Engr.
Perf. 14½x14, 14½x15
412 A144 40c violet blue   12.00   .25
413 A145 50c brown red   16.00   .25
414 A144 75c olive green   2.00   1.40
415 A144 $1 deep claret   3.25   .45
a.   Perf 15x14   125.00   32.50
416 A145 $2 purple   8.00   2.25
417 A145 $4 sepia   8.00   5.00
    Nos. 394-417 (26)   91.10   17.70

No. 398 issued in booklets only.
Booklet panes of 10 of No. 399, and of 5 No. 400, are torn from sheets. They were issued for the use of "Australian Defence Forces," as the covers read, in Viet Nam.
Issued: Nos. 398, 399, 9/29/67; No. 401A, 9/28/70; No. 402A, 10/1/71; No. 415a, 1973; others, 2/14/66.

Coil Stamps
1966-67   Photo.   Perf. 15 Horiz.
418 A157 3c emerald, blk & buff   .60   .50
419 A157 4c org red, blk & buff   .70   .50
420 A157 5c blue, black & buff   .85   .25
    Nos. 418-420 (3)   2.15   1.25
Issued: 5c, 9/29/67; others, 2/14/66.

Rescue
A159

1966, July 6   Photo.   Perf. 13½
421 A159 4c blue, ultra & black   .30   .25
Royal Life Saving Society, 75th anniv.

Adoration of the Shepherds
A160

1966, Oct. 19   Photo.   Perf. 13½
422 A160 4c olive & black   .30   .25
a.   Olive omitted   7,250.
Christmas.

Dutch Sailing Ship,
17th
Century — A161

1966, Oct. 24   Photo.   Perf. 13½
423 A161 4c bl, blk, dp org & gold   .30   .25
a.   Deep orange omitted   6,000.
b.   Gold omitted   2,000.
350th anniv. of Dirk Hartog's discovery of the Australian west coast, and his landing on the island named after him.

Hands Reaching for
Bible — A162

1967, Mar. 7   Photo.   Perf. 13½
424 A162 4c multicolored   .30   .25
British and Foreign Bible Soc., 150th anniv.

Combination
Lock and
Antique
Keys — A163

1967, Apr. 5   Photo.   Perf. 13½
425 A163 4c emerald, blk & lt blue   .30   .25
150th anniv. of banking in Australia (Bank of New South Wales).

Lions Intl., 50th
Anniv. — A164

1967, June 7   Photo.   Perf. 13½
426 A164 4c ultra, black & gold   .30   .25

YWCA
Emblems
and Flags
A165

1967, Aug. 21   Photo.   Perf. 13½
427 A165 4c dk blue, lt bl & lilac   .30   .25
World Council Meeting of the YWCA, Monash University, Victoria, Aug. 14-Sept. 1.

Seated Women Symbolizing Obstetrics and Gynecology, Female Symbol
A166

1967, Sept. 20   Photo.   Perf. 13½
428 A166 4c lilac, dk blue & blk   .30   .25
5th World Congress of Gynecology and Obstetrics, Sydney, Sept. 23-30.

Gothic
Arches and
Christmas
Bell Flower
A167

Cross, Stars of David
and Yin Yang
Forming
Mandala — A168

1967   Photo.   Perf. 13½
429 A167 5c multicolored   .30   .25
430 A168 25c multicolored   2.25 2.00
Christmas.
Issue dates: 5c, Oct. 18; 25c, Nov. 27.

Satellite Orbiting
Earth — A169

Satellite and
Antenna,
Moree,
N.S.W. — A170

Design: 20c, World weather map connecting Washington, Moscow and Melbourne, and computer and teleprinter tape spools.

1968, Mar. 20   Photo.   Perf. 13½
431 A169 5c dull yel, red, bl & dk blue   .90   .50
432 A169 20c blue, blk & red   2.50 2.40
a.   Red omitted   3,000.
433 A170 25c Prus blue, blk & lt green   4.00 4.00
    Nos. 431-433 (3)   7.40 6.90
Use of satellites for weather observations and communications.

Kangaroo Paw,
Western
Australia — A171

State Flowers: 13c, Pink heath, Victoria. 15c, Tasmanian blue gum, Tasmania. 20c, Sturt's desert pea, South Australia. 25c, Cooktown orchid, Queensland. 30c, Waratah, New South Wales.

1968, July 10   Photo.   Perf. 13½
Flowers in Natural Colors
434 A171 6c multicolored   .55   .50
435 A171 13c multicolored   .65   .55
436 A171 15c multicolored   2.25   .45
437 A171 20c multicolored   5.00   .75
438 A171 25c multicolored   4.75   .75
439 A171 30c multicolored   1.25   .25
a.   Green omitted   3,750.
    Nos. 434-439 (6)   14.45 3.25
A 1971 reprinting of No. 439 shows more areas of white in the pink petals. This is scarcer than the first printing. Value, $4.75.

Sturt's Desert Rose,
Northern Territory —
A171a

Designs: 5c, Golden wattle, national flower. 7c, 10c, Sturt's desert pea.

Coil Stamps
1970-75   Perf. 14½ Horiz.
439A A171a 2c dk grn & multi   .25   .25
i.   Lettering and value bolder   .25   .25
439B A171a 4c gray & multi   .70   .45
439C A171a 5c gray & multi   .25   .25
439D A171a 6c gray & multi   1.40   .55
h.   Green omitted   2,250.
439E A171a 7c blk, red & grn   .40   .25
f.   Green omitted   110.00

439G A171a 10c blk, red &
grn .35 .25
Nos. 439A-439G (6) 3.35 2.00

Issued: 4c, 5c, 4/27; 6c, 10/28; 2c, 7c, 10/1/71; 10c, 1/15/75; No. 439Ai, 11/73.

Soil Testing
Through
Chemistry &
by Computer
A172

Hippocrates
& Hands
Holding
Hypodermic
A173

1968, Aug. 6   Photo.   Perf. 13½
440 A172 5c multicolored .30 .25
441 A173 5c multicolored .30 .25

9th Intl. Congress of Soil Science, University of Adelaide, Aug. 6-16 (No. 440); General Assembly of World Medical Associations, Sydney, Aug. 6-9 (No. 441). Nos. 440-441 printed in sheets of 100 in two separate panes of 50 connected by a gutter. Each sheet contains 10 gutter pairs.

Runner and Aztec
Calendar
Stone — A174

Design: 25c, Aztec calendar stone and Mexican flag, horiz.

1968, Oct. 2
442 A174 5c multicolored .55 .25
443 A174 25c multicolored 2.00 1.75
a. Green omitted 3,500.

19th Olympic Games, Mexico City, Oct. 12-27. Nos. 442-443 printed in sheets of 100 in two separate panes of 50 connected by a gutter. Each sheet contains 10 gutter pairs.

Symbolic House and
Money — A175

1968, Oct. 16
444 A175 5c multicolored .35 .35

11th Triennial Congress of the Intl. Union of Building Societies and Savings Associations, Sydney, Oct. 20-27.

View of Bethlehem
and Church
Window — A176

1968, Oct. 23   Photo.   Perf. 13½
445 A176 5c lt bl, red, grn
& gold .30 .25
a. Red omitted 3,500. 2,000.
b. Gold omitted 850.00 500.00

Christmas.

Edgeworth David (1858-1934),
Geologist — A177

Famous Australians: No. 447, Caroline Chisholm (1808-77), social worker, reformer. No. 448, Albert Namatjira (1902-59), aborigine, artist. No. 449, Andrew Barton (Banjo) Paterson 1864-1941), poet, writer.

1968, Nov. 6   Engr.   Perf. 15x14
446 A177 5c green, *greenish* 1.20 .35
a. Booklet pane of 5 + label 6.50
447 A177 5c purple, *pink* 1.20 .35
a. Booklet pane of 5 + label 6.50
448 A177 5c dark brown, *buff* 1.20 .35
a. Booklet pane of 5 + label 6.50
449 A177 5c indigo, *lt blue* 1.20 .35
a. Booklet pane of 5 + label 6.50
Nos. 446-449 (4) 4.80 1.40

Sir Edmund Barton
(1849-1920) — A178

Prime Ministers: No. 451, Alfred Deakin (1856-1919). No. 452, John C. Watson (1867-1941). No. 453, Sir George H. Reid (1845-1918).

1969, Oct. 22   Engr.   Perf. 15x14
450 A178 5c indigo, *greenish* 1.20 .35
a. Booklet pane of 5 + label 6.50
451 A178 5c indigo, *greenish* 1.20 .35
a. Booklet pane of 5 + label 6.50
452 A178 5c indigo, *greenish* 1.20 .35
a. Booklet pane of 5 + label 6.50
453 A178 5c indigo, *greenish* 1.20 .35
a. Booklet pane of 5 + label 6.50
Nos. 450-453 (4) 4.80 1.40

Reginald C. and John
R. Duigan,
Aviators — A179

Famous Australians: No. 455, Lachlan Macquarie (1761-1824), Governor of New South Wales. No. 456, Adam Lindsay Gordon (1833-70), poet. No. 457, Edward John Eyre (1815-1901), explorer.

1970, Nov. 16   Engr.   Perf. 15x14
454 A179 6c dark blue 1.20 .50
a. Booklet pane of 5 + label 6.50
455 A179 6c dk brn, *salmon* 1.20 .50
a. Booklet pane of 5 + label 6.50
456 A179 6c magenta, *brt pink* 1.20 .50
a. Booklet pane of 5 + label 6.50
457 A179 6c brown red, *salmon* 1.20 .50
a. Booklet pane of 5 + label 6.50
Nos. 454-457 (4) 4.80 2.00

Nos. 446-457 were issued in booklet panes only; all stamps have 1 or 2 straight edges.

Macquarie
Lighthouse — A180

1968, Nov. 27   Engr.   Perf. 14½x13½
458 A180 5c indigo, *buff* .45 .50

Macquarie Lighthouse, Outer South Head, Sydney, 150th anniv.

Surveyor George W. Goyder and
Assistants, 1869; Building in Darwin,
1969 — A181

1969, Feb. 5   Photo.   Perf. 13½
459 A181 5c black brn & dull yel .30 .25

First permanent settlement of the Northern Territory of Australia, cent.

Melbourne
Harbor
Scene
A182

1969, Feb. 26   Photo.   Perf. 13½
460 A182 5c dull blue & multi .30 .25

6th Biennial Conference of the Intl. Assoc. of Ports and Harbors, Melbourne, March 3-8.

Overlapping
Circles
A183

1969, June 5   Photo.   Perf. 13½
461 A183 5c gray, vio bl, bl &
gold .30 .25
a. Gold omitted 3,000.

ILO, 50th anniv.

Sugar Cane — A184

Primary industries: 15c, Eucalyptus (timber). 20c, Wheat. 25c, Ram, ewe, lamb (wool).

1969, Sept. 17   Perf. 13½x13
462 A184 7c blue & multi 1.60 1.00
463 A184 15c emerald & multi 4.75 3.00
a. Black omitted 1,750. —
464 A184 20c org brn & multi 2.40 1.20
465 A184 25c gray, black & yel 3.25 1.20
Nos. 462-465 (4) 12.00 6.40

Nativity — A185

Tree of
Life — A186

Perf. 13½x13, 13x13½
1969, Oct. 15   Photo.
466 A185 5c multicolored .40 .25
a. Yellow omitted 1,800.
b. Magenta omitted 1,800.
467 A186 25c multicolored 3.00 2.75

Christmas.

Vickers Vimy
Flown by
Ross Smith,
England to
Australia
A187

Designs: No. 469, B.E. 2E plane, automobile, spectators. No. 470, Ford truck, surveyors Lieuts. Hudson Fysh & P.J. McGinness.

1969, Nov. 12   Perf. 13x13½
468 A187 5c bl, blk, cop red & ol .75 .35
469 A187 5c bl, blk, cop red & ol .75 .35
470 A187 5c cop red, black & ol .75 .35
a. Strip of 3, #468-470 3.75 3.50
Nos. 468-470 (3) 2.25 1.05

1st England to Australia flight by Capt. Ross Smith & Lieut. Keith Smith, 50th anniv. No. 470a has various combinations possible.

Diesel Locomotive and New Track
Linking Melbourne, Sydney and
Brisbane with Perth
A188

1970, Feb. 11   Photo.   Perf. 13x13½
471 A188 5c multicolored .35 .25

Completion of the standard gauge railroad between Sydney and Perth.

EXPO '70
Australian
Pavilion
A189

Design: 20c, Southern Cross and Japanese inscription: "From the country of the south with warm feeling."

1970, Mar. 16   Photo.   Perf. 13x13½
472 A189 5c bl, blk, red & brnz .30 .25
473 A189 20c red & black .75 .45

EXPO '70 Intl. Exhib., Osaka, Japan, Mar. 15-Sept. 13.

Queen
Elizabeth II
and Prince
Philip
A190

Australian
Flag — A191

1970, Mar. 31
474 A190 5c yel bister & black .50 .30
475 A191 30c vio blue & multi 2.25 1.50

Visit of Queen Elizabeth II, Prince Philip and Princess Anne to Australia.

Steer, Alfalfa
and Native
Spear Grass
A192

1970, Apr. 13   Photo.   Perf. 13x13½
476 A192 5c emerald & multi .30 .35

11th Intl. Grasslands Congress, Surfers Paradise, Queensland, Apr. 13-23.

Capt. James Cook and "Endeavour" — A193

Designs: No. 478, Sextant, "Endeavour." No. 479, "Endeavour," landing party, kangaroo. No. 480, Daniel Charles Solander, Sir Joseph Banks, Cook, map, botanical drawing. No. 481, Cook taking possession with Union Jack; "Endeavour," coral. 30c, Cook, "Endeavour," sextant, kangaroo, aborigines.

1970, Apr. 20   Perf. 13½x13
Size: 24x35½mm
477	A193	5c org brn & multi	.35	.25
478	A193	5c org brn & multi	.35	.25
479	A193	5c org brn & multi	.35	.25
480	A193	5c org brn & multi	.35	.25
481	A193	5c org brn & multi	.35	.25
a.		Strip of 5, #477-481	2.40	2.40

Size: 62x29mm
482	A193	30c org brn & multi	2.40	2.25
a.		Souv. sheet, #477-482, imperf	16.00	12.00
		Nos. 477-482 (6)	4.15	3.50

Cook's discovery and exploration of the eastern coast of Australia, 200th anniv.
No. 481a has continuous design.
No. 482a with brown marginal overprint "Souvenir Sheet ANPEX 1970. . ." is of private origin. Value $27.50.

Snowy Mountains Hydroelectric Project A194

Designs: 8c, Ord River hydroelectric project (dam, cotton plant and boll). 9c, Bauxite and aluminum production (mine, conveyor belt and aluminum window frame). 10c, Oil and natural gas (off-shore drilling rig and pipelines).

1970, Aug. 31 Photo. Perf. 13x13½
483	A194	7c multicolored	1.20	.40
484	A194	8c multicolored	.25	.25
485	A194	9c multicolored	.50	.25
486	A194	10c multicolored	.60	.30
		Nos. 483-486 (4)	2.55	1.20

Australian economic development.

Flame Symbolizing Democracy and Freedom of Speech — A195

1970, Oct. 2 Photo. Perf. 13½x13
| 487 | A195 | 6c green & multi | .30 | .25 |

16th Commonwealth Parliamentary Assoc. Conference, Canberra, Oct. 2-9.

Herd of Illawarra Shorthorns and Laboratory A196

1970, Oct. 7   Perf. 13x13½
| 488 | A196 | 6c multicolored | .30 | .25 |

18th Intl. Dairy Cong., Sydney, Oct. 12-16.

Madonna and Child, by William Beasley — A197

1970, Oct. 14   Perf. 13½x13
| 489 | A197 | 6c multicolored | .30 | .25 |

Christmas.

UN Emblem, Dove and Symbols — A198

1970, Oct. 19
| 490 | A198 | 6c blue & multi | .30 | .25 |

25th anniversary of the United Nations.

Qantas Boeing 707, and Avro 504 — A199

30c, Sunbeam Dyak powered Avro 504 on ground and Qantas Boeing 707 in the air.

1970, Nov. 2   Perf. 13x13½
| 491 | A199 | 6c multicolored | .40 | .25 |
| 492 | A199 | 30c multicolored | 1.25 | 1.25 |

Qantas, Australian overseas airlines, 50th anniv.

Japanese Noh Actor, Australian Dancer and Chinese Opera Character — A200

15c, Chinese pipe, trumpet, Australian aboriginal didgeridoo, Thai fiddle, Indian double oboe, Tibetan drums. 20c, Red Sea dhow, Chinese junk, Australian lifeguard's surfboat, Malaysian & South Indian river boats.

1971, Jan. 6 Photo. Perf. 13½x13
493	A200	7c multicolored	1.20	.55
494	A200	15c multicolored	1.60	1.25
495	A200	20c multicolored	1.45	.70
		Nos. 493-495 (3)	4.25	2.50

Link between Australia and Asia; 28th Intl. Congress of Orientalists, Canberra, Jan. 6-12.

Southern Cross A201

1971, Apr. 21 Photo. Perf. 13x13½
| 496 | A201 | 6c multicolored | .30 | .25 |

Australian Natives Assoc., cent.

Symbolic Market Graphs — A202

1971, May 5   Perf. 13½x13
| 497 | A202 | 6c silver & multi | .30 | .25 |

Centenary of Sydney Stock Exchange.

Rotary Emblem A203

1971, May 17   Perf. 13x13½
| 498 | A203 | 6c multicolored | .30 | .25 |

First Intl. Rotary Convention held in Australia, Sydney, May 16-20.

DH-9A, Australian Mirage Jet Fighters — A204

1971, June 9   Perf. 13½x13
| 499 | A204 | 6c multicolored | .55 | .25 |

Royal Australian Air Force, 50th anniv.

RSPCA Centenary — A205

Designs: 12c, Man and lamb (animal science). 18c, Kangaroo (fauna conservation). 24c, Seeing eye dog (animals' aid to man).

1971, July 5 Photo. Perf. 13½x13
500	A205	6c blk, brown & org	.25	.25
501	A205	12c blk, dk grn & yel	.45	.25
502	A205	18c brown & multi	.65	.35
a.		Litho., perf. 14¾x14, dated "2013" (#1003b)	.45	.45
503	A205	24c blue & multi	1.20	.70
		Nos. 500-503 (4)	2.55	1.55

Royal Society for Prevention of Cruelty to Animals in Australia, cent.
Issued: No. 502a, 5/10/2013.

Longnecked Tortoise, Painted on Bark — A206

Aboriginal Art: 25c, Mourners' body paintings, Warramunga tribe. 30c, Cave painting, Western Arnhem Land, vert. 35c, Graveposts, Bathurst and Melville Islands, vert.

Perf. 13x13½, 13½x13
1971, Sept. 29
504	A206	20c multicolored	.45	.30
505	A206	25c multicolored	.45	.45
506	A206	30c multicolored	1.50	.45
507	A206	35c multicolored	.55	.45
		Nos. 504-507 (4)	2.95	1.65

Three Kings and Star — A207

1971, Oct. 13 Photo. Perf. 13½x13
508	Block of 7		45.00	35.00
a.	A207 7c brt grn, dk bl (Kings) & lil		12.00	1.50
b.	A207 7c lil, red brn, grn & dk bl		3.25	.70
c.	A207 7c red brown & lilac		4.00	.80
d.	A207 7c lilac, red brn & brt grn		3.25	.70
e.	A207 7c red brn & dark blue		3.25	.70
f.	A207 7c lilac, green & dk blue		15.00	3.00
g.	A207 7c brt grn, dk bl & lilac (Kings)		3.25	.70

Christmas. Nos. 508a-508g printed se-tenant in sheets of 50. Each sheet contains 2 green crosses formed by 4 No. 508g and three No. 508a.

Andrew Fisher (1862-1928) — A208

Prime Ministers: No. 515, Joseph Cook (1860-1947). No. 516, William Morris Hughes (1864-1952). No. 517, Stanley Melbourne Bruce (1883-1967).

1972, Mar. 8 Engr. Perf. 15x14
514	A208	7c dark blue	.70	.40
a.		Booklet pane of 5 + label	3.50	
515	A208	7c dark red	.70	.40
a.		Booklet pane of 5 + label	3.50	
516	A208	7c dark blue	.70	.40
a.		Booklet pane of 5 + label	3.50	
517	A208	7c dark red	.70	.40
a.		Booklet pane of 5 + label	3.50	
		Nos. 514-517 (4)	2.80	1.60

Nos. 514-517 were issued in booklets only; all stamps have one or two straight edges.

Cameo Brooch — A209

1972, Apr. 18 Photo. Perf. 13½
| 518 | A209 | 7c multicolored | .35 | .25 |

Country Women's Assoc., 50th anniv.

Apple and Banana A210

1972, June 14
519	A210	20c shown	2.40	1.50
520	A210	25c Rice	2.40	1.75
521	A210	30c Fish	1.75	1.75
522	A210	35c Cattle	4.00	3.00
		Nos. 519-522 (4)	10.55	8.00

Worker in Sheltered Workshop — A211

18c, Amputee assembling electrical circuit. 24c, Boy wearing Toronto splint, playing ball.

1972, Aug. 2   Perf. 13½x13
523	A211	12c grn & brn	.30	.25
524	A211	18c org & ol, horiz.	1.25	.60
525	A211	24c brn & ultra	.50	.25
		Nos. 523-525 (3)	2.05	1.10

Rehabilitation of the handicapped.

Overland Telegraph Line — A212

1972, Aug. 22 Photo. Perf. 13x13½
526 A212 7c dk red, blk & lemon .30 .30
Centenary of overland telegraph line.

Athlete, Olympic Rings — A213

1972, Aug. 28 Perf. 13½x13
527 A213 7c shown .45 .45
528 A213 7c Swimming .45 .45
529 A213 7c Rowing .45 .45
530 A213 35c Equestrian 3.25 2.75
Nos. 527-530 (4) 4.60 4.10

20th Olympic Games, Munich, 8/26-9/11.

Abacus, Numerals, Computer Circuits A214

1972, Oct. 16 Photo. Perf. 13x13½
531 A214 7c multicolored .30 .30
10th Intl. Congress of Accountants.

19th Cent. Combine Harvester A215

5c, Pioneer family, vert. 10c, Water pump, vert. 40c, Pioneer house. 50c, Cobb & Co. coach. 60c, Early Morse key, vert. 80c, Paddle-wheel steamer.

Perf. 13½x13, 13x13½
1972, Nov. 15 Photo.
532 A215 5c multicolored .25 .25
533 A215 10c multicolored .35 .25
534 A215 15c shown .30 .25
535 A215 40c multicolored .60 .25
536 A215 50c multicolored 1.00 .25
537 A215 60c multicolored .90 .55
538 A215 80c multicolored 1.25 .65
Nos. 532-538 (7) 4.65 2.45

Australian pioneer life.

Jesus and Children A216

Dove, Cross and "Darkness into Light" — A217

Perf. 14½x14, 13½x13
1972, Nov. 29
539 A216 7c tan & multi .35 .25
540 A217 35c blue & multi 8.00 6.50
Christmas.

Metric Conversion, Mass — A218

Metric conversion: No. 542, Temperature, horiz. No. 543, Length. No. 544, Volume.

1973, Mar. 7 Photo. Perf. 14x14½
541 A218 7c pale vio & multi .60 .40
542 A218 7c yellow & multi .60 .40
543 A218 7c yel green & multi .60 .40
544 A218 7c brt rose & multi .60 .40
Nos. 541-544 (4) 2.40 1.60

Conversion to metric system.

Stylized Caduceus and Laurel A219

1973, Apr. 4 Photo. Perf. 14½x14
545 A219 7c dk bl, emer & lil rose .40 .30
WHO, 25th anniv.

Dame Mary Gilmore, Writer — A220

Famous Australians: No. 547, William Charles Wentworth, explorer. No. 548, Sir Isaac Isaacs, lawyer, 1st Australian-born Governor-General. No. 549, Marcus Clarke, writer.

Engr. & Litho.
1973, May 16 Perf. 15x14
546 A220 7c bister & black .80 .30
547 A220 7c bister & black .80 .30
548 A220 7c black & violet .80 .30
549 A220 7c black & violet .80 .30
a. Block of 4, #546-549 4.00 4.00

Shipping Industry — A221

Designs: 25c, Iron ore and steel. 30c, Truck convoy (beef road). 35c, Aerial mapping.

1973, June 6 Photo. Perf. 13½x13
550 A221 20c ultra & multi 1.75 1.40
551 A221 25c red & multi 1.50 1.40
552 A221 30c ol brn & multi 3.00 1.75
553 A221 35c olive & multi 2.00 1.75
Nos. 550-553 (4) 8.25 6.30

Australian economic development.

Banded Coral Shrimp — A222

Chrysoprase A223

Helichrysum Thomsonii A223a

Wombat A224

Radio Astronomy A225

Red Gums of the Far North, by Hans Heysen — A226

Coming South (Immigrants), by Tom Roberts — A226a

2c, Fiddler crab. 3c, Coral crab. 4c, Mauve stinger. 7c, Agate. 8c, Opal. 9c, Rhodonite. 10c, Star sapphire. 11c, Atomic absorption spectrophotometry. 25c, Spiny anteater. 30c, Brushtail possum. 33c, Immunology. 45c, Callistemon teretifolius, horiz. 48c, Oceanography. 75c, Feather-tailed glider.

Paintings: $1, Sergeant of Light Horse, by George Lambert. No. 575, On the Wallaby Track. $4, Shearing the Rams, by Tom Roberts. No. 577, McMahon's Point, by Arthur Streeton. No. 578, Mentone.

Perf. 14x15, 15x14 (A222, A223, A223a); Perf. 14x14½ (A224); Perf. 13x13½ (A225, A226, $1)
1973-84 Photo.
554 A222 1c shown .25 .25
555 A222 2c multi .25 .25
556 A222 3c multi .25 .25
557 A222 4c multi .25 .25
558 A223 6c shown .25 .25
559 A223 7c multi .30 .25
560 A223 8c multi .30 .25
561 A223 9c multi .30 .25
562 A223 10c multi ('74) .35 .25
563 A225 11c multi ('75) .65 .30
564 A223a 18c shown ('75) .60 .25
565 A224 20c multi ('74) .45 .25
566 A225 24c shown ('75) 1.00 .45
567 A224 25c multi ('74) 1.25 .60
568 A224 30c multi ('74) .65 .25
569 A225 33c multi ('75) 1.00 .80
570 A223a 45c multi ('75) .80 .35
571 A223 48c multi ('75) 1.25 1.00
572 A224 75c multi ('74) 1.25 .60
573 A226a $1 multi ('74) 1.60 .40
574 A226 $2 multi ('74) 3.25 .75
575 A226 $2 multi ('81) 3.25 .75
576 A226 $4 multi ('74) 6.00 2.75

Litho.
Perf. 14½
577 A226a $5 multi ('79) 8.00 2.75
578 A226a $5 multi ('84) 7.50 3.50
579 A226a $10 shown ('77) 16.00 4.00
Nos. 554-579 (26) 57.00 22.00

Issued: 1c-9c, 7/11; 20c, 25c, 30c, 75c, 2/13; $1, No. 574, $4, 4/24; 10c, 10/16; 11c, 24c, 33c, 48c, 5/14; 18c, 45c, 8/27; $10, 10/19; No. 577, 3/14; No. 575, 6/17; No. 578, 4/4.

No. 560 Surcharged in Red

Perf. 15x14
580 A223 9c on 8c multi ('74) .30 .35

Hand Protecting Playing Children A227

1973, Sept. 5 Photo. Perf. 13x13½
581 A227 7c bis brn, grn & plum .30 .25

50th anniv. of Legacy, an ex-servicemen's organization concerned with the welfare of widows and children of servicemen.

Baptism of Christ A228

The Good Shepherd A229

1973, Oct. 3 Perf. 14x14½
582 A228 7c gold & multi .30 .25
a. Perf. 14x15 3.00 .75

Perf. 13½
583 A229 30c gold & multi 2.25 2.25
Christmas.

Buchanan's Hotel, Townsville A230

St. James' Church, Sydney — A231

Designs: 7c, Opera House, Sydney. 40c, Como House, Melbourne.

1973, Oct. 17 Photo. Perf. 14½x14
584 A230 7c lt blue & ultra .35 .35
a. Perf. 15x14 4.50 .90
585 A230 10c bister & black .50 .35

Perf. 13x13½, 13½x13
586 A230 40c dl pink, gray & blk .65 .75
587 A231 50c gray & multi 1.60 1.25
Nos. 584-587 (4) 3.10 2.60

Australian architecture; opening of the Sydney Opera House, Oct. 14, 1973 (No. 584).

Radio and Gramophone Speaker A232

1973, Nov. 21 Photo. Perf. 13½x13
588 A232 7c dull blue, blk & brn .35 .25
Broadcasting in Australia, 50th anniv.

Supreme Court
Judge on
Bench — A233

1974, May 15   Photo.   Perf. 14x14½
589 A233 7c multicolored   .35 .25

150th anniv. of the proclamation of the
Charter of Justice in New South Wales and
Van Diemen's Land (Australia's Third
Charter).

Australian
Football — A234

1974, July 24   Photo.   Perf. 14x14½
590 A234 7c shown   .35 .25
591 A234 7c Cricket   .35 .25
  a.   Booklet pane of 1, litho., perf.
        14¾x14, dated "2007"   .25 —
592 A234 7c Golf   .35 .25
593 A234 7c Surfing   .35 .25
594 A234 7c Tennis   .35 .25
595 A234 7c Bowls, horiz.   .35 .25
596 A234 7c Rugby, horiz.   .35 .25
      Nos. 590-596 (7)   2.45 1.75

No. 591a issued 11/14/2007.

Carrier
Pigeon
A235

Designs: 30c, Carrier pigeons, vert.

1974, Oct. 9   Photo.   Perf. 14½x14
597 A235 7c multicolored   .60 .35
  a.   Perf. 15x14   .60 .35

Perf. 13½x13
598 A235 30c multicolored   1.60 1.20

UPU, cent. A booklet containing a strip of 5
each of Nos. 597-598 was produced and sold
for $4 Australian by the National Stamp Week
Promotion Council with government approval.

William Charles
Wentworth — A236

Typo. & Litho.
1974, Oct. 9   Perf. 14x15
599 A236 7c bister & black   .40 .25
  a.   Perf. 14x14½   1.60 .40

Sesquicentennial of 1st Australian independent newspaper. W. C. Wentworth and Dr.
Robert Wardell were the editors and the "A" is
type from masthead of "The Australian."

Adoration of the
Kings, by
Dürer — A237

Christmas: 35c, Flight into Egypt, by
Albrecht Dürer.

1974, Nov. 13   Engr.   Perf. 14x14½
600 A237 10c buff & black   .40 .25
601 A237 35c buff & black   .90 .90

Pre-school
Education
A238

Correspondence Schools — A239

Science
Education
A240

Advanced
Education — A241

Perf. 13x13½, 13½x13
1974, Nov. 20   Photo.
602 A238 5c multicolored   .60 .25
603 A239 11c multicolored   .60 .25
604 A240 15c multicolored   .60 .40
605 A241 60c multicolored   1.60 1.20
      Nos. 602-605 (4)   3.40 2.10

"Avoid
Pollution"
A242

"Road
Safety" — A243

Design: No. 607, "Avoid bush fires."

1975, Jan. 29   Photo.   Perf. 14½x14
606 A242 10c multicolored   .55 .45
  a.   Perf. 15x14   9.50 5.00
607 A242 10c multicolored   .55 .45
  a.   Perf. 15x14   1.50 1.10

Perf. 14x14½
608 A243 10c multicolored   .55 .45
      Nos. 606-608 (3)   1.65 1.35
      Environmental dangers.

Symbols of
Womanhood, Sun,
Moon — A244

1975, Mar. 12   Photo.   Perf. 14x14½
609 A244 10c dk vio blue & grn   .35 .25
      International Women's Year.

Joseph B. Chifley
(1885-1951) — A245

No. 611, John Curtin, 1885-1945. No. 612,
Arthur W. Fadden, 1895-1973. No. 613,
Joseph A. Lyons, 1879-1939. No. 614, Earle
Page, 1880-1963. No. 615, John H. Scullin,
1876-1953.

1975, Mar. 26
610 A245 10c shown   .35 .25
611 A245 10c multicolored   .35 .25
612 A245 10c multicolored   .35 .25
613 A245 10c multicolored   .35 .25
614 A245 10c multicolored   .35 .25
615 A245 10c multicolored   .35 .25
      Nos. 610-615 (6)   2.10 1.50
      Australian Prime Ministers.

Australian
Postal
Commission
A246

Design: No. 617, Australian Telecommunications Commission.

1975, July 1   Photo.   Perf. 14½x14
616 A246 10c red, black & gray   .65 .45
  a.   Perf. 15x14   .85 .45
617 A246 10c yel, black & gray   .65 .45
  a.   Perf. 15x14   .85 .45
  b.   Pair, #616-617   1.60 1.25
  c.   Pair, #616a, 617b   3.50 3.50

Formation of Australian Postal and Telecommunications Commissions. Printed
checkerwise.

Edith Cowan,   Truganini, Last
Judge and   Tasmanian
Legislator   Aborigine
A247   A248

Portraits: No. 619, Louisa Lawson (1848-
1920), journalist. No. 620, Ethel Florence
(Henry Handel) Richardson (1870-1946), novelist. No. 621, Catherine Spence (1825-1910),
teacher, journalist, voting reformer. No. 622,
Emma Constance Stone (1856-1902), first
Australian woman physician.

1975, Aug. 6   Photo.   Perf. 14x14½
618 A247 10c olive grn & multi   .60 .30
  a.   Perf. 14x15   .60 .30
619 A247 10c yel bister & multi   .60 .30
  a.   Perf. 14x15   .60 .30
620 A248 10c olive & multi   .60 .30
  a.   Perf. 14x15   .60 .30
621 A247 10c gray & multi   .60 .30
  a.   Perf. 14x15   .60 .30
622 A247 10c violet & multi   .60 .30
  a.   Perf. 14x15   .60 .30
623 A248 10c brown & multi   .60 .30
  a.   Perf. 14x15   .60 .30
      Nos. 618-623 (6)   3.60 1.80
      Famous Australian women.

Spirit House (PNG)
and Sydney Opera
House — A249

Bird in Flight
and Southern
Cross
A250

1975, Sept. 16   Photo.   Perf. 13½
624 A249 18c multicolored   .45 .25
625 A250 25c multicolored   .80 .65

Papua New Guinea independence, Sept.
16, 1975.

Adoration of the
Kings — A251

"The Light
Shineth in
the
Darkness"
A252

1975, Oct. 29   Photo.   Perf. 14½x14
626 A251 15c multicolored   .40 .25
627 A252 45c silver & multi   1.60 1.50
      Christmas.

Australian
Coat of
Arms
A253

Type I   Type II

Type I — Kangaroo: eye is dot, right paw
has 1 toe, left foot has 1 toe. Emu: feet have 1
toe.
Type II — Kangaroo: eye is line, right paw
has 3 toes, left foot has 2 toes. Emu: feet have
2 toes.
Other differences exist.

1976, Jan. 5   Photo.   Perf. 14½x14
628 A253 18c multicolored, type I .40 .25
  a.   Type II   .95 .40

"Williams'
Coffin"
Telephone,
1878 — A254

1976, Mar. 10   Photo.   Perf. 13½
629 A254 18c buff & multi   .40 .30

Centenary of first telephone call by Alexander Graham Bell, Mar. 10, 1876.

John Oxley
A255

Australian explorers: No. 631, Hamilton
Hume and William Hovell. No. 632, John For-
rest. No. 633, Ernest Giles. No. 634, Peter
Warburton. No. 635, William Gosse.

1976, June 9 Photo. *Perf. 13½*
630	A255	18c shown	.35	.25
631	A255	18c multicolored	.35	.25
632	A255	18c multicolored	.35	.25
633	A255	18c multicolored	.35	.25
634	A255	18c multicolored	.35	.25
635	A255	18c multicolored	.35	.25
		Nos. 630-635 (6)	2.10	1.50

Survey Rule, Graph, Punched Tape — A256

1976, June 15 *Perf. 15x14*
636	A256	18c multicolored	.40	.25

Commonwealth Scientific and Industrial Research Organization, 50th anniv.

Soccer Goalkeeper A257

Olympic Rings and: No. 638, Woman gymnast, vert. 25c, Woman diver, vert. 40c, Bicycling.

Perf. 13x13½, 13½x13
1976, July 14 Photo.
637	A257	18c multicolored	.30	.25
638	A257	18c multicolored	.30	.25
639	A257	25c multicolored	.40	.40
640	A257	40c multicolored	.60	.50
		Nos. 637-640 (4)	1.60	1.40

21st Olympic Games, Montreal, Canada, July 17-Aug. 1.

Richmond Bridge, Tasmania A258

Mt. Buffalo, Victoria — A259

Designs: 25c, Broken Bay, New South Wales. 35c, Wittenoom Gorge, Western Australia. 70c, Barrier Reef, Queensland. 85c, Ayers Rock, Northern Territory.

Perf. 14½x14, 14x14½
1976, Aug. 25 Photo.
641	A258	5c multicolored	.30	.25
642	A258	25c multicolored	.45	.25
643	A258	35c multicolored	.50	.30
644	A259	50c multicolored	.70	.30
645	A258	70c multicolored	1.00	.40
646	A258	85c multicolored	1.10	.70
		Nos. 641-646 (6)	4.05	2.20

Blamire Young and Australia No. 59 — A260

1976, Sept. 27 Photo. *Perf. 13½*
647	A260	18c apple grn & multi	.40	.25

Miniature Sheet
648		Sheet of 4	1.60 1.60
a.		A260 18c yellow & dark brown	.40 .40
b.		A260 18c rose, dk brown & yel	.40 .40
c.		A260 18c bl, dk brn, rose & yel	.40 .40

Natl. Stamp Week, Sept. 27-Oct. 3. Blamire Young (1862-1935), designer of Australia's 1st issue. No. 648 shows different stages of 4-

---

color printing. The 4th stamp in sheet is identical with No. 647.

Virgin and Child, after Simone Cantarini A261

Holly, Toy Koala, Christmas Tree and Decoration, Partridge A262

1976, Nov. 1 Photo. *Perf. 14½x14*
649	A261	15c brt car & lt blue	.40	.25

Perf. 13½
650	A262	45c multicolored	.80	.80

Christmas.

John Gould (1804-1881) Ornithologist A263

Famous Australians: No. 652, Thomas Laby (1880-1946), nuclear scientist. No. 653, Sir Baldwin Spencer (1860-1929), anthropologist (aborigines). No. 654, Griffith Taylor (1880-1963), geographer and antarctic explorer.

1976, Nov. 10 *Perf. 15x14*
651	A263	18c shown	.35	.25
652	A263	18c Laby	.35	.25
653	A263	18c Spencer	.35	.25
654	A263	18c Taylor	.35	.25
		Nos. 651-654 (4)	1.40	1.00

Violinists — A264

1977, Jan. 19 Photo. *Perf. 14x14½*
655	A264	20c shown	.30	.25
656	A264	30c Dramatic scene	.35	.25
657	A264	40c Dancer	.45	.30
658	A264	60c Opera singer	.90	.40
		Nos. 655-658 (4)	2.00	1.20

Performing arts in Australia.

Elizabeth II — A265

Design: 45c, Elizabeth II and Prince Philip.

1977, Feb. 2 *Perf. 14x14½*
659	A265	18c multicolored	.40	.30
660	A265	45c multicolored	.75	.75

Reign of Queen Elizabeth II, 25th anniv. Perf 14½x14 examples of Nos. 659-660 are from a booklet pane containing 2 of each stamp, found in the booklet footnoted under No. 2507.

Wicket Keeper, Slip Fieldsman — A266

Cricket match, 19th century: No. 662, Umpire and batsman. No. 663, Two fieldsmen. No. 664, Batsman and umpire. No. 665, Bowler and fieldsman. 45c, Batsman facing bowler.

1977, Mar. 9 Photo. *Perf. 13½*
661	A266	18c gray & multi	.45	.45
a.		Litho., perf. 14¾x14, dated "2007"	.55	.55
662	A266	18c gray & multi	.45	.45
a.		Litho., perf. 14¾x14, dated "2007"	.55	.55
663	A266	18c gray & multi	.45	.45
a.		Litho., perf. 14¾x14, dated "2007"	.55	.55
664	A266	18c gray & multi	.45	.45
a.		Litho., perf. 14¾x14, dated "2007"	.55	.55
665	A266	18c gray & multi	.45	.45
a.		Strip of 5, #661-665	3.00	3.00
b.		Litho., perf. 14¾x14, dated "2007"	.55	.55
666	A266	45c gray & multi	1.00	1.00
a.		Litho., imperf., dated "2007"	1.25	1.25
b.		Booklet pane of 6, #661a, 662a, 663a, 664a, 665b, 666a	4.00	—
		Nos. 661-666 (6)	3.25	3.25

Nos. 661a, 662a, 663a, 664a, 665b, 666a, 666b issued 11/14/2007.

Parliament House, Canberra A267

1977, Apr. 13 *Perf. 14½x14*
667	A267	18c multicolored	.40	.25

Parliament House, Canberra, 50th anniv.

Trade Union Workers A268

1977, May 9 Photo. *Perf. 13*
668	A268	18c multicolored	.40	.25

Australian Council of Trade Unions (ACTU), 50th anniv.

Surfing Santa — A269

Virgin and Child — A270

1977, Oct. 31 Photo. *Perf. 14x14½*
669	A269	15c multicolored	.40	.25

Perf. 13½x13
670	A270	45c multicolored	.75	.75

Christmas.

Australian Flag — A271

1978, Jan. 26 Photo. *Perf. 13x13½*
671	A271	18c multicolored	.40	.30

Australia Day, 190th anniversary of first permanent settlement in New South Wales.

Harry Hawker and Sopwith "Camel" A272

Australian Aviators and their Planes: No. 673, Bert Hinkler and Avro Avian. No. 674, Charles Kingsford-Smith and Fokker "Southern Cross." No. 675, Charles Ulm and "Southern Cross."

1978, Apr. 19 Litho. *Perf. 15½*
672	A272	18c ultra & multi	.40	.30
673	A272	18c blue & multi	.40	.30
674	A272	18c orange & multi	.40	.30
675	A272	18c yellow & multi	.40	.30
a.		Souv. sheet, 2 each #674-675, imperf.	2.25	2.00
		Nos. 672-675 (4)	1.60	1.20

No. 675a for 50th anniv. of first Trans-Pacific flight from Oakland, Cal., to Brisbane.

Beechcraft Baron Landing A273

1978, May 15 Photo. *Perf. 13½*
676	A273	18c multicolored	.40	.30

Royal Flying Doctor Service, 50th anniv.

Illawarra Flame Tree — A274

Australian trees: 25c, Ghost gum. 40c, Grass tree. 45c, Cootamundra wattle.

1978, June 1
677	A274	18c multicolored	.25	.25
678	A274	25c multicolored	.50	.50
679	A274	40c multicolored	.65	.65
680	A274	45c multicolored	.70	.70
		Nos. 677-680 (4)	2.10	2.10

Sturt's Desert Rose, Map of Australia — A275

1978, June 19 Litho. *Perf. 15½*
681	A275	18c multicolored	.40	.25

Establishment of Government of the Northern Territory.

Hooded Dotterel — A276

Australian birds: 20c, Little grebe. 25c, Spur-wing Plover. 30c, Pied oystercatcher. 55c, Lotus bird.

1978 Photo. *Perf. 13½*
682	A276	5c multicolored	.25	.25
683	A276	20c multicolored	.40	.25
684	A276	25c multicolored	.45	.25
685	A276	30c multicolored	.70	.35
686	A276	55c multicolored	.90	.60
		Nos. 682-686 (5)	2.70	1.70

Issued: Nos. 683, 686, July 3; others, July 17. See Nos. 713-718, 732-739, 768.

Australia No. 95 on Album Page — A277

1978, Sept. 25   Litho.   Perf. 15½
| 687 | A277 20c multicolored | .40 | .25 |
| a. | Miniature sheet of 4 | 1.60 | 1.60 |

National Stamp Week; 50th anniv. of Melbourne Intl. Phil. Exhib., Oct. 1928.

Virgin and Child, by Simon Marmion — A278

Paintings from National Gallery, Victoria: 15c, Virgin and Child, after Van Eyck. 55c, Holy Family, by Perino del Vaga.

1978   Perf. 15
688	A278 15c multicolored	.40	.25
689	A278 25c multicolored	.55	.55
690	A278 55c multicolored	1.00	.80
	Nos. 688-690 (3)	1.95	1.60

Christmas. Issued: 25c, 10/3; others, 11/1.

Tulloch A279

Race horses: 35c, Bernborough, vert. 50c, Phar Lap, vert. 55c, Peter Pan.

Perf. 15x14, 14x15
1978, Oct. 18   Photo.
691	A279 20c multicolored	.40	.30
692	A279 35c multicolored	.60	.40
693	A279 50c multicolored	.80	.80
694	A279 55c multicolored	1.00	.90
	Nos. 691-694 (4)	2.80	2.40

Australian horse racing.

Flag Raising at Sydney Cove — A280

1979, Jan. 26   Litho.   Perf. 15½
| 695 | A280 20c multicolored | .40 | .30 |

Australia Day, Jan. 26.

Passenger Steamer Canberra A281

Ferries and Murray River Steamers: 35c, M.V. Lady Denman. 50c, P.S. Murray River Queen. 55c, Hydrofoil Curl Curl.

Perf. 13½, 15x14 (20c)
1979, Feb. 14   Photo.
696	A281 20c multicolored	.40	.30
697	A281 35c multicolored	.60	.40
698	A281 50c multicolored	.80	.80
699	A281 55c multicolored	.90	.90
	Nos. 696-699 (4)	2.70	2.40

Port Campbell A282

Designs: Australian National Parks.

1979, Apr. 9   Litho.   Perf. 15½
700	A282 20c shown	.35	.35
701	A282 20c Uluru	.35	.35
702	A282 20c Royal	.35	.35
703	A282 20c Flinders Ranges	.35	.35
704	A282 20c Nambung	.35	.35
a.	Strip of 5, #700-704	2.00	2.00
705	A282 20c Girraween, vert.	.35	.35
706	A282 20c Mount Field, vert.	.35	.35
a.	Pair, #705-706	.75	.75
	Nos. 700-706 (7)	2.45	2.45

Double Fairlie A283

Australian steam locomotives: 35c, Puffing Billy. 50c, Pichi Richi. 55c, Zig Zag.

Perf. 13½, 15x14 (20c)
1979, May 16   Photo.
707	A283 20c multicolored	.40	.30
708	A283 35c multicolored	.75	.40
709	A283 50c multicolored	.90	.80
710	A283 55c multicolored	.95	.80
	Nos. 707-710 (4)	3.00	2.30

"Black Swan" A284

1979, June 6   Photo.   Perf. 13½
| 711 | A284 20c multicolored | .40 | .25 |

150th anniversary of Western Australia.

Children Playing, IYC Emblem A285

1979, Aug. 13   Litho.   Perf. 13½x13
| 712 | A285 20c multicolored | .40 | .25 |

International Year of the Child.

Bird Type of 1978

Australian birds: 1c, Zebra finch. 2c, Crimson finch. 15c, Forest kingfisher, vert. 20c, Eastern yellow robin. 40c, Lovely wren, vert. 50c, Flame robin, vert.

1979, Sept. 17   Photo.   Perf. 13½
713	A276 1c multicolored	.25	.25
714	A276 2c multicolored	.25	.25
715	A276 15c multicolored	.35	.25
716	A276 20c multicolored	.45	.25
717	A276 40c multicolored	.75	.35
718	A276 50c multicolored	1.00	.40
	Nos. 713-718 (6)	3.05	1.75

Christmas Letters, Flag-wrapped Parcels — A286

Christmas: 15c, Nativity, icon. 55c, Madonna and Child, by Buglioni.

1979   Litho.   Perf. 13
719	A286 15c multicolored	.35	.25
720	A286 25c multicolored	.45	.30
721	A286 55c multicolored	1.00	.90
	Nos. 719-721 (3)	1.80	1.45

Issue dates: 25c, Sept. 24. Others, Nov. 1.

Trout Fishing — A287

Sport fishing: 35c, Angler. 50c, Black marlin fishing. 55c, Surf fishing.

1979, Oct. 24   Photo.   Perf. 14x14½
722	A287 20c multicolored	.35	.30
723	A287 35c multicolored	.50	.35
724	A287 50c multicolored	.80	.65
725	A287 55c multicolored	1.20	.80
	Nos. 722-725 (4)	2.85	2.10

Matthew Flinders, Map of Australia A288

1980, Jan. 23   Litho.   Perf. 13½
| 726 | A288 20c multicolored | .40 | .25 |

Australia Day, Jan. 28.

Dingo A289

1980, Feb. 20   Litho.   Perf. 13½x13
727	A289 20c shown	.35	.25
728	A289 25c Border collie	.45	.45
729	A289 35c Australian terrier	.55	.50
730	A289 50c Australian cattle dog	.75	.70
731	A289 55c Australian kelpie	.85	.80
	Nos. 727-731 (5)	2.95	2.70

Bird Type of 1978

10c, Golden-shoulder parrot, vert. 22c, White-tailed kingfisher, vert. 28c, Rainbow bird, vert. 35c, Regent bower bird, vert. 45c, Masked woodswallow. 60c, King parrot, vert. 80c, Rainbow pitta. $1, Western magpie, vert.

Perf. 13x12½ (10c, 28c, 35c, 60c, $1), 14x15 (22c), 12½x13 (45c, 80c)
1980   Litho., Photo. (22c)
732	A276 10c multicolored	.30	.25
a.	Perf. 14½x14	1.75	.60
733	A276 22c multicolored	.40	.30
734	A276 28c multicolored	.60	.45
735	A276 35c multicolored	.70	.45
736	A276 45c multicolored	.95	.60
a.	Perf. 14x14½	3.50	2.00
737	A276 60c multicolored	1.25	.60
738	A276 80c multicolored	1.60	1.00
739	A276 $1 multicolored	2.00	.45
	Nos. 732-739 (8)	7.80	4.10

Issued: Nos. 733, 734, 737, 3/31; others, 7/1.

Queen Elizabeth II, 54th Birthday — A290

1980, Apr. 21   Litho.   Perf. 13x13½
| 740 | A290 22c multicolored | .35 | .25 |

Wanderer — A291

1980, May 7   Litho.   Perf. 13x13½
741	Strip of 5	2.00	2.00
a.	A291 22c shown	.35	.35
b.	A291 22c Stealing sheep	.35	.35
c.	A291 22c Squatter on horseback	.35	.35
d.	A291 22c Three troopers	.35	.35
e.	A291 22c Wanderer's ghost	.35	.35

"Waltzing Matilda", poem by Andrew Barton Patterson (1864-1941). No. 741 in continuous design.

High Court Building, Canberra — A292

1980, May 19
| 742 | A292 22c multicolored | .40 | .25 |

Opening of High Court of Australia Building, Canberra, May 26.

Salvation Army Officers A294

No. 748, St. Vincent de Paul Society, vert. No. 749, Meals on Wheels, vert. No. 750, "Life. Be in it." (Joggers, bicyclists).

Perf. 13x13½, 13½x13
1980, Aug. 11
747	A294 22c shown	.40	.30
748	A294 22c multicolored	.40	.30
749	A294 22c multicolored	.40	.30
750	A294 22c multicolored	.40	.30
	Nos. 747-750 (4)	1.60	1.20

Mailman c. 1900 — A295

1980, Sept. 29   Litho.   Perf. 13x13½
751	A295 22c Mailbox	.40	.25
752	A295 22c shown	.40	.25
753	A295 22c Mail truck	.40	.25
754	A295 22c Mailman, mailbox	.40	.25
755	A295 22c Mailman, diff.	.40	.25
a.	Souvenir sheet of 3	1.50	1.50
b.	Strip of 5, #751-755	2.00	2.00
	Nos. 751-755 (5)	2.00	1.25

Natl. Stamp Week, Sept. 29-Oct. 5. Nos. 755a contains stamps similar to #751, 753, 755.

No. 755a overprinted "SYDPEX 80" was privately produced.

Holy Family, by Prospero Fontana — A296

Christmas: 15c, Virgin Enthroned, by Justin O'Brien. 60c, Virgin and Child, by Michael Zuern the Younger, 1680.

1980   Perf. 13x13½
756	A296 15c multicolored	.30	.25
757	A296 28c multicolored	.55	.45
758	A296 60c multicolored	.90	.65
	Nos. 756-758 (3)	1.75	1.35

Issued: 15c, 60c, Nov. 3; 28c, Oct. 1.

CA-6
Wackett
Trainer,
1941 — A297

Designs: Australian military training planes.

1980, Nov. 19   **Perf. 13½x14**
759	A297	22c shown	.40	.30
760	A297	40c Winjeel, 1955	.65	.40
761	A297	45c Boomerang, 1944	.75	.50
762	A297	60c Nomad, 1975	.95	.80
		Nos. 759-762 (4)	2.75	2.00

Bird Type of 1978
1980, Nov. 17   **Litho.**   **Perf. 13½**
768	A276	18c Spotted catbird, vert.	.50	.25

Flag on Map
of Australia
A298

1981, Jan. 21   **Perf. 13½x13**
771	A298	22c multicolored	.40	.25

Australia Day, Jan. 21.

Jockey Darby
Munro (1913-
1966), by Tony
Rafty — A299

Australian sportsmen (Caricatures by Tony Rafty): 35c, Victor Trumper (1877-1915), cricket batsman. 55c, Norman Brookes (1877-1968), tennis player. 60c, Walter Lindrum (1898-1960), billiards player.

1981, Feb. 18   **Perf. 14x13½**
772	A299	22c multicolored	.40	.25
773	A299	35c multicolored	.65	.60
a.		Booklet pane of 1, perf. 14¾x14, dated "2007"	1.10	—
774	A299	55c multicolored	1.00	.90
775	A299	60c multicolored	1.10	1.00
		Nos. 772-775 (4)	3.15	2.75

No. 773a issued 11/14/2007.

Australia
No. C2 and
Cover
A300

22c, Australia No. C2, vert.

    Perf. 13x13½, 13½x13
1981, Mar. 25   **Litho.**
776	A300	22c multicolored	.45	.45
777	A300	60c shown	1.10	.80

Australia-United Kingdom official airmail service, 50th anniv.

Map of
Australia,
APEX
Emblem
A301

1981, Apr. 6   **Photo.**   **Perf. 13x13½**
778	A301	22c multicolored	.40	.25

50th anniv. of APEX (young men's service club).

Queen
Elizabeth's
Personal Flag
of Australia
A302

1981, Apr. 21   **Litho.**   **Perf. 13**
779	A302	22c multicolored	.40	.25

Queen Elizabeth II, 55th birthday.
Perf 14x14¾ examples in a booklet pane of 4 come from the booklet footnoted under No. 2507.

License Inspected,
Forrest Creek, by
S.T. Gill — A303

Gold Rush Era (Sketches by S.T. Gill): No. 781, Puddling. No. 782, Quality of Washing Stuff. No. 783, Diggers on Route to Deposit Gold.

1981, May 20   **Perf. 13x13½**
780	A303	22c multicolored	.40	.30
781	A303	22c multicolored	.40	.30
782	A303	22c multicolored	.40	.30
783	A303	22c multicolored	.40	.30
		Nos. 780-783 (4)	1.60	1.20

Lace Monitor —
A303a

Tasmanian
Tiger — A304

Two Types of A304:
Type I — Indistinct line at right of ear, stripes even with base of tail.
Type II — Heavy line at right of ear, stripes longer.
3c, Corroboree frog. 5c, Queensland hairy-nosed wombat, vert. 15c, Eastern snake-necked tortoise. 25c, Greater bilby, vert. 27c, Blue Mountains tree frog. 30c, Bridled nail-tailed wallaby, vert. 40c, Smooth knob-tailed gecko. 50c, Leadbeater's opossum. 55c, Stick-nest rat, vert. 65c, Yellow-faced whip snake. 70c, Crucifix toad. 75c, Eastern water dragon. 85c, Centralian blue-tongued lizard. 90c, Freshwater crocodile. 95c, Thorny devil.

1981-83   **Litho.**
784	A303a	1c shown	.25	.25
785	A303a	3c multicolored	.40	.25
786	A304	5c multicolored	.35	.35
b.		Imperf., dated "2007"	.25	.25
787	A303a	15c multicolored	.40	.25
788	A304	24c Type I, photo. & litho.	.50	.40
a.		Shown, type II, litho.	.70	.40
b.		Imperf., dated "2007"	.50	.50
789	A304	25c multicolored	.65	.45
b.		Imperf., dated "2007"	.60	.60
790	A303a	27c multicolored	.60	.25
791	A304	30c multicolored	.90	.60
a.		Imperf., dated "2007"	.70	.70
792	A304	40c multicolored	.85	.45
793	A304	50c multicolored	1.10	.70
b.		Imperf., dated "2007"	1.10	1.10
c.		Booklet pane, 2 each #788b, 793b	3.50	—
794	A304	55c multicolored	1.10	.70
a.		Imperf., dated "2007"	1.25	1.25
b.		Booklet pane #786b, 789b, 791a, 794a	2.75	—
795	A303a	65c multicolored	1.40	.70
796	A303a	70c multicolored	1.40	.75
797	A303a	75c multicolored	1.60	.75
798	A303a	85c multicolored	1.75	1.00
799	A303a	90c multicolored	1.90	.95
800	A303a	95c multicolored	2.00	1.00
		Nos. 784-800 (17)	17.15	9.80

Perfs: 1c, 70c, 85c, 95c, 13½; 3c, 15c, 27c, 40c, 50c, 65c, 75c, 90c, 12½x13; 5c, 25c, 30c, 55c, 13x12½; 24c, 13x13½.

Issued: 24c, 7/1/81; 5c, 25c, 30c, 50c, 55c, 7/15/81; 3c, 27c, 65c, 75c, 4/19/82; 15c, 40c, 90c, 6/16/82. 1c, 70c, 85c, 95c, 2/2/83.

Nos. 786b, 788b, 789b, 791a, 793b. 793c, 794a, 794b issued 6/26/07. No. 788b has wider spacing between text lines than on the original stamps.

1982-84   **Perf. 14x14½, 14½x14**
785a	A303a	3c ('84)	.70	.45
786a	A304	5c ('84)	1.40	.50
787a	A304	15c ('84)	1.25	.60
789a	A304	25c ('83)	1.40	.60
790a	A303a	27c	1.10	.30
792a	A304	40c ('84)	3.00	1.10
793a	A304	50c ('83)	2.25	1.10
795a	A303a	65c ('84)	2.25	1.40
797a	A303a	75c ('84)	2.60	1.40
		Nos. 785a-797a (9)	15.95	7.45

Prince
Charles and
Lady Diana
A305

1981, July 29   **Litho.**   **Perf. 13**
804	A305	24c multicolored	.45	.25
805	A305	60c multicolored	1.25	1.25

Royal Wedding.

Fungi — A306

24c, Cortinarius cinnabarinus. 35c, Coprinus comatus. 55c, Armillaria luteo-obubalina. 60c, Cortinarius austro-venetus.

1981, Aug. 19   **Litho.**   **Perf. 13**
806	A306	24c multicolored	.55	.40
807	A306	35c multicolored	.70	.70
808	A306	55c multicolored	1.00	.80
809	A306	60c multicolored	1.00	1.00
		Nos. 806-809 (4)	3.25	2.90

Intl. Year of the
Disabled — A307

1981, Sept. 16   **Perf. 14x13½**
810	A307	24c multicolored	.45	.30

Christmas Bush for
His
Adorning — A308

Christmas (Carols by William James and John Wheeler): 30c, The Silver Stars are in the Sky. 60c, Noeltime.

1981   **Litho.**   **Perf. 13x13½**
811	A308	18c multicolored	.35	.25
812	A308	30c multicolored	.60	.60
813	A308	60c multicolored	1.00	1.00
		Nos. 811-813 (3)	1.95	1.85

Issue dates: 30c, Sept. 28; others, Nov. 2.

Globe — A309

1981, Sept. 30
814	A309	24c multicolored	.55	.40
815	A309	60c multicolored	1.00	.95

Commonwealth Heads of Government Meeting, Melbourne, Sept. 30-Oct. 7.

Yacht — A310

24c, Ocean racer. 35c, Lightweight sharpie. 55c, 12-Meter. 60c, Sabot.

1981, Oct. 14   **Litho.**   **Perf. 13x13½**
816	A310	24c multicolored	.45	.30
817	A310	35c multicolored	.60	.50
818	A310	55c multicolored	.85	.80
819	A310	60c multicolored	1.00	.85
		Nos. 816-819 (4)	2.90	2.45

Australia
Day, Jan. 26
A311

1982, Jan. 20   **Litho.**   **Perf. 13x13½**
820	A311	24c multicolored	.45	.30

Sperm Whale
A312

35c, Southern right whale, vert. 55c, Blue whale, vert. 60c, Humpback whale.

1982, Feb. 17   **Perf. 13x13½, 13½x13**
821	A312	24c shown	.50	.40
822	A312	35c multicolored	.75	.70
823	A312	55c multicolored	1.00	1.00
824	A312	60c multicolored	1.20	1.10
		Nos. 821-824 (4)	3.45	3.20

A trial printing of No. 824 exists with a greenish blue background and no white streaks at the UL. A small number of these stamps were sold by mistake.

Elizabeth II, 56th
Birthday — A313

1982, Apr. 21   **Perf. 13½**
825	A313	27c multicolored	.50	.40

Roses — A314

27c, Marjorie Atherton. 40c, Imp. 65c, Minnie Watson. 75c, Satellite.

1982, May 19   **Perf. 13x13½**
826	A314	27c multicolored	.50	.30
827	A314	40c multicolored	.60	.60
828	A314	65c multicolored	1.00	1.00
829	A314	75c multicolored	1.20	1.10
		Nos. 826-829 (4)	3.30	3.00

50th Anniv.
of Australian
Broadcasting
Commission
A315

No. 830, Announcer, microphone. No. 831,
Emblem.

1982, June 16   **Perf. 13½x13**
830 A315 27c multicolored   .45   .35
831 A315 27c multicolored   .45   .35
  a.   Pair, #830-831   1.60   1.30

Nos. 830-831 se-tenant in continuous design.

Alice Springs
Post Office,
1872 — A316

No. 833, Kingston, 1869. No. 834, York,
1893. No. 835, Flemington, 1890, vert. No.
836, Forbes, 1881, vert. No. 837, Launceston,
1889, vert. No. 838, Rockhampton, 1892, vert.

1982, Aug. 4   **Perf. 13½x14, 14x13½**
832 A316 27c shown   .40   .30
833 A316 27c multicolored   .40   .30
834 A316 27c multicolored   .40   .30
835 A316 27c multicolored   .40   .30
836 A316 27c multicolored   .40   .30
837 A316 27c multicolored   .40   .30
838 A316 27c multicolored   .40   .30
      Nos. 832-838 (7)   2.80   2.10

Christmas — A317

1st Australian Christmas cards, 1881. 21c,
horiz.

1982   **Litho.**   **Perf. 14½**
839 A317 21c multicolored   .35   .25
840 A317 35c multicolored   .60   .35
841 A317 75c multicolored   1.20   1.00
      Nos. 839-841 (3)   2.15   1.60

Issue dates: 35c, Sept. 15; others, Nov. 1.

12th Commonwealth Games,
Brisbane, Sept. 30-Oct. 9 — A318

1982, Sept. 22 Litho.   Perf. 14x14½
842 A318 27c Archery   .50   .25
843 A318 27c Boxing   .50   .25
844 A318 27c Weightlifting   .50   .25
  a.   Pair, 3, #842-844   1.75   1.75
845 A318 75c Pole vault   1.25   1.25
  a.   Booklet pane of 4, #842-845,
         perf. 14x14¾ ('06)   3.00   —
      Nos. 842-845 (4)   2.75   2.00

Nos. 842-842 are perf 14½. No. 844a is perf
13½x13.

No. 845a issued 3/1/2006.

Natl. Stamp
Week
A319

1982, Sept. 27   **Perf. 13x13½**
846 A319 27c No. 132   .50   .30

A320

Design: Gurgurr (Moon Spirit), Bark Painting
by Yirawala Gunwinggu Tribe.

1982, Oct. 12   **Perf. 14½**
847 A320 27c multicolored   .50   .30
      Opening of Natl. Gallery, Canberra.

A321

Various eucalypts (gum trees): 1c, Pink-
flowered marri. 2c, Gungurru. 3c, Red-flower-
ing gum. 10c, Tasmanian blue gum. 27c, Forrest's marlock.

Perf. 12½x13½
1982, Nov. 17   **Photo.**
848 A321   1c multicolored   .25   .25
849 A321   2c multicolored   .25   .25
850 A321   3c multicolored   .65   .35
851 A321 10c multicolored   .65   .40
852 A321 27c multicolored   .65   .40
  a.   Bklt. pane, #850-851, 2 #848-
         849, 3 #852 + label   4.00
  b.   Bklt. pane, 2 ea #848-849, 852 2.00
      Nos. 848-852 (5)   2.45   1.65

Nos. 848-852 issued in booklets only.

Mimi Spirits
Singing and
Dancing, by
David
Milaybuma
A322

Aboriginal Bark Paintings: Music and dance
of the Mimi Spirits, Gunwinggu Tribe. 40c,
Lofty Nabardayal. 65c, Jimmy Galareya. 75c,
Djalt Nguleingulei Murrumurru.

1982, Nov. 17 Litho.   Perf. 13½x14
853 A322 27c shown   .50   .30
854 A322 40c multicolored   .60   .40
855 A322 65c multicolored   1.00   .80
856 A322 75c multicolored   1.25   .90
      Nos. 853-856 (4)   3.35   2.40

Historic Fire
Engines
A323

27c, Shand Mason Steam, 1891. 40c,
Hotchkiss, 1914. 65c, Ahrens-Fox PS2, 1929.
75c, Merryweather Manual, 1851.

1983, Jan. 12   **Perf. 13½x14**
857 A323 27c multicolored   .50   .30
858 A323 40c multicolored   .75   .50
859 A323 65c multicolored   1.00   .80
860 A323 75c multicolored   1.20   1.20
      Nos. 857-860 (4)   3.45   2.80

Australia
Day — A324

1983, Jan. 26 Litho.   Perf. 14½
861 A324 27c Sirius   .45   .30
862 A324 27c Supply   .45   .30
  a.   Pair, #861-862   1.10   1.10

A325

1983, Feb. 2   **Perf. 14x13½**
863 A325 27c multicolored   .50   .30
863a   Perf. 14¾x14, dated "2013"
         (#1003b)   .70   .70
      Australia-New Zealand Closer Economic
      Relationship agreement (ANZCER).
      Issued: No. 863a, 5/10/2013.

A326

No. 864, Equality, dignity. No. 865, Social
justice, cooperation. No. 866, Liberty, freedom. No. 867, Peace, harmony.

1983, Mar. 9 Litho.   Perf. 14½
864 A326 27c multicolored   .45   .30
865 A326 27c multicolored   .45   .30
866 A326 27c multicolored   .45   .30
867 A326 75c multicolored   1.20   1.00
      Nos. 864-867 (4)   2.55   1.90

      Commonwealth day.

Queen
Elizabeth II,
57th Birthday
A327

1000, Apr. 20   **Perf. 14½**
868 A327 27c Britannia   .45   .35

World Communications Year — A328

1983, May 18 Litho.   Perf. 13½x14
869 A328 27c multicolored   .45   .35

50th Anniv.
of Australian
Jaycees
Youth
Organization
A329

1983, June 8
870 A329 27c multicolored   .45   .35

St. John Ambulance
Cent. — A330

1983, June 8   **Perf. 13½x14**
871 A330 27c multicolored   .45   .35

Regent
Skipper — A331

10c, Cairn's birdwing. 20c, Macleay's swallowtail. 27c, Ulysses. 30c, Chlorinda hairstreak. 35c, Blue tiger. 45c, Big greasy. 60c,
Wood white. 80c, Amaryllis azure. $1, Sword
grass brown.

1983   **Perf. 13½, 14½x14 (30c)**
872 A331   4c shown   .60   .40
873 A331 10c multicolored   .60   .40
874 A331 20c multicolored   .45   .25
875 A331 27c multicolored   .65   .25
875A A331 30c multicolored   .80   .25
876 A331 35c multicolored   .80   .35
877 A331 45c multicolored   1.00   .45
878 A331 60c multicolored   1.20   .55
879 A331 80c multicolored   1.40   .80
880 A331 $1 multicolored   2.25   1.00
      Nos. 872-880 (10)   9.75   4.70

Issue dates: 30c, Oct. 24; others, June 15.

The Sentimental
Bloke, by C.J.
Dennis,
1909 — A332

Folktale scenes: a, The bloke. b, Doreen-the
intro. c, The stror at coot. d, Hitched. e, The
mooch of life.

1983, Aug. 3   **Perf. 14½**
881   Strip of 5   2.50   2.50
  a.-e. A332 27c multi, any single   .45   .40

Kookaburra
Bird Wearing
Santa
Hat — A333

24c, Nativity. 85c, Holiday beach scene.

1983   **Litho.**   **Perf. 13½x14**
882 A333 24c multicolored   .40   .30
883 A333 35c multicolored   .60   .35
884 A333 85c multicolored   1.30   .90
      Nos. 882-884 (3)   2.30   1.55

Christmas. Issued: No. 883, 9/14; Nos. 882,
884, 11/2.

Inland
Explorers — A334

Clay sculptures by Dianne Quinn: No. 885,
Ludwig Leichhardt (1813-48). No. 886, William
John Wills (1834-61), Robert O'Hara Burke
(1821-61). No. 887, Paul Edmund de
Strzelecki (1797-1873). No. 888, Alexander
Forrest (1849-1901).

1983, Sept. 26   **Perf. 14½**
885 A334 30c multicolored   .50   .35
886 A334 30c multicolored   .50   .35
887 A334 30c multicolored   .50   .35
888 A334 30c multicolored   .50   .35
      Nos. 885-888 (4)   2.00   1.40

Australia
Day — A335

1984, Jan. 26   Litho.   Perf. 13½x14
889 A335 30c Cooks' Cottage   .45 .30

50th Anniv. of Official Air Mail
Service — A336

Pilot Charles Ulm (1898-1934); his plane,
"Faith in Australia," and different flight covers:
No. 890, Australia-New Zealand. No. 891,
Australia-Papua New Guinea.

1984, Feb. 22   Litho.   Perf. 13½
890 A336 45c multicolored   .75 .75
891 A336 45c multicolored   .75 .75
  a. Pair, #890-891   2.25 2.25

Thomson,
1898 — A337

Australian-made vintage cars: b, Tarrant,
1906. c, Australian Six, 1919. d, Summit,
1923. e, Chic, 1924.

1984, Mar. 14   Perf. 14½
892 Strip of 5   2.40 2.40
  a.-e. A337 30c any single   .45 .35

Queen
Elizabeth II,
58th Birthday
A338

1984, Apr. 18   Perf. 14½
893 A338 30c multicolored   .45 .30

Clipper Ships
A339

30c, Cutty Sark, 1869, vert. 45c, Orient,
1853. 75c, Sobraon, 1866. 85c, Thermopylae,
1868, vert.

1984, May 23   Perf. 14x13½, 13½x14
894 A339 30c multicolored   .45 .35
895 A339 45c multicolored   .80 .80
896 A339 75c multicolored   1.25 1.00
897 A339 85c multicolored   1.40 1.25
  Nos. 894-897 (4)   3.90 3.40

Freestyle
Skiing — A340

No. 899, Slalom, horiz. No. 900, Cross-
country, horiz. No. 901, Downhill.

1984, June 6   Litho.   Perf. 14½
898 A340 30c shown   .50 .35
899 A340 30c multicolored   .50 .35
900 A340 30c multicolored   .50 .35
901 A340 30c multicolored   .50 .35
  Nos. 898-901 (4)   2.00 1.40

Coral
Hopper — A341

3c, Jimble. 5c, Tasseled anglerfish. 10c,
Stonefish. 20c, Red handfish. 25c, Orange-
tipped cowrie. 30c, Choat's wrasse. 33c, Leafy
sea dragon. 40c, Red velvet fish. 45c, Textile
cone shell. 50c, Blue-lined surgeonfish. 55c,
Bennett's nudibranch. 60c, Lionfish. 65c,
Stingray. 70c, Blue-ringed octopus. 80c, Pineapple fish. 85c, Regal angelfish. 90c, Crab-
eyed goby. $1, Crown of thorns starfish.

Perf. 13½, 14x14½ (30c, 33c)
1984-86   Litho.
902 A341 2c shown   .25 .25
903 A341 3c multicolored   .25 .25
904 A341 5c multicolored   .40 .40
905 A341 10c multicolored   .25 .25
906 A341 20c multicolored   .40 .35
907 A341 25c multicolored   .40 .35
908 A341 30c multicolored   .65 .25
909 A341 33c multicolored   .80 .25
910 A341 40c multicolored   .80 .35
911 A341 45c multicolored   .80 .35
912 A341 50c multicolored   1.00 .40
913 A341 55c multicolored   1.10 .80
914 A341 60c multicolored   1.00 .80
915 A341 65c multicolored   1.05 .80
916 A341 70c multicolored   1.15 1.00
917 A341 80c multicolored   1.50 1.00
918 A341 85c multicolored   1.60 1.00
919 A341 90c multicolored   1.40 1.00
920 A341 $1 multicolored   1.60 1.10
  Nos. 902-920 (19)   16.40 10.95

Issued: 2c, 25c, 30c, 50c, 55c, 85c, 6/18;
33c, 1/20/85; 5c, 20c, 40c, 80c, 90c, 6/12/85;
3c, 10c, 45c, 60c, 65c, 70c, $1, 6/11/86.

1984
Summer
Olympics
A342

Event stages: No. 922, Start (facing down).
No. 923, Competing (facing right). No. 924,
Finish, vert.

Perf. 13½x14, 14x13½
1984, July 25   Litho.
922 A342 30c multicolored   .60 .35
923 A342 30c multicolored   .60 .35
924 A342 30c multicolored   .60 .35
  Nos. 922-924 (3)   1.80 1.05

Ausipex '84 — A343

Designs: No. 926: a, Victoria #3. b, New
South Wales #1. c, Tasmania #1. d, South
Australia #1. e, Western Australia #1. f,
Queensland #3.

1984   Litho.   Perf. 14½
925 A343 30c No. 2   .50 .35
Souvenir Sheet
926 Sheet of 7   4.00 4.75
  a.-f. A343 30c any single   .50 .40

No. 926 contains Nos. 925, 926a-926f.
Issued: No. 925, Aug. 22; No. 926, Sept. 21.

Christmas — A344

24c, Angel and Child. 30c, Veiled Virgin and
Child. 40c, Angel. 50c, Three Kings. 85c,
Madonna and Child.

1984   Litho.   Perf. 14x13½
927 A344 24c multicolored   .40 .25
928 A344 30c multicolored   .45 .30
929 A344 40c multicolored   .60 .65
930 A344 50c multicolored   .80 .60
931 A344 85c multicolored   1.40 1.25
  Nos. 927-931 (5)   3.65 3.05

Stained-glass windows. Issue dates: 40c,
Sept. 17; others, Oct. 30.

European
Settlement
Bicentenary
A345

Design: No. 932, Bicentennial Emblem.
Rock paintings: No. 933, Stick figures,
Cobar Region, New South Wales. No. 934,
Bunjil's Cave, Grampians, Western Victoria.
No. 935, Quinkan Gallery, Cape York, Queens-
land. No. 936, Wandjina Spirit and Snake
Babies, Gibb River, Western Australia. No.
937, Rock Python, Western Australia. No. 938,
Silver Barramundi, Kakadu Natl. Park, North-
ern Territory. 85c, Rock Possum, Kakadu Natl.
Park.

1984, Nov. 7   Litho.   Perf. 14½
932 A345 30c multicolored   .55 .30
933 A345 30c multicolored   .55 .30
934 A345 30c multicolored   .55 .30
935 A345 30c multicolored   .55 .30
936 A345 30c multicolored   .55 .30
937 A345 30c multicolored   .55 .30
938 A345 30c multicolored   .55 .30
939 A345 85c multicolored   1.75 1.90
  Nos. 932-939 (8)   5.60 4.00

Settlement of
Victoria
Sesquicentenary
A346

No. 940, Helmeted honeyeater. No. 941,
Leadbeater's possum.

1984, Nov. 19
940 A346 30c multicolored   .50 .40
941 A346 30c multicolored   .50 .40
  a. Pair, #940-941   1.25 1.25

Australia
Day
A347

No. 942, Musgrave Ranges, by Sidney
Nolan. No. 943, The Walls of China, by Russell Drysdale.

1985, Jan. 25   Litho.
942 30c multicolored   .55 .35
  a. Pair #942 tete-beche   2.50 2.50
943 30c multicolored   .55 .35
  a. A347 Pair, #942-943   1.50 1.40
  b. Pair, #943 tete-beche   2.50 2.50

Intl. Youth
Year — A348

1985, Feb. 13   Litho.   Perf. 14x13½
944 A348 30c multicolored   .55 .35

Royal Victorian
Volunteer
Artillery — A349

Colonial military uniforms: b, Western Australian Pinjarrah Cavalry. c, New South Wales
Lancers. d, New South Wales Contingent to
the Sudan. e, Victorian Mounted Rifles.

1985, Feb. 25   Perf. 14½
945 Strip of 5   2.50 2.40
  a.-e. A349 33c any single   .50 .30

District Nursing
Service
Centenary — A350

1985, Mar. 13
946 A350 33c multicolored   .60 .35

Australian Cockatoo — A351

Perf. 14 Horiz. on 1 or 2 sides
1985, Mar. 13
947 A351 1c apple grn, yel &
      buff   1.40 1.25
948 A351 33c apple grn, yel, & lt
      grnsh blue   1.40 .75
  a. Bklt. pane, 1 #947, 3 #948   6.50

Issued in booklets only.

A352

No. 949, Abel Tasman, explorer. No. 950,
The Eendracht. No. 951, William Dampier. No.
952, Globe and hand.

1985, Apr. 10   Perf. 13
949 A352 33c multicolored   .60 .40
950 A352 33c multicolored   .60 .40
951 A352 33c multicolored   .60 .40
952 A352 90c multicolored   1.90 1.90
  a. Souvenir sheet of 4, #949-952   5.00 5.00
  Nos. 949-952 (4)   3.70 3.10

Queen Elizabeth II,
59th
Birthday — A353

33c, Queen's Badge, Order of Australia.

1985, Apr. 22   *Perf. 14x13½*
953 A353 33c multicolored   .50 .35
  a.   Perf. 14¾x14, dated "2013"
    (#1003b)   .85 .85
    Issued: No. 953a, 5/10/2013.

A354

1985, May 15   **Litho.**   *Perf. 14x13*
954 A354 33c Soil   .50 .25
955 A354 50c Air   1.00 .75
956 A354 80c Water   1.20 1.00
957 A354 90c Energy   1.40 1.25
    Nos. 954-957 (4)   4.10 3.25
    Environmental conservation.

A356

Illustrations from classic children's books: a, Elves & Fairies, by Annie Rentoul. b, The Magic Pudding, text and illustrations by Norman Lindsay. c, Ginger Meggs, by James Charles Bancks. d, Blinky Bill, by Dorothy Wall. e, Snugglepot and Cuddlepie, by May Gibbs.

1985, July 17   **Litho.**   *Perf. 14½*
960 A356 Strip of 5   3.25 3.00
  a.-e.   33c any single   .50 .35

Electronic
Mail — A357

1985, Sept. 18   **Litho.**
961 A357 33c multicolored   .55 .30

Christmas
A358

Angel in a ship, detail from a drawing by Albrecht Durer (1471-1528).

1985, Sept. 18   **Litho.**
962 A358 45c multicolored   .80 .35
    See Nos. 967-970.

Coastal
Shipwrecks
A359

Salvaged antiquities: 33c, Astrolabe from Batavia, 1629. 50c, German beardman (Bellarmine) jug from Vergulde Draeck, 1656. 90c, Wooden bobbins from Batavia, and scissors from Zeewijk, 1727. $1, Silver buckle from Zeewijk.

1985, Oct. 2   **Litho.**   *Perf. 13*
963 A359 33c multicolored   .65 .25
964 A359 50c multicolored   1.00 .95
965 A359 90c multicolored   1.90 1.75
966 A359 $1 multicolored   2.40 2.00
    Nos. 963-966 (4)   5.95 4.95

Christmas Type of 1985
Illustrations by Scott Hartshorne.

1985, Nov. 1   **Litho.**   *Perf. 14*
967 A358 27c Angel with trumpet   .50 .25
968 A358 33c Angel with bells   .60 .35
969 A358 55c Angel with star   1.00 .80
970 A358 90c Angel with ornament   1.40 1.40
    Nos. 967-970 (4)   3.50 2.80

Australia
Day — A360

1986, Jan. 24   **Litho.**   *Perf. 14½*
971 A360 33c Aboriginal painting   .55 .35

AUSSAT — A361

Various communications satellites.

1986, Jan. 24
972 A361 33c multicolored   .65 .30
973 A361 90c multicolored   1.05 1.05

South
Australia,
Sesquicent.
A362

No. 974, Sailing ship Buffalo. No. 975, City Sign, sculpture by O.H. Hajek.

1986, Feb. 12   *Perf. 13½x14*
974 A362 33c multicolored   .50 .40
975 A362 33c multicolored   .50 .40
  a.   Pair, #974-975   1.40 1.40

Cook's New
Holland
Expedition
A363

No. 976, Hibiscus merankensis. No. 977, Banksia serrata. No. 978, Dillenia alata. No. 979, Corria reflexa. No. 980, Parkinson. No. 981, Banks.

1986, Mar. 12   *Perf. 13*
976 A363 33c multicolored   .65 .35
977 A363 33c multicolored   .65 .35
978 A363 33c multicolored   1.10 1.25
979 A363 80c multicolored   1.60 1.40
980 A363 90c multicolored   1.75 1.75
981 A363 90c multicolored   1.75 1.75
    Nos. 976-981 (6)   7.50 6.85
Australian bicentennial. Sydney Parkinson (d. 1775), artist. Sir Joseph Banks (1743-1820), naturalist.

Halley's
Comet — A364

33c, Radio telescope, trajectory diagram.

1986, Apr. 9   *Perf. 14x13½*
982 A364 33c multicolored   .60 .40

Elizabeth II, 60th
Birthday — A365

1986, Apr. 21   *Perf. 14½*
983 A365 33c multicolored   .60 .40

Horses
A366

33c, Brumbies. 80c, Stock horse mustering. 90c, Show-jumping. $1, Australian pony.

1986, May 21
984 A366 33c multicolored   .60 .30
985 A366 80c multicolored   1.40 1.25
986 A366 90c multicolored   1.60 1.40
987 A366 $1 multicolored   2.00 1.60
    Nos. 984-987 (4)   5.60 4.55

Click Go the
Shears, Folk Song
— A366a

Lines from the song: b, Old shearer stands. c, Ringer looks around. d, Boss of the board. e, Tar-boy is there. f, Shearing is all over.

1986, July 21   **Litho.**   *Perf. 14½*
987A   Strip of 5   3.00 3.00
  b.-f.   A366a 33c, any single   .50 .40
Amalgamated Shearers' Union, predecessor of the Australian Workers' Union, cent.

Australia
Bicentennial
A367

Settling of Botany Bay penal colony: No. 988, King George III, c. 1767, by A. Ramsay. No. 989, Lord Sydney, secretary of state, 1783-1789, by Gilbert Stuart. No. 990, Capt. Arthur Phillip, 1st penal colony governor, by F. Wheatley, 1786. $1, Capt. John Hunter, governor, 1795-1800, by W. B. Bennett, 1815.

1986, Aug. 6   **Litho.**   *Perf. 13*
988 A367 33c multicolored   .80 .45
989 A367 33c multicolored   .80 .45
990 A367 33c multicolored   .80 .45
991 A367 $1 multicolored   2.25 2.25
    Nos. 988-991 (4)   4.65 3.60

Wildlife — A368

Designs: a, Red kangaroo. b, Emu. c, Koala. d, Kookaburra. e, Platypus.

1986, Aug. 13   *Perf. 14½x14*
992   A368 Strip of 5   3.50 3.50
  a.-e.   A368 36c any single   .70 .60

Alpine
Wildflowers — A369

3c, Royal bluebell. 5c, Alpine marsh marigold. 25c, Mount Buffalo sunray. 36c, Silver snow daisy.

Rouletted 9½ Vert. on 1 or 2 sides
1986, Aug. 25   **Booklet Stamps**
993 A369 3c multicolored   1.10 1.25
994 A369 5c multicolored   1.60 1.60
995 A369 25c multicolored   1.60 1.60
996 A369 36c multicolored   1.00 .80
  a.   Bklt. pane, #993, #994, 2 #996   5.00
  b.   Bklt. pane, #993, #995, 2 #996   5.25
    Nos. 993-996 (4)   5.30 5.25

Orchids — A370

36c, Elythranthera emarginata. 55c, Dendrobium nindii. 90c, Caleana major. $1, Thelymitra variegata.

1986, Sept. 18   *Perf. 14½*
997 A370 36c multicolored   .60 .25
998 A370 55c multicolored   .90 .90
999 A370 90c multicolored   1.75 1.75
1000 A370 $1 multicolored   2.00 2.00
    Nos. 997-1000 (4)   5.25 4.90

America's Cup
Triumph '83 — A371

No. 1001, Australia II crossing finish line. No. 1002, Trophy. No. 1003, Boxing kangaroo.

1986, Sept. 26   *Perf. 14x13½*
1001 A371 36c multicolored   .60 .40
1002 A371 36c multicolored   .60 .40
1003 A371 36c multicolored   .60 .40
  a.   Perf. 14¾x14, dated "2013" (#1003b)   .95 .95
  b.   Booklet pane of 4, #502a, 863a, 953a, 1003a   3.50
    Nos. 1001-1003 (3)   1.80 1.20
    Issued: Nos. 1003a, 1003b, 5/10/2013. No. 1003b was issued in a booklet also containing Nos. 1284b, 3534d and 3918.

Intl. Peace
Year — A372

1986, Oct. 22   Litho.   Perf. 14x13½
1004 A372 36c multicolored   .55 .35

Christmas
A373

Kindergarten nativity play: No. 1005, Holy
Family, vert. No. 1006, Three Kings, vert. No.
1007, Angels. No. 1008a, Angels, peasants.
No. 1008b, Holy Family, angels, vert. No.
1008c, Shepherd, angels, vert. No. 1008d,
Three Kings. No. 1008e, Shepherds.

1986, Nov. 3   Litho.
1005 A373 30c multicolored   .60 .35
  a.   Perf 14x13½   1.25 1.25
1006 A373 36c multicolored   .60 .40
1007 A373 60c multicolored   1.10 1.10
    Nos. 1005-1007 (3)   2.30 1.85
          Souvenir Sheet
1008   Sheet of 5   2.75 2.75
  a.-e. A373 30c any single   .55 .45

Perfs: Nos. 1005-1006, 1008c, 15x14½;
Nos. 1007, 1008a 1008e, 14½x15.
No. 1008b, 15x14½x15x15; No. 1008d,
14½x15x14½x14½.

Australia
Day — A374

No. 1009, Flag, circuit board. No. 1010,
Made in Australia campaign emblem.

1987, Jan. 23   Litho.   Perf. 13½x14
1009 A374 36c multicolored   .60 .40
1010 A374 36c multicolored   .60 .40

America's
Cup — A375

Views of yachts racing.

1987, Jan. 28   Perf. 15x14½
1011 A375 36c multicolored   .60 .30
1012 A375 55c multicolored   1.00 1.10
1013 A375 90c multicolored   1.60 1.60
1014 A375 $1 multicolored   1.90 1.75
    Nos. 1011-1014 (4)   5.10 4.75

Fruits — A376

36c, Melons, grapes. 65c, Tropical fruit. 90c,
Pears, apples, oranges. $1, Berries, peaches.

1987, Feb. 11   Perf. 14x13½
1015 A376 36c multicolored   .60 .30
1016 A376 65c multicolored   1.00 1.00
1017 A376 90c multicolored   1.40 1.40
1018 A376 $1 multicolored   2.00 1.75
    Nos. 1015-1018 (4)   5.00 4.45

Agricultural
Shows — A377

1987, Apr. 10   Litho.   Perf. 14x13½
1019 A377 36c Livestock   .60 .30
1020 A377 65c Produce   1.00 1.00
1021 A377 90c Carnival   1.40 1.40
1022 A377 $1 Farmers   2.00 2.00
    Nos. 1019-1022 (4)   5.00 4.70

Queen
Elizabeth II,
61st Birthday
A378

1987, Apr. 21   Perf. 13½x14
1023 A378 36c multicolored   .60 .40

First Fleet
Leaving
England
A379

Continuous design: No. 1024a, Convicts
awaiting transportation. b, Capt. Arthur Phillip,
Mrs. Phillip, longboat on shore. c, Sailors
relaxing and working. d, Longboats heading
from and to fleet. 4e, Fleet in harbor.
No. 1025a, Longboat approaching Tenerife,
The Canary Isls. b, Fishing in Tenerife Harbor.
$1, Fleet, dolphins.

1987   Perf. 13
1024   Strip of 5   3.75 3.75
  a.-e. A379 36c any single   .70 .40
1025   Pair   1.60 1.50
  a.-b. A379 36c any single   .70 .40
1026 A379 $1 multicolored   2.25 2.00
    Nos. 1024-1026 (3)   7.60 7.25

Australia bicent.; departure of the First
Fleet, May 13, 1787; arrival at Tenerife, June
1787.
  Issued: No. 1024, 5/13; Nos. 1025-1026,
6/3.

1987, Aug. 6

First Fleet arrives at Rio de Janeiro, Aug.
1787: a, Whale, storm in the Atlantic. b, Citrus
grove. c, Market. d, Religious procession. e,
Fireworks over harbor.

1027   Strip of 5   3.75 3.75
  a.-e. A379 37c any single   .60 .40

No. 1027 has a continuous design.

1987, Oct. 13

First Fleet arrives at Cape of Good Hope,
Oct. 1787: No. 1028a, British officer surveys
livestock and supplies, Table Mountain. No.
1028b, Ships anchored in Table Bay. No.
1029, Fishermen pull in nets as the Fleet
approaches the Cape.

1028   Pair   1.75 1.75
  a.-b. A379 37c any single   .75 .40
1029 A379 $1 multicolored   1.90 1.40

No. 1028 has a continuous design.

1988, Jan. 26

Arrival of the First Fleet, Sydney Cove, Jan.
1788: a, Five aborigines on shore. b, Four
aborigines on shore. c, Kangaroos. d, White
cranes. e, Flag raising.

1030   Strip of 5   4.00 3.75
  a.-e. A379 37c any single   .60 .40

Printed se-tenant in a continuous design.

The Early
Years: Sydney
Cove and
Parramatta
Colonies
A380

Details from panorama "View of Sydney
from the East Side of the Cove," 1808, painted
by convict artist John Eyre to illustrate The
Present Picture of New South Wales, published in London in 1811, and paintings in British and Australian museums: a, Government
House, 1790, Sydney, by midshipman George
Raper. b, Government Farm, Parramatta,
1791, attributed to the Port Jackson Painter. c,
Parramatta Road, 1796, attributed to convict
artist Thomas Watling. d, The Rocks and Sydney Cove, 1800, an aquatint engraving by
Edward Dayes. e, Sydney Hospital, 1803, by
George William Evans, an explorer and sur-
veyor-general of New South Wales. Printed
se-tenant in a continuous design.

1988, Apr. 13   Perf. 13
1031   Strip of 5   3.75 3.50
  a.-e. A380 37c any single   .60 .40

Australia Bicentennial.

The Man from
Snowy River, 1890,
Ballad by A.B.
Paterson — A381

Excerpts: a, At the station. b, Mountain
bred. c, Terrible descent. d, At their heels. e,
Brought them back.

1987, June 24   Perf. 14x13½
1034   Strip of 5   4.00 4.00
  a.-e. A381 36c any single   .60 .40

Printed se-tenant in a continuous design.

Fauna — A382

Designs: a, Possum. b, Cockatoo. c, Wombat. d, Rosella. e, Echidna.

1987, July 1   Perf. 14½x14
1035   Strip of 5   3.75 3.75
  a.-e. A382 37c any single   .60 .40

Printed se-tenant in a continuous design.

Technology — A383

1987, Aug. 19   Perf. 14½
1036 A383 37c Bionic ear   .60 .30
1037 A383 53c Microchips   1.00 .60
1038 A383 63c Robotics   1.25 1.00
1039 A383 68c Zirconia ceramics   1.40 1.25
    Nos. 1036-1039 (4)   4.25 3.15

Children
A384

37c, Crayfishing. 55c, Cat's cradle. 90c,
Eating meat pies. $1, Playing with a joey.

1987, Sept. 16
1040 A384 37c multicolored   .60 .25
1041 A384 55c multicolored   1.00 1.10
1042 A384 90c multicolored   1.60 1.40
1043 A384 $1 multicolored   2.10 1.60
    Nos. 1040-1043 (4)   5.30 4.35

Christmas
A385

Carolers: a, Woman, two girls. b, Man, two
girls. c, Four children. d, Man, two women,
boy. e, Six youths. 37c, three women, two
men. Nos. 1044a-1044e are vert.

1987, Nov. 2   Litho.   Perf. 14½
1044   Strip of 5   3.75 3.50
  a.-e. A385 30c any single   .60 .35
                  Perf. 13½x14
1045 A385 37c multicolored   .60 .40
1046 A385 63c shown   1.50 1.00
    Nos. 1044-1046 (3)   5.85 4.90

Carols by Candlelight, Christmas Eve, Sidney Myer Bowl, Melbourne.

Aboriginal Crafts — A386

Designs: 3c, Spearthrower, Western Austra-
lia. 15c, Shield, New South Wales. No. 1049,
Basket, Queensland. No. 1050, Bowl, Central
Australia. No. 1051, Belt, Northern Territory.

                  Perf. 15½ Horiz.
1987, Oct. 13   Photo.
1047 A386 3c multicolored   1.60 1.50
1048 A386 15c multicolored   4.00 4.00
1049 A386 37c multicolored   1.00 1.00
  a.   Bklt. pane, 2 ea #1047, 1049 5.75
1050 A386 37c multicolored   1.00 1.00
1051 A386 37c multicolored   1.00 1.00
  a.   Bklt. pane, #1048, 3 x1050, 2
          #1051   9.00
    Nos. 1047-1051 (5)   8.60 8.50

Issued only in booklets.

Caricature of
Australian
Koala and
American Bald
Eagle — A387

1988, Jan. 26   Perf. 13
1052 A387 37c multicolored   .75 .40

Australia bicentennial. See No. 1086 and
US No. 2370.

Living
Together — A388

Cartoons: 1c, Religion. 2c, Industry. 3c,
Local government. 4c, Trade unions. 5c, Parliament. 10c, Transportation. 15c, Sports. 20c,
Commerce. 25c, Housing. 30c, Welfare. 37c,
Postal services. 39c, Tourism. 40c, Recreation. 45c, Health. 50c, Mining. 53c, Primary
industry. 55c, Education. 60c, Armed Forces.
63c, Police. 65c, Telecommunications. 68c,
The media. 70c, Science and technology. 75c,
Visual arts. 80c, Performing arts. 90c, Banking. 95c, Law. $1, Rescue and emergency
services.

1988   Perf. 14
1053 A388 1c multi   .25 .25
1054 A388 2c multi   .25 .25
1055 A388 3c multi   .25 .25
1056 A388 4c multi   .25 .25
1057 A388 5c multi   .30 .25

1058	A388	10c multi	.30	.25
1059	A388	15c multi	.40	.25
1060	A388	20c multi	.60	.25
1061	A388	25c multi	.60	.25
1062	A388	30c multi	.60	.25
1063	A388	37c multi	.75	.25
a.		Booklet pane of 10	10.50	
1063B	A388	39c multi	.80	.35
c.		Booklet pane of 10	9.00	
1064	A388	40c multi	.80	.45
1065	A388	45c multi	.90	.45
1066	A388	50c multi	1.00	.50
1067	A388	53c multi	1.60	1.00
1068	A388	55c multi	1.30	.65
1069	A388	60c multi	1.25	.80
1070	A388	63c multi	2.00	1.60
1071	A388	65c multi	1.60	.80
1072	A388	68c multi	2.00	1.10
1073	A388	70c multi	1.60	.80
1074	A388	75c multi	1.60	.80
1075	A388	90c multi	1.60	.80
1076	A388	90c multi	1.90	1.00
1077	A388	95c multi	2.00	1.10
1078	A388	$1 multi	2.00	1.25
		Nos. 1053-1078 (27)	28.50	16.20

Issued: 1c, 2c, 3c, 5c, 30c, 40c, 55c, 60c, 63c, 65c, 68c, 75c, 95c, 3/16; 39c, 9/28; others, 2/17.

Queen Elizabeth II, 62nd Birthday A389

1988, Apr. 21   *Perf. 14½*
1079 A389 37c multicolored 1.00 .50

EXPO '88, Brisbane, Apr. 30-Oct. 30 — A390

1988, Apr. 29   *Perf. 13*
1080 A390 37c multicolored 1.00 .50

Opening of Parliament House, Canberra A391

1988, May 9   *Perf. 14½*
1081 A391 37c multicolored 1.00 .50

Australia Bicentennial A392

Designs: No. 1082, Colonist, clipper ship. No. 1083, British and Australian parliaments, Queen Elizabeth II. No. 1084, Cricketer W.G. Grace. No. 1085, John Lennon (1940-1980), William Shakespeare (1564-1616) and Sydney Opera House. Nos. 1083a, 1085a have continuous design picturing flag of Australia.

1988, June 21   Litho.   *Perf. 13*
1082 A392 37c multicolored .85 .40
1083 A392 37c multicolored .85 .40
  a. Pair, #1082-1083 2.00 1.60
1084 A392 $1 multicolored 1.75 1.40
  a. Booklet pane of 1, imperf., dated "2007" 3.25 —
1085 A392 $1 multicolored 1.75 1.40
  a. Pair, #1084-1085 4.00 4.00
  Nos. 1082-1085 (4) 5.20 3.60

No. 1084a issued 11/14/2007.
See Great Britain Nos. 1222-1225.

Caricature Type of 1988
Design: Caricature of an Australian koala and New Zealand kiwi.

1988, June 21   Litho.   *Perf. 13½*
1086 A387 37c multicolored 1.00 .60
Australia bicentennial. See New Zealand No. 907.

"Dream" Lore on Art of the Desert A393

Aboriginal paintings from Papunya Settlement in the Flinders University Art Museum: 37c, Bush Potato Country, by Turkey Tolsen Tjupurrula with by David Corby Tjapaltjarri. 55c, Courtship Rejected, by Limpi Puntungka Tjapangati. 90c, Medicine Story, anonymous. $1, Ancestor Dreaming, by Tim Leura Tjapaltjarri.

1988, Aug. 1   Litho.   *Perf. 13*
1087 A393 37c multicolored .80 .40
1088 A393 55c multicolored 1.25 1.00
1089 A393 90c multicolored 2.00 2.00
1090 A393 $1 multicolored 2.25 2.00
  Nos. 1087-1090 (4) 6.30 5.40

1988 Summer Olympics, Seoul — A394

37c, Basketball. 65c, Running. $1, Rhythmic gymnastics.

1988, Sept. 14   *Perf. 14½*
1091 A394 37c multicolored .80 .50
1092 A394 65c multicolored 1.60 1.25
1093 A394 $1 multicolored 2.00 2.00
  Nos. 1091-1093 (3) 4.40 3.75

34th Commonwealth Parliamentary Conference, Canberra — A395

37c, Scepter and mace.

1988, Sept. 19
1094 A395 37c multicolored .80 .40

Works in the Contemporary Decorative Arts Collection at the Natl. Gallery — A396

2c, "Australian Fetish," by Peter Tully. 5c, Vase by Colin Levy. 39c, Teapot by Frank Bauer.

Roulette 9 Horiz.
1988, Sept. 28   Litho.
1095 A396 2c multicolored 3.75 4.00
1096 A396 5c multicolored 4.00 4.00
1097 A396 39c multicolored 1.60 .60
  a. Bkt. pane of 3 (2c, 2 39c) 6.75
  b. Bkt. pane of 6 (5c, 5 39c) 8.25
  Nos. 1095-1097 (3) 9.35 8.60

Nos. 1095-1097 issued in booklets only.

Views — A397

1988, Oct. 17   Photo.   *Perf. 13*
1098 A397 39c The Desert .80 .40
1099 A397 55c The Top End 1.20 .80
1100 A397 65c The Coast 1.60 1.20
1101 A397 70c The Bush 1.90 1.60
  Nos. 1098-1101 (4) 5.50 4.00

Christmas A398

Children's design contest winning drawings: 32c, Nativity scene, by Danielle Hush, age 7. 39c, Koala wearing a Santa hat, by Kylie Courtney, age 6. 63c, Cockatoo wearing a Santa hat, by Benjamin Stevenson, age 10.

1988, Oct. 31   *Perf. 13½x13*
1102 A398 32c multicolored .80 .30
1103 A398 39c multicolored .80 .40
1104 A398 63c multicolored 1.60 1.20
  Nos. 1102-1104 (3) 3.20 1.90

Sir Henry Parkes (1815-1896), Advocate of the Federation of the Six Colonies — A399

1989, Jan. 25   Litho.   *Perf. 14x13½*
1105 A399 39c multicolored .80 .40
Australia Day.

Sports — A400

1989, Feb. 13   *Perf. 14x14½*
1106 A400 1c Bowls .30 .25
  a. Perf. 13¼x13¾ ('90) .40 .35
1107 A400 2c Bowling .25 .25
  a. Perf. 13¼x13¾ ('91) .25 .25
1108 A400 3c Football .35 .25
1109 A400 39c Fishing 1.00 .35
  a. Booklet pane of 10 12.00
  d. Perf. 13¼x13¾ on sides ('90) 2.25 3.00
  e. Booklet pane of 10, #1109d 22.50
1109B A400 41c Cycling .80 .25
  c. Booklet pane of 8 8.00
1110 A400 55c Kite-flying 1.10 .85
1111 A400 70c Cricket 1.60 1.10
  a. Imperf., dated "2007" (from booklet pane No. 1302b) 2.25 2.25
1112 A400 $1.10 Golf 2.00 1.40

No. 1109d also exists perfed on 4 sides from sheets. These are scarcer. Value, unused or used $17.50.
No. 1111a issued 11/14/2007.

1990-94
1114 A400 5c Kayaking, canoeing 1.00 1.00
  a. Perf. 13¼x13¾ .35 .25
1115 A400 10c Windsurfing 1.00 1.00
  a. Perf. 13¼x13¾ .70 .70
1116 A400 20c Tennis 1.00 .35
  a. Perf. 13¼x13¾ 2.00 .35
1117 A400 65c Rock climbing 2.60 1.00
  a. Perf. 13¼x13¾ 3.50 1.40
1118 A400 $1 Running 2.25 1.60
  a. Perf. 13¼x13¾ 4.75 3.50

Issued: Nos. 1114a, 1115a, 1116a, 1117a, 1118, 1/17/90; No. 1118a, 1/91; Nos. 1115, 1117, 2/92; No. 1116, 7/93; No. 1114, 3/94.

The 1990 year date on the original printing of No. 1117 is in serif type. The date on the 4 koala reprint of 2005 is in san-serif type.

1990, Aug. 27
1119 A400 43c Skateboarding .85 .60
  a. Booklet pane of 10 8.50
Perf. 13½
1120 A400 $1.20 Hang-gliding 2.00 1.10

1991, Aug. 22   *Perf. 14x14½*
1121 A400 75c Netball 1.25 .80
1122 A400 80c Squash 1.25 .80
1123 A400 85c Diving 1.40 .80
1124 A400 90c Soccer 1.60 .80
  Nos. 1106-1124 (19) 23.60 14.55

For self-adhesive stamps see Nos. 1185-1186.

Botanical Gardens — A401

Designs: $2, Nooroo, New South Wales. $5, Mawarra, Victoria. $10, Palm House, Adelaide Botanical Garden. $20, A View of the Artist's House and Garden in Mills Plains, Van Diemen's Land by John Glover.

1989-90   Litho. & Engr.   *Perf. 14*
1132 A401 $2 multicolored 4.00 1.60
  a. Perf. 13¼x13¾ ('91) 7.50 4.00
1133 A401 $5 multicolored 8.00 2.40
  a. Perf. 13¼x13¾ 20.00 9.25
1134 A401 $10 multicolored 15.00 5.75

Litho with Foil Application   *Perf. 14½x14*
1135 A401 $20 multicolored 30.00 14.00
  Nos. 1132-1135 (4) 57.00 23.75

Issued: $10, 4/12; $2, $5, 9/13; $20, 8/15/90.

Sheep A402

1989, Feb. 27   Litho.   *Perf. 13½x14*
1136 A402 39c Merino .80 .40
1137 A402 39c Poll Dorset .80 .40
1138 A402 85c Polwarth 1.75 1.60
1139 A402 $1 Corriedale 2.00 1.60
  Nos. 1136-1139 (4) 5.35 4.00

World Sheep and Wool Congress, Tasmania, Feb. 27-Mar. 6.

Queen Elizabeth II, 63rd Birthday — A403

1989, Apr. 21   Litho.   *Perf. 14½*
1140 A403 39c Statue by John Dowie 1.00 .30

Colonial Australia — A404

Pastoral Era: a, Immigrant ship in port, c. 1835. b, Pioneer's hut, wool bales in dray. c, Squatter's homestead. d, Shepherds. e, Explorers.

1989, May 10
1141 A404 Strip of 5 5.00 4.75
  a.-e. 39c any single .80 .80

Stars of Stage and Screen — A405

Performers and directors: 39c, Gladys Moncrieff and Roy Rene, the stage, 1920's. 85c, Charles Chauvel and Chips Rafferty, talking films. $1, Nellie Stewart and James Cassius Williamson, the stage, 1890's. $1.10, Lottie Lyell and Raymond Longford, silent films.

1989, July 12   Litho.   Perf. 14½
1142	A405	39c multicolored	.80	.25
a.		Perf. 14x13½	11.50	11.50
1143	A405	85c multicolored	1.75	1.60
1144	A405	$1 multicolored	2.10	1.50
1145	A405	$1.10 multicolored	2.10	1.60
		Nos. 1142-1145 (4)	6.75	4.95

Impressionist Paintings A406

Paintings by Australian artists: No. 1146, *Impression for Golden Summer*, by Sir Arthur Streeton. No. 1147, *All on a Summer's Day*, by Charles Conder, vert. No. 1148, *Petit Dejeuner*, by Frederick McCubbin. No. 1149, *Impression*, by Tom Roberts.

Perf. 13½x14, 14x13½
1989, Aug. 23   Litho.
1146	A406	41c shown	.80	.40
1147	A406	41c multicolored	.80	.40
1148	A406	41c multicolored	.80	.40
1149	A406	41c multicolored	.80	.40
		Nos. 1146-1149 (4)	3.20	1.60

The Urban Environment — A407

1989, Sept. 1   Litho.   Perf. 15½
Booklet Stamps
1150	A407	41c Freeways	.80	.45
1151	A407	41c Architecture	.80	.45
1152	A407	41c Commuter train	.80	.45
a.		Bklt. pane, 2 ea #1150, 1152, 3 #1151	7.50	
		Nos. 1150-1152 (3)	2.40	1.35

No. 1152a sold for $3.

Australian Youth Hostels, 50th Anniv. A408

1989, Sept. 13   Perf. 14½
1153	A408	41c multicolored	1.00	.40

Street Cars — A409

Designs: No. 1154, Horse-drawn tram, Adelaide, 1878. No. 1155, Steam tram, Sydney, 1884. No. 1156, Cable car, Melbourne, 1886. No. 1157, Double-deck electric tram, Hobart, 1893. No. 1158, Combination electric tram, Brisbane, 1901.

1989, Oct. 11   Litho.   Perf. 13½x14
1154	A409	41c multicolored	.90	.40
1155	A409	41c multicolored	.90	.40
1156	A409	41c multicolored	.90	.40
a.		Perf. 14½ on 3 sides	3.25	3.25
b.		Booklet pane of 10, #1156a	25.00	
1157	A409	41c multicolored	.90	.40
1158	A409	41c multicolored	.90	.40
		Nos. 1154-1158 (5)	4.50	2.00

Purchase of booklet containing No. 1156b included STAMPSHOW '89 admission ticket and a Melbourne one-day transit pass. Sold for $8.

Christmas — A410

Illuminations: 36c, Annunciation, from the Nicholai Joseph Foucault Book of Hours, c. 1510-20. 41c, Annunciation to the Shepherds, from the Wharncliffe Hours, c. 1475. 80c, Adoration of the Magi, from Parisian Book of Hours, c. 1490-1500.

1989, Nov. 1   Perf. 14x13½
1159	A410	36c multicolored	.60	.40
a.		Booklet pane of 10	7.25	

Perf. 15x14½
1160	A410	41c multicolored	.80	.40
1161	A410	80c multicolored	1.40	1.20
		Nos. 1159-1161 (3)	2.80	2.00

Radio Australia, 50th Anniv. — A411

1989, Nov. 1   Perf. 14x13½
1162	A411	41c multicolored	1.00	.40

Australia Day — A412

1990, Jan. 17   Litho.   Perf. 15x14½
1163	A412	41c Golden wattle	1.00	.40

Special Occasions — A413

1990, Feb. 7   Perf. 14x13½
1164	A413	41c Thinking of You	.80	.40
a.		Booklet pane of 10	8.00	
b.		Perf. 14½ on 3 sides	3.50	1.10
c.		Booklet pane of 10, #1164b	35.00	

See No. 1193.

Women Practicing Medicine in Australia, Cent. A414

1990, Feb. 7   Perf. 14½x15
1165	A414	41c Constance Stone	.80	.40

Dr. Constance Stone, Australia's first woman doctor.

A415

Fauna of the High Country: 41c, Greater glider. 65c, Spotted-tailed quoll. 70c, Mountain pygmy-possum. 80c, Brush-tailed rock-wallaby.

1990, Feb. 21   Perf. 14x13½
1166	A415	41c multicolored	.80	.40
1167	A415	65c multicolored	1.40	1.20
1168	A415	70c multicolored	1.50	1.20
1169	A415	80c multicolored	1.60	1.40
		Nos. 1166-1169 (4)	5.30	4.20

A416

No. 1170, Quit smoking. No. 1171, Don't drink and drive. No. 1172, Eat right. No. 1173, Medical check-ups.

1990, Mar. 14
1170	A416	41c multicolored	.80	.40
1171	A416	41c multicolored	.80	.40
1172	A416	41c multicolored	.80	.40
1173	A416	41c multicolored	.80	.40
		Nos. 1170-1173 (4)	3.20	1.60

Community health.

A417

Scenes from WW II, 1940-41: No. 1174, Anzacs at the front. No. 1175, Women working in factories, aircraft at the ready. 65c, Veterans and memorial parade. $1, Helicopters picking up wounded, cemetery. $1.10, Anzacs reading mail from home, 5 women watching departure of 2 ships.

1990-2005   Litho.   Perf. 14½
1174	A417	41c shown	.80	.35
1175	A417	41c multicolored	.80	.35
1176	A417	65c multicolored	1.25	1.00
a.		Booklet pane of 2, perf. 14½x14 ('05)	9.75	—
1177	A417	$1 multicolored	1.75	1.40
1178	A417	$1.10 multicolored	2.10	1.60
		Nos. 1174-1178 (5)	6.70	4.70

Australia and New Zealand Army Corps (ANZAC).
Issued: Nos. 1174-1178, 4/12/90. No. 1176a, Apr. 2005.

A418

1990, Apr. 19   Perf. 14½
1179	A418	41c multicolored	1.00	.40

Queen Elizabeth's 64th birthday.

Penny Black, 150th Anniv. A419

Stamps on stamps: a, New South Wales #44. b, South Australia #4. c, Tasmania #2. d, Victoria #120. e, Queensland #111A. f, Western Australia #3a.

1990, May 1   Perf. 13½x14
1180		Block of 6	5.25	4.75
a.-f.		A419 41c any single	.80	.40
g.		Souvenir sheet of 6	5.75	5.50
h.		As "g," with Stamp World London '90 emblem ovpt. in silver in sheet margin	16.00	16.00

No. 1180h issued 5/3.

The Gold Rush — A420

a, Off to the diggings. b, The diggings. c, Panning for gold. d, Commissioner's tent. e, Gold escort.

1990, May 16   Perf. 13
1181		Strip of 5	3.75	3.75
a.-e.		A420 41c any single	.80	.40

Cooperation in Antarctic Research A421

41c, Glaciology. $1.10, Krill (marine biology).

1990, June 13   Litho.   Perf. 14½x14
1182	A421	41c multi	.80	.40
1183	A421	$1.10 multi	1.75	1.10
a.		Min. sheet of 2, #1182-1183	2.75	2.75
b.		#1183a overprinted	8.00	8.00

No. 1183 is overprinted in gold, in sheet margin only, for NZ 1990 International Stamp Exhibition, Auckland, Aug. 24-Sept. 2, 1990. See Russia Nos. 5902-5903.

Colonial Australia A422

Boom Time: a, Land boom. b, Building boom. c, Investment boom. d, Retail boom. e, Factory boom.

1990, July 12   Litho.   Perf. 13
1184		Strip of 5	4.50	4.50
a.-e.		A422 41c any single	.80	.40

Sports Type of 1989
1990-91   Typo.   Die Cut Perf. 11½
Self-Adhesive
1185	A400	41c Cycling	1.00	.75
1186	A400	43c Skateboarding	1.00	.25
a.		Litho.	1.10	.25

Blue background has large dots on No. 1186 and smaller dots on No. 1186a. No. 1186 is on waxed paper backing printed with 0 to 4 koalas. No. 1186a is on plain paper backing printed with one kangaroo.
Issued: 41c, 5/16; No. 1186, 8/27; No. 1186a, 1991.

Salmon Gums by Robert Juniper — A423

43c, The Blue Dress by Brian Dunlop.

Perf. 15½ Vert.
1990, Sept. 3   Litho.
Booklet Stamps
1191 A423 28c multicolored   2.00 1.25
   a.   Perf. 14½ vert.   2.00 1.50
1192 A423 43c multicolored   1.00 .85
   a.   Bklt. pane, #1191, 4 #1192   9.50
   b.   Perf. 14½ vert.   1.20 .60
   c.   Bklt. pane, #1191a, 4 #1192b   5.00

Thinking Of You Type
1990, Sept. 3   Perf. 14½
1193 A413 43c multicolored   .85 .50
   a.   Booklet pane of 10   8.00

Christmas A424

1990, Oct. 31   Litho.   Perf. 14½
1194 A424 38c Kookaburras   .75 .35
   a.   Booklet pane of 10   8.00
1195 A424 43c Nativity, vert.   .80 .40
   a.   Perf. 14¾x14, additionally dated "2013" (#3534d)   1.25 1.25
1196 A424 80c Opossum   1.60 1.60
   Nos. 1194-1196 (3)   3.15 2.35

Issued: No. 1195a, 5/10/2013.

Local Government in Australia, 150th Anniv. — A425

43c, Town Hall, Adelaide.

1990, Oct. 31
1197 A425 43c multi   1.00 .40

Flags A426

43c, National flag. 90c, White ensign. $1, Air Force ensign. $1.20, Red ensign.

1991, Jan. 10   Litho.   Perf. 14½
1199 A426 43c multi   .80 .45
1200 A426 90c multi   1.40 1.40
1201 A426 $1 multi   1.75 1.40
1202 A426 $1.20 multi   2.10 1.60
   Nos. 1199-1202 (4)   6.05 4.85

Australia Day.

Water Birds — A427

No. 1203, Black swan. No. 1204, Black-necked stork, vert. No. 1205, Cape Barren goose, vert. No. 1206, Chestnut teal.

1991, Feb. 14
1203 A427 43c multicolored   .80 .40
1204 A427 43c multicolored   .80 .40
1205 A427 85c multicolored   2.00 1.50
1206 A427 $1 multicolored   1.75 1.60
   Nos. 1203-1206 (4)   5.35 3.90

Women's Wartime Services, 50th Anniv. A428

50th Anniv: No. 1208, Siege of Tobruk. $1.20, Australian War Memorial, Canberra.

1991-2005   Litho.   Perf. 14½
1207 A428 43c shown   .80 .40
   a.   Booklet pane of 4, perf. 14x14½ ('05)   9.75 —
1208 A428 43c multicolored   .80 .40
1209 A428 $1.20 multicolored   2.10 1.60
   Nos. 1207-1209 (3)   3.70 2.40

Issued: Nos. 1207-1209, 3/14/91. No. 1207a, Apr. 2005.

Queen Elizabeth II's 65th Birthday — A429

1991, Apr. 11   Litho.   Perf. 14½
1210 A429 43c multicolored   1.00 .80

Insects A430

No. 1211, Hawk moth. No. 1212, Cotton harlequin bug. No. 1213, Leichhardt's grasshopper. No. 1214, Jewel beetle.

1001, Apr. 11
1211 A430 43c multicolored   .80 .40
1212 A430 43c multicolored   .80 .40
1213 A430 80c multicolored   1.75 1.50
1214 A430 $1 multicolored   1.75 1.60
   Nos. 1211-1214 (4)   5.10 3.90

Australian Photography, 150th Anniv. — A431

Designs: No. 1215a, Bondi, by Max Dupain, 1939. No. 1215b, Gears for the Mining Industry, Vickers Ruwolt Melbourne, by Wolfgang Sievers, 1967. 70c, Wheel of Youth, by Harold Cazneaux, 1929. $1.20, Teacup Ballet, by Olive Cotton, 1935.

1991, May 13   Litho.   Perf. 14½
1215   Pair   2.00 1.60
   a.-b.   A431 43c any single   .85 .40
1216 A431 70c blk, olive & cl   1.50 1.25
1217 A431 $1.20 blk, gray & Prus bl   2.00 1.60
   Nos. 1215-1217 (3)   5.50 4.45

Golden Days of Radio — A432

No. 1218, Music & variety shows. No. 1219, Soap operas. No. 1220, Quiz shows. No. 1221, Children's stories.

1991, June 13   Litho.   Perf. 14½
1218 A432 43c multicolored   .80 .40
1219 A432 43c multicolored   .80 .40
1220 A432 85c multicolored   1.25 1.60
1221 A432 $1 multicolored   2.10 1.75
   Nos. 1218-1221 (4)   4.95 4.15

Pets — A433

1991, July 25   Litho.   Perf. 14½
1222 A433 43c Puppy   .80 .40
1223 A433 43c Kitten   .80 .40
1224 A433 70c Pony   1.50 1.25
1225 A433 $1 Cockatoo   1.75 1.60
   Nos. 1222-1225 (4)   4.85 3.65

George Vancouver (1757-1798) and Edward John Eyre (1815-1901), Explorers — A434

1991, Sept. 26   Litho.   Perf. 14½
1226 A434 $1.05 multicolored   1.75 1.25
   a.   Souvenir sheet of 1   2.25 2.25
   b.   As "a," overprinted in gold   7.50 7.50

Vancouver's visit to Western Australia, 200th anniv. and Eyre's journey to Albany, Western Australia, 150th anniv.
No. 1226b overprinted in sheet margin with show emblem and: "PHILANIPPON / WORLD STAMP / EXHIBITION / TOKYO / 16-24 NOV 1991" followed by Japanese inscription.
Issued: No. 1226b, Nov. 16.

Australian Literature of the 1890's A435

Designs: 43c, Seven Little Australians by Ethel Turner. 75c, On Our Selection by Steele Rudd. $1, Clancy of the Overflow by A.B. "Banjo" Paterson, vert. $1.20, The Drover's Wife by Henry Lawson, vert.

1991, Oct. 10
1227 A435 43c multicolored   .80 .40
1228 A435 75c multicolored   1.10 1.00
1229 A435 $1 multicolored   1.75 1.25
1230 A435 $1.20 multicolored   2.10 1.40
   Nos. 1227-1230 (4)   5.75 4.05

Christmas A436

38c, Shepherd. 43c, Baby Jesus. 90c, Wise man, camel.

1991, Nov. 1
1231 A436 38c multi   .60 .30
   a.   Booklet pane of 20   12.50
1232 A436 43c multi   .65 .30
1233 A436 90c multi   1.60 1.60
   Nos. 1231-1233 (3)   2.85 2.20

Thinking of You — A437

1992, Jan. 2   Litho.   Perf. 14½
1234 A437 45c Wildflowers   .85 .30
   a.   Booklet pane of 10   8.75

Threatened Species — A438

Designs: Nos. 1235a, 1241, Parma wallaby. Nos. 1235b, 1242, Ghost bat. Nos. 1235c, 1243, Long-tailed dunnart. Nos. 1235d, 1244, Little pygmy possum. Nos. 1235e, 1245, Dusky hopping mouse. Nos. 1235f, 1246, Squirrel glider.

1992, Jan. 2   Litho.   Perf. 14x14½
1235   Block of 6   5.25 5.25
   a.-f.   A438 45c any single   .80 .40

Die Cut
Perf. 11½
Self-Adhesive
Size: 31x22mm

1241 A438 45c multicolored   1.00 .40
   a.   Typo.   1.00 .40
1242 A438 45c multicolored   1.00 .40
   a.   Typo.   1.00 .40
1243 A438 45c multicolored   1.00 .40
   a.   Typo.   1.00 .40
1244 A438 45c multicolored   1.00 .40
   a.   Typo.   1.00 .40
1245 A438 45c multicolored   1.00 .40
   a.   Typo.   1.00 .40
1246 A438 45c multicolored   1.00 .40
   a.   Typo.   1.00 .40
   b.   Bklt. pane, 2 each #1241-1244, 1 each #1245-1246   10.00
   c.   Pane of 5, #1242-1246   6.00
   d.   Strip of 6, #1241-1246   6.00
   e.   Strip of 6, #1241a-1246a   6.00
   f.   #1246c overprinted   6.00
   g.   As "f," no die cutting   210.00
   Nos. 1241-1246 (6)   6.00 2.40

Litho. stamps are sharper in appearance than typo. stamps, most notably on the black lettering. Nos. 1246b and 1246c have tagging bars which make the right portion of the stamps appear toned.
No. 1246f — overprinted in Gold on sheet margin of No. 1246c with emblem of "WORLD COLUMBIAN / STAMP EXPO '92 / MAY 22-31, 1992 - CHICAGO." Issued in May.
See Nos. 1271-1293.

Wetlands A439

20c, Noosa River, Queensland. 45c, Lake Eildon, Victoria.

Perf. 14½ Horiz.
1992, Jan. 2   Litho.
Booklet Stamps
1247 A439 20c multi   1.20 .85
   a.   Perf. 14 horiz.   2.50 .85
1248 A439 45c multi   .80 .80
   a.   Bklt. pane, #1247, 4 #1248   5.50
     Complete booklet, #1248a   5.50
   b.   Perf. 14 horiz.   .80 .65
   c.   Bklt. pane, #1247a, 4 #1248b   6.50
     Complete booklet, #1248c   6.50

Sailing Ships A440

No. 1249, Young Endeavour. No. 1250, Britannia, vert. No. 1251, Akarana, vert. No. 1252, John Louis.

1992, Jan. 15   Litho.   Perf. 14½
1249 A440 45c multi   .80 .40
1250 A440 45c multi   .80 .40
1251 A440 $1.05 multi   1.75 1.60
1252 A440 $1.20 multi   2.10 1.60
   a.   Sheet of 4, #1249-1252   6.50 6.50
   b.   As "a," overprinted   6.50 9.25
   c.   As "a," overprinted   13.00 10.50
   Nos. 1249-1252 (4)   5.45 4.00

Australia Day. Discovery of America, 500th anniv. (No. 1252a).
Overprint in gold on sheet margin of No. 1252b contains emblem and "WORLD COLUMBIAN / STAMP EXPO '92 / MAY 22-31, 1992-CHICAGO." No. 1252b issued in May.

Overprint in gold on sheet margin of No. 252c contains emblem and "GENOVA '92 / 8-27 SEPTEMBER." No. 1252c issued in ept.

Australian Battles, 1942 — A441

No. 1253, Bombing of Darwin. No. 1254, Milne Bay. No. 1255, Kokoda Trail. No. 1256, Coral Sea. No. 1257, El Alamein.

992-2005		**Litho.**	**Perf. 14½**	
253	A441	45c multi	.80	.40
254	A441	75c multi	1.25	.80
255	A441	75c multi	1.25	.80
256	A441	$1.05 multi	1.75	1.25
a.		Booklet pane, #1253-1256, perf. 14x14½ ('05)	11.00	—
257	A441	$1.20 multi	2.00	1.25
		Nos. 1253-1257 (5)	7.05	4.50

No. 1256a issued Apr. 2005.

Intl. Space Year — A442

45c, Helix Nebula. $1.05, The Pleiades. $1.20, Spiral Galaxy NGC 2997.

1992, Mar. 19				
258	A442	45c multi	.80	.40
259	A442	$1.05 multi	1.60	1.25
260	A442	$1.20 multi	2.40	1.60
a.		Sheet of 3, #1258-1260	5.00	5.00
b.		As "a," overprinted	9.00	9.00
		Nos. 1258-1260 (3)	4.80	3.25

Overprint on sheet margin of No. 1260b contains emblem of "WORLD COLUMBIAN / STAMP EXPO '92 / MAY 22-31, 1992-CHICAGO." No. 1260b issued in May.

Queen Elizabeth II, 66th Birthday A443

1992, Apr. 9			**Perf. 14x14½**	
1261	A443	45c Wmk. 228 & #258	.90	.25

Vineyard Regions A444

Designs: No. 1262, Hunter Valley New South Wales. No. 1263, North Eastern Victoria. No. 1264, Barossa Valley South Australia. No. 1265, Coonawarra South Australia. No. 1266, Margaret River Western Australia.

1992, Apr. 9				
1262	A444	45c multicolored	.80	.55
1263	A444	45c multicolored	.80	.55
1264	A444	45c multicolored	.80	.55
1265	A444	45c multicolored	.80	.55
1266	A444	45c multicolored	.80	.55
		Nos. 1262-1266 (5)	4.00	2.75

Land Care — A445

a, Salt action. b, Farm planning. c, Erosion control. d, Tree planting. e, Dune care.

1992 Summer Olympics and Paralympics, Barcelona A446

1992, June 11		**Litho.**	**Perf. 14½x14**	
1267		Strip of 5	4.25	4.00
a.-e.		A445 45c Any single	.80	.40

1992, July 2			**Perf. 14½**	
1268	A446	45c Cycling	1.40	.70
1269	A446	$1.20 Weight lifting	2.40	2.00
1270	A446	$1.20 High jump	2.40	2.00
		Nos. 1268-1270 (3)	6.20	4.70

Threatened Species Type of 1992

Designs: 30c, Saltwater crocodile. 35c, Echidna. 40c, Platypus. No. 1274, Kangaroo. No. 1275, Adult kangaroo with joey. No. 1276, Two adult kangaroos. No. 1277, Four koalas. No. 1278, Koala walking. No. 1279, Koala in tree. 50c, Koala. 60c, Common brushtail possum. 70c, Kookaburra. Nos. 1283, 1283A, Pelican. 90c, Eastern gray kangaroo. 95c, Common wombat. $1.20, Pink cockatoo. $1.35, Emu.

1992-98		**Litho.**	**Perf. 14x14½**	
1271	A438	30c multi	.80	.40
1272	A438	35c multi	.70	.35
1273	A438	40c multi	.80	.30
1274	A438	45c orange & multi	.80	.25
a.		Brown panel	6.00	6.00
b.		Bright orange panel	4.00	3.50
c.		Additionally dated "2013" (#1284b)	1.50	1.50
1275	A438	45c orange & multi	.80	.25
a.		Brown panel	6.00	6.00
b.		Bright orange panel	4.00	3.50
c.		Additionally dated "2013" (#1284b)	1.50	1.50
1276	A438	45c orange & multi	.80	.25
a.		Sheet of 3, #1274-1276	10.00	10.00
b.		Brown panel	6.00	6.00
c.		Bright orange panel	4.00	3.50
d.		Additionally dated "2013" (#1284b)	1.50	1.50
1277	A438	45c orange & multi	.80	.25
a.		Brown panel	6.00	6.00
b.		Bright orange panel	4.00	3.50
1278	A438	45c orange & multi	.80	.25
a.		Brown panel	6.00	6.00
b.		Bright orange panel	4.00	3.50
1279	A438	45c orange & multi	.80	.25
a.		Block of 6, #1274-1279	6.50	6.50
b.		Souv. sheet, #1274-1279	20.00	20.00
c.		Brown panel	6.00	5.00
d.		Block, #1274a-1275a, 1276b, 1277a-1278a, 1279c	36.00	36.00
e.		Bright orange panel	4.00	3.50
f.		Block, #1274b-1275b, 1276c, 1277b-1278b, 1279e	24.00	24.00

On No. 1279a Australia and denomination are orange, "KANGAROO" is 9mm long, and date is 1½mm long. Date is 1mm long and "KANGAROO" 8mm long on Nos. 1279d and 1279f. No. 1279d comes from 2 Koala printing. No. 1279f comes from 3 Koala printing.

1280	A438	50c multi	.80	.35
1281	A438	60c multi	1.00	.65
1282	A438	70c multi	1.00	.60
a.		"Australia 70c" in brn ('96)	2.75	2.50
1283	A438	85c peach panel at bottom	1.60	.80
1283A	A438	85c yellow panel at bottom	3.25	3.00
1284	A438	90c multi	1.35	.80
a.		Additionally dated "2013" (#1284b)	3.25	3.00
b.		Booklet pane of 4, #1274c, 1275c, 1276d, 1284a	6.50	—
1285	A438	95c multi	1.60	.80
1286	A438	$1.20 multi	1.90	1.60
a.		"Australia $1.20" in brown ('98)	3.75	3.25
1287	A438	$1.35 multi	2.40	2.00
		Nos. 1271-1287 (18)	22.00	13.05

PHILAKOREA '94 (No. 1279b). "Australia" and denominations on Nos. 1282, 1286 are in orange.

No. 1276a inscribed in sheet margin with "CHINA '96 — 9th Asian International Exhibition" in Chinese and English and exhibition emblems.

No. 1282a comes from 3 Koala or 1 Kangaroo and 1 Koala printing. No. 1286a comes from 1 Kangaroo printing.

No. 1283A is from the three koala printing.

Issued: 35c, 50c, 60c, 95c, 8/13; 40c, 70c, 90c, $1.20, 8/12/93; 30c, 85c, $1.35, 3/10/94; 45c, 5/12/94; No. 1279b, 8/94; No. 1282a, 3/96; No. 1276a, 5/18/96; No. 1283A, 1997; No. 1286a, 12/98; Nos. 1274c, 1275c, 1276d, 1284a, 1284b, 5/10/13. No. 1284b was issued

---

in a booklet also containing Nos. 1003b, 3534d and 3918.

Die Cut Perf. 11

1994, May 12			**Litho.**	
		Self-Adhesive		
1288	A438	45c like #1274	1.75	.75
1289	A438	45c like #1275	1.75	.75
1290	A438	45c like #1276	1.75	.75
1291	A438	45c like #1277	1.75	.75
1292	A438	45c like #1278	1.75	.75
1293	A438	45c like #1279	1.75	.75
a.		Bklt. pane, #1290, 1293, 2 each #1288-1289, 1291-1292	17.50	
b.		Strip of 6, #1288-1293	11.50	
		Nos. 1288-1293 (6)	10.50	4.50

Serpentine Die Cut 11½

1995		**Typo.**	**Self-Adhesive**	
		Coil Stamps		
1294	A438	45c Like #1274	1.00	.40
1294A	A438	45c Like #1275	1.00	.40
1294B	A438	45c Like #1276	1.00	.40
1294C	A438	45c Like #1277	1.00	.40
1294D	A438	45c Like #1278	1.00	.40
1295	A438	45c Like #1279	1.00	.40
a.		Strip of 6, #1294, 1294A-1294D, 1295	8.00	
		Nos. 1294-1295 (6)	6.00	2.40

Nos. 1294-1295 come from the third through seventh Koala printings by Pemara.

Opening of Sydney Harbor Tunnel, August 29 — A447

Sydney Harbor Bridge and Tunnel: a, Left side. b, Right side.

1992, Aug. 28		**Litho.**	**Perf. 14½**	
1296	A447	45c Pair, #a.-b.	4.50	4.50
c.		Pair, #d.-e., perf 15½	4.00	4.00

Buildings in Western Australia Goldfield Towns A448

Designs: No. 1297, Warden's Courthouse, Coolgardie. No. 1298, Post Office, Kalgoorlie. $1.05, York Hotel, Kalgoorlie. $1.20, Town Hall, Kalgoorlie.

1992, Sept. 17		**Litho.**	**Perf. 14x14½**	
1297	A448	45c multicolored	.80	.40
1298	A448	45c multicolored	.80	.40
1299	A448	$1.05 multicolored	1.60	1.60
1300	A448	$1.20 multicolored	2.00	1.60
		Nos. 1297-1300 (4)	5.20	4.00

Sheffield Shield Cricket Competition, Cent. — A449

Cricket match, 1890s: 45c, Bowler. $1.20, Batsman, wicket keeper.

1992, Oct. 15		**Litho.**	**Perf. 14½**	
1301	A449	45c multicolored	.75	.40
a.		Perf. 14¾x14, dated "2007"	1.40	1.40
1302	A449	$1.20 multicolored	2.00	1.60
a.		Perf. 14¾x14, dated "2007"	3.75	3.75
b.		Booklet pane of 3, #1111a, 1301a, 1302a	7.50	—

Nos. 1301a, 1302a, 1302b issued 11/14/2007.

Christmas A450

Designs: 40c, Children dressed as Mary and Joseph with baby carriage. 45c, Boy jumping from bed Christmas morning. $1, Boy and girl singing Christmas carol.

1992, Oct. 30		**Litho.**	**Perf. 14x14½**	
1303	A450	40c multicolored	.75	.35
a.		Booklet pane of 20	14.00	
1304	A450	45c multicolored	.75	.35
1305	A450	$1 multicolored	1.60	1.25
		Nos. 1303-1305 (3)	3.10	1.95

Watercolor Paintings by Albert Namatjira — A451

Designs: No. 1306a, Ghost Gum, Central Australia. b, Across the Plain to Mount Giles.

1993, Jan. 14		**Litho.**	**Perf. 14x15**	
1306	A451	45c Pair, #a.-b.	1.90	1.90

Australia Day.

Dreamings — A452

Aboriginal paintings: 45c, Wild Onion Dreaming, by Pauline Nakamarra Woods. 75c, Yam Plants, by Jack Wunuwun, vert. 85c, Goose Egg Hunt, by George Milpurrurru, vert. $1, Kalumpiwarra-Ngulalintji, by Rover Thomas.

	Perf. 14x14½, 14½x14			
1993, Feb. 4				**Litho.**
1307	A452	45c red & multi	.80	.40
1308	A452	75c org yel & multi	1.40	.80
1309	A452	85c buff & multi	1.60	1.10
1310	A452	$1 salmon & multi	1.75	1.50
		Nos. 1307-1310 (4)	5.55	3.80

World Heritage Sites in Australia — A453

1993, Mar. 4		**Litho.**	**Perf. 14½x14**	
1311	A453	45c Uluru (Ayers Rock)	.80	.40
1312	A453	85c Fraser Island	1.60	.80
1313	A453	95c Shark Bay	1.90	1.00
1314	A453	$2 Kakadu	3.25	2.00
		Nos. 1311-1314 (4)	7.55	4.20

See Nos. 1485-1488.

World War II Ships A454

45c, Cruiser HMAS Sydney II. 85c, Corvette HMAS Bathurst. $1.05, Destroyer HMAS Arunta. $1.20, Hospital Ship Centaur.

1993-2005   Litho.   Perf. 14x14½

1315	A454	45c multicolored	.80	.40
1316	A454	85c multicolored	1.25	1.00
1317	A454	$1.05 multicolored	1.60	1.60
a.		Booklet pane, #1315, 1317 ('05)	11.75	—
1318	A454	$1.20 multicolored	2.40	1.60
		Nos. 1315-1318 (4)	6.05	4.60

Issued: Nos. 1315-1318, 4/7/93. No. 1317a, April 2005.

Queen Elizabeth II, 67th Birthday — A455

1993, Apr. 7   Perf. 14½x14

1319	A455	45c multicolored	.90	.40

A456

Designs based on 19th cent. trade union banners: No. 1320, Baker, shoe maker. No. 1321, Stevedore, seamstresses. $1, Blacksmith, telephone operator, cook. $1.20, Carpenters.

1993, May 7   Litho.   Perf. 14½x14

1320	A456	45c multicolored	.90	.40
1321	A456	45c multicolored	.90	.40
1322	A456	$1 multicolored	1.60	1.20
1323	A456	$1.20 multicolored	2.40	1.60
		Nos. 1320-1323 (4)	5.80	3.60

Working life in the 1890s.

Trains A457

Designs: No. 1324, Centenary Special, Tasmania. No. 1325, Spirit of Progress. No. 1326, Western Endeavour. No. 1327, Silver City Comet. No. 1328, Kuranda Tourist Train. No. 1329, The Ghan.

1993, June 1   Perf. 14x14½

1324	A457	45c multicolored	.80	.80
1325	A457	45c multicolored	.80	.80
1326	A457	45c multicolored	.80	.80
1327	A457	45c multicolored	.80	.80
1328	A457	45c multicolored	.80	.80
1329	A457	45c multicolored	.80	.80
a.		Block of 6, #1324-1329	7.75	7.75
		Nos. 1324-1329 (6)	4.80	4.80

Die Cut Perf. 11½x12
Self-Adhesive

1330	A457	45c like No. 1324	1.60	.40
1331	A457	45c like No. 1325	1.60	.40
1332	A457	45c like No. 1326	1.60	.40
1333	A457	45c like No. 1327	1.60	.40
1334	A457	45c like No. 1328	1.60	.40
1335	A457	45c like No. 1329	1.60	.40
a.		Strip of 6, #1330-1335	10.50	
b.		Bklt. pane, #1332, 1335, 2 ea #1330-1331, 1333-1334	12.00	
		Nos. 1330-1335 (6)	9.60	2.40

Aboriginal Art — A458

Aboriginal paintings: 45c, Black Cockatoo Feather, by Fiona Foley, vert. 75c, Ngarrgooroon Country, by Hector Jandany. $1, Ngak Ngak, by Ginger Riley. $1.05, Untitled work, by Robert Cole, vert.

Perf. 14½x14, 14x14½
1993, July 1   Litho.

1336	A458	45c henna brown & multi	.80	.40
1337	A458	75c brown & multi	1.25	.80
1338	A458	$1 gray & multi	1.75	1.25
1339	A458	$1.05 olive & multi	2.00	1.40
		Nos. 1336-1339 (4)	5.80	3.85

Dame Enid Lyons, MP, and Sen. Dorothy Tangney A459

No. 1340, Stylized globe, natl. arms, Inter-Parliamentary Conf. emblem.

1993, Sept. 2   Litho.   Perf. 14½

1340	A459	45c multicolored	.80	.80
1341	A459	45c multicolored	.80	.80
a.		Pair, #1340-1341	2.25	1.40

90th Inter-Parliamentary Union Conference (No. 1340). First women in Australian Federal Parliament, 50th anniv. (No. 1341). Nos. 1340-1341 printed in panes of 25 with 16 #1340 and 9 #1341. Panes with 16 #1341 and 9 #1340 were issued Nov. 19, but were available only through Philatelic Agency.

A460   A461

Dinosaurs: Nos. 1342, 1348, Ornithocheirus. Nos. 1343, 1349, Leaellynasaura. No. 1344, Allosaurus. No. 1345, Timimus. No. 1346, Muttaburrasaurus. No. 1347, Minmi.

1993, Oct. 1   Perf. 14x14½, 14½x14

1342	A460	45c multi, horiz.	.80	.40
1343	A460	45c multi	.80	.40
1344	A461	45c multi	.80	.40
1345	A461	45c multi	.80	.40

Size: 30x50mm

1346	A461	75c multi	1.25	.80
1347	A461	$1.05 multi horiz.	1.60	1.60
a.		Souvenir sheet of 6, #1342-1347, perf. 14¼	6.00	6.00
b.		As "a," overprinted	10.00	10.00
c.		As "a," overprinted	10.00	10.00
		Nos. 1342-1347 (6)	6.05	4.00

Self-Adhesive
Die Cut Perf. 11½

1348	A460	45c multi horiz.	2.10	.80
1349	A460	45c multi	2.10	.80
a.		Bklt. pane, 5 each #1348-1349	22.00	

Overprint in gold on sheet margin of No. 1347b contains "BANGKOK 1993" show emblem and "WORLD PHILATELIC / EXHIBITION / BANGKOK 1-10 OCTOBER 1993."
Overprint in gold on sheet margin of No. 1347c contains dinosaur and "Sydney / STAMP & COIN / SHOW / 15-17 October 1993."

Christmas — A462

1993, Nov. 1   Litho.   Perf. 14½x14

1354	A462	40c Goodwill	.70	.40
a.		Booklet pane of 20	14.00	
1355	A462	45c Joy	.80	.40
1356	A462	$1 Peace	1.60	1.20
		Nos. 1354-1356 (3)	3.10	2.00

Australia Day — A463

Landscape paintings: 45c, Shoalhaven River Bank-Dawn, by Arthur Boyd. 85c, Wimmera (from Mt. Arapiles), by Sir Sidney Nolan. $1.05, Lagoon, Wimmera, by Nolan. $2, White Cockatoos in Paddock with Flame Trees, by Boyd, vert.

Perf. 14½x14, 14x14½
1994, Jan. 13   Litho.

1357	A463	45c multicolored	.80	.40
1358	A463	85c multicolored	1.40	.80
1359	A463	$1.05 multicolored	2.10	2.10
1360	A463	$2 multicolored	4.00	2.40
		Nos. 1357-1360 (4)	8.30	5.70

See Nos.1418-1421, 1476-1479, 1572-1574.

Royal Life Saving Society, Cent. A464

1994, Jan. 20   Litho.   Perf. 14x14½

1361	A464	45c Vigilance	.80	.40
1362	A464	45c Education	.80	.40
1363	A464	95c Drill	1.60	1.20
1364	A464	$1.20 Fitness	2.00	1.40
		Nos. 1361-1364 (4)	5.20	3.40

Die Cut Perf. 11½
Self-Adhesive

1365	A464	45c like #1361	1.60	.80
1366	A464	45c like #1362	1.60	.80
a.		Pair, #1365-1366	3.75	
b.		Booklet pane, 5 #1366a	19.00	

Thinking of You — A465

1994, Feb. 3   Litho.   Perf. 14½x14

1367	A465	45c Rose	.90	.40
1368	A465	45c Tulips	.80	.40
1369	A465	45c Poppies	.80	.40
a.		Pair, #1368-1369	2.00	1.75
b.		Booklet pane, 5 #1369a	10.00	
		Nos. 1367-1369 (3)	2.50	1.20

A466

1994, Apr. 8   Litho.   Perf. 14½

1370	A466	45c multicolored	1.25	.80

Queen Elizabeth II, 68th birthday.

A467

1994, Apr. 8   Perf. 14½x14

1371	A467	95c multicolored	1.90	1.60

Opening of Friendship Bridge, Thailand-Laos.

Intl. Year of the Family A468

Children's paintings of their families: 45c Bobbie Lea Blackmore. 75c, Kathryn Teoh. $1 Maree McCarthy.

1994, Apr. 14   Litho.   Perf. 14x14½

1372	A468	45c multicolored	.80	.40
1373	A468	75c multicolored	1.40	.80
1374	A468	$1 multicolored	1.90	1.20
		Nos. 1372-1374 (3)	4.10	2.40

Australian Women's Right to Vote, Cent. A469

1994, June 9   Litho.   Perf. 14x14½

1375	A469	45c multicolored	1.00	.50

Bunyips Folklore Creatures A470

Types of Bunyips: No. 1376, Aboriginal legend. No. 1377, Nature Spirit. 90c, Berkeley's Creek. $1.35, Natural history.

1994, July 14   Litho.   Perf. 14x14½

1376	A470	45c multicolored	.80	.80
1377	A470	45c multicolored	.80	.80
a.		Pair, #1376-1377	1.60	1.60
1378	A470	90c multicolored	2.00	1.60
1379	A470	$1.35 multicolored	2.40	2.40
		Nos. 1376-1379 (4)	6.00	5.60

World War II Prime Ministers A471

Designs: a, Robert Menzies. b, Arthur Fadden. c, John Curtin. d, Francis (Frank) Forde. e, Joseph Benedict (Ben) Chifley.

1994-2005

1380		Strip of 5	6.00	6.00
a.-e.		A471 45c any single	.80	.80
f.		Booklet pane, #1380a, 1380c ('05)	9.75	—

Issued: No. 1380, 8/11/94. No. 1380f, April 2005.

Aviation Pioneers — A472

Designs: No. 1381, Lawrence Hargrave, box kites. No. 1382, Ross and Keith Smith, Vickers Vimy. $1.35, Ivor McIntyre, Stanley Goble, Fairey IIID A10-3 seaplane. $1.80, Freda Thompson, DeHavilland Moth Major.

1994, Aug. 29   Engr.   Perf. 12

1381	A472	45c multicolored	.80	.80
1382	A472	45c multicolored	.80	.80
1383	A472	$1.35 multicolored	2.40	1.60
1384	A472	$1.80 multicolored	3.00	2.40
		Nos. 1381-1384 (4)	7.00	5.60

First England-Australia flight within 30-day time span (No. 1382). First aerial circumnavigation of Australia (No. 1383). First woman to fly solo from England-Australia (No. 1384).

A473   Australian Zoo
Animals — A474

Perf. 14x14½, 14½x14

	1994, Sept. 28		**Litho.**
1385	A473 45c Scarlet macaw	.80	.80
1386	A473 45c Cheetah, vert.	.80	.80
1387	A474 45c Fijian crested		
	iguana	.80	.80
1388	A474 45c Orangutan	.80	.80

Size: 50x30mm
Perf. 14½x14

1389	A473 $1 Asian elephant	1.60	1.20
a.	Souv. sheet of 5, #1385-1389, perf. 14½	6.00	6.00
b.	As "a," ovptd.	13.50	13.50
c.	As "a," ovptd.	13.50	13.50
d.	As "a," ovptd.	13.00	13.00
e.	As "a," ovptd.	12.00	12.00
	Nos. 1385-1389 (5)	4.80	4.40

Self-Adhesive
Die Cut Perf. 11½

1390	A473 45c like #1385	3.00	.80
1391	A473 45c like #1386	3.00	.80
a.	Bklt. pane, 6 #1390, 4 #1391	25.00	

Denomination is in LL corner on No. 1391.
Overprint in gold on sheet margin:

No. 1389b, show emblem and "Brisbane Stamp Show Zoos / October 21-23, 1994."
No. 1389c, show emblem and "SYDNEY / STAMP / AND / COIN / SHOW / 30/9/94 TO 2/10/94."
No. 1389d, show emblem and "Stampshow '94 Melbourne October 27-30 / National/State Centennial Exhibition 1894-1994."
No. 1389e, show emblem and "STAMP SHOW 94 / Fremantle Convention Centre / 5-6 November 1994."

Christmas
A475

Details from Adoration of the Magi, by Giovanni Toscani: 40c, Madonna and Child, vert. 45c, One of Magi, horse and groom. $1, Joseph receiving frankincense from Magi. $1.80, Entire painting.

1994, Oct. 31		**Litho.**	**Perf. 14½x14**
1392	A475 40c multicolored	.80	.35
a.	Booklet pane of 20	16.00	
	Complete booklet, #1392a	16.00	

Perf. 14x14½

1393	A475 45c multicolored	.80	.35
1394	A475 $1 multicolored	1.60	1.25

Size: 50x30mm

1395	A475 $1.80 multicolored	2.80	2.40
	Nos. 1392-1395 (4)	6.00	4.35

50th Sydney-Hobart Yacht
Race — A476

Designs: a, Yachts bow-on, Sydney Opera House, Harbor Bridge. b, Two yachts abeam.

1994, Oct. 31			**Perf. 14½**
1396	Pair	3.25	3.25
a.-b.	A476 45c any single	1.10	.80

Self-Adhesive
Die Cut Perf. 11½

1397	A476 45c like #1396a	3.00	.60
1397A	A476 45c like #1396b	3.00	.60

A477

Self-Adhesive
Booklet Stamps
Background Color
Die Cut Perf. 17

1994, Nov. 2			**Litho.**
1398	A477 45c bluish green	1.20	1.00
1399	A477 45c blue	1.20	1.00
1400	A477 45c purple	1.20	1.00
1401	A477 45c yellow green	1.20	1.00
1402	A477 45c pale yel green	1.20	1.00
1403	A477 45c pale red brown	1.20	1.00
1404	A477 45c rose	1.20	1.00
1405	A477 45c orange yellow	1.20	1.00
a.	Booklet pane of 20	24.00	
	Nos. 1398-1405 (8)	9.60	8.00

No. 1405a contains 3 each of Nos.1399, 1401, 1403, 1405 and 2 each of Nos. 1398, 1400, 1402, 1404. No. 1405a was sold in ATM machines, at the Natl. Philatelic Center, and Australian Philatelic Bureau.
Two printings differ slightly in shade and advertisement on back of pane.

Nos. 1406-1417 were deleted from the 2003 Standard catalogue. These self-adhesive stamps of design No. A438 have computer-generated denominations and exist with a large variety of different inscriptions for shows and other purposes.

Australia Day Type of 1994

Paintings: No. 1418, Back Verandah, by Russell Drysdale. No. 1419, Skull Springs Country, by Guy Grey-Smith. $1.05, Outcamp, by Robert Juniper. $1.20, Kite Flying, by Ian Fairweather.

1995, Jan. 12		**Litho.**	**Perf. 15x14½**
1418	A463 45c multicolored	.80	.80
1419	A463 45c multicolored	.80	.80
1420	A463 $1.05 multicolored	2.00	1.60
1421	A463 $1.20 multicolored	2.40	1.60
	Nos. 1418-1421 (4)	6.00	4.80

St. Valentine's
Day — A478

Various designs: a, Red heart. b, Red & gold heart. c, Gold heart.

1995, Feb. 6		**Litho.**	**Perf. 14½x14**
1422	Strip of 3	2.75	2.40
a.-c.	A478 45c any single	.80	.40

See No. 1480.

Endeavour
A479

No. 1423: a, Captain Cook's Endeavour. b, Replica.

1995, Feb. 9		**Litho.**	**Perf. 14x14½**
1423	Pair	2.75	2.75
a.-b.	A479 45c any single	.80	.80

Booklet Stamps
Size: 44x26mm
Perf. 14 Horiz.

1424	A479 20c like #1423b	2.40	2.40
1425	A479 45c like #1423a	2.40	2.40
a.	Bklt. pane, #1424, 4 #1425	8.50	8.50
	Complete booklet, #1425a	8.50	

Natl. Trust,
50th Anniv.
A480

Designs: No. 1426a, Coalport plate, Regency style bracket clock. No. 1426b, 15th-16th cent. x-frame Italian style chair, 19th cent. Steiner doll. $1, Advance Australia teapot, neo-classical parian-ware statuette. $2, China urn, silver bowl.

1995, Mar. 16		**Engr.**	**Perf. 14x14½**
1426	Pair	2.00	1.60
a.-b.	A480 45c any single	.75	.40
1427	A480 $1 red brn & bl	2.00	1.60
1428	A480 $2 blue & green	3.00	2.00
	Nos. 1426-1428 (3)	7.00	5.20

Opals — A481

1995, Apr. 5		**Litho.**	**Perf. 14½x14**
1429	A481 $1.20 Light opal	2.00	1.60
1430	A481 $2.50 Black opal	4.00	3.25

Nos. 1429-1430 each contain a holographic image. Soaking in water may affect the hologram.
See Nos. 1554-1555.

Australia 45c
A482

1995, Apr. 20		**Litho.**	**Perf. 14½**
1431	A482 45c multicolored	.80	.40

Queen Elizabeth II, 69th birthday.

A483

Famous Australians from World War II — No. 1432, Sir Edward Dunlop. No. 1433, Mrs. Jessie Vasey. No. 1434, Tom Derrick. No. 1435, Rawdon Hume Middleton.

1995, Apr. 20		**Litho.**	**Perf. 14½x14**
1432	A483 45c multi	1.00	.80
1433	A483 45c multi	1.00	.80
1434	A483 45c multi	1.00	.80
1435	A483 45c multi	1.00	.80
a.	Block of 4, #1432-1435	4.75	4.75
	Nos. 1432-1435 (4)	4.00	3.20

Self-Adhesive
Die Cut Perf. 11½

1436	A483 45c like #1432	1.60	.80
1437	A483 45c like #1433	1.60	.80
1438	A483 45c like #1434	1.60	.80
1439	A483 45c like #1435	1.60	.80
a.	Booklet pane, #1436, 2 each #1437-1439	16.00	
b.	Strip of 4, #1436-1439	12.00	
	Nos. 1436-1439 (4)	6.40	3.20

See Nos. 1452-1455.

UN, 50th
Anniv.
A484

1995, May 11		**Litho.**	**Perf. 14x14½**
1440	A484 45c + label, multi	1.10	.40
a.	Block of 4 + 4 labels	5.75	5.25

No. 1440 was issued se-tenant with label in blocks of 4 + 4 labels in four designs. In alternating rows, labels appear on left or right side of stamp.

A485

Poster, scene from: No. 1441, The Story of the Kelly Gang, 1906. No. 1442, On Our Selection, 1932. No. 1443, Jedda, 1955. No. 1444, Picnic at Hanging Rock, 1970s. No. 1445, Strictly Ballroom, 1992.

1995, June 8		**Litho.**	**Perf. 14½x14**
1441	A485 45c multicolored	.80	.80
1442	A485 45c multicolored	.80	.80
1443	A485 45c multicolored	.80	.80
1444	A485 45c multicolored	.80	.80
1445	A485 45c multicolored	.80	.80
a.	Strip of 5, #1441-1445	5.75	5.75
	Nos. 1441-1445 (5)	4.00	4.00

Self-Adhesive
Die Cut Perf. 11½

1446	A485 45c like #1441	.80	.80
1447	A485 45c like #1442	.80	.80
1448	A485 45c like #1443	.80	.80
1449	A485 45c like #1444	.80	.80
1450	A485 45c like #1445	.80	.80
a.	Strip of 5, #1446-1450	20.00	
b.	Bklt. pane, 2 ea #1446-1450	16.00	
	Nos. 1446-1450 (5)	4.00	4.00

Motion Pictures, cent.
By its nature No. 1450b constitutes a complete booklet. The peelable backing serves as a booklet cover.

A486

People with Disabilities: No. 1451a, Person flying kite from wheelchair. b, Blind person playing violin, guide dog.

1995, July 13		**Litho.**	**Perf. 14½x14**
1451	Pair	2.25	2.25
a.-b.	A486 45c any single	.80	.40

Famous Australians from World War II Type of 1995

1995-2005		**Litho.**	**Perf. 14½x14**
1452	A483 45c Leon Goldsworthy	.80	.80
a.	Booklet pane, #1432, 1434, 1435, 1452 ('05)	9.75	
1453	A483 45c Len Waters	.80	.80
1454	A483 45c Ellen Savage	.80	.80
a.	Booklet pane, #1433, 1454 ('05)	10.75	
1455	A483 45c Percy Collins	.80	.80
a.	Block of 4, #1452-1455	6.00	6.00
	Nos. 1452-1455 (4)	3.20	3.20

Issued: Nos. 1452-1455, 8/10/95. Nos 1452a and 1454a, April 2005.

Peace Types of 1946
Perf. 14x14½, 14½x14

1995, Aug. 10			**Engr.**
1456	A43 45c red brown	.95	.40
1457	A45 45c dark green	.95	.40
1458	A44 $1.50 dark blue	2.75	2.00
	Nos. 1456-1458 (3)	4.65	2.80

End of World War II, 50th anniv.

Wildlife
A487

Designs: a, Koalas. b, Pandas.

1995, Sept. 1   Litho.   *Perf. 14*
1459		Pair	2.25	2.25
a.-b.	A487	45c any single	.80	.80
c.		Souv. sheet #1459a, perf. 11x11½	2.25	2.25
d.		Souv. sheet #1459b, perf. 11x11½	2.50	2.50
e.		#1459c Ovptd. in sheet margin	4.50	4.50
f.		#1459d Ovptd. in sheet margin	4.50	4.50

Overprints read: No. 1459e: "AUSTRALIAN STAMP EXHIBITION." No. 1459f: "INTERNATIONAL STAMP & COIN EXPO. / BEIJING '95."

Issued: No. 1459f, 9/14/95.
See People's Republic of China Nos. 2597-2598.

Australian Medical Discoveries A488

Designs: No. 1461a, Joseph Slattery, Thomas Lyle, Walter Filmer, x-ray pioneers. No. 1461b, Jean Macnamara, Macfarlane Burnet, viruses and immunology. No. 1461C, Fred Hollows, eye care, vert. $2.50, Howard Florey, co-discoverer of penicillin, vert.

1995, Sept. 7   *Perf. 14x14½, 14½x14*
1461		Pair	2.40	1.60
a.-b.	A488	45c any single	.85	.80
1461C	A488	45c multicolored	1.10	.75
1461D	A488	$2.50 multicolored	4.00	4.00
		Nos. 1461-1461D (3)	7.50	6.35

No. 1461D exists in sheetlets of 10.

The World Down Under A489

Designs: Nos. 1462a, 1465a, Flatback turtle. Nos. 1462b, 1465b, Flame angelfish, nudibranch. Nos. 1463a, 1465c, Potato cod, giant maori wrasse. Nos. 1463b, 1465d, Giant trevally. Nos. 1464a, 1465e, Black marlin. Nos. 1464b, 1465f, Mako & tiger sharks.

1995, Oct. 3   Litho.   *Perf. 14x14½*
1462		Pair	2.25	2.25
a.-b.	A489	45c any single	.80	.80
1463		Pair	2.25	2.25
a.-b.	A489	45c any single	.80	.80
1464		Pair	2.25	2.25
a.-b.	A489	45c any single	.80	.80
		Nos. 1462-1464 (3)	6.75	6.75

Miniature Sheet of 6
1465	A489	45c #a.-f.	6.50	6.50
g.		Ovptd. in sheet margin	9.00	9.00
h.		Ovptd. in sheet margin	9.00	9.00
i.		Ovptd. in sheet margin	9.00	9.00
j.		Ovptd. in sheet margin	9.00	9.00
k.		Ovptd. in sheet margin	9.00	9.00

Nos. 1462-1464 have pale blue border on three sides. No. 1465 is a continuous design and does not have the pale border. Fish on No. 1465 are printed with additional phosphor ink producing a glow-in-the-dark effect under ultraviolet light.

Overprints in gold in sheet margin of No. 1465 include show emblems and text:
No. 1465g: "ADELAIDE / STAMP AND / COLLECTIBLES / FAIR / 14/10/95 - / 15/10/95."
No. 1465h: "SYDNEY / CENTREPOINT 95 / STAMPSHOW."
No. 1465i: "Brisbane Stamp Show / 20-22 October 1995."
No. 1465j: "Melbourne Stamp & Coin Fair / 27-29 October 1995."
No. 1465k: "Swanpex WA / 28-29 October 1995."

Booklet Stamps
Self-Adhesive
Die Cut Perf. 11½
1466	A489	45c like #1462a	1.20	.40
1467	A489	45c like #1462b	1.20	.40
1468	A489	45c like #1463a	1.20	.40
1469	A489	45c like #1463b	1.20	.40
1470	A489	45c like #1464a	1.20	.40
1471	A489	45c like #1464b	1.60	.40
a.		Booklet pane of #1470-1471, 2 each #1466-1469	14.00	
b.		Strip of 6, #1466-1471	14.00	
		Nos. 1466-1471 (6)	7.60	2.40

By its nature, No. 1471a constitutes a complete booklet. The peelable backing serves as a booklet cover.

Christmas — A490

Stained glass windows, Our Lady Help of Christians Church, Melbourne: 40c, Madonna and Child. 45c, Angel carrying banner. $1, Three rejoicing angels.

1995, Nov. 1   Litho.   *Perf. 14½x14*
1472	A490	40c multicolored	.80	.40
1473	A490	45c multicolored	1.25	.40
1474	A490	$1 multicolored	1.60	1.20
		Nos. 1472-1474 (3)	3.65	2.00

Booklet Stamp
Self-Adhesive
Die Cut Perf. 11½
1475	A490	40c multicolored	1.25	.40
a.		Booklet pane of 20	25.00	

Madonna and Child on No. 1475 are printed with additional phosphor ink giving parts of the stamp a rough texture.
By its nature, No. 1475a constitutes a complete booklet. The peelable backing serves as a booklet cover, which also contains 20 labels. The complete booklet is available with backing showing two different advertisements.

Australia Day Type of 1994

Paintings by Australian women: 45c, West Australian Banksia, by Margaret Preston, vert. 85c, The Babe is Wise, by Lina Bryans, vert. $1, The Bridge in Curve, by Grace Cossington Smith. $1.20, Beach Umbrellas, by Vida Lahey.

Perf. 14x14½, 14½x14
1996, Jan. 16   Litho.
1476	A463	45c multicolored	1.00	.35
1477	A463	85c multicolored	1.25	1.10
1478	A463	$1 multicolored	2.00	1.25
1479	A463	$1.20 multicolored	2.40	1.60
a.		Block of 4, #1476-1479	8.00	6.50
		Nos. 1476-1479 (4)	6.65	4.30

Heart and Roses A491

1996, Jan. 30   *Perf. 14x14½*
1480	A491	45c gold & multi	1.00	.40

See No. 1422.

Military Aviation A492

Airplanes: No. 1481, Firefly, Sea Fury. No. 1482, Beaufighter, Kittyhawk. No. 1483, Hornet. No. 1484, Kiowa.

1996-2005   Litho.   *Perf. 14x14½*
1481	A492	45c multicolored	.80	.80
1482	A492	45c multicolored	.80	.80
a.		Booklet pane, #1481, 1482 ('05)	10.00	—
1483	A492	45c multicolored	.80	.80
1484	A492	45c multicolored	.80	.80
a.		Block of 4, #1481-1484	4.00	4.00

Issued: 1481-1484, 2/26/96. No. 1482a, April 2005.

Australian World Heritage Sites Type of 1993

Designs: 45c, Tasmanian Wilderness. 75c, Willandra Lakes. 95c, Fossil Cave, Naracoorte. $1, Lord Howe Island.

1996, Mar. 14   Litho.   *Perf. 14½x14*
1485	A453	45c multicolored	.75	.75
1486	A453	75c multicolored	1.25	1.25
1487	A453	95c multicolored	1.60	1.25
1488	A453	$1 multicolored	2.00	1.60
a.		Booklet pane, #1311, 1314, 1485, 1488 ('06)	8.25	—
		Nos. 1485-1488 (4)	5.60	4.85

No. 1488a issued 3/15/2006.

Indonesian Bear Cuscus — A493

No. 1489, Australian Spotted Cuscus.

1996, Mar. 22
1489	A493	45c multicolored	.80	.80
1490	A493	45c multicolored	.80	.80
a.		Pair, Nos. 1489-1490	2.50	2.50
b.		Souvenir sheet, No. 1490a	4.00	4.00
c.		As "b," with World Philatelic Youth Exhibition emblem in sheet margin	9.25	9.25

No. 1490a has continuous design.
See Indonesia Nos. 1640-1642.

Queen Elizabeth II, 70th Birthday A494

Litho. & Engr.
1996, Apr. 11   *Perf. 14x14½*
1491	A494	45c multicolored	1.00	.40

North Melbourne Kangaroos A495

Brisbane Bears A496

Sydney Swans — A497

Carlton Blues — A498

Adelaide Crows — A499

Fitzroy Lions — A500

Richmond Tigers — A501

St. Kilda Saints — A502

Melbourne Demons — A503

Collingwood Magpies — A504

Fremantle Dockers — A505

Footscray Bulldogs — A506

West Coast Eagles A507

Essendon Bombers A508

Geelong Cats — A509

Hawthorn Hawks — A510

1996, Apr. 23   Litho.   *Perf. 14½x14*
1492	A495	45c multicolored	.75	.75
1493	A496	45c multicolored	.75	.75
1494	A497	45c multicolored	.75	.75
1495	A498	45c multicolored	.75	.75
1496	A499	45c multicolored	.75	.75
1497	A500	45c multicolored	.75	.75
1498	A501	45c multicolored	.75	.75
1499	A502	45c multicolored	.75	.75
1500	A503	45c multicolored	.75	.75
1501	A504	45c multicolored	.75	.75
1502	A505	45c multicolored	.75	.75
1503	A506	45c multicolored	.75	.75
1504	A507	45c multicolored	.75	.75
1505	A508	45c multicolored	.75	.75
1506	A509	45c multicolored	.75	.75
1507	A510	45c multicolored	.75	.75
a.		Min. sheet of 16, #1492-1507	15.00	
		Nos. 1492-1507 (16)	12.00	12.00

Booklet Stamps
Self-Adhesive
Serpentine Die Cut 11½
1508	A495	45c multicolored	1.00	.40
a.		Booklet pane of 10	10.00	
1509	A496	45c multicolored	1.00	.40
a.		Booklet pane of 10	10.00	
1510	A497	45c multicolored	1.00	.40
a.		Booklet pane of 10	10.00	
1511	A498	45c multicolored	1.00	.40
a.		Booklet pane of 10	10.00	
1512	A499	45c multicolored	1.00	.40
a.		Booklet pane of 10	10.00	
1513	A500	45c multicolored	1.00	.40
a.		Booklet pane of 10	10.00	
1514	A501	45c multicolored	1.00	.40
a.		Booklet pane of 10	10.00	
1515	A502	45c multicolored	1.00	.40
a.		Booklet pane of 10	10.00	
1516	A503	45c multicolored	1.00	.40
a.		Booklet pane of 10	10.00	
1517	A504	45c multicolored	1.00	.40
a.		Booklet pane of 10	10.00	
1518	A505	45c multicolored	1.00	.40
a.		Booklet pane of 10	10.00	
1519	A506	45c multicolored	1.00	.40
a.		Booklet pane of 10	10.00	
1520	A507	45c multicolored	1.00	.40
a.		Booklet pane of 10	10.00	
1521	A508	45c multicolored	1.00	.40
a.		Booklet pane of 10	10.00	
1522	A509	45c multicolored	1.00	.40
a.		Booklet pane of 10	10.00	

1523	A510	45c multicolored	1.00	.40
a.		Booklet pane of 10	10.00	
		Nos. 1508-1523 (16)	16.00	6.40

By their nature, Nos. 1508a-1523a are complete booklets. The peelable paper backing serves as a booklet cover.

Australian Football League, cent.

Flora and Fauna — A511

Designs: 5c, Leadbeater's possum. 10c, Powerful owl. 20c, Saltwater crocodile, Kangkong flower. 25c, Northern dwarf tree frog, red lily. No. 1528, Little kingfisher. No. 1529, Jacana. No. 1530, Jabiru. No. 1531, Brolga. $1, Big greasy butterfly, water lily. $2, Blackwood wattle. $5, Mountain ash, fern. $10, Kakadu Wetlands during lightning storm, great egret, red lily.

Perf. 14x14½, 14½x14 (#1535)

1996-99				Litho.
1524	A511	5c multi	.25	.25
1525	A511	10c multi	.30	.25
1526	A511	20c multi	.40	.40
1527	A511	25c multi	.55	.40
1528	A511	45c multi	.95	.40
1529	A511	45c multi	.95	.40
1530	A511	45c multi	.95	.40
1531	A511	45c multi	.95	.40
a.		Block of 4, #1528-1531	4.50	4.00
b.		Souvenir sheet of 2, #1530-1531	7.50	
1532	A511	$1 multi	2.10	.65
1533	A511	$2 multi	3.25	1.25

Size: 30x50mm

1534	A511	$5 multi, vert.	7.50	3.25

Size: 50x30mm

1535	A511	$10 multi	15.00	5.75
a.		Souvenir sheet of 1	18.00	18.00
b.		As "a," ovptd. in sheet margin	30.00	30.00
c.		As "a," ovptd in sheet margin	25.00	25.00
d.		As "a," ovptd in sheet margin	29.00	21.00
		Nos. 1524-1535 (12)	33.15	13.80

Self-Adhesive

Serpentine Die Cut 11½, 11¼ (#1539i)

1536	A511	45c like #1529	1.00	.35
1537	A511	45c like #1528	1.00	.35
1538	A511	45c like #1531	1.00	.35
1539	A511	45c like #1530	1.00	.35
a.		Booklet pane, 3 ea #1536, #1538, 2 ea #1537, #1539	10.00	
b.		Strip of 4, #1536-1539	4.75	
h.		Sheet of 5, #1537-1539, 2 #1536	6.00	
i.		Booklet pane, 5 each #1536-1539	28.00	

Serpentine Die Cut 12½x13

1539C	A511	45c like #1529	1.50	.55
1539D	A511	45c like #1528	1.50	.55
1539E	A511	45c like #1531	1.50	.55
1539F	A511	45c like #1530	1.50	.55
g.		Strip of 4, #1539C-1539F	8.50	
		Nos. 1536-1539F (8)	10.00	3.60

Nos. 1536-1539 are booklet stamps.

No. 1531b is inscribed in sheet margin with Shanghai '97 emblem and "International Stamp & Coin Exposition Shanghai '97" in Chinese and English.

No. 1535b is overprinted in silver in sheet margin with PACIFIC 97 emblem and "Australia Post Exhibition Sheet No. 4."

No. 1535c is overprinted in sheet margin for "Italia '98" in Milan.

No. 1535d is overprinted in copper in sheet margin with "PHILA NIPPON '01" and show emblem. Issued: No. 1535c, 8/1/01.

By its nature No. 1539a is a complete booklet. The peelable backing serves as a booklet cover.

Issued: 5c, 10c, $2, $5, 5/9/96; 20c, 25c, $1, $10, 4/10/97; #1528-1531, 1536-1539, 6/2/97; #1531b, 11/17/97; #1539C-1539F, 11/13/99; No. 1539i, 9/1/98.

No. 1539i is a complete booklet.

See Nos. 1734-1746L, 1984-1995, 2060-2063, 2111-2114, 2159-2170, 2235-2238.

Modern Olympic Games, Cent. A512

Designs: No. 1540, Edwin Flack, 1st Australian gold medalist, runners. No. 1541, Fanny

Durack, 1st Australian woman gold medalist, swimmers. $1.05, Paralympics, Atlanta.

Litho. & Engr.

1996, June 6			**Perf. 14x14½**	
1540	A512	45c multicolored	.75	.30
1541	A512	45c multicolored	.75	.30
a.		Pair, #1540-1541	2.25	1.75
1542	A512	$1.05 multicolored	2.40	1.20
		Nos. 1540-1542 (3)	3.90	1.80

Transfer of Olympic Flag from Atlanta to Sydney A513

1996, July 22			Litho.
1543	A513	45c multicolored	1.10	.40

Issued in sheets of 10.

Children's Book Council, 50th Anniv. A514

Covers from "Book of the Year" books: No. 1544, "Animalia." No. 1545, "Greetings from Sandy Beach." No. 1546, "Who Sank the Boat?" No. 1547, "John Brown, Rose and the Midnight Cat."

1996, July 4		Litho.	**Perf. 14x14½**	
1544	A514	45c multicolored	1.00	1.00
1545	A514	45c multicolored	1.00	1.00
1546	A514	45c multicolored	1.00	1.00
1547	A514	45c multicolored	1.00	1.00
a.		Block of 4, #1544-1547	4.50	4.50
		Nos. 1544-1547 (4)	4.00	4.00

Serpentine Die Cut 11½

Self-Adhesive

1548	A514	45c like #1544	1.10	.40
1549	A514	45c like #1546	1.10	.40
1550	A514	45c like #1547	1.10	.40
1551	A514	45c like #1545	1.10	.40
a.		Booklet pane, 4 #1548, 2 each #1549-1551	12.00	
b.		Strip of 4, #1548-1551	8.00	
		Nos. 1548-1551 (4)	4.40	1.60

By its nature, No. 1551a is a complete booklet. The peelable paper backing serves as a booklet cover.

National Council of Women, Cent. — A515

Designs: 45c, Margaret Windeyer (1866-1939), honorary life president. $1, Rose Scott (1847-1925), founding executive member.

1996, Aug. 8		Litho.	**Perf. 14½x14**	
1552	A515	45c claret & yellow	.80	.30
1553	A515	$1 blue & yellow	2.00	1.10

Gems Type of 1995

1996, Sept. 5		Litho.	**Perf. 14½x14**	
1554	A481	45c Pearl	1.60	.30
1555	A481	$1.20 Diamond	3.00	2.50

No. 1555 contains a round foil design. Soaking in water may affect the design.

Arts Councils in Regional Australia A516

Silhouettes of performing artists, outdoor scene: 20c, Ballet dancer, violinist, field, bales, trees. 45c, Violinist, hand holding flower, dancer, tree in field.

Perf. 14 Horiz.

1996, Sept. 12			Litho.
		Booklet Stamps	
1556	A516	20c multicolored	1.75	1.50
1557	A516	45c multicolored	1.50	.60
a.		Bklt. pane, #1556, 4 #1557	5.75	
		Complete booklet, #1557a	5.75	

A517   Pets — A518

1996-97		**Perf. 14x14½, 14½x14**		
1558	A517	45c Cockatoo	.75	.75
1559	A517	45c Ducks, vert.	.75	.75
1560	A517	45c Dog, cat, vert.	.75	.40
a.		Pair, #1559-1560	2.00	2.00
1561	A518	45c Dog, puppy	.75	.75
1562	A518	45c Kittens	.75	.75
a.		Pair, #1561-1562	2.60	2.60

Size: 30x50mm

1563	A518	45c Pony mare, foal	.75	.40
a.		Souvenir sheet, #1558-1563, perf. 14¼	6.00	6.00
b.		As "a," ovptd.	8.00	8.00
c.		As "a," ovptd.	8.00	8.00
d.		As "a," ovptd.	8.00	8.00
e.		As "a," ovptd.	8.00	8.00
f.		As "a," ovptd.	8.00	8.00
g.		As "a," ovptd.	8.00	8.00
h.		As "a," ovptd.	8.00	8.00
		Nos. 1558-1563 (6)	4.50	3.80

Self-Adhesive

Serpentine Die Cut 11½

1564	A518	45c like #1561	1.60	.80
1565	A518	45c like #1562	1.60	.80
a.		Bklt. pane, 6 #1564, 4 #1565	15.00	

No. 1563a is a continuous design.

Overprints in gold on sheet margin: No. 1563b, show emblem and "10TH ASIAN INTERNATIONAL PHILATELIC EXHIBITION 1996" in Chinese and English. No. 1563c, pets emblem and, "ASDA CENTREPOINT '96 STAMP AND COIN SHOW / 5-7 October 1996." No. 1563d, pets emblem and "ST PETERS STAMP & COLLECTIBLE FAIR / 12-13 OCTOBER 1996." No. 1563e, pets emblem and "MELBOURNE '96 NATIONAL PHILATELIC EXHIBITION / 17-20 OCTOBER 1996." No. 1563f, pets emblem and "QUEENSLAND SPRING STAMP AND COIN SHOW / 25-27 OCTOBER 1996." No. 1563g, pets emblem and "SWANPEX '96 / 26-27 OCTOBER 1996." No. 1563h: Hong Kong '97 emblem and "11TH ASIAN INTERNATIONAL STAMP EXHIBITION / 12-16 FEBRUARY 1997."

By its nature, No. 1565a is a complete booklet. The peelable paper backing serves as a booklet cover.

Issued: Nos. 1558-1563, 1563a, 1564-1565, 10/1/96; Nos. 1563b-1563g, 10/3/96; No. 1563h, 2/12/97.

Baron Ferdinand von Mueller (1825-96), Botanist — A519

1996, Oct. 9			**Perf. 14**
1566	A519	$1.20 multicolored	2.40	2.40

See Germany No. 1949.

Christmas — A520

40c, Madonna and Child. 45c, Wise man. $1, Shepherd boy, lamb.

1996, Nov. 1			**Perf. 14½x14**	
1567	A520	40c multicolored	.80	.35
1568	A520	45c multicolored	.90	.35
1569	A520	$1 multicolored	1.60	1.25
		Nos. 1567-1569 (3)	3.30	1.95

Self-Adhesive

Serpentine Die Cut 12

1570	A520	40c like #1567	2.00	.40
a.		Booklet pane of 20	40.00	

By its nature, No. 1570a is a complete booklet. The peelable paper backing serves as a booklet cover.

Exploration of Australian Coast & Christmas Island by Willem de Vlamingh, 300th Anniv. — A521

Portrait of a Dutch Navigator, by Jan Verkolje.

1996, Nov. 1			**Perf. 14x14½**	
1571	A521	45c multicolored	.90	.30
a.		Pair, #1571 & Christmas Is. #404	2.25	2.25

Australia Day Type of 1994

Paintings: 85c, Landscape '74, by Fred Williams. 90c, The Balcony 2, by Brett Whiteley. $1.20, Fire Haze at Gerringong, by Lloyd Rees.

1997, Jan. 16		Litho.	**Perf. 14½x14**	
1572	A463	85c multicolored	1.50	.75
1573	A463	90c multicolored	1.60	1.25
1574	A463	$1.20 multicolored	2.50	1.60
		Nos. 1572-1574 (3)	5.60	3.60

Sir Donald Bradman, Cricketer A522

1997, Jan. 23		Litho.	**Perf. 14¼**	
1575	A522	45c Portrait	.80	.40
a.		Without gold highlights, dated "2007"	1.40	1.40
1576	A522	45c At bat	.80	.40
a.		Pair, No. 1575-1576	2.40	2.25
b.		Booklet pane, #1575-1576	1.90	
c.		Without gold highlights, dated "2007"	1.40	1.40

No. 1576b issued 1/24/07. Nos. 1575a, 1576c issued 11/14/2007.

See Nos. 1634-1646, 1719-1722, 1800-1807, 1933-1936, 1941-1942, 2021-2030, 2125-2132, 2207-2210.

Greetings — A523

1997, Jan. 29			**Perf. 14½x14**	
1577	A523	45c Rose	.80	.40

Serpentine Die Cut 11½

Booklet Stamp

Self-Adhesive

1578	A523	45c like #1577	1.50	.30
a.		Booklet pane of 10	15.00	

By its nature, No. 1578a is a complete booklet. The peelable paper backing, which also contains 12 labels, serves as a booklet cover.

Classic
Cars — A524

Automobiles: No. 1579, 1934 Ford Coupe
Utility. No. 1580, 1948 GMH Holden 48-215
(FX). No. 1581, 1958 Austin Lancer. No. 1582,
1962 Chrysler Valiant R Series.

1997, Feb. 27 Litho. Perf. 14x14½
1579	A524	45c multicolored	.90	.90
a.		Booklet pane of 4	3.75	
1580	A524	45c multicolored	.90	.90
a.		Booklet pane of 4	3.75	
1581	A524	45c multicolored	.90	.90
a.		Booklet pane of 4	3.75	
1582	A524	45c multicolored	.90	.90
a.		Booklet pane of 4	3.75	
b.		Block of 4, #1579-1582	4.50	4.50
		Complete booklet, #1579a, 1580a, 1581a, 1582a	19.00	
		Nos. 1579-1582 (4)	3.60	3.60

Complete booklet contains 2 postal cards
and 16 self-adhesive labels.

Serpentine Die Cut 12
Booklet Stamps
Self-Adhesive
1583	A524	45c like #1579	1.25	.40
1584	A524	45c like #1580	1.25	.40
1585	A524	45c like #1581	1.25	.40
1586	A524	45c like #1582	1.25	.40
a.		Bkt. pane, 2 ea #1583, 1585, 3 ea #1584, 1586	12.50	
b.		Strip of 4, #1583-1586	12.50	
		Nos. 1583-1586 (4)	5.00	1.60

By its nature, No. 1586a is a complete booklet. The peelable backing serves as a booklet
cover. The backing for No. 1586b is inscribed
with a 3x8mm black vertical box and "SNP
CAMBEC."

Circuses in
Australia, 150th
Anniv. — A525

Designs: No. 1591, Queen of the Arena,
May Wirth (1894-1978). No. 1592, Wizard of
the Wire, Con Colleano (1899-1973). No.
1593, Clowns. No. 1594, Tumblers.

1997, Mar. 13 Litho. Perf. 14½x14
1591	A525	45c multicolored	.80	.35
1592	A525	45c multicolored	.80	.35
1593	A525	45c multicolored	.80	.35
1594	A525	45c multicolored	.80	.35
a.		Block of 4, #1591-1594	4.50	4.50
		Nos. 1591-1594 (4)	3.20	1.40

A526

1997, Apr. 17 Engr. Perf. 14x14½
1595	A526	45c Design A50	1.00	.40

Queen Elizabeth II, 71st birthday, 50th wedding anniv.

A527

1997, Apr. 17 Perf. 14½x14
1596	A527	45c multicolored	1.00	.40

Lions Clubs of Australia, 50th anniv.

A528

Dolls and Teddy Bears: No. 1597, Doll wearing red hat. No. 1598, Bear standing. No.
1599, Doll wearing white dress holding teddy
bear. No. 1600, Doll in brown outfit. No. 1601,
Teddy bear seated.

1997, May 8 Litho. Perf. 14½x14
1597	A528	45c multicolored	.80	.80
1598	A528	45c multicolored	.80	.80
1599	A528	45c multicolored	.80	.80
1600	A528	45c multicolored	.80	.80
1601	A528	45c multicolored	.80	.80
a.		Strip of 5, #1597-1601	5.50	5.50
		Nos. 1597-1601 (5)	4.00	4.00

Nos. 1597-1601 were printed in sheets containing two strips of five. Some sheets exist
overprinted in margin with picture of teddy
bear and inscription "Brisbane Stamp & Coin
Expo / 7-9 June 1997."

Emergency
Services
A529

Designs: No. 1602, Disaster victim evacu-
ated. No. 1603, Police rescue saves home. $1.05,
Rapid response saves home. $1.20, Ambu-
lance dash saves life.

1997, July 10 Litho. Perf. 14x14½
1602	A529	45c multicolored	.80	.80
1603	A529	45c multicolored	.80	.80
a.		Pair, #1602-1603	2.00	1.60
1604	A529	$1.05 multicolored	1.75	1.50
1605	A529	$1.20 multicolored	2.40	1.60
		Nos. 1602-1605 (4)	5.75	4.70

Arrival of
Merino
Sheep in
Australia,
Bicent.
A530

Designs: No. 1606, George Peppin, Junior
(1827-76), breeder, Merino sheep. No. 1607,
"Pepe" chair, uses of wool.

1997, Aug. 7 Litho. Perf. 14x14½
1606	A530	45c multicolored	.80	.40
1607	A530	45c multicolored	.80	.40
a.		Pair, #1606-1607	2.00	2.00

Scenes from
"The
Dreaming,"
Animated
Stories for
Children
A531

Designs: 45c, Dumbi the Owl. $1, The Two
Willy-Willies. $1.20, How Brolga Became a
Bird. $1.80, Tuggan-Tuggan.

1997, Aug. 21 Perf. 14½
1608	A531	45c multicolored	.80	.40
1609	A531	$1 multicolored	1.75	1.25
1610	A531	$1.20 multicolored	2.40	1.60
1611	A531	$1.80 multicolored	3.25	2.00
		Nos. 1608-1611 (4)	8.20	5.25

Prehistoric
Animals — A532

Designs: No. 1612, Rhoetosaurus brownei.
No. 1613, Mcnamaraspis kaprios. No. 1614,
Ninjemys oweni. No. 1615, Paracyclotosaurus
davidi. No. 1616, Woolungasaurus
glendowerensis.

1997, Sept. 4 Litho. Perf. 14½x14
1612	A532	45c multicolored	.80	.40
1613	A532	45c multicolored	.80	.40
1614	A532	45c multicolored	.80	.40
1615	A532	45c multicolored	.80	.40
1616	A532	45c multicolored	.80	.40
a.		Strip of 5, #1612-1616	6.50	5.00
		Nos. 1612-1616 (5)	4.00	2.00

Printed in sheets of 10 stamps.

A533   Nocturnal
Animals — A534

No. 1617, Barking owl. No. 1618, Spotted-
tailed quoll. No. 1619, Platypus. No. 1620,
Brown antechinus. No. 1621, Dingo. No. 1622,
Yellow-bellied glider.

Perf. 14½x14, 14x14½
1997, Oct. 1   Litho.
1617	A533	45c multicolored	.80	.80
1618	A533	45c multicolored	.80	.80
a.		Pair, #1617-1618	2.00	1.60
1619	A534	45c multicolored	.80	.80
1620	A534	45c multicolored	.80	.80
1621	A534	45c multicolored	.80	.80
a.		Strip of 3, #1619-1621	3.25	3.25

Size: 50x30mm
1622	A534	45c multicolored	1.40	.80
a.		Souvenir sheet, #1617-1622, perf. 14¼	6.00	6.00
		Nos. 1617-1622 (6)	5.40	4.80

No. 1622a is printed with additional
phosphor ink revealing a glow-in-the-dark spider and web under ultraviolet light.

Size: 21x32mm
Serpentine Die Cut Perf. 11½
Self-Adhesive
1623	A533	45c like #1617	1.25	.40
1624	A533	45c like #1618	1.25	.40
a.		Booklet pane, 5 each #1623-1624	12.50	
b.		Pair, #1623-1624	4.00	

By its nature No. 1624a is a complete booklet. The peelable paper backing serves as a
booklet cover.

Breast
Cancer
Awareness
A535

1997, Oct. 27 Litho. Perf. 14x14½
1625	A535	45c multicolored	1.00	.40

Christmas
A536

Children in Christmas Nativity pageant: 40c,
Angels. 45c, Mary holding Baby Jesus. $1,
Three Wise Men.

1997, Nov. 3
1626	A536	40c multicolored	.65	.35
1627	A536	45c multicolored	.75	.35
1628	A536	$1 multicolored	1.60	1.25
		Nos. 1626-1628 (3)	3.00	1.95

Booklet Stamps
Serpentine Die Cut Perf. 11½
Self-Adhesive
1629	A536	40c multicolored	.75	.40
a.		Booklet pane of 20	15.00	

By its nature No. 1629a is a complete booklet. The peelable paper backing serves as a
booklet cover, which also contains 20 labels.

Maritime
Heritage — A537

1998, Jan. 15 Litho. Perf. 14½x14
1630	A537	45c Flying Cloud	.80	.40
a.		Pane of 10	9.00	9.00
1631	A537	85c Marco Polo	1.25	.80
a.		Sheet of 2, #1631 perf. 13½ & Canada #1779b	7.00	7.00
1632	A537	$1 Chusan	1.60	.80
1633	A537	$1.20 Heather Belle	2.00	1.25
		Nos. 1630-1633 (4)	5.65	3.25

Australia '99 (No. 1630a). World Stamp
Expo. (No. 1631a).
See Canada No. 1779a.
Issued: No. 1630a, 6/17/98; No. 1631a,
3/19/99.

Legends Type of 1997

Olympians: No. 1634: a, Betty Cuthbert. b,
Cuthbert running. c, Herb Elliott. d, Elliott running. e, Dawn Fraser. f, Fraser swimming. g,
Marjorie Jackson. h, Jackson running. i, Murray Rose. j, Rose swimming. k, Shirley Strickland. l, Strickland clearing hurdle.

1998, Jan. 21   Perf. 14x14½
Size: 34x26mm
1634		Sheet of 12	14.00	14.00
a.-l.		A522 45c any single	.80	.80
m.		Booklet pane, #1634a-1634d	5.50	—
n.		Booklet pane, #1634e-1634h	5.50	—
o.		Booklet pane, #1634i-1634l	5.50	—

Booklet Stamps
Self-Adhesive
Serpentine Die Cut 11½
Size: 34x25mm
1635	A522	45c like #1634a	1.10	.40
1636	A522	45c like #1634b	1.10	.40
1637	A522	45c like #1634c	1.10	.40
1638	A522	45c like #1634d	1.10	.40
1639	A522	45c like #1634e	1.10	.40
1640	A522	45c like #1634f	1.10	.40
1641	A522	45c like #1634g	1.10	.40
1642	A522	45c like #1634h	1.10	.40
1643	A522	45c like #1634i	1.10	.40
1644	A522	45c like #1634j	1.10	.40
1645	A522	45c like #1634k	1.10	.40
1646	A522	45c like #1634l	1.10	.40
a.		Bkt. pane of 12, #1635-1646	20.00	
		Nos. 1635-1646 (12)	13.20	4.80

By its nature, No. 1646a is a complete booklet. The peelable backing serves as a booklet
cover.
Nos. 1634m-1634o issued 1/24/07.

Greetings — A538

1998, Feb. 12 Litho. Perf. 14½x14
1647	A538	45c Champagne roses	.90	.40

Booklet Stamp
Self-Adhesive
Serpentine Die Cut 11½
1648	A538	45c like #1647	.90	.65
a.		Booklet pane of 10	11.00	

By its nature No. 1648a is a complete booklet. The peelable paper backing, which contains 12 labels, serves as a booklet cover.

Queen
Elizabeth II,
72nd
Birthday
A539

1998, Apr. 9 Litho. Perf. 14x14½
1649	A539	45c multicolored	1.10	.65

Royal Australian Navy Fleet Air Arm, 50th Anniv. A540

1998, Apr. 9
1650 A540 45c multicolored   1.10 .40

Farming in Australia A541

Designs: No. 1651, Sheep for producing wool. No. 1652, Sheaves of wheat. No. 1653, Herding cattle on horseback. No. 1654, Harvesting sugar cane. No. 1655, Dairy cattle, man on motorcycle.

1998, Apr. 21
1651	A541	45c multicolored	.80 .40
1652	A541	45c multicolored	.80 .40
1653	A541	45c multicolored	.80 .40
1654	A541	45c multicolored	.80 .40
1655	A541	45c multicolored	.80 .40
a.		Strip of 5, #1651-1655	4.75 4.75
		Nos. 1651-1655 (5)	4.00 2.00

Booklet Stamps
Self-Adhesive
Serpentine Die Cut 11½
Size: 37x25mm

1656	A541	45c like #1651	1.25 .40
1657	A541	45c like #1652	1.25 .40
1658	A541	45c like #1653	1.25 .40
1659	A541	45c like #1654	1.25 .40
1660	A541	45c like #1655	1.25 .40
a.		Bklt. pane, 2 ea #1656-1660	16.00
		Nos. 1656-1660 (5)	6.25 2.00

The peelable backing of No. 1660a serves as a booklet cover.

Heart Health A542

1998, May 4   Litho.   Perf. 14x14½
1661 A542 45c multicolored   1.10 .40

Rock and Roll in Australia A543

a, "The Wild One," by Johnny O'Keefe, 1958. b, "Oh Yeah Uh Huh," by Col Joye and the Joye Boys, 1959. c, "He's My Blonde-headed Stompie Wompie Real Gone Surfer Boy," by Little Pattie, 1963. d, "Shakin' All Over," by Normie Rowe, 1965. e, "She's So Fine," by The Easybeats, 1965. f, "The Real Thing," by Russell Morris, 1969. g, "Turn Up Your Radio," by The Masters Apprentices, 1970. h, "Eagle Rock," by Daddy Cool, 1971. i, "Most People I Know Think That I'm Crazy," by Billy Thorpe & the Aztecs, 1972. j, "Horror Movie," by Skyhooks, 1974. k, "It's a Long Way to the Top," by AC/DC, 1975. l, "Howzat," by Sherbet, 1976.

1998, May 26
1662	A543	Sheet of 12	12.00 12.00
a.-l.		45c any single	.80 .80

Coil Stamps
Self-Adhesive
Serpentine Die Cut 11½
Size: 37x25mm

1663	A543	45c like #1662a	1.10 .50
1664	A543	45c like #1662b	1.10 .50
1665	A543	45c like #1662c	1.10 .50
1666	A543	45c like #1662d	1.10 .50
1667	A543	45c like #1662e	1.10 .50
1668	A543	45c like #1662f	1.10 .50
1669	A543	45c like #1662g	1.10 .50
1670	A543	45c like #1662h	1.10 .50
1671	A543	45c like #1662i	1.10 .50
1672	A543	45c like #1662j	1.10 .50
1673	A543	45c like #1662k	1.10 .50

1674	A543	45c like #1662l	1.10 .50
a.		Strip of 12 + label	18.00
		Nos. 1663-1674 (12)	13.20 6.00

Endangered Birds — A544

World Wildlife Fund: No. 1675, Helmeted honeyeater. No. 1676, Orange-bellied parrot. No. 1677, Red-tailed black cockatoo. No. 1678, Gouldian finch.

1998, June 25   Perf. 14x14½
1675	A544	5c multicolored	.40 .40
1676	A544	5c multicolored	.40 .40
a.		Pair, #1675-1676	1.60 1.60
1677	A544	45c multicolored	.80 .80
1678	A544	45c multicolored	.80 .80
a.		Pair, #1677-1678	2.40 2.40

Performing and Visual Arts — A545

Young people: No. 1679, Playing French horn. No. 1680, Dancing.

1998, July 16   Litho.   Perf. 14x14½
1679	A545	45c multicolored	.80 .80
1680	A545	45c multicolored	.80 .80
a.		Pair, #1679-1680	2.25 2.25

Orchids — A546

Designs: 45c, Phalaenopsis rosenstromii. 85c, Arundina graminifolia. $1, Grammatophyllum speciosum. $1.20, Dendrobium phalaenopsis.

1998, Aug. 6   Litho.   Perf. 14½x14
1681	A546	45c multicolored	.80 .40
1682	A546	85c multicolored	1.30 .75
1683	A546	$1 multicolored	1.60 1.00
1684	A546	$1.20 multicolored	2.00 1.75
a.		Souvenir sheet, #1681-1684	6.50 6.50
		Nos. 1681-1684 (4)	5.70 3.90

See Singapore Nos. 858-861b.

The Teapot of Truth, by Cartoonist Michael Leunig A547

Designs: No. 1685, Angel carrying teapot, bird with flower. No. 1686, Birds perched on heart-shaped vine. No. 1687, Characters using their heads to pour tea into cup. $1, Stylized family. $1.20, Stylized teapot with face & legs.

1998, Aug. 13   Perf. 14x14½
1685	A547	45c multicolored	1.60 1.25
a.		Booklet pane of 4	6.50
1686	A547	45c multicolored	1.60 1.25
a.		Booklet pane of 4	6.50
1687	A547	45c multicolored	1.60 1.25
a.		Booklet pane of 4	6.50

Size: 30x25mm
1688	A547	$1 multicolored	2.60 2.60
a.		Booklet pane of 2	5.25
1689	A547	$1.20 multicolored	3.25 3.25
a.		Booklet pane of 2	6.25
		Complete booklet, #1685a, 1686a, 1687a, 1688a, 1689a, 1 postal card & 16 self-adhesive labels	35.00
		Nos. 1685-1689 (5)	10.65 9.60

A548

Butterflies — No. 1690, Red lacewing. No. 1691, Dull oakblue. No. 1692, Meadow argus. No. 1693, Ulysses. No. 1694, Common redeye.

1998, Sept. 3   Litho.   Perf. 14½x14
1690	A548	45c multicolored	.80 .80
1691	A548	45c multicolored	.80 .80
1692	A548	45c multicolored	.80 .80
1693	A548	45c multicolored	.80 .80
1694	A548	45c multicolored	.80 .80
a.		Strip of 5, #1690-1694	5.50 5.25
b.		Souv. sheet of 5, #1690-1694	7.00 7.00
		Nos. 1690-1694 (5)	4.00 4.00

No. 1694b for China 1999 World Philatelic Exhibition. Issued 8/21/99.

Self-Adhesive
Serpentine Die Cut 11½
1695	A548	45c like #1690	1.00 .40
1696	A548	45c like #1691	1.00 .40
1697	A548	45c like #1692	1.00 .40
1698	A548	45c like #1693	1.00 .40
1699	A548	45c like #1694	1.00 .40
a.		Strip of 5, #1695-1699	8.75
		Nos. 1695-1699 (5)	5.00 2.00

A549

Designs: No. 1700, Sextant, map of Bass Strait. No. 1701, Telescope, map of Van Diemen's Land (Tasmania).

1998, Sept. 10   Perf. 14½x14
1700	A549	45c multicolored	1.00 .40
1701	A549	45c multicolored	1.00 .40
a.		Pair, #1700-1701	2.40 2.25

Circumnavigation of Tasmania by George Bass (1771-c. 1803) and Matthew Flinders (1774-1814), bicent.

A550   Marine Life — A551

Designs: No. 1702, Fiery squid. No. 1703, Manta ray. No. 1704, Bottlenose dolphin. No. 1705, Weedy seadragon. No. 1706, Southern right whale. No. 1707, White pointer shark.

Perf. 14½x14, 14x14½
1998, Oct. 1   Litho.
1702	A550	45c multicolored	.80 .80
1703	A550	45c multi, horiz.	.80 .80
1704	A551	45c multi	.80 .80
1705	A551	45c multi	.80 .80
a.		Pair, #1704-1705	2.25 2.25

Size: 50x30mm
1706	A551	45c multi, horiz.	.80 .80
1707	A551	45c multi	.80 .80
a.		Souvenir sheet, #1702-1707	6.00 5.75
		Nos. 1702-1707 (6)	4.80 4.80

Booklet Stamps
Self-Adhesive
Serpentine Die Cut Perf. 11½
1708	A551	45c like #1704	1.10 .40
1709	A551	45c like #1705	1.10 .40
a.		Bklt. pane, 5 ea #1708-1709	11.00

No. 1709a is a complete booklet. The peelable paper backing serves as a booklet cover. Nos. 1708-1709 also exist in coils, issued in rolls of 100 with surrounding selvage removed. Value, set of singles $4.50.

Universal Declaration of Human Rights, 50th Anniv. — A552

1998, Oct. 22   Litho.   Perf. 14½x14
1712 A552 45c multicolored   1.10 .60

Christmas A553

40c, Magi. 45c, Nativity. $1, Journey to Bethlehem.

1998, Nov. 2   Perf. 14x14½
1713	A553	40c multicolored	.80 .55
1714	A553	45c multicolored	.90 .80
1715	A553	$1 multicolored	2.00 2.00
		Nos. 1713-1715 (3)	3.70 3.35

Booklet Stamp
Self-Adhesive
Serpentine Die Cut Perf. 11½
1716	A553	40c multicolored	1.10 .55
a.		Booklet pane of 20	22.00

No. 1716a is a complete booklet.

Nationality and Citizenship Act, 50th Anniv. A554

1999, Jan. 14   Litho.   Perf. 14x14½
1717 A554 45c multicolored   1.10 .50

Die Cut Perf. 11¾
Self-Adhesive
1718 A554 45c multicolored   1.10 .55

Legends Type of 1997
Designs: Nos. 1719, 1721, Arthur Boyd, artist. Nos. 1720, 1722, "Nebuchadnezzar on Fire Falling over a Waterfall," by Boyd.

1999, Jan. 22   Litho.   Perf. 14x14½
1719	A522	45c multicolored	.80 .80
1720	A522	45c multicolored	.80 .80
a.		Pair, #1719-1720	2.25 2.25
b.		Booklet pane, #1719-1720	3.00 —

Booklet Stamps
Self-Adhesive
Serpentine Die Cut Perf. 11½
1721	A522	45c multicolored	1.10 .55
1722	A522	45c multicolored	1.10 .55
a.		Bklt. pane, 5 ea #1721-1722	11.00

No. 1722a is a complete booklet.
No. 1720b issued 1/24/07.

Love — A555

1999, Feb. 4   Perf. 14x14½
1723 A555 45c Red roses   .75 .65

Booklet Stamp
Self-adhesive
Serpentine Die Cut Perf. 11½
1724	A555	45c like #1723	1.10 .55
a.		Booklet pane of 10	11.00

No. 1724a is a complete booklet.

Intl. Year of
Older
Persons
A556

Designs: No. 1725, Woman walking with girl, man up close. No. 1726, Woman up close, man playing soccer with boy.

1999, Feb. 11   **Perf. 14x14½**

1725	A556	45c multicolored	.80	.40
1726	A556	45c multicolored	.80	.40
a.	Pair, #1725-1726		1.60	2.25

Early Navigators Type of 1963

No. 1727: a, like #374. b, like #376. c, like #377.
No. 1728: a, like #375. b, like #379. c, like #378.

Perf. 14x14½, 14½x14

1999, Mar. 19   **Litho.**

1727	Sheet of 3	5.25	5.00
a.-c.	A144 45c any single	1.00	1.00
d.	As #1727, imperf.	12.00	12.00
e.	As #1727, perfin "A99" in sheet margin	45.00	45.00
1728	Sheet of 3	5.25	5.00
a.-c.	A145 45c any single	1.00	1.00
d.	As #1728, imperf.	12.00	12.00
e.	As #1728, perfin "A99" in sheet margin	45.00	45.00

Australia '99, World Stamp Expo.
Nos. 1727e-1728e were made from Nos. 1727d-1728d at Australia '99. Examples different perforations or with the perforating and "A99" inverted were intentionally misperfed personally by patrons of the show.

Sailing
Ships — A557

1999, Mar. 19   **Perf. 14½x14**

1729	A557	45c Polly Woodside	.90	.55
a.	Perf 14x14½		3.00	3.00
b.	Souvenir sheet of 2, #1729a, Ireland #1173a		6.00	6.00
1730	A557	85c Alma Doepel	1.75	1.60
1731	A557	$1 Enterprize	1.90	1.60
1732	A557	$1.05 Lady Nelson	2.00	1.60
	Nos. 1729-1732 (4)		6.55	5.35

Australia '99, World Stamp Expo (No. 1729a). See Ireland No. 1173.
No. 1729 was issued in sheets of 20 with a se-tenant label showing Australia '99 logo. Panes of 10 No. 1729 with labels were sold only at the show, where patrons could have their photos printed on the label.

Olympic
Torch — A558

1999, Mar. 22

1733	A558 $1.20 #289	2.00	2.00

Flora & Fauna Type of 1996

Flowers: Nos. 1734, 1742A, 1743, 1746B, 1746I, Correa reflexa. Nos. 1735, 1744, 1746C, 1746J, Hibbertia scandens. Nos. 1736, 1745, 1746D, 1746K, Ipomoea pescaprae. No. 1737, 1746, 1746E, 1746L, Wahlenbergia stricta.
70c, Humpback whales, zebra volute. No. 1739, Brahminy kite, checkerboard helmet shell. No. 1740, Fraser Island, chambered nautilus. $1.05, Loggerhead turtle, baler. $1.20, White-bellied sea eagle, Campbell's stromb.

1999   **Litho.**   **Perf. 14x14½**

1734	A511	45c multicolored	.80	.40
1735	A511	45c multicolored	.80	.40
1736	A511	45c multicolored	.80	.40
1737	A511	45c multicolored	.80	.40
a.	Block of 4, #1734-1737		3.75	3.75
1738	A511	70c multicolored	1.40	1.40
1739	A511	90c multicolored	1.60	1.25
1740	A511	90c multicolored	1.60	1.25
a.	Pair, #1739-1740		3.50	3.25

1741	A511	$1.05 multicolored	2.10	1.90
1742	A511	$1.20 multicolored	2.40	2.40
	Nos. 1734-1742 (9)		12.30	9.80

Booklet Stamps
Serpentine Die Cut 11, 11¼
(#1742Df)
Self-Adhesive

1742A	A511	45c like #1734	1.00	.40
1742B	A511	45c like #1735	1.00	.40
1742C	A511	45c like #1736	1.00	.40
1742D	A511	45c like #1737	1.00	.40
e.	Booklet pane, 3 each #1742A, 1742C, 2 each #1742B, 1742D		10.00	
f.	Booklet pane, 5 each #1742A-1742D		19.00	

Die Cut perf. 12½x12¾

1743	A511	45c like #1734	1.00	.40
1744	A511	45c like #1735	1.00	.40
1745	A511	45c like #1736	1.00	.40
1746	A511	45c like #1737	1.00	.40
a.	Booklet pane, 3 each #1743, 1745, 2 each #1744, 1746		10.00	
g.	Strip of 4, #1743-1746		4.50	
	Nos. 1742A-1746 (8)		8.00	3.20

Nos. 1742De, 1746a are complete booklets.

Coil Stamps
Serpentine Die Cut 11½

1746B	A511	45c like #1734	1.10	.40
1746C	A511	45c like #1735	1.10	.40
1746D	A511	45c like #1736	1.10	.40
1746E	A511	45c like #1737	1.10	.40
f.	Strip of 4, #1746B-1746E		5.25	
h.	Pane, #1746B, 1746D-1746E, 2 #1746C		5.75	

Serpentine Die Cut 13

1746I	A511	45c like #1734	1.10	.40
1746J	A511	45c like #1735	1.10	.40
1746K	A511	45c like #1736	1.10	.40
1746L	A511	45c like #1737	1.10	.40
m.	Strip of 4, #1746I-1746K		5.25	
	Nos. 1746B-1746L (8)		8.80	3.20

Issued: Nos. 1738-1742, 7/8; 1746B-1746E, 1746I-1746L, 4/8.
No. 1742Df is a complete booklet.

Queen
Mother and
Queen
Elizabeth
II — A559

1999, Apr. 15   **Perf. 14x14½**

1747	A559 45c multicolored	1.00	.75

Queen Elizabeth II, 73rd birthday.

Children's Television
Programs — A560

Designs: Nos. 1748, 1753, "Here's Humphrey." Nos. 1749, 1754, "Bananas in Pajamas." Nos. 1750, 1755, "Mr. Squiggle." Nos. 1751, 1756, Teddy bears from "Play School." Nos. 1752, 1757, Clock, dog, boy from "Play School."

1999, May 6   **Litho.**   **Perf. 14½x14**

1748	A560	45c multicolored	1.00	.75
1749	A560	45c multicolored	1.00	.75
1750	A560	45c multicolored	1.00	.75
1751	A560	45c multicolored	1.00	.75
1752	A560	45c multicolored	1.00	.75
a.	Strip of 5, #1748-1752		5.75	5.75
	Nos. 1748-1752 (5)		5.00	3.75

Self-Adhesive
Serpentine Die Cut 11½x11¼

1753	A560	45c like #1748	1.10	.40
1754	A560	45c like #1749	1.10	.40
1755	A560	45c like #1750	1.10	.40
1756	A560	45c like #1751	1.10	.40
1757	A560	45c like #1752	1.10	.40
a.	Bklt. pane, 2 ea #1753-1757		18.00	
	Nos. 1753-1757 (5)		5.50	2.00

No. 1757a is a complete booklet.

$2
Perth
Mint,
Cent.
A561

1999, May 13   **Litho.**   **Perf. 14¼x14**

1758	A561 $2 gold & multi	4.00	3.75

Test Rugby in
Australia,
Cent.
A562

Designs: Nos. 1759, 1763, Kicking ball, vert. Nos. 1760, 1764, Catching ball. $1, Diving with ball. $1.20, Being tackled.

1999, June 8   **Litho.**   **Perf. 14½x14**

1759	A562	45c multi	1.00	.75
1760	A562	45c multi, vert.	1.00	.75
a.	Pair, #1759-1760		2.25	2.25

Perf. 14x14½

1761	A562	$1 multi	2.25	2.25
1762	A562	$1.20 multi	2.50	2.50

Serpentine Die Cut 11½
Self-Adhesive
Coil Stamps

1763	A562	45c like #1759	1.75	.60
1764	A562	45c like #1760	1.75	.60
a.	Pair, #1763-1764		3.50	

Snowy
Mountains
Hydroelectric
Projects,
50th Anniv.
A563

Designs: No. 1765, Rock bolters at Tumut 2 Power Station Hall, driller at Tooma-Tumut Tunnel. No. 1766, English class for migrant workers at Cooma. No. 1767, Eucumbene Dam, Tumut 2 Tailwater Tunnel. No. 1768, Island Bend Dam, German carpenters.

1999, Aug. 12   **Litho.**   **Perf. 14x14½**

1765	A563	45c multicolored	1.00	.75
1766	A563	45c multicolored	1.00	.75
1767	A563	45c multicolored	1.00	.75
1768	A563	45c multicolored	1.00	.75
a.	Block of 4, #1765-1768		4.50	4.50
	Nos. 1765-1768 (4)		4.00	3.00

Self-Adhesive
Coil Stamps
Litho.
Serpentine Die Cut 11¾

1769	A563	45c Like #1765	1.25	.40
1770	A563	45c Like #1766	1.25	.40
1771	A563	45c Like #1767	1.25	.40
1772	A563	45c Like #1768	1.25	.40
a.	Strip of 4, #1769-1772		6.00	5.25
	Nos. 1769-1772 (4)		5.00	1.60

Teddy
Bear — A564

Birthday cake —
A564a

Roses, Rings —
A564b

Pen, Letter —
A564c

Christmas
Ornament —
A564d

Koala — A564e

1999-2003   **Litho.**   **Perf. 14½x14**

1773	A564	45c multicolored	.90	.65
1774	A564a	45c multicolored	.90	.65
1775	A564b	45c multicolored	.90	.65
a.	Booklet pane of 4 + 4 labels ('02)		3.75	
	Booklet, 5 #1775a		27.50	
1776	A564c	45c multicolored	.90	.65
1777	A564d	45c multicolored	.90	.65
a.	Booklet pane of 4 + 4 labels		3.75	
	Complete booklet, 5 #1777a		27.50	
1778	A564e	$1 multicolored	2.60	2.60
	Nos. 1773-1778 (6)		7.10	5.95

Greetings.
Nos. 1773-1778 each were printed with a se-tenant label at right in sheets of 20. Size of label is 24mm wide on No. 1777, 19mm wide on No. 1775a, 17mm on others. Labels were inscribed with phrases appropriate to the stamp design, or blank, upon which Australia Post printed photographs, sent to them through special orders. No. 1775a and 1777a each come with five different margins, each of which is found in the respective booklet, which sold for $9.95.
Issued: Nos. 1773-1778, 9/1/99; No. 1775a, 3/12/02. No. 1777a, 10/31/03.
See No. 1926.
Compare with types A631, A633, A634.

2000 Olympic
Games,
Sydney — A565

1999, Sept. 14   **Litho.**   **Perf. 14½x14**

1779	A565 45c multicolored	1.00	.75

Sydney
Design 99,
Intl. Design
Congress
A566

Designs: 45c, Australia Post emblem. 90c, Embryo chair. $1.35, Possum skin textile design. $1.50, Storey Hall, Royal Melbourne Institute of Technology.

1999, Sept. 16   **Litho.**   **Perf. 14x14½**

1780	A566	45c multicolored	1.25	.75
1781	A566	90c multicolored	1.60	1.25
1782	A566	$1.35 multicolored	2.40	2.00
1783	A566	$1.50 multicolored	2.75	2.75
	Nos. 1780-1783 (4)		8.00	6.75

Pond
Fauna — A567

Designs: Nos. 1784, 1790c, Roth's tree frog. Nos. 1785, 1790d, Dragonfly. Nos. 1786,

1790b, Sacred kingfisher. Nos. 1787, 1790f, Magnificent tree frog. Nos. 1788, 1790e, 1791, Northern dwarf tree frog. Nos. 1789, 1790a, 1792, Javelin frog.
No. 1793, Sacred kingfisher. No. 1794, Magnificent tree frog.

1999, Oct. 1   Litho.   Perf. 14x14½

1784	A567	45c multicolored	.95	.80
1785	A567	45c multicolored	.95	.80
a.		Pair, #1784-1785	2.25	2.25

Size: 26x38mm

Perf. 14½x14

1786	A567	45c multicolored	.95	.80
1787	A567	45c multicolored	.95	.80
a.		Pair, #1786-1787	2.25	2.25

Size: 25x30mm

1788	A567	50c multicolored	1.10	.90
1789	A567	50c multicolored	1.10	.90
a.		Pair, #1788-1789	2.40	2.40
		Nos. 1784-1789 (6)	6.00	5.00

Souvenir Sheet

Perf. 14½

1790	A567	Sheet of 6, #a-f	7.00	7.00
g.		Ovptd. in sheet margin for Bangkok 2000 Exhibition	12.00	12.00
h.		Ovptd. in gold in sheet margin for Adelaide Stamp '99 Exhibition	15.00	15.00

No. 1790d has foil impression on dragonfly's wings.
No. 1790 with overprints for Victorian and South Australian Philatelic Congresses in 1999 are unofficial.
No. 1790h was issued by Australia Post. Another, unofficial, overprint in black (with an orange and black sticker affixed) was applied to other souvenir sheets by the event organizers using the same logo.

Self-Adhesive

Serpentine Die Cut 11¼

Size: 25x30mm

1791	A567	50c multicolored	1.40	.60
1792	A567	50c multicolored	1.40	.60
a.		Bklt. pane, 5 ea #1791-1792	17.00	

Nos. 1791-1792 are booklet stamps. No. 1792a is a complete booklet.

Die Cut Perf. 11¾

Size: 26x38mm

1793	A567	45c multicolored	1.25	.60
1794	A567	45c multicolored	1.25	.60
a.		Pair, #1793-1794	4.25	4.25

Christmas A568

1999, Nov. 1   Perf. 14½x14

1795	A568	40c Madonna and child, vert.	1.00	.75

Perf. 14x14½

1796	A568	$1 Tree	2.25	2.25

Booklet Stamp

Self-Adhesive

Serpentine Die Cut 11¾

1797	A568	Like #1795	1.00	.40
a.		Booklet pane of 20	20.00	

Celebrate 2000 — A569

1999, Nov. 1   Litho.   Perf. 14½x14

1798	A569	45c multicolored	1.10	.75

No. 1798 has a holographic image. Soaking in water may affect hologram.
Sheets of 10 exist with 10 labels inscribed "Celebrate 2000."
No. 1798 was also printed with a se-tenant label at right in sheets of 20. Labels were inscribed "Celebrate 2000" or blank, upon which Australia Post printed photographs, sent to them through special orders.
Sheets of 10 stamps plus 10 photo labels have been available at special events. These have the sheet salvage inscribed for each event. Most of these have been available only at the event and exist in very limited quantities.

Faces of Australia — A570

Ordinary people: a, Nicholle and Meghan Triandis, baby twins. b, David Willis, cattleman with hat. c, Natasha Bramley, with snorkel gear. d, Cyril Watson, Aboriginal boy. e, Mollie Dowdall, with red hat. f, Robin Dicks, in khaki uniform. g, Mary Simons, with gray hair. h, Peta and Samantha Nieuwerth, mother and daughter. i, Dr. John Matthews, with stethoscope. j, Edith Dizon-Fitzsimmons, with large earrings. k, Philippa Weir, with brown hat. l, John Thurgar, with suit, tie and hat. m, Miguel Alzona, with large, multicolored hat. n, Rachael Thomson, girl with wavy hair. o, Necip Akarsu, with mustache. p, Justin Allan, with HMAS Brisbane cap. q, Wadad Dennaoui, with checked blouse. r, Jack Laity, with hat and jacket. s, Kelsey Stubbin, with Australia cap. t, Gianna Rossi, with hand on chin. u, Paris Hansch, young girl. v, Donald George Whatham, in shirt and tie. w, Stacey Coull, Aboriginal girl in patterned blouse. x, Alex Payne, with bicycle helmet. y, John Lodge, with Salvation Army hat.

2000, Jan. 1   Litho.   Perf. 14¾x13¾

1799	A570	Sheet of 25	24.00	24.00
a.-y.		45c Any single	.95	.80

Legends Type of 1997

Aging veterans of World War I: Nos. 1800, 1804, Walter Parker. Nos. 1801, 1805, Roy Longmore. Nos. 1802, 1806, Alec Campbell. Nos. 1803, 1807, 1914-15 Star.

2000, Jan. 21   Litho.   Perf. 14x14¾

Size: 34x26mm

1800	A522	45c multi	.95	.80
1801	A522	45c multi	.95	.80
1802	A522	45c multi	.95	.80
1803	A522	45c multi	.95	.80
a.		Block of 4, #1800-1803	4.00	3.60
b.		Booklet pane, #1800-1803	6.00	—
		Nos. 1800-1803 (4)	3.80	3.20

Self-Adhesive

Die Cut Perf. 11¾

1804	A522	45c multi	1.00	.75
1805	A522	45c multi	1.00	.75
1806	A522	45c multi	1.00	.75
1807	A522	45c multi	1.00	.75
a.		Complete booklet, 2 each #1804-1806, 4 #1807	13.00	
		Nos. 1804-1807 (4)	4.00	3.00

No. 1803b issued 1/24/07.

A571

Arts festivals.

2000, Feb. 24   Litho.   Perf. 14¾x14

1808	A571	45c Perth	.95	.75
1809	A571	45c Adelaide	.95	.75
1810	A571	45c Sydney	.95	.75
1811	A571	45c Melbourne	.95	.75
1812	A571	45c Brisbane	.95	.75
a.		Strip of 5, #1808-1812	4.75	4.75
		Nos. 1808-1812 (5)	4.75	3.75

A572

Gardens: Nos. 1813, 1818, 1823, Coast banksia, false sarsaparilla, swamp bloodwood (denomination at UR). Nos. 1814, 1819, 1824, Swamp bottlebrush, Eastern spinebill (denomination at UL). Nos. 1815, 1820, 1825, Canna X generalis varieties (denomination at LL). Nos. 1816, 1821, 1826, Pond, roses, purple swamphen (denomination at UR). Nos. 1817, 1822, 1827, Pond, hibiscus, nerium oleander (denomination at UL).

2000, Mar. 23   Litho.   Perf. 14¾x14

1813	A572	45c multi	.95	.95
1814	A572	45c multi	.95	.95
1815	A572	45c multi	.95	.95
1816	A572	45c multi	.95	.95
1817	A572	45c multi	.95	.95
a.		Horiz. strip, #1813-1817	4.75	4.75
		Nos. 1813-1817 (5)	4.75	4.75

Booklet Stamps

Self-Adhesive

Serpentine Die Cut 11½x11¼

Pale Green Frames

1818	A572	45c multi	1.10	.75
1819	A572	45c multi	1.10	.75
1820	A572	45c multi	1.10	.75
1821	A572	45c multi	1.10	.75
1822	A572	45c multi	1.10	.75
a.		Booklet, 2 each #1818-1822	11.50	
		Nos. 1818-1822 (5)	5.50	3.75

Coil Stamps

Self-Adhesive

Serpentine Die Cut 11¾

Pale Green Frames

1823	A572	45c multi	1.25	.75
1824	A572	45c multi	1.25	.75
1825	A572	45c multi	1.25	.75
1826	A572	45c multi	1.25	.75
1827	A572	45c multi	1.25	.75
a.		Strip of 5, #1823-1827	7.50	
		Nos. 1823-1827 (5)	6.25	3.75

Queen Elizabeth II, 74th Birthday A573

2000, Apr. 13   Litho.   Perf. 14x14¾

1828	A573	45c multi	1.00	.75

Korean War, 50th Anniv. A574

2000, Apr. 18

1829	A574	45c multi	1.00	.75

Daisy — A575

Australia on Globe, Southern Cross — A576

Kangaroo and Flag — A577

Sand, Sea and Sky — A578

Rainforest A579

2000, May 11   Perf. 14½x14

1830	A575	45c multi + label	1.20	.75
1831	A576	45c multi + label	1.20	.75
1832	A577	45c multi + label	1.20	.75
1833	A578	45c multi + label	1.20	.75
1834	A579	45c multi + label	1.20	.75
		Nos. 1830-1834 (5)	6.00	3.75

Nos. 1830-1834 each issued in sheets of 20 stamps and labels, with and without decorative selvage.
Sheets containing 10 No. 1831 with margins and ten labels that could be personalized were sold for $12, $2 of which was donated to volunteer organizations of the purchaser's choice. Volunteer organizations could purchase these sheets and offer them for resale in fundraising projects.
No. 1832 exists in a sheet of 10+10 labels that sold sold for $16. Sheet has decorative selvage and labels showing stock photo.

The Move Towards Federation — A580

Designs: No. 1835, Taking the vote. No. 1836, Waiting for the results. No. 1837, The fair new nation. No. 1838, Queen Victoria.

2000, May 22   Perf. 14¾x14

1835	A580	45c multi	.90	.75
1836	A580	45c multi	.90	.75
a.		Pair, #1835-1836	2.00	2.00

Size: 30x50mm

Perf. 14x14½

1837	A580	$1.50 multi	2.40	2.40
1838	A580	$1.50 multi	2.40	2.40
a.		Pair, #1837-1838	5.00	5.00
b.		Souvenir sheet, #1836a, 1838a	7.25	7.25
c.		As "b," with marginal inscription for The Stamp Show 2000, London	14.00	14.00
		Nos. 1835-1838 (4)	6.60	6.30

Tourist Attractions — A581

Designs: 50c, Sydney Opera House. $1, Nandroya Falls. $1.50, Sydney Harbour Bridge. $2, Cradle Mountain. $3, The Pinnacles. $4.50, Flinders Ranges. $5, Twelve Apostles. $10, Devils Marbles.

2000, June 20   Litho.   Perf. 14½x14

1839	A581	50c multi	.80	.75
1840	A581	$1 multi	1.60	1.50
1841	A581	$1.50 multi	2.40	2.25
1842	A581	$2 multi	3.25	2.75
1843	A581	$3 multi	4.75	4.50

Size: 56x25mm
Perf. 14x14½

1844	A581	$4.50 multi	7.25	6.75
1845	A581	$5 multi	8.00	7.25
1846	A581	$10 multi	16.00	14.40
	Nos. 1839-1846 (8)		44.05	40.15

See Nos. 1925, 1979-1983, 2055-2059, 2077-2080, 2280-2283.

2000 Paralympics,
Sydney — A582

Designs: Nos. 1847, 1855, Wheelchair tennis. Nos. 1848, 1856, Amputee running. Nos. 1849, 1853, Wheelchair basketball. Nos. 1850, 1852, Cycling for the visually impaired. Nos. 1851, 1854, Amputee shot put.

2000, July 3   Litho.   Perf. 14¾x14

1847	A582	45c multi	.75	.75
1848	A582	45c multi	.75	.75
a.	Pair, #1847-1848		2.00	2.00
1849	A582	49c multi	1.00	1.00
1850	A582	49c multi	1.00	1.00
1851	A582	49c multi	1.00	1.00
a.	Strip of 3, #1849-1851		3.25	3.25
	Nos. 1847-1851 (5)		4.50	4.50

Booklet Stamps
Self-Adhesive
Die Cut Perf. 11½x11¾

1852	A582	49c multi	1.25	.75
1853	A582	49c multi	1.25	.75
1854	A582	49c multi	1.25	.75
a.	Bklt., 4 ea #1852-1853, 2 #1854		14.50	

Coil Stamps
Self-Adhesive
Serpentine Die Cut 11¾

1855	A582	45c multi	1.10	.85
1856	A582	45c multi	1.10	.85
a.	Pair, #1855-1856		3.00	3.00
	Nos. 1852-1856 (5)		5.95	3.95

No. 1851 exists without Tasmania in the map of Australia at LL. Value $20.

Australian Victoria
Cross,
Cent. — A583

Designs: No. 1857, Sir Neville Howse. No. 1858, Sir Arthur Roden Cutler. No. 1859, Victoria Cross. No. 1860, Edward Kenna. No. 1861, Keith Payne.

2000, July 24   Litho.   Perf. 14¾x14

1857	A583	45c multi	.95	.75
1858	A583	45c multi	.95	.75
1859	A583	45c multi	.95	.75
1860	A583	45c multi	.95	.75
1861	A583	45c multi	.95	.75
a.	Horiz. strip of 5, #1857-1861		5.00	5.00
	Nos. 1857-1861 (5)		4.75	3.75

Olympic
Sports — A584

Designs: Nos. 1862a, 1869, Water polo. Nos. 1862b, 1870, Women's field hockey. Nos. 1862c, 1863, Swimming. Nos. 1862d, 1865, Basketball. Nos. 1862e, 1866, Triathlon cycling. Nos. 1862f, 1871, Equestrian. Nos. 1862g, 1872, Tennis. Nos. 1862h, 1864, Rhythmic gymnastics. Nos. 1862i, 1867, Runner. Nos. 1862j, 1868, Rowing.

2000, Aug. 17   Litho.   Perf. 14¾x14

1862		Sheet of 10	11.50	11.50
a.-j.	A584 45c Any single		.80	.80
k.	As #1862, with inscription added in sheet margin		20.00	20.00

No. 1862k was issued 9/15/00 and has additional multicolored inscription in upper sheet margin reading "15-28 / September / 2000 / OLYMPHILEX 2000" and show emblem.

Booklet Stamps
Self-Adhesive
Serpentine Die Cut 11½x11¼

1863	A584	45c multi	1.00	.70
1864	A584	45c multi	1.00	.70
1865	A584	45c multi	1.00	.70
1866	A584	45c multi	1.00	.70
1867	A584	45c multi	1.00	.70
1868	A584	45c multi	1.00	.70
1869	A584	45c multi	1.00	.70
1870	A584	45c multi	1.00	.70
1871	A584	45c multi	1.00	.70
1872	A584	45c multi	1.00	.70
a.	Booklet, #1863-1872		14.00	
	Nos. 1863-1872 (10)		10.00	7.00

Sydney and
Athens — A585

Olympic torch, flag and: 45c, Parthenon. $1.50, Sydney Opera House.

2000, Sept. 15   Litho.   Perf. 14½x14

1873	A585	45c multi + label	1.00	.60
1874	A585	$1.50 multi + label	2.40	2.40

Nos. 1873-1874 were issued in sheets of 20 stamps and 20 se-tenant labels. Labels were inscribed "Sydney Athens." These sheets could be ordered with personalized labels, as could sheets with a stock photo.
See Greece Nos. 1968-1969.

Australian
Gold Medalists
at 2000
Olympics
A586

Cathy
Freeman
Lighting
Olympic
Flame — A587

Medal Winners: Nos. 1875, 1891, Ian Thorpe. Nos. 1876, 1892, Men's 4x100-meter freestyle swimming team. Nos. 1877, 1893, Michael Diamond. Nos. 1878, 1894, Three day event equestrian team. Nos. 1879, 1895, Susie O'Neill. Nos. 1880, 1896, Men's 4x200-meter freestyle swimming team. Nos. 1881, 1897, Simon Fairweather. Nos. 1882, 1898, Brett Aitken, Scott McGrory. Nos. 1883, 1899, Grant Hackett. Nos. 1884, 1900, Women's water polo team. Nos. 1885, 1901, Natalie Cook, Kerri Pottharst. Nos. 1886, 1902, Cathy Freeman. Nos. 1887, 1903, Lauren Burns. Nos. 1888, 1904, Women's field hockey team. Nos. 1889, 1905, Jenny Armstrong, Belinda Stowell. Nos. 1890, 1906, Tom King, Mark Turnbull.

2000   Digitally Printed   Perf. 14¼

1875	A586	45c multi	1.00	.80
1876	A586	45c multi	1.00	.80
1877	A586	45c multi	1.00	.80
1878	A586	45c multi	1.00	.80
1879	A586	45c multi	1.00	.80
1880	A586	45c multi	1.00	.80
1881	A586	45c multi	1.00	.80
1882	A586	45c multi	1.00	.80
1883	A586	45c multi	1.00	.80
1884	A586	45c multi	1.00	.80
1885	A586	45c multi	1.00	.80
1886	A586	45c multi	1.00	.80
1887	A586	45c multi	1.00	.80
1888	A586	45c multi	1.00	.80
1889	A586	45c multi	1.00	.80
1890	A586	45c multi	1.00	.80

Litho.

1891	A586	45c multi	1.10	1.10
1892	A586	45c multi	1.10	1.10
1893	A586	45c multi	1.10	1.10
1894	A586	45c multi	1.10	1.10
1895	A586	45c multi	1.10	1.10
1896	A586	45c multi	1.10	1.10
1897	A586	45c multi	1.10	1.10
1898	A586	45c multi	1.10	1.10
1899	A586	45c multi	1.10	1.10
1900	A586	45c multi	1.10	1.10
1901	A586	45c multi	1.10	1.10
1902	A586	45c multi	1.10	1.10
1903	A586	45c multi	1.10	1.10
1904	A586	45c multi	1.10	1.10
1905	A586	45c multi	1.10	1.10
1906	A586	45c multi	1.10	1.10
1907	A587	45c multi	1.60	1.60
	Nos. 1875-1907 (33)		35.20	32.00

Issued: Nos. 1875-1876, 9/17; No. 1877, 9/18; Nos. 1891-1892, 9/19; Nos. 1878-1880, 1893, 9/20; No. 1881, 9/21; Nos. 1882, 1894-1896, 9/22; No. 1897, 9/23; Nos. 1883-1884, 1898, 9/24; Nos. 1885-1886, 1899-1900, 9/26; Nos. 1887, 1901-1902, 9/28; Nos. 1888, 1903, 9/30; Nos. 1889-1890, 10/1; No. 1904, 10/2; Nos. 1905-1906, 10/3; No. 1907, 10/10.

Nos. 1875-1890 have shinier appearance than Nos. 1891-1906. Olympic rings, flag stars and flag edge on Nos. 1875-1890 have a more ragged appearance than Nos. 1891-1906, which have crisp details.

Nos. 1875-1907 printed in sheets of 10. Sheets of Nos. 1875-1890 exist rouletted at either the right or left and have one of six red animal imprints in lower right margin representing where the sheets were made (Platypus, Sydney; Kookaburra, Canberra; Koala, Brisbane; Swan, Perth; Kangaroo, Adelaide; Opossum, Melbourne). Sheets of Nos. 1875-1890 were placed on sale at 67 outlets within 24 hours of the awarding of the medals to the athletes. Sheets of Nos. 1891-1906, which have a straight-edged right margin and a red Australia map imprint in lower right margin, gradually became available nationwide as stocks were printed and shipped.

A sheet containing Nos. 1891-1907 and 8 labels was available only in the Australia Post annual collection. Value, $50.

Space — A588

Designs: Nos. 1908, 1914a, Flight crew. Nos. 1909, 1914b, Robots, vert. Nos. 1910, 1914c, 1915, 1917, Astronaut, vert. Nos. 1911, 1914d, 1916, 1918, Terrain, vert. Nos. 1912, 1914e, Spacecraft. Nos. 1913, 1914f, Launch site, vert.

Perf. 14x14½, 14½x14

2000, Oct. 3			**Litho.**	
1908	A588	45c multi	.95	.95
1909	A588	45c multi	.95	.95

Size: 26x38mm

1910	A588	45c multi	.95	.95
1911	A588	45c multi	.95	.95
a.	Pair, #1910-1911		2.25	2.25

Size: 50x30mm

1912	A588	45c multi	.95	.95

Size: 30x50mm

1913	A588	45c multi	.95	.95
	Nos. 1908-1913 (6)		5.70	5.70

Souvenir Sheet
Litho. with Translucent Foil
Perf. 14½

1914		Sheet of 6	5.00	5.00
a.-f.	A588 45c any single		.80	.80
g.	As #1914, ovptd. in margin in gold		14.00	14.00

Booklet Stamps
Litho.
Self-Adhesive
Serpentine Die Cut 11½x11¼

1915	A588	45c multi	1.00	.60
1916	A588	45c multi	1.00	.60
a.	Booklet, 5 each #1915-1916		12.00	

Coil Stamps
Serpentine Die Cut 11½

1917	A588	45c multi	1.10	.60
1918	A588	45c multi	1.10	.60
a.	Pair, #1917-1918		2.50	2.50

Nos. 1915-1918 have pink and gray frames.
No 1914g overprinted with emblem of Hong Kong 2001 Stamp Exhibition. Issued 2/1/01.

2000
Paralympics,
Sydney — A589

Designs: No. 1919, Paralympics emblem. No. 1920, Runner with torch.

2000, Oct. 18   Litho.   Perf. 14½x14

1919	A589	45c multi + label	1.25	1.00
1920	A589	45c multi + label	1.25	1.00

Siobhan Paton,
Paralympian of
the
Year — A590

2000, Oct. 31   Perf. 14¼

1921	A590	45c multi	1.00	.75

Christmas — A591

40c, Madonna and child. 45c, Manger.

2000, Nov. 1   Litho.   Perf. 14½x14

1922	A591	40c multi	.75	.50
1923	A591	45c multi	.75	.50
a.	Souvenir sheet, #1922-1923		2.25	2.25

Booklet Stamp
Serpentine Die Cut 11¾

1924	A591	40c multi	.85	.70
a.	Booklet of 20 + 20 stickers		17.25	

Tourist Attractions Type of 2000

2000, Nov. 1   Perf. 14½x14

1925	A581	80c Byron Bay	1.75	1.50

No. 1778 Digitally
Overprinted in
Dark Blue

2001, Jan.   Litho.   Perf. 14½x14

1926	A564	$1 multi + label	17.50	17.50

Federation of
Australia,
Cent. — A592

Designs: Nos. 1927, 1931, Federation Arch, Sydney. Nos. 1928, 1932, Sir Edmund Barton, first prime minister. No. 1929, National celebrations, horiz (50x30mm). No. 1930, State banquet (30x50mm).

Perf. 14¾x14, 14x14¾

2001, Jan.			**Litho.**	
1927	A592	49c multi	1.00	.80
1928	A592	49c multi	1.00	.80
a.	Pair, #1927-1928		3.00	2.50
1929	A592	$2 multi	3.25	2.75
1930	A592	$2 multi	3.25	2.75
a.	Souvenir sheet, #1927-1930, perf. 14½		10.00	10.00
	Nos. 1927-1930 (4)		8.50	7.10

Self-Adhesive Booklet Stamps

Serpentine Die Cut 11½x11

1931	A592	49c multi	1.00	.30
a.	Serpentine die cut 11½x11¾		—	—
1932	A592	49c multi	1.00	.30
a.	Booklet, 5 each # 1931-1932		11.50	

Australian Legends Type of 1997

Slim Dusty, musician: Nos. 1933, 1935, With guitar. Nos. 1934, 1936, Wearing blue shirt.

2001, Jan. 25   **Perf. 14x14¾**

Size: 34x26mm

1933	A522	45c multi	1.10	1.00
1934	A522	45c multi	1.10	1.00
a.	Pair, #1933-1934		2.50	2.00
b.	Booklet pane, #1933-1934		3.00	

Self-Adhesive Booklet Stamps

Serpentine Die Cut 11x11½

1935	A522	45c multi	1.10	.75
1936	A522	45c multi	1.10	.75
a.	Booklet, 5 each #1935-1936		11.50	
	Nos. 1933-1936 (4)		4.40	3.50

No. 1934b issued 1/24/07.

Australian Army, Cent. A593

Rising Sun badge and: No. 1937, Light Horse Brigade, 1940, soldiers in New Guinea, 1943. No. 1938, Soldier in UN peacekeeping mission carrying Rwandan child, 1995, soldiers on commando officer selection course, 1997.

2001-05   **Perf. 14x14¾**

1937	A593	45c multi	1.10	.75
a.	Additionally dated "2013" (#1938d)		1.10	1.10
1938	A593	45c multi	1.10	.75
a.	Pair, #1937-1938		2.50	2.00
b.	Booklet pane, #1937-1938		16.00	—
c.	Additionally dated "2013" (#1938d)		1.10	1.10
d.	Booklet pane of 2, #1937a, 1938c		2.25	—
	Complete booklet, #1176a, 1207a, 1256a, 1317a, 1380f, 1452a, 1454a, 1482a, 1938b		100.00	

Issued: Nos. 1937-1938, 2/15/01. No. 1938b, 4/05. Complete booklet sold for $14.95.

Issued: Nos. 1937a, 1938c, 1938d, 3/5/13. No. 1938d was issued in booklet along with Nos. 2710c, 2869e, 3107c, 3349b and 3877a.

Opening of National Museum, Canberra A594

Designs: No. 1939, Museum floor plan. No. 1940, Pangk (wallaby sculpture), by George MacNaught and Joe Ngallametta.

2001, Mar. 8

1939	A594	49c multi	1.00	.85
1940	A594	49c multi	1.00	.85
a.	Pair, #1939-1940		2.25	2.00

Australian Legends Type of 1997

Similar to Nos. 1575-1576, but with cropped designs and "1908-2001" inscription added.

2001, Mar. 13   **Perf. 14¼**

1941	A522	45c Like #1575	1.00	.80
a.	Without gold highlights, dated "2007"		1.40	1.40
1942	A522	45c Like #1576	.80	.80
a.	Pair, #1941-1942		2.25	2.00
b.	Without gold highlights, dated "2007"		1.40	1.40

Nos. 1941a, 1942b issued 11/14/07.

Rock Music A595

Designs: Nos. 1943a, 1953, Khe Sanh, by Cold Chisel, 1978. Nos. 1943b, 1952, Down Under, by Men at Work, 1981. Nos. 1943c, 1951, Power and the Passion, by Midnight Oil, 1983. Nos. 1943d, 1950, Original Sin, by INXS. Nos. 1943e, 1949, You're the Voice, by John Farnham, 1986. Nos. 1943f, 1948, Don't Dream It's Over, by Crowded House, 1986. Nos. 1943g, 1947, Treaty, by Yothu Yindi, 1991. Nos. 1943h, 1946, Tomorrow, by Silverchair, 1994. Nos. 1943i, 1945, Confide in Me, by Kylie Minogue, 1994. Nos. 1943j, 1944, Truly, Madly, Deeply, by Savage Garden, 1997.

2001, Mar. 20   **Litho.**   **Perf. 14x14¾**

1943		Sheet of 10	10.00	10.00
a.-j.	A595 45c Any single		1.00	.80

Self-Adhesive

Serpentine Die Cut 11¼x11½

1944	A595	45c multi	1.00	.80
1945	A595	45c multi	1.00	.80
1946	A595	45c multi	1.00	.80
1947	A595	45c multi	1.00	.80
1948	A595	45c multi	1.00	.80
1949	A595	45c multi	1.00	.80
1950	A595	45c multi	1.00	.80
1951	A595	45c multi	1.00	.80
1952	A595	45c multi	1.00	.80
1953	A595	45c multi	1.00	.80
a.	Horiz. strip of 10, #1944-1953		14.50	
b.	Booklet, #1944-1953		10.00	
	Nos. 1944-1953 (10)		10.00	8.00

Queen Elizabeth II, 75th Birthday — A596

2001, Apr. 12   **Litho.**   **Perf. 14¾x14**

1954	A596	45c multi	1.00	.75

Flower — A597

Balloons — A598

Streamers — A599

Kangaroos — A600

Bayulu Banner — A601

Litho., Litho with Hologram (#1957)

2001-03   **Perf. 14½x14**

1955	A597	45c multi + label	.80	.80
1956	A598	45c multi + label	.80	.80
1957	A599	45c multi + label	.80	.80
1958	A600	$1 multi + label	2.00	1.60
a.	Booklet pane of 4 + 4 labels		8.75	
	Complete booklet, 2 #1958a		22.00	
1959	A601	$1.50 multi + label	2.50	2.50
	Nos. 1955-1959 (5)		6.90	6.50

Issued: Nos. 1955-1959, 4/24/01. No. 1958a, 10/31/03.

The complete booklet, which sold for $10.95, contains two panes of No. 1958a with different margins.

Federal Parliament, Cent. — A602

Designs: No. 1960, The Opening of the First Federal Parliament, 9 May 1901, by Charles Nuttall. No. 1961, Opening of the First Parliament of the Commonwealth of Australia by H.R.H. The Duke of Cornwall and York (Later King George V), May 9, 1901, by Tom Roberts.

2001, May 3   **Litho.**   **Perf. 14¼**

1960	A602	45c multi	1.00	.65
a.	Souvenir sheet of 1		2.00	2.00
1961	A602	$2.45 multi	4.00	4.00
a.	Souvenir sheet of 1		5.50	5.50

Outback Services A603

Designs: Nos. 1962, 1967, 1972, Telecommunications. Nos. 1963, 1968, 1973, Transport. Nos. 1964, 1969, 1974, School of the Air. Nos. 1965, 1970, 1975, Postal service. Nos. 1966, 1971, 1976, Royal flying Doctor Service.

2001, June 5   **Perf. 14x14½**

1962	A603	45c multi	1.00	.75
1963	A603	45c multi	1.00	.75
1964	A603	45c multi	1.00	.75
1965	A603	45c multi	1.00	.75
1966	A603	45c multi	1.00	.75
a.	Horiz. strip, #1962-1966		5.00	4.75
	Nos. 1962-1966 (5)		5.00	3.75

Self-Adhesive Coil Stamps

Serpentine Die Cut 11¼

1967	A603	45c multi	1.25	.95
1968	A603	45c multi	1.25	.95
1969	A603	45c multi	1.25	.95
1970	A603	45c multi	1.25	.95
1971	A603	45c multi	1.25	.95
a.	Horiz. strip, #1967-1971		8.00	

Booklet Stamps

Serpentine Die Cut 11¾

1972	A603	45c multi	1.00	.75
1973	A603	45c multi	1.00	.75
1974	A603	45c multi	1.00	.75
1975	A603	45c multi	1.00	.75
1976	A603	45c multi	1.00	.75
a.	Booklet, 2 each #1972-1976		11.00	
	Nos. 1967-1976 (10)		11.25	8.50

Dragon Boat Races A604

Dragon boats and: 45c, Hong Kong Convention and Exhibition Center. $1, Sydney Opera House.

2001, June 25   **Perf. 14x14½**

1977	A604	45c multi	1.10	.85
1978	A604	$1 multi	2.25	2.25
a.	Souvenir sheet, #1977-1978		3.50	3.50

See Hong Kong Nos. 938-939.

Tourist Attraction Type of 2000

Designs: 50c, Blue Mountains. $1, Murrumbidgee River. $1.50, Port Douglas. $20, Uluru.

Litho., Litho with Foil Application ($20)

2001, July 12   **Perf. 14½x14**

1979	A581	50c multi	1.00	1.00
1980	A581	$1 multi	2.00	2.00
1981	A581	$1.50 multi	3.00	3.00

Size: 56x25mm

Perf. 14x14½

1982	A581	$20 multi	24.00	24.00
	Nos. 1979-1982 (4)		30.00	30.00

Booklet Stamp

Self-Adhesive

Serpentine Die Cut 11¼x10½

1983	A581	50c multi	1.10	1.00
a.	Booklet, 10 #1983		11.50	

Flora & Fauna Type of 1996

Birds: Nos. 1984, 1988, 1992, Variegated fairy wren. Nos. 1985, 1989, 1993, Painted firetail. Nos. 1986, 1990, 1994, Crimson chat. Nos. 1987, 1991, 1995, Budgerigar.

2001-02   **Litho.**   **Perf. 14x14½**

1984	A511	45c multi	1.00	.75
1985	A511	45c multi	1.00	.75
1986	A511	45c multi	1.00	.75
1987	A511	45c multi	1.00	.75
a.	Block of 4, #1984-1987		4.25	4.25
	Nos. 1984-1987 (4)		4.00	3.00

Self-Adhesive Coil Stamps

Die Cut Perf. 12½x12¾

1988	A511	45c multi	1.25	.75
1989	A511	45c multi	1.25	.75
1990	A511	45c multi	1.25	.75
1991	A511	45c multi	1.25	.75
a.	Horiz. strip of 4, #1988-1991		5.25	5.25

Booklet Stamps

Serpentine Die Cut 11¼

1992	A511	45c multi	1.25	.75
1993	A511	45c multi	1.25	.75
1994	A511	45c multi	1.25	.75
1995	A511	45c multi	1.25	.75
a.	Booklet pane, #1993, 1995		4.50	
b.	Booklet pane, #1992-1995, rouletted at bottom		7.50	
	Booklet, #1995a 2 #1995b		12.00	
c.	Booklet pane, #1992-1995, rouletted at side		15.00	
	Booklet, 5 #1995c		85.00	
d.	Pane, #1992-1994, 2 #1995		9.50	
e.	Coil strip, #1992-1995		5.50	
f.	As "d," with Philakorea 2002 ovpt. in margin ('02)		15.00	
g.	As "d," with China 2002 Stamp & Coin Expo ovpt. in margin ('02)		15.00	
h.	As "d," with Hafnia '01 ovpt. in margin		27.50	
	Nos. 1988-1995 (8)		10.00	6.00

Issued: No. 1995f, 8/2/02; No. 1995g, 9/28/02. No. 1995h, 10/16/01. Rest of set, 8/9/01.

Daniel Solander (1733-82), Botanist on Endeavour A605

Designs: 45c, Barringtonia calyptrata and Solander. $1.50, Cachlospermum gillivraei and Endeavour.

Perf. 12½x12¾

2001, Aug. 16   **Litho. & Engr.**

1996	A605	45c multi	1.25	.90
1997	A605	$1.50 multi	3.25	3.25

See Sweden No. 2419.

Commonwealth Heads of Government Meeting, Brisbane — A606

2001, Sept. 4 Litho. Perf. 14½x14

1998	A606	45c Southern Cross	1.00	.75
1999	A606	45c Australia on globe	1.00	.75
a.		Pair, #1998-1999	2.25	2.25

Christmas — A607

2001, Sept. 4 Perf. 14½x14

Stamp + Label

2000	A607	40c Christmas tree	.85	.70
2001	A607	80c Star	1.60	1.60

Nos. 2000-2001 were each printed in sheets of 20 + 20 labels. The labels could be personalized.

Birds of Prey — A608

Designs: No. 2002, Wedge-tailed eagle. No. 2003, Nankeen kestrel. No. 2004, Red goshawk, vert. No. 2005, Spotted harrier, vert.

Perf. 14x14½, 14½x14

2001, Sept. 11

2002	A608	49c multi	1.00	.80
2003	A608	49c multi	1.00	.80
a.		Pair, #2002-2003	2.50	2.50
2004	A608	98c multi	1.60	1.60
2005	A608	98c multi	1.60	1.60
a.		Pair, #2004-2005	4.00	2.50
		Nos. 2002-2005 (4)	5.20	4.80

Caricatures of Australian Wildlife by Roland Harvey — A609

Designs: Nos. 2006, 2012, Bilby and antechinus musicians, dancing cockatoo. Nos. 2007, 2013, Koala with birthday cake. Nos. 2008, 2014, Ring-tailed possums with drinks and food. Nos. 2009, 2015, Bilbies, crocodile, emu, koala and gifts. Nos. 2010, 2016, Wombat and ladder. Nos. 2011, 2017, Wallabies, echidnas, platypus and ladder.

2001, Oct. 2 Perf. 14½x14

2006	A609	45c multi	1.00	.80
2007	A609	45c multi	1.00	.80
2008	A609	45c multi	1.00	.80
a.		Horiz. strip of 3, #2006-2008	3.00	3.00
b.		Souvenir sheet, #2006-2008	3.50	3.50
2009	A609	45c multi	1.00	.80
2010	A609	45c multi	1.00	.80
2011	A609	45c multi	1.00	.80
a.		Horiz. strip, #2009-2011	3.00	3.00
b.		Souvenir sheet, #2009-2011	3.00	3.00
		Nos. 2006-2011 (6)	6.00	4.80

Self-Adhesive

Serpentine Die Cut 11½x11

2012	A609	45c multi	1.00	.80
2013	A609	45c multi	1.00	.80
2014	A609	45c multi	1.00	.80
2015	A609	45c multi	1.00	.80
2016	A609	45c multi	1.00	.80
2017	A609	45c multi	1.00	.80
a.		Coil strip, 2012-2017	7.50	
b.		Booklet, #2014-2015, 2 each #2012-2013, 2016-2017	12.00	
		Nos. 2012-2017 (6)	6.00	4.80

Christmas — A610

Illuminations from the Wharncliffe Hours, by Maitre Francois: 40c, Adoration of the Magi. 45c, Flight into Egypt.

2001, Nov. 1 Perf. 14½x14

2018	A610	40c multi	1.00	.60
2019	A610	45c multi	1.25	.65

Self-Adhesive

Serpentine Die Cut 11½x11¼

2020	A610	40c multi	1.10	.25
a.		Booklet of 20 + 20 labels	22.00	

Australian Legends Type of 1997

Medical researchers: Nos. 2021, 2026, Sir Gustav Nossal. Nos. 2022, 2027, Nancy Mills. No. 2023, 2028, Peter Doherty. Nos. 2024, 2029, Fiona Stanley. Nos. 2025, 2030, Donald Metcalf.

2002, Jan. 23 Litho. Perf. 14x14¾

Size: 34x26mm

2021	A522	45c multi	.95	.75
2022	A522	45c multi	.95	.75
2023	A522	45c multi	.95	.75
2024	A522	45c multi	.95	.75
2025	A522	45c multi	.95	.75
a.		Vert. strip, #2021-2025	5.00	5.00
b.		Booklet pane, #2021-2025	8.00	8.00
		Nos. 2021-2025 (5)	4.75	3.75

Booklet Stamps

Self-Adhesive

Serpentine Die Cut 11x11½

2026	A522	45c multi	1.00	1.00
2027	A522	45c multi	1.00	1.00
2028	A522	45c multi	1.00	1.00
2029	A522	45c multi	1.00	1.00
2030	A522	45c multi	1.00	1.00
a.		Booklet, 2 each #2026-2030	12.50	
		Nos. 2026-2030 (5)	5.00	5.00

No. 2025b issued 1/24/07.

Reign of Queen Elizabeth II, 50th Anniv. — A611

Queen: 45c, As young woman. $2.45, In 2000.

2002, Feb. 6 Perf. 14¾x14

2031	A611	45c multi	.95	.70
2032	A611	$2.45 multi	5.00	5.00
a.		Souvenir sheet, #2031-2032	6.25	6.25

A booklet pane containing 2 each of Nos. 2031-2032 is found in the booklet footnoted under No. 2507.

Gold Medalists at 2002 Winter Olympics, Salt Lake City — A612

Designs: No. 2033, Steven Bradbury. No. 2034, Alisa Camplin.

2002 Perf. 14¼

2033	A612	45c multi	1.10	1.00
2034	A612	45c multi	1.10	1.00

Issued: No. 2033, 2/20; No. 2034, 2/22.

Race Cars — A613

Designs: Nos. 2035, 2041, Victoria Austin 7 and Bugatti Type 40, Phillip Island, Victoria, 1928. Nos. 2036, 2042, Jaguar Mark II, Mallala, South Australia, 1963. Nos. 2037, 2043, Repco-Brabham, Sandown, Victoria, 1966. Nos. 2038, 2044, Holden Torana XU1 and Ford Falcon XY GTHO, Bathurst, New South Wales, 1972. Nos. 2039, 2045, Williams FW07 Ford, Calder, Victoria, 1980. Nos. 2040, 2046, Benetton-Renault, Albert Park, Victoria, 2001.

2002, Feb. 27 Perf. 14x14¾

2035	A613	45c multi	1.00	.75
2036	A613	45c multi	1.00	.75
2037	A613	45c multi	1.00	.75
2038	A613	45c multi	1.00	.75
2039	A613	45c multi	1.00	.75
2040	A613	45c multi	1.00	.75
a.		Block of 6, #2035-2040	7.00	7.00
		Nos. 2035-2040 (6)	6.00	4.50

Self-Adhesive

Serpentine Die Cut 11¼x11½

2041	A613	45c multi	1.00	.80
2042	A613	45c multi	1.00	.80
2043	A613	45c multi	1.00	.80
2044	A613	45c multi	1.00	.80
2045	A613	45c multi	1.00	.80
2046	A613	45c multi	1.00	.80
a.		Coil strip, #2041-2046	9.00	
b.		Booklet, #2045-2046, 2 each #2041-2044	10.00	
		Nos. 2041-2046 (6)	6.00	4.80

Lighthouses and Maps — A614

Designs: 45c, Macquarie, New South Wales. Nos. 2048, 2051, Troubridge Island, South Australia. Nos. 2049, 2052, Cape Naturaliste, Western Australia. $1.50, Cape Bruny, Tasmania.

2002, Mar. 12 Perf. 14½x14

2047	A614	45c multi	1.40	.60
a.		Booklet pane of 4	5.75	
2048	A614	49c multi	1.40	.90
a.		Booklet pane of 2	2.75	
2049	A614	49c multi	1.40	.90
a.		Horiz. pair, #2048-2049	2.75	2.00
b.		Booklet pane of 2	2.75	
2050	A614	$1.50 multi	2.25	2.00
a.		Booklet pane of 2	7.00	—
b.		Booklet pane, #2047-2050	7.75	—
		Booklet, #2047a, 2048a, 2049b, 2050a, 2050b	25.75	

Booklet Stamps

Self-Adhesive

Serpentine Die Cut 11¾

2051	A614	49c multi	1.00	.50
2052	A614	49c multi	1.00	.50
a.		Booklet, 5 each #2051-2052	13.50	
		Nos. 2047-2052 (6)	8.45	5.40

Booklet containing Nos. 2047a-2050b sold for $9.95.

Encounter of Matthew Flinders and Nicolas Baudin, Bicent. A615

Map, ship and: 45c, Baudin and kangaroo. $1.50, Flinders and Port Lincoln parrot.

2002, Apr. 4 Perf. 14x14¾

2053	A615	45c multi	1.25	.75
2054	A615	$1.50 multi	2.50	2.10

See France Nos. 2882-2883.

Tourist Attractions Type of 2000

Designs: 50c, Walker Flat. $1, Mt. Roland. $1.50, Cape Leveque.

2002, May 1 Perf. 14½x14

2055	A581	50c multi	1.10	1.00
2056	A581	$1 multi	2.25	2.25
2057	A581	$1.50 multi	3.25	3.25

Booklet Stamps

Self-Adhesive

Serpentine Die Cut 11¼x10½

2058	A581	50c multi	1.40	.85
2059	A581	$1 multi	2.25	2.00
a.		Booklet, 6 #2058, 4 #2059	18.00	
		Nos. 2055-2059 (5)	10.25	9.35

Flora & Fauna Type of 1996

Designs: 50c, Desert star flower. $1, Bilby. $1.50, Thorny devil. $2, Great Sandy Desert.

2002, June 4 Litho. Perf. 14x14½

2060	A511	50c multi	.75	.55
2061	A511	$1 multi	1.50	1.25
2062	A511	$1.50 multi	2.25	1.75

Perf. 14½x14

Size: 50x30mm

2063	A511	$2 multi	3.00	2.40
		Nos. 2060-2063 (4)	7.50	5.95

See Nos. 2112-2114 for self-adhesive versions of 50c stamp.

Paintings by Albert Namatjira (1902-59) A616

Designs: Nos. 2064, 2068, Ghost Gum Mt. Sonder, MacDonnel Ranges. Nos. 2065, 2069, Mt. Hermannsburg. Nos. 2066, 2070, Glen Helen Country. Nos. 2067, 2071, Simpsons Gap.

2002, July 2 Litho. Perf. 14x14¾

2064	A616	45c multi	.95	.75
a.		Booklet pane of 4	4.00	4.00
2065	A616	45c multi	.95	.75
a.		Booklet pane of 4	4.00	4.00
2066	A616	45c multi	.95	.75
a.		Booklet pane of 4	4.00	4.00
2067	A616	45c multi	.95	.75
a.		Block of 4, #2064-2067	4.25	3.75
b.		Souvenir sheet of 4, #2064-2067	4.25	3.75
c.		Booklet pane of 4	4.00	4.00
d.		Booklet pane, #2067b	4.25	4.00
		Booklet, #2064a, 2065a, 2066a, 2067c, 2067d	20.75	
		Nos. 2064-2067 (4)	3.80	3.00

Serpentine Die Cut 11x11½

Self-Adhesive

2068	A616	45c multi	1.00	.75
2069	A616	45c multi	1.00	.75
2070	A616	45c multi	1.00	.75
2071	A616	45c multi	1.00	.75
a.		Booklet pane of 10, 3 each #2068-2069, 2 each #2070-2071	10.00	
b.		Coil strip of 4, #2068-2071	4.50	
		Nos. 2068-2071 (4)	4.00	3.00

Australia — Thailand Diplomatic Relations, 50th Anniv. A617

Designer: 45c, Nelumbo nucifera. $1, Nymphaea immutabilis.

2002, Aug. 6 Litho. Perf. 14x14½

2072	A617	45c multi	1.00	.75
2073	A617	$1 multi	2.25	2.00
a.		Souvenir sheet, #2072-2073	3.25	2.75
b.		As "a," overprinted in gold in margin	8.50	8.50

Overprint on margin of No. 2073b has IFSDA and APTA emblems and text reading "50th Anniversary International Federation / of Stamp Dealers Associations."

See Thailand Nos. 2028-2029.

Christmas — A618

Koala A619

Puja, by Ngarralja Tommy May — A620

2002   *Perf. 14¼x14*
2074	A618	90c multi + label	1.90	1.90
2075	A619	$1.10 multi + label	2.25	2.25
2076	A620	$1.65 multi + label	3.50	3.50
a.		Booklet pane of 4 + 4 labels	13.75	—
		Complete booklet, 3 #2076a	50.00	
		Nos. 2074-2076 (3)	7.65	7.65

Issued: 2074-2076, 8/23. No. 2076a, 10/31.
Nos. 2074-2076 were each printed in sheets of 20 stamps + 20 labels. Labels on some sheets could be personalized for an additional fee.
The complete booklet, which sold for $20.75, contains three panes of No. 2076a with different margins.

Tourist Attractions Type of 2000

Designs: $1.10, Coonawarra. $1.65, Gariwerd-Grampians Natl. Park. $2.20, National Library. $3.30, Cape York.

2002, Aug. 23   *Litho.*   *Perf. 14½x14*
2077	A581	$1.10 multi	2.25	2.25
2078	A581	$1.65 multi	3.50	3.50
2079	A581	$2.20 multi	4.50	4.50
2080	A581	$3.30 multi	7.00	6.00
		Nos. 2077-2080 (4)	17.25	16.25

Aboriginal Food Plants — A621

Designs: Nos. 2081, 2088, Murnong. Nos. 2082, 2087, Acacia seeds. Nos. 2083, 2086, Quandong. Nos. 2084, 2090, Honey grevillea. Nos. 2085, 2089, Lilly-pilly.

2002, Sept. 3   *Litho.*   *Perf. 14¾x14*
2081	A621	49c multi	1.00	.75
2082	A621	49c multi	1.00	.75
2083	A621	49c multi	1.00	.75
2084	A621	49c multi	1.00	.75
2085	A621	49c multi	1.00	.75
a.		Horiz. strip of 5, #2081-2085	5.00	4.75
b.		Tete beche block of 10, 2 each # 2081-2085	10.00	11.50
		Nos. 2081-2085 (5)	5.00	3.75

Booklet Stamps
Self-Adhesive
Serpentine Die Cut 11¾
2086	A621	49c multi	1.00	.80
2087	A621	49c multi	1.00	.80
2088	A621	49c multi	1.00	.80
2089	A621	49c multi	1.00	.80
2090	A621	49c multi	1.00	.80
a.		Booklet pane, 2 each #2086-2090	11.00	
		Nos. 2086-2090 (5)	5.00	4.00

Bunyip — A622   Fairy — A623

Gnome — A624   Goblin — A625

Wizard — A626   Sprite — A627

2002, Sept. 25   *Perf. 14¾x14*
2091	A622	45c multi	1.00	.75
2092	A623	45c multi	1.00	.75
2093	A624	45c multi	1.00	.75
a.		Horiz. strip of 3, #2091-2093	3.00	3.00
2094	A625	45c multi	1.00	.75
2095	A626	45c multi	1.00	.75
2096	A627	45c multi	1.00	.75
a.		Horiz. strip of 3, #2094-2096	3.00	3.00
b.		Souvenir sheet, #2091-2096	6.50	6.50
		Nos. 2091-2096 (6)	6.00	4.50

Self-Adhesive
Serpentine Die Cut 11½x11
2097	A622	45c multi	1.00	.75
2098	A623	45c multi	1.00	.75
2099	A624	45c multi	1.00	.75
2100	A625	45c multi	1.00	.75
2101	A626	45c multi	1.00	.75
2102	A627	45c multi	1.00	.75
a.		Vert. coil strip of 6, #2097-2102	6.00	
b.		Booklet pane #2097, 2102, 2 each #2098-2101	10.00	
		Nos. 2097-2102 (6)	6.00	4.50

Characters from The Magic Rainforest, by John Marsden.

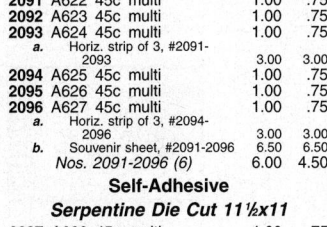

Race Horses A628

2002, Oct. 15   *Litho.*   *Perf. 14x14½*
2103	A628	45c Wakeful	1.00	.75
2104	A628	45c Rising Fast	1.00	.75
2105	A628	45c Manikato	1.00	.75
2106	A628	45c Might and Power	1.00	.75
2107	A628	45c Sunline	1.00	.75
a.		Horiz. strip of 5, #2103-2107	5.25	5.25
		Nos. 2103-2107 (5)	5.00	3.75

Christmas — A629

2002, Nov. 1   *Perf. 14½x14*
2108	A629	40c Nativity	1.00	.80
2109	A629	45c Magi	1.00	.70

Self-Adhesive
Booklet Stamp
Serpentine Die Cut 11¼
2110	A629	40c Nativity	1.00	.70
a.		Booklet pane of 20 + 20 labels	20.00	
		Nos. 2108-2110 (3)	3.00	2.20

Flora and Fauna Type of 1996

Designs: 50c, Desert star flower. $1.45, Blue orchid.

2003   *Litho.*   *Perf. 14x14½*
2111	A511	$1.45 multi	3.25	3.25

Self-Adhesive
Coil Stamps
Serpentine Die Cut 11¼
2112	A511	50c multi	1.00	.50

Serpentine Die Cut 12¾
2113	A511	50c multi	1.00	.50

Booklet Stamp
Serpentine Die Cut 11¼x11
2114	A511	50c multi	1.00	.50
a.		Booklet pane of 10	10.00	
b.		Booklet pane of 20	22.50	
		Nos. 2111-2114 (4)	6.25	4.75

Issued: 50c, 1/7; $1.45, 2/11.

Flowers — A630

Roses and Wedding Rings — A631

Roses and Hearts — A632

Birthday Cake, Balloons and Gifts — A633

Teddy Bear A634

Balloons and Streamers — A635

Kangaroo and Australian Flag — A636

Australia on Globe — A637

Automobile — A638

Rose and Wedding Rings — A639

2003   *Perf. 14½x14*
2115	A630	50c multi + label	1.50	.85
a.		Booklet pane of 4 + 4 labels	6.00	
		Booklet, 5 #2115a	30.00	
2116	A631	50c multi + label	1.50	.85
a.		Booklet pane of 4 + 4 labels	6.00	
		Booklet, 5 #2116a	30.00	

2117	A632	50c multi + label	1.50	.85
a.		Booklet pane of 4 + 4 labels	6.00	
		Booklet, 5 #2117a	30.00	
b.		Strip of 3, #2115-2117, + 3 labels	4.50	
2118	A633	50c multi + label	1.50	.85
a.		Booklet pane of 4 + 4 labels	6.00	
		Booklet, 5 #2118a	30.00	
2119	A634	50c multi + label	1.50	.85
a.		Booklet pane of 4 + 4 labels	6.00	—
		Complete booklet, 5 #2119a	30.00	
2120	A635	50c multi + label	1.50	.85
a.		Booklet pane of 4 + 4 labels	6.00	
		Booklet, 5 #2120a	30.00	
b.		Strip of 3, #2118-2120, + 3 labels	3.50	
2121	A636	50c multi + label	1.50	.85
2122	A637	50c multi + label	1.50	.85
a.		Booklet pane of 4 + 4 labels	6.00	—
		Complete booklet, 5 #2122a	30.00	
2123	A638	50c multi + label	1.50	.85
a.		Strip of 3, #2121-2123, + 3 labels	4.50	
2124	A639	$1 multi + label	1.75	1.75
a.		Booklet pane of 4 + 4 labels	7.00	
		Booklet, 5 #2124a	35.00	
		Nos. 2115-2124 (10)	15.25	9.40

Issued: No. 2119a, 10/31/03; No. 2122a, 3/16/04. Rest of set, 1/7/03.
Panes of 20 stamps containing the same design could have labels personalized. The personalized panes sold for a higher price.
Nos. 2115a, 2116a, 2117a, 2118a, 2119a, 2120a, 2122a and 2124a come in complete booklets, each containing 5 panes, each pane having different margins. Some panes are found in a number of different booklets.

Australian Legends Type of 1997

Tennis players: Nos. 2125, 2129, Margaret Court with Wimbledon trophy. Nos. 2126, 2131, Court in action. Nos. 2127, 2130, Rod Laver with Wimbledon trophy. Nos. 2128, 2132, Laver in action.

2003, Jan. 24   *Perf. 14x14¾*
Size: 34x26mm
2125	A522	50c multi	1.00	.70
2126	A522	50c multi	1.00	.70
2127	A522	50c multi	1.00	.70
2128	A522	50c multi	1.00	.70
a.		Block of 4, #2125-2128	5.25	4.75
b.		Booklet pane, #2125-2128	6.00	—
		Nos. 2125-2128 (4)	4.00	2.80

Self-Adhesive
Booklet Stamps
Serpentine Die Cut 11x11½
2129	A522	50c multi	1.00	.50
2130	A522	50c multi	1.00	.50
2131	A522	50c multi	1.00	.50
2132	A522	50c multi	1.00	.50
a.		Booklet pane, 3 each #2129-2130, 2 each #2131-2132	10.00	
		Nos. 2129-2132 (4)	4.00	2.00

No. 2128b issued 1/24/07.

Fish A640

2003, Feb. 11   *Perf. 14½x14*
2133	A640	50c Snapper	1.00	.60
2134	A640	50c Murray cod	1.00	.60
2135	A640	50c Brown trout	1.00	.60
2136	A640	50c Yellowfin tuna	1.00	.60
2137	A640	50c Barramundi	1.00	.60
a.		Horiz. strip of 5, #2133-2137	5.75	4.50
		Nos. 2133-2137 (5)	5.00	3.00

Australian Cultivars — A641

Designs: Nos. 2138, 2143, Hari Withers camellia. Nos. 2139, 2144, Victoria Gold rose. Nos. 2140, 2145, Superb grevillea. Nos. 2141, 2146, Bush Tango kangaroo paw. Nos. 2142, 2147, Midnight rhododendron.

2003, Mar. 25   *Perf. 14¾x14*
2138	A641	50c multi	.95	.70
2139	A641	50c multi	.95	.70
2140	A641	50c multi	.95	.70
2141	A641	50c multi	.95	.70
2142	A641	50c multi	.95	.70
a.		Horiz. strip of 5, #2138-2142	5.75	5.00
		Nos. 2138-2142 (5)	4.75	3.50

Self-Adhesive
Serpentine Die Cut 11½x11¼

2143	A641	50c multi	1.00	.35
2144	A641	50c multi	1.00	.35
2145	A641	50c multi	1.00	.35
2146	A641	50c multi	1.00	.35
2147	A641	50c multi	1.00	.35
a.	Coil strip of 5, #2143-2147		5.00	
b.	Booklet pane, 2 each #2143-2147		10.00	
	Nos. 2143-2147 (5)		5.00	1.75

Paintings — A642

Designs: No. 2148, Ned Kelly, by Sidney Nolan. No. 2149, Family Home, Suburban Exterior, by Howard Arkley. $1.45, Cord Drawn Long, Expectant, by Robert Jacks. $2.45, Girl, by Joy Hester.

2003, May 6   Litho.   Perf. 14½x14

2148	A642	$1 multi	1.75	1.50
2149	A642	$1 multi	1.75	1.50
a.	Horiz. pair, #2148-2149		3.50	3.25
2150	A642	$1.45 multi	3.25	2.75
2151	A642	$2.45 multi	4.75	4.00
	Nos. 2148-2151 (4)		11.50	9.75

Coronation of Queen Elizabeth II, 50th Anniv. — A643

Designs: 50c, Queen Elizabeth II, 1953. $2.45, St. Edward's Crown.

2003, June 2   Litho.   Perf. 14¾x14

2152	A643	50c multi	1.00	1.00
2153	A643	$2.45 multi	4.00	3.25
a.	Souvenir sheet, #2152-2153		6.50	6.50

Booklet Stamp
Self-Adhesive
Serpentine Die Cut 11¼x11¼

2154	A643	50c multi	.90	.40
a.	Booklet pane of 10		9.00	
	Nos. 2152-2154 (3)		5.90	4.65

Papunya Tula Aboriginal Art A644

Untitled works by: $1.10, Ningura Napurrula. $1.65, Naata Nungurrayi. $2.20, Graham Tjupurrula. $3.30, Dini Campbell Tjampitjinpa.

2003, June 17   Perf. 14½x14

2155	A644	$1.10 multi	2.00	2.00
2156	A644	$1.65 multi	3.00	3.00

Size: 56x25mm
Perf. 14x14½

2157	A644	$2.20 multi	4.00	4.00
2158	A644	$3.30 multi	5.75	5.75
	Nos. 2155-2158 (4)		14.75	14.75

Flora & Fauna Type of 1996

Designs: Nos. 2159, 2163, 2167, Orange-thighed tree frog. Nos. 2160, 2164, 2168, Green-spotted triangle butterfly. Nos. 2161, 2165, 2169, Striped possum. Nos. 2162, 2166, 2170, Yellow-bellied sunbird.

2003, July 8   Litho.   Perf. 14x14¼

2159	A511	50c multi	.85	.40
2160	A511	50c multi	.85	.40
2161	A511	50c multi	.85	.40
2162	A511	50c multi	.85	.40
a.	Block of 4, #2159-2162		3.75	3.75
	Nos. 2159-2162 (4)		3.40	1.60

Self-Adhesive
Serpentine Die Cut 11¼

2163	A511	50c multi	1.00	.40
2164	A511	50c multi	1.00	.40
a.	Booklet pane of 2, #2163-2164		2.25	
2165	A511	50c multi	1.00	.40
2166	A511	50c multi	1.00	.40
a.	Booklet pane of 4, #2163-2166, rouletted at bottom		4.50	

	Complete booklet, #2164a, 2 #2166a		10.25	
b.	Booklet pane of 4, #2163-2166, rouletted at side		4.50	
	Complete booklet, 5 #2166b		23.00	
c.	Coil strip of 4, #2163-2166		4.50	

Coil Stamps
Serpentine Die Cut 12¾

2167	A511	50c multi	1.10	.40
2168	A511	50c multi	1.10	.40
2169	A511	50c multi	1.10	.40
2170	A511	50c multi	1.10	.40
a.	Strip of 4, #2167-2170		5.25	
	Nos. 2163-2170 (8)		8.40	3.20

Genetics A645

Map of Australia and: No. 2171, DNA molecule. No. 2172, Kangaroo chromosomes in cell division.

2003, July 8   Litho.   Perf. 14x14¾

2171	A645	50c red & multi	1.00	.80
2172	A645	50c grn & multi	1.00	.80
a.	Horiz. pair, #2171-2172		2.50	2.50

Murray River Shipping, 150th Anniv. A646

Murray River vessels: Nos. 2173, 2178, Oscar W. Nos. 2174, 2179, Marion. Nos. 2175, 2180, Ruby. Nos. 2176, 2181, Pyap. Nos. 2177, 2182, Adelaide.

2003, Aug. 5   Litho.   Perf. 14x14¾

2173	A646	50c multi	.90	.70
a.	Booklet pane of 4		3.75	—
2174	A646	50c multi	.90	.70
a.	Booklet pane of 4		3.75	—
2175	A646	50c multi	.90	.70
a.	Booklet pane of 4		3.75	—
2176	A646	50c multi	.90	.70
a.	Booklet pane of 4		3.75	—
2177	A646	50c multi	.90	.70
a.	Booklet pane of 4		3.75	—
	Complete booklet, #2173a-2177a		20.00	
b.	Horiz. strip of 5, #2173-2177		4.50	4.00
	Nos. 2173-2177 (5)		4.50	3.50

Self-Adhesive
Serpentine Die Cut 11¼x11½

2178	A646	50c multi	1.10	.45
2179	A646	50c multi	1.10	.45
2180	A646	50c multi	1.10	.45
2181	A646	50c multi	1.10	.45
2182	A646	50c multi	1.10	.45
a.	Horiz. coil strip of 5, #2178-2182		5.75	
b.	Booklet pane, 2 each #2178-2182		11.00	
	Nos. 2178-2182 (5)		5.50	2.25

The booklet containing Nos. 2173a-2177a sold for $10.95.

Christmas — A647

2003, Aug. 5   Litho.   Perf. 14½x14

2183	A647	50c Christmas tree	.80	.60
a.	Sheet of 20 + 20 labels		35.00	
2184	A647	90c Star	1.60	1.50
a.	Sheet of 20 + 20 labels		50.00	

Labels on Nos. 2183a and 2184a could be personalized. No. 2183a sold for $23 on day of issue; No. 2184a for $32.

High Court of Australia, Cent. A648

Designs: 50c, Sir Samuel Griffith (1845-1920), first Chief Justice, text from Constitution about High Court. $1.45, "Justice," names of significant cases.

2003, Sept. 2   Litho.   Perf. 14x14¾

2185	A648	50c multi	.80	.80
2186	A648	$1.45 multi	2.50	2.50
a.	Souvenir sheet, #2185-2186		4.00	4.25

Insects A649

Designs: Nos. 2187, 2198, Ulysses butterfly. Nos. 2188, 2197, Leichhardt's grasshopper. Nos. 2189, 2196, Vedalia ladybird. Nos. 2190, 2195, Green mantid and damselfly. Nos. 2191, 2194, Emperor gum moth caterpillar. Nos. 2192, 2193, Fiddler beetle.

2003, Sept. 24   Perf. 14x14¾

2187	A649	50c multi	.80	.60
2188	A649	50c multi	.80	.60
2189	A649	50c multi	.80	.60
a.	Horiz. strip, #2187-2189		3.25	3.25
2190	A649	50c multi	.80	.60
2191	A649	50c multi	.80	.60
2192	A649	50c multi	.80	.60
a.	Horiz. strip, #2190-2192		3.25	3.25
b.	Souvenir sheet, #2187-2192		5.75	5.75
c.	As "b," with Bangkok 2003 emblem in margin in gold		8.00	8.00
	Nos. 2187-2192 (6)		4.80	3.60

Self-Adhesive
Serpentine Die Cut 11x11¼

2193	A649	50c multi	1.00	.40
2194	A649	50c multi	1.00	.40
2195	A649	50c multi	1.00	.40
2196	A649	50c multi	1.00	.40
2197	A649	50c multi	1.00	.40
2198	A649	50c multi	1.00	.40
a.	Horiz. coil strip, #2193-2198		6.75	
b.	Booklet pane, #2193-2194, 2 each #2195-2198		12.00	
	Nos. 2193-2198 (6)		6.00	2.40

No. 2193c issued 10/4.

2003 Rugby World Cup — A650

Designs: 50c, Players running with ball, hands and ball. $1.10, Webb Ellis Cup, Telstra Stadium. $1.65, Player kicking at goal, ball in hand.

2003, Oct. 8   Litho.   Perf. 14½x14

2199	A650	50c multi	1.00	.85
a.	Booklet pane of 3		3.50	
2200	A650	$1.10 multi	2.25	2.25
a.	Booklet pane of 3		7.00	
2201	A650	$1.65 multi	3.25	3.25
a.	Booklet pane of 3		10.50	
	Complete booklet, #2199a, 2200a, 2201a		24.00	
b.	Souvenir sheet, #2199-2201		7.00	7.00
	Nos. 2199-2201 (3)		6.50	6.35

Booklet sold for $10.95.

Active With Asthma A651

2003, Oct. 14   Perf. 14x14½

2202	A651	50c multi	1.00	.70

Christmas — A652

Designs: 45c, Madonna and Child with Angels. 50c, Three Wise Men. 90c, Angel Appearing to the Shepherds.

2003, Oct. 31   Perf. 14½x14

2203	A652	45c multi	.75	.80
2204	A652	50c multi	.80	.80
2205	A652	90c multi	1.60	1.60

Booklet Stamp
Self-Adhesive
Serpentine Die Cut 11½x11¼

2206	A652	45c multi	.95	.60
a.	Booklet pane of 20 + 20 labels		20.00	
	Nos. 2203-2206 (4)		4.10	3.80

Australian Legends Type of 1997

Dame Joan Sutherland, opera singer: Nos. 2207, 2209, In costume. Nos. 2208, 2210, In black and red dress.

2004, Jan. 23   Litho.   Perf. 14x14¾
Size: 37x26mm

2207	A522	50c multi	.90	.70
2208	A522	50c multi	.90	.70
a.	Horiz. pair, #2207-2208		2.00	2.00
b.	Booklet pane, #2207-2208		3.00	—

Booklet Stamps
Self-Adhesive
Serpentine Die Cut 11x11½

2209	A522	50c multi	1.00	.40
2210	A522	50c multi	1.00	.40
a.	Booklet pane, 5 each #2209-2210		11.00	
	Nos. 2207-2210 (4)		3.80	2.20

No. 2208b issued 1/24/07.

Settlement of Hobart Town, Tasmania, Bicent. A653

Segment of shell necklace, map of Tasmania and: No. 2211, Cheshunt House, Deloraine. No. 2212, Complete shell necklace. No. 2213, Mount Wellington. No. 2214, Hobart Town from Kangaroo Point, by John Glover.

2004, Feb. 3   Litho.   Perf. 14x14½

2211	A653	50c multi	1.00	.70
2212	A653	50c multi	1.00	.70
a.	Pair, #2211-2212		2.00	1.60
2213	A653	$1 multi	2.00	1.60
2214	A653	$1 multi	2.00	1.60
a.	Pair, #2213-2214		4.00	3.50
b.	Souvenir sheet, #2211-2214		6.25	6.25
c.	As "b," ovptd. for Paris Exhib. 2004		35.00	35.00
d.	As "b," ovptd. for China 2005 exhibition		20.00	20.00
	Nos. 2211-2214 (4)		6.00	4.60

Historic Bridges A654

Designs: Nos. 2215, 2220, Ross Bridge, Tasmania, 1836. Nos. 2216, 2221, Lockyer Creek Bridge, Queensland, 1911. Nos. 2217, 2222, Sydney Harbour Bridge, 1932. Nos. 2218, 2223, Birkenhead Bridge, Adelaide, 1940. Nos. 2219, 2224, Bolte Bridge, Melbourne, 1999.

2004, Mar. 2   Litho.   Perf. 14x14½

2215	A654	50c multi	.90	.70
a.	Booklet pane of 4		4.00	
2216	A654	50c multi	.90	.70
a.	Booklet pane of 4		4.00	
2217	A654	50c multi	.90	.70
a.	Booklet pane of 4		4.00	
2218	A654	50c multi	.90	.70
a.	Booklet pane of 4		4.00	
2219	A654	50c multi	.90	.70
a.	Booklet pane of 4		4.00	
	Complete booklet, #2215a, 2216a, 2217a, 2218a, 2219a		21.00	
b.	Horiz. strip of 5, #2215-2219		5.25	4.00
c.	Booklet pane of 6 ('06)		6.25	
	Nos. 2215-2219 (5)		4.50	3.50

The complete booklet No. 2219a sold for $10.95.
No. 2219c issued 3/1/06.

Self-Adhesive
Serpentine Die Cut 11x11½

2220	A654	50c multi	1.40	.90
2221	A654	50c multi	1.40	.90
2222	A654	50c multi	1.40	.90
2223	A654	50c multi	1.40	.90
2224	A654	50c multi	1.40	.90
a.	Horiz. coil strip of 5, #2220-2224		7.25	
b.	Booklet pane, 2 each #2220-2224		14.50	
	Nos. 2220-2224 (5)		7.00	4.50

Southern
Cross — A655

2004-05   **Perf. 14½x14**
2225	A655	50c multi	.90	.70
a.		Booklet pane of 4 + 4 labels	4.25	—
		Complete booklet, 5 #2225a	22.00	

Issued: No. 2225, 3/16/04. No. 2225a, Jan. 2005. No. 2225a was issued in a variety of complete booklets, each containing 5 panes with different margins. Each complete booklet sold for $10.95.

Renewable
Energy
A656

Designs: Nos. 2226, 2230, Solar energy. Nos. 2227, 2231, Wind energy. Nos. 2228, 2232, Hydroelectric energy. Nos. 2229, 2233, Biomass energy.

2004, Mar. 30   **Perf. 14x14½**
2226	A656	50c multi	.90	.70
2227	A656	50c multi	.90	.70
2228	A656	50c multi	.90	.70
2229	A656	50c multi	.90	.70
a.		Block of 4, #2226-2229	3.75	3.75
		Nos. 2226-2229 (4)	3.60	2.80

Coil Stamps
Self-Adhesive
Serpentine Die Cut 11x11½
2230	A656	50c multi	1.00	.50
2231	A656	50c multi	1.00	.50
2232	A656	50c multi	1.00	.50
2233	A656	50c multi	1.00	.50
a.		Horiz. strip of 4, #2230-2233	4.25	
		Nos. 2230-2233 (4)	4.00	2.00

Royal Visit, 50th
Anniv. — A657

2004, Apr. 13   **Perf. 14½x14**
2234	A657	50c multi	.90	.70
a.		Booklet pane of 4	4.25	—
		Complete booklet, 5 #2234a	22.00	

The booklet, which contains five panes with different margins, sold for $10.95. Another booklet pane, with a different margin, is found in the booklet footnoted under No. 2507.

Flora & Fauna Type of 1996

Designs: 5c, Red lacewing butterfly. 10c, Blue-banded eggfly butterfly. 75c, Cruiser butterfly. $2, Butterflies, Daintree National Park rainforest.

2004, May 4   **Litho.**   **Perf. 14x14½**
2235	A511	5c multi	.25	.25
2236	A511	10c multi	.25	.25
2237	A511	75c multi	1.60	.95

Size: 50x30mm
Perf. 14½x14
2238	A511	$2 multi	3.50	3.00
		Nos. 2235-2238 (4)	5.60	4.45

Australian
Innovations
A658

Designs: Nos. 2239, 2248, Black box flight recorder, 1961. Nos. 2240, 2247, Ultrasound imaging equipment, 1976. Nos. 2241, 2246, Racecam television sports coverage, 1979. Nos. 2242, 2245, Baby safety capsule, 1984. Nos. 2243, 2244, Polymer banknotes, 1988.

2004, May 18   **Perf. 14x14½**
2239	A658	50c multi	1.00	.70
2240	A658	50c multi	1.00	.70
2241	A658	50c multi	1.00	.70
2242	A658	50c multi	1.00	.70
2243	A658	50c multi	1.00	.70
a.		Horiz. strip, #2239-2243	5.00	5.00
		Nos. 2239-2243 (5)	5.00	3.50

Booklet Stamps
Self-Adhesive
Serpentine Die Cut 11x11½
2244	A658	50c multi	1.10	.50
2245	A658	50c multi	1.10	.50
2246	A658	50c multi	1.10	.50
2247	A658	50c multi	1.10	.50
2248	A658	50c multi	1.10	.50
a.		Booklet pane, 2 each #2244-2248	11.00	
		Nos. 2244-2248 (5)	5.50	2.50

Passenger Ship
Travel
Posters — A659

Designs: 50c, Shaw Savill Lines. $1, Awatea, Union Steam Ship Co. $1.45, Orient Line. $2, Aberdeen & Commonwealth Line.

2004, June 1   **Litho.**   **Perf. 14½x14**
2249	A659	50c multi	1.00	.70
2250	A659	$1 multi	1.60	1.25
2251	A659	$1.45 multi	2.40	1.75
2252	A659	$2 multi	3.25	2.40
		Nos. 2249-2252 (4)	8.25	6.10

Serpentine Die Cut 11½x11¼
Syncopated
2252A	A659	50c Like #2249,		
		2005	5.00	2.50

Booklet Stamp
Self-Adhesive
Serpentine Die Cut 11½x11¼
2253	A659	50c multi	1.10	.50
a.		Booklet pane of 10	11.00	

Issued: Nos. 2249-2252, 2253, 6/1/04. No. 2252A, 2/22/05. No. 2252A issued in sheet of 10.

Eureka
Stockade,
150th Anniv.
A660

Designs: 50c, Eureka flag. $2.45, Peter Lalor (1827-89), leader of rebellious gold diggers.

2004, June 29   **Perf. 14x14½**
2254	A660	50c multi	1.00	.70
a.		Booklet pane of 2	2.25	
2255	A660	$2.45 multi	4.00	3.25
a.		Booklet pane of 2	10.25	—
b.		Booklet pane, #2254-2255	6.25	
		Complete booklet, #2255a, 2255b, 2 #2254a	25.00	
c.		Souvenir sheet, #2254-2255	5.75	5.75

No. 2255b has perfs that extend to the right margin. No. 2255c does not have perfs that extend through the margin. The margin is larger on No. 2255b than on No. 2255c. The complete booklet sold for $10.95.

Tourist Attractions — A661

Designs: No. 2256, Koala, Eastern Australia, vert. No. 2257, Little penguin, Phillip Island, vert. $1.45, Clown anemonefish, Great Barrier Reef. $2.45, Beach, Gold Coast.

Perf. 14x14½, 14½x14
2004, July 13				**Litho.**
2256	A661	$1 multi	1.50	1.25
2257	A661	$1 multi	1.60	1.25
a.		Horiz. pair, #2256-2257	4.50	4.50
2258	A661	$1.45 multi	3.00	2.00

Litho. With Foil Application
2259	A661	$2.45 multi	5.00	4.75
		Nos. 2256-2259 (4)	11.10	9.25

2004
Summer
Olympics
and
Paralympics,
Athens
A662

2004, Aug. 3   **Litho.**   **Perf. 14x14½**
2260	A662	50c Swimmer	1.00	.70
2261	A662	$1.65 Runner	2.75	2.75
2262	A662	$1.65 Cyclist	2.75	2.75
		Nos. 2260-2262 (3)	6.50	6.20

Gold Medalists
at 2004
Summer
Olympics,
Athens
A663

Designs: No. 2263, Ian Thorpe, Men's swimming 400m freestyle. No. 2264, Women's 4x100m medley relay swimming team. No. 2265, Sara Carrigan, Women's cycling road race. No. 2266, Petria Thomas, Women's swimming 100m butterfly. No. 2267, Suzanne Balogh, Women's trap shooting. No. 2268, Ian Thorpe, Men's swimming 200m freestyle. No. 2269, Jodie Henry, Women's swimming 100m freestyle. No. 2270, Anna Meares, Women's cycling 500m time trial. No. 2271, James Tomkins and Drew Ginn, Men's rowing pairs. No. 2272, Grant Hackett, Men's swimming 1500m freestyle. No. 2273, Women's 4x100 freestyle relay swimming team. No. 2274, Chantelle Newbery, Women's diving 10m platform. No. 2275, Men's 4000m team pursuit cycling team. No. 2276, Ryan Bayley, Men's cycling individual sprint. No. 2277, Graeme Brown and Stuart O'Grady, Men's cycling Madison. No. 2278, Ryan Bayley, Men's cycling Keirin. No. 2279, Men's field hockey team.

2004   **Litho.**   **Perf. 14¼**
2263	A663	50c multi	1.00	.80
2264	A663	50c multi	1.00	.80
2265	A663	50c multi	1.00	.80
2266	A663	50c multi	1.00	.80
2267	A663	50c multi	1.00	.80
2268	A663	50c multi	1.00	.80
2269	A663	50c multi	1.00	.80
2270	A663	50c multi	1.00	.80
2271	A663	50c multi	1.00	.80
2272	A663	50c multi	1.00	.80
2273	A663	50c multi	1.00	.80
2274	A663	50c multi	1.00	.80
2275	A663	50c multi	1.00	.80
2276	A663	50c multi	1.00	.80
2277	A663	50c multi	1.00	.80
2278	A663	50c multi	1.00	.80
2279	A663	50c multi	1.00	.80
		Nos. 2263-2279 (17)	17.00	13.60

Issued: Nos. 2263-2264, 8/16; Nos. 2265-2266, 8/17; Nos. 2267-2268, 8/18; Nos. 2269-2273, 8/23; No. 2274, 8/24; No. 2275, 8/25; No. 2276, 8/26; Nos. 2277-2278, 8/27; No. 2279, 8/30.

A sheet containing Nos. 2263-2279 was available only in the Australia Post annual collection. Value, $50.

Tourist Attractions Type of 2000

Designs: $1.20, Entrance Beach, Broome, Western Australia. $1.80, Mt. William National Park, Tasmania. $2.40, Potato Point, Bodalla, New South Wales. $3.60, Point Gibbon, South Australia.

2004, Sept. 6   **Perf. 14½x14**
2280	A581	$1.20 multi	2.40	1.75
2281	A581	$1.80 multi	3.25	2.75
2282	A581	$2.40 multi	4.00	4.00
2283	A581	$3.60 multi	5.50	5.50
		Nos. 2280-2283 (4)	15.15	14.00

Block of £2 Kangaroo & Map Stamps
from Australia Post Archives — A664

2004, Sept. 7   **Perf. 14¼**
2284	A664	$5 multi	11.00	9.25

Souvenir Sheet
Self-Adhesive
Serpentine Die Cut 11¼
2285	A664	$5 multi	11.00	11.00

Australian
Railways,
150th Anniv.
A665

Designs: Nos. 2286, 2291, Melbourne to Sandridge line, 1854. Nos. 2287, 2292, Sydney to Parramatta line, 1855. Nos. 2288, 2293, Helidon to Toowoomba line, 1867. Nos. 2289, 2294, Kalgoorlie to Port Augusta line, 1917. Nos. 2290, 2295, Alice Springs to Darwin line, 2004.

2004, Sept. 7   **Perf. 14x14¾**
2286	A665	50c multi	.95	.70
a.		Booklet pane of 4	4.25	—
2287	A665	50c multi	.95	.70
a.		Booklet pane of 4	4.25	—
2288	A665	50c multi	.95	.70
a.		Booklet pane of 4	4.25	—
2289	A665	50c multi	.95	.70
a.		Booklet pane of 4	4.25	—
2290	A665	50c multi	.95	.70
a.		Booklet pane of 4	4.25	—
		Complete booklet, #2286a-2290a	22.00	
b.		Horiz. strip, #2286-2290	5.25	5.25
		Nos. 2286-2290 (5)	4.75	3.50

Complete booklet of Nos. 2286a-2290a sold for $10.95.

Self-Adhesive
With Designs Lightened at Stamp Edges
Serpentine Die Cut 11¼x11½
2291	A665	50c multi	1.00	.60
2292	A665	50c multi	1.00	.60
2293	A665	50c multi	1.00	.60
2294	A665	50c multi	1.00	.60
2295	A665	50c multi	1.00	.60
a.		Horiz. coil strip, #2291-2295	5.50	
b.		Booklet pane, 2 each #2291-2295	11.00	
		Nos. 2291-2295 (5)	5.00	3.00

Cats and
Dogs — A666

Designs: Nos. 2296, 2302, Cat (fish background). Nos. 2297, 2304, Cat (mouse background). Nos. 2298, 2301, Labrador retriever puppy (ball background). Nos. 2299, 2303, West Highland terriers (paw print background). $1, Jack Russell terrier (bone background).

2004, Sept. 21   **Perf. 14¾x14**
2296	A666	50c multi	1.00	.70
a.		Booklet pane of 4	4.25	—
2297	A666	50c multi	1.00	.70
a.		Horiz. pair, #2296-2297	2.25	1.60
b.		Booklet pane of 4	4.25	—
c.		Booklet pane, 2 each #2296-2297	4.50	—
		Complete booklet, #2296a, 2297b, 3 #2297c	21.00	
2298	A666	50c multi	1.00	.70
a.		Booklet pane of 4	4.25	—
2299	A666	50c multi	1.00	.70
a.		Horiz. pair, #2298-2299	2.25	1.60
b.		Booklet pane of 4	4.25	—
c.		Booklet pane, 2 each #2298-2299	4.50	—

2300 A666 $1 multi 2.00 1.60
  a. Booklet pane of 2 4.25 —
    Complete booklet, #2298a,
    2299b, 2300a, 2 #2299c 21.00
  b. Souvenir sheet, #2296-2300 5.50 5.50
    Nos. 2296-2300 (5) 6.00 4.40

The complete booklets each sold for $10.95. The Cat booklet contains three examples of No. 2297c, each with different margins and stamp arrangements. The Dog booklet contains two examples of No. 2299c with different margins and stamp arrangements.

Self-Adhesive
Booklet Stamps
Serpentine Die Cut 11¼ Syncopated

2301 A666 50c multi .80 .60
2302 A666 50c multi .80 .60
2303 A666 50c multi .80 .60
  a. Booklet pane, 3 #2301, 2
    #2303 5.25
2304 A666 50c multi .80 .60
  a. Booklet pane, 3 each
    #2301-2302, 2 each
    #2303-2304 9.00
  b. Booklet pane, 3 #2302, 2
    #2304 5.25
2305 A666 $1 multi 2.25 1.25
  a. Booklet pane of 5 11.00
    Nos. 2301-2305 (5) 5.45 3.65

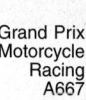

Grand Prix
Motorcycle
Racing
A667

Designs: Nos. 2306, 2311, Mick Doohan (motorcycle #1, red panel). Nos. 2307, 2312, Wayne Gardner (motorcycle #1, blue panel). Nos. 2308, 2313, Troy Bayliss (motorcycle #12, orange red panel). Nos. 2309, 2314, Daryl Beattie (motorcycle #4, green panel). Nos. 2310, 2315, Garry McCoy (motorcycle #8, yellow orange panel).

2004, Oct. 12 Litho. Perf. 14x14¾
2306 A667 50c multi .95 .70
2307 A667 50c multi .95 .70
2308 A667 50c multi .95 .70
2309 A667 50c multi .95 .70
2310 A667 50c multi .95 .70
  a. Horiz. strip of 5, #2306-
    2310 5.25 4.00
    Nos. 2306-2310 (5) 4.75 3.50

Self-Adhesive
Serpentine Die Cut 11¼ Syncopated

2311 A667 50c multi 1.00 .70
2312 A667 50c multi 1.00 .70
2313 A667 50c multi 1.00 .70
2314 A667 50c multi 1.00 .70
2315 A667 50c multi 1.00 .70
  a. Horiz. coil strip, #2311-2315 6.00
  b. Booklet pane, 2 each
    #2311-2315 11.00
    Nos. 2311-2315 (5) 5.00 3.50

Christmas — A668

Designs: 45c, Madonna and Child. 50c, Shepherds. $1, Magi, horiz.

2004, Nov. 1 Perf. 14¾x14, 14x14¾
2316 A668 45c multi .80 .65
2317 A668 50c multi .85 .75
2318 A668 $1 multi 1.60 1.60
    Nos. 2316-2318 (3) 3.25 3.00

Self-Adhesive
Booklet Stamps
Serpentine Die Cut 11¼ Syncopated

2319 A668 45c multi .95 .85
  a. Booklet pane of 20 + 20 eti-
    quettes 20.00
2320 A668 $1 multi 2.00 1.60
  a. Booklet pane of 5 10.00

Australian
Tennis
Open, Cent.
A669

Designs: 50c, Male player, tennis court and stands, 1905. $1.80, Female player, tennis court and stands, 2005.

2005, Jan. 11 Litho. Perf. 14x14¾
2321 A669 50c multi 1.00 .65
  a. Booklet pane of 2 2.25 —
2322 A669 $1.80 multi 3.50 2.00
  a. Booklet pane of 2 8.50 —
    Complete booklet, 2 each
    #2321a, 2322a 25.00

The complete booklet contains two examples of Nos. 2321a and 2322a, each with different margins.

Australian Legends
— Fashion
Designers — A670

Designs: Nos. 2323, 2329, Prue Acton. Nos. 2324, 2330, Jenny Bannister. Nos. 2325, 2331, Collette Dinnigan. Nos. 2326, 2332, Akira Isogawa. Nos. 2327, 2333, Joe Saba. Nos. 2328, 2334, Carla Zampatti.

2005, Jan. 21 Perf. 14¾x14
2323 A670 50c multi .80 .70
2324 A670 50c multi 1.00 .70
  a. I horiz. pair, #2323-2324 1.75 1.00
  b. Booklet pane, #2323-2324 3.00 —
2325 A670 50c multi .80 .70
2326 A670 50c multi .80 .70
  a. Horiz. pair, #2325-2326 1.75 1.60
  b. Booklet pane, #2325-2326 3.00 —
2327 A670 50c multi .80 .70
2328 A670 50c multi .80 .70
  a. Horiz. pair, #2327-2328 1.75 1.60
  b. Booklet pane, #2327-2328 3.00 —
    Nos. 2323-2328 (6) 5.00 4.20

Self-Adhesive
Booklet Stamps
Serpentine Die Cut 11¼ Syncopated

2329 A670 50c multi .90 .60
2330 A670 50c multi .90 .60
  a. Booklet pane, 5 each
    #2329-2330 10.00
2331 A670 50c multi .90 .60
2332 A670 50c multi .90 .60
  a. Booklet pane, 5 each
    #2331-2332 10.00
2333 A670 50c multi .90 .60
2334 A670 50c multi .90 .60
  a. Booklet pane, 5 each
    #2333-2334 10.00
    Nos. 2329-2334 (6) 5.40 3.60

Nos. 2324b, 2326b, 2328b, 1/24/07.

Parrots — A671

Designs: Nos. 2335, 2340, Princess parrot. Nos. 2336, 2344, Rainbow lorikeet. Nos. 2337, 2343, Green rosella. Nos. 2338, 2342, Red-capped parrot. Nos. 2339, 2341, Purple-crowned lorikeet.

2005, Feb. 8 Perf. 14¾x14
2335 A671 50c multi 1.00 .70
2336 A671 50c multi 1.00 .70
2337 A671 50c multi 1.00 .70
2338 A671 50c multi 1.00 .70
2339 A671 50c multi 1.00 .70
  a. Horiz. strip of 5, #2335-2339 5.50 4.75
    Nos. 2335-2339 (5) 5.00 3.50

A sheet containing Nos. 2335-2339 + 4 labels was available only with purchase of the "2005 Collection of Australian Stamps." Value $24.

Self-Adhesive
Coil Stamps
Serpentine Die Cut 11¼ Syncopated

2340 A671 50c multi 1.10 .60
2341 A671 50c multi 1.10 .60
2342 A671 50c multi 1.10 .60
2343 A671 50c multi 1.10 .60
2344 A671 50c multi 1.10 .60
  a. Vert. strip of 5, #2340-2344 6.00
    Nos. 2340-2344 (5) 5.50 3.00

Sports Memorabilia
A672

Designs: No. 2345, Sir Donald Bradman's cricket cap. No. 2346, Lionel Rose's boxing gloves. No. 2347, Marjorie Jackson's running spikes. No. 2348, Racing silks of Phar Lap's jockeys.

2005, Mar. 8 Litho. Perf. 14¾x14
2345 A672 50c multi .90 .70
  a. Booklet pane of 5, #1575a,
    1576c, 1941a, 1942b, 2345
    dated "2007" 7.50 —
2346 A672 50c multi .90 .70
2347 A672 $1 multi 1.60 1.20
2348 A672 $1 multi 1.60 1.20
  a. Horiz. pair, #2347-2348 4.50 4.50
    Nos. 2345-2348 (4) 5.00 3.80

No. 2345a issued 11/14/2007.

Child's Plush
Toy — A673

Red
Roses — A674

Gifts
A675

Kangaroos
A676

White
Roses — A677

Yellow Roses and
Woman's
Hand — A678

Koala — A679

Shell on
Beach — A680

Sydney Opera
House — A681

2005, Mar. 22 Perf. 14¾x14
2349 A673 50c multi .90 .70
2350 A674 50c multi .90 .70
2351 A675 50c multi .90 .70
2352 A676 50c multi .90 .70
  a. Additionally dated "2013"
    (#3534d) 1.25 1.25
2353 A677 50c multi .90 .70
  a. Horiz. strip, #2349-2353 5.00 5.00
2354 A678 $1 multi 1.60 1.60
2355 A679 $1.10 multi 2.25 2.25
2356 A680 $1.20 multi 2.40 2.40
2357 A681 $1.80 multi 3.50 3.50
    Nos. 2349-2357 (9) 14.25 13.25

Issued: No. 2352a, 5/10/2013.

Booklet Stamps
Self-Adhesive
*Serpentine Die Cut 11x11¼
Syncopated*

2358 A673 50c multi 3.75 *3.25*
  a. Booklet pane of 4 15.00
    Complete booklet, 5 #2358a 75.00
2359 A674 50c multi 3.75 *3.25*
  a. Booklet pane of 4 15.00
    Complete booklet, 5 #2359a 75.00
2360 A675 50c multi 3.75 *3.25*
  a. Booklet pane of 4 15.00
    Complete booklet, 5 #2360a 75.00
2361 A677 50c multi 3.75 *3.25*
  a. Booklet pane of 4 15.00
    Complete booklet, 5 #2361a 75.00
2362 A678 $1 multi 6.25 *6.25*
  a. Booklet pane of 4 25.00
    Complete booklet, 5 #2362a 125.00
2363 A679 $1.10 multi 6.50 *8.00*
  a. Booklet pane of 4 26.00
    Complete booklet, 2 #2363a 130.00
2364 A680 $1.20 multi 7.00 *9.00*
  a. Booklet pane of 2 14.00
2365 A681 $1.80 multi 7.50 *13.00*
  a. Booklet pane of 2 30.00
    Complete booklet, 2 each
    #2364a, 2365a 30.00
    Nos. 2358-2365 (8) 42.25 49.25

Each pane in the various complete booklets has a different margin. The complete booklets containing Nos. 2358-2361 each sold for $10.95, the complete booklet containing No. 2362 sold for $20.95, and the complete booklets containing Nos. 2363-2365 sold for $12.95.
See Nos. 2439-2447.

First
Australian
Coin, 150th
Anniv.
A682

Designs: One sovereign coin. Nos. 2000, 2368a, Obverse. Nos. 2367, 2368b, Reverse.

2005, Apr. 21 Litho. Perf. 14x14¾
2366 A682 50c multi 1.00 .75
2367 A682 $2.45 multi 4.00 3.60
  a. Booklet pane, #2366-2367 7.75 —

Litho. & Embossed with Foil
Application

2368 Sheet of 2 6.00 6.00
  a. A682 50c multi .90 .90
  b. A682 $2.45 multi 5.00 5.00

UNESCO
World Heritage
Sites in
Australia and
Great
Britain — A683

Designs: No. 2369, Wet Tropics of Queensland, Australia. No. 2370, Stonehenge, England. No. 2371, Greater Blue Mountains Area, New South Wales, Australia. No. 2372, Blenheim Castle, England. No. 2373, Purnululu National Park, Western Australia. No. 2374, Heart of Neolithic Orkney, Scotland. No. 2375, Ayers Rock, Uluru-Kata Tjuta National Park, Northern Territory, Australia. No. 2376, Hadrian's Wall, England.

2005, Apr. 21 Litho. Perf. 14¼
2369 A683 50c multi .95 .70
2370 A683 50c multi .95 .70
  a. Horiz. pair, #2369-2370 2.00 2.00
2371 A683 50c multi 1.00 .70
2372 A683 50c multi 1.00 .70
  a. Horiz. pair, #2371-2372 2.00 2.00
2373 A683 $1 multi 1.60 1.20
2374 A683 $1 multi 1.60 1.20
  a. Horiz. pair, #2373-2374 3.60 3.60
  b. Booklet pane, #2369-2370,
    2373-2374, + 4 labels 7.75

2375	A683 $1.80 multi	3.75	3.25
2376	A683 $1.80 multi	3.75	3.25
a.	Horiz. pair, #2375-2376	7.50	7.50
b.	Booklet pane, #2371-2372, 2375-2376, + 4 labels	11.50	—
	Nos. 2369-2376 (8)	14.60	11.70

See Great Britain Nos. 2280-2287.

Creatures of the Slime A684

2005, Apr. 21   **Perf. 14x14¾**

2377	A684 50c Tribrachidium	.90	.70
2378	A684 50c Dickinsonia	.90	.70
2379	A684 50c Spriggina	.90	.70
2380	A684 50c Kimberella	.90	.70
2381	A684 50c Inaria	.90	.70
a.	Horiz. strip of 5, #2377-2381	5.00	4.75
2382	A684 $1 Charnodiscus	1.75	1.60
a.	Souvenir sheet, #2377-2382	7.50	7.50
b.	Booklet pane, #2377-2382	9.00	—
	Nos. 2377-2382 (6)	6.25	5.10

Rotary International, Cent. — A685

2005, Apr. 21   **Perf. 14¾x14**

2383	A685 50c multi	.90	.65
a.	Imperf.	8.00	8.00

Self-Adhesive
Serpentine Die Cut 11½x11¼ Syncopated

2384	A685 50c multi	.90	.65
a.	Booklet pane of 10	10.25	
b.	Booklet pane of 1	1.40	—
	Complete booklet, #2367a, 2374b, 2376b, 2382b, 2384b	40.00	

No. 2383a was sold at the Pacific Explorer Intl. Philatelic Exhibition 2005.

Queen Elizabeth II, 79th Birthday A686

2005, May 10   **Perf. 14x14¾**

2385	A686 50c multi	1.00	.70
a.	Booklet pane of 4	4.00	
	Complete booklet, 5 #2385a	29.00	

2006 Commonwealth Games, Melbourne. No. 2385a was issued in a booklet that sold for $10.95, with the 5 panes having different margins.

Bush Wildlife A687

No. 2386, Superb lyrebird. Nos. 2387, 2390, Laughing kookaburra. Nos. 2388, 2391, Koala. Nos. 2389, 2392, Red kangaroo.

2005, June 7   **Perf. 14x14¾**

2386	A687 $1 multi	1.75	1.20
2387	A687 $1.10 multi	1.90	1.50
2388	A687 $1.20 multi	2.10	1.60
2389	A687 $1.80 multi	3.25	2.40
	Nos. 2386-2389 (4)	9.00	6.70

Serpentine Die Cut 11¼x11½ Syncopated
Self-Adhesive
Booklet Stamps

2390	A687 $1.10 multi	1.75	1.60
a.	Booklet pane of 5	10.00	
2391	A687 $1.20 multi	2.40	2.25
a.	Booklet pane of 5	12.00	
2392	A687 $1.80 Red kangaroo	3.25	3.25
a.	Booklet pane of 5	17.00	
	Nos. 2390-2392 (3)	7.40	7.10

Wild Flowers — A688

Designs: Nos. 2393, 2397, 2401, Sturt's desert pea. Nos. 2394, 2398, 2402, Coarse-leaved mallee. Nos. 2395, 2399, 2403, Common fringe lily. Nos. 2396, 2400, 2404, Swamp daisy.

2005, July 5   **Perf. 14x14½**

2393	A688 50c multi	1.00	.40
2394	A688 50c multi	1.00	.40
2395	A688 50c multi	1.00	.40
2396	A688 50c multi	1.00	.40
a.	Horiz. strip of 4, #2393-2396	4.00	3.75
	Nos. 2393-2396 (4)	4.00	1.60

Self-Adhesive
Serpentine Die Cut 11¼x11

2397	A688 50c multi	1.25	.70
2398	A688 50c multi	1.25	.70
2399	A688 50c multi	1.25	.70
2400	A688 50c multi	1.25	.70
a.	Horiz. coil strip of 4, #2397-2400	5.00	
b.	Booklet pane of 10, 3 each #2397-2398, 2 each #2399-2400	11.00	
c.	Booklet pane of 20, 5 each #2397-2400	20.00	
d.	Booklet pane of 10, 3 each #2398-2400, 2 #2397	6.50	

Coil Stamps
Die Cut Perf. 12¾

2401	A688 50c multi	1.35	.70
2402	A688 50c multi	1.35	.70
2403	A688 50c multi	1.35	.70
2404	A688 50c multi	1.35	.70
a.	Horiz. coil strip of 4, #2401-2404	5.50	
	Nos. 2397-2404 (8)	10.40	5.60

Australian Wine — A689

Designs: Nos. 2405, 2410, Grapevine, vineyard. Nos. 2406, 2411, Grapes, grape leaves. No. 2407, Grape pickers, basket of grapes, wine bottle. No. 2408, Wine bottle, corkscrew, wine barrels. $1.45, Wine glasses, cheese.

2005, July 19   **Perf. 14x14¾**

2405	A689 50c multi	.90	.70
2406	A689 50c multi	.90	.70
a.	Horiz. pair, #2405-2406	2.00	1.60
b.	Booklet pane, #2406a	2.25	
c.	Booklet pane, 2 #2406a	4.50	
2407	A689 $1 multi	1.60	1.25
2408	A689 $1 multi	1.60	1.25
a.	Horiz. pair, #2407-2408	3.75	2.75
b.	Booklet pane, 2 #2408a	9.25	
2409	A689 $1.45 multi	2.75	2.40
a.	Booklet pane of 2	6.25	—
	Complete booklet, #2406b, 2406c, 2408b, 2409a	22.50	
	Nos. 2405-2409 (5)	7.75	6.30

Booklet Stamps
Self-Adhesive
Serpentine Die Cut 11¼x11½ Syncopated

2410	A689 50c multi	1.00	.65
2411	A689 50c multi	1.00	.65
a.	Booklet pane, 5 each #2410-2411	11.00	

Complete booklet sold for $10.95.

Trees A690

Designs: Nos. 2412, 2417, Snowgum. Nos. 2413, 2418, Wollemi pine. Nos. 2414, 2419, Boab. Nos. 2415, 2420, Karri. Nos. 2416, 2421, Moreton Bay fig.

2005, Aug. 8   **Perf. 14x14¾**

2412	A690 50c multi	1.00	.70
2413	A690 50c multi	1.00	.70
2414	A690 50c multi	1.00	.70
2415	A690 50c multi	1.00	.70
2416	A690 50c multi	1.00	.70
a.	Horiz. strip of 5, #2412-2416	5.00	4.00
	Nos. 2412-2416 (5)	5.00	3.50

Coil Stamps
Serpentine Die Cut 11¼x11½ Syncopated

2417	A690 50c multi	1.00	.70
2418	A690 50c multi	1.00	.70
2419	A690 50c multi	1.00	.70
2420	A690 50c multi	1.00	.70
2421	A690 50c multi	1.00	.70
a.	Horiz. strip of 5, #2417-2421	6.00	
	Nos. 2417-2421 (5)	5.00	3.50

Nos. 2417-2421 have "frames" that are faded portions of the design.

Portion of Specimen Pane of New South Wales No. 86 from Australia Post Archives — A691

2005, Sept. 6   **Litho.**   **Perf. 14¼**

2422	A691 $5 multi	10.00	10.00

No. 2422 exists imperf.

Southern Cross — A692

Southern Cross and: 45c, Christmas tree. 50c, Map of Oceania and East Asia.

2005   **Perf. 14½x14**

2423	A692 45c multi	.90	.35
a.	Booklet pane of 4	5.75	
	Complete booklet (see footnote)	24.00	
2424	A692 50c multi	1.00	.60

Issued: Nos. 2423, 2424, 9/6. No. 2423a, 11/1. No. 2423a exists with three different margins, each of which appear in a booklet also containing two examples of Christmas Island No. 452a. The complete booklet sold for $9.95.

Southern Cross With Personalized Picture — A692a

Serpentine Die Cut 11½x11¼ Syncopated
2005, Sept. 6   **Litho.**
Self-Adhesive

2425	A692a 45c Like #2423	2.50	2.50
2426	A692a 50c Like #2424	2.50	2.50

Nos. 2425-2426 were sold in sheets of 20 and have personalized pictures and a straight edge at right, and lack separations between the stamp and the picture. Sheets of 20 of No. 2425 sold for $22, and of No. 2426, $23.

Down on the Farm — A693

Designs: Nos. 2427, 2433, Hen and chicks. Nos. 2428, 2434, Lambs and insects. Nos. 2429, 2437, Goats and rabbit. Nos. 2430,

2435, Pigs and frog. Nos. 2431, 2436, Cow and bird. $1, Horse, dogs, birds, lizard.

2005, Oct. 4   **Litho.**   **Perf. 14x14¾**

2427	A693 50c multi	1.00	.70
a.	Booklet pane of 1	1.40	
2428	A693 50c multi	1.00	.70
a.	Booklet pane of 1	1.40	
2429	A693 50c multi	1.00	.70
a.	Booklet pane of 1	1.40	
2430	A693 50c multi	1.00	.70
a.	Booklet pane of 1	1.40	
2431	A693 50c multi	1.00	.70
a.	Booklet pane of 1	1.40	
b.	Horiz. strip of 5, #2427-2431	5.00	4.00
2432	A693 $1 multi	2.00	1.60
a.	Booklet pane of 1	2.75	
b.	Souvenir sheet, #2427-2432	7.00	7.00
c.	Booklet pane of 1 #2432b (120x190mm)	10.00	—
	Complete booklet, #2427a-2432a, 2432c	20.00	
	Nos. 2427-2432 (6)	7.00	5.10

The complete booklet containing Nos. 2427a-2432a and 2432c sold for $9.95.

Booklet Stamps
Self-Adhesive
Serpentine Die Cut 11¼ Syncopated

2433	A693 50c multi	1.00	.70
2434	A693 50c multi	1.00	.70
2435	A693 50c multi	1.00	.70
2436	A693 50c multi	1.00	.70
2437	A693 50c multi	1.00	.70
a.	Booklet pane of 5, #2433-2437	6.75	—
b.	Booklet pane of 10, 2 each #2433-2437	10.00	
c.	Booklet pane of 20, 4 each #2433-2437	20.00	
2438	A693 $1 multi	2.00	1.60
a.	Booklet pane of 5	12.00	
	Nos. 2433-2438 (6)	7.00	5.10

Greetings Types of 2005 With Personalized Photo at Right Like Type A692a
Serpentine Die Cut 11½x11¼ Syncopated

2005   **Self-Adhesive**

2439	A673 50c multi	5.00	5.00
2440	A674 50c multi	5.00	5.00
2441	A675 50c multi	5.00	5.00
2442	A676 50c multi	5.00	5.00
2443	A677 50c multi	5.00	5.00
2444	A678 $1 multi	8.00	8.00
2445	A679 $1.10 multi	5.75	7.25
2446	A680 $1.20 multi	6.50	8.00
2447	A681 $1.80 multi	5.50	5.50
	Nos. 2439-2447 (9)	50.75	53.75

Nos. 2439-2447 were sold in sheets of 20 and have personalized pictures and a straight edge at right, and lack separations between the stamp and the picture. Sheets of 20 of Nos. 2439-2443 sold for $23 each, of No. 2444, $33.50, of No. 2445, $35, of No. 2446, $37, of No. 2447, $48.

Christmas — A694

Designs: Nos. 2448, 2450, Madonna and Child. Nos. 2449, 2451, Angel, horiz.

2005, Nov. 1   **Litho.**   **Perf. 14½x14**

2448	A694 45c multi	.80	.35

Perf. 14x14½

2449	A694 $1 multi	1.60	1.60

Booklet Stamps
Self-Adhesive
Serpentine Die Cut 11½x11¼ Syncopated

2450	A694 45c multi	1.00	.75
a.	Booklet pane of 20	20.00	

Serpentine Die Cut 11¼x11½ Syncopated

2451	A694 $1 multi	2.25	2.00
a.	Booklet pane of 5	11.00	
	Nos. 2448-2451 (4)	5.65	4.70

Emblem of 2006 Commonwealth Games, Melbourne — A695

Commonwealth Games Athletes — A696

Highlights of Commonwealth Games — A697

Medalists at Commonwealth Games — A698

"Equality, Humanity, Destiny" — A699

"Destiny, Equality, Humanity" — A700

"Humanity, Destiny, Equality" — A701

Designs: Nos. 2455, 2458, Runner crouching before race. $1.25, Cyclist. $1.85, Athlete holding ball.

No. 2459 — Sheet #1: a, Trolley car with wings. b, Fish sculpture. c, Cat and mouse puppets. d, Queen Elizabeth II. e, Opening ceremony crowd and fireworks.

No. 2460 — Sheet #2: a, Anna Meares. b, Equality, Humanity, destiny. c, Stephanie Rice swimming. d, Destiny, Equality, Humanity. e, Ben Kersten.

No. 2461 — Sheet #3: a, Ryan Bayley holding flag. b, Adam Vella & Michael Diamond. c, Sean Finning. d, Deserie Baynes & Suzanne Balogh. e, Danni Miatke. f, Women's Artistic Gymnastics team. g, Kate Bates. h, Leisel Jones wearing swim cap and waving. i, David Moore & Daniel Repacholi.

No. 2462 — Sheet #4: a, Brad Kahlfeldt. b, Libby Lenton, lane marker in background. c, Josh Jefferis on pommel horse. d, Emma Snowsill.

No. 2463 — Sheet #5: a, Leisel Jones wearing sweatsuit. b, Ryan Bayley wearing cycling

helmet. c, Matthew Cowdrey in water. d, Chloe Sims. e, Sophie Edington in water. f, Women's 4x200m freestyle swim team. g, Ben Turner.

No. 2464 — Sheet #6: a, Katie Mactier. b, Russell Mark & Craig Trembath. c, Jessicah Schipper in water. d, Kerryn McCann. e, Lalita Yauhleuskaya & Dina Aspandiyarova.

No. 2465 — Sheet #7: a, Lauryn Mark & Natalia Rahman. b, Jane Saville. c, Libby Lenton, pushing on lane marker. d, Nathan Deakes in 20km walk. e, Lisa McIntosh.

No. 2466 — Sheet #8: a, Leisel Jones with fist raised. b, Men's triples lawn bowling team. c, Sophie Edington holding medal. d, Matthew Cowdrey wearing sweatsuit. e, Brooke Krueger-Billett. f, Josh Jefferis kissing medal. g, Natalie Grinham. h, Women's 4x100m freestyle swim team. i, Joanna Fargus.

No. 2467 — Sheet #9: a, Alex Karapetyan. b, Jessicah Schipper wearing sweatsuit. c, Nathan O'Neill. d, Lalita Yauhleuskaya holding medal.

No. 2468 — Sheet #10: a, Hollie Dykes. b, Men's 4x100m medley swim team. c, Oenone Wood. d, Women's 4x100m medley swim team. e, Stephanie Rice with arm raised. f, Damian Istria. g, Deborah Lovely.

No. 2469 — Sheet #11: a, Chantelle Newbery & Loudy Tourky. b, John Steffensen. c, Bree Cole & Sharleen Stratton. d, Lynsey Armitage & Karen Murphy.

No. 2470 — Sheet #12: a, Heath Francis. b, Jana Pittman. c, Lalita Yauhleuskaya wearing sight. d, Scott Martin. e, Loudy Tourky. f, Women's basketball team. g, Chris Rae. h, Bruce Scott.

No. 2471 — Sheet #13: a, Nathan Deakes in 50km walk. b, Bronwyn Thompson. c, Robert Newbery & Mathew Helm. d, Steven Hooker. e, Stuart Rendell. f, Kelvin Kerkow. g, Men's basketball team.

No. 2472 — Sheet #14: a, Women's 4x400m relay team. b, Kym Howe. c, Women's field hockey team. d, Mathew Helm. e, Men's 4x400m relay team. f, Bradley Pitt. g, Jarrod Fletcher.

No. 2473 — Sheet #15: a, Natalie Bates. b, Natalie Grinham & Joe Kneipp. c, Men's field hockey team. d, Rachael Grinham & Natalie Grinham. e, Mathew Hayman.

No. 2474 — Sheet #16: a, Dancer on hoops. b, Women wearing hats. c, Dancer. d, Lit-up stadium and fireworks. e, Darkened stadium and fireworks.

No. 2475 — Sheet #17 — Kerryn McCann: a, Running, with opponents in background. b, Drinking from water bottle. c, Running past opponent, profile. d, Running on track with opponent. e, With hands over mouth. f, Collapsed on track. g, With both arms raised. h, Holding flag. i, Raising flower bouquet. j, Holding medal.

2006	**Litho.**	**Perf.**	**14¾x14**
2452 A695	50c shown	.90	.75
a.	Sheet of 9 + 9 labels	27.50	—
b.	Booklet pane of 4	4.25	

Self-Adhesive (#2453-2454)

Serpentine Die Cut 11¼ Syncopated

2453 A695	50c multi	.75	.75
a.	Booklet pane of 4	4.50	

With Personalized Photo at Right Like Type A692a

Booklet Stamp

Serpentine Die Cut 11½x11¼ on 3 Sides, Syncopated

2454 A695	50c multi	1.50	1.50
a.	Booklet pane of 4	7.00	

Perf. 14x14¾

2455 A696	50c shown	.80	.60
2456 A696	$1.25 multi	2.00	2.00
2457 A696	$1.85 multi	2.75	2.75
a.	Souvenir sheet, #2455-2457, 142x75mm sheet	5.50	5.50
b.	Booklet pane, #2455-2457, in 168x118mm pane	7.75	
	Complete booklet, #1488a, 2457b, 2 each #2453a, 2454a, + 3 postal cards	37.50	
c.	Booklet pane, #2455-2457, in 156x103mm pane	7.75	—
	Complete booklet, #845a, 2219c, 2452b, 2457c	22.00	
	Nos. 2455-2457 (3)	5.55	5.35

Booklet Stamp

Self-Adhesive

Serpentine Die Cut 11¼ Syncopated

2458 A696	50c multi	.90	.75
a.	Booklet pane of 10	10.00	

Miniature Sheets

Perf. 14½x14

2459	Sheet of 5	7.25	15.00
a.-e.	A697 50c any single	1.40	3.00
2460	Sheet of 5	7.25	11.00
a.	A698 50c multi	1.40	3.00
b.	A699 50c multi	1.40	1.00
c.	A698 50c multi	1.40	3.00
d.	A700 50c multi	1.40	1.00
e.	A698 50c multi	1.40	3.00
2461	Sheet of 10, #2460b, 2461a-2461i	14.50	28.00
a.-i.	A698 50c any single	1.40	3.00

2462	Sheet of 5, #2460b, 2462a-2462d	7.25	13.00
a.-d.	A698 50c any single	1.40	3.00
2463	Sheet of 10, #2460b, 2460d, 2463a-2463h	14.50	24.00
a.-g.	A698 50c any single	1.40	3.00
h.	A701 50c multi	1.40	1.00
2464	Sheet of 5	7.25	15.00
a.-e.	A698 50c any single	1.40	3.00
2465	Sheet of 5	7.25	15.00
a.-e.	A698 50c any single	1.40	3.00
2466	Sheet of 10, #2460b, 2466a-2466i	14.50	28.00
a.-i.	A698 50c any single	1.40	3.00
2467	Sheet of 5, #2460b, 2467a-2467d	7.25	13.00
a.-d.	A698 50c any single	1.40	3.00
2468	Sheet of 10, #2460b, 2460d, 2463a, 2468a-2468g	14.50	24.00
a.-g.	A698 50c any single	1.40	3.00
2469	Sheet of 5, #2460b, 2469a-2469d	7.25	13.00
a.-d.	A698 50c any single	1.40	3.00
2470	Sheet of 10, #2460b, 2460d, 2470a-2470h	14.50	26.00
a.-h.	A698 50c any single	1.40	3.00
2471	Sheet of 10, #2460b, 2460d, 2463h, 2471a-2471g	14.50	24.00
a.-g.	A698 50c any single	1.40	3.00
2472	Sheet of 10, #2460b, 2460d, 2463h, 2472a-2472g	14.50	24.00
a.-g.	A698 50c any single	1.40	3.00
2473	Sheet of 5	7.25	15.00
a.-e.	A698 50c any single	1.40	3.00
2474	Sheet of 5	7.25	15.00
a.-e.	A697 50c any single	1.40	3.00
2475	Sheet of 10	14.50	30.00
a.-j.	A697 50c any single	1.40	3.00
	Nos. 2459-2475 (17)	181.25	333.00

Issued: Nos. 2452-2453, 1/12; Nos. 2454, 2457b, 3/15; No. 2455, 2455-2458, 2457c, 3/1; No. 2459, 3/16; No. 2460, 3/17; No. 2461, 3/18; Nos. 2462, 2463, 3/19; No. 2464, 3/20; Nos. 2465, 2466, 3/21; Nos. 2467, 2468, 3/22; No. 2469, 3/23; No. 2470, 3/24; No. 2471, 3/25; No. 2472, 3/26; Nos. 2473, 2474, 3/27; No. 2475, 3/28.

No. 2452a sold for $15.95. Labels could be personalized.

Complete booklet containing No. 2454 sold for $19.95. Labels could be personalized.

Complete booklet containing No. 2457c sold for $10.95 and included a booklet pane with perf. 14x14¾ lithographed examples of Nos. 349-350 which were not valid for postage.

A booklet issued 2/1, containing #2452p, an imperf booklet pane of 4 #2452, a booklet pane of 2 #2453, a booklet pane of 1 #2453 and four 50c coins, sold for $24.95.

50c AUSTRALIA
Dame Edna Everage 2004
Dame Edna Everage in 2004 A702

50c AUSTRALIA
Barry Humphries
Barry Humphries A703

Inscriptions: Nos. 2476, 2481, Mrs. Norm Everage, 1969. Nos. 2477, 2482, Mrs. Edna Everage, 1973. Nos. 2478, 2483, Dame Edna Everage, 1982.

2006, Jan. 20	**Litho.**	**Perf.**	**14½x14**
2476 A702	50c multi	.80	.70
2477 A702	50c multi	.80	.70
2478 A702	50c multi	.80	.70
2479 A702	50c shown	.80	.70
2480 A703	50c shown	.80	.70
a.	Horiz. strip of 5, #2476-2480	4.75	4.00
b.	Booklet pane, #2476-2480	5.25	—
	Complete booklet	45.00	
	Nos. 2476-2480 (5)	4.00	3.50

Booklet Stamps

Self-Adhesive

Serpentine Die Cut 11¼ Syncopated

2481 A702	50c multi	.75	.75
2482 A702	50c multi	.75	.75
2483 A702	50c multi	.75	.75
a.	Booklet pane, 4 #2481, 3 each #2482-2483	9.00	

2484 A702	50c multi	.75	.75
2485 A703	50c multi	.75	.75
a.	Booklet pane, 5 each #2484-2485	9.00	
	Nos. 2481-2485 (5)	3.75	3.75

Edna Everage, stage character played by Barry Humphries.

No. 2480b issued 1/24/07. Complete booklet, which sold for $22.95, contains Nos. 1576b, 1634m, 1634n, 1634o, 1720b, 1803b, 1934b, 2025b, 2128b, 2208b, 2324b, 2326b, 2328b, and 2480b.

Rose A704

2006, Jan. 27 Litho.	**Perf. 14x14¾**	
2486 A704	50c multi	1.00 1.00

With White Border

Self-Adhesive

Litho. & Typo.

Serpentine Die Cut 11¼ Syncopated

2487 A704	50c multi	1.60 1.60

Booklet Stamp

Litho.

2488 A704	50c multi	1.00 1.00
a.	Booklet pane of 10	10.00

No. 2487 has a scratch-and-sniff area with a rose scent applied to the center of the rose, has a denomination composed of small black dots, and was printed in sheets of 10. No. 2488 lacks the scratch and sniff panel and has a solid gray denomination.

$1 australia
Pincushion Hakea
Flowers — A705

Designs: $1, Pincushion hakea. $2, Donkey orchid. $5, Mangles kangaroo paw. $10, Waratah.

2006, Feb. 7	**Litho.**	**Perf.**	**14x14½**
2489 A705	$1 multi	2.00	1.40
2490 A705	$2 multi	3.25	2.50

Perf. 14½x14

Size:50x30mm

2491 A705	$5 multi	7.75	6.50
2492 A705	$10 multi	15.50	13.00
	Nos. 2489-2492 (4)	28.50	23.40

Souvenir Sheet

Litho. & Embossed

2493 A705	$10 multi	20.00 20.00

50c
Freestyle Skiing: Men's Moguls
AUSTRALIA TORINO 2006
Dale Begg-Smith, Men's Moguls Gold Medalist at 2006 Winter Olympics, Turin — A706

2006, Feb. 15	**Litho.**	**Perf.**	**14½**
2494 A706	50c multi	2.75	2.00

5c
International POST
AUSTRALIA
PLATYPUS
Animals A707

Royal Exhibition
Building,
Melbourne — A708

Designs: 2495, 5c, Platypus. 2496, 25c, Short-beaked echidna. No. 2497, $1.25, Common wombat. Nos. 2498, $1.25, Koala, vert. No. 2499, $1.85, Tasmanian devil. 2501, $2.50, Greater bilby. 2502, $3.70, Dingo.

2006		Perf. 14x14¾, 14¾x14	
2495	A707	5c multi	.25 .25
2496	A707	25c multi	.50 .35
2497	A707	$1.25 multi	2.00 2.00
2498	A707	$1.25 multi	2.50 2.50
a.		Souvenir sheet of 1, with China 2006 emblem and Great Wall of China in sheet margin	2.25 2.25
b.		As "a," with Sydney landmarks in sheet margin	2.25 2.25
2499	A707	$1.85 multi	3.25 3.25
2500	A708	$1.85 multi	3.75 3.75
2501	A707	$2.50 multi	4.00 4.00
2502	A707	$3.70 multi	6.50 6.50
		Nos. 2495-2502 (8)	22.75 22.60

Self-Adhesive
Booklet Stamps
Serpentine Die Cut 11¼ Syncopated

2503	A707	$1.25 multi	2.50 2.50
a.		Booklet pane of 5	12.75
b.		Booklet pane of 2	5.75
c.		Complete booklet, 4 #2503b	23.00
		As "a," with Washington 2000 Exhib. emblem added to lower right margin of bklt. pane	13.75
2504	A708	$1.85 multi	3.75 3.75
a.		Booklet pane of 5	19.00
b.		Booklet pane of 2	7.50
		Complete booklet, 4 #2504b	30.00

Issued: Nos. 2498, 2500, 2503, 2504, 5/2; No. 2503c, 5/27; others, 3/6.
Each of the four panes of Nos. 2503b and 2504b in the complete booklets have different margins. The complete booklet containing No. 2503b sold for $12.95; the booklet containing No. 2504b sold for $14.95.
Nos. 2498a-2498b issued 10/26.
See Nos. 2542-2543, 2674, 2676, 2678, 5010.

Queen Elizabeth II, 80th Birthday
A709   A710

2006, Apr. 19		Perf. 14¾x14	
2505	A709	50c multi	1.00 1.00
a.		Booklet pane of 2	2.00
b.		Dated "2010"	2.00 1.00
2506	A710	$2.45 multi	4.75 4.75
a.		Booklet pane of 2	10.00
b.		Booklet pane of #2505-2506, 153x104mm pane size	6.00
		Complete booklet, #2506a, 2506b, 2 #2505a	20.00
c.		Souvenir sheet, #2505-2506, 105x70mm sheet size	6.50 6.50

Self-Adhesive
Booklet Stamp
Serpentine Die Cut 11¼ Syncopated

2507	A709	50c multi	1.00 .75
a.		Booklet pane of 10	10.00

Complete booklet containing Nos. 2505-2506 sold for $10.95.

A booklet commemorating royal visits to Australia containing a booklet pane of 2 each of lithographed, perf. 14x14¾ example of Nos. 474-475, a booklet pane of 4 lithographed, perf. 14x14¾ examples of No. 779, a booklet pane of 2 each of lithographed perf. 14½x14 examples of Nos. 659-660, a booklet pane of 2 each Nos. 2031-2032, a booklet pane of No. 2234a with a different margin, a booklet pane of 2 each of perf. 14½x14 examples of Nos. 351-352 (not valid for postage), and a 50c coin was released in 2006. It sold for $15.95.

Lighthouses
A711

Designs: Nos. 2508, 2513, Point Lonsdale Lighthouse, Victoria. Nos. 2509, 2514, Cape Don Lighthouse, Northern Territory. Nos. 2510, 2515, Wollongong Head Lighthouse, New South Wales. Nos. 2511, 2516, Casuarina Point Lighthouse, Western Australia. Nos. 2512, 2517, Point Cartwright Lighthouse, Queensland.

2006, May 2		Perf. 14¾x14	
2508	A711	50c multi	.80 .70
2509	A711	50c multi	.80 .70
2510	A711	50c multi	.80 .70
a.		Booklet pane, #2509, 2510, 2 #2508	4.25 —
b.		Booklet pane, #2508, 2509, 2 #2510	4.25 —
2511	A711	50c multi	.80 .70
2512	A711	50c multi	.80 .70
a.		Horiz. strip, #2508-2512	4.50 4.50
b.		Booklet pane, #2511, 2512, 2 #2509	4.25 —
c.		Booklet pane, #2510, 2512, 2 #2511	4.25 —
d.		Booklet pane, #2508, 2511, 2 #2512	4.25 —
		Complete booklet, #2510a, 2510b, 2512b, 2512c, 2512d	20.00
		Nos. 2508-2512 (5)	4.00 3.50

Coil Stamps
Self-Adhesive
Serpentine Die Cut 11¼ Syncopated

2513	A711	50c multi	.75 .75
2514	A711	50c multi	.75 .75
2515	A711	50c multi	.75 .75
2516	A711	50c multi	.75 .75
2517	A711	50c multi	.75 .75
a.		Vert. strip, #2513-2517	5.75

Complete booklet sold for $10.95.

2006 World Cup Soccer
Championships, Germany — A712

Soccer player, 2006 World Cup emblem and word: Nos. 2518, 2522, "Play." Nos. 2519, 2523, "Goal." $1.25, "Save." $1.85, "Shot."

2006, May 9		Perf. 14x14¾	
2518	A712	50c multi	.80 .70
2519	A712	50c multi	.80 .70
a.		Horiz. pair, #2518-2519	2.25 2.25
2520	A712	$1.25 multi	1.90 1.75
2521	A712	$1.85 multi	3.00 3.00
a.		Souvenir sheet, #2518-2521	8.00 8.00
b.		As "a," with 2006 Paris Exhib. ovpt.	9.25 9.25
		Nos. 2518-2521 (4)	6.50 6.15

Booklet Stamps
Self-Adhesive
Serpentine Die Cut 11¼ Syncopated

2522	A712	50c multi	1.00 .75
2523	A712	50c multi	1.00 .75
a.		Booklet pane, 5 each #2522-2523	11.00

No. 2521b issued 6/17.

Postie
Kate — A713

Kate: Nos. 2524, 2529, Writing address on letter. Nos. 2525, 2530, On motorcycle, delivering letter. Nos. 2526, 2531, With van, delivering package. Nos. 2527, 2532, Riding motorcycle in rain. Nos. 2528, 2533, Waving.

2006, June 1		Litho.	Perf. 14x14¾	
2524	A713	50c multi	.75 .60
a.		Booklet pane of 1	1.75
2525	A713	50c multi	.75 .60
a.		Booklet pane of 1	1.75
2526	A713	50c multi	.75 .60
a.		Booklet pane of 1	1.75
2527	A713	50c multi	.75 .60
a.		Booklet pane of 1	1.75
2528	A713	50c multi	.75 .60
a.		Horiz. strip of 5, #2524-2528	4.00 3.60
b.		Booklet pane of 1	1.75 —
		Nos. 2524-2528 (5)	3.75 3.00

Booklet Stamps
Self-Adhesive
Serpentine Die Cut 11¼ Syncopated

2529	A713	50c multi	1.00 .60
2530	A713	50c multi	1.00 .60
2531	A713	50c multi	1.00 .60
2532	A713	50c multi	1.00 .60
2533	A713	50c multi	1.00 .60
a.		Booklet pane, 2 each #2529-2533	11.00
b.		Booklet pane, 4 each #2529-2533	20.00
c.		Booklet pane, #2529-2533 Complete booklet, #2524a, 2525a, 2526a, 2527a, 2528b, 2533c	5.00 20.00
		Nos. 2529-2533 (5)	5.00 3.00

Complete booklet sold for $9.95.

Worldwide
Fund for
Nature
(WWF)
A714

Designs: Nos. 2534, 2538, Humpback whale. Nos. 2535, 2539, Blue whale. $1.25, Fin whale. $1.85, Southern bottlenose whale.

2006, June 6		Perf. 14x14¾	
2534	A714	50c multi	.75 .60
2535	A714	50c multi	.75 .60
a.		Horiz. pair, #2534-2535	2.00 2.00
2536	A714	$1.25 multi	2.50 2.50
2537	A714	$1.85 multi	3.00 3.00
a.		Souvenir sheet, #2534-2537	6.00 5.25
		Nos. 2534-2537 (4)	7.00 6.70

Self-Adhesive
Serpentine Die Cut 11¼ Syncopated
Coil Stamps

2538	A714	50c multi	1.10 .95
2539	A714	50c multi	1.10 .95
a.		Horiz. pair, #2538-2539	2.25

Booklet Stamps

2540	A714	$1.25 multi	6.50 6.50
a.		Booklet pane of 5	32.50
2541	A714	$1.85 multi	7.25 7.25
a.		Booklet pane of 5	37.50
		Nos. 2538-2541 (4)	15.95 15.65

Types of 2006 With Personalized Photo at Right Like Type A692a

Designs: $1.25, Koala. $1.85, Royal Exhibition Building.

Serpentine Die Cut 11½x11¼ Syncopated

2006		Litho.	
		Self-Adhesive	
2542	A707	$1.25 multi	8.00 8.00
2543	A708	$1.85 multi	12.00 12.00

Nos. 2542-2543 were sold in sheets of 20 and have personalized pictures and a straight edge at right, and lack separations between the stamp and the pictures. Sheets of 20 of No. 2542 sold for $38, and of No. 2543, $49.

Extreme
Sports
A715

Designs: 50c, Surfing. $1, Snowboarding. $1.45, Skateboarding. $2, Freestyle motocross.

2006, July 18		Litho.	Perf. 14x14¾	
2544	A715	50c multi	.75 .70
2545	A715	$1 multi	1.50 1.25
2546	A715	$1.45 multi	2.50 2.50
2547	A715	$2 multi	3.25 3.25
		Nos. 2544-2547 (4)	8.00 7.70

Cars and
Trucks
A716

Designs: Nos. 2548, 2553, 1917 Ford TT Truck. Nos. 2549, 2554, 1956 Holden FE. Nos. 2550, 2555, 1961 Morris 850. Nos. 2551, 2556, 1976 Holden Sandman HX. Nos. 2552, 2557, 1985 Toyota Land Cruiser FJ60.

2006, Aug. 15		Perf. 14x14¾	
2548	A716	50c multi	.75 .70
a.		Booklet pane of 4	3.50 —
2549	A716	50c multi	.75 .70
a.		Booklet pane of 4	3.50
2550	A716	50c multi	.75 .70
a.		Booklet pane of 4	3.50
2551	A716	50c multi	.75 .70
a.		Booklet pane of 4	3.50
2552	A716	50c multi	.75 .70
a.		Booklet pane of 4	3.50
		Complete booklet, #2548a-2552a	18.00
b.		Horiz. strip of 5, #2548-2552	4.75 4.00
		Nos. 2548-2552 (5)	3.75 3.50

Booklet Stamps
Self-Adhesive
Serpentine Die Cut 11¼ Syncopated

2553	A716	50c multi	.90 .70
a.		Booklet pane of 10	11.00
b.		Missing 2006 date	
2554	A716	50c multi	.90 .70
a.		Booklet pane of 10	11.00
2555	A716	50c multi	.90 .70
a.		Booklet pane of 10	11.00
2556	A716	50c multi	.90 .70
a.		Booklet pane of 10	11.00
2557	A716	50c multi	.90 .70
a.		Booklet pane of 10	11.00
b.		Booklet pane, 2 each #2553-2557	16.00
		Nos. 2553-2557 (5)	4.50 3.50

Complete booklet containing Nos. 2548a-2552a sold for $10.95.

Rock
Posters — A717

Designs: Nos. 2558a, 2559a, Sunbury Rock Festival, 1972. Nos. 2558b, 2559b, Magic Dirt Tour, 2002. Nos. 2558c, 2559c, The Masters Apprentices Parramatta concert, 1972. Nos. 2558d, 2559d, Goanna's Spirit of Place album, 1983. Nos. 2558e, 2559e, Angels, Sports and Paul Kelly and the Dots Latrobe concert, 1979. Nos. 2558f, 2559f, Midnight Oil, 1979. Nos. 2558g, 2559g, Big Day Out Festival, 2003. Nos. 2558h, 2559h, Apollo Bay Music Festival, 1999. Nos. 2558i, 2559i, Rolling Stones Australian Tour, 1973. Nos. 2558j, 2559j, Mental as Anything's Another Falcon Tour, 1990.

2006, Sept. 12		Litho.	Perf. 14½x14	
2558		Sheet of 10	16.00 16.00
a.-j.		A717 50c Any single	.95 .95
k.		Booklet pane of 2 #2558a	2.25 —
l.		Booklet pane of 2 #2558b	2.25 —
m.		Booklet pane of 2 #2558c	2.25 —
n.		Booklet pane of 2 #2558d	2.25 —
o.		Booklet pane of 2 #2558e	2.25 —
p.		Booklet pane of 2 #2558f	2.25 —
q.		Booklet pane of 2 #2558g	2.25 —
r.		Booklet pane of 2 #2558h	2.25 —
s.		Booklet pane of 2 #2558i	2.25 —
t.		Booklet pane of 2 #2558j	2.25 —
		Complete booklet, #2558k-2558t	22.00

Self-Adhesive
Serpentine Die Cut 11½x11¼ Syncopated

2559		Booklet pane of 10	16.00
a.-j.		A717 50c Any single	1.00 1.00

Complete booklet containing Nos. 2558t-2558t sold for $10.95.

Dangerous
Australian
Wildlife
A718

Designs: Nos. 2560, 2566, White shark.
Nos. 2561, 2567, Eastern brown snake. Nos.
2562, 2568, Box jellyfish. Nos. 2563, 2569,
Saltwater crocodile. Nos. 2564, 2570, Blue-
ringed octopus. Nos. 2565, 2571, Yellow-bellied sea snake.

2006, Oct. 3   Litho.   Perf. 14x14¾

2560	A718	50c multi	1.00	.70
a.		Booklet pane of 2	2.25	—
2561	A718	50c multi	1.00	.70
a.		Booklet pane of 2	2.25	—
2562	A718	50c multi	1.00	.70
a.		Booklet pane of 2	2.25	—
2563	A718	50c multi	1.00	.70
a.		Booklet pane of 2	2.25	—
2564	A718	50c multi	1.00	.70
a.		Horiz. strip of 5, #2560-2564	5.00	5.00
b.		Booklet pane of 2	2.25	—
2565	A718	$1 multi	1.90	1.90
a.		Booklet pane, 2 each #2561, 2565	6.50	—
b.		Booklet pane, #2560-2565 (page 26)	7.50	—
c.		Souvenir sheet, #2560a, 2562a, 2563a, 2564b, 2565a, 2565b	7.75	7.75
			25.00	
		Nos. 2560-2565 (6)	6.90	5.40

Self-Adhesive

Serpentine Die Cut 11 Syncopated

2566	A718	50c multi	1.00	.70
2567	A718	50c multi	1.00	.70
2568	A718	50c multi	1.00	.70
2569	A718	50c multi	1.00	.70
2570	A718	50c multi	1.00	.70
a.		Horiz. coil strip of 5, #2566-2570	5.75	
b.		Booklet pane, #2566-2570	7.00	
2571	A718	$1 multi	1.75	1.75
a.		Booklet pane of 5	9.00	
		Nos. 2566-2571 (6)	6.75	5.25

Complete booklet sold for $10.95. A souve-
nir sheet similar to No. 2565c containing partially perforated examples of Nos. 2560-2564
and a stamp that is assumed to be invalid
depicting a red-back spider sold for $9.95.
Value $25.

Television in
Australia,
50th Anniv.
A719

Television shows: Nos. 2572, 2577, IMT (In
Melbourne Tonight). Nos. 2573, 2578, Homi-
cide. Nos. 2574, 2579, Dateline. Nos. 2575,
2580, Neighbours. Nos. 2576, 2581, Kath &
Kim.

2006, Oct. 24   Litho.   Perf. 14x14¾

2572	A719	50c multi	.75	.60
2573	A719	50c multi	.75	.60
2574	A719	50c multi	.75	.60
2575	A719	50c multi	.75	.60
2576	A719	50c multi	.75	.60
a.		Horiz. strip of 5, #2572-2576	4.50	4.50
		Nos. 2572-2576 (5)	3.75	3.00

Self-Adhesive

Serpentine Die Cut 11¼x11½ Syncopated

2577	A719	50c multi	.90	.30
a.		Booklet pane of 10 #2577	9.00	
2578	A719	50c multi	.90	.30
2579	A719	50c multi	.90	.30
2580	A719	50c multi	.90	.30
2581	A719	50c multi	.90	.30
a.		Booklet pane of 10 #2581	9.25	
b.		Booklet pane of 10, 2 each #2577-2581	9.25	
c.		Horiz. coil strip of 5, #2577-2581	5.25	
		Nos. 2577-2581 (5)	4.50	1.50

Melbourne
Summer
Olympics,
50th Anniv.
A720

1956 Melbourne Olympics emblem and: No.
2582, Australia #291, Olympic torch. No.
2583, View of Melbourne across Yarra River,
2006, Olympic torch. No. 2584, Australia
#290, runners. No. 2585, Collins Street, Mel-
bourne, 2006, runners.

2006, Nov. 1   Perf. 14¾x14

2582	A720	50c multi	.90	.70
2583	A720	50c multi	.90	.70
a.		Horiz. pair, #2582-2583	2.00	2.00
2584	A720	$1 multi	1.90	1.20
2585	A720	$1 multi	1.90	1.20
a.		Horiz. pair, #2584-2585	4.80	2.75
		Nos. 2582-2585 (4)	5.60	3.80

Christmas — A721

Designs: 45c, Madonna and Child. 50c,
Magus with gift. $1.05, Shepherd and lamb.

2006, Nov. 1   Perf. 14¾x14

2586	A721	45c multi	.80	.40
2587	A721	50c multi	.80	.50
2588	A721	$1.05 multi	1.60	1.60
		Nos. 2586-2588 (3)	3.20	2.50

Self-Adhesive

Booklet Stamps

Serpentine Die Cut 11½x11¼ Syncopated

2589	A721	45c multi	.80	.30
a.		Booklet pane of 20	16.00	
2590	A721	$1.05 multi	1.90	.30
a.		Booklet pane of 5	9.25	

Australian Victory
in 2006 Ashes
Cricket
Match — A722

Designs: 50c, Players celebrating. $1.85,
Players with Ashes Urn.

2007, Jan. 16   Litho.   Perf. 14½x14

2591	A722	50c multi	.75	.65
a.		Imperf.	2.00	2.00
2592	A722	$1.85 multi	2.75	2.40
a.		Souvenir sheet, #2591-2592	4.50	4.50
b.		Imperf.	15.00	12.00
c.		Booklet pane of 2, #2591a, 2592b	7.50	—
		Complete booklet, #591a, 666b, 773a, 1084a, 1302b, 2345a, 2592c	32.00	

Booklet Stamps

Self-Adhesive

Serpentine Die Cut 10¾x11¼ Syncopated

2593	A722	50c multi	1.50	.75
a.		Booklet pane of 5	7.50	
2594	A722	$1.85 multi	5.00	2.50
a.		Booklet pane of 5	25.00	
		Nos. 2591-2594 (4)	10.00	6.30

Nos. 2591a, 2592b, 2592c issued 11/14/07.
Complete booklet sold for $14.95 and was not
made available to foreign addresses.

Horse Racing
Personalities
A723

Designs: Nos. 2595, 2607, Scobie Breasley,
jockey, in silks. No. 2596, Breasley on horse.
Nos. 2597, 2608, Bart Cummings, horse
trainer, with binoculars. No. 2598, Cummings
holding trophy. No. 2599, Roy Higgins, jockey,
in silks. Nos. 2600, 2609, Higgins on horse.
No. 2601, Bob Ingham, horse breeder. Nos.
2602, 2610, Ingham with horse. Nos. 2603,
2611, George Moore, jockey, in silks. No.
2604, Moore on horse. Nos. 2605, 2612, John
Tapp, horse race announcer. No. 2606, Tapp
with binoculars.

2007, Jan. 24   Perf. 14½x14

2595	A723	50c multi	.90	.75
2596	A723	50c multi	.90	.75
2597	A723	50c multi	.90	.75
2598	A723	50c multi	.90	.75
a.		Block of 4, #2595-2598	3.75	3.00
2599	A723	50c multi	.90	.75
2600	A723	50c multi	.90	.75
2601	A723	50c multi	.90	.75
2602	A723	50c multi	.90	.75
a.		Block of 4, #2599-2602	3.75	3.00
2603	A723	50c multi	.90	.75
2604	A723	50c multi	.90	.75
2605	A723	50c multi	.90	.75
2606	A723	50c multi	.90	.75
a.		Block of 4, #2603-2606	3.75	3.00
		Nos. 2595-2606 (12)	10.80	9.00

Booklet Stamps

Self-Adhesive

Serpentine Die Cut 11x11¼ Syncopated

2607	A723	50c multi	.90	.30
2608	A723	50c multi	.90	.30
a.		Booklet pane of 10, 5 each #2607-2608	9.25	
2609	A723	50c multi	.90	.30
2610	A723	50c multi	.90	.30
a.		Booklet pane of 10, 5 each #2609-2610	9.25	
2611	A723	50c multi	.90	.30
2612	A723	50c multi	.90	.30
a.		Booklet pane of 10, 5 each #2611-2612	9.25	
		Nos. 2607-2612 (6)	5.40	1.80

Flowers — A724

Designs: Nos. 2613, 2617, 2621, Tasma-
nian Christmas bell. Nos. 2614, 2618, 2622,
Green spider flower. Nos. 2615, 2619, 2623,
Sturt's desert rose. Nos. 2616, 2620, 2624,
Phebalium whitei.

2007, Feb. 13   Litho.   Perf. 14x14½

2613	A724	50c multi	.90	.40
2614	A724	50c multi	.90	.40
2615	A724	50c multi	.90	.40
2616	A724	50c multi	.90	.40
a.		Horiz. strip of 4, #2613-2616	3.75	3.00
		Nos. 2613-2616 (4)	3.60	1.60

Self-Adhesive

Serpentine Die Cut 11¼

2617	A724	50c multi	.90	.30
2618	A724	50c multi	.90	.30
2619	A724	50c multi	.90	.30
2620	A724	50c multi	.90	.30
a.		Horiz. coil strip of 4, #2617-2620	3.75	
b.		Booklet pane of 10, 3 each #2617-2618, 2 each #2619-2620	9.25	
c.		Booklet pane of 20, 5 each #2617-2620	18.50	

Coil Stamps

Die Cut Perf. 12¾

2621	A724	50c multi	.90	.30
2622	A724	50c multi	.90	.30
2623	A724	50c multi	.90	.30
2624	A724	50c multi	.90	.30
a.		Horiz. strip of 4, #2621-2624	3.75	
		Nos. 2617-2624 (8)	7.20	2.40

12th FINA World
Swimming
Championships,
Melbourne — A725

2007, Feb. 20   Perf. 14½x14

2625	A725	50c multi	1.00	1.00

Coil Stamp

Self-Adhesive

Serpentine Die Cut 11¼ Syncopated

2626	A725	50c multi	1.10	.30

Islands
A726

Designs: 10c, Maria Island, Tasmania. 30c,
Rottnest Island, Western Australia. $1.30,
Green Island, Queensland. $1.95, Fraser
Island, Queensland. $2.60, Kangaroo Island,
South Australia. $3.85, Lord Howe Island, New
South Wales.

2007, Mar. 5   Perf. 14x14½

2627	A726	10c multi	.25	.25
2628	A726	30c multi	.60	.30
2629	A726	$1.30 multi	2.25	1.60
2630	A726	$1.95 multi	3.50	2.40
2631	A726	$2.60 multi	4.50	2.25
2632	A726	$3.85 multi	7.00	3.50
		Nos. 2627-2632 (6)	18.10	10.30

Booklet Stamps

Self-Adhesive

Serpentine Die Cut 11¼ Syncopated

2633	A726	$1.30 multi	2.25	.30
a.		Booklet pane of 5	30.00	
2634	A726	$1.95 multi	3.50	.30
a.		Booklet pane of 5	40.00	

Surf Life
Saving
Australia,
Cent.
A727

Designs: Nos. 2635, 2639, Female lifeguard. Nos. 2636, 2640, Male lifeguards. $1,
Surf boat crew. $2, Nippers (junior lifeguards).
$2.45, Inflatable rescue boat and crew, vert.
(30x50mm).

2007, Mar. 6   Litho.   Perf. 14x14½

2635	A727	50c multi	.90	.90
a.		Booklet pane of 1	1.25	—
2636	A727	50c multi	.90	.90
a.		Horiz. pair, #2635-2636	1.90	1.90
b.		Booklet pane of 1	1.25	—
2637	A727	$1 multi	1.90	1.40
a.		Booklet pane of 1	2.50	—
2638	A727	$2 multi	3.75	2.75
a.		Booklet pane of 1	5.25	—
		Nos. 2635-2638 (4)	7.45	5.95

Self-Adhesive

Coil Stamps (#2639-2640)

Serpentine Die Cut 11¼ Syncopated

2639	A727	50c multi	.90	.30
2640	A727	50c multi	.90	.30
a.		Horiz. pair, #2639-2640	1.90	

Litho. With Three-Dimensional Plastic Affixed

2641	A727	$2.45 multi	4.25	4.25
a.		Souvenir sheet of 2	8.50	
b.		Booklet pane, as "a," with rouletting at left of pane	12.50	
		Complete booklet, #2635a, 2636b, 2637a, 2638a, 2641b	23.00	

Complete booklet sold for $12.95. No.
2641a does not have rouletting at left side of
sheet.

Signs of the
Zodiac — A728

Designs: Nos. 2642, 2654, 2665B, Aries.
Nos. 2643, 2655, 2665C, Taurus. Nos. 2644,
2656, 2665D, Gemini. Nos. 2645, 2657,
2665E, Cancer. Nos. 2646, 2658, 2665F, Leo.
Nos. 2647, 2659, 2665G, Virgo. Nos. 2648,
2660, 2665H, Libra. Nos. 2649, 2661, 2665I,
Scorpio. Nos. 2650, 2662, 2665J, Sagittarius.
Nos. 2651, 2663, 2665K, Capricorn. Nos.
2652, 2664, 2665L, Aquarius. Nos. 2653,
2665, 2665M, Pisces.

2007, Apr. 3   Litho.   Perf. 14½x14

2642	A728	50c multi	.95	.95
2643	A728	50c multi	.95	.95
2644	A728	50c multi	.95	.95
2645	A728	50c multi	.95	.95
a.		Block of 4, #2642-2645	4.00	
2646	A728	50c multi	.95	.95
2647	A728	50c multi	.95	.95
2648	A728	50c multi	.95	.95
2649	A728	50c multi	.95	.95
a.		Block of 4, #2646-2649	4.00	
2650	A728	50c multi	.95	.95
2651	A728	50c multi	.95	.95
2652	A728	50c multi	.95	.95
2653	A728	50c multi	.95	.95
a.		Block of 4, #2650-2653	4.00	
		Nos. 2642-2653 (12)	11.40	11.40

Booklet Stamps

Self-Adhesive

Serpentine Die Cut 11¼ Syncopated

2654	A728	50c multi	1.00	.30
a.		Booklet pane of 10	10.50	
2655	A728	50c multi	1.00	.30
a.		Booklet pane of 10	10.50	

2656	A728	50c multi	1.00	.30
a.		Booklet pane of 10	10.50	
2657	A728	50c multi	1.00	.30
a.		Booklet pane of 10	10.50	
2658	A728	50c multi	1.00	.30
a.		Booklet pane of 10	10.50	
2659	A728	50c multi	1.00	.30
a.		Booklet pane of 10	10.50	
2660	A728	50c multi	1.00	.30
a.		Booklet pane of 10	10.50	
2661	A728	50c multi	1.00	.30
a.		Booklet pane of 10	10.50	
2662	A728	50c multi	1.00	.30
a.		Booklet pane of 10	10.50	
2663	A728	50c multi	1.00	.30
a.		Booklet pane of 10	10.50	
2664	A728	50c multi	1.00	.30
a.		Booklet pane of 10	10.50	
2665	A728	50c multi	1.00	.30
a.		Booklet pane of 10	10.50	
		Nos. 2654-2665 (12)	12.00	3.60

With Personalized Photo at Right Like Type A692a
Serpentine Die Cut 11½x11¼
Syncopated
Self-Adhesive

2665B	A728	50c multi	2.50	*2.50*
2665C	A728	50c multi	2.50	*2.50*
2665D	A728	50c multi	2.50	*2.50*
2665E	A728	50c multi	2.50	*2.50*
2665F	A728	50c multi	2.50	*2.50*
2665G	A728	50c multi	2.50	*2.50*
2665H	A728	50c multi	2.50	*2.50*
2665I	A728	50c multi	2.50	*2.50*
2665J	A728	50c multi	2.50	*2.50*
2665K	A728	50c multi	2.50	*2.50*
2665L	A728	50c multi	2.50	*2.50*
2665M	A728	50c multi	2.50	*2.50*
		Nos. 2665B-2665M (12)	30.00	*30.00*

Nos. 2665B-2665M were sold in sheets of 20 and have personalized pictures and a straight edge at right, and lack separations between the stamp and the pictures. Sheets of 20 of Nos. 2665B-2665M each sold for $23.

Travel Posters of the 1930s — A729

Designs: 50c, At the Beach, by Percy Trompf. $1, Fishing, by John Vickery. $2, Riding in the Country, by James Northfield. $2.45, Winter Sport, by Northfield.

2007, Apr. 10   Perf. 14½x14

2666	A729	50c multi	.95	.95
2667	A729	$1 multi	2.00	1.60
a.		Booklet pane of 2, #2666-2667	3.25	—
2668	A729	$2 multi	4.00	3.00
2669	A729	$2.45 multi	5.00	3.75
a.		Booklet pane of 4, #2666-2669	12.00	—
b.		Booklet pane of 2, #2666, 2669	6.00	—
		Complete booklet #2667a, 2669a, 2669b	21.00	
		Nos. 2666-2669 (4)	11.95	9.10

Queen Elizabeth II, 81st Birthday A730

2007, Apr. 18   Perf. 14x14½

2670	A730	50c multi	.95	.75

Shipwrecks A731

Designs: 50c, Admella, 1859. $1, Loch Ard, 1878. $2, Dunbar, 1857.

2007, May 1   Litho.   Perf. 14x14½

2671	A731	50c multi	.95	.70
2672	A731	$1 multi	2.00	1.60
2673	A731	$2 multi	4.00	3.25
		Nos. 2671-2673 (3)	6.95	5.55

Animals Type of 2006 and

Sydney Harbour Bridge — A732

Design: $1.30, Yellow-footed rock wallaby, vert.

2007   Litho.   Perf. 14½x14

2674	A707	$1.30 multi	2.50	2.50
2675	A732	$1.95 multi	3.75	3.75
a.		Imperf. x perf. 14 x imperf. x imperf.	3.75	3.75
b.		Souvenir sheet, #2675, 2675a	7.50	7.50
c.		Souvenir sheet, 2 #2675	7.75	7.75
d.		As "b," with Sberatel Exhib., Prague ovpt.	9.75	9.75
e.		As "c," with Bangkok 2007 Exhib. ovpt.	9.75	9.75

Self-Adhesive
Booklet Stamps
Serpentine Die Cut 11¼ Syncopated

2676	A707	$1.30 multi	3.25	3.25
a.		Booklet pane of 2	6.25	
		Complete booklet, 4 #2676a	25.00	
2677	A732	$1.95 multi	4.00	4.00
a.		Booklet pane of 1	4.00	
b.		Booklet pane of 2	8.00	
		Complete booklet, #2677a, 3 #2677b	29.00	

With Personalized Photo at Right Like Type A692a
Serpentine Die Cut 11½x11¼

2678	A707	$1.30 multi	4.50	4.50
2679	A732	$1.95 multi	5.75	5.75

Issued: Nos. 2674-2679, 5/8; No. 2675b, 6/15. Complete booklet containing No. 2676 sold for $12.95. It contains four different examples of No. 2676a. The booklet containing No. 2677 sold for $14.95, and it contains three different examples of No. 2677b.

No. 2675c issued 6/15. Margin of No. 2675c is overprinted in gold with emblem for Sydney Philatelic Show.

Nos. 2678-2679 were sold in sheets of 20 and have personalized pictures and a straight edge at right, and lack separations between the stamp and the picture. A sheet of 20 of No. 2678 sold for $39; of No. 2679, $51.

Circus Performers — A733

Circus acts: Nos. 2680, 2685, 2690, Torch juggler. Nos. 2681, 2686, 2691, Contortionist. Nos. 2682, 2687, 2692, Trapeze artists. Nos. 2683, 2688, 2693, Acrobats. Nos. 2684, 2689, 2694, Human cannonball.

2007, May 15   Litho.   Perf. 14½x14

2680	A733	50c multi	.95	.95
2681	A733	50c multi	.95	.95
a.		Booklet pane of 2	2.50	—
2682	A733	50c multi	.95	.95
a.		Booklet pane of 2	2.50	—
2683	A733	50c multi	.95	.95
a.		Booklet pane of 2	2.50	—
2684	A733	50c multi	.95	.95
a.		Horiz. strip of 5, #2680-2684	5.00	5.00
b.		Booklet pane, #2680-2684	6.25	—
c.		Booklet pane, 2 each # 2680, 2684	5.25	—
		Nos. 2680-2684 (5)	4.75	4.75

Booklet Stamps
Self-Adhesive
Serpentine Die Cut 11¼ Syncopated

2685	A733	50c multi	1.10	.40
2686	A733	50c multi	1.10	.40
2687	A733	50c multi	1.10	.40
2688	A733	50c multi	1.10	.40
2689	A733	50c multi	1.10	.40
a.		Booklet pane, 2 each #2685-2689	11.50	

Litho. With Foil Application

2690	A733	50c multi	1.40	1.40
2691	A733	50c multi	1.40	1.40
2692	A733	50c multi	1.40	1.40
2693	A733	50c multi	1.40	1.40

2694	A733	50c multi	1.40	1.40
a.		Booklet pane, #2690-2694	7.25	
		Complete booklet, #2681a, 2682a, 2683a, 2684b, 2684c, 2694a	25.00	
		Nos. 2685-2694 (10)	12.50	9.00

Complete booklet sold for $12.95. Nos. 2690-2694 each have gold stars and a portion of stamp covered by varnish.

Tourist Attractions — A734

Designs: Nos. 2695, 2700, Big Guitar, Tamworth, New South Wales. Nos. 2696, 2701, Big Lobster, Kingston Southeast, South Australia. Nos. 2697, 2702, Big Banana, Coffs Harbour, New South Wales. Nos. 2698, 2703, Big Merino Sheep, Goulburn, New South Wales. Nos. 2699, 2704, Big Pineapple, Nambour, Queensland.

2007, June 5   Perf. 14½x14

2695	A734	50c multi	.95	.95
2696	A734	50c multi	.95	.95
2697	A734	50c multi	.95	.95
2698	A734	50c multi	.95	.95
2699	A734	50c multi	.95	.95
a.		Horiz. strip of 5, #2695-2699	5.00	5.00
		Nos. 2695-2699 (5)	4.75	4.75

Booklet Stamps
Self-Adhesive
Serpentine Die Cut 11¼ Syncopated

2700	A734	50c multi	1.10	.40
2701	A734	50c multi	1.10	.40
2702	A734	50c multi	1.10	.40
2703	A734	50c multi	1.10	.40
2704	A734	50c multi	1.10	.40
a.		Booklet pane, 2 each #2700-2704	11.50	
		Nos. 2700-2704 (5)	5.50	2.00

Endangered Animals — A735

Designs: No. 2705, Gray-headed flying fox. No. 2706, Mountain pygmy possum. $1.25, Flatback turtle, horiz. $1.30, Wandering albatross, horiz.

2007, June 26   Perf. 14½x14

2705	A735	50c multi	.95	.70
a.		Booklet pane of 2 #2705	2.25	
2706	A735	50c multi	.95	.70
a.		Horiz. pair, #2705-2706	2.00	1.40
b.		Booklet pane of 2 #2706	2.25	

Perf. 14x14½

2707	A735	$1.25 multi	2.40	1.90
a.		Booklet pane of 2	5.75	—
2708	A735	$1.30 multi	2.50	2.00
a.		Booklet pane of 2	6.00	—
		Complete booklet, #793c, 794b, 2705a, 2706b, 2707a, 2708a	23.00	

Complete booklet sold for $10.95.

Modern Architecture A736

Designs: No. 2709, Former ICI House, Melbourne. No. 2710, Academy of Science, Canberra. $1, Council House, Perth. $2.45, Sydney Opera House.

2007, July 10   Perf. 14x14¾

2709	A736	50c multi	.95	.70
2710	A736	50c multi	.95	.70
a.		Horiz. pair, #2709-2710	2.00	1.40
b.		Additionally dated "2013" (#2710c)	1.10	1.10
c.		Booklet pane of 2 #2710b	2.25	—

2711	A736	$1 multi	2.00	1.60
2712	A736	$2.45 multi	5.00	3.75
a.		Souvenir sheet, #2709-2712	9.00	9.00

Due to the arrangement of the stamps on No. 2712a, the left side of the top row of perfs on each of the stamps is perf. 14 and the right side of the top row is perf. 14¾.

No. 2712a exists imperf from a telephone drawing at a substantial premium over face value. Value for single souvenir sheet, $17.50.

Issued: Nos. 2710b, 2710c, 3/5/13. No. 2710c was issued in booklet along with Nos. 1939c, 2869e, 3107c, 3349b and 3877a.

Markets — A737

Designs: Nos. 2713, 2718, Queen Victoria Market, Melbourne. Nos. 2714, 2719, Rusty's Market, Cairns. Nos. 2715, 2720, Sydney Fish Market. Nos. 2716, 2721, Adelaide Central Market. Nos. 2717, 2722, Hume Murray Farmers Market, Albury Wodonga.

2007, July 24   Perf. 14½x14

2713	A737	50c multi	.95	.95
2714	A737	50c multi	.95	.95
2715	A737	50c multi	.95	.95
2716	A737	50c multi	.95	.95
2717	A737	50c multi	.95	.95
a.		Horiz. strip of 5, #2713-2717	5.00	5.00
		Nos. 2713-2717 (5)	4.75	4.75

Booklet Stamps
Self-Adhesive
Serpentine Die Cut 11¼ Syncopated

2718	A737	50c multi	1.10	.40
a.		Booklet pane of 10	11.50	
2719	A737	50c multi	1.10	.40
a.		Booklet pane of 10	11.50	
2720	A737	50c multi	1.10	.40
a.		Booklet pane of 10	11.50	
2721	A737	50c multi	1.10	.40
a.		Booklet pane of 10	11.50	
2722	A737	50c multi	1.10	.40
a.		Booklet pane of 10	11.50	
		Nos. 2718-2722 (5)	5.50	2.00

Asia-Pacific Economic Cooperation Forum, Sydney A738

2007, Aug. 28   Perf. 14x14½

2723	A738	50c multi	.95	.95

Coil Stamp
Self-Adhesive
Serpentine Die Cut 11¼x11½
Syncopated

2724	A738	50c multi	.95	.30

Special Air Service, 50th Anniv. A739

2007, Sept. 4   Perf. 14x14½

2725	A739	50c multi	.95	.75

This stamp exists with "SAS" insignia embossed with gold foil. This was a restricted issue sold at far more than face value by the Philatelic Bureau.

Botanical Gardens A740

Designs: Nos. 2726, 2731, Brisbane Botanic Gardens, Mt. Coot-tha. Nos. 2727, 2732, Kings Park and Botanic Gardens, Perth. Nos. 2728, 2733, Royal Botanic Gardens and Domain, Sydney. Nos. 2729, 2734, Royal

Botanic Gardens, Melbourne. Nos. 2730, 2735, Botanic Gardens of Adelaide.

2007, Sept. 12   *Perf. 14x14½*
2726	A740 50c multi	.95	.95
a.	Booklet pane of 4	4.25	—
2727	A740 50c multi	.95	.95
a.	Booklet pane of 4	4.25	—
2728	A740 50c multi	.95	.95
a.	Booklet pane of 4	4.25	—
2729	A740 50c multi	.95	.95
a.	Booklet pane of 4	4.25	—
2730	A740 50c multi	.95	.95
a.	Booklet pane of 4	4.25	—
	Complete booklet, #2726a-2730a	22.00	
b.	Horiz. strip of 5, #2726-2730	5.00	5.00
	Nos. 2726-2730 (5)	4.75	4.75

Self-Adhesive
Serpentine Die Cut 11¼x11½ Syncopated
2731	A740 50c multi	.95	.30
2732	A740 50c multi	.95	.30
2733	A740 50c multi	.95	.30
2734	A740 50c multi	.95	.30
2735	A740 50c multi	.95	.30
a.	Horiz. coil strip of 5, #2731-2735	5.00	
b.	Booklet pane of 20, 5 each #2731-2735, + 10 labels	19.50	
	Nos. 2731-2735 (5)	4.75	1.50

Complete booklet sold for $10.95.

Space Age, 50th Anniv. — A741

Designs: Nos. 2736, 2743, Sputnik, 1957. Nos. 2737, 2744, First space walk, 1965. Nos. 2738, 2745, First Moon walk, 1969. Nos. 2739, 2746, Voyager, 1977. Nos. 2740, 2747, International Space Station, 1998. No. 2741, 2742a, Hubble Space Telescope, 1990, horiz.

2007, Oct. 2   *Litho.*   *Perf. 14½x14*
2736	A741 50c multi	1.00	1.00
a.	Booklet pane of 2	2.40	—
2737	A741 50c multi	1.00	1.00
a.	Booklet pane of 2	2.40	—
2738	A741 50c multi	1.00	1.00
a.	Booklet pane of 2	2.40	—
2739	A741 50c multi	1.00	1.00
a.	Booklet pane of 2	2.40	—
2740	A741 50c multi	1.00	1.00
a.	Horiz. strip of 5, #2736-2740	5.25	5.25
b.	Booklet pane of 2	2.40	—
c.	Booklet pane of 5, #2736-2740	6.00	—
2741	A741 $1 multi, 50x30mm	2.25	2.25
a.	Booklet pane of 5	5.00	—
	Complete booklet, #2736a, 2737a, 2738a, 2739a, 2740b, 2740c, 2741a	23.00	
	Nos. 2736-2741 (6)	7.25	7.25

Souvenir Sheet
2742	Sheet of 6, #2736-2740, 2742a	7.50	7.50
a.	A741 $1 multi, 52x43mm	2.25	2.25

A souvenir sheet in the 50c denomination exists. It was sold in a restricted sale with a normal souvenir sheet and a coin at a price far in advance of face value.

Self-Adhesive
Booklet Stamps
Serpentine Die Cut 11¼ Syncopated
2743	A741 50c multi	1.00	.30
2744	A741 50c multi	1.00	.30
2745	A741 50c multi	1.00	.30
2746	A741 50c multi	1.00	.30
2747	A741 50c multi	1.00	.30
a.	Coil strip of 5, #2743-2747	5.25	
b.	Booklet pane, 2 each #2743-2747	10.00	
	Nos. 2743-2747 (5)	5.00	1.50

Complete booklet sold for $10.95.

Trailer Campers A742

People and trailer campers from: Nos. 2748, 2753, 1950s. Nos. 2749, 2754, 1960s. Nos. 2750, 2755, 1970s. Nos. 2751, 2756, 1980s. Nos. 2752, 2757, Today.

2007, Oct. 16   *Perf. 14x14½*
2748	A742 50c multi	1.10	1.10
a.	Booklet pane of 4	5.00	—

2749	A742 50c multi	1.10	1.10
a.	Booklet pane, 2 each #2748-2749	5.00	—
2750	A742 50c multi	1.10	1.10
a.	Booklet pane of 4	5.00	—
2751	A742 50c multi	1.10	1.10
a.	Booklet pane, 2 each #2750-2751	5.00	—
2752	A742 50c multi	1.10	1.10
a.	Horiz. strip of 5, #2748-2752	5.50	5.50
b.	Booklet pane of 4	5.00	—
	Complete booklet, #2748a, 2749a, 2750a, 2751a, 2752b	25.00	
	Nos. 2748-2752 (5)	5.50	5.50

Self-Adhesive
Booklet Stamps
Serpentine Die Cut 11¼ Syncopated
2753	A742 50c multi	1.10	.30
a.	Booklet pane of 10	11.00	—
2754	A742 50c multi	1.10	.30
a.	Booklet pane of 10	11.00	—
2755	A742 50c multi	1.10	.30
a.	Booklet pane of 10	11.00	—
2756	A742 50c multi	1.10	.30
a.	Booklet pane of 10	11.00	—
2757	A742 50c multi	1.10	.30
a.	Booklet pane of 10	11.00	—
b.	Booklet pane, 2 each #2753-2757	11.00	—
	Nos. 2753-2757 (5)	5.50	1.50

Complete booklet sold for $10.95.

Christmas — A743

Designs of past Australian Christmas stamps with original denominations removed: Nos. 2758, 2763, 2768, #669. Nos. 2759, 2764, 2769, #1195. Nos. 2760, 2765, #1567. Nos. 2761, 2766, #306, horiz. Nos. 2762, 2767, 2770, #931.

2007, Nov. 1   *Litho.*
Perf. 14½x14, 14x14½
2758	A743 45c multi	.95	.95
a.	Booklet pane of 4	4.25	—
2759	A743 45c multi	.95	.95
a.	Booklet pane of 4	4.25	—
2760	A743 45c multi	.95	.95
a.	Horiz. pair, #2759-2760	2.00	2.00
b.	Booklet pane of 4	4.25	—
2761	A743 50c multi	1.10	1.10
a.	Booklet pane of 2	2.25	—
2762	A740 50c multi	1.10	1.10
a.	Booklet pane of 1	2.50	—
	Nos. 2758-2762 (5)	6.35	6.35

Self-Adhesive
Serpentine Die Cut 11¼ Syncopated
2763	A743 45c multi	.95	.30
a.	With varnish block over stamp vignette	.95	.30
2764	A743 45c multi	.95	.30
a.	Booklet pane of 20	20.00	—
2765	A743 45c multi	.95	.95
a.	Booklet pane of 20	20.00	—
2766	A743 50c multi	1.10	1.10
a.	Booklet pane of 5	5.50	—
2767	A743 $1.10 multi	2.40	2.40
a.	Booklet pane of 5	12.00	—
b.	Souvenir sheet, #2763-2767	6.50	—
c.	Booklet pane, #2763-2767	7.00	—
	Complete booklet, #2758a, 2759a, 2760b, 2761a, 2762a, 2767c	25.00	
	Nos. 2763-2767 (5)	6.35	5.05

Complete booklet sold for $10.95. Size of No. 2767b is 156x100mm. Size of No. 2767c is 156x104mm.

With Personalized Photo at Right Like Type A692a
Serpentine Die Cut 11½x11¼ Syncopated
2768	A743 45c multi	2.40	2.40
2769	A743 45c multi	2.40	2.40
2770	A743 $1.10 multi	3.75	3.75
	Nos. 2768-2770 (3)	8.55	8.55

Nos. 2768-2770 were sold in sheets of 20 and have personalized pictures and a straight edge at right, and lack separations between the stamp and the pictures. Sheets of 20 of Nos. 2768 and 2769 sold for $22, and of No. 2770, $35.

A booklet titled "Behind the Stamp," which contained four panes, sold for $19.95. The panes were in two designs, one containing Nos. 740, 1164, 1193, 1891 and a litho. reproduction of No. 277, the other containing Nos. 400, 616-617, 882, 1063 and a reproduction of No. 367. The stamps within both panes were dated "2007" and the panes were either perforated at a different gauge than the original stamps or imperforate.

Red Rose — A744

2008, Jan. 15   *Litho.*   *Perf. 14*
2771	A744 50c multi	1.00	1.00

Litho. With Foil Application
Serpentine Die Cut 11¼ Syncopated
Self-Adhesive
2772	A744 50c multi	1.00	.30

Booklet Stamp
Litho.
2773	A744 50c multi	1.10	.30
a.	Booklet pane of 4	4.50	
	Complete booklet, 5 #2773a	22.50	

With Personalized Photo at Right Like Type A692a
Serpentine Die Cut 11½x11¼ Syncopated
2774	A744 50c multi	2.40	2.40

No. 2772 was printed in a sheet of 10 + 10 labels, having rose-scented scratch and sniff areas on the rose and the labels. No. 2773 lacks the scratch and sniff areas. The complete booklet, which sold for $10.95, contains five examples of No. 2773a, each with a different margin.

No. 2774 was sold in sheets of 20 for $23 and have personalized pictures and a straight edge at right, and lack separations between the stamp and the personalized photo.

Philanthropists A745

Designs: Nos. 2775, 2782, Dame Elisabeth Murdoch. Nos. 2776, 2781, Victor and Loti Smogron. Nos. 2777, 2780, Lady Mary Fairfax. Nos. 2778, 2779, Frank Lowy.

2008, Jan. 23   *Litho.*   *Perf. 14¾x14*
2775	A745 50c multi	1.25	1.25
2776	A745 50c multi	1.25	1.25
2777	A745 50c multi	1.25	1.25
2778	A745 50c multi	1.25	1.25
a.	Horiz. strip of 4, #2775-2778	5.00	5.00
	Nos. 2775-2778 (4)	5.00	5.00

Coil Stamps
Self-Adhesive
Serpentine Die Cut 11¼ Syncopated
2779	A745 50c multi	1.00	.30
2780	A745 50c multi	1.00	.30
2781	A745 50c multi	1.00	.30
2782	A745 50c multi	1.00	.30
a.	Vert. strip of 4, #2779-2782	4.00	
	Nos. 2779-2782 (4)	4.00	1.20

Organ and Tissue Donation — A746

2008, Feb. 5   *Perf. 14¾x14*
2783	A746 50c multi	1.10	1.10

Booklet Stamp
Self-Adhesive
Serpentine Die Cut 11¼ Syncopated
2784	A746 50c multi	1.10	.30
a.	Booklet pane of 10	11.00	

Scouting in Australia, Cent. A747

Australian Scouting emblem and: 50c, Four scouts near tent. $1.35, Scouts from various nations. $2, Lord Robert Baden-Powell.

2008, Feb. 19   *Perf. 14*
2785	A747 50c multi	1.10	1.10
2786	A747 $1.35 multi	2.75	2.75
2787	A747 $2 multi	4.25	4.25
a.	Perf. 14x14½	4.25	4.25
b.	Souvenir sheet, 2 #2787a	8.50	8.50
	Nos. 2785-2787 (3)	8.10	8.10

Self-Adhesive
Serpentine Die Cut 11¼ Syncopated
Coil Stamp
2788	A747 50c multi	1.10	.30

Booklet Stamps
2789	A747 $1.35 multi	2.75	1.40
a.	Booklet pane of 5	14.50	
2790	A747 $2 multi	4.25	2.25
a.	Booklet pane of 5	22.00	
	Nos. 2788-2790 (3)	8.10	3.95

Canberra Stamp Show (No. 2787b).

Gorges — A748

Designs: $1.35, Grose River Gorge, New South Wales. $2, Walpa Gorge, Northern Territory. $2.70, Katherine Gorge, Northern Territory, horiz. $4, Geikie Gorge, Western Australia.

2008, Mar. 3   *Litho.*   *Perf. 14*
2791	A748 $1.35 multi	2.75	2.75
2792	A748 $2 multi	4.25	4.25
2793	A748 $2.70 multi	5.75	2.75
2794	A748 $4 multi	8.50	4.25
	Nos. 2791-2794 (4)	21.25	14.00

Booklet Stamps (#2795-2796)
Self-Adhesive
Serpentine Die Cut 11½x11¼ Syncopated
2795	A748 $1.35 multi	7.50	5.00
a.	Booklet pane of 5	37.50	
b.	Booklet pane of 2	15.00	—
	Complete booklet, 4 #2795b	68.00	
2796	A748 $2 multi	9.00	7.50
a.	Booklet pane of 5	45.00	
b.	Booklet pane of 2	18.00	—
	Complete booklet, 4 #2796b	72.00	

With Personalized Photo at Right Like Type A692a
2797	A748 $1.35 multi	8.00	8.00
2798	A748 $2 multi	12.00	12.00

Nos. 2797-2798 each were sold in sheets of 20 and have personalized pictures and a straight edge at right, and lack separations between the stamp and the personalized photo. Sheets of 20 of No. 2797 sold for $40, and of No. 2798, $52.

Complete booklet containing No. 2795b sold for $10.95, and containing No. 2796b, $16.95. Each booklet contains four panes with differing margins.

World Youth Day — A749

Various depictions of Pope Benedict XVI with "08" in: 50c, Light blue. $1.35, Pink. $2, Light green.

2008, Mar. 4 — **Perf. 14**

2799	A749	50c multi	1.10	.85
2800	A749	$1.35 multi	2.75	2.75
2801	A749	$2 multi	4.25	4.25
		Nos. 2799-2801 (3)	8.10	7.85

Booklet Stamps (#2802-2803)

Self-Adhesive

Serpentine Die Cut 11½x11¼ Syncopated

2802	A749	$1.35 multi	4.75	.40
a.		Booklet pane of 5	22.50	
2803	A749	$2 multi	7.50	2.50
a.		Booklet pane of 5	37.50	

With Personalized Photo at Right Like Type A692a

2804	A749	50c multi	5.00	3.00
2805	A749	$1.35 multi	8.00	8.00
2806	A749	$2 multi	10.00	10.00
		Nos. 2804-2806 (3)	23.00	21.00

Nos. 2804-2806 each were sold in sheets of 20 and have personalized pictures and a straight edge at right, and lack separations between the stamp and the personalized photo. Sheets of 20 of No. 2804 sold for $23, No. 2805, sold for $40, and No. 2806 sold for $52.

Rugby League, Cent. — A750

Players and teams: Nos. 2807, 2823, Andrew Ryan, Bulldogs. Nos. 2808, 2824, Scott Prince, Titans. Nos. 2809, 2825, Brett Kimmorley, Sharks. Nos. 2810, 2826, Danny Buderus, Knights. Nos. 2811, 2827, Johnathan Thurston, Cowboys. Nos. 2812, 2828, Darren Lockyer, Broncos. Nos. 2813, 2829, Matt Orford, Sea Eagles. Nos. 2814, 2830, Cameron Smith, Storm. Nos. 2815, 2831, Craig Fitzgibbon, Roosters. Nos. 2816, 2832, Alan Tongue, Raiders. Nos. 2817, 2833, Dean Widders, Rabbitohs. Nos. 2818, 2834, Tony Puletua, Panthers. Nos. 2819, 2835, Mark Gasnier, Dragons. Nos. 2820, 2836, Nathan Cayless, Eels. Nos. 2821, 2837, Robbie Farah, Wests Tigers. Nos. 2822, 2838, Steve Price, Warriors.

2008, Mar. 24 — **Perf. 14**

2807	A750	50c multi	1.10	1.10
2808	A750	50c multi	1.10	1.10
2809	A750	50c multi	1.10	1.10
2810	A750	50c multi	1.10	1.10
a.		Block of 4, #2807-2810	4.50	4.50
2811	A750	50c multi	1.10	1.10
2812	A750	50c multi	1.10	1.10
2813	A750	50c multi	1.10	1.10
2814	A750	50c multi	1.10	1.10
a.		Block of 4, #2811-2814	4.50	4.50
2815	A750	50c multi	1.10	1.10
2816	A750	50c multi	1.10	1.10
2817	A750	50c multi	1.10	1.10
2818	A750	50c multi	1.10	1.10
a.		Block of 4, #2815-2818	4.50	4.50
2819	A750	50c multi	1.10	1.10
2820	A750	50c multi	1.10	1.10
2821	A750	50c multi	1.10	1.10
2822	A750	50c multi	1.10	1.10
a.		Block of 4, #2819-2822	4.50	4.50
		Nos. 2807-2822 (16)	17.60	17.60

Booklet Stamps

Self-Adhesive

Serpentine Die Cut 11 Syncopated

2823	A750	50c multi	1.10	.30
a.		Booklet pane of 10	11.00	
2824	A750	50c multi	1.10	.30
a.		Booklet pane of 10	11.00	
2825	A750	50c multi	1.10	.30
a.		Booklet pane of 10	11.00	
2826	A750	50c multi	1.10	.30
a.		Booklet pane of 10	11.00	
2827	A750	50c multi	1.10	.30
a.		Booklet pane of 10		

2828	A750	50c multi	1.10	.30
a.		Booklet pane of 10	11.00	
2829	A750	50c multi	1.10	.30
a.		Booklet pane of 10	11.00	
2830	A750	50c multi	1.10	.30
a.		Booklet pane of 10	11.00	
2831	A750	50c multi	1.10	.30
a.		Booklet pane of 10	11.00	
2832	A750	50c multi	1.10	.30
a.		Booklet pane of 10	11.00	
2833	A750	50c multi	1.10	.30
a.		Booklet pane of 10	11.00	
2834	A750	50c multi	1.10	.30
a.		Booklet pane of 10	11.00	
2835	A750	50c multi	1.10	.30
a.		Booklet pane of 10	11.00	
2836	A750	50c multi	1.10	.30
a.		Booklet pane of 10	11.00	
2837	A750	50c multi	1.10	.30
a.		Booklet pane of 10	11.00	
2838	A750	50c multi	1.10	.30
a.		Booklet pane of 10	11.00	
b.		Booklet pane of 20, #2823-2829, 2831-2838, 5 #2830	22.00	
		Nos. 2823-2838 (16)	17.60	4.80

A booklet containing one Rugby League dollar coin, and panes containing Nos. 2810a, 2814a, 2818a, 2822a, and four No. 2814, each in perf. 14½x14, sold for $15.95.

Heavy Haulers — A751

Designs: Nos. 2839, 2844, 2849, Excavator. Nos. 2840, 2845, 2850, Dump truck. Nos. 2841, 2846, 2851, Road train. Nos. 2842, 2847, 2852, Locomotive and ore cars. Nos. 2843, 2848, 2853, Ore carrier MS Berge Stahl.

2008, Apr. 1 — **Perf. 14**

Without White Frames

2839	A751	50c multi	1.10	1.10
2840	A751	50c multi	1.10	1.10
2841	A751	50c multi	1.10	1.10
2842	A751	50c multi	1.10	1.10
2843	A751	50c multi	1.10	1.10
a.		Horiz. strip of 5, #2839-2843	5.50	5.50
		Nos. 2839-2843 (5)	5.50	5.50

Booklet Stamps

Self-Adhesive

Serpentine Die Cut 11 Syncopated

2844	A751	50c multi	1.10	.60
2845	A751	50c multi	1.10	.60
2846	A751	50c multi	1.10	.60
2847	A751	50c multi	1.10	.60
2848	A751	50c multi	1.10	.60
a.		Booklet pane, 4 each #2844-2848	22.00	

Coil Stamps

With White Frames

2849	A751	50c multi	1.10	.60
2850	A751	50c multi	1.10	.60
2851	A751	50c multi	1.10	.60
2852	A751	50c multi	1.10	.60
2853	A751	50c multi	1.10	.60
a.		Vert. strip of 5, #2849-2853	5.50	
		Nos. 2844-2853 (10)	11.00	6.00

ANZAC Day — A752

Designs: Nos. 2854, 2863, Veterans marching. Nos. 2855, 2862, Laying of wreaths at memorial. Nos. 2856, 2861, Buglers. Nos. 2857, 2860, Veteran holding child. Nos. 2858, 2859, Young people at Gallipoli.

2008, Apr. 16 — **Perf. 14**

2854	A752	50c multi	1.10	1.10
a.		Perf. 14¾x14	1.10	1.10
b.		Booklet pane, 4 #2854a	5.00	—
2855	A752	50c multi	1.10	1.10
a.		Perf. 14¾x14	1.10	1.10
b.		Booklet pane, 4 #2855a	5.00	—
c.		Souvenir sheet, 2 each #2854-2855, perf. 14	4.50	4.50
2856	A752	50c multi	1.10	1.10
a.		Perf. 14¾x14	1.10	1.10
b.		Booklet pane, 4 #2856a	5.00	—
c.		Souvenir sheet of 4 #2856a	4.50	4.50
d.		Souvenir sheet, 2 each #2855-2856, perf. 14	4.50	4.50

2857	A752	50c multi	1.10	1.10
a.		Perf. 14¾x14	1.10	1.10
b.		Booklet pane, 4 #2857a	5.00	—
2858	A752	50c multi	1.10	1.10
a.		Perf. 14¾x14	1.10	1.10
b.		Booklet pane, 4 #2858a	5.00	—
		Complete booklet, #2854b-2858b	25.00	
c.		Souvenir sheet, #2854a-2858a		
d.		Horiz. strip of 5, #2854-2858	5.50	5.50
		Nos. 2854-2858 (5)	5.50	5.50

Coil Stamps

Self-Adhesive

Serpentine Die Cut 11 Syncopated

2859	A752	50c multi	1.10	.60
2860	A752	50c multi	1.10	.60
2861	A752	50c multi	1.10	.60
2862	A752	50c multi	1.10	.60
2863	A752	50c multi	1.10	.60
a.		Vert. strip of 5, #2859-2863	5.50	
		Nos. 2859-2863 (5)	5.50	3.00

Complete booklet sold for $10.95.
2008 World Stamp Championships, Israel (No. 2856c). Issued: No. 2855c, 11/3; No. 2856d, 11/5.

Queen's Birthday — A753

Designs: 50c, Queen Elizabeth II. $2, Order of Australia badge.

2008, Apr. 18 — **Perf. 14**

2864	A753	50c multi	1.10	.85
a.		Perf. 14¾x14	1.10	.85
b.		Dated "2010"	2.00	1.00
2865	A753	$2 multi	4.25	2.25
a.		Perf. 14¾x14	4.25	2.25
b.		Souvenir sheet, #2864a, 2865a	5.50	5.50

First Hot-air Balloon Flight in Australia, 150th Anniv. — A754

Hot-air balloons over: Nos. 2866, 2870, Sydney Harbour Bridge and Sydney Opera House. Nos. 2867, 2871, Mount Feathertop, Victoria (red denomination). Nos. 2868, 2873, Western MacDonnell Ranges, Northern Territory (lilac denomination). Nos. 2869, 2872, Canberra.

2008, May 6 — **Litho.** — **Perf. 14x14¾**

2866	A754	50c multi	1.10	1.10
a.		Booklet pane of 4	5.00	—
2867	A754	50c multi	1.10	1.10
a.		Booklet pane of 4	5.00	—
2868	A754	50c multi	1.10	1.10
a.		Booklet pane of 4	5.00	—
2869	A754	50c multi	1.10	1.10
a.		Booklet pane of 4	5.00	—
b.		Booklet pane of 4, #2866-2869	5.00	—
		Complete booklet, #2866a-2869a, 2869b	25.00	
c.		Horiz. strip of 4, #2866-2869	4.50	4.50
d.		Additionally dated "2013" (#2869e)		
e.		Booklet pane of 2 #2869d	1.10	1.10
			2.25	
		Nos. 2866-2869 (4)	4.40	4.40

Issued: Nos. 2869d, 2869e, 3/5/13. No. 2869e was issued in booklet along with Nos. 1939c, 2710c, 3107c, 3349b and 3877a.

Booklet Stamps

Self-Adhesive

Serpentine Die Cut 11 Syncopated

2870	A754	50c multi	1.10	.30
2871	A754	50c multi	1.10	.30
2872	A754	50c multi	1.10	.30
2873	A754	50c multi	1.10	.30
a.		Booklet pane, 4 #2870, 2 each #2871-2873	11.00	
		Nos. 2870-2873 (4)	4.40	1.20

Complete booklet sold for $10.95.

Working Dogs — A755

Designs: Nos. 2874, 2879, German shepherd. Nos. 2875, 2880, Australian cattle dog. Nos. 2876, 2881, Beagle. Nos. 2877, 2882, Border collie. Nos. 2878, 2883, Labrador retriever.

2008, June 10 — **Litho.** — **Perf. 14¾x14**

2874	A755	50c multi	1.10	1.10
a.		Booklet pane of 4	5.00	—
2875	A755	50c multi	1.10	1.10
a.		Booklet pane of 4	5.00	—
2876	A755	50c multi	1.10	1.10
a.		Booklet pane of 4	5.00	—
2877	A755	50c multi	1.10	1.10
a.		Booklet pane of 4	5.00	—
2878	A755	50c multi	1.10	1.10
a.		Booklet pane of 4	5.00	—
		Complete booklet, #2874a-2878a	25.00	
b.		Horiz. strip of 5, #2874-2878	5.50	5.50
		Nos. 2874-2878 (5)	5.50	5.50

Booklet Stamps

Self-Adhesive

Serpentine Die Cut 11 Syncopated

2879	A755	50c multi	1.10	.30
a.		Booklet pane of 10 + 5 stickers	11.00	
2880	A755	50c multi	1.10	.30
a.		Booklet pane of 10 + 5 stickers	11.00	
2881	A755	50c multi	1.10	.30
a.		Booklet pane of 10 + 5 stickers	11.00	
2882	A755	50c multi	1.10	.30
a.		Booklet pane of 10 + 5 stickers	11.00	
2883	A755	50c multi	1.10	.30
a.		Booklet pane of 10 + 5 stickers	11.00	
b.		Booklet pane of 10, 2 each #2879-2883, + 5 stickers	11.00	
		Nos. 2879-2883 (5)	5.50	1.50

Complete booklet sold for $10.95.

2008 Summer Olympics, Beijing — A756

2008, June 24 — **Perf. 14¾x14**

2884	A756	50c multi	1.10	1.10

Coil Stamp

Self-Adhesive

Serpentine Die Cut 11 Syncopated

2885	A756	50c multi	1.10	.30

Ecology A757

Slogans: Nos. 2886, 2890, Save water. Nos. 2887, 2891, Reduce waste. Nos. 2888, 2892, Travel smart. Nos. 2889, 2893, Save energy.

2008, July 8 — **Litho.** — **Perf. 14x14¾**

2886	A757	50c multi	1.10	1.10
2887	A757	50c multi	1.10	1.10
2888	A757	50c multi	1.10	1.10
2889	A757	50c multi	1.10	1.10
a.		Block of 4, #2886-2889	4.50	4.50
		Nos. 2886-2889 (4)	4.40	4.40

Self-Adhesive

Serpentine Die Cut 11¼x11 Syncopated

2890	A757	50c multi	1.10	.30
a.		Booklet pane of 2	2.25	
2891	A757	50c multi	1.10	.30
a.		Booklet pane of 2	2.25	
2892	A757	50c multi	1.10	.30
a.		Booklet pane of 2	2.25	
2893	A757	50c multi	1.10	.30
a.		Booklet pane of 2	2.25	
b.		Booklet pane of 4, #2890-2893	4.50	

c. Double-sided booklet pane of 8, 2 each #2890-2893 9.25
Complete booklet, #2890a, 2891a, 2892a, 2893a, 2893b, 2893c 24.00
d. Double-sided booklet of 20, 5 each #2890-2893 22.00
e. Horiz. coil strip of 4, #2890-2893 4.50
Nos. 2890-2893 (4) 4.40 1.20
Complete booklet sold for $10.95.

Quarantine Laws, Cent. — A758

2008, July 15 *Perf. 14¾x14*
2894 A758 50c multi 1.10 1.10

Coil Stamp
Self-Adhesive
Serpentine Die Cut 11x11¼ Syncopated
2895 A758 50c multi 1.10 .30

Australian Football, 150th Anniv. — A759

2008, July 29 *Perf. 14¾x14*
2896 A759 50c multi 1.10 .85

2008 Summer Olympics, Beijing — A760

No. 2897, Basketball. Nos. 2898, 2900, Cycling. Nos. 2899, 2901, Rhythmic gymnastics.

2008, Aug. 1
2897 A760 50c multi 1.10 .85
2898 A760 $1.30 multi 2.75 2.75
2899 A760 $1.35 multi 2.75 2.75
Nos. 2897-2899 (3) 6.60 6.35
Litho.
Serpentine Die Cut 11¼ Syncopated
Booklet Stamps
Self-Adhesive
2900 A760 $1.30 multi 2.75 .30
a. Booklet pane of 5 14.00
2901 A760 $1.35 multi 2.75 .30
a. Booklet pane of 5 14.50

Scenes From World Youth Day — A761

Designs: No. 2902, Pilgrims at opening mass. No. 2903, Papal welcome. No. 2904, Stations of the Cross. No. 2905, Pilgrimage walk. No. 2906, Pope Benedict XVI at final mass.

2008, July 24 **Litho.** *Perf. 14½x14*
2902 A761 50c multi 2.00 2.00
2903 A761 50c multi 2.00 2.00
2904 A761 50c multi 2.00 2.00
2905 A761 50c multi 2.00 2.00
2906 A761 50c multi 2.00 2.00
a. Vert. strip of 5, #2902-2906 12.00 12.00
Nos. 2902-2906 (5) 10.00 10.00

Aircraft A762

Designs: No. 2907, Bristol Tourer. No. 2908, Short S.30 Empire Flying Boat. No. 2909, Lockheed Super Constellation. $2, Airbus A380.

2008, Aug. 5 *Perf. 14*
2907 A762 50c multi 1.00 .80
a. Perf. 14x14¾ 1.25 1.25
b. Booklet pane of 2, #2907a 2.50
2908 A762 50c multi 1.00 .80
a. Perf. 14x14¾ 1.25 1.25
b. Booklet pane of 2, #2907a 2.50
2909 A762 50c multi 1.00 .80
a. Perf. 14x14¾ 1.25 1.25
b. Booklet pane of 2, #2907a 2.50
c. Horiz. strip of 3, #2907-2909 3.00 2.40
2910 A762 $2 multi 4.00 2.00
a. Perf. 14x14¾ 5.50 5.50
b. Booklet pane of 1, #2907a 5.50
c. Booklet pane of 4, #2907a-2910a 9.50
Complete booklet, #2907b, 2908b, 2909b, 2910b, 2910c 23.00
d. Souvenir sheet, 2 each #2868, 2910a 9.50 9.50
Nos. 2907-2910 (4) 7.00 4.40

Booklet Stamp
Self-Adhesive
Serpentine Die Cut 11¼ Syncopated
2911 A762 $2 multi 4.00 2.00
a. Booklet pane of 5 20.00

Complete booklet sold for $10.95. Issued: No./ 2910d, 8/22. SunStamp 2008 Philatelic Exhibition, Brisbane (No. 2910d).

Gold Medalists at 2008 Summer Olympics, Beijing A763

Designs: No. 2912, Stephanie Rice, Women's swimming 400m individual medley. No. 2913, Lisbeth Trickett, Women's swimming 100m butterfly. No. 2914, Leisel Jones, Women's swimming, 100m breaststroke. No. 2915, Stephanie Rice, Women's swimming 200m individual medley. No. 2916, Women's 4x200m freestyle relay swimming team. No. 2917, Drew Ginn and Duncan Free, Men's rowing pairs. No. 2918, David Crawshay and Scott Brennan, Men's rowing double sculls. No. 2919, Women's 4x100m medley relay swimming team. No. 2920, Emma Snowsill, Women's triathlon. No. 2921, Malcolm Page and Nathan Wilmot, Men's sailing 470 crew. No. 2922, Tessa Parkinson and Elise Rechichi, Women's sailing 470 crew. No. 2923, Ken Wallace, Men's single kayak 500m. No. 2924, Steven Hooker, Men's pole vault. No. 2925, Matthew Mitcham, Men's 10m platform diving.

2008, Aug. **Litho.** *Perf. 14¼*
2912 A763 50c multi .95 .75
2913 A763 50c multi .95 .75
2914 A763 50c multi .95 .75
2915 A763 50c multi .95 .75
2916 A763 50c multi .95 .75
2917 A763 50c multi .95 .75
2918 A763 50c multi .95 .75
2919 A763 50c multi .95 .75
2920 A763 50c multi .95 .75
2921 A763 50c multi .95 .75
2922 A763 50c multi .95 .75
2923 A763 50c multi .95 .75
2924 A763 50c multi .95 .75
2925 A763 50c multi .95 .75
Nos. 2912-2925 (14) 13.30 10.50

Issued: Nos. 2912, 8/11; No. 2913, 8/12; No. 2914, 8/13; No. 2915, 8/14; No. 2916, 8/15; No. 2917-2919, 8/18; Nos. 2920-2922, 8/19; Nos. 2923-2925, 8/25. Nos. 2912-2925 were printed in sheets of 10. Digitally printed versions of Nos. 2912-2925 were printed in Beijing in sheets of 10. The digitally printed stamps were only available in complete sets of 14 sheets to collectors in Australia who pre-ordered the sets, and purchasers at the Olympex Stamp Exhibition in China. The digitally printed stamps have a larger dot pattern, most evident in the background and the Olympic rings, and a browner cast to the orange background.

Waterfalls — A764

Designs: $1.40, Russell Falls, Tasmania. $2.05, Jim Jim Falls, Northern Territory. $2.80, Spa Pool, Hammersley Gorge, Western Australia. $4.10, Mackenzie Falls, Victoria.

2008, Sept. 8 **Litho.** *Perf. 14¾x14*
2926 A764 $1.40 multi 2.50 2.50
2927 A764 $2.05 multi 3.75 3.75
2928 A764 $2.80 multi 5.25 2.50
2929 A764 $4.10 multi 7.50 3.75
Nos. 2926-2929 (4) 19.00 12.50

Booklet Stamps
Self-Adhesive
Serpentine Die Cut 11¼ Syncopated
2930 A764 $1.40 multi 2.50 .30
a. Booklet pane of 5 13.00
b. Booklet pane of 2 5.50
Complete booklet, 4 #2930b 22.00
2931 A764 $2.05 multi 3.75 1.90
a. Booklet pane of 5 19.00
b. Booklet pane of 2 7.75
Complete booklet, 4 #2931b 30.00

With Personalized Photo at Right Like Type A692a
Serpentine Die Cut 11½x11¼ Syncopated
Self-Adhesive
2932 A764 $1.40 multi 3.75 3.75
2933 A764 $2.05 multi 5.00 5.00

Complete booklet containing No. 2930 sold for $11.95; booklet containing No. 2931, $16.95. Margins for each pane in the complete booklets differ.
Nos. 2932-2933 each were sold in sheets of 20 and have personalized pictures and a straight edge at right, and lack separations between the stamp and the personalized photo. Sheets of 20 of No. 2932 sold for $41, and No. 2933 sold for $53.

Tourist Areas of Cities — A765

Designs: Nos. 2934, 2941, 2945, Luna Park, Melbourne. Nos. 2935, 2942, 2946, South Bank, Brisbane. Nos. 2936, 2943, 2947, The Rocks, Sydney. Nos. 2937, 2944, 2948, Fishermans Wharf, Fremantle. $1.10, Foreshore, Cairns. $1.65, Salamanca Place, Hobart. $2.75, Glenelg, Adelaide (50x30mm).

2008, Sept. 8 **Litho.** *Perf. 14x14½*
2934 A765 55c multi .95 .95
2935 A765 55c multi .95 .95
2936 A765 55c multi .95 .95
2937 A765 55c multi .95 .95
a. Block of 4, #2934-2937 4.00 4.00
b. Sheet of 4, #2934-2937 4.00 4.00
c. Block of 4, #2934-2937, perf. 13½x14 18.00 18.00
2938 A765 $1.10 multi 2.00 1.60
2939 A765 $1.65 multi 3.00 2.25
Perf. 14½x14
2940 A765 $2.75 multi 5.00 2.40
Nos. 2934-2940 (7) 13.80 10.05

Self-Adhesive
Coil Stamps
Die Cut Perf. 12¾
2941 A765 55c multi .95 .30
2942 A765 55c multi .95 .30
2943 A765 55c multi .95 .30
2944 A765 55c multi .95 .30
a. Horiz. strip of 4, #2941-2944 4.00

Booklet Stamps
Serpentine Die Cut 11¼
2945 A765 55c multi .95 .30
a. Booklet pane of 10 9.75
2946 A765 55c multi .95 .30
a. Booklet pane of 10 9.75
2947 A765 55c multi .95 .30
a. Booklet pane of 10 9.75
2948 A765 55c multi .95 .30
a. Booklet pane of 10 9.75
b. Booklet pane of 20, 5 each #2945-2948 20.00
Nos. 2941-2948 (8) 7.60 2.40

Issued: No. 2937b, 5/14/09. Hong Kong 2009 Intl. Stamp Exhibition (No. 2937b).

Australia and Southern Cross — A766

Balloons — A767

Bird and Beach — A768

Stylized Map A769

Sparklers A770

Flowers and Silver Wedding Rings — A771

Gold Wedding Rings — A772

Baby's Feet — A773

Heart and Roses — A774

Roses and Wedding Gown — A775

2008, Sept. 23 *Perf. 14½x14*
2949 A766 55c multi .95 .95
Perf. 14¾x14
2950 A767 55c multi .95 .95
2951 A768 55c multi .95 .95
2952 A769 55c multi .95 .95
a. Souvenir sheet of 2 + 2 labels, Chips Rafferty in margin 4.25 4.25
b. As "a," Errol Flynn in margin 4.25 4.25
2953 A770 55c multi .95 .95
a. Block of 4, #2950-2953 4.00 4.00
2954 A771 55c multi .95 .95
2955 A772 55c multi .95 .95
2956 A773 55c multi .95 .95

2957	A774 55c multi	.95	.95
a.	Block of 4, #2954-2957	4.00	4.00
2958	A775 $1.10 multi	2.00	1.60
	Nos. 2949-2958 (10)	10.55	10.15

Nos. 2952a and 2952b were sold with Nos. 3009b and 3010d in a set for $12.95.

Booklet Stamps
Self-Adhesive
Serpentine Die Cut 11¼ Syncopated

2959	A767 55c multi	1.00	.30
a.	Booklet pane of 4	4.25	
	Complete booklet, 5 #2959a	22.00	
b.	Booklet pane of 10	10.50	
2960	A770 55c multi	1.00	.30
a.	Booklet pane of 4	4.25	
	Complete booklet, 5 #2960a	22.00	
b.	Booklet pane of 10	10.50	
2961	A771 55c multi	1.00	.30
a.	Booklet pane of 4	4.25	
	Complete booklet, 5 #2961a	22.00	
b.	Booklet pane of 10	10.50	
2962	A772 55c multi	1.00	.30
a.	Booklet pane of 4	4.25	
	Complete booklet, 5 #2962a	22.00	
b.	Booklet pane of 10	10.50	
2963	A773 55c multi	1.00	.30
a.	Booklet pane of 4	4.25	
	Complete booklet, 5 #2963a	22.00	
b.	Booklet pane of 10	10.50	
2964	A774 55c multi	1.00	.30
a.	Booklet pane of 4	4.25	
	Complete booklet, 5 #2964a	22.00	
2965	A775 $1.10 multi	2.00	2.00
a.	Booklet pane of 4	8.00	
	Complete booklet, 5 #2965a	41.00	
b.	Booklet pane of 10	20.00	
	Nos. 2959-2965 (7)	8.00	3.80

With Personalized Photo at Right Like Type A692a
Serpentine Die Cut 11½x11¼ Syncopated
Self-Adhesive

2966	A767 55c multi	2.25	2.25
2967	A768 55c multi	2.25	2.25
2968	A769 55c multi	2.25	2.25
2969	A770 55c multi	2.25	2.25
2970	A771 55c multi	2.25	2.25
2971	A772 55c multi	2.25	2.25
2972	A773 55c multi	2.25	2.25
2973	A774 55c multi	2.25	2.25
2974	A775 $1.10 multi	3.25	3.25
	Nos. 2966-2974 (9)	21.25	21.25

Issued: Nos. 2959b, 2960b, 2962b, 2963b, 2965b, 3/2/09.

Complete booklet containing No. 2965 sold for $22.95; booklets containing Nos. 2959-2964 each sold for $11.95. Each booklet contained panes with five different margins.

Nos. 2966-2974 each were sold in sheets of 20 and have personalized pictures and a straight edge at right, and lack separations between the stamp and the personalized photo. Sheets of 20 of Nos. 2966-2973 each sold for $24, and No. 2974 sold for $35.

Large Extinct Animals — A776

Designs: Nos. 2975, 2981, Genyornis. Nos. 2976, 2982, Diprotodon. Nos. 2977, 2983, Thylacoleo. Nos. 2978, 2984, Thylacine. No. 2979, Megalania, horiz. (52x37mm). No. 2980, Procoptodon, horiz. (52x37mm).

2008, Oct. 1   Litho.   Perf. 14½x14

2975	A776 55c multi	.95	.95
a.	Perf. 14	.95	.95
b.	Booklet pane of 2 #2975	2.25	—
2976	A776 55c multi	.95	.95
a.	Perf. 14	.95	.95
b.	Booklet pane of 2 #2976	2.25	—
2977	A776 55c multi	.95	.95
a.	Perf. 14	.95	.95
b.	Booklet pane of 2 #2977	2.25	—
2978	A776 55c multi	.95	.95
a.	Perf. 14	.95	.95
b.	Horiz. strip of 4, #2975-2978	4.00	4.00
c.	Booklet pane of 2 #2978	2.25	—
d.	Booklet pane of 4, #2975-2978	4.25	—
2979	A776 $1.10 multi	2.00	1.60
a.	Perf. 14	.95	.95
b.	Booklet pane of 2 #2979	4.25	—
2980	A776 $1.10 multi	2.00	1.60
a.	Perf. 14	.95	.95
b.	Horiz. pair, #2979-2980	4.00	4.00
c.	Souvenir sheet, #2975a-2980a	8.00	8.00
d.	Booklet pane of 2 #2980	4.25	—
e.	Booklet pane of 2, #2979-2980	4.25	—
	Complete booklet, #2975b, 2976b, 2977b, 2978c, 2978d, 2979b, 2980d, 2980e	26.50	
f.	As "c," overprinted with Beijing 2008 Stamp Exposition emblem in margin	7.00	7.00
	Nos. 2975-2980 (6)	7.80	7.00

Self-Adhesive
Serpentine Die Cut 11¼ Syncopated

2981	A776 55c multi	.95	.30
2982	A776 55c multi	.95	.30
2983	A776 55c multi	.95	.30
2984	A776 55c multi	.95	.30
a.	Vert. coil strip of 4, #2981-2984	4.00	
b.	Booklet pane of 10, 3 each #2981-2982, 2 each #2983-2984	9.75	
	Nos. 2981-2984 (4)	3.80	1.20

Complete booklet sold for $13.95. Issued: No. 2980f, 10/24.

Matthew Cowdrey, Paralympian of the Year — A777

2008, Oct. 24   Litho.   Perf. 14¼

2985	A777 55c multi	.85	.70

Christmas
A778   A779

Star of Bethlehem and: Nos. 2987, 2992, 2995, Madonna and child. Nos. 2988, 2996, Angel. Nos. 2989, 2993, Magus.

2008, Oct. 31   Litho.   Perf. 14¾x14

2986	A778 50c multi	.80	.80
2987	A779 50c multi	.80	.80
2988	A779 55c multi	.85	.70
2989	A779 $1.20 multi	1.90	1.90
	Nos. 2986-2989 (4)	4.35	4.20

Booklet Stamps
Self-Adhesive
Litho. & Typo.
Serpentine Die Cut 11¼ Syncopated

2990	A778 50c multi	.80	.30
a.	Booklet pane of 10	8.00	

Litho.

2991	A778 50c multi	.80	.30
a.	Booklet pane of 20	16.00	
2992	A779 50c multi	.80	.30
a.	Booklet pane of 20	16.00	
2993	A779 $1.20 multi	1.90	.30
a.	Booklet pane of 5	9.25	
	Nos. 2990-2993 (4)	4.30	1.20

With Personalized Photo at Right Like Type A692a
Serpentine Die Cut 11½x11¼ Syncopated
Self-Adhesive

2994	A778 50c multi	1.75	1.75
2995	A779 50c multi	1.75	1.75
2996	A779 55c multi	1.75	1.75
	Nos. 2994-2996 (3)	5.25	5.25

Nos. 2994-2996 each were sold in sheets of 20 and have personalized pictures and a straight edge at right, and lack separations between the stamp and the personalized photo. Sheets of 20 of Nos. 2994-2995 each sold for $23, and No. 2996 sold for $24.

Posters for Popular Australian Films — A780

Poster for: Nos. 2997, 3002, The Adventures of Priscilla, Queen of the Desert. Nos. 2998, 3003, The Castle. Nos. 2999, 3004, Muriel's Wedding. Nos. 3000, 3005, Lantana. Nos. 3001, 3006, Gallipoli.

2008, Nov. 3   Litho.   Perf. 14¾x14

2997	A780 55c multi	.85	.85
2998	A780 55c multi	.85	.85
2999	A780 55c multi	.85	.85
3000	A780 55c multi	.85	.85
3001	A780 55c multi	.85	.85
a.	Horiz. strip of 5, #2997-3001	4.25	4.25
	Nos. 2997-3001 (5)	4.25	4.25

Self-Adhesive
Serpentine Die Cut 11¼ Syncopated

3002	A780 55c multi	.85	.30
a.	Booklet pane of 10	8.50	
3003	A780 55c multi	.85	.30
a.	Booklet pane of 10	8.50	
3004	A780 55c multi	.85	.30
a.	Booklet pane of 10	8.50	
3005	A780 55c multi	.85	.30
a.	Booklet pane of 10	8.50	
3006	A780 55c multi	.85	.30
a.	Booklet pane of 10	8.50	
b.	Booklet pane of 10, 2 each #3002-3006	8.50	
c.	Vert. coil strip of 5, #3002-3006	4.25	
d.	Souvenir sheet of 10, 1 ea #3002, 3004-3006, 6 #3003	11.00	
	Nos. 3002-3006 (5)	4.25	1.50

Academy Award-winning Actors and Actresses — A781

Designs: Nos. 3007, 3015, Nicole Kidman. Nos. 3008, 3016, Russell Crowe. Nos. 3009, 3018, Geoffrey Rush. Nos. 3010, 3017, Cate Blanchett. Nos. 3011, 3020, Crowe in *Gladiator*. Nos. 3012, 3019, Kidman in *Moulin Rouge!* Nos. 3013, 3021, Blanchett in *Elizabeth: The Golden Age*. Nos. 3014, 3022, Rush in *Shine*.

2009, Jan. 22   Litho.   Perf. 14¾x14

3007	A781 55c multi	.80	.80
a.	Booklet pane of 4	4.25	
3008	A781 55c multi	.80	.80
a.	Booklet pane of 4	4.25	
b.	Sheet of 10 + 10 labels	14.00	14.00
3009	A781 55c multi	.80	.80
a.	Booklet pane of 4	4.25	
b.	Souvenir sheet of 4	8.25	8.25
3010	A781 55c multi	.85	.85
a.	Booklet pane of 4	4.25	
b.	Block of 4, #3007-3010	3.50	3.50
c.	Booklet pane of 4, #3007-3010	4.25	—
d.	Souvenir sheet of 4, #3007-3010	8.25	8.25
3011	A781 55c multi	.85	.85
a.	Booklet pane of 4	4.25	
b.	Booklet pane of 4, 2 each #3008, 3011	4.25	—
	Complete booklet, #3008a, 3010c, 3011a, 3011b	17.00	
3012	A781 55c multi	.85	.85
a.	Booklet pane of 4	4.25	
b.	Booklet pane of 4, 2 each #3007, 3012	4.25	—
	Complete booklet, #3007a, 3010c, 3012a, 3012b	17.00	
3013	A781 55c multi	.85	.85
a.	Booklet pane of 4	4.25	
b.	Booklet pane of 4, 2 each #3010, 3013	4.25	—
	Complete booklet, #3010a, 3010c, 3013a, 3013b	17.00	
3014	A781 55c multi	.85	.85
a.	Booklet pane of 4	4.25	
b.	Booklet pane of 4, 2 each #3009, 3014	4.25	—
	Complete booklet, #3009a, 3010c, 3014a, 3014b	17.50	
c.	Block of 4, #3011-3014	3.50	3.50
	Nos. 3007-3014 (8)	6.65	6.65

Issued: No. 3008b, 5/6/10. Two sheets of 3008b, each sheet having different labels, were sold together as a set for $13.50. Nos. 3009b and 3010d were sold with Nos. 2952a and 2952b in a set for $12.95.

Self-Adhesive
Booklet Stamps
Serpentine Die Cut 11¼ Syncopated

3015	A781 55c multi	.85	.30
3016	A781 55c multi	.85	.30
3017	A781 55c multi	.85	.30
3018	A781 55c multi	.85	.30
3019	A781 55c multi	.85	.30
a.	Booklet pane of 10, 5 each #3015, 3019	8.50	
3020	A781 55c multi	.85	.30
a.	Booklet pane of 10, 5 each #3016, 3020	8.50	
3021	A781 55c multi	.85	.30
a.	Booklet pane of 10, 5 each #3017 3021	8.50	
3022	A781 55c multi	.85	.30
a.	Booklet pane of 20, 3 each #3015-3018, 2 each #3019-3022	17.00	

b.	Booklet pane of 10, 5 each #3019, 3022	8.50	
	Nos. 3015-3022 (8)	6.80	2.40

Each complete booklet sold for $10.95.

Roses — A782   Heart — A783

Flowers With Heart-Shaped Petals — A784

2009, Feb. 3   Litho.   Perf. 14¾x14

3023	A782 55c multi	.80	.80
3024	A783 55c gray blue	.80	.80
3025	A784 55c multi	.80	.80
a.	Pair, #3024-3025	1.60	1.60
	Nos. 3023-3025 (3)	2.40	2.40

Booklet Stamps
Self-Adhesive
Serpentine Die Cut 11¼ Syncopated

3026	A782 55c multi	.80	.80
a.	Booklet pane of 10	8.00	
3027	A783 55c gray blue	.80	.80
a.	Booklet pane of 10	8.00	
3028	A784 55c multi	.80	.80
a.	Booklet pane of 10	8.00	

Litho. With Foil Application

3029	A784 55c multi	.80	.80

Litho. With Flocking

3030	A783 55c gray blue	.80	.80
a.	Booklet pane of 10, 2 each #3029-3030	8.00	
	Nos. 3026-3030 (5)	4.00	4.00

With Personalized Photo at Right Like Type A692a
Syncopated Die Cut 11½x11¼ Syncopated
Self-Adhesive

3031	A782 55c multi	1.75	1.75
3032	A783 55c multi	1.75	1.75
3033	A784 55c multi	1.75	1.75
	Nos. 3031-3033 (3)	5.25	5.25

Nos. 3031-3033 each were sold in sheets of 20 and have personalized pictures and a straight edge at right and lack separations between the stamp and the personalized photo. Sheets of 20 of each stamp sold for $24.

Australian Inventions — A785

Designs: Nos. 3034, 3039, Esky (insulated cooler), wine cask. Nos. 3035, 3040, Hills hoist (rotatable clothes line frame). Nos. 3036, 3041, Speedos (swim wear), zinc oxide cream. Nos. 3037, 3042, Ute (utility vehicle), B&D Roll-A-Door (garage door). Nos. 3038, 3043, Victa rotary lawnmower.

2009, Feb. 19   Litho.   Perf. 14¾x14

3034	A785 55c multi	.80	.80
a.	Booklet pane of 4	4.00	
b.	As #3034, perf. 14	.80	.80
3035	A785 55c multi	.80	.80
a.	Booklet pane of 4	4.00	
b.	As #3035, perf. 14	.80	.80
3036	A785 55c multi	.80	.80
a.	Booklet pane of 4	4.00	
b.	As #3036, perf. 14	.80	.80
3037	A785 55c multi	.80	.80
a.	Booklet pane of 4	4.00	
b.	As #3037, perf. 14	.80	.80
3038	A785 55c multi	.80	.80
a.	Booklet pane of 4	4.00	
	Complete booklet, #3034a, 3035a, 3036a, 3037a, 3038a	19.50	

b.	As #3038, perf. 14	.80	.80
c.	Souvenir sheet, #3034b-3038b	4.00	4.00
d.	Horiz. strip of 5, #3034-3038	4.00	4.00
	Nos. 3034-3038 (5)	4.00	4.00

Self-Adhesive
Serpentine Die Cut 11¼ Syncopated

3039	A785	55c multi	.80	.30
3040	A785	55c multi	.80	.30
3041	A785	55c multi	.80	.30
3042	A785	55c multi	.80	.30
3043	A785	55c multi	.80	.30
a.	Vert. coil strip of 5, #3039-3043			4.00
b.	Booklet pane of 10, 2 each #3039-3043			8.00
	Nos. 3039-3043 (5)		4.00	1.50

Complete booklet sold for $12.95.

Earth Hour — A786

Animals and slogan: Nos. 3044, 3047, Lights out. No. 3045, 3048, Switch off. $2.05, Save energy.

2009, Mar. 11   Perf. 14¾x14

3044	A786	55c multi	.90	.90
3045	A786	55c multi	.90	.90
a.	Horiz. pair, #3044-3045		1.90	1.90
3046	A786	$2.05 multi	3.50	3.50
	Nos. 3044-3046 (3)		5.30	5.30

Booklet Stamps
Self-Adhesive
Serpentine Die Cut 11¼ Syncopated

3047	A786	55c multi	.90	.30
3048	A786	55c multi	.90	.30
a.	Booklet pane of 20, 10 each #3047-3048			18.50

Australia Post, Bicent. — A787

Inscriptions: Nos. 3049a, 3050, First postmaster. Nos. 3049b, 3051, Early post office. Nos. 3049c, 3052, Early posting box. Nos. 3049d, 3053, News from home. Nos. 3049e, 3054, Early air mail. Nos. 3049f, 3055, Home delivery. Nos. 3049g, 3056, Post-war immigration. Nos. 3049h, 3057, Retail post shop. Nos. 3049i, 3058, Express post. Nos. 3049j, 3059, Part of every day.

2009, Mar. 25   Perf. 14¾x14

3049		Sheet of 10	9.25	9.25
a.-j.	A787 55c Any single		.90	.90
k.	Booklet pane of 10, #3049a-3049j		11.00	
l.	As "k," imperf.		11.00	
	Complete booklet, #3049l, 2 #3049k		32.50	

Self-Adhesive
Serpentine Die Cut 11¼ Syncopated

3050	A787	55c multi	.90	.30
3051	A787	55c multi	.90	.30
3052	A787	55c multi	.90	.30
3053	A787	55c multi	.90	.30
3054	A787	55c multi	.90	.30
3055	A787	55c multi	.90	.30
3056	A787	55c multi	.90	.30
3057	A787	55c multi	.90	.30
3058	A787	55c multi	.90	.30
3059	A787	55c multi	.90	.30
a.	Vert. coil strip of 10, #3050-3059			9.00
b.	Booklet pane of 10, #3050-3059			9.00
	Nos. 3050-3059 (10)		9.00	3.00

Complete booklet sold for $19.95. Compare with type A806.

Aboriginal Art — A788

Designs: No. 3060, Mamu, by Nura Rupert. No. 3061, All the Jila, by Jan Billycan. No. 3062, Mina Mina, by Judy Napangardi Watson. $1.40, Untitled work from the Mission Series, by Elaine Russell. $2.05, Natjula, by Tjuruparu Watson.

2009, Apr. 1   Perf. 14x14¾

3060	A788	55c multi	.90	.70
3061	A788	55c multi	.90	.70
3062	A788	55c multi	.90	.70
a.	Horiz. strip of 3, #3060-3062		2.75	2.00
3063	A788	$1.40 multi	2.25	1.10
3064	A788	$2.05 multi	3.50	1.75
	Nos. 3060-3064 (5)		8.45	4.95

Self-Adhesive
Booklet Stamps
Serpentine Die Cut 11¼ Syncopated

3065	A788	$1.40 multi	2.25	1.10
a.	Booklet pane of 5		11.50	
3066	A788	$2.05 multi	3.50	1.75
a.	Booklet pane of 5		17.50	

Queen's Birthday — A789

Queen Elizabeth II: 55c, In uniform. $2.05, Wearing green coat and hat.

2009, Apr. 15   Perf. 14¾x14

3067	A789	55c multi	.90	.70
a.	Booklet pane of 2		2.25	
b.	Dated "2010"		2.00	1.00
3068	A789	$2.05 multi	3.50	1.75
a.	Booklet pane of 2		8.50	
b.	Souvenir sheet of 2, #3067-3068		4.50	2.40
c.	Complete booklet of #3068a, 3068c, 2 #3067a		18.50	

Complete booklet sold for $10.95.

Eponymous Desserts A790

Designs: Nos. 3069, 3073, Anna Pavlova and Pavlova. Nos. 3070, 3074, Dame Nellie Melba and Peach Melba. Nos. 3071, 3075, Baron and Lady Lamington and Lamingtons. Nos. 3072, 3076, ANZAC soldiers and ANZAC biscuits.

2009, May 15   Litho.   Perf. 14x14¾

3069	A790	55c multi	1.00	1.00
a.	Booklet pane of 4		5.25	
3070	A790	55c multi	1.00	1.00
a.	Booklet pane of 4		5.25	
3071	A790	55c multi	1.00	1.00
a.	Booklet pane of 4		5.25	
3072	A790	55c multi	1.00	1.00
a.	Booklet pane of 4		5.25	
	Complete booklet, #3069a-3072a		20.75	
b.	Horiz. strip of 4, #3069-3072		4.25	4.25
	Nos. 3069-3072 (4)		4.00	4.00

Booklet Stamps
Self-Adhesive
Serpentine Die Cut 11¼ Syncopated

3073	A790	55c multi	1.00	.30
3074	A790	55c multi	1.00	.30
3075	A790	55c multi	1.00	.30
3076	A790	55c multi	1.00	.30
a.	Booklet pane of 10, 3 each #3073-3074, 2 each #3075-3076		11.00	
	Nos. 3073-3076 (4)		4.00	1.20

Complete booklet sold for $10.95.

Worldwide Fund for Nature (WWF) A791

Designs: 55c, Spotted bottlenose dolphins. $1.35, Hourglass dolphins. $1.40, Southern right whale dolphins. $2.05, Dusky dolphins.

2009, May 26   Perf. 14x14¾

3077	A791	55c multi	1.00	.80
3078	A791	$1.35 multi	2.50	2.50
3079	A791	$1.40 multi	2.50	2.50
3080	A791	$2.05 multi	3.75	3.75
a.	Souvenir sheet, #3077-3080		10.00	10.00
	Nos. 3077-3080 (4)		9.75	9.55

Booklet Stamps
Self-Adhesive
Serpentine Die Cut 11¼ Syncopated

3081	A791	$1.35 multi	2.50	2.50
a.	Booklet pane of 5		13.00	
3082	A791	$1.40 multi	2.50	2.50
a.	Booklet pane of 5		13.00	
3083	A791	$2.05 multi	3.75	3.75
a.	Booklet pane of 5		19.00	
	Nos. 3081-3083 (3)		8.75	8.75

Queensland, 150th Anniv. — A792

Designs: 55c, Queensland Parliament, windmill. $2.75, Great Barrier Reef, red-eyed tree frog.

2009, June 9   Litho.   Perf. 14¾x14

3084	A792	55c multi	1.00	.80
3085	A792	$2.75 multi	5.25	4.00
a.	Souvenir sheet, #3084-3085		6.25	6.25

Australia's Favorite Stamps A793

Designs: Nos. 3086, 3091, 3095B, Australia #15. Nos. 3087, 3092, Australia #132. Nos. 3088, 3093, Australia #200. Nos. 3089, 3094, Australia #226. Nos. 3090, 3095, Australia #18.

2009, June 26   Litho.   Perf. 14x14¾

3086	A793	55c multi	1.00	1.00
a.	Booklet pane of 4		4.50	
3087	A793	55c multi	1.00	1.00
a.	Booklet pane of 4		4.50	
3088	A793	55c multi	1.00	1.00
a.	Booklet pane of 4		4.50	
3089	A793	55c multi	1.00	1.00
a.	Booklet pane of 4		4.50	
3090	A793	55c multi	1.00	1.00
a.	Booklet pane of 4		4.50	
	Complete booklet, #3086a-3090a		23.00	
b.	Horiz. strip of 5, #3086-3090		5.25	5.25
	Nos. 3086-3090 (5)		5.00	5.00

Self-Adhesive
Serpentine Die Cut 11¼ Syncopated

3091	A793	55c multi	1.00	.30
3092	A793	55c multi	1.00	.30
3093	A793	55c multi	1.00	.30
3094	A793	55c multi	1.00	.30
3095	A793	55c multi	1.00	.30
a.	Horiz. coil strip of 5, #3091-3095		5.25	
	Nos. 3091-3095 (5)		5.00	1.50

Litho. & Embossed
Serpentine Die Cut 11¼ Syncopated
Self-Adhesive

3095B	A793	55c multi	1.00	.30
c.	Sheet of 13, #3091-3095, 8 #3095B		14.00	

The complete booklet sold for $12.95. Nos. 3091-3095 each were printed by two different printers. There is no noticeable difference between single coil stamps, but Pemara-printed stamps are slightly closer to each other on the strip compared to the McKellar Renown-printed stamps.

Marsupials and Their Young — A794

Designs: $1.45, Koalas. $2.10, Eastern gray kangaroos. $2.90, Brushtail possums, horiz. $4.20, Common wombats, horiz.

2009, July 1   Perf. 14¾x14

3096	A794	$1.45 multi	2.75	2.75
3097	A794	$2.10 multi	4.00	4.00
a.	Additionally dated "2013" (#3534d)		5.50	5.50

Perf. 14x14¾

3098	A794	$2.90 multi	5.50	2.75
3099	A794	$4.20 multi	7.75	4.00
	Nos. 3096-3099 (4)		20.00	13.50

Issued: No. 3097a, 5/10/13.

Booklet Stamps
Self-Adhesive
Serpentine Die Cut 11¼ Syncopated

3100	A794	$1.45 multi	2.75	1.40
a.	Booklet pane of 5		14.00	
3101	A794	$2.10 multi	4.00	2.00
a.	Booklet pane of 5		20.00	

With Personalized Photo at Right
Like Type A692a
Serpentine Die Cut 11¼ Syncopated
Self-Adhesive

3102	A794	$1.45 multi	4.00	4.00
3103	A794	$2.10 multi	5.25	5.25

Nos. 3102-3103 each were sold in sheets of 20 and have personalized pictures and a straight edge at right and lack separations between the stamp and the personalized photo. Sheets of 20 of No. 3102 sold for $42; No. 3103, for $54.

Parks and Gardens A795

Designs: Nos. 3104, 3109, Fitzroy Gardens, Melbourne. Nos. 3105, 3110, Roma Street Parkland, Brisbane. Nos. 3106, 3111, St. David's Park, Hobart. Nos. 3107, 3112, Commonwealth Park, Canberra. Nos. 3108, 3113, Hyde Park, Sydney.

2009, July 14   Litho.   Perf. 14x14¾

3104	A795	55c multi	1.10	1.10
a.	Booklet pane of 4		5.25	—
b.	Sheet of 4, #3072, 3086, 3090, 3104		4.25	4.25
3105	A795	55c multi	1.10	1.10
a.	Booklet pane of 4		5.25	—
3106	A795	55c multi	1.10	1.10
a.	Booklet pane of 4		5.25	—
3107	A795	55c multi	1.10	1.10
a.	Booklet pane of 4		5.25	—
b.	Additionally dated "2013" (#3107c)		1.25	1.25
c.	Booklet pane of 2 #3107b		2.50	
3108	A795	55c multi	1.10	1.10
a.	Booklet pane of 4		5.25	—
	Complete booklet, #3104a-3108a		26.00	
b.	Horiz. strip of 5, #3104-3108		5.50	5.50
	Nos. 3104-3108 (5)		5.50	5.50

Issued: Nos. 3107b, 3107c, 3/5/13. No. 3107c was issued in booklet along with Nos. 1939c, 2710c, 2869e, 3349b and 3877a.

Coil Stamps
Self-Adhesive
Serpentine Die Cut 11¼ Syncopated

3109	A795	55c multi	1.10	.30
3110	A795	55c multi	1.10	.30
3111	A795	55c multi	1.10	.30
3112	A795	55c multi	1.10	.30
3113	A795	55c multi	1.10	.30
a.	Horiz. strip of 5, #3109-3113		5.25	
b.	Booklet pane of 10, 2 each # 3109-3113		11.00	
	Nos. 3109-3113 (5)		5.50	1.50

The complete booklet sold for $12.95. Issued: No. 3104b, 7/23. Melbourne Stamp Show 09 (No. 3104b).

Insects and Spiders A796

Designs: Nos. 3114, 3120a, 3121, Hatchet wasp. Nos. 3115, 3120b, 3122, Praying mantis. Nos. 3116, 3120c, 3123, Ground beetle. Nos. 3117, 3120d, 3124, Jumping spider. Nos. 3118, 3120e, 3125, Ant. 1.10, Weevil.

2009, July 28 Litho. Perf. 14x14¾

3114	A796	55c multi	1.10	1.10
3115	A796	55c multi	1.10	1.10
3116	A796	55c multi	1.10	1.10
3117	A796	55c multi	1.10	1.10
3118	A796	55c multi	1.10	1.10
b.		Horiz. strip of 5, #3114-3118	5.25	5.25
3119	A796	$1.10 multi	2.25	1.60
	Nos. 3114-3119 (6)		7.75	7.10

Miniature Sheet
With Square of Thermochromic Ink
Covering Magnification Squares

3120	Sheet of 6	7.75	7.75
a.-e.	A796 55c Any single	1.10	1.10
f.	A796 $1.10 multi	2.25	2.25

Coil Stamps
Self-Adhesive
Serpentine Die Cut 11¼ Syncopated

3121	A796	55c multi	1.10	.30
3122	A796	55c multi	1.10	.30
3123	A796	55c multi	1.10	.30
3124	A796	55c multi	1.10	.30
3125	A796	55c multi	1.10	.30
a.		Horiz. strip of 5, #3121-3125	5.25	
	Nos. 3121-3125 (5)		5.50	1.50

Endangered Wildlife — A797

Designs: Nos. 3126, 3132, Bridled nailtail wallaby. Nos. 3127, 3133, Norfolk Island green parrot. Nos. 3128, 3134, Subarctic fur seal. Nos. 3129, 3135, Christmas Island blue-tailed skink. Nos. 3130, 3136, Green turtle.

2009, Aug. 4 Litho. Perf. 14¾x14
"Australia" Above Denomination

3126	A797	55c multi	1.10	1.10
3127	A797	55c multi	1.10	1.10
3128	A797	55c multi	1.10	1.10
3129	A797	55c multi	1.10	1.10
3130	A797	55c multi	1.10	1.10
a.		Horiz. strip of 5, #3126-3130	5.25	5.25
	Nos. 3126-3130 (5)		5.50	5.50
3131	A797	55c Sheet of 5, #3126, 3128-3130, Norfolk Island #980	5.25	5.25

Booklet Stamps
Self-Adhesive
Serpentine Die Cut 11¼ Syncopated

3132	A797	55c multi	1.10	.30
3133	A797	55c multi	1.10	.30
3134	A797	55c multi	1.10	.30
3135	A797	55c multi	1.10	.30
3136	A797	55c multi	1.10	.30
a.		Booklet pane of 20, 4 each #3132-3136	22.00	
	Nos. 3132-3136 (5)		5.50	1.50

Inscribed on the left side of Nos. 3128 and 3134 is "Australian Antarctic Territory"; on Nos. 3129 and 3135, "Christmas Island"; and on Nos. 3130 and 3136, "Cocos (Keeling) Islands." All recent stamps of the Australian possessions of Australian Antarctic Territory, Christmas Island and Cocos Islands are doubly-inscribed with "Australia" and the territory's name, and all stamps inscribed "Australia," "Australian Antarctic Territory," "Christmas Island," or "Cocos Islands," are valid for postage anywhere in those four areas. However, because Nos. 3128-3130 and 3134-3136 have the territorial inscriptions at the side rather than above the denomination like similar Norfolk Island stamps, Nos. 979-983, they will be listed here only and not in the listings for each of these territories. No. 3131 is identical to Norfolk Island No. 984. Norfolk Island No. 980 has "Norfolk Island" above the denomination, which differentiates it from Australia No. 3127.

Corrugated Iron Water Tank, Fleurieu Peninsula, South Australia
A798

Corrugated Iron House, Broken Hill, New South Wales
A799

Corrugated Iron Shearing Shed, Bushy Park Cattle Station, Queensland
A800

Magney House, Bingie Bingie Point, New South Wales
A801

2009, Aug. 11 Perf. 14x14¾

3137	A798	55c multi	1.10	1.10
a.		Booklet pane of 4	5.25	
3138	A799	55c multi	1.10	1.10
a.		Booklet pane of 4	5.25	
3139	A800	55c multi	1.10	1.10
a.		Booklet pane of 4	5.25	
3140	A801	55c multi	1.10	1.10
a.		Booklet pane of 4 Complete booklet, #3137a-3140a	22.00	
b.		Horiz. strip of 4, #3137-3140	4.50	4.50
	Nos. 3137-3140 (4)		4.40	4.40

Self-Adhesive
Serpentine Die Cut 11¼ Syncopated

3141	A798	55c multi	1.10	.30
3142	A799	55c multi	1.10	.30
3143	A800	55c multi	1.10	.30
3144	A801	55c multi	1.10	.30
a.		Horiz. coil strip of 4, #3141-3144	4.50	
b.		Booklet pane of 20, 5 each #3141-3144	22.00	
	Nos. 3141-3144 (4)		4.40	1.20

Complete booklet sold for $10.95.

Intl. Year of Astronomy
A802

Designs: 55c, Sombrero Galaxy (M104). $1.45, Reflection Nebula (M78). $2.10, Spiral Galaxy (M83).

2009, Aug. 25 Perf. 14x14¾

3145	A802	55c multi	1.10	.85
3146	A802	$1.45 multi	2.75	2.25
3147	A802	$2.10 multi	4.00	3.00
a.		Souvenir sheet, #3145-3147	8.00	6.00
	Nos. 3145-3147 (3)		7.85	6.10

No. 3147a exists imperf from a telephone drawing at a substantial premium over face value. Value for a single sheet, $22.

Birds — A803

Designs: 55c, Green catbird. $1.10, Noisy scrub-bird. $1.65, Mangrove golden whistler. $2.75, Scarlet honeyeater.

2009, Sept. 9 Litho. Perf. 14¾x14

3148	A803	55c multi	1.10	1.10
a.		Additionally dated "2013"	1.10	1.10
3149	A803	$1.10 multi	2.25	1.60
a.		Booklet pane of 2, #3148-3149	4.25	
b.		Additionally dated "2013"	2.10	2.10
3150	A803	$1.65 multi	3.50	2.50
a.		Booklet pane of 2, #3149-3150	7.25	
b.		Booklet pane of 2, #3148, 3150	6.75	—
c.		Additionally dated "2013"	3.25	3.25
3151	A803	$2.75 multi	5.50	4.25
a.		Booklet pane of 2, #3148, 3151	8.50	—
		Complete booklet, #3149a, 3150a, 3150b, 3151a	26.00	
b.		Additionally dated "2013"	5.50	5.50
c.		Booklet pane of 4, #3148a, 3149b, 3150c, 3151d	12.00	—
	Nos. 3148-3151 (4)		12.35	9.45

Issued: Nos. 3148a, 3149b, 3150c, 3151b, 3151c, 5/11/13. No. 3151c was issued in a booklet also containing Nos. 3376b, 3665b and 3925a.

Self-Adhesive
Serpentine Die Cut 11¼ Syncopated

3152	A803	55c multi	.95	.25
a.		Booklet pane of 20	19.00	

Complete booklet sold for $12.95.

Toys — A804

Children and: Nos. 3153, 3158, Cyclops pedal car. Nos. 3154, 3159, Test Match board game. Nos. 3155, 3160, Barbie doll. Nos. 3156, 3161, Malvern Star Dragstar bicycle. Nos. 3157, 3162, Cabbage Patch Kids doll.

2009, Sept. 25 Perf. 14¾x14

3153	A804	55c multi	1.10	1.10
a.		Booklet pane of 4	5.25	
3154	A804	55c multi	1.10	1.10
a.		Booklet pane of 4	5.25	
3155	A804	55c multi	1.10	1.10
a.		Booklet pane of 4	5.25	
b.		Sheet of 10 #3155 + 10 labels	22.00	22.00
3156	A804	55c multi	1.10	1.10
a.		Booklet pane of 4	5.25	
3157	A804	55c multi	1.10	1.10
a.		Booklet pane of 4 Complete booklet, #3153a, 3154a, 3155a, 3156a, 3157a	26.00	
b.		Horiz. strip of 5, #3153-3157	5.50	5.50
	Nos. 3153-3157 (5)		5.50	5.50

No. 3155b sold for $10.95.

Booklet Stamps
Self-Adhesive
Serpentine Die Cut 11¼ Syncopated

3158	A804	55c multi	1.10	.30
3159	A804	55c multi	1.10	.30
3160	A804	55c multi	1.10	.30
3161	A804	55c multi	1.10	.30
3162	A804	55c multi	1.10	.30
a.		Booklet pane of 10, 2 each #3158-3162	11.00	
	Nos. 3158-3162 (5)		5.50	1.50

Complete booklet sold for $12.95.

"Let's get active" and children playing: Nos. 3163, 3169, Australian rules football. Nos. 3164, 3170, Basketball. Nos. 3165, 3171, Soccer. Nos. 3166, 3172, Netball. Nos. 3167, 3173, Cricket. Nos. 3168, 3174, Tennis.

2009, Oct. 6 Perf. 14¾x14

3163	A805	55c multi	1.10	1.10
3164	A805	55c multi	1.10	1.10
3165	A805	55c multi	1.10	1.10
3166	A805	55c multi	1.10	1.10
3167	A805	55c multi	1.10	1.10
3168	A805	55c multi	1.10	1.10
a.		Block of 6, #3163-3168	7.00	7.00
b.		Souvenir sheet, #3163-3168	7.00	7.00
	Nos. 3163-3168 (6)		6.60	6.60

Booklet Stamps
Self-Adhesive
Serpentine Die Cut 11¼ Syncopated

3169	A805	55c multi	1.10	.30
a.		Booklet pane of 10	11.50	
3170	A805	55c multi	1.10	.30
a.		Booklet pane of 10	11.50	
3171	A805	55c multi	1.10	.30
a.		Booklet pane of 10	11.50	

Children Playing Sports — A805

3172	A805	55c multi	1.10	.30
a.		Booklet pane of 10	11.50	
3173	A805	55c multi	1.10	.30
a.		Booklet pane of 10	11.50	
3174	A805	55c multi	1.10	.30
a.		Booklet pane of 10	11.50	
b.		Booklet pane of 10, #3172, 3174, 2 each #3169-3171, 3173	11.50	
	Nos. 3169-3174 (6)		6.60	1.80

Miniature Sheet

Australia Post Employees — A806

No. 3175: a, Patrica Crabb (with white blouse with red dots). b, Shirley Freeman (at counter, with brochures at left). c, Vinko Romank (lifting mail tubs). d, Valda Knott (sorting boxes in background). e, Gordon Morgan (motorcycle in background). f, Vongpradith Phongsavan (with conveyor belt in background). g, Norma Thomas (with contractor delivery automobile). h, John Marsh (with blue shirt and tie). i, Anne Brun (at desk, with computer keyboard at left). j, Russell Price (with beard).

2009, Oct. 13 Perf. 14¾x14

3175	A806	Sheet of 10	11.50	8.50
a.-j.		55c Any single	1.10	.85

Australia Post, bicent. Compare with Type A787.

Christmas
A807   A808

Designs: Nos. 3176, 3183, Madonna and Child. Nos. 3177, 3184, 3190, 3195, Candles in star frame. Nos. 3178, 3185, 3191, 3196, Tree ornaments in Christmas tree frame. Nos. 3179, 3186, 3192, 3197, Gifts in stocking cap frame. Nos. 3180, 3187, 3193, 3198, Ornaments in bell frame. Nos. 3181, 3188, 3194, 3199, Candy canes in stocking frame. $1.25, Magi.

2009, Nov. 2 Litho. Perf. 14¾x14

3176	A807	50c multi	1.10	1.10
3177	A808	50c multi	1.10	1.10
3178	A808	50c multi	1.10	1.10
3179	A808	50c multi	1.10	1.10
3180	A808	50c multi	1.10	1.10
3181	A808	50c multi	1.10	1.10
a.		Horiz. strip of 5, #3177-3181	5.50	5.50
3182	A807	$1.25 multi	2.75	2.75
a.		Souvenir sheet of 2, #3176, 3182	4.00	4.00
	Nos. 3176-3182 (7)		9.35	9.35

Booklet Stamps (#3183-3194)
Self-Adhesive
Serpentine Die Cut 11¼ Syncopated

3183	A807	50c multi	1.10	.30
a.		Booklet pane of 20	22.00	
3184	A808	50c multi	1.10	.30
3185	A808	50c multi	1.10	.30
3186	A808	50c multi	1.10	.30
3187	A808	50c multi	1.10	.30
3188	A808	50c multi	1.10	.30
a.		Booklet pane of 10, 2 each #3184-3188	11.00	
3189	A807	$1.25 multi	2.75	.30
a.		Booklet pane of 5	14.00	

Litho. With Foil Application
Frames in Gold

3190	A808	50c multi	1.10	.30
3191	A808	50c multi	1.10	.30
3192	A808	50c multi	1.10	.30
3193	A808	50c multi	1.10	.30
3194	A808	50c multi	1.10	.30
a.		Booklet pane of 10, 2 each #3190-3194	11.00	
	Nos. 3183-3194 (12)		14.85	3.60

With Personalized Photo at Right
Like Type A692a

3195	A808	50c multi	2.40	2.40
3196	A808	50c multi	2.40	2.40
3197	A808	50c multi	2.40	2.40

3198	A808	50c multi	2.40	2.40
3199	A808	50c multi	2.40	2.40
		Nos. 3195-3199 (5)	12.00	12.00

Nos. 3195-3199 were sold in sheets of 20 containing 4 of each stamp, have personalized pictures and a straight edge at right and lack separations between the stamp and the personalized photo. Sheets of 20 of sold for $23. No. 3197 exists without "Australia" and the denomination.

Authors — A809

Designs: Nos, 3200, 3212, Color photograph of Peter Carey. No. 3201, Black-and-white photograph of Carey. No. 3202, Black-and-white photograph of David Malouf. Nos. 3203, 3213, Color photograph of Malouf. Nos, 3204, 3214, Color photograph of Colleen McCullough. No. 3205, Black-and-white photograph of McCullough. No. 3206, Black-and-white photograph of Bryce Courtenay. Nos. 3207, 3215, Color photograph of Courtenay. Nos, 3208, 3216, Color photograph of Thomas Keneally. No. 3209, Black-and-white photograph of Keneally. No. 3210, Black-and-white photograph of Tim Winton. Nos. 3211, 3217, Color photograph of Winton.

2010, Jan. 21   Litho.   Perf. 14¾x14

3200	A809	55c multi	1.10	1.10
3201	A809	55c black & gray	1.10	1.10
3202	A809	55c black & gray	1.10	1.10
3203	A809	55c multi	1.10	1.10
a.		Block of 4, #3200-3203	4.50	4.50
b.		Booklet pane of 4, #3203-3203	8.50	—
c.		As "b," with color separations of stamps	8.50	—
3204	A809	55c multi	1.10	1.10
3205	A809	55c black & gray	1.10	1.10
3206	A809	55c black & gray	1.10	1.10
3207	A809	55c multi	1.10	1.10
a.		Block of 4, #3204-3207	4.50	4.50
b.		Booklet pane of 4, #3204-3207	8.50	—
c.		As "b," with color separations of stamps	8.50	—
3208	A809	55c multi	1.10	1.10
3209	A809	55c black & gray	1.10	1.10
3210	A809	55c black & gray	1.10	1.10
3211	A809	55c multi	1.10	1.10
a.		Block of 4, #3208-3211	4.50	4.50
b.		Booklet pane of 4, #3208-3211	8.50	—
c.		As "b," with color separations of stamps	8.50	—
		Complete booklet, #3203b, 3203c, 3207b, 3207c, 3211b, 3211c	52.00	
		Nos. 3200-3211 (12)	13.20	13.20

Booklet Stamps
Self-Adhesive
Serpentine Die Cut 11¼ Syncopated

3212	A809	55c multi	1.10	.30
3213	A809	55c multi	1.10	.30
3214	A809	55c multi	1.10	.30
3215	A809	55c multi	1.10	.30
3216	A809	55c multi	1.10	.30
3217	A809	55c multi	1.10	.30
a.		Booklet pane of 20, 5 #3214, 3 each #3212-3213, 3215-3217	23.00	
		Nos. 3212-3217 (6)	6.60	1.80

Complete booklet sold for $24.95. Color separations were not valid for postage.

Rule of Governor Lachlan Macquarie, Bicent. — A810

Designs: No. 3218, Macquarie (1762-1824) and north view of Sydney. No. 3219, Port Jackson and Sydney Town. No. 3220, Parramatta Female Penitentiary. No. 3221, Governor's Sydney Stables.

2010, Feb. 16   Perf. 14x14¾

3218	A810	55c multi	1.10	.85
a.		Booklet pane of 4	5.75	—
3219	A810	55c multi	1.10	.85
a.		Booklet pane of 4	5.75	—
3220	A810	55c multi	1.10	.85
a.		Booklet pane of 4	5.75	—

3221	A810	55c multi	1.10	.85
a.		Booklet pane of 4	5.75	—
		Complete booklet, #3218a-3221a	23.00	
b.		Block of 4, #3218-3221	4.50	3.50
		Nos. 3218-3221 (4)	4.40	3.40

Complete booklet sold of $10.95.

Coinage of the Australian Commonwealth, Cent. — A811

1910 two shilling coin: Nos. 3222, 3224a, Reverse depicting Australian coat of arms. Nos. 3223, 3224b, Obverse depicting King Edward VII.

2010, Feb. 23   Litho.   Perf. 14x14¾

3222	A811	55c multi	1.10	.85
3223	A811	$2.75 multi	5.75	2.75

Souvenir Sheet
Litho. & Embossed With Foil Application

3224		Sheet of 2	7.00	3.75
a.	A811	55c multi	1.10	.85
b.	A811	$2.75 multi	5.75	2.75

No. 3224 exists imperf from a telephone drawing at a substantial premium over face value. Value for single souvenir sheet, $14.

Gold Medalists at 2010 Winter Olympics, Vancouver A812

Designs: No. 3225, Torah Bright, Snowboard halfpipe. No. 3226, Lydia Lassila, Freestyle skiing aerials.

2010   Litho.   Perf. 14¼

3225	A812	55c multi	1.10	.85
3226	A812	55c multi	1.10	.85

Issued: No. 3225, 2/25; No. 3226, 3/3.

Powered Flight in Australia, Cent. (in 2009) A813

Airplane of: 55c, Colin Defries. $1.45, John Duigan. $2.10, Harry Houdini.

2010, Mar. 9   Perf. 14x14¾

3227	A813	55c multi	1.10	.85
3228	A813	$1.45 multi	3.25	1.60
a.		Souvenir sheet, #3218, 3223, 3227, 3228	11.00	11.00
b.		Sheet of 4, 2 each #3227-3228	9.00	6.75
3229	A813	$2.10 multi	4.50	2.25
		Nos. 3227-3229 (3)	8.85	4.70

Booklet Stamps
Self-Adhesive
Serpentine Die Cut 11¼ Syncopated

3230	A813	$1.45 multi	3.25	1.60
a.		Booklet pane of 5	16.00	
3231	A813	$2.10 multi	4.50	2.25
a.		Booklet pane of 5	23.00	

2010 Canberra Stamp Show (No. 3228a). London 2010 Festival of Stamps (No. 3228b). Issued: No. 3228a, 3/12. No. 3228b, 5/8.

Agricultural Shows — A814

Designs: Nos. 3232, 3237, Prize bull. Nos. 3233, 3238, Cake decorating competition. Nos. 3234, 3239, Horse competition. Nos. 3235, 3240, Wood chopping competition. Nos. 3236, 3241, Dog show.

2010, Mar. 23   Litho.   Perf. 14¾x14

3232	A814	55c multi	1.10	1.10
a.		Booklet pane of 4	5.50	
3233	A814	55c multi	1.10	1.10
a.		Booklet pane of 4	5.50	
3234	A814	55c multi	1.10	1.10
a.		Booklet pane of 4	5.50	
3235	A814	55c multi	1.10	1.10
a.		Booklet pane of 4	5.50	
3236	A814	55c multi	1.10	1.10
a.		Booklet pane of 4	5.50	
		Complete booklet, #3232a-3236a	27.50	
b.		Horiz. strip of 5, #3232-3236	5.75	5.75
c.		Souvenir sheet of 1 #3232-3236	5.75	5.75
		Nos. 3232-3236 (5)	5.50	5.50

Booklet Stamps
Self-Adhesive
Serpentine Die Cut 11¼ Syncopated

3237	A814	55c multi	1.10	.30
3238	A814	55c multi	1.10	.30
3239	A814	55c multi	1.10	.30
3240	A814	55c multi	1.10	.30
3241	A814	55c multi	1.10	.30
a.		Booklet pane of 10, 2 each #3237-3241	11.50	—
		Nos. 3237-3241 (5)	5.50	1.50

Complete booklet sold for $12.95.

Queen's Birthday — A815

2010, Apr. 6   Perf. 14¾x14

3242	A815	55c multi	1.25	1.25
a.		Sheet of 4, #2505b, 2864b, 3067b, 3242	8.00	4.00

Booklet Stamp
Self-Adhesive
Serpentine Die Cut 11¼ Syncopated

3243	A815	55c multi	1.25	.30
a.		Booklet pane of 10	12.75	

Issued: No. 3242a, 5/8. London 2010 Festival of Stamps (No. 3242a).

Kokoda Campaign, 68th Anniv. — A816

Designs: Nos. 3244, 3249, Soldiers in battle. Nos. 3245, 3250, Injured Australian soldier, Papuan natives. Nos. 3246, 3251, Veterans of Kokoda Campaign, Papuan houses. Nos. 3247, 3252, Tourists at Kokoda. $1.45, Veterans at Kokoda Campaign Memorial, Isurava, Papua New Guinea.

2010, Apr. 20   Perf. 14¾x14

3244	A816	55c multi	1.10	1.10
3245	A816	55c multi	1.10	1.10
a.		Booklet pane of 4, 2 each #3244-3245	6.25	—
3246	A816	55c multi	1.10	1.10
3247	A816	55c multi	1.10	1.10
a.		Booklet pane of 4	6.25	—
b.		Horiz. strip of 4, #3244-3247	4.50	4.50
3248	A816	$1.45 multi	3.25	2.40
a.		Booklet pane of 4, 2 each #3246, 3248	11.50	
		Complete booklet, #3245a, 3247a, 3248a	24.00	
b.		Souvenir sheet, #3244-3248	7.75	7.75
		Nos. 3244-3248 (5)	7.65	6.80

Self-Adhesive
Serpentine Die Cut 11¼ Syncopated

3249	A816	55c multi	1.10	.30
3250	A816	55c multi	1.10	.30
3251	A816	55c multi	1.10	.30
3252	A816	55c multi	1.10	.30
a.		Vert. coil strip of 4, #3249-3252	4.50	
b.		Booklet pane of 10, 2 each #3250, 3252, 3 each #3249, 3251	11.50	
		Nos. 3249-3252 (4)	4.40	1.20

Complete booklet sold for $10.95. See Papua New Guinea Nos. 1455-1456.

Queen Victoria ("Chalon Head" Portrait of Tasmania and Queensland Stamps) — A817

2010, May 7   Litho.   Perf. 14x13½

3253	A817	$5 multi	10.00	5.25
a.		Souvenir sheet of 1	10.00	5.25
b.		As "a," with London 2010 emblem in gold in sheet margin	8.25	8.25

No. 3253 has simulated toning. A souvenir sheet with a litho. and engraved stamp sold for $15. Issued: No. 3253b, 5/8.

Railway Journeys A818

Designs: Nos. 3254, 3258, The Ghan. Nos. 3255, 3259, West Coast Wilderness Railway, Tasmania. No. 3256, 3260, The Indian Pacific. $2.10, Kuranda Scenic Railway, Queensland (50x30mm).

2010, May 7   Perf. 14x14¾

3254	A818	55c multi	1.10	1.10
3255	A818	55c multi	1.10	1.10
3256	A818	55c multi	1.10	1.10
a.		Booklet pane of 4, #3254, 3255, 2 #3256	6.50	—
b.		Booklet pane of 4, #3255, 3256, 2 #3254	6.50	—
c.		Booklet pane of 4, #3254, 3256, 2 #3255	6.50	—

Perf. 13½x14

3257	A818	$2.10 multi	4.25	2.25
a.		Booklet pane of 1	6.25	—
		Complete booklet, #3256a-3256c, 3257a	26.50	
b.		Souvenir sheet of 1	4.25	2.25
c.		As "b," with London 2010 emblem in gold in sheet margin	3.50	3.50
		Nos. 3254-3257 (4)	7.55	5.55

Self-Adhesive
Serpentine Die Cut 11¼ Syncopated

3258	A818	55c multi	1.10	.30
3259	A818	55c multi	1.10	.30
3260	A818	55c multi	1.10	.30
a.		Horiz. coil strip of 3, #3258-3260	3.50	
b.		Booklet pane of 20, 8 each #3258-3259, 4 #3260	23.00	

Serpentine Die Cut 11¼

3261	A818	$2.10 multi	4.25	2.25
a.		Booklet pane of 5	22.00	
		Nos. 3258-3261 (4)	7.55	3.15

No. 3257a has blue panels at the sides. Complete booklet sold for $12.95. Issued: No. 3257c, 5/8.

Expo 2010, Shanghai — A819

Designs: No. 3262, Australian Pavilion. No. 3263, Australian kookaburra mascot, Peng Peng.

2010, May 18   Perf. 14¾x14

3262	A819	55c multi	1.00	.80
3263	A819	55c multi	1.00	.80
a.		Pair, #3262-3263	2.00	1.60

UNESCO World
Heritage Sites in
Australia — A820

Designs: Nos. 3264, 3268, Purnululu
National Park. Nos. 3265, 3269, Kakadu
National Park. No. 3266, Gondwana
Rainforests, horiz. No. 3267, Tasmanian Wilderness, horiz.

2010, May 25   **Perf. 14¾x14**
3264 A820 55c multi   1.00 1.00
3265 A820 55c multi   1.00 1.00
  a. Horiz. pair, #3264-3265   2.00 2.00

Perf. 14x14¾
3266 A820 $1.10 multi   2.25 1.60
3267 A820 $1.10 multi   2.25 1.60
  a. Horiz. pair, #3266-3267   4.50 3.25
  Nos. 3264-3267 (4)   6.50 5.20

Self-Adhesive
Serpentine Die Cut 11¼ Syncopated
3268 A820 55c multi   1.00 1.00
3269 A820 55c multi   1.00 1.00
  a. Vert. coil pair, #3268-3269   2.00
  b. Booklet pane of 10, 5 each #3268-3269   10.00

Fish — A821

Designs: 5c, Coral rabbitfish. Nos. 3271, 3278, 3283, Clown triggerfish. Nos. 3272, 3279, 3284, Spotted sweetlips. Nos. 3273, 3280, 3285, Golden damsel. Nos. 3274, 3281, 3286, Regal angelfish. $1.20, Saddle butterflyfish. $1.80, Chevron butterflyfish. $3, Orangefin anemonefish.

2010, June 21   **Litho.**   **Perf. 14x14½**
3270 A821 5c multi   .25 .25
3271 A821 60c multi   1.00 .25
3272 A821 60c multi   1.00 .25
  a. Souvenir sheet, #3271, 3272, 2 #3270   2.40 2.40
3273 A821 60c multi   1.00 .25
3274 A821 60c multi   1.00 .25
  a. Block or strip of 4, #3271-3274   4.00 1.00
3275 A821 $1.20 multi   2.00 1.00
3276 A821 $1.80 multi   3.00 1.50

Perf. 14½x14
Size: 50x30mm (#3277)
3277 A821 $3 multi   5.00 2.50
  Nos. 3270-3277 (8)   14.25 6.25

Coil Stamps
Self-Adhesive
Die Cut Perf. 12¾
3278 A821 60c multi   1.00 .25
3279 A821 60c multi   1.00 .25
3280 A821 60c multi   1.00 .25
3281 A821 60c multi   1.00 .25
  a. Horiz. strip of 4, #3278-3281   4.00

Booklet Stamps
Serpentine Die Cut 11¼
3282 A821 5c multi   .25 .25
  a. Booklet pane of 20   4.00
3283 A821 60c multi   1.00 .25
3284 A821 60c multi   1.00 .25
3285 A821 60c multi   1.00 .25
3286 A821 60c multi   1.00 .25
  a. Booklet pane of 10, 3 each #3283-3284, 2 each #3285-3286   10.00
  b. Booklet pane of 20, 5 each #3283-3286   20.00
  Nos. 3278-3286 (9)   8.25 2.25

Issued: No. 3272a, 8/4/10. Bangkok 2010 Intl. Stamp Exhibition (No. 3272a).

Beaches — A822

Designs: $1.50, Bay of Fires, Tasmania. $2.20, Cape Tribulation, Queensland. $4.30, Hellfire Bay, Western Australia, horiz.

2010, June 28   **Perf. 14¾x14**
3287 A822 $1.50 multi   2.50 1.25
3288 A822 $2.20 multi   3.75 1.90

Size: 50x30mm (#3289)
Perf. 14½x14
3289 A822 $4.30 multi   7.25 3.75
  Nos. 3287-3289 (3)   13.50 6.90

Booklet Stamps
Self-Adhesive
Serpentine Die Cut 11¼ Syncopated
3290 A822 $1.50 multi   2.50 1.25
  a. Booklet pane of 5   12.50
3291 A822 $2.20 multi   3.75 1.90
  a. Booklet pane of 5   19.00

With Personalized Photo at Right Like Type A692a
Serpentine Die Cut 11½x11¼ Syncopated
3292 A822 $1.50 multi   3.75 3.75
3293 A822 $2.20 multi   4.75 4.75

Nos. 3292-3293 each were printed in sheets of 20 and have personalized pictures and a straight edge at right, and lack separations between the stamp and the personalized photo. Sheets of 20 of No. 3292 sold for $43, and No. 3293 sold for $56.

Adopted
Dogs — A823

Designs: Nos. 3294, 3299, Piper. Nos. 3295, 3300, Jessie. Nos. 3296, 3301, Buckley. Nos. 3297, 3302, Daisy. Nos. 3298, 3303, Tigger.

2010, June 29   **Perf. 14¾x14**
3294 A823 60c multi   1.00 1.00
3295 A823 60c multi   1.00 1.00
3296 A823 60c multi   1.00 1.00
3297 A823 60c multi   1.00 1.00
3298 A823 60c multi   1.00 1.00
  a. Horiz. strip of 5, #3294-3298   5.00 5.00
  Nos. 3294-3298 (5)   5.00 5.00

Self-Adhesive
Serpentine Die Cut 11¼ Syncopated
3299 A823 60c multi   1.00 .25
3300 A823 60c multi   1.00 .25
3301 A823 60c multi   1.00 .25
3302 A823 60c multi   1.00 .25
3303 A823 60c multi   1.00 .25
  a. Vert. coil strip of 5, #3299-3303   5.00
  b. Booklet pane of 10, 2 each #3299-3303   10.00
  Nos. 3299-3303 (5)   5.00 1.25

No. 3303a was produced by two different printers, Pemara and McKellar Renown. The stamps have the printer's name on the backing paper, but are essentially identical to each other.

Emergency
Services — A824

000 Emergency Services emblem and: Nos. 3304, 3308, "Stay Focused, Stay Relevant, Stay on Line." Nos. 3305, 3309, Police Helicopter. Nos. 3306, 3310, Fire. Nos. 3307, 3311, Ambulance Cross.

2010, July 13   **Perf. 14¾x14**
3304 A824 60c multi   1.10 1.10
3305 A824 60c multi   1.10 1.10
3306 A824 60c multi   1.10 1.10
3307 A824 60c multi   1.10 1.10
  a. Horiz. strip of 4, #3304-3307   4.40 4.40
  Nos. 3304-3307 (4)   4.40 4.40

Self-Adhesive
Serpentine Die Cut 11¼ Syncopated
3308 A824 60c multi   1.10 .25
3309 A824 60c multi   1.10 .25
3310 A824 60c multi   1.10 .25

3311 A824 60c multi   1.10 .25
  a. Vert. coil strip of 4, #3308-3311   4.40
  b. Booklet pane of 20, 5 each #3308-3311   22.00
  Nos. 3308-3311 (4)   4.40 1.00

Southern
Cross — A825

2010, July 19   **Perf. 14½x14**
3312 A825 60c Blue sky   1.10 1.10
  a. Sheet of 20 + 20 labels   27.00 27.00
3313 A825 60c Purple & orange sky   1.10 1.10
  a. Horiz. pair, #3312-3313   2.25 2.25
  b. Sheet of 20 + 20 labels   27.00 27.00
  c. Perf. 14x14½, + label at bottom   1.40 1.40

Nos. 3312a and 3313b each sold for $12.95 and have labels depicting various National Rugby League and Australian Football League team emblems that could not be personalized. No. 3313c was issued in sheet of 10 + 10 labels depicting race horse Black Caviar that were sold in groups of 2 sheets that sold for $12.95.

Balloons — A826   Teddy
          Bear — A827

Wattle — A828   Flowers — A829

Tulips — A830   Roses — A831

Flowers and   Wedding
Champagne   Rings — A833
Flutes — A832

2010, July 19   **Perf. 14¾x14**
3314 A826 60c multi   1.10 1.10
3315 A827 60c multi   1.10 1.10
3316 A828 60c multi   1.10 1.10
  a. Horiz. strip of 3, #3314-3316   3.30 3.30
3317 A829 60c multi   1.10 1.10
3318 A830 60c multi   1.10 1.10
3319 A831 60c multi   1.10 1.10
3320 A832 60c multi   1.10 1.10
  a. Block of 4, #3317-3320   4.40 4.40
3321 A833 $1.20 multi   2.25 2.25
  Nos. 3314-3321 (8)   9.95 9.95

Booklet Stamps
Self-Adhesive
Serpentine Die Cut 11¼ Syncopated
3322 A826 60c multi   1.10 .25
  a. Booklet pane of 10   11.00
3323 A827 60c multi   1.10 .25
  a. Booklet pane of 10   11.00
3324 A828 60c multi   1.10 .25
  a. Booklet pane of 10   11.00
3325 A830 60c multi   1.10 .25
  a. Booklet pane of 10   11.00
3326 A831 60c multi   1.10 .25
  a. Booklet pane of 10   11.00
3327 A833 $1.20 multi   2.25 1.10
  a. Booklet pane of 10   22.50
  Nos. 3322-3327 (6)   7.75 2.35

With Personalized Photo at Right Like Type A692a
Serpentine Die Cut 11½x11¼ Syncopated
3328 A826 60c multi   2.25 2.25
3329 A827 60c multi   2.25 2.25
3330 A828 60c multi   2.25 2.25
3331 A829 60c multi   2.25 2.25
3332 A830 60c multi   2.25 2.25
3333 A831 60c multi   2.25 2.25
3334 A832 60c multi   2.25 2.25
3335 A833 $1.20 multi   3.50 3.50
  Nos. 3328-3335 (8)   19.25 19.25

Nos. 3328-3335 each were printed in sheets of 20 and have personalized pictures and a straight edge at right, and lack separations between the stamp and the personalized photo. Sheets of 20 of Nos. 3328-3334 each sold for $25, and No. 3335 sold for $37.
See No. 3401.

Australian
Taxation
Office, Cent.
A834

2010, July 27   **Litho.**   **Perf. 14x14¾**
3336 A834 60c multi   1.10 .85

Burke and
Wills
Expedition,
150th Anniv.
A835

Designs: Nos. 3337, 3341, Explorers Robert Burke (1820-61) and William J. Wills (1834-61). Nos. 3338, 3342, Burke and Wills on horses leaving Melbourne. No. 3339, Expedition members returning from Gulf of Carpenteria. No. 3340, Expedition members heading towards Mt. Hopeless.

2010, Aug. 3   **Litho.**   **Perf. 14x14¾**
3337 A835 60c multi   1.10 1.10
  a. Booklet pane of 4   5.00
3338 A835 60c multi   1.10 1.10
  a. Horiz. pair, #3337-3338   2.20 2.20
  b. Booklet pane of 4   5.00
3339 A835 $1.20 multi   2.25 2.25
  a. Booklet pane of 2   5.00
3340 A835 $1.20 multi   2.25 2.25
  a. Horiz. pair, #3339-3340   4.50 4.50
  b. Booklet pane of 2   5.00
  c. Complete booklet, #3337a, 3338b, 3339a, 3340b   20.00
  Nos. 3337-3340 (4)   6.70 6.70

Coil Stamps
Self-Adhesive
Serpentine Die Cut 11¼ Syncopated
3341 A835 60c multi   1.10 .25
3342 A835 60c multi   1.10 .25
  a. Horiz. pair, #3341-3342   2.20

Complete booklet sold for $10.95.
See Australian Antarctic Territory No. L149b.

Girl Guides,
Cent.
A836

Emblem, early Girl Guides and: 60c, Girl Guide with helmet and climbing rope. $1.50, Girl Guides wearing hats. $2.20, Olave Baden-Powell.

2010, Aug. 31 Litho. Perf. 14x14¾
3343	A836	60c multi	1.10	1.10
3344	A836	$1.50 multi	2.75	2.75
3345	A836	$2.20 multi	4.00	4.00
		Nos. 3343-3345 (3)	7.85	7.85

Self-Adhesive
Serpentine Die Cut 11¼ Syncopated
3346	A836	60c multi	1.10	.25
a.		Booklet pane of 20	22.00	

Booklet Stamps
3347	A836	$1.50 multi	2.75	1.40
a.		Booklet pane of 5	14.00	
3348	A836	$2.20 multi	4.00	2.00
a.		Booklet pane of 5	20.00	
		Nos. 3346-3348 (3)	7.85	3.65

Dedication of National Service Memorial, Canberra A837

2010, Sept. 8 Litho. Perf. 14x14¾
3349	A837	60c multi	1.10	1.10
a.		Additionally dated "2013" (#3349b)	1.25	1.25
b.		Booklet pane of 4 #3349a	5.00	

Issued: Nos. 3349a, 3349b, 3/5/13. No. 3349b was issued in booklet along with Nos. 1939c, 2710c, 2869e, 3107c and 3877a.

Booklet Stamp
Self-Adhesive
Serpentine Die Cut 11¼ Syncopated
3350	A837	60c multi	1.10	.25
a.		Booklet pane of 10	11.00	

Long Weekend Vacations A838

People on weekend vacations: Nos. 3351, 3356, Boating at beach, 1950s. Nos. 3352, 3357, Camping, 1960s. Nos. 3353, 3358, Surfing at beach, 1970s. Nos. 3354, 3359, Houseboating on river, 1980s. Nos. 3355, 3360, At winter resort, 1990s.

2010, Sept. 22 Perf. 14x14¾
3351	A838	60c multi	1.25	1.25
a.		Booklet pane of 4	5.50	—
3352	A838	60c multi	1.25	1.25
a.		Booklet pane of 4	5.50	—
3353	A838	60c multi	1.25	1.25
a.		Booklet pane of 4	5.50	—
3354	A838	60c multi	1.25	1.25
a.		Booklet pane of 4	5.50	—
3355	A838	60c multi	1.25	1.25
a.		Booklet pane of 4	5.50	—
		Complete booklet, #3351a-3355a	27.50	
b.		Horiz. strip of 5, #3351-3355	6.25	6.25
		Nos. 3351-3355 (5)	6.25	6.25

Self-Adhesive
Serpentine Die Cut 11¼ Syncopated
3356	A838	60c multi	1.25	.25
3357	A838	60c multi	1.25	.25
3358	A838	60c multi	1.25	.25
3359	A838	60c multi	1.25	.25
3360	A838	60c multi	1.25	.25
a.		Horiz. coil strip of 5, #3356-3360	6.25	
b.		Booklet pane of 10, 2 each #3356-3360	12.50	
		Nos. 3356-3360 (5)	6.25	1.25

Complete booklet sold for $13.95.

Care for Wildlife — A839

Designs: Nos. 3361, 3367, Common wombat. Nos. 3362, 3368, Eastern gray kangaroo. Nos. 3363, 3369, Koala. Nos. 3364, 3370, Gray-headed flying fox. Nos. 3365, 3371, Southern boobook. $1.20, Ringtail possum.

2010, Oct. 5 Litho. Perf. 14¾x14
Denomination Color
3361	A839	60c orange brown	1.25	1.25
3362	A839	60c blue	1.25	1.25
3363	A839	60c green	1.25	1.25
3364	A839	60c red brown	1.25	1.25
3365	A839	60c bister	1.25	1.25
a.		Horiz. strip of 5, #3361-3365	6.25	6.25
3366	A839	$1.20 red	2.40	1.75
a.		Souvenir sheet of 6, #3361-3366	8.75	8.75
		Nos. 3361-3366 (6)	8.65	8.00

Self-Adhesive
Serpentine Die Cut 11¼ Syncopated
3367	A839	60c orange brown	1.25	.25
3368	A839	60c blue	1.25	.25
3369	A839	60c green	1.25	.25
3370	A839	60c red brown	1.25	.25
3371	A839	60c bister	1.25	.25
a.		Vert. coil strip of 5, #3367-3371	6.25	
b.		Booklet pane of 10, 2 each #3367-3371	12.50	
		Nos. 3367-3371 (5)	6.25	1.25

Canonization of St. Mary MacKillop (1842-1909) A840

2010, Oct. 18 Perf. 14¾x14
3372	A840	60c multi	1.25	.95

Kingfishers A841

Designs: 60c, Red-backed kingfisher. $1.20, Sacred kingfisher. $1.80, Blue-winged kookaburra. $3, Yellow-billed kingfisher.

2010, Oct. 26 Perf. 14¾x14
3373	A841	60c multi	1.00	1.00
a.		Additionally dated "2013"	1.25	1.25
3374	A841	$1.20 multi	2.50	1.90
a.		Additionally dated "2013"	2.40	2.40
3375	A841	$1.80 multi	3.75	1.90
a.		Additionally dated "2013"	3.50	3.50
3376	A841	$3 multi	6.25	3.25
a.		Additionally dated "2013"	5.75	5.75
b.		Booklet pane of 4, #3373a, 3374a, 3375a, 3376a	13.00	—
		Nos. 3373-3376 (4)	13.75	8.30

Issued: Nos. 3373a, 3374a, 3375a, 3376a, 3376b, 5/11/13. No. 3376b was issued in a booklet also containing Nos. 3151c, 3665b and 3925a.

Self-Adhesive
Serpentine Die Cut 11¼ Syncopated
3377	A841	60c multi	1.25	.25
a.		Booklet pane of 10	12.50	

150th Running of the Melbourne Cup Horse Race — A842

Designs: No. 3378, Melbourne Cup. Nos. 3379, 3382, Carbine, 1890 winner, horiz. Nos. 3380, 3383, Phar Lap, 1930 winner, horiz. Nos. 3381, 3384, Saintly, 1996 winner, horiz.

2010, Nov. 1 Litho. Perf. 14¾x14
3378	A842	60c multi	1.25	.95
a.		Booklet pane of 4	7.25	

Perf. 14x14¾
3379	A842	60c multi	1.25	1.25
a.		Booklet pane of 4	7.25	
3380	A842	60c multi	1.25	1.25
a.		Booklet pane of 4	7.25	
3381	A842	60c multi	1.25	1.25
a.		Booklet pane of 4	7.25	—
		Complete booklet, #3378a, 3379a, 3380a, 3381a	29.00	
b.		Souvenir sheet, #3378-3381	5.00	5.00
		Nos. 3378-3381 (4)	5.00	4.70

No. 3381b exists imperf from a telephone drawing at a substantial premium over face value. Value for single souvenir sheet, $15.

Booklet Stamps
Self-Adhesive
Serpentine Die Cut 11¼ Syncopated
3382	A842	60c multi	1.25	.25
3383	A842	60c multi	1.25	.25
3384	A842	60c multi	1.25	.25
a.		Booklet pane of 20, 7 each #3382-3383, 6 #3384	25.00	
		Nos. 3382-3384 (3)	3.75	75.00

Complete booklet sold for $13.95 and also included imperforate and gummed lithographed pages reproducing pairs of Nos. 337, 693, 694, 2104 and 2106 that were not valid for postage.

Christmas A843 A844

Designs: Nos. 3385, 3390, 3393, 3396, Girl writing letter to Santa Claus. Nos. 3386, 3389, 3394, 3395, Santa Claus reading letter. Nos. 3387, 3391, Adoration of the Magi. $1.30, Adoration of the Shepherds.

2010, Nov. 1 Litho. Perf. 14¾x14
3385	A843	55c multi	1.10	1.10
3386	A843	55c multi	1.10	1.10
a.		Horiz. pair, #3385-3386	2.25	2.25
3387	A844	55c multi	1.10	1.10
3388	A844	$1.30 multi	2.75	2.75
		Nos. 3385-3388 (4)	6.05	6.05

Booklet Stamps
Self-Adhesive
Serpentine Die Cut 11¼ Syncopated
3389	A843	55c multi	1.10	.25
3390	A843	55c multi	1.10	.25
a.		Booklet pane of 20, 10 each #3389-3390	22.00	
b.		Booklet pane of 20	22.00	
3391	A844	55c multi	1.10	.25
a.		Booklet pane of 20	22.00	
3392	A844	$1.30 multi	2.75	1.40
a.		Booklet pane of 5	14.00	

Litho. With Foil Application
3393	A843	55c multi	1.10	.25
a.		Booklet pane of 10	11.00	
3394	A843	55c multi	1.10	.25
a.		Booklet pane of 10	11.00	
		Nos. 3389-3394 (6)	8.25	2.65

With Personalized Photo at Right Like Type A692a
Litho.
Self-Adhesive
Serpentine Die Cut 11½x11¼ Syncopated
3395	A843	55c multi	2.50	2.50
3396	A843	55c multi	2.50	2.50

Nos. 3395-3396 were printed together in sheets of 20 (10 of each design), and have personalized pictures and a straight edge at right and lack separations between the stamp and the personalized photo. Sheets of 20 sold for $24.

Champagne Flutes Type of 2010 and

Roses — A845   Hearts and Flowers — A846

2011, Jan. 18 Perf. 14¾x14
3397	A845	60c multi	1.25	1.25
3398	A846	60c multi	1.25	1.25
a.		Horiz. pair, #3397-3398	2.50	2.50

Booklet Stamps
Self-Adhesive
Serpentine Die Cut 11¼ Syncopated
3399	A845	60c multi	1.25	.25
a.		Booklet pane of 12	12.50	
3400	A846	60c multi	1.25	.25
a.		Booklet pane of 12	12.50	
3401	A832	60c multi	1.25	.6
a.		Booklet pane of 12	12.50	
		Nos. 3399-3401 (3)	3.75	1.1

With Personalized Photo at Right Like Type A692a
Serpentine Die Cut 11½x11¼ Syncopated
3402	A845	60c multi	2.50	2.5
3403	A846	60c multi	2.50	2.5

Nos. 3395-3396 each were printed in sheet of 20 and have personalized pictures and straight edge at right and lack separation between the stamp and the personalize photo. Sheets of 20 of Nos. 3402-3403 eac sold for $25.
No. 3401 dated 2010.

Famous Women — A848

Designs: Nos. 3404, 3408, Eva Cox, feminist. Nos. 3405, 3409, Germaine Greer, write on feminist topics. Nos. 3406, 3410, Elizabeth Evatt, jurist. Nos. 3407, 3411, Anne Summers writer.

2011, Jan. 20 Perf. 14¾x1(4)
3404	A848	60c multi	1.25	1.2
3405	A848	60c multi	1.25	1.2
3406	A848	60c multi	1.25	1.2
3407	A848	60c multi	1.25	1.2
a.		Horiz. strip of 4, #3404-3407	5.00	5.0
		Nos. 3404-3407 (4)	5.00	5.0

Booklet Stamps
Self-Adhesive
Serpentine Die Cut 11¼ Syncopated
3408	A848	60c multi	1.25	.2
3409	A848	60c multi	1.25	.2
3410	A848	60c multi	1.25	.2
3411	A848	60c multi	1.25	.2
a.		Booklet pane of 20, 5 each #3408-3411	25.00	
		Nos. 3408-3411 (4)	5.00	1.0

Intl. Women's Day, Cent. A849

2011, Feb. 15 Perf. 14x14¾
3412	A849	60c multi	1.25	.95
a.		Miniature sheet of 10	12.50	12.5

Military Aircraft A850

Designs: Nos. 3413, 3417, F-111. Nos 3414, 3418, F/A-18F. $1.20, Wedge Tail. $3 C-17.

2011, Feb. 22 Perf. 14x14¾
3413	A850	60c multi	1.25	1.25
3414	A850	60c multi	1.25	1.25
3415	A850	$1.20 multi	2.40	1.90
a.		Souvenir sheet of 4, #3337, 3339, 3413, 3415	7.75	7.75
3416	A850	$3 multi	6.00	4.50
a.		Souvenir sheet of 4, #3413-3416	11.00	11.00
		Nos. 3413-3416 (4)	10.90	8.90

Booklet Stamps
Self-Adhesive
Serpentine Die Cut 11¼ Syncopated

3417	A850	60c multi	1.25	.25
3418	A850	60c multi	1.25	.25
a.		Booklet pane of 10, 5 each		
		#3417-3418	12.50	

Issued: No. 3415a, 3/31. Sydney Stamp Expo 2011 (No. 3415a).

Flowers — A851

Designs: Nos. 3419, 3424, Gerbera daisy. Nos. 3420, 3425, Jacarandas. Nos. 3421, 3426, Australian everlasting. Nos. 3422, 3427, Violet. Nos. 3423, 3428, Tulip.

2011, Mar. 8   Litho.   Perf. 14¾x14

3419	A851	60c multi	1.25	1.25
a.		Booklet pane of 4	5.25	—
3420	A851	60c multi	1.25	1.25
a.		Booklet pane of 4	5.25	—
3421	A851	60c multi	1.25	1.25
a.		Booklet pane of 4	5.25	—
3422	A851	60c multi	1.25	1.25
a.		Booklet pane of 4	5.25	—
3423	A851	60c multi	1.25	1.25
a.		Booklet pane of 4	5.25	—
		Complete booklet, #3419a, 3420a, 3421a, 3422a, 3423a	27.00	
b.		Horiz. strip of 5, #3419-3423	6.25	6.25
		Nos. 3419-3423 (5)	6.25	6.25

Self-Adhesive
Serpentine Die Cut 11¼ Syncopated

3424	A851	60c multi	1.25	.25
3425	A851	60c multi	1.25	.25
3426	A851	60c multi	1.25	.25
3427	A851	60c multi	1.25	.25
3428	A851	60c multi	1.25	.25
a.		Vert. coil strip of 5, #3424-3428	6.25	
b.		Booklet pane of 20, 4 each #3424-3428	25.00	
		Nos. 3424-3428 (5)	6.25	1.25

Complete booklet sold for $12.95.

Paintings of Flowers in National Gallery of Victoria — A852

Paintings: Nos. 3429, 3434, A Bunch of Flowers, by Nora Heysen. Nos. 3430, 3435, Camellias, by Arnold Shore. Nos. 3431, 3436, Fruit and Flowers, by Vida Lahey. Nos. 3432, 3437, Still Life, Zinnias, by Roy de Maistre. Nos. 3433, 3438, A Cottage Bunch, by Hans Heysen.

2011, Mar. 22   Perf. 14x14¾

3429	A852	60c multi	1.25	1.25
3430	A852	60c multi	1.25	1.25
3431	A852	60c multi	1.25	1.25
3432	A852	60c multi	1.25	1.25
3433	A852	60c multi	1.25	1.25
a.		Horiz. strip of 5, #3429-3433	6.25	6.25
		Nos. 3429-3433 (5)	6.25	6.25

Self-Adhesive
Serpentine Die Cut 11¼ Syncopated

3434	A852	60c multi	1.25	.25
3435	A852	60c multi	1.25	.25
3436	A852	60c multi	1.25	.25
3437	A852	60c multi	1.25	.25
3438	A852	60c multi	1.25	.25
a.		Horiz. coil strip of 5, #3434-3438	6.25	
b.		Booklet pane of 10, 2 each #3434-3438	12.50	
		Nos. 3434-3438 (5)	6.25	1.25

Lake Eyre — A853

Lake Eyre: 60c, In dry season. $1.55, With new growth. $2.25, Bird life. $3.10, In flood.

2011, Apr. 4   Perf. 14½x14

3439	A853	60c multi	1.25	.65
3440	A853	$1.55 multi	3.25	3.25
3441	A853	$2.25 multi	4.75	4.75
3442	A853	$3.10 multi	6.50	3.25
		Nos. 3439-3442 (4)	15.75	11.90

Booklet Stamps
Self-Adhesive
Serpentine Die Cut 11¼

3443	A853	$1.55 multi	3.25	1.60
a.		Booklet pane of 5	16.50	
3444	A853	$2.25 multi	4.75	2.40
a.		Booklet pane of 5	24.00	

A854

Portraits of Queen Elizabeth II by: 60c, Brian Dunlop, 1984. $2.25, Rolf Harris, 2005.

2011, Apr. 5   Perf. 14¾x14

3445	A854	60c multi	1.25	.65
3446	A854	$2.25 multi	4.75	2.40
a.		Souvenir sheet of 2, #3445-3446	6.00	6.00

Queen Elizabeth II, 85th birthday.

A855

Background color: 60c, Pale olive green. $2.25, White.

2011, Apr. 12   Perf. 14¾x14

3447	A855	60c multi	1.25	1.25
3448	A855	$2.25 multi	4.75	2.40
a.		Souvenir sheet of 2, #3447-3448	6.00	6.00

Booklet Stamp
Self-Adhesive
Serpentine Die Cut 11¼ Syncopated

3449	A855	60c multi	1.25	.25
a.		Booklet pane of 10	12.50	

Wedding of Prince William and Catherine Middleton.

Wedding Photograph of Prince William and Wife Catherine — A856

2011, May 4   Perf. 14¼

3450	A856	60c multi	1.25	1.25

Booklet Stamp
Self-Adhesive
Serpentine Die Cut 11¼ Syncopated

3451	A856	60c multi	1.25	.25
a.		Booklet pane of 10	12.50	

Dame Nellie Melba (1861-1931), Operatic Soprano — A857

2011, May 10   Perf. 14¾x14

3452	A857	60c multi	1.25	1.25

Booklet Stamp
Self-Adhesive
Serpentine Die Cut 11¼ Syncopated

3453	A857	60c multi	1.25	.25
a.		Booklet pane of 20	25.00	

Native Agricultural Products — A858

Designs: Nos. 3454, 3458, Eucalyptus oil. Nos. 3455, 3459, Australian honey. Nos. 3456, 3460, Macadamia nuts. Nos. 3457, 3461, Tea tree oil.

2011, May 17   Perf. 14x14¾

3454	A858	60c multi	1.25	1.25
3455	A858	60c multi	1.25	1.25
3456	A858	60c multi	1.25	1.25
3457	A858	60c multi	1.25	1.25
a.		Horiz. strip of 4, #3454-3457	5.00	5.00
		Nos. 3454-3457 (4)	5.00	5.00

Self-Adhesive
Serpentine Die Cut 11¼ Syncopated

3458	A858	60c multi	1.25	.25
3459	A858	60c multi	1.25	.25
3460	A858	60c multi	1.25	.25
3461	A858	60c multi	1.25	.25
a.		Horiz. coil strip of 4, #3458-3461	5.00	
b.		Booklet pane of 10, 4 #3458, 2 each #3459-3461	12.50	
		Nos. 3458-3461 (4)	5.00	1.00

Southern Cross With Sports Team Emblem — A859

Booklet Stamps
Self-Adhesive
Blue Sky
With Emblem of Australian Rules
Football Team
Adelaide Crows
Serpentine Die Cut 10¾x11¼ Syncopated

2011, Apr. 12   Litho.

3462	A859	60c Emblem at R	1.50	.75
3463	A859	60c Emblem at L	1.50	.75
a.		Booklet pane of 10, 5 each #3462-3463	15.00	

Carlton Blues

3464	A859	60c Emblem at R	1.50	.75
3465	A859	60c Emblem at L	1.50	.75
a.		Booklet pane of 10, 5 each #3464-3465	15.00	

Essendon Bombers

3466	A859	60c Emblem at R	1.50	.75
3467	A859	60c Emblem at L	1.50	.75
a.		Booklet pane of 10, 5 each #3466-3467	15.00	

Geelong Cats

3468	A859	60c Emblem at R	1.50	.75
3469	A859	60c Emblem at L	1.50	.75
a.		Booklet pane of 10, 5 each #3468-3469	15.00	

Gold Coast Suns

3470	A859	60c Emblem at R	1.50	.75
3471	A859	60c Emblem at L	1.50	.75
a.		Booklet pane of 10, 5 each #3470-3471	15.00	

North Melbourne Kangaroos

3472	A859	60c Emblem at R	1.50	.75
3473	A859	60c Emblem at L	1.50	.75
a.		Booklet pane of 10, 5 each #3472-3473	15.00	

Port Adelaide Power

3474	A859	60c Emblem at R	1.50	.75
3475	A859	60c Emblem at L	1.50	.75
a.		Booklet pane of 10, 5 each #3474-3475	15.00	

West Coast Eagles

3476	A859	60c Emblem at R	1.50	.75
3477	A859	60c Emblem at L	1.50	.75
a.		Booklet pane of 10, 5 each #3476-3477	15.00	

Western Bulldogs

3478	A859	60c Emblem at R	1.50	.75
3479	A859	60c Emblem at L	1.50	.75
a.		Booklet pane of 10, 5 each #3478-3479	15.00	

Purple & Orange Sky
Brisbane Lions

3480	A859	60c Emblem at R	1.50	.75
3481	A859	60c Emblem at L	1.50	.75
a.		Booklet pane of 10, 5 each #3480-3481	15.00	

Collingwood Magpies

3482	A859	60c Emblem at R	1.50	.75
3483	A859	60c Emblem at L	1.50	.75
a.		Booklet pane of 10, 5 each #3482-3483	15.00	

Fremantle Dockers

3484	A859	60c Emblem at R	1.50	.75
3485	A859	60c Emblem at L	1.50	.75
a.		Booklet pane of 10, 5 each #3484-3485	15.00	

Hawthorn Hawks

3486	A859	60c Emblem at R	1.50	.75
3487	A859	60c Emblem at L	1.50	.75
a.		Booklet pane of 10, 5 each #3486-3487	15.00	

Melbourne Demons

3488	A859	60c Emblem at R	1.50	.75
3489	A859	60c Emblem at L	1.50	.75
a.		Booklet pane of 10, 5 each #3488-3489	15.00	

Richmond Tigers

3490	A859	60c Emblem at R	1.50	.75
3491	A859	60c Emblem at L	1.50	.75
a.		Booklet pane of 10, 5 each #3490-3491	15.00	

St. Kilda Saints

3492	A859	60c Emblem at R	1.50	.75
3493	A859	60c Emblem at L	1.50	.75
a.		Booklet pane of 10, 5 each #3492-3493	15.00	

Sydney Swans

3494	A859	60c Emblem at R	1.50	.75
3495	A859	60c Emblem at L	1.50	.75
a.		Booklet pane of 10, 5 each #3494-3495	15.00	

Blue Sky
With National Rugby League
Emblems
North Queensland Cowboys

3496	A859	60c Emblem at R	1.50	.75
3497	A859	60c Emblem at L	1.50	.75
a.		Booklet pane of 10, 5 each #3496-3497	15.00	

St. George Illawarra Dragons

3498	A859	60c Emblem at R	1.50	.75
3499	A859	60c Emblem at L	1.50	.75
a.		Booklet pane of 10, 5 each #3498-3499	15.00	

Parramatta Eels

3500	A859	60c Emblem at R	1.50	.75
3501	A859	60c Emblem at L	1.50	.75
a.		Booklet pane of 10, 5 each #3500-3501	15.00	

Newcastle Knights

3502	A859	60c Emblem at R	1.50	.75
3503	A859	60c Emblem at L	1.50	.75
a.		Booklet pane of 10, 5 each #3502-3503	15.00	

Penrith Panthers

3504	A859	60c Emblem at R	1.50	.75
3505	A859	60c Emblem at L	1.50	.75
a.		Booklet pane of 10, 5 each #3504-3505	15.00	

Canberra Raiders

3506	A859	60c Emblem at R	1.50	.75
3507	A859	60c Emblem at L	1.50	.75
a.		Booklet pane of 10, 5 each #3506-3507	15.00	

Sydney Roosters

3508	A859	60c Emblem at R	1.50	.75
3509	A859	60c Emblem at L	1.50	.75
a.		Booklet pane of 10, 5 each #3508-3509	15.00	

Cronulla Sutherland Sharks

3510	A859	60c Emblem at R	1.50	.75
3511	A859	60c Emblem at L	1.50	.75
a.		Booklet pane of 10, 5 each #3510-3511	15.00	

Gold Coast Titans

3512	A859	60c Emblem at R	1.50	.75
3513	A859	60c Emblem at L	1.50	.75
a.		Booklet pane of 10, 5 each #3512-3513	15.00	

Purple & Orange Sky
Brisbane Broncos

3514	A859	60c Emblem at R	1.50	.75
3515	A859	60c Emblem at L	1.50	.75
a.		Booklet pane of 10, 5 each		
		#3514-3515	15.00	

Canterbury-Bankstown Bulldogs

3516	A859	60c Emblem at R	1.50	.75
3517	A859	60c Emblem at L	1.50	.75
a.		Booklet pane of 10, 5 each		
		#3516-3517	15.00	

South Sydney Rabbitohs

3518	A859	60c Emblem at R	1.50	.75
3519	A859	60c Emblem at L	1.50	.75
a.		Booklet pane of 10, 5 each		
		#3518-3519	15.00	

Manly Warringah Sea Eagles

3520	A859	60c Emblem at R	1.50	.75
3521	A859	60c Emblem at L	1.50	.75
a.		Booklet pane of 10, 5 each		
		#3520-3521	15.00	

Melbourne Storm

3522	A859	60c Emblem at R	1.50	.75
3523	A859	60c Emblem at L	1.50	.75
a.		Booklet pane of 10, 5 each		
		#3522-3523	15.00	

New Zealand Warriors

3524	A859	60c Emblem at R	1.50	.75
3525	A859	60c Emblem at L	1.50	.75
a.		Booklet pane of 10, 5 each		
		#3524-3525	15.00	

Wests Tigers

3526	A859	60c Emblem at R	1.50	.75
3527	A859	60c Emblem at L	1.50	.75
a.		Booklet pane of 10, 5 each		
		#3526-3527	15.00	
		Nos. 3462-3527 (66)	99.00	49.50

Each booklet, Nos. 3463a-3527a, sold for $6.95. Stamps with team emblem at right have straight edge at right, and stamps with team emblem at left have straight edge at left.

Australian Navy, Cent. — A860

Sailor and: Nos. 3528, 3530, HMAS Australia and biplane. Nos. 3529, 3531, HMAS Sydney and helicopter.

2011, June 14 *Perf. 14x14¾*

3528	A860	60c multi	1.40	1.40
3529	A860	60c multi	1.40	1.40
a.		Horiz. pair, #3528-3529	2.80	2.80

Booklet Stamps
Self-Adhesive

Serpentine Die Cut 11¼ Syncopated

3530	A860	60c multi	1.40	.25
3531	A860	60c multi	1.40	.25
a.		Booklet pane of 20, 10 each		
		#3530-3531	28.00	

A861

Baby animals: 60c, Bilby. $1.60, Dingo. $1.65, Kangaroo. $2.35, Koala. $4.70, Sugar glider.

2011, July 1 Litho. *Perf. 14¾x14*

3532	A861	60c multi	1.40	1.10
3533	A861	$1.60 multi	3.50	1.75
a.		Souvenir sheet of 1	3.50	3.50
3534	A861	$1.65 multi	3.50	3.50
a.		Souvenir sheet of 2, #3533-3534	7.00	7.00
b.		Souvenir sheet of 1	3.50	3.50
c.		Additionally dated "2013"	4.25	4.25
d.		Booklet pane of 4, #1195a, 2352a, 3097a, 3534c	12.50	
3535	A861	$2.35 multi	5.00	5.00
a.		Souvenir sheet of 2	9.75	9.75
3536	A861	$4.70 multi	10.00	5.00
		Nos. 3532-3536 (5)	23.40	16.35

Issued: No. 3534a, 7/28; No. 3535a, 6/18/12. Nos. 3533a, 3534b, 11/11. PhilaNippon '11 World Stamp Exhibition, Yokohama (No. 3534a). 2012 World Stamp Championship, Indonesia (No. 3535a). China 2011 Intl. Stamp Exhibition, Wuxi (Nos. 3533a, 3534b). Nos. 3534c, 3534d, 5/10/13. No. 3534d was

issued in a booklet also containing Nos. 1003b, 1284b, and 3918.

Booklet Stamps
Self-Adhesive

Serpentine Die Cut 11¼ Syncopated

3537	A861	$1.65 multi	3.50	1.75
a.		Booklet pane of 5	17.50	
3538	A861	$2.35 multi	5.00	2.50
a.		Booklet pane of 5	25.00	

With Personalized Photo at Right
Like Type A692a

Serpentine Die Cut 11½x11¼ Syncopated

3539	A861	$1.60 multi	4.75	4.75
3540	A861	$1.65 multi	5.00	5.00
3541	A861	$2.35 multi	11.50	11.50
		Nos. 3539-3541 (3)	21.25	21.25

Nos. 3539-3541 each were printed in sheets of 20 and have personalized pictures and at straight edge at right, and lack separations between the stamp and the personalized photo. Sheets of 20 of No. 3539 sold for $45; No. 3540, $46; No. 3541, $106.

A862

2011, July 5 *Perf. 14¾x14*

3542	A862	60c yellow & black	1.40	1.10

Amnesty International, 50th anniv.

Living Australian — A863

Photographs of Australian scenes: Nos. 3543, 3548, Boy and dog on beach. Nos. 3544, 3549, Children with flags painted on faces hugging. Nos. 3545, 3550, Reflection in sunglasses of sports fans in stadium. Nos. 3546, 3551, Aboriginal boy performing wedge tail eagle dance. Nos. 3547, 3552, Kangaroo resting on beach.

2011, July 5 *Perf. 14x14¾*
Denomination Color

3543	A863	60c orange	1.40	1.40
3544	A863	60c purple	1.40	1.40
3545	A863	60c green	1.40	1.40
3546	A863	60c red violet	1.40	1.40
3547	A863	60c blue	1.40	1.40
a.		Horiz. strip of 5, #3543-3547	7.00	7.00

Self-Adhesive

Serpentine Die Cut 11¼ Syncopated

3548	A863	60c orange	1.40	.25
3549	A863	60c purple	1.40	.25
3550	A863	60c green	1.40	.25
3551	A863	60c red violet	1.40	.25
3552	A863	60c blue	1.40	.25
a.		Horiz. coil strip of 5, #3548-3552	7.00	
b.		Booklet pane of 10, 2 each #3548-3552	14.00	
		Nos. 3548-3552 (5)	7.00	1.25

Skiing — A864

Designs: 60c, Child learning to ski. $1.60, Snowboarder, horiz. $1.65, Downhill skier, horiz.

2011, July 19 *Perf. 14¾x14*

3553	A864	60c multi	1.25	1.25

Perf. 14x14¾

3554	A864	$1.60 multi	3.50	3.50
3555	A864	$1.65 multi	3.50	3.50
		Nos. 3553-3555 (3)	8.25	8.25

Self-Adhesive
Coil Stamp

Serpentine Die Cut 11¼ Syncopated

3556	A864	60c multi	1.25	.25

Booklet Stamps

3557	A864	$1.60 multi	3.50	1.75
a.		Booklet pane of 5	17.50	
3558	A864	$1.65 multi	3.50	1.75
a.		Booklet pane of 5	17.50	
		Nos. 3556-3558 (3)	8.25	3.75

Items Depicted on Australian States Stamps — A865

Designs: No. 3559, Kangaroo and lyrebird. No. 3560, Black swan and Southern Cross.

2011, July 28 *Perf. 14x13½*

3559	A865	$2 pale grn & blue	4.25	2.10
3560	A865	$2 pink & blue	4.25	2.10
a.		Pair, #3559-3560	8.50	4.25
b.		Souvenir sheet of 2, #3559-3560	8.50	4.25

A limited edition of No. 3560b with a gold overprint in the sheet margin exists.

Worldwide Fund for Nature (WWF), 50th Anniv. — A866

Designs: No. 3561, Quokka. No. 3562, Southern elephant seal. No. 3563, Dugong. No. 3564, Christmas Island shrew.

2011, Aug. 30 Litho. *Perf. 14x14¾*

3561	A866	60c multi	1.25	.95
3562	A866	60c multi	1.25	.95
3563	A866	60c multi	1.25	.95
3564	A866	60c multi	1.25	.95
a.		Block of 4, #3561-3564	5.00	4.00
b.		Souvenir sheet of 4, #3561-3564, #3561 at UL	5.00	5.00
c.		Souvenir sheet of 4, #3561-3564, #3562 at UL	5.00	5.00
d.		Souvenir sheet of 4, #3561-3564, #3563 at UL	5.00	5.00
e.		Souvenir sheet of 4, #3561-3564, #3564 at UL	5.00	5.00
		Nos. 3561-3564 (4)	5.00	3.80

Along with the "Australia" inscription at left, inscribed at the bottom above the animal's name is "Australian Antarctic Territory" on No. 3562, "Cocos (Keeling) Islands" on No. 3563, and "Christmas Island" on No. 3564. All recent stamps of the Australian possessions of Australian Antarctic Territory, Cocos Islands and Christmas Island are doubly-inscribed with "Australia" and the possession's name, and all stamps inscribed "Australia," "Australian Antarctic Territory," "Cocos Islands," or "Christmas Island" are valid for postage anywhere in those four areas. As there was no attempt to make the stamps bearing the names of these possessions in this set available separately in those locations they will be listed here only and not in the listings for each of the possessions.

2011 Presidents Cup Golf Tournament, Melbourne — A867

Designs: Nos. 3565, 3570, Hand on golf club. Nos. 3566, 3569B, 3571, Presidents Cup. Nos. 3567, 3572, Golf shoes, glove and ball. $1.65, Golf club and ball. $2.35, Clubs in golf bag.

2011, Sept. 27 *Perf. 14¾x14*

3565	A867	60c multi	1.25	1.25
3566	A867	60c multi	1.25	1.25
3567	A867	60c multi	1.25	1.25
a.		Horiz. strip of 3, #3565-3567	3.75	3.75
3568	A867	$1.65 multi	3.25	3.25
3569	A867	$2.35 multi	4.75	4.75
a.		Souvenir sheet of 5, #3565-3569	12.00	12.00
		Nos. 3565-3569 (5)	11.75	11.75

Litho. & Embossed With Foil Application

3569B	A867	60c multi	1.25	1.25

No. 3569B was printed in sheets of 15 that sold for $9.45.

Litho.
Self-Adhesive

Serpentine Die Cut 11¼ Syncopated

3570	A867	60c multi	1.25	.25
3571	A867	60c multi	1.25	.25
3572	A867	60c multi	1.25	.25
a.		Booklet pane of 10, 4 each # 3570-3571, 2 #3572	12.50	
b.		Vert. coil strip of 3, #3570-3572	3.75	
3573	A867	$1.65 multi	3.25	1.60
a.		Booklet pane of 5	16.50	
3574	A867	$2.35 multi	4.75	2.40
a.		Booklet pane of 5	24.00	
		Nos. 3570-3574 (5)	11.75	4.75

Mythical Creatures — A868

Designs: Nos. 3575, 3581, Fairy. Nos. 3576, 3582, Troll. Nos. 3577, 3583, Mermaid. Nos. 3578, 3584, Griffin. Nos. 3579, 3585, Unicorn. $1.20, Dragon.

2011, Oct. 4 Litho. *Perf. 14¾x14*

3575	A868	60c multi	1.25	1.25
3576	A868	60c multi	1.25	1.25
3577	A868	60c multi	1.25	1.25
3578	A868	60c multi	1.25	1.25
3579	A868	60c multi	1.25	1.25
a.		Horiz. strip of 5, #3575-3579	6.25	6.25
3580	A868	$1.20 multi	2.40	1.90
a.		Souvenir sheet of 6, #3575-3580	8.75	8.75
		Nos. 3575-3580 (6)	8.65	8.15

Booklet Stamps
Self-Adhesive

Serpentine Die Cut 11¼ Syncopated

3581	A868	60c multi	1.25	.25
3582	A868	60c multi	1.25	.25
3583	A868	60c multi	1.25	.25
3584	A868	60c multi	1.25	.25
3585	A868	60c multi	1.25	.25
a.		Booklet pane of 10, 2 each #3581-3585	12.50	
b.		Booklet pane of 20, 4 each #3581-3585	25.00	
		Nos. 3581-3585 (5)	6.25	1.25

Commonwealth Heads of Government Meeting, Perth — A869

2011, Oct. 18 *Perf. 14½x14*

3586	A869	60c multi	1.25	.95

Diplomatic Relations Between Australia and South Korea, 50th Anniv. — A870

Designs: 60c, Korean woman playing haegeum. $1.65, Australian aborigine playing didgeridoo.

2011, Oct. 31 *Perf. 13¼x13*

3587	A870	60c multi	1.25	.95

3588 A870 $1.65 multi   3.50 1.75

Booklet Stamp
Self-Adhesive
Serpentine Die Cut 11¼ Syncopated
3589 A870 $1.65 multi   3.50 1.75
   a. Booklet pane of 5   17.50

See South Korea No. 2373.

Christmas
A871   A872

Designs: Nos. 3590, 3595, Madonna and Child. Nos. 3591, 3596, 3599, 3601, Star on Christmas tree. Nos. 3592, 3597, 3600, 3602, Star and gift. 60c, Star and fruit tree branches. $1.50, Magi and camels, horiz.

2011, Oct. 31   Litho.   Perf. 14¾x14
3590 A871 55c multi   1.10 1.10
3591 A872 55c multi   1.10 1.10
3592 A872 55c multi   1.10 1.10
   a. Horiz. pair, #3591-3592   2.20 2.20
3593 A872 60c multi   1.25 1.25
      Perf. 14x14¾
3594 A871 $1.50 multi   3.25 3.25
   Nos. 3590-3594 (5)   7.80 7.80

Booklet Stamps
Self-Adhesive
Serpentine Die Cut 11¼ Syncopated
3595 A871 55c multi   1.10 .25
   a. Booklet pane of 20 + 20 eti-
     quettes   22.00
3596 A872 55c multi   1.10 .25
3597 A872 55c multi   1.10 .25
   a. Booklet pane of 20, 10 each
     #3596-3597 + 20 eti-
     quettes   22.00
3598 A871 $1.50 multi   3.25 1.60
   a. Booklet pane of 5   16.50

Litho. With Foil Application
3599 A872 55c multi   1.10 .25
   a. Booklet pane of 10   11.00
3600 A872 55c multi   1.10 .25
   a. Booklet pane of 10   11.00
   Nos. 3595-3600 (6)   8.75 2.85

Litho.
With Personalized Photo at Right
Like Type A692a
Serpentine Die Cut 11½x11¼ Syncopated
3601 A872 55c multi   2.50 2.50
3602 A872 55c multi   2.50 2.50
3603 A872 60c multi   2.60 2.60
   Nos. 3601-3603 (3)   7.60 7.60

Nos. 3601-3603 each were printed in sheets of 20 and have personalized pictures and a straight edge at right, and lack separations between the stamp and the personalized photo. Sheets of 20 of Nos. 3601 and 3602 each sold for $24, for No. 3603, $25.

Remembrance Day — A873

Lines from "In Flanders Fields," poem by John McCrae, and: 60c, Poppy, bugler. $1.20, Two poppies, two soldiers.

2011, Nov. 2   Litho.   Perf. 14x14¾
3604 A873 60c multi   1.25 1.25
3605 A873 $1.20 multi   2.50 1.90
   a. Souvenir sheet of 2, #3604-
     3605   3.75 3.25

Self-Adhesive
Serpentine Die Cut 11¼ Syncopated
3606 A873 60c multi   1.25 .25
   a. Booklet pane of 10   12.50

No. 3606 was issued in coils and booklets.

Australian Lieutenant General Sydney F. Rowell, New Zealand Major General William Gentry, and U.S. Admiral Arthur Radford
A874

2011, Nov. 16   Perf. 14x14¾
3607 A874 60c multi   1.25 .95
   ANZUS Treaty, 60th anniv.

Cupcake and   Teddy
Birthday   Bear — A876
Candle — A875

Balloons and   "Love" and
Streamers   Hearts
A877   A878

Birds — A879   Rose — A880

2012, Jan. 17   Perf. 14¾x14
3608 A875   60c multi   1.25 1.25
3609 A876   60c multi   1.25 1.25
3610 A877   60c multi   1.25 1.25
3611 A878   60c multi   1.25 1.25
3612 A879   60c multi   1.25 1.25
   a. Horiz. strip of 5, $3608-
     3612   6.25 6.25
3613 A880 $1.20 multi   2.60 2.60
   Nos. 3608-3613 (6)   8.85 8.85

Booklet Stamps
Self-Adhesive
Serpentine Die Cut 11¼ Syncopated
3614 A875   60c multi   1.25 .25
   a. Booklet pane of 10 + 5
     stickers   12.50
3615 A876   60c multi   1.25 .25
   a. Booklet pane of 10 + 5
     stickers   12.50
3616 A877   60c multi   1.25 .25
   a. Booklet pane of 10 + 5
     stickers   12.50
3617 A878   60c multi   1.25 .25
   a. Booklet pane of 10 + 5
     stickers   12.50
3618 A879   60c multi   1.25 .25
   a. Booklet pane of 10 + 5
     stickers   12.50
3619 A880 $1.20 multi   2.75 1.40
   a. Booklet pane of 4   11.00
     Complete booklet, 5 #3619a   55.00
   Nos. 3614-3619 (6)   9.00 2.65

With Personalized Photo at Right
Like Type A692a
Serpentine Die Cut 11½x11¼ Syncopated
3620 A875   60c multi   2.75 2.75
3621 A876   60c multi   2.75 2.75
3622 A877   60c multi   2.75 2.75
3623 A878   60c multi   2.75 2.75

3624 A879   60c multi   2.75 2.75
3625 A880 $1.20 multi   4.00 4.00
   Nos. 3620-3625 (6)   17.75 17.75

Complete booklet sold for $24.95 and contains five booklet panes of No. 3619a, each with a different margin.

Nos. 3620-3625 each were printed in sheets of 20 and have personalized pictures and a straight edge at right, and lack separations between the stamp and the personalized photo. Sheets of 20 of Nos. 3620-3624 each sold for $25, for No. 3625, $37.

 Athletes — A881

Designs: Nos. 3626, 3634, Ron Barassi, Australian Rules Football player. Nos. 3627, 3635, Gary Ablett, Jr., Australian Rules Football player. Nos. 3628, 3636, John Raper, Rugby League player. Nos. 3629, 3637, Billy Slater, Rugby League player. Nos. 3630, 3638, David Campese, Rugby Union player. Nos. 3631, 3639, David Pocock, Rugby Union player. Nos. 3632, 3640, Joe Marston, soccer player. Nos. 3633, 3641, Mark Schwarzer, soccer player.

2012, Jan. 20   Perf. 14¾x14
3626 A881 60c multi   1.25 1.25
   a. Booklet pane of 4   5.50
3627 A881 60c multi   1.25 1.25
   a. Booklet pane of 4   5.50
3628 A881 60c multi   1.25 1.25
   a. Booklet pane of 4   5.50
3629 A881 60c multi   1.25 1.25
   a. Booklet pane of 4   5.50
3630 A881 60c multi   1.25 1.25
   a. Booklet pane of 4   5.50
3631 A881 60c multi   1.25 1.25
   a. Booklet pane of 4   5.50
3632 A881 60c multi   1.25 —
   a. Booklet pane of 4   5.50
3633 A881 60c multi   1.25 1.25
   a. Booklet pane of 4   5.50
     Complete booklet, #3626a-
     3633a   44.00
   Nos. 3626-3633 (8)   10.00 10.00

Booklet Stamps
Self-Adhesive
Serpentine Die Cut 11¼ Syncopated
3634 A881 60c multi   1.25 .25
   a. Booklet pane of 10   12.50
3635 A881 60c multi   1.25 .25
   a. Booklet pane of 10   12.50
3636 A881 60c multi   1.25 .25
   a. Booklet pane of 10   12.50
3637 A881 60c multi   1.25 .25
   a. Booklet pane of 10   12.50
3638 A881 60c multi   1.25 .25
   a. Booklet pane of 10   12.50
3639 A881 60c multi   1.25 .25
   a. Booklet pane of 10   12.50
3640 A881 60c multi   1.25 .25
   a. Booklet pane of 10   12.50
3641 A881 60c multi   1.25 .25
   a. Booklet pane of 10   12.50
   Nos. 3634-3641 (8)   10.00 2.00

Complete booklet sold for $19.95.

Technological Changes Through the Years — A882

Designs: Nos. 3642, 3647, Woman on pay telephone, 4G phone. Nos. 3643, 3648, Man carrying ice to icebox, modern refrigerator. Nos. 3644, 3649, Family watching black-and-white television, flat-screen television. Nos. 3645, 3650, Man with vinyl records and record player, digital media player. Nos. 3646, 3651, Man reading paper road map, global positioning system.

2012, Feb. 7   Perf. 14x14¾
3642 A882 60c multi   1.40 1.40
3643 A882 60c multi   1.40 1.40
3644 A882 60c multi   1.40 1.40
3645 A882 60c multi   1.40 1.40
3646 A882 60c multi   1.40 1.40
   a. Horiz. strip of 5, #3642-3646   7.00 7.00
   b. Souvenir sheet of 5, #3642-
     3646   7.00 7.00

Self-Adhesive
Serpentine Die Cut 11¼ Syncopated
3647 A882 60c multi   1.40 .25
3648 A882 60c multi   1.40 .25
3649 A882 60c multi   1.40 .25
3650 A882 60c multi   1.40 .25
3651 A882 60c multi   1.40 .25
   a. Horiz. coil strip of 5, #3647-
     3651   7.00
   b. Booklet pane of 10, 2 each
     #3647-3651   14.00
   Nos. 3647-3651 (5)   7.00 1.25

Transportation in State Capitals — A883

Designs: Nos. 3652, 3657, O-Bahn bus system, Adelaide. Nos. 3653, 3658, Ferry in Sydney Harbor. Nos. 3654, 3659, Train in Perth. Nos. 3655, 3660, St. Kilda-bound tram, Melbourne. Nos. 3656, 3661, North Sydney-bound double-decker train, Sydney.

2012, Feb. 21   Perf. 14x14¾
3652 A883 60c multi   1.40 1.40
   a. Booklet pane of 4   5.75
3653 A883 60c multi   1.40 1.40
   a. Booklet pane of 4   5.75
3654 A883 60c multi   1.40 1.40
   a. Booklet pane of 4   5.75
3655 A883 60c multi   1.40 1.40
   a. Booklet pane of 4   5.75
3656 A883 60c multi   1.40 1.40
   a. Booklet pane of 4   5.75
     Complete booklet, #3652a-
     3656a   29.00
   b. Horiz. strip of 5, #3652-3656   7.00 7.00

Booklet Stamps
Self-Adhesive
Serpentine Die Cut 11¼ Syncopated
3657 A883 60c multi   1.40 .25
3658 A883 60c multi   1.40 .25
3659 A883 60c multi   1.40 .25
3660 A883 60c multi   1.40 .25
3661 A883 60c multi   1.40 .25
   a. Booklet pane of 20, 4 each
     #3657-3661   28.00
   Nos. 3657-3661 (5)   7.00 1.25

Complete booklet sold for $12.95.

Ducks
A884

Designs: Nos. 3662, 3666, Radjah shelduck. Nos. 3663, 3667, Pink-eared duck. $1.65, Australian shelduck. $2.35, Plumed whistling duck.

2012, Mar. 6   Perf. 14x14¾
3662 A884   60c multi   1.25 1.25
   a. Additionally dated "2013"   1.25 1.25
3663 A884   60c multi   1.25 1.25
   a. Additionally dated "2013"   1.25 1.25
3664 A884 $1.65 multi   3.50 3.50
   a. Additionally dated "2013"   3.25 3.25
3665 A884 $2.35 multi   5.00 5.00
   a. Additionally dated "2013"   4.50 4.50
   b. Booklet pane of 4, #3662a,
     3663a, 3664a, 3665a   11.00 11.00
   Nos. 3662-3665 (4)   11.00 11.00

Issued: Nos. 3662a, 3663a, 3664a, 3665a, 3665b, 5/11/13. No. 3665b was issued in a booklet also containing Nos. 3151c, 3376b and 3925a.

Self-Adhesive
Serpentine Die Cut 11¼ Syncopated
3666 A884   60c multi   1.25 .25
3667 A884   60c multi   1.25 .25
   a. Horiz. coil pair, #3666-3667   2.50
   b. Booklet pane of 10, 5 each
     #3666-3667   25.00

Booklet Stamps
3668 A884 $1.65 multi   3.50 1.75
   a. Booklet pane of 5   17.50
3669 A884 $2.35 multi   5.00 2.50
   a. Booklet pane of 5   25.00
   Nos. 3666-3669 (4)   11.00 4.75

Farm Products — A885

Designs: 10c, Dairy cows. 20c, Pineapples. $1, Wine grapes. $3, Sunflowers. $5, Apples.

2012, Mar. 20   **Perf. 14x14½**
3670 A885 10c multi   .25   .25
3671 A885 20c multi   .40   .25
  a.   As No. 3671, with part of
        design and 1mm wide
        white space separating
        designs at left side   1.10   1.10

          Size: 50x30mm
          Perf. 14½x14
3672 A885 $1 multi   2.10   1.10
3673 A885 $3 multi   6.25   3.25
3674 A885 $5 multi   10.50   5.25
      Nos. 3670-3674 (5)   19.50 10.10

No. 3671 has a white margin extending to the perforation tips at left. Four of the five stamps in the bottom row of the bottom pane in the sheet of 100 stamps (composed of two panes of 50) are No. 3671a.
See Nos. 3712-3723.

Compulsory Voting Enrollment, Cent. — A886

2012, Mar. 27   Litho.   Perf. 14¾x14
3675 A886 60c multi   1.25   .95

Reign of Queen Elizabeth II, 60th Anniv. — A887

Photograph of Queen Elizabeth II in: 60c, 1952. $2.35, 2012.

2012, Apr. 3   **Perf. 14¾x14**
3676 A887   60c multi   1.25   .95
3677 A887 $2.35 multi   5.00   5.00
  a.   Souvenir sheet of 2, #3676-
        3677   6.25   6.00

       Booklet Stamp
       Self-Adhesive
Serpentine Die Cut 11¼ Syncopated
3678 A887 $2.35 multi   5.00   2.50
  a.   Booklet pane of 5   25.00

Medical Doctors — A888

Designs: Nos. 3679, 3684, Dr. Jane Stocks Greig (1872-1939), public health specialist. Nos. 3680, 3685, Dame Kate Campbell (1899-1986), pediatrician. Nos. 3681, 3686, Dr. Victor Chang (1936-91), cardiac surgeon. Nos. 3682, 3687, Dr. Fred Hollows (1929-93), ophthalmologist. Nos. 3683, 3688, Dr. Chris O'Brien (1952-2009), surgeon.

2012, Apr. 10   **Perf. 14¾x14**
3679 A888 60c multi   1.25   1.25
3680 A888 60c multi   1.25   1.25
3681 A888 60c multi   1.25   1.25
3682 A888 60c multi   1.25   1.25
3683 A888 60c multi   1.25   1.25
      Nos. 3679-3683 (5)   6.25   6.25

       Coil Stamps
       Self-Adhesive
Serpentine Die Cut 11¼ Syncopated
3684 A888 60c multi   1.25   .25
3685 A888 60c multi   1.25   .25
3686 A888 60c multi   1.25   .25
3687 A888 60c multi   1.25   .25
3688 A888 60c multi   1.25   .25
  a.   Vert. coil strip of 5, #3684-3688 6.25
      Nos. 3684-3688 (5)   6.25   1.25

Rising Sun Badge A889

Rising Sun Badge in use from: Nos. 3689, 3694, 1902-04. Nos. 3690, 3695, 1904-49. Nos. 3691, 3696, 1954-69. Nos. 3692, 3697, 1969-91. Nos. 3693, 3698, 1991-present.

2012, Apr. 17   **Perf. 14x14¾**
3689 A889 60c multi   1.25   1.25
3690 A889 60c multi   1.25   1.25
3691 A889 60c multi   1.25   1.25
3692 A889 60c multi   1.25   1.25
3693 A889 60c multi   1.25   1.25
  a.   Horiz. strip of 5, #3689-3693   6.25   6.25
  b.   Souvenir sheet of 5, #3689-
        3693   6.25   6.25

       Booklet Stamps
       Self-Adhesive
Serpentine Die Cut 11¼ Syncopated
3694 A889 60c multi   1.25   .25
3695 A889 60c multi   1.25   .25
3696 A889 60c multi   1.25   .25
3697 A889 60c multi   1.25   .25
3698 A889 60c multi   1.25   .25
  a.   Booklet pane of 10, 2 each
        #3694-3698   12.50
      Nos. 3694-3698 (5)   6.25   1.25

Limited editions exist of No. 3698a with a gold overprint in the margin, and a part-perforate sheet of seven stamps (five similar to Nos. 3689-3693, and two different $1 stamps).

Nudibranchs A890

Designs: Nos. 3699, 3705, Chromodoris westraliensis. Nos. 3700, 3706, Godiva sp. Nos. 3701, 3707, Flabellina rubrolineata. No. 3702, Phyllidia ocellata. No. 3703, Thorunna florens. $1.80, Nembrotha purpureolineata.

2012, May 8   **Perf. 14x14¾**
3699 A890   60c multi   1.25   1.25
  a.   Booklet pane of 4   5.25
3700 A890   60c multi   1.25   1.25
  a.   Booklet pane of 4   5.25
3701 A890   60c multi   1.25   1.25
  a.   Booklet pane of 4   5.25
3702 A890 $1.20 multi   2.40   1.90
3703 A890 $1.20 multi   2.40   1.90
  a.   Booklet pane of 4, #3699-
        3702   6.50   —
3704 A890 $1.80 multi   3.75   1.90
  a.   Booklet pane of 4, #3699-
        3701, 3704   7.75   —
        Complete booklet, #3699a,
        3700a, 3701a, 3703a,
        3704a   30.00
  b.   Souvenir sheet of 6, #3699-
        3704   12.50 12.50
      Nos. 3699-3704 (6)   12.30   9.45

       Booklet Stamps
       Self-Adhesive
Serpentine Die Cut 11¼ Syncopated
3705 A890   60c multi   1.25   .25
3706 A890   60c multi   1.25   .25
3707 A890   60c multi   1.25   .25
  a.   Booklet pane of 20, 7 each
        #3705-3706, 6 #3707   25.00
      Nos. 3705-3707 (3)   3.75   .75

Complete booklet sold for $14.95.

Australian Flag, Olympic Rings, London Tourist Attractions — A891

2012, June 5   **Perf. 14¾x14**
3708 A891 60c multi   1.25   1.25

          Self-Adhesive
Serpentine Die Cut 11¼ Syncopated
3709 A891 60c multi   1.25   .25
  a.   Booklet pane of 10   12.50

2012 Summer Olympics, London.

Colonial Heritage — A892

Designs: No. 3710, Redrawn vignette of New South Wales #1. No. 3710, Redrawn vignette of Tasmania #88.

2012, June 19   **Perf. 14x14½**
3710 A892 $2 yellow & blue   4.25   2.10
  a.   Perf. 14x13½   4.25   2.10
3711 A892 $2 lt blue & blue   4.25   2.10
  a.   Perf. 14x13½   4.25   2.10
  b.   Horiz. pair, #3710-3711   8.50   4.25
  c.   Souvenir sheet of 2, #3710a,
        3711a   8.50   4.25

       Farm Products Type of 2012
Designs: Nos. 3712, 3716, 3720, Beef cattle. Nos. 3713, 3717, 3721, Oranges. Nos. 3714, 3718, 3722, Sugar. Nos. 3715, 3719, 3723, Wool.

2012, June 26   Litho.   Perf. 14x14½
3712 A885 60c multi   1.25   .25
3713 A885 60c multi   1.25   .25
3714 A885 60c multi   1.25   .25
3715 A885 60c multi   1.25   .25
  a.   Block of 4, #3712-3715   5.00   2.50
      Nos. 3712-3715 (4)   5.00   1.00

       Coil Stamps
       Self-Adhesive
   Serpentine Die Cut 12¾
3716 A885 60c multi   1.25   .25
3717 A885 60c multi   1.25   .25
3718 A885 60c multi   1.25   .25
3719 A885 60c multi   1.25   .25
  a.   Horiz. strip of 4, #3716-3719   5.00

       Booklet Stamps
   Serpentine Die Cut 11¼
3720 A885 60c multi   1.25   .25
3721 A885 60c multi   1.25   .25
3722 A885 60c multi   1.25   .25
3723 A885 60c multi   1.25   .25
  a.   Booklet pane of 10, 2 each
        #3720, 3722-3723, 4 #3721   12.50
  b.   Booklet pane of 20, 5 each
        #3720-3723   25.00
      Nos. 3716-3723 (8)   10.00   2.00

Inland Exploration A893

Designs: No. 3724, Explorers crossing Blue Mountains, 1813. No. 3725, Explorers William Lawson, William Charles Wentworth and Gregory Blaxland. No. 3726, Explorer John McDouall Stuart. No. 3727, Stuart Overland Crossing Expedition planting flag on Indian Ocean coast.

2012, July 3   **Perf. 14¾x14**
3724 A893   60c multi   1.25   .95
3725 A893   60c multi   1.25   .95
  a.   Horiz. pair, #3724-3725   2.50   1.90
3726 A893 $1.20 multi   2.50   2.00
3727 A893 $1.20 multi   2.50   2.00
  a.   Horiz. pair, #3726-3727   5.00   4.00
  b.   Souvenir sheet of 4, #3724-
        3727   7.50   6.00
      Nos. 3724-3727 (4)   7.50   5.90

Sports of the Summer Olympics A894

Designs: 60c, Swimming. $1.60, Pole vault. $2.30, Rowing.

2012, July 17   **Perf. 14x14¾**
3728 A894   60c multi   1.25   1.25
3729 A894 $1.60 multi   3.50   3.50
3730 A894 $2.35 multi   5.00   5.00
      Nos. 3728-3730 (3)   9.75   9.75

       Coil Stamp
       Self-Adhesive
Serpentine Die Cut 11¼ Syncopated
3731 A894   60c multi   1.25   .25

       Booklet Stamps
       Self-Adhesive
3732 A894 $1.60 multi   3.50   1.75
  a.   Booklet pane of 5   17.50
3733 A894 $2.35 multi   5.00   2.50
  a.   Booklet pane of 5   25.00
      Nos. 3731-3733 (3)   9.75   4.50

Photographs of Everyday Life in Australia — A895

Designs: Nos. 3734, 3740, Little Wonders, by Ann Clark (children on beach). Nos. 3735, 3742, The Godfathers, by Chevelle Williams (sheep in pen). Nos. 3736, 3741, Is There a Letter for Me?, by Wanda Lach (row of mailboxes in rural area). Nos. 3737, 3743, Lunch on the Harbor, by Damian Madden (seagull with French fry in beak). Nos. 3738, 3739, Fuel Ask at the Store Across the Road, by Ronald Rockman (rural gas station).

2012, July 24   **Perf. 14x14¾**
3734 A895 60c multi   1.25   1.25
3735 A895 60c multi   1.25   1.25
3736 A895 60c multi   1.25   1.25
3737 A895 60c multi   1.25   1.25
3738 A895 60c multi   1.25   1.25
  a.   Horiz. strip of 5, #3734-3738   6.25   6.25
      Nos. 3734-3738 (5)   6.25   6.25

       Booklet Stamps
       Self-Adhesive
Serpentine Die Cut 11¼ Syncopated
3739 A895 60c multi   1.25   .25
3740 A895 60c multi   1.25   .25
3741 A895 60c multi   1.25   .25
3742 A895 60c multi   1.25   .25
3743 A895 60c multi   1.25   .25
  a.   Booklet pane of 20, 4 each
        #3739-3742   25.00
      Nos. 3739-3743 (5)   6.25   1.25

       Souvenir Sheet

Emblem of Australia 2013 World Stamp Expo and Royal Exhibition Building, Melbourne — A896

2012, June 18   Litho.   Perf. 14¾x14
3744 A896 $1.85 multi   3.75   1.90

A limited edition of No. 3744 with a gold overprint in the sheet margin exists.

Australian Gold Medalists at 2012 Summer Olympics, London A897

Designs: No. 3745, Women's 4x100 mete freestyle swimming relay team. No. 3746, Ton Slingsby, men's Laser class sailing. No. 3747 Anna Meares, women's sprint cycling. No 3748, Iain Jensen and Nathan Outteridge men's 49er class sailing. No. 3749, Sally Pear son, women's 100 meter hurdles. No. 3750 Men's 1000 meter kayak fours team. No 3751, Mathew Belcher and Malcolm Page men's 470 class sailing.

2012   *Perf. 14¼*

3745	A897 60c multi	1.25	.95
3746	A897 60c multi	1.25	.95
3747	A897 60c multi	1.25	.95
3748	A897 60c multi	1.25	.95
3749	A897 60c multi	1.25	.95
3750	A897 60c multi	1.25	.95
3751	A897 60c multi	1.25	.95
	Nos. 3745-3751 (7)	8.75	6.65

Nos. 3745-3751 each were printed in sheets of 10. Issued: No. 3745, 7/31; No. 3746, 8/9; No. 3747, 8/10; others, 8/13.
See No. 4506B.

Portraits of Autralian Nobel Prize Winners — A898

Portrait of: Nos. 3752, 3757, Sir Frank Macfarlane Burnet, by Clifton Pugh. Nos. 3753, 3758, Sir John Carew Eccles, by Judy Cassab. Nos. 3754, 3759, Patrick White, by Brett Whiteley. Nos. 3755, 3760, Sir Howard Walter Florey, by Allan Gwynne-Jones. Nos. 3756, 3761, William Lawrence Bragg, by Sir William Dargie.

2012, Aug. 28   Litho.   *Perf. 14¾x14*

3752	A898 60c multi	1.25	1.25
3753	A898 60c multi	1.25	1.25
3754	A898 60c multi	1.25	1.25
3755	A898 60c multi	1.25	1.25
3756	A898 60c multi	1.25	1.25
a.	Horiz. strip of 5, #3752-3756	6.25	6.25
	Nos. 3752-3756 (5)	6.25	6.25

Self-Adhesive
Serpentine Die Cut 11¼ Syncopated

3757	A898 60c multi	1.25	.25
3758	A898 60c multi	1.25	.25
3759	A898 60c multi	1.25	.25
3760	A898 60c multi	1.25	.25
3761	A898 60c multi	1.25	.25
a.	Vert. coil strip of 5, #3757-3761	6.25	
b.	Booklet pane of 10, 2 each #3757-3761	12.50	
	Nos. 3757-3761 (5)	6.25	1.25

Road Trips — A899

Designs: Nos. 3762, 3769, Station wagon at Port Arthur, Tasmania. Nos. 3763, 3767, Volkswagen Bus at Great Barrier Reef, Queensland. Nos. 3764, 3768, Motorcyclists picnicking near Margaret River, Western Australia. $1.65, Station wagon at Phillip Island, Victoria. $2.35, Car at camel race, Alice Springs, Northern Territory.

2012, Sept. 18   *Perf. 14¼*

3762	A899 60c multi	1.25	1.25
3763	A899 60c multi	1.25	1.25
3764	A899 60c multi	1.25	1.25
a.	Horiz. strip of 3, #3762-3764	3.75	3.75
3765	A899 $1.65 multi	3.50	1.75
3766	A899 $2.35 multi	4.75	2.40
a.	Souvenir sheet of 5, #3762-3766	12.00	12.00
	Nos. 3762-3766 (5)	12.00	7.90

Booklet Stamps
Self-Adhesive
Serpentine Die Cut 11¼ Syncopated

3767	A899 60c multi	1.25	.25
3768	A899 60c multi	1.25	.25
3769	A899 60c multi	1.25	.25
a.	Booklet pane of 10, 3 each #3767, 3769, 4 #3768	12.50	
3770	A899 $1.65 multi	3.50	1.75
a.	Booklet pane of 5	17.50	
3771	A899 $2.35 multi	4.75	2.40
a.	Booklet pane of 5	24.00	
	Nos. 3767-3771 (5)	12.00	4.90

Compare with type A933.

Wilderness Areas — A900

Designs: $1.65, Nullarbor Plain, Western Australia. $2.35, Daintree National Park, Queensland. $4.50, Cradle Mountain, Tasmania.

2012, Sept. 25   *Perf. 14¾x14*

3772	A900 $1.65 multi	3.50	1.75
3773	A900 $2.35 multi	4.75	2.40
3774	A900 $4.50 multi	9.25	4.75
	Nos. 3772-3774 (3)	17.50	8.90

Booklet Stamps
Self-Adhesive
Serpentine Die Cut 11¼ Syncopated

3775	A900 $1.65 multi	3.50	1.75
a.	Booklet pane of 5	17.50	
3776	A900 $2.35 multi	4.75	2.40
a.	Booklet pane of 5	24.00	

Animals in Australian Zoos — A901

Designs: No. 3777, Sumatran tiger, Melbourne Zoo, Victoria. Nos. 3778, 3789, Wedge-tailed hawk, Healesville Sanctuary, Victoria. Nos. 3779, 3787. Sumatran orangutan, Perth Zoo, Western Australia. Nos. 3780, 3786, Giant panda, Adelaide Zoo, South Australia. Nos. 3781, 3785, Giraffe, Taronga Zoo, Sydney, New South Wales. Nos. 3782, 3788, Saltwater crocodile, Australia Zoo, Sunshine Coast, Queensland. Nos. 3783, 3784, Black rhinoceros, Taronga Western Plains Zoo, Dubbo, New South Wales.

2012, Sept. 28   *Perf. 13¾x14*

3777	A901 60c multi	1.25	.95

Size: 37x26mm
Perf. 14x14¾

3778	A901 60c multi	1.25	1.25
3779	A901 60c multi	1.25	1.25
3780	A901 60c multi	1.25	1.25
3781	A901 60c multi	1.25	1.25
3782	A901 60c multi	1.25	1.25
3783	A901 60c multi	1.25	1.25
a.	Souvenir sheet of 7, #3777-3783	8.75	8.75
	Nos. 3777-3783 (7)	8.75	8.45

Self-Adhesive
Serpentine Die Cut 11¼ Syncopated

3784	A901 60c multi	1.25	.25
3785	A901 60c multi	1.25	.25
3786	A901 60c multi	1.25	.25
3787	A901 60c multi	1.25	.25
3788	A901 60c multi	1.25	.25
3789	A901 60c multi	1.25	.25
a.	Horiz. coil strip of 6, #3784-3789	7.50	
b.	Booklet pane of 20, 4 each #3784-3785, 3 each #3786-3789	25.00	
	Nos. 3784-3789 (6)	7.50	1.50

Auto Racing at Bathurst, 50th Anniv. A902

Designs: Nos. 3790, 3794, Race car, country name in red. Nos. 3791, 3797, Mount Panorama Race Track, country name in yellow green. Nos. 3792, 3796, Race car, country name in blue. Nos. 3793, 3795, Race car, country name in yellow.

2012, Oct. 2   *Perf. 14x14¾*

3790	A902 60c multi	1.25	1.25
3791	A902 60c multi	1.25	1.25
3792	A902 60c multi	1.25	1.25
3793	A902 60c multi	1.25	1.25
a.	Block of 4, #3790-3793	5.00	5.00
b.	Souvenir sheet of 4, #3790-3793	5.00	5.00
	Nos. 3790-3793 (4)	5.00	5.00

Booklet Stamps
Self-Adhesive
Serpentine Die Cut 11¼ Syncopated

3794	A902 60c multi	1.25	.25
3795	A902 60c multi	1.25	.25
3796	A902 60c multi	1.25	.25
3797	A902 60c multi	1.25	.25
a.	Booklet pane of 10, 2 each #3794-3796, 4 #3797	12.50	
	Nos. 3794-3797 (4)	5.00	1.00

Susie O'Neill, Swimmer — A903

O'Neill: No. 3798, Wearing black jacket. No. 3799, Swimming in pool.

2012, Oct. 12   *Perf. 14¾x14*

3798	A903 60c multi	1.25	.95
3799	A903 60c multi	1.25	.95
a.	Pair, #3798-3799	2.50	1.90

Australian Ballet, 50th Anniv. — A904

Designs: Nos. 3800, 3802, One dancer. Nos. 3801, 3803, Two dancers.

2012, Oct. 16   *Perf. 14¾x14*

3800	A904 60c multi	1.25	1.25
3801	A904 60c multi	1.25	1.25
a.	Pair, #3800-3801	2.50	2.50

Coil Stamps
Self-Adhesive
Serpentine Die Cut 11¼ Syncopated

3802	A904 60c multi	1.25	.25
3803	A904 60c multi	1.25	.25
a.	Vert. pair, #3802-3803	2.50	

Lawn Bowling A905

Designs: 60c, Female bowlers. $1.20, Male bowlers.

2012, Nov. 1   *Perf. 14x14¾*

3804	A905 60c multi	1.25	.95
3805	A905 $1.20 multi	2.50	1.90
a.	Souvenir sheet of 2, #3804-3805	3.75	3.00

Christmas
A906   A907

Designs: Nos. 3806, 3811, Detail of Madonna and Child from Adoration of the Magi tapestry. Nos. 3807, 3812, 3815, 3817, Reindeer. Nos. 3808, 3813, 3816, 3818, Gifts. 60c, Bells. $1.60, Entire Adoration of the Magi tapestry (50x30mm), horiz.

2012, Nov. 1   *Perf. 14¾x14*

3806	A906 55c multi	1.25	1.25
3807	A907 55c multi	1.25	1.25
3808	A907 55c multi	1.25	1.25
3809	A907 60c multi	1.25	.60

Perf. 14½x14

3810	A906 $1.60 multi	3.50	1.75
	Nos. 3806-3810 (5)	8.50	6.10

Booklet Stamps
Self-Adhesive
Serpentine Die Cut 11¼ Syncopated

3811	A906 55c multi	1.25	.25
a.	Booklet pane of 20	25.00	
3812	A907 55c multi	1.25	.25
3813	A907 55c multi	1.25	.25
a.	Booklet pane of 20, 10 each #3812-3813	25.00	
3814	A906 $1.60 multi	3.50	1.75
a.	Booklet pane of 5	17.50	

Litho. With Foil Application

3815	A907 55c multi	1.25	.25
a.	Booklet pane of 10	12.50	

Litho. & Embossed With Foil Application

3816	A907 55c multi	1.25	.25
a.	Booklet pane of 10	12.50	
	Nos. 3811-3816 (6)	9.75	3.00

With Personalized Photo at Right Like Type A692a
Litho.
Serpentine Die Cut 11½x11¼ Syncopated

3817	A907 55c multi	2.50	2.50
3818	A907 55c multi	2.50	2.50

Nos. 3817-3818 each were printed in sheets of 20 and have personalized pictures and straight edge at right, and lack separations between the stamp an the personalized photo. Sheets of 20 of each stamp sold for $24.

Jacqueline Freney, Paralympian of the Year — A908

2012, Nov. 9   *Perf. 14¼*

3819	A908 60c multi	1.25	.95

Musical Legends — A909

Designs: Nos. 3820, 3830, AC/DC (rock band). Nos. 3821, 3831, Cold Chisel (rock band). Nos. 3822, 3832, INXS (rock band). Nos. 3823, 3833, John Farnham (singer). Nos. 3824, 3834, Kylie Minogue (singer). Nos. 3825, 3835, Men At Work (rock band). Nos. 3826, 3836, Ian "Molly" Meldrum (record producer). Nos. 3827, 3837, Olivia Newton-John (singer). No. 3828, 3838, Paul Kelly (singer). Nos. 3829, 3839, The Seekers (rock band).

2013, Jan. 18   *Perf. 14¾x14*

3820	A909 60c multi	1.25	1.25
a.	Booklet pane of 4	5.25	
3821	A909 60c multi	1.25	1.25
a.	Booklet pane of 4	5.25	
b.	Horiz. pair, #3820-3821	2.50	2.50
3822	A909 60c multi	1.25	1.25
a.	Booklet pane of 4	5.25	—
3823	A909 60c multi	1.25	1.25
a.	Booklet pane of 4	5.25	
3824	A909 60c multi	1.25	1.25
a.	Booklet pane of 4	5.25	
3825	A909 60c multi	1.25	1.25
a.	Booklet pane of 4	5.25	—
3826	A909 60c multi	1.25	1.25
a.	Booklet pane of 4	5.25	
b.	Horiz. pair, #3824, 3826	2.50	2.50
3827	A909 60c multi	1.25	1.25
a.	Booklet pane of 4	5.25	
b.	Horiz. pair, #3823, 3827	2.50	2.50
3828	A909 60c multi	1.25	1.25
a.	Booklet pane of 4	5.25	
b.	Horiz. pair, #3822, 3828	2.50	2.50
3829	A909 60c multi	1.25	1.25
a.	Booklet pane of 4	5.25	—
b.	Horiz. pair, #3825, 3829	2.50	2.50
	Complete booklet, #3820a-3829a	52.50	
	Nos. 3820-3829 (10)	12.50	12.50

Booklet Stamps
Self-Adhesive
Serpentine Die Cut 11¼ Syncopated

3830	A909 60c multi	1.25	.25
a.	Booklet pane of 10	12.50	
3831	A909 60c multi	1.25	.25
a.	Booklet pane of 10	12.50	
3832	A909 60c multi	1.25	.25
a.	Booklet pane of 10	12.50	
3833	A909 60c multi	1.25	.25
a.	Booklet pane of 10	12.50	

3834	A909	60c multi	1.25	.25
a.		Booklet pane of 10	12.50	
3835	A909	60c multi	1.25	.25
a.		Booklet pane of 10	12.50	
3836	A909	60c multi	1.25	.25
a.		Booklet pane of 10	12.50	
3837	A909	60c multi	1.25	.25
a.		Booklet pane of 10	12.50	
3838	A909	60c multi	1.25	.25
a.		Booklet pane of 10	12.50	
3839	A909	60c multi	1.25	.25
a.		Booklet pane of 10	12.50	
		Nos. 3830-3839 (10)	12.50	2.50

Complete booklet sold for $24.95.

Eucalyptus Leaves — A910

Map of Australia — A911

Rose Petal — A912

Orchid — A913

Gifts and Champagne Flutes — A914

2013, Feb. 5   Litho.   Perf. 14¾x14

3840	A910	60c multi	1.25	1.25
3841	A911	60c blue & multi	1.25	1.25
3842	A911	60c org & multi	1.00	1.00
3843	A912	60c multi	1.25	1.25
3844	A913	60c multi	1.25	1.25
a.		Horiz. strip of 5, #3840-3844	6.25	6.25
3845	A914	$1.20 multi	2.50	2.50
		Nos. 3840-3845 (6)	8.75	8.75

Booklet Stamps
Self-Adhesive
Serpentine Die Cut 11¼ Syncopated

3846	A910	60c multi	1.25	.25
a.		Booklet pane of 10 + 5 stickers	12.50	
3847	A911	60c blue & multi	1.25	.25
3848	A911	60c org & multi	1.25	.25
a.		Booklet pane of 10, 5 each #3847-3848, + 5 stickers	12.50	
3849	A912	60c multi	1.25	.25
a.		Booklet pane of 10 + 5 stickers	12.50	
3850	A913	60c multi	1.25	.25
a.		Booklet pane of 10 + 5 stickers	12.50	
3851	A914	$1.20 multi	2.50	1.25
a.		Booklet pane of 10 + 5 stickers	25.00	
b.		Booklet pane of 4	10.50	
		Complete booklet, 5 #3851b	52.50	
		Nos. 3846-3851 (6)	8.75	2.50

Complete booklet sold for $24.95 and contains five examples of No. 3851b, each with a different image in pane margin.

With Personalized Photo at Right
Like Type A692a
Serpentine Die Cut 11½x11¼ Syncopated

3852	A910	60c multi	2.60	2.60
3853	A911	60c blue & multi	2.60	2.60
3854	A911	60c org & multi	2.60	2.60
3855	A912	60c multi	2.60	2.60
3856	A913	60c multi	2.60	2.60
3857	A914	$1.20 multi	3.75	3.75
		Nos. 3852-3857 (6)	16.75	16.75

Nos. 3852-3857 each were printed in sheets of 20 and have personalized pictures and a straight edge at right and lack separations between the stamp and the personalized photo. Sheets of 20 of Nos. 3852-3856 sold for $25 each, No. 3857, $37.

Women and Surfboards A915

Surfer and Stylized Waves A916

Surfboards on Automobile Roof — A917

Surfer A918

2013, Feb. 12   Litho.   Perf. 14x14¾

3858	A915	60c multi	1.25	1.25
a.		Booklet pane of 4	5.25	
3859	A916	60c multi	1.25	1.25
a.		Booklet pane of 4	5.25	
3860	A917	60c multi	1.25	1.25
a.		Booklet pane of 4	5.25	
3861	A918	60c multi	1.25	1.25
a.		Booklet pane of 4	5.25	—
b.		Booklet pane of 4, #3858-3861, #3859 in UL	5.25	
		Complete booklet, #3858a, 3859a, 3860a, 3861a, 3861b	26.50	
c.		Block of 4, #3851-3861	5.00	5.00
d.		Souvenir sheet of 4, #3858-3861, #3858 in UL	5.00	5.00
		Nos. 3858-3861 (4)	5.00	5.00

Self-Adhesive
Serpentine Die Cut 11¼ Syncopated

3862	A915	60c multi	1.25	.25
3863	A916	60c multi	1.25	.25
3864	A917	60c multi	1.25	.25
3865	A918	60c multi	1.25	.25
a.		Horiz. coil strip of 4, #3862-3865	5.00	
b.		Booklet pane of 10, 0 each #3862, 3865, 2 each #3863-3864	12.50	
		Nos. 3862-3865 (4)	5.00	1.00

Complete booklet sold for $12.95.

Dogs — A919

Designs: Nos. 3866, 3871, Miniature schnauzer. Nos. 3867, 3872, Miniature dachshund. Nos. 3868, 3873, Cavalier King Charles spaniel. Nos. 3869, 3874, Pug. Nos. 3870, 3875, Australian terrier.

2013, Feb. 19   Perf. 14¾x14

3866	A919	60c multi	1.25	1.25
3867	A919	60c multi	1.25	1.25
3868	A919	60c multi	1.25	1.25
3869	A919	60c multi	1.25	1.25
3870	A919	60c multi	1.25	1.25
a.		Horiz. strip of 5, #3866-3870	6.25	6.25
		Nos. 3866-3870 (5)	6.25	6.25

Booklet Stamps
Self-Adhesive
Serpentine Die Cut 11¼ Syncopated

3871	A919	60c multi	1.25	.25
a.		Booklet pane of 10 + 5 stickers	12.50	
3872	A919	60c multi	1.25	.25
a.		Booklet pane of 10 + 5 stickers	12.50	
3873	A919	60c multi	1.25	.25
a.		Booklet pane of 10 + 5 stickers	12.50	
3874	A919	60c multi	1.25	.25
a.		Booklet pane of 10 + 5 stickers	12.50	

3875	A919	60c multi	1.25	.25
a.		Booklet pane of 10 + 5 stickers	12.50	
		Nos. 3871-3875 (5)	6.25	1.25

Canberra, Cent. A920

Map and: 60c, National Portrait Gallery. $2.35, Parliament House.

2013, Mar. 5   Perf. 14x14¾

3876	A920	60c multi	1.25	1.25
3877	A920	$2.35 multi	4.75	2.40
a.		Booklet pane of 4, 2 each #3876-3877	13.00	
		Complete booklet, #1938d, 2710c, 2869e, 3107c, 3349b, 3877a	27.50	

Self-Adhesive
Serpentine Die Cut 11¼ Syncopated

3878	A920	60c multi	1.25	.25
a.		Booklet pane of 20	25.00	

Complete booklet sold for $12.95. No. 3878 was issued in coils and booklet panes.

Paintings in National Gallery of Australia — A921

Designs: Nos. 3879, 3884, Dandenong Ranges from 'Beleura,' by Eugene von Guérard. Nos. 3880, 3885, In the Flinders - Far North, by Hans Heysen. Nos. 3881, 3886, Land of the Golden Fleece, by Arthur Streetson. Nos. 3882, 3887, Mr. Robinson's House on the Derwent, Van Diemen's Land, by John Glover. Nos. 3883, 3888, Studley Park at Sunrise, by Nicholas Chevalier.

2013, Mar. 19   Perf. 14¾x14

3879	A921	60c multi	1.25	1.25
3880	A921	60c multi	1.25	1.25
3881	A921	60c multi	1.25	1.25
3882	A921	60c multi	1.25	1.25
3883	A921	60c multi	1.25	1.25
a.		Horiz. strip of 5, #3879-3883	6.25	6.25
		Nos. 3879-3883 (5)	6.25	6.25

Booklet Stamps
Self-Adhesive
Serpentine Die Cut 11¼ Syncopated

3884	A921	60c multi	1.25	.25
3885	A921	60c multi	1.25	.25
3886	A921	60c multi	1.25	.25
3887	A921	60c multi	1.25	.25
3888	A921	60c multi	1.25	.25
a.		Booklet pane of 10, 2 each #3884-3888	12.50	
		Nos. 3884-3888 (5)	6.25	1.25

Baby Animals — A922

Designs: $1.70, Kookaburra. $1.75, Wombat. $2.60, Echidna. $4.65, Platypus. $6.45, Possum.

2013, Apr. 2   Perf. 14¾x14

3889	A922	$1.70 multi	3.50	3.50
3890	A922	$1.75 multi	3.75	3.75
3891	A922	$2.60 multi	5.50	5.50
3892	A922	$4.65 multi	9.75	7.50
3893	A922	$6.45 multi	13.50	10.00
		Nos. 3889-3893 (5)	36.00	30.25

Booklet Stamps
Self-Adhesive
Serpentine Die Cut 11¼ Syncopated

3894	A922	$1.70 multi	3.50	1.75
a.		Booklet pane of 5	17.50	
3895	A922	$1.75 multi	3.75	1.90
a.		Booklet pane of 5	19.00	
3896	A922	$2.60 multi	5.50	2.75
a.		Booklet pane of 5	27.50	
		Nos. 3894-3896 (3)	12.75	6.40

With Personalized Photo at Right
Like Type A692a
Serpentine Die Cut 11½x11¼ Syncopated

3898	A922	$1.75 multi	5.00	5.00
3899	A922	$2.60 multi	6.75	6.75

Nos. 3898-3899 each were printed in sheets of 20 and have personalized pictures and a straight edge at right and lack separations between the stamp and the personalized photo. Sheets of 20 of No. 3898 sold for $48, No. 3899, $65.

Coach — A923

Queen Elizabeth II — A924

2013, Apr. 9   Litho.   Perf. 14¾x14

3900	A923	60c multi	1.25	.95
a.		Booklet pane of 1	1.25	—
3901	A924	$2.60 multi	5.50	5.50
a.		Souvenir sheet of 2, #3900-3901	6.75	6.75
b.		Booklet pane of 1	5.50	—
c.		Booklet pane of 3	16.50	—
		Complete booklet, #3901b, 2 each #3900a, 3901c, + 50c coin	41.00	

Complete booklet sold for $19.95.

Booklet Stamp
Self-Adhesive
Serpentine Die Cut 11¼ Syncopated

3902	A924	$2.60 multi	5.50	2.75
a.		Booklet pane of 5	27.50	

Litho. & Embossed
Perf. 14¾x14

3903	A923	60c multi	1.40	1.40

Coronation of Queen Elizabeth II, 60th anniv. Examples of No. 3901a with an overprint for the Australia 2013 World Stamp Expo were made given to the show organizers and sold only by them. No. 3903 was printed in sheets of 10 that sold for $6.45.

Botanical Gardens A925

Designs: Nos. 3904, 3909, Royal Tasmanian Botanical Gardens, Hobart. Nos. 3905, 3910, Australian National Botanic Gardens, Canberra. Nos. 3906, 3911, Blue Mountains Botanic Garden, Mount Tomah, New South Wales. Nos. 3907, 3912, Darwin Botanic Gardens, Darwin, Northern Territory. No. 3908, 3913, Royal Botanic Gardens, Cranbourne, Victoria.

2013, Apr. 23   Litho.   Perf. 14x14¾

3904	A925	60c multi	1.25	1.25
a.		Booklet pane of 4 + 2 labels	5.50	
3905	A925	60c multi	1.25	1.25
a.		Booklet pane of 4 + 2 labels	5.50	
3906	A925	60c multi	1.25	1.25
a.		Booklet pane of 4 + 2 labels	5.50	
3907	A925	60c multi	1.25	1.25
a.		Booklet pane of 4 + 2 labels	5.50	
3908	A925	60c multi	1.25	1.25
a.		Booklet pane of 4 + 2 labels	5.50	
		Complete booklet, #3904a, 3905a, 3906a, 3907a, 3908a	27.50	
b.		Horiz. strip of 5, #3904-3908	6.25	6.25
		Nos. 3904-3908 (5)	6.25	6.25

Coil Stamps
Self-Adhesive
Serpentine Die Cut 11¼ Syncopated

3909	A925	60c multi	1.25	.25
3910	A925	60c multi	1.25	.25
3911	A925	60c multi	1.25	.25

3912 A925 60c multi 1.25 .25
3913 A925 60c multi 1.25 .25
   a. Horiz. strip of 5, #3909-3913 6.25
   Nos. 3909-3913 (5) 6.25 1.25

Complete booklet sold for $12.95. Examples of complete booklets with overprints for the Australia 2013 World Stamp Expo were made given to the show organizers and sold only by them.

Battle of Beersheba, 96th Anniv. A926

Designs: 60c, Statue of Australian Light Horseman, by Peter Corlett, Beersheva, Israel. $2.60, Australian Light Horsemen, photograph of battle re-enactment.

2013, May 10 **Perf. 13x13½**
3914 A926 60c multi 1.25 .95
3915 A926 $2.60 multi 5.00 3.75

See Israel Nos. 1975-1976.

Black Caviar, Undefeated Racehorse — A927

2013, May 10 **Perf. 14¾x14**
3916 A927 60c multi 1.25 1.25

Booklet Stamp
Self-Adhesive

Serpentine Die Cut 11¼ Syncopated

3917 A927 60c multi 1.25 .25
   a. Booklet pane of 10 12.50

Stamps like No. 3916 but with a white frame were printed in limited-quantity sheets of 10 that were sold in special packages only at the Australia 2013 World Stamp Expo.

Stamps Depicting Kangaroos — A928

2013, May 10 **Litho.** **Imperf.**
3918 A928 $1.62 Booklet pane 3.50
   Complete booklet sold for #1003b, 1284h, 3534d, 3918 25.00

No. 3918 contains imperforate examples of Nos. 992a, 1030c, 1063B and 2121, but these stamps were not valid for postage individually as cutouts from the entire booklet pane. Complete booklet sold for $12.95, and also contains a perforated booklet pane containing lithographed reproductions of Nos. 166 and 322 that is invalid for postage.

Kangaroo and Map Stamps, Cent. — A929

2013, May 10 **Litho.** **Perf. 14¼x14**
3919 A929 $10 red 19.00 9.50
   a. Souvenir sheet of 1 19.00 9.50

A booklet containing an imperforate example of No. 3919 sold for $24.95.

First Commonwealth of Australia Banknotes, Cent. — A930

Designs: 60c, Scene from ceremony for numbering first banknote. $2.60, Arms of Australia.

2013, May 11 **Litho.** **Perf. 14x13½**
3920 A930 60c multi 1.25 .95
3921 A930 $2.60 multi 5.00 3.75
   a. Souvenir sheet of 2, #3920-3921 6.25 4.75

Examples of No. 3921a overprinted in the margin with the emblem of the 2013 Melbourne World Stamp Expo were sold by the exhibitions organizers for $15.

Pardalotes A931

Designs: 60c, Forty-spotted pardalote. $1.20, Spotted pardalotes. $1.80, Red-browed pardalote. $3, Striated pardalote.

2013, May 11 **Litho.** **Perf. 14x14¾**
3922 A931 60c multi 1.25 1.25
3923 A931 $1.20 multi 2.25 2.25
3924 A931 $1.80 multi 3.50 2.60
3925 A931 $3 multi 5.75 4.50
   a. Booklet pane of 4, #3922-3925 13.00 —
   Complete booklet, #3151c, 3376b, 3665b, 3925a 48.50
   Nos. 3922-3925 (4) 12.75 10.60

Coil Stamp
Self-Adhesive

Serpentine Die Cut 11¼ Syncopated

3926 A931 60c multi 1.25 .25

Booklet Stamp

3927 A931 $1.20 multi 2.25 .50
   a. Booklet pane of 5 11.50

Complete booklet sold for $24.95.

State Government Houses A932

Government House of: Nos. 3928, 3932, South Australia. Nos. 3929, 3933, Western Australia. Nos. 3930, 3934, New South Wales. Nos. 3931, 3935, Tasmania.

2013, June 11 **Litho.** **Perf. 14x14¾**
3928 A932 60c multi 1.25 1.25
3929 A932 60c multi 1.25 1.25
3930 A932 60c multi 1.25 1.25
3931 A932 60c multi 1.25 1.25
   a. Block of 4, #3928-3931 5.00 5.00
   Nos. 3928-3931 (4) 5.00 5.00

Self-Adhesive

Serpentine Die Cut 11¼ Syncopated

3932 A932 60c multi 1.25 .25
3933 A932 60c multi 1.25 .25
3934 A932 60c multi 1.25 .25
3935 A932 60c multi 1.25 .25
   a. Horiz. coil strip of 4, #3932-3935 5.00
   b. Booklet pane of 20, 5 each #3932-3935 25.00
   Nos. 3932-3935 (4) 5.00 1.00

Road Trips — A933

Designs: Nos. 3936, 3942, Utility vehicle in Sydney. Nos. 3937, 3941, Station wagon in Melbourne. Nos. 3938, 3945, Car on roller coaster tracks, Gold Coast. Nos. 3939, 3943, Utility vehicle and camper in Adelaide. Nos. 3940, 3944, Car and camper in Canberra.

2013, July 2 **Litho.** **Perf. 14¼**
3936 A933 60c multi 1.10 1.10
3937 A933 60c multi 1.10 1.10
3938 A933 60c multi 1.10 1.10
3939 A933 60c multi 1.10 1.10
3940 A933 60c multi 1.10 1.10
   a. Souvenir sheet of 5, #3936-3940 5.50 5.50
   Nos. 3936-3940 (5) 5.50 5.50

Booklet Stamps
Self-Adhesive

Serpentine Die Cut 11¼ Syncopated

3941 A933 60c multi 1.10 .25
3942 A933 60c multi 1.10 .25
   a. Booklet pane of 10, 5 each #3941-3942 11.00
3943 A933 60c multi 1.10 .25
3944 A933 60c multi 1.10 .25
3945 A933 60c multi 1.10 .25
   a. Booklet pane of 20, 7 each #3943, 3945, 6 #3944 22.00
   Nos. 3941-3945 (5) 5.50 1.25

Aboriginal Leaders — A934

Designs: Nos. 3946, 3951, Shirley Smith (1921-98), justice and welfare advocate. Nos. 3947, 3952, Neville Bonner (1922-99), first Aboriginal member of Australian Parliament. Nos. 3948, 3953, Oodgeroo Noonuccal (1920-93), poet. Nos. 3949, 3954, Eddie "Koiki" Mabo (1936-92), plaintiff in historic Aboriginal land rights lawsuit. Nos. 3950, 3955, Charles Perkins (1936-2000), Secretary of the Department of Aboriginal Affairs.

2013, July 9 **Litho.** **Perf. 14¾x14**
3946 A934 60c multi 1.10 1.10
   a. Booklet pane of 4 4.75
3947 A934 60c multi 1.10 1.10
   a. Booklet pane of 4 4.75
3948 A934 60c multi 1.10 1.10
   a. Booklet pane of 4 4.75
3949 A934 60c multi 1.10 1.10
   a. Booklet pane of 4 4.75
3950 A934 60c multi 1.10 1.10
   a. Booklet pane of 4 4.75
   Complete booklet, #3946a, 3947a, 3948a, 3949a, 3950a 24.00
   b. Horiz. strip of 5, #3946-3950 5.50 5.50
   Nos. 3946-3950 (5) 5.50 5.50

Coil Stamps
Self-Adhesive

Serpentine Die Cut 11¼ Syncopated

3951 A934 60c multi 1.10 .25
3952 A934 60c multi 1.10 .25
3953 A934 60c multi 1.10 .25
3954 A934 60c multi 1.10 .25
3955 A934 60c multi 1.10 .25
   a. Vert. coil strip of 5, #3951-3955 5.50
   Nos. 3951-3955 (5) 5.50 1.25

Complete booklet sold for $12.95.

Birth of Prince George of Cambridge A935

2013, July 22 **Litho.** **Perf. 14¼**
3956 A935 60c multi 1.10 1.10

Booklet Stamp
Self-Adhesive

Serpentine Die Cut 11¼ Syncopated

3957 A935 60c multi 1.10 .25
   a. Booklet pane of 10 11.00

Headline News — A936

News stories of: Nos. 3958, 3962, August 15, 1945 (end of World War II). Nos. 3959, 3963, July 21, 1969 (first man on the Moon). Nos. 3960, 3964, December 25, 1974 (destruction of Darwin by Cyclone Tracy). Nos. 3961, 3965, September 27, 1983 (victory of Australia in America's Cup yacht races).

2013, July 23 **Litho.** **Perf. 14¾x14**
3958 A936 60c multi 1.10 1.10
3959 A936 60c multi 1.10 1.10
3960 A936 60c multi 1.10 1.10
3961 A936 60c multi 1.10 1.10
   a. Block of 4, #3958-3961 4.40 4.40
   b. Souvenir sheet of 4, #3958-3961 4.40 4.40
   Nos. 3958-3961 (4) 4.40 4.40

Self-Adhesive

Serpentine Die Cut 11¼ Syncopated

3962 A936 60c multi 1.10 .25
3963 A936 60c multi 1.10 .25
3964 A936 60c multi 1.10 .25
3965 A936 60c multi 1.10 .25
   a. Vert. coil strip of 4, #3962-3965 4.40
   b. Booklet pane of 20, 5 each #3962-3965 22.00
   Nos. 3962-3965 (4) 4.40 1.00

Carnivorous Plants — A937

Designs: Nos. 3966, 3970, Cephalotus follicularis and ants. Nos. 3967, 3971, Drosera rupicola and fly. Nos. 3968, 3972, Drosera lowriei and butterfly. Nos. 3969, 3973, Nepenthes rowanae and frog.

2013, Aug. 13 **Litho.** **Perf. 14¾x14**
3966 A937 60c multi 1.10 1.10
3967 A937 60c multi 1.10 1.10
3968 A937 60c multi 1.10 1.10
3969 A937 60c multi 1.10 1.10
   a. Block of 4, #3966-3969 4.40 4.40
   Nos. 3966-3969 (4) 4.40 4.40

Booklet Stamps
Self-Adhesive

Serpentine Die Cut 11¼ Syncopated

3970 A937 60c multi 1.10 .25
3971 A937 60c multi 1.10 .25
3972 A937 60c multi 1.10 .25
3973 A937 60c multi 1.10 .25
   a. Booklet pane of 10, 3 each #3970, 3972, 2 each #3971, 3973 11.00
   Nos. 3970-3973 (4) 4.40 1.00

Coral Reefs A938

Designs: Nos. 3974, 3979, Underwater view of Ningaloo Reef, Western Australia. Nos. 3975, 3978, Underwater view of Great Barrier Reef, Queensland. Nos. 3976, 3981, Aerial veiw of Ningaloo Reef. Nos. 3977, 3980, Aerial view of Great Barrier Reef.

2013, Aug. 20 **Litho.** **Perf. 14½x14**
3974 A938 60c multi 1.10 1.10
   a. Perf. 13½x14 1.10 1.10
3975 A938 60c multi 1.10 1.10
   a. Horiz. pair, #3974-3975 2.20 2.20
   b. Perf. 13½x14 1.10 1.10
3976 A938 $1.20 multi 2.25 2.25
   a. Perf. 13½x14 2.25 2.25
3977 A938 $1.20 multi 2.25 2.25
   a. Horiz. pair, #3976-3977 4.50 4.50
   b. Perf. 13½x14 2.25 2.25
   c. Souvenir sheet of 4, #3974a, 3975b, 3976a, 3977b 6.75 6.75
   Nos. 3974-3977 (4) 6.70 6.70

Booklet Stamps
Self-Adhesive
Serpentine Die Cut 10½ Syncopated

3978	A938	60c multi	1.10	.25
3979	A938	60c multi	1.10	.25
a.	Booklet pane of 20, 10 each #3978-3979		22.00	
3980	A938	$1.20 multi	2.25	.50
3981	A938	$1.20 multi	2.25	.50
a.	Booklet pane of 5, 3 #3980, 2 #3981		11.50	
	Nos. 3978-3981 (4)		6.70	1.50

Poultry Breeds — A939

Designs: No. 3982, Australian Game hen and rooster. No. 3983, Australian Pit Game hen and chicks. Nos. 3984, 3985, Australorp hens (37x26mm).

2013, Sept. 3   Litho.   Perf. 14x13½

3982	A939	60c multi	1.10	.85
a.	Booklet pane of 4		4.75	
3983	A939	60c multi	1.10	.85
a.	Booklet pane of 4		4.75	
b.	Booklet pane of 4, 2 each #3982-3983		4.75	—
	Perf. 14x14¾			
3984	A939	60c multi	1.10	1.10
a.	Booklet pane of 4		4.75	
b.	Souvenir sheet of 3, #3982-3984		3.30	3.30
	Complete booklet, #3982a, 3983a, 3983b, 2 #3984a		24.00	
	Nos. 3982-3984 (3)		3.30	2.80

Booklet Stamp
Self-Adhesive
Serpentine Die Cut 11¼ Syncopated

3985	A939	60c multi	1.10	.25
a.	Booklet pane of 10		11.00	

Complete booklet sold for $12.95 and contains two examples of No. 3984a having different margins.

Dinosaurs — A940

Designs: Nos. 3986, 3992, Koolasuchus. Nos. 3987, 3995, Serendipaceratops (26x37mm). No. 3988, Timimus (30x50mm). Nos. 3989, 3993, Diamantinasaurus, horiz. No. 3990, Qantassaurus, horiz. (50x30mm). Nos. 3991, 3994, Australovenator (26x37mm).

2013, Sept. 24   Litho.   Perf. 14½x14

3986	A940	60c multi	1.25	1.25
a.	Booklet pane of 4		5.00	
b.	Perf. 14½		1.25	1.25
	Perf. 14¾x14			
3987	A940	60c multi	1.25	1.25
a.	Booklet pane of 4		5.00	
b.	Perf. 14½		1.25	1.25
	Perf. 14x14½			
3988	A940	60c multi	1.25	1.25
a.	Perf. 14x13½		1.25	1.25
b.	Booklet pane of 2 #3988a		2.50	
c.	Perf. 14½		1.25	1.25
	Perf. 14x14½			
3989	A940	60c multi	1.25	1.25
a.	Booklet pane of 4		5.00	—
b.	Perf. 14½		1.25	1.25
	Perf. 14½x14			
3990	A940	60c multi	1.25	1.25
a.	Perf. 13½x14		1.25	1.25
b.	Booklet pane of 2 #3990a		2.50	—
c.	Perf. 14½		1.25	1.25
	Perf. 14¾x14			
3991	A940	60c multi	1.25	1.25
a.	Booklet pane of 4		5.00	—
	Complete booklet, #3986a, 3987a, 3988b, 3989a, 3990b, 3991a		25.00	
b.	Perf. 14½		1.25	1.25
c.	Souvenir sheet of 6, #3986b, 3987b, 3988c, 3989b, 3990c, 3991b		7.50	7.50
	Nos. 3986-3991 (6)		7.50	7.50

Booklet Stamps
Self-Adhesive
Serpentine Die Cut 11¼

3992	A940	60c multi	1.25	.25
3993	A940	60c multi	1.25	.25
a.	Booklet pane of 10, 5 each #3992-3993		12.50	
	Serpentine Die Cut 11¼ Syncopated			
3994	A940	60c multi	1.25	.25
3995	A940	60c multi	1.25	.25
a.	Booklet pane of 20, 10 each #3994-3995		25.00	
	Nos. 3992-3995 (4)		5.00	1.00

Complete booklet sold for $12.95.

Historic Railroad Stations A941

Station at: Nos. 3996, 4000, Maryborough, Victoria. Nos. 3997, 4001, Quorn, South Australia. Nos. 3998, 4002, Hay, New South Wales. Nos. 3999, 4003, Normanton, Queensland.

2013, Oct. 8   Litho.   Perf. 14x14¾

3996	A941	60c multi	1.25	1.25
3997	A941	60c multi	1.25	1.25
3998	A941	60c multi	1.25	1.25
3999	A941	60c multi	1.25	1.25
a.	Block of 4, #3996-3999		5.00	5.00
	Nos. 3996-3999 (4)		5.00	5.00

Self-Adhesive
Serpentine Die Cut 11¼ Syncopated

4000	A941	60c multi	1.25	.25
4001	A941	60c multi	1.25	.25
4002	A941	60c multi	1.25	.25
4003	A941	60c multi	1.25	.25
a.	Horiz. coil strip of 4, #4000-4003		5.00	
b.	Booklet pane of 10, 3 each #4000-4001, 2 each #4002-4003		12.50	
	Nos. 4000-4003 (4)		5.00	1.00

Ludwig Leichhardt (1813-48), Explorer of Outback Region A942

2013, Oct. 15   Litho.   Perf. 14¼

4004	A942	60c multi	1.25	.95

See Germany No. 2752.

Early Australian Coinage A943

Designs: 60c, Holey dollar and dumps. $3, Holey dollars.

2013, Oct. 22   Litho.   Perf. 14x14¾

4005	A943	60c multi	1.25	.95
4006	A943	$3 multi	5.75	4.50

Souvenir Sheet
Litho. & Embossed With Foil Application

4007		Sheet of 2	7.00	7.00
a.	A943 60c multi		1.25	.95
b.	A943 $3 multi		5.75	4.50

Christmas
A944   A945

Designs: Nos. 4008, 4014, Madonna and Child. Nos. 4009, 4015, 4019, Christmas tree.

Nos. 4010, 4016, 4020, Gift. 60c, Candle. Nos. 4012, 4017, Bell. Nos. 4013, 4018, Adoration of the Shepherds.

2013, Nov. 1   Litho.   Perf. 14¾x14

4008	A944	55c multi	1.10	1.10
4009	A945	55c multi	1.10	1.10
4010	A945	55c multi	1.10	1.10
a.	Horiz. pair, #4009-4010		2.20	2.20
4011	A945	60c multi	1.25	.95
4012	A945	$1.70 multi	3.25	1.60
4013	A944	$2.55 multi	4.75	2.40
a.	Souvenir sheet of 2, #4008, 4013		6.00	6.00
	Nos. 4008-4013 (6)		12.55	8.25

Booklet Stamps
Self-Adhesive
Serpentine Die Cut 11¼ Syncopated

4014	A944	55c multi	1.10	.25
a.	Booklet pane of 20 + 10 etiquettes		22.00	
4015	A945	55c multi	1.10	.25
4016	A945	55c multi	1.10	.25
a.	Booklet pane of 20, 10 each #4015-4016, + 10 etiquettes		22.00	
4017	A945	$1.70 multi	3.25	1.60
a.	Booklet pane of 5		16.50	
4018	A944	$2.55 multi	4.75	2.40
a.	Booklet pane of 5		24.00	

Litho. & Embossed With Foil Application

4019	A945	55c multi	1.10	.25
a.	Booklet pane of 10		11.00	
4020	A945	55c multi	1.10	.25
a.	Booklet pane of 10		11.00	
	Nos. 4014-4020 (7)		13.50	5.25

Christening of Prince George of Cambridge — A946

Duke and Duchess of Cambridge with Prince George: 60c, White background. $2.60, Yellow background.

2014, Jan. 7   Litho.   Perf. 14¾x14

4022	A946	60c multi	1.10	1.10
4023	A946	$2.60 multi	4.75	4.75
a.	Souvenir sheet of 2, #4022-4023		6.00	6.00

Booklet Stamps
Self-Adhesive
Serpentine Die Cut 11¼ Syncopated

4024	A946	60c multi	1.10	.25
a.	Booklet pane of 10		11.00	
4025	A946	$2.60 multi	4.75	2.40
a.	Booklet pane of 5		24.00	

Orchids — A947

Designs: Nos. 4026, 4030, Golden rock orchid. Nos. 4027, 4031, Bee orchid. Nos. 4028, 4032, Orange blossom orchid. Nos. 4029, 4033, Shirt orchid.

2014, Jan. 14   Litho.   Perf. 14¾x14

4026	A947	60c multi	1.10	1.10
4027	A947	60c multi	1.10	1.10
4028	A947	60c multi	1.10	1.10
4029	A947	60c multi	1.10	1.10
a.	Horiz. strip of 4, #4026-4029		4.40	4.40
	Nos. 4026-4029 (4)		4.40	4.40

Booklet Stamps
Self-Adhesive
Serpentine Die Cut 11¼ Syncopated

4030	A947	60c multi	1.10	.25
4031	A947	60c multi	1.10	.25
4032	A947	60c multi	1.10	.25
4033	A947	60c multi	1.10	.25
a.	Booklet pane of 10, 2 each #4030, 4032, 3 each #4031, 4033		11.00	
b.	Booklet pane of 20, 5 each #4030-4033		22.00	
	Nos. 4030-4033 (4)		4.40	1.00

Cooking Celebrities — A948

Designs: Nos. 4034, 4039, Margaret Fulton. Nos. 4035, 4040, Maggie Beer. Nos. 4036, 4041, Stephanie Alexander. Nos. 4037, 4042, Neil Perry. Nos. 4038, 4043, Kylie Kwong.

2014, Jan. 17   Litho.   Perf. 14¾x14

4034	A948	60c multi	1.10	1.10
a.	Booklet pane of 4		5.25	—
4035	A948	60c multi	1.10	1.10
a.	Booklet pane of 4		5.25	—
4036	A948	60c multi	1.10	1.10
a.	Booklet pane of 4		5.25	—
4037	A948	60c multi	1.10	1.10
a.	Booklet pane of 4		5.25	—
4038	A948	60c multi	1.10	1.10
a.	Booklet pane of 4		5.25	—
	Complete booklet, #4034a, 4035a, 4036a, 4037a, 4038a		22.00	
	Nos. 4034-4038 (5)		5.50	5.50

Booklet Stamps
Self-Adhesive
Serpentine Die Cut 11¼ Syncopated

4039	A948	60c multi	1.10	.25
a.	Booklet pane of 10		11.00	
4040	A948	60c multi	1.10	.25
a.	Booklet pane of 10		11.00	
4041	A948	60c multi	1.10	.25
a.	Booklet pane of 10		11.00	
4042	A948	60c multi	1.10	.25
a.	Booklet pane of 10		11.00	
4043	A948	60c multi	1.10	.25
a.	Booklet pane of 10		11.00	
	Nos. 4039-4043 (5)		5.50	1.25

Complete booklet sold for $14.95.

Victory of Australian Cricket Team in 2013-14 Ashes Test Matches — A949

Designs: 60c, Ashes urn. $2.60, Australian cricket team.

2014, Jan. 20   Litho.   Perf. 14¾x14

4044	A949	60c multi	1.10	.85
4045	A949	$2.60 multi	4.75	4.75
a.	Souvenir sheet of 2, #4044-4045		6.00	6.00

Booklet Stamp
Self-Adhesive
Serpentine Die Cut 11½x11¼

4046	A949	$2.60 multi	4.75	2.40
a.	Booklet pane of 5		24.00	

 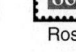

Hearts — A950   Rose — A951

2014, Feb. 4   Litho.   Perf. 14¾x14

4047	A950	60c multi	1.10	1.10
4048	A951	60c multi	1.10	1.10
a.	Pair, #4047-4048		2.20	2.20

Booklet Stamps
Self-Adhesive
Serpentine Die Cut 11¼ Syncopated

4049	A950	60c multi	1.10	.25
a.	Booklet pane of 10		11.00	
4050	A951	60c multi	1.10	.25
a.	Booklet pane of 20		22.00	

With Personalized Photo at Right Like Type A692a
Serpentine Die Cut 11½x11¼ Syncopated

4051	A950	60c multi	2.25	2.25
4052	A951	60c multi	2.25	2.25

Nos, 4051-4052 each were printed in sheets of 20 and have personalized pictures and a straight edge at right and lack separations between the stamp and the personalized photo. Sheets of 20 of each stamp sold for $25.

National and State Floral Emblems — A952

Designs: Nos. 4053, 4060, 4064, Tasmanian blue gum (Tasmania). Nos. 4054, 4061, 4065, Waratah (New South Wales). Nos. 4055, 4062, 4066, Golden wattle (Australia). Nos. 4056, 4063, 4067, Common heath (Victoria). $1.40, Cooktown orchid (Queensland). $2.10, Kangaroo paw (Western Australia). $3.50, Sturt's desert pea (South Australia).

2014, Mar. 24 Litho. Perf. 14½x14

4053	A952	70c multi	1.40	1.40
4054	A952	70c multi	1.40	1.40
4055	A952	70c multi	1.40	1.40
4056	A952	70c multi	1.40	1.40
a.		Horiz. strip of 4, #4053-4056	5.60	5.60
4057	A952	$1.40 multi	2.60	1.40
4058	A952	$2.10 multi	4.00	2.00
4059	A952	$3.50 multi	6.50	3.25
		Nos. 4053-4059 (7)	18.70	12.25

Coil Stamp
Self-Adhesive
Serpentine Die Cut 12¾

4060	A952	70c multi	1.40	.25
4061	A952	70c multi	1.40	.25
4062	A952	70c multi	1.40	.25
4063	A952	70c multi	1.40	.25
a.		Vert. strip of 4, #4060-4063	5.60	

Booklet Stamps
Serpentine Die Cut 11¼

4064	A952	70c multi	1.40	.25
4065	A952	70c multi	1.40	.25
4066	A952	70c multi	1.40	.25
4067	A952	70c multi	1.40	.25
a.		Booklet pane of 10, 3 each #4064-4065, 2 each #4066-4067	14.00	
b.		Booklet pane of 20, 5 each #4064-4067	28.00	
		Nos. 4060-4067 (8)	11.20	2.00

Map of Australia on Beach A953

Kangaroo A954

Serpentine Die Cut 11¼ Syncopated
2014, Mar. 24 Litho.
Booklet Stamps
Self-Adhesive

4068	A953	(70c) multi	1.40	.25
4069	A954	(70c) multi	1.40	.25
a.		Booklet pane of 5, 2#4068, 3 #4069	7.25	

No. 4069a was made available to holders of Australia Post My Post Concession Account card and the general public. Pensioners, veterans, the disabled, and others typically on low or fixed incomes, could apply at their local post office to receive a Concession Account card. Those eligible to receive the card were sent a free example of No. 4069a, which was mailed with the card. Card holders, when showing the card at the post office and having the information recorded, could purchase up to ten No. 4069a every year for $3 (60c per stamp, lower than the 70c letter rate instituted on March 31). 10,000 examples of No. 4069a were made available to the public through the philatelic bureau, but these were sold for $3.95 (79c per stamp). There are no differences between the stamps offered to card holders and the general public, aside from the selling price. Nos. 4068 and 4069 were valid only on letters, and could not be used on parcels or international mail.

Queen Elizabeth II, 88th Birthday — A955

Queen Elizabeth II facing: 70c, Left. $2.60, Right.

2014, Apr. 8 Litho. Perf. 14¾x14

4070	A955	70c multi	1.40	1.10
4071	A955	$2.60 multi	5.00	2.50
a.		Souvenir sheet of 2, #4070-4071	6.50	3.75

Booklet Stamp
Self-Adhesive
Serpentine Die Cut 11¼ Syncopated

4072	A955	$2.60 multi	5.00	2.50
a.		Booklet pane of 5	25.00	

Map of Australia A956

Balloons and Streamers A957

Baby's Mobile A958

Fireworks A959

Rose — A960

Stylized Flowers — A961

Champagne Flutes — A962

Wedding Rings and Roses — A963

Wedding Rings — A964

2014, Apr. 15 Litho. Perf. 14¾x14

4073	A956	70c blue & multi	1.40	.70
4074	A956	70c red & multi	1.40	.70
a.		Horiz. pair, #4073-4074	2.80	1.40
4075	A957	70c multi	1.40	1.40
4076	A958	70c multi	1.40	1.40
4077	A959	70c multi	1.40	1.40
4078	A960	70c multi	1.40	1.40
4079	A961	70c multi	1.40	1.40
4080	A962	70c multi	1.40	1.40
4081	A963	70c multi	1.40	1.40
4082	A964	$1.40 multi	2.60	1.40
		Nos. 4073-4082 (10)	15.20	12.60

Booklet Stamps
Self-Adhesive
Serpentine Die Cut 11¼ Syncopated

4083	A957	70c multi	1.40	.25
a.		Booklet pane of 10	14.00	
4084	A958	70c multi	1.40	.25
a.		Booklet pane of 10	14.00	
4085	A959	70c multi	1.40	.25
a.		Booklet pane of 10	14.00	
4086	A960	70c multi	1.40	.25
a.		Booklet pane of 10	14.00	
4087	A961	70c multi	1.40	.25
a.		Booklet pane of 10	14.00	
4088	A962	70c multi	1.40	.25
a.		Booklet pane of 10	14.00	
4089	A963	70c multi	1.40	.25
a.		Booklet pane of 10	14.00	
4090	A964	$1.40 multi	2.60	1.40
a.		Booklet pane of 4	10.50	
		Complete booklet, 5 #4090a	52.50	
		Nos. 4083-4090 (8)	12.40	3.15

Complete booklet contains 5 examples of No. 4090a, each with different pane margins.

With Personalized Photo at Right Like Type A692a
Serpentine Die Cut 11½x11¼ Syncopated

4091	A956	70c blue & multi	2.50	2.50
4092	A957	70c multi	2.50	2.50
4093	A958	70c multi	2.50	2.50
4094	A959	70c multi	2.50	2.50
4095	A960	70c multi	2.50	2.50
4096	A961	70c multi	2.50	2.50
4097	A962	70c multi	2.50	2.50
4098	A963	70c multi	2.50	2.50
4099	A964	$1.40 multi	3.75	3.75
		Nos. 4091-4099 (9)	23.75	23.75

Nos, 4091-4099 each were printed in sheets of 20 and have personalized pictures and a straight edge at right and lack separations between the stamp and the personalized photo. Sheets of 20 of Nos. 4091-4098 sold for $27 each, No. 4099, $41.

World War I, Cent. — A965

Inscriptions: Nos. 4100, 4105, War Declared! Nos. 4101, 4106, Australians in Action. Nos. 4102, 4107, Troops Depart. Nos. 4103, 4108, Training, Mena Camp (Egypt). Nos. 4104, 4109, Our Boys.

2014, Apr. 22 Litho. Perf. 14¼

4100	A965	70c multi	1.40	1.40
4101	A965	70c multi	1.40	1.40
4102	A965	70c multi	1.40	1.40
4103	A965	70c multi	1.40	1.40
4104	A965	70c multi	1.40	1.40
a.		Souvenir sheet of 5, #4100-4104	7.00	7.00
		Nos. 4100-4104 (5)	7.00	7.00

Booklet Stamps
Self-Adhesive
Serpentine Die Cut 11¼ Syncopated

4105	A965	70c multi	1.40	.25
4106	A965	70c multi	1.40	.25
4107	A965	70c multi	1.40	.25
4108	A965	70c multi	1.40	.25
4109	A965	70c multi	1.40	.25
a.		Booklet pane of 10, 2 each #4105-4109	14.00	
		Nos. 4105-4109 (5)	7.00	1.25

Australian Red Cross, Cent. A966

2014, May 6 Litho. Perf. 14x14¾

4110	A966	70c multi	1.40	1.40

Coil Stamp
Self-Adhesive
Serpentine Die Cut 11¼ Syncopated

4111	A966	70c multi	1.40	.25

Poems by Andrew Barton "Banjo" Paterson (1864-1941) A967

Designs: Nos. 4112, 4116, Clancy of the Overflow. Nos. 4113, 4117, The Man from Snowy River. Nos. 4114, 4118, Waltzing Matilda. Nos. 4115, 4119, Mulga Bill's Bicycle.

2014, May 13 Litho. Perf. 14x14¾

4112	A967	70c multi	1.40	1.40
a.		Booklet pane of 4	5.60	
4113	A967	70c multi	1.40	1.40
a.		Booklet pane of 4	5.60	
4114	A967	70c multi	1.40	1.40
a.		Booklet pane of 4	5.60	
4115	A967	70c multi	1.40	1.40
a.		Block of 4, #4112-4115	5.60	5.60
b.		Souvenir sheet of 4, #4112-4115	5.60	5.60
c.		Booklet pane of 4 #4115	5.60	—
d.		Booklet pane of 4, #4112-4115	5.60	
		Complete booklet, #4112a, 4113a, 4114a, 4115c, 2 #4115d	34.00	
		Nos. 4112-4115 (4)	5.60	5.60

Self-Adhesive
Serpentine Die Cut 11¼ Syncopated

4116	A967	70c multi	1.40	.25
4117	A967	70c multi	1.40	.25
4118	A967	70c multi	1.40	.25
4119	A967	70c multi	1.40	.25
a.		Horiz. coil strip of 4, #4116-4119	5.60	
b.		Booklet pane of 10, 3 each #4116-4117, 2 each #4118-4119	14.00	
		Nos. 4116-4119 (4)	5.60	1.00

The complete booklet sold for $16.95. In the complete booklet, one of the two examples of No. 4115d has a booklet pane margin similar to No. 4115b.

G20 Summit, Brisbane — A968

2014, June 3 Litho. Perf. 14¾x14

4120	A968	70c multi	1.40	1.10

King George V Typographed Stamps, Cent. — A969

2014, June 17 Litho. Perf. 14½x14

4121	A969	70c red	1.40	1.10
a.		Booklet pane of 4	5.60	
4122	A969	70c red brown	1.40	1.10
a.		Booklet pane of 4	5.60	
4123	A969	70c purple	1.40	1.10
a.		Booklet pane of 4	5.60	
4124	A969	70c green	1.40	1.10
a.		Booklet pane of 4	5.60	
b.		Booklet pane of 4, #4121-4124	5.60	
c.		Booklet pane of 4, #4121-4124, imperf.	5.60	
		Complete booklet, #4121a, 4122a, 4123a, 4124a, 4124b, 4124c	34.00	
d.		Block or strip of 4, #4121-4124	5.60	4.40
e.		Souvenir sheet of 4, #4121-4124	5.60	4.40
f.		Sheet of 10, 4 #4121, 2 each #4122-4124	14.00	11.00

Typo.

4125	A969	70c red	1.40	1.10
4126	A969	70c purple	1.40	1.10
4127	A969	70c green	1.40	1.10
4128	A969	70c red brown	1.40	1.10
a.		Horiz. strip of 4, #4125-4128	5.60	4.40
b.		Sheet of 10, 4 #4125, 2 each #4126-4128	14.00	11.00
		Nos. 4121-4128 (8)	11.20	8.80

Complete booklet sold for $16.95. Nos. 4124f and 4128b were sold together for $14.45.

First Air Mail in Australia, Cent. — A970

Designs: 70c, Spectators watching airplane in flight. $2.60, Maurice Guillaux piloting Bleriot XI airplane.

2014, July 1		**Litho.**	**Perf. 14¼**	
4129	A970	70c multi	1.40	1.10
a.		Booklet pane of 4	5.75	—
4130	A970	$2.60 multi	5.00	2.50
a.		Booklet pane of 4	20.50	—
b.		Booklet pane of 2, #4129-4130, 2 #4129a	6.50	—
		Complete booklet, #4130a, 4130b, 2 #4129a	38.50	
c.		Souvenir sheet of 2, #4129-4130	6.50	—

Complete booklet sold for $19.95. The two examples of No. 4129a in the booklet have different pane margins.

Visit of Duke and Duchess of Cambridge and Prince George A971

Designs: 70c, Duke and Duchess, Sydney Harbour Bridge. $2.60, Duke and Duchess, Prince George, and bilby.

2014, July 8		**Litho.**	**Perf. 14¼**	
4131	A971	70c multi	1.40	1.40
4132	A971	$2.60 multi	5.00	5.00
a.		Souvenir sheet of 2, #4131-4132	6.50	6.50

Booklet Stamps
Self-Adhesive

Serpentine Die Cut 11¼ Syncopated

4133	A971	70c multi	1.40	.25
a.		Booklet pane of 10	14.00	
4134	A971	$2.60 multi	5.00	2.50
a.		Booklet pane of 5	25.00	

Equestrian Events — A972

Designs: Nos. 4135, 4140, Pony Club. Nos. 4136, 4141, Polocrosse. Nos. 4137, 4142, Show jumping. Nos. 4138, 4143, Cross-country. Nos. 4139, 4144, Dressage.

2014, July 15		**Litho.**	**Perf. 14¾x14**	
4135	A972	70c multi	1.40	1.40
4136	A972	70c multi	1.40	1.40
4137	A972	70c multi	1.40	1.40
4138	A972	70c multi	1.40	1.40
4139	A972	70c multi	1.40	1.40
		Nos. 4135-4139 (5)	7.00	7.00

Self-Adhesive

Serpentine Die Cut 11¼ Syncopated

4140	A972	70c multi	1.40	.25
a.		Booklet pane of 10	14.00	
4141	A972	70c multi	1.40	.25
a.		Booklet pane of 10	14.00	
4142	A972	70c multi	1.40	.25
a.		Booklet pane of 10	14.00	
4143	A972	70c multi	1.40	.25
a.		Booklet pane of 10	14.00	
4144	A972	70c multi	1.40	.25
a.		Booklet pane of 10	14.00	
b.		Vert. coil strip of 5, #4140-4144	7.00	
		Nos. 4140-4144 (5)	7.00	1.25

Norfolk Island Pine — A973

Norfolk Island Pine and: 70c, Cottesloe Beach, Western Australia. $1.40, Old Military Barracks, Kingston, Norfolk Island.

2014, July 22		**Litho.**	**Perf. 14x14¾**	
4145	A973	70c multi	1.40	1.10
4146	A973	$1.40 multi	2.60	2.00

See Norfolk Island Nos. 1090-1091.

Australian Military Centenaries A974

Designs: Nos. 4147, 4149, Military aviation, cent. Nos. 4148, 4150, Submarines, cent.

2014, Aug. 5		**Litho.**	**Perf. 14x14¾**	
4147	A974	70c multi	1.40	1.40
4148	A974	70c multi	1.40	1.40
a.		Vert. pair, #4147-4148	2.80	2.80
b.		Souvenir sheet of 2, #4147-4148	2.80	2.80

Booklet Stamps
Self-Adhesive

Serpentine Die Cut 11¼ Syncopated

4149	A974	70c multi	1.40	.25
4150	A974	70c multi	1.40	.25
a.		Booklet pane of 20, 10 each #4149-4150	28.00	

Mid-20th Century Advertisements A975

Advertisement for: Nos. 4151, 4156, Phillip Island Tourism. Nos. 4152, 4157, Harper's Empire Self-Raising Flour. Nos. 4153, 4158, Trans-Australian Airways. Nos. 4154, 4159, Jacko Shoe Polish. Nos. 4155, 4160, Swallow & Ariell's Teddy Bear Biscuits.

2014, Aug. 19		**Litho.**	**Perf. 14¾x14**	
4151	A975	70c multi	1.40	1.40
4152	A975	70c multi	1.40	1.40
4153	A975	70c multi	1.40	1.40
4154	A975	70c multi	1.40	1.40
4155	A975	70c multi	1.40	1.40
a.		Horiz. strip of 5, #4151-4155	7.00	7.00
b.		Souvenir sheet of 5, #4151-4155	7.00	7.00
		Nos. 4151-4155 (5)	7.00	7.00

Coil Stamps
Self-Adhesive

Serpentine Die Cut 11¼ Syncopated

4156	A975	70c multi	1.40	.25
4157	A975	70c multi	1.40	.25
4158	A975	70c multi	1.40	.25
4159	A975	70c multi	1.40	.25
4160	A975	70c multi	1.40	.25
a.		Vert. strip of 5, #4156-4160	7.00	
		Nos. 4156-4160 (5)	7.00	1.25

Aurora Australis (Southern Lights) A976

Various photographs of auroras with denomination at: Nos. 4161, 4163, 4165, LL. Nos. 4162, 4164, 4166, LR.

2014, Aug. 26		**Litho.**	**Perf. 14x14¾**	
4161	A976	70c multi	1.40	1.40
4162	A976	70c multi	1.40	1.40
a.		Horiz. pair, #4161-4162	2.80	2.80
4163	A976	$1.40 multi	2.60	2.00
4164	A976	$1.40 multi	2.60	2.00
a.		Horiz. pair, #4163-4164	5.20	4.00
b.		Souvenir sheet of 4, #4161-4164	8.00	8.00
		Nos. 4161-4164 (4)	8.00	6.80

Booklet Stamps
Self-Adhesive

4165	A976	70c multi	1.40	.25
4166	A976	70c multi	1.40	.25
a.		Booklet pane of 10, 5 each #4165-4166	14.00	

On. No. 4164b, Nos. 4162a and 4164a are tete-beche in relationship to each other.

Gardens A977

Designs: Nos. 4167, 4172, Cruden Farm, Victoria. Nos. 4168, 4173, Mendel Gardens, Western Australia. Nos. 4169, 4176, Niwajiri, South Australia. Nos. 4170, 4174, Walcott Gardens, Australian Capital Territory. Nos. 4171, 4175, Wychwood, Tasmania.

2014, Sept. 2		**Litho.**	**Perf. 14x14¾**	
4167	A977	70c multi	1.40	1.40
4168	A977	70c multi	1.40	1.40
4169	A977	70c multi	1.40	1.40
4170	A977	70c multi	1.40	1.40
4171	A977	70c multi	1.40	1.40
a.		Horiz. strip of 5, #4167-4171	7.00	7.00
		Nos. 4167-4171 (5)	7.00	7.00

Booklet Stamps
Self-Adhesive

Serpentine Die Cut 11¼ Syncopated

4172	A977	70c multi	1.40	.25
4173	A977	70c multi	1.40	.25
4174	A977	70c multi	1.40	.25
4175	A977	70c multi	1.40	.25
4176	A977	70c multi	1.40	.25
a.		Booklet pane of 20, 4 each #4172-4176	28.00	
		Nos. 4172-4176 (5)	7.00	1.25

Venomous Creatures A978

Designs: Nos. 4177, 4186, European wasp. Nos. 4178, 4185, Lionfish. Nos. 4179, 4183, Bull ant. Nos. 4180, 4187, Tiger snake. Nos. 4181, 4188, Stonefish. Nos. 4182, 4184, Stingray.

2014, Sept. 23		**Litho.**	**Perf. 14x14¾**	
4177	A978	70c multi	1.25	1.25
4178	A978	70c multi	1.25	1.25
4179	A978	70c multi	1.25	1.25
4180	A978	70c multi	1.25	1.25
a.		Souvenir sheet of 6, 2 each #4177, 4179, 4180, + 6 labels	7.75	7.75
4181	A978	70c multi	1.25	1.25
4182	A978	70c multi	1.25	1.25
a.		Souvenir sheet of 6, #4177-4182	7.50	7.50
b.		Souvenir sheet of 6, 2 each #4176, 4181, 4182, + 6 labels	7.75	7.75
		Nos. 4177-4182 (6)	7.50	7.50

Booklet Stamps
Self-Adhesive

Serpentine Die Cut 11¼ Syncopated

4183	A978	70c multi	1.25	.25
4184	A978	70c multi	1.25	.25
4185	A978	70c multi	1.25	.25
4186	A978	70c multi	1.25	.25
4187	A978	70c multi	1.25	.25
4188	A978	70c multi	1.25	.25
a.		Booklet pane of 10, #4185, 4188, 2 each #4183-4184, 4186-4187	12.50	
b.		Booklet pane of 20, 3 each #4183, 4185, 4187, 4188, 4 each #4184, 4186	25.00	
		Nos. 4183-4188 (6)	7.50	1.50

A souvenir sheet of six containing one each of Nos. 4177-4182 + six labels was sold with a die and game pieces that sold for $9.95. Nos. 4180a and 4182b sold together as a set in a folder for $8.85.

National Parks — A979

Designs: $2.75, Alpine National Park, Victoria. $5.35, Blue Mountains National Park, New South Wales. $7.40, Judbarra/Gregroy National Park, Northern Territory.

2014, Oct. 1		**Litho.**	**Perf. 14¾x14**	
4189	A979	$2.75 multi	5.00	2.50
4190	A979	$5.35 multi	9.50	4.75
4191	A979	$7.40 multi	13.00	6.50
		Nos. 4189-4191 (3)	27.50	13.75

Booklet Stamp
Self-Adhesive

Serpentine Die Cut 11¼ Syncopated

4192	A979	$2.75 multi	5.00	2.50
a.		Booklet pane of 5	25.00	

National Parks Type of 2014 With Personalized Photo at Right Like Type A692a

Serpentine Die Cut 11½x11¼ Syncopated

2014, Oct. 1		**Litho.**	
		Self-Adhesive	
4193	A979	$2.75 multi	6.00 6.00

No. 4193 was printed in sheets of 20 and has personalized picture and a straight edge at right and lack separations between the stamp and personalized photo. Sheets of 20 of No. 4193 sold for $68.

Horse Racing Tracks A980

Designs: Nos. 4194, 4198, Eagle Farm, Queensland. Nos. 4195, 4199, Royal Randwick, New South Wales. Nos. 4196, 4200, Morphettville, South Australia. Nos. 4197, 4201, Flemington, Victoria.

2014, Oct. 7		**Litho.**	**Perf. 14x14¾**	
4194	A980	70c multi	1.25	1.25
4195	A980	70c multi	1.25	1.25
4196	A980	70c multi	1.25	1.25
4197	A980	70c multi	1.25	1.25
a.		Horiz. strip of 4, #4194-4197	5.00	5.00
		Nos. 4194-4197 (4)	5.00	5.00

Self-Adhesive

Serpentine Die Cut 11¼ Syncopated

4198	A980	70c multi	1.25	.25
4199	A980	70c multi	1.25	.25
4200	A980	70c multi	1.25	.25
4201	A980	70c multi	1.25	.25
a.		Horiz. coil strip of 4, #4198-4201	5.00	
b.		Booklet pane of 10, 3 each #4198-4199, 2 each #4200-4201	12.50	
		Nos. 4198-4201 (4)	5.00	1.00

Australian Defense Force, Cent. — A981

Poppies and: Nos. 4202, 4206, Cap of Royal Australian Navy. Nos. 4203, 4209, Hat of Australian Army. Nos. 4204, 4207, Cap of Royal Australian Air Force. Nos. 4205, 4208, Australian Defense Force badge.

2014, Oct. 21		**Litho.**	**Perf. 14¼**	
4202	A981	70c multi	1.25	1.25
4203	A981	70c multi	1.25	1.25
4204	A981	70c multi	1.25	1.25
4205	A981	70c multi	1.25	1.25
a.		Souvenir sheet of 4, #4202-4205	5.00	5.00
		Nos. 4202-4205 (4)	5.00	5.00

Booklet Stamps
Self-Adhesive

Serpentine Die Cut 11¼ Syncopated

4206	A981	70c multi	1.25	.25
4207	A981	70c multi	1.25	.25
4208	A981	70c multi	1.25	.25
4209	A981	70c multi	1.25	.25
a.		Booklet pane of 10, 2 each #4206, 4207, 4209, 4 #4208	12.50	

Christmas
A982   A983

Designs: Nos. 4210, 4216, Madonna and Child. Nos. 4211, 4217, 4221, Snowflake, ornament, Christmas tree, reindeer. Nos. 4212, 4218, 4222, Star, ornament, gift. 70c, Snowflake, ornament, holly leaves, dove, star. Nos. 4214, 4220, Snowflake and bells. Nos. 4215, 4220, Angels.

2014, Oct. 31   Litho.   Perf. 14¾x14
4210	A982	65c multi	1.10	1.10
4211	A983	65c green	1.10	1.10
4212	A983	65c red	1.10	1.10
a.		Horiz. pair, #4211-4212	2.20	2.20
4213	A983	70c blue green	1.25	.95
4214	A983	$1.70 pur & dk bl	3.00	1.50
4215	A982	$2.55 multi	4.50	2.25
a.		Souvenir sheet of 2, #4210, 4215	5.75	5.75
		Nos. 4210-4215 (6)	12.05	8.00

Self-Adhesive
Booklet Stamps
Serpentine Die Cut 11¼ Syncopated
4216	A982	65c multi	1.10	.25
a.		Booklet pane of 20 + 20 etiquettes	22.00	
4217	A983	65c green	1.10	.25
4218	A983	65c red	1.10	.25
a.		Booklet pane of 20, 10 each #4217-4218, + 20 etiquettes	22.00	
4219	A983	$1.70 pur & dk bl	3.00	1.50
a.		Booklet pane of 5	15.00	
4220	A982	$2.55 multi	4.50	2.25
a.		Booklet pane of 5	22.50	

Litho. With Foil Application
4221	A983	65c green	1.10	.25
a.		Booklet pane of 10	11.00	
4222	A983	65c red	1.10	.25
a.		Booklet pane of 10	11.00	
		Nos. 4216-4222 (7)	13.00	5.00

Marsupials
A984

Designs: Nos. 4225, 4234, Echidna. Nos. 4226, 4233, Common wombat. Nos. 4227, 4231, Eastern gray kangaroo. Nos. 4228, 4232, Koala. No. 4229, Numbat. No. 4230, Tasmanian devil.

2015, Jan. 13   Litho.   Perf. 14x14¾
4225	A984	70c multi	1.10	1.10
4226	A984	70c multi	1.10	1.10
4227	A984	70c multi	1.10	1.10
4228	A984	70c multi	1.10	1.10
a.		Block of 4, #4225-4228	4.40	4.40
4229	A984	$1.40 multi	2.25	1.75
4230	A984	$1.40 multi	2.25	1.75
a.		Vert. pair, #4229-4230	4.50	3.50
b.		Souvenir sheet of 6, #4225-4230	9.00	9.00
		Nos. 4225-4230 (6)	8.90	7.90

Booklet Stamps
Self-Adhesive
Serpentine Die Cut 11¼ Syncopated
4231	A984	70c multi	1.10	.25
4232	A984	70c multi	1.10	.25
4233	A984	70c multi	1.10	.25
4234	A984	70c multi	1.10	.25
a.		Booklet pane of 10, 3 each #4231-4232, 2 each #4233-4234	11.00	
b.		Booklet pane of 20, 5 each #4231-4234	22.00	
		Nos. 4231-4234 (4)	4.40	1.00

Victoria Cross
Recipients — A985

Designs: Nos. 4235, 4240, Ben Roberts-Smith. Nos. 4236, 4241, Cameron Baird

(1981-2013). Nos. 4237, 4242, Mark Donaldson. Nos. 4238, 4243, Dan Keighran. Nos. 4239, 4244, Keith Payne.

2015, Jan. 22   Litho.   Perf. 14¾x14
4235	A985	70c multi	1.10	1.10
4236	A985	70c multi	1.10	1.10
4237	A985	70c multi	1.10	1.10
4238	A985	70c multi	1.10	1.10
4239	A985	70c multi	1.10	1.10
a.		Souvenir sheet of 5, #4235-4239	5.50	5.50
		Nos. 4235-4239 (5)	5.50	5.50

Booklet Stamps
Self-Adhesive
Serpentine Die Cut 11¼ Syncopated
4240	A985	70c multi	1.10	.25
a.		Booklet pane of 10	11.00	
4241	A985	70c multi	1.10	.25
a.		Booklet pane of 10	11.00	
4242	A985	70c multi	1.10	.25
a.		Booklet pane of 10	11.00	
4243	A985	70c multi	1.10	.25
a.		Booklet pane of 10	11.00	
4244	A985	70c multi	1.10	.25
a.		Booklet pane of 10	11.00	
		Nos. 4240-4244 (5)	5.50	1.25

Souvenir Sheet

Victoria Cross — A986

2015, Jan. 22   Litho.   Perf. 14x14¾
4245	A986	Sheet of 2	9.00	9.00
a.		70c olive green	1.10	.85
b.		$5 violet	7.75	5.75

Heart-Shaped
Items — A987

Designs: Nos. 4246, 4251, Kite. Nos. 4247, 4252, Airplane contrail. Nos. 4248, 4250, Hot-air balloon. Nos. 4249, 4253, Cloud.

2015, Feb. 3   Litho.   Perf. 14¾x14
4246	A987	70c multi	1.10	1.10
4247	A987	70c multi	1.10	1.10
4248	A987	70c multi	1.10	1.10
4249	A987	70c multi	1.10	1.10
a.		Horiz. strip of 4, #4246-4249	4.40	4.40
		Nos. 4246-4249 (4)	4.40	4.40

Booklet Stamps
Self-Adhesive
Serpentine Die Cut 11¼ Syncopated
4250	A987	70c multi	1.10	.25
4251	A987	70c multi	1.10	.25
4252	A987	70c multi	1.10	.25
4253	A987	70c multi	1.10	.25
a.		Booklet pane of 20, 7 each #4250-4251, 3 each #4252-4253	22.00	
b.		Booklet pane of 10, 5 each #4250-4253	11.00	
		Nos. 4250-4253 (4)	4.40	1.00

Clipper Ships
A988

Designs: No. 4254, Frances Henty. No. 4255, Phoenician. No. 4256, Arabian. No. 4257, Monkchester.

2015, Feb. 17   Litho.   Perf. 14x14¾
4254	A988	70c multi	1.10	.85
4255	A988	70c multi	1.10	.85
a.		Horiz. pair #4254-4255	2.20	1.70
4256	A988	$1.40 multi	2.25	1.75
4257	A988	$1.40 multi	2.25	1.75
a.		Horiz. pair, #4256-4257	4.50	3.50
		Nos. 4254-4257 (4)	6.70	5.20

Tourist
Attractions — A989

Designs: Nos. 4258, 4262, Horse-drawn tram, Victor Harbour, South Australia. Nos. 4259, 4263, Seaplane, Whitsunday Islands, Queensland. Nos. 4260, 4264, Steam train, Dandenong Ranges, Victoria. Nos. 4261, 4265, Cruise boat, Katherine Gorge, Northern Territory.

2015, Mar. 3   Litho.   Perf. 14¾x14
4258	A989	70c multi	1.10	1.10
4259	A989	70c multi	1.10	1.10
4260	A989	70c multi	1.10	1.10
4261	A989	70c multi	1.10	1.10
a.		Horiz. strip of 4, #4258-4261	4.40	4.40
		Nos. 4258-4261 (4)	4.40	4.40

Self-Adhesive
Serpentine Die Cut 11¼ Syncopated
4262	A989	70c multi	1.10	.25
4263	A989	70c multi	1.10	.25
4264	A989	70c multi	1.10	.25
4265	A989	70c multi	1.10	.25
a.		Vert. coil strip of 4, #4262-4265	4.40	
b.		Booklet pane of 10, 3 each #4262, 4264, 2 each #4263, 4265	11.00	
		Nos. 4262-4265 (4)	4.40	1.00

Trees
A990

Designs: 70c, Lemon-scented gum tree. $1.40, Queensland bottle tree. No. 4268, Green fig tree. No. 4269, Moonah tree.

2015, Mar. 17   Litho.   Perf. 14x14¾
4266	A990	70c multi	1.10	.85
4267	A990	$1.40 multi	2.25	1.75
4268	A990	$2.10 multi	3.25	2.50
4269	A990	$2.10 multi	3.25	2.50
a.		Horiz. pair, #4268-4269	6.50	5.00
b.		Souvenir sheet of 4, #4266-4269	10.00	10.00
		Nos. 4266-4269 (4)	9.85	7.60

Self-Adhesive
Printed on Wood Veneer
Serpentine Die Cut 11¼ Syncopated
4270	A990	70c multi	1.25	1.25

No. 4270 was printed in sheets of 10. The sheet was sold only in a package, together with a sheet of 10 of No. 4266. The package sold for $14.95.

Australian and New
Zealand Army
Corps,
Cent. — A991

Soldier and bugler with bugler facing: 70c, Right. $1.85, Left.

2015, Apr. 7   Litho.   Perf. 14¾x14
4271	A991	70c multi	1.10	1.10
4272	A991	$1.85 multi	3.00	3.00
a.		Souvenir sheet of 2, #4271-4272	4.25	4.25

Booklet Stamps
Self-Adhesive
Serpentine Die Cut 11¼ Syncopated
4273	A991	70c multi	1.10	.25
a.		Booklet pane of 10	11.00	
4274	A991	$1.85 multi	3.00	1.50
a.		Booklet pane of 5	15.00	

See New Zealand Nos. 2584-2585.

Queen Elizabeth II,
89th
Birthday — A992

Hat color: 70c, Red. $2.75, Blue.

2015, Apr. 7   Litho.   Perf. 14¾x14
4275	A992	70c multi	1.10	.85
4276	A992	$2.75 multi	4.50	2.25
a.		Souvenir sheet of 2, #4275-4276	5.75	5.75
b.		Booklet pane of 2	9.00	—
c.		Booklet pane of 2, #4275-4276	5.75	—
		Complete booklet, #4276b, 4276c, 2 #4275a	24.50	

Booklet Stamp
Self-Adhesive
Serpentine Die Cut 11¼ Syncopated
4277	A992	$2.75 multi	4.50	2.25
a.		Booklet pane of 5	22.50	

Complete booklet sold for $14.95.

World War I,
Cent. — A993

Australian soldiers involved in Gallipoli campaign: Nos. 4278, 4283, Landing at Gallipoli. Nos. 4279, 4284, Lance Corporal Albert Jacka and Victoria Cross. Nos. 4280, 4285, At Lone Pine. Nos. 4281, 4286, With donkey used for recovering wounded soldiers. Nos. 4282, 4287, Near cannon before evacuation.

2015, Apr. 14   Litho.   Perf. 14¼
4278	A993	70c multi	1.10	1.10
a.		Booklet pane of 4	4.75	
4279	A993	70c multi	1.10	1.10
a.		Booklet pane of 4	4.75	
4280	A993	70c multi	1.10	1.10
a.		Booklet pane of 4	4.75	
4281	A993	70c multi	1.10	1.10
a.		Booklet pane of 4	4.75	
4282	A993	70c multi	1.10	1.10
a.		Booklet pane of 4	4.75	
		Complete booklet, #4278a, 4279a, 4280a, 4281a, 4282a	24.00	
b.		Horiz. strip of 5, #4278-4282	5.50	5.50
c.		Souvenir sheet of 5, #4278-4282	5.50	5.50
		Nos. 4278-4282 (5)	5.50	5.50

Booklet Stamps
Self-Adhesive
Serpentine Die Cut 11¼ Syncopated
4283	A993	70c multi	1.10	.25
4284	A993	70c multi	1.10	.25
4285	A993	70c multi	1.10	.25
4286	A993	70c multi	1.10	.25
4287	A993	70c multi	1.10	.25
a.		Booklet pane of 10, 2 each #4283-4287	11.00	
		Nos. 4283-4287 (5)	5.50	1.25

Complete booklet sold for $14.95.

Cats — A994

Cats named: Nos. 4288, 4293, Charo. Nos. 4289, 4294, Bubu. Nos. 4290, 4295, Sweeie. Nos. 4291, 4296, Cato. Nos. 4292, 4297, Briony.

2015, May 5   Litho.   Perf. 14¾x14
4288	A994	70c multi	1.10	1.10
4289	A994	70c multi	1.10	1.10
4290	A994	70c multi	1.10	1.10
4291	A994	70c multi	1.10	1.10
4292	A994	70c multi	1.10	1.10
a.		Horiz. strip of 5, #4288-4292	5.50	5.50
		Nos. 4288-4292 (5)	5.50	5.50

Self-Adhesive
Serpentine Die Cut 11¼ Syncopated

4293 A994 70c multi		1.10	.25
a.	Booklet pane of 10	11.00	
4294 A994 70c multi		1.10	.25
a.	Booklet pane of 10	11.00	
4295 A994 70c multi		1.10	.25
a.	Booklet pane of 10	11.00	
4296 A994 70c multi		1.10	.25
a.	Booklet pane of 10	11.00	
4297 A994 70c multi		1.10	.25
a.	Booklet pane of 10	11.00	
b.	Vert. coil strip of 5, #4293-4297	5.50	
	Nos. 4293-4297 (5)	5.50	1.25

Items in Australian Museums — A995

Designs: Nos. 4298, 4303, 1907 Model automatic totalizer, from Museum of Applied Arts and Sciences, Sydney. Nos. 4299, 4302, Turtle sculpture by Ellarose Savage, Australian Museum, Sydney. Nos. 4300, 4305, Anchor of HMS Endeavour, National Museum of Australia, Canberra. Nos. 4301, 4304, Replica of "Welcome Stranger" gold nugget, Gold Museum, Sovereign Hill, Victoria.

2015, May 19　Litho.　Perf. 14¾x14

4298 A995 70c multi		1.10	1.10
4299 A995 70c multi		1.10	1.10
4300 A995 70c multi		1.10	1.10
4301 A995 70c multi		1.10	1.10
a.	Block of 4, #4298-4301	4.40	4.40
b.	Souvenir sheet of 4, #4298-4301	4.40	4.40
	Nos. 4298-4301 (4)	4.40	4.40

Coil Stamps
Self-Adhesive
Serpentine Die Cut 11¼ Syncopated

4302 A995 70c multi		1.10	.25
4303 A995 70c multi		1.10	.25
4304 A995 70c multi		1.10	.25
4305 A995 70c multi		1.10	.25
a.	Vert. strip of 4, #4302-4305	4.40	
	Nos. 4302-4305 (4)	4.40	1.00

Islands A996

Designs: Nos. 4306, 4310, Phillip Island, Victoria. Nos. 4307, 4311, Lady Musgrave Island, Queensland. $1.40, Bruny Island, Tasmania. $2.10, Buccaneer Archipelago, Western Australia.

2015, June 2　Litho.　Perf. 14x14¾

4306 A996 70c multi		1.10	1.10
4307 A996 70c multi		1.10	1.10
a.	Horiz. pair, #4306-4307	2.20	2.20
4308 A996 $1.40 multi		2.25	1.10
4309 A996 $2.10 multi		3.25	1.60
	Nos. 4306-4309 (4)	7.70	4.90

Booklet Stamps
Self-Adhesive
Serpentine Die Cut 11¼ Syncopated

4310 A996 70c multi		1.10	.25
4311 A996 70c multi		1.10	.25
a.	Booklet pane of 10, 5 each #4310-4311	11.00	

Walter and Eliza Hall Institute of Medical Research, Cent. — A997

2015, June 30　Litho.　Perf. 14¾x14

4312 A997 70c multi		1.10	.85
a.	Booklet pane of 4	4.50	
	Complete booklet, 5 #4312a	22.50	

Complete booklet sold for $14.95.

Lighthouses — A998

Designs: Nos. 4313, 4317, Cape Byron Lighthouse, New South Wales. Nos. 4314, 4318, Cape Leeuwin Lighthouse, Western Australia. Nos. 4315, 4319, North Reef Lighthouse, Queensland. Nos. 4316, 4320, Tasman Island Lighthouse, Tasmania.

2015, July 7　Litho.　Perf. 14¾x14

4313 A998 70c multi		1.10	1.10
a.	Booklet pane of 4	4.50	
4314 A998 70c multi		1.10	1.10
a.	Booklet pane of 4	4.50	
4315 A998 70c multi		1.10	1.10
a.	Booklet pane of 4	4.50	
4316 A998 70c multi		1.10	1.10
a.	Booklet pane of 4	4.50	
b.	Booklet pane of 4, #4313-4316	4.50	
	Complete booklet, #4313a, 4314a, 4315a, 4316a, 4316b	22.50	
c.	Block of 4, #4313-4316	4.40	4.40
	Nos. 4313-4316 (4)	4.40	4.40

Self-Adhesive
Serpentine Die Cut 11¼ Syncopated

4317 A998 70c multi		1.10	.25
4318 A998 70c multi		1.10	.25
4319 A998 70c multi		1.10	.25
4320 A998 70c multi		1.10	.25
a.	Booklet pane of 20, 5 each #4317-4320	22.00	
b.	Vert. coil strip of 4, #4317-4320	4.40	
	Nos. 4317-4320 (4)	4.40	1.00

Complete booklet sold for $14.95.

Hiking Trails A999

Designs: Nos. 4321, 4326, National Pass Track, New South Wales. Nos. 4322, 4328, Cape to Cape Track, Western Australia. Nos. 4323, 4325, Larapinta Trail, Northern Territory. Nos. 4324, 4327, Overland Track, Tasmania.

2015, July 14　Litho.　Perf. 14x14¾

4321 A999 70c multi		1.10	1.10
4322 A999 70c multi		1.10	1.10
4323 A999 70c multi		1.10	1.10
4324 A999 70c multi		1.10	1.10
a.	Horiz. strip of 4, #4321-4324	4.40	4.40
b.	Souvenir sheet of 4, #4321-4324	4.40	4.40
	Nos. 4321-4324 (4)	4.40	4.40

Self-Adhesive
Serpentine Die Cut 11¼ Syncopated

4325 A999 70c multi		1.10	.25
4326 A999 70c multi		1.10	.25
4327 A999 70c multi		1.10	.25
4328 A999 70c multi		1.10	.25
a.	Booklet pane of 10, 3 each #4325, 4327, 2 each #4326, 4328	11.00	
b.	Horiz. coil strip of 4, #4325-4328	4.40	
	Nos. 4325-4328 (4)	4.40	1.00

2015 Netball World Cup, Sydney — A1000

2015, Aug. 8　Litho.　Perf. 14¾x14

4329 A1000 70c multi		1.10	.85

Booklet Stamp
Self-Adhesive
Serpentine Die Cut 11¼ Syncopated

4330 A1000 70c multi		1.10	.25
a.	Booklet pane of 20	20.00	

Houses of Parliament A1001

Houses of Parliament in: 70c, Australia. $1.85, New Zealand. $1.95, Singapore.

2015, Aug. 14　Litho.　Perf. 14¼

4331 A1001 70c multi		1.10	.85
4332 A1001 $1.85 multi		2.75	1.40
4333 A1001 $1.95 multi		3.00	1.50
a.	Souvenir sheet of 3, #4331-4333	7.00	7.00
	Nos. 4331-4333 (3)	6.85	3.75

Diplomatic relations of Singapore with Australia and New Zealand, 50th anniv.
See New Zealand No. 2600, Singapore Nos. 1743-1745.

Birth of Princess Charlotte of Cambridge A1002

2015, Aug. 25　Litho.　Perf. 14¼

4334 A1002 70c multi		1.00	1.00

Booklet Stamp
Self-Adhesive
Serpentine Die Cut 11¼ Syncopated

4335 A1002 70c multi		1.00	.25
a.	Booklet pane of 10	10.00	

Neon Signs — A1003

Designs: Nos. 4336, 4339, Skipping Girl Vinegar sign, Abbotsford, Victoria, 1936. Nos. 4337, 4340, Pink Poodle Motel sign, Surfers Paradise, Queensland, 1967. $1.40, Dandy Pig sign for Gippsland Co-operative Bacon Curing Company, Dandenong, Victoria, 1950s.

2015, Sept. 1　Litho.　Perf. 14¾x14

4336 A1003 70c multi		1.00	1.00
4337 A1003 70c multi		1.00	1.00
4338 A1003 $1.40 multi		2.00	1.50
a.	Souvenir sheet of 3, #4336-4338	4.00	4.00
	Nos. 4336-4338 (3)	4.00	3.50

Self-Adhesive
Serpentine Die Cut 11¼ Syncopated

4339 A1003 70c multi		1.00	1.00
4340 A1003 70c multi		1.00	1.00
a.	Vert. coil pair, #4339-4340	2.00	
b.	Booklet pane of 10, 5 each #4339-4340	10.00	

A1004

A1006

A1007

Queen Elizabeth II, Longest-Reigning British Monarch — A1008

2015, Sept. 9　Litho.　Perf. 14¾x14

4341 A1004 70c black		1.00	.75
a.	Booklet pane of 4	4.25	—
4342 A1005 70c multi		1.00	.75
a.	Booklet pane of 4	4.25	—
4343 A1006 70c multi		1.00	.75
a.	Booklet pane of 4	4.25	—
b.	Horiz. strip of 3, #4341-4343	3.00	2.25
4344 A1007 $2.75 multi		4.00	4.00
a.	Booklet pane of 2	8.00	
4345 A1008 $2.75 multi		4.00	4.00
a.	Booklet pane of 2	8.00	
	Complete booklet, #4341a, 4342a, 4343a, 4344a, 4345a	29.00	
b.	Horiz. pair, #4344-4345	8.00	8.00
c.	Souvenir sheet of 5, #4341-4345	11.00	11.00
	Nos. 4341-4345 (5)	11.00	10.25

Booklet Stamps
Self-Adhesive
Serpentine Die Cut 11¼ Syncopated

4346 A1007 $2.75 multi		4.00	4.00
4347 A1008 $2.75 multi		4.00	4.00
a.	Booklet pane of 5, 2 #4346, 3 #4347	20.00	

Complete booklet sold for $19.95.

Planets — A1009

Designs: Nos. 4348, 4356a, Mercury. Nos. 4349, 4356b, Mars, horiz. Nos. 4350, 4356c, 4357, Earth. Nos. 4351, 4356d, 4358, Uranus. Nos. 4352, 4356e, 4359, Neptune, horiz. Nos. 4353, 4356f, 4360, Venus, horiz. Nos. 4354, 4356g, Jupiter. Nos. 4355, 4356h, Saturn, horiz.

Litho., Litho. & Silk-Screened
(#4356)

2015, Sept. 22　Perf. 14½x14
Stamps With White Frames on Two Sides

4348 A1009 35c multi		.50	.40

Perf. 14x14½

4349 A1009 35c multi		.50	.40
a.	Pair, #4348-4349	1.00	.80

Size: 26x38mm
Perf. 14¾x14

4350 A1009 70c multi		1.00	1.00
4351 A1009 70c multi		1.00	1.00

Size:36x28mm
Perf. 14x14¾

4352 A1009 70c multi		1.00	1.00
4353 A1009 70c multi		1.00	1.00

Size: 30x50mm
Perf. 14x14½

4354 A1009 70c multi		1.00	1.00

Size: 50x30mm
Perf. 14½x14

4355 A1009 70c multi		1.00	1.00
	Nos. 4348-4355 (8)	7.00	6.80

Miniature Sheet
Stamps Without White Frames
Perf. 14½, 14x14½ (#4356e, 4356f)

4356	Sheet of 8	7.00	7.00
a.	A1009 35c multi	.50	.40
b.	A1009 35c multi	.50	.40
c.	A1009 70c multi, 26x38mm	1.00	.75
d.	A1009 70c multi, 26x38mm	1.00	.75
e.	A1009 70c multi, 38x26mm	1.00	.75
f.	A1009 70c multi, 38x26mm	1.00	.75
g.	A1009 70c multi, 30x50mm	1.00	.75
h.	A1009 70c multi, 50x30mm	1.00	.75

A1005

Litho.
Serpentine Die Cut 11¼ Syncopated
Booklet Stamps
Self-Adhesive
Size: 26x38mm
Stamps With White Frames on Two Sides

4357	A1009 70c multi	1.00	.25
4358	A1009 70c multi	1.00	.25
a.	Booklet pane of 20, 10 each #4357-4358	20.00	

Size: 38x26mm

4359	A1009 70c multi	1.00	.25
4360	A1009 70c multi	1.00	.25
a.	Booklet pane of 10, 5 each #4359-4360	10.00	
	Nos. 4357-4360 (4)	4.00	1.00

Humanitarians Honored by
Australia — A1010

Designs: Nos. 4361, 4364, Mother Teresa (1910-97), Honorary Companion of the Order of Australia. Nos. 4362, 4365, Nelson Mandela (1918-2013), Honorary Companion of the Order of Australia. Nos. 4363, 4366, Raoul Wallenberg (1912-45), Honorary Citizen of Australia.

2015, Oct. 5   Litho.   Perf. 14x14¾

4361	A1010 70c multi	1.00	1.00
4362	A1010 70c multi	1.00	1.00
4363	A1010 70c multi	1.00	1.00
	Nos. 4361-4363 (3)	3.00	3.00

Booklet Stamps
Self-Adhesive
Serpentine Die Cut 11¼ Syncopated

4364	A1010 70c multi	1.00	.25
a.	Booklet pane of 10	10.00	
4365	A1010 70c multi	1.00	.25
a.	Booklet pane of 10	10.00	
4366	A1010 70c multi	1.00	.25
a.	Booklet pane of 10	10.00	
	Nos. 4364-4366 (3)	3.00	.75

Bicycles
A1011

Designs: Nos. 4367, 4371, 1888 Basset & Co. penny-farthing. Nos. 4368, 4372, Sutherland ladies' safety bicycle, c. 1910. $1.85, Finlay Bros. men's sprung-frame saftey bicycle, 1930s. $2.75, Baum Cycles custom-made road bicycle, 2015.

2015, Oct. 13   Litho.   Perf. 14¼

4367	A1011 70c multi	1.00	1.00
a.	Booklet pane of 4	4.00	—
4368	A1011 70c multi	1.00	1.00
a.	Booklet pane of 4	4.00	—
b.	Horiz. pair, #4367-4368	2.00	2.00
4369	A1011 $1.85 multi	2.75	1.40
a.	Booklet pane of 2	5.50	—
4370	A1011 $2.75 multi	4.00	4.00
a.	Booklet pane of 2	8.00	—
	Complete booklet, #4367a, 4368a, 4369a, 4370a	21.50	
	Nos. 4367-4370 (4)	8.75	7.40

Booklet Stamps
Self-Adhesive
Serpentine Die Cut 11¼ Syncopated

4371	A1011 70c multi	1.00	.25
4372	A1011 70c multi	1.00	.25
a.	Booklet pane of 20, 10 each #4371-4372	20.00	
4373	A1011 $2.75 multi	4.00	2.00
a.	Booklet pane of 5	20.00	
	Nos. 4371-4373 (3)	6.00	2.50

Complete booklet sold for $14.95.

Animals in
War — A1012

Poppies, soldiers and: Nos. 4374, 4379, Donkeys. Nos. 4375, 4380, Dogs. Nos. 4376, 4381, Horses. Nos. 4377, 4383, Pigeons. Nos. 4378, 4382, Camels.

2015, Oct. 27   Litho.   Perf. 14¼

4374	A1012 70c multi	1.00	1.00
4375	A1012 70c multi	1.00	1.00
4376	A1012 70c multi	1.00	1.00
4377	A1012 70c multi	1.00	1.00
4378	A1012 70c multi	1.00	1.00
a.	Souvenir sheet of 5, #4374-4378	5.00	5.00
	Nos. 4374-4378 (5)	5.00	5.00

Booklet Stamps
Self-Adhesive
Serpentine Die Cut 11¼ Syncopated

4379	A1012 70c multi	1.00	.25
4380	A1012 70c multi	1.00	.25
4381	A1012 70c multi	1.00	.25
4382	A1012 70c multi	1.00	.25
4383	A1012 70c multi	1.00	.25
a.	Booklet pane of 10, 2 each #4379-4383	10.00	
	Nos. 4379-4383 (5)	5.00	1.25

Christmas
A1013   A1014

Designs: Nos. 4384, 4389, 4394, Gift box with ribbon. Nos. 4385, 4390, 4395, Green doves. Nos. 4386, 4391, Nativity. Nos. 4387, 4392, Blue doves. Nos. 4388, 4393, Magi.

2015, Oct. 30   Litho.   Perf. 14¾x14

4384	A1013 65c multi	.95	.95
4385	A1013 65c multi	.95	.95
a.	Horiz. pair, #4384-4385	1.90	1.90
4386	A1014 65c multi	.95	.95
4387	A1013 $1.70 multi	2.50	2.50
4388	A1014 $2.55 multi	3.75	3.75
a.	Souvenir sheet of 2, #4386, 4388	4.75	4.75
	Nos. 4384-4388 (5)	9.10	9.10

Booklet Stamps
Self-Adhesive
Serpentine Die Cut 11¼ Syncopated

4389	A1013 65c multi	.95	.25
4390	A1013 65c multi	.95	.25
a.	Booklet pane of 20, 10 each #4389-4390	19.00	
4391	A1014 65c multi	.95	.25
a.	Booklet pane of 20	19.00	
4392	A1013 $1.70 multi	2.50	1.25
a.	Booklet pane of 5	12.50	
4393	A1014 $2.55 multi	3.75	1.90
a.	Booklet pane of 5	19.00	

Litho. & Silk-Screened

4394	A1013 65c multi	.95	.25
a.	Booklet pane of 10	9.50	

Litho. With Foil Application

4395	A1013 65c multi	.95	.25
a.	Booklet pane of 10	9.50	
	Nos. 4389-4395 (7)	11.00	4.40

Wildflowers
A1015

Designs: Nos. 4398, 4402, 4405, Rose coneflower. Nos. 4399, 4403, 4406, Spiny mirbelia. Nos. 4400, 4404, 4407, Blue devil. $2, Golden rainbow.

2015, Dec. 15   Litho.   Perf. 14¾x14

4398	A1015 $1 multi	1.50	1.50
4399	A1015 $1 multi	1.50	1.50
4400	A1015 $1 multi	1.50	1.50
a.	Horiz. strip of 3, #4398-4400	4.50	4.50
4401	A1015 $2 multi	3.00	1.50
	Nos. 4398-4401 (4)	7.50	6.00

Self-Adhesive
Serpentine Die Cut 11¼ Syncopated

4402	A1015 $1 multi	1.50	.25
4403	A1015 $1 multi	1.50	.25
4404	A1015 $1 multi	1.50	.25
a.	Vert. coil strip of 3, #4402-4404	4.50	

b.	Booklet pane of 10, 4 #4402, 3 each #4403-4404	15.00	
c.	Booklet pane of 20, 8 #4402, 5 #4403, 7 #4404	30.00	
	Nos. 4402-4404 (3)	4.50	.75

With Personalized Photo at Right
Like Type A692a
Serpentine Die Cut 11½x11¼ Syncopated
Self-Adhesive

4405	A1015 $1 multi	2.40	2.40
4406	A1015 $1 multi	2.40	2.40
4407	A1015 $1 multi	2.40	2.40
4408	A1015 $2 multi	4.00	4.00
	Nos. 4405-4408 (4)	11.20	11.20

Nos. 4405-4408 were each printed in sheets of 20 and have personalized pictures and a straight edge at right and lack separations between the stamp and the personalized photo. Sheets of 20 of Nos. 4405-4407 sold for $33 each, No. 4408, $53.
See No. 4653.

Tennis
Players — A1016

Designs: Nos. 4409, 4412, Tony Roche. Nos. 4410, 4413, Fred Stolle. Nos. 4411a, 4414, Pat Cash. Nos. 4411b, 4415, Ashley Cooper. Nos. 4411c, 4416, Roy Emerson. Nos. 4411d, 4417, Neale Fraser. Nos. 4411e, 4418, Evonne Goolagong Cawley. Nos. 4411f, 4419, John Newcombe. Nos. 4411g, 4420, Patrick Rafter. Nos. 4411h, 4421, Ken Rosewall. Nos. 4411i, 4422, Frank Sedgman. Nos. 4411j, 4423, Lleyton Hewitt.

2016, Jan. 21   Litho.   Perf. 14¾x14

4409	A1016 $1 multi	1.50	1.50
4410	A1016 $1 multi	1.50	1.50
a.	Vert. pair, #4409-4410	3.00	3.00
4411	Sheet of 10	15.00	15.00
a.-j.	A1016 $1 Any single	1.50	1.50

Booklet Stamps
Self-Adhesive
Serpentine Die Cut 11¼ Syncopated

4412	A1016 $1 multi	1.50	.25
a.	Booklet pane of 10	15.00	
4413	A1016 $1 multi	1.50	.25
a.	Booklet pane of 10	15.00	
4414	A1016 $1 multi	1.50	.25
a.	Booklet pane of 10	15.00	
4415	A1016 $1 multi	1.50	.25
a.	Booklet pane of 10	15.00	
4416	A1016 $1 multi	1.50	.25
a.	Booklet pane of 10	15.00	
4417	A1016 $1 multi	1.50	.25
a.	Booklet pane of 10	15.00	
4418	A1016 $1 multi	1.50	.25
a.	Booklet pane of 10	15.00	
4419	A1016 $1 multi	1.50	.25
a.	Booklet pane of 10	15.00	
4420	A1016 $1 multi	1.50	.25
a.	Booklet pane of 10	15.00	
4421	A1016 $1 multi	1.50	.25
a.	Booklet pane of 10	15.00	
4422	A1016 $1 multi	1.50	.25
a.	Booklet pane of 10	15.00	
4423	A1016 $1 multi	1.50	.25
a.	Booklet pane of 10	15.00	
	Nos. 4412-4423 (12)	18.00	3.00

White
Roses — A1017   Champagne
Flutes — A1018

Heart of Red
Roses — A1019   Cake — A1020

Balloons   Handprints
A1021   A1022

Map of Australia   Flowering Gum
A1023   A1024

Wattle — A1025   Engagement and
Wedding
Rings — A1026

2016, Jan. 25   Litho.   Perf. 14¾x14

4424	A1017 $1 multi	1.50	1.50
4425	A1018 $1 multi	1.50	1.50
4426	A1019 $1 multi	1.50	1.50
4427	A1020 $1 multi	1.50	1.50
4428	A1021 $1 multi	1.50	1.50
4429	A1022 $1 multi	1.50	1.50
4430	A1023 $1 multi	1.50	1.10
4431	A1024 $1 multi	1.50	1.10
4432	A1025 $1 multi	1.50	1.10
4433	A1026 $2 multi	3.00	3.00
	Nos. 4424-4433 (10)	16.50	15.30

Booklet Stamps
Self-Adhesive
Serpentine Die Cut 11¼ Syncopated

4434	A1017 $1 multi	1.50	.25
a.	Booklet pane of 10 + 5 stickers	15.00	
4435	A1018 $1 multi	1.50	.25
a.	Booklet pane of 10 + 5 stickers	15.00	
4436	A1019 $1 multi	1.50	.25
a.	Booklet pane of 10 + 5 stickers	15.00	
4437	A1020 $1 multi	1.50	.25
a.	Booklet pane of 10 + 5 stickers	15.00	
4438	A1021 $1 multi	1.50	.25
a.	Booklet pane of 10 + 5 stickers	15.00	
4439	A1022 $1 multi	1.50	.25
a.	Booklet pane of 10 + 5 stickers	15.00	
4440	A1026 $2 multi	3.00	1.50
a.	Booklet pane of 4	12.00	
	Complete booklet, 4 #4440a	48.00	
	Nos. 4434-4440 (7)	12.00	3.00

Complete booklet sold for $32.95 and contains four examples of No. 4440a, each with a different pane margin.

With Personalized Photo at Right
Like Type A692a
Serpentine Die Cut 11½x11¼ Syncopated
Self-Adhesive

4441	A1017 $1 multi	2.40	2.40
4442	A1018 $1 multi	2.40	2.40
4443	A1019 $1 multi	2.40	2.40
4444	A1020 $1 multi	2.40	2.40
4445	A1021 $1 multi	2.40	2.40
4446	A1022 $1 multi	2.40	2.40
4447	A1023 $1 multi	2.40	2.40
4448	A1024 $1 multi	2.40	2.40
4449	A1025 $1 multi	2.40	2.40
4450	A1026 $2 multi	3.75	3.75
	Nos. 4441-4450 (10)	25.35	25.35

Nos. 4441-4450 were each printed in sheets of 20 and have personalized pictures and a straight edge at right and lack separations between the stamp and the personalized photo. Sheets of 20 of Nos. 4441-4449 sold for $33 each, No. 4450, $53.

Australian One Pound Banknote, One
Dollar Banknote and Coin — A1027

2016, Feb. 9   Litho.   Perf. 14½x14
4451 A1027 $1 multi   1.50 1.10
a.   Perf. 13½x14   1.50 1.10
b.   Booklet pane of 4 #4451a   6.00   —
      Complete booklet, 5 #4451b   30.00

Complete booklet sold for $20.95, and con-
tained five examples of No. 4451b, each with
different pane margins.

Items Starting With
Same
Letter — A1028

Designs: Nos. 4452, 4457, Numbat, nippers
(junior lifeguards) on surfboard, New South
Wales map. Nos. 4453, 4458, Quokka, quoll,
queue sign, Quokkair plane, Queensland map.
Nos. 4454, 4459, Surf, surfboard, sand castle,
starfish, sausage, shark toy, shell, snail, South
Australia map. Nos. 4455, 4460, Vegetables,
Victa lawnmower, violins, Vegemite sandwich,
Victoria map. Nos. 4456, 4461, Wombat, wat-
tle, waratah, water hose, Western Australia
Cricket Association bat and ball, Western Aus-
tralia map.

2016, Mar. 1   Litho.   Perf. 14¾x14
4452 A1028 $1 multi   1.50 1.50
4453 A1028 $1 multi   1.50 1.50
4454 A1028 $1 multi   1.50 1.50
4455 A1028 $1 multi   1.50 1.50
4456 A1028 $1 multi   1.50 1.50
a.   Horiz. strip of 5, #4452-4456 7.50 7.50
      Nos. 4452-4456 (5)   7.50 7.50

Booklet Stamps
Self-Adhesive
Serpentine Die Cut 11¼ Syncopated
4457 A1028 $1 multi   1.50   .25
a.   Booklet pane of 10   15.00
4458 A1028 $1 multi   1.50   .25
a.   Booklet pane of 10   15.00
4459 A1028 $1 multi   1.50   .25
a.   Booklet pane of 10   15.00
4460 A1028 $1 multi   1.50   .25
a.   Booklet pane of 10   15.00
4461 A1028 $1 multi   1.50   .25
a.   Booklet pane of 10   15.00
      Nos. 4457-4461 (5)   7.50 1.25

See Nos. 4520-4529, 4697-4706, 4853-
4862, 5027-5038.

Bridges
A1029

Designs: Nos. 4462, 4465, Gladesville
Bridge, New South Wales. Nos. 4463, 4467,
Story Bridge, Queensland. Nos. 4464, 4466,
Tasman Bridge, Tasmania.

2016, Mar. 15   Litho.   Perf. 14x14¾
4462 A1029 $1 multi   1.60 1.60
4463 A1029 $1 multi   1.60 1.60
4464 A1029 $1 multi   1.60 1.60
a.   Horiz. strip of 3, #4462-4464 4.80 4.80
      Nos. 4462-4464 (3)   4.80 4.80

Booklet Stamps
Self-Adhesive
Serpentine Die Cut 11¼ Syncopated
4465 A1029 $1 multi   1.60   .25
4466 A1029 $1 multi   1.60   .25
4467 A1029 $1 multi   1.60   .25
a.   Booklet pane of 20, 7 each
      #4465-4466, 6 #4467   32.00
      Nos. 4465-4467 (3)   4.80   .75

Queen Elizabeth II,
90th
Birthday — A1030

Designs: $1, Queen Elizabeth II. $2.75,
Golden wattle diamond brooch.

2016, Apr. 5   Litho.   Perf. 14¾x14
4468 A1030 $1 multi   1.60 1.25
4469 A1030 $2.75 multi   4.25 4.25
a.   Souvenir sheet of 2, #4468-
      4469   6.00 6.00

Booklet Stamp
Self-Adhesive
Serpentine Die Cut 11¼ Syncopated
4470 A1030 $2.75 multi   4.25 2.10
a.   Booklet pane of 5   21.50

World War I,
Cent. — A1031

Poppy and: Nos. 4471, 4476, Soldiers arriving on the Western Front. Nos. 4472, 4477,
Somme Offensive. Nos. 4473, 4478, Referendum on conscription. Nos. 4474, 4479, Matron
Grace Wilson of Australian Army Nursing Service, and Royal Red Cross, First Class. Nos.
4475, 4480, Soldier writing letter home.

2016, Apr. 12   Litho.   Perf. 14¼
4471 A1031 $1 multi   1.60 1.60
4472 A1031 $1 multi   1.60 1.60
4473 A1031 $1 multi   1.60 1.60
4474 A1031 $1 multi   1.60 1.60
a.   Booklet pane of 4, #4471-
      4474   6.50   —
4475 A1031 $1 multi   1.60 1.60
a.   Booklet pane of 4, #4472-
      4475   6.50   —
b.   Booklet pane of 4, #4471,
      4473-4475   6.50   —
c.   Booklet pane of 4, #4471-
      4472, 4474-4475   6.50   —
d.   Booklet pane of 4, #4471-
      4473, 4475   6.50   —
      Complete booklet, #4474a,
      4475a, 4475b, 4475c,
      4475d   32.50
e.   Souvenir sheet of 5, #4471-
      4475   8.00 8.00
      Nos. 4471-4475 (5)   8.00 8.00

Booklet Stamps
Self-Adhesive
Serpentine Die Cut 11¼ Syncopated
4476 A1031 $1 multi   1.60   .25
4477 A1031 $1 multi   1.60   .25
4478 A1031 $1 multi   1.60   .25
4479 A1031 $1 multi   1.60   .25
4480 A1031 $1 multi   1.60   .25
a.   Booklet pane of 10, 2 each
      #4476-4480   16.00
      Nos. 4476-4480 (5)   8.00 1.25

Complete booklet sold for $20.95.

Butterflies
A1032

Designs: Nos. 4481, 4485, Pale triangle butterfly. Nos. 4482, 4487, Bordered rustic butterfly. Nos. 4483, 4486, Cairns birdwing butterfly.
$2.75, Chequered swallowtail butterfly.

2016, May 3   Litho.   Perf. 14x14¾
4481 A1032 $1 multi   1.50 1.50
4482 A1032 $1 multi   1.50 1.50
4483 A1032 $1 multi   1.50 1.50
4484 A1032 $2.75 multi   4.00 4.00
a.   Souvenir sheet of 4, #4481-
      4484   8.50 8.50
      Nos. 4481-4484 (4)   8.50 8.50

Self-Adhesive
Serpentine Die Cut 11¼ Syncopated
4485 A1032 $1 multi   1.50   .25
4486 A1032 $1 multi   1.50   .25
4487 A1032 $1 multi   1.50   .25
a.   Horiz. coil strip of 3, #4485-
      4487   4.50

---

b.   Booklet pane of 20, 7 each
      #4485, 4487, 6 #4486   30.00
Booklet Stamp
4488 A1032 $2.75 multi   4.00 2.00
a.   Booklet pane of 5   20.00
      Nos. 4485-4488 (4)   8.50 2.75

Returned and
Services League of
Australia,
Cent. — A1033

2016, May 31   Litho.   Perf. 14¾x14
4489 A1033 $1 multi   1.50 1.50

Booklet Stamp
Self-Adhesive
Serpentine Die Cut 11¼ Syncopated
4490 A1033 $1 multi   1.50   .25
a.   Booklet pane of 20   30.00

Early 20th
Century Fruit
Crate Labels
A1034

Labels for: Nos. 4491, 4495, Paterson & Co.
"Red Gum Pack" Apples. Nos. 4492, 4496,
The River's Pride Navel Oranges. Nos. 4493,
4497, L. H. Kile "Robin" Apples. Nos. 4494,
4498, W. H. Price Ltd. Special Ohanez
Grapes.

2016, June 7   Litho.   Perf. 14x14¾
4491 A1034 $1 multi   1.50 1.50
a.   Booklet pane of 4   6.50   —
4492 A1034 $1 multi   1.50 1.50
a.   Booklet pane of 4   6.50   —
4493 A1034 $1 multi   1.50 1.50
a.   Booklet pane of 4   6.50   —
4494 A1034 $1 multi   1.50 1.50
a.   Booklet pane of 4   6.50   —
      Complete booklet, #4491a,
      4492a, 4493a, 4494a   26.00

Self-Adhesive
Serpentine Die Cut 11¼ Syncopated
4495 A1034 $1 multi   1.50   .25
4496 A1034 $1 multi   1.50   .25
4497 A1034 $1 multi   1.50   .25
4498 A1034 $1 multi   1.50   .25
a.   Horiz. coil strip of 4, #4495-
      4498   6.00
b.   Booklet pane of 10, 3 each
      #4496-4497, 2 each
      #4497-4498   15.00
      Nos. 4495-4498 (4)   6.00 1.00

Complete booklet sold for $16.95.

Owls — A1035

Designs: Nos. 4499, 4505, Rufous owl. Nos.
4500, 4503, Eastern grass owl. Nos. 4501,
4504, Sooty owl. Nos. 4502, 4506, Southern
boobook owl.

2016, July 5   Litho.   Perf. 14x13½
4499 A1035 $1 multi   1.50 1.50
a.   Booklet pane of 2   3.25
4500 A1035 $1 multi   1.50 1.50
a.   Booklet pane of 2   3.25
b.   Booklet pane of 2, #4499-
      4500   3.25
4501 A1035 $1 multi   1.50 1.50
a.   Booklet pane of 2   3.25
b.   Booklet pane of 2, #4500-
      4501   3.25
4502 A1035 $1 multi   1.50 1.50
a.   Booklet pane of 2   3.25
b.   Booklet pane of 2, #4501-
      4502   3.25
c.   Booklet pane of 2, #4499,
      4502   3.25
      Complete booklet, #4499a,
      4500a, 4500b, 4501a,
      4501b, 4502a, 4502b,
      4502c   26.00

---

d.   Souvenir sheet of 4, #4499-
      4502   6.00 6.00
      Nos. 4499-4502 (4)   6.00 6.00
Booklet Stamps
Self-Adhesive
Serpentine Die Cut11¼x10¾
Syncopated
4503 A1035 $1 multi   1.50   .25
4504 A1035 $1 multi   1.50   .25
4505 A1035 $1 multi   1.50   .25
4506 A1035 $1 multi   1.50   .25
a.   Booklet pane of 10, 2 each
      #4503, 4506, 3 each
      #4504-4505   15.00

Complete booklet sold for $16.95.

Olympic Gold Medalist Type of 2012

Design: $1, Jared Tallent, men's 50-kilome-
ter walk.

2016, July 23   Litho.   Perf. 14½
4506B A897 $1 multi   1.50 1.10

Tallent originally received a 2012 Olympic
silver medal, but was awarded a gold medal in
2016 after Sergey Kirdyapkin was stripped of
his medal for doping.

Play School
Children's Television
Program, 50th
Anniv. — A1036

Designs: $1, Jemima and Humpty. $2, Big
Ted and Little Ted.

2016, July 26   Litho.   Perf. 14¾x14
4507 A1036 $1 multi   1.50 1.50
4508 A1036 $2 multi   3.00 2.25
a.   Souvenir sheet of 2, #4507-
      4508   4.50 4.50

Booklet Stamp
Self-Adhesive
Serpentine Die Cut 11¼ Syncopated
4509 A1036 $1 multi   1.50   .25
a.   Booklet pane of 10   15.00

With Personalized Photo at Right
Like Type A692a
Serpentine Die Cut 11½x11¼
Syncopated
Self-Adhesive
4510 A1036 $1 multi   2.50 2.50

No. 4510 was printed in a sheet of 20 and
has personalized pictures and a straight edge
at right and lack separations between the
stamp and the personalized photo. Sheets of
20 sold for $33 each.

2016
Summer
Olympics,
Rio de
Janeiro
A1037

2016, Aug. 2   Litho.   Perf. 14x14¾
4511 A1037 $1 multi   1.50 1.10

Australian
Gold Medalists
at 2016
Summer
Olympics, Rio
de Janeiro
A1038

Designs: No. 4512, Mack Horton, men's
400-meter freestyle. No. 4513, Women's
4x100 meter freestyle relay team. No. 4514,
Catherine Skinner, women's trap shooting.
No. 4515, Women's rugby sevens team. No.
4516, Kyle Chalmers, men's 100-meter freestyle. No. 4517, Kimberley Brennan, women's
single sculls. No. 4518, Tom Burton, men's
Laser class sailing. No. 4519, Chloe Esposito,
women's individual modern pentathlon.

2016   Litho.   Perf. 14¼
4512 A1038 $1 multi   1.50 1.10
4513 A1038 $1 multi   1.50 1.10
4514 A1038 $1 multi   1.50 1.10

4515	A1038 $1 multi	1.50	1.10
4516	A1038 $1 multi	1.50	1.10
4517	A1038 $1 multi	1.50	1.10
4518	A1038 $1 multi	1.50	1.10
4519	A1038 $1 multi	1.50	1.10
	Nos. 4512-4519 (8)	12.00	8.80

Nos. 4512-4519 were each printed in sheets of 10. Issued: Nos. 4512-4514, 8/8; No. 4515, 8/9; No. 4516, 8/11; No. 4517, 8/15; No. 4518, 8/17; No. 4519, 8/18.

Items Starting With Same Letter
Type of 2016

Designs: Nos. 4520, 4525, Ant, Australian Rules Footballer players and ball, ANZAC memorial. Nos. 4521, 4526, Couple at campfire with Canberra map, crocodile, cockatoo. Nos. 4522, 4527, Lace monitor, lyrebird on lounge, Lamingtons on log. Nos. 4523, 4528, Rugby ball, refrigerator, rocket, reel, ruler, rope, Red Center poster. Nos. 4524, 4529, Tasmania map, Tasmanian devil, tradesman in tinnie (boat) with toolbelt.

2016, Aug. 16   Litho.   Perf. 14¾x14

4520	A1028 $1 multi	1.50	1.50
4521	A1028 $1 multi	1.50	1.50
4522	A1028 $1 multi	1.50	1.50
4523	A1028 $1 multi	1.50	1.50
4524	A1028 $1 multi	1.50	1.50
	Nos. 4520-4524 (5)	7.50	7.50

Self-Adhesive
Serpentine Die Cut 11¼ Syncopated

4525	A1028 $1 multi	1.50	.25
a.	Booklet pane of 10	15.00	
4526	A1028 $1 multi	1.50	.25
a.	Booklet pane of 10	15.00	
4527	A1028 $1 multi	1.50	.25
a.	Booklet pane of 10	15.00	
4528	A1028 $1 multi	1.50	.25
a.	Booklet pane of 10	15.00	
4529	A1028 $1 multi	1.50	.25
a.	Booklet pane of 10	15.00	
b.	Vert. coil strip of 5, #4525-4529	7.50	
	Nos. 4525-4529 (5)	7.50	1.25

Stigmodera gratiosa

Jewel Beetles — A1039

Designs: Nos. 4530, 4534, Stigmodera gratiosa. Nos. 4531, 4535, Castiarina klugii. No. 4532, Temognatha alternata. No. 4533, Julodimorpha bakewellii.

2016, Sept. 6   Litho.   Perf. 14¾x14

4530	A1039 $1 multi	1.60	1.60
4531	A1039 $1 multi	1.60	1.60
a.	Horiz. pair, #4530-4531	3.20	3.20
4532	A1039 $2 multi	3.25	2.40
4533	A1039 $2 multi	3.25	2.40
a.	Horiz. pair, #4532-4533	6.50	4.80
	Nos. 4530-4533 (4)	9.70	8.00

Self-Adhesive
Serpentine Die Cut 11¼ Syncopated

4534	A1039 $1 multi	1.60	.25
4535	A1039 $1 multi	1.60	.25
a.	Vert. coil pair, #4534-4535	3.20	
b.	Booklet pane of 20, 10 each #4534-4535	32.00	

Landing of Dirk Hartog in Western Australia, 400th Anniv. — A1040

2016, Sept. 13   Litho.   Perf. 14¾x14

4536	A1040 $2 multi	3.25	2.40

Orange-bellied Parrot

A1041

Endangered Animals — A1042

Designs: No. 4537, Orange-bellied parrots. No. 4538, Northern quolls. Nos. 4539, 4544, Snow leopards. Nos. 4540, 4545, Western swamp tortoise. Nos. 4541, 4546, Western lowland gorillas. Nos. 4542, 4547, Asian elephants. Nos. 4543, 4548, Southern corroboree frog.

2016, Sept. 20   Litho.   Perf. 14x14¾

4537	A1041 50c multi	.80	.60
4538	A1041 50c multi	.80	.60
a.	Horiz. pair, #4537-4538	1.60	1.20
4539	A1041 $1 multi	1.60	1.60
4540	A1041 $1 multi	1.60	1.60
4541	A1041 $1 multi	1.60	1.60
4542	A1041 $1 multi	1.60	1.60

Perf. 13¾x14

4543	A1042 $1 multi	1.60	1.60
a.	Souvenir sheet of 7, #4537-4543	9.75	9.75
	Nos. 4537-4543 (7)	9.60	9.20

Self-Adhesive
Serpentine Die Cut 11¼ Syncopated

4544	A1041 $1 multi	1.60	.25
4545	A1041 $1 multi	1.60	.25
4546	A1041 $1 multi	1.60	.25
4547	A1041 $1 multi	1.60	.25
a.	Horiz. coil strip of 4, #4544-4547	6.40	
b.	Booklet pane of 20, 6 each #4544-4545, 4 each #4546, 4547	32.00	

Booklet Stamp
Serpentine Die Cut 10¾x11 Syncopated

4548	A1042 $1 multi	1.60	.25
a.	Booklet pane of 10	16.00	
	Nos. 4544-4548 (5)	8.00	1.25

Taronga Zoo, cent. (Nos. 4543, 4548).

Monotremes A1043

Designs: $2.10, Platypus. $2.95, Short-beaked echidna.

2016, Sept. 26   Litho.   Perf. 14¾x14

4549	A1043 $2.10 multi	3.25	3.25
4550	A1043 $2.95 multi	4.50	4.50
a.	Souvenir sheet of 2, #4549-4550	7.75	7.75

Booklet Stamps
Self-Adhesive
Serpentine Die Cut 11¼ Syncopated

4551	A1043 $2.10 multi	3.25	1.60
a.	Booklet pane of 5	16.50	
4552	A1043 $2.95 multi	4.50	2.25
a.	Booklet pane of 5	22.50	

With Personalized Photo at Right Like Type A692a
Serpentine Die Cut 11½x11¼ Syncopated

4553	A1043 $2.10 multi	4.25	4.25
4554	A1043 $2.95 multi	5.50	5.50

Nos. 4553-4554 were each printed in sheets of 20 and have personalized pictures and a straight edge at right and lack separations between the stamp and the personalized photo. Sheets of 20 of No. 4553 sold for $55 each, No. 4554, $72.

Australian Involvement in Viet Nam War — A1044

Poppies and inscription: Nos. 4555, 4560, In the field. Nos. 4556, 4561, Long Tan Cross.

Nos. 4557, 4562, Aid and recreation. Nos. 4558, 4563, Opposition and withdrawal. Nos. 4559, 4564, Commemoration.

2016, Oct. 11   Litho.   Perf. 14¼

4555	A1044 $1 multi	1.60	1.60
a.	Booklet pane of 4	6.50	
4556	A1044 $1 multi	1.60	1.60
a.	Booklet pane of 4	6.50	
4557	A1044 $1 multi	1.60	1.60
a.	Booklet pane of 4	6.50	
4558	A1044 $1 multi	1.60	1.60
a.	Booklet pane of 4	6.50	
4559	A1044 $1 multi	1.60	1.60
a.	Booklet pane of 4	6.50	
	Complete booklet, #4555a, 4556a, 4557a, 4558a, 4559a	32.50	
b.	Souvenir sheet of 5, #4555-4559	8.00	8.00
	Nos. 4555-4559 (5)	8.00	8.00

Booklet Stamps
Self-Adhesive
Serpentine Die Cut 11¼ Syncopated

4560	A1044 $1 multi	1.60	.25
4561	A1044 $1 multi	1.60	.25
4562	A1044 $1 multi	1.60	.25
4563	A1044 $1 multi	1.60	.25
4564	A1044 $1 multi	1.60	.25
a.	Booklet pane of 10, 2 each #4560-4564	16.00	
	Nos. 4560-4564 (5)	8.00	1.25

Complete booklet sold for $20.95.

Dylan Alcott, Paralympian of the Year — A1045

2016, Oct. 18   Litho.   Perf. 14¼

4565	A1045 $1 multi	1.60	1.25

No. 4565 exists in sheets of 10.

Christmas
A1046   A1047

Designs: Nos. 4566, 4571, 4576, 4578, Star and "Goodwill." Nos. 4567, 4572, 4577, 4579, Gift and "Joy." Nos. 4568, 4573, 4580, Madonna and Child. Nos. 4569, 4574, 4581, Angel, Nos. 4570, 4575, Magi.

2016, Oct. 31   Litho.   Perf. 14¾x14

4566	A1046 65c multi	1.00	1.00
4567	A1046 65c multi	1.00	1.00
a.	Horiz. pair, #4566-4567	2.00	2.00
4568	A1047 65c multi	1.00	1.00
4569	A1047 $1.70 multi	2.60	2.60
4570	A1047 $2.55 multi	4.00	4.00
a.	Souvenir sheet of 3, #4568-4570	7.75	7.75
	Nos. 4566-4570 (5)	9.60	9.60

Booklet Stamps
Self-Adhesive
Serpentine Die Cut 11¼ Syncopated

4571	A1046 65c multi	1.00	.25
4572	A1047 65c multi	1.00	.25
a.	Booklet pane of 20, 10 each #4971-4972, + 20 etiquettes	20.00	
4573	A1047 65c multi	1.00	.25
a.	Booklet pane of 20 + 20 etiquettes	20.00	
4574	A1047 $1.70 multi	2.60	1.40
a.	Booklet pane of 5	13.00	
4575	A1047 $2.55 multi	4.00	2.00
a.	Booklet pane of 5	20.00	

Litho. & Embossed With Foil Application

4576	A1046 65c multi	1.00	.25
a.	Booklet pane of 10	10.00	
4577	A1046 65c multi	1.00	.25
a.	Booklet pane of 10	10.00	
	Nos. 4571-4577 (7)	11.60	4.65

With Personalized Photo at Right Like Type A692a
Litho.
Serpentine Die Cut 11½x11¼ Syncopated

4578	A1046 65c multi	2.00	2.00
4579	A1046 65c multi	2.00	2.00
4580	A1047 65c multi	2.00	2.00
4581	A1047 $1.70 multi	3.50	3.50
	Nos. 4578-4581 (4)	9.50	9.50

Nos. 4578-4581 were each printed in sheets of 20 and have personalized pictures and a straight edge at right and lack separations between the stamp and the personalized photo. Sheets of 20 of No. 4578-4580 each sold for $26 each, No. 4581, $47.

Rose — A1048   Heart — A1049

2017, Feb. 7   Litho.   Perf. 14¾x14

4582	A1048 $1 multi	1.60	1.60
4583	A1049 $1 multi	1.60	1.60

Booklet Stamps
Self-Adhesive
Serpentine Die Cut 11¼ Syncopated

4584	A1048 $1 multi	1.60	.25
a.	Booklet pane of 10	16.00	
4585	A1049 $1 multi	1.60	.25
a.	Booklet pane of 10	16.00	

With Personalized Photo at Right Like Type A692a
Litho.
Serpentine Die Cut 11½x11¼ Syncopated
Self-Adhesive

4586	A1048 $1 multi	2.60	2.60
4587	A1049 $1 multi	2.60	2.60

Nos. 4586-4587 were each printed in sheets of 20 and have personalized pictures and a straight edge at right and lack separations between the stamp and the personalized photo. Sheets of 20 of Nos. 4586-4587 sold for $33 each.

Jetties A1050

Designs: Nos. 4588, 4592, Busselton Jetty, Western Australia. Nos. 4589, 4593, Tumby Bay Jetty, South Australia. $2.10, Shelley Beach Jetty, Victoria. $2.95, Kincumber Jetty, New South Wales.

2017, Feb. 21   Litho.   Perf. 14x14¾

4588	A1050 $1 multi	1.60	1.60
4589	A1050 $1 multi	1.60	1.60
a.	Horiz. pair, #4588-4589	3.20	3.20
4590	A1050 $2.10 multi	3.25	3.25
4591	A1050 $2.95 multi	4.50	4.50
	Nos. 4588-4591 (4)	10.95	10.95

Self-Adhesive
Serpentine Die Cut 11¼ Syncopated

4592	A1050 $1 multi	1.60	1.60
4593	A1050 $1 multi	1.60	1.60
a.	Horiz. coil pair, #4592-4593	3.20	
b.	Booklet pane of 10, 5 each #4592-4593	16.00	

Booklet Stamps

4594	A1050 $2.10 multi	3.25	1.60
a.	Booklet pane of 5	16.50	
4595	A1050 $2.95 multi	4.50	4.50
a.	Booklet pane of 5	22.50	
	Nos. 4592-4595 (4)	10.95	9.30

Paintings and Artists — A1051

Designs: No. 4596, Near Heidelberg, by Sir Arthur Streeton (1867-1943). No. 4597, Footballer, by Sir Sidney Nolan (1917-92).

2017, Mar. 30 Litho. Perf. 14x13½

4596	A1051 $1 multi	1.60	1.25
4597	A1051 $1 multi	1.60	1.25
a.	Horiz. pair, #4596-4597	3.20	2.50

Gems — A1052

Designs: Nos. 4598, 4602, Golden sapphire. Nos. 4599, 4603, Rhodonite. No. 4600, Fluorite. No. 4601, Pink diamond.

2017, Mar. 30 Litho. Perf. 14¾x14

4598	A1052 $1 multi	1.60	1.60
a.	Booklet pane of 4	6.50	—
4599	A1052 $1 multi	1.60	1.60
a.	Horiz. pair, #4598-4599	3.20	3.20
b.	Booklet pane of 4	6.50	—
4600	A1052 $2 multi	3.00	2.25
a.	Booklet pane of 4	12.50	—
4601	A1052 $2 multi	3.00	2.25
a.	Horiz. pair, #4600-4601	6.00	4.50
b.	Booklet pane of 4	12.50	—
c.	Booklet pane of 4, #4598-4601	9.50	—
	Complete booklet, #4598a, 4599b, 4600a, 4601b, 4601c	47.50	
d.	Souvenir sheet of 4, #4598-4601	9.25	7.75
	Nos. 4598-4601 (4)	9.20	7.70

Self-Adhesive

Serpentine Die Cut 11¼ Syncopated

4602	A1052 $1 multi	1.60	1.60
4603	A1052 $1 multi	1.60	1.60
a.	Vert. coil pair, #4602-4603	3.20	
b.	Booklet pane of 10, 5 each #4602-4603	16.00	

Complete booklet sold for $30.95.

A1053

Queen Elizabeth II, 91st Birthday — A1054

2017, Apr. 4 Litho. Perf. 14¾x14

4604	A1053 $1 multi	1.50	1.50
4605	A1054 $2.95 multi	4.50	4.50
a.	Souvenir sheet of 2, #4604-4605	6.00	6.00

Booklet Stamps
Self-Adhesive

Serpentine Die Cut 11¼ Syncopated

4606	A1053 $1 multi	1.50	.25
a.	Booklet pane of 10	15.00	

Serpentine Die Cut 11¼

4607	A1054 $2.95 multi	4.50	2.25
a.	Booklet pane of 5	22.50	

World War I, Cent. — A1055

Poppy and: Nos. 4608, 4613, War in the air. Nos. 4609, 4614, Third Battle of Ypres. Nos. 4610, 4616, Support for the troops. Nos. 4611, 4615, Sinai-Palestine campaign. Nos. 4612, 4617, War correspondent Charles Bean.

2017, Apr. 18 Litho. Perf. 14¼

4608	A1055 $1 multi	1.50	1.50
4609	A1055 $1 multi	1.50	1.50
4610	A1055 $1 multi	1.50	1.50
4611	A1055 $1 multi	1.50	1.50
a.	Booklet pane of 4, #4608-4611	6.50	—
4612	A1055 $1 multi	1.50	1.50
a.	Booklet pane of 4, #4608-4610, 4612	6.50	—
b.	Booklet pane of 4, #4609-4612	6.50	—
c.	Booklet pane of 4, #4608, 4610-4612	6.50	·
d.	Booklet pane of 4, #4608-4609, 4611-4612	6.50	—
	Complete booklet, #4611a, 4612a, 4612b, 4612c, 4612d	32.50	
e.	Souvenir sheet of 5, #4608-4612	7.50	7.50
	Nos. 4608-4612 (5)	7.50	7.50

Booklet Stamps
Self-Adhesive

Serpentine Die Cut 11¼ Syncopated

4613	A1055 $1 multi	1.50	.25
4614	A1055 $1 multi	1.50	.25
4615	A1055 $1 multi	1.50	.25
4616	A1055 $1 multi	1.50	.25
4617	A1055 $1 multi	1.50	.25
a.	Booklet pane of 10, 2 each #4613-4617	15.00	
	Nos. 4613-4617 (5)	7.50	1.25

Complete booklet sold for $20.95.

Caves A1056

Designs: Nos. 4618, 4622, Cliefden Caves, New South Wales. Nos. 4619, 4623, Weebubbie Cave, Western Australia. $2, Undara Lava Tube, Queensland. $3, Kubla Khan Cave, Tasmania.

2017, May 2 Litho. Perf. 14x14¾

4618	A1056 $1 multi	1.50	1.50
4619	A1056 $1 multi	1.50	1.50
a.	Horiz. pair, #4618-4619	3.00	3.00
4620	A1056 $2 multi	3.00	2.25
4621	A1056 $3 multi	4.50	2.25
	Nos. 4618-4621 (4)	10.50	7.50

Self-Adhesive

Serpentine Die Cut 11¼ Syncopated

4622	A1056 $1 multi	1.50	.25
4623	A1056 $1 multi	1.50	.25
a.	Horiz. coil pair, #4622-4623	3.00	
b.	Booklet pane of 20, 10 each #4622-4623	30.00	

Street Art — A1057

Art: Nos. 4624, 4628, Indigenous Boy, by Adnate, Hosier Lane, Melbourne. Nos. 4625, 4631, Woman, by Vans the Omega, Railway Terrace, Adelaide. Nos. 4626, 4630, Forever Curious, by Rone and Phibs, Rutledge Lane,

Melbourne. Nos. 4627, 4629, Shinka, by Fin DAC, Little Rundle Street, Adelaide.

2017, May 16 Litho. Perf. 14¾x14

4624	A1057 $1 multi	1.50	1.50
4625	A1057 $1 multi	1.50	1.50
4626	A1057 $1 multi	1.50	1.50
4627	A1057 $1 multi	1.50	1.50
a.	Souvenir sheet of 4, #4624-4627	6.00	6.00
	Nos. 4624-4627 (4)	6.00	6.00

Booklet Stamps
Self-Adhesive

Serpentine Die Cut 11¼ Syncopated

4628	A1057 $1 multi	1.50	.25
4629	A1057 $1 multi	1.50	.25
4630	A1057 $1 multi	1.50	.25
4631	A1057 $1 multi	1.50	.25
a.	Booklet pane of 10, 2 each #4628, 4631, 3 each #4629-4630	15.00	
	Nos. 4628-4631 (4)	6.00	1.00

1967 Constitutional Amendment Referendum, 50th Anniv. — A1058

2017, May 24 Litho. Perf. 14¾x14

4632	A1058 $1 multi	1.50	1.10

Distinguished Aborigines — A1059

Designs: Nos. 4633, 4636, Tom Calma, University of Canberra Chancellor. Nos. 4634, 4637, Lowitja O'Donoghue, nurse, and first chairperson of Aboriginal and Torres Strait Islander Commission. Nos. 4635, 4638, Galarrwuy Yunupingu, Aboriginal land rights activist.

2017, May 29 Litho. Perf. 14x14¾

4633	A1059 $1 multi	1.50	1.50
4634	A1059 $1 multi	1.50	1.50
4635	A1059 $1 multi	1.50	1.50
	Nos. 4633-4635 (3)	4.50	4.50

Booklet Stamps
Self-Adhesive

Serpentine Die Cut 11¼ Syncopated

4636	A1059 $1 multi	1.50	.25
4637	A1059 $1 multi	1.50	.25
4638	A1059 $1 multi	1.50	.25
a.	Booklet pane of 20, 7 each #4636-4637, 6 #4638	30.00	
	Nos. 4636-4638 (3)	4.50	.75

Lions Clubs International, Cent. A1060

2017, June 7 Litho. Perf. 14x14¾

4639	A1060 $1 multi	1.60	1.60

Booklet Stamp
Self-Adhesive

Serpentine Die Cut 11¼ Syncopated

4640	A1060 $1 multi	1.60	.25
a.	Booklet pane of 20	32.00	

Scenes from Works Written by Henry Lawson (1867-1922) A1061

Scene from: $1, The Drover's Wife. $2.95, Mitchell: A Character Sketch.

2017, June 13 Litho. Perf. 14x14¾

4641	A1061 $1 multi	1.60	1.60
4642	A1061 $2.95 multi	4.50	4.50
a.	Souvenir sheet of 2, #4641-4642	6.25	6.25

Booklet Stamps
Self-Adhesive

Serpentine Die Cut 11¼ Syncopated

4643	A1061 $1 multi	1.60	1.60
a.	Booklet pane of 20	32.00	
4644	A1061 $2.95 multi	4.50	4.50
a.	Booklet pane of 5	22.50	

Succulent Plants A1062

Designs: Nos. 4645, 4649, Portulaca cyclophylla. Nos. 4646, 4650, Tecticornia verrucosa. Nos. 4647, 4651, Calandrinia creethae. Nos. 4648, 4652, Gunniopsis quadrifida.

2017, June 20 Litho. Perf. 14x14¾

4645	A1062 $1 multi	1.60	1.60
4646	A1062 $1 multi	1.60	1.60
4647	A1062 $1 multi	1.60	1.60
4648	A1062 $1 multi	1.60	1.60
	Nos. 4645-4648 (4)	6.40	6.40

Self-Adhesive

Serpentine Die Cut 11¼ Syncopated

4649	A1062 $1 multi	1.60	.25
4650	A1062 $1 multi	1.60	.25
4651	A1062 $1 multi	1.60	.25
4652	A1062 $1 multi	1.60	.25
a.	Horiz. coil strip of 4, #4640-4652	6.40	
b.	Booklet pane of 10, 3 each #4649-4650, 2 each #4651-4652	16.00	
	Nos. 4649-4652 (4)	6.40	1.00

Wildflowers Type of 2015

Serpentine Die Cut 11¼ Syncopated

2017, July 4 Self-Adhesive Litho.
Booklet Stamp

4653	A1015 $2 Golden rainbow	3.25	1.60
a.	Booklet pane of 5	16.50	

Dated 2016.

Trans-Australian Railway Travel Posters

A1063   A1064

2017, July 4 Litho. Perf. 14¾x14

4654	A1063 $1 multi	1.60	1.60
4655	A1064 $1 multi	1.60	1.60
a.	Souvenir sheet of 2, #4654-4655	3.25	3.25

Booklet Stamps
Self-Adhesive

Serpentine Die Cut 11¼ Syncopated

4656	A1063 $1 multi	1.60	.25
4657	A1064 $1 multi	1.60	.25
a.	Booklet pane of 10, 5 each #4656-4657	16.00	

A1065

Dragonflies — A1066

Designs: Nos. 4658, 4663, Scarlet percher. Nos. 4659, 4664, Arrowhead rockmaster. Nos. 4660, 4666, Australian tiger. Nos. 4661, 4667, Jewel flutterer. Nos. 4662, 4665, Beautiful petaltail.

2017, Aug. 1 Litho. Perf. 14x14¾

4658	A1065	$1 multi	1.60	1.60
a.		Perf. 14x14¾x13¾x14¾	1.60	1.60
4659	A1065	$1 multi	1.60	1.60
a.		Perf. 14x14¾x13¾x14¾	1.60	1.60

Perf. 13¾x14

4660	A1066	$1 multi	1.60	1.60
4661	A1066	$1 multi	1.60	1.60
4662	A1066	$1 multi	1.60	1.60
a.		Souvenir sheet of 5, #4658a, 4659a, 4660-4662	8.00	8.00
		Nos. 4658-4662 (5)	8.00	8.00

Self-Adhesive

Serpentine Die Cut 11¼ Syncopated

4663	A1065	$1 multi	1.60	.25
4664	A1065	$1 multi	1.60	.25
a.		Horiz. coil pair, #4663-4664	3.20	
b.		Booklet pane of 20, 10 each #4663-4664		

Booklet Stamps

Serpentine Die Cut 10¾ Syncopated

4665	A1066	$1 multi	1.60	.25
4666	A1066	$1 multi	1.60	.25
4667	A1066	$1 multi	1.60	.25
a.		Booklet pane of 10, 3 each #4665, 4667, 4 #4666	16.00	
		Nos. 4663-4667 (5)	8.00	1.25

Shipwrecks
A1067

Wreck of: Nos. 4668, 4671, HMS Pandora, 1791, and pistol. Nos. 4669, 4672, PS Clonmel, 1841, and decanter. Nos. 4670, 4673, Zuytdorp, 1712, and silver coin.

2017, Aug. 29 Litho. Perf. 14x14¾

4668	A1067	$1 multi	1.60	1.60
4669	A1067	$1 multi	1.60	1.60
4670	A1067	$1 multi	1.60	1.60
a.		Booklet pane of 4, #4669, 4670, 2 #4668	6.75	—
b.		Booklet pane of 4, #4668, 4670, 2 #4669	6.75	—
c.		Booklet pane of 4, #4668, 4669, 2 #4670 (#4670 at UL and LR)	6.75	—
d.		Booklet pane of 4, #4668, 4669, 2 #4670 (#4670 at UR and LL)	6.75	—
		Complete booklet, #4670a, 4670c, 4670d, 2 #4670b	34.00	
		Nos. 4668-4670 (3)	4.80	4.80

Self-Adhesive

Serpentine Die Cut 11¼ Syncopated

4671	A1067	$1 multi	1.60	.25
4672	A1067	$1 multi	1.60	.25
4673	A1067	$1 multi	1.60	.25
a.		Horiz. coil strip of 3, #4671-4673	4.80	
b.		Booklet pane of 10, 4 #4671, 3 each #4672-4673	16.00	
		Nos. 4671-4673 (3)	4.80	.75

Complete booklet sold for $20.95. The pane margins differ on the two examples of No. 4670b in the complete booklet.

Heard Island
A1068

Designs: No. 4674, Southern elephant seals. No. 4675, Kerguelen cabbage. No. 4676, King penguins. No. 4677, Baudissin Glacier.

2017, Sept. 5 Litho. Perf. 14¼

4674	A1068	$1 multi	1.60	1.25
4675	A1068	$1 multi	1.60	1.25
4676	A1068	$1 multi	1.60	1.25
4677	A1068	$1 multi	1.60	1.25
a.		Souvenir sheet of 4, #4674-4677	6.50	5.00
		Nos. 4674-4677 (4)	6.40	5.00

Launch of Weapons
Research Satellite,
50th Anniv. — A1069

2017, Sept. 12 Litho. Perf. 14¾x14

4678	A1069	$1 multi	1.60	1.60

Booklet Stamp
Self-Adhesive

Serpentine Die Cut 11¼ Syncopated

4679	A1069	$1 multi	1.60	.25
a.		Booklet pane of 20	32.00	

Water Plants
A1070

Designs: $2.10, Entire marshwort. $2.30, Giant waterlily. $3, Lotus lily.

2017, Sept. 27 Litho. Perf. 14x14¾

4680	A1070	$2.10 multi	3.25	3.25
4681	A1070	$2.30 multi	3.75	3.75
4682	A1070	$3 multi	4.75	4.75
		Nos. 4680-4682 (3)	11.75	11.75

Booklet Stamps
Self-Adhesive

Serpentine Die Cut 11¼ Syncopated

4683	A1070	$2.10 multi	3.25	1.60
a.		Booklet pane of 5	16.50	
4684	A1070	$2.30 multi	3.75	1.90
a.		Booklet pane of 5	19.00	
4685	A1070	$3 multi	4.75	2.40
a.		Booklet pane of 5	24.00	
		Nos. 4683-4685 (3)	11.75	5.90

"Australia" — A1071

Serpentine Die Cut 11¼ Syncopated
2017, Oct. 2 Self-Adhesive Litho.
Booklet Stamps

4686	A1071	($1) multi	1.75	.25
a.		Booklet pane of 5	8.75	

No. 4686a was made available to holders of Australia Post My Post Concession Account card and the general public. Pensioners, veterans, the disabled, and others typically on low or fixed incomes, could apply at their local post office to receive a Concession Account card. Those eligible to receive the card were sent a free example of No. 4686a, which was mailed with the card. Card holders, when showing the card at the post office and having the information recorded, could purchase up to ten No. 4686a every year for $3 (60c per stamp, lower than the $1 letter rate). The examples of No. 4686a made available to the public through the philatelic bureau sold for $5.45 ($1.09 per stamp). There are no differences between the stamps offered to card holders and the general public, aside from the selling price. No. 4686 was valid only on domestic letters and could not be used on parcels or international mail.

Women at
War — A1072

Poppies and women in: Nos. 4687, 4692, World War I. Nos. 4688, 4693, World War II. Nos. 4689, 4694, Korea and Viet Nam. Nos. 4690, 4695, Afghanistan and Iraq. Nos. 4691, 4696, Peacekeeping.

2017, Oct. 6 Litho. Perf. 14¼

4687	A1072	$1 multi	1.60	1.60
4688	A1072	$1 multi	1.60	1.60
4689	A1072	$1 multi	1.60	1.60
4690	A1072	$1 multi	1.60	1.60
4691	A1072	$1 multi	1.60	1.60
a.		Souvenir sheet of 5, #4687-4691	8.00	8.00
		Nos. 4687-4691 (5)	8.00	8.00

Booklet Stamps
Self-Adhesive

Serpentine Die Cut 11¼ Syncopated

4692	A1072	$1 multi	1.60	.25
4693	A1072	$1 multi	1.60	.25
4694	A1072	$1 multi	1.60	.25
4695	A1072	$1 multi	1.60	.25
4696	A1072	$1 multi	1.60	.25
a.		Booklet pane of 10, 2 each #4692-4696	16.00	
		Nos. 4692-4696 (5)	8.00	1.25

Items Starting With Same Letter
Type of 2016

Designs: Nos. 4697, 4702, Barramundi in billy on barbecue, blowflies, and budgie-smugglers (bathing suit). Nos. 4698, 4703, Galahs, gasket, gecko, gnome, man in gumboots, signs to Gladstone, Great Barrier Reef and Gulargambone. Nos. 4699, 4704, Jabiru, jillaroo, jam and jumbucks. No. 4700, 4705, Kangaroo, koala, kelpie. Nos. 4701, 4706, Ulysses butterfly, ute, uggs, umpire with ukulele, umbrella.

2017, Oct. 17 Litho. Perf. 14¾x14

4697	A1028	$1 multi	1.60	1.60
4698	A1028	$1 multi	1.60	1.60
4699	A1028	$1 multi	1.60	1.60
4700	A1028	$1 multi	1.60	1.60
4701	A1028	$1 multi	1.60	1.60
		Nos. 4697-4701 (5)	8.00	8.00

Self-Adhesive

Serpentine Die Cut 11¼ Syncopated

4702	A1028	$1 multi	1.60	.25
a.		Booklet pane of 10	16.00	
4703	A1028	$1 multi	1.60	.25
a.		Booklet pane of 10	16.00	
4704	A1028	$1 multi	1.60	.25
a.		Booklet pane of 10	16.00	
4705	A1028	$1 multi	1.60	.25
a.		Booklet pane of 10	16.00	
4706	A1028	$1 multi	1.60	.25
a.		Booklet pane of 10	16.00	
b.		Vert. coil strip of 5, #4702-4706	8.00	
		Nos. 4702-4706 (5)	8.00	1.25

Aboriginal
Art — A1073

Designs: Nos. 4707, 4711, Pukumani Poles, by Bede Tungutalum. Nos. 4708, 4712, Waterlili and Gaya, by Banduk Marika. No. 4709, Untitled, by Tungutalum. No. 4710, Guyamala, by Marika.

2017, Oct. 24 Litho. Perf. 14¾x14

4707	A1073	$1 multi	1.60	1.60
4708	A1073	$1 multi	1.60	1.60
4709	A1073	$2 multi	3.25	3.25
4710	A1073	$2 multi	3.25	3.25
		Nos. 4707-4710 (4)	9.70	9.70

Booklet Stamps
Self-Adhesive

Serpentine Die Cut 11¼ Syncopated

4711	A1073	$1 multi	1.60	.25
4712	A1073	$1 multi	1.60	.25
a.		Booklet pane of 20, 10 each #4711-4712	32.00	

Christmas
A1074   A1075

Designs: Nos. 4713, 4718, Madonna and Child projected on St. Mary's Cathedral, Sydney. Nos. 4714, 4719, 4723, Christmas gift boxes. Nos. 4715, 4720, 4724, Star and Christmas tree. $2, Bells. $2.30, Small Cowper Madonna projected on St. Mary's Cathedral.

2017, Nov. 1 Litho. Perf. 14¾x14

4713	A1074	65c multi	1.00	1.00
4714	A1075	65c multi	1.00	1.00
4715	A1075	65c multi	1.00	1.00
a.		Horiz. pair, #4714-4715	2.00	2.00
4716	A1075	$2 multi	3.25	1.60
4717	A1074	$2.30 multi	3.50	1.75
a.		Souvenir sheet of 2, #4713, 4717	4.50	2.75
		Nos. 4713-4717 (5)	9.75	6.35

Booklet Stamps
Self-Adhesive

Serpentine Die Cut 11¼ Syncopated

4718	A1074	65c multi	1.00	.25
a.		Booklet pane of 20 + 20 labels	20.00	
4719	A1075	65c multi	1.00	.25
4720	A1075	65c multi	1.00	.25
a.		Booklet pane of 20, 10 each #4719-4720 + 20 labels	20.00	
4721	A1075	$2 multi	3.25	1.60
a.		Booklet pane of 5	16.50	
4722	A1074	$2.30 multi	3.50	1.75
a.		Booklet pane of 5	17.50	

Litho. With Foil Application

4723	A1075	65c gold & multi	1.00	.25
a.		Booklet pane of 10	10.00	
4724	A1075	65c gold & multi	1.00	.25
a.		Booklet pane of 10	10.00	
		Nos. 4718-4724 (7)	11.75	4.60

Australian
Convict
Heritage
A1076

Designs: Nos. 4730, 4733, Hyde Park Barracks, Sydney, New South Wales Colony, ticket of leave, and chain gang. Nos. 4731, 4734, Penitentiary, Van Diemen's Land, convict love token. $3, Convict Establishment (Fremantle Prison), Swan River Colony, article from newspaper about life on convict transport ships.

2018, Jan. 16 Litho. Perf. 14x14¾

4730	A1076	$1 multi	1.60	1.60
4731	A1076	$1 multi	1.60	1.60
4732	A1076	$3 multi	5.00	2.50
		Nos. 4730-4732 (3)	8.20	5.70

Self-Adhesive

Serpentine Die Cut 11¼ Syncopated

4733	A1076	$1 multi	1.60	.25
4734	A1076	$1 multi	1.60	.25
a.		Horiz. coil pair, #4733-4734	3.20	
b.		Booklet pane of 10, 5 each #4733-4734	16.00	

Booklet Stamp

4735	A1076	$3 multi	5.00	2.50
a.		Booklet pane of 5	25.00	
		Nos. 4733-4735 (3)	8.20	3.00

Nos. 4732 & 4735 are inscribed: "International Post".

Television
Personalities
A1077

Designs: Nos. 4736, 4741, Daryl Somers, television host. Nos. 4737, 4742, Denise Drysdale, singer and dancer. Nos. 4738, 4743, Bert Newton, television host. Nos. 4739, 4744, Kerri-Anne Kennerley, television host. Nos. 4740-4745, Ray Martin, television journalist.

2018, Jan. 18 Litho. Perf. 14¾x14

4736	A1077	$1 multi	1.60	1.60
4737	A1077	$1 multi	1.60	1.60
4738	A1077	$1 multi	1.60	1.60
4739	A1077	$1 multi	1.60	1.60
4740	A1077	$1 multi	1.60	1.60
		Nos. 4736-4740 (5)	8.00	8.00

Booklet Stamps
Self-Adhesive

Serpentine Die Cut 11¼ Syncopated

4741	A1077	$1 multi	1.60	.25
a.		Booklet pane of 10	16.00	
4742	A1077	$1 multi	1.60	.25
a.		Booklet pane of 10	16.00	
4743	A1077	$1 multi	1.60	.25
a.		Booklet pane of 10	16.00	
4744	A1077	$1 multi	1.60	.25
a.		Booklet pane of 10	16.00	
4745	A1077	$1 multi	1.60	.25
a.		Booklet pane of 10	16.00	
		Nos. 4741-4745 (5)	8.00	1.25

Bird — A1078

Flower — A1079

2018, Feb. 6   Litho.   Perf. 14¾x14
| 4746 | A1078 | $1 multi | 1.60 | 1.60 |
| 4747 | A1079 | $2 multi | 3.25 | 1.60 |

Booklet Stamp
Self-Adhesive
Serpentine Die Cut 11¼ Syncopated
| 4748 | A1078 | $1 multi | 1.60 | .25 |
| a. | | Booklet pane of 10 | 16.00 | |

With Personalized Photo at Right
Like Type A692a
Serpentine Die Cut 11½x11¼
Syncopated
| 4749 | A1078 | $1 multi | 2.50 | 2.50 |
| 4750 | A1079 | $1 multi | 2.50 | 2.50 |

Nos. 4749-4750 were each printed in sheets of 20 and have personalized pictures and a straight edge at right and lack separations between the stamp and the personalized photo. Sheets of 20 of Nos. 4749-4750 sold for $33 each.

Banksia
Flowers — A1080

Designs: Nos. 4751, 4755, 4759, Banksia speciosa. Nos. 4752, 4756, 4760, Banksia grossa. Nos. 4753, 4757, 4761, Baksia coccinea. Nos. 4754, 4758, 4762, Banksia cuneata.

2018, Feb. 20   Litho.   Perf. 14¾x14
4751	A1080	$1 multi	1.60	1.60
4752	A1080	$1 multi	1.60	1.60
4753	A1080	$1 multi	1.60	1.60
4754	A1080	$1 multi	1.60	1.60
a.		Souvenir sheet of 4, #4751-4754	6.50	6.50
		Nos. 4751-4754 (4)	6.40	6.40

Booklet Stamps
Self-Adhesive
Serpentine Die Cut 11¼ Syncopated
4755	A1080	$1 multi	1.60	.25
4756	A1080	$1 multi	1.60	.25
4757	A1080	$1 multi	1.60	.25
4758	A1080	$1 multi	1.60	.25
a.		Booklet pane of 20, 5 each #4755-4758	32.00	
		Nos. 4755-4758 (4)	6.40	1.00

With Personalized Photo at Right
Like Type A692a
Serpentine Die Cut 11½x11¼
Syncopated
4759	A1080	$1 multi	2.50	2.50
4760	A1080	$1 multi	2.50	2.50
4761	A1080	$1 multi	2.50	2.50
4762	A1080	$1 multi	2.50	2.50
		Nos. 4759-4762 (4)	10.00	10.00

Nos. 4759-4762 were each printed in sheets of 20 and have personalized pictures and a straight edge at right and lack separations between the stamp and the personalized photo. Sheets of 20 of Nos. 4759-4762 sold for $33 each.

19th and 20th
Century Jam Can
Labels — A1081

Label for: Nos. 4763, 4767, Kingurli Prince Engelbert Plum Jam. Nos. 4764, 4768, Peacock's Apricot Jam. Nos. 4765, 4769, Melray Blackberry Jam. Nos. 4766, 4770, Alva Dark Plum Jam.

2018, Mar. 6   Litho.   Perf. 14¾x14
4763	A1081	$1 multi	1.60	1.60
4764	A1081	$1 multi	1.60	1.60
4765	A1081	$1 multi	1.60	1.60
4766	A1081	$1 multi	1.60	1.60
		Nos. 4763-4766 (4)	6.40	6.40

Booklet Stamps
Self-Adhesive
Serpentine Die Cut 11¼ Syncopated
4767	A1081	$1 multi	1.60	.25
a.		Booklet pane of 10	16.00	
4768	A1081	$1 multi	1.60	.25
a.		Booklet pane of 10	16.00	
4769	A1081	$1 multi	1.60	.25
a.		Booklet pane of 10	16.00	
4770	A1081	$1 multi	1.60	.25
a.		Booklet pane of 10	16.00	
		Nos. 4767-4770 (4)	6.40	1.00

Finches
A1082

Designs: Nos. 4771, 4775, Blue-faced parrot-finch. Nos. 4772, 4776, Double-barred finches. Nos. 4773, 4777, Star finches. Nos. 4774, 4778, Zebra finches.

2018, Mar. 16   Litho.   Perf. 14x14¾
4771	A1082	$1 multi	1.60	1.60
4772	A1082	$1 multi	1.60	1.60
4773	A1082	$1 multi	1.60	1.60
4774	A1082	$1 multi	1.60	1.60
		Nos. 4771-4774 (4)	6.40	6.40

Self-Adhesive
Serpentine Die Cut 11¼ Syncopated
4775	A1082	$1 multi	1.60	.25
4776	A1082	$1 multi	1.60	.25
4777	A1082	$1 multi	1.60	.25
4778	A1082	$1 multi	1.60	.25
a.		Horiz. coil strip of 4, #4775-4778	6.40	
b.		Booklet pane of 10, 3 each #4775-4776, 2 each #4777-4778	16.00	
		Nos. 4775-4778 (4)	6.40	1.00

See Nos. 4811-4813.

2018
Commonwealth
Games, Gold Coast,
Queensland
A1083

2018, Mar. 20   Litho.   Perf. 14¾x14
| 4779 | A1083 | $1 multi | 1.60 | 1.25 |

War
Memorials
A1084

Poppies, silhouette of soldier and: Nos. 4780, 4788, Legacy Memorial, Melbourne. Nos. 4781, 4785, Avenue of Honor, Ballarat. Nos. 4782, 4789, Cobbers Statue, Fromelles, France. Nos. 4783, 4787, Cenotaph, Darwin. Nos. 4784, 4786, Tomb of the Unknown Australian Soldier, Canberra.

2018, Apr. 10   Litho.   Perf. 14¼
4780	A1084	$1 multi	1.50	1.50
a.		Booklet pane of 4	7.50	—
4781	A1084	$1 multi	1.50	1.50
a.		Booklet pane of 4	7.50	—
4782	A1084	$1 multi	1.50	1.50
a.		Booklet pane of 4	7.50	—
4783	A1084	$1 multi	1.50	1.50
a.		Booklet pane of 4	7.50	—
4784	A1084	$1 multi	1.50	1.50
a.		Booklet pane of 4 Complete booklet, #4780a, 4781a, 4782a, 4783a, 4784a	7.50	—
			31.50	
b.		Souvenir sheet of 5, #4780-4784	7.50	7.50
		Nos. 4780-4784 (5)	7.50	7.50

Booklet Stamps
Self-Adhesive
Serpentine Die Cut 11¼ Syncopated
4785	A1084	$1 multi	1.50	.25
4786	A1084	$1 multi	1.50	.25
4787	A1084	$1 multi	1.50	.25
4788	A1084	$1 multi	1.50	.25
4789	A1084	$1 multi	1.50	.25
a.		Booklet pane of 10, 2 each #4785-4789	15.00	
		Nos. 4785-4789 (5)	7.50	1.25

Complete booklet sold for $20.95.

Queen Elizabeth II,
92nd
Birthday — A1085

Queen Elizabeth II: $1, And Queen Elizabeth rose. $3, Holding bouquet of flowers.

2018, Apr. 17   Litho.   Perf. 14¾x14
4790	A1085	$1 multi	1.50	1.50
4791	A1085	$3 multi	4.50	2.25
a.		Souvenir sheet of 2, #4790-4791	6.00	3.75

Booklet Stamps
Self-Adhesive
Serpentine Die Cut 11¼ Syncopated
4792	A1085	$1 multi	1.50	.25
a.		Booklet pane of 10	15.00	
4793	A1085	$3 multi	4.50	2.25
a.		Booklet pane of 5	22.50	

1868
Aboriginal XI
Cricket Team
A1086

2018, May 1   Litho.   Perf. 14x14¾
| 4794 | A1086 | $1 multi | 1.50 | 1.10 |

First overseas tour of an Australian cricket team, 150th anniv.

Clouds
A1087

Cloud type: Nos. 4795, 4799, Lenticularis. Nos. 4796, 4800, Mammatus. Nos. 4797, 4801, Cumulonimbus. Nos. 4798, 4802, Arcus.

2018, May 1   Litho.   Perf. 14¼x14
4795	A1087	$1 multi	1.50	1.50
4796	A1087	$1 multi	1.50	1.50
4797	A1087	$1 multi	1.50	1.50
4798	A1087	$1 multi	1.50	1.50
a.		Souvenir sheet of 4, #4795-4798	6.00	6.00
		Nos. 4795-4798 (4)	6.00	6.00

Booklet Stamps
Self-Adhesive
Serpentine Die Cut 11¼ Syncopated
4799	A1087	$1 multi	1.50	.25
a.		Booklet pane of 10	15.00	
4800	A1087	$1 multi	1.50	.25
a.		Booklet pane of 10	15.00	
4801	A1087	$1 multi	1.50	.25
a.		Booklet pane of 10	15.00	
4802	A1087	$1 multi	1.50	.25
a.		Booklet pane of 10	15.00	
		Nos. 4799-4802 (4)	6.00	1.00

Silo
Art — A1088

Silo from: Nos. 4803, 4807, Brim, Victoria. Nos. 4804, 4808, Ravensthorpe, Western

Australia. Nos. 4805, 4809, Thallon, Queensland. Nos. 4806, 4810, Weethalle, New South Wales.

2018, May 21   Litho.   Perf. 14x14¾
4803	A1088	$1 multi	1.50	1.50
4804	A1088	$1 multi	1.50	1.50
a.		Booklet pane of 4, 2 each #4803, 4804	6.25	—
4805	A1088	$1 multi	1.50	1.50
a.		Booklet pane of 4, 2 each #4803, 4805	6.25	—
4806	A1088	$1 multi	1.50	1.50
a.		Booklet pane of 4, #4803-4806	6.25	—
b.		Booklet pane of 4, #4804, 4806	6.25	—
c.		Booklet pane of 4, 2 each #4805, 4806	6.25	—
		Complete booklet, #4804a, 4805a, 4806a, 4806b, 4806c	31.50	
d.		Souvenir sheet of 4, #4803-4806	6.00	6.00
		Nos. 4803-4806 (4)	6.00	6.00

Booklet Stamps
Self-Adhesive
Serpentine Die Cut 11¼ Syncopated
4807	A1088	$1 multi	1.50	.25
a.		Booklet pane of 10	15.00	
4808	A1088	$1 multi	1.50	.25
a.		Booklet pane of 10	15.00	
4809	A1088	$1 multi	1.50	.25
a.		Booklet pane of 10	15.00	
4810	A1088	$1 multi	1.50	.25
a.		Booklet pane of 10	15.00	
		Nos. 4807-4810 (4)	6.00	1.00

Complete booklet sold for $20.95.

Finches Type of 2018

Designs: No. 4811, Gouldian finches. No. 4812, Beautiful firetail. $2, Black-throated finches.

2018, June 5   Litho.   Perf. 14x13¾
4811	A1082	$1 multi	1.50	1.10
4812	A1082	$1 multi	1.50	1.10
4813	A1082	$2 multi	3.00	2.25
a.		Souvenir sheet of 3, #4811-4813	6.00	4.50
		Nos. 4811-4813 (3)	6.00	4.45

Art in Nature — A1089

Aerial photographs of: Nos. 4814, 4818, 4819, Shark Bay, Western Australia. Nos. 4815, 4819, Lake MacDonnell, South Australia. Nos. 4816, 4820, Wyadup Rocks, Western Australia. Nos. 4817, 4821, Cape Capricorn, Queensland.

2018, June 12   Litho.   Perf. 14½x14
4814	A1089	$1 multi	1.50	1.50
4815	A1089	$1 multi	1.50	1.50
4816	A1089	$1 multi	1.50	1.50
4817	A1089	$1 multi	1.50	1.50
a.		Souvenir sheet of 4, #4814-4817	6.00	6.00
		Nos. 4814-4817 (4)	6.00	6.00

Booklet Stamps
Self-Adhesive
Serpentine Die Cut 10¾x11
Syncopated
4818	A1089	$1 multi	1.50	.25
a.		Booklet pane of 10	15.00	
4819	A1089	$1 multi	1.50	.25
a.		Booklet pane of 10	15.00	
4820	A1089	$1 multi	1.50	.25
a.		Booklet pane of 10	15.00	
4821	A1089	$1 multi	1.50	.25
a.		Booklet pane of 10	15.00	
		Nos. 4818-4821 (4)	6.00	1.00

Birth of Prince
Louis of
Cambridge
A1090

2018, July 3   Litho.   Perf. 14¼
| 4822 | A1090 | $1 multi | 1.50 | 1.10 |

Frogs
A1091

Designs: No. 4823, Armored mist frog. No. 4824, Australian lace-lid. No. 4825, Baw baw frog. No. 4826, Tasmanian tree frog.

2018, July 10   Litho.   Perf. 14x14¾

4823	A1091	$1 multi	1.50	1.10
4824	A1091	$1 multi	1.50	1.10
4825	A1091	$1 multi	1.50	1.10
4826	A1091	$1 multi	1.50	1.10
a.		Souvenir sheet of 4, #4823-4826	6.00	4.50
		Nos. 4823-4826 (4)	6.00	4.40

Reef Animals
A1092

Designs: Nos. 4827, 4832a, 4833, Nautilus. Nos. 4828, 4832b, 4834, Green sea turtle. Nos. 4829, 4832c, 4835, Olive sea snake. Nos. 4830, 4832d, 4836, Emperor angelfish. Nos. 4831, 4832e, Gray reef shark (50x30mm).

Perf. 14x14¾, 14¼x14 (#4431, 4432e)

2018, Aug. 1   Litho.
Stamps With White Frames on Two Sides

4827	A1092	$1 multi	1.50	1.50
a.		Booklet pane of 4	6.25	—
4828	A1092	$1 multi	1.50	1.50
a.		Booklet pane of 4	6.25	—
4829	A1092	$1 multi	1.50	1.50
a.		Booklet pane of 4	6.25	—
4830	A1092	$1 multi	1.50	1.50
a.		Booklet pane of 4	6.25	—
4831	A1092	$2 multi	3.00	3.00
a.		Booklet pane of 2	6.25	—
		Complete booklet, #4827a, 4828a, 4829a, 4830a, 4831a	31.50	
		Nos. 4827-4831 (5)	9.00	9.00

Souvenir Sheet
Stamps Without White Frames

4832		Sheet of 5	9.00	6.75
a.-d.	A1092	$1 Any single	1.50	1.10
e.	A1092	$2 multi	3.00	2.25

Booklet Stamps
Self-Adhesive
Stamps With White Frames on Two Sides

Serpentine Die Cut 11¼ Syncopated

4833	A1092	$1 multi	1.50	.25
4834	A1092	$1 multi	1.50	.25
4835	A1092	$1 multi	1.50	.25
4836	A1092	$1 multi	1.50	.25
a.		Booklet pane of 10, 3 each #4833-4834, 2 each #4835-4836	15.00	
b.		Booklet pane of 20, 5 each #4833-4836	30.00	
		Nos. 4833-4836 (4)	6.00	1.00

Complete booklet sold for $20.95.

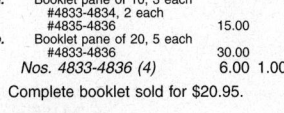

Winx, Winner of 27 Consecutive Stakes Races
A1093

2018, Aug. 18   Litho.   Perf. 14x14¾

4837	A1093	$1 multi	1.50	1.50

Booklet Stamp
Self-Adhesive

Serpentine Die Cut 11¼ Syncopated

4838	A1093	$1 multi	1.50	.25
a.		Booklet pane of 10	15.00	

Illustrations From Children's Novels About the Australian Bush
A1094

Illustration from: No. 4839, *The Magic Pudding*, by Norman Lindsay. No. 4840, *Tales of Snugglepot and Cuddlepie: Their Adventures Wonderful*, by May Gibbs.

2018, Aug. 21   Litho.   Perf. 14x14¾

4839	A1094	$1 multi	1.50	1.10
4840	A1094	$1 multi	1.50	1.10
a.		Souvenir sheet of 2, #4839-4840	3.00	2.25

Motorcycles
A1095

Designs: Nos. 4841, 4845, 4849, 1904 Kelecom. Nos. 4842, 4846, 4850, 1912 The Precision. Nos. 4843, 4847, 4851, 1919 Whiting V4. Nos. 4844, 4848, 4852, 1923 Invincible J.A.P.

2018, Sept. 4   Litho.   Perf. 14x14¾

4841	A1095	$1 multi	1.50	1.50
a.		Booklet pane of 4	6.00	
4842	A1095	$1 multi	1.50	1.50
a.		Booklet pane of 4	6.00	
4843	A1095	$1 multi	1.50	1.50
a.		Booklet pane of 4	6.00	
4844	A1095	$1 multi	1.50	1.50
a.		Booklet pane of 4	6.00	—
b.		Booklet pane of 4, #4841-4844	6.00	
		Complete booklet, #4841a, 4842a, 4843a, 4844a, 4844b	30.00	
		Nos. 4841-4844 (4)	6.00	6.00

Booklet Stamps
Self-Adhesive

Serpentine Die Cut 11¼ Syncopated

4845	A1095	$1 multi	1.50	.25
a.		Booklet pane of 10	15.00	
4846	A1095	$1 multi	1.50	.25
a.		Booklet pane of 10	15.00	
4847	A1095	$1 multi	1.50	.25
a.		Booklet pane of 10	15.00	
4848	A1095	$1 multi	1.50	.25
a.		Booklet pane of 10	15.00	
		Nos. 4845-4848 (4)	6.00	1.00

Typo.
Coil Stamps

4849	A1095	$1 multi	1.50	.25
4850	A1095	$1 multi	1.50	.25
4851	A1095	$1 multi	1.50	.25
4852	A1095	$1 multi	1.50	.25
a.		Horiz. strip of 4, #4849-4852	6.00	
		Nos. 4849-4852 (4)	6.00	1.00

Complete booklet sold for $20.95. Typographed coil stamps have larger dots in images than lithographed booklet stamps.

Items Starting With Same Letter Type of 2016

Designs: Nos. 4853, 4858, Emu, egg. echidna, Eureka flag. Nos. 4854, 4859, Organ, obelisk, oar, oven, octopus, owl, oil heater, oilskin coat, opal opera house. Nos. 4855, 4860, X-ray, xylophone, Xanthorrhea grass tree. XXXX beer, Xerox machine. Nos. 4856, 4861, Yacht, yo-yo, yowie, yabbies (crawfish). Nos. 4857, 4862, Zombie on zebra crossing (crosswalk), zoologist, zebra finches.

2018, Sept. 18   Litho.   Perf. 14¾x14

4853	A1028	$1 multi	1.50	1.50
4854	A1028	$1 multi	1.50	1.50
4855	A1028	$1 multi	1.50	1.50
4856	A1028	$1 multi	1.50	1.50
4857	A1028	$1 multi	1.50	1.50
		Nos. 4853-4857 (5)	7.50	7.50

Booklet Stamps
Self-Adhesive

Serpentine Die Cut 11¼ Syncopated

4858	A1028	$1 multi	1.50	.25
a.		Booklet pane of 10	15.00	
4859	A1028	$1 multi	1.50	.25
a.		Booklet pane of 10	15.00	
4860	A1028	$1 multi	1.50	.25
a.		Booklet pane of 10	15.00	
4861	A1028	$1 multi	1.50	.25
a.		Booklet pane of 10	15.00	
4862	A1028	$1 multi	1.50	.25
a.		Booklet pane of 10	15.00	
		Nos. 4858-4862 (5)	7.50	1.25

Farmers Inspecting Parched Land —
A1095a

Serpentine Die Cut 11¼ Syncopated
2018, Sept. 20   Litho.
Booklet Stamp
Self-Adhesive

4862B	A1095a	$1 multi	1.50	.75
c.		Booklet pane of 5	7.50	

With the sale of each booklet pane of No. 4862Bc, Australia Post donated $2 to Rural Aid Limited to provide drought assistance to farms and communities.

Australian Cities — A1096

Designs: $3, Melbourne. $4.60, Adelaide. $7.50, Brisbane.

2018, Sept. 25   Litho.   Perf. 14¼x14

4863	A1096	$3 multi	4.50	4.50
4864	A1096	$4.60 multi	6.75	3.50
4865	A1096	$7.50 multi	11.00	5.50
		Nos. 4863-4865 (3)	22.25	13.50

Booklet Stamp
Self-Adhesive

Serpentine Die Cut 10¾x11 Syncopated

4866	A1096	$3 multi	4.50	2.25
a.		Booklet pane of 5	22.50	

See Nos. 5011-5013.

World War I, Cent. — A1097

Poppy and: Nos. 4867, 4872, Soldiers resting in last hundred days of war. Nos. 4868, 4873, Lieutenant General Sir John Monash (1865-1931). Nos. 4869, 4874, Armistice declaration. Nos. 4870, 4875, Australian women awaiting return of troops. Nos. 4871, 4876, Children honoring fallen soldiers at cemetery.

2018, Oct. 2   Litho.   Perf. 14¼

4867	A1097	$1 multi	1.50	1.50
4868	A1097	$1 multi	1.50	1.50
4869	A1097	$1 multi	1.50	1.50
4870	A1097	$1 multi	1.50	1.50
a.		Booklet pane of 4, #4867-4870	6.00	—
4871	A1097	$1 multi	1.50	1.50
a.		Booklet pane of 4, #4868-4871	6.00	—
b.		Booklet pane of 4, #4867, 4869-4871	6.00	—
c.		Booklet pane of 4, #4867-4868, 4870-4871	6.00	—
d.		Booklet pane of 4, #4867-4869, 4871	6.00	—
		Complete booklet, #4870a, 4871a, 4871b, 4871c, 4871d	30.00	
e.		Souvenir sheet of 5, #4867-4871	7.50	7.50
		Nos. 4867-4871 (5)	7.50	7.50

Booklet Stamps
Self-Adhesive

Serpentine Die Cut 11¼ Syncopated

4872	A1097	$1 multi	1.50	.25
4873	A1097	$1 multi	1.50	.25
4874	A1097	$1 multi	1.50	.25
4875	A1097	$1 multi	1.50	.25
4876	A1097	$1 multi	1.50	.25
a.		Booklet pane of 10, 2 each #4872-4876	15.00	
		Nos. 4872-4876 (5)	7.50	1.25

Complete booklet sold for $20.95.

Wedding of Prince Harry and Meghan Markle
A1098

2018, Oct. 2   Litho.   Perf. 14¼

4877	A1098	$1 multi	1.50	1.10

Veteran
A1099

Two Veterans
A1100

2018, Oct. 23   Litho.   Perf. 14¾x14

4878	A1099	$1 multi	1.50	1.10
4879	A1100	$1 multi	1.50	1.10
a.		Pair, #4878-4879	3.00	2.25

Repatriation of veterans by Department of Veterans' Affairs, cent.

Lighthouses Near Sydney
A1101

Designs: Nos. 4880, 4883, Hornby Lighthouse. Nos. 4881, 4884, Robertsons Point Lighthouse. Nos. 4882, 4885, Macquarie Lighthouse.

2018, Oct. 23   Litho.   Perf. 14x14¾

4880	A1101	$1 multi	1.50	1.50
4881	A1101	$1 multi	1.50	1.50
4882	A1101	$1 multi	1.50	1.50
a.		Booklet pane of 4, #4881-4882, 2 #4880	6.00	—
b.		Booklet pane of 4, #4880, 4882, 2 #4881	6.00	—
c.		Booklet pane of 4, #4880-4881, 2 #4882 (#4480 at UR)	6.00	—
d.		Booklet pane of 4, 2 each #4880-4881	6.00	—
e.		Booklet pane of 4, #4880-4881, 2 #4882 (#4480 at UL)	6.00	—
		Complete booklet, #4882a, 4882b, 4882c, 4882d, 4882e	30.00	
f.		Souvenir sheet of 3, #4880-4882	4.50	4.50
		Nos. 4880-4882 (3)	4.50	4.50

Self-Adhesive

Serpentine Die Cut 11¼ Syncopated

4883	A1101	$1 multi	1.50	.25
4884	A1101	$1 multi	1.50	.25
4885	A1101	$1 multi	1.50	.25
a.		Horiz. coil strip of 3, #4883-4885	4.50	
b.		Booklet pane of 10, 4 #4883, 3 each #4884-4885	15.00	
		Nos. 4883-4885 (3)	4.50	.75

Complete booklet sold for $20.95.

Christmas
A1102   A1103

Designs: Nos. 4886, 4891, Madonna and Child. Nos. 4887, 4892, 4896, "Jingle Bells" and bell. Nos. 4888, 4893, 4897, "Glad Tidings" and Christmas tree. $2, "Noel" and star. $2.30, Angels.

2018, Nov. 1   Litho.   Perf. 14¾x14

4886	A1102	65c multi	.95	.95
4887	A1103	65c multi	.95	.95
4888	A1103	65c multi	.95	.95
a.		Horiz. pair, #4887-4888	1.90	1.90
4889	A1103	$2 multi	3.00	3.00
4890	A1102	$2.30 multi	3.50	3.50
a.		Souvenir sheet of 2, #4886, 4890	4.50	4.50
		Nos. 4886-4890 (5)	9.35	9.35

Booklet Stamps
Self-Adhesive

Serpentine Die Cut 11¼ Syncopated

4891	A1102 65c multi	.95	.25
a.	Booklet pane of 20 + 20 et-iquettes	19.00	
4892	A1103 65c multi	.95	.25
4893	A1103 65c multi	.95	.25
a.	Booklet pane of 20, 10 each #4892-4893, + 20 etiquettes	19.00	
4894	A1103 $2 multi	3.00	1.50
a.	Booklet pane of 5	15.00	
4895	A1102 $2.30 multi	3.50	1.75
a.	Booklet pane of 5	17.50	

Litho. With Foil Application

4896	A1103 65c multi	.95	.25
a.	Booklet pane of 10 + 10 et-iquettes	9.50	
4897	A1103 65c multi	.95	.25
a.	Booklet pane of 10 + 10 et-iquettes	9.50	
	Nos. 4891-4897 (7)	11.25	4.50

Writers of
Children's
Books and
Their Works
A1104

Designs: Nos. 4903, 4908, Mem Fox, *Where is the Green Sheep?* Nos. 4904, 4909, Morris Gleitzman, *Once.* Nos. 4905, 4910, Leigh Hobbs, *Mr. Chicken Goes to Paris.* Nos. 4906, 4911, Alison Lester, *Magic Beach.* Nos. 4907, 4912, Shaun Tan, *The Lost Thing.*

2019, Jan. 17   Litho.   Perf. 14x14¾

4903	A1104 $1 multi	1.50	1.50
4904	A1104 $1 multi	1.50	1.50
4905	A1104 $1 multi	1.50	1.50
4906	A1104 $1 multi	1.50	1.50
4907	A1104 $1 multi	1.50	1.50
	Nos. 4903-4907 (5)	7.50	7.50

Booklet Stamps
Self-Adhesive

Serpentine Die Cut 11¼ Syncopated

4908	A1104 $1 multi	1.50	.25
a.	Booklet pane of 10	15.00	
4909	A1104 $1 multi	1.50	.25
a.	Booklet pane of 10	15.00	
4910	A1104 $1 multi	1.50	.25
a.	Booklet pane of 10	15.00	
4911	A1104 $1 multi	1.50	.25
a.	Booklet pane of 10	15.00	
4912	A1104 $1 multi	1.50	.25
a.	Booklet pane of 10	15.00	
	Nos. 4908-4912 (5)	7.50	1.25

Wedding
Rings — A1105

Bird Carrying
Flower — A1106

Roses — A1107

Decorated
Cake — A1108

Teddy Bear
A1109

Party Balloons
A1110

Sparkler
A1111

White Rose
A1112

2019, Feb. 5   Litho.   Perf. 14¾x14

4913	A1105 $1 multi	1.50	1.50
4914	A1106 $1 multi	1.50	1.50
4915	A1107 $1 multi	1.50	1.50
4916	A1108 $1 multi	1.50	1.50
4917	A1109 $1 multi	1.50	1.50
4918	A1110 $1 multi	1.50	1.50
4919	A1111 $1 multi	1.50	1.50
4920	A1112 $2 multi	3.00	3.00
	Nos. 4913-4920 (8)	13.50	13.50

Booklet Stamps
Self-Adhesive

Serpentine Die Cut 11¼ Syncopated

4921	A1105 $1 multi	1.50	.25
a.	Booklet pane of 10	15.00	
4922	A1106 $1 multi	1.50	.25
a.	Booklet pane of 10	15.00	
4923	A1107 $1 multi	1.50	.25
a.	Booklet pane of 10	15.00	
4924	A1108 $1 multi	1.50	.25
a.	Booklet pane of 10	15.00	
4925	A1109 $1 multi	1.50	.25
a.	Booklet pane of 10	15.00	
4926	A1110 $1 multi	1.50	.25
a.	Booklet pane of 10	15.00	
4927	A1111 $1 multi	1.50	.25
a.	Booklet pane of 10	15.00	
4928	A1112 $2 multi	3.00	1.50
a.	Booklet pane of 4	12.00	
	Complete booklet, 4 #4928a	48.00	
	Nos. 4921-4928 (8)	13.50	3.25

With Personalized Photo at Right
Like Type A692a

Serpentine Die Cut 11½x11¼ Syncopated

4929	A1105 $1 multi	2.40	2.40
4930	A1106 $1 multi	2.40	2.40
4931	A1107 $1 multi	2.40	2.40
4932	A1108 $1 multi	2.40	2.40
4933	A1109 $1 multi	2.40	2.40
4934	A1110 $1 multi	2.40	2.40
4935	A1111 $1 multi	2.40	2.40

Complete booklet sold for $32.95 and contains four examples of No. 4928a with different pane margins.

An additional stamp was issued in this set. The editors would like to see any example of it.

Nos. 4929-4935 were each printed in sheets of 20 and have personalized pictures and a straight edge at right and lack separations between the stamp and the personalized photo. Sheets of 20 of Nos. 4929-4935 sold for $33 each.

Boyd House II, South Yarra, Victoria,
Designed by Robin Boyd (1919-71)
A1113

2019, Feb. 12   Litho.   Perf. 14x14¾

4937	A1113 $1 multi	1.40	1.10

Discovery of
Welcome
Stranger
Gold
Nugget,
150th Anniv.
A1114

WELCOME
STRANGER
DISCOVERED
1869

2019, Feb. 26   Litho.   Perf. 14x14¾

4938	A1114 $1 multi	1.40	1.10

Booklet Stamp
Self-Adhesive

Serpentine Die Cut 11¼ Syncopated

4939	A1114 $1 multi	1.40	.25
a.	Booklet pane of 20	28.00	

Australian
Animals
A1115

Designs: Nos. 4940, 4944, Galah. Nos. 4941, 4945, Red kangaroo. Nos. 4942, 4946, Tasmanian devil. Nos. 4943, 4947, Blue-tongue lizard.

2019, Mar. 5   Litho.   Perf. 14x14¾

4940	A1115 $1 multi	1.40	1.40
4941	A1115 $1 multi	1.40	1.40
4942	A1115 $1 multi	1.40	1.40
4943	A1115 $1 multi	1.40	1.40
	Nos. 4940-4943 (4)	5.60	5.60

Self-Adhesive

Serpentine Die Cut 11¼ Syncopated

4944	A1115 $1 multi	1.40	.25
a.	Booklet pane of 10	14.00	
4945	A1115 $1 multi	1.40	.25
a.	Booklet pane of 10	14.00	
4946	A1115 $1 multi	1.40	.25
a.	Booklet pane of 10	14.00	
4947	A1115 $1 multi	1.40	.25
a.	Booklet pane of 10	14.00	
b.	Hoirz. coil strip of 4, #4944-4947	5.60	
	Nos. 4944-4947 (4)	5.60	1.00

Sustainable
Fish — A1116

Designs: Nos. 4948, 4951, Patagonian toothfish and fishing boat with bird exclusion device. Nos. 4949, 4952, Blue grenadier and fishing boat with seal excluder device. Nos. 4950, 4953, Tiger flathead and fishing boat with mesh net.

2019, Mar. 14   Litho.   Perf. 14¼

4948	A1116 $1 multi	1.50	1.50
4949	A1116 $1 multi	1.50	1.50
4950	A1116 $1 multi	1.50	1.50
a.	Souvenir sheet of 3, #4948-4950	4.50	4.50
	Nos. 4948-4950 (3)	4.50	4.50

Booklet Stamps
Self-Adhesive

Serpentine Die Cut 11¼ Syncopated

4951	A1116 $1 multi	1.50	.25
4952	A1116 $1 multi	1.50	.25
4953	A1116 $1 multi	1.50	.25
a.	Booklet pane of 10, 4 #4951, 3 each #4952-4953	15.00	
	Nos. 4951-4953 (3)	4.50	.75

Queen Elizabeth II, 93rd Birthday
A1117   A1118

2019, Apr. 9   Litho.   Perf. 14¾x14

4954	A1117 $1 multi	1.40	1.10
4955	A1118 $3 multi	4.25	4.25
a.	Souvenir sheet of 2, #4954-4955	5.75	5.75

Booklet Stamp
Self-Adhesive

Serpentine Die Cut 11¼ Syncopated

4956	A1118 $3 multi	4.25	2.10
a.	Booklet pane of 5	21.50	

ANZAC
Day — A1119

Cover of: $1, 1919 ANZAC Memorial Day souvenir program. $3, 1919 ANZAC Day souvenir program for Australian Depots in France.

2019, Apr. 16   Litho.   Perf. 14¾x14

4957	A1119 $1 blue & multi	1.40	1.40
4958	A1119 $3 red & multi	4.25	3.25
a.	Souvenir sheet of 2, #4957-4958	5.75	5.75

Booklet Stamp
Self-Adhesive

Serpentine Die Cut 11¼ Syncopated

4959	A1119 $1 blue & multi	1.40	.25
a.	Booklet pane of 20	28.00	

International
Year of
Indigenous
Languages
A1120

2019, Apr. 30   Litho.   Perf. 14x14¾

4960	A1120 $1 multi	1.40	1.10

A1121

Flightless
Birds
A1122

Designs: No. 4961, Emu. No. 4962, Southern cassowary. $2.30, Little penguin.

2019, May 7   Litho.   Perf. 14x14½

4961	A1121 $1 multi	1.40	1.10
4962	A1121 $1 multi	1.40	1.10
	Perf. 14x14¾		
4963	A1122 $2.30 multi	3.25	3.25

Booklet Stamp
Self-Adhesive

Serpentine Die Cut 11¼ Syncopated

4964	A1122 $2.30 multi	3.25	1.60
a.	Booklet pane of 5	16.50	

Native Bees
A1123

Designs: Nos. 4965, 4969, Green and gold nomia bee. Nos. 4966, 4970, Neon cuckoo bee. Nos. 4967, 4971, Wasp-mimic bee. Nos. 4968, 4972, Resin bee.

2019, May 14   Litho.   Perf. 14x14¾

4965	A1123 $1 multi	1.40	1.40
4966	A1123 $1 multi	1.40	1.40
4967	A1123 $1 multi	1.40	1.40
4968	A1123 $1 multi	1.40	1.40
	Nos. 4965-4968 (4)	5.60	5.60

Booklet Stamps
Self-Adhesive

Serpentine Die Cut 11¼ Syncopated

4969	A1123 $1 multi	1.40	.25
a.	Booklet pane of 10	14.00	
4970	A1123 $1 multi	1.40	.25
a.	Booklet pane of 10	14.00	
4971	A1123 $1 multi	1.40	.25
a.	Booklet pane of 10	14.00	
4972	A1123 $1 multi	1.40	.25
a.	Booklet pane of 10	14.00	
	Nos. 4969-4972 (4)	5.60	1.00

Sports Stadiums
A1124

Designs: Nos. 4973, 4977, AAMI Park, Melbourne. Nos. 4974, 4978, Optus Stadium, Perth. Nos. 4975, 4979, Sydney Cricket Ground. No. 4976, 4980, Melbourne Cricket Ground.

2019, June 4   Litho.   Perf. 14x14¾

4973	A1124	$1 multi	1.40	1.40
4974	A1124	$1 multi	1.40	1.40
4975	A1124	$1 multi	1.40	1.40
4976	A1124	$1 multi	1.40	1.40
		Nos. 4973-4976 (4)	5.60	5.60

Booklet Stamps
Self-Adhesive

Serpentine Die Cut 11¼ Syncopated

4977	A1124	$1 multi	1.40	.25
a.		Booklet pane of 10	14.00	
4978	A1124	$1 multi	1.40	.25
a.		Booklet pane of 10	14.00	
4979	A1124	$1 multi	1.40	.25
a.		Booklet pane of 10	14.00	
4980	A1124	$1 multi	1.40	.25
a.		Booklet pane of 10	14.00	
		Nos. 4977-4980 (4)	5.60	1.00

Principle of Gender Pay Parity in Australia, 50th Anniv.
A1125

2019, June 18   Litho.   Perf. 14x14¾

4981	A1125	$1 multi	1.40	1.10

Crayfish
A1126

Designs: No. 4982, Cherax cainii. No. 4983, Astacopsis gouldi. No. 4984, Euastacus sulcatus.

2019, July 2   Litho.   Perf. 14x14¾

4982	A1126	$1 multi	1.40	1.10
4983	A1126	$1 multi	1.40	1.10
4984	A1126	$1 multi	1.40	1.10
		Nos. 4982-4984 (3)	4.20	3.30

First Man on the Moon, 50th Anniv. — A1127

Designs: Nos. 4985, 4990, Apollo 11 Lunar Module "Eagle". Nos. 4986, 4991, Parkes Radio Telescope, Parkes, New South Wales. Nos. 4987, 4992, First Moon walk. Nos. 4988, 4993, Telecast of moon walk via Honeysuckle Creek Tracking Station, Australian Capital Territory.

2019, July 16   Litho.   Perf. 14¾x14

4985	A1127	$1 multi	1.40	1.40
4986	A1127	$1 multi	1.40	1.40
4987	A1127	$1 multi	1.40	1.40
4988	A1127	$1 multi	1.40	1.40
		Nos. 4985-4988 (4)	5.60	5.60
4989		Souvenir sheet of 4, #4985, 4987, 4989a, 4989b	5.60	5.60
a.	A1127	$1 As #4986, Litho. with silver foil application	1.40	1.40
b.	A1127	$1 As #4988, Litho. with silver foil application	1.40	1.40

Self-Adhesive

Serpentine Die Cut 11¼ Syncopated

4990	A1127	$1 multi	1.40	.25
a.		Booklet pane of 10	14.00	
4991	A1127	$1 multi	1.40	.25
a.		Booklet pane of 10	14.00	
4992	A1127	$1 multi	1.40	.25
a.		Booklet pane of 10	14.00	

4993	A1127	$1 multi	1.40	.25
a.		Booklet pane of 10	14.00	
b.		Vert. coil strip of 4, #4990-4993	5.60	
		Nos. 4990-4993 (4)	5.60	1.00

Gardening
A1128

Designs: Nos. 4994, 4999, Rainwater garden. Nos. 4995, 5000, Worm farm. Nos. 4996, 5001, Nest box. Nos. 4997, 5002, Pollinators. $2, Vegetable garden.

2019, Aug. 1   Litho.   Perf. 14x14¾

4994	A1128	$1 multi	1.40	1.40
a.		Booklet pane of 4	5.75	
4995	A1128	$1 multi	1.40	1.40
a.		Booklet pane of 4	5.75	
4996	A1128	$1 multi	1.40	1.40
a.		Booklet pane of 4	5.75	

Size: 50x30mm
Perf. 14½x14

4997	A1128	$1 multi	1.40	1.40
a.		Booklet pane of 4	5.75	
4998	A1128	$2 multi	2.75	2.10
a.		Booklet pane of 2	5.75	—
		Complete booklet, #4994a, 4995a, 4996a, 4997a, 4998s	29.00	
b.		Souvenir sheet of 5, #4994-4998	8.50	7.75
		Nos. 4994-4998 (5)	8.35	7.70

Booklet Stamps
Self-Adhesive
Size: 38x26mm

Serpentine Die Cut 11¼ Syncopated

4999	A1128	$1 multi	1.40	.25
5000	A1128	$1 multi	1.40	.25
5001	A1128	$1 multi	1.40	.25
a.		Booklet pane of 20, 6 each #4999, 5001, 7 #5000	28.00	

Size: 50x30mm

Serpentine Die Cut 10¾ Syncopated

5002	A1128	$1 multi	1.40	.25
a.		Booklet pane of 10	14.00	
		Nos. 4999-5002 (4)	5.60	1.00

Complete booklet sold for $20.95.

Bush Citrus
A1129

Designs: Nos. 5003, 5006, Desert lime. Nos. 5004, 5007, Finger lime. Nos. 5005, 5008, Lemon aspen.

2019, Aug. 13   Litho.   Perf. 14x14¾

5003	A1129	$1 multi	1.40	1.40
5004	A1129	$1 multi	1.40	1.40
5005	A1129	$1 multi	1.40	1.40
a.		Souvenir sheet of 3, #5003-5005	4.25	4.25
		Nos. 5003-5005 (3)	4.20	4.20

Coil Stamps
Self-Adhesive

Serpentine Die Cut 11¼ Syncopated

5006	A1129	$1 multi	1.40	.25
5007	A1129	$1 multi	1.40	.25
5008	A1129	$1 multi	1.40	.25
a.		Horiz. coil strip of 3, #5006-5008	4.25	
		Nos. 5006-5008 (3)	4.20	.75

Fall to Earth of Murchison Meteorite, 50th Anniv. — A1130

2019, Sept. 10   Litho.   Perf. 14¾x14

5009	A1130	$1 multi	1.40	1.10

Animals Type of 2006

Design: $2.50, Greater bilby.

Serpentine Die Cut 11¼ Syncopated
2019, Sept. 23   Litho.

Booklet Stamp
Self-Adhesive

5010	A707	$2.50 multi	3.50	1.75
a.		Booklet pane of 5	17.50	

Australian Cities Type of 2018

Designs: $3.20, Sydney. $5, Perth.

2019, Sept. 23   Litho.   Perf. 14¼x14

5011	A1096	$3.20 multi	4.25	4.25
5012	A1096	$5 multi	6.75	3.00

Booklet Stamp
Self-Adhesive

Serpentine Die Cut 10¾x11 Syncopated

5013	A1096	$3.20 multi	4.25	2.10
a.		Booklet pane of 5	21.50	

Australian Team for 2019 The Ashes Test Cricket Series With Trophy
A1131

2019, Oct. 1   Litho.   Perf. 14¼

5014	A1131	$1 multi	1.40	1.10

Marriage Equality
A1132   A1133

2019, Oct. 1   Litho.   Perf. 14¾x14

5015	A1132	$1 multi	1.40	1.10
5016	A1133	$1 multi	1.40	1.10

Vickers Vimy and Crew — A1134

Label and Handstamp for First Great Britain to Australia Airmail Flight — A1135

2019, Oct. 1   Litho.   Perf. 14¾x14

5017	A1134	$1 multi	1.40	1.40
a.		Booklet pane of 4	5.75	
5018	A1135	$3.20 multi	4.25	4.25
a.		Booklet pane of 2	9.25	—
		Complete booklet, #5018a, 4 #5017a	32.50	
b.		Souvenir sheet of 2, #5017-5018	5.75	5.75

Booklet Stamps
Self-Adhesive

Serpentine Die Cut 11¼ Syncopated

5019	A1134	$1 multi	1.40	.25
a.		Booklet pane of 20	28.00	

Serpentine Die Cut 11¾x11½ Syncopated

5020	A1135	$3.20 multi	4.25	2.10
a.		Booklet pane of 5	21.50	—

First Great Britain-Australia airmail flight, captained by Ross Smith, cent. Complete booklet contains four examples of No. 5017a, each with different pane margins, and sold for $23.95.

Seeds of Endangered Plant Species in Seed Banks — A1136

Designs: Nos. 5021, 5024, Rytidosperma clelandii. Nos. 5022, 5025, Epacris petrophila. Nos. 5023, 5026, Petrophile latericola.

2019, Oct. 8   Litho.   Perf. 14¾x14

5021	A1136	$1 multi	1.40	1.40
5022	A1136	$1 multi	1.40	1.40
5023	A1136	$1 multi	1.40	1.40
		Nos. 5021-5023 (3)	4.20	4.20

Booklet Stamps
Self-Adhesive

Serpentine Die Cut 11¼ Syncopated

5024	A1136	$1 multi	1.40	.25
a.		Booklet pane of 10	14.00	
5025	A1136	$1 multi	1.40	.25
a.		Booklet pane of 10	14.00	
5026	A1136	$1 multi	1.40	.25
a.		Booklet pane of 10	14.00	
		Nos. 5024-5026 (3)	4.20	.75

Items Starting With Same Letter Type of 2016

Designs: Nos. 5027, 5033, Dog, digger, Daily News, dentures, dunny (outhouse). Nos. 5028, 5034, Father, fish in fish creel, fishing pole and gear, child with football. Nos. 5029, 5035, Housewife hanging laundry on Hills Hoist, hibiscus. Nos. 5030, 5036, Ibis, ironing board, ironman triathlete holding iron. Nos. 5031, 5037, Mechanic feeding macadamia nuts to mud crab, milk carton, mallet. Nos. 5032, 5038, Platypus eating peach and pineapple pavlova, presents, possum, python, pelican, picket fence.

2019, Oct. 22   Litho.   Perf. 14¾x14

5027	A1028	$1 multi	1.40	1.40
5028	A1028	$1 multi	1.40	1.40
5029	A1028	$1 multi	1.40	1.40
5030	A1028	$1 multi	1.40	1.40
5031	A1028	$1 multi	1.40	1.40
5032	A1028	$1 multi	1.40	1.40
a.		Souvenir sheet of 6, #5027-5032	8.50	8.50
		Nos. 5027-5032 (6)	8.40	8.40

Booklet Stamps
Self-Adhesive

Serpentine Die Cut 11¼ Syncopated

5033	A1028	$1 multi	1.40	.25
a.		Booklet pane of 10	14.00	
5034	A1028	$1 multi	1.40	.25
a.		Booklet pane of 10	14.00	
5035	A1028	$1 multi	1.40	.25
a.		Booklet pane of 10	14.00	
5036	A1028	$1 multi	1.40	.25
a.		Booklet pane of 10	14.00	
5037	A1028	$1 multi	1.40	.25
a.		Booklet pane of 10	14.00	
5038	A1028	$1 multi	1.40	.25
a.		Booklet pane of 10	14.00	
		Nos. 5033-5038 (6)	8.40	1.50

Christmas
A1137   A1138

Designs: Nos. 5039, 5044, 5051 Flight into Egypt. Nos. 5040, 5046, 5049, 5052, Christmas tree. Nos. 5041, 5045, 5050, Star. Nos. 5042, 5047, 5053, Adoration of the Magi. Nos. 5043, 5048, 5054, Christmas gift.

2019, Nov. 1   Litho.   Perf. 14¾x14

5039	A1137	65c multi	.90	.90
5040	A1138	65c multi	.90	.90
5041	A1138	65c multi	.90	.90
a.		Horiz. pair, #5040-5041	1.80	1.80
5042	A1137	$2.20 multi	3.00	3.00
a.		Souvenir sheet of 2, #5039, 5042	4.00	4.00
5043	A1138	$2.20 multi	3.00	3.00
		Nos. 5039-5043 (5)	8.70	8.70

Booklet Stamps
Self-Adhesive

Serpentine Die Cut 11¼ Syncopated

5044	A1137	65c multi	.90	.25
a.		Booklet pane of 20 + 20 et-iquettes	18.00	

5045	A1138	65c multi	.90	.25
5046	A1138	65c multi	.90	.25
a.		Booklet pane of 20, 10 each #5045-5046, + 20 etiquettes	18.00	
5047	A1137	$2.20 multi	3.00	1.50
a.		Booklet pane of 5	15.00	
5048	A1138	$2.20 multi	3.00	1.50
a.		Booklet pane of 5	15.00	

Litho. With Foil Application

5049	A1138	65c multi	.90	.25
a.		Booklet pane of 10 + 10 etiquettes	9.00	
5050	A1138	65c multi	.90	.25
a.		Booklet pane of 10 + 10 etiquettes	9.00	
		Nos. 5044-5050 (7)	10.50	4.25

With Personalized Photo at Right Like Type A692a
Litho.
Serpentine Die Cut 11½x11¼ Syncopated

5051	A1137	65c multi	2.00	2.00
5052	A1138	65c multi	2.00	2.00
5053	A1137	$2.20 multi	6.75	6.75
5054	A1138	$2.20 multi	6.75	6.75
		Nos. 5051-5054 (4)	17.50	17.50

Nos. 5051-5054 were each printed in sheets of 20 and have personalized pictures and a straight edge at right and lack separations between the stamp and the personalized photo. Sheets of 20 of Nos. 5051-5052 sold for $26 each, and sheets of 20 of Nos. 5053-5054 sold for $57 each.

On Dec. 16, 2019, Australia Post began issuing self-adhesive personalizable stamps in nine different shapes (Australia, speech bubble, teddy bear, heart, present, star, house, curved frame and decorative frame), with each shape available initially with six different denominations (65c, $1.10, $2.20, $3.30, $5.50, and $2.20 for international use). These stamps could only be purchased in sheets of 20.

Marsupials
A1139

Designs: Nos. 5055, 5059, Koala. Nos. 5056, 5060, Wombat. $2.20, Echidna, $3.30, Sugar glider.

2019, Dec. 16 Litho. Perf. 14x14¾

5055	A1139	$1.10 multi	1.60	1.60
5056	A1139	$1.10 multi	1.60	1.60
5057	A1139	$2.20 multi	3.25	1.60
5058	A1139	$3.30 multi	4.75	2.40
		Nos. 5055-5058 (4)	11.20	7.20

Self-Adhesive
Serpentine Die Cut 11¼ Syncopated

5059	A1139	$1.10 multi	1.60	.25
a.		Booklet pane of 10	16.00	
5060	A1139	$1.10 multi	1.60	.25
a.		Booklet pane of 20	32.00	
b.		Horiz. coil pair, #5059-5060	3.20	

Teddy Bear
A1140

Gifts — A1142

Party Balloons
A1141

"Let's Party!" — A1143

Flowers
A1144

Champagne Flutes
A1145

Bridal Bouquet
A1146

Map of Australia and Southern Cross Constellation
A1147

Kangaroo's Paw Flower and Southern Cross Constellation
A1148

Wedding Ring
A1149

2020, Jan. 2 Litho. Perf. 14¾x14

5061	A1140	$1.10 multi	1.60	1.60
5062	A1141	$1.10 multi	1.60	1.60
5063	A1142	$1.10 multi	1.60	1.60
5064	A1143	$1.10 multi	1.60	1.60
5065	A1144	$1.10 multi	1.60	1.60
5066	A1145	$1.10 multi	1.60	1.60
5067	A1146	$1.10 multi	1.60	1.60
5068	A1147	$1.10 multi	1.60	1.25
5069	A1148	$1.10 multi	1.60	1.25
5070	A1149	$2.20 multi	3.25	3.25
a.		Souvenir sheet of 10, #5061-5070	18.00	18.00
		Nos. 5061-5070 (10)	17.65	16.95

Booklet Stamps
Self-Adhesive
Serpentine Die Cut 11¼ Syncopated

5071	A1140	$1.10 multi	1.60	.25
a.		Booklet pane of 10 + 5 stickers	16.00	
5072	A1141	$1.10 multi	1.60	.25
a.		Booklet pane of 10 + 5 stickers	16.00	
5073	A1142	$1.10 multi	1.60	.25
a.		Booklet pane of 10 + 5 stickers	16.00	
5074	A1143	$1.10 multi	1.60	.25
a.		Booklet pane of 10 + 5 stickers	16.00	
5075	A1144	$1.10 multi	1.60	.25
a.		Booklet pane of 10 + 5 stickers	16.00	
5076	A1145	$1.10 multi	1.60	.25
a.		Booklet pane of 10 + 5 stickers	16.00	
5077	A1146	$1.10 multi	1.60	.25
a.		Booklet pane of 10 + 5 stickers	16.00	
5078	A1149	$2.20 multi	3.25	1.60
a.		Booklet pane of 4	13.00	
		Complete booklet, 4 #5078a	52.00	
		Nos. 5071-5078 (8)	14.45	3.35

Complete booklet sold for $35.95 and the four panes in it have different pane margins.

Designs: No. 5089, Bennett's tree kangaroo. No. 5090, Spectacled flying fox. No. 5091, Lemuroid ringtail possum.

2020, Jan. 21 Litho. Perf. 14¾x14

5089	A1150	$1.10 multi	1.50	1.10
5090	A1150	$1.10 multi	1.50	1.10
5091	A1150	$1.10 multi	1.50	1.10
a.		Souvenir sheet of 3, #5089-5091	4.50	3.50
		Nos. 5089-5091 (3)	4.50	3.30

Sports Broadcasters
A1151

Designs: No. 5092, Richie Benaud (1930-2015), cricket commentator. No. 5093, Reg Gasnier (1939-2014), rugby commentator. No. 5094, Les Murray (1945-2017), soccer commentator. $2.20, Lou Richards (1923-2017), Jack Dyer (1913-2003), and Bob Davis (1928-2011), Australia rules football commentators.

2020, Feb. 4 Litho. Perf. 14x14¾

5092	A1151	$1.10 multi	1.50	1.10
a.		Booklet pane of 4	6.00	
5093	A1151	$1.10 multi	1.50	1.10
a.		Booklet pane of 4	6.00	
5094	A1151	$1.10 multi	1.50	1.10
a.		Booklet pane of 4	6.00	

Size: 50x30mm
Perf. 14¼x14

5095	A1151	$2.20 multi	3.00	2.25
a.		Booklet pane of 2	6.00	—
		Complete booklet, #5092a, 5093a, 5094a, 3 #5095a	36.00	
		Nos. 5092-5095 (4)	7.50	5.55

Complete booklet sold for $26.95 and the three panes of No. 5095a in it have different pane margins.

Completion of Standard Gauge Transcontinental Rail Line, 50th Anniv. — A1152

2020, Feb. 11 Litho. Perf. 14x14¾

5096	A1152	$1.10 multi	1.50	1.50

Booklet Stamp
Self-Adhesive
Serpentine Die Cut 11¼ Syncopated

5097	A1152	$1.10 multi	1.50	.25
a.		Booklet pane of 20	30.00	

Medical Innovations — A1153

Designs: Nos. 5098, 5102, Human papillomavirus vaccine. Nos. 5099, 5103, Implanted cardiac pacemaker. Nos. 5100, 5104, Spray-on skin cells. $3.20, Medical use of penicillin.

2020, Feb. 18 Litho. Perf. 14¾x14

5098	A1153	$1.10 multi	1.50	1.50
5099	A1153	$1.10 multi	1.50	1.50
5100	A1153	$1.10 multi	1.50	1.50
5101	A1153	$3.20 multi	4.25	4.25
		Nos. 5098-5101 (4)	8.75	8.75

Booklet Stamps
Self-Adhesive
Serpentine Die Cut 11¼ Syncopated

5102	A1153	$1.10 multi	1.50	.25
5103	A1153	$1.10 multi	1.50	.25
5104	A1153	$1.10 multi	1.50	.25
a.		Booklet pane of 20, 8 #5102, 7 #5103, 5 #5104	30.00	
5105	A1153	$3.20 multi	4.25	2.10
a.		Booklet pane of 5	21.50	
		Nos. 5102-5105 (4)	8.75	2.85

S.S. Wonga Wonga
A1154

2020, Mar. 3 Litho. Perf. 14x14¾

5106	A1154	$1.10 multi	1.50	1.10

Mail steamer service between Sydney and San Francisco, 150th anniv.

Sports Stadiums
A1155

Designs: Nos. 5107, 5111, Rod Laver Arena, Melbourne. Nos. 5108, 5112, Adelaide Oval, Adelaide. Nos. 5109, 5113, Anne Meares Velodrome, Brisbane. Nos. 5110, 5114, Sydney Olympic Park Aquatic Center, Sydney.

2020, Mar. 24 Litho. Perf. 14x14¾

5107	A1155	$1.10 multi	1.40	1.40
5108	A1155	$1.10 multi	1.40	1.40
5109	A1155	$1.10 multi	1.40	1.40
5110	A1155	$1.10 multi	1.40	1.40
		Nos. 5107-5110 (4)	5.60	5.60

Self-Adhesive
Serpentine Die Cut 11¼ Syncopated

5111	A1155	$1.10 multi	1.40	.25
a.		Booklet pane of 10	14.00	
5112	A1155	$1.10 multi	1.40	.25
a.		Booklet pane of 10	14.00	
5113	A1155	$1.10 multi	1.40	.25
a.		Booklet pane of 10	14.00	
5114	A1155	$1.10 multi	1.40	.25
a.		Booklet pane of 10	14.00	
b.		Horiz. coil strip of 4, #5111-5114	5.60	
		Nos. 5111-5114 (4)	5.60	1.00

Queen Elizabeth II, 94th Birthday
A1156   A1157

2020, Apr. 7 Litho. Perf. 14¾x14

5115	A1156	$1.10 multi	1.40	1.10
5116	A1157	$3.20 multi	4.25	4.25
a.		Souvenir sheet of 2, #5115-5116	5.75	5.75

Booklet Stamp
Self-Adhesive
Serpentine Die Cut 11¼ Syncopated

5117	A1157	$3.20 multi	4.25	2.10
a.		Booklet pane of 5	21.50	

ANZAC Day — A1158

Paintings: Nos. 5118, 5122, The Sock Knitter, by Grace Cossington Smith (1892-1984). Nos. 5119, 5123, A Man, by Hilda Rix Nicholas (1884-1961). Nos. 5120, 5124, Group of VADS, by William Dargie (1912-2003). Nos. 5121, 5125, Bomber Crew, by Stella Bowen (1893-1947).

2020, Apr. 14 Litho. Perf. 14¾x14

5118	A1158	$1.10 multi	1.40	1.40
5119	A1158	$1.10 multi	1.40	1.40
5120	A1158	$1.10 multi	1.40	1.40
5121	A1158	$1.10 multi	1.40	1.40
a.		Souvenir sheet of 4, #5118-5121	5.75	5.75
		Nos. 5118-5121 (4)	5.60	5.60

Coil Stamps
Self-Adhesive

Serpentine Die Cut 11¼ Syncopated

5122	A1158	$1.10 multi	1.40	.25
5123	A1158	$1.10 multi	1.40	.25
5124	A1158	$1.10 multi	1.40	.25
5125	A1158	$1.10 multi	1.40	.25
a.		Vert. coil strip of 4, #5122-5125	5.60	
		Nos. 5122-5125 (4)	5.60	1.00

Comedians A1159

Designs: Nos. 5126, 5130, Noeline Brown. Nos. 5127, 5131, Adam Hills. Nos. 5128, 5132, Garry McDonald. Nos. 5129, 5133, Magda Szubanski.

2020, Apr. 15   Litho.   Perf. 14x14¾

5126	A1159	$1.10 multi	1.40	1.40
5127	A1159	$1.10 multi	1.40	1.40
5128	A1159	$1.10 multi	1.40	1.40
5129	A1159	$1.10 multi	1.40	1.40
		Nos. 5126-5129 (4)	5.60	5.60

Booklet Stamps
Self-Adhesive

Serpentine Die Cut 11¼ Syncopated

5130	A1159	$1.10 multi	1.40	.25
a.		Booklet pane of 10	14.00	
5131	A1159	$1.10 multi	1.40	.25
a.		Booklet pane of 10	14.00	
5132	A1159	$1.10 multi	1.40	.25
a.		Booklet pane of 10	14.00	
5133	A1159	$1.10 multi	1.40	.25
a.		Booklet pane of 10	14.00	
		Nos. 5130-5133 (4)	5.60	1.00

State and Territory Birds — A1160

Designs: Nos. 5134, 5140, Gang-gang cockatoo, Australian Capital Territory. Nos. 5135, 5141, Helmeted honeyeater, Victoria. Nos. 5136, 5142, Wedge-tailed eagle, Northern Territory. Nos. 5137, 5143, Laughing kookaburra, New South Wales. Nos. 5138, 5144, Brolga, Queensland. Nos. 5139, 5145, Black swan, Western Australia, horiz.

2020, Apr. 21   Litho.   Perf. 14¾x14

5134	A1160	$1.10 multi	1.40	1.40
5135	A1160	$1.10 multi	1.40	1.40
5136	A1160	$1.10 multi	1.40	1.40
5137	A1160	$1.10 multi	1.40	1.40
5138	A1160	$1.10 multi	1.40	1.40

Perf. 14x14¾

5139	A1160	$1.10 multi	1.40	1.40
		Nos. 5134-5139 (6)	8.40	8.40

Booklet Stamps
Self-Adhesive

Serpentine Die Cut 11¼ Syncopated

5140	A1160	$1.10 multi	1.40	.25
a.		Booklet pane of 10	14.00	
5141	A1160	$1.10 multi	1.40	.25
a.		Booklet pane of 10	14.00	
5142	A1160	$1.10 multi	1.40	.25
a.		Booklet pane of 10	14.00	
5143	A1160	$1.10 multi	1.40	.25
a.		Booklet pane of 10	14.00	
5144	A1160	$1.10 multi	1.40	.25
a.		Booklet pane of 10	14.00	
5145	A1160	$1.10 multi	1.40	.25
a.		Booklet pane of 10	14.00	
		Nos. 5140-5145 (6)	8.40	1.50

Miniature Sheet

First Pacific Voyage of the HMS Endeavour, 250th Anniv. — A1161

Nos. 5146 and 5147: a, Southern Cross constellation. b, HMS Endeavour. c, Silhouettes of indigenous Australians. d, Flower and needle. e, Map of Australian coast and Torres Strait Islands. f, Lieutenant James Cook using sextant. g, Map of Australia. h, Expedition member sitting. i, Naturalists Joseph Banks and Daniel Solander. j, Compass rose.

Perf. 14 Syncopated

2020, Apr. 29   Litho.

5146	A1161	Sheet of 10	7.00	7.00
a.-j.		55c Any single	.70	.70

Booklet Stamps
Self-Adhesive

Serpentine Die Cut 11¾ Syncopated on 3 Sides

5147	A1161	Booklet pane of 10	7.00	
a.-j.		55c Any single	.70	.25

Citizen Science A1162

Inscriptions: Nos. 5148, 5152, QuestaGame. Nos. 5149, 5153, Ngukurr Wi Stadi Bla Kantri (We study the country). Nos. 5150, 5154, Butterflies Australia. Nos. 5151, 5155, Zika Mozzie Seeker.

2020, May 19   Litho.   Perf. 14x14¾

5148	A1162	$1.10 multi	1.50	1.50
5149	A1162	$1.10 multi	1.50	1.50
5150	A1162	$1.10 multi	1.50	1.50
5151	A1162	$1.10 multi	1.50	1.50
		Nos. 5148-5151 (4)	6.00	6.00

Booklet Stamps
Self-Adhesive

Serpentine Die Cut 11¼ Syncopated

5152	A1162	$1.10 multi	1.50	.25
a.		Booklet pane of 10	15.00	
5153	A1162	$1.10 multi	1.50	.25
a.		Booklet pane of 10	15.00	
5154	A1162	$1.10 multi	1.50	.25
a.		Booklet pane of 10	15.00	
5155	A1162	$1.10 multi	1.50	.25
a.		Booklet pane of 10	15.00	
		Nos. 5152-5155 (4)	6.00	1.00

Art by Western Desert Aboriginals A1163

Designs: No. 5156, Milnga-Milnga, The Artist's Birthplace, by Boxer Milner (c.1935-2009). No. 5157, Tingarri Mamultjulkulakutu, by Fred Ward Tjungurrayi. No. 5158, Untitled painting by Eubena Nampitjin (c. 1925-2013). $2.20, Kangaroo Dreaming, by Walter Tjampitjinpa (c. 1912-81).

2020, June 9   Litho.   Perf. 14x14¼

5156	A1163	$1.10 multi	1.50	1.10
5157	A1163	$1.10 multi	1.50	1.10
5158	A1163	$1.10 multi	1.50	1.10
5159	A1163	$2.20 multi	3.00	3.00
		Nos. 5156-5159 (4)	7.50	6.30

Booklet Stamp
Self-Adhesive

Serpentine Die Cut 11x10¾ Syncopated

5160	A1163	$2.20 multi	3.00	1.50
a.		Booklet pane of 5	15.00	

Fashion Photography A1164

Photograph from: No. 5161, 1949, by Athol Shmith (1914-90). No. 5162, 1959, by Helmut Newton (1920-2004). No. 5163, 1960s, by Henry Talbot (1920-99). No. 5164, 1972, Bruno Benini (1925-2001).

2020, June 16   Litho.   Perf. 14¾x14

5161	A1164	$1.10 multi	1.50	1.10
5162	A1164	$1.10 multi	1.50	1.10
5163	A1164	$1.10 multi	1.50	1.10
5164	A1164	$1.10 multi	1.50	1.10
a.		Souvenir sheet of 4, #5161-5164	6.00	4.50
		Nos. 5161-5164 (4)	6.00	4.40

Royal Children's Hospital Melbourne, 150th Anniv. A1165

2020, July 7   Litho.   Perf. 14x14¾

5165	A1165	$1.10 multi	1.60	1.60

Booklet Stamp
Self-Adhesive

Serpentine Die Cut 11¼ Syncopated

5166	A1165	$1.10 multi	1.60	.25
a.		Booklet pane of 10	16.00	

Australian Alps A1166

Designs: Nos. 5167, 5170, Snow gum trees, Namadgi National Park, Australian Capital Territory. Nos. 5168, 5171, The Cathedral, Mount Buffalo National Park, Victoria. Nos. 5169, 5172, Swampy Plain River, Kosciuszko National Park, New South Wales.

2020, July 21   Litho.   Perf. 14x14¾

5167	A1166	$1.10 multi	1.60	1.60
5168	A1166	$1.10 multi	1.60	1.60
5169	A1166	$1.10 multi	1.60	1.60
a.		Souvenir sheet of 3, #5167-5169	4.80	4.80
		Nos. 5167-5169 (3)	4.80	4.80

Coil Stamps
Self-Adhesive

Serpentine Die Cut 11¼ Syncopated

5170	A1166	$1.10 multi	1.60	.25
5171	A1166	$1.10 multi	1.60	.25
5172	A1166	$1.10 multi	1.60	.25
a.		Horiz. strip of 3, #5170-5172	4.80	
		Nos. 5170-5172 (3)	4.80	.75

A1167

Wildlife Recovery — A1168

Animals severly affected by loss of habitat in Australian bushfires: Nos. 5173, 5179, Bathurst copper butterfly. Nos. 5174, 5180, Davies' tree frog. Nos. 5175, 5181, Kangaroo Island dunnart. Nos. 5176, 5182, Regent honeyeater. Nos. 5177, 5183, Blue Mountains water skink. No. 5178, Koala.

2020, Aug. 4   Litho.   Perf. 14x14¾

5173	A1167	$1.10 multi	1.60	1.60
5174	A1167	$1.10 multi	1.60	1.60
5175	A1167	$1.10 multi	1.60	1.60
5176	A1167	$1.10 multi	1.60	1.60
5177	A1167	$1.10 multi	1.60	1.60

Perf. 14¼x14

5178	A1168	$1.10 multi	1.60	1.60
a.		Souvenir sheet of 6, #5173-5178	9.75	9.75
		Nos. 5173-5178 (6)	9.60	9.60

Booklet Stamp
Self-Adhesive

Serpentine Die Cut 11¼ Syncopated

5179	A1167	$1.10 multi	1.60	.25
a.		Booklet pane of 10	16.00	
5180	A1167	$1.10 multi	1.60	.25
a.		Booklet pane of 10	16.00	
5181	A1167	$1.10 multi	1.60	.25
a.		Booklet pane of 10	16.00	
5182	A1167	$1.10 multi	1.60	.25
a.		Booklet pane of 10	16.00	
5183	A1167	$1.10 multi	1.60	.25
a.		Booklet pane of 10	16.00	
		Nos. 5179-5183 (5)	8.00	1.25

Princes Highway, Cent. — A1169

Automobile and travel poster for: No. 4184, Mount Gambier. No. 4185, Geelong. No. 4186, Melbourne. No. 4187, Sydney.

2020, Aug. 11   Litho.   Perf. 14¾x14

5184	A1169	$1.10 multi	1.60	1.25
5185	A1169	$1.10 multi	1.60	1.25
5186	A1169	$1.10 multi	1.60	1.25
5187	A1169	$1.10 multi	1.60	1.25
		Nos. 5184-5187 (4)	6.40	5.00

Opalized Fossils A1170

Fossil of: Nos. 5188, 5194, Pine cone. Nos. 5189, 5193, Theropod tooth. Nos. 5190, 5192, Moon snail. Nos. 5191, 5195, Wood.

2020, Aug. 17   Litho.   Perf. 14x14¾

5188	A1170	$1.10 multi	1.60	1.60
5189	A1170	$1.10 multi	1.60	1.60
5190	A1170	$1.10 multi	1.60	1.60
5191	A1170	$1.10 multi	1.60	1.60
a.		Souvenir sheet of 4, #5188-5191	6.50	6.40
		Nos. 5188-5191 (4)	6.40	6.40

Booklet Stamps
Self-Adhesive

Serpentine Die Cut 11¼ Syncopated

5192	A1170	$1.10 multi	1.60	.25
5193	A1170	$1.10 multi	1.60	.25
5194	A1170	$1.10 multi	1.60	.25
5195	A1170	$1.10 multi	1.60	.25
a.		Booklet pane of 10, 3 each #5192-5193, 2 each #5194-5195	16.00	
b.		Booklet pane of 20, 5 each #5192-5195	32.00	
		Nos. 5192-5195 (4)	6.40	1.00

Art on Water
Towers — A1171

Designs: Nos. 5196, 5200, Lucky Dip, by
Jenny McCracken on Gulargambone, New
South Wales water tower. Nos. 5197, 5201,
Man's Face, by Guido van Helten on Winton,
Victoria water tower. Nos. 5198, 5202, East-
ern Bearded Dragon, by Apparition Media on
Narrandera, New South Wales water tower.
No. 5199, 5203, Man with Safety Helmet, by
Vans the Omega, on Snowtown, South Austra-
lia water tower.

2020, Sept. 7   Litho.   Perf. 14¾x14
5196 A1171 $1.10 multi   1.60 1.60
5197 A1171 $1.10 multi   1.60 1.60
5198 A1171 $1.10 multi   1.60 1.60
5199 A1171 $1.10 multi   1.60 1.60
  a.   Souvenir sheet of 4, #5196-
            5199   6.50 6.50
        Nos. 5196-5199 (4)   6.40 6.40

Booklet Stamps
Self-Adhesive

Serpentine Die Cut 11¼ Syncopated
5200 A1171 $1.10 multi   1.60   .25
  a.   Booklet pane of 10   16.00
5201 A1171 $1.10 multi   1.60   .25
  a.   Booklet pane of 10   16.00
5202 A1171 $1.10 multi   1.60   .25
  a.   Booklet pane of 10   16.00
5203 A1171 $1.10 multi   1.60   .25
  a.   Booklet pane of 10   16.00
        Nos. 5200-5203 (4)   6.40 1.00

Civil Aviation in Australia,
Cent. — A1174

Designs: $1.10, Qantas Dreamliner at Syd-
ney Airport. $2.20, Biplane and 1920 Act con-
cerning civil aviation.

2020, Oct. 0   Litho.   Perf. 14½x14
5206 A1174 $1.10 multi   1.60 1.60
5207 A1174 $2.20 multi   3.25 2.40
  a.   Souvenir sheet of 2, #5206-
            5207   5.00 3.75

Booklet Stamp
Self-Adhesive

Serpentine Die Cut 10¾ Syncopated
5208 A1174 $1.10 multi   1.60   .25
  a.   Booklet pane of 10   16.00

Australian
National
Botanic
Gardens,
Canberra,
50th Anniv.
A1175

Designs: Nos. 5209, 5211, Grevillea ias-
picula. Nos. 5210, 5212, Banksia marginata.

2020, Oct. 13   Litho.   Perf. 14x14¾
5209 A1175 $1.10 multi   1.60 1.60
5210 A1175 $1.10 multi   1.60 1.60
  a.   Souvenir sheet of 2, #5209-
            5210   3.25 3.25

Self-Adhesive

Serpentine Die Cut 11¼ Syncopated
5211 A1175 $1.10 multi   1.60   .25
5212 A1175 $1.10 multi   1.60   .25
  a.   Horiz. coil pair, #5211-5212 3.20
  b.   Booklet pane of 10, 5 each
            #5211-5212   16.00

UNESCO World
Heritage Sites in
Australia — A1176

Designs: Nos. 5215, 5219, Royal Exhibition
Building and Carlton Gardens, Melbourne,
Victoria. Nos. 5216, 5220, Budj Bim Cultural
Landscape, Victoria. Nos. 5217, 5221, Cas-
cades Female Factory, Tasmania. Nos. 5218,
5222, Sydney Opera House, Sydney, New
South Wales.

2020, Oct. 20   Litho.   Perf. 14¾x14
5215 A1176 $1.10 multi   1.60 1.60
5216 A1176 $1.10 multi   1.60 1.60
5217 A1176 $1.10 multi   1.60 1.60
5218 A1176 $1.10 multi   1.60 1.60
        Nos. 5215-5218 (4)   6.40 6.40

Booklet Stamps
Self-Adhesive

Serpentine Die Cut 11¼ Syncopated
5219 A1176 $1.10 multi   1.60   .25
  a.   Booklet pane of 10   16.00
5220 A1176 $1.10 multi   1.60   .25
  a.   Booklet pane of 10   16.00
5221 A1176 $1.10 multi   1.60   .25
  a.   Booklet pane of 10   16.00
5222 A1176 $1.10 multi   1.60   .25
  a.   Booklet pane of 10   16.00
        Nos. 5219-5222 (4)   6.40 1.00

100th
Running of
the W. S. Cox
Plate Horse
Race
A1177

Litho. & Embossed With Foil
Application

2020, Oct. 22   Perf. 14¼
5223 A1177 $1.10 dk blue & gold 1.60 1.25

A1178

Christmas — A1179

Designs: Nos. 5224, 5229, Painting of
Madonna and Child, by Leopoldine Mimovich
(1920-2019). Nos. 5225, 5230, Christmas
wreath. Nos. 5226, 5231, Christmas stocking
with flowers. Nos. 5227, 5232, Painting of Holy
Family, by Mimovich. Nos. 5228, 5233, Christmas ornament, flowers and holly.

2020, Oct. 30   Litho.   Perf. 14¾x14
5224 A1178 65c multi   .95   .95
5225 A1179 65c multi   .95   .95
5226 A1179 65c multi   .95   .95
  a.   Horiz. pair, #5225-5226   1.90 1.90
5227 A1178 $2.20 multi   3.25 3.25
  a.   Souvenir sheet of 2, #5224,
            5227   4.25 4.25
5228 A1179 $2.20 multi   3.25 3.25
        Nos. 5224-5228 (5)   9.35 9.35

Booklet Stamps
Self-Adhesive

Serpentine Die Cut 11¼ Syncopated
5229 A1178 65c multi   .95   .25
  a.   Booklet pane of 20 + 20 eti-
            quettes   19.00
5230 A1179 65c multi   .95   .25
  a.   With glossier varnish   .95   .25
  b.   Booklet pane of 10 #5230a +
            10 etiquettes   9.50
5231 A1179 65c multi   .95   .25
  a.   Booklet pane of 20 10 each
            #5230-5231, + 20 eti-
            quettes   19.00
  b.   With glossier varnish   .95   .25
  c.   Booklet pane of 10 #5231b +
            10 etiquettes   9.50
5232 A1178 $2.20 multi   3.25 1.60
  a.   Booklet pane of 5   16.50
5233 A1179 $2.20 multi   3.25 1.60
  a.   Booklet pane of 5   16.50
        Nos. 5229-5233 (5)   9.35 3.95

SEMI-POSTAL STAMPS

**Catalogue values in this section
are for Never Hinged items.**

Queensland Flood
Relief — SP1

Designs: No. B1, Rescuer holding baby. No.
B2, Flooded buildings, ground-level view. No.
B3, Rescuers taking pet from house. No. B4,
Kangaroo stranded on island in flood. No. B5,
Flooded buildings, aerial view.

Serpentine Die Cut 11¼ Syncopated
2011, Jan. 27   Litho.
Self-Adhesive
B1 SP1 60c+(20c) multi   1.75 1.75
B2 SP1 60c+(20c) multi   1.75 1.75
B3 SP1 60c+(20c) multi   1.75 1.75
B4 SP1 60c+(20c) multi   1.75 1.75
B5 SP1 60c+(20c) multi   1.75 1.75
  a.   Sheet of 10, 2 each #B1-B5   17.50
       Nos. B1-B5 (5)   8.75 8.75

Surtax for Premier's Flood Relief Appeal.

Leaves in Ring and
Hands — SP2

2012, June 26   Self-Adhesive
B6 SP2 60c+(20c) multi   1.75 1.75

Printed in sheets of 10. Surtax for Olivia
Newton-John Cancer and Wellness Center.

AIR POST STAMPS

Airplane over
Bush
Lands — AP1

Unwmk.
1929, May 20   Engr.   Perf. 11
C1 AP1 3p deep green   9.25 8.50
       Never hinged   14.50
  a.   Booklet pane of 4 ('30)   450.00

Kingsford-Smith Type of 1931
1931, Mar. 19
C2 A8   6p gray violet   8.00 8.00
       Never hinged   11.50

AP3

1931, Nov. 4
C3 AP3 6p olive brown   17.00 14.00
       Never hinged   35.00

    For overprint see No. CO1.

Mercury and
Hemispheres
AP4

1934, Dec. 1   Perf. 11
C4 AP4 1sh6p violet brown   40.00 8.00
       Never hinged   97.50

**   Perf. 13½x14**
1937, Oct. 22   Wmk. 228
C5 AP4 1sh6p violet brown   8.50 1.40
       Never hinged   14.50

**Catalogue values for unused
stamps in this section, from this
point to the end of the section, are
for Never Hinged items.**

Mercury and
Globe — AP5

1949, Sept. 1   Perf. 14½
C6 AP5 1sh6p sepia   2.25   .60

1956, Dec. 6   Unwmk.
C7 AP5 1sh6p sepia   18.50 1.10

Super-Constellation over Globe — AP6

1958, Jan. 6   Perf. 14½x14
C8 AP6 2sh dark violet blue   2.75 2.25

    Inauguration of Australian "Round the
World" air service.

AIR POST OFFICIAL STAMP

No. C3
Overprinted

**   Perf. 11, 11½**
1931, Nov. 17   Unwmk.
CO1 AP3 6p olive brown   35.00 35.00
       Never hinged   57.50

    Issued primarily for official use, but to pre-
vent speculation, a quantity was issued for
public distribution.

POSTAGE DUE STAMPS

Very fine examples of Nos. J1-J38
will have perforations touching the
design on one or more sides due to the
narrow spacing of the stamps on the
plates. Stamps with perfs clear of the
design on all four sides are scarce and
will command higher prices.

D1

1902 Typo. Wmk. 55 Perf. 11½, 12

J1	D1	½p emerald	5.75	7.00
J2	D1	1p emerald	27.00	14.00
a.		Perf. 11	2,650.	1,000.
b.		Perf. 11x11½	400.00	160.00
J3	D1	2p emerald	67.50	11.50
a.		Perf. 11x11½	525.00	190.00
J4	D1	3p emerald	52.50	32.50
J5	D1	4p emerald	52.50	15.00
J6	D1	6p emerald	62.50	12.50
J7	D1	8p emerald	105.00	90.00
J8	D1	5sh emerald	210.00	80.00
		Nos. J1-J8 (8)	582.75	262.50

D2

Perf. 11½, 12, Compound with 11
1902-04

J9	D2	½p emerald	22.00	18.00
a.		Perf. 11	575.00	325.00
J10	D2	1p emerald, Perf 12x11	21.00	5.00
a.		Perf. 11	170.00	32.50
b.		Perf 11½	200.00	140.00
c.		Perf 11x11½	37.50	11.50
J11	D2	2p emerald	52.50	3.50
a.		Perf. 11	240.00	30.00
b.		Perf 12	—	180.00
c.		Perf 11x11½	120.00	37.50
d.		Perf 11x12	140.00	45.00
J12	D2	3p emerald	95.00	18.00
a.		Perf. 11	160.00	62.50
b.		Perf 12	375.00	110.00
J13	D2	4p emerald	80.00	27.50
a.		Perf. 11	275.00	75.00
J14	D2	5p emerald	70.00	25.00
a.		Perf. 11	400.00	57.50
b.		Perf 12	75.00	20.00
J15	D2	6p emerald	75.00	12.50
a.		Perf. 11	130.00	17.50
J16	D2	8p emerald	150.00	60.00
J17	D2	10p emerald	100.00	25.00
a.		Perf. 11	125.00	20.00
J18	D2	1sh emerald	85.00	20.00
a.		Perf. 11	500.00	45.00
b.		Perf 12x11½	120.00	30.00
J19	D2	2sh emerald	135.00	135.00
a.		Perf 11½, 12	200.00	200.00
J20	D2	5sh emerald	475.00	475.00
a.		Perf. 11	1,700.	300.00

Perf. 11

J21	D2	10sh emerald	2,250.	1,900.
J22	D2	20sh emerald	4,500.	2,750.
		Nos. J9-J20 (12)	1,361.	824.50

Perf. 11½, 12 Compound with 11
1906 Wmk. 12

J23	D2	½p emerald	16.00	18.00
J24	D2	1p emerald	30.00	5.75
a.		Perf. 11	3,250.	1,150.
J25	D2	2p emerald	80.00	10.00
J26	D2	3p emerald	950.00	350.00
J27	D2	4p emerald	77.50	24.00
a.		Perf. 11	5,750.	3,500.
J28	D2	6p emerald	77.50	25.00
		Nos. J23-J28 (6)	1,231.	432.75

1907 Wmk. 13 Perf. 11½x11

J29	D2	½p emerald	37.50	80.00
J30	D2	1p emerald	150.00	80.00
J31	D2	2p emerald	300.00	175.00
J32	D2	4p emerald	300.00	165.00
J33	D2	6p emerald	350.00	250.00
		Nos. J29-J33 (5)	1,138.	750.00

D3

Perf. 11 (2sh, 10sh, 20sh), 11½x11 (1sh, 5sh)
1908-09 Wmk. 12

J34	D3	1sh emer ('09)	125.00	17.50
J35	D3	2sh emerald	1,050.	18,000.
J36	D3	5sh emerald	275.00	52.50
J37	D3	10sh emerald	2,750.	27,500.
J38	D3	20sh emerald	7,500.	52,500.

D4

1909-23 Wmk. 13 Perf. 12x12½

J39	D4	½p grn & car	32.00	45.00
a.		Perf 11, grn & rose ('14)	20.00	17.00

---

b.		Perf 12½, grn & scar ('13)	37.50	29.00
c.		Perf 14 ('19)	20.00	10.00
J40	D4	1p grn & car	23.00	9.75
a.		Perf 11, yel grn & rose, thicker paper, thick yellowish gum	4,000.	1,500.
b.		Perf 14, brt apple grn & rose, thin paper, thin white gum ('14)	20.00	8.50
c.		Perf 14 ('14)	70.00	17.00
J41	D4	2p grn & car	40.00	6.00
a.		Perf 11	25,000.	15,750.
b.		Perf 14 ('18)	29.00	7.50
J42	D4	3p grn & car	35.00	14.50
a.		Perf 14, green & rose ('16)	150.00	52.00
J43	D4	4p grn & car	24.00	11.50
a.		Perf 14 ('21)	200.00	70.00
J44	D4	6p grn & car	30.00	4.50
a.		Perf 11	37,000.	25,000.
J45	D4	1sh grn & car	33.00	9.25
a.		Perf 14, yel grn & scarlet ('23)	45.00	23.00
J46	D4	2sh grn & car	115.00	16.00
J47	D4	5sh grn & car	175.00	17.00
J48	D4	10sh grn & car	275.00	170.00
a.		Perf 14, yel grn & scarlet ('21)	1,500.	
J49	D4	£1 grn & car	525.00	325.00
a.		Perf 14, grn & scar ('21)	1,000.	
		Nos. J39-J49 (11)	1,307.	628.50

Nos. J39-J48 and J40a, J41a, J44a are from the 1909 printings and have thicker paper and thick yellowish gum. The other listings are from the 1912-23 printings on thinner paper with thin white gum.

1922-30 Wmk. 10 Perf. 14, 11 (4p)

J50	D4	½p grn & car ('23)	9.25	7.50
J51	D4	1p green & car	7.50	2.25
J52	D4	1½p grn & rose ('25)	4.25	7.50
J53	D4	2p green & car	9.25	4.25
J54	D4	3p green & car	17.00	3.25
J55	D4	4p grn & car ('30)	17.00	8.00
a.		Perf 14	52.00	23.00
J56	D4	6p green & car	37.50	18.50
		Nos. J50-J56 (7)	101.75	51.25
		Set, never hinged	200.00	

1931-36 Wmk. 228 Perf. 11

J57	D4	½p yel grn & rose ('34)	23.00	23.00
J58	D4	1p yel grn & rose ('32)	9.00	2.25
a.		Perf 14	14.00	11.50
J59	D4	2p yel grn & rose ('33)	10.50	2.25
a.		Perf 14	11.50	11.50
J60	D4	3p yel grn & rose ('36)	140.00	115.00
J61	D4	4p yel grn & rose ('34)	29.00	4.50
J62	D4	6p yel grn & rose ('36)	550.00	500.00
J63	D4	1sh yel grn & rose ('34)	70.00	30.00
		Nos. J57-J63 (7)	831.50	677.00
		Set, never hinged	1,400.	

D5

Engraved; Value Typo.
1938 Perf. 14½x14

J64	D5	½p green & car	3.50	3.50
J65	D5	1p green & car	12.50	1.10
J66	D5	2p green & car	12.50	2.25
J67	D5	3p green & car	55.00	23.00
J68	D5	4p green & car	16.00	1.10
J69	D5	6p green & car	100.00	45.00
J70	D5	1sh green & car	57.50	20.00
		Nos. J64-J70 (7)	257.00	95.95
		Set, never hinged	400.00	

> Catalogue values for unused stamps in this section, from this point to the end of the section, are for Never Hinged items.

Type of 1938
Value Tablet Redrawn

Original

Redrawn

Pence denominations: "D" has melon-shaped center in redrawn tablet. The 1909-45 3p differs slightly, having no vertical white stroke half filling the right side of "D" center.

1sh. 1938: Numeral "1" narrow, with six background lines above.

1sh. 1947: Numeral broader, showing more white space around dotted central ornament. Three lines above.

1946-57 Wmk. 228

J71	D5	½p grn & car ('56)	7.00	5.75
J72	D5	1p grn & car ('47)	4.50	1.10
J73	D5	2p green & car	8.00	1.10
J74	D5	3p green & car	10.00	1.10
J75	D5	4p grn & car ('52)	14.00	1.40
J76	D5	5p grn & car ('48)	18.50	2.25
J77	D5	6p grn & car ('49)	18.50	2.90
J78	D5	7p grn & car ('53)	8.00	7.00
J79	D5	8p grn & car ('57)	26.00	23.00
J80	D5	1sh grn & car ('47)	29.00	4.50
		Nos. J71-J80 (10)	143.50	50.10

D5a

1953-54
White Tablet, Carmine Numeral

J81	D5a	1sh grn & car ('54)	10.00	6.25
J82	D5a	2sh green & car	16.00	14.50
J83	D5a	5sh green & car	15.00	8.50
		Nos. J81-J83 (3)	41.00	29.25

Issued: 2sh, 5sh, Aug. 26; 1sh, Feb. 17.

Redrawn Type of 1947-57

Two Types of Some Pence Values:
Type I — Background lines touch numeral, "D" and period.
Type II — Lines do not touch numeral, etc. Second engraving of 1sh has sharper and thicker lines.
The ½p type II has 7 dots under the "2."
The 8p type II has distinct lines in centers of "8" and between "8" and "D."

Engr.; Value Typo.
1958-60 Unwmk. Perf. 14½x14

J86	D5	½p grn & car, II	7.00	4.25
a.		Six dots under the "2"	9.25	2.25
J87	D5	1p grn & car, II	5.75	1.10
a.		Type I	5.75	2.25
J88	D5	3p grn & car, II	5.75	4.50
J89	D5	4p grn & car, I	11.50	10.00
a.		Type II ('59)	9.25	9.25
J90	D5	5p grn & car, I	29.00	17.50
a.		Type II ('59)	100.00	40.00
J91	D5	6p grn & car, II	10.00	5.25
J92	D5	8p grn & car, II	29.00	29.00
a.		Indistinct lines	23.00	23.00
J93	D5	10p grn & car, II	17.00	6.25

White Tablet, Carmine Numeral

J94	D5a	1sh green & car	29.00	7.00
a.		2nd redrawing ('60)	29.00	5.75
J95	D5a	2sh grn & car	35.00	21.00
		Nos. J86-J95 (10)	179.00	105.85

Issued: 1sh, 9/8/58; 10p, 12/9/59; 2sh, 3/8/60; 3p, 6p, 5/25/60; others, 2/27/58.

MILITARY STAMPS

Nos. 166, 191, 183A, 173, 175, 206 and 177 Overprinted in Black

a

b

---

c

Perf. 14½x14, 15x14, 11½, 13½x13
1946-47 Wmk. 228

M1	A24(a)	½p orange	3.50	3.50
		Never hinged	5.75	
M2	A36(b)	1p brown vio	3.50	3.50
		Never hinged	5.75	
a.		Blue overprint	115.00	77.50
		Never hinged	140.00	
M3	A27(c)	3p dk vio brn	3.50	3.50
		Never hinged	5.75	
a.		Double overprint	1,250.	
M4	A30(a)	6p brn violet	12.00	11.50
		Never hinged	18.00	
M5	A16(a)	1sh gray green	12.00	11.50
		Never hinged	18.00	
M6	A1(c)	2sh dk red brn	35.00	45.00
		Never hinged	70.00	
M7	A32(c)	5sh dl red brn	140.00	200.00
		Never hinged	250.00	
		Nos. M1-M7 (7)	209.50	278.50

"B.C.O.F." stands for "British Commonwealth Occupation Force."

Issue dates: Nos. M1-M3, Oct. 11, 1946, Nos. M4-M7, May 8, 1947.

OFFICIAL STAMPS

Overprinted Official stamps are comparatively more difficult to find well centered than the basic issues on which they are printed. This is because poorly centered sheets that had been discarded were purposely chosen to be overprinted to save money.

Perforated Initials

In 1913-31, postage stamps were perforated "OS" for federal official use. The Scott Standard Catalogues do not list officials with perforated initials, but listings for these Australian stamps will be found in the Scott Classic Specialized Catalogue.

Overprinted

On Regular Issue of 1931
1931, May 4 Unwmk. Perf. 11, 11½

O1	A8	2p dull red	60.00	22.50
O2	A8	3p blue	225.00	35.00

These stamps were issued primarily for official use but to prevent speculation a quantity was issued for public distribution.

Used values are for CTO examples.
Counterfeit overprints exist.

On Regular Issues of 1928-32
1932 Wmk. 203 Perf. 13½x12½

O3	A4	2p red (II)	25.00	13.00
O4	A4	4p olive bister	40.00	26.00

Perf. 11½, 12

O5	A1	6p brown	97.50	90.00

1932-33 Wmk. 228 Perf. 13½x12½

O6	A4	½p orange	11.00	1.65
a.		Inverted overprint	30,000.	21,000.
O7	A4	1p green (I)	6.00	.50
O8	A4	2p red (II)	25.00	.60
a.		Inverted overprint		47,500.
O9	A4	3p ultra (II) ('33)	10.00	5.00
O10	A4	5p brown buff	52.50	30.00

Perf. 11½, 12

O11	A1	6p yel brn	42.50	22.50
a.		Inverted overprint	72,500.	
		Nos. O6-O11 (6)	147.00	60.25
		Set, never hinged	275.00	

1932		Unwmk.	Perf. 11, 11½	
O12	A9	2p red	7.25	6.00
O13	A9	3p blue	24.00	24.00
O14	A16	1sh gray green	72.50	52.50
		Nos. O12-O14 (3)	103.75	82.50
		Set, never hinged	160.00	

AUSTRALIAN ANTARCTIC TERRITORY

Catalogue values for all unused stamps in this section are for Never Hinged items.

All stamps, except Nos. L1-L7, are also valid for postage in Australia.

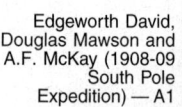

Edgeworth David, Douglas Mawson and A.F. McKay (1908-09 South Pole Expedition) — A1

Australian Explorers and Map of Antarctica — A2

Designs: 8p, Loading weasel (snow truck). 1sh, Dog team and iceberg, vert. 2sh3p, Emperor penguins and map, vert.

Perf. 14½, 14½x14, 14x14½				
1957-59		Engr.	Unwmk.	
L1	A1	5p brown	.65	.30
L2	A2	8p dark blue	2.25	1.00
L3	A2	1sh dark green	2.75	1.75
L4	A2	2sh ultra ('57)	1.50	.90
L5	A2	2sh3p green	7.50	3.50
		Nos. L1-L5 (5)	14.65	7.45
		Set, hinged	8.50	

Nos. L1 and L2 were printed as 4p and 7p stamps and surcharged typographically in black and dark blue before issuance.

Sizes of stamps: No. L2, 34x21mm; Nos. L3, L5, 21x34mm; No. L4, 43½x25½mm.

1961, July 5			Perf. 14½	
L6	A1	5p dark blue	1.00	.45

The denomination on No. L6 is not within a typographed circle, but is part of the engraved design.

Sir Douglas Mawson — A3

1961, Oct. 18				
L7	A3	5p dark green	.50	.40

50th anniv. of the 1911-14 Australian Antarctic Expedition.

Lookout and Iceberg — A4

Designs: 1c, Aurora australis and camera dome. 2c, Banding penguins. 5c, Branding of elephant seals. 7c, Measuring snow strata. 10c, Wind gauges. 15c, Weather balloon. 20c, Helicopter. 25c, Radio operator. 50c, Ice compression tests. $1, "Mock sun" (parahelion) and dogs. 20c, 25c, 50c and $1 horizontal.

Perf. 13½x13, 13x13½				
1966-68		Photo.	Unwmk.	
L8	A4	1c multicolored	.50	.30
L9	A4	2c multicolored	.50	.75
L10	A4	4c multicolored	.60	.50
L11	A4	5c multicolored	1.40	.50
L12	A4	7c multicolored	.75	.50
L13	A4	10c multicolored	1.00	1.00
L14	A4	15c multicolored	4.75	1.40
L15	A4	20c multicolored	8.00	2.75
L16	A4	25c multicolored	2.00	2.00
L17	A4	50c multicolored	5.00	4.00
L18	A4	$1 multicolored	20.00	12.00
		Nos. L8-L18 (11)	44.50	25.70
		Set, never hinged	34.00	

Issued: 5c, 9/25/68; others, 9/28/66. Nos. L8-L18 are on phosphorescent helecon paper. Fluorescent orange is one of the colors used in printing the 10c, 15c, 20c and 50c.

Sastrugi Snow Formation A5

1971, June 23		Photo.	Perf. 13x13½	
L19	A5	6c shown	.85	.65
L20	A5	30c Pancake ice	4.50	3.50

10th anniv. of the Antarctic Treaty pledging peaceful uses of and scientific cooperation in Antarctica.

Capt. Cook, Sextant, Azimuth Compass A6

Design: 35c, Chart of Cook's circumnavigation of Antarctica, and "Resolution."

1972, Sept. 13		Photo.	Perf. 13x13½	
L21	A6	7c bister & multi	1.05	.75
L22	A6	35c buff & multi	4.25	4.25

Bicentenary of Capt. James Cook's circumnavigation of Antarctica.

Plankton and Krill Shrimp — A7

Mawson's D.H. Gipsy Moth, 1931 — A8

Food Chain (Essential for Survival): 7c, Adelie penguin feeding on krill shrimp. 9c, Leopard seal pursuing fish, horiz. 10c, Killer whale hunting seals, horiz. 20c, Wandering albatross, horiz. $1, Sperm whale attacking giant squid.

Explorers' Aircraft: 8c, Rymill's DH Fox Moth returning to Barry Island. 25c, Hubert Wilkins Lockheed Vega, horiz. 30c, Lincoln Ellsworth's Northrop Gamma. 35c, Lars Christensen's Avro Avian and Framnes Mountains, horiz. 50c, Richard Byrd's Ford Tri-Motor dropping US flag over South Pole.

Perf. 13½x13, 13x13½				
1973, Aug. 15				
L23	A7	1c multicolored	.25	.25
L24	A8	5c multicolored	.25	.25
L25	A7	7c multicolored	1.00	.90
L26	A8	8c multicolored	.25	.50
L27	A7	9c multicolored	.25	.25
L28	A7	10c multicolored	2.50	1.75
L29	A7	20c multicolored	.70	.60
L30	A8	25c multicolored	.55	.60
L31	A8	30c multicolored	.55	.70
L32	A8	35c multicolored	.55	.70
L33	A8	50c multicolored	1.00	.75
L34	A7	$1 multicolored	1.75	2.00
		Nos. L23-L34 (12)	9.60	9.25

Adm. Byrd, Plane, Mountains A9

Design: 20c, Adm. Byrd, Floyd Bennett trimotored plane, map of Antarctica.

1979, June 20		Litho.	Perf. 15½	
L35	A9	20c multicolored	.40	.60
L36	A9	55c multicolored	.85	1.10

50th anniv. of first flight over South Pole by Richard Byrd (1888-1957).

"S.Y. Nimrod" A10

Designs: 1c, S.Y. Aurora. 2c, R.Y. Penola. 5c, M.V. Thala Dan. 10c, H.M.S. Challenger. No. L41, S.S. Morning. No. L42, S.Y. Nimrod, stern view. 20c, R.R.S. Discovery II. 22c, R.Y.S. Terra Nova. 25c, S.S. Endurance. 30c, S.S. Fram. 35c, M.S. Nella Dan. 40c, M.S. Kista Dan. 45c, L'Astrolabe. 50c, S.S. Norvegia. 55c, S.Y. Discovery. $1, H.M.S. Resolution.

2c, 5c, 22c, 25c, 40c, 55c, $1 are vertical.

Perf. 13½x13, 13x13½				
1979-81			Litho.	
L37	A10	1c multi	.25	.25
L38	A10	2c multi	.25	.25
L39	A10	5c multi	.25	.25
L40	A10	10c multi	.30	.25
L41	A10	15c multi	1.15	2.60
L42	A10	15c shown	.25	.30
L43	A10	20c multi	.30	1.00
L44	A10	22c multi	.50	.30
L45	A10	25c multi	.50	.70
L46	A10	30c multi	.50	1.30
L47	A10	35c multi	.60	1.30
L48	A10	40c multi	.80	1.30
L49	A10	45c multi	.80	1.30
L50	A10	50c multi	.80	1.00
L51	A10	55c multi	1.00	2.60
L52	A10	$1 multi	2.00	3.25
		Nos. L37-L52 (16)	10.25	17.95

Issued: 5c, 20c, 25c, 30c, 55c, 8/29; 1c, No. L41, 22c, 35c, $1, 5/21/80; 2c, 10c, No. L42, 40c, 45c, 50c, 9/9/81.

A11

1982, May 5		Litho.	Perf. 14x13½	
L53	A11	27c Mawson, landscape	.35	.25
L54	A11	75c Mawson, map	1.00	1.40

Sir Douglas Mawson (1882-1958), explorer.

A12

Local Wildlife: a, Light-mantled sooty albatross. b, Macquarie Isld. shags. c, Elephant seals. d, Royal penguins. e, Antarctic prions.

1983, Apr. 6		Litho.	Perf. 14½	
L55		Strip of 5, multi	3.50	3.50
a.-e.		A12 27c, any single	.70	.50

12th Antarctic Treaty Consultative Meeting, Canberra, Sept. 13-27 — A13

1983, Sept. 7		Litho.	Perf. 14½	
L56	A13	27c multicolored	.45	.50

South Magnetic Pole Expedition, 75th Anniv. A14

1984, Jan. 16				
L57	A14	30c Prismatic compass	.50	.50
L58	A14	85c Aneroid barometer	1.50	2.00

Dog Team, Mawson Station A15

2c, Summer afternoon. 10c, Evening. 15c, Prince Charles Mts. 20c, Morning. 25c, Sea ice, iceberg. 30c, Mt. Coates. 33c, Iceberg Alley, Mawson. 36c, Winter evening. 45c, Brash ice, vert. 60c, Midwinter shadows. 75c, Coastline. 85c, Landing field. 90c, Pancake ice, vert. $1, Emperor penguins, Auster Rookery.

1984-87		Litho.	Perf. 14½x15	
L60	A15	2c multi	.25	.25
L61	A15	5c shown	.25	.25
L62	A15	10c multi	.25	.25
L63	A15	15c multi	.30	.25
L64	A15	20c multi	.35	.30
L65	A15	25c multi	.40	.35
L66	A15	30c multi	.50	.45
L67	A15	33c multi	.55	.45
L68	A15	36c multi	.60	.30
L69	A15	45c multi	.75	.65
L70	A15	60c multi	1.00	.80
L71	A15	75c multi	1.25	1.10
L72	A15	85c multi	1.50	1.25
L73	A15	90c multi	1.50	1.25
L74	A15	$1 multi	1.75	1.40
		Nos. L60-L74 (15)	11.20	9.10

Issued: 5, 25, 30, 75, 85c, 7/18/84; 15, 33, 45, 90c, $1, 8/7/85; 2, 10, 20, 36, 60c, 3/11/87.

Antarctic Treaty, 25th Anniv. — A16

1986, Sept. 17		Litho.	Perf. 14x13½	
L75	A16	36c multicolored	1.00	.85

Environment, Conservation and Technology A17

No. L76: a, Hour-glass dolphins and the Nella Dan. b, Emperor penguins and Davis Station. c, Crabeater seal and helicopters. d, Adelie penguins and snow-ice transport vehicle. e, Gray-headed albatross and photographer.

1988, July 20		Litho.	Perf. 13	
L76		Strip of 5	6.00	6.00
a.-e.		A17 37c any single	1.05	1.05

Paintings by Sir
Sidney Nolan (b.
1917) — A18

No. L77, Antarctica. No. L78, Iceberg Alley.
No. L79, Glacial Flow. No. L80, Frozen Sea.

1989, June 14 Litho. Perf. 14x13½
L77 A18 39c multicolored   .90 .60
L78 A18 39c multicolored   .90 .60
L79 A18 60c multicolored   1.50 1.50
L80 A18 80c multicolored   2.25 2.25
  Nos. L77-L80 (4)   5.55 4.95

Aurora
Australis
A19

Design: $1.20, Research ship Aurora
Australis.

1991, June 20 Litho. Perf. 14½
L81 A19 43c multicolored   .80 .80
L82 A19 $1.20 multicolored   2.25 1.50

Antarctic Treaty, 30th anniv. (No. L81).

Regional
Wildlife
A20

45c, Adelie penguin. 75c, Elephant seal.
85c, Northern giant petrel. 95c, Weddell seal.
$1, Royal penguins. $1.20, Emperor penguin,
vert. $1.40, Fur seals. $1.50, King penguins,
vert.

Perf. 14x14½, 14½x14
1992-93   Litho.
L83 A20 45c multi   .75 .65
L84 A20 75c multi   1.25 1.10
L85 A20 85c multi   1.50 1.40
L86 A20 95c multi   1.60 1.50
L86A A20 $1 multi   1.75 1.60
L87 A20 $1.20 multi   1.90 1.75
L88 A20 $1.40 multi   2.40 2.00
L89 A20 $1.50 multi   2.60 2.25
  Nos. L83-L89 (8)   13.75 12.25

Issued: $1, $1.40, $1.50, 1/14/93; others,
5/14/92.

The Last
Huskies
A21

45c, Dog up close, vert. 75c, Sled team.
85c, Dog seated, vert. $1.05, Three dogs.

1994, Jan. 13 Litho. Perf. 14½
L90 A21 45c multi   1.00 .75
L91 A21 75c multi   1.50 1.50
L92 A21 85c multi   2.25 2.25
L93 A21 $1.05 multi   2.50 2.50
  Nos. L90-L93 (4)   7.25 7.00

Whales &
Dolphins
A22

1995, June 15 Litho. Perf. 14½
L94 A22 45c Humpback whale   .95 .85
L95 A22 45c Hourglass
         dolphin, vert.   .95 .85
L96 A22 45c Minke whale,
         vert.   .95 .85
  a. Pair, #L95-L96   2.25 2.25

L97 A22 $1 Killer whale   2.50 2.50
  a. Souvenir sheet of 4, #L94-L97 7.75 7.75
  b. As "a," overprinted   65.00 65.00
  c. As "a," overprinted   40.00 40.00
    Nos. L94-L97 (4)   5.35 5.05

No. L97b is overprinted in gold in sheet mar-
gin with Singapore '95 emblem and: "Australia
Post Exhibition Sheet No. 2," and, in both Chi-
nese and English, with "Singapore 95 World
Stamp Exhibition."
No. L97c is overprinted in gold in sheet mar-
gin with exhibition emblem, "Australian Post
Exhibition Sheet No. 3" and CAPEX '96
WORLD PHILATELIC EXHIBITION / EXPOSI-
TION PHILATELIQUE MONDIALE
Issued: No. L97b, 9/1/95; No. L97c, 6/15/96.

Landscapes, by
Christian Clare
Robertson — A23

Designs: No. L98, Rafting sea ice. No. L99,
Shadow on the Plateau. $1, Ice cave. $1.20,
Twelve Lake.

1996, May 16 Litho. Perf. 14½x14
L98 A23 45c multicolored   1.25 .95
L99 A23 45c multicolored   1.25 .95
  a. Pair, Nos. L98-L99   2.50 2.25
L100 A23 $1 multicolored   2.25 2.50
L101 A23 $1.20 multicolored   3.00 2.40
  Nos. L98-L101 (4)   7.75 6.80

Australian
Natl.
Antarctic
Research
Expeditions,
50th Anniv.
A24

Designs: No. L102, Apple field huts. No.
L103, Inside an apple hut. 95c, Summer sur-
veying. $1.05, Sea ice research. $1.20,
Remote field camp.

1997, May 15 Litho. Perf. 14x14½
L102 A24 45c multicolored   1.10 .90
L103 A24 45c multicolored   1.10 .90
  a. Pair, #L102-L103   2.25 2.25
L104 A24 95c multicolored   2.50 2.25
L105 A24 $1.05 multicolored   2.10 2.40
L106 A24 $1.20 multicolored   2.75 2.50
  Nos. L102-L106 (5)   9.55 8.95

Modes of
Transportation
A25

Designs: No. L107, Snowmobile. No. L108,
Ship, "Aurora Australis." $1, Helicopter airlift-
ing a four-wheel drive ATV, vert. $2, Antarctic
Hagglunds (rubber-tracked vehicles with fiber-
glass cabins), vert.

Perf. 14x14½, 14½x14
1998, Mar. 5   Litho.
L107 A25 45c multicolored   1.00 1.00
L108 A25 45c multicolored   1.00 1.00
  a. Pair, #L107-L108   2.50 2.50
L109 A25 $1 multicolored   2.50 3.00
L110 A25 $2 multicolored   5.25 4.50
  Nos. L107-L110 (4)   9.75 9.50

Preservation
of Huts used
During
Mawson's
Antarctic
Expedition
A26

Designs: No. L111, Photograph of Mawson,
sailing ship Aurora. No. L112, Photograph,
"Home of the Blizzard," by Frank Hurley. 90c,
Photograph, "Huskie Team," by Xavier Mertz.
$1.35, Huts restoration.

1999, May 13 Litho. Perf. 14x14½
L111 A26 45c multicolored   1.00 1.00
L112 A26 45c multicolored   1.00 1.00
  a. Pair, #L111-L112   2.40 2.40

L113 A26 90c multicolored   2.75 3.00
L114 A26 $1.35 multicolored   4.00 3.50
  Nos. L111-L114 (4)   8.75 8.50

Penguins
A27

2000, July 24 Litho. Perf. 13¾x14½
L115 A27 45c Emperor penguins   1.25 1.25
L116 A27 45c Adelie penguins   1.25 1.25
  a. Pair, #L115-L116   4.75 4.75

Australians in the
Antarctic,
Cent. — A28

No. L117: a, Penguins and icicles. b, Louis
Bernacchi, physicist. c, Nimrod. d, Scientists
at South Magnetic Pole. e, Griffith Taylor and
Frank Debenham, geologists. f, First radio
used in Antarctica. g, First flight over Antarctica. h, Sir Douglas Mawson, explorer. i,
BANZARE (British, Australian and New Zealand Antarctic Research Expedition). j, Australia's claim to territory. k, Establishment of
ANARE (Australian National Antarctic
Research Expeditions). l, Transport. m, Aurora
Australis. n, Climate research. o, Cold-weather
clothing. p, Nella Dan. q, First women on Antarctica. r, Communications. s, Tourism. t, Satellite view of Antarctica.

2001, May 17 Litho. Perf. 14¾x14
L117   Sheet of 20   18.50 18.50
  a.-e. A28 5c Any single   .40 .40
  f.-j. A28 10c Any single   .50 .50
  k.-o. A28 25c Any single   .60 .60
  p.-t. A28 45c Any single   .75 .75

Worldwide Fund for Nature
(WWF) — A29

No. L118: a, Leopard seal and pup on ice. b,
Leopard seal and penguin on ice. c, Penguins,
two leopard seals in water. d, Penguins, leopard seal in water.

2001, Sept. 11 Litho. Perf. 14x14½
L118 A29   Block of 4   6.75 8.00
  a.-d. A29 45c Any single   1.00 1.00

Antarctic Base Stations — A30

Maps showing station locations and: a, Light
Detection and Ranging Instrument, aurora
australis, Davis Station. b, Diatom, Casey Station. c, Wandering albatross, Macquarie Island
Station. d, Adélie penguin, Mawson Station.

2002, July 2 Litho. Perf. 14x14¾
L119 A30   Block of 4, #a-d   7.00 7.00
  a.-d. 45c Any single   1.00 1.00

Ships — A31

Designs: No. L120, Kista Dan, No. L121,
Magga Dan. $1, Thala Dan, vert. $1.45, Nella
Dan, vert.

Perf. 14x14½, 14½x14
2003, Apr. 29   Litho.
L120 A31 50c multi   1.00 1.00
L121 A31 50c multi   1.00 1.00
  a. Horiz. pair, #L120-L121   2.25 2.25
L122 A31 $1 multi   2.25 2.25
L123 A31 $1.45 multi   3.75 3.75
  Nos. L120-L123 (4)   8.00 8.00

Mawson
Station, 50th
Anniv. — A32

Designs: No. L124, Naming ceremony,
1954. No. L125, Station buildings. $1, Barge
and airplane. $1.45, Auster Emperor Penguin
Rookery.

2004, Feb. 13 Litho. Perf. 14x14½
L124 A32 50c multi   1.00 1.00
L125 A32 50c multi   1.00 1.00
  a. Horiz. pair, #L124-L125   2.50 2.50
L126 A32 $1 multi   3.00 3.00
L127 A32 $1.45 multi   4.00 4.00
  Nos. L124-L127 (4)   9.00 9.00

Aircraft
A33

Designs: No. L128, Hughes 500 helicopter.
No. L129, De Havilland DHC-2 Beaver. $1,
Pilatus PC-6 Porter. $1.45, Douglas DC-
3/Dakota C-47.

2005, Sept. 6 Litho. Perf. 14x14½
L128 A33 50c multi   1.00 1.00
L129 A33 50c multi   1.00 1.00
  a. Horiz. pair, #L128-L129   2.25 2.25
L130 A33 $1 multi   2.75 2.75
L131 A33 $1.45 multi   4.50 4.50
  Nos. L128-L131 (4)   9.25 9.25

Fish — A34

Designs: No. L132, Mackerel icefish. No.
L133, Lanternfish. No. L134, Eaton's skate.
No. L135, Patagonian toothfish.

2006, Aug. 1 Litho. Perf. 14x14¾
L132 A34 50c multi   .90 .90
L133 A34 50c multi   .90 .90
  a. Horiz. pair, #L132-L133   2.50 2.50
L134 A34 $1 multi   2.00 2.00
L135 A34 $1 multi   2.00 2.00
  a. Horiz. pair, #L134-L135   5.00 5.00
  Nos. L132-L135 (4)   5.80 5.80

Worldwide Fund
For Nature
(WWF) — A35

Royal penguins: No. L136, Four marching.
No. L137, Nesting. No. L138, Two contesting
territory (denomination at bottom), horiz. No.
L139, Two courting (denomination at left),
horiz.

2007, Aug. 7   Litho.   Perf. 14½x14
L136	A35	50c multi	1.00	1.00
L137	A35	50c multi	1.00	1.00
a.		Horiz. pair, #L136-L137	2.75	2.00

Perf. 14x14½
L138	A35	$1 multi	1.50	1.50
L139	A35	$1 multi	1.50	1.50
a.		Vert. pair, #L138-L139	5.75	4.75
		Nos. L136-L139 (4)	5.00	5.00

International Polar Year — A36

Designs: No. L140, Astronomy. No. L141, Glaciology. No. L142, Marine biology. No. L143, Oceanography.

2008, Sept. 16   Litho.   Perf. 14x14½
L140	A36	55c multi	1.00	1.00
L141	A36	55c multi	1.00	1.00
a.		Vert. pair, #L140-L141	3.00	2.75
L142	A36	$1.10 multi	1.75	1.75
L143	A36	$1.10 multi	1.75	1.75
a.		Vert. pair, #L142-L143	6.00	6.00
b.		Souvenir sheet, #L140-L143	11.50	12.50
		Nos. L140-L143 (4)	5.50	5.50

Discovery of South Magnetic Pole, Cent. — A37

Designs: No. L144, Crew unloading the Nimrod. No. L145, Crew depositing expedition provisions by automobile. No. L146, Men at Northern Party camp. No. L147, Alistair Mackay, Douglas Mawson, and Edgeworth David with flag at South Magnetic Pole.

2009, Jan. 8   Litho.   Perf. 14½x14
L144	A37	55c lt bl & blk	1.00	.75
L145	A37	55c lt bl & multi	1.00	.75
a.		Horiz. pair, #L144-L145	2.40	2.60
L146	A37	$1.10 lt bl & blk	2.40	1.60
L147	A37	$1.10 lt bl & blk	2.40	1.60
a.		Horiz. pair, #L146-L147	5.00	5.00
b.		Souvenir sheet, #L144-L147	7.50	8.00
		Nos. L144-L147 (4)	6.80	4.70

International Polar Year — A38

Designs: 55c, Snow petrel. $2.05, Jade iceberg.

2009, Mar. 4   Litho.   Perf. 14x14¾
L148	A38	55c multi	1.60	1.30
L149	A38	$2.05 multi	5.00	3.25
b.		Souvenir sheet, #L148-L149	8.00	4.50
b.		Sheet of 2, Australia #3337, Australian Antarctic Terr. #L149	10.00	10.00

Issued: No. L149b, 8/20/10. Stampex 2010, Adelaide (No. L149b).

For Endangered Wildlife stamps inscribed "Australian Antarctic Territory" see Australia Nos. 3128 and 3134.

Macquarie Island — A39

Designs: No. L150, Pleurophyllum hookeri (flower). No. L151, Southern elephant seal. No. L152, Mawson Point Stacks (green terrain). No. L153, Caroline Cove (brown terrain).

2010, Oct. 26   Litho.   Perf. 14¼
L150	A39	60c multi	1.00	1.00
L151	A39	60c multi	1.00	1.00
a.		Horiz. pair, #L150-L151	3.00	3.00
L152	A39	$1.20 multi	1.90	1.90
L153	A39	$1.20 multi	1.90	1.90
a.		Horiz. pair, #L152-L153	6.00	6.00
b.		Souvenir sheet, #L150-L153	12.00	12.00
		Nos. L150-L153 (4)	5.80	5.80

A40

A41

A42

Icebergs A43

2011, June 7   Litho.   Perf. 14x14¾
L154		Block of 4	5.00	5.00
a.		A40 60c multi	1.00	1.00
b.		A41 60c multi	1.00	1.00
c.		A42 60c multi	1.00	1.00
d.		A43 60c multi	1.00	1.00
e.		Souvenir sheet of 4, #L154a-L154d	8.00	8.00

Booklet Stamps
Self-Adhesive
Stamps With Grayed Frame
Serpentine Die Cut 11¼ Syncopated
L155	A40	60c multi	1.00	.30
L156	A41	60c multi	1.00	.30
L157	A42	60c multi	1.00	.30
L158	A43	60c multi	1.00	.30
a.		Booklet pane of 10, 3 each #L155-L156, 2 each #L157-L158	12.00	
		Nos. L155-L158 (4)	4.00	1.20

Australasian Antarctic Expedition, Cent. — A44

No. L159: a, Map and mast of SY Aurora. b, John King Davis (1884-1967), captain of the SY Aurora. c, SY Aurora and postmark. d, Expedition members landing at Macquarie Island. e, Birds on Macquarie Island.

2011, Aug. 2   Perf. 14¾x14
L159		Horiz. strip of 5	7.00	7.25
a.-e.		A44 60c Any single	1.00	1.00
f.		Souvenir sheet of 5, #L159a-L159e	9.50	7.25

For WWF stamp inscribed "Australian Antarctic Territory" see Australia No. 3562.

Dr. Philip Law (1912-2010), Polar Explorer — A45

Designs: 60c, Law. $1.20, Map of Antarctica, Law and helicopter at Arthurson Bluff. $1.80, Map of Antarctica, opening of Mawson Station.

2012, Mar. 6   Litho.   Perf. 14¾x14
L160	A45	60c multi	1.75	1.40
L161	A45	$1.20 multi	3.50	2.75
L162	A45	$1.80 multi	5.50	2.75
a.		Souvenir sheet of 3, #L160-L162	11.00	8.50
		Nos. L160-L162 (3)	10.75	6.90

Australasian Antarctic Expedition, Cent. — A46

Designs: No. L163, Main hut. No. L164, Xavier Mertz and dogs. No. L165, Belgrave Ninnis and dogs. No. L166, Bow of SY Aurora, map of Cape Denison, penguins. No. L167, Stern of SY Aurora, expedition members carrying supplies from ship.

2012, Sept. 4
L163	A46	60c multi	1.00	1.00
L164	A46	60c multi	1.00	1.00
L165	A46	60c multi	1.00	1.00
a.		Horiz. strip of 3, #L163-L165	5.00	4.00
L166	A46	$1.20 multi	1.50	1.50
L167	A46	$1.20 multi	1.50	1.50
a.		Horiz. pair, #L166-L167	6.75	5.50
b.		Souvenir sheet of 5, #L163-L167	12.00	9.50
		Nos. L163-L167 (5)	6.00	6.00

Mountains A47

Designs: No. L168, Mt. Parsons. No. L169, Mawson Escarpment. $1.20, South Masson Range. $1.80, David Range.

2013, Mar. 12   Litho.   Perf. 14x14¾
L168	A47	60c multi	.90	.95
L169	A47	60c multi	.90	.95
a.		Horiz. pair, #L168-L169	2.50	1.90
L170	A47	$1.20 multi	2.50	1.90
L171	A47	$1.80 multi	3.75	3.00
a.		Souvenir sheet of 4, #L168-L171	8.75	8.75
		Nos. L168-L171 (4)	8.05	6.80

Australasian Antarctic Expedition, Cent. — A48

Designs: No. L172, Men walking in blizzard. No. L173, Man checking wind recorder. No. L174, Weddell seal, Cape petrels. No. L175, Wireless operator Walter Hannam. No. L176, Frank Wild, leader of Western Party of Expedition.

2013, Sept. 10   Perf. 14¾x14
L172	A48	60c multi	1.10	.85
L173	A48	60c multi	1.10	.85
L174	A48	60c multi	1.10	.85
a.		Horiz. strip of 3, #L172-L174	3.30	2.60
L175	A48	$1.20 multi	2.25	1.75
L176	A48	$1.20 multi	2.25	1.75
a.		Horiz. pair, #L175-L176	4.50	3.50
b.		Souvenir sheet of 5, #L172-L176	8.00	8.00
		Nos. L172-L176 (5)	7.80	6.05

Australasian Antarctic Expedition, Cent. — A49

Designs: No. L177, Scientific researchers with large net. No. L178, Expedition members on SY Aurora. No. L179, Sir Douglas Mawson (1882-1958), expedition leader. No. L180, Mawson on motor launch, Cape Denison. No. L181, Frank Hurley with movie camera.

2014, Feb. 18   Litho.   Perf. 14¾x14
L177	A49	60c multi	1.10	.85
L178	A49	60c multi	1.10	.85
L179	A49	60c multi	1.10	.85
a.		Horiz. strip of 3, #L177-L179	3.30	2.60
L180	A49	$1.20 multi	2.25	1.75
L181	A49	$1.20 multi	2.25	1.75
a.		Horiz. pair, #L180-L181	4.50	3.50
b.		Souvenir sheet of 5, #L177-L181	8.00	8.00
		Nos. L177-L181 (5)	7.80	6.05

Husky — A50

Designs: Nos. L182, L186, Gray husky (shown). Nos. L183, L186, Brown husky. No. L184, Dog team with drivers in orange parkas, horiz. No. L185, Dog team with drivers in black parkas, horiz.

Perf. 14¾x14, 14x14¾
2014, Sept. 9   Litho.
L182	A50	70c multi	1.25	1.25
L183	A50	70c multi	1.25	1.25
a.		Horiz. pair, #L182-L183	2.50	2.50
L184	A50	$1.40 multi	2.50	2.00
L185	A50	$1.40 multi	2.50	2.00
a.		Horiz. pair, #L184-L185	5.00	4.00
b.		Souvenir sheet of 4, #L182-L185	7.50	7.50
		Nos. L182-L185 (4)	7.50	6.50

Booklet Stamps
Self-Adhesive
Serpentine Die Cut 11¼ Syncopated
L186	A50	70c multi	1.25	.25
L187	A50	70c multi	1.25	.25
a.		Booklet pane of 10, 5 each #L186-L187	12.50	

Antarctic Atmospheric Conditions A51

Various Antarctic landscapes and atmospheric conditions with denomination at: No. L188, UR. No. L189, UL. No. L190, UR. No. L191, UL.

2015, May 26   Litho.   Perf. 14x14¾
L188	A51	70c multi	1.10	.85
L189	A51	70c multi	1.10	.85
a.		Horiz. pair, #L188-L189	2.20	1.70
L190	A51	$1.40 multi	2.25	1.75
L191	A51	$1.40 multi	2.25	1.75
a.		Horiz. pair, #L190-L191	4.50	3.50
b.		Souvenir sheet of 4, #L188-L191	6.75	6.75
		Nos. L188-L191 (4)	6.70	5.20

Dogs Involved in Macquarie Island Pest Eradication A52

Dogs and: No. L192, Penguins. No. L193, Man with backpack. No. L194, Woman. No. L195, Man in winter coat.

2015, Sept. 9   Litho.   Perf. 14x14¾

L192	A52	70c multi	1.00	.75
L193	A52	70c multi	1.00	.75
a.		Horiz. pair, #L192-L193	2.00	1.50
L194	A52	$1.40 multi	2.00	1.50
L195	A52	$1.40 multi	2.00	1.50
a.		Horiz. pair, #L194-L195	4.00	3.00
b.		Souvenir sheet of 4, #L192-L195	6.00	6.00
		Nos. L192-L195 (4)	6.00	4.50

Photographs of Ernest Shackleton's Imperial Trans-Antarctic Expedition by Frank Hurley (1885-1962) — A53

Inscriptions: No. L196, Weddell Sea. No. L197, Ice-bound. No. L198, Ocean Camp. No. L199, Rescue Mission. $3, At Work.

2016, June 21   Litho.   Perf. 14¾x14

L196	A53	$1 multi	1.50	1.10
L197	A53	$1 multi	1.50	1.10
a.		Horiz. pair, #L196-L197	3.00	2.25
L198	A53	$2 multi	3.00	2.25
L199	A53	$2 multi	3.00	2.25
a.		Horiz. pair, #L198-L199	6.00	4.50
L200	A53	$3 multi	4.50	3.50
a.		Souvenir sheet of 5, #L196-L200	13.50	13.50
		Nos. L196-L200 (5)	13.50	10.20

Ice Flowers (Frost Formations) A54

Various ice flowers. Denomination at UR on Nos. L201, L203, L205a, L205c, L206, Denomination at UL on Nos. L202, L204, L205b, L205d, L207.

Litho., Litho & Embossed With Foil Application (#L205)

2016, Sept. 20   Perf. 14¼

L201	A54	$1 multi	1.60	1.60
L202	A54	$1 multi	1.60	1.60
a.		Horiz. pair, #L201-L202	3.20	3.20
L203	A54	$2 multi	3.25	1.60
L204	A54	$3 multi	4.75	2.40
		Nos. L201-L204 (4)	11.20	7.20

Miniature Sheet

L205		Sheet of 4	11.50	6.50
a.-b.	A54	$1 Either single	1.60	1.25
c.	A54	$2 multi	3.25	1.60
d.	A54	$3 multi	4.75	2.40

Booklet Stamps
Self-Adhesive

Serpentine Die Cut 11¼ Syncopated

L206	A54	$1 multi	1.60	.25
L207	A54	$1 multi	1.60	.25
a.		Booklet pane of 10, 5 each #L206-L207	16.00	

A55

A56

A57

East Antarctic Deep Sea Creatures A58

2017, Mar. 7   Litho.   Perf. 14¼

L208	A55	$1 multi	1.60	1.25
L209	A56	$1 multi	1.60	1.25
a.		Horiz. pair, #L208-L209	3.20	2.50
L210	A57	$2 multi	3.00	2.25
L211	A58	$2 multi	3.00	2.25
a.		Horiz. pair, #L210-L211	6.00	4.50
b.		Souvenir sheet of 4, #L208-L211	9.25	7.00
		Nos. L208-L211 (4)	9.20	7.00

Cultural Heritage — A59

Designs: No. L212, Aneroid barometer and ship. No. L213, Proclamation of Sir Douglas Mawson and map of Antarctica. $2, Weasel M29 vehicle and mountains.

2017, Sept. 19   Litho.   Perf. 14¾x14

L212	A59	$1 multi	1.60	1.25
L213	A59	$1 multi	1.60	1.25
L214	A59	$2 multi	3.25	1.60
a.		Souvenir sheet of 3, #L212-L214	6.50	4.25
		Nos. L212-L214 (3)	6.45	4.10

Crabeater Seals — A60

Designs: No. L215, Two seals. No. L216, Seal in water. No. L217, Two seals, diff. No. L218, One seal.

2018, Mar. 27   Litho.   Perf. 14x14¾

L215	A60	$1 multi	1.60	1.25
L216	A60	$1 multi	1.60	1.25
L217	A60	$2 multi	3.25	1.60
L218	A60	$2 multi	3.25	1.60
a.		Souvenir sheet of 4, #L215-L218	9.75	5.75
		Nos. L215-L218 (4)	9.70	5.70

RSV Aurora Australis, 30th Anniv. A61

Designs: No. L219, Ship in ice. No. L220, Ship and penguins. No. L221, Wave approaching ship. No. L222, Aerial view of ship in ice.

2018, Sept. 25   Litho.   Perf. 14x14¾

L219	A61	$1 multi	1.50	1.10
L220	A61	$1 multi	1.50	1.10
L221	A61	$2 multi	3.00	2.25
L222	A61	$2 multi	3.00	2.25
a.		Souvenir sheet of 4, #L219-L222	9.00	6.75
		Nos. L219-L222 (4)	9.00	6.70

Carey Research Station, 50th Anniv. A62

Designs: No. L223, Scientist holding equipment at Aurora Basin North, 2013. No. L224, Casey Repstat, 1971. No. L225, Tents at Aurora Basin North, 2013. No. L226, Casey Station, 2015.

2019, Mar. 26   Litho.   Perf. 14x14¾

L223	A62	$1 multi	1.50	1.10
L224	A62	$1 multi	1.50	1.10
L225	A62	$2 multi	3.00	2.25
L226	A62	$2 multi	3.00	2.25
a.		Souvenir sheet of 4, #L223-L226	9.00	6.75
		Nos. L223-L226 (4)	9.00	6.70

Mapping the Australian Antarctic Territory — A63

Maps by: No. L227, Douglas Mawson, 1911. No. L228, Department of the Interior, 1939. No. L229, Division of National Mapping, 1971. No. L230, Australian Antarctic Division, 1993.

2019, Aug. 20   Litho.   Perf. 14¼

L227	A63	$1 multi	1.40	1.10
L228	A63	$1 multi	1.40	1.10
L229	A63	$2 multi	2.75	2.10
L230	A63	$2 multi	2.75	2.10
a.		Souvenir sheet of 4, #L227-L230	8.50	6.50
		Nos. L227-L230 (4)	8.30	6.40

1948 HMAS Wyatt Earp Expedition A64

Designs: No. L231, HMAS Wyatt Earp. No. L232, Royal Australian Air Force Vought Kingfisher. $3.30, HMAS Wyatt Earp and Royal Australian Air Force Vought Kingfisher.

Perf. 12¼x13¼

2020, Mar. 31   Litho. & Engr.

L231	A64	$1.10 multi	1.40	1.10
L232	A64	$1.10 multi	1.40	1.10
L233	A64	$3.30 multi	4.00	3.00
a.		Souvenir sheet of 3, #L231-L233	7.00	5.25
		Nos. L231-L233 (3)	6.80	5.20

A65

A66

A67

Arrival of New Icebreaker RSV Nuyina A68

2020, Sept. 29   Litho.   Perf. 14x14¾

L234	A65	$1.10 multi	1.60	1.25
L235	A66	$1.10 multi	1.60	1.25
L236	A67	$2.20 multi	3.25	2.40
L237	A68	$2.20 multi	3.25	2.40
a.		Souvenir sheet of 4, #L234-L237	9.75	9.75
		Nos. L234-L237 (4)	9.70	7.30

Glossary of philatelic terms

This glossary defines nearly 300 terms frequently encountered by stamp collectors and cover collectors. Precise definitions for many philatelic terms do not exist. One collector, dealer or society may define a term in one way, while others will use the term in a slightly different way.

A

Accessories: Various products and tools commonly used by the stamp collector, including hinges, mounts, stamp tongs, perforation gauges, stock books and magnifiers. Stamp albums, catalogs and philatelic literature can also be regarded as accessories.

Adhesive: 1) The gum on the back of a stamp or label. Some stamps have been issued with no adhesive. Stamp adhesive may be water-activated or pressure-sensitive (self-adhesive). 2) A word generally referring to a stamp that may be affixed to an article to prepay postal fees, in contrast to a design printed directly on an article, as with postal stationery. An adhesive can also refer to a registration label or other label added to a cover.

Admirals: A nickname for three British Commonwealth definitive series, those of Canada, 1912-25 (Scott 104-34); New Zealand, 1926 (182-84); and Rhodesia, 1913-19 (119-38). These stamps depict King George V of Great Britain in naval uniform.

Aerogram: A postage-paid airletter sheet with gummed flaps that is written on and then folded to form an envelope. Aerograms are normally carried at less than the airmail letter rate. No enclosures are permitted.

Aerophilately: A specialized area of collecting concentrating on stamps or covers transported by air.

Agency: 1) An extraterritorial post office maintained at various times by a government within the territory of another government. Examples are the post offices maintained by many European powers in the Turkish Empire until 1923. 2) An organization authorized to publicize or sell new issues of stamps on behalf of a stamp-issuing entity.

Air labels: Air labels, or etiquettes, are used by Universal Postal Union member nations to denote airmail carriage. They are inscribed "Par Avion" (French for "By Airmail"). The text usually includes the same message in the language of the country of origin. Air labels also are adhesives issued by private organizations for specific, unofficial flights.

Airmail: The carriage of mail by air. The first regular airmail service began in 1870, when mail was carried from Paris-then besieged by German forces-over enemy lines by balloon. Many countries have issued postage stamps, stamped envelopes, postal cards and aerograms specially designated for airmail use. The first airmail stamp was issued by Italy in 1917 (Italy Scott C1).

Albino: An uninked impression made by a printing plate. Such errors are scarce on stamps. They are found more frequently on postal stationery.

Album: A binder and pages designed for the mounting and display of stamps or covers. Many early albums were permanently bound books. Albums come in many sizes, styles and themes. See the Album section in this almanac.

Album weed: In general, a forged stamp. It also refers to unusual items that resemble postage stamps but were not intended to pay postage, like publicity labels and bogus issues. Album Weeds is the title of a reference book series on forged stamps, written by the Rev. Robert Brisco Ear E.

Aniline: Ink with a coal-tar base. Aniline inks are very sensitive and may dissolve in water or other liquids or chemicals. To prevent the erasure of cancellations and reuse of stamps, aniline inks were used to print some stamps.

Approvals: Priced selections of stamps or covers sent to collectors by mail. The collector purchases the items he chooses, returning the rest to the approval dealer with payment for the purchased items.

Army Post Office: An official United States post office established for use by U.S. military units abroad. An army post office (APO) or military post office is set up to distribute mail to and from military personnel. The APO is indicated by numbers during wartime to prevent revealing personnel locations. The locations become generally known after the conflict ends.

Arrow: On many sheets of stamps, V-shaped arrowlike markings appear in the selvage, generally serving as guides for cutting the sheets into predetermined units. Some collectors save stamps or blocks displaying these marks.

As is: A term written in auction descriptions, or spoken or written during a retail transaction. It indicates that an item or lot is sold without guarantee or return privilege. Stamps are usually sold "as is" when they are damaged or are possibly not genuine.

ATM: 1) In the United States, panes of self-adhesive stamps on a liner the approximate size and shape of U.S. currency, designed for dispensing from automatic teller machines. 2) "Automatenmarken," automatic stamps produced individually by a machine; see also Frama.

Auction: A sale of stamps, covers and other philatelic items where prospective purchasers place bids in an attempt to obtain the desired items. The highest bidder for each lot (described item or items) makes the purchase. Auctions are generally divided into mail sales, where bids are accepted by mail, and public sales, where mail bids are combined with live bidding from individuals present at the auction or participating by telephone.

Authentication mark: A marking, such as initials, placed on the reverse of a stamp examined and certified to be genuine by an expert. Such markings do not detract from the value of the stamps when they represent the endorsement of recognized authorities.

APO: Army Post Office. An official United States post office established for use by U.S. military units abroad. An army post office or military post office is set up to distribute mail to and from military personnel. The APO is indicated by numbers during wartime to prevent revealing personnel locations. The locations become generally known after the conflict ends.

B

Backprint: Printing on the reverse of a stamp. Some stamps have numbers, symbols, advertising or information about the stamp subject printed on the reverse of the stamp.

Backstamp: A postmark applied to mail by the receiving post office or by a post office handling the piece while it is in transit. Backstamps are usually on the back of a cover, but they can be on the front.

Bank mixture: A high-quality mixture of stamps. It generally represents clippings from the mail of banks or other businesses with extensive overseas correspondence, and thus includes a relatively high proportion of foreign stamps of high face value. See also Mission mixture.

Bantams: The nickname of the South African definitive series of 1942-43 (Scott 90-97). Wartime economy measures prompted the manufacture of stamps of small size to conserve paper.

Batonne: A wove or laid paper with watermarklike lines deliberately added in the papermaking process and intended as a guide for handwriting.

Bicolor: Printed in two colors.

Bilingual: Inscribed in two languages. Most Canadian stamps include both English and French text. South African stamps from 1926-49 were printed alternately with English and Afrikaans inscriptions in the same sheet.

Bisect: A stamp cut or perforated into two parts, each half representing half the face value of the original stamp. Officially authorized bisects have often been used during temporary shortages of commonly used denominations. Unauthorized bisects appear on mail from some countries in some periods. Bisects are usually collected on full cover with the stamp tied by a cancel. At times, some countries have permitted trisects or quadrisects.

Bishop mark: The earliest postmark, introduced by Henry Bishop in England circa 1661. A Bishop mark was used to indicate the month and day that a letter was received by a post office. It encouraged prompt delivery by letter carriers.

Black Jack: The nickname of the United States 2¢ black Andrew Jackson stamp issued between 1863 and 1875.

Blind perforation: Intended perforations that are only lightly impressed by the perforating pins, leaving the paper intact, but cut or with a faint impression. Some stamps that appear to be imperforate really are not if they have blind perfs. Stamps with blind perfs are minor varieties carrying little, if any, price premium over normally perforated copies.

Block: A unit of four or more unsevered stamps, including at least two stamps both vertically and horizontally. Most commonly a block refers to a block of four, or a block of stamps two high and two wide, though blocks often contain more stamps and may be irregularly configured (such as, a block of seven consisting of one row of three stamps and one row of four stamps).

Bluenose: The nickname for Canada Scott 158, the 50¢ issue of 1929, picturing the schooner Bluenose.

Bogus: A fictitious stamplike label created for sale to collectors. Bogus issues include labels for nonexistent countries, nonexistent values appended to regularly issued sets and issues for nations or similar entities without postal systems.

Booklet: A unit of one or more small panes or blocks (known as booklet panes) glued, stitched or stapled together between thin card covers to form a convenient unit for mailers to purchase and carry. The first officially issued booklet was produced by Luxembourg in 1895. For some modern booklets of self-adhesive stamps the liner (backing paper) serves as the booklet cover.

Bourse: A meeting of stamp collectors and/or dealers, where stamps and covers are sold or exchanged. A bourse usually has no competitive exhibits of stamps or covers. Almost all public stamp exhibitions include a dealer bourse, though many bourses are held without a corresponding exhibition.

Bull's-Eyes: 1) The nickname for the 1843 first issue of Brazil, Scott 1-3. The similar but smaller issues are called goat's eyes. 2) A bull's-eye cancel refers to a "socked-on-the-nose" postmark with the impression centered directly on the stamp so that the location and date of mailing are shown on the stamp.

Burelage: A design of fine, intricate lines printed on the face of security paper, either to discourage counterfeiting or to prevent the cleaning and reuse of a stamp. The burelage on some stamps is part of the stamp design.

Burele: Adjective form for burelage, meaning having a fine network of lines. Some stamps of Queensland have a burele band on the back. Also called moir.

C

Cachet: In French, cachet means a stamp or a seal. On a cover, the cachet is an added design or text, often corresponding to the design of the postage stamp, the mailed journey of the cover, or some type of special event. Cachets appear on modern first-day covers, first-flight covers and special-event covers.

Canceled-to-order: Stamps are "canceled to order," usually in full sheets, by many governments. The cancels may be printed on the stamps at the same time that the stamp design is printed. A stamp with a cancel and with full gum is likely a CTO stamp, as CTOs do not see actual postal use. CTO stamps are sold to stamp dealers at large discounts from face value. Most catalogs say whether they price CTO stamps or genuinely used stamps.

Cancel: A marking intended to show a stamp has been used and is no longer valid as postage. Modern cancels usually include the name of the original mailing location or a nearby sorting facility and the date of mailing. Most cancellations also include a section of lines, bars, text or a design that prints upon the postage stamp to invalidate it. This part of a cancel is called the killer.

Cantonal stamps: Issues of Switzerland's cantons (states) used before the release of national stamps. The cantonal issues of Basel (1845), Geneva (1843-50) and Zurich (1843-50) are among the classics of philately.

Cape Triangles: Common name for the triangular Cape of Good Hope stamps of 1853-64, the first stamps printed in triangular format. The distinctive shape helped illiterate postal clerks distinguish letters originating in the colony from those from other colonies.

Catalog: A comprehensive book or similar compilation with descriptive information to help identify stamps. Many catalogs include values for the listed items. An auction catalog is published by the auction firm in advance of a planned sale to notify potential customers of the specific items that will be offered.

Catalog value: The value of a stamp as listed in a given catalog for the most common condition in which the stamp is collected. Some catalogs list stamps at a retail value, though actual dealer prices may vary substantially for reasons of condition, demand or other market factors. Most catalogs have a set minimum value for the most common stamps.

Censored mail: A cover bearing a handstamp or label indicating that the envelope has been opened and the contents inspected by a censor.

Centering: The relative position of the design of a stamp in relation to its margins. Assuming that a stamp is undamaged, centering is generally a very important factor in determining grade and value.

Certified mail: A service of most postal administrations that provides proof of mailing and delivery without indemnity for loss or damage.

Chalky paper: A chalk-surfaced paper for printing stamps. Any attempt to remove the cancel on a used chalky-paper stamp will also remove the design. Immersion of such stamps in water will cause the design to lift off. Touching chalky paper with silver will leave a discernible, pencil-like mark and is a means of distinguishing chalky paper.

Changeling: A stamp whose color has been changed-intentionally or unintentionally-by contact with a chemical or exposure to light.

Charity seals: Stamplike labels that are distributed by a charity. They have no postal validity, although they are often affixed to envelopes. United States Christmas seals are one example.

Charity stamp: see Semipostal.

Cinderella: A stamplike label that is not a postage stamp. Cinderellas include seals and bogus issues, as well as revenue stamps, local post issues and other similar items.

Classic: An early issue, often with a connotation of rarity, although classic stamps are not necessarily rare. A particularly scarce recent item may be referred to as a modern classic.

Cleaning (stamps): Soiled or stained stamps are sometimes cleaned with chemicals or by erasing. The cleaning is usually done to improve the appearance of a stamp. A cleaned stamp can also mean one from which a cancellation has been removed, making a used stamp appear unused.

Cliché: The individual unit consisting of the design of a single stamp, combined with others to make up the complete printing plate. Individual designs on modern one-piece printing plates are referred to as subjects.

Coil: Stamps processed in a long single row and prepared for sale in rolls, often for dispensing from stamp-vending and affixing machines. Some coils, including most U.S. coils, have a straight edge on two parallel sides and perforations on the remaining two parallel sides. Some coils are backprinted with sequence or counting numbers.

Collateral material: Any supportive or explanatory material relating to a given stamp or philatelic topic. The material may be either directly postal in nature (post office news releases, rate schedules, souvenir cards, promotional items) or nonpostal (maps, photos of scenes appearing on stamps).

Combination cover: Cover bearing the stamps of more than one country when separate postal charges are paid for the transport of a cover by each country. Also stamps of the same country canceled at two different times on the same cover as a souvenir.

Commatology: Specialized collecting of postmarks. This term was invented before World War II to describe postmark collecting. It is rarely used. Usually, collectors refer to postmark collecting or marcophily.

Commemorative: A stamp printed in a limited quantity and available for purchase for a limited time. The design may note an anniversary associated with an individual, an historic event, or a national landmark. See also Definitive.

Compound perforations: Different gauge perforations on different sides of a single stamp. The sides with the different gauge measurements are usually perpendicular.

Condition: The overall appearance and soundness of a stamp or cover. Positive condition factors include fresh full color, full original gum on unused stamps, and so on. Damage such as creases, tears, thinned paper, short perforation teeth, toning and so on negatively affect condition.

Controlled mail: A system in which the mailer selects philatelically desirable issues for outgoing mail, arranges for a specific manner of cancellation and secures the stamps' return by the addressee. In some cases such controlled mail operations may provide rare examples of specific rate fulfillment, or other similar postal use.

Copyright block: Block of four or more United States stamps with the copyright notice marginal marking of the United States Postal Service. The copyright marking was introduced in 1978 and replaced the Mail Early marking.

Corner card: An imprinted return address, generally in the upper-left corner of an envelope, from a commercial, institutional or private source, similar to business card or letterhead imprints.

Counterfeit: Any stamp, cancellation or cover created for deception or imitation, intended to be accepted by others as genuine. A counterfeit stamp is designed to deceive postal authorities.

Cover: An envelope or piece of postal stationery, usually one that has been mailed. Folded letters that were addressed and mailed without an envelope and the wrappers from mailed parcels are also covers.

Crash cover: A cover that has been salvaged from the crash of an airplane, train, ship or other vehicle. Such covers often carry a postal marking explaining damage or delay in delivery.

Crease: A noticeable weakening of the paper of a stamp or cover, caused by its being folded or bent at some point. Creases substantially lower a stamp's value. Creases particularly affect cover values when they extend through the attached stamp or a postal marking. Stamp creases are visible in watermark fluid.

Cut cancellation: A cancellation that intentionally slices into the stamp paper. Often a wedge-shaped section is cut away. On many issues, such cancellations indicate use of postage stamps as fiscals (revenues) or telegraph stamps rather than as postage. Cut cancellations were used experimentally on early United States postage stamps to prevent reuse.

Cut square: A neatly trimmed rectangular or square section from a stamped envelope that includes the imprinted postage stamp with ample margin. Collectors generally prefer to collect stationery as entire pieces rather than as cut squares. Some older stationery is available only in cut squares.

Cut-to-shape: A nonrectangular stamp or postal stationery imprint cut to the shape of the design, rather than cut square. Cut-to-shape stamps and stationery generally have lower value than those cut square. One of the world's most valuable stamps, the unique 1856 British Guiana "Penny Magenta" (Scott 13), is a cut-to-shape stamp.

Cylinder: A curved printing plate used on a modern rotary press. The plate has no seams. For United States stamps, cylinders are used to print gravure stamps. See also Sleeve.

Cancellation: A marking intended to show a stamp has been used and is no longer valid as postage. Modern cancels usually include the name of the original mailing location or a nearby sorting facility and the date of mailing. Most cancellations also include a section of lines, bars, text or a design that prints upon the postage stamp to invalidate it. This part of a cancel is called the killer.

CTO: Canceled-to-order. Stamps are "canceled to order," usually in full sheets, by many governments. The cancels may be printed on the stamps at the same time that the stamp design is printed. A stamp with a cancel and with full gum is likely a CTO stamp, as CTOs do not see actual postal use. CTO stamps are sold to stamp dealers at large discounts from face value. Most catalogs say whether they price CTO stamps or genuinely used stamps.

Charity stamp: A stamp sold at a price greater than postal value, with the additional charge dedicated for a special purpose. Usually recognized by the presence of two (often different) values, separated by a "+" sign, on a single stamp.

D

Dead country: A former stamp-issuing entity that has ceased issuing its own stamps. Also, the old name of an active stamp-issuing entity that has changed its name, so that the old name will no longer be used on stamps.

Definitive: Stamp issued in a large indefinite quantity and for an indefinite period, usually several years or more. The United States Presidential issue of 1938 and the 1995 32› Flag Over Porch stamps are examples. Definitive stamp designs usually do not honor a specific time-dated event.

Deltiology: Picture postcard collecting.

Denomination: The face value of a stamp, usually indicated by numerals printed as part of the design. Some modern U.S. stamps produced for rate changes are denominated with a letter. A numerical value is assigned when the letter stamps are issued. An example of this is the H-rate Hat stamp of 1998, which represented the first-class rate of 33¢.

Die: The original engraving of a stamp design, usually recess-engraved in reverse on a small flat piece of soft steel. In traditional intaglio printing, a transfer roll is made from a die and printing plates are made from impressions of the transfer roll. When more than one die is used in the production of an issue, distinctive varieties are often identifiable.

Die cut: A form of separation usually employed on self-adhesive stamps. During processing, an edged tool (die) completely penetrates the stamp paper on all sides of the printed stamp, making the removal of the individual stamps from the liner possible. Die cuts may be straight, shaped in wavy lines to simulate perforation teeth, or take other forms.

Directory markings: Postal indication of failed delivery attempt, stating the reason for failure. Examples are "No Such Number," "Address Unknown" and "Moved."

Duck stamp: Popular name for the United States Migratory Bird Hunting and Conservation stamp, issued for use on hunting licenses. Each annual stamp depicts waterfowl. Also used to describe similar issues from the various states for use by hunters or for sale to collectors.

Dummy stamp: Officially produced imitation stamp used to train employees or to test automatic stamp-dispensing machines. Dummy stamps are usually blank or carry special inscriptions, blocks or other distinguishing ornamentation. They are not valid for postage, nor are they intended to reach the hands of stamp collectors. Some do by favor of postal employees.

Duplex cancel: A two-part postal marking consisting of a canceler and a postmark. The canceler voids the stamp so it cannot be reused. The postmark notes the date and place of mailing.

Duplicate: An additional copy of a stamp that one already has in a collection. Beginners often consider stamps to be duplicates that really are not, because they overlook perforation, watermark or color varieties.

E

Earliest known use: The cover or piece that documents the earliest date on which a stamp or postal stationery item is known to be used. New discoveries can change an established EKU. The EKU for a classic issue may be after the official issue date. Because of accidental early sales, the EKU for modern stamps is often several days before the official first day.

Embossing: The process of giving relief to paper by pressing it with a die. Embossed designs are often found on the printed stamps of postal stationery (usually envelopes and wrappers). Selected stamps of certain countries have been embossed.

Encased postage stamp: A stamp inserted into a small coin-size case with a transparent front or back. Such stamps were circulated as legal coins during periods when coins were scarce.

Entire: An intact piece of postal stationery, in contrast to a cutout of the imprinted stamp. This term is sometimes used in reference to an intact cover or folded letter.

Error: A major mistake in the production of a stamp or postal stationery item. Production errors include imperforate or imperforate-between varieties, missing or incorrect colors, and inversion or doubling of part of the design or overprint. Major errors are usually far scarcer than normal varieties of the same stamp and are highly valued by collectors.

Essay: The artwork of a proposed design for a stamp. Some essays are rendered photographically. Others are drawn in pencil or ink or are painted. Most essays are rejected. One becomes the essay for the accepted design.

Etiquette: A gummed label manufactured for application to an envelope to designate a specific mail service. Airmail etiquettes are most common.

Europa: The "United Europe" theme celebrated annually on stamps of western European nations since 1956. The original Europa stamps were issued by the nations in the European coal and steel association. Today, European nations that are members of the postal and telecommunications association (CEPT) issue Europa stamps.Expertization: The examination of a stamp or cover by an acknowledged expert to determine if it is genuine. As standard procedure, an expert or expertizing body issues a signed certificate, often with an attached photograph, attesting to the item's status.

Exploded: A stamp booklet that has been separated into its various components, usually for purposes of display. Panes are removed intact: individual stamps are not separated from the pane.

Express mail: Next-day mail delivery service in the United States, inaugurated in 1977.

EKU: The cover or piece that documents the earliest date on which a stamp or postal stationery item is known to be used. New discoveries can change an established EKU. The EKU for a classic issue may be after the official issue date. Because of accidental early sales, the EKU for modern stamps is often several days before the official first day.

F

Face: The front of a stamp; the side bearing the design.

Face value: The value of a stamp as inscribed on its face. For letter-denominated or nondenominated stamps, the understood postal value of the stamp.

Facsimile: A reproduction of a genuine stamp or cover. Such items are usually made with no intent to deceive collectors or postal officials. Catalog illustrations may also be considered facsimiles.Fake: A stamp, cover or cancel that has been altered or concocted to appeal to a collector. In a broad sense, fakes include repairs, reperforations and regummed

stamps, as well as painted-in cancels, bogus cancels or counterfeit markings. Sometimes entire covers are faked.

Fancy cancel: A general term to describe any pictorial or otherwise unusual obliterating postmark. More specifically, the term is used to describe elaborate handmade pictorial cancels of the 19th century, such as the Waterbury "Running Chicken" of 1869 or the many intricate geometric shapes used during that period in post offices around the country.

Farley's Follies: During 1933-34, U.S. Postmaster General James A. Farley supplied a few imperforate sheets of current commemorative issues to Pres. Franklin D. Roosevelt and other government officials. The resulting uproar from U.S. collectors forced the government to release for public sale 20 issues in generally imperforate and ungummed sheets. They are United States Scott 752-771. Numbers 752-753 are perforated.

Fast colors: Inks resistant to fading.

Field Post Office: A military postal service operating in the field, either on land or at sea. Frequently abbreviated FPO.

Find: A new discovery, usually of something that was not known to exist. It can be a single item or a hoard of stamps or covers.

First-day cover: A cover bearing a stamp tied by a cancellation showing the date of the official first day of issue of that stamp.

Fiscal: A revenue stamp or similar label denoting the payment of tax. Fiscals are ordinarily affixed to documents and canceled by pen, canceler or mutilation. Because of their similarity to postage stamps, fiscals have occasionally been used either legally or illegally to prepay postage. See also Postal fiscal, Revenues.

Flat plate: A flat metal plate used in a printing press, as opposed to a curved or cylindrical plate.

Flaw: A defect in a plate that reproduces as an identifiable variety in the stamp design.

Fleet Post Office (FPO): An official United States post office for use by U.S. military naval units abroad. Frequently abbreviated FPO.

Forerunner: A stamp or postal stationery item used in a given location prior to the issuing of regular stamps for that location. Turkish stamps before 1918 canceled in Palestine are forerunners of Israeli issues. So are the various European nations' issues for use in Palestine, and the subsequent issues of the Palestine Mandate. The term "forerunner" is also used to describe a stamp issued before another stamp or set, if the earlier issue may have influenced the design or purpose of the later issue.

Forgery: A completely fraudulent reproduction of a postage stamp. There are two general types of forgeries: those intended to defraud the postal authorities (see also Counterfeit), and those intended to defraud the collectors (see also Bogus).

Frama: A general name used for an automatic stamp, derived from the name of the Swiss firm, Frama AG, an early producer of such issues. Automatic stamps are produced individually by a machine on demand in a denomination selected by the customer. There normally is no date on the stamp, as there is on a meter stamp. Also called ATM, from the German word Automatenmarken.

Frame: The outer portion of a stamp design, often consisting of a line or a group of panels.

Frank: An indication on a cover that postage is prepaid, partially prepaid or that the letter is to be carried free of postage. Franks may be written, hand-stamped, imprinted or affixed. Free franking is usually limited to soldiers' mail or selected government correspondence. Postage stamp and postage meter stamps are modern methods of franking a letter.

Freak: An abnormal, usually nonre-petitive occurrence in the production of stamps that results in a variation from the normal stamp, but falls short of producing an error. Most paper folds, overinking and perforation shifts are freaks. Those abnormalities occurring repetitively are called varieties and may result in major errors.

Front: The front of a cover with most or all of the back and side panels torn away or removed. Fronts, while desirable if they bear unusual or uncommon postal markings, are less desirable than an intact cover.

Fugitive inks: Printing inks used in stamp

production that easily fade or break up in water or chemicals. To counter attempts at forgery or the removal of cancellations, many governments have used fugitive inks to print stamps.

FPO: Field Post Office. A military postal service operating in the field, either on land or at sea. Also Fleet Post Office. An official United States post office for use by U.S. military naval units abroad.

FDC: First-day cover. A cover bearing a stamp tied by a cancellation showing the date of the official first day of issue of that stamp.

Franking: An indication on a cover that postage is prepaid, partially prepaid or that the letter is to be carried free of postage. Franks may be written, hand-stamped, imprinted or affixed. Free franking is usually limited to soldiers' mail or selected government correspondence. Postage stamp and postage meter stamps are modern methods of franking a letter.

G

Ghost tagging: The appearance of a faint image impression in addition to the normal inked impression. This is caused by misregistration of the phosphor tagging in relation to the ink. Sometimes, a plate number impression will have an entirely different number from the ink plate, giving the impression of an error: one dark (normal) number and one light (ghost) number.

Glassine: A thin, semitransparent paper that is moderately resistant to the passage of air and moisture. Envelopes made of glassine are commonly used for temporary stamp storage. Glassine is also used in the manufacture of stamp hinges.

Goldbeater's skin: A thin, tough, translucent paper. The 1886 issue of Prussia was printed in reverse on goldbeater's skin, with the gum applied over the printing. These stamps are brittle and virtually impossible to remove from the paper to which they are affixed.

Granite paper: A paper with small colored fibers added when the paper is made. This paper is used as a deterrent against forgery.

Gravure: A printing process utilizing an intaglio printing plate created by photographic and chemical means, rather than by hand engraving. See also Intaglio.

Grill: A pattern of parallel lines (or dots at the points where lines would cross) forming a grid. A grill is usually: 1) the impressed breaks added to stamps as a security measure (United States issues of 1867-71 and Peru issues of 1874-79); or 2) a grill-like canceling device used on various 19th-century issues.

Gum: The mucilage applied to the backs of adhesive postage stamps, revenue stamps or envelope flaps. Gum is an area of concern for stamp collectors. It may crack and harm the paper of the stamp itself. It may stain or adhere to other stamps or album pages under certain climatic conditions. Many collectors are willing to pay extra for 19th- and some 20th-century stamps with intact, undisturbed original gum.

Gutter: The selvage separating panes on a sheet of stamps. The gutter is usually discarded during processing. The gutter may be unprinted, or bear plate numbers, accounting or control numbers, advertising or other words or markings.

Gutter snipe: One or more stamps to which is attached the full gutter from between panes, plus any amount of an adjoining stamp or stamps. This term is typically used in reference to U.S. stamps. Gutter snipes are freaks caused by misregistration of the cutting device or paper foldover.

H

Handstamp: Cancellation or overprint applied by hand to a cover or to a stamp.

Highway Post Office (HPO): Portable mail-handling equipment for sorting mail in transit on highways (normally by truck). The last official U.S. HPO ran June 30, 1974.

Hinge: Stamp hinges are small, rectangular-shaped pieces of glassine paper, usually gummed on one side. Folded with the gummed side out, the hinge is used to mount stamps. Most modern hinges are peelable. Once dry, they may be easily removed from the stamp, leaving little trace of having been applied.

HPO: Highway Post Office. Portable mail-handling equipment for sorting mail in transit on highways (normally by truck). The last official U.S. HPO ran June 30, 1974.

I

Imperforate: Refers to stamps without

perforations or rouletting between the individual stamps in a pane. The earliest stamps were imperforate by design, but after about 1860 most stamps were perforated. Modern imperforates are usually errors or are produced specifically for sale to stamp collectors.

Impression: Any stamped or embossed printing.

Imprimatur: Latin for "let it be printed." The first sheets of stamps from an approved plate, normally checked and retained in a file prior to a final directive to begin stamp production from a plate.

India paper: A thin, tough opaque printing paper of high quality used primarily for striking die proofs.

Indicium: The stamp impression of a postage meter or the imprint on postal stationery (as opposed to an adhesive stamp), indicating prepayment and postal validity. Plural: indicia.

Inscription: The letters, words and numbers that are part of a postage stamp design.

Intaglio: Italian for "in recess." A form of printing in which the inked image is produced by that portion of the plate sunk below the surface. Line engraving and gravure are forms of intaglio printing.

International Reply Coupon: A redeemable certificate issued by member nations of the Universal Postal Union to provide for return postage from recipients in other countries. IRCs are exchangeable for postage at a post office.

Invert: The term generally used to describe any error where one portion of the design is inverted in relation to the other portion(s). An overprint applied upside down is also an invert.

Inverts: The term generally used to describe any error where one portion of the design is inverted in relation to the other portion(s). An overprint applied upside down is also an invert.

IRC: International Reply Coupon. A redeemable certificate issued by member nations of the Universal Postal Union to provide for return postage from recipients in other countries. IRCs are exchangeable for postage at a post office.

J

None

K

Keytype: A basic stamp design utilized for the issues of two or more postal entities, usually differing in the country name and inscription of value. Many of the earlier colonial issues of Britain, France, Spain, Germany and Portugal are keytypes.

Kiloware: A stamp mixture consisting of miscellaneous postally used stamps on envelope corner paper from various sources. Kiloware is sometimes sold by the kilogram (about 2.2 pounds).

L

Label: Any stamplike adhesive that is not a postage stamp or revenue stamp.

Laid paper: One of the two basic types of paper used in stamp printing. Laid paper is distinguished from wove paper by the presence of thin, parallel lines visible when the paper is held to light. The lines are usually a few millimeters apart. See also Batonne.

Letterpress: Printing done directly from the inked, raised surface of the printing plate.

Line engraving: Printing done from an intaglio plate produced from a hand-engraved die and transfer roll rather than by photographic or chemical means. See also Gravure.

Line pair: A pair of coil stamps with a printed line between them. Stamps produced on a flatbed press have a line from the guideline between panes. Stamps produced on a rotary press have a joint line from the space where ink collects between the sections of curved rotary plates.

Liner: Coated paper used as a backing for mint self-adhesive stamps. The liner allows the release of the stamp, which may then be applied with pressure to envelope paper.

Linerless: An experimental form of self-adhesive coil stamp that requires no liner. The mint stamps are rolled upon each other in a manner similar to adhesive tape. See United States Scott 3132, 3133.

Lithography: Printing from a flat surface with a design area that is ink-receptive. The area that is not to print is ink-repellant. The process is based on the principle that an oil-based design surface will attract oily ink.

Locals: Stamps valid within a limited area or within a limited postal system. Local post mail requires the addition of nationally or internationally valid stamps for further service. Locals have been produced both privately and officially.

M

Machin: The name given to a well-known series of British definitive stamps first issued in 1967. The design of the stamp depicts a plaster portrait of Queen Elizabeth II created by artist Arnold Machin.

Mail Early block: U.S. marginal marking block with the selvage bearing the inscription "Mail Early (in the Day)." This first appeared on U.S. marginal selvage in 1968. It was subsequently replaced by the copyright notice. ME blocks typically consist of four or six stamps.

Makeshift booklets: U.S. stamp booklets manufactured using stamps normally issued in individual panes, packaged in generic blue cardboard covers and dispensed by vending machines.

Marcophily: Postmark collecting.

Margin: 1) The selvage surrounding the stamps in a sheet, often carrying inscriptions of various kinds. 2) The unprinted border area around the stamp design. The collectible grades of stamps are determined by the position of the design in relation to the edge of the stamp as perforated or, in the case of imperforate stamps, as cut from the sheet.

Mat: A hard rubber plate used to apply overprints on postage stamps.

Maximaphily: Maximum card collecting.

Maximum card: A picture postcard, a cancel, and a stamp presenting maximum concordance. The stamp is usually affixed to the picture side of the card and is tied by the cancel. Collectors of maximum cards seek to find or create cards with stamp, cancel and picture in maximum agreement, or concordance. The statutes of the International Federation of Philately (FIP) give specific explanatory notes for the postage stamp, the picture postcard, the cancel, concordance of subject, concordance of place and concordance of time. (See Exhibiting chapter.)

Meter: The mechanical or digital device that creates a valid denominated postage imprint known as a meter stamp. Postage is prepaid to the regulating postal authority. Meters were authorized by the UPU in 1920. They are used today by volume mailers to cut the cost of franking mail.

Microprinting: Extremely small letters or numbers added to the designs of selected United States stamps as a security feature. In most cases, 8-power magnification or greater is needed to read microprinting.

Miniature sheet: A smaller-than-normal pane of stamps issued only in that form or in addition to full panes. A miniature sheet is usually without marginal markings or text saying that the sheet was issued in conjunction with or to commemorate some event. See also Souvenir sheet.

Mint: A stamp in the same state as issued by a post office: unused, undamaged and with full original gum (if issued with gum). Over time, handling, light and atmospheric conditions may affect the mint state of stamps.

Mirror image: An offset negative or reverse impression.

Mission mixture: The lowest grade of stamp mixture, containing unsorted but primarily common stamps on paper, as purchased from missions or other institutions. See also Bank mixture.

Missionaries: The first stamps of Hawaii, issued 1851-52, considered among the great classics of philately.

Mixed perforation: See Compound perforation.

Mixed postage: The franking on a cover bearing the stamps of two or more stamp-issuing entities, properly used.

Mixture: A large group of stamps, understood to contain duplication. A mixture is said to be unpicked or picked. A picked mixture may have had stamps removed by a collector or dealer.

Mobile Post Office: Portable mail-handling equipment and personnel, generally in railroad cars, streetcars, trucks or buses.

Mount: Acetate holders, clear on the front and with some sort of adhesive on the back. Collectors use mounts to affix stamps or covers to album or exhibit pages.

Multicolor: More than two colors.

Multiple: An unseparated unit of stamps including at least two stamps, but fewer than the number included in a full pane.

ME block: U.S. marginal marking block with the selvage bearing the inscription "Mail Early (in the Day)." This first appeared on U.S. marginal selvage in 1968. It was subsequently replaced by the copyright notice. ME blocks typically consist of four or six stamps.

MPO: Mobile Post Office. Portable mail-handling equipment and personnel, generally in railroad cars, streetcars, trucks or buses.

N

Native paper: Crude, handmade paper produced locally, as opposed to finer, machine-made paper.

Never hinged: A stamp without hinge marks. A never-hinged (NH) stamp usually has original gum, but this is not always the case.

New issue service: A dealer service that automatically supplies subscribers with new issues of a given country, area or topic. The issues provided are determined by a prearranged standing order that defines the quantity and types of issues.

Newspaper stamps: Stamps issued specifically for the prepayment of mailing rates for newspapers, periodicals and printed matter.

Nondenominated: A stamp with no numerical inscription designating the face value. The value of some nondenominated stamps are marked by a designated letter. Others may have a service inscription that indicates the rate the stamp fulfills.

NH: Never Hinged. A stamp without hinge marks. A never-hinged (NH) stamp usually has original gum, but this is not always the case.

O

Obliteration: 1) A cancellation intended solely to deface a stamp-also called a killer. 2) An overprint intended to deface a portion of the design of a stamp, such as the face of a deposed ruler.

Obsolete: A stamp no longer available from post offices, although possibly still postally valid.

Occupation issue: An issue released for use in territory occupied by a foreign power.

Off-center: A stamp design that is not centered in relation to the edges of the stamp. Generally, off-center stamps are less desirable than stamps more nearly centered in relation to the edges. Stamps that are extremely off-center may be added to collections as production freaks.

Offices abroad: At various times, many nations have maintained post offices in other countries, usually because of the unreliability of the local postal system. In China and the Turkish Empire, especially, many foreign nations maintained their own postal systems as part of their extraterritorial powers. Usually, special stationery and stamps were used by these offices. Most consisted of overprints on the regular issues of the nations maintaining the offices.

Official: Stamp or stationery issued solely for the use of government departments and officials. In many countries such items may be available to collectors in unused condition from the postal authority.

Offset: 1) A printing process that transfers an inked image from a plate to a roller. The roller then applies the ink to paper. 2) The transfer of part of a stamp design or an overprint from one sheet to the back of another, before the ink has dried (also called set off). Such impressions are in reverse (see Mirror image). They are different from stamps printed on both sides.

OHMS: Abbreviation for On His (or Her) Majesty's Service. Used in perfins, overprints or franks to indicate Official use in the British Commonwealth.

Omnibus issue: An issue released by several postal entities to celebrate a common theme. Omnibus issues may or may not share a keytype design.

On paper: Stamps (usually postally used) that are affixed to portions of original envelope or wrapper. Often used to describe stamps prior to soaking.

On piece: A stamp on a portion of the original envelope or wrapper showing all or most of the cancel. Stamps on piece are usually saved that way.

Original gum (OG): The adhesive coating on a mint or unused stamp or envelope

flap applied by a postal authority or security printer, usually before the item was issued. Upon request of stamp collectors, postal authorities have at times offered to add gum to items first issued ungummed. See also Regummed.

Overprint: Any printing over the original completed design of a stamp. An overprint that changes the value of a stamp is also called a surcharge.

Oxidation: Darkening of the ink on certain stamps caused by contact with air or light. Some inks used to print stamps, especially oranges, may in time turn brown or black.

P

Packet: 1) A presorted selection of all-different stamps, a common and economical way to begin a general collection; 2) a ship operating on a regular schedule and contracted by a government or post office to carry mail.

Packet letter: A letter carried by a ship operating on a regular schedule and carrying mail by contract with a government or a post office.

Pair: Two unseparated stamps.

Pane: The unit into which a full press sheet is divided before sale at post offices. What a post office customer may refer to as a "sheet of stamps" is more properly called a pane. Most United States full sheets are divided into four or more regular panes or many more booklet panes before they are shipped to post offices.

Paquebot: Cancellation indicating an item was mailed aboard a ship.

Par Avion: A French phrase meaning "By Air," it appears on airmail etiquettes of most countries, along with a similar phrase in the predominant language of the country of origin.

Parcel post stamps: Special stamps created for payment of parcel post fees.

Part-perforate: A stamp with all perforations missing on one or more sides, but with at least one side perforated.

Paste-up: The ends of rolls of coiled stamps joined together with glue or tape.

Pelure paper: A strong, thin paper occasionally used in stamp printing.

Pelure paper is translucent and resembles a slightly dark, thin onion-skin paper.

Pen canceled: Stamps canceled with an ink pen or marker pen rather than a handstamp or machine cancel. Many early stamps were routinely canceled by pen. A pen cancel may also indicate that a stamp was used as a fiscal. Modern stamps may be pen canceled if a sorting clerk or delivery carrier notices a stamp has been missed by a canceling machine.

Penny Black: The black 1-penny British stamp issued May 6, 1840, bearing the portrait of Queen Victoria. It is the world's first adhesive stamp issued for the prepayment of postage.

Perfins: Stamps perforated through the face with identifying initials, designs or holes in coded positions. Perfins are normally used by a business or government office to discourage pilferage or misuse of stamps by employees. Perfins may be either privately or officially produced.

Perforation: The punching out of holes between stamps to make separation easy. 1) Comb perforation-three sides of a stamp are perforated at once, with the process repeated in rows. 2) Harrow perforation-the entire sheet or unit of stamps is perforated in one operation. 3) Line perforation-holes are punched one row at a time. Line perforations are distinguished by the uneven crossing of perforation lines and irregular corners. Comb and harrow perforations usually show alignment of holes at the corners. Some forms of perforation may be difficult to distinguish.

Perforation gauge: A scale printed or designed on metal, transparent or opaque plastic, cardboard or other material to measure the number of perforation holes or teeth within the space of 2 centimeters.

Permit: Franking by the imprint of a number and additional information that identifies a mailer's prepaid postage account, thereby eliminating the need to affix and cancel stamps on large mailings. The mailer must obtain a document (permit) that authorizes his use of this procedure.

Phantom philately: The collection of bogus stamps. The name is derived from Frederick Melville's book Phantom Philately, one of the pioneer works on bogus issues.

Philatelic cover: An envelope, postal card or other item franked and mailed by a stamp collector to create a collectible object. It may or may not have carried a personal or business message. A nonphilatelic cover is usually one that has carried business or personal correspondence and has had its stamps applied by a noncollector. Some stamps are known only on collector-created covers. It is impossible to say whether some covers are philatelically inspired or not. See also Used and Postally used.

Philately: The collection and study of postage stamps, postal stationery and postal history.

Phosphor: A chemical substance used in the production of selected stamps to activate machines that automatically cancel mail. The machines react to the phosphor under ultraviolet light. In 1959, Great Britain began to print phosphor lines on some of its stamps. See also Tagging.

Photogravure: A modern stamp-printing process that is a form of intaglio printing. Plates are made photographically and chemically, rather than by hand engraving a die and transferring it to a plate. The ink in this process rests in the design depressions. The surface of the printing plate is wiped clean. The paper is forced into the depressions and picks up the ink, in a manner much like the line-engraved printing process.

Pictorial: Stamp bearing a picture of some sort, other than a portrait or coat of arms.

Plate: The basic printing unit on a press used to produce stamps. Early stamps were printed from flat plates. Curved or cylindrical plates are used for most modern stamps. See also Cylinder and Sleeve.

Plate block: A block of stamps from the corner or side of a pane including the selvage bearing the number(s) of the plate(s) used to print the sheet from which the pane was separated. Some stamp production methods, like booklet production, normally cut off plate numbers. In the United States, plate number blocks are collected normally as blocks of four to 20 stamps, depending on the press used to print the stamps. When each stamp in a pane is a different design, the entire pane is collected as the plate block.

Plate number: Numerals or an alphanumeric combination that identifies the printing plate used to print postage stamp images. In the United States, plate numbers on sheet stamps often appear in corner margin paper or side margin paper. Plate numbers on coil stamps were commonly trimmed off until about 1980; since then the number appears on stamps at specific intervals. Booklet plate numbers are often found on selvage attached to the pane.

Plating: The reconstruction of a stamp pane by collecting blocks and individual stamps representing various positions. This is possible for many older issues, but most modern issues are too uniform to make the identification of individual positions possible.

Plebiscite issue: A stamp issue promoting a popular vote. After World War I, a number of disputed areas were placed under temporary League of Nations administration, pending plebiscites to determine which nation the populace wished to join. Special issues note the upcoming vote in several of these areas; among them, Allenstein, Carinthia, Eastern Silesia, Marienwerder, Schleswig and Upper Silesia.

PNC: 1) A plate number coil stamp; that is, a stamp from a coil that is inscribed with a plate number. The abbreviations PNC3 and PNC5 identify strips of three or five coil stamps with the PNC located in the center position of the strip. 2) A philatelic-numismatic combination: a cover bearing a stamp and containing a coin, medal or token. The coin and stamp are usually related in such cases; often the cover is canceled on the first day of use of the coin.

Pneumatic post: Letter distribution through pressurized air tubes. Pneumatic posts existed in many large cities in Europe, and special stamps and stationery were often produced for the service.

Postage dues: Stamps or markings indicating that insufficient postage has been affixed to the mailing piece. Postage dues are usually affixed at the office of delivery. The additional postage is collected from the addressee.

Postal card: A government-produced postcard bearing a stamp imprint in the upper-right corner representing prepayment of postage.

Postal fiscal: Revenue or fiscal stamps used postally.

Postal history: The study of postal markings, rates and routes, or anything to do with the history of the posts.

Postal stationery: Stationery bearing imprinted stamps, as opposed to adhesive stamps. Postal stationery includes postal cards, lettercards, stamped envelopes, wrappers, aerograms, telegraph cards, postal savings forms and similar government-produced items. The cost to the mailer is often the price of postage plus an additional charge for the stationery item.

Postally used: A stamp or cover that has seen legitimate postal use, as opposed to one that has been canceled-to-order or favor-canceled. The term "postally used" suggests that an item exists because it was used to carry a personal or business communication, without the sender thinking of creating an item to be collected.

Postcard: A small card, usually with a picture on one side and a space for a written message on the other. Postcards have no imprinted stamp, so the mailer must also purchase postage to mail the postcard. See also Postal card.

Postmark: Any official postal marking. The term is usually used specifically in reference to cancellations bearing the name of a post office of origin and a mailing date.

Precancel: Stamp with a special overprint cancellation allowing it to bypass normal canceling. In some cases the precancel also designates a specific mail-handling service, such as "Presorted First-Class." Other precancels may include the city and state of the issuing post office. Precanceled stamps are used by volume mailers who hold a permit to use them. U.S. precancels fall into two categories: 1) Locals have the mark or text applied by a town or city post office; 2) Bureaus have the mark or text applied by the U.S. Bureau of Engraving and Printing. See also Service inscribed.

Prestamp covers: Folded letters or their outer enclosures used before the introduction of adhesive postage stamps or postal stationery.

Prestige booklet: A stamp booklet with oversized panes, descriptive information and stamp issues commemorating a special topic. Prestige booklets often include panes with no stamps that instead bear labels or additional information, along with panes bearing stamps.

Prexies: The nickname for the U.S. 1938-54 Presidential definitive series, Scott 803-34, 839-51.

Printer's waste: Misprinted, misperforated or misgummed stamps often created during the normal process of stamp production. Printer's waste is supposed to be destroyed, but such material enters the philatelic market through carelessness and theft.

Printing: The process of imprinting designs on paper from an inked surface.

Processing: Steps that finish a printed stamp sheet. Processing includes perforation, trimming, dividing the sheet into individual panes, and packaging for distribution.

Pro Juventute: Latin, meaning for the benefit of youth. Switzerland has issued Pro Juventute semipostals nearly every year since 1913.

Proofs: Trial impressions from a die or printing plate before actual stamp production. Proofs are made to examine a die or plate for defects or to compare the results of using different inks.

Provisional: A postage stamp issued for temporary use to meet postal demands until new or regular stocks of stamps can be obtained.

Plate number block: A block of stamps from the corner or side of a pane including the selvage bearing the number(s) of the plate(s) used to print the sheet from which the pane was separated. Some stamp production methods, like booklet production, normally cut off plate numbers. In the United States, plate number blocks are collected normally as blocks of four to 20 stamps, depending on the press used to print the stamps. When each stamp in a pane is a different design, the entire pane is collected as the plate block.

Press sheet: A complete unit of stamps as printed. Stamps are usually printed in large sheets and are separated into two or more panes before shipment to post offices.

Q

Quadripartition: A block or strip of four stamps that together complete a single entire design. See United States Scott 1448-51, the 1972 Cape Hatteras National Seashore issue.

R

Railway Post Office: Portable mail-handling equipment for sorting mail in transit on trains. The last official U.S. RPO ran June 30, 1977. RPOs were used in many countries. See also Mobile Post Office.

Receiving mark: A postmark or other postal marking applied by the receiving, rather than the originating, post office. See also Backstamp.

Redrawn: A stamp design that has been slightly altered yet maintains the basic design as originally issued.

Re-engraved: A stamp with an altered design as the result of a change made to a transfer roll or printing plate prior to a later printing, thereby distinguishing it from the original die.

Regional: Stamp sold or valid in a specific area of a stamp-issuing entity. Great Britain has issued stamps for the regions of Guernsey, Jersey, Isle of Man, Northern Ireland, Scotland and Wales. Regionals are usually sold only in a given region but are often valid for postage throughout a country.

Registered mail: First-class mail with a numbered receipt, including a valuation of the registered item, for full or limited compensation if the mail is lost. Some countries have issued registered mail stamps. Registered mail is signed for by each postal employee who handles it.

Registration labels: Adhesive labels indicating the registry number and, often, the city of origin for registered articles sent through the mail.

Regummed: A stamp bearing adhesive from an unauthorized source.

Reissue: An official reprinting of a stamp from an obsolete or discontinued issue. Reissues are valid for postage. See also Reprint.

Remainders: Stocks of stamps remaining unsold at the time that an issue is declared obsolete by a post office. Some countries have sold remainders to the stamp trade at substantial discounts from face value. The countries normally mark the stamps with a distinctive cancel.

Uncanceled remainders usually cannot be distinguished from stamps sold over the counter before the issue was invalidated.

Repaired stamp: A damaged stamp that has been repaired in some way to reinforce it or to make it resemble an undamaged stamp.

Replica: A reproduction of a stamp or cover. In the 19th century, replica stamps were sold as stamp album space fillers. Replica stamps are often printed in one color in a sheet containing a number of different designs. Replicas can sometimes deceive either a postal clerk or collectors.

Reprint: A stamp printed from the original plate, after the issue has ceased to be postally valid. Official reprints are sometimes made for presentation purposes or official collections. They are often distinguishable in some way from the originals: different colors, perforations, paper or gum. Private reprints, on the other hand, are usually produced strictly for sale to collectors and often closely resemble the original stamps. Private reprints normally sell for less than original copies. Reprints are not valid for postage. See also Reissue.

Retouch: The repairing of a damaged plate or die, often producing a minor, but detectable, difference in the design of the printed stamps.

Revenues: Stamps representing the prepayment or payment of various taxes. Revenues are affixed to official documents and to merchandise. Some stamps, including many issues of the British Commonwealth, are inscribed "Postage and Revenue" and were available for either use. Such issues are usually worth less fiscally canceled than postally used. In some cases, revenues have been used provisionally as postage stamps. See also Fiscal.

Rocket mail: Mail flown in a rocket, even if only a short distance. Many rocket mail experiments have been conducted since 1931. Special labels, cachets or cancels usually note that mail was carried on a rocket.

Rotary plate: A curved or cylindrical printing plate used on a press that rotates the plate to make continuous impressions. Flat plates make single impressions.

Rouletting: The piercing of the paper between stamps to make their separation more convenient. No paper is actually removed from the sheet, as it is in perforating. Rouletting has been made by dash, sawtooth or wavy line.

Rural Free Delivery: System for free home delivery of mail in rural areas of the United States, begun just prior to the turn of the 20th century.

Rust: A brown mold resembling the rust in iron. Rust affects stamp paper and gum in tropical regions.

RPO: Railway Post Office. Portable mail-handling equipment for sorting mail in transit on trains. The last official U.S. RPO ran June 30, 1977. RPOs were used in many countries. See also Mobile Post Office.

RFD: Rural Free Delivery. System for free home delivery of mail in rural areas of the United States, begun just prior to the turn of the 20th century.

S

SASE: A self-addressed, stamped envelope. An unused envelope bearing the address of the sender and sufficient return postage. Enclosed with correspondence to make answering easy.

Secret mark: A minute alteration to a stamp design added to distinguish later printings from earlier printings by a different firm. Secret marks may positively distinguish genuine stamps from counterfeits.

Seebeck: The nickname for various Latin American issues produced 1890-99 in contract with Nicholas Frederick Seebeck, the agent for the Hamilton Bank Note Co. of New York. Seebeck agreed to provide new issues of stamps and stationery each year at no charge, in return for the right to sell remainders and reprints to collectors. The resulting furor destroyed Seebeck and blackened the philatelic reputations of the countries involved.

Self-adhesive: Stamp gum that adheres to envelope paper by the application of pressure alone. Most self-adhesive stamps are sold on a coated paper release liner. See also Liner, Linerless, Water-activated.

Selvage: The marginal paper on a sheet or pane of stamps. Selvage may be unprinted or may contain printer's markings or other information.

Semipostal: A stamp sold at a price greater than postal value, with the additional charge dedicated for a special purpose. Usually recognized by the presence of two (often different) values, separated by a "+" sign, on a single stamp.

Series: A group of stamps with a similar design or theme, issued over a period of time. A series may be planned or may evolve.

Service inscribed: A stamp with wording as part of the initial printed design that identifies the mail-handling service for which the stamp is intended, such as "Presorted First-Class." See also Precancel.

Set: Stamps sharing common design elements, often issued at one time and usually collected as a group.

Se-tenant: French for "joined together." Two or more unseparated stamps of different designs, colors, denominations or types.

Shade: The minor variation commonly found in any basic color. Shades may be accorded catalog status when they are very distinctive.

Sheet: A complete unit of stamps as printed. Stamps are usually printed in large sheets and are separated into two or more panes before shipment to post offices.

Ship letter: Mail carried by private ship.

Short set: An incomplete set of stamps, usually lacking either the high value or one or more key values.

Sleeper: Stamp or other collectible item that seems to be underpriced and may have good investment potential.

Sleeve: 1) A seamless cylindrical printing plate used in rotary intaglio printing. 2) A flat transparent holder, often specifically for protecting and storing a cover.

Soaking: Removal of stamps from envelope paper. Most stamps may be safely soaked in water. Fugitive inks, however, will run in water, and chalky-surfaced papers will lose their designs entirely, so some knowledge of stamps is a necessity. Colored envelope paper should be soaked separately.

Souvenir card: A philatelic card, not valid for postage, issued in conjunction with some special event. The souvenir card often illustrates the design of a postage stamp.

Souvenir page: An announcement of a new United States stamp issue created by the U.S. Postal Service, bearing a copy of the new stamp tied by a first day of issue cancellation.

Souvenir sheet: A small sheet of stamps, including one value or a set of stamps. A souvenir sheet usually has a wide margin and an inscription describing an event being commemorated. Stamps on a souvenir sheet may be perforated or imperforate.

Space filler: A stamp in poor condition used to fill the designated space in a stamp album until a better copy can be found.

Special delivery: A service providing expedited delivery of mail. Called Express by some nations.

Special handling: A U.S. service providing expeditious handling for fourth-class material.

Special printing: Reissue of a stamp of current or recent design, often with distinctive color, paper or perforations.

Specialist: A stamp collector who intensively studies and collects the stamps and postal history of a given country, area, or time period, or who has otherwise limited his collecting field.

Special stamps: Regular postage stamp issues that fall outside the traditional definitions of commemorative and definitive stamps. In the United States, holiday issues such as Contemporary Christmas, Traditional Christmas, Hanukkah and the like are considered special stamps. They are printed in substantially greater quantities than commemorative stamps, and sometimes return to press for additional printings. Love stamps are also considered special stamps.

Specimen: Stamp or stationery item distributed to Universal Postal Union members for identification purposes and to the philatelic press and trade for publicity purposes. Specimens are overprinted or punched with the word "SPECIMEN" or its equivalent, or are overprinted or punched in a way to make them different from the issued stamps. Specimens of scarce stamps tend to be less valuable than the actual stamps. Specimens of relatively common stamps

are more valuable.

Speculative issue: A stamp or issue released primarily for sale to collectors, rather than to meet any legitimate postal need.

Splice: The repair of a break in a roll of stamp paper, or the joining of two rolls of paper for continuous printing. Stamps printed over a splice are usually removed and destroyed before the normal stamps are issued.

Stamp: An officially issued postage label, often adhesive, attesting that payment has been rendered for mail delivery. Initially used as a verb, meaning to imprint or impress; as in, to stamp a design.

Stampless cover: A folded sheet or envelope carried as mail without a postage stamp. This term usually refers to covers predating the requirement that stamps be affixed to all letters (in the United States, 1856).

Stock book: A specially manufactured blank book containing rows of pockets on each page to hold stamps.

Straight edge: Flat-plate or rotary-plate stamps from the margins of panes where the sheets were cut apart. Straight-edge stamps have no perforations on one or two adjacent sides. Sometimes straight-edge stamps show a guideline.

Strip: Three or more unseparated stamps in a row, vertically or horizontally.

Surcharge: An overprint that changes or restates the denomination of a stamp or postal stationery item.

Surface-colored paper: Paper colored on the surface only, with a white or uncolored back.

Surtax: The portion of a semipostal stamp purchase price exceeding the postage value. The surtax is designated for donation to a charity or some other purpose.

Sweatbox: A closed box containing dampened spongelike material, over which stuck-together unused stamps are placed on a grill. Humidity softens the gum, allowing separation of stamps. In some cases, the sweatbox may be used to help remove a postally used stamp from envelope paper.

T

T: Abbreviation for the French "Taxe."

Handstamped on a stamp, the T indicates the stamp's use as a postage due. Handstamped on a cover, it indicates that postage due has been charged. Several countries have used regular stamps with a perforated initial T as postage dues.

Tagging: Phosphor material on stamps used to activate automatic mail-handling equipment. This may be lines, bars, letters, part of the design area or the entire stamp surface. The tagging may also permeate the stamp paper. Some stamps are issued both with and without tagging. Catalogs describe them as tagged or untagged.

Teeth: The protruding points along the outer edge of a perforated postage stamp when it has been removed from the pane.

Telegraph stamp: Label used for the prepayment of telegraph fees. Telegraph stamps resemble postage stamps.

Tete-beche: French for "head to tail." Two or more unsevered stamps, one of which is inverted in relation to the other.

Thematic: A collection of stamps or covers relating to a specific topic. The topic is expanded by careful inquiry and is presented as a logical story. See also Topical.

Tied: A stamp is said to be tied to a cover when the cancel extends over both the stamp and the envelope paper. Stamps can also be tied by the aging of the mucilage or glue that holds them to the paper.

Tong: Tweezerlike tool with rounded, polished tips, used to handle stamps. Tongs prevent stamps from being soiled by dirt, oil or perspiration.

Topical: 1) Stamp or cover showing a given subject. Examples are flowers, art, birds, elephants or the Statue of Liberty. 2) The collection of stamps by the topic depicted on them, rather than by country of origin. See also Thematic.

Transit mark: A postal marking applied by a post office between the originating and receiving post offices. It can be on the front or back of a cover, card or wrapper.

Triptych: A se-tenant strip of three related stamps forming one overall design. See United States Scott 1629-31, the 1976 Spirit of 76 issue.

Type: A basic design of a stamp or

884

a set. Catalogs use type numbers or letters to save space. Catalogs show a typical design of one type rather than every stamp with that design or a similar design.

U

Underprint: A fine printing underlying the design of a stamp, most often used to deter counterfeiting.

Ungummed: A stamp without gum. Ungummed stamps are either stamps issued without gum or an uncanceled gummed stamp that has had its gum soaked off. Many countries in tropical climates have issued stamps without gum.

Unhinged: A stamp without hinge marks, but not necessarily with original gum.

Universal Postal Union: An international organization formed in Bern, Switzerland, in 1874, to regulate and standardize postal usage and to facilitate the movement of mail between member nations. Today, most nations belong to the UPU. (See UPU section of this almanac.)

Unused: An uncanceled stamp that has not been used but has a hinge mark or some other characteristic or defect that keeps it from being considered a mint stamp. Uncanceled stamps without gum may have been used and missed being canceled, or they may have lost their gum by accident.

Used: A stamp or stationery item that has been canceled by a postal authority to prevent its reuse on mail. In general, a used stamp is any stamp with a cancel or a precanceled stamp without gum. See also Postally Used and Philatelic Cover.

UPU: Universal Postal Union. An international organization formed in Bern, Switzerland, in 1874, to regulate and standardize postal usage and to facilitate the movement of mail between member nations. Today, most nations belong to the UPU.

V

Variety: A variation from the standard form of a stamp. Varieties include different watermarks, inverts, imperforates, missing colors, wrong colors and major color shifts. See also Freak, Error.

Vignette: The central part of a stamp design, usually surrounded by a border.

In some cases the vignette shades off gradually into the surrounding area.

W

Want list: A list of needed stamps or covers, identified by catalog number or some other description, submitted by a collector to a dealer, usually including requirements on condition and price.

Water-activated adhesive: Stamp gum designed to adhere to envelope paper only if the gum is moistened. All gummed stamps before 1963 used water-activated adhesive.

Watermark: A deliberate thinning of paper during its manufacture to produce a semitranslucent pattern. Watermarks appear frequently in paper used in stamp printing or envelope manufacture. See also Batonne.

Web: A continuous roll of paper used in stamp printing.

Wing margin: Early British stamps from the side of a pane with selvage attached. British sheets printed before 1880 were perforated down the center of the gutter, producing oversized margins on one side of stamps adjacent to the gutter. Such copies are distinctive and scarcer than normal copies.

Wove paper: A paper showing few differences in texture and thickness when held to light. In the production of wove paper, the pulp is pressed against a very fine netting, producing a virtually uniform texture. Wove paper is the most commonly used paper in stamp production.

Wrapper: A flat sheet or strip open at both ends that can be folded and sealed around a newspaper or periodical. Wrappers can have an imprinted stamp or have a stamp attached.

X

None

Y

None

Z

Zemstvo: A local stamp issued by Russian municipal governments or zemstvos, in accordance with an imperial edict of 1870.

Zeppelins: The stamps issued for, or in honor of, zeppelin flights. Cacheted covers carried on such flights are Zeppelin covers.

ZIP block: U.S. marginal marking block with the selvage bearing the image of the "Mr. ZIP" cartoon character and/or an inscription urging the use of ZIP code. This first appeared on U.S. marginal selvage in 1964. Typically a ZIP block is a block of four stamps.

ZIP code: The U.S. numerical post code used to speed and mechanize mail handling and delivery. The letters stand for Zoning Improvement Plan.

INDEX AND IDENTIFIER

All page numbers shown are
those in this Volume 1A.

Postage stamps that do not have
English words on them are shown in the
Scott *Stamp Illustrated Identifier*. To
purchase it visit AmosAdvantage.com or
call Amos Media at 800-572-6885.

Currency conversion

Country	Dollar	Pound	S Franc	Yen	HK $	Euro	Cdn $	Aus $
Australia	1.3588	1.8139	1.5031	0.0130	0.1753	1.6295	1.0484	—
Canada	1.2961	1.7302	1.4337	0.0124	0.1672	1.5543	—	0.9539
European Union	0.8339	1.1132	0.9225	0.0080	0.1076	—	0.6434	0.6137
Hong Kong	7.7522	10.348	8.5754	0.0743	—	9.2963	5.9812	5.7052
Japan	104.40	139.36	115.49	—	13.467	125.20	80.549	76.832
Switzerland	0.9040	1.2067	—	0.0087	0.1166	1.0841	0.6975	0.6653
United Kingdom	0.7491	—	0.8287	0.0072	0.0966	0.8983	0.5780	0.5513
United States	—	1.3349	1.1062	0.0096	0.1290	1.1992	0.7715	0.7359

Country	Currency	U.S. $ Equiv.
Afghanistan	afghani	.0130
Aitutaki	New Zealand dollar	.7042
Albania	lek	.0096
Algeria	dinar	.0077
Andorra (French)	euro	1.1992
Andorra (Spanish)	euro	1.1992
Angola	kwanza	.0015
Anguilla	East Caribbean dollar	.3704
Antigua	East Caribbean dollar	.3704
Argentina	peso	.0123
Armenia	dram	.0021
Aruba	guilder	.5587
Ascension	British pound	1.3349
Australia	dollar	.7359
Australian Antarctic Territory	dollar	.7359
Austria	euro	1.1992
Azerbaijan	manat	.5886
Bahamas	dollar	1.00
Bahrain	dinar	2.6596
Bangladesh	taka	.0118
Barbados	dollar	.5000
Barbuda	East Caribbean dollar	.3704
Belarus	ruble	.3866
Belgium	euro	1.1992
Belize	dollar	.4967
Benin	Community of French Africa (CFA) franc	.0018
Bermuda	dollar	1.00
Bhutan	ngultrum	.0136
Bolivia	boliviano	.1452
Bosnia & Herzegovina	convertible mark	.6129
Botswana	pula	.0907
Brazil	real	.1896
British Antarctic Territory	British pound	1.3349
British Indian Ocean Territory	British pound	1.3349
Brunei	dollar	.7464
Bulgaria	lev	.6128
Burkina Faso	CFA franc	.0018
Burma	kyat	.0008
Burundi	franc	.0005
United Nations-New York	U.S. dollar	1.00
United Nations-Geneva	Swiss franc	1.1062
United Nations-Vienna	euro	1.1992
United States	dollar	1.00

Source: xe.com Dec. 1, 2020. Figures reflect values as of Dec. 1, 2020.

Vols. 1A-1B number additions, deletions and changes

Number in 2021 Catalogue	Number in 2022 Catalogue

United States

new	527d
new	1384t
new	2150c
new	2216q
new	5335c

Semi-postal Stamps

new	B5b

Official Stamps

new	O136b

Confederate Postmasters' Provisionals

new	153XU1

Afghanistan

4	deleted
4A	4

Aitutaki

642	641
641	642

Albania

new	18a
new	19a
new	19b
new	19c
new	J1a
new	J1b
new	J2a
new	J2b
new	J3a

Argentina

new	C20a
O129	deleted

Australian States – New South Wales

new	71b

Belgium

new	82a
new	J17a
new	J18a
new	J19a
new	J21a

Bolivia

new	450a

INDEX TO ADVERTISERS
2022 VOLUME 1A

2022
VOLUME 1A
DEALER DIRECTORY
YELLOW PAGE LISTINGS

This section of your Scott Catalogue contains advertisements to help you conveniently find what you need, when you need it...!

Albania

WORLDSTAMPS/
FRANK GEIGER PHILATELISTS
PO Box 4743
Pinehurst, NC 28374
PH: 910-295-2048
Frank@WorldStamps.com
www.WorldStamps.com

Andorra

WORLDSTAMPS/
FRANK GEIGER PHILATELISTS
PO Box 4743
Pinehurst, NC 28374
PH: 910-295-2048
Frank@WorldStamps.com
www.WorldStamps.com

Appraisals

DR. ROBERT FRIEDMAN &
SONS STAMP & COIN
BUYING CENTER
2029 W. 75th St.
Woodridge, IL 60517
PH: 800-588-8100
FAX: 630-985-1588
stampcollections@drbobstamps.com
www.drbobfriedmanstamps.com

MILLER'S STAMP COMPANY
P.O. Box 1011
Niantic, CT 06357
www.millerstamps.com
PH: 860-908-6200

Auctions

DUTCH COUNTRY AUCTIONS
The Stamp Center
4115 Concord Pike
Wilmington, DE 19803
PH: 302-478-8740
FAX: 302-478-8779
auctions@dutchcountryauctions.com
www.dutchcountryauctions.com

Australia

COLONIAL STAMP COMPANY
5757 Wilshire Blvd. PH #8
Los Angeles, CA 90036
PH: 323-933-9435
FAX: 323-939-9930
info@colonialstamps.com
www.colonialstamps.com

WORLDSTAMPS/
FRANK GEIGER PHILATELISTS
PO Box 4743
Pinehurst, NC 28374
PH: 910-295-2048
Frank@WorldStamps.com
www.WorldStamps.com

Austria

HENRY GITNER
PHILATELISTS, INC.
PO Box 3077-S
Middletown, NY 10940
PH: 845-343-5151
PH: 800-947-8267
FAX: 845-343-0068
hgitner@hgitner.com
www.hgitner.com

WORLDSTAMPS/
FRANK GEIGER PHILATELISTS
PO Box 4743
Pinehurst, NC 28374
PH: 910-295-2048
Frank@WorldStamps.com
www.WorldStamps.com

Bangkok

COLONIAL STAMP COMPANY
5757 Wilshire Blvd. PH #8
Los Angeles, CA 90036
PH: 323-933-9435
FAX: 323-939-9930
info@colonialstamps.com
www.colonialstamps.com

Belgium

WORLDSTAMPS/
FRANK GEIGER PHILATELISTS
PO Box 4743
Pinehurst, NC 28374
PH: 910-295-2048
Frank@WorldStamps.com
www.WorldStamps.com

Bermuda

COLONIAL STAMP COMPANY
5757 Wilshire Blvd. PH #8
Los Angeles, CA 90036
PH: 323-933-9435
FAX: 323-939-9930
info@colonialstamps.com
www.colonialstamps.com

Bhutan

WORLDSTAMPS/
FRANK GEIGER PHILATELISTS
PO Box 4743
Pinehurst, NC 28374
PH: 910-295-2048
Frank@WorldStamps.com
www.WorldStamps.com

British Asia

THE STAMP ACT
PO Box 1136
Belmont, CA 94002
PH: 650-703-2342
thestampact@sbcglobal.net

British Commonwealth

COLLECTORS EXCHANGE
ORLANDO STAMP SHOP
1814A Edgewater Drive
Orlando, FL 32804
PH: 407-620-0908
PH: 407-947-8603
FAX: 407-730-2131
jlatter@cfl.rr.com
www.OrlandoStampShop.com

ARON R. HALBERSTAM
PHILATELISTS, LTD.
PO Box 150168
Van Brunt Station
Brooklyn, NY 11215-0168
PH: 718-788-3978
arh@arhstamps.com
www.arhstamps.com

ROY'S STAMPS
PO Box 28001
600 Ontario Street
St. Catharines, ON
CANADA L2N 7P8
Phone: 905-934-8377
Email: roystamp@cogeco.ca
www.roysstamps.com

THE STAMP ACT
PO Box 1136
Belmont, CA 94002
PH: 650-703-2342
thestampact@sbcglobal.net

British Commonwealth

WORLDSTAMPS/
FRANK GEIGER PHILATELISTS
PO Box 4743
Pinehurst, NC 28374
PH: 910-295-2048
Frank@WorldStamps.com
www.WorldStamps.com

British E. Africa

COLONIAL STAMP COMPANY
5757 Wilshire Blvd. PH #8
Los Angeles, CA 90036
PH: 323-933-9435
FAX: 323-939-9930
info@colonialstamps.com
www.colonialstamps.com

British Guiana

COLONIAL STAMP COMPANY
5757 Wilshire Blvd. PH #8
Los Angeles, CA 90036
PH: 323-933-9435
FAX: 323-939-9930
info@colonialstamps.com
www.colonialstamps.com

Buying

DR. ROBERT FRIEDMAN &
SONS STAMP & COIN
BUYING CENTER
2029 W. 75th St.
Woodridge, IL 60517
PH: 800-588-8100
FAX: 630-985-1588
stampcollections@drbobstamps.com
www.drbobfriedmanstamps.com

British Commonwealth

Canada

CANADA STAMP FINDER
PO Box 92591
Brampton, ON L6W 4R1
PH: 514-238-5751
Toll Free in North America:
877-412-3106
FAX: 323-315-2635
canadastampfinder@gmail.com
www.canadastampfinder.com

ROY'S STAMPS
PO Box 28001
600 Ontario Street
St. Catharines, ON
CANADA L2N 7P8
Phone: 905-934-8377
Email: roystamp@cogeco.ca
www.roysstamps.com

China - PRC

THE STAMP ACT
PO Box 1136
Belmont, CA 94002
PH: 650-703-2342
thestampact@sbcglobal.net

Collections

DR. ROBERT FRIEDMAN &
SONS STAMP & COIN
BUYING CENTER
2029 W. 75th St.
Woodridge, IL 60517
PH: 800-588-8100
FAX: 630-985-1588
stampcollections@drbobstamps.com
www.drbobfriedmanstamps.com

Ducks

MICHAEL JAFFE
PO Box 61484
Vancouver, WA 98666
PH: 360-695-6161
PH: 800-782-6770
FAX: 360-695-1616
mjaffe@brookmanstamps.com
www.brookmanstamps.com

Europe-Western

HENRY GITNER PHILATELISTS, INC.
PO Box 3077-S
Middletown, NY 10940
PH: 845-343-5151
PH: 800-947-8267
FAX: 845-343-0068
hgitner@hgitner.com
www.hgitner.com

German Colonies

COLONIAL STAMP COMPANY
5757 Wilshire Blvd. PH #8
Los Angeles, CA 90036
PH: 323-933-9435
FAX: 323-939-9930
info@colonialstamps.com
www.colonialstamps.com

Great Britain

COLONIAL STAMP COMPANY
5757 Wilshire Blvd. PH #8
Los Angeles, CA 90036
PH: 323-933-9435
FAX: 323-939-9930
info@colonialstamps.com
www.colonialstamps.com

New Issues

DAVIDSON'S STAMP SERVICE
Personalized Service since 1970
PO Box 36355
Indianapolis, IN 46236-0355
PH: 317-826-2620
ed-davidson@earthlink.net
www.newstampissues.com

WORLDSTAMPS/ FRANK GEIGER PHILATELISTS
PO Box 4743
Pinehurst, NC 28374
PH: 910-295-2048
Frank@WorldStamps.com
www.WorldStamps.com

Stamp Stores
California

COLONIAL STAMP COMPANY
5757 Wilshire Blvd. PH #8
Los Angeles, CA 90036
PH: 323-933-9435
FAX: 323-939-9930
info@colonialstamps.com
www.colonialstamps.com

Connecticut

MILLER'S STAMP COMPANY
P.O. Box 1011
Niantic, CT 06357
www.millerstamps.com
PH: 860-908-6200

Delaware

DUTCH COUNTRY AUCTIONS
The Stamp Center
4115 Concord Pike
Wilmington, DE 19803
PH: 302-478-8740
FAX: 302-478-8779
auctions@dutchcountryauctions.com
www.dutchcountryauctions.com

Florida

DR. ROBERT FRIEDMAN & SONS STAMP & COIN BUYING CENTER
PH: 800-588-8100
FAX: 630-985-1588
stampcollections@drbobstamps.com
www.drbobfriedmanstamps.com

Illinois

DR. ROBERT FRIEDMAN & SONS STAMP & COIN BUYING CENTER
2029 W. 75th St.
Woodridge, IL 60517
PH: 800-588-8100
FAX: 630-985-1588
stampcollections@drbobstamps.com
www.drbobfriedmanstamps.com

New Jersey

BERGEN STAMPS & COLLECTIBLES
306 Queen Anne Rd.
Teaneck, NJ 07666
PH: 201-836-8987
bergenstamps@gmail.com

Stamp Stores
New Jersey

TRENTON STAMP & COIN
Thomas DeLuca
Store: Forest Glen Plaza
1804 Highway #33
Hamilton Square, NJ 08690
Mail: PO Box 8574
Trenton, NJ 08650
PH: 609-584-8100
FAX: 609-587-8664
TOMD4TSC@aol.com
www.trentonstampandcoin.com

New York

CK STAMPS
42-14 Union St. # 2A
Flushing, NY 11355
PH: 917-667-6641
ckstampsllc@yahoo.com

Ohio

HILLTOP STAMP SERVICE
Richard A. Peterson
PO Box 626
Wooster, OH 44691
PH: 330-262-8907 (O)
PH: 330-201-1377 (H)
hilltopstamps@sssnet.com
www.hilltopstamps.com

Supplies

BROOKLYN GALLERY COIN & STAMP, INC.
8725 4th Ave.
Brooklyn, NY 11209
PH: 718-745-5701
FAX: 718-745-2775
info@brooklyngallery.com
www.brooklyngallery.com

Topicals

E. JOSEPH McCONNELL, INC.
PO Box 683
Monroe, NY 10949
PH: 845-783-9791
FAX: 845-782-0347
ejstamps@gmail.com
www.EJMcConnell.com

WORLDSTAMPS/ FRANK GEIGER PHILATELISTS
PO Box 4743
Pinehurst, NC 28374
PH: 910-295-2048
Frank@WorldStamps.com
www.WorldStamps.com

Topicals - Columbus

MR. COLUMBUS
PO Box 1492
Fennville, MI 49408
PH: 269-543-4755
David@MrColumbus1492.com
www.MrColumbus1492.com

United Nations

BRUCE M. MOYER
Box 12031
Charlotte, NC 28220
PH: 908-237-6967
moyer@unstamps.com
www.unstamps.com

United States

ACS STAMP COMPANY
2914 W 135th Ave
Broomfield, Colorado 80020
303-841-8666
www.ACSStamp.com

BROOKMAN STAMP CO.
PO Box 90
Vancouver, WA 98666
PH: 360-695-1391
PH: 800-545-4871
FAX: 360-695-1616
info@brookmanstamps.com
www.brookmanstamps.com

HENRY GITNER PHILATELISTS, INC.
PO Box 3077-S
Middletown, NY 10940
PH: 845-343-5151
PH: 800-947-8267
FAX: 845-343-0068
hgitner@hgitner.com
www.hgitner.com

MILLER'S STAMP COMPANY
P.O. Box 1011
Niantic, CT 06357
www.millerstamps.com
PH: 860-908-6200

WORLDSTAMPS/ FRANK GEIGER PHILATELISTS
PO Box 4743
Pinehurst, NC 28374
PH: 910-295-2048
Frank@WorldStamps.com
www.WorldStamps.com

U.S. Classics/Moderns

BARDO STAMPS
PO Box 7437
Buffalo Grove, IL 60089
PH: 847-634-2676
jfb7437@aol.com
www.bardostamps.com

**HENRY GITNER
PHILATELISTS, INC.**
PO Box 3077-S
Middletown, NY 10940
PH: 845-343-5151
PH: 800-947-8267
FAX: 845-343-0068
hgitner@hgitner.com
www.hgitner.com

U.S.-Collections Wanted

DUTCH COUNTRY AUCTIONS
The Stamp Center
4115 Concord Pike
Wilmington, DE 19803
PH: 302-478-8740
FAX: 302-478-8779
auctions@dutchcountryauctions.com
www.dutchcountryauctions.com

**DR. ROBERT FRIEDMAN &
SONS STAMP & COIN
BUYING CENTER**
2029 W. 75th St.
Woodridge, IL 60517
PH: 800-588-8100
FAX: 630-985-1588
stampcollections@drbobstamps.com
www.drbobfriedmanstamps.com

MILLER'S STAMP COMPANY
P.O. Box 1011
Niantic, CT 06357
www.millerstamps.com
PH: 860-908-6200

Want Lists - British Empire 1840-1935 German Cols./Offices

COLONIAL STAMP COMPANY
5757 Wilshire Blvd. PH #8
Los Angeles, CA 90036
PH: 323-933-9435
FAX: 323-939-9930
info@colonialstamps.com
www.colonialstamps.com

Want Lists - U.S.

**HENRY GITNER
PHILATELISTS, INC.**
PO Box 3077-S
Middletown, NY 10940
PH: 845-343-5151
PH: 800-947-8267
FAX: 845-343-0068
hgitner@hgitner.com
www.hgitner.com

Wanted - Worldwide Collections

DUTCH COUNTRY AUCTIONS
The Stamp Center
4115 Concord Pike
Wilmington, DE 19803
PH: 302-478-8740
FAX: 302-478-8779
auctions@dutchcountryauctions.com
www.dutchcountryauctions.com

Wanted - U.S.

**HENRY GITNER
PHILATELISTS, INC.**
PO Box 3077-S
Middletown, NY 10940
PH: 845-343-5151
PH: 800-947-8267
FAX: 845-343-0068
hgitner@hgitner.com
www.hgitner.com

Websites

ACS STAMP COMPANY
2914 W 135th Ave
Broomfield, Colorado 80020
303-841-8666
www.ACSStamp.com

MILLER'S STAMP COMPANY
P.O. Box 1011
Niantic, CT 06357
www.millerstamps.com
PH: 860-908-6200

Wholesale - Dealers

**HENRY GITNER
PHILATELISTS, INC.**
PO Box 3077-S
Middletown, NY 10940
PH: 845-343-5151
PH: 800-947-8267
FAX: 845-343-0068
hgitner@hgitner.com
www.hgitner.com

Worldwide

GUILLERMO JALIL
Maipu 466, local 4
1006 Buenos Aires
Argentina
guillermo@jalilstamps.com
philatino@philatino.com
www.philatino.com (worldwide
stamp auctions)
www.jalilstamps.com (direct sale,
worldwide stamps)

Worldwide-Collections

**DR. ROBERT FRIEDMAN &
SONS STAMP & COIN
BUYING CENTER**
2029 W. 75th St.
Woodridge, IL 60517
PH: 800-588-8100
FAX: 630-985-1588
stampcollections@drbobstamps.com
www.drbobfriedmanstamps.com